Small Business Sourcebook

ISSN 0883-3397

Small Business Sourcebook

The Entrepreneur's Resource

THIRTIETH EDITION

Volume 1

Specific Small Business Profiles

(Entries 1-9230)

Sonya D. Hill
Project Editor

GALE
CENGAGE Learning

Detroit • New York • San Francisco • New Haven, Conn • Waterville, Maine • London

Small Business Sourcebook, 30th edition

Project Editor: Sonya D. Hill

Editorial Support Services: Charles Beaumont

Composition and Electronic Prepress: Gary Leach

Manufacturing: Rita Wimberley

For product information and technology assistance, contact us at
Gale Customer Support, 1-800-877-4253.
For permission to use material from this text or product,
submit all requests online at **www.cengage.com/permissions.**
Further permissions questions can be emailed to
permissionrequest@cengage.com

While every effort has been made to ensure the reliability of the information presented in this publication, Gale, a part of Cengage Learning, does not guarantee the accuracy of the data contained herein. Gale accepts no payment for listing; and inclusion in the publication of any organization, agency, institution, publication, service, or individual does not imply endorsement of the editors or publisher. Errors brought to the attention of the publisher and verified to the satisfaction of the publisher will be corrected in future editions.

EDITORIAL DATA PRIVACY POLICY. Does this publication contain information about you as an individual? If so, for more information about our data privacy policies, please see our Privacy Statement at www.gale.cengage.com.

Gale
27500 Drake Rd.
Farmington Hills, MI, 48331-3535

ISBN-13: 978-1-4144-7957-6 (set)
ISBN-10: 1-4144-7957-3 (set)
ISBN-13: 978-1-4144-7958-3 (vol. 1)
ISBN-10: 1-4144-7958-1 (vol. 1)
ISBN-13: 978-1-4144-7959-0 (vol. 2)
ISBN-10: 1-4144-7959-X (vol. 2)
ISBN-13: 978-1-4144-7960-6 (vol. 3)
ISBN-10: 1-4144-7960-3 (vol. 3)
ISBN-13: 978-1-4144-7961-3 (vol. 4)
ISBN-10: 1-4144-7961-1 (vol. 4)
ISBN-13: 978-1-4144-7962-0 (vol. 5)
ISBN-10: 1-4144-7962-X (vol. 5)
ISBN-13: 978-1-4144-7963-7 (vol. 6)
ISBN-10: 1-4144-7963-8 (vol. 6)

ISSN 0883-3397

Printed in the United States of America
1 2 3 4 5   17 16 15 14 13

Contents

The appeal of small business ownership remains perpetually entrenched in American culture as one of the most viable avenues for achieving the American Dream. To many entrepreneurs going into business for themselves represents financial independence, an increased sense of identity and self-worth, and the fulfillment of personal goals. Small business owners strive to make their mark in today's competitive marketplace by establishing healthy businesses that can, over time, become legacies handed down from one generation to the next. Entrepreneurs from each generation tackle the obstacles and adversities of the current business and economic climate to test their business savvy and generate opportunities. Today's entrepreneurs face many of the problems of their predecessors, as well as some distinctly new challenges.

With the rightsizing, downsizing, and reorganization of-corporate America, many individuals have decided to confront the risks of developing and operating their own businesses. Small business ownership is rapidly becoming a viable alternative to what is perceived as an equally unstable corporate environment. These entrepreneurs, many of whom have firsthand experience with the problems and inefficiencies inherent in today's large corporations, seek to improve upon an archaic business model and to capitalize on their own ingenuity and strengths. Led by their zeal, many would-be entrepreneurs let their desire, drive, and determination overshadow the need for business knowledge and skill. Ironically, aids in obtaining these components of entrepreneurial success are widely available, easily accessible, and often free of charge.

Small Business Sourcebook (*SBS*) is a six-volume annotated guide to more than 21,310 listings of live and print sources of information designed to facilitate the start-up, development, and growth of specific small businesses, as well as over 26,280 similar listings on general small business topics. An additional 12,367 state-specific listings and over 2,220 U.S. federal government agencies and offices specializing in small business issues, programs, and assistance are also included. *SBS* covers 340 specific small business profiles and 99 general small business topics.

Features of This Edition

This edition of *Small Business Sourcebook* has been revised and updated, incorporating thousand of changes to names, addresses, contacts, and descriptions of listings from the previous edition.

Contents and Arrangement

The geographical scope of *SBS* encompasses the United States and Canada, with expanded coverage for resources pertaining to international trade and for resources that have a U.S. or Canadian distributor or contact. Internet sites that are maintained outside of the U.S. and Canada are also included if they contain relevant information for North American small businesses. Resources that do not relate specifically to small businesses are generally not included.

The information presented in *SBS* is grouped within four sections: Specific Small Business Profiles, General Small Business Topics, State Listings, and Federal Government Assistance. Detailed outlines of these sections may be found in the Users' Guide following this Introduction. Also included is a Master Index to Volumes 1 through 6.

Specific Small Business Profiles This section includes the following types of resources: start-up information, associations and other organizations, educational programs, directories of educational programs, reference works, sources of supply, statistical sources, trade periodicals, videocassettes/audiocassettes, trade shows and conventions, consultants, franchises and business opportunities, computerized databases, computer systems/software, Internet databases, libraries, and research centers-all arranged by business type. Entries range from Accounting Service to Word Processing Service, and include such businesses as Airbag Replacement Service Centers, Computer Consulting, Damage Restoration Service, and Web Site Design.

General Small Business Topics This section offers such resources as associations, books, periodicals, articles, pamphlets, educational programs, directories of educational programs,videocassettes/audiocassettes, trade shows and conventions, consultants, computerized databases, Internet databases, software, libraries, and research centers, arranged alphabetically by business topic.

State Listings Entries include government, academic, and commercial agencies and organizations, as well as select coverage of relevant state-specific publications; listings are arranged alphabetically by state, territory, and Canadian province. Some examples include small business development consultants, educational programs, financing and loan programs, better business bureaus, and chambers of commerce.

Federal Government Assistance Listings specializing in small business issues, programs, assistance, and policyare arranged alphabetically by U.S. government agency or office; regional or branch offices are listed alphabetically by state.

Master Index All entries in Volumes 1 through 6 are arranged in one alphabetic index for convenience.

Entries in *SBS* include (as appropriate andavailable):

- Organization, institution, or product name

- Contact information, including contact name, address and phone, toll-free, and fax numbers

- Author/editor, date(s), and frequency

- Availability, including price

- Brief description of purpose, services, or content

- Company and/or personal E-mail addresses

- Web site addresses

SBS also features the following:

Guide to Publishers—An alphabetic listing of 2,470 companies, associations, institutions, and individuals that publish the periodicals, directories, guidebooks, and other publications noted in the Small Business Profiles and General Topics sections. Users are provided with full contact information, including address, phone, fax,and e-mail and URL when available. The Guide to Publishers facilitates contact with publishers and provides a one- stop resource for valuable information.

Method of Compilation

SBS was compiled by consulting small business experts and entrepreneurs, as well as a variety of resources, including direct contact with the associations, organizations, and agencies through telephone surveys, Internet research, or through materials provided by those listees; government resources; and data obtained from other relevant Gale directories. *SBS* was reviewed by a team of small business advisors, all of whom have numerous years of expertise in small business counseling and identification of small business information resources. The last and perhaps most important resource we utilize is direct contact with our readers, who provide valuable comments and suggestions to improve our publication. *SBS* relies on these comprehensive market contacts to provide today's entrepreneurs with relevant, current, and accurate informationon all aspects of small business.

Available in Electronic Formats

Licensing. *Small Business Sourcebook* is available for licensing. The complete database is provided in a fielded format and is deliverable on such media as disk or CD-ROM. For more information, contact Gale's Business Development Group at1-800-877-GALE, or visit our website at www.gale.com/bizdev.

Comments and Suggestions Welcome

Associations, agencies, business firms, publishers, and other organizations that provide assistance and information to the small business community are encouraged to submit material about their programs, activities, services, or products. Comments and suggestions from users of this directory are also welcomed and appreciated. Please contact:

Project Editor
Small Business Sourcebook
Gale, Cengage Learning
27500 Drake Rd.
Farmington Hills, MI 48331-3535
Phone: (248) 699-4253
Fax: (248) 699-8070
E-mail: BusinessProductsgale.com
URL: www.gale.com

Small Business Sourcebook (*SBS*) provides information in a variety of forms and presentations for comprehensive coverage and ease of use. The directory contains four parts within two volumes:

- Specific Small Business Profiles
- General Small Business Topics
- State Listings
- Federal Government Assistance

Information on specific businesses is arranged by type of business; the many general topics that are of interest to the owners, operators, or managers of all small businesses are grouped in a separate section for added convenience. Users should consult the various sections to benefit fully from the information *SBS* offers. For example, an entrepreneur with a talent or interest in the culinary arts could peruse a number of specific small business profiles, such as Restaurant, Catering, Cooking School, Specialty Food/Wine Shop, Bakery/Doughnut Shop, Healthy Restaurant, or Candy/Chocolate Store. Secondly, the General Small Business Topics section could be consulted for any applicable subjects, such as Service Industry, Retailing, Franchising, and other relevant topics. Then, the appropriate state within the State Listings section would offer area programs and offices providing information and support to small businesses, including venture capital firms and small business development consultants. Finally, the Federal Government Assistance section could supply relevant government offices, such as procurement contacts.

Features Included in Volumes 1 through 3

List of Small Business Profiles. This list provides an alphabetic outline of the small businesses profiled, with cross-references for related profiles and for alternate names by which businesses may be identified. The page number for each profile is indicated.

Standard Industrial Classification (SIC) Codes for Profiled Small Businesses. This section lists four-digit SIC codes and corresponding classification descriptions for the small businesses profiled in this edition. The SIC system, which organizes businesses by type, is a product of the Statistical Policy Division of the U.S. Office of Management and Budget. Statistical data produced by government, public, and private organizations is usually categorized according to SIC codes, thereby facilitating the collection, comparison, and analysis of data as well as providing a uniform method for presenting statistical information. Hence, knowing the SIC code for a particular small business increases access and the use of a variety of statistical data from many sources.

Guide to Publishers. This resource lists alphabetically the companies, associations, institutions, and individuals that publish the periodicals, directories, guidebooks, and other publications noted in the "Small Business Profiles" and "General Topics" sections. Users are provided with full contact information, including address, phone, fax, and e-mail and URL when available. The "Guide" facilitates contact with publishers and provides a one-stop resource for valuable information.

Glossary of Small Business Terms. This glossary defines nearly 400 small business terms, including financial, governmental, insurance, procurement, technical, and general business definitions. Cross-references and acronyms are also provided.

Small Business Profiles A-Z. A total of 340 small businesses is represented in volumes 1 through 3. Profiles are listed alphabetically by business name. Entries within each profile are arranged alphabetically by resource type, within up to 17 subheadings. These subheadings are detailed below:

- *Start-up Information*—Includes periodical articles, books, manuals, book excerpts, kits, and other sources of information. Entries offer title; publisher; address; phone, fax, toll-free numbers; company e-mail and URL addresses; and a description. Bibliographic data is provided for cited periodical articles whenever possible.

- *Associations and Other Oganizations*—Includes trade and professional associations whose members gather and disseminate information of interest to small business owners. Entries offer the association's name; address; phone, toll-free and fax numbers; company e-mail address; contact name; purpose and objective; a description of membership; telecommunication services; and a listing of its publications, including publishing frequency.

- *Educational Programs*—Includes university and college programs, schools, training opportunities, association seminars, correspondence courses, and other educational programs.Entries offer name of program or institution, sponsor name, address, phone, toll-free and fax numbers, e-mail and URL addresses; and description of program.

- *Directories of Educational Programs*—Includes directories and other publications that list educational programs. Entries offer name of publication; publisher name, address, and phone, toll-free and fax numbers; editor; frequency or date of publication; price; and description of contents, including directory arrangement and indexes.

- *Reference Works*—Includes handbooks, manuals, textbooks, guides, directories, dictionaries, encyclopedias, and other published reference materials. Entries offer name of publication; publisher name, address, and phone, toll-free and fax numbers; e-mail and URL addresses; and, when available, name of author or editor, publication year or frequency, and price. A brief description is often featured.

- *Sources of Supply*—Includes buyer's guides,directories, special issues of periodicals, and other publications that list sources of equipment, supplies, and services related to the operation of the profiled small business. Entries offer publication name; publisher name, address, and phone, toll-free and fax numbers; e-mail and URL addresses; and, when available, editor's name, frequency or publication year, and price. A brief description of the publication, including directory arrangement and indexes, is often provided.

- *Statistical Sources*—Includes books, reports, pamphlets, and other sources of statistical data of interest to an owner, operator or manager of the profiled small business, such as wage, salary, and compensation data; financial and operating ratios; prices and costs; demographics; and other statistical information. Entries offer publication/data source name; publisher (if applicable); address; phone, toll-free and fax numbers of data source; publication date or frequency; and price. A brief description of the publication/data source is often provided.

- *Trade Periodicals*—Includes trade journals, newsletters, magazines, and other serials that offer information about the management and operation of the profiled small business. Such periodicals often contain industry news; trends and developments; reviews; articles about new equipment and supplies;

and other information related to business operations. Entries offer publication name; publisher name, address, phone, toll-free and fax numbers, and e-mail and URL addresses; editor name; publication frequency; andprice. A brief description of the publication's content is also included, when known.

- *Videocassettes/Audiocassettes*—Includes videocassettes, audiocassettes, and other audiovisual media offering information on the profiled small business. Entries offer program title; distributor name, address, phone, toll-free and fax numbers, and e-mail and URL addresses; description of program; release date; price; and format(s).

- *Trade Shows and Conventions*—Includes tradeshows, exhibitions, expositions, conventions, and other industry meetings that provide prospective and existing business owners with the opportunity to meet and exchange information with their peers, review commercial exhibits, establish business or sales contacts, and attend educational programs. Entries offer event name; sponsor or management company name, address, phone, toll-free and fax numbers, and e-mail and URL addresses; a description of the event, including audience, frequency, principal exhibits, and dates and locations of event for as many years ahead as provided by the event's sponsor.

- *Consultants*—Includes consultants and consulting organizations that provide services specifically related to the profiled small business. Entries offer individual consultant or consulting organization name, address, and phone, toll-free and fax numbers; company and individual e-mail addresses; and a brief description of consulting services. (For e-mail and URL addresses, see the Small Business Development Consultants subheadings in the State Listings section in Volume 2.)

- *Franchises and Business Opportunities*—Includes companies granting franchise licenses for enterprises falling within the scope of the profiled small business, as well as other non-franchised business opportunities that operate within a given network or system. Entries offer franchise name, address, phone, toll-free and fax numbers, and e-mail and URL addresses, as well as a description of the franchise or business opportunity, which has been expanded whenever possible to include the number of existing franchises, the founding date of the franchise, franchise fees, equity capital requirements, royalty fees, any managerial assistance offered, and available training.

- *Computerized Databases*—Includes diskettes, magnetic tapes, CD-ROMs, online systems, and other computer-readable databases. Entries offer database name; producer name, address, phone, toll-free and fax numbers, e-mail and URL addresses; description; and available format(s), including vendor name.

(Many university and public libraries offer online information retrieval services that provide searches of databases, including those listed in this category.)

- **Computer Systems/Software**—Includes software-eand computerized business systems designed to assist in the operation of the profiled small business. Entries offer name of the software or system; publisher name, address, phone, toll-free and fax-numbers; price; and description.

- **Libraries**—Includes libraries and special collections that contain material especially applicable to the profiled small business. Entries offer library or collection name; parent organization (where applicable); address; phone, toll-free and fax numbers; e-mail and URL addresses; contact name and title; scope of collection; and description of holdings, subscriptions, and services.

- **Research Centers**—Includes university-related and independently operated research institutes and information centers that generate, through their research programs, data related to the operation of the profiled small business. Also listed are associations and other business-related organizations that conduct research programs. Entries offer name of organization; address; phone, toll-free and fax numbers; company web site address; contact name and personale-mail; a description of principal fields of research or services; publications, including title and frequency; and related conferences.

Features Included in Volumes 2 through 6

General Small Business Topics. This section offers chapters on different topics in the operation of any small business, for example, venture capital and other funding, or compensation. Chapters are listed alphabetically by small business topic; entries within each chapter are arranged alphabetically, within up to 14 subheadings, by resource type:

- **Associations and Other Organizations**—Includes trade and professional associations that gather and disseminate information of interest to small business owners. Entries offer the association's name; address; phone, toll-free and fax numbers; organization e-mail and URL addresses; contact name;purpose and objectives; a description of membership; telecommunication services; and a listing of its publications, including publishing frequency.

- **Educational Programs**—Includes university and college programs, schools, training opportunities, association seminars, correspondence courses, and other educational programs. Entries offer name of program or institution, sponsor name, address, phone, toll-free and fax numbers, e-mail and URL addresses, and description of program.

- **Directories of Educational Programs**—Includes directories and other publications that list educational programs. Entries offer name of publication; publisher name, address, phone, toll-free and fax numbers, and e-mail and URL addresses; editor; frequency or date of publication; price; and description of contents, including arrangement and indexes.

- **Reference Works**—Includes articles, handbooks, manuals, textbooks, guides, directories, dictionaries, encyclopedias, and other published reference materials. Entries offertitle of article, including bibliographic information; name of publication; publisher name, address, phone, toll-free and fax numbers, and e-mail and URL addresses; and, when available, name of author oreditor, publication year or frequency, and price. A brief descriptionis often featured.

- **Sources of Supply**—Includes buyer's guides,directories, special issues of periodicals, and other publications that list sources of equipment, supplies, and services. Entries offer publication name; publisher name, address, phone, toll-free and fax numbers, and e-mail and URL addresses; editor's name, frequency or publication year, price, and a brief description of the publication, when available.

- **Statistical Sources**—Includes books, reports, pamphlets, and other sources of statistical data of interest to an owner, operator, or manager of a small business, such as wage, salary, and compensation data; financial and operating ratios; prices and costs; demographics; and other statistical information. Entries offer publication/data source name; publisher (if applicable); address; phone, toll-free and fax numbers of data source; publication date or frequency; and price. A brief description is often provided.

- **Trade Periodicals**—Includes journals, newsletters, magazines, and other serials. Entries offer name of publication; publisher name, address, phone, toll-free and fax numbers, and e-mail and URL addresses; and name of editor, frequency, and price.A brief description of the periodical's content is included when known.

- **Videocassettes/Audiocassettes**—Includes videocassettes, audiocassettes, and other audiovisual media. Entries offer program title; distributor name, address, phone, toll-free and fax numbers, and e-mail and URL addresses; price; description of program; release date; and format(s).

- **Trade Shows and Conventions**—Includes tradeshows, exhibitions, expositions, seminars, and conventions. Entries offer event name; sponsor or management company name, address, phone, toll-free and fax numbers, and e-mail and URL addresses; frequency of event; and dates and locations of the event for as many years ahead as known.

- *Consultants*—Includes consultants and consulting organizations. Entries offer individual consultant or-consulting organization name, address, and phone, toll-free and fax numbers; company and individual e-mail addresses; and a brief description of consulting services. (See also Consultants in the State Listings section.)

- *Computerized Databases*—Includes diskettes, CD-ROMs, magnetic tape, online systems and other computer-readable databases. Entries offer database name; producer, address, phone, toll-free and fax numbers, and e-mail and URL addresses; description; and available format(s), including vendor name. (Many university and public libraries offer online information retrieval services that provide searches of databases, including those listed in this category.)

- *Computer Systems/Software*—Includes software and computerized business systems. Entries offer name of the software or system; publisher name, ad-dress, phone, toll-free and fax numbers, and e-mail and URL addresses; price; and description.

- *Libraries*—Includes libraries and special collections that contain material applicable to the small business topic. Entries offer library or collection name, parent organization (where applicable), address, phone and fax numbers, e-mail and URL addresses, scope of collection, and description of holdings and services.

- *Research Centers*— Includes university-related and independently operated research institutes and information centers that generate, through their research programs, data related to specific small business topics. Entries offer name of organization, address, phone, toll-free and fax numbers, e-mail and URL addresses, a description of principal fields of research or services, and related conferences.

State Listings. This section lists various sources of information and assistance available within given states, ter-ritories, and Canadian provinces; entries include governmen-tal, academic, and commercial agencies, and are arranged alphabetically within up to 15 subheadings by resource type:

- *Small Business Development Center Lead Of-fice*— Includes the lead small business development center (SBDC) for each state.

- *Small Business Development Centers*—Includes any additional small business development centers (SBDC) in the state, territory, or province. SBDCs provide support services to small businesses, includ-ing individual counseling, seminars, conferences, and learning center activities.

- *Small Business Assistance Programs*—Includes state small business development offices and other programs offering assistance to small businesses.

- *SCORE Offices*—Includes SCORE office(s) for each state. The Service Corps of Retired Executives As-sociation (SCORE), a volunteer program sponsored by the Small Business Administration, offers counsel-ing, workshops, and seminars across the U.S. for small business entrepreneurs.

- *Better Business Bureaus*—Includes various better business bureaus within each state. By becoming a member of the local Better Business Bureau, a small business owner can increase the prestige and cred-ibility of his or her business within the community, as well as make valuable business contacts.

- *Chambers of Commerce*—Includes various chambers of commerce within each state. Chambers of Commerce are valuable sources of small business advice and information; often, local chambers sponsor SCORE counseling several times per month for a small fee, seminars, conferences, and other workshops to its members. Also, by becoming a member of the local Chamber of Commerce, a small business owner can increase the prestige and cred-ibility of his or herbusiness within the community, as well as make valuable business contacts.

- *Minority Business Assistance Programs*—Includes minority business development centers and other sources of assistance for minority-owned business.

- *Financing and Loan Programs*—Includes venture capital firms, small business investment companies (SBIC), minority enterprise small business investment companies (MESBIC), and other programs that provide funding to qualified small businesses.

- *Procurement Assistance Programs*—Includes state services such as counseling, set-asides, and sheltered-market bidding, which are designed to aid small businesses in bidding on government contracts.

- *Incubators/Research and Technology Parks*— Includes small business incubators, which provide newly established small business owners with work sites, business services, training, and consultation; also includes research and technology parks, which sponsor research and facilitate commercialization of new technologies.

- *Educational Programs*—Includes university and col-lege programs, as well as those sponsored by other organizations that offer degree, nondegree, certificate, and correspondence programs in entrepreneurship and in small business development.

- *Legislative Assistance*—Includes committees, subcommittees, and joint committees of each state's senate and house of representatives that are concerned with small business issues and regulations.

- **Consultants**—Includes consultants and consulting firms offering expertise in small business development.

- **Publications**—Includes publications related to small business operations within the profiled state.

- **Publishers**—Includes publishers operating in or for the small business arena within the profiled state.

Federal Government Assistance. This section lists federal government agencies and offices, many with additional listings for specific offices, as well as regional or district branches. Main agencies or offices are listed alphabetically; regional, branch, ordistrict offices are listed after each main office or agency.

Master Index. This index provides an alphabetic listing of all entries contained in Volumes 1 throgh 6. Citations are referenced by their entry numbers. Publication titles are rendered in italics.

Acknowledgements

The editors would like to extend sincere thanks to the following members of the Small Business Sourcebook advisory board for their expert guidance, recommendations, and suggestions for the ongoing development of this title:

Susan C. Awe
Assistant Director,
William J. Parish Memorial Business Library

Jill Clever
Business Technology Specialist,
Toledo-Lucas County Public Library

Jules Matsoff
District Manager,
Service Corps of Retired Executives (SCORE) Milwaukee
  Chapter

Ken MacKenzie
President,
Southeast Business Appraisal

The editors would also like to thank the individuals from associations and other organizations who provided information for the compilation of this directory.

List of Small Business Profiles

This list is an outline of the 341 small businesses profiled in this edition of Small Business Sourcebook. The beginning page number of each profile is provided. For convenience, this index also provides cross-references to small businesses known by alternate names, businesses contained within other small business profiles, and synonymous or related businesses.

Standard Industrial Classification (SIC) Codes for Profiled Small Businesses

Included here are the four-digit SIC codes and corresponding classification descriptions for the businesses profiled in this edition. The SIC system, which organizes businesses by type, is a product of the Statistical Policy Division of the U.S. Office of Management and Budget. Statistical data produced by government, public, and private organizations usually are categorized according to SIC codes, thereby facilitating the collection, comparison, and analysis of data as well as providing a uniform method for presenting statistical information. Hence, knowing the SIC code for a particular small business increases the access to, and the use of, a variety of statistical data from many sources. The following SIC codes were obtained from the 1987 edition of the Standard Industrial Classification Manual, the most recent version available. (The term "nec" stands for "not elsewhere classified.")

Accounting Service

7291   Tax return preparation services

8721   Accounting, auditing, and bookkeeping services

Adult Day Care Center

8322   Individual and family social services (includes adult day carecenters)

Advertising Service

7311   Advertising agencies (includes advertising consultants)

7312   Outdoor advertising agencies

7313   Radio, television, and publishers' advertising representatives

7319   Advertising, nec

7331   Direct mail advertising services

8999   Services, nec (includes advertising copywriters)

Airbag Replacement Service Centers

7538   General automotive repair shops

7539   Automotive repair shops, nec

Air Charter Service

4512   Air transportation, scheduled (includes air cargo and passenger carriers)

4513   Air courier services

4522   Air transportation, nonscheduled (includes charter service)

Air-conditioning/Heating and Cooling Contractor

1711   Plumbing, heating, and air-conditioning contractors

Air Purification/Cleaning Service

7699   Repair shops and related services, nec (includes furnace cleaning service)

Ambulance Service

4119   Local passenger transportation, nec (includes ambulance service, road)

4522   Air transportation, nonscheduled (includes ambulance service, air)

Amusement Arcade

7993   Coin-operated amusement devices

Amusement/Water Park

7996   Amusement parks

7999   Amusement and recreation services, nec (includes waterslides and wave pools)

Animal Breeder

0279   Animal specialties, nec (includes kennels, breeding and raising own stock)

0752   Animal specialty services, except veterinary (includes breeding of animals other than farm animals)

Animal Clinic

0742   Veterinary service for animal specialties (includes animal hospitals for pets and other animals)

Antique Shop

5932   Used merchandise stores (includes retail antique stores)

Reupholstery (continued)

7641   Reupholstery and furniture repair (includes antique furniture repair and restoration)

7699   Repair shops and related services, nec (includes antique repair and restoration, except furniture)

Apartment Locating Service

6531   Real Estate Agents and Managers

Appliance Store

5722   Household appliance stores

Appraisal Service

7389   Business services, nec (includes appraisers, except real estate)

6531   Real estate agents and managers (includes appraisers, realestate)

Aquarium Maintenance/Leasing Service

7359   Equipment rental and leasing, nec

8999   Services, nec

Archery/Target/Shooting Range

7999   Amusement and recreation services, nec (includes archery ranges, shooting galleries, shooting ranges, and trap-shooting facilities, except membership)

Architectural Restoration/Conservation

8712   Architectural Services

Art Gallery

5932   Used merchandise stores (includes retailers of art objects)

5999   Miscellaneous retail stores, nec (includes art dealers)

8412   Museums and art galleries (includes noncommercial art galleries)

Art Supplies Store

5999   Miscellaneous retail stores, nec (includes retail artists' supplies and materials stores)

Assisted Living Facilities

8051   Skilled nursing care facilities (includes extended care facilities and skilled nursing homes)

8052   Intermediate care facilities (includes intermediate care nursing homes)

8059   Nursing and personal care facilities, nec (includes rest homeswith health care)

Association Management Service

8611   Business associations

8621   Professional membership organizations

8631   Labor unions and similar labor organizations

8641   Civic, social, and fraternal associations

8699   Membership organizations, nec

8741   Management services (does not include operating staff)

Auctioneer

5154   Livestock (includes wholesale livestock auctioning)

5999   Miscellaneous retail stores, nec (includes retail general merchandise auction rooms)

7389   Business services, nec (includes auctioneering services)

Auto Supply Store

5531   Auto and home supply stores

Automobile Detailing/Painting Service

7532   Automotive paint shops

7542   Carwashes (includes detailing, cleaning and polishing, new autos on a contract or fee basis; washing and polishing, automotive; waxing and polishing, automotive)

Automobile/Truck Leasing Service

7513   Truck rental and leasing, without drivers

7514   Passenger car rental, without drivers

7515   Passenger car leasing, without drivers

Baby Store

5999   Miscellaneous retail stores, nec (includes retail baby)

Bagel Shop

2051   Bread and other bakery products, except cookies and crackers (includes bagels)

5461   Retail bakeries (includes retail bagel stores)

Bait and Tackle Shop

5941   Sporting goods stores and bicycle shops (includes bait and tackle shops and fishing equipment, retail)

Bakery/Doughnut Shop

5461   Retail bakeries

Bar/Cocktail Lounge

5813   Drinking places alcoholic beverages (includes bars, cocktail lounges, saloons, tap rooms, taverns, and like establishments)

Beauty Supply Center

5087   Service establishment equipment and supplies (includes wholesale barber shop and beauty parlor equipment and supplies)

Bed and Breakfast Operation

7011   Hotels and motels (includes bed and breakfast inns)

Beekeeping

0279   Animal specialties, nec (includes apiaries and bee farms)

Beeper/Paging Service

4812   Radiotelephone communications (includes beeper and paging services)

Bicycle Shop

5941   Sporting goods stores and bicycle shops

7699   Repair shops and related services, nec (includes bicycle repair shops)

Billiards Hall

7999   Amusement and recreation services, nec (includes billiard parlors)

Blacktop Surfacing Business

1771   Concrete work (includes blacktop work: private driveways and private parking areas contractors)

Blind Cleaning/Installation

2431   Millwork (includes wood blinds and shutters)

2591   Drapery hardware and window blinds and shades

Body Care Shop

5999   Miscellaneous retail stores, nec (includes cosmetics stores)

Book Publishing

2731   Books; publishing or publishing and printing

Bookbinder

2789   Bookbinding and related work

Bookkeeping

8721   Accounting, auditing, and bookkeeping services

Bookstore

5932   Used merchandise stores (includes used book retailers)

5942   Bookstores

Bottled Water Service

5149   Groceries and related products, nec (includes natural spring and mineral water bottling and distribution services)

5499   Miscellaneous food stores (includes mineral water, retail)

Bowling Alley

7933   Bowling centers

Brewery Operation

2082   Malt beverages

Bridal Shop/Bridal Consultant

5621   Women's clothing stores (includes retail bridal shops, exceptcustom designers)

Building/Home Inspection

7389   Business services, nec (includes safety inspection, except automotive)

Building Maintenance/Custodial Service

7349   Building cleaning and maintenance services, nec (includes interior building cleaning services, contract janitorial services, and like enterprises)

Bulletin Board Service

4822   Telegraph and other message communications (includes electronic mail services)

7379   Computer related services, nec

Business Broker Service

7389   Business services, nec (includes business brokers buying andselling business enterprises)

Business Consulting Service

8748   Business consulting services, nec

Business Services Operation

8744   Facilities support management services (includesbasemaintenance, providing personnel on continuing basis)

Butcher Shop

5423   Meat and fish (seafood) markets, including freezer provisioners

---

5499   Miscellaneous food stores (includes retail poultry dealers)

Cable Network

1623   Water, Sewer, Pipeline, and Communications and Power Line Construction (includes cable television line construction-contractors)

1731   Electrical Work (includes cable television hookup-contractors)

4841   Cable and Other Pay Television Services

Calligraphy Service

7389   Business services, nec (includes lettering services)

Camera Shop

5946   Camera and photographic supply stores

7699   Repair shops and related services, nec (includes camera repair shops)

Campground Management

7033   Recreational vehicle parks and campsites

Candy/Chocolate Shop

5441   Candy, nut, and confectionery stores

Car Alarm and Stereo Store

5531   Auto and home supply stores (includes automobile accessorydealers, retail)

5731   Radio, television, and consumer electronics stores (includesautomotive stereo equipment, retail)

Car Inspection Service

7549   Automotive services, except repair services and car washes(includes inspection service, automotive)

Car Towing Service

7549   Automotive services, except repair services and car washes(includes automotive towing and wrecker services)

Car Wash

7542   Car washes

Career Counseling

7389   Business services, nec (includes career counseling service)

Carpentry Service

1751   Carpentry work

Catering Service

5812   Eating places (includes caterers)

CD-ROM Developer/Producer

7372   Prepackaged software (includes pre-packaged computer software publishers)

7379   Computer related services, nec (includes database developers)

Cellular Phone/Telephone Business

4812   Radiotelephone communications

5999   Miscellaneous retail stores, nec (includes telephone stores, retail)

Charter Boat Service

4499   Water transportation service, nec (includes boat rental, commercial)

Check Cashing Service

6099   Functions related to depository banking, nec (includes check cashing agencies)

Children's Apparel Shop

5611   Men's and boys' clothing stores

5641   Children's and infants' wear stores

5651   Family clothing stores

5699   Miscellaneous apparel and accessory stores (includes children's wear)

5932   Used merchandise stores (includes retail second hand clothing stores)

Children's Day Care Center

8351   Child day care services

Chimney Sweeping Business

7349   Building cleaning and maintenance services, nec (includeschimney cleaning service)

Christmas Decoration Store

5999   Miscellaneous retail stores, nec

Christmas Tree Farm

0811   Timber tracts (includes Christmas tree growing)

Clipping Service

7389   Business services, nec (includes press clipping service)

Clothing Designer

2311   Men's and boys' suits, coats, and overcoats

2325   Men's and boys' separate trousers and slacks

2329   Men's and boys' clothing, nec

2331   Women's, misses', and juniors' blouses and shirts

2335   Women's, misses', and juniors' dresses

2337   Women's, misses', and juniors' suits, skirts, and coats

2361   Girls', children's, and infants' dresses, blouses, and shirts

Clothing Store

5611   Men's and boys' clothing and accessory stores

5621   Women's clothing stores

5632   Women's accessory and specialty stores

5641   Children's and infants' wear stores

5651   Family clothing stores

5699   Miscellaneous apparel and accessory stores

5932   Used merchandise stores (includes retail secondhand clothing stores)

Coffee Service

5149   Groceries and related products, nec (includes coffee, wholesale)

Coin/Stamp Dealer

5961   Catalog and mail order houses (includes retail mail order coinand stamp businesses)

5999   Miscellaneous retail stores, nec

Comedy Club

5813   Drinking placesMalcoholic beverages (includes nightclubs)

Comic Book/Collectibles Store

5999   Miscellaneous retail stores, nec

Commercial/Graphic Art Business

7336   Commercial art and graphic design

Commercial Mail Receiving Agency

7389   Business services, nec (includes post office contract stations)

Compact Disc/Record Store

5735   Recorded and prerecorded tape stores

Computer Consulting

7379   Computer related services, nec (includes computer consultants

Computer Data Storage Company

3572   Computer storage devices

Computer Learning/Training Center

8243   Data processing schools

Computer Maintenance and Repair Service

7378   Computer maintenance and repair

Computer Programming and Data Processing Service

7374   Computer processing and data preparation services

Computer Store

5734   Computer and computer software stores

Computer System Integrators

7371   Computer programming services

7373   Computer integrated systems design

7379   Computer related services, nec (includes computer consultants and database developers)

Computerized Billing Service

7374   Computer processing and data preparation and processing services

Computerized Matching Service

7299   Miscellaneous personal services, nec (includes dating services)

7375   Information retrieval services

Concession Stand Business

5812   Eating places (includes concession stands in airports and sports arenas, and refreshment stands)

7999   Amusement and recreation services, nec (concession operators andamusement concessions)

Consignment Shop

5932   Used merchandise stores (includes clothing stores, secondhand retail; furniture stores, secondhand retail; home furnishing stores, secondhand retail)

Construction Company

1521   General contractors—single family houses

1522   General contractors—residential buildings other than single-family

Consumer Electronics Store

5731   Radio, television, and consumer electronics stores

Convenience Store

5411   Grocery stores (includes retail convenience food stores)

Cooking School

8299   Schools and educational services, nec (includes cooking schools)

Copy Shop

7334   Photocopying and duplicating services

Cosmetics Business

2844   Perfumes, cosmetics, and other toilet preparations

5122   Drugs, drug proprietaries, and druggists' sundries (includes cosmetics—wholesale)

5963   Direct selling establishments (includes canvassers, headquarters for retail sale of merchandise, and direct selling organizations—retail)

5999   Miscellaneous retail stores, nec (includes cosmeticsstores—retail)

Costume Shop

7299   Miscellaneous personal services, nec (includes costume rental)

7922   Theatrical producers and miscellaneous theatrical services(includes theatrical costume design)

Craft Artisan

3269   Pottery products, nec (includes art and ornamental ware; pottery; ceramic articles for craft shops; cookware; crockery; china, earthenware and stoneware figures; kitchen articles; coarse earthenware; lamp bases; and vases)

Craft/Hobby Shop

5945   Hobby, toy, and game shops (includes retail hobby stores and craft kit and supply retailers)

5947   Gift, novelty, and souvenir shops pottery; ceramic articles for craft shops; cookware; crockery; china, earthenware and stoneware figures; kitchen articles; coarse earthenware; lamp bases; and vases)

Create Your Own...Store

3269   Pottery Products, nec

5947   Gift, Novelty, and Souvenir Shops

5999   Micellaneous Retail Stores, nec

Credit Card Issuing Service

6153   Short-Term Business Credit Institutions, Except Agricultural (includes credit card service, collection by central agency)

7389   Business Services, nec (includes credit card service collection by individual firms)

Credit Repair Service

7299   Miscellaneous personal services, nec (includes debt counseling and adjustment services)

Credit Reporting and Collection Service

7322   Adjustment and collection services

7323   Credit reporting services

Damage Restoration Service

1790   Special trade contractors, nec (includes cleaning building exteriors, dampproofing buildings, dewatering, fireproofing buildings, steam cleaning of building exteriors, and waterproofing)

Dance School

7911   Dance studios, schools, and halls

Delicatessen/Sandwich Shop

5812   Eating places (includes sandwich bars or shops and submarine sandwich shops)

Desktop Publishing Company

2711   Publishing, or publishing and printing newspapers

2721   Publishing, or publishing and printing periodicals

2731   Publishing, or publishing and printing books

2741   Miscellaneous publishing

Dial-it Services

4813   Telephone communications, except radio-telephone

Diaper Service

7219   Laundry and garment services, nec

Disc Jockey Service

8999   Services, nec

Domestic Help/Maid Service

7349   Building cleaning and maintenance services, nec (includes housekeeping and office cleaning services)

8811   Private households (includes private households employing cooks, maids, and other domestic help)

Driving School

8249   Vocational schools, nec (includes truck driving schools)

8299   Schools and educational services, nec (includes automobile driving instruction)

Drug Store/Pharmacy

5912   Drug stores and proprietary stores

Dry Cleaning Service/Coin-Operated Laundry

7215   Coin-operated laundries and dry cleaning services

7216   Dry cleaning plants, except rug cleaning

Editorial/Freelance Writing Business

8999   Services, nec (includes writing and ghostwriting services)

Electrical Contractor

1731   Electrical work (includes trade contractors engaged in on-site electrical work)

Electrical Lighting Supply Store

5719   Miscellaneous home furnishings stores (includes retail lamp and shade shops)

Employee Leasing Service

7363   Help supply services

Employment Agency

361   Employment agencies

Engraving/Monogramming Service

3479   Coating, engraving, and allied services, nec (includes jewelryand silverware engraving)

7389   Business services, nec (includes advertising embroidery services, embossing services, and identification engraving services)

Environmental Consultant

8748   Business consulting services, nec

Environmental Store

5999   Miscellaneous retail stores, nec

Estate Planning

8811   Private Households

Estate Sales Business

6530   Real estate agents and managers

Executive Recruiting Agency

7361   Employment agencies (includes executive placement)

Fashion Accessories Business

3961   Costume jewelry and costume novelties, except precious metal

5137   Women's, children's, and infants' clothing and accessories

5632   Women's accessory and specialty stores

Fax Service

4822   Telegraph and other message communications (includes facsimile transmission services)

Film and Video Production Operation

7812   Motion picture and videotape production services

Financial Planning Service

282   Investment Advice

Fish and Seafood Store

5421   Meat and fish (seafood) markets, including freezer provisioners

Fish Farm

0273   Animal aquaculture (includes fish farms except hatcheries)

Floor Covering/Restoration Business

5713   Floor covering stores—retail

Florist

5992   Florists

Food Delivery Service

5812   Eating places

5963   Direct selling establishments (includes door-to-door selling organizations and mobile lunch wagons)

5999   Miscellaneous retail stores, nec

Formalwear Rental Business

7299   Miscellaneous personal services, nec (includes tuxedo rental)

Freight Forwarding Service

4731   Arrangement of transportation of freight and cargo (includes freight forwarding services)

Fund Raising Consultant

7389   Business services, nec (includes fund raising on a contract or fee basis)

Funeral Service

7261   Funeral services and crematories

Fur Farm

0271   Fur-bearing animals and rabbits

Fur Store

5632   Women's accessory and specialty stores (includes fur shops and furriers)

Furniture Restoration Service

7641   Reupholstery and furniture repair

Gambling Organizations/Service

7011   Hotels and Motels (includes casino hotels)

7993   Coin-Operated Amusement Devices

7999   Amusement and Recreation Services, nec (includes gambling establishments not primarily operating coin-operated machines and lotteries, operation of)

9311   Public Finance Taxation, and Monetary Policy (includes gambling control boards-government and lottery control boards-government)

Genealogy Service

7299   Miscellaneous personal services, nec (includes genealogical investigation service)

Gift Basket Service

5961   Catalog and mail-order houses

Gift/Card Shop

5943   Stationery stores

5947   Gift, novelty, and souvenir shops (includes card shops)

Glass Repair and Replacement Service

1751   Carpentry work (includes prefabricated window and door installation)

7536   Automotive glass replacement shops

Golf Shop

5941   Sporting goods stores and bicycle shops (includes retail golf goods and equipment stores)

Gourmet Coffee/Tea House

5499   Miscellaneous food stores (includes coffee stores, retail)

5812   Eating places (includes coffee shops)

Greenhouse/Garden Center/Nursery Business

0181   Ornamental floricultural and nursery products (includes greenhouses for floral products, growing of nursery stock, growing of potted plants)

5261	Retail nurseries, lawn and garden supply stores (includes nursery stock, seeds, and bulbs, retail)

Greeting Card Publishing

2771	Greeting card publishing and printing
8999	Services, nec (includes hand painting of greeting cards)

Grocery Store

5411	Grocery stores

Gunsmith/Gun Shop

5941	Sporting good stores and bicycle shops (includes firearms,retail)
7699	Repair shops and related services, nec (includes gunsmith shops)

Hair Replacement/Electrolysis Clinic

7299	Miscellaneous personal services, nec (includes depilatory salons, electrolysis, and hair weaving or replacement services)

Hair Salon/Barber Shop

7231	Beauty shops (includes beauty and barber shops combined)
7241	Barber shops

Handwriting Analysis Consultant

7389	Business services, nec (includes handwriting analysis)

Hardware Store

5251	Hardware stores

Hat Store

5611	Men's and boys' clothing and accessory stores (includes retail hat stores)
5621	Women's accessory and specialty stores (includes retail millinery stores)

Hazardous Waste Disposal Business

4953	Refuse systems (includes hazardous waste material disposal sites)

Healthy Restaurants

5812	Eating Places

Health Food Store

5499	Miscellaneous food stores (includes health food stores)

Hearing Aid Testing and Fitting Service

5999	Miscellaneous retail stores, nec (includes hearing aids, retail)
8099	Health and allied services, nec (includes hearing testing service)

Herb Farm

0191	General farms, primarily crop
2833	Medical chemicals and botanical products (includes herb grinding, grading, and milling)
5499	Miscellaneous food stores (includes spice and herb stores)

Home Accessory Store

5714	Drapery, curtain, and upholstery stores
5719	Miscellaneous home furnishings stores

Home Furnishings Store

5712	Furniture stores
5719	Miscellaneous home furnishings stores
5932	Used merchandise stores (including antique and secondhand retail furniture stores)

Home Health Care Service

8082	Home health care services

Horse Riding Academy

752	Animal specialty services, except veterinary (includes boarding and training horses)

Hotel/Motel/Resort Operation

7011	Hotels and motels (includes resort hotels)

Housesitting Service

8999	Services, nec

Ice Cream/Frozen Yogurt Shop

5451	Dairy products stores (includes retail packaged ice cream stores)

5812	Eating places (includes retail dairy bars)
563	Direct selling establishments (includes ice cream wagons)

Image Consultant

8299	Schools and educational services, nec (includes personal development schools)
8743	Public relations services

Import/Export Service

4731	Arrangement of the transportation of freight and cargo

Incubator

7389	Business services, nec
8748	Business consulting services, nec

Information Broker

7375	Information retrieval services

Insulation Contractor

1742	Plastering, dry wall, acoustical, and insulation work (includes insulation installation contractors)

Insurance Agency

6411	Insurance agents, brokers, and services

Interior Design Service

7389	Business services, nec (includes interior decoration consulting services and interior design services)

Internet/Online Service Provider

4822	Telegraph and other message communications (includes electronicmail services)
7379	Computer related services, nec

Investment/Securities Broker

6211	Security brokers, dealers, and flotation companies

Jewelry Store

5632	Women's accessory and specialty stores (includes costume jewelry stores)

| 5944 | Jewelry stores |
| 7631 | Watch, clock, and jewelry repair |

Job Training/Retraining

| 8331 | Job training and vocational rehabilitation services (includesjob training) |

Kiosk/Pushcart/Vendor Business

| 5812 | Eating places (includes box lunch stands, concession stands,food bars, hamburger and hot dog stands, ice cream stands, refreshment stands, and soft drink stands) |

Landscaping Service

0781	Landscape counseling and planning services
0782	Lawn and garden services
0783	Ornamental shrub and tree services

Lawn Maintenance Service

| 0782 | Lawn and garden services |
| 0783 | Ornamental shrub and tree services |

Limousine Service

| 4119 | Local passenger transportation, nec (includes hearse and limousine rental, with drivers) |
| 7514 | Passenger car rental (includes limo rental, w/o drivers) |

Lingerie Shop

| 5632 | Lingerie storesMretail |

Liquor Store

| 5921 | Liquor stores |

Literary Agency

| 7389 | Business services, nec (includes agents and brokers for authors and non-performing artists) |

Locksmith

| 7699 | Repair shops and related services, nec (includes locksmith shops and made-to order lock parts) |

Luggage and Leather Goods Business

| 5948 | Luggage and leather goods stores |

Lumberyard

| 5211 | Lumber and other building materials dealers |

Machine Shop/Metalorking Shop

3541	Machine tools, metal cutting types
3542	Machine tools, metal forming types
3544	Special dies and tools, die sets, jigs and fixtures, and industrial molds
3545	Cutting tools, machine tool accessories, and machinists' precision measuring devices
3549	Metalworking machinery, nec

Mail Order Business

| 5961 | Catalog and mail order houses |

Management Consulting Service

| 8742 | Management consulting services |

Manufacturer's Representative

| 7389 | Business services, nec |

Marine Shop

| 5551 | Boat dealers (includes retail marine supply dealers) |

Market Research and Analysis

| 8732 | Commercial, economic, sociological, and educational research |
| 8742 | Management consulting services |

Martial Arts Studio

| 7999 | Amusement and recreation services, nec (includes Judo and Karate instruction) |

Masonry, Stonework, and Plastering Contractors

| 1741 | Masonry, stone setting, and other stonework |
| 1742 | Plastering, dry wall, acoustical, and insulation work |

Massage Therapist

| 7299 | Massage parlor 8049 Offices and clinics of health practitioners,nec |

Mediation Service

| 7389 | Business services, nec (includes arbitration and conciliationservices) |

Medical and Dental Instrument Manufacturing

| 3841 | Surgical and medical instruments and apparatus |
| 3843 | Dental equipment and supplies |

Medical Claims Service

| 6411 | Insurance agents, brokers, and service (includes processing ofmedical claims on a contract or fee basis) |

Medical Laboratory Service

| 8071 | Medical laboratories |

Medical Supplies Store

| 5047 | Medical, dental, and hospital equipment and supplies |

Medical Transcription Service

| 7374 | Computer processing and data preparation and processing services |

Messenger/Delivery/Subpoena Service

4215	Courier services, except by air (includes letter, mail, package,and parcel delivery services)
4822	Telegraph and other message communication (includes cablegrams, mailgrams, electronic mail, and other message services)
7389	Business services, nec (includes process serving services)

Miniature Golf Course Operation

| 7999 | Amusement and recreation services, nec (includes miniature golf course operations) |

Modeling School/Agency

| 7363 | Help supply services (includes modeling services) |

8299   Schools and educational services, nec (includes modeling schools)

Mortgage Broker

6162   Mortgage bankers and loan correspondents (includes mortgage brokers using own money)

6163   Loan brokers (includes mortgage brokers arranging for loans but using money of others)

6211   Security brokers, dealers, and flotation companies (includes buying and selling mortgages)

Motorcycle/Moped Store

5571   Motorcycle dealers

Movie Theatre Operation

7832   Motion picture theatres, except drive-ins

7833   Drive-in motion picture theatres

Moving Service

4212   Local trucking, without storage (includes furniture and other moving services)

4214   Local trucking, with storage (includes furniture and household goods moving services)

Music School

8299   Schools and educational services, nec (includes music schools)

Music Shop

5736   Musical instrument stores

5932   Used merchandise stores (includes retailers of secondhand musical instruments)

7699   Repair shops and related services, nec (includes musical instrument repair shops)

Musical Instrument Repair/Piano Tuning Service

7699   Repair shops and related services, nec (includes musical instrument repair shops and piano tuning and repair)

Nail Salon

7231   Beauty shops (includes manicure and pedicure salons)

Nanny Service

7299   Miscellaneous personal services, nec (includes babysitting bureaus)

New Age Services and Supplies

5999   Miscellaneous retail stores, nec

8999   Services, nec

New and Used Car Dealer

5511   Motor vehicle dealers (new and used)

5521   Motor vehicle dealers (used only)

Newsletter Publishing

2721   Periodicals; publishing or publishing and printing

2741   Miscellaneous publishing (includes business service newsletterspublishing and/or printing)

Novelty Items Business

2499   Wood products, nec (includes wood and wood fiber novelties)

2514   Metal household furniture (includes metal novelty furniture)

2679   Converted paper and paperboard products, nec (includes papernovelties)

3199   Leather goods, nec (includes leather novelties)

3229   Pressed and blown glass and glassware, nec (includes novelty glassware made in glassmaking plants)

3231   Glass products, made of purchased glass (includes glassnovelties)

3499   Fabricated metal products, nec (includes metal novelties and specialties, except advertising novelties)

3961   Costume jewelry and costume novelties, except precious metal andgems

3999   Manufacturing industries, nec (includes bone, beaded and shell novelties)

Nursing Home/Long-Term Care Center

8051   Skilled nursing care facilities

8052   Intermediate care facilities (includes intermediate care nursing homes)

8059   Nursing and personal care facilities, nec (includes convalescent homes, rest homes, and like facilities)

Nutritional Consultant/Diet Planner

7299   Miscellaneous personal services, nec (includes diet workshops)

8049   Offices and clinics of health practitioners, nec (includes offices of nutritionists and offices of dietitians)

Office Design Service

7389   Business services, nec (includes interior decorating and design services)

Office Supply/Equipment Store

5943   Stationery stores (includes retail office forms and supplies stores)

Online Store

5734   Computer and computer software stores

7375   Information retrieval services

Paint/Wall Covering Center

5231   Paint, glass, and wallpaper stores

Painting Contractors

1721   Painting and paperhanging contractors

Party Entertainment Services

7929   Bands, orchestras, actors, and other entertainers and entertainment groups

Party/Reunion Planning Service

7359   Equipment rental and leasing, nec (includes party supplies rental and leasing)

8999   Services, nec

Pawnbroker

5932   Used merchandise stores (includes pawnshops)

Payroll Preparation Service

8721   Accounting, auditing, and bookkeeping services (includes payrollaccounting service)

Periodical/Newspaper Publishing

2721   Periodicals; publishing or publishing and printing

Personal Shopping Service

7299   Miscellaneous personal services, nec (includes shopping servicesfor individuals)

Pest Control Service

0851   Forestry services (includes forest pest control)

7342   Disinfecting and pest control services

Pet Boarding/Grooming Service

0279   Animal specialties, nec (includes breeding kennels)

0752   Animal specialty services (includes boarding kennels, doggrooming services, and related services)

Pet Cemetery

0782   Lawn and garden services (includes independent cemetery upkeep services)

6531   Real estate agents and managers (includes cemetery management services)

6553   Cemetery subdividers and developers (includes animal cemetery operations)

Pet Obedience School

0752   Animal specialty services, except veterinary (includes training of pets and other animal specialties)

Pet Shop

5999   Miscellaneous retail stores, nec (includes pet shops)

Pet Sitting Service

0752   Animal specialty services, except veterinary

Photo Finishing Center

7384   Photo finishing laboratories

7819   Services allied to motion picture production (includes motion picture film processing)

Photographer, Commercial

7335   Commercial photography

Photographic Studio

7221   Photographic studios, portrait

Physical Fitness Center

7991   Physical fitness facilities

Physical Therapy Clinic/Practice

8049   Offices and clinics of health practitioners, nec (includes offices of physical therapists)

Pizzeria

5812   Eating places (includes pizza parlors and pizzerias)

Plant Leasing Service

7359   Equipment rental and leasing, nec (includes plants)

Plumbing Service

1711   Plumbing, heating, and air-conditioning contractors

Porcelain Refinishing Service

1799   Special trade contractors, nec

Power Washing Service

1799   Special trade contractors, nec (includes cleaning of building exteriors)

7349   Building cleaning and maintenance services, nec (includes cleaning of building interiors)

7542   Car washes (includes automotive washing and polishing)

Prepaid Phone Card Business

4812   Radiotelephone communications

4813   Telephone communications, except radiotelephone

Print/Frame Shop

7699   Repair shops and related services, nec (includes custom picture framing services)

Printing Business

2752   Commercial printing, lithographic

2754   Commercial printing, gravure

2759   Commercial printing, nec

2761   Manifold business form printers

Private Investigation/Personal Security Service

7381   Detective, guard, and armored car services

Private Label Product Manufacturer/Retailer

3999   Manufacturing industries, nec

5399   Miscellaneous general merchandise stores

5499   Miscellaneous food stores 5699 Miscellaneous apparel and accessory stores

5999   Miscellaneous retail stores, nec

Professional Organizer

7299   Miscellaneous personal services, nec

7389   Business services, nec

Property Management

6531   Real estate agents and managers

Public Relations Consultant

8743   Public relations services

Public Warehousing/Ministorage Operation

4221   Farm product warehousing and storage

4222   Refrigerated warehousing and storage

4225   General warehousing and storage

4226   Special warehousing and storage, nec (includes fur storage, household goods warehousing and storage, whiskey warehousing, and like enterprises)

Quick Oil Change Service

5541　Gasoline service stations (includes automobile ser-vicestations—retail)

7538　General automotive repair shops

Radio Station

4832　Radio broadcasting stations

Radon Testing Service

1799　Special trade contractors, nec

8734　Testing laboratories

Real Estate Agency

6531　Real estate agents and managers

Real Estate Investment Service

6798　Real estate investment trusts

Recording Studio

7399　Business services, nec (includes recording studios operating on a contract or fee basis)

Recreational Vehicle Dealer

5561　Recreational vehicle dealers

Recycling Business

5093　Scrap and waste materials

Rental Service

7299　Miscellaneous personal services, nec (includes clothing rental)

7352　Medical equipment rental and leasing

7353　Heavy construction equip-ment and leasing

7359　Equipment rental and leas-ing, nec

7377　Computer rental and leasing

7999　Amusement and recreation services, nec (includes pleasure boat rental, canoe and rowboat rental, bicycle, motorcycle and moped rental, and sporting goods rental)

Restaurant

5812　Eating places (includes sit-down, carry-out, and fast food)

Resume Service

7338　Secretarial anc court report-ing services (includes re-sumewriting services)

Roofing Contractor

1761　Roofing, siding, and sheet metal work

Satellite Dish Service

4841　Cable and other pay televi-sion services (includes di-rectbroadcast satellite services and satellite master antenna systems services)

Screen Printing Business

2261　Finishers of broadwoven fabrics of cotton (includes printing andfinishing of cot-ton broadwoven fabrics)

2262　Finishers of broadwoven fabrics of manmade fiber and silk(includes printing manmade fiber and silk broadwoven fabrics)

2759　Commercial printing, nec (includes screen printing on glass, plastics, paper, and metal, including highway signs)

Security Systems Service

7382　Security systems services

Seminar Planner/Lecturer

8999　Services, nec (including lecturers)

Service Station/Auto Repair and Service Shop

5541　Gasoline service stations

7532　Top, body, and upholstery repair shops and paint shops

7533　Automotive exhaust system repair shops

7534　Tire retreading and repair shops

7536　Automotive glass replace-ment shops

7537　Automotive transmission repair shops

7538　General automotive repair shops

7539　Automotive repair shops, nec

Sewer and Drain Cleaning Business

7699　Repair shops and related services, nec (includes sewer cleaning and rodding and septic tank cleaning) Sewing Center 5722 Household appliance stores (includes retail sew-ing machine stores)

5949　Sewing, needlework, and piece goods stores

7699　Repair shops and related services, nec (includes sewing machine repair shops)

Shoe Repair Shop

7251　Shoe repair shops and shoe-shine parlors

Shoe Store

5661　Shoe stores

Sign Shop

3993　Signs and advertising specialties

7389　Business services, nec (includes sign painting shops)

Silk Plant Shop

5999　Miscellaneous retail stores, nec (includes artificial flow-ers—retail)

Skating Rink Operation

7999　Amusement and recreation services, nec (includes ice and rollerskating rink operations)

Ski Shop

5941　Sporting goods stores and bicycle shops

Software Publishing

7372　Packaged software

Solar Energy Design/Contracting Busi-ness

1711　Plumbing, heating, and air-conditioning contractors (includes solar heating ap-paratus contractors)

1742   Plastering, dry wall, acoustical, and insulation work (includes solar reflecting insulation film contractors)

Specialized Staffing

7361   Employment Agencies

7363   Help Supply Services

Specialty Foods/Wine Shop

5499   Miscellaneous food stores

5921   Liquor stores (includes packaged wine—retail)

Sports Promotional Services

7941   Professional Sports Clubs and Promoters

Sporting Goods Store

5941   Sporting goods stores and bicycle shops

Surveying Service

8713   Surveying services (includes surveying: land, water, and aerial)

Swimming Pool/Hot Tub Business

1799   Special trade contractors, nec (includes swimming pool construction contractors)

5999   Miscellaneous retail stores, nec (includes hot tubs, retail)

7389   Business services, nec (includes swimming pool cleaning and maintenance services)

7999   Amusement and recreation services, nec (includes swimming pooloperations)

Tailor Shop

5699   Miscellaneous apparel and accessory stores (includes customtailor shops) 7219 Laundry and garment services, nec (includes tailorshops, except custom or merchant tailors)

Talent Agency

7922   Theatrical producers and miscellaneous theatrical services (includes agents)

Tanning Parlor/Sauna

7299   Miscellaneous personal services (includes steam baths and tanning salons)

Tattoo Parlor

7299   Miscellaneous personal services, nec (includes tattoo parlors)

Tax Preparation Business

7291   Tax return preparation services

8721   Accounting, auditing, and bookkeeping services

Taxicab/Van Shuttle Service

4121   Taxicabs

Taxidermy Service

7699   Repair shops and related services, nec (includes taxidermy)

Teacher Supply Store

5999   Miscellaneous retail stores, nec

Telemarketing Service

7389   Business services, nec (includes telemarketing services operating on a contract or fee basis)

Telephone Answering Service

7389   Business services, nec (includes answering services)

Television/Radio Repair Service

7622   Radio and television repair shops

Television Station

4833   Television broadcasting stations

Temporary Employment Agency

7363   Help supply services (includes temporary help services)

Tennis Court/Racquet Club Operation

7997   Membership sports and recreation clubs (includes racquetball and tennis clubs)

7999   Amusement and recreation services, nec (includes nonmembership racquetball and tennis court operations)

Tire Dealer

5531   Auto and home supply stores (includes retail tire dealers) 7534 Tire retreading and repair shops

Tobacco Shop

5993   Tobacco stores and stands

Tour Guide Operation/Adventure Service

4725   Tour operations

7999   Amusement and recreation services, nec (includes tour guides)

Toy Business

5945   Hobby, toy, and game shops

Trade Show/Conference Management Service

7389   Business services, nec (includes trade show arrangement)

Translating/Interpreting Service

7389   Business services, nec (includes translation service)

Travel Agency

4724   Travel agencies

Trucking Business

4212   Local trucking, without storage services

4213   Trucking, except local

4214   Local trucking, with storage services

Tutoring Service

8299   Schools and educational services, nec (includes tutoring services)

Typesetting Business

2791   Typesetting

Typing/Stenographic Service

7338   Secretarial and court reporting services (includes stenographic and typing services)

Upholstery/Carpet Services

1752   Floor laying and other floor work, nec (includes carpet laying and removing services)

5714   Drapery, curtain, and upholstery stores (includes upholstery materials stores)

7217   Carpet and upholstery cleaning

Vending Machine Merchandising and Service Business

5962   Automatic merchandising machine operators (includes retail sale of products through vending machines)

7359   Equipment rental and leasing services, nec (includes vending machine rental businesses)

Videocassette Rental Store

5735   Recorded and prerecorded tape stores (includes retail videotape stores)

7841   Videotape rental establishments

Vision Center

5995   Optical goods stores

Voice Mail Service

4813   Telephone communications, except radiotelephone (includes voice telephone communications)

Water Conditioning Service

7389   Business services, nec (includes water softener services)

Web Site Design

7371   Computer programming services (includes custom computer programsor systems software development and computer software systems analysis and design)

Weight Reduction/Control Center

7991   Physical fitness facilities (includes reducing facilities and slenderizing salons)

Welcome Service

7389   Business service, nec (includes welcoming service)

Window Dressing Business

3993   Signs and advertising specialties (includes advertising displays, except printed, and window and lobby cutouts and displays)

7319   Advertising, nec (includes display advertising services, exceptoutdoor)

Word Processing Service

7338   Secretarial and court reporting services (includes wordprocessing services)

Included here are state offices that provide information and assistance to small business owners and entrepreneurs concerning business licensing requirements and regulations.

ALABAMA

Dept. of Revenue—Business Licensing
50 N. Ripley
Montgomery, AL 36132
334-242-1170
URL: http://www.revenue.alabama.gov/
 licenses/index.html

ALASKA

Corporations, Business and Professional Licensing
PO Box 110806
Juneau, AK 99811-0806
907-465-2534
Fax: 907-465-2974
Email: businesslicense@alaska.gov
URL: http://www.dced.state.ak.us/occ/
 home.htm

ARIZONA

Arizona Dept. of Commerce
1700 W. Washington, Ste. 600
Phoenix, AZ 85007
602-771-1100
Toll-Free: 800-528-8421
URL: http://www.azcommerce.com/
 BusAsst/SmallBiz

CALIFORNIA

Consumer Affairs Dept
1625 N. Market Blvd., Ste. 112
Sacramento, CA 95814
916-445-1254
Toll-Free: 800-952-5210
URL: http://www.dca.ca.gov
URL: http://www.2dca.ca.gov/licensee/
 shtml

COLORADO

Dept. of Regulatory Agencies
1560 Broadway, Ste. 1550
Denver, CO 80202
303-894-7855

Fax: 303-894-7885
URL: http:// www.dora.state.co.us

CONNECTICUT

Dept. of Consumer Protection—DCP License Services Division
165 Capitol Ave.
Hartford, CT 06106
800-842-2649
Fax: 860-713-7239
Email: license.services@po.state.ct.us
URL: http://www.ct.gov/dcp/site/default.asp
URL: http://www.ct-clic.com

DELAWARE

Dept. of State — Professional Regulation Division
Cannon Bldg.
861 Silver Lake Blvd., Ste. 203
Dover, DE 19904
302-744-4500
Fax: 302-739-2711
URL: http://dpr.delaware.gov

DISTRICT OF COLUMBIA

Dept. of Consumer and Regulatory Affairs
1100 4th St., SW
Washington, DC 20024
202-442-4400
URL: http://dcra.dc.gov/drca/site/default.
 asp

FLORIDA

Business & Professional Regulation Dept.
1940 N. Monroe St.
Tallahassee, FL 32399
850-487-1395
http://www.myfloridalicense.com/dbpr

GEORGIA

Georgia Secretary of State— Professional Licensing Boards Division
237 Coliseum Dr.
Macon, GA 31217-3858
478-207-2440

Fax: 877-588-0446
URL: http://www.sos.georgia.gov/plb/
URL: http://www.georgia.gov

HAWAII

State Dept. of Commerce and Consumer Affairs—Professional and Vocational Licensing
Street Address:
335 Merchant St. 3rd Fl, Rm. 301
Honolulu, HI 96813

Mailing Address:
PO Box 3469
Honolulu, HI 96801
808-587-3295
URL: http:// hawaii.gov/dbedt/business

IDAHO

Occupational Licenses Bureau
Owyhee Plaza
1109 Main St., Ste. 220
Boise, ID 83702-5642
208-334-3233
Fax: 208-334-3945
Email: ibol@ibol.idaho.gov
URL: http://wwwv.secure.ibol.idaho.gov/
 IBOL/home.aspx

ILLINOIS

Illinois Professional Regulation Dept
320 W. Washington St.
Springfield, IL 62786
217-785-0800
URL: http://www.idfpr.com

INDIANA

Professional Licensing Agency
302 W. Washington St., Rm. EO-34
Indianapolis, IN 46204
317-232-2980

Fax: 317-232-231
URL: http://www.in.gov/pla/

IOWA

Professional Licensing Division
1920 SE Hulsizer Rd.
Ankeny, IA 50021
515-281-7393
Fax: 515-281-7411
URL: http://www.state.ia.us/government/
com/prof/home.html

KENTUCKY

Secretary of State—One-Stop Business Licensing Program
700 Capital Ave., Ste. 152
State Capitol Frankfurt, KY 40601
502-564-3490
Fax: 502-564-5687
URL: http://sos.ky.gov/business/onestop.
htm

LOUISIANA

Secretary of State—Commercial Div.
URL: http://www.sos.louisiana.gov

MAINE

URL: http://www.maine.gov/portal/busi-
ness/licensing.html

MARYLAND

Labor, Licensing and Regulation Dept— Division of Occupational and Professional Licensing
500 N. Calvert St., 3rd. Fl.
Baltimore, MD 21202
410-230-6020
Email: op@dllr.state.md.us
URL: http://www.dllr.state.md.us/license/

MASSACHUSETTS

Division of Professional Licensure
239 Causeway
Boston, MA 02114
617-727-3074
Fax: 517-727-2197
URL: http://www.mass.gov/dpl

MICHIGAN

Dept. of Energy, Labor and Economic Growth
525 W. Ottawa
PO Box 30004
Lansing, MI 48909
517-373-1820

Fax: 517-373-2129
URL: http://www.michigan.gov/dleg

MINNESOTA

Commerce Dept.
85 7th Place East, Ste. 500
St Paul, MN 55101
651-296-6319
Toll-Free: 800-657-3978
Email: licensing.commerce@state.mn.us
URL: http://www.state.mn.us/

MISSISSIPPI

Mississippi Secretary of State— Business Services
PO Box 136
Jackson, MS 39205
601-359-1350
Fax: 601-359-1633
Email: Wthompson@sos.state.ms.us
URL: http://www.sos.ms.gov/business_ser
vices.aspx
URL: http://www.ms.gov

MISSOURI

Dept. of Economic Development— Professional Registration Division
3605 Missouri Blvd.
Jefferson City, MO 65102 PO Box 1335
573-751-0293
Email: profreg@pr.mo.gov
URL: http://www.pr.mo.gov/

MONTANA

Department of Labor and Industry
PO Box 1728
Helena, MT 59624
406-841-2300
URL: http:// dli.mt.gov

NEBRASKA

See Nebraska Online for more information
Toll Free: 800-747-8177
URL: http://www.nol.org/business/
URL: http://www.sos.ne.gov

NEVADA

Nevada Secretary of State
101 North Carson St.
Carson City, NV 89701-4786
775-684-5708
URL: http://www.nvsos.gov

NEW HAMPSHIRE

Joint Board of Licensure & Certification
57 Regional Dr.
Concord, NH 03301
603-271-2219

Fax: 603-271-6990
Email: llavertu@nhsa.state.nh.us
URL: http://www.nh.gov/jtboard/

NEW JERSEY

New Jersey Dept. of Law and Public Safety—Consumer Affairs Division
124 Halsey St.
Newark, NJ 07102
973-504-6534
URL: http://www.state.nj.us/lps/ca/boards.
htm

NEW MEXICO

Regulation & Licensing Dept
2550 Cerrillos Rd
Santa Fe, NM 87505
505-476-4500
URL: http://www.rld.state.nm.us/

NEW YORK

New York State Dept. of State, Division of Licensing Services
99 Washington Ave.
Albany, NY 12231
518-474-4752
Fax: 518-474-4597
Email: licensing@dos.state.ny.us
URL: http://www.dos.state.ny.us/lcns/
licensing.html

NORTH CAROLINA

Dept. of the Secretary of State— Busirof/ ness License Information Office (BLIO)
301 N. Wilmington St.
Raleigh, NC 27601
919-733-4151
Toll-Free: 800-228-8443
URL: http://www.nccomerce.com/en/
BusinessServices/startyourbusiness

NORTH DAKOTA

Secretary of State—Business Information and Registration
600 E. Boulevard Ave., Dept. 108
Bismarck, ND 58505-0500
701-328-4284
800-352-0867 ext. 4284
Fax: 701-328-2992
Email: sosbir@nd.gov
URL: http://www.nd.gov/sos/
Businessserve/

OHIO

Commerce Dept.
77 S. High St.
Columbus, OH 43215
614-466-4100
URL: http://www.com.ohio.gov/

OKLAHOMA

Dept. of Commerce—Oklahoma Business Licensing System
877-879-6552
URL: http://www.okonestop.com

OREGON

Secretary of State—Corporate Division
255 Capitol St. NE, Ste. 151
Salem, OR 97310-1327
503-986-2200
URL: http://www.oregon.gov/lic

Portland Bureau of Licenses
111 SW Columbia St., Ste. 600
Portland, OR 97201
503-823-5157
Fax: 503-823-5192
URL: http://www.pdxbl.org

PENNSYLVANIA

Professional & Occupational Affairs Bureau
Secretary of Commonwealth (State Dept.)
302 North Office Bldg.
Harrisburg, PA 17120
717-787-8503
URL: http://www.mylicense.state.pa.us/

RHODE ISLAND

Office of the Secretary of State
82 Smith St., Rm. 217
Providence, RI 02903
401-222-2357
Fax: 401-222-1356
URL: http://www.state.ri.us/

SOUTH CAROLINA

Dept. of Labor, Licensing and Regulation Dept.
PO Box 11329
Columbia, SC 29211
803-896-4300

Email: contactllr@mail.llr.state.sc.us
URL: http://www.llr.state.sc.us/pol.asp

SOUTH DAKOTA

Dept. of Labor Boards, Commissions and Councils
700 Governors Dr.
Pierre, SD 57501
605-773-3101
Fax: 605-773-6184
URL: http://www.state.sd.us
URL: http://dol.sd.gov/bdcomm/

TENNESSEE

State of Tennessee
500 James Robertson Pkwy.
Nashville, TN 37243-0572
615-741-3449
URL: www.state.tn.us/
URL: http://www.tennesseeanytime.org/
business

TEXAS

Licensing and Regulation Dept.
PO Box 12157
Austin, TX 78711
512-463-6599
Toll-Free: 800-803-9202
Fax: 512-475-2854
URL: http://www.license.state.tx.us

UTAH

Occupational & Professional Licensing Div.—Commerce Dept.
PO Box 146741
Salt Lake City, UT 84114-6741
801-530-6628
Toll-Free: 866-275-3675
Fax: 801-530-6511
URL: http://www.commerce.state.ut.us/

VERMONT

Office of Professional Regulation
26 Terrace St.
Montpelier, VT 05609
802-828-2363
URL: http://www.sec.state.vt.us/
URL: http://vtprofessionals.org

VIRGIN ISLANDS

Licensing & Consumer Affairs Dept.
Golden Rock Shopping Ctr.
Christiansted
340-773-2226
Fax: 340-778-8250
URL: http:// dlca.vi.gov/links/

VIRGINIA

Professional and Occupational Regulations Dept.
9960 Maryland Dr., Ste. 400
Richmond, VA 23233
804-367-8500
Email: dpor@dpor.state.va.us
URL: http://www.state.va.us/dpor/

WASHINGTON

Dept. of Licensing
405 Black Lake Blvd., Bldg. 2
Olympia, WA 98502
360-664-1400
URL: http://www.dol.wa.gov/business

WISCONSIN

Regulation and Licensing Dept.
PO Box 8935
Madison, WI 53708-8935
URL: http://www.drl.state.wi.us/

This Guide lists alphabetically by name the companies, associations, institutions, and individuals who publish the periodicals (magazines, journals, etc.), directories, guide books, and other publications noted in the "Small Business Profiles" and "General Topics" sections. In these two sections, you will see "Pub:" (publisher) noted following publication names. This note provides the name of the entity that publishes the work.

If you should need to directly contact the publisher, you can locate the contact information in this Guide. Note that some publications listed provide the specific name and e-mail address of an individual to be contacted regarding the publication; this information can be found in the text of the entry. Please use that contact information when available. Listings in this Guide provide full publisher name, address, phone and fax numbers, and e-mail and URL when available.

NUMERICS

101 Communications
9121 Oakdale Ave., Ste. 101
Chatsworth, CA 91311
Ph: (818)814-5200
Fax: (818)734-1522
Co. E-mail: info@1105media.com
URL: http://www.1105media.com/

1105 Media, Inc.
14901 Quorum Dr., Ste. 425
Dallas, TX 75254
Ph: (972)687-6700
Fax: (972)687-6799
URL: http://1105media.com

124 S Mercedes Rd.
Fallbrook
CA 92028
URL: http://www.encorepublishers.com

360 Youth L.L.C.
151 W 26th St., 9th Fl.
New York, NY 10001
Ph: (212)244-4307
Fax: (212)244-4311
Co. E-mail: marketing@360youth.com
URL: http://www.360youth.com/

A

A and C Black Publishers Ltd.
50 Bedford Sq.
London WC1B 3DP, United Kingdom
Ph: 020 7631 5600
Fax: 020 7631 5800
Co. E-mail: customerservices@acblack.
com
URL: http://www.acblack.com

A. & C. Black
38 Soho Sq.
London W1D 3QY, United Kingdom
Ph: 44 20 77580200
Fax: 44 20 77580222
Co. E-mail: customerservices@acblack.
com
URL: http://www.acblack.com

The A.I. Root Co.
PO Box 706
Medina, OH 44258-0706
Ph: (330)725-6677
Free: 800-289-7668
Fax: (330)725-5624
Co. E-mail: beeculture@airoot.com
URL: http://www.rootcandles.com

A.M. Best Company Inc.
1 Ambest Rd.
Oldwick, NJ 08858-7000
Ph: (908)439-2200
Fax: (908)439-3296
Co. E-mail: customer_service@ambest.
com
URL: http://www.ambest.com

A/N Group Inc.
17 Scott Dr.
Melville, NY 11747
Ph: (631)549-4090
Fax: (631)385-9858
Co. E-mail: angroup@pb.net
URL: http://www.smbiz.com

AACC International
3340 Pilot Knob Rd.
St. Paul, MN 55121
Ph: (651)454-7250
Free: 800-328-7560
Fax: (651)454-0766
Co. E-mail: aacc@scisoc.org
URL: http://www.aaccnet.org

AACSB--American Assembly of Collegiate Schools of Business
777 South Harbour Island Blvd., Ste. 750
Tampa, FL 33602-5730
Ph: (813)769-6500
Fax: (813)769-6559
URL: http://www.aacsb.edu

Abbeyfield Houses Society of Canada
427 Bloor St. W, Box 1
Toronto, ON, Canada M5S 1X7
Ph: (416)920-7483
Fax: (416)920-6956
Co. E-mail: info@abbeyfield.ca

ABC Book Publishing
20609 NE Lakeside Dr.
Fairview, OR 97024
Ph: (503)780-7322

ABC-Clio Inc.
130 Cremona Dr.
Santa Barbara, CA 93117-5516
Ph: (805)968-1911
Free: 800-368-6868
Fax: (805)685-9685
Co. E-mail: crussell@abc-clio.com
URL: http://www.abc-clio.com

The ABWA Company Inc.
9100 Ward Pky.
Kansas City, MO 64114-0728
Free: 800-228-0007
Fax: (816)361-4991
Co. E-mail: abwa@abwa.org
URL: http://www.abwa.org/

ACA International
4040 W 70th St.
Minneapolis, MN 55439
Ph: (952)926-6547
Fax: (612)926-1624
Co. E-mail: aca@acainternational.org
URL: http://www.acainternational.org

Academic Press
525 B St., Ste. 1900
San Diego, CA 92101-4495
Free: 800-545-2522
URL: http://www.elsevierdirect.com/imprint.
jsp?iid=5

Academy of Doctors of Audiology
3493 Lansdowne Dr., Ste. 2
Lexington, KY 40517-1147
Ph: (859)271-0607
Free: 866-493-5544
Fax: (859)977-7441
Co. E-mail: info@audiologist.org
URL: http://www.audiologist.org

Academy of Management (AOM)
PO Box 3020
Briarcliff Manor, NY 10510
Ph: (914)923-2607
Fax: (914)923-2615

Co. E-mail: academy@pace.edu
URL: http://www.aom.pace.edu

Access Intelligence L.L.C.
2700 Westchester Ave., Ste. 107
Purchase, NY 10577
Ph: (914)251-4705
Free: 800-800-5474
Fax: (914)251-7107
Co. E-mail: clientservices@pbimedia.com

Accordionists and Teachers Guild, International
c/o Joan Sommers
2312 W 71st Ter.
Prairie Village, KS 66208-3322

Accrediting Commission of Career Schools and Colleges of Technology
2101 Wilson Blvd., Ste. 302
Arlington, VA 22201
Ph: (703)247-4212
Fax: (703)247-4533
Co. E-mail: info@accsc.org
URL: http://www.accsc.org

Accudata America
4210 Metro Pkwy., Ste. 300
Fort Myers, FL 33916
Ph: (239)425-4400
Free: 800-732-3440
Fax: (239)425-4401
Co. E-mail: info@accudata.com

Accuity Inc.
4709 W Golf Rd.
Skokie, IL 60076-1231
Ph: (847)676-9600
Free: 800-321-3373
Fax: (847)933-8101
Co. E-mail: custserv@accuitysolutions.
 com
URL: http://www.accuitysolutions.com

Accurate Writing & More
16 Barstow Ln.
Hadley, MA 01035
Ph: (413)586-2388
URL: http://www.principledprofit.com

Achill River Corp.
PO Box 1409
Arden, NC 28704
Ph: (828)687-0011
Fax: (828)681-0601
Co. E-mail: circulations@aquaculturemag.
 com
URL: http://www.aquaculturemag.com

Acoustic Guitar
PO Box 767
San Anselmo, CA 94979
Ph: (415)485-6946
Free: 800-827-6837
Fax: (415)485-0831
Co. E-mail: acousticguitar@pcspublink.
 com

URL: http://www.acousticguitar.com/

ACTA Press
Bldg. B6, Ste. 101
Calgary, AB, Canada T3E 7J9
Ph: (403)288-1195
Fax: (403)247-6851
Co. E-mail: journals@actapress.com
URL: http://www.actapress.com/

Action Communication Inc.
135 Spy Ct.
Markham, ON, Canada L3R 5H6
Ph: (905)477-3222
Fax: (905)477-4320

Active Interest Media
300 Continental Blvd., Ste. 650
El Segundo, CA 90245-5067
Ph: (310)356-4100
Fax: (310)356-4110
URL: http://www.aimmedia.com

Adams Business Media
50 Washington St., 10th Fl.
Norwalk, CT 06854
Ph: (203)855-8499
Fax: (203)855-9446

Adams Business Media/Green Media
833 W Jackson Blvd.
7th Fl.
Chicago, IL 60607
Ph: (312)846-4600
Fax: (312)846-4638
URL: http://www.aip.com

Adams Media Corporation
57 Littlefield St.
Avon, MA 02322
Ph: (508)247-6733
Free: 800-872-5627
Fax: (508)427-6790
URL: http://www.adamsmedia.com

Advanced Medical Technology Association
701 Pennsylvania Ave. NW, Ste. 800
Washington, DC 20004-2654
Ph: (202)783-8700
Fax: (202)783-8750
Co. E-mail: info@advamed.org
URL: http://www.advamed.org

Advanced Research Press Inc.
690 Rte. 25A, Ste. 150
Setauket, NY 11733
Ph: (631)751-9696
Free: 800-653-1151
Fax: (631)751-9699
URL: http://www.fitnessrxmag.com

Advanstar Communications Inc.
2501 Colorado Ave., Ste. 280
Santa Monica, CA 90404
Ph: (310)857-7500
Fax: (310)857-7510

Co. E-mail: info@advanstar.com
URL: http://www.advanstar.com

Advanstar Communications
641 Lexington Ave., 8th Fl.
New York, NY 10022
Ph: (212)951-6600
Free: 800-346-0085
Fax: (212)951-6793
Co. E-mail: info@advanstar.com
URL: http://www.advanstar.com

Advantage Business Media L.L.C.
100 Enterprise Dr., Ste. 600, Box 912
Rockaway, NJ 07866-0912
Ph: (973)920-7000
Co. E-mail: advantagecommunications@
 advantagemedia.com
URL: http://www.advantagebusinessmedia.
 com

Adventure Cycling Association
150 E Pine St.
Missoula, MT 59807
Ph: (406)721-1776
Free: 800-755-2453
Fax: (406)721-8754
Co. E-mail: info@adventurecycling.org
URL: http://www.adventurecycling.org

Adventure Publishing Group Inc.
286 5th Ave., 3rd Fl.
New York, NY 10001
Ph: (212)575-4510
Fax: (212)575-4521
URL: http://www.
 adventurepublishinggroup.com/

Advertising Research Foundation
432 Park Ave. S, 6th Fl.
New York, NY 10016-8013
Ph: (212)751-5656
Fax: (212)319-5265
Co. E-mail: info@thearf.org
URL: http://www.thearf.org

Adweek L.P.
100 Boylston St., Ste. 210
Boston, MA 02116
Free: 800-641-2030
URL: http://www.adweek.com

Agate Publishing
1045 Westgate Dr.
Saint Paul, MN 55114
Ph: (847)475-4457
Fax: (847)475-1045
Co. E-mail: seibold@agatepublishing.com
URL: http://www.agatepublishing.com

Agate Publishing, Incorporated
1501 Madison St.
Evanston, IL 60202

AGCD Brandspa Books
215 Glenridge Ave.
Montclair, NJ 07042
Ph: (973)509-2728
Co. E-mail: inquiry@brandspa.net
URL: http://www.brandspa-llc.com

Agricore United
PO Box 9800
Winnipeg, MB, Canada R3C 3K7
Ph: (204)954-1400
Free: 800-782-0794
Fax: (204)954-1422
URL: http://www.agcanada.com

Agricultural Resources & Communications Inc.
4210 Wam-Teau Dr.
Wamego, KS 66547
Ph: (785)456-9705
Free: 800-404-7940
Fax: (785)456-1654
Co. E-mail: chris@agresources.com
URL: http://www.agresources.com

Aha! House
1519 Oakmoor Pl.
Marietta, GA 30062-2745
Ph: (770)565-1231
Fax: (770)565-9712

Aiken Standard
326 Rutland Dr. NW
Aiken, SC 29801
Ph: (803)648-2311
Fax: (803)648-6052

Air Age Publishing Inc.
20 Westport Rd.
Wilton, CT 06897
Ph: (203)431-9000
Fax: (203)761-8744
Co. E-mail: production@airage.com
URL: http://www.airage.com

Air Conditioning Contractors of America
2800 Shirlington Rd., Ste. 300
Arlington, VA 22206
Ph: (703)575-4477
Free: 888-290-2220
Fax: (703)575-4449
Co. E-mail: info@acca.org
URL: http://www.acca.org

Air-Conditioning and Refrigeration Institute
4100 N Fairfax Dr., Ste. 200
Arlington, VA 22203-1627
Ph: (703)524-8800
Fax: (703)528-3816
URL: http://ari.org

AKTRIN Furniture Research
2267 Daffodil Ct.
Oakville, ON, Canada L6J 5Y2
Ph: (905)845-3474

Fax: (905)841-7459
Co. E-mail: aktrin@aktrin.com
URL: http://www.aktrin.com

Alan B. Lancz and Associates Inc.
2400 N Reynolds Rd.
Toledo, OH 43615-2800
Ph: (419)536-5200
Fax: (419)536-5401
Co. E-mail: info@ablonline.com
URL: http://www.ablonline.com

Alaska Business Publishing Company
501 W Northern Lights Blvd., Ste. 100
Anchorage, AK 99503
Ph: (907)276-4373
Free: 800-770-4373
Fax: (907)279-2900

Alberta Association of Optometrists
10724-113 St.
Edmonton, AB, Canada T5H 3H8
Ph: (780)451-6824
Free: 800-272-8843
Fax: (780)452-9918
Co. E-mail: alberta.association@
  optometrists.ab.ca

Alberta Veterinary Medical Association
Weber Centre, No. 950
5555 Calgary Trail NW
Edmonton, AB, Canada T6H 5P9
Ph: (780)489-5007
Free: 800-404-2862
Fax: (780)484-8311
Co. E-mail: avma@avma.avma.ab.ca

Alcuin Society
PO Box 3216
Vancouver, BC, Canada V6B 3X8
Ph: (604)937-3293
Co. E-mail: info@alcuinsociety.com
URL: http://www.alcuinsociety.com

Alexander Communications Group Inc.
712 Main St., Ste. 187B
Boonton, NJ 07005
Ph: (973)265-2300
Free: 800-232-4317
Fax: (972)492-6056
Co. E-mail: info@alexcommgrp.com
URL: http://www.alexcommgrp.com

Alexander Communications Group Inc.
28 W 25th St., 8th Fl.
New York, NY 10010
Ph: (212)228-0246
Free: 800-232-4317
Fax: (212)228-0376
Co. E-mail: info@alexcommgrp.com
URL: http://www.alexcommgrp.com

The Alexander Graham Bell Association for the Deaf and Hard of Hearing
3417 Volta Pl. NW
Washington, DC 20007
Ph: (202)337-5220

Free: 866-337-5220
Fax: (202)337-8314
Co. E-mail: info@agbell.org
URL: http://nc.agbell.org

Alexander Hamilton Institute Inc.
70 Hilltop Rd.
Ramsey, NJ 07446-1119
Ph: (201)825-3377
Free: 800-879-2441
Fax: (201)825-8696
Co. E-mail: editorial@ahipubs.com
URL: http://www.ahipubs.com

Alexander Research & Communications Inc.
712 Main St., Ste. 187B
Boonton, NJ 07005
Ph: (973)265-2300
Free: 800-232-4317
Fax: (973)402-6065
Co. E-mail: info@distributiongroup.com

Algonquin Publishing
PO Box 2225
Chapel Hill, NC 27515
Ph: (919)967-0108
Fax: (919)933-0272
Co. E-mail: inquiry@algonquin.com
URL: http://www.algonquin.com

Alive Publishing Group Inc.
100-12751 Vulcan Way
Richmond, BC, Canada V6V 3C8
Ph: (604)295-9333
Free: 800-663-6580
Fax: (800)663-6597
Co. E-mail: editorial@alive.com
URL: http://www.alive.com

All American Crafts Inc.
7 Waterloo Rd.
Stanhope, NJ 07874-3250
Ph: (973)347-6900
Fax: (973)347-6909
Co. E-mail: readersvc@allamericancrafts.
  com
URL: http://www.allamericancrafts.com

Allen & Unwin Pty., Limited
83 Alexander St.
Crows Nest, NSW 2065, Australia
Ph: 61 2 84250178
Fax: 61 2 84250065

Allen & Unwin
PO Box 8500
Saint Leonards, NSW 1590, Australia
Ph: 2 8425 0100
URL: http://www.allenandunwin.com

Allen-Reed Publishing Company
160 W Foothill Pkwy., Ste. 105-125
Corona, CA 92882
Ph: (951)340-9024
Free: 866-336-2927
Fax: (951)340-9024

Allied Distribution Inc.
PO Box 607
Eagle River, WI 54521
Ph: (715)479-3530
Fax: (715)479-3551
Co. E-mail: info@warehousenetwork.com
URL: http://www.warehousenetwork.com/

Allworth Press
10 E 23rd St., Ste. 510
New York, NY 10010
Ph: (212)777-8395
Fax: (212)777-8261

Allyear Tax Guides
20484 Glen Brae Dr.
Saratoga, CA 95070
Ph: (408)867-2628
Fax: (408)867-6466

ALM Media Inc.
1 SE 3rd Ave., Ste. 900
Miami, FL 33158
Ph: (305)377-3721
Free: 800-777-7300

Alpha Forum Inc.
104 Enterprise Dr.
Kingston, NY 12401-7002

Alpha Publishing House
411 Eagleview Blvd., Ste. 100
Exton, PA 19341
Free: 800-992-9124
URL: http://www.alphapub.com

Alternative Aquaculture Association
630 Independent Rd.
Breinigsville, PA 18031
Ph: (610)398-1062
Fax: (610)395-8202
Co. E-mail: altaqua@ptd.net

Altitude Publishing
1500 Railway Ave.
Canmore, AB, Canada T1W 1P6
Ph: (403)678-6888
Free: 800-957-6888
Fax: (403)678-6951

AMACOM
1601 Broadway
New York, NY 10019
Ph: (212)586-8100
Free: 800-262-9699
Fax: (212)903-8168
Co. E-mail: customerservice@amanet.org
URL: http://www.amanet.org

Amber Books
1334 E Chandler Blvd., Ste. 5-D67
Phoenix, AZ 85048
Ph: (480)460-1660
Fax: (480)283-0991

AMC Institute
100 N 20th St., 4th Fl.
Philadelphia, PA 19103-1443
Ph: (215)564-3484
Fax: (215)564-2175
Co. E-mail: info@amcinstitute.org
URL: http://www.amcinstitute.org

American Academy of Sleep Medicine
2510 N Frontage Rd.
Darien, IL 60561
Ph: (630)737-9700
Fax: (630)737-9790
Co. E-mail: inquiries@aasmnet.org
URL: http://www.aasmnet.org

American Accounting Association
5717 Bessie Dr.
Sarasota, FL 34233-2399
Ph: (941)921-7747
Fax: (941)923-4093
Co. E-mail: info@aaahq.org
URL: http://aaahq.org/index.cfm

American Advertising Federation
1101 Vermont Ave. NW, Ste. 500
Washington, DC 20005-6306
Ph: (202)898-0089
Free: 800-999-2231
Fax: (202)898-0159
Co. E-mail: aaf@aaf.org
URL: http://www.aaf.org

American Alliance for Health, Physical Education, Recreation and Dance
1900 Association Dr.
Reston, VA 20191-1598
Ph: (703)476-3400
Free: 800-213-7193
Fax: (703)476-9527
Co. E-mail: membership@aahperd.org
URL: http://www.aahperd.org

American Animal Hospital Association
12575 W Bayaud Ave.
Lakewood, CO 80228
Ph: (303)986-2800
Free: 800-883-6301
Fax: (303)986-1700
Co. E-mail: info@aahanet.org
URL: http://www.aahanet.org

American Arbitration Association, Inc.
335 Madison Ave.
New York, NY 10017
Ph: (212)716-5800
Free: 800-778-7879
Fax: (212)716-5905
Co. E-mail: websitemail@adr.org
URL: http://www.adr.org

American Association for Career Education
2900 Amby Pl.
Hermosa Beach, CA 90254-2216
Ph: (310)376-7378
Fax: (310)376-2926

American Association for Employment in Education
3040 Riverside Dr., Ste. 117
Columbus, OH 43221
Ph: (614)485-1111
Fax: (360)244-7802
Co. E-mail: execdir@aaee.org
URL: http://www.aaee.org/cwt/external/wcpages/index.aspx

American Association for Homecare
2011 Crystal Dr., Ste. 725
Arlington, VA 22202
Ph: (703)836-6263
Fax: (703)836-6730
Co. E-mail: info@aahomecare.org

American Association for Laboratory Accreditation
5301 Buckeystown Pke., Ste. 350
Frederick, MD 21704-8307
Ph: (301)644-3248
Fax: (301)662-2974
Co. E-mail: info@a2la.org
URL: http://www.a2la.org

American Association of Bioanalysts
906 Olive St., Ste. 1200
Saint Louis, MO 63101-1434
Ph: (314)241-1445
Fax: (314)241-1449
Co. E-mail: aab@aab.org

American Association of Clinical Chemistry
1850 K St. NW, Ste. 625
Washington, DC 20006-2215
Ph: (202)857-0717
Free: 800-892-1400
Fax: (202)887-5093
Co. E-mail: info@aacc.org
URL: http://www.aacc.org

American Association of Fund-Raising Counsel Inc.
4700 W Lake Ave.
Glenview, IL 60025
Ph: (847)375-4709
Free: 800-462-2372
Co. E-mail: info@aafrc.org
URL: http://www.aafrc.org

American Association of Individual Investors
625 N Michigan Ave.
Chicago, IL 60611
Ph: (312)280-0170
Free: 800-428-2244
Fax: (312)280-9883
Co. E-mail: members@aaii.com
URL: http://www.aaii.com

American Association of Insurance Services
1745 S Naperville Rd.
Wheaton, IL 60189-8132
Ph: (630)681-8347

Free: 800-564-AAIS
Fax: (630)681-8356
Co. E-mail: info@aaisonline.com
URL: http://www.aaisonline.com

American Association of Meat Processors
1 Meating Pl.
Elizabethtown, PA 17022-2883
Ph: (717)367-1168
Fax: (717)367-9096
Co. E-mail: info@aamp.com
URL: http://www.aamp.com

American Association of Medical Assistants
20 N Wacker Dr., Ste. 1575
Chicago, IL 60606
Ph: (312)899-1500
Fax: (312)899-1259
URL: http://www.aama-ntl.org

American Bar Association (ABA)
321 N Clark St.
Chicago, IL 60654-7598
Ph: (312)988-5522
Free: 800-285-2221
Fax: (312)988-5177
Co. E-mail: service@americanbar.org
URL: http://www.americanbar.org

American Beekeeping Federation Inc.
115 Morning Glory Circle
Jesup, GA 31546
Ph: (912)427-4233
Fax: (912)427-8447
Co. E-mail: info@abfnet.org

American Board of Family Medicine
1648 McGrathiana Pkwy., Ste. 550
Lexington, KY 40511-1342
Ph: (859)269-5626
Free: 888-995-5700
Fax: (859)335-7501
Co. E-mail: help@theabfm.org
URL: http://www.theabfm.org

American Boat & Yacht Council Inc.
613 3rd St., Ste. 10
Annapolis, MD 21403
Ph: (410)990-4460
Fax: (410)990-4466
Co. E-mail: info@abycinc.org
URL: http://www.abycinc.org

American Booksellers Association
200 White Plains Rd., Ste. 600
Tarrytown, NY 10591
Ph: (914)591-2665
Free: 800-637-0037
Fax: (914)591-2720
Co. E-mail: info@bookweb.org
URL: http://www.bookweb.org

American Business Women's Association
PO Box 8728
Kansas City, MO 64114
Free: 800-228-0007
URL: http://www.abwa.org/

American Business Women's Association
11050 Roe Ave., Ste. 200
Overland Park, KS 66211
Free: 800-228-0007

American Camping Association
5000 State Rd., 67 N
Martinsville, IN 46151-7902
Ph: (765)342-8456
Free: 800-428-2267
Fax: (765)342-2065
Co. E-mail: exhibitors@acacamps.org
URL: http://www.acacamps.org

American Cat Fanciers Association Inc.
PO Box 203
Point Lookout, MO 65726
Ph: (417)334-5430
Fax: (417)334-5540
Co. E-mail: info@acfacat.com

American Ceramic Society
600 N Cleveland Ave., Ste. 210
Westerville, OH 43082
Ph: (240)646-7054
Free: 866-721-3322
Fax: (204)396-5637
Co. E-mail: customerservice@ceramics.org
URL: http://ceramics.org

American Chain of Warehouses
156 Flamingo Dr.
Beecher, IL 60401
Ph: (708)946-9792
Fax: (708)946-9793
Co. E-mail: bjurus@acwi.org
URL: http://www.acwi.org

American Chemical Society
1155 16th St. NW
Washington, DC 20036
Ph: (202)872-4600
Free: 800-227-5558
Fax: (202)872-6067
Co. E-mail: help@acs.org
URL: http://portal.acs.org/portal/acs/corg/content

American City Business Journals
111 Congress Ave., Ste. 750
Austin, TX 78701
Ph: (512)494-2500
Fax: (512)494-2525

American City Business Journals
1 E Pratt St., Ste. 205
Baltimore, MD 21202
Ph: (410)576-1161

Fax: (410)752-3112
Co. E-mail: baltimore@bizjournals.com
URL: http://baltimore.bizjournals.com

American City Business Journals
303 W Nationwide Blvd.
Columbus, OH 43215
Ph: (614)461-4040
Fax: (614)365-2980

American City Business Journals
1233 West Loop S, Ste. 1300
Houston, TX 77027
Ph: (713)688-8811
Fax: (713)963-0482
Co. E-mail: Houston@bizjournals.com

American City Business Journals Inc.
160 Federal St., 12th Fl.
Boston, MA 02110
Ph: (617)330-1000
Fax: (617)330-1015

American City Business Journals Inc.
400 Market St., Ste. 1200
Philadelphia, PA 19106
Ph: (215)238-1450
Fax: (215)238-9489

American City Business Journals Inc.
851 SW 6th Ave., Ste. 500
Portland, OR 97204
Ph: (503)274-8733
Fax: (502)219-3450
URL: http://portland.bizjournals.com

American City Business Journals
825 N Jefferson St., Ste. 200
Milwaukee, WI 53202
Ph: (414)278-7788
Fax: (414)278-7028
Co. E-mail: Milwaukee@bizjournals.com
URL: http://milwaukee.bizjournals.com/milwaukee

American City Business Journals
255 S Orange Ave., Ste. 700
Orlando, FL 32801
Ph: (407)649-8470
Fax: (407)420-1625
Co. E-mail: Orlando@bizjournals.com
URL: http://Orlando.bizjournals.com/orlando

American City Business Journals
801 Second Ave., Ste. 210
Seattle, WA 98104
Ph: (206)876-5500
Fax: (206)447-8510

American City Business Journals
4890 W Kennedy Blvd., Ste. 850
Tampa, FL 33609
Ph: (813)873-8225
Fax: (813)876-1827
Co. E-mail: tampabay@bizjournals.com

URL: http://tampabay.bizjournals.com/
tampabay/

American City Business Journals, Inc.
465 Main St.
Buffalo, NY 14203
Ph: (716)541-1600
Fax: (716)854-3394

American City Business Journals, Inc.
120 W Morehead St.
Charlotte, NC 28202
Ph: (704)973-1000
Fax: (704)973-1001

American City Business Journals, Inc.
1100 Main St., Ste. 210
Kansas City, MO 64105-5123
Ph: (816)421-5900
Fax: (816)472-4010

American City Business Journals, Inc.
40 British American Blvd.
Latham, NY 12110
Ph: (518)640-6800
Fax: (518)640-6801

American City Business Journals, Inc.
600 Virginia Ave., Ste. 500
Milwaukee, WI 53204
Ph: (414)278-7788
Fax: (414)278-7028

American City Business Journals, Inc.
101 N 1st Ave., Ste. 2300
Phoenix, AZ 85003
Ph: (602)230-8400
Fax: (602)230-0955

American College of Apothecaries
2830 Summer Oaks Dr.
Bartlett, TN 38134
Ph: (901)383-8119
Free: 800-828-5933
Fax: (901)383-8882
Co. E-mail: aca@acainfo.org
URL: http://www.americancollegeofapoth-
ecaries.com

American College of Healthcare Executives
1 N Franklin St., Ste. 1700
Chicago, IL 60606-3529
Ph: (312)424-2800
Fax: (312)424-0023
Co. E-mail: contact@ache.org
URL: http://www.ache.org

American College of Physician Executives
400 N Ashley Dr., Ste. 400
Tampa, FL 33602-4322
Ph: (813)287-2000
Free: 800-562-8088
Fax: (813)287-8993
Co. E-mail: acpe@acpe.org
URL: http://www.acpe.org

American Counseling Association
5999 Stevenson Ave.
Alexandria, VA 22304
Ph: (703)823-6862
Free: 800-347-6647
Fax: (703)823-0252
Co. E-mail: ryep@counseling.org
URL: http://www.counseling.org

American Craft Council
1224 Marshall St. NE, Ste. 200
Minneapolis, MN 55413-1089
Ph: (612)206-3100
Free: 800-836-3470
Fax: (612)355-2330
Co. E-mail: council@craftcouncil.org
URL: http://www.craftcouncil.org

American Edged Products Manufacturers Association
21165 Whitfield Pl., No. 105
Potomac Falls, VA 20165
Ph: (703)433-9281
Fax: (703)433-0369
Co. E-mail: info@aepma.org
URL: http://www.aepma.org

American Farm Bureau Federation
600 Maryland Ave. SW, Ste. 1000W
Washington, DC 20024
Ph: (202)406-3600
Fax: (202)406-3602
Co. E-mail: jap@fb.org
URL: http://www.fb.org

American Financial Services Association
919 18th St. NW, Ste. 300
Washington, DC 20006-5526
Ph: (202)296-5544
Fax: (202)223-0321
Co. E-mail: cstinebert@afsamail.org
URL: http://www.afsaonline.org

American Fisheries Society
5410 Grosvenor Ln., Ste. 110
Bethesda, MD 20814-2199
Ph: (301)897-8616
Fax: (301)897-8096
Co. E-mail: main@fisheries.org
URL: http://www.fisheries.org

American Fitness
15250 Ventura Blvd., Ste. 200
Sherman Oaks, CA 91403
Free: 877-968-7263
URL: http://www.americanfitness.com

American Foundry Society, Inc.
1695 N Penny Ln.
Schaumburg, IL 60173
Ph: (847)824-0181
Free: 800-537-4237
Fax: (847)824-2174
Co. E-mail: jcall@afsinc.org
URL: http://www.afsinc.org

American Health Assistance Foundation
22512 Gateway Center Dr.
Clarksburg, MD 20871-2005
Ph: (301)948-3244
Free: 800-437-2423
Fax: (301)258-9454
Co. E-mail: jphilabaum@ahaf.org
URL: http://www.ahaf.org

American Health Care Association
1201 L St. NW
Washington, DC 20005
Ph: (202)842-4444
Free: 800-321-0343
Fax: (202)842-3860
Co. E-mail: hr@ahca.org
URL: http://www.ahcancal.org/Pages/
Default.aspx

American Health Consultants
3235 Piedmont Rd.
Bldg. 6., Ste. 400
Atlanta, GA 30305
Ph: (404)262-5476
Free: 800-688-2421
Fax: (404)262-7837
Co. E-mail: editorial_questions@ahcme-
dia.com
URL: http://www.ahcmedia.com/

American Home Furnishings Alliance
317 W High Ave., 10th Fl.
High Point, NC 27260
Ph: (336)884-5000
Fax: (336)884-5303
URL: http://www.ahfa.us

American Horse Council
1616 H St. NW, 7th Fl.
Washington, DC 20006
Ph: (202)296-4031
Fax: (202)296-1970
Co. E-mail: ahc@horsecouncil.org
URL: http://www.horsecouncil.org

American Horticultural Society
7931 East Blvd. Dr.
Alexandria, VA 22308-1300
Ph: (703)768-5700
Free: 800-777-7931
Fax: (703)768-7533
Co. E-mail: editor@ahs.org
URL: http://www.ahs.org

American Hospital Association
155 N Wacker Dr.
Chicago, IL 60606
Ph: (312)422-3000
Free: 800-242-2626
Fax: (312)422-4796
Co. E-mail: rich@aha.org
URL: http://www.aha.org

American Humane
63 Inverness Dr. E
Englewood, CO 80112-5117
Ph: (303)792-9900
Free: 800-227-4645
Fax: (303)792-5333
Co. E-mail: info@americanhumane.org
URL: http://www.americanhumane.org

American Institute for Economic Research
PO Box 1000
Great Barrington, MA 01230
Ph: (413)528-1216
Free: 888-528-1216
Fax: (413)528-0103
Co. E-mail: info@aier.org
URL: http://www.aier.org

American Institute of Baking Research Dept.
1213 Bakers Way
Manhattan, KS 66505-3999
Ph: (785)537-4750
Free: 800-633-5137
Fax: (785)537-1493
URL: http://www.aibonline.org

American Institute of Certified Public Accountants (AICPA)
1211 Avenue of the Americas
New York, NY 10036-8775
Ph: (212)596-6200
Free: 888-777-7077
Fax: (212)596-6213
Co. E-mail: service@aicpa.org
URL: http://www.aicpa.org

American Institute of Graphic Arts
164 5th Ave.
New York, NY 10010
Ph: (212)807-1990
Free: 800-548-1634
Fax: (212)807-1799
Co. E-mail: comments@aiga.org
URL: http://www.aiga.org

American International Automobile Dealers Association
211 N Union St., Ste. 300
Alexandria, VA 22314
Ph: (703)519-7800
Free: 800-462-4232
Fax: (703)519-7810
Co. E-mail: membership@aiada.org
URL: http://www.aiada.org

American Law Institute-American Bar Association Continuing Professional Education
4025 Chestnut St.
Philadelphia, PA 19104-3099
Free: 800-253-6397
Fax: (215)243-1664
URL: http://www.ali-aba.org

American Lighting Association
2050 N Stemmons Fwy., Unit 100
Dallas, TX 75207-3206
Ph: (214)698-9898
Free: 800-605-4448
Fax: (214)698-9899
Co. E-mail: skelley@americanlightingassoc.com
URL: http://www.americanlightingassoc.com

American Lock Collectors Association
8576 Barbara Dr.
Mentor, OH 44060
Ph: (440)257-2346
Co. E-mail: dixlock@aol.com
URL: http://www.alca-online.org/

American Management Association (AMA)
1601 Broadway
New York, NY 10019-7420
Ph: (212)586-8100
Free: 877-566-9441
Fax: (212)903-8168
Co. E-mail: customerservice@amanet.org
URL: http://www.amanet.org

American Marketing Association
311 S Wacker Dr., Ste. 5800
Chicago, IL 60606
Ph: (312)542-9000
Free: 800-262-1150
Fax: (312)542-9001
URL: http://www.marketingpower.com

American Massage Therapy Association
500 Davis St., Ste. 900
Evanston, IL 60201-4695
Ph: (847)864-0123
Free: 877-905-0577
Fax: (847)864-5196
Co. E-mail: info@amtamassage.org
URL: http://www.amtamassage.org

American Media, Inc.
4 New York Plaza
New York, NY 10004
Ph: (212)545-4800
URL: http://www.americanmediainc.com/

American Medical Association
515 N State St.
Chicago, IL 60610
Ph: (312)464-4430
Free: 800-621-8335
Fax: (312)464-4189
Co. E-mail: jasupport@ama-assn.org
URL: http://www.ama-assn.org

American Motorcyclist Association
13515 Yarmouth Dr.
Pickerington, OH 43147
Ph: (614)856-1900
Free: 800-262-5646
Fax: (614)856-1920

URL: http://www.americanmotorcyclist.com

American Musicological Society Inc.
6010 College Sta.
Brunswick, ME 04011-8451
Ph: (207)798-4243
Free: 877-679-7648
Fax: (207)798-4254
Co. E-mail: ams@ams-net.org
URL: http://www.ams-net.org/

American Numismatic Association
818 N Cascade Ave.
Colorado Springs, CO 80903-3208
Ph: (719)632-2646
Free: 800-367-9723
Fax: (719)634-4085
Co. E-mail: ana@money.org
URL: http://www.money.org

American Numismatic Society
75 Varick St., 11th Fl.
New York, NY 10038
Ph: (212)571-4470
Fax: (212)571-4479
Co. E-mail: meadows@numismatics.org
URL: http://www.numismatics.org

American Nurseryman Publishing Co.
223 W Jackson Blvd., Ste. 500
Chicago, IL 60606-6904
Ph: (312)427-7339
Free: 800-621-5727
Fax: (312)427-7346
Co. E-mail: admin@amerinursery.com
URL: http://www.amerinursery.com/

American Optometric Association
243 N Lindbergh Blvd.
Saint Louis, MO 63141
Ph: (314)983-4133
Free: 800-365-2219
Fax: (314)991-4101
Co. E-mail: rbrauns@aoa.org
URL: http://www.aoa.org/

American Pharmacists Association
2215 Constitution Ave. NW
Washington, DC 20005-1707
Ph: (202)628-4410
Free: 800-237-2742
Fax: (202)783-2351
Co. E-mail: infocenter@aphanet.org
URL: http://www.pharmacist.com

American Philatelic Society
100 Match Factory Pl.
Bellefonte, PA 16823
Ph: (814)933-3803
Free: 800-782-9580
Fax: (814)933-6128
Co. E-mail: flsente@stamps.org
URL: http://www.stamps.org/

American Physical Therapy Association
1111 N Fairfax St.
Alexandria, VA 22314-1488
Ph: (703)684-2782
Free: 800-999-2782
Fax: (703)706-8536
Co. E-mail: memberservices@apta.org
URL: http://www.apta.org

American Polygraph Association
PO Box 8037
Chattanooga, TN 37414-0037
Ph: (423)892-3992
Free: 800-272-8037
Fax: (423)894-5435
Co. E-mail: manager@polygraph.org
URL: http://www.polygraph.org

American Public Health Association
800 I St. NW
Washington, DC 20001-3710
Ph: (202)777-2742
Fax: (202)777-2534
Co. E-mail: comments@apha.org
URL: http://www.apha.org

American Public Human Services Association
1133 19th St. NW, Ste. 400
Washington, DC 20036
Ph: (202)682-0100
Fax: (202)289-6555
Co. E-mail: tracy.wareing@aphsa.org

American Publishing Co.
85 Canisteo St.
Hornell, NY 14843-1544
URL: http://oaspub.epa.gov/

American Purchasing Society
PO Box 256
Aurora, IL 60506
Ph: (630)859-0250
Fax: (630)859-0270
Co. E-mail: propurch@propurch.com
URL: http://www.american-purchasing.com

American Quarter Horse Association
1600 Quarter Horse Dr.
Amarillo, TX 79104
Ph: (806)376-4811
URL: http://www.aqha.com

American Quilt Study Group
1610 L St.
Lincoln, NE 68508-2509
Ph: (402)477-1181
Fax: (402)477-1181
Co. E-mail: aqsg2@americanquiltstudy-group.org
URL: http://www.americanquiltstudygroup.org

American Rental Association
1900 19th St.
Moline, IL 61265-4179
Ph: (309)764-2475
Free: 800-334-2177
Fax: (309)764-1533
URL: http://www.ararental.org

American Riding Instructors Association
28801 Trenton Ct.
Bonita Springs, FL 34134-3337
Ph: (239)948-3232
Fax: (239)948-5053
Co. E-mail: aria@riding-instructor.com
URL: http://www.riding-instructor.com

American Salers Association
19590 E Main St., Ste. 202
Parker, CO 80138
Ph: (303)770-9292
Fax: (303)770-9302
Co. E-mail: sherry@salersusa.org
URL: http://www.salersusa.org

American School Health Association
7263 State Route 43
Kent, OH 44240
Ph: (330)678-1601
Free: 800-445-2742
Fax: (330)678-4526
Co. E-mail: asha@ashaweb.org
URL: http://www.ashaweb.org

American Self-Protection Association
825 Greengate Oval
Sagamore Hills, OH 44067-2311
Ph: (330)467-1750
Co. E-mail: ebaltazzi@windstream.net
URL: http://www.americanselfprotection.org

American Society for Clinical Pathology
33 W Monroe, Ste. 1600
Chicago, IL 60603
Ph: (312)541-4999
Free: 800-267-2727
Fax: (312)541-4998
Co. E-mail: info@ascp.org
URL: http://www.ascp.org

American Society for Nutrition
9650 Rockville Pike
Bethesda, MD 20814-3998
Ph: (301)634-7050
Fax: (301)634-7892
Co. E-mail: info@nutrition.org
URL: http://www.nutrition.org

American Society for Public Administration
1301 Pennsylvania Ave. NW, Ste. 700
Washington, DC 20004-1735
Ph: (202)393-7878
Fax: (202)638-4952
Co. E-mail: info@aspanet.org

URL: http://www.aspanet.org

American Society for Quality
PO Box 3005
Milwaukee, WI 53201-3005
Ph: (414)272-8575
Free: 800-248-1946
Fax: (414)272-1734
Co. E-mail: help@asq.org
URL: http://www.asq.org

American Society of Agricultural Engineers
2950 Niles Rd.
Saint Joseph, MI 49085
Ph: (269)429-0300
Fax: (269)429-3852
Co. E-mail: hq@asabe.org
URL: http://www.asae.org

American Society of Andrology
1100 E Woodfield Rd., Ste. 520
Schaumburg, IL 60173
Ph: (847)619-4909
Fax: (847)517-7229
Co. E-mail: info@andrologysociety.com
URL: http://www.andrologysociety.com

American Society of Artists
PO Box 1326
Palatine, IL 60078-1326
Ph: (312)751-2500
Co. E-mail: asoaartists@aol.com
URL: http://www.americansocietyofartists.org

American Society of Association Executives
1575 I St. NW
Washington, DC 20005-1103
Ph: (202)371-0940
Free: 888-950-2723
Fax: (202)371-8315
Co. E-mail: asaeservice@asaecenter.org
URL: http://www.asaecenter.org

American Society of Civil Engineers Architectural Engineering Institute
1801 Alexander Bell Dr.
Reston, VA 20191-4400
Ph: (703)295-6300
Free: 800-548-2723
Fax: (703)295-6222
Co. E-mail: aei@asce.org
URL: http://content.aeinstitute.org

American Society of Consultant Pharmacists
1321 Duke St.
Alexandria, VA 22314-3563
Ph: (703)739-1300
Free: 800-355-2727
Fax: (703)739-1321
Co. E-mail: info@ascp.com
URL: http://www.ascp.com

American Society of Consulting Arborists
15245 Shady Grove Rd., Ste. 130
Rockville, MD 20850
Ph: (301)947-0483
Fax: (301)990-9771
Co. E-mail: asca@mgmtsol.com

American Society of Electroneurodiagnostic Technologists
402 E Bannister Rd., Ste. A
Kansas City, MO 64131-3019
Ph: (816)931-1120
Fax: (816)931-1145
Co. E-mail: info@aset.org
URL: http://www.aset.org

American Society of Furniture Designers
144 Woodland Dr.
New London, NC 28127
Ph: (910)576-1273
Fax: (910)576-1573
Co. E-mail: info@asfd.com
URL: http://www.asfd.com

American Society of Journalists & Authors
1501 Broadway, Ste. 302
New York, NY 10036
Ph: (212)997-0947
Fax: (212)937-2315
Co. E-mail: 75227.1650@compuserve.
com
URL: http://www.asja.org/index.php

American Society of Landscape Architects
636 Eye St. NW
Washington, DC 20001-3736
Ph: (202)898-2444
Free: 888-999-ASLA
Fax: (202)898-1185
Co. E-mail: info@asla.org
URL: http://www.asla.org

American Society of Mechanical Engineers
3 Park Ave.
New York, NY 10016-5990
Ph: (973)882-1170
Free: 800-843-2763
Fax: (973)882-1717
Co. E-mail: infocentral@asme.org
URL: http://www.asme.org

American Society of Media Photographers Inc.
150 N 2nd St.
Philadelphia, PA 19106-1912
Ph: (215)451-2767
Fax: (215)451-0880
Co. E-mail: info@asmp.org
URL: http://www.asmp.org

American Society of Plant Biologists
15501 Monona Dr.
Rockville, MD 20855-2768
Ph: (301)251-0560
Fax: (301)279-2996
Co. E-mail: info@aspb.org
URL: http://www.aspb.org

American Society of Professional Estimators
2525 Perimeter Place Dr., Ste. 103
Nashville, TN 37214
Ph: (615)316-9200
Free: 888-EST-MATE
Fax: (615)316-9800
Co. E-mail: psmith@aspenational.org
URL: http://www.aspenational.org

American Society of Safety Engineers
1800 E Oakton St.
Des Plaines, IL 60018
Ph: (847)699-2929
Fax: (847)768-3434
Co. E-mail: customerservice@asse.org
URL: http://www.asse.org

American Society of Women Accountants
1760 Old Meadow Rd., Ste. 500
McLean, VA 22102
Ph: (703)506-3265
Free: 800-326-2163
Fax: (703)506-3266
Co. E-mail: aswa@aswa.org
URL: http://www.aswa.org

American Society on Aging (ASA)
71 Stevenson St., Ste. 1450
San Francisco, CA 94105-2938
Ph: (415)974-9600
Free: 800-537-9728
Fax: (415)974-0300
Co. E-mail: membership@asaging.org
URL: http://www.asaging.org

American Sociological Association
1430 K St. NW, Ste. 600
Washington, DC 20005
Ph: (202)383-9005
Fax: (202)638-0882
Co. E-mail: executive.office@asanet.org
URL: http://www.asanet.org

American Solar Energy Society
4760 Walnut St., Ste. 106
Boulder, CO 80301-2843
Ph: (303)443-3130
Fax: (303)443-3212
Co. E-mail: info@solartoday.org
URL: http://www.ases.org

American String Teachers Association with National School Orchestra Association--Michigan Chapter
4153 Chain Bridge Rd.
5670 Commerce Rd.
Fairfax, VA 22030

Ph: (703)279-2113
Fax: (703)279-2114
URL: http://www.astaweb.com/

American Supply Association
1200 N Arlington Heights Rd., Ste. 150
Itasca, IL 60143
Ph: (630)467-0000
Fax: (630)467-0001
Co. E-mail: info@asa.net
URL: http://www.asa.net

American Tort Reform Association
1101 Connecticut Ave. NW, Ste. 400
Washington, DC 20036
Ph: (202)682-1163
Fax: (202)682-1022
Co. E-mail: sjoyce@atra.org
URL: http://www.atra.org

American Trade Magazines Crain Associated Enterprises Inc.
360 N Michigan Ave.
Chicago, IL 60601-3806
Ph: (312)649-5200
URL: http://www.crain.com/index.html

American Translators Association
225 Reinekers Ln., Ste. 590
Alexandria, VA 22314
Ph: (703)683-6100
Fax: (703)683-6122
Co. E-mail: ata@atanet.org
URL: http://www.atanet.org

American Trucking Associations
950 N Glebe Rd., Ste. 210
Arlington, VA 22203-4181
Ph: (703)838-1700
Free: 800-517-7370
Fax: (703)683-2292
Co. E-mail: media@trucking.org
URL: http://www.truckline.com

American Typecasting Fellowship
PO Box 263
Terra Alta, WV 26764
Ph: (304)789-2455
Fax: (304)789-2300
Co. E-mail: wvtypenut@aol.com

American Veterinary Medical Association
1931 N Meacham Rd., Ste. 100
Schaumburg, IL 60173-4360
Ph: (847)925-8070
Free: 800-248-2862
Fax: (847)925-1329
Co. E-mail: avmainfo@avma.org
URL: http://www.avma.org

American Water Works Association
6666 W Quincy Ave.
Denver, CO 80235-3098
Ph: (303)794-7711
Free: 800-926-7337
Fax: (303)347-0804

URL: http://www.awwa.org

American Wholesale Marketers Association
2750 Prosperity Ave., Ste. 530
Fairfax, VA 22031
Ph: (703)208-3358
Free: 800-482-2962
Fax: (703)573-5738
Co. E-mail: info@awmanet.org
URL: http://www.awmanet.org

American Wind Energy Association
1101 14th St. NW, Ste. 1000
Washington, DC 20005
Ph: (202)383-2500
Fax: (202)383-2505
Co. E-mail: windmail@awea.org
URL: http://www.awea.org

American Window Cleaner Magazine
750-B NW Broad St.
Southern Pines, NC 28387
Ph: (910)693-2644
Fax: (910)246-1681
Co. E-mail: info@awcmag.com
URL: http://www.awcmag.com/information.
  html#staff

American Woman's Society of Certified Public Accountants
136 S Keowee St.
Dayton, OH 45402
Ph: (973)222-1872
Free: 800-297-2721
Fax: (937)222-5794
Co. E-mail: info@awscpa.org
URL: http://www.awscpa.org

American-International Charolais Association
11700 NW Plaza Cir.
Kansas City, MO 64153
Ph: (816)464-5977
Fax: (816)464-5759
Co. E-mail: north@charolaisusa.com
URL: http://www.charolaisusa.com

Americana Unit
PO Box 127
New Britain, CT 06050

AMIDEAST Publications
1730 M St. NW, Ste. 1100
Washington, DC 20036-4505
Ph: (202)776-9600
Free: 800-368-5720
Fax: (202)776-7000
Co. E-mail: inquiries@amideast.org
URL: http://www.amideast.org

Amos Press Inc.
911 S Vandemark Rd.
Sidney 45365
Ph: (937)498-2111
Free: 800-673-8311
Fax: (937)498-0806

Co. E-mail: cweditor@amospress.com
URL: http://www.amospress.com

Ancestry.com Inc.
360 West 4800 North
Provo, UT 84604
Ph: (801)705-7000
Free: 800-262-3787
Fax: (801)705-7001
Co. E-mail: support@ancestry.com
URL: http://corporate.ancestry.com

Anchor Press
77 Accord Park Dr., Unit C4
Norwell, MA 02061
Ph: (781)982-9510
Fax: (781)982-9511
Co. E-mail: info@anchorpress.com
URL: http://www.anchorpress.com

Andersen Horticultural Library
University of Minnesota Landscape
3675 Arboretum Dr.
Chaska, MN 55318
Ph: (952)443-1405
Co. E-mail: hortlib@umn.edu
URL: http://www.arboretum.umn.edu/
  library.aspx

Animal Health Institute
1325 G St. NW, Ste. 700
Washington, DC 20005-3127
Ph: (202)637-2440
Fax: (202)393-1667
Co. E-mail: rphillips@ahi.org
URL: http://www.ahi.org

Animal Rights Network Inc.
3500 Boston St., Ste. 325
Baltimore, MD
Ph: (410)675-4566
Fax: (410)675-0066

Annex Publishing & Printing Inc.
PO Box 530
105 Donly Drive St.
Simcoe, ON, Canada N3Y 4N5
Ph: (519)429-3966
Free: 800-265-2827
Fax: (519)429-3094
URL: http://www.annexweb.com

Antique Bottle and Glass Collector
PO Box 180
East Greenville, PA 18041
Ph: (215)679-5849
Fax: (215)679-3068
Co. E-mail: glswrk@enter.net
URL: http://www.glswrk-auction.com

AOCS Press
2710 S Boulder Rd.
Urbana, IL 61802-6996
Ph: (217)359-2344
Fax: (217)351-8091
Co. E-mail: general@aocs.org
URL: http://www.aocs.org

APA: The Engineered Wood Association
7011 S 19th St.
Tacoma, WA 98466
Ph: (253)565-6600
Fax: (253)565-7265
Co. E-mail: help@apawood.org
URL: http://www.apawood.org

Apartment News Publications Inc.
15502 Graham St.
Huntington Beach, CA 92649
Ph: (714)893-3971
Free: 800-931-6666
Fax: (714)893-6484
Co. E-mail: aptmags@aptmags.com
URL: http://www.aptmags.com

Apex Publications Inc.
185 St. Paul
Quebec, QC, Canada G1K 3W2
Free: 800-905-7468
Fax: (800)664-2739
Co. E-mail: info@photolife.com
URL: http://www.photolife.com/

Apparel News Group
110 E 9th St., Ste. A-777
Los Angeles, CA 90079-1777
Ph: (213)627-3737
Co. E-mail: info@apparelnews.net
URL: http://www.apparelnews.net

Appendx
PO Box 382806
Cambridge, MA 02238
Ph: (617)495-4115
Fax: (617)495-8916
Co. E-mail: appendx@gsd.harvard.edu
URL: http://www.appendx.org

Applied Arts Inc.
18 Wynford Dr., Ste. 705
Toronto, ON, Canada M3C 3S2
Ph: (416)510-0909
Free: 800-646-0347
Fax: (416)510-0913
URL: http://www.appliedartsmag.com

The Appraisal Institute of American Inc.
386 Park Ave. S, Ste. 2000
New York, NY 10016
Ph: (212)889-5404
Fax: (212)889-5503
Co. E-mail: aaa1@rcn.com

Appraisal Institute of Canada
403-200 Catherine St.
Ottawa, ON, Canada K2P 2K9
Ph: (613)234-6533
Free: 866-726-5996
Fax: (613)234-7197
Co. E-mail: info@aicanada.org
URL: http://www.aicanada.ca

Appraisers Association of America Inc.
386 Park Ave. S, Ste. 2000
New York, NY 10016
Ph: (212)889-5404
Fax: (212)889-5503
Co. E-mail: aaa@appraisersassoc.org
URL: http://www.appraisersassoc.org

Apress
2855 Telegraph Ave., Ste. 600
Berkeley, CA 94705
Ph: (510)549-5930
Fax: (510)549-5939
Co. E-mail: info@apress.com
URL: http://www.apress.com/

Apress L.P.
2560 9th St., Ste. 219
Berkeley, CA 94710
Ph: (510)549-5930
Fax: (510)549-5939

Aquarian Research Foundation
5620 Morton St.
Philadelphia, PA 19144
Ph: (215)848-2292
Free: 800-254-8291
Co. E-mail: judyrosenblum@juno.com
URL: http://www.aquarian.cjb.net/

Arbor Day Foundation
100 Arbor Ave.
Nebraska City, NE 68410
Ph: (402)474-5655
Free: 888-448-7337
Fax: (402)474-0820
Co. E-mail: info@arborday.org
URL: http://www.arborday.org

The Arc of Carroll County Inc.
180 Kriders Church Rd.
Westminster, MD 21158
Ph: (410)848-4124
Fax: (410)876-5317

Architectural Designs Inc.
57 Danbury Rd.
Wilton, CT 06897-4439
Ph: (262)521-4596
Free: 800-854-7852
Fax: (203)761-8600
Co. E-mail: info@architecturaldesigns.com
URL: http://www.architecturaldesigns.com

Arizona Daily Star
4850 S Park Ave.
Tucson, AZ 85714
Free: 800-695-4492

Arizona Farm Bureau Federation
PO Box 9000
PO Box 9000
Higley, AZ 85236-9000
Ph: (480)635-3604
Fax: (480)635-3781

Arkansas Business Publishing Group
122 E 2nd St.
Little Rock, AR 72201
Ph: (501)372-1443
Fax: (501)375-7933

Art Dealers Association of America
205 Lexington Ave., Ste. 901
New York, NY 10016
Ph: (212)488-5550
Fax: (646)688-6809
Co. E-mail: lmitchem@artdealers.org
URL: http://www.artdealers.org

Art Now Inc.
601 W 26th St., Ste. 410
New York, NY 10001
Ph: (212)447-9555
Co. E-mail: northamericapress@artinfo.
  com
URL: http://www.artinfo.com/galleryguide/

The Art of Eating
PO Box 242
Peacham, VT 05862
Free: 800-495-3944
URL: http://www.artofeating.com/

Artech House, Incorporated
685 Canton St.
Norwood, MA 02062
Ph: (781)769-9750
Free: 800-225-9977
Fax: (781)769-6334

Artificial Language Laboratory
Michigan State University
405 Computer Ctr.
East Lansing, MI 48824-1042
Ph: (517)353-0870
Fax: (517)353-4766
Co. E-mail: artlang@pilot.msu.edu
URL: http://www.msu.edu/artlang/Com-
  mOut.html

ARTnews L.L.C.
48 W 38th St.
New York, NY 10018-6248
Ph: (212)398-1690
Free: 800-284-4625
Fax: (212)819-0394
Co. E-mail: info@artnews.com
URL: http://www.artnewsonline.com

Arts & Media Inc.
PO Box 678
Richboro, PA 18954
Ph: (215)968-4655
Fax: (215)968-4766
Co. E-mail: info@glasscraftsman.com
URL: http://www.glasscraftsman.com

ARTWEEK
PO Box 52100
Palo Alto, CA 94303-0751
Free: 800-733-2916
Co. E-mail: info@artweek.com

URL: http://www.artweek.com

Ascend Integrated Media
7015 College Blvd., Ste. 600
Overland Park, KS 66211
Ph: (913)469-1110
Fax: (913)469-0806
Co. E-mail: info@ascendmedia.com
URL: http://www.ascendmedia.com/

ASIS International
1625 Prince St.
Alexandria, VA 22314-2818
Ph: (703)519-6200
Fax: (703)519-6299
Co. E-mail: asis@asisonline.org
URL: http://www.asisonline.org

ASM International
9639 Kinsman Rd.
Materials Park, OH 44073-0001
Ph: (440)338-5151
Free: 800-336-5152
Fax: (440)338-4634
Co. E-mail: CustomerService@asminter-
  national.org
URL: http://asmcommunity.
  asminternational.org/portal/site/www/

ASM Journals
1752 North St. NW
Washington, DC 20036-2904
Ph: (202)737-3600
Fax: (202)942-9335
Co. E-mail: journals@asmusa.org
URL: http://www.journals.asm.org

Aspatore Books, Incorporated
264 Beacon St., 2nd Fl.
Boston, MA 02116
Ph: (617)369-7007
Fax: (617)249-1970

Aspen Publishers Inc.
76 9th Ave., 7 Fl.
New York, NY 10011-4962
Ph: (212)771-0786
Free: 800-234-1660
Fax: (212)771-0796
Co. E-mail: aspen-customerservice@
  wolterskluwer.com
URL: http://www.aspenpublishers.com

Aspen Publishers, Inc.
7201 McKinney Cir.
Frederick, MD 21704
Ph: (301)698-7100
Free: 800-234-1660
Fax: (800)901-9075
Co. E-mail: customerservice@aspenpub-
  lisher.com
URL: http://www.aspenpublishers.com

The Asphalt Contractor
1233 Janesville Ave.
Fort Atkinson, WI 53538-0803
Ph: (920)563-6388

Free: 800-547-7377
Fax: (920)328-9029
URL: http://www.forconstructionpros.com

Asphalt Emulsion Manufacturers Association
3 Church Cir.
Annapolis, MD 21401
Ph: (410)267-0023
Fax: (410)267-7546
Co. E-mail: krissoff@aema.org
URL: http://www.aema.org

Asphalt Recycling and Reclaiming Association
PMB 250
Annapolis, MD 21401
Ph: (410)267-0023
Fax: (410)267-7546
Co. E-mail: krissoff@arra.org
URL: http://www.arra.org

Asset International Inc.
1055 Washington Blvd.
Stamford, CT 06901
Free: 888-374-3722
Fax: (203)595-3201
URL: http://home.globalcustodian.com

Associated Builders and Contractors Inc.
4250 N Fairfax Dr., 9th Fl.
Arlington, VA 22203-1607
Ph: (703)812-8201
Fax: (703)812-8235
Co. E-mail: gotquestions@abc.org
URL: http://www.abc.org

Associated Equipment Distributors Inc.
600 Hunter Dr., Ste. 220
Oak Brook, IL 60523
Ph: (630)574-0650
Free: 800-388-0650
Fax: (630)574-0132
Co. E-mail: info@aednet.org
URL: http://www.aednet.org

Associated General Contractors of America
2300 Wilson Blvd., Ste. 400
Arlington, VA 22201
Ph: (703)548-3118
Free: 800-242-1767
Fax: (703)548-3119
Co. E-mail: info@agc.org
URL: http://www.agc.org

Associated Humane Societies
124 Evergreen Ave.
Newark, NJ 07114-2133
Ph: (973)824-7080
Fax: (973)824-2720
Co. E-mail: associatedhumane@aol.com
URL: http://www.ahscares.org

Associated Locksmiths of America
3500 Easy St.
Dallas, TX 75247
Ph: (214)819-9733
Free: 800-532-2562
Fax: (214)819-9736
Co. E-mail: president@aloa.org
URL: http://www.aloa.org

Associated Plumbing Heating & Cooling
PO Box 36972
Birmingham, AL 35236-6972
Ph: (205)985-9488
Co. E-mail: dconsult1@bellsouth.net
URL: http://www.alphccapprentice.org/

Associated Press
1120 John St.
Seattle, WA 98111
Ph: (206)464-2111
Fax: (206)464-2261

Associated Warehouses Inc.
1740 W Katella Ave., Ste. M
Orange, CA 92867
Ph: (973)539-1277
Co. E-mail: barb@awilogistics.com
URL: http://www.awilogistics.com/

Association de la construction du Quebec
7400, Blvd. les Galeries d'Anjou, Bureau 205
Montreal, QC, Canada H1M 3M2
Ph: (514)354-0609
Fax: (514)354-8292
Co. E-mail: info@prov.acq.org
URL: http://www.acq.org

Association for Childhood Education International
17904 Georgia Ave., Ste. 215
Olney, MD 20832
Ph: (301)570-2111
Free: 800-423-3563
Fax: (301)570-2212
Co. E-mail: headquarters@acei.org
URL: http://www.acei.org

Association for Computing Machinery
2 Penn Pl., Ste. 701
New York, NY 10121-0701
Ph: (212)626-0500
Free: 800-342-6626
Fax: (212)944-1318
Co. E-mail: infodir_sigmis@acm.org
URL: http://www.sigmis.org

Association for Computing Machinery Special Interest Group on Array Programming Languages
Department of Computer Science
151 Engineer's Way
Charlottesville, VA 22904
Ph: (212)869-7440
Free: 800-342-6626

Fax: (212)944-1318
Co. E-mail: acmhelp@acm.org
URL: http://www.sigir.org/index.html

Association for Computing Machinery
Editorial Offices
Baylor University, Hankamer School of Business
Waco, TX 76798-8005

Association for Educational Communications and Technology
1800 N Stonelake Dr., Ste. 2
Bloomington, IN 47404
Ph: (812)335-7675
Free: 877-677-AECT
Fax: (812)335-7678
Co. E-mail: aect@aect.org
URL: http://www.aect.org

Association for Manufacturing Technology
7901 West Park Dr.
McLean, VA 22102
Ph: (703)893-2900
Free: 800-524-0475
Fax: (703)893-1151
Co. E-mail: amtT@amtonline.org
URL: http://www.amtonline.org

Association for Technology in Music Instruction
312 E Pine St.
Missoula, MT 59802
Ph: (406)721-1152
Fax: (406)721-9419
Co. E-mail: jimf@soundtree.com
URL: http://www.atmionline.org

Association for the Advancement of Medical Instrumentation
1110 N Glebe Rd., Ste. 220
Arlington, VA 22201-4795
Ph: (703)525-4890
Free: 800-332-2264
Fax: (703)276-0793
Co. E-mail: publications@aami.org
URL: http://www.aami.org

Association for the Advancement of Medical Instrumentation
4301 N Fairfax Dr., Ste. 301
Arlington, VA 22203-1633
Ph: (703)525-4890
Free: 800-332-2264
Fax: (703)276-0793
Co. E-mail: customerservice@aami.org
URL: http://www.aami.org

Association of American Publishers Inc.
50 F St. NW, Ste. 400
Washington, DC 20001
Ph: (202)347-3375
Fax: (202)347-3690

Association of American University Presses
28 W 36th St., Ste. 602
New York, NY 10018
Ph: (212)989-1010
Fax: (212)989-0275
Co. E-mail: info@aaupnet.org
URL: http://www.aaupnet.org

Association of Asphalt Paving Technologists
6776 Lake Dr., Ste. 215
Lino Lakes, MN 55014-1191
Ph: (651)293-9188
Fax: (651)293-9193
Co. E-mail: aaptinfo@gmail.com
URL: http://www.asphalttechnology.org

Association of Bridal Consultants
56 Danbury Rd., Ste. 11
New Milford, CT 06776
Ph: (860)355-7000
Fax: (860)354-1404
Co. E-mail: office@bridalassn.com
URL: http://www.bridalassn.com

Association of Clinicians for the Underserved
1420 Spring Hill Rd., Ste. 600
Tysons Corner, VA 22102
Ph: (703)442-5318
Fax: (703)562-8801
Co. E-mail: acu@clinicians.org
URL: http://www.clinicians.org

Association of Directory Marketing
1187 Thorn Run Rd., Ste. 630
Moon Township, PA 15108-3198
Ph: (412)269-0663
Fax: (412)269-0655
Co. E-mail: nmd@localsearchassociation.
  org
URL: http://www.admworks.org

Association of Machinery and Equipment Appraisers
315 S Patrick St.
Alexandria, VA 22314
Ph: (703)836-7900
Free: 800-537-8629
Fax: (703)836-9303
Co. E-mail: amea@amea.org
URL: http://www.amea.org/

Association of Millwork Distributors
10047 Robert Trent Jones Pkwy.
New Port Richey, FL 34655-4649
Ph: (727)372-3665
Fax: (727)372-2879
Co. E-mail: mail@amdweb.com

Association of Ontario Land Surveyors
1043 McNicoll Ave.
Toronto, ON, Canada M1W 3W6
Ph: (416)491-9020
Free: 800-268-0718
Fax: (416)491-2576

Co. E-mail: admin@aols.org
URL: http://www.aols.org/

Association of Professional Genealogists
11207 Wyandot St.
Westminster, CO 80035-0998
Ph: (303)422-9371
Fax: (303)456-8825
Co. E-mail: admin@apgen.org
URL: http://www.apgen.org

Association of Registered Interior Designers of Ontario
717 Church St.
Toronto, ON, Canada M4W 2M5
Ph: (416)921-2127
Free: 800-334-1180
Fax: (416)921-3660
Co. E-mail: adminoffice@arido.ca

Association of Retail Travel Agents
73 White Bridge Rd., Box 238
Nashville, TN 37205
Free: 800-969-6069
Fax: (615)985-0600
Co. E-mail: info@artaonline.com

Association of Schools and Colleges of Optometry
6110 Executive Blvd., Ste. 420
Rockville, MD 20852
Ph: (301)231-5944
Fax: (301)770-1828
Co. E-mail: carmstrong@opted.org
URL: http://www.opted.org/i4a/pages/
  index.cfm?pageid=1

Association of the Wall and Ceiling Industries International
513 W Broad St., Ste. 210
Falls Church, VA 22046
Ph: (703)538-1600
Fax: (703)534-8307
Co. E-mail: info@awci.org
URL: http://www.awci.org

Association of Writers and Writing Programs
George Mason University
Fairfax, VA 22030-4444
Ph: (703)993-4301
Fax: (703)993-4302
Co. E-mail: awp@awpwriter.org
URL: http://www.awpwriter.org

ASTD
1640 King St.
Alexandria, VA 22314-2746
Ph: (703)683-8100
Free: 800-628-2783
Fax: (703)683-1523
Co. E-mail: customercare@astd.org
URL: http://www.astd.org

Athletic Business Publications Inc.
4130 Lien Rd.
Madison, WI 53704
Ph: (608)249-0186
Free: 800-722-8764
Fax: (608)249-1153
Co. E-mail: editors@hardwoodfloorsmag.
  com
URL: http://www.athleticbusiness.com

Atlanta Journal Constitution
223 Perimeter Center Pkwy.
Atlanta, GA 30346
Ph: (404)526-5151

Atlantic Boating Almanac
3 Church Cir., Ste. 109
Annapolis, MD 21401
Free: 800-481-6277
Fax: (800)487-6277
Co. E-mail: editor@prostarpublications.
  com
URL: http://www.prostarpublications.com

Atlantic Monthly Press
841 Broadway, 4th Fl.
New York, NY 10003
Ph: (212)614-7850
Fax: (212)614-7886
URL: http://www.groveatlantic.com/

Atlantic Publishing Company
1405 SW 6th Ave.
Ocala, FL 34471
Free: 800-814-1132
URL: http://www.atlantic-pub.com

Atlantic Publishing Company
1210 SW 23rd Pl.
Ocala, FL 34474
Ph: (352)622-1825
Fax: (352)622-1875
Co. E-mail: sales@atlantic-pub.com
URL: http://www.atlantic-pub.com

Atlantic Spinners & Handweavers Nova Scotia Museum
1747 Summer St.
Halifax, NS, Canada B3H 3A6
Ph: (902)865-3641

Audio Engineering Society Inc.
60 E 42nd St., Rm. 2520
New York, NY 10165-2520
Ph: (212)661-8528
Free: 800-541-7299
Fax: (212)682-0477
Co. E-mail: hq@aes.org
URL: http://www.aes.org

Audiotex News
2362 Hempstead Tpke., 2nd Fl.
East Meadow, NY 11554
Fax: (516)735-3682

August Home Publishing
2200 Grand Ave.
Des Moines, IA 50312
Ph: (515)875-7000
Free: 800-311-5441
Fax: (515)283-0447
URL: http://www.augusthome.com

Austin & Company, Incorporated
104 S Union St., Ste. 202
Traverse City, MI 49684
Ph: (231)933-4649
Fax: (231)933-4659

Austrian Press and Information Service
3524 International Ct. NW
Washington, DC 20008
Ph: (202)895-6700
Fax: (202)895-6772
Co. E-mail: austroinfo@austria.org
URL: http://www.austrianinformation.org

AuthorHouse
1663 Liberty Dr., Ste. 200
Bloomington, IN 47403
Free: 888-519-5121
URL: http://www.authorhouse.com

Automotive Body Parts Association
PO Box 820689
Houston, TX 77282-0689
Ph: (281)531-0809
Free: 800-323-5832
Fax: (281)531-9411
Co. E-mail: autobpa@infohwy.com
URL: http://www.autobpa.com

Automotive Engine Rebuilders Association
330 Lexington Dr.
Buffalo Grove, IL 60089-6998
Ph: (847)541-6550
Free: 888-326-2372
Fax: (847)541-5808
Co. E-mail: info@aera.org

Automotive Fleet and Leasing Association
21061 S Western Ave.
Torrance, CA 90501
Ph: (651)203-7247
Fax: (310)533-2506

Automotive Parts International
PO Box 5950
Bethesda, MD 20824-5950
Ph: (301)229-2077
Fax: (301)229-3995

Automotive Service Association
PO Box 929
Bedford, TX 76095-0929
Ph: (817)283-6205
Free: 800-272-7467
Fax: (817)685-0225
Co. E-mail: asainfo@asashop.org
URL: http://www.asashop.org

Automotive Warehouse Distributors Association
7101 Wisconsin Ave., Ste. 1300
Bethesda, MD 20814
Ph: (301)654-6664
Fax: (301)654-3299
Co. E-mail: info@awda.org

Available from U.S. Government Printing Office
732 N Capitol St. NW
Washington, DC 20401
Ph: (202)512-1800
Free: 800-432-2250
Fax: (202)728-1863
Co. E-mail: customerservice@cqpress.com
URL: http://www.gpo.gov

Awards and Recognition Association
4700 W Lake Ave.
Glenview, IL 60025
Ph: (847)375-4800
Free: 800-344-2148
Fax: (847)375-6480
Co. E-mail: info@ara.org
URL: http://www.ara.org

Axios Press
94 Landfill Rd.
Edinburg, VA 22824-9421
Ph: (540)984-3829
Free: 888-542-9467
Fax: (540)984-3843
Co. E-mail: info@axiospress.com
URL: http://www.axiospress.com

Azure Publishing Inc.
460 Richmond St. W, Ste. 601
Toronto, ON, Canada M5V 1Y1
Ph: (416)203-9674
Fax: (416)203-9842
Co. E-mail: azure@azureonline.com
URL: http://www.azuremagazine.com/

B

The B&B and Country Inn Marketplace
926 Lenoir Rhyne Blvd. SE
Hickory, NC 28602
Ph: (828)324-7291
Free: 800-871-8977
Co. E-mail: innsales@charter.net
URL: http://www.innmarketing.com

Babcox
3550 Embassy Pky.
Akron, OH 44333
Ph: (330)670-1234
Co. E-mail: bbabcox@babcox.com
URL: http://www.babcox.com/

Back Bay/Little, Brown
PO Box 8828
Boston, MA 02114
Free: 800-759-0190
Fax: (800)331-1664

URL: http://www.hachettebookgroupusa.com/publishing_back-bay-books.aspx

Baker & Taylor
1120 Rte. 22 E
Bridgewater, NJ 08807
Ph: (908)541-7000
Free: 800-775-1500
Co. E-mail: btinfo@btol.com
URL: http://www.baker-taylor.com/

Bale Publications
5121 St. Charles Ave., Ste. 13
New Orleans, LA 70115

Ball Publishing
622 Town Rd.
West Chicago, IL 60186
Ph: (630)231-3675
Free: 888-888-0013
Fax: (630)231-5254
Co. E-mail: info@ballpublishing.com
URL: http://www.ballpublishing.com

Ballantine/Random House
1745 Broadway
New York, NY 10019
Ph: (212)782-9000
Fax: (212)572-8700
Co. E-mail: customerservice@random-house.com

Baltimore Business Journal
1 E Pratt St., Ste. 205
Baltimore, MD 21202
Ph: (410)576-1161
Fax: (410)752-3112
Co. E-mail: baltimore@bizjournals.com
URL: http://baltimore.bizjournals.com/baltimore

Bangor Daily News
491 Main St.
Bangor, ME 04402
Ph: (207)990-8000
Free: 800-432-7964

Bantam Books
Front Porch Institute
964 17th St.
Astorta, OR 97103
Ph: (503)338-6218
URL: http://patrickoverton.com

Bantam Books
1745 Broadway
New York, NY 10019
Ph: (212)782-9000
Fax: (212)572-6066
URL: http://www.randomhouse.com/bantamdell/

Barbara Wallraff
1010 E Missouri Ave.
Phoenix, AZ 85014
Ph: (602)395-5850
Free: 888-626-8779

Fax: (602)395-5853

Bard Press
5275 McCormick Mt. Dr.
Austin, TX 78734
Ph: (512)266-2112
Fax: (512)266-2749
Co. E-mail: info@bardpress.com
URL: http://www.bardpress.com

Barger & Wolen
515 S Flower St., 34th Fl.
Los Angeles, CA 90071-2205
Ph: (213)680-2800
Fax: (213)614-7399

Barnard Enterprises Inc.
17 Kenneth Rd.
Upper Montclair, NJ 07043
Ph: (973)655-8888

Barron's Editorial & Corporate Headquarters
Dow Jones & Company
1211 Ave. of the Americas
New York, NY 10036
Ph: (212)416-2000

Barron's Educational Series Inc.
250 Wireless Blvd.
Hauppauge, NY 11788
Ph: (631)434-3311
Free: 800-645-3476
Fax: (631)434-3723
Co. E-mail: barrons@barronseduc.com
URL: http://www.barronseduc.com

Basic Books
387 Park Ave. S
New York, NY 10016
Free: 800-810-4145
Co. E-mail: special.markets@perseus-books.com
URL: http://www.perseusbooks.com

Basic Books/Perseus Books Group
387 Park Ave. S, 12th Fl.
New York, NY 10016
Ph: (212)340-8100

BASS/ESPN
5845 Carmichael Rd.
Montgomery, AL 36117-2329
Ph: (334)272-9530
Fax: (334)270-8549
Co. E-mail: customerservice@bassmaster.com
URL: http://espn.go.com/

Baum Publications Ltd.
201 - 2323 Boundary Rd.
Vancouver, BC, Canada V5M 4V8
Ph: (604)291-9900
Fax: (604)291-1906
URL: http://www.baumpub.com

Bay Area Independent Publishers Association
PO Box E
Corte Madera, CA 94976
Ph: (415)456-0247
Free: 866-622-1325
Co. E-mail: board@baipa.org
URL: http://www.baipa.org

Bay Area Poets Coalition Inc.
PO Box 11435
Berkeley, CA 94712-2435
Co. E-mail: poetalk@aol.com

Baylor University Dept. of Management
1 Bear Pl.
Waco, TX 76798
Ph: (254)710-4290
Fax: (254)710-2271
Co. E-mail: sharon_k_johnson@baylor.edu
URL: http://www.baylor.edu

Baywood Publishing Company Inc.
26 Austin Ave.
Amityville, NY 11701
Ph: (631)691-1270
Free: 800-638-7819
Fax: (631)691-1770
Co. E-mail: info@baywood.com
URL: http://www.baywood.com

Beacon Health Corp.
12308 N Corporate Pkwy., Ste. 100
Mequon, WI 53092-3380
Ph: (262)243-6100
Free: 800-553-2041
Fax: (262)243-1207
Co. E-mail: info@beaconhealth.org

Beacon Press
25 Beacon St.
Boston, MA 02108-2892
Ph: (617)742-2110
Fax: (617)723-3097

The Beauty Industry Report
22287 Mulholland Hwy.
PMB 403
Calabasas, CA 91302-5157
Ph: (818)225-8353
Fax: (818)222-7828
Co. E-mail: mike@beautyindustryreport.com
URL: http://www.bironline.com

Bee Publishing Company Inc.
PO Box 5503
Newtown, CT 06470-5503
Ph: (203)426-3141
Fax: (203)426-5169
URL: http://newtownbee.com/

Bell Springs Publishing
106 State St.
Willits, CA 95490
Ph: (707)459-6372
Free: 800-515-8050

Fax: (707)459-8614

Bellingham Herald
1155 N State St., Ste. 200
Bellingham, WA 98225
Ph: (360)676-2660

BenBella Books
6440 N Central Expy., Ste. 503
Dallas, TX 75206
Ph: (214)750-3600
Fax: (214)750-3645
Co. E-mail: feedback@benbellabooks.com
URL: http://www.benbellabooks.com

Benzinga.com
160 Greentree, Ste. 101
Dover, DE 19904
Free: 877-440-9464

Berens & Tate, P.C.
10050 Regency Cir., Ste. 400
Omaha, NE 68114
Ph: (402)391-1991
Free: 800-729-1441
Fax: (402)391-7363
Co. E-mail: berens@berenstate.com
URL: http://www.berenstate.com

Berkley Trade
Penguin Group
375 Hudson St.
New York, NY 10014
Ph: (212)366-2372
Fax: (212)366-2933
URL: http://us.penguingroup.com/static/html/aboutus/adult.berkley.html

Berkley Trade/Penguin Group USA Inc.
375 Hudson St.
New York, NY 10014
Ph: (212)366-2000
Fax: (212)366-2666
Co. E-mail: fran.corea@us.penguingroup.com
URL: http://www.penguin.com

Berlitz International Inc.
400 Alexander Park
Princeton, NJ 08540
Ph: (609)514-3400
Free: 800-528-8908
Fax: (609)514-3405

Bermuda Department of Tourism
675 3rd Ave., 20th Fl.
New York, NY 10017
Ph: (212)818-9800
Free: 800-223-6106
Fax: (212)983-5289
Co. E-mail: fdesk@bermudatourism.com
URL: http://www.gotobermuda.com

Berrett-Koehler Publishers
235 Montgomery St., Ste. 650
San Francisco, CA 94104
Ph: (415)288-0260

Fax: (415)362-2512
Co. E-mail: bkpub@bkpub.com
URL: http://www.bkconnection.com/

Best-Met Publishing Company Inc.
5537 Twin Knolls Rd., Ste. 438
Columbia, MD 21045
Ph: (410)730-5013
Fax: (410)740-4680
Co. E-mail: office@best-met.com
URL: http://www.best-met.com

Beverage Information Group
17 High St., 2nd Fl.
Norwalk, CT 06851
Ph: (203)855-8499
Fax: (203)855-9446
URL: http://www.bevinfogroup.com

Beverage Marketing Corp.
PO Box 126
Mingo Junction, OH 43938
Ph: (740)598-4133
Free: 800-275-4630
Fax: (740)598-3977
Co. E-mail: consulting@beveragemarket-ing.com
URL: http://www.beveragemarketing.com

Beverage World
200 E Randolph St., 7th fl.
Chicago, IL 60601
Ph: (646)708-7300
Free: 866-890-8541
Fax: (646)708-7399
Co. E-mail: info@beverageworld.com
URL: http://www.beverageworld.com

BIA Financial Network Inc.
15120 Enterprise Ct., Ste. 100
Chantilly, VA 20151
Ph: (703)818-2425
Free: 800-331-5086
Fax: (703)803-3299
Co. E-mail: info@bia.com
URL: http://www.bia.com

Bibliographical Center for Research, Rocky Mountain Region Inc.
14394 E Evans Ave.
Aurora, CO 80014-1478
Ph: (303)751-6277
Free: 800-392-1552
Fax: (303)751-9787
Co. E-mail: admin@bcr.org

Bibliotheca Press
c/o Prosperity & Profits Unltd.
Denver, CO 80201-0416
Ph: (303)575-5676

Bicycling
33 E Minor St.
Emmaus, PA 18098
URL: http://www.bicycling.com/

Bill Communications Inc.
1115 Northmeadow Pkwy.
Roswell, GA 30076
Ph: (770)569-1540
Free: 800-241-9034
Fax: (770)569-5105

Billiards and Bowling Institute of America
615 Six Flags Dr.
Arlington, TX 76011
Ph: (817)385-8120
Fax: (817)633-2940
Co. E-mail: bbia@billiardandbowling.org
URL: http://www.billiardandbowling.org/

Billings Gazette
PO Box 36300
Billings, MT 59107-6300
Ph: (406)657-1200
Free: 800-543-2505

Bio-Integral Resource Center
PO Box 7414
Berkeley, CA 94707
Ph: (510)524-2567
Fax: (510)524-1758
Co. E-mail: birc@igc.org
URL: http://www.birc.org

Bissett Communications Corp.
12844 Berkhamsted St.
Cerritos, CA 90703
Ph: (562)809-8917
Fax: (562)809-1627
Co. E-mail: bbissett@mfpreport.com

Black Book Marketing Group Inc.
740 Broadway, Ste. 202
New York, NY 10003
Ph: (212)979-6700
Free: 800-841-1246
Fax: (212)673-4321
Co. E-mail: info@blackbook.com
URL: http://www.blackbook.com

Black Tennis Magazine
PO Box 210767
Dallas, TX 75211
Ph: (214)339-7370
Fax: (214)339-7370
Co. E-mail: marcus.freeman.tennis@airmail.net
URL: http://www.btmag.com/

Blackwell Publishers Ltd.
111 River St.
Hoboken, NJ 07030
Ph: (201)748-6000
Fax: (201)748-6088

Blackwell Publishing Inc.
350 Main St.
Malden, MA 02148
Ph: (781)388-8200
Free: 800-216-2522
Fax: (781)388-8210

Co. E-mail: journaladsusa@bos.blackwell-publishing.com
URL: http://www.blackwellpublishing.com

Bloomberg Press
731 Lexington Ave.
New York, NY 10022
Co. E-mail: press@bloomberg.com
URL: http://www.bloomberg.com

Bloomberg Press
734 Lexington Ave.
New York, NY 10022-1265
Ph: (212)318-2000
Free: 800-869-1231
Fax: (917)369-5000
Co. E-mail: press@bloomberg.com
URL: http://www.bloomberg.com/books

Bloomsbury USA
175 5th Ave.
New York, NY 10010
URL: http://www.bloomsburyusa.com

Blue Dolphin Publishing Inc.
13340-D Grass Valley Ave.
Grass Valley, CA 95945-7706
Ph: (530)477-1503
Free: 800-643-0765
Fax: (530)477-8342
Co. E-mail: bdolphin@bluedolphinpublish-ing.com
URL: http://www.bluedolphinpublishing.com

Bluestocking Press
3333 Gold Country Dr.
Placerville, CA 95667
Ph: (530)622-8586
Free: 800-959-8586
Fax: (530)642-9222
Co. E-mail: customerservice@bluestock-ingpress.com
URL: http://www.bluestockingpress.com

BNA Tax and Accounting
9435 Key West Ave.
Rockville, MD 20850
Ph: (800)372-1033
Free: 800-223-7270
Fax: (301)294-6760
Co. E-mail: tm@bna.com
URL: http://www.bnatax.com

BNP Media
1050 Illinois Rte. 83, Ste. 200
Bensenville, IL 60106
Ph: (630)694-4353

BNP Media
2401 W Big Beaver Rd., Ste. 700
Troy, MI 48084
Ph: (248)362-3700
Free: 800-952-6643
Fax: (248)362-5103
Co. E-mail: privacy@bnpmedia.com
URL: http://www.bnpmedia.com

Boat Owners Association of the United States
880 S Pickett St.
Alexandria, VA 22304-4695
Ph: (703)461-4666
Free: 800-395-2628
Fax: (703)461-2847
Co. E-mail: membership@boatus.com
URL: http://www.boatus.com

Bobit Business Media
3520 Challenger St.
Torrance, CA 90503
Ph: (310)533-2400
Fax: (310)533-2500
Co. E-mail: webmaster@bobit.com
URL: http://www.bobit.com

Bohman Industrial Traffic Consultants Inc.
116 Deer Meadow Lane
Chatham, MA 02633
Ph: (508)945-2272
Fax: (978)630-2917

Bollinger Capital Management Inc.
PO Box 3358
Manhattan Beach, CA 90266
Ph: (310)798-8855
Free: 800-888-8400
Fax: (310)798-8858
Co. E-mail: bbands@bollingerbands.com

Book Industry Study Group (BISG)
370 Lexington Ave., Ste. 900
New York, NY 10017
Ph: (646)336-7141
Fax: (646)336-6214
Co. E-mail: info@bisg.org
URL: http://www.bisg.org

Booklocker.com Inc.
PO Box 2399
Bangor, ME 04402-2399
Fax: (207)262-5544
URL: http://booklocker.com

Booklocker.com, Incorporated
PO Box 2399
Bangor, ME 04402
Fax: (207)262-5544

BookSurge LLC
7290 B Investment Dr.
Charleston, SC 29418
Ph: (843)789-5000
Free: 866-308-6235
Co. E-mail: customerservice@booksurge.
  com
URL: http://www.booksurge.com

Booksurge, LLC
5341 Dorchester Rd., Ste. 16
North Charleston, SC 29418
Ph: (843)579-0000
Free: 866-308-6235
Fax: (843)577-7506

Boston Business Journal
160 Federal St., 12th Fl.
Boston, MA 02110-1700
Ph: (617)330-1000
Fax: (617)330-1015

Bowhunters of North America
1811 E Thayer Ave.
Bismarck, ND 58501-4780

BowTie Inc.
PO Box 6050
Mission Viejo, CA 92690-6040
Ph: (949)855-8822
Fax: (949)855-3045

Bowtie, Inc. Fancy Publications Pet Product News Magazine
PO Box 6050
Mission Viejo, CA 92690-6040
Ph: (949)855-8822
Fax: (949)855-3045
URL: http://www.watergardennews.com/
  contact-us.aspx

BPS Communications
PO Box 340
Willow Grove, PA 19090-0340
Ph: (215)830-8467
Fax: (215)830-8490
Co. E-mail: info@natclo.com
URL: http://www.natclo.com

Bradenton Herald
102 Manatee Ave. W
Bradenton, FL 34205-8810
Ph: (941)748-0411
Free: 800-748-6666

Brain Brew Books
Eureka Institute
3849 Edwards Rd.
Cincinnati, OH 45244
Ph: (513)271-9911
Co. E-mail: Doug@DougHall.com
URL: http://www.DougHall.com

Brant Publications Inc.
575 Broadway
New York, NY 10012
Ph: (212)941-2800
Fax: (212)941-2844
URL: http://www.themagazineantiques.
  com/

Brazilian-American Chamber of Commerce
509 Madison Ave., Ste. 304
New York, NY 10022
Ph: (212)751-4691
Fax: (212)751-7692
Co. E-mail: info@brazilcham.com
URL: http://www.brazilcham.com

Brewers Publications
736 Pearl St.
Boulder, CO 80302
Ph: (303)447-0816
Free: 888-822-6273
Fax: (303)447-2825
Co. E-mail: info@brewersassociation.org
URL: http://www.brewerspublications.com

Brewery Collectibles Club of America
747 Merus Ct.
Fenton, MO 63026-2092
Ph: (636)343-6486
Fax: (636)343-6486
Co. E-mail: bcca@bcca.com
URL: http://www.bcca.com

Brick Industry Association
1850 Centennial Park Dr., Ste. 301
Reston, VA 20191
Ph: (703)620-0010
Fax: (703)620-3928
Co. E-mail: brickinfo@bia.org
URL: http://www.gobrick.com

Brick Tower Press
1230 Park Ave., No. 10A
New York, NY 10128
Ph: (212)427-7139
Free: 800-682-7425
Fax: (212)427-7139

Briefings Media Group
2807 N Parham Rd., Ste. 200
Richmond, VA 23294
Ph: (804)762-9600
Free: 800-791-8699
Fax: (804)217-8999
Co. E-mail: briefingsweborders@publish-
  ersserviceassociates.com
URL: http://www.briefingsmediagroup.com

Briefings Publishing Group
2807 N. Parham Rd., Ste. 200
Richmond, VA 23294
Ph: (800)791-8699
Free: 800-722-9221
Fax: (804)217-8999
Co. E-mail: customerservice@douglaspub-
  lications.com
URL: http://www.briefings.com

Broadcast Education Association
1771 N St. NW
Washington, DC 20036-2800
Ph: (202)429-5355
Free: 888-380-7222
Fax: (202)775-2981
Co. E-mail: hbirks@nab.org
URL: http://www.beaweb.org

Broadcast Interview Source Inc.
2233 Wisconsin Ave. NW, Ste. 301
Washington, DC 20007-4132
Ph: (202)333-5000
Free: 866-639-7735
Fax: (202)342-5411

Co. E-mail: editor@yearbook.com
URL: http://www.expertclick.com

Broadway Books
1745 Broadway
New York, NY 10019
Ph: (212)572-6066
Free: 800-726-0600
Fax: (800)659-2436
Co. E-mail: bwaypub@randomhouse.com
URL: http://crownpublishing.com/imprint/
  broadway-books/

**Broadway Books, a Division of
Random House**
1745 Broadway
New York, NY 10019
Ph: (212)782-9000
Fax: (212)572-6066
Co. E-mail: ddaypub@randomhouse.com
URL: http://www.broadwaybusinessbooks.
  com

Brookings Institution Press
1775 Massachusetts Ave. NW
Washington, DC 20036-2188
Ph: (202)797-6252
Free: 800-275-1447
Fax: (202)797-6195

Brooklyn Botanic Garden
1000 Washington Ave.
Brooklyn, NY 11225
Ph: (718)623-7200
URL: http://www.bbg.org

Brown Books Publishing Group
16200 N Dallas Pkwy., Ste. 170
Dallas, TX 75248
Ph: (972)381-0009

Brownstone Publishers Inc.
149 Fifth Ave., 16th Fl.
New York, NY 10010
Ph: (212)473-8200
Free: 800-643-8095
Fax: (212)473-8786
Co. E-mail: custserv@brownstone.com
URL: http://www.brownstone.com

Bruce Mooney Associates Inc.
PO Box 749
Marlton, NJ 08053
Ph: (856)797-9164
Free: 800-454-2686
Fax: (856)797-9165
Co. E-mail: remgro@brucemooney.com

Bryan Sadoff
250 W Coventry Ct., No. 109
Milwaukee, WI 53217-3961
Ph: (414)352-8460
Fax: (414)352-3681
Co. E-mail: info@sadoffinvestments.com

BUC International Corp.
1314 NE 17th Ct.
Fort Lauderdale, FL 33305
Ph: (954)565-6715
Free: 800-327-6929
Fax: (954)561-3095
Co. E-mail: info@buc.com
URL: http://www.buc.com

Buffalo News
1 News Plz.
Buffalo, NY 14240
Ph: (716)849-4444

The Buffalo News
1 News Plaza
Buffalo, NY 14240
Ph: (716)856-5555
Free: 800-777-8653
Fax: (716)856-5150

Building Green Inc.
122 Birge St., Ste. 30
Brattleboro, VT 05301-3206
Ph: (802)257-7300
Free: 800-861-0954
Fax: (802)257-7304
Co. E-mail: info@buildinggreen.com

**Building Industry Association of
Southeastern Michigan**
2075 Walnut Lake Rd.
West Bloomfield, MI 48323
Ph: (248)737-4477
Fax: (248)538-4078
Co. E-mail: susanas@builders.org
URL: http://www.builders.org

**Building Service Contractors Associa-
tion Int'l.**
401 N Michigan Ave., Ste. 2200
Chicago, IL 60611
Ph: (312)321-5167
Free: 800-368-3414
Fax: (312)673-6735
Co. E-mail: info@bscai.org
URL: http://www.bscai.org

**Bureau of Business & Economic
Research**
University of Montana
Gallagher Business Bldg., Ste. 231
32 Campus Dr., Ste. 6840
Missoula, MT 59812
Ph: (406)243-3113
Fax: (406)243-2086

Bureau of Labor Statistics
2 Massachusetts Ave. NE, PSB Ste. 2850
Washington, DC 20212-0001
Ph: (202)691-5200

Bureau of National Affairs Inc.
9435 Key West Ave.
Rockville, MD 20850
Ph: (703)341-3000
Free: 800-372-1033

Co. E-mail: customercare@bna.com
URL: http://www.bna.com

BurrellesLuce
75 E Northfield Rd.
Livingston, NJ 07039
Ph: (973)992-6600
Free: 800-631-1160
Fax: (973)992-7675
Co. E-mail: sross@burrelleluce.com
URL: http://www.burrellesluce.com/

Business & Legal Resources, Inc.
141 Mill Rock Rd., E
Old Saybrook, CT 06475
Ph: (860)510-0100
Free: 800-454-0404
Fax: (860)510-7220
Co. E-mail: service@blr.com
URL: http://www.blr.com

**Business and Professional Women/
USA**
1718 M St. NW, Ste. 148
Washington, DC 20036
Ph: (202)293-1100
Free: 888-491-8833
Fax: (202)861-0298
Co. E-mail: foundation@bpwusa.org
URL: http://www.bpwfoundation.org

Business Communications Co., Inc.
70 New Canaan Ave.
Norwalk, CT 06850
Ph: (203)750-9783
Fax: (203)229-0087
Co. E-mail: info@bccresearch.com
URL: http://wwww.bccresearch.com

**Business Communications Company
Inc.**
35 Walnut St., Ste 100
Wellesley, MA 02481
Ph: (781)489-7301
Free: 866-285-7215
Fax: (781)489-7308
Co. E-mail: sales@bccresearch.com
URL: http://www.bccresearch.com

Business Courier
101 W 7th St.
Cincinnati, OH 45202
Ph: (513)621-6665
Fax: (513)621-2462

Business Ethics
55 W 39th St., Ste. 800
New York, NY 10018
Ph: (646)688-3620
Fax: (212)202-3561
URL: http://business-ethics.com/

Business First
303 W Nationwide Blvd.
Columbus, OH 43215
Ph: (614)461-4040
Fax: (614)365-2980

Business Information Group
80 Valleybrook Dr.
Toronto, ON, Canada M3B 2S9
Ph: (416)442-5600
Free: 800-668-2374
Fax: (416)442-2191
Co. E-mail: rgreif@businessinformation-
 group.com
URL: http://businessinformationgroup.ca

Business Insurance
360 N Michigan Ave.
Chicago, IL 60601-3806
Ph: (312)649-5200
Free: 888-446-1422
Fax: (312)280-3174
Co. E-mail: biweb@crain.com
URL: http://www.businessinsurance.com

Business Intelligence Program
333 Ravenswood Ave.
Menlo Park, CA 94025
Ph: (650)859-4600
Fax: (650)859-4544
Co. E-mail: E-mail: info@sric-bi.com

Business Journals, Inc.
50 Day St.
Norwalk, CT 06854
Ph: (203)853-6015
Fax: (203)852-8175
Co. E-mail: macb@busjour.com
URL: http://www.busjour.com

Business Marketing & Publishing Inc.
PO Box 7457
Wilton, CT 06897
Ph: (203)834-9959
Co. E-mail: info@epnweb.com

Business Marketing Association
1833 Centre Point Cir., Ste. 123
Naperville, IL 60563
Ph: (630)544-5054
Fax: (630)544-5055
Co. E-mail: info@marketing.org
URL: http://www.marketing.org

Business North Carolina
5435 77 Center Dr., Ste. 50
Charlotte, NC 28217-0711
Ph: (704)523-6987
Fax: (704)523-4211

Business Plus
PO Box 8828
Boston, MA 02114
Free: 800-759-0190
Fax: (800)331-1664
URL: http://www.hachettebookgroupusa.
 com

Business Plus/Warner Business Books
PO Box 8828
Boston, MA 02114
Free: 800-759-0190
Fax: (800)331-1664

URL: http://www.hachettebookgroupusa.
 com

Business Publications Inc.
93 High St.
Portsmouth, NH 03801
Ph: (603)436-9401

Business Research Services Inc.
7720 Wisconsin Ave., Ste. 213
Bethesda, MD 20814
Ph: (301)229-5561
Free: 800-845-8420
Fax: (301)229-6133
Co. E-mail: brspubs@sba8a.com
URL: http://www.sba8a.com

The Business Review
40 British American Blvd.
Latham, NY 12110
Ph: (518)640-6825
Fax: (518)640-6801

Business Service Corp.
2185 Faraday Ave., Ste. 110
Carlsbad, CA 92008-7206
Free: 800-809-1763
Fax: (619)263-1763
Co. E-mail: boj@boj.com
URL: http://www.boj.com/

**Business Success Systems,
Incorporated**
49 Cliffwood Ave., Ste. 200
Cliffwood, NJ 07721
Ph: (732)566-3660
Free: 800-748-5433
Fax: (732)566-3565

Business Trend Analysts
38 E 29th St., 6th Fl.
New York, NY 10016
Ph: (212)807-2629
Free: 800-866-4648
Fax: (212)807-2676
Co. E-mail: customerservice@marketre-
 search.com
URL: http://www.marketresearch.com

**Business Trend Analysts, Inc. Industry
Studies**
2171 Jericho Tpke., Ste. 200
Commack, NY 11725
Ph: (631)462-5454
Free: 800-866-4648
Fax: (631)462-1842
Co. E-mail: sales@bta-ler.com
URL: http://www.businesstrendanalysts.
 com

**Business Trend Analysts, Inc. Leading
Edge Reports**
38 E 29th St., 6th Fl.
New York, NY 10016
Ph: (212)807-2629
Free: 800-866-4648
Fax: (212)807-2676

Co. E-mail: customerservice@marketre-
 search.com
URL: http://www.marketresearch.com

Business Vision Group
4914 Country Club Dr.
Highland, UT 84003
Ph: (801)420-2838

The Business Word
11211 E Arapahoe Rd., Ste. 101
Centennial, CO 80112-3851
Ph: (303)290-8500
Free: 800-328-3211
Fax: (303)290-9025
Co. E-mail: thebusinessword@yahoo.com
URL: http://www.businessword.com

Butterworth-Heinemann
225 Wildwood Ave.
Woburn, MA 01801
Ph: (781)904-2500
Free: 800-366-2665
Fax: (800)568-5136
Co. E-mail: custserv.bh@elsevier.com
URL: http://www.bh.com

Buyers Laboratory Inc.
20 Railroad Ave.
Hackensack, NJ 07601-4130
Ph: (201)488-0404
Fax: (201)488-0461
Co. E-mail: info@buyers-lab.com
URL: http://www.buyerslab.com

C

C.E. Publications Inc.
PO Box 3006
Bothell, WA 98041-3006
Ph: (425)806-5200
Fax: (425)806-5585
Co. E-mail: staff@cjhunter.com
URL: http://www.cjhunter.com

Cabletelevision Advertising Bureau
830 3rd Ave., 2nd Fl.
New York, NY 10022
Ph: (212)508-1200
Fax: (212)832-3268
URL: http://www.thecab.tv

Cadmus Journal Services
8621 Robert Fulton Dr., Ste. 100
Columbia, MD 21046
Ph: (410)850-0500
Free: 800-257-5529
URL: http://www.cadmus.com/locations.
 htm

Cahners Publishing Co.
245 W 17th St.
New York, NY 10010

California Builder & Engineer Inc.
1200 Madison Ave., LL20
Indianapolis, IN 46225
Ph: (317)423-7080
Fax: (317)426-7094
URL: http://www.acppubs.com

California Trucking Association
3251 Beacon Blvd.
West Sacramento, CA 95691
Ph: (916)373-3500
Fax: (916)371-3639
Co. E-mail: cta@caltrux.org

The California Wine Club
2175 Goodyear Ave., Ste. 102
Ventura, CA 93006-3699
Ph: (805)650-4330
Free: 800-777-4443
Fax: (805)650-6016
Co. E-mail: info@cawineclub.com

California Women's Caucus
2900 Amby Pl.
Hermosa Beach, CA 90254-2216
Ph: (310)376-7378
Fax: (310)376-2926

Calorie Control Council
1100 Johnson Ferry Rd., Ste. 300
Atlanta, GA 30342
Ph: (404)252-3663
Free: 800-215-3553
Fax: (404)252-0774
Co. E-mail: ccc@kellencompany.com
URL: http://www.caloriecontrol.org

Cambridge Scientific Abstracts L.P.
7200 Wisconsin Ave., Ste. 601
Bethesda, MD 20814
Ph: (301)961-6700
Free: 800-843-7751
Fax: (301)961-6720
Co. E-mail: sales@proquest.com
URL: http://www.proquest.co.uk

Cambridge University Press (CUP)
32 Ave. of the Americas
New York, NY 10013-2473
Ph: (212)924-3900
Free: 800-872-7423
Fax: (212)691-3239
Co. E-mail: newyork@cambridge.org
URL: http://www.cambridge.org/us

Campground Data Resource
1004 Tequesta Trl.
Lake Wales, FL 33898
Ph: (863)676-0009
Free: 800-889-0355
Fax: (863)676-0009
Co. E-mail: db@campground-data.com
URL: http://www.campground-data.com

Camping Programs YMCA of the USA
101 N Wacker Dr.
Chicago, IL 60606
Ph: (312)977-0031
Free: 800-872-9622
Co. E-mail: fulfillment@ymca.net
URL: http://www.ymca.net

Canada Wide Magazines & Communications Ltd.
4180 Lougheed Hwy., 4th Fl.
Burnaby, BC, Canada V5C 6A7
Ph: (604)299-7311
Fax: (604)299-9188
Co. E-mail: cwm@canadawide.com
URL: http://www.canadawide.com

Canadian Apparel Federation
151 Slater St., Ste. 708
Ottawa, ON, Canada K1P 5H3
Ph: (613)231-3220
Fax: (613)231-2305
Co. E-mail: info@apparel.ca
URL: http://www.apparel.ca

Canadian Association of Moldmakers
St. Clair College
2000 Talbot Rd. W
Box 16
Windsor, ON, Canada N9A 6S4
Ph: (519)255-7863
Free: 800-567-CAMM
Fax: (519)255-9446
Co. E-mail: info@camm.ca
URL: http://www.camm.ca

Canadian Co-Operative Wool Growers Ltd.
c/o Ontario Stockyards Inc.
Box 1051, 3807 Hwy. No. 89
Cookstown, ON, Canada L0L 1L0
Ph: (705)458-4800
Free: 866-458-4800
Fax: (705)458-0186
Co. E-mail: ccwgosy@bellnet.ca
URL: http://www.seregonmap.com/SCM/index.htm

Canadian Council for Small Business and Entrepreneurship
Faculty of Administration
University of Regina
Regina, SK, Canada S4S 0A2
Ph: (306)585-4728
Fax: (206)585-4805

Canadian Federation of Chefs & Cooks
582 Somerset St. W
Ottawa, ON, Canada K1R 5K2
Ph: (613)562-0123
Free: 877-470-2483
Fax: (613)237-9900
Co. E-mail: cfcc@cfcc.ca

Canadian Honey Council
234-5149 Country Hills Blvd. NW, Ste. 235
Calgary, AB, Canada T3A 5K8
Ph: (403)208-7141
Fax: (403)547-4317
Co. E-mail: chc-ccm@honeycouncil.ca

Canadian Innovation Centre
490 Dutton Dr., Unit 1A
Waterloo, ON, Canada N2L 6H7
Ph: (519)885-5870
Free: 800-265-4559
Fax: (519)885-5729
Co. E-mail: moreinfo@innovationcentre.ca

Canadian Institute of Geomatics
900 rue Dynes Rd., Ste. 100 D
Ottawa, ON, Canada K2C 3L6
Ph: (613)224-9851
Fax: (613)224-9577
Co. E-mail: admincig@magma.ca
URL: http://www.cig-acsg.ca

Canadian Pharmacists Association
1785 Alta Vista Dr.
Ottawa, ON, Canada K1G 3Y6
Ph: (613)523-7877
Free: 800-917-9489
Fax: (613)523-0445
Co. E-mail: info@pharmacists.ca
URL: http://www.pharmacists.ca/

Canadian Public Health Association
300-1565 Carling Ave.
Ottawa, ON, Canada K1Z 8R1
Ph: (613)725-3769
Fax: (613)725-9826
Co. E-mail: info@cpha.ca
URL: http://www.cpha.ca

Canadian Restaurant and Foodservices Association
316 Bloor St. W
Toronto, ON, Canada M5S 1W5
Ph: (416)923-8416
Free: 800-387-5649
Fax: (416)923-1450
Co. E-mail: info@crfa.ca
URL: http://www.crfa.ca

Canadian Society of Cinematographers
3007 Kingston Rd., Ste. 131
Toronto, ON, Canada M1M 1P1
Ph: (416)266-0591
Fax: (416)266-3996
Co. E-mail: admin@csc.ca
URL: http://www.csc.ca/default_home.asp

Canadian Society of Respiratory Therapists
400-331 Cooper St.
Ottawa, ON, Canada K2P 0G5
Ph: (613)731-3164
Free: 800-267-3422
Fax: (613)521-4314
Co. E-mail: adminasst@csrt.com

URL: http://www.csrt.com/en/index.asp

Canadian Wood Council
99 Bank St., Ste. 400
Ottawa, ON, Canada K1P 6B9
Ph: (613)747-5544
Free: 800-463-5091
Fax: (613)747-6264
Co. E-mail: info@cwc.ca
URL: http://www.cwc.ca

Canola Council of Canada
167 Lombard Ave., Ste. 400
Winnipeg, MB, Canada R3B 0T6
Ph: (204)982-2100
Fax: (204)942-1841
Co. E-mail: admin@canola-council.org
URL: http://www.canola-council.org/

Canon Communications L.L.C.
201 28th St., Ste. 100
Santa Monica, CA 90405
Ph: (310)445-4200
Fax: (310)445-4299
Co. E-mail: info@cancom.com
URL: http://www.ubmcanon.com

Cape Cod Media Group
319 Main St.
Hyannis, MA 02601
Ph: (508)775-1200

Cape Cod Times
319 Main St.
Hyannis, MA 02601
Ph: (508)775-1200

Cape Project Management Inc.
12 Remington Ln.
Plymouth, MA 02360-1424

Capital Newspapers
1901 Fish Hatchery Rd.
Madison, WI 53713
Ph: (252)-6200

Capitol Information Group Inc.
PO Box 9070
McLean, VA 22102
Free: 800-543-2055
Fax: (703)905-8040

Career Planning and Adult Development Network
543 Vista Mar Ave.
Pacifica, CA 94044
Ph: (650)773-0982
Fax: (650)359-3089
Co. E-mail: admin@careernetwork.org
URL: http://www.careernetwork.org

Career Press
3 Tice Rd.
Franklin Lakes, NJ 07417
Ph: (201)848-0310
Free: 800-227-3371
Fax: (201)848-1727

Co. E-mail: contact@careerpress.com
URL: http://www.careerpress.com

Career Press, Inc.
PO Box 687
Franklin Lakes, NJ 07417
Ph: (201)848-0310
Free: 800-227-3371
Fax: (201)848-1727

Career Press, Inc.
220 W Parkway, Unit 12
Pompton Plains, NJ 07417
Ph: (201)848-0310
Free: 800-227-3371
Fax: (201)848-0310
Co. E-mail: sales@careerpress.com
URL: http://www.careerpress.com

Career Recruitment Media
2 LAN Dr., Ste. 100
Westford, MA 01886
Ph: (978)692-5092
Fax: (978)692-4174
Co. E-mail: hshulick@alloyeducation.com
URL: http://www.alloyeducation.com/
    request.htm

Career Steps
4112 Park Blvd.
Oakland, CA 94602
Ph: (510)531-2071

Carpet Cleaners Institute of the Northwest
2661 N Pearl St.
Tacoma, WA 98407
Ph: (253)759-5762
Free: 877-692-2469
Fax: (253)761-9134
Co. E-mail: info@ccinw.org
URL: http://www.ccinw.org/

Carstens Publications Inc.
108 Phil Hardin Rd.
Newton, NJ 07860-5223
Ph: (973)383-3355
Free: 888-526-5365
Fax: (973)383-4064
Co. E-mail: carstens@carstens-publica-
    tions.com
URL: http://www.carstens-publications.com

Carswell
One Corporate Plz.
2075 Kennedy Rd.
Toronto, ON, Canada M1T 3V4
Ph: (416)609-8000
Free: 800-342-6288
Fax: (416)298-5094
Co. E-mail: carswell.customerrelations@
    thomson.com
URL: http://www.carswell.com

Casket and Funeral Supply Association of America
49 Sherwood Terr., Ste. Y
Lake Bluff, IL 60044-2231
Ph: (847)295-6630
Fax: (847)295-6647
Co. E-mail: brussell@cfsaa.org
URL: http://www.cfsaa.org

Castle Publications Ltd.
PO Box 580
Van Nuys, CA 91408
Ph: (818)708-3208
Fax: (818)708-9287
Co. E-mail: info@castlepublications.com

Cat Fanciers' Association Inc.
260 E Main St.
Alliance, OH 44601
Ph: (330)680-4070
Fax: (330)680-4633
Co. E-mail: cfa@cfa.org
URL: http://www.cfa.org

Catawba County Chamber of Commerce
PO Box 1828
Hickory, NC 28603-1828
Ph: (828)328-6111
Fax: (828)328-1175
Co. E-mail: pmanfredi@catawbachamber.
    org
URL: http://www.catawbachamber.org

Catholic Charities USA
66 Canal Center Pl., Ste. 600
Alexandria, VA 22314-1583
Ph: (703)549-1390
Free: 800-919-9338
Fax: (703)549-1656
Co. E-mail: info@catholiccharitiesusa.org
URL: http://www.catholiccharitiesusa.org

CBA Service Corp.
9240 Explorer Dr., Ste. 200
Colorado Springs, CO 80920
Ph: (719)265-9895
Free: 800-252-1950
Fax: (719)272-3510
Co. E-mail: info@cbaonline.org
URL: http://www.cbaonline.org

CCH Canadian Ltd.
90 Sheppard Ave. E, Ste. 300
Toronto, ON, Canada M2N 6X1
Ph: (416)224-2224
Free: 800-268-4522
Fax: (416)224-2243
Co. E-mail: cservice@cch.ca
URL: http://www.cch.ca

CCH Inc.
2700 Lake Cook Rd.
Riverwoods, IL 60015
Ph: (847)267-7000
Free: 888-224-7377
Fax: (847)267-2873

Co. E-mail: info@cch.com
URL: http://www.cch.com

CCIM Institute
430 N Michigan Ave.
Chicago, IL 60611-4092
Ph: (312)321-4460
Free: 800-621-7027
Fax: (312)321-4530
Co. E-mail: magazine@ccim.com
URL: http://www.ccim.com

CD Publications
8204 Fenton St.
Silver Spring, MD 20910
Ph: (301)588-6380
Free: 800-666-6380
Fax: (301)588-6385
Co. E-mail: info@cdpublications.com
URL: http://www.cdpublications.com/

CDG Books Canada, Incorporated
99 Yorkville Ave., Ste. 400
Toronto, ON, Canada M5R 3K5
Ph: (416)963-8830
Free: 877-963-8830
Fax: (416)923-4821

Ceilings and Interior Systems Construction Association
405 Illinois Ave., Ste. 2B
Saint Charles, IL 60174-2963
Ph: (630)584-1919
Fax: (866)560-8537
Co. E-mail: cisca@cisca.org
URL: http://www.cisca.org

Celestial Arts Publishing Co.
999 Harrison St.
Berkeley, CA 94710-1455
Ph: (510)559-1600
Free: 800-841-2665
Fax: (510)559-1629
Co. E-mail: sales@tenspeed.com
URL: http://crownpublishing.com/imprint/
ten-speed-press/2/?sort=Release
20Date&cf

Cenflo Inc.
PO Box 44040
Rio Rancho, NM 87174
Ph: (505)771-8841
Free: 800-732-4581
Fax: (505)892-0986
Co. E-mail: info@cenflo.com
URL: http://www.cenflo.com

Cengage Gale
27500 Drake Rd.
Farmington Hills, MI 48331-3535
Ph: (248)699-4253
Free: 800-877-4253
Fax: (248)699-8065
Co. E-mail: galeord@thomson.com
URL: http://www.gale.com

Cengage Learning Inc.
10650 Toebben Dr.
Independence, KY 41051
Free: 800-354-9706
Fax: (800)487-8488
Co. E-mail: investors@cengage.com
URL: http://www.gale.cengage.com

Cengage Learning Inc.
200 1st Stamford Pl., Ste. 400
Stamford, CT 06902-6753
Ph: (203)965-8600
Free: 800-354-9706
Fax: (800)487-8488
Co. E-mail: investors@cengage.com
URL: http://www.cengage.com

Cengage South-Western
5191 Natorp Blvd.
Mason, OH 45040
Ph: (513)229-1000
Free: 800-543-0487
Fax: (800)437-8488
URL: http://www.cengage.com

Center for Ethics and Social Policy
Graduate Theological Union
2400 Ridge Rd.
Berkeley, CA 94709
Ph: (510)649-2560
Co. E-mail: cesp@gtu.edu

Center For Health, Environment and Justice
PO Box 6806
Falls Church, VA 22040-6806
Ph: (703)237-2249
Fax: (703)237-8389
Co. E-mail: chej@chej.org
URL: http://chej.org

Center for Hearing and Communication
50 Broadway, 6th Fl.
New York, NY 10004
Ph: (917)305-7700
Fax: (917)305-7888
Co. E-mail: info@chchearing.org
URL: http://www.chchearing.org

Center for Labor Research and Education
Box 951478
Los Angeles, CA 90095-1478
Ph: (510)642-0323
Fax: (510)642-6432
Co. E-mail: osmer@vclink.berkley.edu

Center for Science in the Public Interest
1875 Connecticut Ave. NW, Ste. 300
Washington, DC 20009
Ph: (202)332-9110
Fax: (202)265-4954
Co. E-mail: cspi@cspinet.org
URL: http://www.cspinet.org

Centers for Disease Control and Prevention Office of Scientific and Health Communications
1600 Clifton Rd.
Atlanta, GA 30329-4018
Ph: (404)639-3311
Free: 800-232-4636
Fax: (888)232-6348
Co. E-mail: cdcinfo@cdc.gov
URL: http://www.cdc.gov

CFA Institute
560 Ray C. Hunt Dr.
Charlottesville, VA 22903-2981
Ph: (434)951-5499
Free: 800-247-8132
Fax: (434)951-5262
Co. E-mail: info@cfainstitute.org
URL: http://www.cfainstitute.org

CFO Publishing Corporation
111 W 57th St., 12th Fl.
New York, NY 10019
Ph: (212)698-9787
Fax: (212)459-3007

Chain Store Age
425 Park Ave.
New York, NY 10022
Ph: (212)756-5118
Fax: (212)756-5256
URL: http://www.chainstoreage.com/

Chain Store Guide Information Services
3922 Coconut Palm Dr.
Tampa, FL 33619
Ph: (813)627-6800
Free: 800-252-9764
Fax: (813)627-6882
Co. E-mail: info@csgis.com
URL: http://www.csgis.com

Chain Store Guide
10117 Princess Palm Dr.
Tampa, FL 33610
Ph: (813)627-6800
Free: 800-927-9292
Fax: (813)627-6888
Co. E-mail: info@csgis.com
URL: http://www.chainstoreguide.com

Chamber Music America
243 5th Ave.
New York, NY 10016
Ph: (212)242-2022
Fax: (646)430-5667
Co. E-mail: mlioi@chamber-music.org
URL: http://www.chamber-music.org

Charles River Media
10 Downer Ave.
Hingham, MA 02043
Ph: (781)740-0400
Fax: (781)740-8816

Charlotte Business Journal
1100 S Tryon St., Ste. 100
Charlotte, NC 28203
Ph: (704)973-1100
Fax: (704)973-1102

Chart Your Course International Inc.
2814 Hwy. 212 SW
Conyers, GA 30094
Ph: (770)860-9464
Free: 800-821-2487
Fax: (770)760-0581
Co. E-mail: info@chartcourse.com
URL: http://www.chartcourse.com

Chartcraft Inc.
30 Church St.
New Rochelle, NY 10801
Ph: (914)632-0422
Fax: (914)632-0335
Co. E-mail: customers@mplcomm.com

Chase Online Marketing Strategies,Inc
29 John St. No.102
New York, NY 10038
Ph: (212)619-4780
Fax: (212)876-1098
Co. E-mail: me@larrychase.com

Chattanooga Publishing Company
400 E 11th St.
Chattanooga, TN 37403
Ph: (423)756-6900
URL: http://www.timesfreepress.com/
contactus/

Chattanooga Times/Free Press
400 E 11th St.
Chattanooga, TN 37403
Ph: (423)756-6900

Cheese Reporter Publishing Company Inc.
2810 Crossroads Dr., Ste. 3000
Madison, WI 53718
Ph: (608)246-8430
Fax: (608)246-8431
Co. E-mail: info@cheesereporter.com
URL: http://www.cheesereporter.com/

Chelsea Green Publishing
85 N Main St., Ste. 120
White River Junction, VT 05001
Ph: (802)295-6300
Free: 800-639-4099
Fax: (802)295-6444

The Chemical Educator
1910 University Dr.
Boise, ID 83725
Ph: (208)440-1866
Fax: (208)426-4493
Co. E-mail: chemeducator@gmail.org
URL: http://chemeducator.org/

Chemical Week Associates
2 Grand Central Tower
140 E 45th St., 40th Fl.
New York, NY 10017
Ph: (212)884-9528
Free: 800-774-5733
Fax: (212)883-9514
Co. E-mail: webmaster@chemweek.com
URL: http://www.chemweek.com/

The Chemists' Club Library
40 W 45th St.
New York, NY 10036
Ph: (212)626-9300
Fax: (212)626-9393
Co. E-mail: info@thechemistsclub.com
URL: http://www.thechemistsclub.com

Chicago Home & Garden
435 N Michigan Ave., Ste. 1100
Chicago, IL 60611
Ph: (312)222-8999
Fax: (312)222-0287
Co. E-mail: chicagohome@chicagomag.
com
URL: http://www.chicagohomemag.com/

Child Welfare League of America Inc.
1726 M St. NW, Ste. 500
Washington, DC 20036
Ph: (202)688-4200
Free: 800-407-6273
Fax: (202)833-1689
Co. E-mail: order@cwla.org
URL: http://www.cwla.org

Children of Aging Parents
1609 Woodbourne Rd., Ste 302A
Richboro, PA 18954-0167
Ph: (215)355-6611
Free: 800-227-7294
Co. E-mail: info@caps4caregivers.org
URL: http://www.caps4caregivers.org

Children's Apparel Manufacturers' Association
6900 Decarie, Ste. 3110
Montreal, QC, Canada H3X 2T8
Ph: (514)731-7774
Fax: (514)731-7459
Co. E-mail: cama@cama-apparel.org
URL: http://www.cama-apparel.org

Children's Book Insider L.L.C.
901 Columbia Rd., Ste. 204
Ste. 204
Fort Collins, CO 80525
Ph: (970)495-0056
Free: 800-807-1916
Fax: (970)493-1810
Co. E-mail: mail@write4kids.com
URL: http://www.write4kids.com

Christian Camping International/USA
405 W Rockrimmon Blvd.
Colorado Springs, CO 80919
Ph: (719)260-9400

Fax: (719)260-6398
Co. E-mail: ghunter@ccca.org
URL: http://www.cciworldwide.org/regions/
north-america/usa

Chronicle Books LLC
85 2nd St., 6th Fl.
San Francisco, CA 94105
Ph: (415)537-4200
Free: 800-722-6657
Fax: (415)537-4460
Co. E-mail: frontdesk@chroniclebooks.
com
URL: http://www.chroniclebooks.com

Chronicle Books LLC
680 2nd St.
San Francisco, CA 94107
Ph: (415)537-4200
Free: 800-722-6657
Fax: (415)537-4460

The Chronicle of Philanthropy
1255 23rd St. NW, Ste. 700
Washington, DC 20037
Ph: (202)466-1200
Co. E-mail: help@philanthropy.com
URL: http://philanthropy.com/

Cincinnati Magazine Inc.
441 Vine St., Ste. 200
Cincinnati, OH 45202-2039
Ph: (513)421-4300
Fax: (513)562-2746
Co. E-mail: cmletters@cintimag.emmis.
com
URL: http://www.cincinnatimagazine.com/

CIO
PO Box 9208
Framingham, MA 01701
Ph: (508)872-0080

Cisco Press
800 E 96th St.
Indianapolis, IN 46240-3770
Free: 800-545-5914

Cision Canada Inc.
1100-150 Ferrand Dr.
Toronto, ON, Canada M3C 3E5
Ph: (416)750-2220
Free: 877-269-3367
Fax: (416)750-2223
Co. E-mail: info.ca@cision.com
URL: http://ca.cision.com

Cision US Inc.
332 S Michigan Ave., Ste. 900
Chicago, IL 60604-4393
Free: 866-639-5087
Co. E-mail: info.us@cision.com
URL: http://us.cision.com

CITA International
5331 W Montebello Ave.
Glendale, AZ 85301
Ph: (602)447-0480
Fax: (623)847-4454
Co. E-mail: esammorsy@qwestoffice.net
URL: http://www.citainternational.com/
contact.htm

Citadel Press
c/o Kensington Publishing
119 W 40th St.
New York, NY 10018
Ph: (212)407-1500
Free: 800-221-2647
Fax: (212)935-0699
Co. E-mail: publicity@kensingtonbooks.
com
URL: http://www.kensingtonbooks.com

**The City Centre Business Association
of Windsor**
474 Oullette Ave.
Windsor, ON, Canada N9A 1B2
Ph: (519)252-5723
Fax: (519)252-6817
Co. E-mail: ccba@windsordowntown.ca

Clayton-Fillmore Ltd.
125 Dorset Ct.
Castle Rock, CO 80108-9285
Ph: (303)663-0606
Fax: (303)663-1616
Co. E-mail: ht@clayfil.com
URL: http://www.clayfil.com

CLB Media Inc.
240 Edward St.
Aurora, ON, Canada L4G 3S9
Ph: (905)727-0077
Fax: (905)727-0017

Clearbridge Publishing
PO Box 33772
Seattle, WA 98133
Ph: (206)533-9357
Fax: (206)546-9756

Clement Communications Inc.
3 Creek Pky.
Upper Chichester, PA 19061
Ph: (800)253-6368
Free: 888-358-5858
Fax: (800)459-1933
Co. E-mail: customerservice@clement.
com
URL: http://www.clement.com/

**Clinical Laboratory Management As-
sociation**
401 N Michigan Ave., Ste. 2200
Chicago, IL 60611
Ph: (312)321-5111
Fax: (312)673-6927
Co. E-mail: info@clma.org
URL: http://www.clma.org

Clintron Publishers
PO Box 30998
Spokane, WA 99223-3016
Ph: (509)458-3924
Free: 800-869-7923
Fax: (866)259-4786
Co. E-mail: info@agpowermag.com
URL: http://www.agpowermag.com

Close-Up Media Inc.
13400 Sutton Park Dr. S, Ste. 1504
Jacksonville, FL 32224
Ph: (904)223-3377
Fax: (904)223-4211

Closing the Gap Inc.
526 Main St.
Henderson, MN 56044-7709
Ph: (507)248-3294
Fax: (507)248-3810
Co. E-mail: mturek@closingthegap.com
URL: http://www.closingthegap.com

**Clothing Manufacturers Association of
the U.S.A.**
1330 Ave. of the Americas, 19th Fl.
New York, NY 10019-5400

**The Clute Institute for Academic
Research**
6901 S Pierce St., Ste. 239
Littleton, CO 80128
Ph: (303)904-4750
Fax: (303)259-2420
Co. E-mail: staff@cluteinstitute.com
URL: http://www.cluteinstitute.com/

CN Publishing
PO Box 5084
Costa Mesa, CA 92628-5084
Ph: (714)751-7433
Fax: (714)751-6685
Co. E-mail: editor@cyclenews.com
URL: http://www.cyclenews.com

CNW Group
WaterPark Pl.
20 Bay St., Ste. 1500
Toronto, ON, Canada M5J 2N8
Ph: (416)863-9350
Free: 877-269-7890
Fax: (877)269-5044
Co. E-mail: info@newswire.ca
URL: http://www.newswire.ca

**CNW Publishing, Editing and Promo-
tion Inc.**
45 Main St.
North Stratford, NH 03590
Ph: (603)922-8338
Fax: (603)922-8339
Co. E-mail: info@writers-editors.com
URL: http://www.writers-editors.com

Coastal Communications Corp.
2700 N Military Trl., Ste. 120
Boca Raton, FL 33431-6394
Ph: (561)989-0600
Fax: (561)989-9509
Co. E-mail: ccceditor2@att.net
URL: http://www.themeetingmagazines.
com/index/Default.aspx?tabid=197

Coin Laundry Association
1 S 660 Midwest Rd., Ste. 205
Oakbrook Terrace, IL 60181
Ph: (630)953-7920
Free: 800-570-5629
Fax: (630)953-7925
Co. E-mail: info@coinlaundry.org
URL: http://coinlaundry.org

Collectors Club
22 E 35th St.
New York, NY 10016-3806
Ph: (212)683-0559
Fax: (212)481-1269
Co. E-mail: collectorsclub@verizon.net
URL: http://www.collectorsclub.org

Collectors Information Bureau
PO Box 306
Grundy Center, IA 50638
Ph: (319)824-6981
Fax: (319)824-3414
Co. E-mail: cib@thepioneergroup.com
URL: http://www.collectorsinfo.com

College Art Association
50 Broadway, 21st Fl.
New York, NY 10004
Ph: (212)691-1051
Fax: (212)627-2381
Co. E-mail: nyoffice@collegeart.org
URL: http://www.collegeart.org

College of Veterinarians of Ontario
2106 Gordon St.
Guelph, ON, Canada N1L 1G6
Ph: (519)824-5600
Free: 800-424-2856
Fax: (519)824-6497
Co. E-mail: inquiries@cvo.org

Collins Publications
3233 Grand Ave., Ste. N-294C
Chino Hills, CA 91709-1489
Ph: (909)590-2471
Free: 800-795-8999
Fax: (909)628-9330
Co. E-mail: collins@collinspub.com
URL: http://www.collinspub.com

Color Association of the United States
315 W 39th St., Studio 507
New York, NY 10018
Ph: (212)947-7774
Fax: (212)594-6987
Co. E-mail: caus@colorassociation.com

Colorado Calligraphers' Guild
Box 6746
Denver, CO 80206
Co. E-mail: info@coloradocalligrahers.com

Colorado Municipal League
1144 Sherman St.
Denver, CO 80203
Ph: (303)831-6411
Fax: (303)860-8175
Co. E-mail: cml@cml.org

Colorado Society of Certified Public Accountants
7979 E Tufts Ave., Ste. 1000
Denver, CO 80237-2847
Ph: (303)773-2877
Free: 800-523-9082
Fax: (303)773-6344
Co. E-mail: mmedley@cocpa.org
URL: http://www.cocpa.org

Colorado Springs Fine Arts Center
30 W Dale St.
Colorado Springs, CO 80903
Ph: (719)634-5581
Fax: (719)634-0570
Co. E-mail: info@csfineartscenter.org
URL: http://www.csfineartscenter.org

Columbia Books and Information Services
8120 Woodmont Ave., Ste. 110
Bethesda, MD 20814
Ph: (202)464-1662
Free: 888-265-0600
Fax: (202)464-1775
Co. E-mail: info@columbiabooks.com
URL: http://www.columbiabooks.com

The Columbian
701 W 8th St.
Vancouver, WA 98666
Ph: (360)694-3391
Free: 800-743-3391

Columbus Times
PO Box 2845
Columbus, GA 31902
Ph: (706)324-2404
Fax: (706)596-0657
Co. E-mail: hgertjegerdes@columbus-times.com
URL: http://www.columbustimes.com

Commercial Appeal
495 Union Ave.
Memphis, TN 38103
Ph: (901)529-2345
Free: 800-444-6397

Commercial Finance Association
370 7th Ave., Ste. 1801
New York, NY 10001-3979
Ph: (212)792-9390
Fax: (212)564-6053
Co. E-mail: info@cfa.com

URL: http://www.cfa.com

Communications Concepts Inc.
7481 Huntsman Blvd., No. 720
Springfield, VA 22153-1648
Ph: (703)643-2200
Fax: (703)643-2329
Co. E-mail: concepts@writingthatworks.com

Community Information & Referral Inc.
2200 N Central Ave., Ste. 601
Phoenix, AZ 85004
Ph: (602)263-8856
Free: 800-352-3792
Fax: (602)263-0979
URL: http://www.cirs.org

Compliance Action
PO Box 1632
Doylestown, PA 18901
Ph: (215)230-8661
Free: 800-660-0080
Fax: (215)230-8318
Co. E-mail: milner@bankersonline.com
URL: http://www.BankersOnline.com/

Computer Industry Almanac Inc.
PO Box 53
Arlington Heights, IL 60006
Ph: (847)758-3687
Fax: (847)758-3686
Co. E-mail: ej@c-i-a.com
URL: http://www.c-i-a.com

ComputerTalk Associates Inc.
492 Norristown Rd., Ste. 160
Blue Bell, PA 19422
Ph: (610)825-7686
Fax: (610)825-7641
Co. E-mail: wal@computertalk.com
URL: http://www.computertalk.com

Computing Technology Industry Association
3500 Lacey Rd., Ste. 100
Downers Grove, IL 60515
Ph: (630)678-8300
Fax: (630)678-8384
URL: http://www.comptia.org

Comtex
625 N Washington St., Ste. 301
Alexandria, VA 22314
Ph: (703)820-2000

Comtex News Network Inc.
625 N Washington St., Ste. 301
Alexandria, VA 22314
Ph: (703)820-2000

Comtex News Network Inc.
950 3rd Ave., 9th Fl.
New York, NY 10022
Ph: (212)688-6240
Fax: (212)688-6241

Concepts Travel Media Ltd.
282 Richmond St. E, Ste. 100
Toronto, ON, Canada M5A 1P4
Ph: (416)365-1500
Free: 800-727-1429
Fax: (416)365-1504
Co. E-mail: travelweek@travelweek.ca
URL: http://www.travelweek.ca

Conde Nast Publications
4 Times Sq.
New York, NY 10036-6518
Ph: (212)286-2860
Free: 800-289-9330
Fax: (212)286-6763
Co. E-mail: contact@condenast.com
URL: http://www.condenast.com

Consensus Inc.
PO Box 520526
Independence, MO 64052-0526
Ph: (816)373-3700
Free: 800-383-1441
Fax: (816)373-3701
Co. E-mail: editor@consensus-inc.com
URL: http://www.consensus-inc.com/

Conservative Publishing Corp.
751 W Camelback Rd.
Phoenix, AZ 85013
Ph: (602)390-3391
Fax: (602)390-3391

Consolidated Marketing Services, Inc.
PO Box 7838
New York, NY 10150
Ph: (212)688-8797
Co. E-mail: nschneel@drop-shipping-news.com
URL: http://www.drop-shipping-news.com

Construction Financial Management Association
100 Village Blvd., Ste. 200
Princeton, NJ 08540
Ph: (609)452-8000
Free: 888-421-9996
Fax: (609)452-0474
Co. E-mail: sbinstock@cfma.org
URL: http://www.cfma.org

Construction Management Association of America
7926 Jones Branch Dr., Ste. 800
McLean, VA 22102
Ph: (703)356-2622
Fax: (703)356-6388
Co. E-mail: info@cmaanet.org
URL: http://cmaanet.org

The Construction Specifications Institute
110 S Union St., Ste. 100
Alexandria, VA 22314
Ph: (800)689-2900
Fax: (703)236-4600
Co. E-mail: csi@csinet.org

URL: http://www.csinet.org

Consumer Electronics Association
1919 S Eads St.
Arlington, VA 22202
Ph: (703)907-7600
Free: 866-858-1555
Fax: (703)907-7675
Co. E-mail: info@ce.org
URL: http://www.ce.org

Contact Lens Manufacturers Association
PO Box 29398
Lincoln, NE 68529
Ph: (402)465-4122
Free: 800-344-9060
Fax: (402)465-4187
Co. E-mail: clmassociation@aol.com
URL: http://www.clma.net

Contact Lens Society of America
441 Carlisle Dr.
Herndon, VA 20170
Ph: (703)437-5100
Free: 800-296-9776
Fax: (703)437-0727
Co. E-mail: clsa@clsa.info
URL: http://www.clsa.info

Contemporary A Cappella Society of America
325 Sharon Park Dr. Ste. 110
Menlo Park, CA 94025-6805
Ph: (415)358-8067
Co. E-mail: casa@casa.org

Continental Records Company Ltd.
2665 Thomas St., Ste. 37
Mississauga, ON, Canada L5M 6G4
Ph: (905)813-9544
Free: 800-494-6129
Fax: (905)812-4993
Co. E-mail: conrecs@gocontinental.com
URL: http://www.gocontinental.com

Continnuus
PO Box 416
Denver, CO 80201-0416
Ph: (303)575-5676
Fax: (303)575-1187
Co. E-mail: mail@contentprovidermedia.
 com

Continuing Education of the Bar-California
300 Frank H. Ogawa Plz., Ste. 410
Oakland, CA 94612
Ph: (510)302-0770
Free: 800-232-3444
Fax: (510)302-0768

Conway Data Inc.
6625 The Corners Parkway, Ste. 200
Norcross, GA 30092-3334
Ph: (770)446-6996
Free: 800-554-5686

Fax: (770)263-8825
Co. E-mail: editor@siteselection.com
URL: http://www.conway.com

COR Healthcare Resources
PO Box 50507
Santa Barbara, CA 93150
Ph: (805)564-2177
Fax: (805)564-2146
Co. E-mail: info@corhealth.com

Corbin Manufacturing & Supply Inc.
600 Industrial Cir.
White City, OR 97503
Ph: (541)826-5211
Fax: (541)826-8669
Co. E-mail: sales@corbins.com
URL: http://www.corbins.com

CoreNet Global
133 Peachtree St. NE, Ste. 3000
Atlanta, GA 30303-1815
Ph: (404)589-3200
Free: 800-726-8111
Fax: (404)589-3201
Co. E-mail: acain@corenetglobal.org
URL: http://www.corenetglobal.org

Cornell Feline Health Center
College of Veterinary Medicine
Ithaca, NY 14853
Ph: (607)253-3414
Fax: (607)253-3419
Co. E-mail: kmm8@cornell.edu
URL: http://www.vet.cornell.edu/fhc

Cornell University Press
Sage House, 512 E State St.
Ithaca, NY 14850
Ph: (607)277-2338
Free: 800-666-2211
Fax: (607)277-2374
Co. E-mail: cupressinfo@cornell.edu
URL: http://www.cornellpress.cornell.edu

Cornell University School of Hotel Administration
489 Statler Hall
Ithaca, NY 14853
Ph: (607)255-9780
Fax: (607)254-2922
Co. E-mail: hosp_research@cornell.edu
URL: http://www.hotelschool.cornell.edu/
 research/chr/

Corporation for Public Broadcasting
401 9th St. NW
Washington, DC 20004
Ph: (202)879-9600
Free: 800-272-2190
Fax: (202)879-9700
Co. E-mail: nstaples@cpb.org
URL: http://www.cpb.org

Cosmic Awareness Communications
PO Box 115
Olympia, WA 98507
Fax: (360)352-6294
Co. E-mail: cosmiccomm@aol.com

Council for Community and Economic Research
PO Box 100127
Arlington, VA 22210
Ph: (703)522-4980
Fax: (480)393-5098
Co. E-mail: info@crec.net
URL: http://www.c2er.org

Council for Exceptional Children
2900 Crystal Dr., Ste. 1000
Arlington, VA 22202-3557
Ph: (703)620-3660
Free: 866-509-0218
Fax: (703)264-9494
Co. E-mail: service@cec.sped.org
URL: http://www.cec.sped.org

Council of Residential Specialists
430 N Michigan Ave.
Chicago, IL 60611
Ph: (312)321-4444
Free: 800-462-8841
Fax: (312)329-8882
Co. E-mail: crshelp@crs.com
URL: http://crs.com

Council on Foundations
2121 Crystal Dr., Ste. 700
Arlington, VA 22202
Ph: (703)879-0600
Free: 800-673-9036
Fax: (703)879-0802
Co. E-mail: membership@cof.org
URL: http://www.cof.org

The Counselor
33 Irving Pl.
New York, NY 10003
Ph: (212)460-1400
Fax: (212)995-0757

Country Dance and Song Society
132 Main St.
Haydenville, MA 01039-0338
Ph: (413)268-7426
Fax: (413)268-7471
Co. E-mail: office@cdss.org
URL: http://www.cdss.org/

Country Sampler Group
707 Kautz Rd.
Saint Charles, IL 60174-5302
Ph: (630)377-8000
Fax: (630)377-8194
URL: http://www.sampler.com

Country Skier L.L.C.
PO Box 550
Cable, WI 54821
Ph: (715)798-5500

URL: http://www.crosscountryskier.com

Course Technology
20 Channel Center St.
Boston, MA 02210-3402
Ph: (617)757-7900
Free: 800-881-8922
Fax: (617)757-7951
URL: http://www.coursetechnology.com

CP Publishing Inc.
P.O. Box 267
Fond du Lac, WI 54936-0267
Ph: (920)923-3700
Fax: (920)923-6805
Co. E-mail: comments@cookingforprofit.
  com
URL: http://www.cookingforprofit.com/
  home.html

CQ Roll Call
1255 22nd St. NW
Washington, DC 20037
Ph: (202)419-8500

**Craft Council of Newfoundland and La-
brador**
Devon House Craft Ctr.
59 Duckworth St.
Saint John's, NL, Canada A1C 1E6
Ph: (709)753-2749
Fax: (709)753-2766
Co. E-mail: info@craftcouncil.nl.ca
URL: http://www.craftcouncil.nl.ca/

The Crafts Center
8601 Georgia Ave., Ste. 800
Silver Spring, MD 20910
Ph: (301)587-4700
Fax: (301)587-7315
Co. E-mail: craftscenter@chfhq.org
URL: http://www.craftscenter.org

The Crafts Fair Guide
PO Box 39429
Downey, CA 90239-0429
Ph: (415)924-3259
Co. E-mail: info@craftsfairguide.com
URL: http://www.craftsfairguide.com

**The Crafts Report News, Editorial &
Advertising Offices**
PO Box 5000
Iola, WI 54945
Ph: (715)445-5000
Free: 800-777-7398
Fax: (715)445-4053
Co. E-mail: jonespub@jonespublishing.
  com
URL: http://www.craftsreport.com/

Crain Communications Inc.
77 Franklin St., Ste. 809
Boston, MA 02110-1510
Ph: (617)292-3385
Co. E-mail: info@crain.com
URL: http://www.crain.com

Crain Communications Inc.
360 N Michigan Ave.
Chicago, IL 60601
Ph: (312)649-5200
Fax: (312)280-3150

Crain Communications Inc.
150 N Michigan Ave.
Chicago, IL 60601-7553
Ph: (312)649-5200
URL: http://www.crain.com/

Crain Communications Inc.
700 W Saint Clair Ave., Ste. 300
Cleveland, OH 44113
Ph: (216)522-1383
Fax: (216)649-4264

Crain Communications Inc.
1155 Gratiot Ave.
Detroit, MI 48207-2732
Ph: (313)446-6000
Co. E-mail: info@crain.com
URL: http://www.crain.com

Crain Communications Inc.
711 3rd Ave.
New York, NY 10017
Ph: (212)210-0100
Free: 888-909-9111

Crain Communications, Inc.
711 3rd Ave.
New York, NY 10017
Ph: (212)210-0111
Free: 888-909-9111

CRC Press
c/o Taylor & Francis Group, LLC
6000 Broken Sound Pkwy., NW
Boca Raton, FL 33487
Ph: (561)994-0555
Free: 800-272-7737
Fax: (800)374-3401
Co. E-mail: orders@taylorandfrancis.com
URL: http://www.crcpress.com

Creative Book Publishers
PO Box 1421
Ridgefield, WA 98642
Ph: (360)887-8356
Co. E-mail: creativebookpublishers@
  yahoo.com
URL: http://www.creativebookpublishers.
  com

Crittenden Research Inc.
45 Leveroni Ct., Ste. 204
Novato, CA 94949
Ph: (619)393-1814
Free: 800-421-3483
Fax: (619)923-3518
Co. E-mail: market@crittendenonline.com
URL: http://www.crittendenonline.com

Crossing Press, Incorporated
PO Box 7123
Berkeley, CA 94707
Ph: (510)559-1600
Free: 800-841-2665
Fax: (510)453-1629

Crown Business
1745 Broadway
New York, NY 10019
Ph: (212)782-9000
Fax: (212)572-6066
Co. E-mail: crownpublicity@randomhouse.
  com
URL: http://www.randomhouse.com/crown/
  crownbusiness.html

Crown Publishing Company
1745 Broadway
New York, NY 10019
Ph: (212)751-2600
Fax: (800)659-2436

Crown Publishing Group
Random House, Inc.
Department of Library Marketing
280 Park Ave. (11-3)
New York, NY 10017
Free: 800-733-3000
Fax: (212)940-7381
URL: http://www.randomhouse.com/crown/

**The Croydon Group Ltd. Fabricators &
Manufacturers Association**
833 Featherstone Rd.
Rockford, IL 61107-6302
Ph: (815)399-8700
Free: 888-394-4362
Fax: (815)381-1370
Co. E-mail: info@thefabricator.com
URL: http://www.fmanet.org

CSIRO Publishing
PO Box 1139
Collingwood, VIC 3066, Australia
Ph: 61 396 627500
Fax: 61 396 627555
Co. E-mail: publishing@csiro.au
URL: http://www.publish.csiro.au

CTE Publications Inc.
40 Skokie Blvd., Ste. 450
Northbrook, IL 60062
Ph: (847)498-9100
Fax: (847)559-4444
Co. E-mail: info@ctemag.com
URL: http://www.ctemag.com

CTVglobemedia Publishing Inc.
444 Front St. W
Toronto, ON, Canada M5V 2S9
Ph: (416)585-5000

**Currency/Doubleday Broadway
Publishing Group**
1745 Broadway
New York, NY 10019
Ph: (212)782-9000

Free: 800-733-3000
Fax: (212)302-7985

Custom Tailors and Designers Association of America
CTDA Headquarters
42732 Ridgeway Dr.
Broadlands, VA 20148
Ph: (888)248-CTDA
Free: 888-248-CTDA
Fax: (866)661-1240
Co. E-mail: CTDAHQ@talley.com
URL: http://www.ctda.com

Cutler Publishing Inc.
4500 Campus Dr., Ste. 480
Newport Beach, CA 92660-1872
Ph: (949)852-1990
Fax: (949)852-0231
URL: http://www.building-products.com/

Cutter Information Corp.
37 Broadway, Ste. 1
Arlington, MA 02474
Ph: (781)648-8700
Free: 800-964-5118
Fax: (781)648-8707
Co. E-mail: service@cutter.com
URL: http://www.cutter.com

Cygnus Business Media
1233 Janesville Ave.
Fort Atkinson, WI 53538-0803
Ph: (920)563-6388
Free: 800-547-7377
Fax: (920)563-1706
Co. E-mail: jeff.reinke@cygnuspub.com
URL: http://www.cygnusb2b.com

Cygnus Business Media
3 Huntington Quad., Ste. 301N
Melville, NY 11747
Ph: (631)845-2700
Free: 800-308-6397
Fax: (631)845-7109

D

Dadant and Sons Inc.
51 S 2nd St., Ste. 2
Hamilton, IL 62341-1397
Ph: (217)847-3324
Free: 888-922-1293
Fax: (217)847-3660
Co. E-mail: dadant@dadant.com
URL: http://www.dadant.com

Daily Journal Corp.
915 E 1st St.
Los Angeles, CA 90012
Ph: (213)229-5300
Fax: (213)229-5481
URL: http://www.dailyjournal.com

Daily News
724 Bell Fork Rd.
Jacksonville, NC 28546
Ph: (910)353-1171

The Daily Record Corp.
6 Century Dr.
Parsippany, NJ 07054
Fax: (973)428-6200
URL: http://www.dailyrecord.com/

Dale Ennis
5540 Loyalist Pkwy.
5540 Loyalist Parkway
Bath, ON, Canada K0H 1G0
Ph: (613)352-7448
Fax: (613)352-7700
Co. E-mail: moneyinfo@canadianmoney-saver.ca

Dan Kiedrowski Co.
PO Box A
La Honda, CA 94020
Ph: (650)747-0549
Fax: (650)747-0549

Dan Newman Co.
1051 Bloomfield Ave.
Clifton, NJ 07012

Dana Chase Publications Inc.
PO Box 3247
Oak Brook, IL 60522-3247
URL: http://www.appliance.com

Dance Magazine Inc.
333 7th Ave., 11th Fl.
New York, NY 10001
Ph: (646)459-4800
Free: 800-331-1750
Fax: (646)459-4900
Co. E-mail: dancemag@dancemagazine.com
URL: http://www.dancemagazine.com

Dance Research Foundation Inc.
37 W 12th St., No. 7/J
New York, NY 10011
Ph: (212)924-5183
Fax: (212)924-2176
Co. E-mail: info@balletreview.com
URL: http://www.balletreview.com/

Dark Horse, Incorporated
22331 Mandarin Ln.
Saugus, CA 91390

Dartnell Publications
PO Box 12038
Durham, NC 27709
Ph: (800)477-4030
Free: 800-621-5463
Co. E-mail: customerservice@dartnellcorp.com
URL: http://www.dartnellcorp.com

Data & Analysis Center for Software
775 Daedalian Dr.
Rome, NY 13441-4909
Ph: (315)334-4905
Free: 800-214-7921
Fax: (315)334-4964
Co. E-mail: dacs@dtic.mil

Data Conversion Laboratory
61-18 190th St., 2nd Fl.
Fresh Meadows, NY 11365-2723
Ph: (718)357-8700
Free: 800-321-2816
Fax: (718)357-8776
Co. E-mail: info@dclab.com
URL: http://www.dclab.com

Data Driven Publishing, LLC
PO Box 340
Newburyport, MA 01950
Ph: (603)969-5020
Fax: (978)499-8886

Data Storage Systems Center
Carnegie Mellon University
ECE Dept.
Pittsburgh, PA 15213
Ph: (412)268-6600
Fax: (412)268-3497
Co. E-mail: dssc@ece.cmu.edu
URL: http://www.dssc.ece.cmu.edu

David Hall Rare Coins
PO Box 6220
Newport Beach, CA 92658
Ph: (949)567-1325
Free: 800-759-7575
Fax: (949)477-5874
Co. E-mail: info@davidhall.com
URL: http://www.davidhall.com

David W. Wood
503 E Deering Rd.
Deering, NH 03244
Ph: (603)529-2355
Free: 800-439-9663
Fax: (603)529-3180
Co. E-mail: woody@wordsfromwoody.com

The Davlin Report Inc.
PO Box 60040
Boulder City, NV 89006-0040
Ph: (702)293-6400
Fax: (702)293-5100

Days Communications
1208 Juniper St.
Quakertown, PA 18951-1520
Ph: (215)538-1240
Fax: (215)538-1208
Co. E-mail: subscriptions@policeandsecuritynews.com
URL: http://policeandsecuritynews.com

DC & D Technologies Inc.
PO Box 948
Valrico, FL 33595-0948
Ph: (813)662-6830
Free: 800-533-5680
Fax: (813)662-6793
Co. E-mail: info@dcd.com
URL: http://www.dcd.com

Dearborn Trade Publishing Inc.
30 S Wacker Dr., Ste. 2500
Chicago, IL 60606-7481
Ph: (312)836-4400
Free: 800-621-9621
Fax: (312)836-1146
Co. E-mail: trade@dearborn.com
URL: http://www.dearborn.com

Decatur Daily
201 1st Ave. SE
Decatur, AL 35609
Ph: (256)353-4612
Free: 888-353-4612

Delahaye Medialink
195 New Hampshire Ave., Ste. 225
Portsmouth, NH 03801-2875
Free: 800-926-0028

The Denver Post
101 W Colfax Ave.
Denver, CO 80202-5177
Ph: (303)954-1010
Free: 800-336-7678
URL: http://www.denverpost.com

Department of Economic and Community Development
William Snodgrass Tennessee Twr., 11th Fl.
312 8th Ave. N
Nashville, TN 37243-0405
Ph: (615)741-1888
Fax: (615)741-7306
URL: http://www.state.tn.us/ecd/

Desktop Wings Inc.

The Destin Log
PO Box 339
Destin, FL 32540
Ph: (850)837-2828
Fax: (850)654-5982

Destiny Productions for Print, Radio & Cable Promotions
3395 S Jones Blvd., No. 217
Las Vegas, NV 89146-6729
Ph: (702)438-1470
Fax: (702)438-2790
Co. E-mail: destinymag@aol.com

DIANE Publishing Co.
601 Upland Ave.
Upland, PA 19015
Ph: (610)499-7415
Fax: (610)499-7429

Co. E-mail: dianepub@erols.com
URL: http://www.dianepublishing.com

DIANE Publishing Company
330 Pusey Ave., Unit 3 Rear
Collingdale, PA 19023-8428
Ph: (610)461-6200
Free: 800-782-3833
Fax: (610)461-6130

DIANE Publishing Company
PO Box 617
Darby, PA 19023-0617
Ph: (610)461-6200
Free: 800-782-3833
Fax: (610)461-6130

Dickinson Press
1815 1st St. W
Dickinson, ND 58602
Ph: (701)225-8111
Fax: (701)225-4205

Diesel & Gas Turbine Publications
20855 Watertown Rd., Ste. 220
Waukesha, WI 53189
Ph: (262)754-4100
Free: 800-558-4322
Fax: (262)754-4175
URL: http://storefront.dieselpub.com

Dietary Managers Association
406 Surrey Woods Dr.
St. Charles, IL 60174
Ph: (630)587-6336
Free: 800-323-1908
Fax: (630)587-6308
Co. E-mail: info@dmaonline.org
URL: http://www.dmaonline.org

Dietitians of Canada
480 University Ave., Ste. 604
Toronto, ON, Canada M5G 1V2
Ph: (416)596-0857
Fax: (416)596-0603
Co. E-mail: centralinfo@dietitians.ca
URL: http://www.dietitians.ca

Direct Marketing Association of Washington, DC
11709 Bowman Green Dr.
Reston, VA 20190
Ph: (703)689-3629
Fax: (703)481-3629
Co. E-mail: Info@dmaw.org

Direct Marketing Club of New York
54 Adams St.
Garden City, NY 11530
Ph: (516)746-6700
Fax: (516)294-8141
Co. E-mail: admin@dmcny.info
URL: http://www.dmcny.org

Directors Guild of America Inc.
7920 Sunset Blvd.
Los Angeles, CA 90046
Ph: (310)289-2000
Free: 800-421-4173
Fax: (310)289-2029
Co. E-mail: dgawebsupport@dga.org
URL: http://www.dga.org

Discovery Publications Inc.
1501 Burlington, Ste. 207
Kansas City, MO 64116
Ph: (816)474-1516
Free: 800-899-9730
Fax: (816)474-1427
Co. E-mail: dispub@discoverypub.com
URL: http://www.discoverypub.com/
    contacts.htm

Distance Education and Training Council
1601 18th St. NW, Ste. 2
Washington, DC 20009
Ph: (202)234-5100
Fax: (202)332-1386
Co. E-mail: mike@detc.org
URL: http://www.detc.org

Diversity Information Resources
2105 Central Ave. NE
Minneapolis, MN 55418
Ph: (612)781-6819
Fax: (612)781-0109
Co. E-mail: info@diversityinforesources.
    com
URL: http://www.diversityinforesources.
    com

DK Publishing/Penguin Group
375 Hudson St.
New York, NY 10014
Ph: (212)366-2679
Fax: (212)366-2612

DL Perkins Company
PO Box 700570
Tulsa, OK 74170
Free: 800-634-0605
Fax: (707)221-3501

DM News
114 W 26th St., 4th Fl.
New York, NY 10001
Ph: (646)638-6000
Fax: (646)638-6159
Co. E-mail: news@dmnews.com
URL: http://www.dmnews.com

DNA Press
Pottstown, PA
Free: 800-888-4741
Fax: (312)337-5985
Co. E-mail: editor@dnapress.com
URL: http://www.dnapress.com

Doane Agricultural Services
77 Westport Plz., Ste. 250
Saint Louis, MO 63146-4193
Ph: (314)569-2700
Free: 866-647-0918
Co. E-mail: doane@doane.com
URL: http://www.doane.com

Doctorow Communications Inc.
180 Phillips Hill Rd., Ste. 1B
New City, NY 10956
Ph: (973)779-1600
Free: 800-361-1400
Fax: (845)708-5166
Co. E-mail: email@homelighting.com
URL: http://www.homelighting.com

Document Center Inc.
121 Industrial Rd., Ste. 8
Belmont, CA 94002
Ph: (650)591-7600
Fax: (650)591-7617
Co. E-mail: info@document-center.com
URL: http://www.document-center.com

Doggone
PO Box 1846
Estes Park, CO 80517
Ph: (303)449-2527
Free: 888-364-8728
Fax: (303)449-2705

Dogwise Publishing
403 S Mission
Wentachee, WA 98801
Ph: (509)663-9115
Fax: (509)662-7233
URL: http://www.dogwise.com

Dohmen Capital Research Institute
PO Box 49-2433
Los Angeles, CA 90049
Ph: (310)476-6933
Free: 800-992-9989
Fax: (310)440-2919
Co. E-mail: client@dohmencapital.com

Dolan Company
11 Saratoga St.
Baltimore, MD 21202
Ph: (443)524-8100

Dolan Media Co.
333 S 7th St., Ste. 2180
Minneapolis, MN 55402-2432
Ph: (612)333-4244

Dolan Media
31 E Platte Ave., Ste. 300
Colorado Springs, CO 80903
Ph: (719)634-5905
Fax: (719)227-5865

Dolan Media Newswires
855 W Broad St., Ste. 103
Boise, ID 83702
Ph: (208)336-3768

Fax: (208)336-5534

Dolan Media Newswires
31 E Platte Ave., Ste. 300
Colorado Springs, CO 80903
Ph: (719)634-5905

Dolan Media Newswires
U.S. Trust Bldg., Ste. 100
730 2nd Ave. S
Minneapolis, MN 55402
Ph: (612)333-4244
Fax: (612)333-3243

Dolan Media Newswires
921 SW Washington St., Ste. 210
Portland, OR 97205
Ph: (503)226-1311

Dolan Media Newswires
2150 Smithtown Ave., Ste. 7
Ronkonkoma, NY 11779
Ph: (631)737-1700
Fax: (631)737-1890

Dolan Media Newswires
401 S Boston Ave., Ste. 105
Tulsa, OK 74103
Ph: (918)295-0098

Dolan Media
921 SW Washington St., Ste. 210
Portland, OR 97205
Ph: (503)226-1311

Dominion Enterprises
150 Granby St.
Norfolk, VA 23510-1604
Ph: (757)351-7000
Fax: (757)314-2512
Co. E-mail: clay.gill@dominionenterprises.
com
URL: http://www.dominionenterprises.com

Donald H. Rowe The Wall Street Digest
2 N Tamiami Trl.
Sarasota, FL 34236
Ph: (941)954-5500
Free: 800-785-5050
Fax: (941)364-8447
Co. E-mail: subscribe@wallstreetdigest.
com
URL: http://www.wallstreetdigest.com

Donrey Media Group
700 Brookside Ave.
Redlands, CA 92373
Ph: (909)793-3221
Fax: (909)793-9588
URL: http://www.redlandsdailyfacts.com

Double Storey Books
PO Box 24309
Cape Town 7779, South Africa
Ph: 27 21 7975101
Fax: 27 21 7624523
URL: http://www.doublestorey.com/

Doubleday Broadway Publishing Group
1745 Broadway
New York, NY 10019
Ph: (212)782-9000
Free: 800-733-3000
Fax: (212)302-7985
Co. E-mail: ddaypub@randomhouse.com
URL: http://www.randomhouse.com/
doubleday/

Doubleday Canada, Limited
1 Toronto St., Unit 300
Toronto, ON, Canada M5C 2V6
Ph: (416)364-4449
Free: 800-668-4247
Fax: (416)364-6863
URL: http://www.randomhouse.ca

Doubleday
Random House/Doubleday Business
1745 Broadway
New York, NY 10019
Ph: (212)782-9000
Free: 800-733-3000
Fax: (212)302-7985
Co. E-mail: ddaypub@randomhouse.com
URL: http://www.randomhouse.com/

**Doubleday, a Division of Random
House**
1745 Broadway
New York, NY 10019
Ph: (212)782-9000
Fax: (212)572-6066
Co. E-mail: ddaypub@randomhouse.com
URL: http://www.randomhouse.com

**Dow Jones & Company Inc. Enterprise
Media Group**
1211 Ave. of the Americas, Ste. 8
New York, NY 10036-8706
Ph: (212)416-2000
Free: 800-544-0422
Fax: (212)416-2524
URL: http://www.dowjones.com

Dow Jones & Company Inc.
1211 Ave. of the Americas
New York, NY 10036
Ph: (212)416-2000

Dow Jones & Company Inc.
1 World Financial Ctr.
200 Liberty St.
New York, NY 10281
Ph: (212)416-2000
URL: http://www.dowjones.com

DP Group, Incorporated
30 S Wacker, No. 2500
Chicago, IL 60606
Ph: (312)894-0361
Free: 800-824-8742
Fax: (312)836-1146

Dreamscape Productions
510 Woodhaven
Aptos, CA 95003-5522
URL: http://www.sfdreamscape.com/

Driving School Association of Americas
3090 E Gause Blvd., Ste. 425
Slidell, LA 70461
Ph: (985)649-9877
Free: 800-270-3722
Co. E-mail: info@thedsaa.org

Drug Store News
425 Park Ave.
New York, NY 10022
Free: 800-766-6999

Drycleaning & Laundry Institute
14700 Sweitzer Ln.
Laurel, MD 20707
Ph: (301)622-1900
Free: 800-638-2627
Fax: (240)295-0685
Co. E-mail: techline@ifi.org
URL: http://www.ifi.org/

Dun and Bradstreet Corp.
103 JFK Pkwy.
Short Hills, NJ 07078
Ph: (973)921-5500
Free: 800-526-0651
Fax: (866)560-7035
Co. E-mail: info@dnb.com
URL: http://www.dnb.com

Dundurn Group
8 Market St., Ste. 200
Toronto, ON, Canada M5E 1M6
Ph: (416)214-5544
Fax: (416)214-5556

Dundurn Press
3 Church St., Ste. 500
Toronto, ON, Canada M5E 1M2
Ph: (416)214-5544
Fax: (416)214-5556
URL: http://www.dundurn.com/

duPont Publishing Inc.
3051 Tech Dr.
Saint Petersburg, FL 33716
Ph: (727)573-9339
Free: 800-233-1731
URL: http://www.dupontregistry.com

Dustbooks
PO Box 100
Paradise, CA 95967
Ph: (530)877-6110
Free: 800-477-6110
Fax: (530)877-0222
Co. E-mail: info@dustbooks.com
URL: http://www.dustbooks.com

Dynamic Graphics Inc.
6000 N Forest Park Dr.
Peoria, IL 61614-3592
Ph: (309)688-8800
Free: 800-255-8800
Fax: (309)688-3075
Co. E-mail: service@dgusa.com
URL: http://www.dgusa.com

E

E.W. Williams Publications Co.
2125 Center Ave., Ste. 305
Fort Lee, NJ 07024-5898
Ph: (201)592-7007
Fax: (201)592-7171
Co. E-mail: philpl@ewwpi.com
URL: http://www.williamspublications.com

Eagle Newspapers
4901 Indian School Rd. NE
Salem, OR 97305
Ph: (503)393-1774
URL: http://www.eaglenewspapers.com/

Eagle Publications Inc.
42400 Grand River, Ste. 103
Novi, MI 48375
Ph: (248)347-3486
Free: 800-783-3491
Fax: (248)347-3492
Co. E-mail: info@ameritooldie.com
URL: http://www.ameritooldie.com/atds-Contact.html

Earl G. Graves Publishing Co. Inc.
130 5th Ave.
New York, NY 10011
Ph: (212)242-8000
Fax: (212)896-9600

Earl Graves Publishing Co.
130 5th Ave., 10th Fl.
New York, NY 10011-4399
Ph: (212)242-8000
Co. E-mail: benyc_ads@blackenterprise.com
URL: http://www.blackenterprise.com

Earth Action Network
1536 Crest Dr.
Los Angeles, CA 90035
Co. E-mail: eanla@aol.com
URL: http://www.emagazine.com/view/?289&printview

Earth Island Institute
2150 Allston Way, Ste. 460
Berkeley, CA 94704-1375
Ph: (510)859-9100
Fax: (510)859-9091
Co. E-mail: johnknox@earthisland.org
URL: http://www.earthisland.org

Earthscan
Dunstan House
14a St. Cross St.
London EC1N 8XA, United Kingdom
Ph: (440) 2078411930
Fax: (440) 2072421474
URL: http://www.earthscan.co.uk

East Coast Publications
57 Washington St.
Norwell, MA 02061
Ph: (781)878-4540
Free: 800-654-4993
Fax: (781)871-1853
Co. E-mail: nyrej@rejournal.com
URL: http://www.rejournal.com

Eastern Perishable Products Association Inc.
PO Box 4878
Colts Neck, NJ 07722
Ph: (973)831-4100
Fax: (973)831-8100
Co. E-mail: eppa@eppainc.org
URL: http://www.eppainc.org

Eating Well Inc.
823A Ferry Rd.
Charlotte, VT 05445
Ph: (802)425-5700
Free: 800-337-0402
Fax: (802)425-3700
Co. E-mail: eatingwell@emailcustomerservice.com
URL: http://www.eatingwell.com

Eaton Publishing
1 Research Dr. Sui 400A
Westborough, MA 01581-6070
Ph: (508)614-1414
Fax: (508)616-2930
Co. E-mail: info@biotechniques.com
URL: http://www.biotechniques.com

Eaton-Moghannam Publishing
696 San Ramon Valley Blvd., Ste. 214
Danville, CA 94526
Ph: (925)743-1083

EBSCO Publishing
10 Estes St.
Ipswich, MA 01938-2106
Ph: (978)356-6500
Free: 800-653-2726
Fax: (978)356-6565
Co. E-mail: information@ebscohost.com
URL: http://www.ebscohost.com

Ebury Press
c/o Random House
1745 Broadway
New York, NY 10019
Ph: (212)782-9000
Fax: (212)572-8700
Co. E-mail: customerservice@random-house.com

Ecco
10 E 53rd St.
New York, NY 10022
Ph: (212)207-7000
Free: 800-242-7737
URL: http://www.harpercollins.com/
imprints/index.aspx?imprintid=517997

Ecco/HarperCollins
10 E 53rd St.
New York, NY 10022
Ph: (212)207-7000
URL: http://www.harpercollins.com/
imprints/index.aspx?imprintid-517997

Economic Development Institute Georgia Tech
O'Keefe Bldg., Rm. 205
Atlanta, GA 30332-0640
Ph: (404)894-3475
Fax: (404)894-0069

Economics Dept.
1201 15th St. NW
Washington, DC 20005
Ph: (202)266-8200
Free: 800-368-5242
Fax: (202)266-8400

Economist Intelligence Unit
111 W 57th St.
New York, NY 10019
Ph: (212)554-0600
Free: 800-938-4685
Fax: (212)586-1181
Co. E-mail: newyork@eiu.com

The Economist Newspaper Inc.
90 New Montgomery St., Ste. 201
San Francisco, CA 94105
Ph: (415)278-0880
Fax: (415)278-0884

Economist Newspaper Ltd.
90 New Montgomery St., Ste. 201
San Francisco, CA 94105
Ph: (415)278-0880
Fax: (415)278-0884

ECRI Institute
5200 Butler Pke.
Plymouth Meeting, PA 19462-1298
Ph: (610)825-6000
Fax: (610)834-1275
Co. E-mail: info@ecri.org
URL: http://www.ecri.org

Ed Varney
PO Box 3655
Vancouver, BC, Canada V6B 3Y8
Ph: (604)266-8289
Fax: (604)266-8289

Edgell Communications Inc.
4 Middlebury Blvd., Ste. 1
Randolph, NJ 07869-1121
Ph: (973)607-1300

Fax: (973)252-9020
Co. E-mail: gedgell@edgellmail.com
URL: http://www.edgellcommunications.
com

Editorial Freelancers Association Inc.
71 W 23rd St., 4th Fl.
New York, NY 10010-4181
Ph: (212)929-5400
Co. E-mail: office@the-efa.org
URL: http://www.the-efa.org

Editorial Projects in Education
6935 Arlington, Ste. 100
Bethesda, MD 20814
Ph: (301)280-3100
Free: 800-346-1834
Fax: (301)280-3200
Co. E-mail: kdorko@epe.org
URL: http://www.edweek.org

Educational Technology Publ
700 E Palisade Ave.
Englewood Cliffs 07632
Ph: (201)871-4007
Free: 800-952-2665
Fax: (201)871-4009
Co. E-mail: edtecpubs@aol.com
URL: http://www.bookstoread.com/etp

Edward Elgar Publishing, Inc.
9 Dewey Ct.
Northampton, MA 01060-3815
Ph: (413)584-5551
Fax: (413)584-9933
Co. E-mail: elgarinfo@e-elgar.com
URL: http://www.e-elgar-business.com

Edward Elgar Publishing, Incorporated
136 West St., Ste. 202
Northampton, MA 01060
Ph: (413)584-5551
Fax: (413)584-9933

Edwin Mellen Press
PO Box 450
Lewiston, NY 14092-0450
Ph: (716)754-2266
Fax: (716)754-2788

EGW.com Inc.
4075 Papazian Way, No. 208
Fremont, CA 94538
URL: http://www.egw.com

ELF Publications Inc.
5285 W Louisiana Ave.
Lakewood, CO 80232-5976
Ph: (303)975-0075
Free: 800-922-8513
Fax: (303)975-0132
Co. E-mail: elfpub@qwest.net
URL: http://www.elfpublications.com/

Elsevier Advanced Technology Publications
Kelly School of Business
Indiana University
1309 E 10th St.
Bloomington, IN 47405
Ph: (812)855-6342
Fax: (812)856-4971

Elsevier Business Intelligence
5635 Fishers Ln., Ste. 6000
Rockville, MD 20852
Ph: (212)633-3648
Free: 800-332-2181
Fax: (240)221-4400
Co. E-mail: fdc.customer.service@fdcreports.com
URL: http://www.elsevierbi.com/contactus.
html

Elsevier
1600 John F. Kennedy Blvd., Ste. 1800
Philadelphia, PA 19103-2899
Ph: (215)239-3900
Free: 800-523-1649
Fax: (215)238-7883
Co. E-mail: healthpermissions@elsevier.
com
URL: http://www.elsevier.com

Elsevier Science & Technology Books
c/o Elsevier Inc.
30 Corporate Dr., Ste. 400
Burlington, MA 01803
Free: 866-607-1417
Co. E-mail: textbook@elsevier.com
URL: http://www.elsevierdirect.com

Elsevier Science & Technology Books
11830 Westline Industrial Dr.
Saint Louis, MO 63146
Ph: (314)453-7010
Free: 800-545-2522
Fax: (800)535-9935

Elsevier Science & Technology Books
525 B St., Ste. 1900
San Diego, CA 92101
Ph: (781)313-4700

Elsevier Science B.V.
Radarweg 29
NL-1043 Amsterdam, Netherlands
Ph: 31 204 853911
Fax: 31 204 852457
URL: http://www.elsevier.com/wps/find/
homepage.cws_home

Elsevier Science Inc.
Secondary Publishing Division
650 Ave. of the Americas
New York, NY 10011
Ph: (212)633-3980
Free: 888-437-4636
Fax: (212)633-3975

Elsevier Technology Publications
360 Park Ave. S
New York, NY 10010
Ph: (212)633-3730
Free: 888-437-4636
Fax: (212)462-1974

Elton Stephens Investments
PO Box 476
South Bend, IN 46614
Ph: (574)291-3823
Free: 800-553-5866
Fax: (574)291-3823
URL: http://www.eltonstephens.com

Emerald Group Publishing Inc.
Brickyard Office Park
84 Sherman St.
Cambridge, MA 02140
Ph: (617)945-9130
Free: 888-622-0075
Fax: (617)945-9136
Co. E-mail: america@emeraldinsight.com
URL: http://www.emeraldinsight.com

Emerald Inc.
Harvard Square
1 Mifflin Place, Ste. 400
Cambridge, MA 02138
Ph: (617)576-5782

Emmis Books
Old Firehouse, 1700 Madison Rd.
Cincinnati, OH 45206
Ph: (513)861-4045
Free: 800-913-9563
Fax: (513)861-4430
Co. E-mail: info@emmis.com

Employee Morale and Recreation Association
PO Box 10517
Rockville, MD 20849
Ph: (630)559-0020
Fax: (630)559-0025
Co. E-mail: esmahq@esmassn.org
URL: http://www.esmassn.org

Employee Relocation Council
4401 Wilson Blvd., Ste. 510
Arlington, VA 22203
Ph: (703)842-3400
Fax: (703)527-1552
Co. E-mail: emea@worldwideerc.org
URL: http://www.erc.org

Employer Resource Institute Inc.
1819 Polk St. No. 290
San Francisco, CA 94109
Free: 800-695-7178
Fax: (888)321-5066
Co. E-mail: custserv@employeradvice.
com

Enfield Publishing
217 W 2nd St.
Whitefish, MT 59937
Ph: (406)862-1233
Fax: (406)862-1053

Engineering Contractors Association
8310 Florence Ave.
Downey, CA 90240
Ph: (562)861-0929
Free: 800-293-2240
Fax: (562)923-6179
Co. E-mail: info.eca@verizon.net
URL: http://www.ecaonline.net

Enterprise Magazines Inc.
5555 N Port Washington Rd., Ste. 305
Milwaukee, WI 53217
Ph: (414)882-2878
Free: 800-272-0246
Fax: (414)882-2877
Co. E-mail: info@franchisehandbook.com
URL: http://www.franchisehandbook.com

Enterprise Technology Corp.
6 Hemlock Dr.
Greenwich, CT 06831-5218

Entree Travel
695 Olive Rd.
Santa Barbara, CA 93108
Ph: (805)969-5848
Fax: (805)966-7095
Co. E-mail: wtomicki@aol.com
URL: http://www.entreenews.com

Entrepreneur Media Inc.
2445 McCabe Way, Ste. 400
Irvine, CA 92614
Ph: (949)261-2325
Free: 800-274-6229

Entrepreneur Press
2445 McCabe Way
Irvine, CA 92614
Ph: (949)261-2325
Fax: (949)261-7729
URL: http://www.smallbizbooks.com

Entrepreneur Press
McGraw-Hill
55 Francisco St., Ste. 200
San Francisco, CA 94133
Ph: (415)433-2821
Free: 800-435-2665
Fax: (415)989-7702

Entrepreneurial Press
2445 McCabe Way, Ste. 400
Irvine, CA 92614-6244
Ph: (949)261-2325
Free: 800-864-6864
Fax: (949)261-7729

Environmental News Network
402 N B St.
Fairfield, IA 52556
Ph: (319)217-2362
Fax: (866)435-1513
URL: http://www.enn.com/

EPM Communications Inc.
19 W 21 St., Ste. 303
New York, NY 10010
Ph: (212)941-0099
Free: 888-852-9467
Fax: (212)941-1622
Co. E-mail: info@epmcom.com
URL: http://www.epmcom.com

EPRI
3420 Hillview Ave.
Palo Alto, CA 94304
Ph: (650)855-2121
Free: 800-313-3774
Fax: (925)609-1310
Co. E-mail: askepri@epri.com
URL: http://www.epri.com

Erie Times-News
205 W 12th St.
Erie, PA 16534
Ph: (814)878-1943

Escapees, Inc.
100 Rainbow Dr.
Livingston, TX 77351
Ph: (936)327-8873
Free: 888-757-2582
Fax: (936)327-4388
Co. E-mail: editor@escapees.com

ETA International
5 Depot St.
Greencastle, IN 46135
Ph: (765)653-8262
Free: 800-288-3824
Fax: (765)653-4287
Co. E-mail: eta@eta-i.org
URL: http://www.eta-i.org

Ethics Resource Center Inc.
1747 Pennsylvania Ave. NW, Ste. 400
Washington, DC 20006-4604
Ph: (202)737-2258
Free: 800-777-1285
Fax: (202)737-2227
Co. E-mail: ethics@ethics.org
URL: http://www.ethics.org

Everton Publishers
3223 S Main St.
Logan, UT 84321-7903
Ph: (435)752-6022
Free: 800-443-6325
Fax: (435)752-1541
Co. E-mail: ed@everton.com
URL: http://www.everton.com

Executive Business Media Inc.
825 Old Country Rd.
Westbury, NY 11590-0812
Ph: (516)334-3030
Fax: (516)334-3059
Co. E-mail: ebm-mail@ebmpubs.com
URL: http://www.ebmpubs.com

Executive Protection Institute
276 Journeys End Ln.
Bluemont, VA 20135
Ph: (540)554-2540
Fax: (540)554-2558
Co. E-mail: info@personalprotection.com
URL: http://www.personalprotection.com

Exhibit Builder Magazine
22900 Ventura Blvd., Ste. 245
Woodland Hills, CA 91364
Ph: (818)225-0100
Free: 800-356-4451
Fax: (818)225-0138
Co. E-mail: jillb@exhibitbuilder.net
URL: http://www.exhibitbuilder.net

EXPO Magazine Inc.
PO Box 2160
Skokie, IL 60076
Ph: (847)763-9618
URL: http://www.expoweb.com

Export Institute
6901 W 84th St., Ste. 301
Minneapolis, MN 55438
Ph: (952)943-1505
Free: 800-943-3171
Fax: (952)943-1535
Co. E-mail: jrj@exportinstitute.com
URL: http://www.exportinstitute.com

Eye Contact Media
1344 Disc Dr., No. 105
Sparks, NV 89436

F

F & W Publications, Incorporated
4700 E Galbraith Rd.
Cincinnati, OH 45236
Ph: (513)531-2690

F and W Publications, Inc.
4700 E Galbraith Rd.
Cincinnati, OH 45236
Ph: (513)531-2690
Free: 800-289-0963
Fax: (888)590-4082

F-D-C Reports Inc.
5635 Fishers Ln., Ste. 6000
Rockville, MD 20852
Ph: (800)332-2181
Free: 800-332-2181
Fax: (240)221-4400
Co. E-mail: fdc.customer.service@fdcreports.com
URL: http://www.elsevierbi.com

Faber & Faber, Inc.
19 Union Sq. W
New York, NY 10003
Ph: (212)741-7900
Fax: (212)633-9385
URL: http://us.macmillan.com/faberandfaber.aspx

Fabricare Canada
PO Box 968
Oakville, ON, Canada L6J 5E8
Ph: (905)337-0516
Fax: (905)337-0525
URL: http://www.fabricarecanada.com

Fabricators and Manufacturers Association International
833 Featherstone Rd.
Rockford, IL 61107-6301
Ph: (815)399-8775
Free: 888-394-4362
Fax: (815)484-7701
Co. E-mail: info@fmanet.org
URL: http://www.fmanet.org

Fahy-Williams Publishing Inc.
171 Reed St.
Geneva, NY 14456
Ph: (315)789-0458
Free: 800-344-0559
Fax: (315)789-4263
Co. E-mail: kfahy@fwpi.com
URL: http://www.fwpi.com

Fairchild Publications
750 Third Ave.
New York, NY 10017
Ph: (212)630-4600
Free: 800-360-1700
Fax: (212)630-3675
Co. E-mail: hillary_kribben@condenast.com
URL: http://www.fairchildmediakit.com/

Fairchild Tropical Botanic Garden
10901 Old Cutler Rd.
Coral Gables, FL 33156
Ph: (305)667-1651
Fax: (305)661-8953
Co. E-mail: webmaster@fairchildgarden.org

Family Enterprise Publishers
1220-B Kennestone Cir.
Marietta, GA 30061
Ph: (770)421-0110
Free: 800-551-0633
Fax: (770)425-1776
Co. E-mail: info@efamilybusiness.com

Family Firm Institute (FFI)
200 Lincoln St., Ste. 201
Boston, MA 02111
Ph: (617)482-3045
Fax: (617)482-3049
Co. E-mail: ffi@ffi.org
URL: http://www.ffi.org

Fandata Publications
7614 Cervantes Ct.
Springfield, VA 22153-1608
Ph: (703)913-5575
Fax: (703)913-5575
Co. E-mail: email@fandata.com
URL: http://www.fandata.com

Fantagraphics Books Inc.
7563 Lake City Way Ne
Seattle, WA 98115-4218
Ph: (206)524-1967
Free: 800-657-1100
Fax: (206)524-2104
Co. E-mail: fbicomix@fantagraphics.com
URL: http://www.fantagraphics.com

Farm & Ranch News
PO Box 160
Lithia, FL 33547-0160
Ph: (813)737-6397
Co. E-mail: farmranchnews@aol.com
URL: http://www.farmandranchnews.com/

Farrar, Straus and Giroux
18 W 18th St.
New York, NY 10011
URL: http://www.fsgbooks.com

Fastline
4900 Fox Run Rd.
Buckner, KY 40010
Ph: (502)222-0146
Free: 800-626-6409
Fax: (502)222-0615
Co. E-mail: custcare@fastline.com
URL: http://www.fastline.com

Faulkner Information Services Inc.
7905 Browning Rd.
Pennsauken, NJ 08109-4323
Ph: (856)662-2070
Free: 800-843-0460
Fax: (856)662-0905
Co. E-mail: faulkner@faulkner.com
URL: http://www.faulkner.com

FCW
50 Charles Lindbergh Blvd., Ste. 100
Uniondale, NY 11553
Ph: (516)229-3600
Fax: (516)227-1342
URL: http://www.floorcoveringweekly.com

FDA News
300 N Washington St., Ste. 200
Falls Church, VA 22046-3431
Ph: (703)538-7600
Fax: (703)538-7676
Co. E-mail: customerservice@fdanews.com

Feature Publishing Ltd.
1800 McGill College Ave., Ste. 1600
Montreal, QC, Canada H3A 3J6
Ph: (514)939-5024
Free: 866-332-8878

Co. E-mail: editor@feature.ca
URL: http://www.movieentertainment.ca/

Federal Jobs Digest
326 Main St.
Emmaus, PA 18049
Free: 800-824-5000
Co. E-mail: webmaster@jobsfed.com
URL: http://www.jobsfed.com

**Federal Library and Information
Network**
Library of Congress
101 Independence Ave., SE
Adams Bldg., Rm. 217
Washington, DC 20540-4935
Ph: (202)707-4800
Fax: (202)707-4825
Co. E-mail: fliccfpe@loc.gov

Federal Reserve Bank of Dallas
2200 N Pearl St.
Dallas, TX 75201-2216
Ph: (214)922-6000
Free: 800-333-4460
Fax: (214)922-6500
Co. E-mail: info@dallasfed.org
URL: http://www.dallasfed.org

Federick News-Post
351 Ballenger Center Dr.
Frederick, MD 21703
Ph: (301)662-1177

Feed-Lot Magazine
116 E Long
Dighton, KS 67839
Free: 800-798-9515
Fax: (620)397-2839
URL: http://www.feedlotmagazine.com/
   contact.html

FERA Inc.
1810 Warrington Cir.
Ann Arbor, MI 48103
Ph: (734)994-9060
Fax: (248)446-8789
Co. E-mail: jskiff@feraonline.com
URL: http://www.feraonline.com

Ferdic Inc.
PO Box 28
Camp Hill, PA 17011
Ph: (717)731-1426
Fax: (717)731-1427
Co. E-mail: ferdic@ix.netcom.com

Ferney Scribes Inc.
PO Box 1118
Mill Valley, CA 94942

Fiction Writer's Connection
PO Box 72300
Albuquerque, NM 87195
Ph: (505)352-9490
Free: 800-248-2758
Fax: (505)352-9495

Fifth Estate
PO Box 201016
Ferndale, MI 48220
Co. E-mail: fe@fifthestate.org
URL: http://www.fifthestate.org

Film Society of Lincoln Center
70 Lincoln Center Plz.
New York, NY 10023-6595
Ph: (212)875-5610
Free: 888-313-6085
Co. E-mail: filminfo@filmlinc.com
URL: http://www.filmlinc.com

Financial Executives International
PO Box 303
Uxbridge, MA 01569
Ph: (502)278-8006
Fax: (866)582-6227

Financial Planning Association
4100 E. Mississippi Ave., Ste. 400
Denver, CO 80246-3053
Ph: (800)322-4237
Free: 800-322-4237
Fax: (303)759-0749
URL: http://www.fpanet.org

Financial Research Association Inc.
203 A Ave, NW., Ste. 202
Winter Haven, FL 33881
Ph: (863)299-3969
Fax: (863)299-2131
Co. E-mail: sales@frafssb.com

Financial Times/Prentice Hall (FTPH)
1 Lake St.
Upper Saddle River, NJ 07458-1813
Ph: (201)236-7000
Free: 800-922-0579
Fax: (201)236-3400
Co. E-mail: liz.gooster@pearson.com
URL: http://www.pearsoned.co.uk/Imprints/
   FTPrenticeHall

Find/SVP
17 Oxford St.
Rochester, NY 14607
Ph: (212)645-4500
Free: 800-346-3787
Fax: (212)645-7681
Co. E-mail: infoadvisor@findsvp.com

Fireside Publishing
Rockefeller Center
1230 Ave. of the Americas
New York, NY 10020

Fitch IPCA Inc.
1 State St. Plz.
New York, NY 10004
Ph: (212)908-0500
Free: 800-753-4824
Fax: (212)480-4435
Co. E-mail: usaclientservices@fitchratings.
   com

Fleisher Fine Arts Inc.
15 McMurrich St., Ste. 706
Toronto, ON, Canada M5R 3M6
Ph: (416)925-5564
Fax: (416)925-2972
URL: http://www.fleisher.org/

**Floor Covering Installation Contractors
Association**
7439 Millwood Dr.
West Bloomfield, MI 48322
Ph: (248)661-5015
Fax: (248)661-5018
Co. E-mail: keo@fcica.com
URL: http://www.fcica.com

Floor Focus Inc.
3001 S Broad St., Ste. 100
Chattanooga, TN 37408
Ph: (423)752-0400
Co. E-mail: info@floorfocus.com
URL: http://www.floordaily.net/

**Florida Department of Agriculture and
Consumer Services, Division of Plant
Industry**
The Capitol
Tallahassee, FL 32399-0800
Ph: (850)488-3022
URL: http://www.doacs.state.fl.us/

**Florida International University School
of Hospitality Management**
3000 NE 151st St.
North Miami, FL 33181
Ph: (305)919-4500
Fax: (305)919-4555
Co. E-mail: hospitality@fiu.edu
URL: http://hospitality.fiu.edu/

Florida Publishers Association
PO Box 430
Highland City, FL 33846-0430
Ph: (863)647-5951
Fax: (863)647-5951
Co. E-mail: fpabooks@aol.com

Florida Times-Union
1 Riverside Ave.
Jacksonville, FL 32202
Ph: (904)359-4111

Florist's Review Enterprises Inc.
PO Box 4368
Topeka, KS 66604
Ph: (785)266-0888
Free: 800-367-4708
Fax: (785)266-0333
Co. E-mail: mail@floristsreview.com
URL: http://www.floristsreview.com/main/
   contactus.html

FM Atlas Publishing
PO Box 336
Esko, MN 55733-0336
Ph: (218)879-7676
Free: 800-605-2219

Co. E-mail: fmatlas@aol.com
URL: http://members.aol.com/fmatlas/
home.html

Food Institute
10 Mountainview Rd., Ste. S125
Upper Saddle River, NJ 07458
Ph: (201)791-5570
Free: 800-966-5225
Fax: (201)791-5222
Co. E-mail: questions@foodinstitute.com
URL: http://www.foodinstitute.com

Foodservice Consultants Society International
144 Parkedge Str.
Rockwood, ON, Canada N0B 2K0
Ph: (519)856-0783
Fax: (519)856-0648
Co. E-mail: info@fcsi.org
URL: http://www.fcsi.org

Forbes Inc.
60 5th Ave.
New York, NY 10011
Ph: (212)620-2200
Fax: (212)620-2332
Co. E-mail: subscriber@forbes.com
URL: http://www.forbes.com

Forbes Magazine
60 5th Ave.
New York, NY 10011
Ph: (212)366-8900
Free: 800-295-0893
URL: http://www.forbes.com

Ford Dealers Alliance
401 Continental Plz.
Hackensack, NJ 07601
Ph: (201)342-4542
Fax: (201)342-3997

Ford Investor Services Inc.
11722 Sorrento Valley Rd., Ste. I
San Diego, CA 92121
Ph: (858)755-1327
Fax: (858)455-6316

Forensic Drug Abuse Advisor Inc.
PO Box 5139
Berkeley, CA 94705-5139
Ph: (510)849-0923
Fax: (510)849-0958
Co. E-mail: info@fdaa.com

Forum Publishing Co.
383 E Main St.
Centerport, NY 11721
Ph: (631)754-5000
Free: 800-635-7654
Co. E-mail: forumpublishing@aol.com
URL: http://www.forum123.com

Foundation Center
79 5th Ave., 16th St.
New York 10003-3076
Ph: (212)620-4230
Free: 800-424-9836
Fax: (212)807-3677
Co. E-mail: feedback@foundationcenter.
org
URL: http://foundationcenter.org/newyork

Foundation for American Communications
85 S Grand Ave.
Pasadena, CA 91105
Ph: (626)584-0010
Fax: (626)584-0627
URL: http://www.facsnet.org

Foundation of Flexographic Technical Association
900 Marconi Ave.
Ronkonkoma, NY 11779-7212
Ph: (631)737-6020
Fax: (631)737-6813
Co. E-mail: memberinfo@flexography.org
URL: http://www.flexography.org

Fourth Seacoast Publishing Company Inc.
25300 Little Mack Ave.
Saint Clair Shores, MI 48081
Ph: (586)779-5570
Fax: (586)779-5547
URL: http://www.fourthseacoastonline.com

The Fragrance Foundation Inc.
545 5th Ave., Ste. 900
New York, NY 10017
Ph: (212)725-2755
Fax: (212)779-9058
Co. E-mail: info@fragrance.org
URL: http://www.fragrance.org

Frances Lincoln Limited
4 Torriano Mews
Torriano Ave.
London NW5 2RZ, United Kingdom
Ph: (440) 2072844009
Fax: (440) 2074850490
URL: http://www.franceslincoln.com

Franchise News
PMB 240
540 S Mendenhall Rd., Ste. 12
Memphis, TN 38117-4245
Co. E-mail: franmark@msn.com

Fraud & Theft Information Bureau
9770 S Military Trl., Ste. 380
Boynton Beach, FL 33436
Ph: (561)737-8700
Fax: (561)737-5800
Co. E-mail: sales@fraudandtheft.com
URL: http://www.fraudandtheft.com

Free Press Media Group Inc.
PO Box 362
Hendersonville, TN 37075
Ph: (615)822-1186

Free Press
1230 Ave. of the Americas
New York, NY 10020
Ph: (212)698-7000
Free: 800-897-7650
Fax: (212)698-7007
URL: http://www.simonandschuster.net/

Free Press/Simon & Schuster Inc.
Simon & Schuster Bldg.
1230 Avenue of the Americas
New York, NY 10020
Ph: (212)698-7000
Free: 800-223-2336
Fax: (212)698-7007
URL: http://www.simonsays.com

FreeBridge Publishing, Inc.
8105 Pinehurst Harbour Way
Pasadena, MD 21122
Ph: (231)933-0445

Freedom Communications
2 Eglin Pkwy. NE
Fort Walton Beach, FL 32548
Ph: (850)863-1111
Free: 800-755-1185

Freedom Communications Inc.
521 Pile St.
Clovis, NM 88101
Ph: (575)763-3431
Fax: (575)762-3879

Freedom Communications Inc.
3200 Wellons Blvd.
New Bern, NC 28562
Ph: (252)638-8101
Fax: (252)638-4664

French-Canadian Genealogical Society of Connecticut Inc.
Box 928
Tolland, CT 06084-0928
Ph: (860)872-2597

Fresh Produce and Floral Council
16700 Valley View Ave., Ste. 130
La Mirada, CA 90638
Ph: (714)739-0177
Fax: (714)739-0226
Co. E-mail: info@fpfc.org
URL: http://www.fpfc.org

Frontline Publishers, Incorporated
8268 Streamwood Dr.
Baltimore, MD 21208-8674
Ph: (410)922-4903
Fax: (410)922-8009

FSBO Publishing
Livonia, MI
Ph: (734)629-7222
Co. E-mail: info@fsbo-cd.com
URL: http://www.fsbo-cd.com

FT Press
800 E 96th St.
Indianapolis, IN 46240
URL: http://www.ftpress.com

FT Press
1 Lake St.
Upper Saddle River, NJ 37458
URL: http://www.ftpress.com/index.asp

FundWorks, Inc.
186 Crescent Rd.
Needham, MA 02494
Ph: (781)433-0909
Free: 800-718-8291
Fax: (781)453-1066
Co. E-mail: jimlowell@fidelityinvestor.com

Funeral Consumers Alliance
33 Patchen Rd.
South Burlington, VT 05403
Ph: (802)865-8300
Free: 800-765-0107
Fax: (802)865-2626
Co. E-mail: fca@funerals.org
URL: http://www.funerals.org/

Future Network USA
4000 Shoreline Ct., Ste. 400
South San Francisco, CA 94080
Ph: (650)872-1642
URL: http://www.futureus.com/contact/

Futures Magazine, Inc.
250 S. Wacker Dr. Suite 1150
Chicago, IL 60606
Ph: (312)977-0999
Free: 800-972-9316
Fax: (312)977-1042
Co. E-mail: gszala@futuresmag.com
URL: http://www.futuresmag.com

FW Publications
c/o Aero Fulfillment Services
6023 Union Centre Blvd.
Fairfield, OH 45014
Ph: (513)531-2690
Free: 800-258-0929
Fax: (513)531-0798
Co. E-mail: bookorders@krause.com
URL: http://www.fwbookstore.com

FXC Investors Corp.
PO Box 1366
Selden, NY 11784
Ph: (800)392-0992
Free: 800-FXC-0992
Fax: (631)218-8187

Co. E-mail: fxcmgt@aol.com

G

G.I.E. Media Inc.
4020 Kinross Lake Pkwy.
Richfield 44286
Ph: (216)961-4130
Free: 800-456-0707
Fax: (330)659-0823
Co. E-mail: bharbison@gie.net
URL: http://www.giemedia.com

G.R. Leonard & Co.
181 N Vermont Ave.
Glendora, CA 91741
Ph: (626)914-3200
Free: 800-574-5250
URL: http://www.leonardsguide.com

G2 Computer Intelligence Inc.
11 Danis Ave.
Glen Cove, NY 11542
Ph: (516)759-7025
Free: 877-426-3971
Fax: (516)759-7028
Co. E-mail: news@g2news.com
URL: http://www.g2news.com/

Gallup Press
1251 Ave. of the Americas, 23rd Fl.
New York, NY 10020
URL: http://www.gallup.com/press/gallup-
press.aspx

Gallup
Gallup Bldg.
901 F St. NW
Washington, DC 20004
Ph: (202)715-3030
Fax: (202)715-3045

Gannett Co.
PO Box 357
Granville, OH 43023-0357
Ph: (740)587-3397
Fax: (740)587-3398
Co. E-mail: cpeterson@nncogannett.com
URL: http://www.granvillesentinel.com

Gardner Business Media, Inc.
6915 Valley Ave.
Cincinnati, OH 45244-3029
Ph: (513)527-8800
Free: 800-950-8020
Fax: (513)527-8801
Co. E-mail: orderbooks@gardnerweb.com
URL: http://www.gardnerweb.com

Gasoline and Automotive Service Dealers Association
18 Liberty St 2nd FL
Stamford, CT 06902
Ph: (203)327-4773
Fax: (203)323-6935
Co. E-mail: info@gasda.org

Gay-Lesbian History Stamp Club
PO Box 190842
Dallas, TX 75219-0842

Gazette
500 3rd Ave. SE
Cedar Rapids, IA 52401
Ph: (319)398-8333
Free: 800-397-8333

The Gazette
30 S Prospect St.
Colorado Springs, CO 80903
Ph: (719)632-5511
URL: http://www.gazette.com/

GC Publishing Company Inc.
744 Main St., Rte. 6A
Dennis, MA 02638
Ph: (508)385-7700
Fax: (508)385-0089
Co. E-mail: sgriffin@gccomm.net
URL: http://www.gccomm.net/contact/
index.asp

Gearhead Communications, LLC
Three Research Ctr.
Marion, IA 52302
Ph: (319)447-5550
Free: 877-704-4327
URL: http://www.premierguitar.com/
Privacy.asp

Gebbie Press Inc.
143 Glford Schoolhouse Rd.
New Paltz, NY 12561
Ph: (845)255-7560
Fax: (888)345-2790
Co. E-mail: gebbiepress@pipeline.com
URL: http://www.gebbiepress.com

GemStone Press
Sunset Farms Offices
Rte. 4
Woodstock, VT 05091
Ph: (802)457-4000
Free: 800-962-4544
Fax: (802)457-4004
Co. E-mail: persmissions@gemstone-
press.com
URL: http://www.gemstonepress.com/

Genealogical Institute
56 W Main St.
Tremonton, UT 84337-0129
Ph: (435)257-3185
Free: 800-377-6058
Fax: (435)257-8622
Co. E-mail: arlene@arleneeakle.com
URL: http://arleneeakle.com

Genealogical Publishing Company Inc.
3600 Clipper Mill Rd., Ste. 260
Baltimore, MD 21211
Ph: (410)837-8271
Free: 800-599-9561
Fax: (410)752-8492

Co. E-mail: info@genealogical.com
URL: http://www.genealogical.com

General Books LLC
PO Box 29000, NAS485
Miami, FL 33102
URL: http://www.general-books.net

General Learning Communications
900 Skokie Blvd., Ste. 200
Northbrook, IL 60062-4031
Ph: (847)205-3000
Free: 800-641-3912
Fax: (847)564-8197
Co. E-mail: info@glcomm.com
URL: http://www.glcomm.com

George Brooks
7925 Looking Glass Ct.
Raleigh, NC 27612-7346
Ph: (919)787-4133

George K. Schweitzer
407 Ascot Ct.
Knoxville, TN 37923
Ph: (865)690-7831
URL: http://www.gensources.com/gen-
sources/Prattsite.htm

George W. Southerland
PO Box 4254
Chattanooga, TN 37405-0254
Ph: (423)886-1628
Fax: (423)886-3537

Georgia Tech University
Center for Sports Performance
Atlanta, GA 30332-1009

Gift and Decorative Accessories Center Association
360 Park Ave. S
New York, NY 10010
Ph: (646)746-6400
Free: 800-309-3332
Fax: (646)746-7431
Co. E-mail: gdacustserv@cdsfulfillment.
com
URL: http://www.giftsanddec.com

Gilston-Kalin Communications, LLC
P.O. Box 5325
Rockville, MD 20848-5325
Ph: (202)463-1250
Fax: (301)570-4545

Glass Patterns Quarterly Inc.
8300 Hidden Valley Rd.
Westport, KY 40077-9797
Ph: (502)222-5631
Free: 800-719-0769
Fax: (502)222-4527
Co. E-mail: info@glasspatterns.com
URL: http://www.glasspatterns.com/

Glaucoma Research Foundation
251 Post St., Ste. 600
San Francisco, CA 94108
Ph: (415)986-3162
Free: 800-826-6693
Fax: (415)986-3763
Co. E-mail: tbrunner@glaucoma.org
URL: http://www.glaucoma.org

Global Health Council
PO Box 13469
Baltimore, MD 21203
Co. E-mail: membership@globalhealth.org
URL: http://www.globalhealth.org

Global Sports Productions Ltd.
16810 Crystal Dr. E
Enumclaw, WA 98022-8044
Ph: (310)454-9480
Co. E-mail: globalnw@earthlink.net
URL: http://www.sportsbooksempire.com

Globe Pequot Press
246 Goose Ln.
Guilford, CT 06437
Ph: (203)458-4500
Fax: (203)458-4604
URL: http://www.globepequot.com

The Globe Pequot Press
246 Goose Ln.
Guilford, CT 06437
Ph: (203)458-4500
Free: 888-249-7586
Fax: (203)458-4604
URL: http://www.globepequot.com

Gloucester Publishers
108 E Main St.
Gloucester, MA 01930
Ph: (978)283-3200
Co. E-mail: info@oldhouseinteriors.com
URL: http://www.oldhouseinteriors.com

Gold Leaf Publishing
PO Box 800041
Roswell, GA 30075
Ph: (678)248-3558

Gold Pen Publishing
PO Box 70057
Sunnyvale, CA 95054
Co. E-mail: info@goldenpress.com
URL: http://www.goldenpress.com

Golden Bell Press
2403 Champa St.
Denver, CO 80205
Ph: (303)296-1600
Fax: (303)295-2159
URL: http://www.goldenbellpress.com

Gom Publishing, LLC
6052 Coventry Hurst Ln.
Hilliard, OH 43026
Ph: (614)876-7097
Free: 866-466-2608

Fax: (866)422-8292

Gotham
375 Hudson St.
New York, NY 10014-3657
Ph: (212)366-2933
Free: 800-847-5515
Co. E-mail: academics@us.penguingroup.
com
URL: http://us.penguingroup.com

Gotham/Penguin Group Incorporated
375 Hudson St.
New York, NY 10014
Ph: (212)366-2000
Free: 800-631-8571
Fax: (212)366-2666
Co. E-mail: customerservice@penguinput-
nam.com
URL: http://www.penguinputnam.com

Government Data Publications Inc.
2300 M St., NW
Washington, DC 20037
Ph: (202)627-0819
Free: 800-275-4688
Fax: (202)998-5960
Co. E-mail: gdp@govdata.com
URL: http://www.govdata.com

Government Development Bank for Puerto Rico
PO Box 42001
San Juan, PR 00940-2001
Ph: (787)728-9200
Fax: (787)268-5496
Co. E-mail: gdbcomm@bgf.gobierno.pr

Government Institutes
15200 NBN Way, Bldg. B
Blue Ridge Summit, PA 17214-0191
Ph: (717)794-3800
Free: 800-462-6420
Fax: (717)794-3803
Co. E-mail: orders@rowman.com
URL: http://www.govinstpress.com

Government Printing Office
732 N Capitol St. NW
Washington, DC 20401
Ph: (202)512-1800
Free: 866-512-1800
Fax: (202)512-2104

Government Relations Section
1575 I St. NW
Washington, DC 20005-1103
Ph: (202)371-0940
Fax: (202)371-8315

Graham & Whiteside
Cengage Learning
Cheriton House
North Way Andover
Hampshire SP10 5BE, United Kingdom
Ph: 44 1264 332424
Fax: 44 1264 342763

Co. E-mail: emea.enquiries@cengage.
com
URL: http://gale.cengage.co.uk/graham--
whiteside.aspx

Graham Communications
40 Oval Rd., Ste. 2
Quincy, MA 02170-3813
Ph: (617)328-0069
Fax: (617)471-1504
Co. E-mail: info@grahamcomm.com
URL: http://www.grahamcomm.com/

Grand Central Publishing
237 Park Ave.
New York, NY 10017
Free: 800-759-0190

Grand Central Publishing
1271 Ave. of the Americas
New York, NY 10020
Ph: (212)364-1200
Fax: (800)286-9471
URL: http://www.hachettebookgroup.com

Grand Circle Corporation
85 Main St., Ste. 101
Watertown, MA 02472
URL: http://odysseys-unlimited-catalog.
com

Grandich Publications
PO Box 243
Perrineville, NJ 08535
Ph: (732)642-3992
Fax: (732)446-0960
Co. E-mail: peter@grandich.com
URL: http://www.grandich.com

**Graphic Arts Center Publishing
Company**
PO Box 10306
Portland, OR 97296-0306
Ph: (503)226-2402

**Graphic Communication Conference of
the International Brotherhood of
Teamsters**
25 Louisiana Ave. NW
Washington, DC 20001
Ph: (202)624-6800
Co. E-mail: webmessenger@gciu.org
URL: http://gciu.org/index.shtml

Graphic Dimensions
9065 Taverna Way
Boynton Beach, FL 33472
Ph: (585)381-3428
Fax: (585)385-9723
Co. E-mail: mkleper@printerport.com
URL: http://www.printerport.com/kdp

Graphico Publishing Company
1601 W 5th Ave., Ste. 123
Columbus, OH 43212-2303
Ph: (614)801-9977

Great American Publishing Co.
75 Applewood Dr. Ste. A
Sparta, MI 49345
Ph: (616)887-9008
Fax: (616)887-2666
URL: http://www.fruitgrowersnews.com

Great Lakes Publishing Co.
1422 Euclid Ave., No. 730
Cleveland, OH 44115
Ph: (216)771-2833
Fax: (216)781-6318
Co. E-mail: webmaster@glpublishing.com
URL: http://www.glpublishing.com

**Greater Phoenix Chamber of Com-
merce**
201 N Central Ave., 27th Fl.
Phoenix, AZ 85004
Ph: (602)495-2195
Fax: (602)495-8913
Co. E-mail: info@phoenixchamber.com
URL: http://www.phoenixchamber.com

Green Mountain Coffee
33 Coffee Ln.
Waterbury, VT 05676-1529
Ph: (802)244-5621
Free: 800-223-6768
Fax: (802)244-6565

Greenleaf Book Group Press
4425 S Mo Pac Expy., Ste. 600
Austin, TX 78735
Ph: (512)891-6100

The Greenmoney Journal
PO Box 67
Santa Fe, NM 87504
Ph: (505)988-7423
Co. E-mail: info@greenmoneyjournal.com

Greenpeace U.S.A.
702 H St. NW, Ste. 300
Washington, DC 20001
Ph: (202)462-1177
Free: 800-722-6995
Fax: (202)462-4507
Co. E-mail: info@wdc.greenpeace.org
URL: http://www.greenpeace.org/usa

Greenwood Press
c/o ABC-CLIO
130 Cremona Dr.
Santa Barbara, CA 93117
Ph: (805)968-1911
Free: 800-368-6868
Fax: (866)270-3856
Co. E-mail: customerservice@abc-clio.
com
URL: http://www.abc-clio.com

**Greenwood Publishing Group Inc.
(GPG)**
88 Post Rd. W
Westport, CT 06881
Ph: (203)226-3571

Free: 800-225-5800
Fax: (203)222-1502
Co. E-mail: orders@greenwood.com
URL: http://www.greenwood.com

Greenwood Publishing Group, Inc.
214 Bald Eagle Ln.
Cary, NC 27518-9681
Ph: (203)226-3571
Fax: (203)226-2540

Greenwood Publishing Group, Inc.
PO Box 6926
Portsmouth, NH 03802
Ph: (603)431-2214
Free: 800-225-5800
URL: http://www.greenwood.com/

Greeting Card Association
1133 Westchester Ave., Ste. N136
White Plains, NY 10604-3547
Ph: (914)421-3331
Fax: (914)948-1484
Co. E-mail: gca@gcamail.org
URL: http://www.greetingcard.org/

Greg and Pat Williams
750 Black Lick Rd.
Gravel Switch, KY 40328
Ph: (859)332-7606

Grey House Publishing
4919 Rte. 22
Amenia, NY 12501
Ph: (518)789-8700
Free: 800-562-2139
Fax: (518)789-0556
Co. E-mail: books@greyhouse.com
URL: http://www.greyhouse.com

Grey House Publishing Canada Inc.
555 Richmond St. W, Ste. 301
Toronto, ON, Canada M5V 3B1
Free: 866-433-4739
Fax: (416)644-1904
Co. E-mail: info@greyhouse.ca
URL: http://www.greyhouse.ca

Griffin Publishing Group
18022 Cowan, Ste. 202
Irvine, CA 92614-6811
Free: 800-472-9741

Grimes and Associates
24 Daisy St.
Ladera Ranch, CA 92694
Ph: (949)388-4848
Fax: (949)388-8448
Co. E-mail: info@vowsmagazine.com
URL: http://www.vowsmagazine.com

Group C Communications Inc.
44 Apple St., Ste. 3
Tinton Falls, NJ 07724
Ph: (732)842-7433
Free: 800-524-0337
Fax: (732)758-6634

Co. E-mail: lconnor@groupc.com
URL: http://www.groupc.com

Grove/Atlantic Inc.
841 Broadway, Fl. 4
New York, NY 10003
Ph: (212)614-7850
Free: 800-521-0178
Fax: (212)614-7886
Co. E-mail: info@groveatlantic.com
URL: http://www.groveatlantic.com

Gruner & Jahr USA
350 Fifth Ave., Ste. 4610
New York, NY 10118
Ph: (212)268-3344
Fax: (212)268-3355
Co. E-mail: dustin.guzowski@husonmedia.
com
URL: http://www.gujmedia.com//

Gruner & Jahr USA Publishing
1716 Locust St.
Des Moines, IA 50309-3023
Ph: (515)284-3000
URL: http://www.meredith.com

Gruner & Jahr USA Publishing
375 Lexington Ave.
New York, NY 10017-5514
Ph: (212)499-2000

Guild of Book Workers Inc.
521 5th Ave.
New York, NY 10175-0038
Ph: (212)757-6454
Co. E-mail: secretary@guildofbookwork-
ers.org
URL: http://www.guildofbookworkers.org

H

H.H. Backer Associates Inc.
18 S Michigan Ave., Ste. 1100
Chicago, IL 60603
Ph: (312)578-1818
Fax: (312)578-1819
Co. E-mail: hhbacker@hhbacker.com
URL: http://www.hhbacker.com/

H.I.C. Corp.
38 Executive Park Ste. 300
Irvine, CA 92614-6755
Ph: (949)261-1636
URL: http://www.heavydutytrucking.com

The H.W. Wilson Co.
950 University Ave.
Bronx, NY 10452
Ph: (718)588-8400
Free: 800-367-6770
Fax: (718)590-1617
Co. E-mail: custserv@hwwilson.com
URL: http://www.hwwilson.com

Hachette Filipacchi Media U.S. Inc.
1271 Ave. of the Americas
New York, NY 10020
Ph: (212)649-4115
Free: 800-544-6748
Fax: (212)767-5612
Co. E-mail: jdeval@hearst.com
URL: http://www.hearst.com/

Hagedorn Communications
PO Box 680
New Rochelle, NY 10801
Ph: (914)636-7400
Fax: (914)636-2957
URL: http://www.rew-online.com

Halle House Publishing
5966 Halle Farm Dr.
Willoughby, OH 44094-3076
Ph: (440)585-8687

Halper Publishing Co.
210 Skokie Valley Rd., Ste. 4
Highland Park, IL 60035
Free: 877-415-3300
Fax: (847)780-2902
Co. E-mail: info@halper.com
URL: http://www.halper.com/

Hanley Wood L.L.C.
1 Thomas Cir. NW, Ste. 600
Washington, DC 20005
Ph: (202)452-0800
Free: 877-275-8647
Fax: (202)785-1974
Co. E-mail: hwmicustomerservice@han-
leywood.com
URL: http://www.hwmarketintelligence.com

Happy About
20660 Stevens Creek Blvd., Ste. 210
Cupertino, CA 95014
Ph: (408)257-3000
Co. E-mail: questions@happyabout.com
URL: http://www.happyabout.com

Hardwood Plywood and Veneer Association
1825 Michael Faraday Dr.
Reston, VA 20190
Ph: (703)435-2900
Fax: (703)435-2537
Co. E-mail: hpva@hpva.org
URL: http://www.hpva.org

Harper Associates Inc.
PO Box 50
Sun Valley, ID 83353-0050
Ph: (208)622-3183
Free: 800-235-9622
Fax: (208)622-2716
Co. E-mail: harper@andrewharpertravel.
com

Harper Business
10 E 53rd St.
New York, NY 10022
Ph: (212)207-7969
Free: 800-242-7737
Fax: (212)207-6961
Co. E-mail: harperbiz@harpercollins.com
URL: http://www.harpercollins.com

Harper Press
10 E 53rd St.
New York, NY 10022
Ph: (212)207-7000
Free: 800-242-7737
Co. E-mail: orders@harpercollins.com
URL: http://www.harpercollins.com

Harperaudio
10 E 53rd St.
New York, NY 10022
Ph: (212)207-7969
Co. E-mail: kyran.cassidy@harpercollins.
com
URL: http://www.harpercollins.com/
templates.asp?page=privacypolicy

HarperBusiness
10 E 53rd St.
New York, NY 10022
Ph: (212)207-7000
Free: 800-242-7737
Co. E-mail: orders@harpercollins.com
URL: http://www.harpercollins.com

HarperCollins
10 E 53rd St.
New York, NY 10022
Ph: (212)207-7000
Free: 800-242-7737
Fax: (212)207-7909
Co. E-mail: orders@harpercollins.com
URL: http://www.harpercollins.com

HarperCollins Publishers Inc.
10 E 53rd St.
New York, NY 10022
Ph: (212)207-7791
Fax: (212)207-7902
URL: http://www.harpercollins.com

HarperInformation
10 E 53rd St.
New York, NY 10022-5299
Ph: (212)207-7000
Free: 800-242-7737
Fax: (800)822-4090

HarperOne
10 E 53rd St.
New York, NY 10022
Ph: (212)207-7000
Free: 800-242-7737
Co. E-mail: orders@harpercollins.com
URL: http://www.harpercollins.com

HarperStudio/HarperCollins
10 E 53rd St.
New York, NY 10022
Ph: (212)207-7000
Free: 800-242-7737
Fax: (212)207-7145
URL: http://www.harpercollins.com

Harris InfoSource
2057 E Aurora Rd.
Twinsburg, OH 44087-1999
Ph: (330)425-9000
Free: 800-888-5900
Fax: (800)643-5997
Co. E-mail: customerservice@harrisinfo.
com
URL: http://www.harrisinfo.com

Harris Publications Inc.
1115 Broadway
New York, NY 10010
Ph: (212)807-7100
Fax: (212)924-8416

Harris Publishing Inc.
360 B St.
Idaho Falls, ID 83402
Ph: (208)524-7000
Free: 800-638-0135
Fax: (208)522-5241
Co. E-mail: customerservice@harrispub-
lishing.com
URL: http://www.harrispublishing.com

Harrison Scott Publications Inc.
5 Marine View Plz., Ste. 400
Hoboken, NJ 07030
Ph: (201)659-1700
Free: 800-283-9363
Fax: (201)659-4141
Co. E-mail: info@hspnews.com

Harvard Business Press
300 N Beacon St.
Watertown, MA 02472
Ph: (617)783-7600
Free: 800-545-7685
Fax: (617)783-7666
Co. E-mail: custserv@hbsp.harvard.edu
URL: http://hbsp.harvard.edu

Harvard Business School (HBS)
Soldiers Field Rd.
Boston, MA 02163
Ph: (617)495-1003
Fax: (617)495-0594
Co. E-mail: wfriedman@hbs.edu
URL: http://www.hbs.edu

Harvard Business School Press
60 Harvard Way
Boston, MA 02163
Co. E-mail: permissions@hbsp.harvard.
edu
URL: http://www.harvard.edu

Harvard Business School Press
300 N Beacon St.
Watertown, MA 02472
Ph: (617)783-7500
Free: 800-988-0886
Fax: (617)783-7555
Co. E-mail: corpcustserv@hbsp.harvard.
edu
URL: http://www.hbsp.harvard.edu

Harvard Business School Publishing
60 Harvard Way
Boston, MA 02163
Co. E-mail: permissions@hbsp.harvard.
edu
URL: http://www.harvard.edu

Harvard Business School Publishing
300 N Beacon St.
Watertown, MA 02472
Ph: (617)783-7500
Free: 800-988-0886
Fax: (617)783-7555
Co. E-mail: corpcustserv@hbsp.harvard.
edu
URL: http://www.hbsp.harvard.edu

Harvey W. Watt & Company Inc.
PO Box 20787
Atlanta, GA 30320
Ph: (404)767-7501
Free: 800-241-6103
Fax: (404)761-8326
Co. E-mail: pilot@harveywatt.com

Hatton-Brown Publishers Inc.
225 Hanrick St.
Montgomery, AL 36102
Ph: (334)834-1170
Free: 800-669-5613
Fax: (334)834-4525
Co. E-mail: dianne@hattonbrown.com
URL: http://www.hattonbrown.net

Hawaii Business Publishing
1000 Bishop St., Ste. 405
Honolulu, HI 96813
Ph: (808)537-9500
Fax: (808)537-6455

Haymarket Group Ltd.
12 W 37th St., 9th fl.
New York, NY 10018
Ph: (212)239-0855
Fax: (212)967-4184
URL: http://www.pastryartanddesign.com/

Haymarket Media Inc.
114 W 26th St., 4th Fl.
New York, NY 10001
Ph: (646)638-6000
Fax: (646)638-6110

Haymarket Media, Inc.
25 Philips Pkwy., Ste. 105
Montvale, NJ 07645
Ph: (201)505-9730

Hazelden Foundation
PO Box 11
Center City, MN 55012-0011
Ph: (651)213-4200
Free: 800-257-7810
Fax: (651)213-4411
Co. E-mail: info@hazelden.org
URL: http://www.hazelden.org

HCM Publishing
c/o Mapletree Publishing
6233 Howard Ln.
Highland Ranch, CO 80130-3773
Ph: (303)791-9024
Free: 800-537-0414
Fax: (303)791-9028

Healing Ministry of Catholic Health Care
4455 Woodson Rd.
Saint Louis, MO 63134
Ph: (314)427-2500
Free: 800-230-7823
Fax: (314)427-0029
Co. E-mail: servicecenter@chausa.org
URL: http://www.chausa.org

Health Administration Press
1 N Franklin St., Ste. 1700
Chicago, IL 60606-3529
Ph: (312)424-2800
Fax: (312)424-0023
Co. E-mail: geninfo@ache.org
URL: http://www.ache.org/hap.cfm

Health Care Financing Administration U.S. Department of Health & Human Service
200 Independence Ave. SW
Washington, DC 20201
Ph: (202)619-0257
Free: 877-696-6775
URL: http://www.os.dhhs.gov/about/opdivs/
hcfa.html

Health Communications, Inc. (HCI)
3201 SW 15th St.
Deerfield Beach, FL 33442
Ph: (954)360-0909
Free: 800-441-5569
Fax: (954)360-0034
Co. E-mail: doreenh@hcibooks.com
URL: http://www.hcibooks.com

Health Forum L.L.C.
155 N Wacker Dr., Ste. 400
Chicago, IL 60606
Ph: (312)893-6800
Free: 800-821-2039
Fax: (312)422-4500
URL: http://www.healthforum.com

Health Resources Publishing
1913 Atlantic Ave., Ste. 200
Manasquan, NJ 08736
Ph: (732)292-1100
Free: 800-516-4343

Fax: (732)292-1111
Co. E-mail: hrp@healthrespubs.com
URL: http://www.healthrespubs.com/

Healthcare Convention and Exhibitors Association
1100 Johnson Ferry Rd., Ste. 300
Atlanta, GA 30342
Ph: (404)252-3663
Fax: (404)252-0774
Co. E-mail: hcea@kellencompany.com
URL: http://www.hcea.org

Heart of America Genealogical Society
PO Box 481727
Kansas City, MO 64148-1727
Ph: (816)701-3445

Heartland Communications Group Inc.
1003 Central Ave., Ste. 1052
Fort Dodge, IA 50501
Ph: (515)955-1600
Free: 800-247-2000
Fax: (515)955-1668
Co. E-mail: sales@hlipublishing.com
URL: http://www.hlipublishing.com

Heavy Duty Representatives Association
160 Symphony Way
Elgin, IL 60120
Ph: (847)760-0067
Co. E-mail: bill.wade@wade-partners.com
URL: http://www.hdra.org

Heldref Publications
325 Chestnut St., Ste. 800
Philadelphia, PA 19106
Ph: (215)625-8900
Free: 800-354-1420
Co. E-mail: customer.service@taylorand-
   francis.com
URL: http://www.heldref.org

Hemmings Motor News
222 W Main St.
Bennington, VT 05201
Ph: (802)442-3101
Free: 800-227-4373
Fax: (802)447-9631
Co. E-mail: hmnmail@hemmings.com
URL: http://www.hemmings.com

Hemophilia Ontario
45 Charles St. E, Ste. 708
Toronto, ON, Canada M4Y 1S2
Ph: (416)972-0641
Free: 888-838-8846
Fax: (416)972-0307
Co. E-mail: info@hemophilia.on.ca

Henry Holt & Company
115 W 18th St., 5th Fl.
New York, NY 10011
Ph: (212)886-9200
Fax: (212)633-0748
Co. E-mail: info@hholt.com

URL: http://www.henryholt.com

Henry Holt and Co.
175 5th Ave.
New York, NY 10010-7703
Ph: (646)307-5095
Free: 888-330-8477
Fax: (212)633-0748
Co. E-mail: publicity@hholt.com
URL: http://us.macmillan.com/HenryHolt.
   aspx

Herb Growing and Marketing Network
PO Box 245
Silver Spring, PA 17575-0245
Ph: (717)393-3295
Fax: (717)393-9261
Co. E-mail: herbworld@aol.com
URL: http://www.herbworld.com

Herb Society of America
9019 Kirtland Chardon Rd.
Kirtland, OH 44094
Ph: (440)256-0514
Fax: (440)256-0541
Co. E-mail: herbs@herbsociety.org
URL: http://www.herbsociety.org

Heritage Books Inc.
5810 Ruatan St.
Berwyn Heights, MD 20740
Ph: (410)876-6101
Free: 800-876-6103
Fax: (410)558-6574
Co. E-mail: info@heritagebooks.com
URL: http://www.heritagebooks.com

Hiaring Co.
1800 Lincoln Ave.
San Rafael, CA 94901-1298
Ph: (415)453-9700
Free: 866-453-9701
Fax: (415)453-2517
Co. E-mail: info@winesandvines.com
URL: http://www.winesandvines.com

Hideaways International
767 Islington St.
Portsmouth, NH 03801
Ph: (603)430-4433
Free: 800-843-4433
Fax: (603)430-4444
Co. E-mail: info@hideaways.com
URL: http://hideaways.com

HighBeam Research
65 E Wacker Pl., Ste. 400
Chicago, IL 60601
Ph: (312)782-3900
Fax: (312)782-3901

HighBeam Research
c/o Cengage Learning
1 N State St., Ste. 900
Chicago, IL 60602
Free: 800-860-9227

Highway Safety Research Center
CB No. 3430
CB 3430
Chapel Hill, NC 27599
Ph: (919)962-2202
Fax: (919)962-8710

Hispanic Business Inc.
425 Pine Ave.
Santa Barbara, CA 93117-3709
Ph: (805)964-4554
Fax: (805)964-5539
URL: http://www.hispanicbusiness.com

Hispanic Business
425 Pine Ave.
Santa Barbara, CA 93117-3709
Ph: (805)964-4554
Free: 800-957-9724
Fax: (805)964-5539

Historical Trends Corp.
69A 7th Ave.
Brooklyn, NY 11217
Ph: (718)636-0788
Fax: (718)636-0750
Co. E-mail: htcstaff@traditional-building.
   com

Hobby Publications Inc.
207 Commercial Ct.
Morganville, NJ 07751-1070
Ph: (732)536-5160
Free: 800-969-7176
Fax: (732)536-5761
Co. E-mail: info@hobbymerchandiser.com
URL: http://www.hobbypub.com

Home Furnishings Retailer
3910 Tinsley Dr., Ste. 101
High Point, NC 27265
Ph: (336)886-6100
Free: 800-888-9590
Fax: (336)801-6102
Co. E-mail: info@nhfa.org
URL: http://www.nhfa.org/

The Home Shop Machinist
PO Box 629
Traverse City, MI 49685
Free: 800-447-7367
URL: http://www.homeshopmachinist.net/

Home-Based Working Moms
PO Box 500164
Austin, TX 78750-0164
Ph: (281)757-2207
Co. E-mail: hbwm@hbwm.com

Homeworkers Organized for More Employment
PO Box 10
Orland, ME 04472
Ph: (207)469-7961
Fax: (207)469-1023
Co. E-mail: info@homecoop.net
URL: http://www.homecoop.net

Horizon Publishing Company L.L.C.
7412 Calumet Ave.
Hammond, IN 46324
Ph: (219)852-3200
Free: 800-233-5922
Fax: (219)931-6487
URL: http://www.horizonpublishing.com/

The Horn Book Inc.
56 Roland St., Ste. 200
Boston, MA 02129
Ph: (617)628-0225
Free: 800-325-1170
Fax: (617)628-0882
Co. E-mail: info@hbook.com
URL: http://www.hbook.com

Horticultural Data Processors
PO Box 489
New York, NY 10028

Horticultural Research Institute
1200 G St. NW, Ste. 800
Washington, DC 20005
Ph: (202)789-2900
Fax: (888)761-7883
Co. E-mail: tjodon@hriresearch.org
URL: http://www.hriresearch.org

Hot To Books Ltd.
3 Newtec Pl.
Magdalen Rd.
Oxford OX4 1RE, United Kingdom
Ph: 44 1865 793806
Fax: 44 1865 248780
Co. E-mail: info@howtobooks.co.uk
URL: http://www.howtobooks.co.uk

Hotel & Travel Index International Edition Northstar Travel Group
100 Lightning Way
Secaucus, NJ 07094-3626
Ph: (201)902-2000
Fax: (201)902-2034
Co. E-mail: tweditorial@ntmllc.com
URL: http://www.travelweekly.com/ManualPages.aspx?id=4834

Houghton Mifflin Books
222 Berkeley St.
Boston, MA 02116
Ph: (617)351-3101
Free: 800-597-6127
Fax: (617)351-1185
Co. E-mail: trade_specialsales@hmco.com
URL: http://www.houghtonmifflinbooks.com

Houghton Mifflin
222 Berkeley St.
Boston, MA 02116
Ph: (617)351-5000
URL: http://www.hmco.com/

Houghton Mifflin College Division
222 Berkeley St.
Boston, MA 02116-3764
Ph: (617)351-5000

Houghton Mifflin Company
222 Berkeley St.
Boston, MA 02116-3764
Ph: (617)351-5000

Houghton Mifflin Harcourt
222 Berkeley St.
Boston, MA 02116-3748
Ph: (617)351-5000
Free: 800-225-1464
Fax: (617)351-1105
Co. E-mail: investors@hmhpub.com
URL: http://www.hmhco.com

House of White Birches
306 E Parr Rd.
Berne, IN 46711-1138
Ph: (260)589-4000
Fax: (260)589-8093
URL: http://drgnetwork.com

Houston Chronicle
PO Box 4260
Houston, TX 77210
Ph: (713)362-7171
Fax: (713)362-3575

Houston Chronicle Publishing Company
PO Box 4260
Houston, TX 77210-4260
Ph: (713)362-7171
Fax: (713)362-3575

How To Books
Spring Hill House
Spring Hill Rd.
Oxford 0X5 1RX, United Kingdom
Ph: (440) 1865375794
Fax: (440) 1865379162
URL: http://www.howtobooks.co.uk

How To Books
3 Newtec Pl.
Magdalen Rd.
Oxford OX4 1RE, United Kingdom
Ph: 44 18 65793806
Fax: 44 18 65248780

Hudson River Sloop Clearwater Inc.
112 Little Market St.
Poughkeepsie, NY 12601
Ph: (845)454-7673
Free: 800-67-SLOOP
Fax: (845)454-7953
Co. E-mail: office@clearwater.org
URL: http://www.Clearwater.org

Hulbert Financial Digest
PO Box 300
Princeton, NJ 08543
Ph: (866)428-6568

Co. E-mail: orders@marketwatch.com

Human Factors and Ergonomics Society
1124 Montana Ave., Ste. B
Santa Monica, CA 90403-1617
Ph: (310)394-1811
Fax: (310)394-2410
Co. E-mail: info@hfes.org
URL: http://www.hfes.org

Hunt Personnel Ltd.
1050 Wall St. W, Ste. 330
Lyndhurst, NJ 07071-3615
Ph: (201)438-8200
Fax: (201)438-8372

Hunterdon County Historical Society
114 Main St.
Flemington, NJ 08822
Ph: (908)782-1091

Huntington Press
3687 S Procyon Ave.
Las Vegas, NV 89103-1907
Ph: (702)252-0655
Free: 800-244-2224
Fax: (702)252-0675
Co. E-mail: customerservice@huntington-press.com
URL: http://www.huntingtonpress.com

Hyperion Books
77 W 66th St., 11th Fl.
New York, NY 10023
Ph: (212)633-4400
Free: 800-242-7737
Fax: (800)822-4090

Hyperion
114 5th Ave.
New York, NY 10011
Free: 800-242-7737
Fax: (800)822-4090
URL: http://www.hyperionbooks.com

Hyperion
77 W 66th St., 11th Fl.
New York, NY 10023
Free: 800-242-7737
Fax: (800)822-4090
URL: http://www.hyperionbooks.com

Hyperion Press
77 W 66th St., 11th Fl.
New York, NY 10023-6298
Ph: (212)456-0100
Fax: (212)456-0108

Hyperion Special Markets
77 W 66th St., 11th Fl.
New York, NY 10023
Ph: (212)456-0100

I

I.T. Financial Management Association
PO Box 30188
Santa Barbara, CA 93130
Ph: (805)687-7390

Fax: (805)687-7382
Co. E-mail: info@itfma.com
URL: http://www.itfma.com

IAPMO
5001 E Philadelphia St.
Ontario, CA 91761-2816
Ph: (909)472-4100
Free: 800-854-2766
Fax: (909)472-4150
Co. E-mail: iapmo@iapmo.org
URL: http://www.iapmo.org

ICD Publications
45 Research Way, Ste. 106
East Setauket, NY 11733
Ph: (631)246-9300
Fax: (631)246-9496
Co. E-mail: info@hotelbusiness.com
URL: http://www.homeworldbusiness.com

Ice Cream Reporter
7 Hilton Terr.
Willsboro, NY 12996
Ph: (518)963-4333
Fax: (518)963-4999

Ice Skating Institute
6000 Custer Rd., Bldg. 9
Plano, TX 75023
Ph: (972)735-8800
Fax: (972)735-8815
Co. E-mail: isi@skateisi.org
URL: http://www.skateisi.org

ICON Inc.
211 S 45th St.
Philadelphia, PA 19104
Ph: (215)349-6500
Fax: (215)349-6502
Co. E-mail: wasterec@icon-info.com

Idaho Business Review
855 W Broad St., Ste. 103
Boise, ID 83702
Ph: (208)336-3768
Fax: (208)336-5534
URL: http://idahobusinessreview.com/

Idea Group Publishing
701 E Chocolate Ave., Ste. 200
Hershey, PA 17033
Ph: (717)533-8845
Fax: (717)533-8661

IDEA Inc.
10455 Pacific Center Ct.
San Diego, CA 92121-4339
Ph: (858)535-8979
Free: 800-999-4332
Fax: (858)535-8234
Co. E-mail: contact@ideafit.com
URL: http://www.ideafit.com

Ideal Media
90 Broad St., Ste. 402
New York, NY 10004
Ph: (646)708-7327
Fax: (646)708-7399

IGI Global
701 E Chocolate Ave., Ste. 200
Hershey, PA 17033
Ph: (717)533-8845
Fax: (717)533-7115
URL: http://www.igi-global.com

Illinois Landscape Contractor Association
2625 Butterfield Rd., Ste. 204-W
Oak Brook, IL 60523
Ph: (630)472-2851
Fax: (630)472-3150
Co. E-mail: information@ilca.net
URL: http://www.ilca.net

Illinois State Genealogical Society
PO Box 10195
Springfield, IL 62791-0195
Ph: (217)789-1968
Co. E-mail: isgsoffice@a5.com
URL: http://www.rootsweb.ancestry.com/
ilsgs/

Illuminating Engineering Society of North America
120 Wall St., 17th Fl.
New York, NY 10005-4001
Ph: (212)248-5000
Fax: (212)248-5017
Co. E-mail: ies@ies.org
URL: http://www.iesna.org

IMAS Publishing Inc.
810 7th Ave., 27th Fl.
New York, NY 10019
Ph: (212)378-0400
Fax: (212)378-0470
URL: http://www.imaspub.com

iMoneyNet Inc.
1 Research Dr.
Westborough, MA 01581-5193
Ph: (508)616-6600
Free: 800-343-5413
Fax: (508)616-5511
Co. E-mail: info@imoneynet.com
URL: http://www.ibcdata.com

Impact Publications
9104 Manassas Dr., Ste. N
Manassas Park, VA 20111
Ph: (703)361-7300
Fax: (703)335-9486
Co. E-mail: query@impactpublications.
com
URL: http://www.impactpublications.com

Imperial College Press
Imperial College
London SW7 2BT, United Kingdom
Ph: 44 20 75949568
Fax: 44 20 75892790

Inc. Magazine
477 Madison Ave.
New York, NY 10022
Ph: (212)326-2600

Incisive Media
120 Broadway, 5th Fl.
New York, NY 10271
Ph: (212)457-9400
Fax: (646)417-7705
Co. E-mail: customerservices@incisiveme-
dia.com
URL: http://www.incisivemedia.com

Independent Book Publishers Association
1020 Manhattan Beach Blvd., Ste. 204
Manhattan Beach, CA 90266
Ph: (310)546-1818
Fax: (310)546-3939
Co. E-mail: info@ibpa-online.org
URL: http://www.pma-online.org

Independent Computer Consultants Association
11131 S Towne Sq., Ste. F
Saint Louis, MO 63123
Ph: (314)892-1675
Free: 800-774-4222
Fax: (314)487-1345
Co. E-mail: info@icca.org

Independent Electrical Contractors Inc.
4401 Ford Ave., Ste. 1100
Alexandria, VA 22302-1432
Ph: (703)549-7351
Free: 800-456-4324
Fax: (703)549-7448
Co. E-mail: info@ieci.org
URL: http://www.ieci.org

Independent Lubricant Manufacturers Association
400 N Columbus St., Ste. 201
Alexandria, VA 22314-2264
Ph: (703)684-5574
Fax: (703)836-8503
Co. E-mail: ilma@ilma.org
URL: http://www.ilma.org

Indiana Association of Plumbing, Heating, Cooling Contractors
c/o Brenda A. Dant, CAE
9595 Whitley Dr., Ste. 208
Indianapolis, IN 46240
Ph: (317)575-9292
Free: 888-717-4835
Fax: (317)575-9378
Co. E-mail: bradisley@isleyplumbing.com
URL: http://www.iaphcc.com

Indiana Historical Society Press
450 W Ohio St.
Indianapolis, IN 46202-3269
Ph: (317)232-1882
Free: 800-447-1830
Fax: (317)234-0427
Co. E-mail: ihspress@indianahistory.org
URL: http://www.indianahistory.org/

Indiana University Press
601 N Morton St.
Bloomington, IN 47404-3797
Ph: (812)855-8817
Free: 800-842-6796
Fax: (812)855-7931
Co. E-mail: iupress@indiana.edu
URL: http://www.iupress.indiana.edu/

Indianapolis Business Journal Corporation
41 E Washington St., Ste. 200
Indianapolis, IN 46204-3592
Ph: (317)634-6200
Fax: (317)263-5060

Industrial Fabrics Association International
1801 County Rd. B W
Roseville, MN 55113-4061
Ph: (651)222-2508
Free: 800-225-4324
Fax: (651)631-9334
Co. E-mail: generalinfo@ifai.com
URL: http://www.ifai.com

Industrial Relations Center
Gregg M. Sinclair Library
2425 Campus Rd.
Honolulu, HI 96822
Ph: (808)956-8132
Fax: (808)956-3609
Co. E-mail: uhirc@hawaii.edu

Industry Publications Inc.
3621 Hill Rd.
Parsippany, NJ 07054
Ph: (973)331-9545610

Infinity Publishing
1094 New Dehaven St., Ste. 100
West Conshohocken, PA 19424
Ph: (610)941-9999
Fax: (610)941-9959
URL: http://www.infinitypublishing.com

Infocom Group
124 Linden St.
Oakland, CA 94607
Ph: (510)596-9300
Free: 800-959-1059
Fax: (510)596-9331
URL: http://www.bulldogreporter.com/

Informa Healthcare
52 Vanderbilt Ave., 7th Fl.
New York, NY 10017-3846
Ph: (212)520-2777

Co. E-mail: healthcare.enquiries@informa.
   com
URL: http://informahealthcare.com

Informa Publishing Group
BioTechniques
One Research Dr. Ste. 400A
Westborough, MA 01581
Ph: (508)614-1414
Fax: (508)616-2930
URL: http://www.informa.com

Information Age Publishing
PO Box 79049
Charlotte, NC 28271-7047
Ph: (704)752-9125
Fax: (704)752-9113
URL: http://www.infoagepub.com

Information Gatekeepers Inc.
1340 Soldiers Field Rd., Ste. 2
Boston, MA 02135
Ph: (617)782-5033
Free: 800-323-1088
Fax: (617)782-5735
Co. E-mail: info@igigroup.com
URL: http://www.igigroup.com

Information Gatekeepers Inc.
320 Washington St., Ste. 302
Brighton, MA 02135
Ph: (617)782-5033
Free: 800-323-1088
Fax: (617)782-5735
Co. E-mail: info@igigroup.com
URL: http://www.igigroup.com

Information Today Inc.
143 Old Marlton Pke.
Medford, NJ 08055
Ph: (609)654-6266
Free: 800-300-9868
Fax: (609)654-4309

infoUSA Inc.
5711 S 86th Cir.
Omaha, NE 68127-0347
Ph: (402)593-4500
Free: 800-321-0869
Fax: (402)331-1505
Co. E-mail: internet@abii.com
URL: http://www.infousa.com

InfoWorld Media Group
501 2nd St.
San Francisco, CA 94107
Free: 800-227-8365
Co. E-mail: feedback@infoworld.com
URL: http://www.infoworld.com/

Inn Room Visitors Magazine
1400 Quail St., Ste. 138
Newport Beach, CA 92660
Ph: (949)833-2550
Free: 888-990-6901
Fax: (949)833-3505

Inside Mortgage Finance Publications Inc.
7910 Woodmont Ave., Ste. 1000
Bethesda, MD 20814
Ph: (301)951-1240
Fax: (301)656-1709
Co. E-mail: service@imfpubs.com
URL: http://www.imfpubs.com/

Inside Washington Publishers
1225 S. Clark St., Ste. 1400
Ben Franklin Sta.
Arlington, VA 22202
Ph: (703)416-8500
Free: 800-424-9068
Fax: (703)415-8543
Co. E-mail: custsvc@iwpnews.com
URL: http://www.iwpnews.com

INSIGHT Into Diversity
c/o Potomac Publishing, Inc.
225 Meramec Ave., Ste. 400
Saint Louis, MO 63105
Ph: (314)863-2900
Free: 800-537-0655
Fax: (314)863-2905
Co. E-mail: info@aarjobs.com
URL: http://www.insightintodiversity.com/

Institute for Supply Management
PO Box 22160
Tempe, AZ 85285-2160
Ph: (480)752-6276
Free: 800-888-6276
Fax: (480)752-7890
URL: http://www.ism.ws

Institute of Business Appraisers
6950 Cypress Rd.
Plantation, FL 33317-2370
Ph: (954)584-1144
Free: 800-299-4130
Fax: (954)584-1184
Co. E-mail: hqiba@go-iba.org
URL: http://www.go-iba.org

Institute of Business Appraisers
PO Box 17410
Plantation, FL 33318
Ph: (954)584-1144
Free: 800-299-4130
Fax: (954)584-1184
Co. E-mail: ibahq@go-iba.org
URL: http://www.go-iba.org

Institute of Electrical and Electronics Engineers Inc.
3 Park Ave., 17th Fl.
New York, NY 10016-5997
Ph: (212)705-8900
Free: 800-678-4333
Fax: (212)705-8999
Co. E-mail: society@comsoc.org
URL: http://www.comsoc.org

Institute of Governmental Studies
109 Moses Hall, Ste. 2370
Berkeley, CA 94720-2370
Ph: (510)642-1474
Fax: (510)642-3020
Co. E-mail: igspress@uclink4.berkeley.edu
URL: http://www.igs.berkeley.edu

Institute of Industrial Engineers
3377 Parkway Ln., Ste. 200
Norcross, GA 30092
Ph: (770)449-0460
Free: 800-494-0460
Fax: (770)441-3295
Co. E-mail: executiveoffices@iienet.org
URL: http://www.iienet2.org

Institute of Management & Administration
1 Washington Park, Ste. 1300
Newark, NJ 07102-3130
Ph: (973)718-4700
Free: 800-401-5937
Fax: (973)622-0595

Institute of Museum & Library Services
1800 M St. NW, 9th Fl.
Washington, DC 20036-5802
Ph: (202)653-4657
Fax: (202)653-4600
Co. E-mail: imlsinfo@imls.gov
URL: http://www.imls.gov

Institute of Public Administration of Canada
1075 Bay St., Ste. 401
Toronto, ON, Canada M5S 2B1
Ph: (416)924-8787
Fax: (416)924-4992
Co. E-mail: rtaylor@ipac.ca
URL: http://www.ipac.ca

Institute of Real Estate Management
430 N Michigan Ave.
Chicago, IL 60611-4090
Ph: (312)329-6000
Free: 800-837-0706
Fax: (800)338-4736
Co. E-mail: custserv@irem.org
URL: http://www.irem.org

Institute of Scrap Recycling Industries
1615 L St. NW, Ste. 600
Washington, DC 20036-5610
Ph: (202)662-8500
Fax: (202)626-0900
Co. E-mail: robinwiener@isri.org
URL: http://www.isri.org

Institutional Investor
225 Park Ave. S, 8th Fl.
New York, NY 10003-1604
Ph: (212)224-3300
URL: http://www.institutionalinvestor.com/

Institutional Real Estate Inc.
2274 Camino Ramon
San Ramon, CA 94583
Ph: (925)244-0500
Fax: (925)244-0520
Co. E-mail: g.dohrmann@irei.com
URL: http://www.irei.com

Instrumentalist Co.
200 Northfield Rd.
Northfield, IL 60093
Ph: (847)446-5000
Free: 888-446-6888
Fax: (847)446-6263
Co. E-mail: advertising@theinstrumental-ist.com
URL: http://www.instrumentalistmagazine.com

Insurance Forum Inc.
PO Box 245
Ellettsville, IN 47429-0245
Ph: (812)876-6502
Free: 888-876-9590

Insurance Institute of Southern Alberta
150, 707 Tenth Ave. SW
Calgary, AB, Canada T2R 0B3
Ph: (403)266-3427
Fax: (403)269-3199
Co. E-mail: genmail@iisalberta.org

Insurance Marketing and Management Services
17280 Newhope St., Ste. 15
Fountain Valley, CA 92708
Ph: (800)753-4467
Free: 800-753-4467
Fax: (714)242-0213
Co. E-mail: sales@imms.com
URL: http://www.imms.com/

Integrated Research Services Inc.
66 Club Rd., Ste. 370
Eugene, OR 97401
Ph: (541)683-9278
Free: 800-929-2955
Fax: (541)683-2621

International Advertising Association
275 Madison Ave., Ste. 2102
New York, NY 10016
Ph: (212)557-1133
Fax: (212)983-0455
Co. E-mail: membership@iaaglobal.org
URL: http://www.iaaglobal.org

International Association of Electrical Inspectors
PO Box 830848
Richardson, TX 75083-0848
Ph: (972)235-1455
Free: 800-786-4234
Fax: (972)235-6858
Co. E-mail: iaei@iaei.org
URL: http://www.iaei.org

International Association of Financial Crimes Investigators
1020 Suncast Ln., Ste. 102
El Dorado Hills, CA 95762
Ph: (916)939-5000
Fax: (916)939-0395
Co. E-mail: admin@iafci.org
URL: http://www.iafci.org

International Association of Venue Managers
635 Fritz Dr., Ste. 100
Coppell, TX 75019-4442
Ph: (972)906-7441
Free: 800-935-4226
Fax: (972)906-7418
Co. E-mail: vicki.hawarden@iavm.org
URL: http://www.iavm.org

International Bottled Water Association
1700 Diagonal Rd., Ste. 650
Alexandria, VA 22314
Ph: (703)683-5213
Free: 800-WATER-11
Fax: (703)683-4074
Co. E-mail: ibwainfo@bottledwater.org
URL: http://www.bottledwater.org

International Brotherhood of Magicians
13 Point West Blvd.
Saint Charles, MO 63301-4431
Ph: (636)724-2400
Fax: (636)724-8566
Co. E-mail: office@magician.org
URL: http://www.magician.org/

International Business Affairs Corp.
5523 Brige Dr
Bethesda, MD 20817
Ph: (301)907-8647
Fax: (301)907-8650

International Business Machines Corp.
1 New Orchard Rd.
Armonk, NY 10504-1722
Ph: (914)499-1900
Free: 800-426-4968
Fax: (914)945-2018
Co. E-mail: info@ibm.com
URL: http://www.ibm.com

International Cinematographers Guild
7755 Sunset Blvd.
Los Angeles, CA 90046
Ph: (323)876-0160
Fax: (323)876-6383
URL: http://www.cameraguild.com

International City/County Management Association
777 N Capitol St., NE, Ste. 500
Washington, DC 20002-4201
Ph: (202)289-4262
Free: 800-745-8780
Fax: (202)962-3500
Co. E-mail: ldanielpour@icma.org
URL: http://www.icma.org

International Code Council
500 New Jersey Ave. NW, 6th Fl.
Washington, DC 20001-2070
Ph: (202)370-1800
Free: 888-422-7233
Fax: (202)783-2348
Co. E-mail: webmaster@iccsafe.org
URL: http://www.iccsafe.org

International Code Council
5360 Workman Mill Rd.
Whittier, CA 90601
Ph: (562)699-0543
Free: 800-423-6587
Fax: (562)695-4694
URL: http://www.icbo.org

International Commission for the Prevention of Alcoholism and Drug Dependency
12501 Old Columbia Pke.
Silver Spring, MD 20904
Ph: (301)680-6719
Fax: (301)680-6707
Co. E-mail: landlessp@gc.adventist.org

International Council on Hotel, Restaurant, and Institutional Education
2810 N Parham Rd., Ste. 230
Richmond, VA 23294
Ph: (804)346-4800
Fax: (804)346-5009
Co. E-mail: publications@chrie.org
URL: http://www.chrie.org

International Dairy-Deli-Bakery Association
PO Box 5528
Madison, WI 53705-0528
Ph: (608)310-5000
Fax: (608)238-6330
Co. E-mail: iddba@iddba.org
URL: http://www.iddba.org

International Data Corp.
5 Speen St.
Framingham, MA 01701
Ph: (508)872-8200
Fax: (508)935-4271

International Directory of Importers
1741 Kekamek NW
Poulsbo, WA 98370
Ph: (360)779-1511
Free: 800-818-0140
Fax: (360)697-4696
Co. E-mail: helpdesk@export-leads.com
URL: http://www.export-leads.com

International Economic Development Council
734 15th St. NW, Ste. 900
Washington, DC 20005
Ph: (202)223-7800
Fax: (202)223-4745
Co. E-mail: kbielen@iedconline.org
URL: http://www.iedconline.org

International Federation of Accountants
529 5th Ave., 6th Fl.
New York, NY 10017
Ph: (212)286-9344
Fax: (212)286-9570
Co. E-mail: communications@ifac.org
URL: http://www.ifac.org

International Formalwear Association
401 N Michigan Ave.
Chicago, IL 60611
Ph: (312)644-6610
Fax: (312)321-4098
Co. E-mail: ifa@sba.org

International Foundation of Employee Benefit Plans (IFEBP)
18700 W Bluemound Rd.
Brookfield, WI 53045
Ph: (262)786-6700
Free: 888-334-3327
Fax: (262)364-1818
Co. E-mail: membership@ifebp.org
URL: http://www.ifebp.org

International Franchise Association
1501 K St. NW, Ste. 350
Washington, DC 20005
Ph: (202)628-8000
Fax: (202)628-0812

International Graphoanalysis Society
842 5th Ave.
New Kensington, PA 15068
Ph: (724)472-9701
Fax: (509)271-1149
Co. E-mail: greg@igas.com
URL: http://www.igas.com

International Hearing Society
16880 Middlebelt Rd., Ste. 4
Livonia, MI 48154
Ph: (734)522-7200
Free: 800-521-5247
Fax: (734)522-0200
URL: http://www.ihsinfo.org

International Home Furnishings Center
210 E Commerce Ave.
High Point, NC 27260-5238
Ph: (336)888-3700
Co. E-mail: marketing@ihfc.com
URL: http://www.ihfc.com

International Informatics Institute
405 4th St.
Brooklyn, NY 11215
Ph: (718)499-1884
Fax: (718)499-1970

International Labour Office
1828 L St. NW, Ste. 600
Washington, DC 20036-5121
Ph: (202)653-7652
Fax: (202)653-7687

International Life Sciences Institute Subscription Office
1 Thomas Cir., 9th Fl.
Washington, DC 20005-5802
Ph: (202)659-0074
Fax: (202)659-3859
Co. E-mail: ilsi@ilsi.org
URL: http://www.ilsi.org

International Midas Dealers Association
14 W 3rd St., Ste. 200
Kansas City, MO 64105
Ph: (816)472-6632
Free: 877-543-6203
Fax: (816)472-7765

International Personnel Management Association
1617 Duke St.
Alexandria, VA 22314
Ph: (703)549-7100
Fax: (703)684-0948
Co. E-mail: publications@ipma-hr.org
URL: http://www.ipma-hr.org/

International Risk Management Institute Inc.
12222 Merit Dr., Ste. 1450
Dallas, TX 75251-2276
Ph: (972)960-7693
Free: 800-827-4242
Fax: (972)371-5120
Co. E-mail: info@irmi.com
URL: http://www.irmi.com

International Schizophrenia Foundation
16 Florence Ave.
Toronto, ON, Canada M2N 1E9
Ph: (416)733-2117
Fax: (416)733-2352
Co. E-mail: centre@orthomed.org
URL: http://www.orthomed.org/isf/isf.html

International Scientific Communications Inc.
30 Controls Dr.
Shelton, CT 06484-0870
Ph: (650)243-5600
Fax: (203)926-9310
Co. E-mail: iscpubs@iscpubs.com
URL: http://www.americanlaboratory.com/

International Self-Counsel Press, Limited
1481 Charlotte Rd.
North Vancouver, BC, Canada V7J 1H1
Ph: (604)986-3366
Free: 800-663-3007
Fax: (604)986-3947

International Society for Technology in Education
1710 Rhode Island Ave. NW Ste. 900
Washington, DC 20036
Ph: (541)302-3777
Free: 800-336-5191
Fax: (541)302-3778

Co. E-mail: iste@iste.org
URL: http://www.iste.org

International Society for Terrain-Vehicle Systems
US Army Cold Reg. Researchlab
Applied Research Division
Hanover, NH 03755-1290
Ph: (603)646-4362
Fax: (603)646-4640
Co. E-mail: rliston@crrel.usace.army.mil
URL: http://www.istvs.org/

International Society for Vehicle Preservation
PO Box 50046
Tucson, AZ 85703-1046
Ph: (520)622-2201
Fax: (520)792-8501
Co. E-mail: isvp@earthlink.net
URL: http://www.aztexcorp.com/root/isvp.html

International Society of Certified Employee Benefit Specialists
PO Box 209
Brookfield, WI 53008-0209
Ph: (262)786-8771
Fax: (262)786-8650
Co. E-mail: iscebs@iscebs.org
URL: http://www.iscebs.org

International Specialized Books Services
5602 NE Hassalo St.
Portland, OR 97213
Ph: (503)287-3093
Fax: (503)284-8859

International Textile and Apparel Association
PO Box 70687
Knoxville, TN 37938-0687
Ph: (865)992-1535
Co. E-mail: info@itaaonline.org
URL: http://www.itaaonline.org

International Trumpet Guild
c/o David C. Jones, ITG Treasurer
241 E Main St., No. 247
Westfield, MA 01086-1633
Ph: (413)568-1239
Fax: (413)568-1913
Co. E-mail: info@trumpetguild.org

International Warehouse Logistics Association
2800 S River Rd., Ste. 260
Des Plaines, IL 60018
Ph: (847)813-4699
Fax: (847)813-0115
Co. E-mail: email@iwla.com
URL: http://www.iwla.com

International Wealth Success, Inc.
PO Box 186
Merrick, NY 11566-0186
Ph: (516)766-5850
Free: 800-323-0548
Fax: (516)766-5919
Co. E-mail: admin@iwsmoney.com
URL: http://www.iwsmoney.com

International Wealth Success, Inc.
24 Canterbury Rd.
Rockville Center, NY 11570-1310
Ph: (516)766-5850
Free: 800-323-0548
Fax: (516)766-5919

International Wood Products Association
4214 King St.
Alexandria, VA 22302
Ph: (703)820-6696
Fax: (703)820-8550
Co. E-mail: info@iwpawood.org
URL: http://www.iwpawood.org

Internet/Media Strategies Inc.
Old City Hall
625 Commerce St., Ste. 330
Tacoma, WA 98402

The Intrepid Traveler
371 Walden Green Rd., Box 531
Branford, CT 06405

Investment Adviser Association
1050 17th St. NW, Ste. 725
Washington, DC 20036-5514
Ph: (202)293-4222
Fax: (202)293-4223
Co. E-mail: info@investmentadviser.org
URL: http://www.investmentadviser.org

Investment Advisor Group
33-41 Newark St., 2nd Fl.
Hoboken, NJ 07030
Ph: (732)389-8700
Fax: (732)276-2493
URL: http://www.advisorone.com

Investment Div. Small Business Administration
409 3rd St. SW
Washington, DC 20416
Ph: (202)205-6586
Free: 800-659-2955
Fax: (202)481-5881
URL: http://www.sba.gov/

Investment Media Inc.
909 3rd Ave., 27th Fl.
New York, NY 10022
Ph: (212)370-3700
Fax: (212)370-4606
Co. E-mail: info@globalinv.com
URL: http://www.globalinv.com

Investment Weekly News
2727 Paces Ferry Rd. SE, Ste. 2-440
Atlanta, GA 30339
Ph: (770)435-8286
Fax: (770)435-6800
Co. E-mail: phil@newsrx.com
URL: http://verticalnews.com/

Investor's Business Daily
12655 Beatrice St.
Los Angeles, CA 90066
Ph: (310)448-6600
Free: 800-831-2525
Fax: (310)577-7301
Co. E-mail: custcare@investors.com
URL: http://www.investors.com/

Iowa Grocery Industry Association
2540 106th St., Ste. 102
Des Moines, IA 50322-3736
Ph: (515)270-2628
Free: 800-383-3663
Fax: (515)270-0316
Co. E-mail: info@iowagrocers.com
URL: http://www.iowagrocers.com

Irish Genealogical Foundation
PO Box 7575
Kansas City, MO 64116
Ph: (816)454-2410
Fax: (816)256-3360
Co. E-mail: mike@irishroots.com
URL: http://www.irishroots.com

Irving Levin Associates Inc.
268 1/2 Main Ave.
Norwalk, CT 06851
Ph: (203)846-6800
Free: 800-248-1668
Fax: (203)846-6800
Co. E-mail: general@levinassociates.com

Island Press-Center For Resource Economics
1718 Connecticut Ave. Nw Ste. 300
Washington, DC 20009-1148
Ph: (202)232-7933
Free: 800-621-2736
Fax: (202)234-1328
Co. E-mail: info@islandpress.org
URL: http://www.islandpress.org

Islands Publishing Co.
6267 Carpinteria Ave., Ste. 200
Carpinteria, CA 93013
Ph: (805)745-7100
Free: 888-881-5861
Fax: (805)745-7105
Co. E-mail: info@resortsgreathotels.com

Italy-America Chamber of Commerce
730 5th Ave., Ste. 600
New York, NY 10019
Ph: (212)459-0044
Fax: (212)459-0090
Co. E-mail: info@italchamber.org
URL: http://www.italchamber.org

iUniverse
1663 Liberty Dr.
Bloomington, IN 47403
Free: 800-288-4677
Fax: (812)355-4085
URL: http://www.iuniverse.com

iUniverse, Incorporated
2021 Pine Lake Rd., Ste. 100
Lincoln, NE 68512
Ph: (402)323-7800
Free: 800-288-4677
Fax: (402)323-7824

Ivan Levison & Associates
14 Los Cerros Dr.
Greenbrae, CA 94904
Ph: (415)461-0672
Fax: (415)461-7738
Co. E-mail: ivan@levison.com
URL: http://www.levison.com

Ivy Sea, Inc.
3701 Sacramento St., No. 199
San Francisco, CA 94118-1705
Ph: (415)752-6317
Fax: (415)752-6317
Co. E-mail: info@ivysea.com
URL: http://www.ivysea.com

J

J.R. O'Dwyer Company Inc.
271 Madison Ave., No. 600
New York, NY 10016
Ph: (212)679-2471
Free: 866-395-7710
Fax: (212)683-2750
URL: http://www.odwyerpr.com

Jack Erickson
PO Box 2184
Reston, VA 22090
URL: http://www.realbeer.com/redbrick-
   press/jack.html

James H. Schmidt
PO Box 1688
Greenwich, CT 06836
Ph: (203)629-3503
Free: 800-356-2527
Fax: (203)629-2175
Co. E-mail: contact@timerdigest.com

James Lorimer & Company Ltd.
35 Britain St.
Toronto, ON, Canada M5A 1R7

James R. Tolliver

Jason Kelly
11032 Moorpark St., No. 17
North Hollywood, CA 91602
Free: 800-339-5671

Jay Conrad Levinson
PO Box 1336
Mill Valley, CA 94942
Ph: (415)381-8361
Free: 800-748-6444
Fax: (415)381-8361

Jenkins Group Inc.
1129 Woodmere Ave., Ste. B
Traverse City, MI 49686
Ph: (231)933-0445
Free: 800-706-4636
Fax: (231)933-0448
Co. E-mail: info@bookpublishing.com
URL: http://www.jenkinsgroupinc.com

Jet Airtransport Exchange Inc.
52 W Main St.
Milford, CT 06460-3310
Ph: (203)301-0255
Free: 800-952-9329
Fax: (203)301-0250
Co. E-mail: editor@jaxfax.com
URL: http://www.jaxfaxmagazine.com

JL Com Publishing Company L.L.C.
26 Hawthorn Dr.
Succasunna, NJ 07876-2112
Ph: (973)252-7552
Free: 888-235-2997
Fax: (973)252-7552
Co. E-mail: lawpublish@aol.com

JMS Publishing L.L.C.
323 Lincoln St.
Roseville, CA 95678-2229
Ph: (916)784-3880
Fax: (916)784-3995
URL: http://www.bamagazine.com

Joan Stewart
3434 County KK
Port Washington, WI 53074
Ph: (262)284-7451
Fax: (262)284-1737
Co. E-mail: jstewart@publicityhound.com

John Baer's Sons
PO Box 328
Lancaster, PA 17608
Ph: (717)392-0733
Fax: (717)392-1341
Co. E-mail: info@johnbaer.com

John Wiley & Sons
111 River St.
Hoboken, NJ 07030
Ph: (201)748-6000
Fax: (201)748-6088
URL: http://www.wiley.com

John Wiley & Sons, Inc.
10475 Crosspoint Blvd.
Indianapolis, IN 46256
Ph: (877)762-2974
Free: 800-225-5945
Fax: (800)597-3299

Co. E-mail: consumers@wiley.com
URL: http://www.wiley.com

John Wiley and Sons Canada Ltd.
22 Worcester Rd.
Etobicoke, ON, Canada M9W 1L1
Co. E-mail: info@wiley.com
URL: http://www.wiley.com

John Wiley and Sons Inc.
111 River St.
Hoboken, NJ 07030-5774
Ph: (201)748-6000
Free: 800-825-7550
Fax: (201)748-6088
Co. E-mail: info@wiley.com
URL: http://www.wiley.com

John Wiley
111 River St.
Hoboken, NJ 07030-5774
Ph: (201)748-6000
Fax: (201)748-6088

Johns Hopkins University Press
2715 N. Charles St.
Baltimore, MD 21218
Ph: (800)537-5487
Free: 800-537-5487
Fax: (410)516-6998
Co. E-mail: jhopkins@mail.press.jhu.edu
URL: http://www.press.jhu.edu/

The Joint Commission Journal on Quality Improvement
1 Renaissance Blvd.
Oakbrook Terrace, IL 60181
Ph: (630)792-5453
Fax: (630)792-4453
Co. E-mail: sberman@jcrinc.com
URL: http://www.jcrinc.com

Jola Publications
2933 N 2nd St.
Minneapolis, MN 55411
Ph: (612)529-5001
Free: 866-565-2782
Fax: (612)521-2289
Co. E-mail: medical@jolapub.com
URL: http://www.jolapub.com

Jordans Publishing Limited
21 St. Thomas St.
Bristol BS1 6JS, United Kingdom
Ph: 44 117 9230600
Fax: 44 117 9250486

Joseph Schlussel
580 5th Ave., Ste. 806
New York, NY 10036
Ph: (212)575-0444
Free: 800-223-7955
Fax: (212)575-0722
Co. E-mail: diamond58@aol.com

Jossey Bass
c/o John Wiley and Sons, Inc.
111 River St.
Hoboken, NJ 07030
Ph: (201)748-6000
Fax: (201)748-6088

Jossey-Bass Publishers
989 Market St.
San Francisco, CA 94103
Ph: (415)433-1740
Free: 888-378-2537
Fax: (415)951-8553
Co. E-mail: jbsubs@jbp.com
URL: http://www.josseybass.com

Jossey-Bass
989 Market St.
San Francisco, CA 94103
Ph: (415)433-1740
Fax: (415)951-8553
Co. E-mail: jbsubs@jbp.com
URL: http://www.joseybass.com

Journal of the Canadian Economics Association
CP 35006
1221 Fleury E
Montreal, QC, Canada H2C 3K4
Ph: (646)257-5906

Journal Publications Inc.
4343 Sonoma Hwy.
Santa Rosa, CA 95409
Ph: (707)566-9734
Fax: (707)568-5980
Co. E-mail: ewalsh@fbworld.com
URL: http://www.fbworld.com

Journal Publishing Inc.
PO Box 909
Tupelo, MS 38802
Ph: (662)678-1536

Journal Register Ohio
7085 Mentor Ave.
Willoughby, OH 44094
Ph: (440)951-0000
Free: 800-947-2737

Journal Star
1 News Plaza
Peoria, IL 61643
Ph: (309)686-3000

Journeywoman
50 Prince Arthur Ave.
Toronto, ON, Canada M5R 1B5
Ph: (416)929-7654
Co. E-mail: editor@journeywoman.com
URL: http://www.journeywoman.com

Junior Achievement
1 Education Way
Colorado Springs, CO 80906
Ph: (719)540-8000
Free: 888-4JA-ALUM

Fax: (719)540-6299
Co. E-mail: newmedia@ja.org
URL: http://www.ja.org

K

KAL Publications Inc.
559 S Harbor Blvd., Ste. A
Anaheim, CA 92805-4525
Ph: (714)563-9300
Fax: (714)563-9310
URL: http://www.kalpub.com

Kalmbach Publishing Co.
21027 Crossroads Cir.
Waukesha, WI 53187-1612
Ph: (262)796-8776
Free: 800-533-6644
Fax: (262)796-1615
Co. E-mail: customerservice@kalmbach.
com
URL: http://corporate.kalmbach.com/kpc/
default.aspx?c=a&id=34#contact

Kane Communications Inc.
10 E Athens Ave., Ste. 208
Ardmore, PA 19003
Ph: (610)645-6940
Fax: (610)645-6943
Co. E-mail: sounovmag@aol.com
URL: http://www.kanec.com

Kaplan Books
1230 Avenue of the Americas, 1st Fl.
New York, NY 10020
Ph: (212)698-7000
Fax: (212)698-7007

Kaplan Publishing
30 N Wacker Dr., No. 2500
Chicago, IL 60606-7481
Ph: (312)836-4400
Free: 800-245-2665
Fax: (312)836-1021

Kaplan Publishing
1 Liberty Plz., 24th Fl.
New York, NY 10006
Ph: (212)632-4973
Free: 800-223-2336
Fax: (800)943-9831
Co. E-mail: kaplanpubsales@kaplan.com
URL: http://www.kaplanpublishing.com

Katydid Press
4736 Meadowview Blvd.
Sarasota, FL 34233
Ph: (941)924-4142
Fax: (941)922-5902

Kazak Communications
16 Ottawa St.
Toronto, ON, Canada M4T 2B6

Keith Key
2451 Cumberland Pkwy., Ste. 3374
Atlanta, GA 30339
Ph: (404)419-6701
Free: 800-633-4931
Fax: (404)419-6702
Co. E-mail: info@fertiltyweekly.com

Kenilworth Media Inc.
15 Wertheim Ct., Ste. 710
Richmond Hill, ON, Canada L4B 3H7
Ph: (905)771-7333
Free: 800-409-8688
Fax: (905)771-7336
Co. E-mail: editor@kenilworth.com
URL: http://www.kenilworth.com

Kennedy Information Inc.
1 Phoenix Mill Ln., 3rd Fl.
Peterborough, NH 03458
Ph: (603)924-1006
Free: 800-531-0007
Fax: (603)924-4460
Co. E-mail: customerservice@kennedy-
info.com
URL: http://www.kennedyinfo.com

Kensington Publishing Corporation
850 3rd Ave.
New York, NY 10022
Free: 800-221-2647
URL: http://www.kensingtonbooks.com

The Kerner Group Inc.
1319 Howard Ln.
Palmer, PA 18045-2153

Key Communications Inc.
385 Garrisonville Rd.
Stafford, VA 22554
Ph: (540)720-5584
Fax: (540)720-5687
Co. E-mail: info@glass.com
URL: http://www.key-com.com

Kiplinger Books and Tapes
1729 H St. NW
Washington, DC 20006
Ph: (202)887-6680
Free: 800-544-0155
Fax: (202)223-8990
Co. E-mail: books@kiplinger.com
URL: http://www.kiplinger.com

Kluwer Academic/Plenum Publishing Corp.
101 Philip Dr.
Norwell, MA 02061
Ph: (781)871-6600
Fax: (781)871-6528
Co. E-mail: kluwer@wkap.com
URL: http://www.springeronline.com

Knight-Ridder/Tribune Business News
600 S Tryon St.
Charlotte, NC 28202-1880
Ph: (704)358-5000

Knopf Publishing/Random House
1745 Broadway
New York, NY 10019
Ph: (212)782-9000
Fax: (212)572-8700
Co. E-mail: customerservice@random-house.com

Knowledge Technology Inc.
PO Box 30130
Phoenix, AZ 85046-0130
Ph: (602)971-1869
Fax: (602)971-2321
Co. E-mail: info@pcai.com
URL: http://www.pcai.com

Knoxville News Sentinel
2332 News Sentinel Dr.
Knoxville, TN 37921
Ph: (865)521-8181

Kodaly Society of Canada
198 Davenport Rd.
Toronto, ON, Canada M5R 1J2
URL: http://www.kodalysocietyofcanada.ca

Kogan Page, Limited
120 Pentonville Rd.
London N1 9JN, United Kingdom
Ph: 44 20 72780433
Fax: 44 20 78376348
Co. E-mail: kpinfo@kogan-page.co.uk
URL: http://www.kogan-page.co.uk/

Kogan Page, Ltd.
525 S 4th St., No. 241
Philadelphia, PA 19147
Ph: (215)928-9112
Fax: (215)928-9113
Co. E-mail: info@koganpage.com
URL: http://www.koganpageusa.com

Kon-Lin Research & Analysis Corp.
5 Water Rd.
Rocky Point, NY 11778
Ph: (631)744-8536
Fax: (631)744-3096

Kona Communications Inc.
707 Lake Cook Rd.
Deerfield, IL 60015
Ph: (847)498-3180
Fax: (847)498-3197
Co. E-mail: truckbooks@konacommunications.com
URL: http://www.truckpartsandservice.com/

Korean Chamber of Commerce & Industry in USA Inc.
460 Park Ave., Ste. 410
New York, NY 10022
Ph: (212)644-0140
Fax: (212)644-9106
Co. E-mail: admin@kocham.org
URL: http://www.kocham.org

Kostuch Publications Ltd.
23 Lesmil Rd., Ste. 101
Toronto, ON, Canada M3B 3P6
Ph: (416)447-0888
Fax: (416)447-5333
URL: http://www.foodserviceworld.com/

Krause Publications Inc.
700 E State St.
Iola, WI 54990-0001
Ph: (715)445-2214
Free: 800-726-9966
Fax: (715)445-4087
Co. E-mail: info@krause.com
URL: http://www.krause.com

L

L.C. Clark Publishing Company Inc.
840 U.S. Hwy., 1 Ste. 330
North Palm Beach, FL 33408
Ph: (561)627-3393
Free: 800-537-4271
Fax: (561)627-1447
Co. E-mail: info@dwconline.com
URL: http://www.dwconline.com/

L/L Research
PO Box 5195
Louisville, KY 40255-0195
Ph: (502)245-6495
Fax: (502)245-6495

La Crosse Tribune
401 3rd St. N
La Crosse, WI 54601
Ph: (608)782-9710
URL: http://www.lacrossetribune.com/

La Leche League International
PO Box 4079
Schaumburg, IL 60168-4079
Ph: (847)519-7730
Free: 800-525-3243
Fax: (847)969-0460
Co. E-mail: fdassociate@llli.org
URL: http://www.llli.org

Lafayette Instrument Company Inc.
3700 Sagamore Pkwy. N
Lafayette, IN 47903
Ph: (765)423-1505
Free: 800-428-7545
Fax: (765)423-4111
Co. E-mail: sales@lafayetteinstrument.com
URL: http://www.lafayetteinstrument.com

Landscape Communications Inc.
14771 Plaza Dr., Ste. M
Tustin, CA 92780
Ph: (714)979-5276
URL: http://www.landscapeonline.com

Landscape Ontario Horticultural Trades Association
7856 5th Line S
Milton, ON, Canada L9T 2X8
Ph: (905)875-1805
Free: 800-265-5656
Fax: (905)875-3942
Co. E-mail: stevemoyer@landscapeontario.com
URL: http://www.landscapeontario.com/

Lapidary Journal
300 Chesterfield Pkwy., Ste. 100
Malvern, PA 19355
Ph: (610)232-5700
Free: 800-676-4336
Fax: (610)232-5756
Co. E-mail: ljeditorial@interweave.com
URL: http://www.jewelryartistmagazine.com

Lark Books
67 Broadway St.
Asheville, NC 28801-2919
Ph: (828)253-0467
Co. E-mail: customerservice@larkbooks.com/
URL: http://www.larkbooks.com/

Las Vegas Insider
PO Box 1185
Chino Valley, AZ 86323
Free: 800-628-1686
Co. E-mail: amchb@primnet.com

Latest Scoop Publishing
PO Box 7477
Loveland, CO 80537-0477
Ph: (970)686-6155
Fax: (970)686-6155
Co. E-mail: SCOOPautovents@aol.com

Laughing Bear Press
PO Box 613322
Dallas, TX 75261-3322
Co. E-mail: editor@laughingbear.com
URL: http://www.laughingbear.com

Lawrence Erlbaum Associates Inc. (LEA Online)
10 Industrial Ave.
Mahwah, NJ 07430-2262
Ph: (201)258-2200
Free: 800-9BO-OKS9
Fax: (201)236-0072
Co. E-mail: orders@erlbaum.com
URL: http://www.leaonline.com

Lawrence Oakly
5 Savage Ct.
Bluffton, SC 29910-4430
Ph: (843)705-5591
Fax: (843)705-5592
Co. E-mail: up415@aol.com

Lawrence Ragan Communications Inc.
111 E Wacker Dr., Ste. 500
Chicago, IL 60601
Ph: (312)960-4100
Free: 800-493-4867
Fax: (312)861-3592
Co. E-mail: cservice@ragan.com
URL: http://www.ragan.com

Learning House Publishing, Inc.
110 1st Ave.
Charlestown, MA 02629
Co. E-mail: info@practicalactionlearning.
  com
URL: http://www.practicalactionlearning.
  com

Lebhar-Friedman Inc.
425 Park Ave.
New York, NY 10022
Ph: (212)756-5000
Fax: (212)756-5295
Co. E-mail: info@lf.com

Lee Enterprises Inc.
201 N Harrison St.
Davenport, IA 52801-1932
Ph: (563)383-2100
Fax: (563)323-9609
Co. E-mail: information@lee.net
URL: http://www.lee.net

Lee Enterprises Inc.
207 E Pennsylvania Ave.
Escondido, CA 92025
Ph: (760)745-6611
URL: http://www.nctimes.com

Lee Enterprises
501 Commercial St.
Waterloo, IA 50704
Ph: (319)291-1400
Free: 800-798-1717

Leisure Publications Inc.
4160 Wilshire Blvd.
Los Angeles, CA 90010-3500
Ph: (323)964-4800
Fax: (323)417-4840

Lessons Professional Publishing
Fitzroy House
11 Chenies St.
London WC1E 7EY, United Kingdom
Ph: (440) 2076364777
Fax: (440) 2076364888

Lewis and Renn Associates
4860 E Main St., No. A128
Mesa, AZ 85205
Ph: (231)275-7287
Fax: (480)830-1187

Lexington Books
4501 Forbes Blvd., Ste. 200
Lanham, MD 20706
Ph: (301)459-3366

Free: 800-338-4550
Fax: (301)459-5748

LexisNexis
9443 Springboro Pke.
Dayton, OH 45342
Ph: (937)865-6800
Free: 800-227-4908
Co. E-mail: customerservice.customer.
  support@lexisnexis.com
URL: http://www.bender.com/

LexisNexis
1016 W Ninth Ave.
King of Prussia, PA 19406-1225
Ph: (215)564-1788
Free: 800-448-1515
URL: http://www.lexisnexis.com/contact-
  us/

LFB Scholarly Publishing LLC
24 W 27th St., No. 1108
New York, NY 10010
Ph: (212)337-3487
Fax: (212)229-1620

Lightner Publishing Corp.
1006 S Michigan Ave.
Chicago, IL 60605
Free: 800-762-7576
Fax: (312)939-0053

LIMS/Letter
PO Box 935
Kenwood, CA 95452
Ph: (707)526-6885
Fax: (707)526-6889
Co. E-mail: webmaster@limsletter.com

Linn's Stamp News
911 Vandemark Rd.
Sidney, OH 45365-0926
Ph: (937)498-0801
Free: 800-572-6885
Fax: (937)498-0807
Co. E-mail: cuserv@amospress.com
URL: http://www.linns.com

Lippincott Williams & Wilkins
16522 Hunters Green Pky.
Hagerstown, MD 21740
Ph: (301)233-2300
Free: 800-638-3030
Fax: (301)233-2398
Co. E-mail: orders@lww.com
URL: http://www.lww.com/

Lippincott Williams & Wilkins
530 Walnut St.
Philadelphia, PA 19106-3619
Ph: (215)521-8300
Free: 800-638-3030
Fax: (215)521-8902
Co. E-mail: customerservice@lww.com
URL: http://www.lww.com

Little Brown & Company
1271 Avenue of the Americas
New York, NY 10020
Ph: (212)522-8700
Fax: (212)522-2067
URL: http://www.twbookmark.com

**Little Brown Company/Time Warner
Book Group**
1271 Avenue of the Americas
New York, NY 10020
Ph: (212)522-8700
Fax: (212)522-2067

Little Mountain Corp.
PO Box 178
Westpoint, TN 38486-0178
Ph: (931)766-6066
Free: 888-218-9226
Fax: (931)766-1128
Co. E-mail: moneychanger@compuserve.
  com

Little, Brown and Company
237 Park Ave.
New York, NY 10017
URL: http://www.HachetteBookGroup.com

LLM Publications Inc.
8201 SE 17th Ave.
Portland, OR 97202
Ph: (503)445-2220
Free: 800-647-1511
Fax: (503)655-0778
Co. E-mail: erin@llm.com
URL: http://www.llm.com

Lockwood Publications Inc.
26 Broadway, Fl. 9M
New York, NY 10004
Ph: (212)391-2060
Fax: (212)827-0945
Co. E-mail: operations@lockwoodpublica-
  tions.com
URL: http://www.lockwoodpublications.com

Loeb Associates Inc.
PO Box 1155
New York, NY 10018
Ph: (212)819-6440
Co. E-mail: loeb@idt.net

Lovejoy Corp.
Palmer Sq.
Princeton, NJ 08542
Ph: (609)989-9484

LRP Publications
lrp.com Technology Contacts
747 Dresher Rd., Ste. 500
Horsham, PA 19044
Ph: (215)784-0860
Free: 800-341-7874
Fax: (215)784-9639
Co. E-mail: techsup@lrp.com
URL: http://www.lrp.com

LRP Publications
360 Hiatt Dr.
Palm Beach Gardens, FL 33418
Ph: (561)622-6529
Free: 800-341-7874
Fax: (561)622-0757
Co. E-mail: custserve@lrp.com
URL: http://www.lrp.com

LRP Publications
PO Box 24668
West Palm Beach, FL 33416-4668
Ph: (800)341-7874
Free: 800-341-7874
Fax: (561)622-2423
Co. E-mail: custserve@lrp.com
URL: http://www.lrp.com

Luce Press Clippings
42 S. Ctr. St.
Mesa, AZ 85210
Ph: (480)834-4884
Free: 800-528-8226
Fax: (480)834-3821
Co. E-mail: clip@lucepress.com
URL: http://www.burrellesluce.com

Lucis Trust
120 Wall St., 24th Fl.
New York, NY 10005
Ph: (212)292-0707
Fax: (212)292-0808
Co. E-mail: newyork@lucistrust.org
URL: http://www.lucistrust.org

Lulu.com
860 Aviation Pkwy., Ste. 300
Morrisville, NC 27560
Fax: (919)459-5867

M

M. Evans & Company Inc.
4501 Forbes Blvd., Ste. 200
Lanham, MD 20706-4346
Ph: (301)459-3366
Free: 800-462-6420
Fax: (301)429-5748
Co. E-mail: custserv@nbnbooks.com
URL: http://www.rlpgtrade.com

M. Evans and Company, Incorporated
216 E 49th St.
New York, NY 10017
Ph: (212)688-2810
Fax: (212)486-4544

M. Shanken Communications Inc.
387 Park Ave. S
New York, NY 10016
Ph: (212)684-4224
Free: 800-227-1617
Fax: (212)481-1540
Co. E-mail: mmorgenstern@mshanken.com
URL: http://www.mshanken.com

M.E. Sharpe Inc.
80 Business Park Dr.
Armonk, NY 10504
Ph: (914)273-1800
Free: 800-541-6563
Fax: (914)273-2106
Co. E-mail: info@mesharpe.com
URL: http://www.mesharpe.com

Mac Publishing
501 2nd St.
San Francisco, CA 94107
Ph: (415)243-0500
Fax: (415)442-1891

Macfadden Communications Group L.L.C.
333 7th Ave., 11th Fl.
New York, NY 10001
Ph: (212)979-4800
URL: http://www.macfad.com/

Machinery Dealers National Association
315 S Patrick St.
Alexandria, VA 22314-3501
Ph: (703)836-9300
Free: 800-872-7807
Fax: (703)836-9303
Co. E-mail: office@mdna.org
URL: http://www.mdna.org

Macmillan Publishers Limited
2 Penn Plz., 5th Fl.
New York, NY 10121-2298
Ph: (212)904-3834
Fax: (212)904-4878
Co. E-mail: international_school@mcgraw-hill.com
URL: http://www.mmhschool.com

Macmillan Reference USA
12 Lunar Dr.
Woodbridge, CT 06525-2322
Ph: (203)397-2600
Free: 800-444-0799
Fax: (800)414-5043
Co. E-mail: gale.galeord@cengage.com
URL: http://gale.cengage.com/macmillan/

Macon Telegraph
120 Broadway
Macon, GA 31201
Ph: (478)744-4200
Free: 800-342-5845

Magazines/Creative Inc.
31 Merrick Ave.
Merrick, NY 11566
Ph: (516)378-0800
Co. E-mail: info@creativemag.com
URL: http://www.creativemag.com/homepage.html

Magill's Choice
2 University Plz., Ste. 121
Hackensack, NJ 07601
Ph: (201)968-9899
Free: 800-221-1592
Fax: (201)968-1411
Co. E-mail: csr@salempress.com
URL: http://salempress.com

Maher Publications Inc.
102 N Haven Rd.
Elmhurst, IL 60126
Ph: (630)941-2030
Free: 800-554-7470
Fax: (630)941-3210
Co. E-mail: service@downbeat.com
URL: http://www.downbeat.com/

Mail Tribune
111 N Fir St.
Medford, OR 97501
Ph: (541)776-4411
Fax: (541)776-4376

Making Waves, Publishers
7 Ripley Rd.
Montague, MA 01351
Ph: (800)267-6388
Free: 800-267-6388
Fax: (413)267-6388
Co. E-mail: info@changingcourse.com

MANA
16 A Journey, Ste. 200
Aliso Viejo, CA 92656
Ph: (949)859-4040
Free: 877-626-2776
Fax: (949)855-2973
URL: http://www.manaonline.org/

Management Accounting Quarterly
10 Paragon Dr., Ste. 1
Montvale, NJ 07645
Ph: (201)573-9000
Free: 800-638-4427

Manitoba Beekeepers' Association
204-545 University Crescent
Winnipeg, MB, Canada R3T 5S6
Ph: (204)945-3861
Fax: (204)945-4327
Co. E-mail: lsimpson@mb.sympatico.ca

Manitoba Child Care Association
2nd Fl., 2350 McPhillips St.
Winnipeg, MB, Canada R2V 4J6
Ph: (204)586-8587
Free: 888-323-4676
Fax: (204)589-5613
Co. E-mail: info@mccahouse.org

Mansueto Ventures LLC
7 World Trade Center
New York, NY 10007
Ph: (212)389-5377

Manufacturers' Agents National Association
16 Journey, Ste. 200
Aliso Viejo, CA 92656
Ph: (949)859-4040
Free: 877-626-2776
Fax: (949)855-2973
Co. E-mail: mana@manaonline.org
URL: http://www.manaonline.org

Manufacturers' Mart Publications
PO Box 310
Georgetown, MA 01833
Free: 800-835-0017
Fax: (978)352-4829
Co. E-mail: info@manufacturesmart.com
URL: http://www.manufacturersmart.com

Manufacturing Confectioner Publishing Corp.
711 W Water St.
Princeton, WI 54968
Ph: (920)295-6969
Fax: (920)295-6843
Co. E-mail: mcinfo@gomc.com
URL: http://www.gomc.com

Manufacturing Jewelers & Suppliers of America
45 Royal Little Dr.
Providence, RI 02904-1861
Ph: (401)274-3840
Free: 800-444-MJSA
Fax: (401)274-0265
Co. E-mail: mjsa@mjsainc.com

Maria C. Smith
PO Box 75064
Houston, TX 77234
Ph: (281)857-6571
Fax: (301)261-5010
Co. E-mail: tp@globalwaterintel.com

Marine Business Journal Inc.
330 N Andrews Ave.
Fort Lauderdale, FL 33301
Ph: (954)522-5515
Fax: (954)522-2260
Co. E-mail: mbj@marinebusinessjournal.com
URL: http://www.marinebusinessjournal.com/

Maritime Activity Reports Inc.
118 E 25th St., 2nd Fl.
New York, NY 10010
Ph: (212)477-6700
Fax: (212)254-6271
Co. E-mail: jomalley@marinelink.com
URL: http://www.marinelink.com

Market Search Inc.
2727 Holland Sylvania Rd., Ste. A
Toledo, OH 43615
Ph: (419)535-7899
Fax: (419)535-1243
Co. E-mail: jb@cbrief.biz

Marketing & Technology Group Inc.
1415 N Dayton St.
Chicago, IL 60622
Ph: (312)266-3311
Fax: (312)266-3363
Co. E-mail: webinars@meatingplace.com

Marketing Research Association
110 National Dr., 2nd Fl.
Glastonbury, CT 06033-1212
Ph: (860)682-1000
Fax: (860)682-1010
Co. E-mail: email@mra-net.org
URL: http://www.mra-net.org/

Marketing Research Association
1156 15th St. NW, Ste. 302
Washington, DC 20005
Ph: (202)800-2545
Fax: (888)512-1050
Co. E-mail: membership@marketingresearch.org
URL: http://www.marketingresearch.org

MarketResearch.com
38 E 29th St., 6th Fl.
New York, NY 10011
Ph: (212)807-2629
Free: 800-298-5699
Fax: (212)807-2676
Co. E-mail: customerservice@marketresearch.com
URL: http://www.marketresearch.com

MarketResearch.com
11200 Rockville Pke., Ste. 504
Rockville, MD 20852
Ph: (240)747-3093
Free: 800-298-5699
Fax: (240)747-3004
Co. E-mail: customerservice@marketresearch.com
URL: http://www.marketresearch.com

The Markets Directory
320 E 42 St., Ste. 2018
New York, NY 10017
Ph: (212)490-1212
Fax: (212)490-1221
Co. E-mail: jimroxton@marketsdirectory.com
URL: http://www.focusgroups.com

MarketWire Canada
25 York St., Ste. 900
Toronto, ON, Canada M5J 2V5
Ph: (416)362-0885
Free: 888-299-0338
Fax: (416)362-6669

Marketwire
48 Yonge St., 8th Fl.
Toronto, ON, Canada M5E 1G6
Ph: (416)362-0885
Free: 888-299-0338
Fax: (416)362-9693
URL: http://www.marketwire.com

Markkula Center for Applied Ethics
Santa Clara University
500 El Camino Real
Santa Clara, CA 95053-0633
Ph: (408)554-5319
Fax: (408)554-2373
Co. E-mail: ethics@scu.edu

Marquis Who's Who L.L.C.
300 Connell Dr., Ste. 2000
Berkeley Heights, NJ 07922
Ph: (908)673-1000
Free: 800-473-7020
Fax: (908)673-1179
Co. E-mail: customerservice@marquiswhoswho.com
URL: http://www.marquiswhoswho.com

Martha Stewart Living Omnimedia Inc.
601 W 26th St.
New York, NY 10001-1101
Ph: (212)827-8000
Fax: (212)827-8204
Co. E-mail: mstewart@marthastewart.com
URL: http://www.marthastewart.com

Martindale-Hubbell Inc.
121 Chanlon Rd.
New Providence, NJ 07974
Ph: (908)464-6800
Free: 800-526-4902
Fax: (908)771-8704
Co. E-mail: info@martindale.com
URL: http://www.martindale.com

Martineau Corp.
7910 Woodmont Ave., No. 1150
Bethesda, MD 20814-3088
Ph: (301)652-8666
Fax: (301)656-8654
Co. E-mail: associationtrends@associationtrends.com
URL: http://www.associationtrends.com

Mary Ann Liebert Inc. Publishers
140 Huguenot St., 3rd Fl.
New Rochelle, NY 10801-5215
Ph: (914)740-2100
Free: 800-654-3237
Fax: (914)740-2101
Co. E-mail: info@liebertpub.com
URL: http://www.liebertpub.com

The Masonry Society
105 S Sunset St., Ste. Q
Longmont, CO 80501-6172
Ph: (303)939-9700
Fax: (303)541-9215
Co. E-mail: info@masonrysociety.org
URL: http://www.masonrysociety.org

Mass Market Retailers
220 5th Ave.
New York, NY 10001
Ph: (212)213-6000

Master Associates
PO Box 116
Livingston Manor, NY 12758-0116
Ph: (845)439-8177
Fax: (801)788-9747

Masthead Publishing Ltd.
8-1606 Sedlescomb Dr.
Mississauga, ON, Canada L4X 1M6
Ph: (905)625-7070
Fax: (905)625-4856
Co. E-mail: circulation@graphicmonthly.ca
URL: http://www.mastheadonline.com

Mavora Publications Inc.
86 Kingsway Cres.
Toronto, ON, Canada M8X 2R6
Ph: (416)233-5490
Fax: (416)239-2757
Co. E-mail: info@canadian-charities.com
URL: http://www.canadian-charities.com

Maximum Press
605 Silverthorn Rd.
Gulf Breeze, FL 32561
Ph: (850)934-0819
Free: 800-989-6733
Fax: (850)934-9981
URL: http://www.maxpress.com/

McClatchy Company
124 Main St.
Fort Mill, SC 29715
Ph: (803)547-2353
Fax: (803)547-2321

McClatchy Company
150 W Brambleton Ave.
Norfolk, VA 23510
Ph: (757)446-2000
Free: 800-446-2004

McClatchy Company
315 S Boulder Ave.
Tulsa, OK 74103
Ph: (918)581-8418

McClatchy Tribune Information Services
120 S Lawler
Mitchell, SD 57301
Ph: (605)996-5514
Fax: (605)996-5020

McClatchy-Tribune Information Services
800 S Main St.
Burlington, IA 52601
Ph: (319)754-8461

McClatchy-Tribune Information Services
435 N Michigan Ave., Ste. 1500
Chicago, IL 60611
Ph: (847)635-6550
Free: 800-374-7985
Fax: (847)635-6968

McClatchy-Tribune Regional News
1320 SW Broadway
Portland, OR 97123
Ph: (503)648-1131

McClatchy-Tribune Regional News
345 Cedar St.
Saint Paul, MN 55101
Ph: (651)222-1111
Free: 800-950-9080

McClathcy-Tribune
333 W Canal Dr.
Kennewick, WA 99336
Ph: (509)582-1500
Free: 800-874-0445

McEntee Media Corp.
9815 Hazelwood Ave.
Cleveland, OH 44149
Ph: (440)238-6603
Fax: (440)238-6712
Co. E-mail: ken@recycle.cc
URL: http://www.recycle.cc

McFarland & CPI, Publishers
960 NC Hwy 88 W
Jefferson, NC 28640
Ph: (336)246-4460
Free: 800-253-2187
Fax: (336)246-5018
Co. E-mail: info@mcfarlandpub.com
URL: http://www.mcfarlandbooks.com

McGraw-Hill
PO Box 545
Blacklick, OH 43004
Ph: (800)262-4729
Free: 800-323-4900
Fax: (847)679-2494
URL: http://www.mcgrawhill.com

The McGraw-Hill Companies
860 Taylor Station Rd.
Blacklick, OH 43004
Ph: (800)352-3566
Free: 800-722-4726
Fax: (614)755-5645
URL: http://www.mcgraw-hill.com

McGraw-Hill Companies
PO Box 182604
Columbus, OH 43272
Free: 877-833-5524
Fax: (614)759-3749
URL: http://www.mcgraw-hill.com/

McGraw-Hill Companies Inc.
1221 Avenue of the Americas
New York, NY 10020
Ph: (212)512-2000
Free: 866-436-8502
Fax: (212)512-3840
Co. E-mail: info@mcgraw-hill.com
URL: http://www.mcgraw-hill.com

McGraw-Hill Higher Education
1333 Burr Ridge Pkwy.
Burr Ridge, IL 60521
Free: 800-338-3987

McGraw-Hill Inc.
PO Box 182604
Columbus, OH 43218
Free: 877-833-5524
Fax: (614)759-3749
URL: http://construction.com

McGraw-Hill Inc.
1221 Avenue of the Americas
New York, NY 10020
Ph: (212)512-2000
Free: 866-436-8502
Fax: (212)512-3840
Co. E-mail: customer.service@mcgraw-hill.com
URL: http://www.mcgraw-hill.com

McGraw-Hill Ryerson Ltd.
300 Water St.
Whitby, ON, Canada L1N 9B6
Ph: (905)430-5000
Free: 800-565-5758
Fax: (905)430-5020
Co. E-mail: orders@mcgrawhill.ca
URL: http://www.mcgrawhill.ca

McGraw-Hill
160 Spear St., 7th Fl.
San Francisco, CA 94105
Ph: (415)357-8000
Free: 800-435-2665
Fax: (415)989-7702
Co. E-mail: customer.service@mcgraw-hill.com
URL: http://www.mcgraw-hill.com/

McGraw-Hill
55 Francisco St., Ste. 200
San Francisco, CA 94133
Ph: (415)433-2821
Free: 800-435-2665
Fax: (415)989-7702

McIlvaine Co.
191 Waukegan Rd., Ste. 208
Northfield, IL 60093
Ph: (847)784-0012
Fax: (847)784-0061
Co. E-mail: editor@mcilvainecompany.com
URL: http://www.mcilvainecompany.com/

McMillan Analysis Corp.
PO Box 1323
Morristown, NJ 07962-1323
Ph: (973)328-1674
Free: 800-724-1817
Fax: (973)328-1303
Co. E-mail: info@optionsstrategist.com

MD Publications Inc.
3057 E Cairo St.
Springfield, MO 65802
Ph: (417)866-3917
Free: 800-274-7890
Fax: (417)866-2781
URL: http://www.mdpublications.com

Meadow Books
Three Rivers
Minions
Liskeard 44 15 7936, United Kingdom

Mechanical Contractors Association of America Inc.
1385 Piccard Dr.
Rockville, MD 20850
Ph: (301)869-5800
Free: 800-556-3653
Fax: (301)990-9690
Co. E-mail: abreedlove@mcaa.org
URL: http://www.mcaa.org

Media Enterprises L.P.
155 S El Molino Ave, Ste. 100
Pasadena, CA 91101
Ph: (626)396-0250
Fax: (626)396-0248
Co. E-mail: editorial@boxoffice.com

Mediacorp Canada Inc.
21 New St.
Toronto, ON, Canada M5R 1P7
Ph: (416)964-6069
Free: 800-361-2580
Fax: (416)964-3202
Co. E-mail: info@mediacorp.ca
URL: http://www.mediacorp.ca

Meister Publishing Co.
37733 Euclid Ave.
Willoughby, OH 44094-5992
Ph: (440)942-2000
Free: 800-572-7740
Fax: (440)975-3447
Co. E-mail: info@meistermedia.com
URL: http://www.meistermedia.com

Membership Section
The ASAE Bldg. 1575 I St. NW
Washington, DC 20005-1103
Ph: (202)371-0940
Free: 888-950-2723
Fax: (202)371-8315
Co. E-mail: mbrshpsec@asaenet.org

MENC: The National Association for Music Education
1806 Robert Fulton Dr.
Reston, VA 20191
Ph: (703)860-4000
Free: 800-336-3768
Fax: (703)860-1531
Co. E-mail: michaelb@nafme.org
URL: http://musiced.nafme.org

The Mercier Press, Ltd.
16 Hume St.
Dublin, Ireland
Ph: (353) 1 6615299
Fax: (353) 1 6618583
URL: http://www.mercierpress.ie/

Mercor Media
330 N Wabash, Ste. 3201
Chicago, IL 60611
Ph: (312)628-5870
Free: 800-254-2123
Fax: (312)628-5878
Co. E-mail: info@zweigwhite.com
URL: http://www.nhmroshow.com

Meredith Corp.
125 Park Ave.
New York, NY 10017-5529
Ph: (212)557-6600
URL: http://www.meredith.com

Merriman Market Analyst
PO Box 250012
West Bloomfield, MI 48325-0012
Ph: (248)626-3034
Free: 800-962-4613
Fax: (248)626-5674
Co. E-mail: mmacycles@msn.com

Messenger Courier Association of America
750 National Press Bldg.
Washington, DC 20045
Ph: (202)591-2460
Fax: (202)223-9741
Co. E-mail: info@mcaa.com
URL: http://www.mcaa.com

Messenger-Inquirer
1401 Frederica St.
Owensboro, KY 42301
Ph: (270)926-0123

Metropolitan Books
175 5th Ave.
New York, NY 10010
Ph: (212)982-9300
Free: 800-221-7945
Fax: (212)777-6359
URL: http://us.macmillan.com/
Metropolitan.aspx

Meyers Publishing
799 Camarillo Springs Rd.
Camarillo, CA 93012-8111
Ph: (805)445-8881
Fax: (805)445-8882
Co. E-mail: len@meyerspublishing.com
URL: http://www.meyerspublishing.com

Michigan Association of CPAs
PO Box 5068
Troy, MI 48007-5068
Ph: (248)267-3700
Fax: (248)267-3737
Co. E-mail: macpa@michcpa.org

URL: http://www.michcpa.org

Michigan Department of Consumer and Industry Services
7150 Harris Dr.
Lansing, MI 48909-8143
Ph: (517)322-1791
Fax: (517)322-1374

Michigan Floral Association
1152 Haslett Rd.
Haslett, MI 48840
Ph: (517)575-0110
Fax: (517)575-0115
URL: http://www.michiganfloral.org

MicroDesign Resources
298 S Sunnyvale Ave. Ste. 101
Sunnyvale, CA 94086-6245
Ph: (408)328-3900
Free: 800-527-0288
Fax: (408)737-2242
Co. E-mail: cs@mdr.cahners.com

Microsoft Press
1 Microsoft Way
Redmond, WA 98052-6399
Ph: (425)882-8080
Fax: (425)936-7329

Mid-America Lumbermens Association
PO Box 419264
Kansas City, MO 64141-9264
Ph: (816)561-5323
Free: 800-747-6529
Fax: (816)561-1249
Co. E-mail: mail@themla.com
URL: http://www.themla.com

Mid-West Truckers Association
2727 N Dirksen Pkwy.
Springfield, IL 62702
Ph: (217)525-0310
Fax: (217)525-0342
Co. E-mail: info@mid-westtruckers.com
URL: http://www.mid-westtruckers.com

Midwest Travel Writers Association
PO Box 409
Fayette, MO 65248
Ph: (660)248-3455
Fax: (866)365-4851
Co. E-mail: sylvia@forbesfreelance.com
URL: http://www.mtwa.org

Mike French Publishing
1619 Front St.
Lynden, WA 98264
Ph: (360)354-8326
Free: 800-238-3934
Fax: (360)354-3013

Millennium Publishing Inc.
1170 Ridge Rd., Ste. 217
Webster, NY 14580
Ph: (585)797-4399
Fax: (585)219-5686

URL: http://www.techny.com/

Miller Publishing Company
12400 Whitewater Dr., Ste. 160
Minnetonka, MN 55343
Ph: (952)930-4343

Miller Publishing Company, Inc.
1235 Sycamore View Rd.
Memphis, TN 38134
Ph: (901)372-8280
Free: 800-844-1280
Fax: (901)373-6180

Miller Publishing Group L.L.C.
1918 Main St., 3rd Fl.
Santa Monica, CA 90405
Ph: (310)893-5300
URL: http://www.tennis.com/

Miller Sports Group L.L.C.
79 Madison Ave., 8th Fl.
New York, NY 10016-7802
Ph: (212)636-2700
URL: http://www.tennis.com

Milwaukee Business Journal
825 N Jefferson St., Ste. 200
Milwaukee, WI 53202
Ph: (404)278-7788
Fax: (404)278-7028

Mini-Storage Messenger
2531 W Dunlap Ave.
Phoenix, AZ 85021
Free: 800-352-4636
Fax: (602)678-3511
Co. E-mail: info@minico.com
URL: http://www.ministoragemessenger.
  com/

Minneapolis Business Journal
120 S 6th St., Ste. 900
Minneapolis, MN 55402
Ph: (612)288-2100
Fax: (612)288-2121

Minnesota Center for Book Arts
1011 Washington Ave.S., Ste. 100
Minneapolis, MN 55415
Ph: (612)215-2520
Fax: (612)215-2545
Co. E-mail: mcba@mnbookarts.org
URL: http://www.mnbookarts.org

Minnesota Department of Transportation, Office of Aeronautics
222 E Plato Blvd.
Saint Paul, MN 55107-1618
Ph: (651)234-7200
Free: 800-657-3922
Fax: (651)234-7261
Co. E-mail: aeroinfo@dot.state.mn.us
URL: http://www.dot.state.mn.us/aero

Minority Business Entrepreneur
3528 Torrance Blvd., Ste. 101
Torrance, CA 90503
Ph: (310)540-9398
Fax: (310)792-8263
Co. E-mail: gconrad@mbemag.com
URL: http://www.mbemag.com

Mint Publishing
10532 Los Vaqueros Cir.
Los Alamitos, CA 90720
Ph: (562)252-4010
Free: 888-372-8702
Fax: (562)415-2689
Co. E-mail: support@hatlife.com
URL: http://www.hatlife.com

MIS Research Center
University of Minnesota
Carlson School of Management
321 19th Ave. S, Ste. 3-365
Minneapolis, MN 55455-0438
Ph: (612)624-0862
Fax: (612)626-1600
Co. E-mail: misrc@umn.edu
URL: http://www.misrc.umn.edu/

Missouri Botanical Garden Press
PO Box 299
Saint Louis, MO 63166-0299
Ph: (314)577-9594
Fax: (314)577-9594
URL: http://www.mbgpress.info/

Missouri Municipal League
1727 Southridge Dr.
Jefferson City, MO 65109
Ph: (573)635-9134
Fax: (573)635-9009
Co. E-mail: info@mocities.com
URL: http://www.mocities.com

Missouri State Genealogical Association
PO Box 833
Columbia, MO 65205-0833
Co. E-mail: mosga@mosga.org
URL: http://www.mosga.org/

The MIT Press
55 Hayward St.
Cambridge, MA 02142-1493
Ph: (617)253-5646
Free: 800-356-0343
Fax: (617)258-6779
Co. E-mail: ewfaran@mit.edu
URL: http://mitpress.mit.edu

Mobile Air Conditioning Society Worldwide
225 S Broad St.
Lansdale, PA 19446
Ph: (215)631-7020
Fax: (215)631-7017
Co. E-mail: info@macsw.org

Moby Press
5375 SW Humphrey Blvd.
Portland, OR 97221
Ph: (503)292-6504
Fax: (503)297-6138

Modern Trade Communications Inc.
7450 Skokie Blvd.
Skokie, IL 60077
Ph: (847)674-2200
Fax: (847)674-3676
Co. E-mail: boneill@moderntrade.com
URL: http://www.moderntrade.com

Montana Standard
25 W Granite St.
Butte, MT 59701
Ph: (406)496-5500
Free: 800-877-1074
Fax: (406)496-5569
URL: http://www.mtstandard.com/

The Mood Disorders Association of Ontario
40 Orchard View Blvd., Ste. 222
Toronto, ON, Canada M4R 1B9
Ph: (416)486-8046
Free: 888-486-8236
Fax: (416)486-8127
Co. E-mail: info@mooddisorders.on.ca

Morehouse Publishing
4775 Linglestown Rd.
Harrisburg, PA 17112-8509
Ph: (212)545-2614
Free: 800-242-1918
URL: http://www.morehousegroup.com

Morgan & Claypool Publishers
1537 4th St., Ste. 228
San Rafael, CA 94901
Ph: (415)462-0004
Fax: (206)285-4653
URL: http://www.cled.biz/books/intedition.
  htm

Morgan James Publishing LLC
1225 Franklin Ave., Ste. 325
Garden City, NY 11530
Ph: (516)620-2528
Free: 800-485-4943
Fax: (516)908-4496
URL: http://publishing.morgan-james.com

Morning Sentinel
31 Front St.
Waterville, ME 04901
Ph: (207)873-3341

Morris Animal Foundation
10200 E Girard Ave., Ste. B430
Denver, CO 80231
Ph: (303)790-2345
Free: 800-243-2345
Fax: (303)790-4066
URL: http://www.morrisanimalfoundation.
  org

Morrow/HarperCollins
10 E 53rd St.
New York, NY 10022
Ph: (212)207-7000
URL: http://www.harpercollins.com

Mortgage Bankers Association of America
1717 Rhode Island Ave., NW, Ste. 400
Washington, DC 20036
Ph: (202)557-2700
Free: 800-793-MBAA
Fax: (202)721-0245
URL: http://www.mbaa.org/

Mortgage Bankers Association
1331 L St. NW
Washington, DC 20005
Ph: (202)557-2700
Free: 800-793-MBAA
Fax: (202)721-0245
Co. E-mail: info@mbaa.org
URL: http://www.mbaa.org/

Mosby An Imprint of Elsevier Science Inc. Elsevier Inc. Health Sciences
1600 John F. Kennedy Blvd., Ste. 1800
Philadelphia, PA 19103-2899
Ph: (215)239-3275
Fax: (215)239-3286
Co. E-mail: h.licensing@elsevier.com
URL: http://www.us.elsevierhealth.com/
article.jsp?pageid=368

Mosby Inc.
10801 Executive Center Dr., Ste. 509
Little Rock, AR 72211
Ph: (501)223-5165
Fax: (501)223-0519
URL: http://www.mosbysdrugconsult.com/
HS/Help/officesUS.html

Mosby Inc.
11830 Westline Industrial Dr.
Saint Louis, MO 63146-3326
Ph: (314)872-8370
Free: 800-325-4177
Fax: (314)432-1380
URL: http://www.us.elsevierhealth.com/
home.jsp?sgCountry=PH

Motion Picture Enterprises Publications Inc.
PO Box 276
Tarrytown, NY 10591-0276
Ph: (212)245-0969
Fax: (212)245-0974
Co. E-mail: info@mpe.net
URL: http://www.mpe.net

Motor and Equipment Manufacturers Association
10 Laboratory Dr.
Research Triangle Park, NC 27709
Ph: (919)549-4800
Fax: (919)406-1465
Co. E-mail: info@mema.org

URL: http://www.mema.org

Motor Information Systems
1301 W Long Lake Rd., Ste. 300
Troy, MI 48098
Free: 800-426-6867
Co. E-mail: motormagazine@motor.com
URL: http://www.motor.com/

The Motorcyclist's Post
c/o Leo Castell
11 Haven Ln.
Huntington, CT 06484
Co. E-mail: lcastell@snet.net
URL: http://www.motorcyclistspost.com

Mountain Bike Magazine
33 E Minor St.
Emmaus, PA 18098-0099
Free: 800-666-3434
URL: http://www.bicycling.com/
mountainbikecom

Mountain Publishing Company
PO Box 1747
Hillsboro, OR 97123-1747
Ph: (503)628-3995
Free: 800-879-8719
Fax: (503)628-0203
Co. E-mail: info@mountainpublishingusa.
com
URL: http://www.mountainpublishingusa.
com

Moyer Bell
549 Old North Rd.
Kingston, RI 02881-1220
Ph: (401)783-5480
Free: 888-789-1945
Fax: (401)284-0959

MPL Communications Inc.
133 Richmond St. W
Ste. 700
Toronto, ON, Canada M5H 3M8
Ph: (416)869-1177
Free: 800-804-8846
Fax: (416)869-0456
Co. E-mail: investors@mplcomm.com
URL: http://www.adviceforinvestors.com

MSW Research
1111 Marcus Ave., Ste. MZ 200
Lake Success, NY 11042
Ph: (516)394-6000
Fax: (516)394-6001
Co. E-mail: mail@mswrearch.com
URL: http://www.mswresearch.com

Multicultural Marketing Resources Inc.
101 Fifth Ave., Ste. 10B
New York, NY 10003
Ph: (212)242-3351
Fax: (212)691-5969
Co. E-mail: lisa@multicultural.com

Multimed Inc.
66 Martin St.
Milton, ON, Canada L9T 2R2
Ph: (905)875-2456
Free: 888-834-1001
Fax: (905)875-2864
Co. E-mail: order@multi-med.com
URL: http://www.multi-med.com

Municipal Art Society
457 Madison Ave.
New York, NY 10022
Ph: (212)935-3960
Fax: (212)753-1816
Co. E-mail: info@mas.org

Municipal World Inc.
42860 Sparta Line
Union, ON, Canada N0L 2L0
Ph: (519)633-0031
Free: 888-368-6125
Fax: (519)633-1001
Co. E-mail: mwadmin@municipalworld.
com
URL: http://www.municipalworld.com/
index.php/Home/Contact

Music Teachers National Association
441 Vine St., Ste. 3100
Cincinnati, OH 45202-2811
Ph: (513)421-1420
Free: 888-512-5278
Fax: (513)421-2503
URL: http://www.mtna.org

Music Trades Corp.
80 W St.
Englewood, NJ 07631
Ph: (201)871-1965
Free: 800-423-6530
Fax: (201)871-0455
Co. E-mail: music@musictrades.com
URL: http://www.musictrades.com

N

NACE International: The Corrosion Society
1440 S Creek Dr.
Houston, TX 77084-4906
Ph: (281)228-6200
Free: 800-797-6223
Fax: (281)228-6300
Co. E-mail: firstservice@nace.org
URL: http://www.nace.org

NACOMEX USA Inc.
PO Box 394
Tivoli, NY 12583
Ph: (212)808-3062
Free: 800-NAC-OMEX
Fax: (212)681-9211
Co. E-mail: info@nacomex.com

NAGMR Consumer Products Sales Agencies
766 W Algonquin Rd.
Arlington Heights, IL 60005
Ph: (312)644-6610
Fax: (312)245-1080
Co. E-mail: nagmr@sba.com

NAMM - The International Music Products Association
5790 Armada Dr.
Carlsbad, CA 92008-4608
Ph: (760)438-8001
Free: 800-767-6266
Fax: (760)438-7327
Co. E-mail: info@namm.org
URL: http://www.namm.org

NARSA
300 Village Run Rd., Ste. 103, No. 221
Wexford, PA 15090-6315
Ph: (724)799-8415
Fax: (724)799-8416
Co. E-mail: info@narsa.org
URL: http://www.narsa.org/

National Accrediting Agency for Clinical Laboratory Sciences
8410 W Bryn Mawr Ave., Ste. 670
Chicago, IL 60631-3415
Ph: (773)714-8880
Fax: (773)714-8886
Co. E-mail: info@naacls.org

National Agri-Marketing Association
11020 King St., Ste. 205
Overland Park, KS 66210
Ph: (913)491-6500
Free: 800-530-5646
Fax: (913)491-6502
Co. E-mail: agrimktg@nama.org
URL: http://www.nama.org

National Agricultural Aviation Association
1005 E St. SE
Washington, DC 20003-2847
Ph: (202)546-5722
Fax: (202)546-5726
Co. E-mail: information@agaviation.org
URL: http://www.agaviation.org

National Air Transportation Association
4226 King St.
Alexandria, VA 22302
Ph: (703)845-9000
Free: 800-808-6282
Fax: (703)845-8176
URL: http://www.nata.aero/

National Antique & Art Dealers Association of America Inc.
220 E 57th St.
New York, NY 10022
Ph: (212)826-9707
Fax: (212)832-9493
Co. E-mail: paulh@naada.org

URL: http://www.naadaa.org

National Appliance Parts Suppliers Association
4015 W Marshall Ave.
Longview, TX 75604
Ph: (903)759-3983
Co. E-mail: board06@napsaweb.org
URL: http://www.napsaweb.org

National Association for Drama Therapy
44365 Premier Plz., Ste. 220
Ashburn, VA 20147
Ph: (571)333-2991
Free: 888-416-7167
Fax: (571)223-6440
Co. E-mail: office@nadt.org
URL: http://www.nadt.org

National Association for Healthcare Quality
4700 W Lake Ave.
Glenview, IL 60025
Ph: (847)375-4720
Free: 800-966-9392
Fax: (847)375-6320
Co. E-mail: info@nahq.org
URL: http://www.nahq.org

National Association for Home Care and Hospice
228 7th St. SE
Washington, DC 20003
Ph: (202)547-7424
Fax: (202)547-3540
Co. E-mail: exec@nahc.org
URL: http://www.nahc.org

National Association for Home Care
228 Seventh St. SE
Washington, DC 20003
Ph: (202)547-7424
Fax: (202)547-3540
URL: http://www.nahc.org

National Association for Printing Leadership
75 W. Century Rd., Ste. 100
Paramus, NJ 07652-1408
Ph: (201)634-9600
Free: 800-642-6275
Fax: (201)634-0324
Co. E-mail: Information@napl.org
URL: http://www.napl.org

National Association for the Education of Young Children
1313 L St. NW, Ste. 500
Washington, DC 20005
Ph: (202)232-8777
Free: 800-424-2460
Fax: (202)328-1846
Co. E-mail: naeyc@naeyc.org
URL: http://www.naeyc.org

National Association of Attorneys General
2030 M St. NW, 8th Fl.
Washington, DC 20036-3306
Ph: (202)326-6000
Fax: (202)331-1427
Co. E-mail: jhunter@naag.org
URL: http://www.naag.org

National Association of Black Accountants
7474 Greenway Center Dr., Ste. 1120
Greenbelt, MD 20770
Ph: (301)474-6222
Free: 888-571-2939
Fax: (301)474-3114
Co. E-mail: customerservice@nabainc.org
URL: http://www.nabainc.org

National Association of Black Journalists
University of Maryland
8701-A Adelphi Rd.
Adelphi, MD 20783-1716
Ph: (301)445-7100
Fax: (301)445-7101
Co. E-mail: nabj@nabj.org

National Association of Colleges and Employers
62 Highland Ave.
Bethlehem, PA 18017-9481
Ph: (610)868-1421
Free: 800-544-5272
Fax: (610)868-0208
Co. E-mail: mmackes@naceweb.org
URL: http://www.naceweb.org

National Association of Concessionaires
35 E Wacker Dr., Ste. 1816
Chicago, IL 60601
Ph: (312)236-3858
Fax: (312)236-7809
Co. E-mail: info@naconline.org
URL: https://www.b-online.com/secure/nac/

National Association of Convenience Stores
1600 Duke St., 7th Fl.
Alexandria, VA 22314
Ph: (703)684-3600
Free: 800-966-6227
Fax: (703)836-4564
Co. E-mail: information@nacsonline.com
URL: http://www.nacsonline.com

National Association of Educational Procurement
5523 Research Park Dr., Ste. 340
Baltimore, MD 21228
Ph: (443)543-5540
Fax: (443)543-5550
Co. E-mail: dmurner@naepnet.org
URL: http://www.naepnet.org

National Association of Electrical Distributors Inc.
1181 Corporate Lake Dr.
Saint Louis, MO 63132
Ph: (314)991-9000
Free: 888-791-2512
Fax: (314)991-3060
Co. E-mail: customerservice@naed.org
URL: http://www.naed.org

National Association of Exposition Managers, Inc.

National Association of Home and Workshop Writers
c/o Richard Day
3131 Tori Trl.
Templeton, CA 93465-5906
Co. E-mail: writer@danramsey.com

National Association of Home Builders
1201 15th St. NW
Washington, DC 20005
Ph: (202)266-8200
Free: 800-368-5242
Fax: (202)266-8400
Co. E-mail: 76176.2456@compuserve.
  com
URL: http://www.nahb.org/

National Association of Independent Fee Appraisers
330 N Wabash Ave., Ste. 2000
Chicago, IL 60611
Ph: (312)321-6830
Fax: (312)673-6652
Co. E-mail: info@naifa.com
URL: http://www.naifa.com

National Association of Insurance Commissioners
2301 McGee St., Ste. 800
Kansas City, MO 64108-2662
Ph: (816)842-3600
Fax: (816)783-8175
Co. E-mail: prodserv@naic.org
URL: http://www.naic.org/

National Association of Insurance Women International
9343 E 95th Ct. S
Tulsa, OK 74133
Ph: (918)294-3700
Free: 800-766-6249
Fax: (918)294-3711
Co. E-mail: joinnaiw@naiw.org
URL: http://www.naiw.org

National Association of Investors Corp.
711 W 13 Mile Rd.
Madison Heights, MI 48071
Ph: (248)583-6242
Free: 877-275-6242
Fax: (248)583-4880
Co. E-mail: service@betterinvesting.org
URL: http://www.betterinvesting.org/Public/
  ContactUs/ContactUs/default.htm

National Association of Jewelry Appraisers
PO Box 18
Rego Park, NY 11374-0018
Ph: (718)896-1536
Fax: (718)997-9057
Co. E-mail: office@najaappraisers.com
URL: http://www.najaappraisers.com

National Association of Marine Surveyors
PO Box 9306
Chesapeake, VA 23321-9306
Ph: (757)638-9638
Free: 800-822-6267
Fax: (757)638-9639
Co. E-mail: office@namsglobal.org
URL: http://namsglobal.org

National Association of Pizza Operators
908 S 8th St., Ste. 200
Louisville, KY 40203
Ph: (502)736-9500
Free: 800-489-8324
Co. E-mail: plachapelle@pizzatoday.com
URL: http://www.pizzatoday.com

National Association of Realtors
430 N Michigan Ave.
Chicago, IL 60611
Ph: (312)329-8495
Free: 800-441-5263
Fax: (312)329-8633
Co. E-mail: rli@realtors.org
URL: http://www.realtor.org

National Association of Schools of Music
11250 Roger Bacon Dr., Ste. 21
Reston, VA 20190-5248
Ph: (703)437-0700
Fax: (703)437-6312
Co. E-mail: info@arts-accredit.org
URL: http://nasm.arts-accredit.org

National Association of State Boards of Accountancy
150 Fourth Ave. N Ste. 700
Nashville, TN 37219-2417
Ph: (615)880-4200
Fax: (615)880-4290

National Association of State Procurement Officials
201 E Main St., Ste. 1405
Lexington, KY 40507-2004
Ph: (859)514-9159
Fax: (859)231-1928
Co. E-mail: naspo@amrms.com
URL: http://www.naspo.org

National Association of Tax Professionals
720 Association Dr.
Appleton, WI 54912-8002
Ph: (920)749-1040
Free: 800-558-3402

Fax: (800)747-0001
Co. E-mail: natp@natptax.com
URL: http://www.natptax.com/contact_us.
  html

National Association of Wholesaler-Distributors
1325 G St. NW, Ste. 1000
Washington, DC 20005
Ph: (202)872-0885
Fax: (202)785-0586
Co. E-mail: naw@naw.org
URL: http://www.naw.org

National Association of Women Artists
80 5th Ave., Ste. 1405
New York, NY 10011
Ph: (212)675-1616
Fax: (212)675-1616
Co. E-mail: office@nawanet.org
URL: http://www.thenawa.org

National Association of Women in Construction
327 S Adams St.
Fort Worth, TX 76104
Ph: (817)877-5551
Free: 800-552-3506
Fax: (817)877-0324
Co. E-mail: nawic@nawic.org
URL: http://www.nawic.org

National Auctioneers Association
8880 Ballentine St.
Overland Park, KS 66214
Ph: (913)541-8084
Fax: (913)894-5281
Co. E-mail: support@auctioneers.org
URL: http://www.auctioneers.org

National Auto Auction Association
5320 Spectrum Dr., Ste. D
Frederick, MD 21703
Ph: (301)696-0400
Fax: (301)631-1359
Co. E-mail: naaa@naaa.com
URL: http://www.naaa.com

National Automotive Radiator Service Association
15000 Commerce Pkwy., Ste. C
Mount Laurel, NJ 08054
Ph: (856)439-1575
Free: 800-551-3232
Fax: (856)439-9596
Co. E-mail: info@narsa.org
URL: http://www.narsa.org/

National Bicycle Dealers Association
3176 Pullman St., No. 117
Costa Mesa, CA 92626
Ph: (949)722-6909
Fax: (949)722-1747
Co. E-mail: info@nbda.com
URL: http://nbda.com

National Burglar and Fire Alarm Association
2300 Valley View Ln., Ste. 230
Irving, TX 75062
Ph: (214)260-5970
Fax: (214)260-5979
Co. E-mail: staff@alarm.org
URL: http://www.alarm.org

National Bus Trader Inc.
9698 W Judson Rd.
Polo, IL 61064-9049
Ph: (815)946-2341
Fax: (815)946-2347
Co. E-mail: info@busmag.com
URL: http://www.busmag.com/

National Career Development Association
305 N Beech Cir.
Broken Arrow, OK 74012
Ph: (918)663-7060
Free: 866-367-6232
Fax: (918)663-7058
Co. E-mail: dosborn@fsu.edu
URL: http://associationdatabase.com/aws/
    NCDA/pt/sp/Home_Page

National Catholic Partnership on Disability
415 Michigan Ave. NE, Ste. 95
Washington, DC 20017-4501
Ph: (202)529-2933
Fax: (202)529-4678
Co. E-mail: ncpd@ncpd.org
URL: http://www.ncpd.org

National Chamber of Commerce for Women
10 Waterside Plz., Ste. 6H
New York, NY 10010
Ph: (212)685-3454
Fax: (212)685-4547
Co. E-mail: commerce-for-women@juno.
    com

National Christmas Tree Association
16020 Swingley Ridge Rd., Ste. 300
Chesterfield, MO 63017
Ph: (636)449-5070
Fax: (636)449-5051
Co. E-mail: info@realchristmastrees.org
URL: http://www.christmastree.org

National Community Pharmacists Association
100 Daingerfield Rd.
Alexandria, VA 22314
Ph: (703)683-8200
Free: 800-544-7447
Fax: (703)683-3619
Co. E-mail: info@ncpanet.org
URL: http://www.ncpanet.org

National Concrete Masonry Association
13750 Sunrise Valley Dr.
Herndon, VA 20171-4662
Ph: (703)713-1900
Free: 877-627-3976
Fax: (703)713-1910
Co. E-mail: rthomas@ncma.org
URL: http://www.ncma.org

National Conference of State Liquor Administrators
c/o Pamela D. Salario
6183 Beau Douglas Ave.
Gonzales, LA 70737
Ph: (225)473-7209
Co. E-mail: pamsalario@cox.net
URL: http://www.ncsla.org

The National Consumer Voice for Quality Long-Term Care
1828 L St. NW, Ste. 801
Washington, DC 20036
Ph: (202)332-2275
Fax: (202)332-2949
Co. E-mail: nccnhr@nccnhr.org
URL: http://www.nursinghomeaction.org

National Council for GeoCosmic Research
531 Main St., No. 1612
New York, NY 10044
Ph: (212)838-6247
Co. E-mail: execsec@geocosmic.org
URL: http://www.geocosmic.org

National Council of Acoustical Consultants
9100 Purdue Rd., Ste. 200
Indianapolis, IN 46268
Ph: (317)328-0642
Fax: (317)328-4629
Co. E-mail: info@ncac.com
URL: http://www.ncac.com

National Council on the Aging (NCOA)
1901 L St. NW 4th Fl.
Washington, DC 20036
Ph: (202)479-1200
Free: 800-373-4906
Fax: (202)479-0735
Co. E-mail: info@ncoa.org
URL: http://www.ncoa.org

National Customs Brokers and Forwarders Association of America
1200 18th St. NW, No. 901
Washington, DC 20036
Ph: (202)466-0222
Fax: (202)466-0226
Co. E-mail: staff@ncbfaa.org
URL: http://www.ncbfaa.org

National Cutting Horse Association
260 Bailey Ave.
Fort Worth, TX 76107-1862
Ph: (817)594-2068
Fax: (817)244-2015

Co. E-mail: youth@nchacutting.com
URL: http://www.nchacutting.com

National Dance Association
1900 Association Dr.
Reston, VA 20191-1502
Ph: (703)476-3400
Free: 800-213-7193
Fax: (703)476-9527
Co. E-mail: lhelms@aahperd.org
URL: http://www.aahperd.org/nda

The National Dipper
1028 W Devon Ave.
Elk Grove Village, IL 60007
Ph: (847)301-8400
Fax: (847)301-8402
URL: http://www.nationaldipper.com/

National Electrical Contractors Association
3 Bethesda Metro Ctr., Ste. 1100
Bethesda, MD 20814
Ph: (301)657-3110
Fax: (301)215-4500
Co. E-mail: neca@necanet.org
URL: http://www.necanet.org

National Electrical Manufacturers Representatives Association
28 Deer St., Ste. 302
Portsmouth, NH 03801
Ph: (914)524-8650
Free: 800-446-3672
Fax: (914)524-8655
Co. E-mail: nemra@nemra.org
URL: http://www.nemra.org

National Electronic Distributors Association
1111 Alderman Dr., Ste. 400
Alpharetta, GA 30005-4175
Ph: (678)393-9990
Fax: (678)393-9998
Co. E-mail: admin@nedassoc.org
URL: http://www.nedassoc.org

National Federation of Community Broadcasters
1970 Broadway, Ste. 1000
Oakland, CA 94612
Ph: (510)451-8200
Fax: (510)451-8208
Co. E-mail: newsletter@nfcb.org

National Federation of Independent Business (NFIB)
7315 Wisconsin Ave., Ste. 750
Bethesda, MD 20814
Ph: (615)872-5800
Free: 800-634-2669
URL: http://www.nfib.com/

National Federation of Independent Business
1201 F St. NW, Ste. 200
Washington, DC 20004
Ph: (615)82-5800

Free: 800-634-2669

National Fisherman
PO Box 7438
Portland, ME 04112-7437
Ph: (207)842-5608
Fax: (207)842-5609
Co. E-mail: info@nationalfisherman.com
URL: http://www.nationalfisherman.com

National Foundation for Credit Counseling
801 Roeder Rd., Ste. 900
Silver Spring, MD 20910
Ph: (301)589-5600
Free: 800-388-2227
Fax: (301)495-5623
Co. E-mail: nfcc@nfcc.org
URL: http://www.debtadvice.org/

National Frozen & Refrigerated Foods Association Inc.
4755 Linglestown Rd., Ste. 300
Harrisburg, PA 17112-8547
Ph: (717)657-8601
Fax: (717)657-9862
Co. E-mail: info@nfraweb.org
URL: http://www.nfraweb.org

National Funeral Directors Association
13625 Bishop's Dr.
Brookfield, WI 53005-6607
Ph: (262)789-1880
Free: 800-228-6332
Fax: (262)789-6977
Co. E-mail: nfda@nfda.org
URL: http://www.nfda.org

National Genealogical Society
3108 Columbia Pike, Ste. 300
Arlington, VA 22204-4370
Ph: (703)525-0050
Free: 800-473-0060
Fax: (703)525-0052
Co. E-mail: ngs@ngsgenealogy.org
URL: http://www.ngsgenealogy.org

National Geographic
1145 17th St. NW
Washington, DC 20036
Ph: (202)857-7027
Fax: (202)828-6679
Co. E-mail: pressroom@ngs.org
URL: http://www.ngsp.com

National Glass Association
1945 Old Gallows Rd., Ste. 750
Vienna, VA 22182
Ph: (703)442-4890
Free: 866-342-5642
Fax: (703)442-0630
Co. E-mail: pjames@glass.org
URL: http://www.glass.org

National Guild for Community Arts Education
520 8th Ave., Ste. 302
New York, NY 10018
Ph: (212)268-3337
Fax: (212)268-3995
Co. E-mail: guildinfo@nationalguild.org
URL: http://www.nationalguild.org

National Guild of Decoupeurs
1017 Pucker St.
Stowe, VT 05672
Ph: (802)253-3903
Fax: (802)253-9552
Co. E-mail: decoupageartistworldwide@
gmail.com
URL: http://www.decoupage.org

National Hardwood Lumber Association
6830 Raleigh La Grange Rd.
Memphis, TN 38134-0518
Ph: (901)377-1818
Free: 800-933-0318
Fax: (901)382-6419
Co. E-mail: info@nhla.com
URL: http://www.nhla.com

National Health Association
PO Box 30630
Tampa, FL 33630
Ph: (813)961-6100
Fax: (813)961-6114
Co. E-mail: lgrudnik@healthscience.org
URL: http://healthscience.org

National Health Council
1730 M St. NW, Ste. 500
Washington, DC 20036
Ph: (202)785-3910
Fax: (202)785-5923
Co. E-mail: info@nhcouncil.org
URL: http://www.nationalhealthcouncil.org

National Highway Carriers Directory Inc.
4432 Pebble Creek Ln.
Long Grove, IL 60047
Ph: (847)634-0606
Fax: (847)634-1026
Co. E-mail: nhcd2@aol.com
URL: http://www.national-highway.com/
index2.html

National Hispanic Council on Aging
734 15th St. NW, Ste. 1050
Washington, DC 20005
Ph: (202)347-9733
Fax: (202)347-9735
Co. E-mail: nhcoa@nhcoa.org
URL: http://www.nhcoa.org

National Independent Automobile Dealers Association
2521 Brown Blvd.
Arlington, TX 76006
Ph: (817)640-3838
Free: 800-682-3837

Fax: (817)649-5866
Co. E-mail: mike@niada.com
URL: http://www.niada.com

National Information Standards Organization
1 N Charles St., Ste. 1905
Baltimore, MD 21201
Ph: (301)654-2512
Free: 866-957-1593
Fax: (410)685-5278
Co. E-mail: nisohq@niso.org
URL: http://www.niso.org

National Institute for Automotive Service Excellence
101 Blue Seal Dr. SE, No. 101
Leesburg, VA 20175
Ph: (703)669-6600
Free: 877-ASE-TECH
Fax: (703)669-6123

National Institute of Business Management
1750 Old Meadow Rd., Ste. 302
Mc Lean, VA 22102
Ph: (703)905-8000
Free: 800-543-2049
Fax: (703)905-8042
Co. E-mail: customer@nibm.net

National Insulation Association
12100 Sunset Hills Rd., Ste. 330
Reston, VA 20190
Ph: (703)464-6422
Fax: (703)464-5896
Co. E-mail: mjones@insulation.org
URL: http://www.insulation.org

National League for Nursing
61 Broadway, 33rd Fl.
New York, NY 10006
Ph: (212)363-5555
Free: 800-669-1656
Fax: (212)812-0391
Co. E-mail: generalinfo@nln.org
URL: http://www.nln.org

National Marine Fisheries Service Fisheries Statistics & Economics Division, F/ST1
1315 EW Hwy.
Silver Spring, MD 20910
Co. E-mail: st1help@noaa.gov
URL: http://www.st.nmfs.gov/st1/

National Marine Manufacturers Association
200 E Randolph Dr. Ste. 5100
Chicago, IL 60601
Ph: (312)946-6200
Fax: (212)922-9607

National Marine Representatives Association
1333 Delany Rd., Ste. 500
Gurnee, IL 60031
Ph: (847)662-3167

Fax: (847)336-7126
Co. E-mail: info@nmraonline.org
URL: http://www.nmraonline.org

National Meat Association
1970 Broadway, Ste. 825
Oakland, CA 94612
Ph: (510)763-1533
Fax: (510)763-6186
Co. E-mail: staff@nmaonline.org
URL: http://www.nmaonline.org/

National Minority Business Council Inc.
25 W 45th St., Ste. 301
New York, NY 10036
Ph: (212)997-4753
Fax: (212)997-5102
Co. E-mail: nmbc@msn.com

National Opera Association
PO Box 60869
Canyon, TX 79016-0869
Ph: (806)651-2857
Fax: (806)651-2958
Co. E-mail: rhansen@noa.org
URL: http://www.noa.org

National Publishing Company Inc.
1533 Burgundy Pkwy.
Streamwood, IL 60107
Ph: (630)837-2044
Fax: (630)837-1210
Co. E-mail: natllock@aol.com
URL: http://www.thenationallocksmith.com/
    index.asp

National Recreation and Park Association
22377 Belmont Ridge Rd.
Ashburn, VA 20148-4501
Ph: (703)858-0784
Free: 800-626-6772
Fax: (703)858-0794
Co. E-mail: membership@nrpa.org
URL: http://www.nrpa.org

National Register Publishing Co.
300 Connell Dr., Ste. 2000
Berkeley Heights, NJ 07922
Free: 800-473-7020
Fax: (908)673-1189
Co. E-mail: nrpeditorial@mar-
    quiswhoswho.com
URL: http://www.nationalregisterpub.com

**National Research Council Canada,
NRC Research Press NRC Corporate
Communications**
1200 Montreal Rd., Bldg. M-58
Ottawa, ON, Canada K1A 0R6
Ph: (613)993-9101
Free: 877-672-2672
Fax: (613)952-9907
Co. E-mail: info@nrc-cnrc.gc.ca
URL: http://www.nrc-cnrc.gc.ca

National Rifle Association of America
11250 Waples Mill Rd.
Fairfax, VA 22030
Free: 800-672-3888
Co. E-mail: info@nraila.org
URL: http://www.nrahq.org

National Roofing Contractors Association
10255 W Higgins Rd., Ste. 600
Rosemont, IL 60018-5607
Ph: (847)299-9070
Free: 800-323-9545
Fax: (847)299-1183
Co. E-mail: llewis@nrca.net
URL: http://www.nrca.net

National Sculpture Society
75 Varick St., 11th Fl.
New York, NY 10017
Ph: (212)764-5645
Fax: (212)764-5651
Co. E-mail: gwen@nationalsculpture.org
URL: http://www.nationalsculpture.org/
    nssN/index.cfm

National Shoe Retailers Association
3037 W Ina Rd., Ste. 101
Tucson, AZ 85741
Ph: (520)209-1710
Fax: (520)209-5595
Co. E-mail: info@nsra.org
URL: http://www.nsra.org

National Skeet Shooting Association
5931 Roft Rd.
San Antonio, TX 78253
Ph: (210)688-3371
Free: 800-877-5338
Fax: (210)688-3014
Co. E-mail: nssa@nssa-nsca.com
URL: http://www.mynssa.com

National Ski and Snowboard Retailers Association
1601 Feehanville Dr., Ste. 300
Mount Prospect, IL 60056-6035
Ph: (847)391-9825
Free: 888-257-1168
Fax: (847)391-9827
Co. E-mail: info@nssra.com
URL: http://www.nssra.com

National Sporting Goods Association
1601 Feehanville Dr., Ste. 300
Mount Prospect, IL 60056
Ph: (847)296-6742
Free: 800-815-5422
Fax: (847)391-9827
Co. E-mail: info@nsga.org
URL: http://www.nsga.org

National Strength and Conditioning Association
1885 Bob Johnson Dr.
Colorado Springs, CO 80906
Ph: (719)632-6722

Free: 800-815-6826
Fax: (719)632-6367
Co. E-mail: nsca@nsca.com
URL: http://www.nsca-lift.org

National Tank Truck Carriers
950 N Glebe Rd., Ste. 520
Arlington, VA 22203
Ph: (703)838-1960
Free: 800-441-1414
Fax: (703)838-8860
Co. E-mail: nttcstaff@tanktruck.org
URL: http://www.tanktruck.org

National Taxpayers Union
108 N Alfred St.
Alexandria, VA 22314-3053
Ph: (703)683-5700
Fax: (703)683-5722
Co. E-mail: ntu@ntu.org
URL: http://www.ntu.org

**National Technical Information Service
U.S. Department of Commerce Technology Administration**
5285 Port Royal Rd.
Springfield, VA 22161
Ph: (703)605-6585
Free: 888-584-8332
Fax: (703)605-6900
Co. E-mail: helpdesk@ntis.gov
URL: http://www.ntis.gov/

National Tour Association
546 E Main St.
Lexington, KY 40508
Ph: (859)226-4444
Free: 800-682-8886
Fax: (859)226-4414
Co. E-mail: questions@ntastaff.com

National Trade Publications Inc.
13 Century Hill Dr.
Latham, NY 12110
Ph: (518)783-1281
Fax: (518)783-1386
Co. E-mail: hstyler@ntpinc.com
URL: http://www.ntpinc.com

National Truck Equipment Association
37400 Hills Tech Dr.
Farmington Hills, MI 48331-3414
Ph: (248)489-7090
Free: 800-441-6832
Fax: (248)489-8590
Co. E-mail: info@ntea.com
URL: http://www.ntea.com

National Vehicle Leasing Association
7250 Pkwy. Dr., Ste. 510
Hanover, MD 21076
Ph: (410)782-2342
Free: 800-225-6852
Fax: (410)712-4038
Co. E-mail: info@nvla.org
URL: http://www.nvla.org

National Venture Capital Association
1655 N Ft. Myer Dr., Ste. 850
Arlington, VA 22209
Ph: (703)524-2549
Fax: (703)524-3940
Co. E-mail: mheesen@nvca.org
URL: http://www.nvca.org

National Wellness Institute
PO Box 827
Stevens Point, WI 54481-0827
Ph: (715)342-2969
Free: 800-243-8694
Fax: (715)342-2979
Co. E-mail: nwi@nationalwellness.org
URL: http://www.nationalwellness.org

National Wood Carvers Association
PO Box 43218
Cincinnati, OH 45243
Ph: (513)561-0627
Co. E-mail: nwca@chipchats.org
URL: http://www.chipchats.org

National Writers Association
10940 S Parker Rd., No. 508
Parker, CO 80134
Ph: (303)841-0246
Fax: (303)841-2607
Co. E-mail: natlwritersassn@hotmail.com
URL: http://www.nationalwriters.com

NATSO
1737 King St., Ste. 200
Alexandria, VA 22314
Ph: (703)549-2100
Free: 888-275-6287
Fax: (703)684-4525
Co. E-mail: tpmembership@natso.com
URL: http://www.natso.com

Natural Hazards Research and Applications Information Center
482 UCB
Institute of Behavioral Science, No. 6
University of Colorado
Boulder, CO 80309-0482
Ph: (303)492-6818
Fax: (303)492-2151
Co. E-mail: hazctr@colorado.edu
URL: http://www.colorado.edu/hazards/

Navellier-MPT Review Inc.
1 E Liberty, 3rd Fl.
Reno, NV 89501
Ph: (775)785-2300
Free: 800-887-8671
Fax: (775)562-8212
Co. E-mail: info@navellier.com
URL: http://navellier.com

Neal-Schuman Publishers Inc.
100 William St., Ste. 2004
New York, NY 10038-5018
Ph: (212)925-8650
Free: 866-672-6657
Fax: (212)219-8916

Co. E-mail: info@neal-schuman.com
URL: http://www.neal-schuman.com

Ned Davis Research Inc.
600 Bird Bay Dr.
Venice, FL 34285
Ph: (941)484-6107
Free: 800-241-0621
Fax: (941)484-8693
URL: http://www.ndr.com

The Needlecraft Shop L.L.C.
23 Old Pecan Rd.
Big Sandy, TX 75755-2200
Fax: (903)636-4088
Co. E-mail: privacy@drgnetwork.com
URL: http://www.needlecraftshop.com

Nelson Business
PO Box 141000
Nashville, TN 37214
Free: 800-251-4000
URL: http://www.thomasnelson.com

Nelson Information
195 Broadway
New York, NY 10007
Ph: (914)937-8400
Free: 800-333-6357
Fax: (646)822-3000
Co. E-mail: nelson.support@thomson.com

Nelson Publishing Inc.
2506 Tamiami Trl. N
Nokomis, FL 34275
Ph: (941)966-9521
Fax: (941)966-2590
URL: http://www.nelsonpub.com/

Nelson Thomson Learning
1120 Birchmount Rd.
Scarborough, ON, Canada M1K 5G4
Ph: (416)752-9100
Free: 800-268-2222
Fax: (416)752-9646

New American Library/Penguin Group
375 Hudson St.
New York, NY 10014-3657
Free: 800-847-5515
Co. E-mail: insidesales@us.penguingroup.com
URL: http://us.penguingroup.com/static/pages/publishers/adult/nal.html

New England Appraisers Association
5 Gill Ter.
Ludlow, VT 05149
Ph: (802)228-7444
Co. E-mail: llt44@tds.net
URL: http://www.newenglandappraisers.net/

New England Bride Inc.
29 Durham Dr.
Lynnfield, MA 01940
Ph: (978)535-4186

Free: 800-241-5458
Fax: (978)535-3090
URL: http://www.nebride.com/

New England Connexion
PO Box 621
Goshen, NY 10924-0621
Ph: (845)294-6867
Fax: (845)291-7114
Co. E-mail: nhsip@frontiernet.net

New England Historic Genealogical Society
101 Newbury St.
Boston, MA 02116
Ph: (617)536-5740
Free: 888-296-3447
Fax: (617)536-7307
Co. E-mail: administration@nehgs.org
URL: http://www.americanancestors.org

New Jersey Law Journal
238 Mulberry St.
Newark, NJ 07101-6081
Ph: (973)642-0075
Fax: (973)642-0920
Co. E-mail: njlj@aol.com
URL: http://www.law.com/jsp/nj/index.jsp?slreturn=1&hbxlogin=1

New Orleans Lettering Arts Association Inc.
PO Box 4117
New Orleans, LA 70178
Ph: (504)861-1807
Co. E-mail: nolaa@gnofn.org
URL: http://www.gnofn.org/nolaa/

New Paradigm Media
11661 W 14th Ave.
Golden, CO 80401
URL: http://holistic-books.ning.com

New Road Publishing
3650 Rogers Rd., Ste. 328
Wake Forest, NC 27587
Ph: (919)453-2850
Fax: (866)808-2851
Co. E-mail: info@newroadpublishing.com
URL: http://www.newroadpublishing.com

New Society Publishers
PO Box 189
Gabriola Island, BC, Canada V0R 1X0
Ph: (250)247-9737
Free: 800-567-6772
Fax: (250)247-7471
Co. E-mail: info@newsociety.com
URL: http://www.newsociety.com/

New Writer's Magazine
PO Box 5976
Sarasota, FL 34277
Ph: (941)953-7903
Fax: (941)953-7903
Co. E-mail: newriters@aol.com
URL: http://www.pspcom.com/

New York AMA Communication Services Inc.
116 E 27th St., 6th Fl.
New York, NY 10016
Ph: (212)849-2752
Free: 800-792-9202
Fax: (212)202-7920
Co. E-mail: info@greenbook.org
URL: http://www.greenbook.org

The New York Review of Books
435 Hudson St., Ste. 300
New York, NY 10014
Ph: (212)757-8070
Free: 800-354-0050
Fax: (212)333-5374
Co. E-mail: nyrb@nybooks.com
URL: http://www.nybooks.com

New York State Society of Certified Public Accountants
3 Park Ave., 18th Fl.
New York, NY 10016-5991
Ph: (212)719-8300
Free: 800-633-6320
Fax: (212)719-3364
Co. E-mail: info@nysscpa.org
URL: http://www.nysscpa.org

The New York Times Co.
620 Eighth Ave.
New York, NY 10018
Ph: (212)556-1234
Fax: (212)556-7088
Co. E-mail: letters@nytimes.com
URL: http://www.nytimes.com

New York Times Co./Globe Newspaper Co.
135 Morrissey Blvd.
Boston, MA 02107-3310
Ph: (617)929-2935
Fax: (617)929-3192

The New York Times Company
229 W 43rd St.
New York, NY 10036-3913
Ph: (212)556-7652
Free: 888-698-6397
Fax: (212)556-4603
URL: http://www.nytimes.com

New York University Press (NYU Press)
838 Broadway, 3rd Fl.
New York, NY 10003-4812
Ph: (212)998-2575
Free: 800-996-6987
Fax: (212)995-3833
Co. E-mail: information@nyupress.org
URL: http://www.nyupress.org

New-Sentinel
600 W Main St.
Fort Wayne, IN 46802
Ph: (260)461-8298
Fax: (260)461-8817

NewBay Media, LLC
28 E 28th St., 12th Fl.
New York, NY 10016
Ph: (212)378-0400
Fax: (917)281-4704
URL: http://www.nbmedia.com/

Newmarket Press
18 E 48th St.
New York, NY 10017
Ph: (212)832-3575
Free: 800-233-4830
Fax: (212)832-3629
URL: http://www.newmarketpress.com

Newport Communications Div. HIC Corp.
38 Executive Park, Ste. 300
Irvine, CA 92614
Ph: (949)261-1636
Fax: (949)261-2904
URL: http://www.newportcommunications-group.com

News & Observer
215 S McDowell St.
Raleigh, NC 27602
Ph: (919)829-4500
Free: 800-522-4205

News Media Directories
PO Box 316
Mount Dora, FL 32756
Free: 800-749-6399
Fax: (866)586-7020
Co. E-mail: newsmedia@comcast.net
URL: http://www.newsmediadirectories.net

News-Herald
7085 Mentor Ave.
Willoughby, OH 44094
Ph: (440)951-0000
Free: 800-947-2737
Fax: (440)951-7853

The News-Herald
7085 Mentor Ave.
Willoughby, OH 44094
Ph: (440)951-0000
Free: 800-947-2737
Fax: (440)951-7653

The Newsletter Factory
1775 The Exchange, Ste. 300
Atlanta, GA 30339
Ph: (770)955-1600
Free: 800-788-9550
Fax: (770)955-3313

Newsletter on Newsletters
20 W Chestnut St.
Rhinebeck, NY 12572
Ph: (845)876-5222
Fax: (845)876-4943
Co. E-mail: newsonnews@newsletterbiz. com
URL: http://www.newsletterbiz.com

Newsletter Publishing Corp.
117 Mercer St., Ste. 200
Seattle, WA 98119-3960
Ph: (206)281-9609
Fax: (206)281-8035

NewsLinc
15115 S 76th Ave.
Bixby, OK 74008

NewsRX
2727 Paces Ferry Rd. SE, Ste. 2-440
Atlanta, GA 30339
Ph: (770)507-7777
Free: 800-726-4550
Fax: (770)435-6800
Co. E-mail: techsupport@newsrx.com
URL: http://www.newsrx.com

NewYorkAncestry.com
PO Box 4311
Boise, ID 83711
Ph: (208)469-0673
Co. E-mail: newyorkancestry@aol.com
URL: http://www.newyorkancestry.com

Nielsen Business Media Inc.
770 Broadway
New York, NY 10003-9522
Ph: (866)890-8541
Fax: (646)654-5584
URL: http://www.nielsenbusinessmedia. com

Nielsen Business Media
90 Broad St., Rm. 402
New York, NY 10004-3312
Ph: (646)654-5000
Fax: (646)654-7265
URL: http://www.nielsenbusinessmedia. com/

Nielsen Co.
770 Broadway
New York, NY 10003-9595
Ph: (646)654-5000
Fax: (646)654-5002
Co. E-mail: pr.us@nielsen.com
URL: http://www.nielsen.com

Nielsen Company
VNU Business Media Inc.
770 Broadway, 7th Fl.
New York, NY 10003
Ph: (818)487-4596
Free: 866-851-6513

The Ninety-Nines Inc.
4300 Amelia Earhart Rd.
Oklahoma City, OK 73159
Ph: (405)685-7969
Free: 800-994-1929
Fax: (405)685-7985
Co. E-mail: president@ninety-nines.org

NOLO
950 Parker St.
Berkeley, CA 94710
Ph: (510)549-1976
Free: 800-728-3555
Fax: (510)548-5902

NOLO Publications
950 Parker St.
Berkeley, CA 94710
Free: 800-728-3555
Fax: (800)645-0895
URL: http://www.nolo.com

Nomis Publications Inc.
8570 Foxwood Ct.
Youngstown, OH 44514-4301
Ph: (330)965-2380
Free: 800-321-7479
Fax: (330)965-2381
Co. E-mail: info@nomispublications.com
URL: http://www.nomispublications.com

NorlightsPress.com
2323 State Rd. 252
Martinsville, IN 46151-7401
Free: 888-558-4354
Fax: (888)558-4356
Co. E-mail: info@norlightspress.com
URL: http://NorlightsPress.com

North American Association of Floor Covering Distributors
401 N Michigan Ave., Ste. 1900
Chicago, IL 60611
Ph: (312)321-6836
Fax: (312)673-6962
Co. E-mail: info@nafcd.org
URL: http://www.nafcd.org/

North American Bookdealers Exchange
77009 London Rd.
Cottage Grove, OR 97424
Ph: (541)942-7455
Fax: (541)942-7455
Co. E-mail: nabe@bookmarketingprofits.
  com
URL: http://www.bookmarketingprofits.com

North American Building Material Distribution Association
401 N Michigan Ave.
Chicago, IL 60611
Ph: (312)321-6845
Free: 888-747-7862
Fax: (312)644-0310
Co. E-mail: info@nbmda.org
URL: http://www.nbmda.org

North American Die Casting Association
241 Holbrook Dr.
Wheeling, IL 60090-5809
Ph: (847)279-0001
Fax: (847)279-0002
Co. E-mail: nadca@diecasting.org
URL: http://www.diecasting.org

North American Publishing Co.
1500 Spring Garden St., Ste. 1200
Philadelphia, PA 19130-4069
Ph: (215)238-5300
Free: 800-777-8074
Fax: (215)238-5412
Co. E-mail: customerservice@napco.com
URL: http://www.napco.com

North American Retail Hardware Association (NRHA)
6325 Digital Way, Ste. 300
Indianapolis, IN 46278-1787
Ph: (317)275-9400
Free: 800-772-4424
Fax: (317)275-9403
Co. E-mail: pfbowman@nrha.org
URL: http://www.nrha.org

North County Times
207 E Pennsylvania Ave.
Escondido, CA 92025
Ph: (760)745-6611
Fax: (760)740-5464
URL: http://www.nctimes.com

North Island Publishing
1606 Sedlescomb Dr., Unit 8
Mississauga, ON, Canada L4X 1M6
Ph: (905)625-7070
Free: 800-331-7408
Fax: (905)625-4856
URL: http://www.northisland.ca/

North Jersey Media Group
150 River St.
Hackensack, NJ 07601
Ph: (201)646-4000

North-South Center Press at the University of Miami
1320 S Dixie Hwy.
Coral Gables, FL 33146-3027
Ph: (305)284-2211
Fax: (305)284-4985
Co. E-mail: nscenter@miami.edu
URL: http://www.miami.edu

Northeast Mississippi Daily Journal
1242 S Green St.
Tupelo, MS 38804
Ph: (662)842-2611

Northeastern Lumber Manufacturers Association
272 Tuttle Rd.
Cumberland Center, ME 04021
Ph: (207)829-6901
Fax: (207)829-4293
Co. E-mail: info@nelma.org
URL: http://www.nelma.org/

Northeastern Retail Lumber Association
585 N Greenbush Rd.
Rensselaer, NY 12144
Ph: (518)286-1010

Free: 800-292-6752
Fax: (518)286-1755
URL: http://www.nrla.org

Northern Arizona Genealogical Society
Box 695
Prescott, AZ 86302
Co. E-mail: sunshinegirl@isp.com

Northern Lights Internet Solutions Ltd.
438 - 5th St.
Saskatoon, SK, Canada S7H 1E9
Ph: (306)931-0020
Fax: (306)931-7667
Co. E-mail: info2@lights.ca
URL: http://www.lights.ca

Northstar Travel Media L.L.C.
100 Lighting Way, 2nd Fl.
Secaucus, NJ 07094
Ph: (201)902-2000
Free: 800-742-7076
Fax: (201)902-2045
Co. E-mail: secausushelpdesk@ntmllc.
  com
URL: http://www.northstartravelmedia.com

NorthStar Travel Media LLC
116 W 32nd St., 14th Fl.
New York, NY 10001
Ph: (646)380-6240

Northwest Fuchsia Society
Box 33071, Bitter Lake Sta.
Seattle, WA 98133
Ph: (253)588-4541

Northwestern Lumber Association
5905 Golden Valley Rd., Ste. 110
Minneapolis, MN 55422
Ph: (763)544-6822
Free: 800-331-0193
Fax: (763)595-4060
Co. E-mail: nlassn@nlassn.org
URL: http://www.nlassn.org

Nouveau Connoisseurs Corporation
Ph: (503)590-4329
Co. E-mail: Monique@nouveauconnois-
  seurs.com
URL: http://moniquehayward.com

Nova Publishing Company
1103 W College
Carbondale, IL 62901
Ph: (618)457-3521
Free: 800-748-1175
Fax: (618)457-2541

Nova Science Publishers, Inc.
400 Oser Ave., Ste. 1600
Hauppauge, NY 11788
Ph: (631)231-7269
Fax: (631)231-8175
URL: http://www.novapublishers.com

Novicom Inc.
6100 Center Dr., Ste. 1000
Los Angeles, CA 90045
Ph: (310)642-4400
Fax: (310)641-4444
URL: http://www.ptproductsonline.com

NPT Publishing Group Inc.
201 Littleton Rd., 2nd Fl.
Morris Plains, NJ 07950
Ph: (973)401-0202
Free: 800-535-8207
Fax: (973)401-0404
Co. E-mail: ednchief@nptimes.comcirculation@nptimes.com
URL: http://www.nptimes.com

NRF Enterprises Inc.
325 7th St. NW, Ste. 1100
Washington, DC 20004
Ph: (202)783-7971
Free: 800-673-4692
Fax: (202)737-2849
URL: http://www.nrf.com

NSBE Publications
205 Daingerfield Rd.
Alexandria, VA 22314
Ph: (703)549-2207
Fax: (703)683-5312
Co. E-mail: info@nsbe.org
URL: http://www.nsbe.org/

NSC Press
1121 Spring Lake Dr.
Itasca, IL 60143-3201
Ph: (630)285-1121
Free: 800-621-7615
Fax: (630)285-1315
Co. E-mail: customerservice@nsc.org
URL: http://www.nsc.org

NueMedia LLC
819 Berry St.
Stoughton, WI 53589
Ph: (608)873-6268
Fax: (608)873-7211
URL: http://www.nuemediallc.net

Numismatic Counseling Inc.
PO Box 38
Plainview, NY 11803
Ph: (516)433-5800
Fax: (516)433-5801
Co. E-mail: mauricerosen@aol.com

Nurre Ink
PO Box 670705
Dallas, TX 75367-0705
Ph: (972)243-1356
Fax: (972)243-1357

NVST Inc.
1100 Dexter Ave. N
Seattle, WA 98109
Ph: (206)676-3802
Free: 800-910-6878

Fax: (206)273-7401
Co. E-mail: info@nvst.com
URL: http://www.nvst.com

NYFEA--The Association for Educating Agricultural Leaders
PO Box 20326
Montgomery, AL 36120
Ph: (334)288-0097
Fax: (334)288-0097
Co. E-mail: natloffice@nyfea.org

O

O Books
46A West St.
Alresford SO24 9AU, United Kingdom
Ph: 44 1962 736880
Fax: 44 1962 736881
URL: http://www.obooks.com

Obsidian Launch LLC
239 Myrtle Ave.
Boonton, NJ 07005
Ph: (973)453-4534
Co. E-mail: info@obsidianlaunch.com
URL: http://www.obsidianlaunch.com

Ocala Star-Banner
2121 SW 19th Ave.
Ocala, FL 34471
Ph: (352)867-4010

Office for History of Science and Technology
543 Stephens Hall, Ste. 2350
Berkeley, CA 94720-2350
Ph: (510)642-4581
Fax: (510)643-5321
Co. E-mail: ohst@berkeley.edu
URL: http://www.ohst.berkeley.edu

Office of Advocacy
409 3rd St. SW
Washington, DC 20416
Ph: (202)205-6533
Fax: (202)205-6928

Office of Product Management National Technical Information Service
5285 Port Royal Rd.
Springfield, VA 22161
Ph: (703)605-6515
Fax: (703)605-6900
Co. E-mail: info@ntis.gov
URL: http://www.ntis.gov

Office of Research and Creative Activity
207 Montana Hall
Bozeman, MT 59717-2460
Ph: (406)994-5607
Fax: (406)994-2893
Co. E-mail: research@montana.edu

Official Airline Guides
3025 Highland Pkwy., Ste. 200
Downers Grove, IL 60515-5561
Ph: (630)515-5300
Free: 800-342-5624
Fax: (630)515-5301
Co. E-mail: contactus@oag.com
URL: http://www.oag.com

Ohara
24715 Rockefeller
Santa Clarita, CA 91355
Co. E-mail: rainbow@rsabbs.com

Ohio State University Moritz College of Law
Enarson Hall
154 W 12th Ave.
Columbus, OH 43210
Ph: (614)292-6446
URL: http://www.osu.edu/

Ohio United Way
88 E Broad St., Ste. 620
Columbus, OH 43215-3506
Ph: (614)224-8146
Fax: (614)224-6597
Co. E-mail: oh_unitedway@ouw.org

Oildom Publishing Company of Texas Inc.
1160 Dairy Ashford Rd., Ste. 610
Houston, TX 77079
Ph: (281)558-6930

Oklahoma Genealogical Society
PO Box 12986
Oklahoma City, OK 73157
Ph: (405)286-1190
Co. E-mail: okgensoc@aol.com

OMB Watch
1742 Connecticut Ave. NW
Washington, DC 20009
Ph: (202)234-8494
Fax: (202)234-8584
Co. E-mail: ombwatch@ombwatch.org
URL: http://www.ombwatch.org

Omnigraphics Inc.
PO Box 31-1640
Detroit, MI 48231
Ph: (313)961-1340
Free: 800-234-1340
Fax: (313)961-1383
Co. E-mail: info@omnigraphics.com
URL: http://www.omnigraphics.com

Online, A Division of Information Today Inc.
143 Old Marlton Pke.
Medford, NJ 08055-8750
Ph: (609)654-6266
Free: 800-300-9868
Fax: (609)654-4309
Co. E-mail: custserv@infotoday.com
URL: http://www.infotoday.com

Ontario Accommodation Association
347 Pido Rd., Unit 2
RR 6
Peterborough, ON, Canada K9J 6X7
Ph: (705)745-4982
Free: 800-461-1972
Fax: (705)745-4983
Co. E-mail: info@ontarioaccommodation.
com

Ontario Beekeepers' Association
Bayfield, ON, Canada N0M 1G0
Ph: (519)674-1007
Fax: (519)565-5452
Co. E-mail: info@ontariobee.com

Ontario Long Term Care Association
345 Renfrew Dr., 3rd Fl.
Markham, ON, Canada L3R 9S9
Ph: (905)470-8995
Fax: (905)470-9595
Co. E-mail: info@oltca.com
URL: http://www.oltca.com/

Ontario Public Buyers Association
Ste. 361, 111 4th Ave., Ridley Sq.
Ridley Sq.
Saint Catharines, ON, Canada L2S 3P5
Ph: (905)682-2644
Fax: (905)682-2644
Co. E-mail: opbasup@vaxxine.com

Ontario Safety League
2595 Skymark Ave Ste. 212
Mississauga, ON, Canada L4W 4L4
Ph: (905)625-0556
Fax: (905)625-0677

Open Horizons
PO Box 2887
Taos, NM 87571
Ph: (641)472-6130
Free: 800-796-6130
Fax: (641)472-1560
Co. E-mail: info@bookmarket.com
URL: http://www.bookmarket.com

Optical Society of America
2010 Massachusetts Ave. NW
Washington, DC 20036-1023
Ph: (202)223-8130
Free: 800-766-405A
Fax: (202)223-1096
Co. E-mail: info@osa.org
URL: http://www.osa.org

Oregon Genealogical Society Inc.
PO Box 10306
Eugene, OR 97440-2306
Ph: (541)345-0399

Oregon Newspaper Publishers Association
7150 SW Hampton St., Ste. 111
Portland, OR 97223
Ph: (503)624-6397
Fax: (503)639-9009

Co. E-mail: onpa@orenews.com
URL: http://www.orenews.com

The Oregonian
1320 SW Broadway
Portland, OR 97201
Ph: (503)221-8327

Organization of American Kodaly Educators
10951 Pico Blvd., Ste. 405
Los Angeles, CA 90064-2191
Ph: (310)441-3555
Fax: (310)441-3577
Co. E-mail: info@oake.org
URL: http://www.oake.org

Orion Research Corp.
14555 N Scottsdale Rd., Ste. 330
Scottsdale, AZ 85254-3457
Ph: (480)951-1114
Co. E-mail: support@usedprice.com
URL: http://www.usedprice.com

Out Your Backdoor
4686 Meridian Rd.
Williamston, MI 48895
Ph: (517)347-1689
Fax: (517)347-7884
Co. E-mail: jeff@outyourbackdoor.com
URL: http://www.outyourbackdoor.com/
list_articles.php?catid=20

Outskirts Press, Incorporated
10940 S Parker Rd., No. 515
Parker, CO 80134
Free: 888-672-6657

Owl Books
1021 Rte. 109
Farmingdale, NY 11735
Ph: (631)249-9803
URL: http://www.owlbooks.com

Owner-Operator Independent Drivers Association
1 NW OOIDA Dr.
Grain Valley, MO 64029-7903
Ph: (816)229-5791
Free: 800-444-5791
Fax: (816)229-0518
Co. E-mail: jim_johnston@ooida.com
URL: http://www.ooida.com

Oxbridge Communications Inc.
186 5th Ave.
New York, NY 10010
Ph: (212)741-0231
Free: 800-955-0231
Fax: (212)633-2938
Co. E-mail: info@oxbridge.com
URL: http://www.oxbridge.com

Oxford University Press
2001 Evans Rd.
Cary, NC 27513
Ph: (919)677-0977

Free: 800-852-7323
Fax: (919)677-1714
Co. E-mail: esl.us@oup.com
URL: http://www.oup.com

Oxford University Press
198 Madison Ave.
New York, NY 10016
Ph: (212)726-0977
Free: 800-445-9714
Fax: (919)677-1303
Co. E-mail: custserv.us@oup.com
URL: http://www.oup.com/us

Oxford University Press, Inc.
198 Madison Ave.
New York, NY 10016-4314
Ph: (212)726-6000
Fax: (212)726-6440
Co. E-mail: custserv.us@oup.com
URL: http://www.oup.com/us

P

Pace Communications Inc.
1301 Carolina St.
Greensboro, NC 27401
Ph: (336)378-6065
URL: http://www.pacecommunications.com

Pace Law School
78 North Broadway
White Plains, NY 10603
Ph: (914)422-4210

Pacific Northwest Christmas Tree Association
4093 12th St., Cutoff SE
Salem, OR 97302-1741
Ph: (503)364-2942
Fax: (503)581-6819
URL: http://www.nwtrees.com

Pacific Resource Development Group, Inc.
1651 NE, 185th St.
Seattle, WA 98155
Free: 800-767-3062
Co. E-mail: pacres@shadesofgray.com

PageFree Publishing, Incorporated
109 S Farmer St.
Otsego, MI 49078
Ph: (269)692-3926
Free: 866-462-6657
Fax: (269)692-3927

Paint and Decorating Retailers Association
1401 Triad Center Dr.
St. Peters, MO 63376-7353
Ph: (636)326-2636
Free: 800-737-0107
Fax: (636)229-4750
Co. E-mail: info@pdra.org
URL: http://www.pdra.org

Painting and Decorating Contractors of America
1801 Park 270 Dr.
St. Louis, MO 63146-4020
Ph: (314)514-7322
Free: 800-332-7322
Fax: (314)890-2068
Co. E-mail: rbright@pdca.org
URL: http://www.pdca.org

Paisano Publications L.L.C.
28210 Dorothy Dr.
Agoura Hills, CA 91301
Ph: (818)889-8740
Free: 800-247-6246
Fax: (818)735-6518
Co. E-mail: bulkmagazines@paisanopub.
  com
URL: http://www.easyriders.com

Palgrave Macmillan
175 5th Ave.
New York, NY 10010
Ph: (212)982-9300
Free: 800-221-7945
Fax: (212)777-6359

Palm Beach County Genealogical Society
PO Box 17617
West Palm Beach, FL 33416
Ph: (561)616-3455
Co. E-mail: ancestry@pbcgensoc.org
URL: http://www.gensocofpbc.org

Palm Beach Post
2751 S Dixie Hwy.
West Palm Beach, FL 33416
Ph: (561)820-4100
Free: 800-432-7595
Fax: (561)820-4407
Co. E-mail: pb_metro@pbpost.com
URL: http://www.palmbeachpost.com

Pan American Health Organization
Publications Program, PAHO
Washington, DC 20037
Ph: (202)974-3000
Fax: (202)974-3663
URL: http://new.paho.org

Panoptic Enterprises
6055 Ridge Ford Dr.
Burke, VA 22009-1220
Ph: (703)451-5953
Free: 800-594-4766
Fax: (703)451-5953
URL: http://www.fedgovcontracts.com

The Pantagraph
301 W Washington St.
Bloomington, IL 61702
Ph: (309)829-9000
Free: 800-747-7323

Pantheon Books
1745 Broadway
New York, NY 10019
Ph: (212)782-9000
Fax: (212)572-6066
URL: http://pantheon.knopfdoubleday.com

Para Publishing
530 Ellwood Ridge Rd.
Santa Barbara, CA 93117-1047
Ph: (805)968-7277
Free: 800-727-2782
Fax: (805)968-1379
Co. E-mail: info@parapublishing.com
URL: http://www.parapublishing.com

Para Publishing
PO Box 8206-240
Santa Barbara, CA 93118
Ph: (805)968-7277
Fax: (805)968-1379
Co. E-mail: info@parapublishing.com
URL: http://www.parapublishing.com

Parkwest Publications, Incorporated
PO Box 310251
Miami, FL 33231
Ph: (305)256-7880
Fax: (305)256-7816

PartiLife Publications
65 Sussex St.
Hackensack, NJ 07601
Ph: (201)441-4224
Fax: (201)342-8118
Co. E-mail: info@balloonsandparties.com
URL: http://www.balloonsandparties.com/

Paul Turok
Old Chelsea Sta.
New York, NY 10113-0202
Ph: (212)691-9229
Co. E-mail: tcpublication@verizon.net

PC Magazine
28 E 28th St.
New York, NY 10016
Ph: (212)503-3500

PCS Mailing List Company
39 Cross St.
Peabody, MA 01960-1628
Ph: (978)532-7100
Free: 800-532-LIST
Fax: (978)532-9181
Co. E-mail: info@pcslist.com

Peachpit Press
1249 8th St.
Berkeley, CA 94710
Ph: (510)524-2178
Free: 800-283-9444
Fax: (510)524-2221

Peanut Butter and Jelly Press LLC (PBJ)
PO Box 590239
Newton, MA 02459
Ph: (617)630-0945
Fax: (617)630-0945
Co. E-mail: info@pbjpress.com
URL: http://www.pbjpress.com

Pearson Education Canada
26 Prince Andrew Pl.
Don Mills, ON, Canada M3C 2T8
Ph: (416)447-5101
Fax: (416)443-0948

Pearson Education Inc.
1 Lake St.
Upper Saddle River, NJ 07458
Free: 800-922-0579
Co. E-mail: corpsales@pearsontechgroup.
  com

Pearson Education Ltd.
Edinburgh Gate
Harlow CM20 2JE, United Kingdom
Ph: 01279 623 623
Fax: 0870 850 5255
URL: http://www.pearsoned.co.uk

Pearson Education, Limited
1 Lake St.
Upper Saddle River, NJ 07458
Ph: (201)236-7000
Free: 800-745-8489
Co. E-mail: communications@pearsoned.
  com
URL: http://www.pearsoned.com

Pearson Technology Group Canada
10 Alcorn Ave., Ste. 304
Toronto, ON, Canada M4V 3B2
Free: 800-567-3800
Fax: (800)263-7733

Penguin Books USA Inc.
375 Hudson St.
New York, NY 10014
Ph: (212)366-2000
Free: 800-631-8571
Fax: (212)366-2666
Co. E-mail: online@penguinputnam.com
URL: http://www.penguinputnam.com

Penguin Group Incorporated
375 Hudson St.
New York, NY 10014
Ph: (212)366-2000
Free: 800-631-8571
Fax: (212)366-2666
Co. E-mail: customerservice@penguinput-
  nam.com
URL: http://www.penguinputnam.com

Penguin Group
375 Hudson St.
New York, NY 10014
Ph: (212)366-2679

Fax: (212)366-2612

Penguin Group USA Inc.
375 Hudson St.
New York, NY 10014
Ph: (212)366-2000
Fax: (212)366-2666
Co. E-mail: fran.corea@us.penguingroup.
  com
URL: http://www.penguin.com

Pennsylvania State University Press
820 N University Dr., USB-1, Ste. C
University Park, PA 16802
Ph: (814)865-1327
Free: 800-326-9180
Fax: (814)863-1408

Pennsylvania State University
116 Deike Bldg.
University Park, PA 16802
Ph: (814)865-6546
Fax: (814)863-7708
URL: http://www.ems.psu.edu

PennWell Corp.
1421 S Sheridan Rd.
Tulsa, OK 74112
Ph: (918)835-3161
Free: 800-331-4463
Fax: (918)831-9497
Co. E-mail: headquarters@pennwell.com
URL: http://www.pennwell.com

PennWell Publishing Co.
98 Spit Brook Rd.
Nashua, NH 03062
Ph: (603)891-0123
Fax: (603)891-0574
URL: http://www.ils.pennet.com

Penton Business Media Inc.
7900 International Dr., Ste. 300
Minneapolis, MN 55425
Ph: (952)851-9329
Fax: (952)851-4601

Penton Business Media Inc.
249 W 17th St.
New York, NY 10011
Ph: (212)204-4200

Penton Media Inc.
2100 West Loop S, Ste. 900
Houston, TX 77027
Ph: (713)300-0674

Penton Media Inc.
249 W 17th St.
New York, NY 10011
Ph: (212)204-4200
Fax: (212)206-3622
Co. E-mail: bethany.weaver@penton.com
URL: http://www.penton.com

Penton Media Inc.
1166 Avenue of the Americas, 10th Fl.
New York, NY 10036-2708
Ph: (212)204-4200
URL: http://www.penton.com

Penton
9800 Metcalf Ave.
Overland Park, KS 66212
Ph: (913)341-1300
Free: 866-748-4926
Fax: (913)967-1905
Co. E-mail: corporatecustomerservice@
  penton.com
URL: http://www.penton.com

Percussive Arts Society
110 W Washington St., Ste. A
Indianapolis, IN 46204
Ph: (317)974-4488
Fax: (317)974-4499
Co. E-mail: percarts@pas.org
URL: http://www.pas.org

Perseus Books Group
387 Park Ave. S, 12th Fl.
New York, NY 10016
Ph: (212)340-8100

Personal Care Products Council
1101 17th St. NW, Ste. 300
Washington, DC 20036-4702
Ph: (202)331-1770
Fax: (202)331-1969
Co. E-mail: publications@ctfa.org
URL: http://www.personalcarecouncil.org

Personal Selling Power Inc.
1140 International Pkwy.
Fredericksburg, VA 22406-1126
Ph: (540)752-7000
Free: 800-752-7355
Fax: (540)752-7001
Co. E-mail: editorial@sellingpower.com
URL: http://www.sellingpower.com

The Pet Care Services Association
2760 North Academy Blvd.
Colorado Springs, CO 80917
Ph: (719)667-1600
Free: 877-570-7788
Fax: (719)667-0116
Co. E-mail: webmaster@PetCareServices.
  org
URL: http://www.petcareservices.org/

Pet Industry Distributors Association
2105 Laurel Bush Rd., Ste. 200
Bel Air, MD 21015
Ph: (443)640-1060
Fax: (443)640-1031
Co. E-mail: pida@ksgroup.org

Peter Baylies
61 Brightwood Ave.
Durham, NC 27707
Ph: (978)685-7931

Co. E-mail: athomedad@aol.com

Peter Glenn Publications
777 E Atlantic Ave., Ste. C2337
Delray Beach, FL 33483
Ph: (561)404-4290
Free: 888-332-6700
Fax: (561)892-5786
URL: http://www.pgdirect.com

Peter Katz Productions Inc.
9 Romar Ave.
White Plains, NY 10605
Ph: (914)949-7443
URL: http://www.aviationmonthly.com

Pfingsten Publishing, LLC
6000 Lombardo Center Dr., Ste. 420
Seven Hills, OH 44131
Ph: (216)328-8926
Free: 888-772-8926

PG Publishing Company
34 Blvd. of the Allies
Pittsburgh, PA 15222
Ph: (412)263-1100
Free: 800-228-6397

Pharmacy Week
7780 Elmwood Ave, Ste. 210
Madison, WI 53562
Ph: (608)251-1112
Fax: (608)251-1155
Co. E-mail: info@pharmacyweek

Pheasant Meadow Farm
1338 Hughes Shop Rd.
Westminster, MD 21158
Fax: (410)857-9145
URL: http://www.qis.net/minidonk/donktext.
  htm

Philadelphia Inquirer
400 N Broad St.
Philadelphia, PA 19130
Ph: (215)854-2000

Philadelphia Media Network
400 N Broad St.
Philadelphia, PA 19130
Ph: (215)854-2000

Phillips Business Information Inc. Access Intelligence L.L.C.
4 Choke Cherry Rd., 2nd Fl.
Rockville, MD 20850
Ph: (301)354-2000
Free: 800-777-5006
Fax: (301)309-3847
Co. E-mail: info@accessintel.com
URL: http://www.accessintel.com/

Phoenix Business Journal
101 N 1st Ave., Ste. 2300
Phoenix, AZ 85003
Ph: (602)230-8400
Fax: (602)230-0955

Phoenix Media Corporation
100 Cummings Center, Ste. 211-C
Beverly, MA 01915
Ph: (978)338-6545

The Photo Review
140 E Richardson Ave., Ste. 301
Langhorne, PA 19047
Co. E-mail: info@photoreview.org
URL: http://www.photoreview.org

The Photograph Collector
140 E Richardson Ave., Ste. 301
Langhorne, PA 19047-2824
Ph: (215)891-0214
Fax: (215)891-9358
Co. E-mail: info@photoreview.org

Photographic Society of America
3000 United Founders Blvd., Ste. 103
Oklahoma City, OK 73112-4294
Ph: (405)843-1437
Free: 855-772-4636
Fax: (405)843-1438
Co. E-mail: hq@psa-photo.org
URL: http://www.psa-photo.org

PhotoSource International
Pine Lake Farm
1910 35th Rd.
Osceola, WI 54020-5602
Ph: (715)248-3800
Free: 800-624-0266
Fax: (715)248-7394
Co. E-mail: info@photosource.com
URL: http://www.photosource.com

Pi Yee Press
4855 W Nevso Dr.
Las Vegas, NV 89103
Ph: (702)579-7711
Fax: (702)579-2665
Co. E-mail: info@bj21.com
URL: http://www.bj21.com

Piano Today
PO Box 58629
Boulder, CO 80323
Free: 800-759-3036
URL: http://www.allaboutjazz.com/php/
    entity.php?id=1194

Picador USA
175 5th Ave.
New York, NY 10010
Ph: (212)674-5151
Fax: (212)253-9627
Co. E-mail: academic@hholt.com
URL: http://www.picadorusa.com

Pictorial Photographers of America
PO Box 2234
Ogunquit, ME 03907-2234

Pierian Press
3196 Maple Dr.
Ypsilanti, MI 48197
Ph: (734)434-4074
Free: 800-678-2435
Co. E-mail: mew_42strat@yahoo.com
URL: http://www.pierianpress.com

Pinnacle Publishing Inc. Lawrence Ragan Communications, Inc.
316 N Michigan Ave., Ste. 300
Chicago, IL 60601
Ph: (312)960-4209
Free: 800-493-4867
Fax: (312)960-4106
Co. E-mail: pinpub@ragan.com
URL: http://www.pinpub.com

Pioneer Communications Inc.
218 6th Ave., Ste. 610
Des Moines, IA 50309
Ph: (515)246-0402
Free: 877-899-9977
Fax: (515)246-0398
Co. E-mail: kroberson@thepioneergroup.
    com
URL: http://www.thepioneergroup.com/
    aboutus.htm

Pitney Bowes Inc.
1 Elmcroft Rd.
Stamford, CT 06926
Ph: (203)356-5000
Fax: (203)351-6059
Co. E-mail: info@pitneybowes.com
URL: http://www.pitneybowes.com

Pittsburgh-Post Gazette
34 Blvd. of the Allies
Pittsburgh, PA 15222
Ph: (412)263-1100
Free: 800-228-6397

Planning Shop
555 Bryant St., No. 180
Palo Alto, CA 94301
Ph: (650)289-9120
Fax: (650)289-9125

Playtonic Communications
3409 Yonge St.
Toronto, ON, Canada M4N 3R1
Ph: (416)487-1869
Co. E-mail: editor@toysandgamesmaga-
    zine.ca
URL: http://toysandgamesmagazine.ca

Polar Bear Alumni Association
165 Morse Rd.
Columbus, OH 43214
Ph: (614)263-8317
Co. E-mail: lfaustcoloradoumbus.rr.com

Polaris International
9200 S Dadeland Blvd., Ste. 510
Miami, FL 33156
Ph: (305)670-0580

Fax: (305)670-3818
Co. E-mail: info@accountants.org
URL: http://www.accountants.org

Polish Genealogical Society of America
984 N Milwaukee Ave.
Chicago, IL 60622-4101
Ph: (773)384-3352
Fax: (773)384-3799
Co. E-mail: pgsamerica@pgsa.org
URL: http://www.pgsa.org

Portbook Publications Inc.
PO Box 462
Belfast, ME 04915
Ph: (207)338-1619
Fax: (207)338-6025
Co. E-mail: info@portbook.net
URL: http://www.portbook.net

Porter Sargent Publishers Inc.
2 LAN Dr., Ste. 100
Westford, MA 01886
Ph: (978)842-2812
Fax: (978)692-2304
Co. E-mail: info@portersargent.com
URL: http://www.portersargent.com

Portfolio Hardcover
375 Hudson St.
New York, NY 10014-3657
Ph: (212)366-2372
Fax: (212)366-2933
Co. E-mail: info@us.penguingroup.com
URL: http://us.penguingroup.com

Portfolio
375 Hudson St.
New York, NY 10014
Ph: (212)366-2000
Fax: (212)366-2666
URL: http://us.penguingroup.com/static/
    pages/publishers/adult/portfolio.html

Portfolio Publishing
375 Hudson St.
New York, NY 10014
Ph: (212)366-2372
Fax: (212)366-2933
URL: http://www.penguingroup.com

Portland Business Journal
851 SW 6th Ave., Ste. 500
Portland, OR 97204
Ph: (503)274-8733
Fax: (503)219-3450

Portland Press Herald
PO Box 1460
Portland, ME 04101
Ph: (207)791-6920

Postcard History Society
1795 Kleinfeltersvil Rd.
Stevens, PA 17578
Ph: (717)721-9273

Potomac Books
PO Box 605
Herndon, VA 20172
Free: 800-775-2518
Fax: (703)661-1501
Co. E-mail: pbimail@presswarehouse.com
URL: http://www.potomacbooksinc.com/

Power Trade Media L.L.C.
4742 N 24th St., Ste. 340
Phoenix, AZ 85016
Ph: (602)265-7600
Free: 800-541-2670
Fax: (602)227-7588
URL: http://www.powertrademedia.com

Powershift Communications Inc.
245 Fairview Mall Dr., 5th Fl.
Toronto, ON, Canada M2J 4T1
Ph: (416)494-1066
Fax: (416)494-2536
Co. E-mail: dbm@powershift.ca
URL: http://www.powershift.ca

Poynter Center for the Study of Ethics and American Institutions
618 3rd St.
Bloomington, IN 47405
Ph: (812)855-0261
Fax: (812)855-3315
Co. E-mail: poynter@indiana.edu

PR Newswire Association LLC
350 Hudson St., Ste. 300
New York, NY 10014
Free: 888-776-0942

PR Newswire
350 Hudson St., Ste. 300
New York, NY 10014
Free: 800-776-8090
Fax: (800)793-9313

Practitioners Publishing Company
PO Box 966
Fort Worth, TX 76101-0966

Precision Metalforming Association MetalForming Magazine
6363 Oak Tree Blvd.
Independence, OH 44131-2500
Ph: (216)901-8800
Fax: (216)901-9190
URL: http://www.metalforming.com/

Precision Shooting Inc.
222 McKee St.
Manchester, CT 06040
Ph: (860)645-8776
Fax: (860)643-8215
URL: http://www.precisionshooting.com

Premiere Publications
14531 Jefferson St.
Midway City, CA 92655
Ph: (714)893-0053
Fax: (714)893-5085
Co. E-mail: editor@the-royal-spaniels.com
URL: http://www.the-royal-spaniels.com/

Prentice Hall Business Publishing (PHBP)
1 Lake St.
Upper Saddle River, NJ 07458
Ph: (201)236-7000
Free: 800-227-1816
Fax: (201)236-3400
URL: http://phbusiness.prenhall.com

Prentice Hall Higher Education
75 Arlington St.
Boston, MA 02116

Prentice Hall
375 Hudson St.
New York, NY 10014
URL: http://www.pearsonhighered.com

Prentice Hall Press
240 Frisch Ct.
Paramus, NJ 07652
Ph: (201)909-6200
Free: 800-288-4745
Fax: (201)909-6360

Prentice Hall Press
1 Lake St.
Upper Saddle River, NJ 07458-1813
Ph: (201)236-7000
Free: 800-745-8489
Fax: (201)236-3290
URL: http://www.pearsoned.com

Prentice Hall PTR
1 Lake St.
Upper Saddle River, NJ 07458
Ph: (201)236-7676
Free: 800-227-1816
Fax: (800)445-6991
URL: http://phbusiness.prenhall.com

Prentiss Publishing
PO Box 1257
Prentiss, MS
Ph: (601)792-4221
Fax: (601)792-4222

Presidential Families of America
10939 West 59th Pl.
Arvada, CO 80004-4732
Ph: (305)493-0003

Preston Publications
6600 W Touhy Ave.
Niles, IL 60714
Ph: (847)647-2900
Free: 800-229-7569
Fax: (847)647-1155
Co. E-mail: tpreston@prestonpub.com

URL: http://www.prestonpub.com

Prima Publishing
3875 Atherton Rd.
Rocklin, CA 95765
Ph: (916)632-4400

Primedia Business
PO Box 603
Indianapolis, IN 46206
Ph: (317)297-5500
Free: 800-827-7468
Fax: (317)299-1356
Co. E-mail: atmarketing@primediabusiness.com
URL: http://www.primediabusiness.com

Primedia Business Magazines & Media
3585 Engineering Dr., Ste. 100
Norcross, GA 30092
Ph: (678)421-3000
Fax: (800)216-1423
URL: http://www.primedia.com/contact-us.aspx

Primedia Business Magazines
PO Box 66010
Houston, TX 77266
Ph: (713)523-8124
Free: 800-880-0368
Fax: (713)523-8384
Co. E-mail: inquiries@prismb2b.com
URL: http://www.primediabusiness.com

Primedia Business
3585 Engineering Dr., Ste. 100
Norcross, GA 30092
Ph: (678)421-3000
Free: 800-216-1423
URL: http://www.primedia.com

Primedia Consumer Media and Magazine Group
3585 Engineering Dr., Ste. 100
Norcross, GA 30092
Ph: (678)421-3000
Free: 800-216-1423
Co. E-mail: nbigley@primedia.com
URL: http://www.primedia.com/

PRIMEDIA Los Angeles
3585 Engineering Dr., Ste. 100
Norcross, GA 30092
Ph: (678)421-3000
Free: 800-216-1423
URL: http://www.primedia.com

Primedia Power & Motoryacht Magazine
261 Madison Ave., 6th Fl.
New York, NY 10016
Free: 800-284-8036
Fax: (212)915-4000
Co. E-mail: power&motoryacht@palmcoastd.com
URL: http://www.powerandmotoryacht.com/contacts/

Primedia Special Interest Publications
3585 Engineering Dr., Ste. 100
Norcross, GA 30092
Ph: (678)421-3000
Free: 800-216-1423
URL: http://www.primedia.com/

Princeton University Press
41 William St.
Princeton, NJ 08540
Ph: (609)258-4900
Fax: (609)258-6305

Print It Design and Publishing, Inc.
191 Blossom Ct.
Paso Robles, CA 93446
Ph: (805)237-7906
Co. E-mail: trq@printitdesign.com
URL: http://printitdesign.com/contact_me.
   html

Print Services and Distribution Association
401 N Michigan Ave., Ste. 2200
Chicago, IL 60611
Free: 800-230-0175
Fax: (312)673-6880
Co. E-mail: psda@psda.org
URL: http://www.psda.org

PrintImage International
2250 East Devon Ave., Ste. 245
Chicago, IL 60018
Ph: (800)234-0040
Free: 800-234-0040
Fax: (847)298-8705
Co. E-mail: info@printimage.org
URL: http://www.naqp.com

Printing Industries of America
200 Deer Run Rd.
Sewickley, PA 15143-2324
Ph: (412)741-6860
Free: 800-910-4283
Fax: (412)741-2311
Co. E-mail: printing@printing.org
URL: http://www.printing.org

Printworld International Inc.
PO Box 1957
West Chester, PA 19380
Ph: (610)431-6654
Free: 800-788-9101
Fax: (610)431-6653
URL: http://www.printworlddirectory.com/
   printworld

Product News Network
5 Penn Plz., 14th Fl.
New York, NY 10001
Free: 888-846-6638
Fax: (212)613-3499

Productive Publications
Entrepreneurship Institute of Canada
75 King St. S
Waterloo, ON, Canada N2J 4V1

Ph: (519)885-1559
Free: 800-665-4497
Fax: (519)885-0990

Professional and Technical Consultants Association
PO Box 2261
Santa Clara, CA 95055
Ph: (408)971-5902
Free: 800-747-2822
Fax: (866)746-1053
Co. E-mail: info@patca.org
URL: http://www.patca.org

Professional Association of Canadian Theatres PACT Communications Centre
215 Spadina Ave., Ste. 555
Toronto, ON, Canada M5T 2C7
Ph: (416)595-6455
Fax: (416)595-6450
Co. E-mail: info@pact.ca
URL: http://www.pact.ca

Professional Association of Innkeepers International
207 White Horse Pke.
Haddon Heights, NJ 08035-1703
Co. E-mail: info@paii.org

Professional Grounds Management Society
720 Light St.
Baltimore, MD 21230-3816
Ph: (410)223-2861
Free: 800-609-7467
Fax: (410)752-8295
Co. E-mail: pgms@assnhqtrs.com
URL: http://www.pgms.org

Professional Landcare Network
950 Herndon Pky., Ste. 450
Herndon, VA 20170-5528
Ph: (703)736-9666
Free: 800-395-2522
Fax: (703)736-9668
Co. E-mail: info@landcarenetwork.org
URL: http://www.landcarenetwork.org

Professional Photographers of America
229 Peachtree St. NE, Ste. 2200
Atlanta, GA 30303-1608
Ph: (404)522-8600
Free: 800-786-6277
Fax: (404)614-6406
Co. E-mail: csc@ppa.com
URL: http://www.ppa.com

Professional School Photographers of America
3000 Picture Pl.
Jackson, MI 49201
Ph: (517)788-8100
Free: 800-762-9287
Fax: (517)788-8371
Co. E-mail: pma_trade_exhibits@pmai.org
URL: http://www.pmai.org

Professional Writers Association of Canada
215 Spadina Ave., Ste. 123
Toronto, ON, Canada M5T 2C7
Ph: (416)504-1645
Fax: (416)913-2327
Co. E-mail: info@pwac.ca
URL: http://www.pwac.ca

Profile Books Limited
Exmouth Market
3A Exmouth House
Pine St.
London EC1R 0JH, United Kingdom
Ph: (440) 2078416300
Fax: (440) 2078333969
URL: http://www.profilebooks.com

Progressive Business Publications
370 Technology Dr.
193
Malvern, PA 19355
Ph: (610)695-8600
Free: 800-220-5000
Fax: (610)647-8089
Co. E-mail: customer_service@pbp.com
URL: http://www.pbp.com

Project HOPE
255 Carter Hall Ln.
Millwood, VA 22646
Ph: (540)837-2100
Free: 800-544-HOPE
Fax: (540)837-1813
Co. E-mail: hope@projecthope.org
URL: http://www.projecthope.org

Project Management Institute (PMI)
14 Campus Blvd.
Newtown Square, PA 19073-3299
Ph: (610)356-4600
Free: 855-746-4849
Fax: (610)482-9971
Co. E-mail: customercare@pmi.org
URL: http://www.pmi.org

Promociones Tyson S.A. de C.V. Tyson Promotions
7770 Regents Rd., No. 113-387
San Diego, CA 92122
Ph: (858)569-0172
Free: 800-208-3924
Fax: (858)777-3569
Co. E-mail: tyson@tysonpromotions.com
URL: http://promocionestyson.com/

Promotion Marketing Association Inc.
257 Park Ave. S., Ste. 1102
New York, NY 10010
Ph: (212)420-1100
Fax: (212)533-7622
Co. E-mail: pma@pmalink.org

Property Management Association
7508 Wisconsin Ave., 4th Fl.
Bethesda, MD 20814
Ph: (301)657-9200

Fax: (301)907-9326
Co. E-mail: info@pma-dc.org
URL: http://www.pma-dc.org/

Prosperity & Profits Unlimited, Distribution Services
PO Box 416
Denver, CO 80201-0416
Ph: (303)575-5676
Fax: (303)575-1187
Co. E-mail: mail@prosperityandprofitsun-
  limited.com
URL: http://www.gumbomedia.com

Prostar Publications Inc.
3 Church Cir., Ste. 109
Annapolis, MD 21401
Ph: (310)280-1010
Free: 800-481-6277
Fax: (800)487-6277
Co. E-mail: editor@prostarpublications.
  com
URL: http://www.prostarpublications.com

The PRS Group Inc.
5800 Heritage Landing Dr., Ste. E
East Syracuse, NY 13057-9378
Ph: (315)431-0511
Fax: (315)431-0200
Co. E-mail: custserv@prsgroup.com
URL: http://www.prsgroup.com

Public Affairs
250 W 57th St., Ste. 1321
New York, NY 10107
Free: 800-810-8145
URL: http://www.perseus.com/

Public Relations Society of America
33 Maiden Ln., 11th Fl.
New York, NY 10038-5150
Ph: (212)460-1400
Fax: (212)995-0757
Co. E-mail: william.murray@prsa.org
URL: http://www.prsa.org

Publicom, Inc.
2800 E Fort Lowell Rd.
Tucson, AZ 85716
Ph: (520)323-6144
Fax: (520)323-7412
Co. E-mail: info@wcponline.com
URL: http://www.wcponline.com

PublishAmerica, Incorporated
111/113 E Church St.
Frederick, MD 21701
Ph: (301)695-1707
Fax: (301)631-9073

Publishers & Producers
PO Box 36
Annandale, VA 22003
Ph: (703)750-2664
Fax: (703)750-0064
Co. E-mail: subscriptions@manufacturing-
  news.com

Publishers Communication Group
875 Massachusetts Ave., 7th Fl.
Cambridge, MA 02139
Ph: (617)497-6514
Fax: (617)354-6875

Publishers Development Corp.
12345 World Trade Dr.
San Diego, CA 92128
Fax: (858)605-0247
Co. E-mail: subs@shootingindustry.com
URL: http://www.shootingindustry.com

Publishers Media
PO Box 1295
El Cajon, CA 92022-1295
Fax: (619)588-2155
Co. E-mail: rvhmedia@aol.com
URL: http://www.rvhfreegate.com

Publishers Weekly
360 Park Ave. S.
New York, NY 10010
Ph: (646)746-6758
Free: 800-278-2991
Fax: (646)746-6631

Pubsun Corp.
244 W 49th St., Ste. 305
New York, NY 10019
Ph: (212)246-6460
Fax: (212)265-6428
Co. E-mail: robert.sunshine@nielsen.com
URL: http://www.filmjournal.com/filmjour-
  nal/index.jsp

The Pueblo Chieftain
825 W 6th St.
Pueblo, CO 81003
Ph: (719)544-3520
Free: 800-279-6397
Co. E-mail: newsroom@chieftain.com
URL: http://www.chieftain.com

Pulsus Group Inc.
2902 S Sheridan Way
Oakville, ON, Canada L6J 7L6
Ph: (905)829-4770
Fax: (905)829-4799
Co. E-mail: pulsus@pulsus.com
URL: http://www.pulsus.com

Purchasing Management Association of Canada
2 Carlton St., Ste. 1414
Toronto, ON, Canada M5B 1J3
Ph: (416)977-7111
Free: 888-799-0877
Fax: (416)977-8886
Co. E-mail: info@pmac.ca

Purdue University Press
504 W State St.
West Lafayette, IN 47907-2058
Free: 800-247-6553
Fax: (419)281-6883
Co. E-mail: order@bookmasters.com

URL: http://www.thepress.purdue.edu

Q

Qualitative Research Consultants Association
1000 Westgate Dr., Ste. 252
St. Paul, MN 55114-8679
Ph: (651)290-7491
Free: 888-674-7722
Fax: (651)290-2266
Co. E-mail: inquiries@qrca.org
URL: http://www.qrca.org

Que
201 W 103rd St.
Indianapolis, IN 46290-1094
Ph: (317)581-3500
Free: 800-428-5331

Quebec Dans Le Monde
404-1001, Rte. de l'Eglise
Sainte-Foy, QC, Canada G1V 4N5
Ph: (418)659-5540
Fax: (418)659-4143
Co. E-mail: info@quebecmonde.com
URL: http://www.quebecmonde.com

Quebecor Media
612 Rue Saint-Jacques St.
Montreal, QC, Canada H3C 4M8
Ph: (514)597-2231
URL: http://www.quebecor.com/

Queens Chamber of Commerce
75-20 Astoria Blvd., Ste. 140
Jackson Heights, NY 11372-1131
Ph: (718)898-8500
Fax: (718)898-8599
Co. E-mail: queenschamber@worldnet.att.
  net

Questex Media Group Inc.
275 Grove St., Ste. 2-130
Newton, MA 02466
Ph: (617)219-8300
Free: 888-552-4346
Fax: (617)219-8310

Quigley Publishing Co.
64 Wintergreen Ln.
Groton, MA 01450
Ph: (978)448-0272
Free: 800-231-8239
Fax: (860)228-0157
Co. E-mail: quigleypub@quigleypublishing.
  com
URL: http://www.quigleypublishing.com

Quinlan Publishing Co.
610 Opperman Dr.
Eagan, MN 55123
Ph: (651)687-7000
Free: 800-229-2084
URL: http://west.thomson.com/quinlan/

Quirk Enterprises Inc.
4662 Slater Rd.
Eagan, MN 55122
Ph: (651)379-6200
Co. E-mail: info@quirks.com
URL: http://www.quirks.com

R

R & R Publishing
446 N Wells St., Ste. 254
Chicago, IL 60610
Ph: (312)952-4900
Fax: (312)276-8001
Co. E-mail: info@rnrpublishing.com
URL: http://www.rnrpublishing.com

R I D Publications
333 Commerce St.
Alexandria, VA 22314
Ph: (703)838-0030
Fax: (703)838-0454
Co. E-mail: views@rid.org
URL: http://www.rid.org

R. Max Bowser
PO Box 6278
Newport News, VA 23606
Ph: (757)877-5979
Fax: (757)595-0622
Co. E-mail: ministocks@aol.com

R. S. Means Co., Inc.
63 Smiths Ln.
Kingston, MA 02364
Ph: (800)334-3509
Free: 800-448-8182
Fax: (800)632-6732
URL: http://www.rsmeans.com

R.R. Bowker L.L.C.
630 Central Ave.
New Providence, NJ 07974
Ph: (908)286-1090
Free: 888-269-5372
URL: http://www.bowker.co.uk/en-UK

R.R. Bowker
630 Central Ave
New Providence, NJ 07974
Ph: (888)269-5372
Free: 888-269-5372
Fax: (908)464-3553
Co. E-mail: info@bowker.com
URL: http://www.ulrichsweb.com

Racher Press Inc.
220 5th Ave., Ste. 18
New York, NY 10001
Ph: (646)763-8268

Radio-Television News Directors Association
529 14th St., N.W., Ste. 425
Washington, DC 20045
Ph: (202)659-6510
Free: 800-807-8632

Fax: (202)223-4007
Co. E-mail: rtnda@rtnda.org
URL: http://www.rtnda.org

Raising Capital
1729 H St. NW
Washington, DC 20006
Ph: (202)887-6400
Free: 800-544-0155
Fax: (202)223-8990
Co. E-mail: books@kiplinger.com
URL: http://www.kiplinger.com

RAM Research Group
Rockefeller Ctr.
1230 Ave. of the Americas, 7th Fl.
New York, NY 10020
Ph: (212)745-1362
Fax: (917)639-4005
Co. E-mail: cardstaff@ramresearch.com

RAND Corp.
1776 Main St.
Santa Monica, CA 90401-3208
Ph: (310)393-0411
Fax: (310)393-4818
Co. E-mail: mweden@rand.org
URL: http://www.rand.org

Randall Publishing Inc.
1425 Lunt Ave.
Elk Grove Village, IL 60007
Ph: (847)437-6604
Fax: (847)437-6618
Co. E-mail: publisher@geartechnology.com
URL: http://www.geartechnology.com

Randall-Reilly Publishing Co.
3200 Rice Mine Rd. NE
Tuscaloosa, AL 35406
Ph: (205)345-0958
Free: 800-633-5953
Fax: (205)345-0958
Co. E-mail: mreilly@randallpub.com
URL: http://www.randallpub.com

Random House Inc.
1745 Broadway
New York, NY 10019-4305
Ph: (212)782-9000
Free: 800-733-3000
Fax: (212)572-6066
Co. E-mail: ecustomerservice@random-house.com
URL: http://www.randomhouse.com

Random House Information Group
1745 Broadway 15-3
New York, NY 10019-4343
Ph: (212)782-9000
Fax: (212)302-7985
URL: http://www.randomhouse.com

Random House
1745 Broadway
New York, NY 10019
Ph: (212)782-9000
Fax: (212)572-8700
Co. E-mail: customerservice@random-house.com

Random House Publishing Group
1745 Broadway
New York, NY 10019
Ph: (212)751-2600
Free: 800-726-0600
Fax: (212)572-4949
Co. E-mail: bwaypub@randomhouse.com
URL: http://www.randomhouse.com

Random Lengths Publications, Inc.
450 Country Club Rd., Ste. 240
Eugene, OR 97441-6053
Ph: (541)686-9925
Free: 888-686-9925
Fax: (541)686-9629
Co. E-mail: rlmail@ripl.com
URL: http://www.randomlengths.com

The Rangefinder Publishing Company Inc.
6059 Bristol Pky., Ste. 100
Culver City, CA 90230
Ph: (310)846-4770
Fax: (310)846-5995
URL: http://www.rangefindermag.com

Rayve Productions, Inc.
PO Box 726
Windsor, CA 95492
Ph: (707)838-6200
Free: 800-832-4890
Fax: (707)838-2220

RB Publishing Co.
2901 International Ln.
Madison, WI 53704
Ph: (608)241-8777
URL: http://www.rbpub.com/ME2/Default.asp

ReadHowYouWant.com, Ltd.
1201 11871 Horseshoe Way
Richmond, BC, Canada V7A 5H5
Free: 800-693-9050
URL: http://ReadHowYouWant.com

Reading Eagle/Reading Times
345 Penn St.
Reading, PA 19603
Ph: (610)371-5000

Realtor Magazine
430 N Michigan Ave.
Chicago, IL 60811
Free: 800-874-6500

Realtors Land Institute
430 N Michigan Ave.
Chicago, IL 60611
Ph: (800)441-5263
Free: 800-441-LAND
Fax: (312)329-8633
Co. E-mail: rli@realtors.org
URL: http://www.rliland.com

Realty Publications Inc.
PO Box 20069
Riverside, CA 92516
Ph: (951)781-7300
Free: 800-794-0494
Fax: (951)781-4721
Co. E-mail: customerservice@firsttuesday.
  us
URL: http://www.firsttuesdayonline.com/

Record
150 River St.
Hackensack, NJ 07601
Ph: (201)646-4000

Recreation Vehicle Dealers Association of North America
3930 University Dr.
Fairfax, VA 22030-2515
Ph: (703)591-7130
Fax: (703)359-0152
Co. E-mail: info@rvda.org
URL: http://www.rvda.org

Recreation Vehicle Industry Association
1896 Preston White Dr.
Reston, VA 20191
Ph: (703)620-6003
Free: 800-336-0154
Fax: (703)620-5071
Co. E-mail: rvia@rvia.org
URL: http://www.rvia.org

Rector Press, Ltd.
130 Rattlesnake Gutter Rd.
Leverett, MA 01054-9726
Ph: (413)367-0303
Free: 800-247-3473
Fax: (413)367-0303
Co. E-mail: info@rectorpress.com
URL: http://www.rectorpress.com

Recycling Council of Ontario
215 Spadina Ave., Ste. 225
Toronto, ON, Canada M5T 2C7
Ph: (416)657-2797
Fax: (416)960-8053
Co. E-mail: rco@rco.on.ca
URL: http://www.rco.on.ca

RedCoat Publishing Inc.
900 Cummings Center, Ste. 222-T
Beverly, MA 01915
Ph: (978)232-9494
Fax: (978)232-0225

RedCoat Publishing, Inc.
900 Cummings Ctr., Ste. 222-T
Beverly, MA 01915
Ph: (978)232-9494
Fax: (978)232-0225
URL: http://www.redcoatpublishing.com/

Reed Business Geo, Inc.
20 W 3rd St.
Frederick, MD 21701
Ph: (301)682-6101
Fax: (301)682-6105
Co. E-mail: psm@profsurv.com
URL: http://www.profsurv.com/reedbusi-
  nessgeo.aspx

Reed Business Information (RBI)
360 Park Ave. S
New York, NY 10010
Ph: (646)746-6400
Free: 800-446-6551
Fax: (646)746-7028
Co. E-mail: corporatecommunications@
  reedbusiness.com
URL: http://www.reedbusiness.com

Reed Business Information Inc.
360 Park Ave. S
New York, NY 10010
Ph: (646)746-6400

Reed Business Information
2000 Clearwater Dr.
Oak Brook, IL 60523
Ph: (630)288-8000
Fax: (630)288-8750
Co. E-mail: packagingdigest@reedbusi-
  ness.com
URL: http://www.packagingdigest.com/
  newsite/cover/contact.php

Reed Construction Data Inc.
30 Technology Pky. S, Ste. 100
Norcross, GA 30092
Ph: (770)417-4000
Free: 800-424-3996
Fax: (770)417-4002
Co. E-mail: marketing@reedbusiness.com
URL: http://www.reedconstructiondata.com

Reed Elsevier Reference Publishing
125 Park Ave., 23rd Fl.
New York, NY 10017
Ph: (212)309-8100
Fax: (212)309-8187

Reed Reference Publishing
125 Park Ave., 23rd Fl.
New York, NY 10017
Ph: (212)309-8100
Fax: (212)309-8187

Reed Travel Group OAG Travel Services Div.
3025 Highland Pky., Ste. 200
Downers Grove, IL 60515-5561
Ph: (630)515-5300

Free: 800-DIA-LOAG
Fax: (630)515-5301
Co. E-mail: custsvc@oag.com
URL: http://www.oag.com

Reflector Publishing
1150 Sugg Pky.
Greenville, NC 27834
Ph: (252)329-9500
Free: 800-849-6166
URL: http://www.reflector.com

The Register-Guard
3500 Chad Dr.
Eugene, OR 97408
Ph: (541)485-1234
Free: 800-377-7428

Rehabilitation Research and Training Center on Blindness and Low Vision
PO Box 6189
Mississippi State, MS 39762
Ph: (662)325-2001
Free: 800-675-7782
Fax: (662)225-8989
Co. E-mail: rrtc@ra.msstate.edu

Reilly Publishing Co.
16 E. Schaumberg Rd.
Schaumberg,, IL 60194-3536
Ph: (847)882-6336
Fax: (847)519-0166
Co. E-mail: rcgroup@flash.net
URL: http://www.rcgonline.com

Rent-A-Wreck of America Inc.
Licensee Service Center
105 Main St.
Laurel, MD 20707
Free: 800-944-7501
URL: http://www.rentawreck.com

RePlay Magazine
18757 Burbank Blvd., No. 105
Tarzana, CA 91356
Ph: (818)776-2880
Fax: (818)776-2888
Co. E-mail: editor@replaymag.com
URL: http://www.replaymag.com/

Research Institute of America
395 Hudson St.
New York, NY 10014
Ph: (212)367-6300
Free: 800-950-1216
Fax: (212)367-6305
Co. E-mail: ria@thomson.com
URL: http://ria.thomsonreuters.com/

Resort and Commercial Recreation Association
PO Box 1564
Dubuque, IA 52004
Co. E-mail: info@rcra.org
URL: http://www.rcra.org

Resource Recycling
PO Box 42270
Portland, OR 97242-0270
Ph: (503)233-1305
Fax: (503)233-1356
Co. E-mail: info@resource-recycling.com
URL: http://www.resource-recycling.com

Restoration Industry Association
12339 Carroll Ave.
Rockville, MD 20852
Ph: (301)231-6505
Free: 800-272-7012
Fax: (301)231-6569
Co. E-mail: tshaw@restorationindustry.org
URL: http://www.ascr.org

The Retailer's Bakery Association
8201 Greensboro Dr., Ste. 300
McLean, VA 22102
Ph: (703)610-9035
Free: 800-638-0924
Fax: (703)610-9005
Co. E-mail: info@rbanet.com

Retired Persons Services Inc.
500 Montgomery St.
Alexandria, VA 22314
Ph: (703)684-0245
Fax: (703)684-0246

RIA Group
395 Hudson St.
New York, NY 10014
Ph: (212)367-6300
Fax: (212)367-6314

Rich Publishing LLC
4330 N Civic Center Plz., Ste. 100
Scottsdale, AZ 85251
Free: 800-317-3905
Co. E-mail: customerservice@richdad.com
URL: http://www.richdad.com

Richard T. Scofield
PO Box 476
New Albany, OH 43054
Ph: (614)855-9315
Free: 800-410-8780
Fax: (614)855-9325

Rick Chapman
34 Sugar Hill Rd.
Killingworth, CT 06419
Ph: (860)663-0552
Fax: (617)924-7288
Co. E-mail: customer@softletter.com

Ridgewood Press
728 Glendale Dr.
Jefferson City, MO 65109
Ph: (573)636-7472
Fax: (309)438-3755

Rimbach Publishing Inc.
8650 Babcock Blvd.
Pittsburgh, PA 15237
Ph: (412)364-5366
Free: 800-245-3182
Co. E-mail: info@rimbach.com
URL: http://www.rimbach.com/

Risk Management Association (RMA)
1801 Market St., Ste. 300
Philadelphia, PA 19103-1613
Ph: (215)446-4000
Fax: (215)446-4101
Co. E-mail: RMAAR@rmahq.org
URL: http://www.rmahq.org

Riverhead Booksk
375 Hudson St.
New York, NY 10014
Ph: (212)366-2000
Fax: (212)366-2666
Co. E-mail: riverhead.web@us.penguin-
  group.com
URL: http://www.riverheadbooks.com

RO-EL Productions Inc.
550 W Old Country Rd., Ste. 204
Hicksville, NY 11801
Ph: (516)932-7860
Fax: (516)932-7639
URL: http://www.fcnews.net

Roanoke Times
201 W Campbell Ave.
Roanoke, VA 24010
Ph: (540)981-3211
Free: 800-346-1234

Robert M. Parker, Jr.
PO Box 311
Monkton, MD 21111
Ph: (410)329-6477
Fax: (410)357-4504
Co. E-mail: wineadvocate@erobertparker.
  com

The Robert Wood Johnson Foundation
College Rd. E, Rte. 1
Princeton, NJ 08543-2316
Ph: (609)452-8701
Free: 877-843-7953
Fax: (609)987-8845

Robotic Industries Association
PO Box 3724
Ann Arbor, MI 48106-3724
Ph: (734)994-6088
Free: 800-994-6099
Fax: (734)994-3338
Co. E-mail: ria@robotics.org
URL: http://www.roboticsonline.com

Rodale Inc.
400 S 10th St.
Emmaus, PA 18098-0001
Ph: (610)967-5171
Free: 800-848-4735

Fax: (610)967-9863
Co. E-mail: customer_service@rodale.com
URL: http://www.rodaleinc.com/

Rodale Press, Inc.
400 S 10th St.
Emmaus, PA 18098
Ph: (610)967-8775
Fax: (610)967-8962
URL: http://www.rodale.com

Rogers Media Ltd.
1 Mt. Pleasant Rd., 11th Fl.
Toronto, ON, Canada M4Y 2Y5
Ph: (416)764-1200
Fax: (416)764-1404

**Rogers Media Publishing Marketing
Media Group**
One Mount Pleasant Rd., 7th Fl.
Toronto, ON, Canada M4Y 2Y5
Ph: (416)764-2000
Fax: (416)764-7730
URL: http://www.rogers.com

Rogers Media Publishing
Box 860
Markham, ON, Canada L3P 8H8
Ph: (905)946-0084
Fax: (905)946-1679
Co. E-mail: service@rmpublishing.com
URL: http://www.rogersmagazines.com

Rogers Media
1 Mt. Pleasant Rd., 11th Fl.
Toronto, ON, Canada M4Y 2Y5
Ph: (416)764-1200
Fax: (416)764-1404

Rogers Publishing Ltd.
333 Bloor St. E, 6th Fl.
Toronto, ON, Canada M4W 1G9
Ph: (416)764-2000

Roll Call CQ
1255 22nd St. NW
Washington, DC 20037
Ph: (202)419-8500
Free: 800-432-2250

Ron Mader
12345 SW 18th St., No. 417
Miami, FL 33175

RosettaBooks LLC
200 W 57th St., Ste. 904
New York, NY 10019
Ph: (646)274-1970
Co. E-mail: editor@rosettabooks.com
URL: http://www.rosettabooks.com

Roswell Park Cancer Institute
Elm & Carlton St.
Buffalo, NY 14263
Ph: (716)845-8182
Free: 877-275-7724
Fax: (716)845-4565

Co. E-mail: askrpci@roswellpark.org
URL: http://www.roswellpark.org

Routledge Inc.
270 Madison Ave.
New York, NY 10016-0702
Ph: (212)216-7800
Free: 800-634-7064
Fax: (212)564-7854
Co. E-mail: info@routledge-ny.com
URL: http://www.routledge-ny.com

Routledge Journals Taylor & Francis Group
270 Madison Ave.
New York, NY 10016-0601
Ph: (212)216-7800
Fax: (212)563-2269
URL: http://www.routledge.com/

Routledge
270 Madison Ave., Ste. 3
New York, NY 10016
Ph: (212)216-7800
Free: 800-634-7064
Fax: (212)564-7854
URL: http://www.routledge.com

Routledge
711 3rd Ave., 8th Fl.
New York, NY 10017
Ph: (212)216-7800
Fax: (212)563-2269

Routledge, Taylor & Francis Group
711 3rd Ave., 8th Fl.
New York, NY 10016
Ph: (212)216-7800
Fax: (212)563-2269
URL: http://www.routledge.com

Rowman & Littlefield Publishers Inc.
4501 Forbes Blvd., Ste. 200
Lanham, MD 20706
Ph: (301)459-3366
Free: 800-462-6420
Fax: (301)459-5748
Co. E-mail: custserv@rowman.com

Royal Historical Society
University College London
Gower St.
London WC1E 6BT, United Kingdom
Ph: 44 20 73877532
Fax: 44 20 73877532

RSVP: The Directory of Illustration and Design
PO Box 050314
Brooklyn, NY 11205
Ph: (718)857-9267
Co. E-mail: info@rsvpdirectory.com
URL: http://www.rsvpdirectory.com

Rubber Division American Chemical Society
PO Box 499
Akron, OH 44309-0499
Ph: (330)972-7814
Fax: (330)972-5269
URL: http://www.rubber.org

Rug News Magazine
5 Hanover Sq., 21st Fl.
New York, NY 10004
Ph: (212)269-2016
Fax: (212)269-2740
Co. E-mail: rugnews@museumbooks.com
URL: http://www.rugnewsdesign.com/

Runzheimer International
1 Runzheimer Pkwy.
Waterford, WI 53185-3599
Ph: (262)971-2200
Free: 800-558-1702
Fax: (262)971-2254
Co. E-mail: marketing@runzheimer.com
URL: http://www.runzheimer.com

Russell Sage Foundation Publications
112 E 64th St.
New York, NY 10065
Ph: (212)750-6000
Fax: (212)371-4761

Ruth Finley
153 E 87th St.
New York, NY 10128
Ph: (212)289-0420
Fax: (212)289-5917
URL: http://www.fashioncalendar.net/

Rutledge Books Inc.
107 Mill Plain Rd., Ste. 302
Danbury, CT 06811
Ph: (203)778-5925
Free: 800-278-8533
Fax: (203)798-7272
Co. E-mail: info@rutledgebooks.com

S

S. Harman & Associates Inc.
PO Box 1129
Sykesville, MD 21784-1129
Ph: (410)795-9296
Fax: (410)549-1261
Co. E-mail: sharmaninc@aol.com
URL: http://www.sharmansite.com

Sacramento Bee
2100 Q St.
Sacramento, CA 95816
Ph: (916)321-1000

Sacramento Business Journal
1400 X St.
Sacramento, CA 95818
Ph: (916)447-7661
Fax: (916)444-7779

Saddle & Bridle Inc.
375 Jackson Ave.
Saint Louis, MO 63130-4243
Ph: (314)725-9115
Fax: (314)725-6440
Co. E-mail: editor@saddleandbridle.com
URL: http://www.saddleandbridle.com

SAGE Publications USA
2455 Teller Rd.
Thousand Oaks, CA 91320
Ph: (805)499-9774
Free: 800-818-7243
Fax: (805)583-2665
Co. E-mail: info@sagepub.com
URL: http://www.sagepub.com

Saint Louis Business Journal
815 Olive St., Ste. 100
Saint Louis, MO 63101
Ph: (314)421-6200
Fax: (314)621-5031

Salesforce Training & Consulting Inc.
2005 Sheppard Ave. E, Ste. 109
Toronto, ON, Canada M2J 5B4
Ph: (800)461-7355
Free: 800-461-7355
Co. E-mail: info@salesforcetraining.com
URL: http://www.salesforcetraining.com

San Diego Business Journal
4909 Murphy Canyon Rd., Ste. 200
San Diego, CA 92123
Ph: (858)277-6359

San Diego Community Newspaper Group
4645 Cass St., 2nd Fl.
San Diego, CA 92109
Ph: (858)270-3103
Free: 800-669-3103
Fax: (858)713-0095
Co. E-mail: sales@sdnews.com
URL: http://www.sdnews.com

San Diego Floral Association
1650 El Prado, Rm. 105
San Diego, CA 92101-1684
Ph: (619)232-5762
Fax: (619)232-5762
Co. E-mail: info@sdfloral.org
URL: http://www.sdfloral.org

San Diego Union-Tribune
PO Box 120191
San Diego, CA 92112-0191
Ph: (619)299-3131
Free: 800-244-6397
Fax: (619)293-1896
Co. E-mail: subscriber.services@uniontrib.
  com
URL: http://www.signonsandiego.com/

San Fernando Valley Association for the Retarded
15725 Parthenia St.
North Hills, CA 91343
Ph: (818)894-9301
Fax: (818)894-7801
Co. E-mail: hrasey@nhsfvar.org

San Francisco AIDS Foundation
995 Market St., Ste. 200
San Francisco, CA 94103
Ph: (415)487-3000
Free: 800-367-AIDS
Fax: (415)487-3009
Co. E-mail: feedback@sfaf.org
URL: http://www.sfaf.org/

San Jose Mercury News
750 Ridder Park Dr.
San Jose, CA 95190
Ph: (408)288-8060
Fax: (408)920-5331

Sandow Media Corp.
3731 NW 8th Ave.
Boca Raton, FL 33431
Ph: (561)750-0151
Fax: (561)750-0152
Co. E-mail: sandowinfo@sandowmedia.
  com
URL: http://www.sandowmedia.com

Sara Wyant
191 S Gary Ave.
Carol Stream, IL 60188
Ph: (630)462-2266
Fax: (630)462-2869
Co. E-mail: swyant@farmprogress.com

Saskatchewan Pulse Corp.
PO Box 516
Regina, SK, Canada S4P 3A2
Fax: (306)525-4173

Scandinavian Collectors Club
PO Box 13196
El Cajon, CA 92022
Co. E-mail: sccwebman@gmail.com
URL: http://www.scc-online.org/

Scarecrow Press Inc.
c/o Rowman & Littlefield Publishing Group
PO Box 191
Blue Ridge Summit, PA 17214
Ph: (717)794-3800
Free: 800-462-6420
Fax: (717)794-3803
Co. E-mail: customercare@rowman.com
URL: http://rowman.com/Scarecrow

Scentouri
PO Box 416
Denver, CO 80201
Ph: (303)575-5676
Fax: (303)575-1187
Co. E-mail: mail@contentprovidermedia.
  com

Schaeffer's Investment Research Inc.
1259 Kemper Meadow Dr.
Cincinnati, OH 45240
Ph: (513)589-3800
Free: 800-448-2080
Fax: (513)589-3810
Co. E-mail: service@sir-inc.com

Schiffer Publishing Ltd.
4880 Lower Valley Rd.
Atglen, PA 19310-1768
Ph: (610)593-1777
Fax: (610)593-2002
Co. E-mail: schifferbk@aol.com
URL: http://www.schifferbooks.com

Schneider Publishing Company Inc.
11835 W Olympic Blvd., 12th Fl.
Los Angeles, CA 90064
Ph: (310)577-3700
Fax: (310)577-3715
Co. E-mail: info@schneiderpublishing.com
URL: http://www.schneiderpublishing.com/

Schofield Media Group
200 E Randolph St., 70th Fl.
Chicago, IL 60601
Ph: (312)236-4090
Fax: (312)240-0686

ScholarOne, Inc.
275 Greenbriar Dr., Ste. 200
Charlottesville, VA 22901
Ph: (434)817-2040
Fax: (434)817-2020

Schonfeld and Associates Inc.
1931 Lynn Cir.
Libertyville, IL 60048-1323
Ph: (847)816-4870
Free: 800-205-0030
Fax: (847)816-4872
Co. E-mail: SAinfo@saibooks.com
URL: http://www.saibooks.com

School of Labor and Industrial Relations
Michigan State University
405 S Kedzie
East Lansing, MI 48823
Ph: (517)355-1800
Fax: (517)355-7656
Co. E-mail: shrm@lir.msu.edu

Schoolhouse Press
6899 Cary Bluff
Pittsville, WI 54466
Ph: (715)884-2799
Free: 800-968-5648
Fax: (715)884-2829
Co. E-mail: info@schoolhousepress.com
URL: http://www.schoolhousepress.com/

Scotsman Community Publications
750 W Genesee St.
Syracuse, NY 13221-4970
Ph: (315)472-7825

Fax: (315)478-1434
Co. E-mail: pennysaver@scotsmanpress.
  com
URL: http://www.scotsmanonline.com

Scott Advertising & Publishing Co.
30595 W Eight Mile Rd.
Livonia, MI 48152-1798
Ph: (248)477-6650
Free: 800-458-8237
Fax: (248)477-6795
Co. E-mail: contactus@scottpublications.
  com
URL: http://www.scottpublications.com

Scott American Corp.
PO Box 88
West Redding, CT 06896-0088
Ph: (203)938-2955
Free: 800-726-8839
Fax: (203)938-2955
Co. E-mail: service@travelpublicityleads.
  com
URL: http://www.scottamerican.com

Scott Publishing
911 S Vandemark Rd.
Sidney, OH 45365-8974
Ph: (937)498-0802
Free: 800-488-5349
Fax: (937)498-0807
Co. E-mail: cuserv@amospress.com
URL: http://www.linns.com

Scott's Directories
12 Concorde Pl., Ste. 800
Toronto, ON, Canada M3C 4J2
Ph: (416)442-2122
Free: 800-668-2374
Fax: (416)510-6870
Co. E-mail: customercare@scottsdirecto-
  ries.com
URL: http://www.scottsdirectories.com

SCP Journal
PO Box 4308
Berkeley, CA 94704
Ph: (510)540-0300
Fax: (510)540-1107
Co. E-mail: scp@scp-inc.org
URL: http://www.scp-inc.org/

Scribner Educational Publishers
1230 Ave. of the Americas
New York, NY 10020
Ph: (212)632-4915
Fax: (212)632-4957
URL: http://www.simonandschuster.com

Seahorse Financial Advisers Inc.
359 Shunpike
Millbrook, NY 12545
Ph: (845)677-6865
Fax: (845)677-0317
URL: http://www.seahorseadvisers.com

Seal Press
Perseus Books Group
1700 4th St.
Berkeley, CA 94710
Ph: (212)340-8100
Free: 800-285-4078
Fax: (510)595-4228
URL: http://www.sealpress.com

Securities Industry and Financial Markets Association
120 Broadway, 35th Fl.
New York, NY 10271
Ph: (212)313-1200

Security Letter Inc.
166 E 96th St., Ste. Grb
New York, NY 10128-2512
Ph: (212)348-1553
Fax: (212)534-2957
Co. E-mail: rmccrie@mindspring.com

Sedgwick Publishing
PO Box 328
Boyds, MD 20841-0328
Ph: (301)528-0011
Fax: (240)599-7679
Co. E-mail: support@pnmsi.com
URL: http://www.businessmailersreview.
  com

Seed Savers Exchange
3094 N Winn Rd.
Decorah, IA 52101-7776
Ph: (563)382-5990
Fax: (563)382-6511
Co. E-mail: john@seedsavers.org
URL: http://www.seedsavers.org

Self-Counsel Press Inc.
1704 N State St.
Bellingham, WA 98225
Ph: (360)676-4530
Free: 877-877-6490
Fax: (360)676-4549
Co. E-mail: orderdesk@self-counsel.com
URL: http://www.self-counsel.com

Self-Counsel, Incorporated
1704 N State St.
Bellingham, WA 98225
Ph: (360)676-4530
Free: 877-877-6490
Fax: (360)676-4549

Self-Help Publishers
3-445 Pioneer Dr.
Kitchner, ON, Canada N2P 1L8
URL: http://www.selfhelppublishers.com

SER-Jobs for Progress National
100 E Royal Ln., Ste. 130
Irving, TX 75039
Ph: (469)549-3600
Free: 800-427-2306
Fax: (469)549-3684
Co. E-mail: info@ser-national.org

URL: http://www.ser-national.org

Serves You Right!, Incorporated
6105 E Osborn Rd.
Scottsdale, AZ 85251
Ph: (480)994-1918
Fax: (480)994-5966

Service Directions Inc.
PO Box 380
Pelham, NY 10803
Ph: (914)738-3800
Free: 800-666-0505
Fax: (914)738-3241
Co. E-mail: SDIWECARE@aol.com

Sexuality Information and Education Council of the U.S.
90 John St., Ste. 402
New York, NY 10038
Ph: (212)819-9770
Fax: (212)819-9776
Co. E-mail: mrodriguez@siecus.org
URL: http://www.siecus.org

SGC Horizon LLC
3030 W Salt Creek Ln., Ste. 201
Arlington Heights, IL 60005
Ph: (847)391-1000
Fax: (847)390-0408
URL: http://www.sgchorizon.com/

Shane Downing
PO Box 7939
Torrance, CA 90504
Ph: (310)515-7369
Fax: (310)515-7534
Co. E-mail: orders@greysheet.com

SHARE
1501 Broadway, Ste. 704A
between W. 43rd & W. 44th Sts.
New York, NY 10036
Ph: (212)719-0364
Free: 866-891-2392
Fax: (212)869-3431

Shelby Publishing Company Inc.
517 Green St. NW
Gainesville, GA 30501
Ph: (770)534-8380
Fax: (678)343-2197
Co. E-mail: editor@shelbypublishing.com
URL: http://www.shelbypublishing.com

Sheltie Pacesetter
9428 Blue Mound Dr.
Fort Wayne, IN 46804
Ph: (260)434-1566
Fax: (260)434-1566
Co. E-mail: sheltiepacesetter@charter.net
URL: http://www.sheltie.com

Shoe Trades Publishing Co.
241 Senneville Rd.
Senneville, QC, Canada H9X 3X5
Ph: (514)457-8787

Fax: (514)457-5832
Co. E-mail: books@shoetrades.com
URL: http://www.shoetrades.com

Shrimp World Inc.
417 Eliza St.
New Orleans, LA 70114
Ph: (504)368-1571
Fax: (504)368-1573

Shugar's Publishing The Purple Directory
15873 Hartwell St.
Detroit, MI 48238-0665
Ph: (313)836-8600
Free: 800-377-9129
Fax: (313)836-8600
Co. E-mail: purfuneral@aol.com
URL: http://www.purpledirectory.com

Siefer Consultants Inc.
524 Cayuga St.
Storm Lake, IA 50588
Ph: (712)732-7340
Free: 800-747-7342
Fax: (712)732-7906
Co. E-mail: info@siefer.com
URL: http://www.siefer.com

Signcraft Publishing Co.
10271 Deer Run Farms Rd.
Fort Myers, FL 33966
Ph: (239)939-4644
Free: 800-204-0204
Fax: (239)939-0607
Co. E-mail: signcraft@signcraft.com
URL: http://www.signcraft.com/

Silver Lake Publishing
1119 N Broadway St.
Aberdeen, WA 98520-2433
Free: 800-663-3091

SIMBA Information Inc.
11200 Rockville Pk., Ste. 504
Rockville, MD 20852
Ph: (240)747-3096
Free: 800-307-2529
Fax: (240)747-3004
Co. E-mail: customerservice@simbainfor-
  mation.com
URL: http://www.simbanet.com/

Simon & Shuster
135 S Mt. Zion Rd.
Lebanon, IN 46052
URL: http://www.simonandschuster.com

Simon and Schuster Inc.
1230 Ave. Of The Americas
New York, NY 10020-1513
Ph: (212)698-7000
Free: 800-943-9831
Fax: (212)698-7099
Co. E-mail: contact@simonandschuster.
  com
URL: http://www.simonandschuster.com

Simon and Schuster
100 Front St.
Riverside, NJ 08075
Ph: (800)223-2348
Free: 800-223-2336
Fax: (800)943-9831

Simon Foundation for Continence
PO Box 815
Wilmette, IL 60091
Ph: (847)864-3913
Free: 800-237-4666
Fax: (847)864-9758
Co. E-mail: cbgartley@simonfoundation.
 org
URL: http://www.simonfoundation.org

Singles in the Suburbs Inc.
PO Box 952
Winchester, MA 01890-8252
Ph: (781)721-4220
Co. E-mail: singlessuburbs@yahoo.com

SK Publications
PO Box 6983
Huntington Beach, CA 92615
Ph: (714)963-1558
Co. E-mail: sk_publishing@yahoo.com
URL: http://skinnedknuckles.net/pages/
 index.htm

Skilled Learning Incorporated
20 Townsite Rd., 2nd Fl.
Nanaimo, BC, Canada V9S 5T7
Ph: (250)244-2937
Fax: (250)244-2970

Small Business Advisors Inc.
11 Franklin Ave.
Hewlett, NY 11557
Ph: (516)374-1387
Fax: (720)294-3202
Co. E-mail: letters@smallbusinessadvice.
 com
URL: http://www.smallbusinessadvice.com/

Small Business Council of America Inc.
4800 Hampton Lane 7th FL
Bethesda, DE 20814
Ph: (301)656-7603
Free: 877-404-1329
Fax: (301)654-7354

Small Farm Center
University of California
One Shields Ave.
Davis, CA 95616-8699
Ph: (530)752-8136
Fax: (530)752-7716
Co. E-mail: sfcenter@ucdavis.edu

Smaller Business Association of New England
1601 Trapelo Rd., Ste. 212
Waltham, MA 02451
Ph: (781)890-9070
Free: 800-366-6803

Fax: (781)890-4567
Co. E-mail: info@sbane.org
URL: http://www.sbane.org

SNL Financial L.C.
1 SNL Plz.
Charlottesville, VA 22902
Ph: (434)977-1600
Free: 888-275-2822
Fax: (434)977-4466
Co. E-mail: CustomerService@snl.com

SnowSports Industries America
8377-B Greensboro Dr.
McLean, VA 22102
Ph: (703)556-9020
Fax: (703)821-8276
Co. E-mail: siamail@snowsports.org
URL: http://www.snowsports.org

Society for Business Ethics (SBE)
c/o Jeff Frooman, Exec. Dir.
University of New Brunswick
PO Box 4400
Fredericton, NB, Canada E3B 5A3
Co. E-mail: frooman@unb.ca
URL: http://www.societyforbusinessethics.
 org

Society for Calligraphy
PO Box 64174
Los Angeles, CA 90064-0174
Co. E-mail: president@societyforcalligra-
 phy.org
URL: http://www.societyforcalligraphy.org

Society for Human Resource Management (SHRM)
1800 Duke St.
Alexandria, VA 22314
Ph: (703)548-3440
Free: 800-283-7476
Fax: (703)535-6490
Co. E-mail: shrm@shrm.org
URL: http://www.shrm.org

Society for Scholarly Publishing
10200 W 44th Ave., Ste. 304
Wheat Ridge, CO 80033
Ph: (303)422-3914
Fax: (303)422-8894
Co. E-mail: info@sspnet.org
URL: http://www.sspnet.org

Society for the Preservation and Advancement of the Harmonica
PO Box 865
Troy, MI 48099-0865
Ph: (586)771-4866
Co. E-mail: harpspah@spah.org
URL: http://www.spah.org

Society of Actuaries
475 N Martingale Rd., Ste. 600
Schaumburg, IL 60173-2226
Ph: (847)706-3500
Fax: (847)706-3599

Co. E-mail: bhaynes@soa.org
URL: http://www.soa.org

Society of American Travel Writers
7044 S 13th St.
Oak Creek, WI 53154
Ph: (414)908-4949
Fax: (414)768-8001
Co. E-mail: satw@satw.org

Society of Architectural Historians
1365 N Astor St.
Chicago, IL 60610-2144
Ph: (312)573-1365
Fax: (312)573-1141
Co. E-mail: info@sah.org
URL: http://www.sah.org

Society of Automotive Engineers (SAE)
400 Commonwealth Dr.
Warrendale, PA 15096-0001
Ph: (724)776-4970
Free: 877-606-7323
Fax: (724)776-0790
Co. E-mail: customerservice@sae.org
URL: http://www.sae.org

Society of Automotive Engineers International
400 Commonwealth Dr.
Warrendale, PA 15096-0001
Ph: (724)776-4841
Free: 877-606-7323
Fax: (724)776-0790
Co. E-mail: customerservice@sae.org
URL: http://www.sae.org

Society of Environmental Toxicology and Chemistry
229 S Baylen St., 2nd Fl.
Pensacola, FL 32502
Ph: (850)469-1500
Fax: (850)469-9778
Co. E-mail: setac@setac.org
URL: http://www.setac.org

Society of Financial Service Professionals
17 Campus Blvd., Ste. 100
Newtown Square, PA 19073-3230
Ph: (610)526-2500
Free: 800-392-6900
Fax: (610)527-1499
Co. E-mail: custserv@financialpro.org
URL: http://www.financialpro.org

Society of Industrial and Office Realtors
1201 New York Ave. NW, Ste. 350
Washington, DC 20005-6126
Ph: (202)449-8200
Free: 888-891-7467
Fax: (202)449-8201
Co. E-mail: admin@sior.com
URL: http://www.sior.com

Society of Manufacturing Engineers
One SME Dr.
Dearborn, MI 48121
Ph: (313)425-3000
Free: 800-733-4763
Fax: (313)425-3401
Co. E-mail: service@sme.org
URL: http://www.sme.org

Society of Professional Audio Recording Services
9 Music Sq. S., Ste. 222
Nashville, TN 37203
Ph: (615)846-6161
Free: 800-771-7727
Fax: (615)846-5123
Co. E-mail: spars@spars.com

Society of Satellite Professionals International
The New York Information Technology
  Ctr., 250 Park Ave., 7th Fl.
New York, NY 10177
Ph: (212)809-5199
Fax: (212)825-0075
Co. E-mail: rbell@sspi.org
URL: http://www.sspi.org

Software and Information Industry Association
1090 Vermont Ave. NW, 6th Fl.
Washington, DC 20005-4095
Ph: (202)289-7442
Free: 800-388-7478
Fax: (202)289-7097
Co. E-mail: info@siia.net
URL: http://www.siia.net

Solar Rating and Certification Corporation
400 High Point Dr., Ste. 400
Cocoa, FL 32926
Ph: (321)213-6037
Fax: (321)821-0910
Co. E-mail: srcc@solar-rating.org
URL: http://www.solar-rating.org

SoloDining.com
PO Box 2664
Carlsbad, CA 92018
Ph: (760)720-1011
Free: 800-299-1079
Fax: (760)720-1049
Co. E-mail: editor@solodining.com
URL: http://www.solodining.com

Sortis Publishing
2193 E Claxton Ave.
Gilbert, AZ 85296
Free: 866-375-9744
Fax: (480)287-8318
Co. E-mail: info@sortispublishing.com
URL: http://www.sortispublishing.com

Sosland Publishing Co.
4800 Main St., Ste. 100
Kansas City, MO 64112
Ph: (816)756-1000
Fax: (816)756-0494
Co. E-mail: nwages@sosland.com
URL: http://www.sosland.com

Sound Publishing Inc.
1321 King St., Ste. 4
Bellingham, WA 98229
Ph: (360)647-8805
Fax: (360)647-0502
Co. E-mail: editor@bbjtoday.com
URL: http://bbjtoday.com/

Soundings Publications L.L.C.
10 Bokum Rd.
Essex, CT 06426
Ph: (860)767-3200
Free: 800-444-7686
Fax: (860)767-0642
Co. E-mail: info@soundingspub.com
URL: http://www.soundingsonline.com/
  about-us

Source Book Publications
1814 Franklin St., Ste. 815
Oakland, CA 94612
Ph: (510)839-5471
Free: 800-841-0873
Fax: (510)839-2104
URL: http://www.sourcebookpublications.
  com

Source Interlink Media L.L.C.
261 Madison Ave., 6th Fl.
New York, NY 10016
Ph: (212)915-4000
Co. E-mail: webmastersim@sourceinter-
  link.com
URL: http://www.sourceinterlinkmedia.com/
  contact/

Sourcebooks Mediafusion
1935 Brookdale Rd., Ste. 139
Naperville, IL 60563
Ph: (630)961-3900
Free: 800-432-7448
Fax: (630)961-2168
URL: http://www.sourcebooks.com/
  content/books_mediafusion.asp

Sourcebooks, Inc.
1935 Brookdale Rd., Ste. 139
Naperville, IL 60563
Ph: (630)961-3900
Free: 800-432-7444
Fax: (630)961-2168
Co. E-mail: info@sourcebooks.com
URL: http://www.sourcebooks.com

SourceMedia Inc.
1 State St. Plaza, 27th Fl.
New York, NY 10004
Ph: (212)803-8200
Fax: (212)843-9600

SourceMedia Inc.
55 Broadway, 6th Fl.
New York, NY 10006
Ph: (212)803-8200

South Carolina Department of Natural Resources
1000 Assembly St.
Columbia, SC 29201
Ph: (803)734-4007
URL: http://www.dnr.sc.gov/

South Carolina Poultry Federation
c/o Connie Smith, Pres.
1921-A Pickens St.
Columbia, SC 29201
Ph: (803)779-4700
Fax: (803)779-5002
Co. E-mail: chick@scpoultry.com
URL: http://www.scpoultry.org

South-Western
5191 Natorp Blvd.
Mason, OH 45040
Ph: (513)229-1000
Free: 800-543-0487
Fax: (800)437-8488

Southern California Genealogical Society & Family Research Library
417 Irving Dr.
Burbank, CA 91504
Ph: (818)843-7247
Fax: (818)843-7262
Co. E-mail: scgs@earthlink.net

Southern Festivals
PO Box 390
Blakely, GA 39823
Free: 800-558-3378
Fax: (229)723-2779
Co. E-mail: jimtaylor@alltel.net
URL: http://www.southfest.com/festival-
  _list/georgia.html

Southern Oregon Media Group
111 N Fir St.
Medford, OR 97501
Ph: (541)776-4411

Southwest Farm Press Agribusiness Div.
7900 International Dr., Ste. 300
Minneapolis, MN 55425-1510
Ph: (952)851-4631
Fax: (952)851-4701
URL: http://southwestfarmpress.com

Special Events Magazine
17383 Sunset Blvd., Ste. A220
Pacific Palisades, CA 90272
Ph: (310)230-7160
Free: 800-543-4116
Fax: (310)230-7168

Special Interest Group on Data Communication
1515 Broadway, 17th Fl.
New York, NY 10036

Special Interest Group on Programming Languages
50 Central Campus Dr., Rm. 3190
Salt Lake City, UT 84112
Ph: (801)587-9091
Fax: (801)581-5843
Co. E-mail: mflatt@cs.utah.edu
URL: http://www.sigplan.org

Specialist Publications Inc.
22801 Ventura Blvd., Ste. 115
Woodland Hills, CA 91364
Ph: (818)224-8035
Free: 800-835-4398
Fax: (818)224-8042
URL: http://www.bnpmedia.com

Specialized Carriers and Rigging Association
2750 Prosperity Ave., Ste. 620
Fairfax, VA 22031-4312
Ph: (703)698-0291
Fax: (571)722-1698
Co. E-mail: info@scranet.org
URL: http://www.scranet.org

Specialty Equipment Market Association
1575 S Valley Vista Dr.
Diamond Bar, CA 91765-0910
Ph: (909)396-0289
Fax: (909)860-1709
Co. E-mail: sema@sema.org
URL: http://www.sema.org

Specialty Graphic Imaging Association
10015 Main St.
Fairfax, VA 22031-3489
Ph: (703)330-5600
Free: 888-385-3588
Fax: (703)330-5357
Co. E-mail: sgia@sgia.org
URL: http://www.sgia.org

The Speedy Bee
PO Box 1317
Jesup, GA 31598
Ph: (912)427-4018
Fax: (912)427-8447
Co. E-mail: speedybee@bellsouth.net
URL: http://thespeedybee.com

Sphinx Publishing
1935 Brookdale Rd. Ste. 139
Naperville, IL 60563
Ph: (630)961-3900
Fax: (630)961-2168

Spiegel & Grau
1745 Broadway
New York, NY 10019
Ph: (212)782-9000

Fax: (212)572-6066
URL: http://www.randomhouse.com/
spiegelandgrau/

SPIN
408 Broadway, 4th Fl.
New York, NY 10013
Ph: (515)242-0297
Free: 800-274-7597

Spiritual Massage Healing Ministry
6907 Sherman St.
Philadelphia, PA 19119
Ph: (215)842-0265
Fax: (215)842-2388
Co. E-mail: aschatz@unix.temple.edu
URL: http://www.healingandlaw.com/

Splash Magazine
8033 Sunset Blvd., No. 841
Los Angeles, CA 90046
Ph: (323)650-0084
Co. E-mail: contact@lasplash.com
URL: http://www.lasplash.com

Spokesman Review
999 W Riverside
Spokane, WA 99201
Ph: (509)459-5000
Free: 800-338-8801

Spoon River Press
2319-C W Rohmann Ave.
Peoria, IL 61604-5072

Springer Netherlands
Van Godewijckstraat 30
3311 GX Dordrecht, Netherlands
Ph: 31 786 576000
Fax: 31 786 576555
URL: http://www.springer.com

Springer
233 Spring St.
New York, NY 10013
Ph: (212)460-1500
Fax: (212)473-6262

Springer
Assinippi Pk.
101 Philip Dr.
Norwell, MA 02061
Ph: (781)681-0537
Fax: (781)681-9045
URL: http://www.springer-sbm.com

Springer Publishing Co.
11 W 42nd St., 15th Fl.
New York, NY 10036
Ph: (212)431-4370
Free: 877-687-7476
Fax: (212)941-7842
Co. E-mail: cs@springerpub.com
URL: http://www.springerpub.com

Springer Publishing Company
233 Spring St.
New York, NY 10013
Ph: (212)460-1500
Free: 800-777-4643
Fax: (212)473-6272
URL: http://www.springerpub.com

Springer-Verlag New York Inc.
233 Spring St.
New York, NY 10013
Ph: (212)460-1500
Free: 800-777-4643
Fax: (212)460-1575
Co. E-mail: service-ny@springer.com
URL: http://www.springer.com

Springfield Resources
205 Ash Ln.
Lafayette hill, PA 19444
Ph: (610)278-7550
Free: 800-242-5656
Fax: (610)278-7552
Co. E-mail: jdl@maintrainer.com

ST Media Group International Inc.
11262 Cornell Park Dr.
Cincinnati, OH 45242
Ph: (513)421-2050
Free: 800-421-1321
Fax: (513)421-5144
URL: http://stmediagroup.com

St. James Press
PO Box 9187
Farmington Hills, MI 48333-9187
Ph: (248)699-4253
Free: 800-877-4253
Fax: (248)699-8035
Co. E-mail: gale.galeord@cengage.com
URL: http://www.gale.cengage.com/
stjames

St. Louis Post-Dispatch
900 N Tucker Blvd.
Saint Louis, MO 63101
Ph: (314)340-8000

St. Martin's Press LLC
175 5th Ave.
New York, NY 10010
Ph: (212)674-5151
Free: 888-330-8477
Fax: (212)674-6132
URL: http://www.stmartins.com

St. Martins Press/Macmillan
175 5th Ave.
New York, NY 10010
Ph: (646)307-5151
Co. E-mail: customerservice@mpsvirginia.
com
URL: http://us.macmillan.com/smp.aspx

Staffing Industry Analysts Inc.
1975 W El Camino Real, Ste. 304
Mountain View, CA 94040
Ph: (650)232-2350
Free: 800-950-9496
Fax: (650)232-2360
Co. E-mail: subservices@sireport.com
URL: http://www.staffingindustry.com

Stagewrite Publishing Inc.
6220 Stevenson Way
Las Vegas, NV 89120-2722
Ph: (702)798-0099
Fax: (702)798-0220
Co. E-mail: editor@magicmagazine.com
URL: http://www.magicmagazine.com/
   contacts.html

Standard & Poor's Corp.
55 Water St.
New York, NY 10041
Ph: (212)438-2000
Free: 800-221-5277
Fax: (212)438-3395
URL: http://www.standardandpoors.com

Standard & Poor's
55 Water St.
New York, NY 10041
Ph: (212)438-1000
Co. E-mail: questions@standardandpoors.
   com

Standard Publishing Corp.
155 Federal St., 13th Fl.
Boston, MA 02110
Ph: (617)457-0600
Free: 800-682-5759
Fax: (617)457-0608
Co. E-mail: customerservice@spcpub.com
URL: http://www.spcpub.com

Standard Rate and Data Service
1700 Higgins Rd.
Des Plaines, IL 60018-5605
Ph: (847)375-5000
Free: 800-232-0772
Fax: (847)375-5001
Co. E-mail: next@srds.com
URL: http://www.srds.com

Standard-Examiner
332 Standard Way
Ogden, UT 84412
Ph: (801)625-4400
Free: 800-651-2105
URL: http://www.standard.net

Stanford University Press
11030 S Langley Ave.
Chicago, IL 60628
Ph: (773)702-7000
Free: 800-621-2736
Fax: (800)621-8471

Stanford University Press
1450 Page Mill Rd.
Palo Alto, CA 94304
Ph: (650)723-9434
Fax: (650)725-3457
Co. E-mail: info@www.sup.org
URL: http://www.sup.org/

Star-News Media
1003 S 17th St.
Wilmington, NC 28401
Ph: (910)343-2000
Fax: (910)343-2210

Star-News
1003 S 17th St.
Wilmington, NC 28401
Ph: (910)343-2000
URL: http://www.starnewsonline.com/

StartingUp Now

State Bar of California
180 Howard St.
San Francisco, CA 94105
Ph: (415)538-2590
Fax: (415)538-2368

State University of New York Press
90 State St., Ste. 700
Albany, NY 12207
Ph: (518)472-5000
Fax: (518)472-5038

Stevens Publishing Corp.
5151 Beltline Rd., 10th Fl.
Dallas, TX 75254
Ph: (972)687-6700
Fax: (972)687-6799
URL: http://www.pollutiononline.com/
   storefronts/stevenspub.html

Stoddart Publishing Company, Ltd.
895 Don Mills Rd.
Toronto, ON, Canada M3C 1W3
Ph: (416)445-3333
Fax: (416)445-5967

Storey Publishing, LLC
210 Mass Moca Way
North Adams, MA 01247
Ph: (413)346-2100
Free: 800-827-7444
Fax: (413)346-2198
URL: http://www.storey.com

Stork Technimet Inc.
662 Cromwell Ave.
St. Paul, MN 55114
Ph: (651)645-3601
Fax: (651)659-7348
Co. E-mail: info.tct@stork.com

Strafford Publications Inc.
590 Dutch Valley Rd.
Atlanta, GA 30324-0729
Ph: (404)881-1141

Free: 800-926-7926
Fax: (404)881-0074
Co. E-mail: custservice@staffordpub.com
URL: http://www.straffordpub.com

Successful Meetings
770 Broadway
New York, NY 10003-9595
Ph: (646)654-5000
Fax: (646)654-5004
URL: http://www.mimegasite.com/

Successful Publishing
7933 Glacier Club Dr.
Washington, MI 48094
Ph: (586)786-1897
Fax: (586)786-1976
URL: http://marksaid.com/_wsn/page2.
   html

Summit Business Media
5081 Olympic Blvd.
Erlanger, KY 41018
Ph: (859)692-2100
Fax: (859)692-2000

Summit Business Media
33-41 Newark St., 2nd Fl.
Hoboken, NJ 07030
Ph: (201)526-1230
Fax: (201)526-1260

Sun News Inc.
1321 King St., Ste. 4
Bellingham, WA 98229
Ph: (360)647-8805

The Sun News
PO Box 406
Myrtle Beach, SC 29578
Ph: (843)626-8555
Free: 800-568-1800

Survey Research Laboratory
505 E Green St., Ste. 3
Champaign, IL 61820-5723
Ph: (217)333-7109
Fax: (217)244-4408
Co. E-mail: info@srl.uic.edu

Suzuki Association of Americas
PO Box 17310
Boulder, CO 80308
Ph: (303)444-0948
Free: 888-378-9854
Fax: (303)444-0984
Co. E-mail: info@suzukiassociation.org
URL: http://www.suzukiassociation.org/

Swedish-American Chamber of Commerce
570 Lexington Ave., 20th Fl.
New York, NY 10022
Ph: (212)838-5530
Fax: (212)755-7953
URL: http://www.saccny.org

Sybex
111 River St.
Hoboken, NJ 07030
Ph: (201)748-6000
Fax: (201)748-6088
URL: http://www.wiley.com/WileyCDA/
   Brand/id-23.html

SYS-CON Media
577 Chestnut Ridge Rd.
Woodcliff Lake, NJ 07677
Ph: (201)802-3000
Fax: (201)782-9601
Co. E-mail: subscribe@sys-con.com
URL: http://www.sys-con.com

T

T.E. Smith Inc.
PO Box 14-2096
Coral Gables, FL 33114
Ph: (305)740-7170
Fax: (305)740-7153
URL: http://www.thewinenews.com/

T.F.H. Publications Inc.
PO Box 427
Neptune, NJ 07754-0427
Ph: (732)988-8400
Fax: (732)988-5466
Co. E-mail: info@tfh.com
URL: http://www.tfhpublications.com/

T.T. Publications Inc.
203 W State Road 434
Winter Springs, FL 32708
Ph: (407)327-4817
Free: 800-308-3745
Fax: (407)327-2603
Co. E-mail: news@towtimes.com
URL: http://www.towtimes.com

TAB Computer Systems, Incorporated
31 Beechwood Ln.
South Windsor, CT 06074
Ph: (860)289-8850
Fax: (860)289-8847

Talcott Communication Corp.
233 N Michigan Ave., Ste. 1780
Chicago, IL 60601
Ph: (312)849-2220
Fax: (312)849-2174
Co. E-mail: talcottpub@talcott.com
URL: http://www.talcott.com

Tampa Bay Business Journal
4890 W Kennedy Blvd., Ste. 850
Tampa, FL 33609
Ph: (813)873-8225
Fax: (813)876-1827

Target Communications Corp.
7626 W Donges Bay Rd.
Mequon, WI 53097
Ph: (262)242-3990
Free: 800-324-3337

Fax: (262)242-7391
Co. E-mail: judy@deerinfo.com
URL: http://www.deerinfo.com

Target Publishing Company Inc.
2470 E Main St.
Columbus, OH 43209
Ph: (614)235-1022
Fax: (614)235-3584
Co. E-mail: rinksider@rinksider.com
URL: http://www.rinksider.com

Target Research
PO Box 1345
Wheaton, MD 20915
Ph: (301)452-1105
Free: 800-376-3324
Fax: (301)949-0065

Targetmark Books
PO Box 421428
Atlanta, GA 30342
Ph: (404)705-9093

Tate Publishing and Enterprises, LLC
127 E Trade Center Terr.
Mustang, OK 73064
Ph: (405)376-4900
Free: 888-361-9473
Fax: (405)376-4401

Taunton Press Inc.
63 S Main St.
Newtown, CT 06470
Ph: (203)426-8171
Free: 800-477-8727
Fax: (203)426-3434
Co. E-mail: booksales@taunton.com
URL: http://www.taunton.com

Tax Analysts
400 S Maple Ave., Ste. 400
Falls Church, VA 22046-4245
Ph: (703)533-4400
Free: 800-955-2444
Fax: (703)533-4444
Co. E-mail: cservice@tax.org
URL: http://www.tax.org

Tax Executives Institute
1200 G St. NW, Ste. 300
Washington, DC 20005-3814
Ph: (202)638-5601
Fax: (202)638-5607
URL: http://www.tei.org

Tax Management Inc.
9435 Key West Ave.
Rockville, MD 20850
Ph: (800)372-1033
Free: 800-223-7270
Fax: (301)294-6760
Co. E-mail: tm@bna.com
URL: http://www.bnatax.com

Taxicab, Limousine and Paratransit Association
3200 Tower Oaks Blvd., Ste. 220
Rockville, MD 20852
Ph: (301)984-5700
Fax: (301)984-5703
Co. E-mail: info@tlpa.org
URL: http://www.tlpa.org

Taylor & Francis Group Journals
325 Chestnut St., Ste. 800
Philadelphia, PA 19106-2608
Ph: (215)625-8900
Free: 800-354-1420
Fax: (215)625-2940
Co. E-mail: customerservice@taylorand-
   francis.com
URL: http://www.tandf.co.uk

Taylor & Francis Group Ltd.
711 3rd Ave., 8th Fl.
New York, NY 10017
Ph: (212)216-7800
Free: 800-634-7064
Fax: (212)563-2269
Co. E-mail: info@taylorandfrancis.com
URL: http://www.routledge.com/

Taylor & Francis Group
325 Chestnut St., Ste. 800
Philadelphia, PA 19106
Ph: (215)625-8900
Free: 800-821-8312
Fax: (215)625-2940
Co. E-mail: info@taylorandfrancis.com
URL: http://www.taylorandfrancis.com

Taylor and Francis Group Ltd
2 Park Sq., Milton Park
Abingdon OX14 4RN, United Kingdom
Ph: 44 22 70176000
Fax: 44 22 70176336
URL: http://www.taylorandfrancis.com

TEACH Magazine
87 Barford Rd.
Toronto, ON, Canada M9W 4H8
Ph: (416)537-2103
Fax: (416)537-3491
Co. E-mail: info@teachmag.com
URL: http://www.teachmag.com

Technical Insights
111 River St.
Hoboken, NJ 07030-5774
Ph: (201)748-6000
Free: 800-245-6217
Fax: (201)748-6088
Co. E-mail: insights@wiley.com
URL: http://www.wiley.com

Technology Marketing Corp.
800 Connecticut Ave, 1st Fl. E.
Norwalk, CT 06854
Ph: (203)852-6800
Free: 800-243-6002
Fax: (203)866-3326

Co. E-mail: tmc@tmcnet.com
URL: http://www.tmcnet.com

Technology Student Association
1914 Association Dr.
Reston, VA 20191-1540
Ph: (703)860-9000
Free: 888-860-9010
Fax: (703)758-4852
Co. E-mail: general@tsaweb.org
URL: http://www.tsaweb.org

Technomic Information Services
300 S. Riverside Plz., Ste. 1200
Chicago, IL 60606
Ph: (312)876-0004
Fax: (312)876-1156
Co. E-mail: foodinfo@technomic.com
URL: http://www.technomic.com/

Telecommunications Industry Association
2500 Wilson Blvd., Ste. 300
Arlington, VA 22201
Ph: (703)907-7700
Free: 703-907-7776
Fax: (703)907-7727
Co. E-mail: tia@tiaonline.org
URL: http://www.tiaonline.org

Teleflora
11444 W Olympic Blvd.
Los Angeles, CA 90064
Ph: (310)966-3517
Free: 800-321-2665
URL: http://www.teleflora.com

The Telegraph
111 E Broadway
Alton, IL 62002
Ph: (618)463-2500
Co. E-mail: telegraph@thetelegraph.com
URL: http://www.thetelegraph.com/

Tennessee Municipal League
226 Capitol Blvd., Ste. 710
Nashville, TN 37219
Ph: (615)255-6416
Fax: (615)255-4752
URL: http://www.tml1.org

Tenth House Enterprises
244 E 86th St., Ste. 65
New York, NY 10028
Ph: (212)737-7536
Fax: (212)737-9469
Co. E-mail: dirhahn@iwwg.org
URL: http://www.iwwg.org

Testa Communications
25 Willowdale Ave.
Port Washington, NY 11050-3716
Ph: (516)767-2500
Fax: (516)767-9335
Co. E-mail: testa@testa.com
URL: http://www.testa.com

Teton Media Inc.
20917 Higgins Ct.
Torrance, CA 90501
Free: 800-777-4320
URL: http://www.cableyellowpages.com/

Theatre Communications Group
520 8th Ave., 24th Fl.
New York, NY 10018-4156
Ph: (212)609-5900
Fax: (212)609-5901
Co. E-mail: tcg@tcg.org
URL: http://www.tcg.org

Theta Corp. Reports
38 E 29th St., 6th Fl.
New York, NY 10016
Ph: (212)807-2629
Free: 800-995-1550
Fax: (212)807-2676
Co. E-mail: customerservice@marketresearch.com
URL: http://www.marketresearch.com

Thin Book Publishing Co. (TB)
70 SW Century Dr., Ste. 100-446
Bend, OR 97702-1047
Ph: (541)382-7579
Free: 888-316-9544
Fax: (541)317-8606
Co. E-mail: info@thinbook.com
URL: http://www.thinbook.com

Think Services
600 Harrison St., 6th Fl.
San Francisco, CA 94017
Ph: (415)947-6224

Thomas Nelson Inc.
501 Nelson Pl.
Nashville, TN 37214-1000
Free: 800-251-4000
Fax: (615)902-1866

Thomas Publishing Company
5 Penn Plz., 14th Fl.
New York, NY 10001
Free: 888-846-6638
Fax: (212)613-3499

Thompson Publishing Group Inc.
805 15th St. NW, 3rd Fl.
Washington, DC 20005
Ph: (202)872-4000
Free: 800-444-8741
Fax: (800)999-5661
Co. E-mail: service@thompson.com
URL: http://www.thompson.com

Thomson CompuMark Americas
500 Victory Rd.
North Quincy, MA 02171-3139
Ph: (617)479-1600
Free: 800-692-8833
Fax: (617)786-8273
Co. E-mail: compumark.us@thomson.com
URL: http://www.thomson-thomson.com

Thomson Financial
195 Broadway, 4th Fl.
New York, NY 10007
Ph: (212)953-3570
Free: 800-953-3570
Fax: (212)953-0353
Co. E-mail: tfonlinerequests@thomson.
com
URL: http://www.thomsonreuters.com/
business_units/financial

Thomson South-Western
5191 Natorp Blvd.
Mason, OH 45040
Ph: (513)229-1000
Free: 800-543-0487
Fax: (513)229-1614
Co. E-mail: swinformation@thomsonlearning.com
URL: http://www.swlearning.com

Thomson South-Western/Texere
10650 Toebben Dr.
Independence, KY 41051
Free: 800-842-3636
Fax: (800)487-8488
URL: http://www.swlearning.com

Thomson West
610 Opperman Dr.
Eagan, MN 55123
Ph: (651)687-7000
Free: 800-328-9352
Co. E-mail: west.customerservice@thomson.com
URL: http://www.andrewsonline.com/

Thomson-Shore Inc.
7300 W Joy Rd.
Dexter, MI 48130-9492
Ph: (734)426-3939
Free: 800-706-4545
Fax: (800)706-4545
URL: http://www.thomsonshore.com

Thorsons
HarperCollins Publishers Inc.
10 E 53rd St.
New York, NY 10022
Ph: (212)207-7791
Fax: (212)207-7902
URL: http://www.thorsons.com

Three Rivers Press
1745 Broadway
New York, NY 10019
Ph: (212)782-9000
Fax: (212)940-7868
URL: http://www.randomhouse.com/crown/
three-rivers-press

Tilden Press Inc.
Six Hillwood Pl.
Oakland, CA 94610
Ph: (510)451-3100
Free: 800-955-4733
Co. E-mail: gbl@greenbiz.com

URL: http://www.greenbizletter.com

Tile and Stone Inc.
18 E 41st St.
New York, NY 10017
Ph: (212)376-7722
Fax: (212)376-7723
Co. E-mail: publisher@ashlee.com

Timber Framers Guild
PO Box 295
Alstead, NH 03602-0295
Ph: (559)834-8453
Free: 888-453-0879
Fax: (559)834-8453
Co. E-mail: info@tfguild.org
URL: http://www.tfguild.org

Time Inc.
Time-Life Bldg.
1271 Ave. of the Americas
New York, NY 10020
Ph: (212)522-1212
Free: 800-843-8463
Fax: (212)522-0602
Co. E-mail: letters@time.com
URL: http://www.time.com

Time Warner Paperbacks
1 Time Warner Center
New York, NY 10019-8016
Ph: (212)484-8000
URL: http://www.timewarner.com

Time4 Media
2 Park Ave., Fl. 9
New York, NY 10016-5600
Ph: (212)779-5000
Fax: (212)779-5599
URL: http://www.time4.com/

The Times and Democrat
1010 Broughton St.
Orangeburg, SC 29115
Ph: (803)533-5500
Free: 877-534-1060
Fax: (803)533-5526
URL: http://www.thetandd.com/

The Times
3410 Delta Dr.
Portage, IN 46368
Ph: (219)762-4334
Fax: (219)762-8386

Times-News
707 S Main St.
Burlington, NC 27215
Ph: (336)227-0131
Fax: (336)228-1889

Times-News Publishing Company
707 S Main St.
Burlington, NC 27215
Ph: (336)227-0131
Fax: (336)228-1889

Tire Guides Inc.
1101 S Rogers Cir., Ste. 6
Boca Raton, FL 33487-2748
Ph: (561)997-9229
Fax: (561)997-9233
URL: http://tireguides.com

Tire Industry Association
1532 Pointer Ridge Pl., Ste. G
Bowie, MD 20716-1883
Ph: (301)430-7280
Free: 800-876-8372
Fax: (301)430-7283
Co. E-mail: info@tireindustry.org
URL: http://www.tireindustry.org

TKG Publishing
1800 S Robertson Blvd., Ste. 125
Los Angeles, CA 90035
Ph: (310)827-9060
Fax: (310)827-9460

TKO/Real Estate Advisory Group Inc.
PO Box 2630
Mercerville, NJ 08690
Ph: (609)587-6200
Free: 800-732-5856
Fax: (609)587-3511
Co. E-mail: aoneal@specialtyretail.net

TL Enterprises Inc. Affinity Group Inc.
2575 Vista Del Mar
Ventura, CA 93001
Ph: (805)667-4100
Fax: (805)667-4419
Co. E-mail: info@affinitygroup.com
URL: http://www.affinitygroup.com

TMB Publishing Inc.
1838 Techny Ct.
Northbrook, IL 60062
Ph: (847)564-1127
URL: http://www.plumbingengineer.com

TMR Publications
PO Box 381822
Cambridge, MA 02238-1822
Ph: (617)489-9120
Free: 877-532-1838
Fax: (617)489-3437
Co. E-mail: customer.service@tmreview.
com
URL: http://www.tmreview.com

Toastmasters International
PO Box 9052
Mission Viejo, CA 92690-9052
Ph: (949)858-8255
Fax: (949)858-1207
Co. E-mail: tminfo@toastmasters.org
URL: http://www.toastmasters.org

Tobacco Merchants Association of the U.S. Inc.
PO Box 8019
Princeton, NJ 08543-8019
Ph: (609)275-4900

Fax: (609)275-8379
Co. E-mail: tmg@tma.org
URL: http://www.tma.org/

Toledo Times
541 N Superior St.
Toledo, OH 43660
Ph: (419)724-6000

Tom Hendricks
4000 Hawthorne Ave., No. 5
Dallas, TX 75219
Co. E-mail: tomHendricks474@cs.com

Toolkit Media Group
2700 Lake Cook Rd.
Riverwoods, IL 60015
Ph: (847)267-7000
Free: 800-248-3248

Touchpoint Publishing
505 N Hwy. 169, Ste. 465
Minneapolis, MN 55441
Ph: (763)595-0808
Free: 800-597-5656
Fax: (763)595-0016
Co. E-mail: info@touchpointpublishing.
com
URL: http://www.tpgsports.com

Touchstone/Simon & Schuster Inc.
1230 Ave. of the Americas
New York, NY 10020
Free: 866-506-1949
Co. E-mail: business@simonandschuster.
com

Towing and Recovery Association of America
2121 Eisenhower Ave., Ste. 200
Alexandria, VA 22314
Ph: (703)684-7713
Free: 800-728-0136
Fax: (703)684-6720
Co. E-mail: towserver@aol.com
URL: http://www.towserver.net

Towse Publishing Co.
1333A N Ave.
New Rochelle, NY 10804
Ph: (914)235-3095
Free: 877-235-3095
Fax: (914)235-3278
Co. E-mail: info@furninfo.com
URL: http://www.furninfo.com/

Toy Industry Association
1115 Broadway, Ste. 400
New York, NY 10010
Ph: (212)675-1141
Free: 888-884-TOYS
Fax: (212)633-1429
Co. E-mail: info@toyassociation.org
URL: http://www.toyassociation.org

Trade Dimensions
55 Greens Farms Rd., Ste. 2
Westport, CT 06880-6149
Free: 800-291-0410
Fax: (203)222-5701

Trade Press Media Group
2100 W Florist Ave.
Milwaukee, WI 53209
Ph: (414)228-7701
Free: 800-727-7995
Fax: (414)228-1134
Co. E-mail: info@tradepress.com
URL: http://www.tradepress.com

Trade Show Exhibitors Association
2301 S Lake Shore Dr., Ste. 1005
Chicago, IL 60616
Ph: (312)842-8732
Fax: (312)842-8744
Co. E-mail: tsea@tsea.org
URL: http://www.tsea.org

Trader Media Corp.
15 Apex Rd.
Toronto, ON, Canada M6A 2V6
Ph: (416)781-5516
Fax: (416)781-5499

Tradeshow Week Inc.
5900 Wilshire Blvd., Ste. 3100
Los Angeles, CA 90036-5804
Ph: (323)617-9100
Fax: (323)965-5334
URL: http://www.tradeshowweek.com

Trafford Publishing
2333 Government St., Ste. 6E
Victoria, BC, Canada V8T 4P4
Ph: (250)383-6864
Free: 888-232-4444
Fax: (250)383-6804
Co. E-mail: sales@trafford.com
URL: http://www.trafford.com/

Trafford Publishing
2657 Wilfert Rd.
Victoria, BC, Canada V9B 5Z3
Ph: (250)383-6864
Free: 888-232-4444
Fax: (250)383-6804
URL: http://www.trafford.com

Training Education Management
1874 S Pacific Coast Hwy.
Redondo Beach, CA 90277
Ph: (310)316-2240
Fax: (310)316-2240
Co. E-mail: info@trainingeducationman-
agement.com
URL: http://www.trainingeducationmanage-
ment.com

Trajan Publishing Corp.
PO Box 28103, Lakeport PO
St. Catharines, ON, Canada L2N 7P8
Ph: (905)646-7744

Free: 800-408-0352
Fax: (905)646-0995
Co. E-mail: office@trajan.ca
URL: http://trajan.com/

Transitions Abroad Publishing
18 Hulst Rd.
Amherst, MA 01002
Free: 800-293-0373
Co. E-mail: senioreditor@transitionsa-
broad.com
URL: http://www.transitionsabroad.com

**Transportation Consumer Protection
Council Inc.**
120 Main St.
Huntington, NY 11743
Ph: (631)549-8984
Fax: (631)549-8962
Co. E-mail: tcpc@transportlaw.com

Travel Goods Association
301 N Harrison St., No. 412
Princeton, NJ 08540-3512
Ph: (877)842-1938
Free: 877-TGA-1938
Fax: (877)842-1938
Co. E-mail: info@travel-goods.org
URL: http://travel-goods.org

Travel Industry Network Inc.
28 Knight St.
Norwalk, CT 06851-4719
Ph: (203)286-6679
Fax: (203)286-6681
URL: http://www.travelworldnews.com

Travelers Aid Society of Rhode Island
177 Union St.
Providence, RI 02903
Ph: (401)521-2255
URL: http://riroads.com/links/listdetail.cgi?
  Lookup=378039

Traveling Times Inc.
25061 Ave. Stanford, Ste. 10
Valencia, CA 91355-4551
Ph: (661)295-1250
Fax: (661)295-8558

Tree Care Industry Association
136 Harvey Rd., Ste. 101
Londonderry, NH 03053
Ph: (603)314-5380
Free: 800-733-2622
Fax: (603)314-5386
Co. E-mail: garvin@tcia.org
URL: http://www.tcia.org

Tree Publishers Inc.
PO Box 107
Lecompton, KS 66050-0170
Ph: (785)887-6324
Co. E-mail: ctreesmag@gmail.com
URL: http://www.christmastreesmagazine.
  com/

Trend Publishing
625 N Michigan Ave., Ste. 1100
Chicago, IL 60611-3118
Ph: (312)654-2300
Free: 800-278-7363
Fax: (312)654-2323
URL: http://www.trendpublishing.com/

TRI-M Music Honor Society
1806 Robert Fulton Dr.
Reston, VA 20191
Ph: (703)860-4000
Free: 800-336-3768
Fax: (703)860-1531
Co. E-mail: michaelb@nafme.org
URL: http://www.menc.org

Truck Renting and Leasing Association
675 N Washington St., Ste. 410
Alexandria, VA 22314
Ph: (703)299-9120
Fax: (703)299-9115
Co. E-mail: smurray@trala.org
URL: http://www.trala.org

Truck-frame & Axle Repair Association
3741 Enterprise Dr. SW
Rochester, MN 55902
Free: 800-232-8272
Fax: (866)529-0380
Co. E-mail: w.g.reich@att.net
URL: http://www.taraassociation.com

Trucker's Connection Inc.
5960 Crooked Creek Rd., Ste. 15
Norcross, GA 30092
Free: 800-948-0154
Fax: (770)416-1734
URL: http://www.truckersconnection.com

Tufts University
P.O Box 420235
Palm Coast, FL 32142
Ph: (800)829-5116
Free: 800-829-5116

Tulsa World
PO Box 1770
Tulsa, OK 74102
Ph: (918)581-8400

Tulsa World
315 S Boulder Ave.
Tulsa, OK 74103
Ph: (918)581-8400

Turley Publications
24 Water St.
Palmer, MA 01069
Ph: (413)283-8393
Free: 800-824-6548
Fax: (413)289-1977
URL: http://www.turley.com

Turnaround Associates
1120 Avenue of the Americas, 4th Fl.
New York, NY 10036
Ph: (212)626-6940
Fax: (212)626-6941
Co. E-mail: info@turnaroundassociates.
 com
URL: http://www.turnaroundassociates.
 com

Tuscarora Inc.
643 Elm St.
Maywood, NJ 07607-2048
Free: 800-351-2537
URL: http://www.alestreetnews.com/

Twelve Books/Hachette Book Group USA
PO Box 8828
Boston, MA 02114
Free: 800-759-0190
Fax: (800)331-1664
URL: http://www.hachettebookgroupusa.
 com

Twelve/Hatchette Book Group
237 Park Ave.
New York, NY 10017
URL: http://www.hatchettebookgroup.com

U

U.S. Bureau of Labor Statistics
Postal Square Bldg.
2 Massachusetts Ave. NE
Washington, DC 20212-0001
Ph: (202)691-5200
Free: 800-877-8339

U.S. Chamber of Commerce
1615 H St. NW
Washington, DC 20062-2000
Ph: (202)659-6000
Free: 800-638-6582
Fax: (800)638-6582
Co. E-mail: custsvc@uschamber.com
URL: http://www.uschamber.com

U.S. Department of Agriculture
2202 Monterey St., Ste. 104-F
Fresno, CA 93721-3129
Ph: (559)487-5178
Free: 800-487-8796
Fax: (559)487-5199

U.S. Economic Development Administration
111 N Canal St., Ste. 855
Chicago, IL 60606
Ph: (312)353-8143
Fax: (312)353-8575
Co. E-mail: jeannette.p.tamayo@eda.gov
URL: http://www.eda.gov

U.S. Food and Drug Administration
10903 New Hampshire Ave.
Silver Spring, MD 20993-0002
Ph: (301)594-1086
Free: 888-463-6332
Fax: (301)210-2849
URL: http://www.fda.gov

U.S. Government Printing Office (GPO)
732 N Capitol St. NW
Washington, DC 20401
Ph: (202)512-1800
Free: 866-512-1800
Fax: (202)512-2250
Co. E-mail: gpoaccess@gpo.gov
URL: http://www.access.gpo.gov

U.S.A. Table Tennis
4065 Sinton Rd., Ste 120
Colorado Springs, CO 80907-5093
Ph: (719)866-4583
Fax: (719)632-6071
Co. E-mail: usatt@usatt.org
URL: http://www.usatt.org

UBM Global Trade
400 Windsor Corporate Pk.
50 Millstone Rd., Ste. 200
East Windsor, NJ 08520-1415
Ph: (609)371-7700
Free: 800-221-5488
Fax: (609)371-7885
Co. E-mail: customerservice@cbizmedia.
 com
URL: http://www.cbizmedia.com

UBM PLC
Ludgate House, 245 Blackfriars Rd.
London SE1 9UY, United Kingdom
Ph: 020 7921 5000
Fax: 020 7928 2717
Co. E-mail: communications@unitedbusi-
 nessmedia.com
URL: http://www.ubm.com

Underwriters Laboratories
2600 NW Lake Rd.
Camas, WA 98607-8542
Free: 877-854-3577
Fax: (360)817-6278
Co. E-mail: cec.us@us.ul.com
URL: http://www.ul.com

UNICOL Inc.
PO Box 260550
Pembroke Pines, FL 33026
Ph: (954)430-7271
Fax: (954)430-7227
Co. E-mail: customerservice@unicol-
 publishing.com
URL: http://www.unicol-publishing.com

United Association of Manufacturers' Representatives
PO Box 784
Branson, MO 65615
Ph: (417)779-1575

Fax: (417)779-1576
Co. E-mail: info@uamr.com

United Brotherhood of Carpenters and Joiners of America, AFL-CIO
101 Constitution Ave. NW
Washington, DC 20001
Ph: (202)546-6206
Fax: (202)547-8979
URL: http://www.carpenters.org/

United Business Media
350 Hudson St., Ste. 300
New York, NY 10014
Free: 800-776-8090
Fax: (800)793-9313

United Comunications Group
11300 Rockville Pike, Suite 1100
Rockville, MD 20852-3030
Ph: (301)816-8950
Free: 800-929-4824
Fax: (301)816-8945
Co. E-mail: dhernan@ucg.com
URL: http://www.ucg.com

United Empire Loyalists' Association of Canada
50 Baldwin St., Ste. 202
Toronto, ON, Canada M5T 1L4
Ph: (416)591-1783
Co. E-mail: uelac@uelac.org
URL: http://www.uelac.org

United Nations Publications
c/o National Book Network
15200 NBN Way
Blue Ridge Summit, PA 17214
Ph: (212)963-7680
Free: 888-254-4286
Fax: (800)338-4550
Co. E-mail: unpublications@nbnbooks.
 com
URL: https://unp.un.org

United Press International-USA
1133 19th St. NW
Washington, DC 20036
Ph: (202)898-8000
Fax: (202)898-8048

United Publications Inc.
106 Lafayette St.
Yarmouth, ME 04096
Ph: (207)846-0600
Free: 800-441-6982
Fax: (207)846-0657
Co. E-mail: spfeifle@securitysystem-
 snews.com
URL: http://www.unitedpublications.com

University Film and Video Association
PO Box 1777
Edwardsville, IL 62026
Ph: (914)761-1187
Free: 866-647-8382
Fax: (914)761-3115

Co. E-mail: ufvahome@aol.com
URL: http://www.ufva.org

University of California Press
2120 Berkeley Way
Berkeley, CA 94704
Ph: (510)642-4247
Free: 800-822-6657
Fax: (510)643-7127
Co. E-mail: askucp@ucpress.edu
URL: http://www.ucpress.edu

University of Chicago Graduate School of Business
5807 S Woodlawn Ave.
Chicago, IL 60637
Ph: (773)702-7743
Co. E-mail: helpdesk@chicagobooth.edu
URL: http://www.chicagobooth.edu/

University of Chicago Press
1427 E 60th St.
Chicago, IL 60637
Ph: (773)702-7700
Free: 800-521-8412
Fax: (773)702-9756
Co. E-mail: custserv@press.uchicago.edu
URL: http://www.press.uchicago.edu

University of Georgia Press
330 Research Dr.
Athens, GA 30602
Ph: (706)369-6130
Free: 800-266-5842
Fax: (706)369-6131
Co. E-mail: books@ugapress.uga.edu
URL: http://www.ugapress.uga.edu

University of Illinois
1 University Plz.
Springfield, IL 62703
Ph: (217)206-6600
URL: http://www.uis.edu/index.html

The University of Montana
32 Campus Dr.
Missoula, MT 59812
Ph: (406)243-0211
Fax: (406)243-4520
URL: http://www.umt.edu/

University of Nebraska
PO Box 880407
Lincoln, NE 68588-0407
Ph: (402)472-7931
Co. E-mail: qjbe@unlnotes.unl.edu
URL: http://www.qjbe.unl.edu

University of North Carolina Press
116 S Boundary St.
Chapel Hill, NC 27514-3808
Ph: (919)966-3561
Free: 800-848-6224
Fax: (919)966-3829
Co. E-mail: Kate_Torrey@unc.edu
URL: http://www.uncpress.unc.edu

University of Toronto Press
Black Rose Books
5201 Dufferin St.
Downsview, ON, Canada M3H 5T8
Free: 800-565-9523
Fax: (800)221-9985
Co. E-mail: utpbooks@utpress.utoronto.ca
URL: http://www.blackrosebooks.net

University of Toronto Press
10 St. Mary St., Ste. 700
Toronto, ON, Canada M4Y 2W8
Ph: (416)978-2239
Free: 800-565-9523
Fax: (416)978-4738

University of Toronto Press-Journal Div.
5201 Dufferin St.
Toronto, ON, Canada M3H 5T8
Ph: (416)667-7810
Free: 800-221-9985
Fax: (416)667-7881
Co. E-mail: journals@utpress.utoronto.ca
URL: http://www.utpjournals.com

University of Wisconsin Press
1930 Monroe St., 3rd Fl.
Madison, WI 53711-2059
Ph: (608)263-0734
Free: 800-621-2736
Fax: (608)263-1132
Co. E-mail: uwiscpress@uwpress.wisc.edu
URL: http://uwpress.wisc.edu

University of Wisconsin-Eau Claire Department of English
405 Hibbard Hall
Eau Claire, WI 54702-4004
Ph: (715)836-2639
Fax: (715)836-5996
Co. E-mail: engl.contact@uwec.edu
URL: http://www.uwec.edu/english/graduate/admissionqualifications.htm

University Press of America Inc.
4501 Forbes Blvd., Ste. 200
Lanham, MD 20706
Ph: (301)459-3366
Free: 800-462-6420
Fax: (301)429-5748
Co. E-mail: customercare@rowman.com
URL: http://rowman.com

Uniworld Business Publications Inc.
6 Seward Ave.
Beverly, MA 01915
Ph: (978)927-0219
Fax: (978)927-0219
Co. E-mail: info@uniworldbp.com
URL: http://www.uniworldbp.com

Update Publicare Co.
c/o Prosperity & Profits Unlimited
Denver, CO 80201-0416
Ph: (303)575-5676

Fax: (303)575-1187
Co. E-mail: mail@contentprovidermedia.com
URL: http://www.gumbomedia.com

Urban Land Institute
1025 Thomas Jefferson St., NW, Ste. 500 W
Washington, DC 20007
Ph: (202)624-7000
Free: 800-321-5011
Fax: (202)624-7140
Co. E-mail: customerservice@uli.org
URL: http://www.uli.org/

Urner Barry Publications Inc.
PO Box 389
Toms River, NJ 08754
Ph: (732)240-5330
Free: 800-932-0617
Fax: (732)341-0891
Co. E-mail: help@urnerbarry.com
URL: http://www.urnerbarry.com

USA International Business Publications
1466 Broadway, No. 910
New York, NY 10036
Ph: (212)490-3999
Fax: (212)986-7864

Utah Department of Workforce Services
140 E 300 S.
Salt Lake City, UT 84145-0249
Ph: (801)526-9675
Fax: (801)526-9211
Co. E-mail: dwscontactus@utah.gov

V

Valley Calligraphy Guild
278 Hambletonian Dr.
Eugene, OR 97401
Ph: (503)343-9094

Valuation Research Corp.
330 E Kilbourn Ave., Ste. 1020
Milwaukee, WI 53202-3141
Ph: (414)271-8662
Free: 800-558-1546
Fax: (414)271-2294

Vancouver Ballet Society
Scotiabank Dance Ctr.
677 Davie St., Level 6
Vancouver, BC, Canada V6B 2G6
Ph: (604)681-1525
Fax: (604)681-7732
Co. E-mail: vbs@telus.net
URL: http://www.vancouverballetsociety.ca/

Vanguard Press (VP)
387 Park Ave. S, 12th Fl.
New York, NY 10016
Ph: (212)340-8100
Free: 877-493-3197

Fax: (212)340-8105
Co. E-mail: perseus.promos@perseus-
books.com
URL: http://www.vanguardpressbooks.com

VBM Printers Inc.
2115 NE McDonald Ln.
McMinnville, OR 97128
Ph: (503)434-5386
Free: 877-452-1235
Fax: (503)435-0990
Co. E-mail: ron@oldstuffnews.com
URL: http://www.oldstuffnews.com

The Vegetarian Resource Group
PO Box 1463
Baltimore, MD 21203
Ph: (410)366-8343
Fax: (410)366-8804
Co. E-mail: vrg@vrg.org
URL: http://www.vrg.org

Vending Times Inc.
55 Maple Ave., Ste. 102
Rockville Centre, NY 11570
Ph: (516)442-1850
Fax: (516)442-1849
Co. E-mail: subscriptions@vendingtimes.
net
URL: http://www.vendingtimes.com

Venice Family Clinic
604 Rose Ave.
Venice, CA 90291
Ph: (310)392-8630
Fax: (310)392-7875
Co. E-mail: vfcinfo@mednet.ucla.edu
URL: http://www.venicefamilyclinic.org/

Ventura County Star
550 Camarillo Center Dr.
Camarillo, CA 93011
Ph: (805)437-0000

Venture Economics Inc.
195 Broadway
New York, NY 10007
Ph: (646)822-2000
Free: 888-605-3385
Fax: (646)822-3230
Co. E-mail: ve.cs@tfn.com
URL: http://www.ventureeconomics.com

VerticalNews
2727 Paces Ferry Rd. SE, Ste. 2-440
Atlanta, GA 30339
Ph: (770)435-8286
Fax: (770)435-6800

Vickers Stock Research Corp.
61 Broadway St., Ste. 1700
New York, NY 10006
Ph: (212)425-7500
Free: 800-645-5043
Fax: (212)809-2975
Co. E-mail: info@vickers-stock.com
URL: http://www.vickers-stock.com

Video Watchdog
PO Box 5283
Cincinnati, OH 45205-0283
Ph: (513)297-1855
Free: 800-275-8395
Fax: (206)333-1405
Co. E-mail: orders@videowatchdog.com
URL: http://www.videowatchdog.com

Viking Press/Penguin Group
375 Hudson St.
New York, NY 10014
Ph: (212)366-2679
Fax: (212)366-2612

Village Press Publications
2779 Aero Park Dr.
Traverse City, MI 49685
Ph: (231)946-3712
Free: 800-327-7377
Fax: (231)946-3289
Co. E-mail: info@villagepress.com
URL: http://www.villagepress.com

Vindicator
107 Vindicator Sq.
Youngstown, OH 44503
Ph: (330)747-1471

Virgin Books/Random House
20 Vauxhall Bridge Rd.
London SW1V 2SA, United Kingdom
Co. E-mail: editorial@virgin-books.co.uk
URL: http://www.virginbooks.co.uk

Virginia Food Dealers Association Inc.
5937 Hopkins Rd., Ste. 201 1/2
Richmond, VA 23234-5412
Ph: (804)271-5964
Free: 800-552-9819
Fax: (804)271-5991
Co. E-mail: vfda@mindspring.com

Virginia Native Plant Society
400 Blandy Farm Ln., Unit 2
Boyce, VA 22620
Ph: (540)837-1600
Co. E-mail: rccsca@comcast.net
URL: http://www.vnps.org

The Virginia-Pilot
Box 449
150 W Brambleton Ave.
Norfolk, VA 23510
Ph: (757)446-2000
Free: 800-446-2004

Virginian-Pilot
150 W Brambleton Ave.
Norfolk, VA 23510
Ph: (757)446-2000
Free: 800-446-2004

Visionaire Publishing
11 Mercer St.
New York, NY 10013
Ph: (212)274-8959

Fax: (212)343-2595
Co. E-mail: info@visionaireworld.com
URL: http://www.visionaireworld.com

VNU Business Media, Inc.
770 Broadway, 4th Fl.
New York, NY 10003
Ph: (646)654-5000

The Voice of Florida
PO Box 030397
Fort Lauderdale, FL 33303-0397
Ph: (954)463-5556
Fax: (954)463-2674

Voyageur Magazine
PO Box 8085
Green Bay, WI 54308-8085
Ph: (920)465-2446
Fax: (920)465-2890
Co. E-mail: voyageur@uwgb.edu
URL: http://www.uwgb.edu/voyageur/ar-
chive.html

W

W. W. Norton & Company, Inc.
500 5th Ave.
New York, NY 10110
Ph: (212)354-5500
Fax: (212)869-0856
URL: http://wwnorton.com

W.W. Norton & Company
500 5th Ave.
New York, NY 10110
Ph: (212)354-5500
Fax: (212)869-0856
URL: http://wwnorton.com

W.W. Norton & Company, Inc.
500 5th Ave.
New York, NY 10110
Free: 800-233-4830
Co. E-mail: specialsales@wwnorton.com
URL: http://www.norton.com

Waco Tribune-Herald
900 Franklin Ave.
Waco, TX 76702
Ph: (254)757-5757
Free: 800-678-8742
Fax: (254)757-0302
URL: http://www.wacotrib.com

Wakeman/Walworth Inc.
PO Box 7376
Alexandria, VA 22307-7376
Ph: (703)768-9600
Free: 800-876-2545
Fax: (703)768-9690
Co. E-mail: newsletters@statecapitals.com
URL: http://statecapitals.com/

Walker & Company
104 5th Ave.
New York, NY 10011
Ph: (212)727-8300
Free: 800-289-2553
Fax: (800)218-9367
URL: http://www.walkerbooks.com

Ward's Communications
3000 Town Ctr., Ste. 2750
Southfield, MI 48075
Ph: (248)357-0800
Fax: (248)357-0810
Co. E-mail: wards@wardsauto.com
URL: http://wardsauto.com

Warner Books Inc.
PO Box 8828
Boston, MA 02114
Free: 800-759-0190
Fax: (800)331-1664
URL: http://www.hachettebookgroupusa.
com

Warner Books, Incorporated
1271 Avenue of the Americas
New York, NY 10020
Ph: (212)522-7200
Free: 800-759-0190
Fax: (800)286-9471

Warner Business Books
1271 Avenue of the Americas
New York, NY 10020-1300
Ph: (212)522-7200
Free: 800-759-0190
Fax: (212)522-7991
Co. E-mail: rick.wolff@twbg.com
URL: http://www.twbookmark.com/

Warren Communications News Inc.
2115 Ward Ct. NW
Washington, DC 20037
Ph: (202)872-9200
Free: 800-771-9202
Fax: (202)318-8350
Co. E-mail: info@warren-news.com
URL: http://www.warren-news.com

Washington Business Information Inc.
300 N Washington St., Ste. 200
Falls Church, VA 22046
Ph: (703)538-7600
Fax: (703)538-7676

Washington Independent Writers
1001 Connecticut Ave. NW, Ste. 701
Washington, DC 20036
Ph: (202)775-5150
Fax: (202)775-5810
Co. E-mail: info@washwriter.org
URL: http://www.amerindywriters.org/
home/

Washington Information Source
6506 Old Stage Rd., Ste. 100
Rockville, MD 20852-4326
Ph: (703)779-8777
Fax: (301)468-0475
Co. E-mail: wis@fdainfo.com
URL: http://www.fdainfo.com

Waste Equipment Technology Association
4301 Connecticut Ave. NW, Ste. 300
Washington, DC 20008-2304
Ph: (202)244-4700
Free: 800-424-2869
Fax: (202)966-4824
Co. E-mail: jbradley@wastec.org
URL: http://www.wastec.org

Water Environment Federation
601 Wythe St.
Alexandria, VA 22314-1994
Free: 800-666-0206
Fax: (703)684-2492
Co. E-mail: inquiry@wef.org
URL: http://www.wef.org

Water Quality Association
4151 Naperville Rd.
Lisle, IL 60532-3696
Ph: (630)505-0160
Fax: (630)505-9637
Co. E-mail: info@wqa.org
URL: http://www.wqa.org

Waterways Journal Inc.
319 N 4th St., Ste. 650
Saint Louis, MO 63102
Ph: (314)241-7354
Free: 800-366-9630
Fax: (314)241-4207
Co. E-mail: info@waterwaysjournal.net
URL: http://www.waterwaysjournal.net/

Wayfarer Publications
2601 Silver Ridge Ave.
Los Angeles, CA 90039
Ph: (323)665-7773
Free: 800-888-9119
Fax: (323)665-1627
Co. E-mail: taichi@tai-chi.com
URL: http://www.tai-chi.com

Wedding & Portrait Photographers International
1312 Lincoln Blvd.
Santa Monica, CA 90406-2003
Ph: (310)451-0090
Fax: (310)395-9058

Weekly Reader Corp.
3001 Cindel Dr.
Delran, NJ 08075
Free: 800-446-3355
Fax: (856)786-3360
Co. E-mail: customerservice@week-
lyreader.com
URL: http://www.weeklyreader.com

Weidenbum Center
Washington University
1 Brookings Dr.
Campus Box 1027
St. Louis, MO 63130-4899
Ph: (314)935-5630
Fax: (314)935-5688
URL: http://www.wustl.edu

Wells Publishing Inc.
3570 Camino del Rio N, Ste. 200
San Diego, CA 92108
Ph: (619)584-1100
Free: 800-897-9965
Fax: (619)584-1200
URL: http://www.wellspublishing.com

West Group
19 Corbin Pl.
Brooklyn, NY 11235
Ph: (718)646-0932
Free: 800-344-5009
Fax: (718)646-7773

Western Association of Venture Capitalists
3000 Sand Hill Rd., Ste. 2-290
Menlo Park, CA 94025-7156
Ph: (650)854-1322
Co. E-mail: kimyatesgrosso@wavc.org
URL: http://www.wavc.net

Western English Retailers Association
451 E 58th Ave., Ste. 4781
Denver, CO 80216
Fax: (303)292-8468
Co. E-mail: wera@frii.com

Western League of Savings Institutions
9841 Airport Blvd., Ste. 418
Los Angeles, CA 90045-5416
Ph: (310)414-8300
Fax: (310)440-0372
URL: http://www.westernleague.org

Westminster John Knox Press
100 Witherspoon St.
Louisville, KY 40202-1396
Ph: (502)569-5052
Free: 800-227-2872
Fax: (800)541-5113
Co. E-mail: annie.mcclure@pcusa.org
URL: http://www.wjk.org

Westview Press
2465 Central Ave.
Boulder, CO 80301-5728
Ph: (303)444-3541
Free: 800-343-4499
Fax: (720)406-7336
Co. E-mail: westview.orders@perseus-
books.com
URL: http://www.westviewpress.com

Wet Feet, Incorporated
101 Howard St., Ste. 300
San Francisco, CA 94105-1619
Ph: (415)284-7900
Free: 800-926-4562
Fax: (415)284-7910

WFC Inc.
4041 G Hadley Rd.
South Plainfield, NJ 07080
Ph: (908)769-1160
Fax: (908)769-1171
Co. E-mail: info@wholefoodsmagazineon-
line.com
URL: http://www.wholefoodsmagazineon-
line.com

Wharton School Publishing
Pearson Technology Group
800 E 96th St.
Indianapolis, IN 46240
Ph: (317)428-3341
URL: http://www.whartonsp.com

Wharton School Publishing
1 Lake St.
Upper Saddle River, NJ 07458
Ph: (201)236-7113

Wheatmark
610 E Delano St., Ste. 104
Tucson, AZ 85705
Ph: (520)798-0888
Free: 888-934-0888
Fax: (520)798-3394

White Publishing Co.
Box 3343
Jackson, TN 38303-0343

Wholesale Florists & Florist Supplier Association
105 Eastern Ave., Ste. 104
Annapolis, MD 21403
Ph: (410)940-6580
Free: 888-289-3372
Fax: (410)263-1659
Co. E-mail: info@wffsa.org
URL: http://www.wffsa.org

Wiley Publishing Inc.
111 River St.
Hoboken, NJ 07030-5774
Ph: (201)748-6000
Free: 800-762-2974
Fax: (201)748-6088
URL: http://www.wiley.com

Wiley-Blackwell
111 River St.
Hoboken, NJ 07030
Ph: (201)748-6000
Fax: (201)748-6088

Wilkes-Barre Publishing Company
15 N Main St.
Wilkes-Barre, PA 18711
Ph: (570)829-7101
Free: 800-427-8649
Fax: (570)831-7362

William Morrow
10 E 53rd St.
New York, NY 10022
Ph: (212)207-7000
Free: 800-242-7737
URL: http://www.harpercollins.com/
imprints/index.aspx?imprintid=518003

WindStar Wildlife Institute
10072 Vista Ct.
Myersville, MD 21773
Ph: (301)293-3351
Co. E-mail: wildlife@windstar.org

Wine & Spirits Magazine Inc.
2 W 32nd St., Ste. 601
New York, NY 10001
Ph: (212)695-4660
Co. E-mail: info@wineandspiritsmagazine.
com
URL: http://www.wineandspiritsmagazine.
com

Wine Appreciation Guild
360 Swift Ave.
San Francisco, CA 94080-6220
Ph: (650)866-3020
Free: 800-231-9463
Fax: (650)866-3513
Co. E-mail: info@wineappreciation.com
URL: http://www.wineappreciation.com

The Wine Enthusiast Inc.
333 N Bedford Rd.
Mount Kisco, NY 10549
Ph: (914)345-8463
Free: 800-648-6058
Fax: (914)592-0105
Co. E-mail: custserv@wineenthusiast.net
URL: http://www.wineenthusiast.com

Winston J. Brill & Associates
12529 237th Way, NE
Redmond, WA 98053
Ph: (425)898-1077
Co. E-mail: office@winstonbrill.com

Wireless Week
199 E Badger Rd., Ste. 201
Madison, WI 53713
Ph: (973)920-7783
URL: http://www.wirelessweek.com

Wisconsin State Journal
1901 Fish Hatchery Rd.
Madison, WI 53713
Ph: (608)252-6110
Fax: (608)252-6119
Co. E-mail: tkelley@madison.com
URL: http://www.madison.com/wsj

Wisconsin Taxpayers Alliance
401 N Lawn Ave.
Madison, WI 53704
Ph: (608)241-9789
Fax: (608)241-5807
Co. E-mail: wistax@wistax.org
URL: http://www.wistax.org/

Wm. K. Walthers Inc.
5601 W Florist Ave.
Milwaukee, WI 53218-1622
Ph: (414)527-0770
Free: 800-487-2467
Fax: (414)527-4423
Co. E-mail: custserv@walthers.com
URL: http://www.walthers.com

Wolf Rinke Associates,Inc.
PO Box 350
Clarksville, MD 21029-0350
Ph: (410)531-9280
Free: 800-828-WOLF
Fax: (410)531-9282
Co. E-mail: wolfrinke@aol.com
URL: http://www.wolfrinke.com/MIWL-
NEWSLETTER/miwlnl.html

Wolfe Publishing Co.
2180 Gulfstream, Ste. A
Prescott, AZ 86301
Ph: (928)445-7810
Free: 800-899-7810
Fax: (928)778-5124
Co. E-mail: circ@riflemag.com
URL: http://www.riflemagazine.com

Wolters Kluwer Pharma Solutions Inc.
323 Norristown Rd., Ste. 200
Ambler, PA 19002
Ph: (215)646-8700
URL: http://www.boucher1.com

Woman's Missionary Union
100 Missionary Ridge
Birmingham, AL 35242
Ph: (205)991-8100
Free: 800-968-7301
Fax: (205)995-4825

Women's Council of Realtors
430 N Michigan Ave.
Chicago, IL 60611
Ph: (312)329-8483
Free: 800-245-8512
Fax: (312)329-3290
Co. E-mail: wcr@wcr.org

Women's National Book Association
PO Box 237
New York, NY 10150
Ph: (615)386-6760
Fax: (212)208-4629
Co. E-mail: info@wnba-books.org
URL: http://www.wnba-books.org

Woodall Publications Corp.
2575 Vista Del Mar Dr.
Ventura, CA 93001-3920
Free: 877-680-6155
Co. E-mail: info-woodalls@woodallsbooks.
  com
URL: http://www.woodalls.com

Woodenboat Publications Inc.
41 Woodenboat Ln.
Brooklin 04616
Ph: (207)359-4651
Free: 800-877-7447
Fax: (207)359-8920
Co. E-mail: woodenboat@woodenboat.
  com
URL: http://www.woodenboat.com

Woodhead Publishing Ltd.
80 High St.
Sawston
Cambridge CB22 3HJ, United Kingdom
Ph: 44 12 23499140
Fax: 44 12 23832819
Co. E-mail: wp@woodheadpublishing.com
URL: http://www.woodheadpublishing.com/
  en/

Wordstar Processing Users' Group Inc.
PO Box 16-1443
Miami, FL 33116-1443

Workman Publishing Company
225 Varick St.
New York, NY 10014
Ph: (212)254-5900
Fax: (212)254-8098
Co. E-mail: info@workman.com
URL: http://www.workman.com

World Organization of China Painters
2641 NW 10th St.
Oklahoma City, OK 73107-5400
Ph: (405)521-1234
Fax: (405)521-1265
Co. E-mail: wocporg@theshop.net
URL: http://www.wocporg.com

World Proof Numismatic Association
PO Box 4094
Pittsburgh, PA 15201
Ph: (412)782-4477
Fax: (412)782-0227

World Publications Inc.
460 N Orlando Ave., Ste. 200
Winter Park, FL 32789
Ph: (407)628-4802
Fax: (407)628-7061
Co. E-mail: info@worldpub.net
URL: http://www.bonniercorp.com

World Publishing Co.
990 Grove St.
Evanston, IL 60201
Ph: (847)491-6440
Free: 800-392-2203

Fax: (847)491-0459
Co. E-mail: cs@centurysports.net
URL: http://www.cruisetravelmag.com

World Publishing
324 S Main St.
Tulsa, OK 74103
Free: 800-444-6552

World Scientific Publishing Company Inc.
27 Warren St., Ste. 401-402
Hackensack, NJ 07601
Ph: (201)487-9655
Free: 800-227-7562
Fax: (201)487-9656
Co. E-mail: wspc@wspc.com
URL: http://www.worldscinet.com

World Trade Press
800 Lindberg Ln., Ste. 190
Petaluma, CA 94952
Ph: (707)778-1124
Free: 800-833-8586
Fax: (707)778-1329
Co. E-mail: accounting@worldtradepress.
  com
URL: http://www.worldtradepress.com

World Wide Gun Report Inc.
110 S College Ave.
Aledo, IL 61231
Ph: (309)582-5311
Co. E-mail: contactus@thegunreport.com

WorldatWork
14040 N Northsight Blvd.
Scottsdale, AZ 85260
Ph: (480)922-2020
Free: 866-816-2962
Fax: (480)483-8352
Co. E-mail: customerrelations@worldat-
  work.org
URL: http://www.worldatwork.org

Worldprofit Inc.
No. 205, 17505 - 107 Ave.
Edmonton, AB, Canada T5S 1E5
Ph: (780)444-7477
Fax: (780)483-8672

Worldwide Videotex
PO Box 3273
Boynton Beach, FL 33424-3273
Ph: (561)738-2276
Co. E-mail: markedit@juno.com

Worm Digest
1455 E 185th St.
Cleveland, OH 44145
Ph: (216)531-5374
Co. E-mail: mail@wormdigest.org
URL: http://www.wormdigest.org/

Writers' Union of Canada
90 Richmond St. E, Ste. 200
Toronto, ON, Canada M5C 1P1
Ph: (416)703-8982
Fax: (416)504-9090
Co. E-mail: info@writersunion.ca
URL: http://www.writersunion.ca

Y

Y-Visionary Publishing L.P.
265 S Anita Dr., Ste. 120
Orange, CA 92868
URL: http://www.bowhunting.net/
  bow&arrow/default.htm

Yakima Herald-Republic
114 N 4th St.
Yakima, WA 98901
Ph: (509)248-1251
Free: 800-343-2799
Fax: (509)577-7767
Co. E-mail: circulation@yakimaherald.com
URL: http://www.yakimaherald.com/

Yale University Press
302 Temple St.
New Haven, CT 06511
Ph: (203)432-0960
Fax: (203)432-0948
URL: http://www.yale.edu/yup/

Yale University Press
PO Box 209040
New Haven, CT 06520-9040
Ph: (203)432-0960
Free: 800-405-1619
Fax: (203)432-0948
Co. E-mail: customer.care@triliteral.org
URL: http://yalepress.yale.edu

The Yamamoto Forecast
PO Box 573
Kahului, HI 96733
Ph: (808)877-2690

Yarn Tree Design Inc.
117 Alexander Ave.
Ames, IA 50010
Ph: (515)232-3121
Free: 800-247-3952
Fax: (515)232-0789
Co. E-mail: info@yarntree.com
URL: http://yarntree.com

Ye Olde Genealogie Shoppe
9605 Vandergriff Rd.
Indianapolis, IN 46239-9591
Ph: (317)862-3330
Free: 800-419-0200
Fax: (317)862-2599
Co. E-mail: yogs@iquest.net
URL: http://www.yogs.com

York Publishing Inc.
1350 E 9th St.
Chico, CA 95927
Ph: (530)891-8410
Free: 800-284-3226
Fax: (530)891-8443
Co. E-mail: customerservice@videomaker.
  com
URL: http://www.videomaker.com

Yuill & Associates
Box 11373
Ottawa, ON, Canada K2H 7V1
Ph: (613)265-1997
Fax: (613)721-1410
Co. E-mail: info@yuill-associates.com
URL: http://www.yuill-associates.com

The Yuma Sun
2055 Arizona Ave.
Yuma, AZ 85364
Ph: (928)783-3333

Z

Zackin Publications Inc.
PO Box 2180
Waterbury, CT 06722
Ph: (203)262-4670
Free: 800-325-6745
Fax: (203)262-4680
Co. E-mail: info@zackin.com
URL: http://www.zackin.com

Zen-Do Kai Martial Arts Association
12 W Main St., 2nd Fl.
Johnstown, NY 12095
Ph: (518)762-4723

Fax: (518)762-4723
Co. E-mail: zendokai@superior.net

Ziff Davis Enterprise
28 E 28th St.
New York, NY 10016
Ph: (212)503-5900

Ziff-Davis Inc.
28 E 28th St.
New York, NY 10016-7939
Ph: (212)503-3500
Fax: (212)503-4599
Co. E-mail: randy_zane@ziffdavis.com
URL: http://www.ziffdavis.com

Absolute liability ▮ Liability that is incurred due to product defects or negligent actions. Manufacturers or retail establishments are held responsible, even though the defect or action may not have been intentional or negligent.

ACE ▮ See Active Corps of Executives.

Accident and health benefits ▮ Benefits offered to employees and their families in order to offset the costs associated with accidental death, accidental injury, or sickness.

Account statement ▮ A record of transactions, including payments, new debt, and deposits, incurred during a defined period of time.

Accounting system ▮ System capturing the costs of all employees and/or machinery included in business expenses.

Accounts payable ▮ See Trade credit.

Accounts receivable ▮ Unpaid accounts which arise from unsettled claims and transactions from the sale of a company's products or services to its customers.

Active Corps of Executives (ACE) ▮ (See also Service Corps of Retired Executives) A group of volunteers for a management assistance program of the U.S. Small Business Administration; volunteers provide one-on-one counseling and teach workshops and seminars for small firms.

ADA ▮ See Americans with Disabilities Act.

Adaptation ▮ The process whereby an invention is modified to meet the needs of users.

Adaptive engineering ▮ The process whereby an invention is modified to meet the manufacturing and commercial requirements of a targeted market.

Adverse selection ▮ The tendency for higher-risk individuals to purchase health care and more comprehensive plans, resulting in increased costs.

Advertising ▮ A marketing tool used to capture public attention and influence purchasing decisions for a product or service. Utilizes various forms of media to generate consumer response, such as flyers, magazines, newspapers, radio, and television.

Age discrimination ▮ The denial of the rights and privileges of employment based solely on the age of an individual.

Agency costs ▮ Costs incurred to insure that the lender or investor maintains control over assets while allowing the borrower or entrepreneur to use them. Monitoring and information costs are the two major types of agency costs.

Agribusiness ▮ The production and sale of commodities and products from the commercial farming industry.

America Online ▮ (See also Prodigy) An online service which is accessible by computer modem. The service features Internet access, bulletin boards, online periodicals, electronic mail, and other services for subscribers.

Americans with Disabilities Act (ADA) ▮ Law designed to ensure equal access and opportunity to handicapped persons.

Annual report ▮ (See also Securities and Exchange Commission) Yearly financial report prepared by a business that adheres to the requirements set forth by the Securities and Exchange Commission (SEC).

Antitrust immunity ▮ (See also Collective ratemaking) Exemption from prosecution under antitrust laws. In the transportation industry, firms with antitrust immunity are permitted—under certain conditions—to set schedules and sometimes prices for the public benefit.

Applied research ▮ Scientific study targeted for use in a product or process.

Asians ▮ A minority category used by the U.S. Bureau of the Census to represent a diverse group that includes Aleuts, Eskimos, American Indians, Asian Indians, Chinese, Japanese, Koreans, Vietnamese, Filipinos, Hawaiians, and other Pacific Islanders.

Assets ▮ Anything of value owned by a company.

Audit ▮ The verification of accounting records and business procedures conducted by an outside accounting service.

Average cost ▮ Total production costs divided by the quantity produced.

Balance Sheet ▮ A financial statement listing the total assets and liabilities of a company at a given time.

Bankruptcy ▮ (See also Chapter 7 of the 1978 Bankruptcy Act; Chapter 11 of the 1978 Bankruptcy Act) The condition in which a business cannot meet its debt obligations and petitions a federal district court either for reorganization of its debts (Chapter 11) or for liquidation of its assets (Chapter 7).

Basic research ▮ Theoretical scientific exploration not targeted to application.

Basket clause ▮ A provision specifying the amount of public pension funds that may be placed in investments not included on a state's legal list (see separate citation).

BBS ❚ *See* Bulletin Board Service.

BDC ❚ *See* Business development corporation.

Benefit ❚ Various services, such health care, flextime, day care, insurance, and vacation, offered to employees as part of a hiring package. Typically subsidized in whole or in part by the business.

BIDCO ❚ *See* Business and industrial development company

Billing cycle ❚ A system designed to evenly distribute customer billing throughout the month, preventing clerical backlogs.

Birth ❚ *See* Business birth.

Blue chip security ❚ A low-risk, low-yield security representing an interest in a very stable company.

Blue sky laws ❚ A general term that denotes various states' laws regulating securities.

Bond ❚ (*See also* General obligation bond; Taxable bonds; Treasury bonds) A written instrument executed by a bidder or contractor (the principal) and a second party (the surety or sureties) to .assure fulfillment of the principal's obligations to a third party (the obligee or government) identified in the bond. If the principal's obligations are not met, the bond assures payment to the extent stipulated of any loss sustained by the obligee.

Bonding requirements ❚ Terms contained in a bond (*see* separate citation).

Bonus ❚ An amount of money paid to an employee as a reward for achieving certain business goals or objectives.

Brainstorming ❚ A group session where employees contribute their ideas for solving a problem or meeting a company objective without fear of retribution or ridicule.

Brand name ❚ The part of a brand, trademark, or service mark that can be spoken. It can be a word, letter, or group of words or letters.

Bridge financing ❚ A short-term loan made in expectation of intermediate-term or long-term financing. Can be used when a company plans to go public in the near future.

Broker ❚ One who matches resources available for innovation with those who need them.

Budget ❚ An estimate of the spending necessary to complete a project or offer a service in comparison to cash-on-hand and expected earnings for the coming year, with an emphasis on cost control.

Bulletin Board Service (BBS) ❚ An online service enabling users to communicate with each other about specific topics.

Business birth ❚ The formation of a new establishment or enterprise. The appearance of a new establishment or enterprise in the Small Business Data Base (*see* separate citation).

Business conditions ❚ Outside factors that can affect the financial performance of a business.

Business contractions ❚ The number of establishments that have decreased in employment during a specified time.

Business cycle ❚ A period of economic recession and recovery. These cycles vary in duration.

Business death ❚ The voluntary or involuntary closure of a firm or establishment. The disappearance of an establishment or enterprise from the Small Business Data Base (*see* separate citation).

Business development corporation (BDC) ❚ A business financing agency, usually composed of the financial institutions in an area or state, organized to assist in financing businesses unable to obtain assistance through normal channels; the risk is spread among various members of the business development corporation, and interest rates may vary somewhat from those charged by member institutions. A venture capital firm in which shares of ownership are publicly held and to which the Investment Act of 1940 applies.

Business dissolution ❚ For enumeration purposes, the absence of a business that was present in the prior time period from any current record.

Business entry ❚ *See* Business birth.

Business ethics ❚ Moral values and principles espoused by members of the business community as a guide to fair and honest business practices.

Business exit ❚ *See* Business death.

Business expansions ❚ The number of establishments that added employees during a specified time.

Business failure ❚ Closure of a business causing a loss to at least one creditor.

Business format franchising ❚ (*See also* Franchising) The purchase of the name, trademark, and an ongoing business plan of the parent corporation or franchisor by the franchisee.

Business and industrial development company (BIDCO) ❚ A private, for-profit financing corporation chartered by the state to provide both equity and long-term debt capital to small business owners (*see* separate citations for equity and debt capital).

Business license ❚ A legal authorization issued by municipal and state governments and required for business operations.

Business name ❚ (*See also* Business license; Trademark) Enterprises must register their business names with local governments usually on a "doing business as" (DBA) form. (This name is sometimes referred to as a "fictional name.") The procedure is part of the business licensing process and prevents any other business from using that same name for a similar business in the same locality.

Business norms ❚ *See* Financial ratios.

Business permit ❚ *See* Business license.

Business plan ❚ A document that spells out a company's expected course of action for a specified period, usually including a detailed listing and analysis of risks and uncertainties. For the small busi-ness, it should examine the proposed products, the market, the industry, the management policies, the marketing policies, produc-tion needs, and financial needs. Frequently, it is used as a pros-pectus for potential investors and lenders.

Business proposal ❚ *See* Business plan.

Business service firm ❚ A business primarily engaged in rendering services to other businesses on a fee or contract basis.

Business start ❚ For enumeration purposes, a business with a name or similar designation that did not exist in a prior time period.

Cafeteria plan ▮ *See* Flexible benefit plan.

Capacity ▮ Level of a firm's, industry's, or nation's output corresponding to full practical utilization of available resources.

Capital ▮ Assets less liabilities, representing the ownership interest in a business. A stock of accumulated goods, especially at a specified time and in contrast to income received during a specified time period. Accumulated goods devoted to production. Accumulated possessions calculated to bring income.

Capital expenditure ▮ Expenses incurred by a business for improvements that will depreciate over time.

Capital gain ▮ The monetary difference between the purchase price and the selling price of capital. Capital gains are taxed at a rate of 28% by the federal government.

Capital intensity ▮ (*See also* Debt capital; Equity midrisk venture capital; Informal capital; Internal capital; Owner's capital; Secondhand capital; Seed capital; Venture capital) The relative importance of capital in the production process, usually expressed as the ratio of capital to labor but also sometimes as the ratio of capital to output.

Capital resource ▮ The equipment, facilities and labor used to create products and services.

Caribbean Basin Initiative ▮ An interdisciplinary program to support commerce among the businesses in the nations of the Caribbean Basin and the United States. Agencies involved include: the Agency for International Development, the U.S. Small Business Administration, the International Trade Administration of the U.S. Department of Commerce, and various private sector groups.

Catastrophic care ▮ Medical and other services for acute and long-term illnesses that cost more than insurance coverage limits or that cost the amount most families may be expected to pay with their own resources.

CDC ▮ *See* Certified development corporation.

CD-ROM ▮ Compact disc with read-only memory used to store large amounts of digitized data.

Certified development corporation (CDC) ▮ A local area or statewide corporation or authority (for profit or nonprofit) that packages U.S. Small Business Administration (SBA), bank, state, and/or private money into financial assistance for existing business capital improvements. The SBA holds the second lien on its maximum share of 40 percent involvement. Each state has at least one certified development corporation. This program is called the SBA 504 Program.

Certified lenders ▮ Banks that participate in the SBA guaranteed loan program (*see* separate citation). Such banks must have a good track record with the U.S. Small Business Administration (SBA) and must agree to certain conditions set forth by the agency. In return, the SBA agrees to process any guaranteed loan application within three business days.

Champion ▮ An advocate for the development of an innovation.

Channel of distribution ▮ The means used to transport merchandise from the manufacturer to the consumer.

Chapter 7 of the 1978 Bankruptcy Act ▮ Provides for a court-appointed trustee who is responsible for liquidating a company's assets in order to settle outstanding debts.

Chapter 11 of the 1978 Bankruptcy Act ▮ Allows the business owners to retain control of the company while working with their creditors to reorganize their finances and establish better business practices to prevent liquidation of assets.

Closely held corporation ▮ A corporation in which the shares are held by a few persons, usually officers, employees, or others close to the management; these shares are rarely offered to the public.

Code of Federal Regulations ▮ Codification of general and permanent rules of the federal government published in the Federal Register.

Code sharing ▮ *See* Computer code sharing.

Coinsurance ▮ (*See also* Cost sharing) Upon meeting the deductible payment, health insurance participants may be required to make additional health care cost-sharing payments. Coinsurance is a payment of a fixed percentage of the cost of each service; copayment is usually a fixed amount to be paid with each service.

Collateral ▮ Securities, evidence of deposit, or other property pledged by a borrower to secure repayment of a loan.

Collective ratemaking ▮ (*See also* Antitrust immunity) The establishment of uniform charges for services by a group of businesses in the same industry.

Commercial insurance plan ▮ *See* Underwriting.

Commercial loans ▮ Short-term renewable loans used to finance specific capital needs of a business.

Commercialization ▮ The final stage of the innovation process, including production and distribution.

Common stock ▮ The most frequently used instrument for purchasing ownership in private or public companies. Common stock generally carries the right to vote on certain corporate actions and may pay dividends, although it rarely does in venture investments. In liquidation, common stockholders are the last to share in the proceeds from the sale of a corporation's assets; bondholders and preferred shareholders have priority. Common stock is often used in first-round start-up financing.

Community development corporation ▮ A corporation established to develop economic programs for a community and, in most cases, to provide financial support for such development.

Competitor ▮ A business whose product or service is marketed for the same purpose/use and to the same consumer group as the product or service of another.

Computer code sharing ▮ An arrangement whereby flights of a regional airline are identified by the two-letter code of a major carrier in the computer reservation system to help direct passengers to new regional carriers.

Consignment ▮ A merchandising agreement, usually referring to secondhand shops, where the dealer pays the owner of an item a percentage of the profit when the item is sold.

Consortium ▮ A coalition of organizations such as banks and corporations for ventures requiring large capital resources.

Consultant ▮ An individual that is paid by a business to provide advice and expertise in a particular area.

Consumer price index ❙ A measure of the fluctuation in prices between two points in time.

Consumer research ❙ Research conducted by a business to obtain information about existing or potential consumer markets.

Continuation coverage ❙ Health coverage offered for a specified period of time to employees who leave their jobs and to their widows, divorced spouses, or dependents.

Contractions ❙ *See* Business contractions.

Convertible preferred stock ❙ A class of stock that pays a reasonable dividend and is convertible into common stock (*See* separate citation). Generally the convertible feature may only be exercised after being held for a stated period of time. This arrangement is usually considered second-round financing when a company needs equity to maintain its cash flow.

Convertible securities ❙ A feature of certain bonds, debentures, or preferred stocks that allows them to be exchanged by the owner for another class of securities at a future date and in accordance with any other terms of the issue.

Copayment ❙ *See* Coinsurance.

Copyright ❙ A legal form of protection available to creators and authors to safeguard their works from unlawful use or claim of ownership by others. Copyrights may be acquired for works of art, sculpture, music, and published or unpublished manuscripts. All copyrights should be registered at the Copyright Office of the Library of Congress.

Corporate financial ratios ❙ (*See also* Industry financial ratios) The relationship between key figures found in a company's financial statement expressed as a numeric value. Used to evalu-ate risk and company performance. Also known as Financial averages, Operating ratios, and Business ratios.

Corporation ❙ A legal entity, chartered by a state or the federal government, recognized as a separate entity having its own rights, privileges, and liabilities distinct from those of its members.

Cost containment ❙ Actions taken by employers and insurers to curtail rising health care costs; for example, increasing employee cost sharing (*see* separate citation), requiring second opinions, or preadmission screening.

Cost sharing ❙ The requirement that health care consumers contribute to their own medical care costs through deductibles and coinsurance (*see* separate citations). Cost sharing does not include the amounts paid in premiums. It is used to control utilization of services; for example, requiring a fixed amount to be paid with each health care service.

Cottage industry ❙ (*See also* Home-based business) Businesses based in the home in which the family members are the labor force and family-owned equipment is used to process the goods.

Credit Rating ❙ A letter or number calculated by an organization (such as Dun & Bradstreet) to represent the ability and disposition of a business to meet its financial obligations.

Customer service ❙ Various techniques used to ensure the satisfaction of a customer.

Cyclical peak ❙ The upper turning point in a business cycle.

Cyclical trough ❙ The lower turning point in a business cycle.

DBA ❙ *See* Business name.

Death ❙ *See* Business death.

Debenture ❙ A certificate given as acknowledgment of a debt (*see* separate citation) secured by the general credit of the issuing corporation. A bond, usually without security, issued by a corporation and sometimes convertible to common stock.

Debt ❙ (*See also* Long-term debt; Mid-term debt; Securitized debt; Short-term debt) Something owed by one person to another. Financing in which a company receives capital that must be repaid; no ownership is transferred.

Debt capital ❙ Business financing that normally requires periodic interest payments and repayment of the principal within a specified time.

Debt financing ❙ *See* Debt capital.

Debt securities ❙ Loans such as bonds and notes that provide a specified rate of return for a specified period of time.

Deductible ❙ A set amount that an individual must pay before any benefits are received.

Demand shock absorbers ❙ A term used to describe the role that some small firms play by expanding their output levels to accommodate a transient surge in demand.

Demographics ❙ Statistics on various markets, including age, income, and education, used to target specific products or services to appropriate consumer groups.

Demonstration ❙ Showing that a product or process has been modified sufficiently to meet the needs of users.

Deregulation ❙ The lifting of government restrictions; for example, the lifting of government restrictions on the entry of new businesses, the expansion of services, and the setting of prices in particular industries.

Desktop Publishing ❙ Using personal computers and specialized software to produce camera-ready copy for publications.

Digital cash ❙ A system that allows a person to make financial transactions over the Internet. This system allows a person to purchase goods or services by transmitting a number from one computer to another.

Disaster loans ❙ Various types of physical and economic assistance available to individuals and businesses through the U.S. Small Business Administration (SBA). This is the only SBA loan program available for residential purposes.

Discrimination ❙ The denial of the rights and privileges of employment based on factors such as age, race, religion, or gender.

Diseconomies of scale ❙ The condition in which the costs of production increase faster than the volume of production.

Dissolution ❙ *See* Business dissolution.

Distribution ❙ Delivering a product or process to the user.

Distributor ❙ One who delivers merchandise to the user.

Diversified company ❙ A company whose products and services are used by several different markets.

Doing business as (DBA) ❙ *See* Business name.

Dow Jones ❚ An information services company that publishes the Wall Street Journal and other sources of financial information.

Dow Jones Industrial Average ❚ An indicator of stock market performance.

Earned income ❚ A tax term that refers to wages and salaries earned by the recipient, as opposed to monies earned through interest and dividends.

E-commerce ❚ See Electronic commerce.

Economic efficiency ❚ The use of productive resources to the fullest practical extent in the provision of the set of goods and services that is most preferred by purchasers in the economy.

Economic indicators ❚ Statistics used to express the state of the economy. These include the length of the average work week, the rate of unemployment, and stock prices.

Economically disadvantaged ❚ See Socially and economically disadvantaged.

Economies of scale ❚ See Scale economies.

EEOC ❚ See Equal Employment Opportunity Commission.

8(a) Program ❚ A program authorized by the Small Business Act that directs federal contracts to small businesses owned and operated by socially and economically disadvantaged individuals.

Electronic mail (e-mail) ❚ The electronic transmission of mail via phone lines.

Electonic commerce (e-commerce) ❚ Buying and selling goods and services through the Internet.

E-mail ❚ See Electronic mail.

Employee leasing ❚ A contract by which employers arrange to have their workers hired by a leasing company and then leased back to them for a management fee. The leasing company typically assumes the administrative burden of payroll and provides a benefit package to the workers.

Employee tenure ❚ The length of time an employee works for a particular employer.

Employer identification number ❚ The business equivalent of a social security number. Assigned by the U.S. Internal Revenue Service.

Enterprise ❚ An aggregation of all establishments owned by a parent company. An enterprise may consist of a single, independent establishment or include subsidiaries and other branches under the same ownership and control.

Enterprise zone ❚ A designated area, usually found in inner cities and other areas with significant unemployment, where businesses receive tax credits and other incentives to entice them to establish operations there.

Entrepreneur ❚ A person who takes the risk of organizing and operating a new business venture.

Entry ❚ See Business entry

Equal Employment Opportunity Commission (EEOC) ❚ A federal agency that ensures nondiscrimination in the hiring and firing practices of a business.

Equal opportunity employer ❚ An employer who adheres to the standards set by the Equal Employment Opportunity Commission (see separate citation).

Equity ❚ (See also Common Stock; Equity midrisk venture capital) The ownership interest. Financing in which partial or total ownership of a company is surrendered in exchange for capital. An investor's financial return comes from dividend payments and from growth in the net worth of the business.

Equity capital ❚ See Equity; Equity midrisk venture capital.

Equity financing ❚ See Equity; Equity midrisk venture capital.

Equity midrisk venture capital ❚ An unsecured investment in a company. Usually a purchase of ownership interest in a company that occurs in the later stages of a company's development.

Equity partnership ❚ A limited partnership arrangement for providing start-up and Seed capital to businesses.

Equity securities ❚ See Equity.

Equity-type ❚ Debt financing subordinated to conventional debt.

Establishment ❚ A single-location business unit that may be independent (a single-establishment enterprise) or owned by a parent enterprise.

Establishment and Enterprise Microdata File ❚ See U.S. Establishment and Enterprise Microdata File.

Establishment birth ❚ See Business birth.

Establishment Longitudinal Microdata File ❚ See U.S. Establishment Longitudinal Microdata File.

Ethics ❚ See Business ethics.

Evaluation ❚ Determining the potential success of translating an invention into a product or process.

Experience rating ❚ See Underwriting.

Exit ❚ See Business exit.

Export ❚ A product sold outside of the country.

Export license ❚ A general or specific license granted by the U.S. Department of Commerce required of anyone wishing to export goods. Some restricted articles need approval from the U.S. Departments of State, Defense, or Energy.

Extranet ❚ (See also Intranet) An intranet that provides various levels of accessibility to outsiders. Access to an extranet can only be obtained if you have a valid username and password.

Failure ❚ See Business failure.

Fair share agreement ❚ (See also Franchising) An agreement reached between a franchisor and a minority business organization to extend business ownership to minorities by either reducing the amount of capital required or by setting aside certain marketing areas for minority business owners.

Feasibility study ❚ A study to determine the likelihood that a proposed product or development will fulfill the objectives of a particular investor.

Federal Trade Commission (FTC) ❚ Federal agency that promotes free enterprise and competition within the U.S.

Federal Trade Mark Act of 1946 ❚ *See* Lanham Act.

Fictional name ❚ *See* Business name.

Fiduciary ❚ An individual or group that hold assets in trust for a beneficiary.

Financial analysis ❚ The techniques used to determine money needs in a business. Techniques include ratio analysis, calculation of return on investment, guides for measuring profitability, and break-even analysis to determine ultimate success.

Financial intermediary ❚ A financial institution that acts as the intermediary between borrowers and lenders. Banks, savings and loan associations, finance companies, and venture capital companies are major financial intermediaries in the United States.

Financial ratios ❚ *See* Corporate financial ratios; Industry financial ratios.

Financial statement ❚ A written record of business finances, including balance sheets and profit and loss statements.

Financing ❚ *See* First-stage financing; Second-stage financing; Third-stage financing.

First-stage financing ❚ (*See also* Second-stage financing; Third-stage financing) Financing provided to companies that have expended their initial capital, and require funds to start full-scale manufacturing and sales. Also known as First-round financing.

Fiscal year ❚ Any twelve-month period used by businesses for accounting purposes.

504 Program ❚ *See* Certified development corporation.

Flexible benefit plan ❚ A plan that offers a choice among cash and/or qualified benefits such as group term life insurance, accident and health insurance, group legal services, dependent care assistance, and vacations.

FOB ❚ *See* Free on board

Format franchising ❚ *See* Business format franchising; Franchising.

401(k) plan ❚ A financial plan where employees contribute a percentage of their earnings to a fund that is invested in stocks, bonds, or money markets for the purpose of saving money for retirement.

Four Ps ❚ Marketing terms: Product, Price, Place, and Promotion.

Franchising ❚ A form of licensing by which the owner—the franchisor—distributes or markets a product, method, or service through affiliated dealers called franchisees. The product, method, or service being marketed is identified by a brand name, and the franchisor maintains control over the marketing methods employed. The franchisee is often given exclusive access to a defined geographic area.

Free on board (FOB) ❚ A pricing term indicating that the quoted price includes the cost of loading goods into transport vessels at a specified place.

Frictional unemployment ❚ *See* Un-employment.

FTC ❚ *See* Federal Trade Commission.

Fulfillment ❚ The systems necessary for accurate delivery of an ordered item, including subscriptions and direct marketing.

Full-time workers ❚ Generally, those who work a regular schedule of more than 35 hours per week.

Garment registration number ❚ A number that must appear on every garment sold in the U.S. to indicate the manufacturer of the garment, which may or may not be the same as the label under which the garment is sold. The U.S. Federal Trade Commission assigns and regulates garment registration numbers.

Gatekeeper ❚ A key contact point for entry into a network.

GDP ❚ *See* Gross domestic product.

General obligation bond ❚ A municipal bond secured by the taxing power of the municipality. The Tax Reform Act of 1986 limits the purposes for which such bonds may be issued and establishes volume limits on the extent of their issuance.

GNP ❚ *See* Gross national product.

Good Housekeeping Seal ❚ Seal appearing on products that signifies the fulfillment of the standards set by the Good Housekeeping Institute to protect consumer interests.

Goods sector ❚ All businesses producing tangible goods, including agriculture, mining, construction, and manufacturing businesses.

GPO ❚ *See* Gross product originating.

Gross domestic product (GDP) ❚ The part of the nation's gross national product (*see* separate citation) generated by private business using resources from within the country.

Gross national product (GNP) ❚ The most comprehensive single measure of aggregate economic output. Represents the market value of the total output of goods and services produced by a nation's economy.

Gross product originating (GPO) ❚ A measure of business output estimated from the income or production side using employee compensation, profit income, net interest, capital consumption, and indirect business taxes.

HAL ❚ *See* Handicapped assistance loan program.

Handicapped assistance loan program (HAL) ❚ Low-interest direct loan program through the U.S. Small Business Administration (SBA) for handicapped persons. The SBA requires that these persons demonstrate that their disability is such that it is impossible for them to secure employment, thus making it necessary to go into their own business to make a living.

Health maintenance organization (HMO) ❚ Organization of physi-cians and other health care professionals that provides health services to subscribers and their dependents on a prepaid basis.

Health provider ❚ An individual or institution that gives medical care. Under Medicare, an institutional provider is a hospital, skilled nursing facility, home health agency, or provider of certain physical therapy services.

Hispanic ❚ A person of Cuban, Mexican, Puerto Rican, Latin American (Central or South American), European Spanish, or other Spanish-speaking origin or ancestry.

HMO ❚ *See* Health maintenance organization.

Home-based business ❚ (*See also* Cottage industry) A business with an operating address that is also a residential address (usually the residential address of the proprietor).

Hub-and-spoke system ❙ A system in which flights of an airline from many different cities (the spokes) converge at a single airport (the hub). After allowing passengers sufficient time to make connections, planes then depart for different cities.

Human Resources Management ❙ A business program designed to oversee recruiting, pay, benefits, and other issues related to the company's work force, including planning to determine the optimal use of labor to increase production, thereby increasing profit.

Idea ❙ An original concept for a new product or process.

Import ❙ Products produced outside the country in which they are consumed.

Income ❙ Money or its equivalent, earned or accrued, resulting from the sale of goods and services.

Income statement ❙ A financial statement that lists the profits and losses of a company at a given time.

Incorporation ❙ The filing of a certificate of incorporation with the secretary of state, thereby limiting the business owner's liability.

Incubator ❙ A facility designed to encourage entrepreneurship and minimize obstacles to new business formation and growth, particularly for high-technology firms, by housing a number of fledgling enterprises that share an array of services, such as meeting areas, secretarial services, accounting, research library, on-site financial and management counseling, and word processing facilities.

Independent contractor ❙ An individual considered self-employed (*see* separate citation) and responsible for paying Social Security taxes and income taxes on earnings.

Indirect health coverage ❙ Health insurance obtained through another individual's health care plan; for example, a spouse's employer-sponsored plan.

Industrial development authority ❙ The financial arm of a state or other political subdivision established for the purpose of financing economic development in an area, usually through loans to nonprofit organizations, which in turn provide facilities for manufacturing and other industrial operations.

Industry financial ratios ❙ (*See also* Corporate financial ratios) Corporate financial ratios averaged for a specified industry. These are used for comparison purposes and reveal industry trends and identify differences between the performance of a specific company and the performance of its industry. Also known as Industrial averages, Industry ratios, Financial averages, and Business or Industrial norms.

Inflation ❙ Increases in volume of currency and credit, generally resulting in a sharp and continuing rise in price levels.

Informal capital ❙ Financing from informal, unorganized sources; includes informal debt capital such as trade credit or loans from friends and relatives and equity capital from informal investors.

Initial public offering (IPO) ❙ A corporation's first offering of stock to the public.

Innovation ❙ The introduction of a new idea into the marketplace in the form of a new product or service or an improvement in organization or process.

Intellectual property ❙ Any idea/work that can be considered proprietary in nature and thus protected from infringement by others.

Internal capital ❙ Debt or equity financing obtained from the owner or through retained business earnings.

Internet ❙ A government-designed computer network that contains large amounts of information and is accessible through various vendors for a fee.

Intranet ❙ (*See also* Extranet) A web site belonging to an organization or a corporation, that is accessible only to employees, members, or others that have authorization.

Intrapreneurship ❙ The state of employing entrepreneurial principles to nonentrepreneurial situations.

Invention ❙ The tangible form of a technological idea, which could include a laboratory prototype, drawings, formulas, etc.

IPO ❙ *See* Initial public offering.

Job description ❙ The duties and responsibilities required in a particular position.

Job tenure ❙ A period of time during which an individual is continuously employed in the same job.

Joint marketing agreements ❙ Agree-ments between regional and major airlines, often involving the coordination of flight schedules, fares, and baggage transfer. These agreements help regional carriers operate at lower cost.

Joint venture ❙ Venture in which two or more people combine efforts in a particular business enterprise, usually a single transaction or a limited activity, and agree to share the profits and losses jointly or in proportion to their contributions.

Keogh plan ❙ Designed for self-employed persons and unincorporated businesses as a tax-deferred pension account.

Labor force ❙ Civilians considered eligible for employment who are also willing and able to work.

Labor force participation rate ❙ The civilian labor force as a percentage of the civilian population.

Labor intensity ❙ (*See also* Capital intensity) The relative importance of labor in the production process, usually measured as the capital-labor ratio; i.e., the ratio of units of capital (typically, dollars of tangible assets) to the number of employees. The higher the capital-labor ratio exhibited by a firm or industry, the lower the capital intensity of that firm or industry is said to be.

Labor surplus area ❙ An area in which there exists a high unemployment rate. In procurement (*see* separate citation), extra points are given to firms in counties that are designated a labor surplus area; this information is requested on procurement bid sheets.

Labor union ❙ An organization of similarly-skilled workers who collectively bargain with management over the conditions of employment.

Laboratory prototype ❙ *See* Prototype.

LAN ❙ *See* Local Area Network.

Lanham Act ❙ Refers to the Federal Trade Mark Act of 1946. Protects registered trademarks, trade names, and other service marks used in commerce.

Large business-dominated industry ❙ Industry in which a minimum of 60 percent of employment or sales is in firms with more than 500 workers.

LBO ❚ *See* Leveraged buy-out.

Leader pricing ❚ A reduction in the price of a good or service in order to generate more sales of that good or service.

Legal list ❚ A list of securities selected by a state in which certain institutions and fiduciaries (such as pension funds, insurance companies, and banks) may invest. Securities not on the list are not eligible for investment. Legal lists typically restrict investments to high quality securities meeting certain specifications. Generally, investment is limited to U.S. securities and investment-grade blue chip securities (*see* separate citation).

Leveraged buy-out (LBO) ❚ The purchase of a business or a division of a corporation through a highly leveraged financing package.

Liability ❚ An obligation or duty to perform a service or an act. Also defined as money owed.

License ❚ (*See also* Business license) A legal agreement granting to another the right to use a technological innovation.

Limited partnerships ❚ *See* Venture capital limited partnerships

Liquidity ❚ The ability to convert a security into cash promptly.

Loans ❚ *See* Commercial loans; Disaster loans; SBA direct loans; SBA guaranteed loans; SBA special lending institution categories.

Local Area Network (LAN) ❚ Computer networks contained within a single building or small area; used to facilitate the sharing of information.

Local development corporation ❚ An organization, usually made up of local citizens of a community, designed to improve the economy of the area by inducing business and industry to locate and expand there. A local development corporation establishes a capability to finance local growth.

Long-haul rates ❚ Rates charged by a transporter in which the distance traveled is more than 800 miles.

Long-term debt ❚ An obligation that matures in a period that exceeds five years.

Low-grade bond ❚ A corporate bond that is rated below investment grade by the major rating agencies (Standard and Poor's, Moody's).

Macro-efficiency ❚ (*See also* Economic efficiency) Efficiency as it pertains to the operation of markets and market systems.

Managed care ❚ A cost-effective health care program initiated by employers whereby low-cost health care is made available to the employees in return for exclusive patronage to program doctors.

Management and technical assistance ❚ A term used by many programs to mean business (as opposed to technological) assistance.

Management Assistance Programs ❚ *See* SBA Management Assistance Programs

Mandated benefits ❚ Specific treatments, providers, or individuals required by law to be included in commercial health plans.

Market evaluation ❚ The use of market information to determine the sales potential of a specific product or process.

Market failure ❚ The situation in which the workings of a competitive market do not produce the best results from the point of view of the entire society.

Market information ❚ Data of any type that can be used for market evaluation, which could include demographic data, technology forecasting, regulatory changes, etc.

Market research ❚ A systematic collection, analysis, and reporting of data about the market and its preferences, opinions, trends, and plans; used for corporate decision-making.

Market share ❚ In a particular market, the percentage of sales of a specific product.

Marketing ❚ Promotion of goods or services through various media.

Master Establishment List (MEL) ❚ A list of firms in the United States developed by the U.S. Small Business Administration; firms can be selected by industry, region, state, standard metropolitan statistical area (*see* separate citation), county, and zip code.

Maturity ❚ (*See also* Term) The date upon which the principal or stated value of a bond or other indebtedness becomes due and payable.

Medicaid (Title XIX) ❚ A federally aided, state-operated and administered program that provides medical benefits for certain low-income persons in need of health and medical care who are eligible for one of the government's welfare cash payment programs, including the aged, the blind, the disabled, and members of families with dependent children where one parent is absent, incapacitated, or unemployed.

Medicare (Title XVIII) ❚ A nationwide health insurance program for disabled and aged persons. Health insurance is available to insured persons without regard to income. Monies from payroll taxes cover hospital insurance and monies from general revenues and beneficiary premiums pay for supplementary medical insurance.

MEL ❚ *See* Master Establishment List.

Metropolitan statistical area (MSA) ❚ A means used by the government to define large population centers that may transverse different governmental jurisdictions. For example, the Washington, D.C., MSA includes the District of Columbia and contiguous parts of Maryland and Virginia because all of these geopolitical areas comprise one population and economic operating unit.

Mezzanine financing ❚ *See* Third-stage financing.

MESBIC ❚ *See* Minority enterprise small business investment corporation.

MET ❚ *See* Multiple employer trust.

Micro-efficiency ❚ (*See also* Economic efficiency) Efficiency as it pertains to the operation of individual firms.

Microdata ❚ Information on the characteristics of an individual business firm.

Mid-term debt ❚ An obligation that matures within one to five years.

Midrisk venture capital ❚ *See* Equity midrisk venture capital.

Minimum premium plan ❚ A combination approach to funding an insurance plan aimed primarily at premium tax savings. The employer self-funds a fixed percentage of estimated monthly claims and the insurance company insures the excess.

Minimum wage ❚ The lowest hourly wage allowed by the federal government.

Minority Business Development Agency ❚ Contracts with private firms throughout the nation to sponsor Minority Business Development Centers which provide minority firms with advice and technical assistance on a fee basis.

Minority Enterprise Small Business Investment Corporation (MESBIC) ❚ A federally funded private venture capital firm licensed by the U.S. Small Business Administration to provide capital to minority-owned businesses (*see* separate citation).

Minority-owned business ❚ Businesses owned by those who are socially or economically disadvantaged (*see* separate citation).

Mom and Pop business ❚ A small store or enterprise having limited capital, principally employing family members.

Moonlighter ❚ A wage-and-salary worker with a side business.

MSA ❚ *See* Metropolitan statistical area.

Multi-employer plan ❚ A health plan to which more than one employer is required to contribute and that may be maintained through a collective bargaining agreement and required to meet standards prescribed by the U.S. Department of Labor.

Multi-level marketing ❚ A system of selling in which you sign up other people to assist you, and they, in turn, recruit others to help them. Some entrepreneurs have built successful companies on this concept because the main focus of their activities is their product and product sales.

Multimedia ❚ The use of several types of media to promote a product or service. Also refers to the use of several different types of media (sight, sound, pictures, text) in a CD-ROM (*see* separate citation) product.

Multiple employer trust (MET) ❚ A self-funded benefit plan generally geared toward small employers sharing a common interest.

NAFTA ❚ *See* North American Free Trade Agreement.

NASDAQ ❚ *See* National Association of Securities Dealers Automated Quotations.

National Association of Securities Dealers Automated Quotations ❚ Provides price quotes on over-the-counter securities as well as securities listed on the New York Stock Exchange.

National income ❚ Aggregate earnings of labor and property arising from the production of goods and services in a nation's economy.

Net assets ❚ *See* Net worth.

Net income ❚ The amount remaining from earnings and profits after all expenses and costs have been met or deducted. Also known as Net earnings.

Net profit ❚ Money earned after production and overhead expenses (*see* separate citations) have been deducted.

Net worth ❚ (*See also* Capital) The difference between a company's total assets and its total liabilities.

Network ❚ A chain of interconnected individuals or organizations sharing information and/or services.

New York Stock Exchange (NYSE) ❚ The oldest stock exchange in the U.S. Allows for trading in stocks, bonds, warrants, options, and rights that meet listing requirements.

Niche ❚ A career or business for which a person is well-suited. Also, a product which fulfills one need of a particular market segment, often with little or no competition.

Nodes ❚ One workstation in a network, either local area or wide area (*see* separate citations).

Nonbank bank ❚ A bank that either accepts deposits or makes loans, but not both. Used to create many new branch banks.

Noncompetitive awards ❚ A method of contracting whereby the federal government negotiates with only one contractor to supply a product or service.

Nonmember bank ❚ A state-regulated bank that does not belong to the federal bank system.

Nonprofit ❚ An organization that has no shareholders, does not distribute profits, and is without federal and state tax liabilities.

Norms ❚ *See* Financial ratios.

North American Free Trade Agreement (NAFTA) ❚ Passed in 1993, NAFTA eliminates trade barriers among businesses in the U.S., Canada, and Mexico.

NYSE ❚ *See* New York Stock Exchange

Occupational Safety & Health Administration (OSHA) ❚ Federal agency that regulates health and safety standards within the workplace.

Optimal firm size ❚ The business size at which the production cost per unit of output (average cost) is, in the long run, at its minimum.

Organizational chart ❚ A hierarchical chart tracking the chain of command within an organization.

OSHA ❚ *See* Occupational Safety & Health Administration.

Overhead ❚ Expenses, such as employee benefits and building utilities, incurred by a business that are unrelated to the actual product or service sold.

Owner's capital ❚ Debt or equity funds provided by the owner(s) of a business; sources of owner's capital are personal savings, sales of assets, or loans from financial institutions.

P & L ❚ *See* Profit and loss statement.

Part-time workers ❚ Normally, those who work less than 35 hours per week. The Tax Reform Act indicated that part-time workers who work less than 17.5 hours per week may be excluded from health plans for purposes of complying with federal nondiscrimination rules.

Part-year workers ❚ Those who work less than 50 weeks per year.

Partnership ❚ Two or more parties who enter into a legal relationship to conduct business for profit. Defined by the U.S. Internal Revenue Code as joint ventures, syndicates, groups, pools, and other associations of two or more persons organized for profit that are not specifically classified in the IRS code as corporations or proprietorships.

Patent ❚ A grant by the government assuring an inventor the sole right to make, use, and sell an invention for a period of 17 years.

PC ❚ *See* Professional corporation.

Peak ❚ *See* Cyclical peak.

Pension ❚ A series of payments made monthly, semiannually, annually, or at other specified intervals during the lifetime of the pensioner for distribution upon retirement. The term is sometimes used to denote the portion of the retirement allowance financed by the employer's contributions.

Pension fund ❚ A fund established to provide for the payment of pension benefits; the collective contributions made by all of the parties to the pension plan.

Performance appraisal ❚ An established set of objective criteria, based on job description and requirements, that is used to evaluate the performance of an employee in a specific job.

Permit ❚ *See* Business license.

Plan ❚ *See* Business plan.

Pooling ❚ An arrangement for employers to achieve efficiencies and lower health costs by joining together to purchase group health insurance or self-insurance.

PPO ❚ *See* Preferred provider organization

Preferred lenders program ❚ *See* SBA special lending institution categories

Preferred provider organization (PPO) ❚ A contractual arrangement with a health care services organization that agrees to discount its health care rates in return for faster payment and/or a patient base.

Premiums ❚ The amount of money paid to an insurer for health insurance under a policy. The premium is generally paid periodically (e.g., monthly), and often is split between the employer and the employee. Unlike deductibles and coinsurance or co-payments, premiums are paid for coverage whether or not benefits are actually used.

Prime-age workers ❚ Employees 25 to 54 years of age.

Prime contract ❚ A contract awarded directly by the U.S. Federal Government.

Private company ❚ *See* Closely held corporation. Private placement A method of raising capital by offering for sale an investment or business to a small group of investors (generally avoiding registration with the Securities and Exchange Commis-sion or state securities registration agencies). Also known as Private financing or Private offering.

Pro forma ❚ The use of hypothetical figures in financial statements to represent future expenditures, debts, and other potential financial expenses.

Proactive ❚ Taking the initiative to solve problems and anticipate future events before they happen, instead of reacting to an already existing problem or waiting for a difficult situation to occur.

Procurement ❚ (*See also* 8(a) Program; Small business set asides) A contract from an agency of the federal government for goods or services from a small business.

Prodigy ❚ (*See also* America Online) An online service which is accessible by computer modem. The service features Internet access, bulletin boards, online periodicals, electronic mail, and other services for subscribers.

Product development ❚ The stage of the innovation process where research is translated into a product or process through evaluation, adaptation, and demonstration.

Product franchising ❚ An arrangement for a franchisee to use the name and to produce the product line of the franchisor or parent corporation.

Production ❚ The manufacture of a product.

Production prototype ❚ *See* Prototype.

Productivity ❚ A measurement of the number of goods produced during a specific amount of time.

Professional corporation (PC) ❚ Organized by members of a pro-fession such as medicine, dentistry, or law for the purpose of con-ducting their professional activities as a corporation. Liability of a member or shareholder is limited in the same manner as in a business corporation.

Profit and loss statement (P & L) ❚ The summary of the incomes and costs of a company's operation during a specific period of time. Also known as Income and expense statement.

Proposal ❚ *See* Business plan.

Proprietorship ❚ The most common legal form of business ownership; about 85 percent of all small businesses are proprietorships. The liability of the owner is unlimited in this form of ownership.

Prospective payment system ❚ A cost-containment measure included in the Social Security Amendments of 1983 whereby Medicare payments to hospitals are based on established prices, rather than on cost reimbursement.

Prototype ❚ A model that demonstrates the validity of the concept of an invention (laboratory prototype); a model that meets the needs of the manufacturing process and the user (production prototype).

Prudent investor rule or standard ❚ A legal doctrine that requires fiduciaries to make investments using the prudence, diligence, and intelligence that would be used by a prudent person in making similar investments. Because fiduciaries make investments on behalf of third-party beneficiaries, the standard results in very conservative investments. Until recently, most state regulations required the fiduciary to apply this standard to each investment. Newer, more progressive regulations permit fiduciaries to apply this standard to the portfolio taken as a whole, thereby allowing a fiduciary to balance a portfolio with higher-yield, higher-risk invest-ments. In states with more progressive regulations, practically every type of security is eligible for inclusion in the portfolio of investments made by a fiduciary, provided that the portfolio investments, in their totality, are those of a prudent person.

Public equity markets ❚ Organized markets for trading in equity shares such as common stocks, preferred stocks, and warrants. Includes markets for both regularly traded and nonregularly traded securities.

Public offering ❚ General solicitation for participation in an investment opportunity. Interstate public offerings are supervised by the U.S. Securities and Exchange Commission (*see* separate citation).

Quality control ❚ The process by which a product is checked and tested to ensure consistent standards of high quality.

Rate of return z ❚ (*See also* Yield) The yield obtained on a security or other investment based on its purchase price or its current market price. The total rate of return is current income plus or minus capital appreciation or depreciation.

Real property ❚ Includes the land and all that is contained on it.

Realignment ❚ *See* Resource realignment.

Recession ❚ Contraction of economic activity occurring between the peak and trough (*see* separate citations) of a business cycle.

Regulated market ❚ A market in which the government controls the forces of supply and demand, such as who may enter and what price may be charged.

Regulation D ❚ A vehicle by which small businesses make small offerings and private placements of securities with limited disclosure requirements. It was designed to ease the burdens imposed on small businesses utilizing this method of capital formation.

Regulatory Flexibility Act ❚ An act requiring federal agencies to evaluate the impact of their regulations on small businesses before the regulations are issued and to consider less burdensome alternatives.

Research ❚ The initial stage of the innovation process, which includes idea generation and invention.

Research and development financing ❚ A tax-advantaged partnership set up to finance product development for start-ups as well as more mature companies.

Resource mobility ❚ The ease with which labor and capital move from firm to firm or from industry to industry.

Resource realignment ❚ The adjustment of productive resources to interindustry changes in demand.

Resources ❚ The sources of support or help in the innovation process, including sources of financing, technical evaluation, market evaluation, management and business assistance, etc.

Retained business earnings ❚ Business profits that are retained by the business rather than being distributed to the shareholders as dividends.

Revolving credit ❚ An agreement with a lending institution for an amount of money, which cannot exceed a set maximum, over a specified period of time. Each time the borrower repays a portion of the loan, the amount of the repayment may be borrowed yet again.

Risk capital ❚ *See* Venture capital.

Risk management ❚ The act of identifying potential sources of financial loss and taking action to minimize their negative impact.

Routing ❚ The sequence of steps necessary to complete a product during production.

S corporations ❚ *See* Sub chapter S corporations.

SBA ❚ *See* Small Business Administration.

SBA direct loans ❚ Loans made directly by the U.S. Small Business Administration (SBA); monies come from funds appropriated specifically for this purpose. In general, SBA direct loans carry interest rates slightly lower than those in the private financial markets and are available only to applicants unable to secure private financing or an SBA guaranteed loan.

SBA 504 Program ❚ *See* Certified development corporation.

SBA guaranteed loans ❚ Loans made by lending institutions in which the U.S. Small Business Administration (SBA) will pay a prior agreed-upon percentage of the outstanding principal in the event the borrower of the loan defaults. The terms of the loan and the interest rate are negotiated between the borrower and the lending institution, within set parameters.

SBA loans ❚ *See* Disaster loans; SBA direct loans; SBA guaranteed loans; SBA special lending institution categories.

SBA Management Assistance Programs ❚ (*See also* Active Corps of Executives; Service Corps of Retired Executives; Small business institutes program) Classes, workshops, counseling, and publications offered by the U.S. Small Business Administration.

SBA special lending institution categories ❚ U.S. Small Business Administration (SBA) loan program in which the SBA promises certified banks a 72-hour turnaround period in giving its approval for a loan, and in which preferred lenders in a pilot program are allowed to write SBA loans without seeking prior SBA approval.

SBDB ❚ *See* Small Business Data Base.

SBDC ❚ *See* Small business development centers.

SBI ❚ *See* Small business institutes program.

SBIC ❚ *See* Small business investment corporation.

SBIR Program ❚ *See* Small Business Innovation Development Act of 1982.

Scale economies ❚ The decline of the production cost per unit of output (average cost) as the volume of output increases.

Scale efficiency ❚ The reduction in unit cost available to a firm when producing at a higher output volume.

SCORE ❚ *See* Service Corps of Retired Executives.

SEC ❚ *See* Securities and Exchange Commission.

SECA ❚ *See* Self-Employment Contribu-tions Act.

Second-stage financing ❚ (*See also* First-stage financing; Third-stage financing) Working capital for the initial expansion of a com-pany that is producing, shipping, and has growing accounts receiv-able and inventories. Also known as Second- round financing.

Secondary market ❚ A market established for the purchase and sale of outstanding securities following their initial distribution.

Secondary worker ❚ Any worker in a family other than the person who is the primary source of income for the family.

Secondhand capital ❚ Previously used and subsequently resold capital equipment (e.g., buildings and machinery).

Securities and Exchange Commission (SEC) ❚ Federal agency charged with regulating the trade of securities to prevent unethical practices in the investor market.

Securitized debt ❚ A marketing technique that converts long-term loans to marketable securities.

Seed capital ❚ Venture financing provided in the early stages of the innovation process, usually during product development.

Self-employed person ❚ One who works for a profit or fees in his or her own business, profession, or trade, or who operates a farm.

Self-Employment Contributions Act (SECA) ❚ Federal law that governs the self-employment tax (*see* separate citation).

Self-employment income ❚ Income covered by Social Security if a business earns a net income of at least $400.00 during the year. Taxes are paid on earnings that exceed $400.00.

Self-employment retirement plan ❚ *See* Keogh plan.

Self-employment tax ❚ Required tax imposed on self-employed individuals for the provision of Social Security and Medicare. The tax must be paid quarterly with estimated income tax statements.

Self-funding ❚ A health benefit plan in which a firm uses its own funds to pay claims, rather than transferring the financial risks of paying claims to an outside insurer in exchange for premium payments.

Service Corps of Retired Executives (SCORE) ❚ (*See also* Active Corps of Executives) Volunteers for the SBA Management Assistance Program who provide one-on-one counseling and teach workshops and seminars for small firms.

Service firm ❚ *See* Business service firm.

Service sector ❚ Broadly defined, all U.S. industries that produce intangibles, including the five major industry divisions of transportation, communications, and utilities; wholesale trade; retail trade; finance, insurance, and real estate; and services.

Set asides ❚ *See* Small business set asides.

Short-haul service ❚ A type of transportation service in which the transporter supplies service between cities where the maximum distance is no more than 200 miles.

Short-term debt ❚ An obligation that matures in one year.

SIC codes ❚ *See* Standard Industrial Classification codes.

Single-establishment enterprise ❚ *See* Establishment.

Small business ❚ An enterprise that is independently owned and operated, is not dominant in its field, and employs fewer than 500 people. For SBA purposes, the U.S. Small Business Administration (SBA) considers various other factors (such as gross annual sales) in determining size of a business.

Small Business Administration (SBA) ❚ An independent federal agency that provides assistance with loans, management, and advocating interests before other federal agencies.

Small Business Data Base ❚ (*See also* U.S. Establishment and Enterprise Microdata File; U.S. Establishment Longitudinal Microdata File) A collection of microdata (*see* separate citation) files on individual firms developed and maintained by the U.S. Small Business Administration.

Small business development centers (SBDC) ❚ Centers that provide support services to small businesses, such as individual counseling, SBA advice, seminars and conferences, and other learning center activities. Most services are free of charge, or available at minimal cost.

Small business development corporation ❚ *See* Certified development corporation.

Small business-dominated industry ❚ Industry in which a minimum of 60 percent of employment or sales is in firms with fewer than 500 employees.

Small Business Innovation Development Act of 1982 ❚ Federal statute requiring federal agencies with large extramural research and development budgets to allocate a certain percentage of these funds to small research and development firms. The program, called the Small Business Innovation Research (SBIR) Program, is designed to stimulate technological innovation and make greater use of small businesses in meeting national innovation needs.

Small business institutes (SBI) program ❚ Cooperative arrangements made by U.S. Small Business Administration district offices and local colleges and universities to provide small business firms with graduate students to counsel them without charge.

Small business investment corporation (SBIC) ❚ A privately owned company licensed and funded through the U.S. Small Business Administration and private sector sources to provide equity or debt capital to small businesses.

Small business set asides ❚ Procurement (*see* separate citation) opportunities required by law to be on all contracts under $10,000 or a certain percentage of an agency's total procurement expenditure.

Smaller firms ❚ For U.S. Department of Commerce purposes, those firms not included in the Fortune 1000.

SMSA ❚ *See* Metropolitan statistical area.

Socially and economically disadvantaged ❚ Individuals who have been subjected to racial or ethnic prejudice or cultural bias without regard to their qualities as individuals, and whose abilities to compete are impaired because of diminished opportunities to obtain capital and credit.

Sole proprietorship ❚ An unincorporated, one-owner business, farm, or professional practice.

Special lending institution categories ❚ *See* SBA special lending institution categories.

Standard Industrial Classification (SIC) codes ❚ Four-digit codes established by the U.S. Federal Government to categorize businesses by type of economic activity; the first two digits correspond to major groups such as construction and manufacturing, while the last two digits correspond to subgroups such as home construction or highway construction.

Standard metropolitan statistical area (SMSA) ❚ *See* Metropolitan statistical area.

Start-up ❚ A new business, at the earliest stages of development and financing.

Start-up costs ❚ Costs incurred before a business can commence operations.

Start-up financing ❚ Financing provided to companies that have either completed product development and initial marketing or have been in business for less than one year but have not yet sold their product commercially.

Stock ❚ (*See also* Common stock; Convertible preferred stock) A certificate of equity ownership in a business.

Stop-loss coverage ‖ Insurance for a self-insured plan that reimburses the company for any losses it might incur in its health claims beyond a specified amount.

Strategic planning ‖ Projected growth and development of a business to establish a guiding direction for the future. Also used to determine which market segments to explore for optimal sales of products or services.

Structural unemployment ‖ *See* Un-employment.

Sub chapter S corporations ‖ Corpora-tions that are considered noncorporate for tax purposes but legally remain corporations.

Subcontract ‖ A contract between a prime contractor and a subcontractor, or between subcontractors, to furnish supplies or services for performance of a prime contract (*see* separate citation) or a subcontract.

Surety bonds ‖ Bonds providing reimbursement to an individual, company, or the government if a firm fails to complete a contract. The U.S. Small Business Administration guarantees surety bonds in a program much like the SBA guaranteed loan program (*see* separate citation).

Swing loan ‖ *See* Bridge financing.

Target market ‖ The clients or customers sought for a business' product or service.

Targeted Jobs Tax Credit ‖ Federal legislation enacted in 1978 that provides a tax credit to an employer who hires structurally unemployed individuals.

Tax number ‖ (*See also* Employer identification number) A number assigned to a business by a state revenue department that enables the business to buy goods without paying sales tax.

Taxable bonds ‖ An interest-bearing certificate of public or private indebtedness. Bonds are issued by public agencies to finance economic development.

Technical assistance ‖ *See* Management and technical assistance

Technical evaluation ‖ Assessment of technological feasibility.

Technology ‖ The method in which a firm combines and utilizes labor and capital resources to produce goods or services; the application of science for commercial or industrial purposes.

Technology transfer ‖ The movement of information about a tech-nology or intellectual property from one party to another for use.

Tenure ‖ *See* Employee tenure.

Term ‖ (*See also* Maturity) The length of time for which a loan is made.

Terms of a note ‖ The conditions or limits of a note; includes the interest rate per annum, the due date, and transferability and convertibility features, if any.

Third-party administrator ‖ An outside company responsible for handling claims and performing administrative tasks associated with health insurance plan maintenance.

Third-stage financing ‖ (*See also* First-stage financing; Second-stage financing) Financing provided for the major expansion of a company whose sales volume is increasing and that is break-ing even or profitable. These funds are used for further plant expansion, marketing, working capital, or development of an improved product. Also known as Third-round or Mezzanine financing.

Time deposit ‖ A bank deposit that cannot be withdrawn before a specified future time.

Time management ‖ Skills and scheduling techniques used to maximize productivity.

Trade credit ‖ Credit extended by suppliers of raw materials or finished products. In an accounting statement, trade credit is referred to as "accounts payable."

Trade name ‖ The name under which a company conducts business, or by which its business, goods, or services are identified. It may or may not be registered as a trademark.

Trade periodical ‖ A publication with a specific focus on one or more aspects of business and industry.

Trade secret ‖ Competitive advantage gained by a business through the use of a unique manufacturing process or formula.

Trade show ‖ An exhibition of goods or services used in a particular industry. Typically held in exhibition centers where exhibitors rent space to display their merchandise.

Trademark ‖ A graphic symbol, device, or slogan that identifies a business. A business has property rights to its trademark from the inception of its use, but it is still prudent to register all trade marks with the Trademark Office of the U.S. Department of Commerce.

Translation ‖ *See* Product development.

Treasury bills ‖ Investment tender issued by the Federal Reserve Bank in amounts of $10,000 that mature in 91 to 182 days.

Treasury bonds ‖ Long-term notes with maturity dates of not less than seven and not more than twenty-five years.

Treasury notes ‖ Short-term notes maturing in less than seven years.

Trend ‖ A statistical measurement used to track changes that oc-cur over time.

Trough ‖ *See* Cyclical trough.

UCC ‖ *See* Uniform Commercial Code. UL *See* Underwriters Laboratories.

Underwriters Laboratories (UL) ‖ One of several private firms that tests products and processes to determine their safety. Although various firms can provide this kind of testing service, many local and insurance codes specify UL certification.

Underwriting ‖ A process by which an insurer determines whether or not and on what basis it will accept an application for insur-ance. In an experience-rated plan, premiums are based on a firm's or group's past claims; factors other than prior claims are used for community-rated or manually rated plans.

Unfair competition ‖ Refers to business practices, usually unethi-cal, such as using unlicensed products, pirating merch-andise, or misleading the public through false advertising, which give the offending business an unequitable advantage over others.

Unfunded accrued liability ‖ The excess of total liabilities, both present and prospective, over present and prospective assets.

Unemployment ▮ The joblessness of individuals who are willing to work, who are legally and physically able to work, and who are seeking work. Unemploy-ment may represent the temporary joblessness of a worker between jobs (frictional unemployment) or the joblessness of a worker whose skills are not suitable for jobs available in the labor market (structural unemployment).

Uniform Commercial Code (UCC) ▮ A code of laws governing commercial transactions across the U.S., except Louisiana. Their purpose is to bring uniformity to financial transactions.

Uniform product code (UPC symbol) ▮ A computer-readable label comprised of ten digits and stripes that encodes what a product is and how much it costs. The first five digits are assigned by the Uniform Produce Code Council, and the last five digits by the individual manufacturer.

Unit cost ▮ *See* Average cost.

UPC symbol ▮ *See* Uniform product code.

US Establishment and Enterprise Microdata (USEEM) File ▮ A cross-sectional database containing information on employment, sales, and location for individual enterprises and establishments with employees that have a Dun & Bradstreet credit rating.

US Establishment Longitudinal Microdata (USELM) File ▮ A database containing longitudinally linked sample microdata on establishments drawn from the U.S. Establishment and Enterprise Microdata file (*see* separate citation).

US Small Business Administration 504 Program ▮ *See* Certified development corporation.

USEEM ▮ *See* U.S. Establishment and Enterprise Microdata File.

USELM ▮ *See* U.S. Establishment Longitudinal Microdata File.

VCN ▮ *See* Venture capital network.

Venture capital ▮ (*See also* Equity; Equity midrisk venture capital) Money used to support new or unusual business ventures that exhibit above-average growth rates, significant potential for market expansion, and are in need of additional financing to sustain growth or further research and development; equity or equity- type financing traditionally provided at the commercialization stage, increasingly available prior to commercialization.

Venture capital company ▮ A company organized to provide seed capital to a business in its formation stage, or in its first or second stage of expansion. Funding is obtained through public or private pension funds, commercial banks and bank holding companies, small business investment corporations licensed by the U.S. Small Business Administration, private venture capital firms, insurance companies, investment management companies, bank trust departments, industrial companies seeking to diversify their investment, and investment bankers acting as intermediaries for other investors or directly investing on their own behalf.

Venture capital limited partnerships ▮ Designed for business development, these partnerships are an institutional mechanism for providing capital for young, technology-oriented businesses. The investors' money is pooled and invested in money market assets until venture investments have been selected. The general partners are experienced investment managers who select and invest the equity and debt securities of firms with high growth potential and the ability to go public in the near future.

Venture capital network (VCN) ▮ A computer database that matches investors with entrepreneurs.

WAN ▮ *See* Wide Area Network.

Wide Area Network (WAN) ▮ Computer networks linking systems throughout a state or around the world in order to facilitate the sharing of information.

Withholding ▮ Federal, state, social security, and unemployment taxes withheld by the employer from employees' wages; employers are liable for these taxes and the corporate umbrella and bankruptcy will not exonerate an employer from paying back payroll withholding. Employers should escrow these funds in a separate account and disperse them quarterly to withholding authorities.

Workers' compensation ▮ A state-mandated form of insurance covering workers injured in job-related accidents. In some states, the state is the insurer; in other states, insurance must be acquired from commercial insurance firms. Insurance rates are based on a number of factors, including salaries, firm history, and risk of occupation.

Working capital ▮ Refers to a firm's short-term investment of current assets, including cash, short-term securities, accounts receivable, and inventories.

Yield ▮ (*See also* Rate of return) The rate of income returned on an investment, expressed as a percentage. Income yield is obtained by dividing the current dollar income by the current market price of the security. Net yield or yield to maturity is the current income yield minus any premium above par or plus any discount from par in purchase price, with the adjustment spread over the period from the date of purchase to the date of maturity.

ASSOCIATIONS AND OTHER ORGANIZATIONS

1 ■ American Society for Indexing (ASI)
10200 W 44th Ave., Ste. 304
Wheat Ridge, CO 80033
Ph: (303)463-2887
Fax: (303)422-8894
Co. E-mail: info@asindexing.org
URL: http://www.asindexing.org
Contact: Richard S. Shrout, President
E-mail: richard.shrout@potomacindexing.com
Description: Professional indexers, librarians, editors, publishers, and organizations employing indexers. Works to improve the quality of indexing and adherence to indexing standards; to encourage members to increase their professional indexing capabilities and performance; to advise authors, editors, and publishers on the qualifications and remuneration of indexers; to protect the professional interests of indexers; to facilitate communication among members concerning methods and developments in the field; to maintain liaison with related organizations. Members' activities include indexing books, databases, and periodicals, teaching indexing courses, and conducting research on indexing problems. **Publications:** *The Indexer: The International Journal of Indexing*; *A Guide to Indexing Software*; *Generic Markup of Electronic Index Manuscripts*; *The Indexer* (Semiannual); *Indexing from A to Z*; *Key Words: American Society of Indexers* (Bimonthly); *Indexer Locater*; *Education and Training in Indexing and Abstracting: A Directory*; *Directory of Indexing and Abstracting Courses and Seminars*. **Educational Activities:** American Society for Indexing Conference (Annual). **Awards:** H.W. Wilson Award (Annual); Hines Award (Annual).

2 ■ Indexing Society of Canada (ISC)—Societe Canadienne D'indexation
PO Box 664, Sta. P
Toronto, ON, Canada M5S 2Y4
Co. E-mail: mary.newberry@rogers.com
URL: http://indexers.ca
Contact: Mary Newberry, Co-President
Description: Indexing and abstracting services; corporations; institutions; interested individuals. Works to: promote production and use of indexes and abstracts; further the recognition of indexers and abstracters; develop improvements in indexing and abstracting techniques; facilitate communication among members. **Founded:** 1977. **Publications:** *ISC/SCI Bulletin* (3/year); *Register of Indexers* (Annual).

3 ■ *ISC/SCI Bulletin*
PO Box 664, Sta. P
Toronto, ON, Canada M5S 2Y4
Co. E-mail: mary.newberry@rogers.com
URL: http://indexers.ca
Contact: Mary Newberry, Co-President
Released: 3/year **Price:** free to members.

4 ■ *Register of Indexers*
PO Box 664, Sta. P
Toronto, ON, Canada M5S 2Y4
Co. E-mail: mary.newberry@rogers.com
URL: http://indexers.ca
Contact: Mary Newberry, Co-President
Released: Annual

REFERENCE WORKS

5 ■ *"IRS Announces New Standards for Tax Preparers"* in *Bellingham Business Journal* (Vol. February 2010, pp. 9)
Pub: Sound Publishing Inc.
Ed: Isaac Bonnell. **Description:** A new oversight plan was announced by the Internal Revenue Services (IRS) that will require tax professionals to pass a competency test and register with the government in order to ensure greater accountability in the industry.

START-UP INFORMATION

6 ■ *The 100 Best Businesses to Start When You Don't Want To Work Hard Anymore*
Pub: Career Press Inc.
Ed: Lisa Rogak. **Price:** $16.99. **Description:** Author helps burned-out workers envision a new future as a small business owner. Systems analysis, adventure travel outfitting, bookkeeping, food delivery, furniture making, and software development are among the industries examined.

7 ■ *Start and Run a Bookkeeping Business*
Pub: Self-Counsel, Incorporated
Ed: Angie Mohr. **Released:** October 2005. **Price:** $17.95 (US), $22.95 (Canadian). **Description:** Advice for starting and running a bookkeeping service business. Includes MS Word and PDF formats for use in Windows-based PC.

8 ■ *Working for Yourself: An Entrepreneur's Guide to the Basics*
Pub: Kogan Page, Limited
Contact: Ben Glover, Director of Marketing
Ed: Jonathan Reuvid. **Released:** September 2006. **Description:** Guide for starting a new business venture, focusing on raising financing, legal and tax issues, marketing, information technology, and site location.

ASSOCIATIONS AND OTHER ORGANIZATIONS

9 ■ Accountants Global Network (AGN)
2851 S Parker Rd., Ste. 850
Aurora, CO 80014
Ph: (303)743-7880
Free: 800-782-2272
Fax: (303)743-7660
Co. E-mail: rhood@agn.org
URL: http://www.agn.org
Contact: Rita J. Hood, Executive Director
Description: Represents and promotes the fields of separate and independent accounting and consulting firms serving business organizations. **Founded:** 1978.

10 ■ Accounting and Finance Benchmarking Consortium
4606 FM 1960 W, Ste. 250
Houston, TX 77069-9949
Ph: (281)440-5044
URL: http://www.afbc.org
Description: Accounting and finance managers of corporations with an interest in benchmarking. Promotes the use of benchmarking, wherein businesses compare their processes with those of their competitors, as a means of improving corporate efficiency and profitability. Facilitates exchange of information among members; conducts target operations, procurement, development, and maintenance studies; identifies model business practices. **Founded:** 1998.

11 ■ *Accounting Perspective*
3997 Chesswood Dr.
Toronto, ON, Canada M3J 2R8
Ph: (416)486-5361
Fax: (416)486-6158
Co. E-mail: admin@caaa.ca
URL: http://www.caaa.ca/
Contact: Vaughan S. Radcliffe, President
E-mail: vradcliffe@ivey.uwo.ca
Released: Quarterly **Price:** C$90, /year for individuals; C$185, /year for institutions.

12 ■ AGN International North America (AGN-NA)
2851 S Parker Rd., Ste. 850
Aurora, CO 80014
Ph: (303)743-7880
Fax: (303)743-7660
Co. E-mail: rhood@agn.org
URL: http://www.agn-na.org
Contact: Rita Hood, Executive Director
Description: Certified public accounting firms. Provides networking resources, technical and marketing assistance, and staff training programs to members. Compiles statistics. Maintains networking share groups. **Scope:** accounting, auditing, marketing, tax, management. **Founded:** 1978. **Subscriptions:** audiovisuals books. **Publications:** *Client Newsletter* (Quarterly); *Tax Brochures*. **Awards:** Chairman's Award (Annual).

13 ■ American Accounting Association (AAA)
5717 Bessie Dr.
Sarasota, FL 34233-2399
Ph: (941)921-7747
Fax: (941)923-4093
Co. E-mail: info@aaahq.org
URL: http://aaahq.org/index.cfm
Contact: Greg Waymire, President
URL(s): aaahq.org/ata/index.htm, aaahq.org, www.rutgers.edu/. **Description:** Represents professors, practitioners of accounting and other persons interested in accounting education and research. Promotes worldwide excellence in accounting education, research and practice. **Founded:** 1916. **Publications:** *The Accounting Review* (Quarterly); *Journal of Information Systems* (Semiannual); *Issues in Accounting Education* (Quarterly); *Behavioral Research in Accounting* (Semiannual); *Journal of the American Taxation Association* (Semiannual); *Auditing: A Journal of Practice & Theory* (Semiannual); *Journal of Management Accounting Research* (Annual); *Accounting Horizons* (Quarterly); *Accounting Horizons* (Quarterly); *Issues in Accounting Education* (Quarterly); *Journal of the American Taxation Association* (Semiannual); *Accounting Review*, *ATA Journal of Legal Tax Research* (Annual). **Educational Activities:** American Accounting Association Annual Meeting (Annual); ATA Midyear Meeting (Annual). **Telecommunication Services:** accounting-review@terry.uga.edu; fayres@ou.edu.

14 ■ American Association of Attorney-Certified Public Accountants (AAA-CPA)
8647 Richmond Hwy., Ste. 639
Alexandria, VA 22309
Ph: (703)352-8064
Free: 888-288-9272
Fax: (703)352-8073
Co. E-mail: info@attorney-cpa.com
URL: http://netforum.avectra.com/eWeb/StartPage.aspx?Site=AAA-CPA
Contact: John Akard, Jr., President
E-mail: johnakard@attorney-cpa.com
Description: Represents persons who are licensed both as attorneys and as certified public accountants (CPAs). Promotes high professional and ethical standards; seeks to safeguard and defend the professional and legal rights of attorney-CPAs. Conducts research on dual licensing and dual practice; maintains speakers' bureau, placement service. Has compiled a list of attorney-CPAs in the United States; conducts biennial economic and practice survey. Maintains liaison with bar associations and accounting groups and offers referral service of potential clients. State groups conduct extensive self-education programs. **Founded:** 1964. **Publications:** *Attorney-CPA Directory* (Annual); *The Attorney-CPA* (Quarterly); *Membership Directory--American Association of Attorney-Certified Public Accountants Inc.* (Annual); *American Association of Attorney-Certified Public Accountants--Membership List* (Periodic). **Educational Activities:** American Association of Attorney-Certified Public Accountants Annual Meeting and Educational Conference (Annual). **Awards:** Attorney-CPA Foundation Scholarships.

15 ■ American Institute of Certified Public Accountants (AICPA)—American Institute of CPAs
1211 Avenue of the Americas
New York, NY 10036-8775
Ph: (212)596-6200
Free: 888-777-7077
Fax: (212)596-6213
Co. E-mail: service@aicpa.org
URL: http://www.aicpa.org
Contact: Barry C. Melancon, President
E-mail: bmelancon@aicpa.org
Description: Professional society of accountants certified by the states and territories. Responsibilities include establishing auditing and reporting standards; influencing the development of financial accounting standards underlying the presentation of U.S. corporate financial statements; preparing and grading the national Uniform CPA Examination for the state licensing bodies. Conducts research and continuing education programs and oversight of practice. Maintains over 100 committees including Accounting Standards, Accounting and Review Services, AICPA Effective Legislation Political Action, Auditing Standards, Taxation, Consulting Services, Professional Ethics, Quality Review, Women and Family Issues, and Information Technology. **Founded:** 1887. **Publications:** *The Tax Adviser* (Monthly); *Journal of Accountancy*; *AICPA Online*; *Accounting Research Studies*; *Auditing Research Monographs*; *Journal of Accountancy* (Monthly); *Accountant's Business Manual*; *Accounting Trends and Techniques - Not-for-Profit Entities*; *The Practicing CPA*; *CPA Client Tax Letter*; *Macroeconomics and Company Planning*; *Manage-*

ment Advisory Services Guideline Series; CPA Client Bulletin; The Inside Track to Careers in Accounting. **Educational Activities:** AICPA Personal Financial Planning Technical Conference (Annual). **Awards:** Public Service Award; Special Recognition Award; AICPA/AAA Notable Contributions to Accounting Literature Award; Distinguished Achievement in Accounting Education Award; Business and Industry Hall of Fame; Outstanding CPA in Government Award; Business Valuation Hall of Fame Award.

16 ■ American Society of Women Accountants (ASWA)
1760 Old Meadow Rd., Ste. 500
McLean, VA 22102
Ph: (703)506-3265
Free: 800-326-2163
Fax: (703)506-3266
Co. E-mail: aswa@aswa.org
URL: http://www.aswa.org
Contact: Mrs. Monika P. Miles, President

Description: Professional society of women accountants, educators and others in the field of accounting dedicated to the achievement of personal, professional and economic potential. Assists women accountants in their careers and promotes development in the profession. Conducts educational and research programs. **Founded:** 1938. **Publications:** The Edge (Bimonthly); The Edge (Monthly); American Society of Women Accountants--Membership Directory (Annual). **Educational Activities:** American Society of Women Accountants Conference (ASWA) (Annual). **Awards:** ASWA Scholarship Award (Annual); Balance Award (Annual); ASWA 2-Year College Scholarships; ASWA Undergraduate Scholarships.

17 ■ American Taxation Association (ATA)
9201 University City Blvd.
Charlotte, NC 28223
Ph: (704)687-7696
Co. E-mail: americantaxationassociation@aaahq.org
URL: http://aaahq.org/ata/index.htm
Contact: Sandy Callaghan, President

Description: Membership comprises primarily university professors teaching federal income tax, federal estate, and/or gift tax courses; other members are practitioners, including certified public accountants. Seeks to further taxation education. Researches the impact of the tax process, particularly tax code sections, on the social and economic structure of the U.S. Maintains speakers' bureau. **Founded:** 1974. **Awards:** Dissertation Award; Outstanding Service Award (Annual); Ray M. Sommerfeld Outstanding Tax Educator Award (Annual); Tax Manuscript Award; Teaching Innovation Award (Annual).

18 ■ American Woman's Society of Certified Public Accountants (AWSCPA)
136 S Keowee St.
Dayton, OH 45402
Ph: (973)222-1872
Free: 800-297-2721
Fax: (937)222-5794
Co. E-mail: info@awscpa.org
URL: http://www.awscpa.org
Contact: Ivy L. Defino, President

Description: Citizens who hold Certified Public Accountant certificates as well as those who have passed the CPA examination but do not have certificates. Works to improve the status of professional women and to make the business community aware of the professional capabilities of the woman CPA. Conducts semiannual statistical survey of members; offers specialized education and research programs. **Founded:** 1933. **Publications:** Membership Roster; AWSCPA Newsletter; American Woman's Society of Certified Public Accountants--Roster (Annual). **Awards:** National Scholarships (Annual); Public Service Award (Annual); AWSCPA National Scholarships; Educator of the Year (Annual); Woman CPA of the Year (Annual); Woman of Courage Award (Annual); Educator of the Year Award; National Scholarships; Public Service Award; Woman CPA of the Year Award.

19 ■ Association for Accounting Administration (AAA)
136 S Keowee St.
Dayton, OH 45402
Ph: (937)222-0030
Co. E-mail: aaainfo@cpaadmin.org
URL: http://www.cpaadmin.org
Contact: Nigel Jacobs, President

Description: Promotes the profession of accounting administration and office management in accounting firms and corporate accounting departments. Sponsors activities, including consulting and placement services, seminars, salary and trends surveys, and speakers' bureau. Provides a forum for representation and exchange. Offers group purchasing opportunities. **Scope:** personnel, firm administration, management. **Founded:** 1984. **Subscriptions:** 250. **Publications:** AAA Report (Bimonthly). **Awards:** Achievement, Commitment and Excellence Award (Annual); Distinguished Service Award (Annual).

20 ■ Association of Chartered Accountants in the United States (ACAUS)
3887 Punahele Rd.
Princeville, HI 96722
Ph: (508)395-0224
Co. E-mail: admin@acaus.org
URL: http://www.acaus.org
Contact: Mark Coles, President

Description: Chartered accountants from England, Wales, Scotland, Ireland, Canada, Australia, New Zealand and South Africa in commerce and public practice. Represents the interests of chartered accountants; promotes career development and international mobility of professionals. Offers educational and research programs. Maintains speakers' bureau and placement service. **Scope:** international mobility and licensing of professionals. **Founded:** 1980. **Subscriptions:** clippings. **Publications:** Member's Directory and Handbook (Annual). **Awards:** Chartered Accountants/Beta Alpha Psi Scholarship (Annual); Chartered Accountants International Education Award (Annual).

21 ■ BKR International (BKR)
19 Fulton St., Ste. 306
New York, NY 10038
Ph: (212)964-2115
Free: 800-BKR-INTL
Fax: (212)964-2133
Co. E-mail: bkr@bkr.com
URL: http://www.bkr.com
Contact: Don Timmins, Chairman

Description: Accounting firms in the U.S. and abroad. Seeks to create an international group of competent professional firms, which will provide full services in major markets of the world and enable member firms to send and receive referrals. Helps reduce operating costs of member firms by: developing consolidated purchasing arrangements for services and supplies at the lowest possible cost; developing recruiting programs, marketing materials, and advertising to reduce the collective recruiting effort of group members; expanding the group to reduce the burden on individual member firms and increase their potential scope of services. Compiles statistics to provide member firms with data helpful to sound management decisions. Organizes clinical and administrative peer reviews to insure quality and provide management with professional counsel. Develops forms, procedures, and manuals to provide guidance and accommodate the needs of partners. Conducts 12 continuing education programs per year in all areas of expertise. **Founded:** 1989. **Publications:** Worldwide Bulletin (Bimonthly).

22 ■ Canadian Academic Accounting Association (CAAA)—Association Canadienne des Professeurs de Comptabilite
3997 Chesswood Dr.
Toronto, ON, Canada M3J 2R8
Ph: (416)486-5361
Fax: (416)486-6158
Co. E-mail: admin@caaa.ca
URL: http://www.caaa.ca/
Contact: Vaughan S. Radcliffe, President
E-mail: vradcliffe@ivey.uwo.ca

Description: Post-secondary school accounting professors and students, accounting organizations, accountants, and accounting firms. Seeks to advance the study, teaching, and practice of accounting, broadly defined to include many related areas and disciplines of study. **Founded:** 1976. **Publications:** Accounting Perspective (Quarterly); Canadian Accounting Education and Research News (Quarterly); Contemporary Accounting Research (Quarterly); Accounting Perspectives (Quarterly); Contemporary Accounting Research: Recherche Comptable Contemporaine (Quarterly).

23 ■ Canadian Accounting Education and Research News
3997 Chesswood Dr.
Toronto, ON, Canada M3J 2R8
Ph: (416)486-5361
Fax: (416)486-6158
Co. E-mail: admin@caaa.ca
URL: http://www.caaa.ca/
Contact: Vaughan S. Radcliffe, President
E-mail: vradcliffe@ivey.uwo.ca
Released: Quarterly

24 ■ Canadian Institute of Chartered Accountants (CICA)—L'Institut Canadien des comptables agrees - Institut Canadien des Comptables Agrees
277 Wellington St. W
Toronto, ON, Canada M5V 3H2
Ph: (416)977-3222
Free: 800-268-3793
Fax: (416)977-8585
Co. E-mail: member.services@cica.ca
URL: http://www.cica.ca
Contact: Kevin J. Dancey, President
E-mail: kevin.dancey@cica.ca

Description: Sets national accounting, auditing, and financial reporting standards. Maintains an active professional development program for its members. Represents the profession's viewpoint on federal legislation issues and matters of national concern. Confers with other national organizations to achieve worldwide harmonization of accounting and auditing standards. **Founded:** 1902. **Publications:** Directory of Canadian Chartered Accountants (Periodic); Directory of Canadian Chartered Accountants (Periodic); Directory of Canadian Chartered Accountants (Biennial); CA Magazine: For Canada's Chartered Accountants. **Telecommunication Services:** jan.burns@cica.ca.

25 ■ Canadian Institute of Quantity Surveyors (CIQS)—Institut Canadien des Economistes en Construction
90 Nolan Ct., Unit 19
Markham, ON, Canada L3R 4L9
Ph: (905)477-0008
Free: 866-345-1168
Fax: (905)477-6774
Co. E-mail: info@ciqs.org
URL: http://www.ciqs.org
Contact: Roy Lewis, President

Description: Quantity surveyors and construction estimators. Establishes and maintains standards for certification and provides through advice to members relating to construction costs, management and administration of construction projects. Conducts continuing professional development programs for members. **Founded:** 1959. **Publications:** The Construction Economist (Quarterly). **Awards:** Buster Vermeulen Memorial Award (Annual); Frank Helyar Memorial Award (Annual); Buster Vermeulen Memorial Award; Frank Helyar Memorial Award. **Telecommunication Services:** president@ciqs.org.

26 ■ Canadian Insurance Accountants Association (CIAA)—Association Canadienne du Comptables d'Assurance
2175 Sheppard Ave. E, Ste. 310
Toronto, ON, Canada M2J 1W8
Ph: (416)971-7800
Fax: (416)491-1670
Co. E-mail: ciaa@ciaa.org
URL: http://www.ciaa.org
Contact: Annette Pohle, President

Description: Accountants employed in the insurance industry. Promotes excellence in the practice of insurance accounting; seeks to insure continuing professional development among members. Serves as a forum for the exchange of information among members; sponsors educational programs. **Founded:** 1934. **Telecommunication Services:** sandrat@os-bie.on.ca.

27 ■ Canadian Tax Foundation (CTF)—L'Association Canadienne d'Études Fiscales (ACEF)
595 Bay St., Ste. 1200
Toronto, ON, Canada M5G 2N5
Ph: (416)599-0283
Free: 877-733-0283
Fax: (416)599-9283
Co. E-mail: admin@ctf.ca
URL: http://www.ctf.ca
Contact: Larry Chapman, Chief Executive Officer
E-mail: lchapman@ctf.ca
Description: Individuals and organizations with an interest in taxation. Promotes increased awareness of the Canadian Tax Code and the social ramifications of taxation. Serves as a clearinghouse on taxation; sponsors research and educational programs. **Services:** Information service: for members. **Founded:** 1945. **Publications:** *Annual Conference Report*; *CTF Annual Report* (Monthly); *Canadian Tax Highlights* (Monthly); *Canadian Tax Journal* (Bimonthly; Quarterly); *Canadian Tax Papers Series* (Occasionally); *Finances of the Nation* (Annual); *Tax Memos*; *Tax for the Owner Manager* (Quarterly); *Taxation of Private Corporations and Their Shareholders* (Occasionally). **Educational Activities:** National tax and corporate management tax conferences (Annual); Regional conferences (Annual). **Telecommunication Services:** srichardson@ctf.ca.

28 ■ Canadian Tax Journal
595 Bay St., Ste. 1200
Toronto, ON, Canada M5G 2N5
Ph: (416)599-0283
Free: 877-733-0283
Fax: (416)599-9283
Co. E-mail: admin@ctf.ca
URL: http://www.ctf.ca
Contact: Larry Chapman, Chief Executive Officer
E-mail: lchapman@ctf.ca
URL(s): www.ctf.ca/ctfweb/en/. **Ed:** Brian R. Carr. **Released:** Bimonthly; Quarterly **Price:** C$55, Single issue mailing cost, outside Canada; $295, Individuals.

29 ■ CMA Management Magazine
1 Robert Speck Pkwy., Ste. 1400
Mississauga, ON, Canada L4Z 3M3
Ph: (905)949-4200
Free: 800-263-7622
Fax: (905)949-0888
Co. E-mail: info@cma-canada.org
URL: http://www.cma-canada.org
Contact: Susan David, Manager
E-mail: sdavid@cma-canada.org
Released: 9/year **Price:** C$15, /year.

30 ■ Community Banking Advisory Network (CBAN)
624 Grassmere Park Dr., Ste. 15
Nashville, TN 37211
Ph: (615)377-3392
Free: 800-231-2524
Fax: (615)377-7092
Co. E-mail: info@bankingcpas.com
URL: http://www.bankingcpas.com
Contact: Patrick Pruett, Executive Director
Description: Certified Public Accounting (CPA) firms providing financial and consulting services to community banks. Seeks to advance CPA services to the community banking industry. Sponsors continuing education and training courses; conducts industry and member surveys; facilitates formation of joint ventures; makes available marketing assistance; facilitates resource sharing among members. **Founded:** 1995. **Publications:** *Community Banking Advisor* (Quarterly). **Educational Activities:** Community Banking Track at Super Conference (Annual); Community Banking Advisory Network Conference (Annual).

31 ■ The Construction Economist
90 Nolan Ct., Unit 19
Markham, ON, Canada L3R 4L9
Ph: (905)477-0008
Free: 866-345-1168
Fax: (905)477-6774
Co. E-mail: info@ciqs.org
URL: http://www.ciqs.org
Contact: Roy Lewis, President
Released: Quarterly

32 ■ Construction Industry CPAs/Consultants Association (CICPAC)
15011 E Twilight View Dr.
Fountain Hills, AZ 85268
Ph: (480)836-0300
Free: 800-864-0491
Fax: (480)836-0400
Co. E-mail: jcorcoran@cicpac.com
URL: http://www.cicpac.com
Contact: John J. Corcoran, Executive Director
Description: Certified Public Accounting (CPA) firms providing financial and consulting services to construction companies. Seeks to advance CPA services to the construction industries. Sponsors continuing education and training courses; conducts industry and member surveys; facilitates formation of joint ventures; makes available marketing assistance; facilitates resource sharing among members. **Educational Activities:** Construction Industry CPAs/Consultants Association Conference (Annual); CICPAC Education Conference and Annual Meeting (Annual).

33 ■ Contemporary Accounting Research
3997 Chesswood Dr.
Toronto, ON, Canada M3J 2R8
Ph: (416)486-5361
Fax: (416)486-6158
Co. E-mail: admin@caaa.ca
URL: http://www.caaa.ca/
Contact: Vaughan S. Radcliffe, President
E-mail: vradcliffe@ivey.uwo.ca
Released: Quarterly **Price:** C$155, /year for individuals; C$315, /year for institutions.

34 ■ CPA Associates International Inc.
Meadows Office Complex
Rutherford, NJ 07070
Ph: (201)804-8686
Fax: (201)804-9222
Co. E-mail: homeoffice@cpaai.com
URL: http://www.cpaai.com
Contact: James Flynn, President
Description: Independent firms of Certified Public Accountants (CPAs) offering professional accounting, auditing, tax, and management advisory services. Fosters exchange of ideas and information among members; works to improve the profitability and practice of the accounting profession. **Scope:** An association of independent CPA and chartered accounting firms that provide clients with professional accounting, auditing, tax and a variety of consulting services. Key objectives to assist members in expanding professional expertise, enhance members' ability to manage in a changing environment, help members boost profitability, enhance members' ability to market services, assist members in meeting regulatory and legal requirements, facilitate communication and exchange of resources among member and provide referral opportunities for members. **Publications:** *Client Newsletter Tax Outlook* (Quarterly); *CPA Associates Directory* (Annual); *Financial Executives International Directory*. **Educational Activities:** CPA Associates International Meeting (Annual); CPA Associates International Annual Meeting (Annual). **Seminars:** Fall Practice Management Seminar; Spring Managing Partners Seminar; Accounting & Assurance Seminar; Tax Seminar; Marketing Workshop; Information Technology Seminar; Business Valuations Seminar; Leadership Development Program; Accounting & Auditing and Tax Staff Training; Regional Training; Telephone Round tables.

35 ■ CPA Auto Dealer Consultants Association (CADCA)
624 Grassmere Park Dr., Ste. 15
Nashville, TN 37211

Ph: (615)377-3392
Free: 800-231-2524
Fax: (615)377-7092
Co. E-mail: info@autodealercpas.net
URL: http://www.autodealercpas.net
Contact: Patrick Pruett, Executive Director
Description: Certified Public Accounting (CPA) firms providing financial and consulting services to automobile dealers. Seeks to advance CPA services to automobile dealers. Sponsors continuing education and training courses; conducts industry and member surveys; facilitates formation of joint ventures; makes available marketing assistance; facilitates resource sharing among members. **Founded:** 1996. **Publications:** *Auto Focus* (Quarterly). **Educational Activities:** Education and Networking Conference (Semiannual).

36 ■ CPA Manufacturing Services Association (MSA)
624 Grassmere Park Dr., Ste. 15
Nashville, TN 37211
Ph: (615)373-9880
Free: 800-231-2524
Fax: (615)377-7092
Co. E-mail: info@manufacturingcpas.com
URL: http://www.manufacturingcpas.com
Contact: Erik Horstmann, President
Description: Certified Public Accounting (CPA) firms providing financial and consulting services to the manufacturing industries. Seeks to advance CPA services to manufacturers. Sponsors continuing education and training courses; conducts industry and member surveys; facilitates formation of joint ventures; makes available marketing assistance; facilitates resource sharing among members. **Publications:** *Client* (Periodic).

37 ■ Directory of Canadian Chartered Accountants
277 Wellington St. W
Toronto, ON, Canada M5V 3H2
Ph: (416)977-3222
Free: 800-268-3793
Fax: (416)977-8585
Co. E-mail: member.services@cica.ca
URL: http://www.cica.ca
Contact: Kevin J. Dancey, President
E-mail: kevin.dancey@cica.ca
Released: Periodic

38 ■ Educational Foundation for Women in Accounting (EFWA)
136 S Keowee St.
Dayton, OH 45402
Ph: (937)424-3391
Fax: (937)222-5794
Co. E-mail: info@efwa.org
URL: http://www.efwa.org
Contact: Laurie Burney, President
Description: Women in the accounting field. Supports the advancement of women in the accounting profession through funding of education, research, career literature, publications, and other projects. **Founded:** 1966. **Publications:** *The Educator* (Semiannual). **Awards:** Laurels (Periodic); Women in Need (Periodic); Women in Transition (Periodic); Michele L. McDonald Scholarships; Seattle Chapter ASWA Scholarships; Women In Need Scholarships; Women In Transition Scholarships; EFWA Moss Adams Foundation Scholarships.

39 ■ Institute of Management Accountants (IMA)
10 Paragon Dr., Ste. 1
Montvale, NJ 07645-1774
Ph: (201)573-9000
Free: 800-638-4427
Fax: (201)474-1600
Co. E-mail: ima@imanet.org
URL: http://www.imanet.org
Contact: Jeffrey C. Thomson, President
E-mail: jthomson@imanet.org
URL(s): www.strategicfinancemag.com. **Description:** Management accountants in industry, public accounting, government, and academia; other persons interested in internal and management uses of accounting. Conducts research on accounting methods

and procedures and the management purposes served. Established Institute of Certified Management Accountants to implement and administer examinations for the Certified Management Accountant (CMA) program and the Certified in Financial Management (CFM) program. Annually presents chapter medals for competition, manuscripts and for the highest scores on the CMA Examination. Offers continuing education programs comprising courses, conferences, and a self-study program in management accounting areas. Offers ethics counseling services for members by telephone. Sponsors the Foundation for Applied Research. **Scope:** accounting, financial management. **Founded:** 1919. **Subscriptions:** 20000 archival material books periodicals. **Publications:** *Management Accounting Quarterly* (Quarterly); *Strategic Finance*; *Management Accounting Quarterly* (Quarterly); *Strategic TechNotes* (Semimonthly); *Strategic Finance: Leadership Strategies in Accounting, Finance, and Information Management* (Monthly). **Educational Activities:** Institute of Management Accountants Conference (Annual). **Awards:** IMA Memorial Education Fund Scholarships (MEF); Chapter Competition; Stevenson Trophy; Clark Johnson Achievement Award (Annual); Stuart Cameron and Margaret McLeod Memorial Scholarships (SCMS); Institute of Management Accountants FAR Doctoral Student Grants Program. **Telecommunication Services:** info@strategicfinancemag.com.

40 ■ Interamerican Accounting Association (IAA)
275 Fountainebleau Blvd., Ste. 245
Miami, FL 33172
Ph: (305)225-1991
Fax: (305)225-2011
Co. E-mail: oficina@contadoresaic.org
URL: http://www.contadores-aic.org
Contact: Victor Manuel Abreu Paez, Executive Director

URL(s): www.contadoresaic.org. **Description:** National associations representing 1,100,000 accountants in the Americas. Objectives are to maintain high technical and ethical standards for the accounting profession; further accounting as a scientific discipline by fostering contacts between members and institutions of higher learning; provide members with information on current accounting practices and concepts; encourage members to establish ties with accounting groups worldwide; assure that professional services rendered by members contribute to the social and economic development of their community. Operates speakers' bureau. **Scope:** Interamerican accounting. **Founded:** 1949. **Subscriptions:** archival material. **Publications:** *IAA Directory* (Biennial); *Interamerican Accounting Magazine* (Quarterly); *Interamerican Accounting Association--Directory* (Irregular); *Interamerican Bulletin* (Monthly). **Educational Activities:** Conferencia Interamericana de Contabilidad (Biennial); Interamerican Accounting Association Biennial Conference (Biennial). **Awards:** Meritorious Accountant of the Americas; Meritorious Accountant of the Americas (Biennial). **Telecommunication Services:** vvargas@terra.com.pe.

41 ■ International Budget Partnership (IBP)
820 1st St. NE, Ste. 510
Washington, DC 20002
Ph: (202)408-1080
Fax: (202)408-8173
Co. E-mail: info@internationalbudget.org
URL: http://internationalbudget.org
Contact: Warren Krafchik, Director

Description: Works to assist civil society organizations globally to improve budget policies and decision-making processes. **Founded:** 1997. **Publications:** *IBP Newsletter* (Bimonthly); *A Guide to Budget Work for NGOs*; *Budgeting for the Future, Building another Europe*. **Educational Activities:** International Budget Conference (Biennial).

42 ■ Moore Stephens North America (MSNA)
250 Pehle Ave.
Park 80 West
Plaza II, Ste. 200
Saddle Brook, NJ 07663
Ph: (201)291-2660
Fax: (201)368-1944
Co. E-mail: theteam@msnainc.org
URL: http://www.msnainc.com
Contact: Steven E. Sacks, Executive Director
Description: North American public accounting and consulting firms. Aids certified public accounting firms in increasing, expanding, and diversifying their practices. Capitalizes on diversity of resources resident throughout the network to build a stronger revenue base for all members. Sponsors training programs in areas such as industry niche development, service niche development tax, staff, and computer auditing; conducts tax and management seminars. Compiles statistics. Offers networking forums, marketing assistance, and technology consulting to member firms. **Scope:** accounting, consulting. **Founded:** 1966. **Subscriptions:** 750 periodicals. **Publications:** *MSNA Membership Directory* (Annual); *MSNA Networker* (Monthly).

43 ■ National Association of Black Accountants (NABA)
7474 Greenway Center Dr., Ste. 1120
Greenbelt, MD 20770
Ph: (301)474-6222
Free: 888-571-2939
Fax: (301)474-3114
Co. E-mail: customerservice@nabainc.org
URL: http://www.nabainc.org
Contact: Calvin Harris, Jr., President
Description: Represents minority students and professionals currently working, or interested in the fields of accounting, finance, technology, consulting or general business. Seeks, promotes, develops, and represents the interests of current and future minority business professionals. **Founded:** 1969. **Publications:** *Spectrum* (Annual); *Achieve* (3/year); *Spectrum* (Annual); *National Association of Black Accountants-News Plus*; *National Association of Black Accountants--News Plus*. **Educational Activities:** National Association of Black Accountants Annual Convention (Annual). **Awards:** NABA National Scholarship Program; Corporate Diversity Award; Microsoft Innovation Award (Annual).

44 ■ National Association of State Boards of Accountancy (NASBA)
150 4th Ave. N, Ste. 700
Nashville, TN 37219-2417
Ph: (615)880-4200
Free: 866-MY-NASBA
Fax: (615)880-4290
Co. E-mail: cpaexam@nasba.org
URL: http://www.nasba.org
Contact: Ken L. Bishop, President
Description: Comprises 54 state boards of accountancy. Serves as a forum for the boards, which administer the Uniform CPA Examination, license certified public accountants, and regulate the practice of public accountancy in the United States. Sponsors committee meetings, conferences, programs and services designed to enhance the effectiveness of its member boards. **Founded:** 1908. **Publications:** *State Board Report* (Monthly); *State Boards of Accountancy of the United States* (Periodic). **Awards:** Distinguished Service Award (Annual); William H. Van Rensselaer Public Service Award (Annual).

45 ■ National Association of Tax Professionals (NATP)
PO Box 8002
Appleton, WI 54914-8002
Free: 800-558-3402
Co. E-mail: natp@natptax.com
URL: http://www.natptax.com
Contact: Jo Ann Schoen, President
Description: Serves professionals who work in all areas of tax practice, including individual practitioners, enrolled agents, certified public accountants, accountants, attorneys and certified financial planners. **Founded:** 1979. **Publications:** *TAXPRO Journal* (Quarterly); *TAXPRO Weekly E-Mail* (Weekly). **Awards:** Tax Professional of the Year (Annual).

46 ■ National Conference of CPA Practitioners (NCCPAP)
22 Jericho Tpke., Ste. 110
Mineola, NY 11501
Ph: (516)333-8282
Free: 888-488-5400
Fax: (516)333-4099
Co. E-mail: execdir@nccpap.org
URL: http://www.nccpap.org
Contact: Lana Kupferschmid
Description: Represents the interests of CPA regional and local accounting firms. Works to enhance the professionalism of local firms. Works with the IRS and local and national government. **Scope:** accounting. **Founded:** 1979. **Subscriptions:** books periodicals photographs. **Awards:** Gold Award (Annual); NCCPAP and AICPA Scholarships for Graduating High School Seniors.

47 ■ National Society of Accountants (NSA)
1010 N Fairfax St.
Alexandria, VA 22314
Ph: (703)549-6400
Free: 800-966-6679
Fax: (703)549-2984
Co. E-mail: members@nsacct.org
URL: http://www.nsacct.org
Contact: Sharon E. Cook, President
Description: Professional organization and its affiliates represent 30,000 members who provide auditing, accounting, tax preparation, financial and estate planning, and management services to approximately 19 million individuals and business clients. Most members are sole practitioners or partners in small to mid-size accounting firms. **Founded:** 1945. **Publications:** *Income and Fees of Accountants in Public Practice*; *NSA Practice Advisor* (8/year); *NSAlert* (Biweekly); *National Public Accountant*; *NSPA Washington Reporter*; *National Society of Public Accountants - Yearbook*. **Awards:** National Society of Accountants Scholarship Program; The Stanley H. Stearman Awards; Accountant of the Year (Annual); ASO of the Year (Annual). **Telecommunication Services:** arichman@nsacct.org; arichman@nsacct.orgg.

48 ■ National Society of Accountants for Cooperatives (NSAC)
136 S Keowee St.
Dayton, OH 45402
Ph: (937)222-6707
Fax: (937)222-5794
Co. E-mail: info@nsacoop.org
URL: http://www.nsacoop.org
Contact: Lawrence D. Romuald, President
Description: Employees of cooperatives, certified public accountants, auditors, chief financial officers, attorneys and bankers. Unites persons performing accounting, auditing, financial and legal services for cooperative and non-profit associations. Holds technical sessions annually. Compiles statistics. **Scope:** cooperative accounting, financial reporting by cooperatives. **Founded:** 1936. **Subscriptions:** 55. **Publications:** *The Cooperative Accountant* (Quarterly). **Awards:** Silver Bowl Award.

49 ■ National Tax Association (NTA)
725 15th St. NW, No. 600
Washington, DC 20005-2109
Ph: (202)737-3325
Fax: (202)737-7308
Co. E-mail: natltax@aol.com
URL: http://www.ntanet.org
Contact: Matthew N. Murray, President
Description: Government and corporate tax officials, accountants, consultants, economists, attorneys, and others interested in the field of taxation. Promotes nonpartisan academics, study of taxation; encourages better understanding of the common interests of national, state, and local governments in matters of taxation and public finance; and disseminates higher quality research through publications and conferences. **Founded:** 1907. **Publications:** *National Tax Journal* (Quarterly). **Educational Activities:** Conference on Taxation; Spring Symposium (Annual). **Awards:** Daniel M. Holland Medal (Annual); Outstanding Doctoral Dissertation Award (Annual); Daniel M. Holland Medal; Jeanne S. Mattersdorf Memorial Fund Award; Outstanding Doctoral Dissertation Award; NTA-TIA Outstanding Doctoral Dissertation Honorable Mention Award (Annual).

50 ■ PrimeGlobal
3235 Satellite Blvd., Bldg. 400, Ste. 300
Duluth, GA 30096
Ph: (678)417-7730
Fax: (678)999-3959
Co. E-mail: kmead@primeglobal.net
URL: http://www.primeglobal.net
Contact: Kevin Mead, President
Description: Works to ensure that the standard for accounting, auditing, and management services are maintained. **Founded:** 1977.

51 ■ *Professional Accountant*
250 Consumers Rd., Ste. 1007
Toronto, ON, Canada M2J 4V6
Ph: (416)350-8145
Free: 877-515-4447
Fax: (416)350-8146
Co. E-mail: president@professionalaccountant.org
URL: http://www.professionalaccountant.org
Contact: Mr. John Singer, Vice President
Released: Quarterly

52 ■ Society of Depreciation Professionals (SDP)
555 8th Ave., Ste. 1902
New York, NY 10018
Ph: (212)804-7178
Fax: (646)417-6378
Co. E-mail: admin@depr.org
URL: http://www.depr.org
Contact: John Spanos, President
Description: Accountants and other individuals with an interest in the depreciation of assets. Promotes "professionalism and ethics within the art of depreciation." Serves as a forum for the discussion of issues affecting depreciation; sponsors continuing professional development courses for members. **Founded:** 1987.

53 ■ Society of Management Accountants of Canada (CMA)—Certified Management Accountants of Canada
1 Robert Speck Pkwy., Ste. 1400
Mississauga, ON, Canada L4Z 3M3
Ph: (905)949-4200
Free: 800-263-7622
Fax: (905)949-0888
Co. E-mail: info@cma-canada.org
URL: http://www.cma-canada.org
Contact: Susan David, Manager
E-mail: sdavid@cma-canada.org
Description: Certified Management Accountants (CMAs). Provides business advice and direction to improve organizational decisions. Offers educational and research programs. **Founded:** 1920. **Subscriptions:** monographs. **Publications:** *CMA Management Magazine* (9/year). **Awards:** FCMA (Annual).

54 ■ Society of Professional Accountants of Canada (SPAC)—La societe des comptables professionnels du Canada
250 Consumers Rd., Ste. 1007
Toronto, ON, Canada M2J 4V6
Ph: (416)350-8145
Free: 877-515-4447
Fax: (416)350-8146
Co. E-mail: president@professionalaccountant.org
URL: http://www.professionalaccountant.org
Contact: Mr. John Singer, Vice President
Description: Professional accountants and individuals working to pass qualifying accountancy examinations. Promotes ongoing professional education among accountants; encourages students to enter the accounting field; works to advance the profession of accounting. Gathers and disseminates information on accounting; sponsors educational programs; conducts professional accountancy qualifying examinations. **Founded:** 1978. **Publications:** *Professional Accountant* (Quarterly).

DIRECTORIES OF EDUCATIONAL PROGRAMS

55 ■ *Directory of Private Accredited Career Schools and Colleges of Technology*
Pub: Accrediting Commission of Career Schools and Colleges of Technology
Contact: Michale S. McComis, Executive Director
Released: On web page. **Price:** Free. **Description:** Covers 3900 accredited post-secondary programs

that provide training programs in business, trade, and technical fields, including various small business endeavors. Entries offer school name, address, phone, description of courses, job placement assistance, and requirements for admission. Arrangement is alphabetical.

REFERENCE WORKS

56 ■ *"2011 Tax Information of Interest" in Business Owner (Vol. 35, November-December 2011, No. 6, pp. 10)*
Pub: DL Perkins Company
Description: Compilation of 2011 tax information to help small business take advantage of all tax incentives.

57 ■ *"Accountants Get the Hook" in Canadian Business (Vol. 80, October 22, 2007, No. 21, pp. 19)*
Pub: Rogers Media
Ed: John Gray. **Description:** Chartered Accountants of Ontario handed down the decision on Douglas Barrington, Anthony Power and Claudio Russo's professional misconduct case. The three accountants of Deloitte & Touche LLP must pay C$100,000 in fines and C$417,000 in costs. Details of the disciplinary case are presented.

58 ■ *Accounting and Finance for Your Small Business*
Pub: John Wiley & Sons, Incorporated
Ed: Steven M. Bragg; E. James Burton. **Released:** April 2006. **Price:** $49.00. **Description:** Financial procedures and techniques for establishing and maintaining a profitable small company are outlined.

59 ■ *"Accrual vs. Cash Accounting, Explained" in Business Owner (Vol. 35, July-August 2011, No. 4, pp. 13)*
Pub: DL Perkins Company
Description: Cash method versus accrual accounting methods are examined, using hypothetical situations.

60 ■ *"Adler Blanchard & Freeman Reports New SmartKeeper Bookkeeping Service" in Professional Services Close-Up (March 24, 2011)*
Pub: Close-Up Media
Description: Profile of Adler Blanchard & Freeman (AB&F) accountants and business advisors. The firm has expanded its client offerings to include their new SmartKeeper Business and Personal Bookkeeping Service for small to mid-sized companies and individuals.

61 ■ *American Society of Women Accountants--Membership Directory*
Pub: American Society of Women Accountants
Contact: Mrs. Monika P. Miles, President
URL(s): www.aswa.org. **Released:** Annual **Covers:** Approximately 5,000 members in accounting and accounting-related fields. **Entries include:** Name, address, phone, fax, e-mail. **Arrangement:** Classified by chapter, then alphabetical.

62 ■ *"Bar Hopping: Your Numbers At a Glance" in Inc. (January 2008, pp. 44-45)*
Pub: Gruner & Jahr USA Publishing
Ed: Michael Fitzgerald. **Description:** Software that helps any company analyze data include Crystal Xcelsius, a program that takes data from Excel documents and turns them into animated gauges, charts and graphs; CashView, a Web-based application that tracks receivables and payables; iDashboards, a Web-based programs that produces animated gauges, maps, pie charts and graphs; Corda Human Capital Management, that transforms stats like head count, productivity, and attrition into graphs and dials; NetSuite, a Web-based application that tracks key indicators; and Cognos Now, that gauges, dials, and graphs data.

63 ■ *"Battling Back from Betrayal" in Harvard Business Review (Vol. 88, December 2010, No. 12, pp. 130)*
Pub: Harvard Business School Publishing
Ed: Daniel McGinn. **Description:** Stephen Greer's scrap metal firm, Hartwell Pacific, lost several million dollars due to a lack of efficient and appropriate

inventory audits, accounting procedures, and new-hire reference checks for his foreign operations. Greer believes that balancing growth with control is a key component of success.

64 ■ *"A Bigger Deal" in Crain's Cleveland Business (Vol. 28, November 12, 2007, No. 45, pp. 1)*
Pub: Crain Communications, Inc.
Ed: Shawn A. Turner. **Description:** In an attempt to boost its revenue CBiz Inc., a provider of accounting and business services, is looking to balance its acquisitions of smaller companies with larger ones as part of its overall growth strategy.

65 ■ *"Book of Lists 2010" in Philadelphia Business Journal (Vol. 28, December 25, 2009, No. 45, pp. 1)*
Pub: American City Business Journals
Description: Rankings of companies and organizations within the banking, biotechnology, economic development, healthcare, hospitality, law and accounting, marketing and media, real estate, and technology industries in the Philadelphia, Pennsylvania area are presented. Rankings are based on sales, business size, and more.

66 ■ *"Bookkeeping Service Opens First Sacramento Franchise" in Sacramento Bee (April 13, 2011)*
Pub: Sacramento Bee
Ed: Mark Glover. **Description:** Franchise bookkeeping service called BookKeeping Express opened its new office in Roseville, California; its first shop in the area.

67 ■ *"Businesses Balk at 1099 Provision in Health Reform Law" in Baltimore Business Journal (Vol. 28, August 13, 2010, No. 14, pp. 1)*
Pub: Baltimore Business Journal
Ed: Scott Dance. **Description:** Small business advocates and accountants have criticized the Internal Revenue Service Form 1099 provision in the health care reform law as not worth the cost of time and money. Critics believe the policy would create a deluge of the documents that is too much for the companies or the IRS to handle. Details of the provision are also discussed.

68 ■ *"Cautions On Loans With Your Business" in Business Owner (Vol. 35, July-August 2011, No. 4, pp. 5)*
Pub: DL Perkins Company
Description: Caution must be used when borrowing from or lending to any small business. Tax guidelines for the borrowing and lending practice are also included.

69 ■ *"Changing the Rules of the Accounting Game" in Canadian Business (Vol. 81, December 8, 2008, No. 21, pp. 19)*
Pub: Rogers Media Ltd.
Ed: Al Rosen. **Description:** Interference from world politicians in developing accounting standards is believed to have resulted in untested rules that are inferior to current standards. European lawmakers have recently asked to change International Financial Reporting Standards.

70 ■ *"Channeling for Growth" in The Business Journal-Serving Greater Tampa Bay (Vol. 28, July 11, 2008, No. 29, pp. 1)*
Pub: American City Business Journals, Inc.
Ed: Margie Manning. **Description:** HSN Inc., one of the largest employers in Tampa Bay, Florida, is expected to spend an additional $9.7 million annually as it plans to hire more accounting, internal audit, legal, treasury and tax personnel after its spin-off to a public company. Details on the company's sales growth are provided.

71 ■ *Computer Accounting Essentials with Microsoft Office Accounting 2010*
Pub: McGraw-Hill Higher Education
Ed: Carol Yacht, Susan Crosson. **Released:** March 10, 2010. **Description:** Step-by-step guide to using Microsoft's Office Professional 2007 Accounting program.

72 ■ *"Convergence Collaboration: Revising Revenue Recognition" in Management Accounting Quarterly (Vol. 12, Spring 2011, No. 3, pp. 18)*
Pub: Management Accounting Quarterly
Ed: Jack T. Ciesielski, Thomas R. Weirich. **Description:** While revenue recognition is critical, regulations have been developed on an ad hoc basis until now. The joint FASB/IASB proposed accounting standard on revenue recognition is a meaningful convergence of standards that will require a major adjustment for financial statement preparers. The proposal is a radical departure from the way revenue has been recognized by the U.S. GAAP. For industries such as consulting, engineering, construction, and technology, it could dramatically change revenue recognition, impacting the top line. The new proposed standard, its potential impact, and the critical role that contracts play is examined thoroughly.

73 ■ *Deduct It!: Lower Your Small Business Taxes*
Pub: NOLO
Ed: Stephen Fishman. **Released:** November 2009. **Price:** $34.99. **Description:** Ways to make the most of tax deductions for any small business are covered. The book is organized into categories featuring common deductions, start-up expenses, health deductions, entertainment, travel, inventory, equipment and more. Current tax laws and numbers for 2008 are included.

74 ■ *"DHS Finalizes Rules Allowing Electronic I-9s" in HR Specialist (Vol. 8, September 2010, No. 9, pp. 5)*
Pub: Capitol Information Group Inc.
Description: U.S. Department of Homeland Security issued regulations that give employers more flexibility to electronically sing and store I-9 employee verification forms.

75 ■ *"Different Aspects of Project Management" in Contractor (Vol. 57, February 2010, No. 2, pp. 30)*
Pub: Penton Media, Inc.
Ed: H. Kent Craig. **Description:** There are differences when managing a two-man crew as a foreman and a 2,000 employee company as a corporate president. A project manager should have good skills in human psychology, accounting, and the knowledge of a mechanical engineer, architect, civil engineer, and also the meditative skills of a Zen master.

76 ■ *Directory of Global Professional Accounting and Business Certifications*
Pub: John Wiley & Sons, Incorporated
Ed: Lal Balkaran. **Released:** February 9, 2007. **Price:** $35.00. **Description:** Resource for international accounting, auditing, and business professions.

77 ■ *"Do Fair Value Adjustments Influence Dividend Policy?" in Accounting and Business Research (Vol. 41, Spring 2011, No. 2, pp. 51)*
Pub: American Institute of Certified Public Accountants
Contact: Barry C. Melancon, President
E-mail: bmelancon@aicpa.org
Ed: Igor Goncharov, Sander van Triest. **Description:** The impact of positive fair value adjustments on corporate distributions is examined using a Russian setting that requires disclosure of unrealized fair value adjustments in income. It was found that there is no rise in dividends due to positive fair value adjustments and that on the contrary, a negative relationship exists between adjustments and dividend changes.

78 ■ *"Economic Crisis and Accounting Evolution" in Accounting and Business Research (Vol. 41, Summer 2011, No. 3, pp. 2159)*
Pub: American Institute of Certified Public Accountants
Contact: Barry C. Melancon, President
E-mail: bmelancon@aicpa.org
Ed: Gregory Waymire, Sudipta Basu. **Description:** Financial reporting changes at the face of economic crises are studied using a punctuated equilibrium

evolution. Findings show that financial reporting has a minor impact but may amplify economic crises. Attempts to enhance accounting amid economic crises may not be as beneficial as planned.

79 ■ *"Economic Crisis and Accounting Evolution" in Accounting and Business Research (Vol. 41, Summer 2011, No. 3, pp. 2159)*
Pub: Routledge
Ed: Gregory Waymire, Sudipta Basu. **Description:** Financial reporting changes at the face of economic crises are studied using a punctuated equilibrium evolution. Findings show that financial reporting has a minor impact but may amplify economic crises. Attempts to enhance accounting and economic crises may not be as beneficial as planned.

80 ■ *Electronic Commerce: Technical, Business, and Legal Issues*
Pub: Prentice Hall PTR
Ed: Oktay Dogramaci; Aryya Gangopadhyay; Yelena Yesha; Nabil R. Adam. **Released:** August 1998. **Description:** Provides insight into the goals of using the Internet to grow a business in the areas of networking and telecommunication, security, and storage and retrieval; business areas such as marketing, procurement and purchasing, billing and payment, and supply chain management; and legal aspects such as privacy, intellectual property, taxation, contractual and legal settlements.

81 ■ *Employer Legal Forms Simplified*
Pub: Nova Publishing Company
Ed: Daniel Sitarz. **Released:** August 2007. **Price:** $24.95. **Description:** Business reference containing the following forms needed to handle employees in any small business environment: application, notice, confidentiality, absence, federal employer forms and notices, and many payroll forms. All forms are included on a CD that comes in both PDF and text formats. Adobe Acrobat Reader software is also included on the CD. The forms are valid in all fifty states and Washington, DC.

82 ■ *"Ethics Commission May Hire Collection Agency" in Tulsa World (August 21, 2010)*
Pub: World Publishing
Ed: Barbara Hoberock. **Description:** Oklahoma Ethics Commission is considering a more to hire a collection agency or law firm in order to collect fees from candidates owing money for filing late financial reports.

83 ■ *"The File On..Skoda Minotti" in Crain's Cleveland Business (Vol. 28, October 8, 2007, No. 40, pp. 26)*
Pub: Crain Communications, Inc.
Ed: Kimberly Bonvissuto. **Description:** Overview of Skoda Minotti, the accounting and financial services firm located in Mayfield Village; the company has 140 employees and an expanded slate of services.

84 ■ *"Finally, Justice" in Canadian Business (Vol. 82, April 27, 2009, No. 7, pp. 12)*
Pub: Rogers Media
Ed: John Gray. **Description:** Former investment adviser Alex Winch feels that he was vindicated with the Canadian Court's ruling that Livent Inc. founders Garth Drabinsky and Myron Gottlieb were guilty of fraud. Drabinsky filed a libel case on Winch over Winch's letter that complained over Livent's accounting procedures. Winch also criticized the inconsistent accounting during Drabinsky's term as chief executive of another firm.

85 ■ *Finance & Accounting: How to Keep Your Books and Manage Your Finances with an MBA, a CPA, or a Ph.D*
Pub: Adams Media Corporation
Ed: Suzanne Caplan. **Price:** $19.95.

86 ■ *"The Finance Function In A Global Corporation" in Harvard Business Review (Vol. 86, July-August 2008, No. 8, pp. 108)*
Pub: Harvard Business School Press
Ed: Mihir A. Desai. **Description:** Designing and implementing a successful finance function in a global setting is discussed. Additional topics include the internal capital market, managing risk and budgeting capital internationally.

87 ■ *Financial Management 101: Get a Grip on Your Business Numbers*
Pub: Self-Counsel Press, Incorporated
Ed: Angie Mohr. **Released:** November 2007. **Price:** $16.95. **Description:** An overview of business planning, financial statements, budgeting and advertising for small businesses. s.

88 ■ *Financial Times Guide to Business Start Up 2007*
Pub: Pearson Education, Limited
Contact: Steven A. Dowling, President
Ed: Sara Williams; Jonquil Lowe. **Released:** November 2006. **Price:** $52.50. **Description:** Guide for starting and running a new business is presented. Sections include ways to get started, direct marketing, customer relations, management and accounting.

89 ■ *The Flaw of Averages: Why We Underestimate Risk in the Face of Uncertainty*
Pub: John Wiley & Sons, Inc.
Ed: Sam L. Savage. **Released:** June 3, 2009. **Price:** $22.95. **Description:** Personal and business plans are based on uncertainties on a daily basis. The common avoidable mistake individuals make in assessing risk in the face of uncertainty is defined. The explains why plans based on average assumptions are wrong, on average, in areas as diverse as finance, healthcare, accounting, the war on terror, and climate change.

90 ■ *"Function Over Forms?" in Barron's (Vol. 88, June 30, 2008, No. 26, pp. 17)*
Pub: Dow Jones & Co., Inc.
Ed: Eric Savitz. **Description:** Securities and Exchange Commission (SEC) chairman Christopher Cox wants the SEC to consider an overhaul of the forms used to meet the agency's disclosure requirements. Cox also said that the U.S. Generally Accepted Accounting Standards has too many rules with exceptions and alternative interpretations.

91 ■ *"Getting More Out of Retirement" in Agency Sales Magazine (Vol. 39, November 2009, No. 10, pp. 48)*
Pub: MANA
Ed: Joshua D. Mosshart. **Description:** Overview of the Tax Increase Prevention and Reconciliation Act, which lets employees convert to a Roth IRA in 2010. The benefits of conversion depend on age and wealth and it is best to consult a tax advisor to determine the best strategy for retirement planners.

92 ■ *Getting Rich In Your Underwear: How To Start and Run a Profitable Home-Based Business*
Pub: HCM Publishing
Ed: Peter I. Hupalo. **Released:** April 1, 2005. **Price:** $17.95. **Description:** Book offers insight into starting a home-based business. Entrepreneurs will learn about business models and the home business; distribution and fulfillment of product or service; marketing and sales; how to overcome the fear of starting a business; personal success characteristics; naming a business; zoning and insurance; intellectual capital; copyrights, trademarks, and patents; limited liability companies and S-corporations; business expenses and accounting; taxes; fifteen basic steps for starting a home-based business, state resources for starting a home company; and seven home-based business ideas.

93 ■ *"Give Until It Works" in Hispanic Business (Vol. 30, March 2008, No. 3, pp. 26)*
Pub: Hispanic Business
Ed: Rick Munarriz. **Description:** Donating to qualified charities and non-profit organizations for maximizing tax advantage to be availed on the income tax bill is examined. The amount that can be deducted from the total taxable amount is usually less then the actual amount donated and must be made during that calendar year.

94 ■ *"Growing Strong" in Entrepreneur (Vol. 35, November 2007, No. 11, pp. 36)*
Pub: Entrepreneur Media Inc.
Ed: Nichole L. Torres. **Description:** Amy Langer founded Salo LL with partner John Folkestad. The company is growing fast since its 2002 launch, with

over $40 million in projections for 2007. The finance and accounting staffing company tops the list of the fastest-growing women-led companies in North America.

95 ■ "Handle With Care" in Hawaii Business (Vol. 53, October 2007, No. 5, pp. 66)
Pub: Hawaii Business Publishing
Ed: Kenneth Sheffield. **Description:** Discusses a fiduciary, who may be a board member, business owner, or a trustee, and is someone who supervises and manages the affairs and the resources of a principal. Fiduciary duties, which include accounting, cost review and risk management, must be served with the benefit of the principal as the priority. Ways of breaching fiduciary duties and how to avoid them are discussed.

96 ■ "The Hidden Tax" in Canadian Business (Vol. 81, April 14, 2008, No. 6, pp. 28)
Pub: Rogers Media
Ed: Al Rosen. **Description:** Accounting fraud could take out a sizable sum from one's retirement fund when computed over a long period of time. The much bigger tax on savings is the collective impact of the smaller losses that do not attract the attention they deserve. Ensuring that investors are not unnecessarily taxed 2 percent of their total investments every year outweighs the benefit of a 2 percent reduction in personal tax rates.

97 ■ How to Start an Internet Sales Business
Pub: Lulu.com
Ed: Dan Davis. **Released:** August 2005. **Price:** $19.95. **Description:** Small business guide for launching an Internet sales company. Topics include business structure, licenses, and taxes.

98 ■ How to Start and Run a Small Book Publishing Company: A Small Business Guide to Self-Publishing and Independent Publishing
Pub: HCM Publishing
Ed: Peter I. Hupalo. **Released:** August 30, 2002. **Price:** $18.95. **Description:** The book teaches all aspects of starting and running a small book publishing company. Topics covered include: inventory accounting in the book trade, just-in-time inventory management, turnkey fulfillment solutions, tax deductible costs, basics of sales and use tax, book pricing, standards in terms of the book industry, working with distributors and wholesalers, cover design and book layout, book promotion and marketing, how to select profitable authors to publish, printing process, printing on demand, the power of a strong backlist, and how to value copyright.

99 ■ "How To: Manage Your Cash Better" in Inc. (Volume 32, December 2010, No. 10, pp. 69)
Pub: Inc. Magazine
Description: A monthly guide to policies, procedures and practices for managing cash for a small business.

100 ■ "IFRS Monopoly: the Pied Piper of Financial Reporting" in Accounting and Business Research (Vol. 41, Summer 2011, No. 3, pp. 291)
Pub: American Institute of Certified Public Accountants
Contact: Barry C. Melancon, President
E-mail: bmelancon@aicpa.org
Ed: Shyam Sunder. **Description:** The disadvantages of granting monopoly to the international financial reporting standards (IFRS) are examined. Results indicate that an IFRS monopoly removes the chances for comparing alternative practices and learning from them. An IFRS monopoly also eliminates customization of financial reporting to fit local differences in governance, business, economic, and legal conditions.

101 ■ "Internal Auditor Wants Ethics Review of City's Casper Golf Contract" in Business Courier (Vol. 27, September 10, 2010, No. 19, pp. 1)
Pub: Business Courier
Ed: Dan Monk. **Description:** Mark Ashworth, an internal auditor for Cincinnati, Ohio is pushing for an ethics review of management contract for seven city-owned golf courses. Ashworth wants the Ohio Ethics Commission to investigate family ties between a superintendent for the Cincinnati Recreation Commission and Billy Casper Golf.

102 ■ "Kaboom!" in Canadian Business (Vol. 81, November 10, 2008, No. 19, pp. 18)
Pub: Rogers Media Ltd.
Ed: Al Rosen, Mark Rosen. **Description:** International Financial Reporting Standards (IFRS) is a good idea in theory but was implemented in a hurry and had poor quality standards from the beginning.

103 ■ "Know Your Numbers" in Inc. (Volume 32, December 2010, No. 10, pp. 39)
Pub: Inc. Magazine
Ed: Norm Brodsky. **Description:** Ways to maximize profit and minimize tax burden are presented.

104 ■ "Lifesavers" in Black Enterprise (Vol. 41, December 2010, No. 5, pp. 38)
Pub: Earl G. Graves Publishing Co. Inc.
Ed: Tamara E. Holmes. **Description:** Profile of Interventional Nephrology Specialists Access Center and founders Dr. Omar Davis and Dr. Natarsha Grant; the center generated $5.5 million in revenue for 2009. Details on how they run their successful center are included.

105 ■ "Living in a 'Goldfish Bowl'" in WorkingUSA (Vol. 11, June 2008, No. 2, pp. 277)
Pub: Blackwell Publishers Ltd.
Ed: John Lund. **Description:** Recent changes in laws, regulations and even the reporting format of labor organization annual financial reports in both the U.S. and Australia have received surprisingly little attention, yet they have significantly increased the amount of information available both to union members and the public in general, as reports in both countries are available via government Websites. While such financial reporting laws are extremely rare in European countries, with the exception of the UK and Ireland, the U.S. and Australian reporting systems have become among the most detailed in the world. After reviewing these changes in financial reporting and the availability of these reports, as well as comparing and contrasting the specific reporting requirements of each country, this paper then examines the cost-benefit impact of more detailed financial reporting.

106 ■ "May I Handle That For You?" in Inc. (March 2008, pp. 40, 42)
Pub: Gruner & Jahr USA Publishing
Ed: Taylor Mallory. **Description:** According to a recent survey, 53 percent of all companies outsource a portion of their human resources responsibilities. Ceridian, Administaff, Taleo, KnowledgeBank, and CheckPoint HR are among the companies profiled.

107 ■ MBA In a Day
Pub: John Wiley and Sons, Inc.
Ed: Steven Stralser, PhD. **Released:** 2004. **Price:** $34.95. **Description:** Management professor presents important concepts, business topics and strategies that can be used by anyone to manage a small business or professional practice. Topics covered include: human resources and personal interaction, ethics and leadership skills, fair negotiation tactics, basic business accounting practices, project management, and the fundamentals of economics and marketing.

108 ■ "Merger Mania: Regional Snaps Up HVS" in The Business Journal-Serving Greater Tampa Bay (Vol. 28, September 26, 2008, No. 40, pp. 1)
Pub: American City Business Journals, Inc.
Ed: Alexis Muellner. **Description:** It was reported that Harper Van Scoik & Co. LLP has finalized a merger with Carr Riggs & Ingram LLC. The agreement, effective October 1, 2008, is a merger of HVS assets into CRI. Bill Carr, a managing partner, revealed that HVS' $5 million in revenue will take CRI from $78 million to $82 million in revenue.

109 ■ Mergers and Acquisitions from A to Z
Pub: Amacom
Ed: Andrew J. Sherman, Milledge A. Hart. **Released:** January 2006. **Price:** $35.00. **Description:** Guide for the entire process of mergers and acquisitions, including taxes, accounting, laws, and projected financial gain.

110 ■ Microfinance
Pub: Palgrave Macmillan
Ed: Mario La Torre; Gianfranco A. Vento; Philip Molyneux. **Released:** October 2006. **Price:** $80.00. **Description:** Microfinance involves the analysis of operational, managerial and financial aspects of a small business.

111 ■ Minding Her Own Business, 4th Ed.
Pub: Sphinx Publishing
Ed: Jan Zobel. **Released:** January 1, 2005. **Price:** $16.95. **Description:** A guide to taxes and financial records for women entrepreneurs is presented.

112 ■ "My Favorite Tool for Managing Expenses" in Inc. (Volume 32, December 2010, No. 10, pp. 60)
Pub: Inc. Magazine
Ed: J.J. McCorvey. **Description:** Web-based service called Expensify is outlined. The service allows companies to log expenses while away from the office using the service's iPhone application.

113 ■ "A Necessary Balancing Act: Bookkeeping" in Contractor (Vol. 56, November 2009, No. 11, pp. 22)
Pub: Penton Media, Inc.
Ed: Al Schwartz. **Description:** Pros and cons of getting a bookkeeper or a certified public accountant for the subcontractor are discussed. A bookkeeper can help a subcontractor get new accounting software up and running while an accountant will more than likely keep after the books at regular intervals throughout the year.

114 ■ "New Century's Fall Has a New Culprit" in Barron's (Vol. 88, March 31, 2008, No. 13, pp. 20)
Pub: Dow Jones & Company, Inc.
Ed: Jonathan R. Laing. **Description:** Court examiner Michael Missal reports that New Century Financial's auditor contributed to New Century's demise by its negligence in permitting improper and imprudent practices related to New Century's accounting processes. New Century's bankruptcy filing is considered the start of the subprime-mortgage crisis.

115 ■ "New Institutional Accounting and IFRS" in Accounting and Business Research (Vol. 41, Summer 2011, No. 3, pp. 309)
Pub: American Institute of Certified Public Accountants
Contact: Barry C. Melancon, President
E-mail: bmelancon@aicpa.org
Ed: Peter Wysocki. **Description:** A new framework for institutional accounting research is presented. It has five fundamental components — efficient versus inefficient results, interdependencies, level of analysis, and institutional structure. The use of the framework for evaluation accounting institutions such as the international financial reporting standards is discussed.

116 ■ "New Institutional Accounting and IFRS" in Accounting and Business Research (Vol. 41, Summer 2011, No. 3, pp. 309)
Pub: Routledge
Ed: Peter Wysocki. **Description:** A new framework for institutional accounting research is presented. It has five fundamental components: efficient versus inefficient results, interdependencies, causation, level of analysis, and institutional structure. The use of the framework for evaluation accounting institutions such as the international financial reports standards (IFRS) is discussed.

117 ■ "New Money" in Entrepreneur (Vol. 36, February 2008, No. 2, pp. 62)
Pub: Entrepreneur Media Inc.
Ed: C.J. Prince. **Description:** Tips on how to handle business finance, with regard to the tightened credit standards imposed by leading institutions, are provided. These include: selling receivables, margining blue chips, and selling purchase orders.

118 ■ *"Olympus is Urged to Revise Board" in Wall Street Journal Eastern Edition (November 28, 2011, pp. B3)*
Pub: Dow Jones & Company Inc. Enterprise Media Group
Contact: Clare Hart, President
Ed: Phred Dvorak. **Description:** Koji Miyata, once a director on the board of troubled Japanese photographic equipment company, is urging the company to reorganize its board, saying the present group should resign their board seats but keep their management positions. The company has come under scrutiny for its accounting practices and costly acquisitions.

119 ■ *The One Minute Entrepreneur*
Pub: Doubleday
Ed: Ken Blanchard; assisted by Don Hutson and Ethan Willis. **Released:** 2008. **Price:** $19.95. **Description:** Four traditional business ideas are covered including: revenue needs to exceed expenses, bill collection, customer service, and employee motivation in order to be successful.

120 ■ *Open Source Solutions for Small Business Problems*
Pub: Charles River Media
Ed: John Locke. **Released:** May 2004. **Price:** $35.95. **Description:** Open source software provides solutions to many small business problems such as tracking electronic documents, scheduling, accounting functions, managing contact lists, and reducing spam.

121 ■ *Outfoxing the Small Business Owner*
Pub: Adams Media Corporation
Ed: Gene Marks. **Released:** January 2005. **Description:** Special skill sets are required to sell, service or deal with small business customers.

122 ■ *"Paperless Bookkeeping Program" in Fleet Owner Online (February 15, 2011)*
Pub: Penton Business Media Inc.
Description: TruckTax launched its new paperless bookkeeping system to help manage bookkeeping tasks, accounting and business tax information and filings for truckers.

123 ■ *"Pick and Save" in Entrepreneur (Vol. 36, April 2008, No. 4, pp. 66)*
Pub: Entrepreneur Media, Inc.
Ed: C.J. Prince. **Description:** Business owners can purchase the needed big equipment to offset this year's expected profit. They can also switch to annualized computing of quarterly income and estimated tax payments to pay less estimated taxes for the first half of the year. Other tips on tax planning are provided.

124 ■ *"Piece of Health Law 'A Goner'" in Baltimore Business Journal (Vol. 28, November 19, 2010, No. 28, pp. 1)*
Pub: Baltimore Business Journal
Ed: Kent Hoover. **Description:** Montana Senator Max Baucus, a Democrat who heads the Senate Finance Committee, has revealed his plan to push legislation that would repeal the 1099 IRS provision that was created by the health care reform law and will result in more paperwork for small businesses when it goes into effect in 2012.

125 ■ *"Place Restrictions on Your Stock Shares" in Business Owner (Vol. 35, July-August 2011, No. 4, pp. 14)*
Pub: DL Perkins Company
Description: It is critical for any small business owner to be certain that the buyer or recipient of any part of the company represents that the stock is being acquired or given for investment purposes only.

126 ■ *"Privacy Concern: Are 'Group' Time Sheets Legal?" in HR Specialist (Vol. 8, September 2010, No. 9, pp. 4)*
Pub: Capitol Information Group Inc.
Description: Under the Fair Labor Standards Act (FLSA) employers are required to maintain and preserve payroll or other records, including the number of hours worked, but it does not prescribe a particular order or form in which these records must be kept.

127 ■ *"Proposed Accounting Changes Could Complicate Tenant's Leases" in Baltimore Business Journal (Vol. 28, July 2, 2010, No. 8, pp. 1)*
Pub: Baltimore Business Journal
Ed: Daniel J. Sernovitz. **Description:** The Financial Accounting Standards Board has proposed that companies must indicate the value of real estate leases as assets and liabilities on balance sheets instead of expenses. The proposals could cause some companies to document millions of dollars in charges on their books or find difficulty in getting loans.

128 ■ *"Prosecutors Dish Sordid AIPC Story" in The Business Journal-Serving Metropolitan Kansas City (Vol. 27, September 19, 2008, No. 1)*
Pub: American City Business Journals, Inc.
Ed: Suzanna Stagemeyer. **Description:** Prosecutors in the American Italian Pasta Co.'s accounting fraud case have revealed evidence on the schemes used by then-officers of the company to commit fraud. District attorney John Wood has dubbed the case as the largest corporate fraud lawsuit in the history of the district of Missouri. How AIPC fell from being an industry leader is also discussed.

129 ■ *QuickBooks All-in-One Desk Reference for Dummies*
Pub: John Wiley & Sons, Incorporated
Ed: Stephen L. Nelson. **Released:** January 2007. **Price:** $29.99 (US), $42.99 (Canadian). **Description:** Compilation of nine self-contained minibooks to get the most from QuickBooks accounting software. Companion Web site with sample business plan workbook and downloadable profit-volume cost analysis workbook included.

130 ■ *QuickBooks for the New Bean Counter: Business Owner's Guide 2006*
Pub: Wheatmark
Ed: Joseph L. Catallini. **Released:** July 2006. **Price:** $21.95. **Description:** Profile of QuickBooks software, offering insight into using the software's accounting and bookkeeping functions.

131 ■ *QuickBooks Simple Start for Dummies*
Pub: John Wiley and Sons, Inc.
Ed: Stephen L. Nelson. **Released:** October 2004. **Price:** $21.99. **Description:** Profile of Intuits new accounting software geared to micro businesses. Advice is offered on daily, monthly, and yearly accounting activities covering records, sales tax, and reports.

132 ■ *QuickBooks X on Demand*
Pub: Que
Ed: Gail Perry. **Released:** December 2006. **Price:** $34.99. **Description:** Step-by-step training for using various small business financial software programs; includes illustrated, full color explanations.

133 ■ *QuickBooks X for Dummies*
Pub: John Wiley & Sons, Incorporated
Ed: Stephen L. Nelson. **Released:** November 2006. **Price:** $21.99. **Description:** Key features of QuickBooks software for small business are introduced. Invoicing and credit memos, recoding sales receipts, accounting, budgeting, taxes, payroll, financial reports, job estimating, billing, tracking, data backup, are among the features.

134 ■ *"Quicken Starter Edition 2008" in Black Enterprise (Vol. 38, March 2008, No. 8, pp. 54)*
Pub: Earl G. Graves Publishing Co. Inc.
Ed: Sonya A. Donaldson. **Description:** Profile of Quicken Starter Edition 2008 offering programs that track spending; it will also categorize tax deductible expenses.

135 ■ *Reading Financial Reports for Dummies*
Pub: John Wiley and Sons, Inc.
Ed: Lita Epstein. **Released:** January 2009. **Price:** $21.99. **Description:** This second edition contains more new and updated information, including new information on the separate accounting and financial reporting standards for private/small businesses versus public/large businesses; updated information reflecting 2007 laws on international financial report-

ing standards; new content to match SEC and other governmental regulatory changes over the last three years; new information about how the analyst-corporate connection has changed the playing field; the impact of corporate communications and new technologies; new examples that reflect the current trends; and updated Websites and resources.

136 ■ *"Reform or Perish" in Canadian Business (Vol. 82, April 27, 2009, No. 7, pp. 20)*
Pub: Rogers Media
Ed: Al Rosen. **Description:** It is believed that Canada needs to fix its financial regulatory framework in order to provide more oversight on accounting procedures that is often left up to auditors. While the U.S. has constantly rebuilt its regulatory framework, Canada has not instituted reforms on its regulations. Canada entered the recession with a strong system but needs to build more substance into it.

137 ■ *Running Your Small Business on a MAC*
Pub: Peachpit Press
Ed: Doug Hanley. **Released:** November 2007. **Price:** $29.99. **Description:** Information to effectively start and run a small business using a MAC, including setting up a network and accounting.

138 ■ *Sarbanes-Oxley for Dummies, 2nd Ed.*
Pub: John Wiley and Sons, Inc.
Ed: Jill Gilbert Welytok. **Released:** February 2008. **Price:** $21.99. **Description:** Provides the latest Sarbanes-Oxley (SOX) legislation with procedures to safely and effectively reduce compliance costs. Topics include way to: establish SOX standards for IT professionals, minimize compliances costs for every aspect of a business, survive a Section 404 audit, avoid litigation under SOX, anticipate future rules and trends, create a post-SOX paper trail, increase a company's standing and reputation, work with SOX in a small business, meet new SOX standards, build a board that can't be bought, and to comply with all SOX management mandates.

139 ■ *Schaum's Outline Financial Management, Third Edition*
Pub: McGraw-Hill
Ed: Jae K. Shim; Joel G. Siegel. **Released:** May 2007. **Price:** $22.95 (CND). **Description:** Rules and regulations governing corporate finance, including the Sarbanes-Oxley Act are discussed.

140 ■ *"Scottsdale Bank Plans 4Q Opening" in The Business Journal - Serving Phoenix and the Valley of the Sun (Vol. 28, August 15, 2008, No. 50)*
Pub: American City Business Journals, Inc.
Ed: Chris Casacchia. **Description:** Arizona's Department of Financial Institutions has approved Scottsdale Business Bank, a community bank which plans to open in the fourth quarter of 2008. The bank, which is to be located near McCormick Ranch in Scottsdale, Arizona, will cater to small business owners in the professional sector, such as accountants and doctors.

141 ■ *"SEC Extends Small Business Deadline for SOX Audit Requirement" in HRMagazine (Vol. 53, August 2008, No. 8, pp. 20)*
Pub: Society for Human Resource Management
Contact: Henry G. Jackson, President
E-mail: hjackson@shrm.org
Description: Securities and Exchange Commission has approved a one-year extension of the compliance date for smaller public companies to meet the Section 404(b) auditor attestation requirement of the Sarbanes-Oxley Act.

142 ■ *Self-Employed Tax Solutions: Quick, Simple, Money-Saving, Audit-Proof Tax and Recordkeeping Basics*
Pub: The Globe Pequot Press
Ed: June Walker. **Released:** January 1, 2009. **Price:** $17.95. **Description:** A simple system for maintaining tax records and filing tax forms for any small business is explored.

143 ■ *Six SIGMA for Small Business*
Pub: Entrepreneur Press
Ed: Greg Brue. **Released:** October 2005. **Price:** $19.95 (US), $26.95 (Canadian). **Description:** Jack Welch's Six SIGMA approach to business covers accounting, finance, sales and marketing, buying a business, human resource development, and new product development.

144 ■ *"Small is Bountiful for Intuit" in Barron's (Vol. 90, September 13, 2010, No. 37, pp. 22)*
Pub: Barron's Editorial & Corporate Headquarters
Ed: Mark Veverka. **Description:** Finance software maker Intuit wants to tap the underserved small business market. One analyst sees Intuit's shares rising 25 percent to 55 percent in the next 12 months from September 2010.

145 ■ *The Small Business Bible: Everything You Need to Know to Succeed in Your Small Business*
Pub: John Wiley and Sons, Inc.
Ed: Steven D. Strauss. **Released:** September 2008. **Price:** $19.95 (US), $28.99 (Canadian). **Description:** Comprehensive guide to starting and running a successful small business. Topics include bookkeeping and financial management, marketing, publicity, and advertising.

146 ■ *Small Business Desk Reference*
Pub: Penguin Books USA Inc.
Ed: Gene Marks. **Released:** December 2004. **Description:** Comprehensive guide for starting or running a successful small business, focusing on buying a business or franchise, writing a business plan, financial management, accounting, legal issues, human resources management, operations, marketing, sales, customer service, taxes, insurance, and ethics. Information for launching a restaurant, property management firm, retail outlet, consulting firm, and service business is included.

147 ■ *Small Business for Dummies, 3rd Ed.*
Pub: John Wiley and Sons, Inc.
Ed: Eric Tyson; Jim Schell. **Released:** March 2008. **Price:** $21.99. **Description:** Guidebook for anyone wanting to start or grow a small business; topics include information financing, budgeting, marketing, management and more.

148 ■ *The Small Business Owner's Manual: Everything You Need to Know to Start Up and Run Your Business*
Pub: Career Press, Incorporated
Ed: Joe Kennedy. **Released:** June 2005. **Price:** $19.99 (US), $26.95 (Canadian). **Description:** Comprehensive guide for starting a small business, focusing on twelve ways to obtain financing, business plans, selling and advertising products and services, hiring and firing employees, setting up a Web site, business law, accounting issues, insurance, equipment, computers, banks, financing, customer credit and collection, leasing, and more.

149 ■ *Small Business Survival Guide*
Pub: Adams Media Corporation
Contact: Gary Krebs, Director
E-mail: swatrous@adamsmedia.com
Ed: Cliff Ennico. **Price:** $12.95. **Description:** Small business expert provides strategies to start a company and survive in the 21st Century. He shows small business owners how to succeed despite challenges that can defeat any firm. His advice covers suppliers; customers and contractors; competitors and creditors; spouses, family and friends; as well as the ways lawyers, accountants and other can steal an entrepreneur's success. Ennico also describes how startups can comply with local regulations.

150 ■ *Small Business Survival Guide: Starting, Protecting, and Securing Your Business for Long-Term Success*
Pub: Adams Media Corporation
Ed: Cliff Ennico. **Released:** September 2005. **Price:** $12.95 (US), $17.95 (Canadian). **Description:** Entrepreneurship in the new millennium. Topics include creditors, taxes, competition, business law, and accounting.

151 ■ *Smart Tax Write-Offs, 5th Ed.*
Pub: Rayve Productions, Inc.
Ed: Norm Ray. **Released:** February 2008. **Price:** $15.95. **Description:** Guidebook to help small business owners take advantage of legitimate tax deductions for home-based and other entrepreneurial businesses.

152 ■ *"Smart Year-End Tax Moves" in Business Owner (Vol. 35, November-December 2011, No. 6, pp. 8)*
Pub: DL Perkins Company
Description: Managing small business and individual taxes is more important in a bad economy. It is imperative to seek all tax incentives that apply to your business.

153 ■ *"Spotlight on Pensions" in Business Horizons (Vol. 51, March-April 2008, No. 2, pp. 105)*
Pub: Elsevier Advanced Technology Publications
Ed: Laureen A. Maines. **Description:** Perceptions of pension burden and risk among financial statement users is likely to increase with changes in pension accounting. These perceptions might affect decisions on pension commitments and investments.

154 ■ *"Spotlight on Principles-based Financial Reporting" in Business Horizons (September-October 2007, pp. 359)*
Pub: Elsevier Technology Publications
Ed: Laureen A. Maines. **Description:** Employment of principles-based standards in order to generate reliable financial reporting and to reduce misrepresentations is discussed. Rules-based standards are distinguished from principles-based standards.

155 ■ *"Staffing Firm Grows by Following Own Advice-Hire a Headhunter" in Crain's Detroit Business (Vol. 24, October 6, 2008, No. 40, pp. 1)*
Pub: Crain Communications, Inc.
Ed: Sherri Begin. **Description:** Profile of Venator Holdings L.L.C., a staffing firm that provides searches for companies in need of financial-accounting and technical employees; the firm's revenue has increased from $1.1 million in 2003 to a projected $11.5 million this year due to a climate in which more people are exiting the workforce than are coming in with those particular specialized skills and the need for a temporary, flexible workforce for contract placements at companies that do not want to take on the legacy costs associated with permanent employees. The hiring of an external headhunter to find the right out-of-state manager for Venator is also discussed.

156 ■ *Streetwise Finance and Accounting for Entrepreneurs: Set Budgets, Manage Costs, Keep Your Business Profitable*
Pub: Adams Media Corporation
Ed: Suzanne Caplan. **Released:** November 2006. **Price:** $25.95. **Description:** Book offers a basic understanding of accounting and finance for small businesses, including financial statements, credits and debits, as well as establishing a budget. Strategies for small companies in financial distress are included.

157 ■ *Streetwise Small Business Book of Lists: Hundreds of Lists to Help You Reduce Costs, Increase Revenues, and Boost Your Profits!*
Pub: Adams Media Corporation
Contact: Gary Krebs, Director
E-mail: swatrous@adamsmedia.com
Ed: Gene Marks. **Released:** September 2006. **Price:** $25.95. **Description:** Strategies to help small business owners locate services, increase sales, and lower expenses.

158 ■ *"Surviving an IRS Audit: Tips for Small Businesses" in Agency Sales Magazine (Vol. 39, July 2009, No. 7, pp. 52)*
Pub: MANA
Ed: Joshua D. Mosshart. **Description:** It is a good idea to enlist the services of a tax professional even if an audit is expected to go smoothly since the IRS

is likely to scrutinize the unreported income and personal as well as business expenses of a small business during an audit.

159 ■ *"Technology and Returnable Asset Management" in Canadian Electronics (Vol. 23, February 2008, No. 1, pp. 6)*
Pub: CLB Media Inc.
Ed: Mark Borkowski. **Description:** Peter Kastner, president of Vestigo Corporation, believes that public companies without an asset track, trace, and control system in place could face Sarbanes-Oakley liability if error-prone processes result to misstatements of asset inventory positions. He also thinks that the system can improve return on assets by increasing the utilization of returnables.

160 ■ *"Test Your Structural Integrity" in Entrepreneur (Vol. 37, August 2009, No. 8, pp. 60)*
Pub: Entrepreneur Media, Inc.
Ed: Jennifer Lawler. **Description:** Tax considerations can be important when choosing a business structure. For example, profits are taxed to the corporation in a C corp while profits are taxed only once at an S corp or a limited liability company. Meeting a tax professional should be done prior to switching to a different structure.

161 ■ *"Throughput Metrics Meet Six Sigma" in Management Accounting Quarterly (Vol. 12, Spring 2011, No. 3, pp. 12)*
Pub: Management Accounting Quarterly
Ed: Shaun Aghili. **Description:** Throughput accounting (TA) metrics can be combined with six sigma's DMAIC methodology and various time-tested analysis and measurement tools for added effectiveness in resolving resource constraint issues. The goal is to optimize not only the output of a specific department but that of the entire system, by implementing a cost accounting system that is conducive to system optimization while increasing product quality, process integrity, or ideally, both.

162 ■ *"ValienteHernandez Acquired" in The Business Journal-Serving Greater Tampa Bay (Vol. 28, September 12, 2008, No. 38, pp. 1)*
Pub: American City Business Journals, Inc.
Ed: Alexis Muellner. **Description:** Minnesota accounting firm LarsonAllen LLP has acquired Florida-based ValienteHernandez PA, creating a company with 35 employees to be based in ValienteHernandez's newly built office in Tampa Bay Area. Other details about the merger are provided.

163 ■ *"Welcome Back" in Canadian Business (Vol. 82, April 27, 2009, No. 7, pp. 25)*
Pub: Rogers Media
Ed: Sarka Halas. **Description:** Some Canadian companies such as Gennum Corporation have taken advantage of corporate sale-leasebacks to raise money at a time when credit is hard to acquire. Corporate sale-leasebacks allow companies to sell their property assets while remaining as tenants of the building. Sale-leasebacks allow firms to increase capital while avoiding the disruptions that may result with moving.

164 ■ *"Where Women Work" in Marketing to Women (Vol. 21, April 2008, No. 4, pp. 8)*
Pub: EPM Communications Inc.
Contact: Ira Mayer, President
E-mail: imayer@epmcom.com
Description: According to the U.S. Census Bureau, 60 percent of America's professional tax preparers are women. Also features additional trends concerning women in the workplace. Statistical data included.

165 ■ *Working Papers, Chapters 1-14 for Needles/Powers/Crosson's Financial and Managerial Accounting*
Pub: Cengage South-Western
Ed: Belverd E. Needles, Marian Powers, Susan V. Crosson. **Released:** May 10, 2010. **Price:** $62.95. **Description:** Appropriate accounting forms for completing all exercises, problems and cases in the text are provided for financial management of a small company.

STATISTICAL SOURCES

166 ■ RMA Annual Statement Studies
Pub: Risk Management Association
Contact: Kevin M. Blakey, President
Released: Annual. **Price:** $175.00 2006-07 edition, $105.00. **Description:** Contains composite balance sheets and income statements for more than 360 industries, including the accounting, auditing, and bookkeeping industries. Also contains five years of comparative historical data for discerning trends. Includes 16 commonly used ratios, computed for most of the size groupings for nearly every industry.

TRADE PERIODICALS

167 ■ The Accounting Review
Pub: American Accounting Association
Contact: Greg Waymire, President
URL(s): aaahq.org/pubs/acctrev.htm. **Ed:** Michael L. Ettredge, Prof. Stephen Zeff. **Released:** Quarterly **Price:** $410, Institutions print; $400, Institutions online from volume 74 through current issue; $465, Institutions online and print.

168 ■ Auditing: A Journal of Practice & Theory
Pub: American Accounting Association
Contact: Greg Waymire, President
URL(s): aaahq.org/audit/ajpt.htm. **Ed:** Jean Bedard, Jeff Cohen. **Released:** Semiannual **Price:** $120, Individuals print only; $160, Individuals online only; $175, Individuals online and print.

169 ■ AWSCPA Newsletter
Pub: American Woman's Society of Certified Public Accountants
Contact: Ivy L. Defino, President
Released: 3/year. **Description:** Concerned with future developments within the accounting profession for women CPA's. Carries items on new accounting methods, member profiles, and other topics of interest.

170 ■ Behavioral Research in Accounting
Pub: American Accounting Association
Contact: Greg Waymire, President
URL(s): aaahq.org/abo/bria/briahome.htm. **Ed:** Prof. Theresa Libby. **Released:** Semiannual **Price:** $150, Individuals print; $160, Individuals electronic from volume 13 to current issue; $175, Individuals print & electronic.

171 ■ CFO & Controller Alert
Pub: Progressive Business Publications
Ed: John Hiatt, Editor, hiatt@pbp.com. **Released:** Semimonthly. **Price:** $299, individuals. **Description:** Assists busy financial executives to boost cash flow, control expenses, manage resources, and comply with changing regulations. Recurring features include case studies, success stories, financial and tax developments, cost-saving ideas and columns titled Management and Sharpen Your Judgment.

172 ■ CPA Client Bulletin
Pub: American Institute of Certified Public Accountants
Contact: Barry C. Melancon, President
E-mail: bmelancon@aicpa.org
Ed: Maria Luzarraga Albanese, Editor. **Released:** Monthly. **Price:** $195, members $174/year for members only; $243.75, nonmembers. **Description:** Discusses business-related topics, including taxes, management, and government regulation. Recurring features include news briefs on personal financial planning and taxes.

173 ■ CPA Client Tax Letter
Pub: American Institute of Certified Public Accountants
Contact: Barry C. Melancon, President
E-mail: bmelancon@aicpa.org
Ed: Maria Luzarraga Albanese, Editor. **Released:** Quarterly. **Price:** $119, members; $148.75, nonmembers. **Description:** Covers tax planning, including laws and legislation.

174 ■ The CPA Journal (Certified Public Accoutants)
Pub: New York State Society of Certified Public Accountants
Contact: Patrick Payano, Controller
URL(s): www.cpajournal.com/www.nysscpa.org/page/society-publications. **Released:** Monthly **Price:** $42, Individuals; $135, Other countries 3 years; $98, Other countries 2 years; $54, Other countries; $74, Two years; $99, Individuals 3 years.

175 ■ IFAC News
Pub: International Federation of Accountants
Released: Quarterly. **Price:** Included in membership. **Description:** Focuses on the activities of the Federation, whose goal is to coordinate efforts to achieve international, technical, ethical, and educational guidelines for the accountancy profession. Also reports on member accounting bodies and on regional groups with similar goals. Recurring features include news of research, a calendar of events, and reports of meetings.

176 ■ Journal of Accountancy
Pub: American Institute of Certified Public Accountants
Contact: Barry C. Melancon, President
E-mail: bmelancon@aicpa.org
URL(s): www.journalofaccountancy.com/. **Released:** Monthly **Price:** $75, Individuals; $60, Members.

177 ■ Journal of Accounting Research
Pub: University of Chicago Graduate School of Business
URL(s): www.chicagogsb.edu/jar/index.aspx. **Ed:** Ray Ball, Philip Berger. **Released:** Semiannual; 5/yr.

178 ■ Journal of the American Taxation Association (JATA)
Pub: American Accounting Association
Contact: Greg Waymire, President
URL(s): aaahq.org/ata/_ATAMenu/ATAPubJATA.html. **Ed:** John Phillips. **Released:** Semiannual; with a third conference supplement. **Price:** $120, Individuals print; $160, Individuals online from volume 21 to current issue; $175, Individuals online and print.

179 ■ Journal of Management Accounting Research
Pub: American Accounting Association
Contact: Greg Waymire, President
URL(s): aaahq.org/mas/jmar/jmar.cfm. **Ed:** Prof. Ramji Balakrishnan. **Released:** Annual **Price:** $125, Individuals print; $160, Individuals online only (vol. 12 through current issue); $175, Individuals online and print.

180 ■ Leader's Edge
Pub: Michigan Association of CPAs
Ed: Marla Janness, Editor, mjanness@ix.netcom.com. **Released:** Bimonthly, 10/year. **Price:** $20. **Description:** Contains professional and technical information for certified public accountants.

181 ■ NACOMEX Insider
Pub: NACOMEX USA Inc.
Ed: Robert Zises, Editor, zises@nacomex.com. **Released:** Quarterly. **Price:** $199, U.S.. **Description:** Provides information on historical values, current tactics, and residual value forecasting for ad valorem tax, bankruptcy, loss compensation, and related purposes. Recurring features include news of research and a column titled Industry Round-up.

182 ■ National Association of Black Accountants--News Plus
Pub: National Association of Black Accountants
Contact: Calvin Harris, Jr., President
Released: Quarterly. **Price:** Included in membership; $20, nonmembers. **Description:** Addresses concerns of black business professionals, especially in the accounting profession. Reports on accounting education issues, developments affecting the profession, and the Association's activities on the behalf of minorities in the accounting profession. Recurring features include member profiles, job listings, reports of meetings, news of research, and a calendar of events.

183 ■ NewsAccount
Pub: Colorado Society of Certified Public Accountants
Contact: Mary E. Medley, Chief Executive Officer
Released: 6/year. **Description:** Relays information on issues and trends affecting the Society, its members, and the accounting profession. Recurring features include letters to the editor, job listings, a calendar of events and columns titled Committees in Action, Student Corner, SEC Corner, and Technical Update.

184 ■ Polaris International
Pub: Polaris International
Ed: Jonathan Hume, Editor, jon@accountants.org.
Released: Monthly. **Price:** Included in membership. **Description:** Advises independent accounting firms worldwide on management of accounting practices. Covers topics such as marketing, employee training, and office products and equipment. Provides news of research, and information about educational opportunities. Recurring features include meeting reports and a calendar of events.

185 ■ The Practical Accountant
Pub: SourceMedia Inc.
Contact: Douglas J. Manoni, Chief Executive Officer
E-mail: doug.manoni@sourcemedia.com
URL(s): www.accountingtoday.com/. **Released:** 12/yr. **Price:** $89, Individuals; $158, Two years; $109, Other countries; $218, Other countries two years.

186 ■ The Practicing CPA
Pub: American Institute of Certified Public Accountants
Contact: Barry C. Melancon, President
E-mail: bmelancon@aicpa.org
Ed: William Moran, Editor, wmoran@aicpa.org. **Released:** Monthly. **Price:** Included in membership. **Description:** Focuses on accounting practice management and the practical application of professional standards. Recurring features include letters to the editor, announcements of seminars and conferences, and bizsites.

187 ■ Public Accounting Report
Pub: CCH Inc.
Contact: Mike Sabbatis, President
Ed: Jon McKenna, Editor. **Released:** Bimonthly. **Price:** $449, U.S. **Description:** Provides public accounting firms and other interested parties with authoritative news and analysis of developments in the accounting profession today and emerging trends for the future. Reports mergers, acquisitions, auditor changes, and related events.

188 ■ Single Audit Information Service
Pub: Thompson Publishing Group Inc.
Contact: Denise Lamoreaux, Manager
Ed: Lisa Hayes, Editor, lisa_hayes@thompson.com. **Released:** Monthly. **Price:** $399. **Description:** Covers single audit developments.

189 ■ Spectrum
Pub: National Association of Black Accountants
Contact: Calvin Harris, Jr., President
URL(s): www.nabainc.org/Publications/Publications/tabid/100/Default.aspx. **Released:** Annual **Price:** $20, Nonmembers.

190 ■ State Board Report
Pub: National Association of State Boards of Accountancy
Ed: Louise Dratler Haberman, Editor. **Released:** Monthly. **Price:** $85, individuals. **Description:** Describes the activities and concerns of the National Association of State Boards of Accountancy. Recurring features include reports of meetings.

191 ■ Taxes--The Tax Magazine
Pub: CCH Inc.
Contact: Mike Sabbatis, President
URL(s): onlinestore.cch.com/productdetail.asp?productid=591. **Ed:** Shannon Jett Fischer. **Released:** Monthly **Price:** $349, Individuals.

VIDEOCASSETTES/ AUDIOCASSETTES

192 ■ *The Accountant as a Business Advisor*
SmartPros Ltd.
12 Skyline Dr.
Hawthorne, NY 10532-2133
Ph: (914)345-2620
Co. E-mail: admin@smartpros.com
URL: http://www.smartpros.com
Contact: Jack Fingerhut, President
Released: 1988. **Price:** $449.00. **Description:** Independent public accountancy can also include management and financial consulting, this video claims, and then provides information to help accountants lay claim to this new field of endeavor. **Availability:** VHS.

193 ■ *Accounting & Auditing Update: Implementation of Recent Developments*
Bisk Education
9417 Princess Palm Ave.
Tampa, FL 33619
Free: 800-874-7877
Co. E-mail: info@bisk.com
URL: http://www.bisk.com
Released: 19??. **Price:** $179.00. **Description:** Details techniques for implementing the latest changes in accounting principles and auditing. Provides information on post-retirement benefits, market value, income taxes, and GAAP. Includes workbook and quizzer. **Availability:** VHS.

194 ■ *Accounting Library*
Moonbeam Publications, Inc.
PO Box 5150
Traverse City, MI 49696
Ph: (616)922-0533
Free: 800-445-2391
Fax: (800)334-9789
Co. E-mail: custserv@moonbeampublications.com
URL: http://www.moonbeampublications.com
Released: 1992. **Price:** $229.65. **Description:** Covers accounting software Quicken, Peachtree, DacEasy Accounting, and DacEasy Payroll for IBM and IBM-compatible computers. Each of the seven tapes is available individually. **Availability:** VHS.

195 ■ *Basic Accounting Video Series*
Cambridge Educational
c/o Films Media Group
132 West 31st Street, 17th Floor
Ste. 124
New York, NY 10001
Free: 800-257-5126
Fax: (609)671-0266
Co. E-mail: custserve@films.com
URL: http://www.cambridgeol.com
Released: 1988. **Price:** $98.00. **Description:** The four parts of this tape cover all pertinent information about learning accounting. Worksheets are included. The tapes can be purchased individually or as a set. **Availability:** VHS.

196 ■ *CPE Network: Accounting and Auditing Report*
Bisk Education
9417 Princess Palm Ave.
Tampa, FL 33619
Free: 800-874-7877
Co. E-mail: info@bisk.com
URL: http://www.bisk.com
Released: 1994. **Price:** $799.00. **Description:** Outlines informaton on current industry issues, pronouncements, new standards, recent decisions, insider reports on exposure drafts, and other early indicators of upcoming changes in the accounting and auditing areas. Video newsletter published 11 times per year. **Availability:** VHS.

197 ■ *CPE Network: Tax & Accounting Report*
Bisk Education
9417 Princess Palm Ave.
Tampa, FL 33619

Free: 800-874-7877
Co. E-mail: info@bisk.com
URL: http://www.bisk.com
Released: 19??. **Price:** $1200.00. **Description:** Provides information on current tax regulations and current accounting and auditing changes. Video newsletter published 11 times per year. **Availability:** VHS.

198 ■ *FMN: Financial Management Network*
SmartPros Ltd.
12 Skyline Dr.
Hawthorne, NY 10532-2133
Ph: (914)345-2620
Co. E-mail: admin@smartpros.com
URL: http://www.smartpros.com
Contact: Jack Fingerhut, President
Released: 1993. **Price:** $4320.00. **Description:** This monthly video magazine keeps accountants up-to-date on the latest occurances in their field, and helps them earn continuing education CPE credits. The price given is for a yearly subscription. **Availability:** VHS.

TRADE SHOWS AND CONVENTIONS

199 ■ American Accounting Association Annual Meeting
American Accounting Association (AAA)
5717 Bessie Dr.
Sarasota, FL 34233-2399
Ph: (941)921-7747
Fax: (941)923-4093
Co. E-mail: info@aaahq.org
URL: http://aaahq.org/index.cfm
Contact: Greg Waymire, President
URL(s): aaahq.org. **Frequency:** Annual. **Principal Exhibits:** Accounting equipment, supplies, and services. **Telecommunication Services:** info@aaahq.org.

200 ■ American Association of Attorney-Certified Public Accountants Annual Meeting and Educational Conference
American Association of Attorney-Certified Public Accountants (AAA-CPA)
8647 Richmond Hwy., Ste. 639
Alexandria, VA 22309
Ph: (703)352-8064
Free: 888-288-9272
Fax: (703)352-8073
Co. E-mail: info@attorney-cpa.com
URL: http://netforum.avectra.com/eWeb/StartPage.aspx?Site=AAA-CPA
Contact: John Akard, Jr., President
E-mail: johnakard@attorney-cpa.com
URL(s): www.attorney-cpa.com. **Frequency:** Annual. **Principal Exhibits:** Exhibits for persons licensed both as attorneys and CPAs.

201 ■ Business & Technology Solutions Show
Illinois Certified Public Accounting Society
550 W Jackson, Ste. 900
Chicago, IL 60661-5716
Ph: (312)933-0407
Free: 800-993-0407
Fax: (312)993-9954
URL: http://www.icpas.org
Contact: Teresa Bates, Coordinator, Conferences
URL(s): www.icpas.org. **Frequency:** Annual. **Audience:** Certified public accountants and their clients, business owners and managers, and others from the financial and business community. **Principal Exhibits:** Computers, office equipment, software publishing and educational supplies, and financial services. **Dates and Locations:** , Donald E. Stephens Convention Center.

202 ■ Institute of Internal Auditors - USA International Conference
Institute of Internal Auditors
247 Maitland Ave.
Altamonte Springs, FL 32701
Ph: (407)937-1111

Fax: (407)937-1101
Co. E-mail: customerrelations@theiia.org
URL: http://na.theiia.org/Pages/IIAHome.aspx
Contact: Richard F. Chambers, President
Frequency: Annual. **Audience:** All levels of internal auditors from every industry. **Principal Exhibits:** Internal auditing equipment, supplies, and services, software, computer related equipment.

203 ■ New Jersey Accounting, Business & Technology Show & Conference
Flagg Management, Inc.
353 Lexington Ave.
New York, NY 10016
Ph: (212)286-0333
Fax: (212)286-0086
Co. E-mail: flaggmgmt@msn.com
URL: http://www.flaggmgmt.com
URL(s): www.flaggmgmt.com/nj. **Frequency:** Annual. **Audience:** CPAs, accounting professionals, business and financial executives of New Jersey, Fortune 1000 corporations, business owners and managers, IT managers. **Principal Exhibits:** Information and technology, financial and business services, computer accounting systems, software, tax preparation, accounting, audit, practice management software - windows, and computer and business systems. Banking, insurance, financial and business software. Internet, online systems and middle market software and investment services. **Telecommunication Services:** flaggmgmt@msn.com.

CONSULTANTS

204 ■ Accounting Systems
PO Box 1720
Santa Monica, CA 90402
Ph: (310)393-5887
Fax: (310)393-5887
Contact: Deborah Peters, Principal
Scope: Trains companies on bookkeeping procedures and consults on selecting appropriate accounting systems. Installs accounting software and trains on system usage. Teaches how to interpret financial statements. Also offers a variety of accounting and bookkeeping services.

205 ■ Achieve Management Inc.
2215 E Henry Ave.
Tampa, FL 33610-4432
Ph: (813)239-1179
Free: 800-749-5155
Co. E-mail: kryals@achievemanagement.com
Contact: John Porter, President
Scope: Firm's management services organization provides customized direct services, focused consultation, and strategic planning. These services include general management (strategic planning, sustainability planning, contract management, quality improvement, policies/procedures development, partnership development); accounting; human resources (hiring process, performance management, compliance, payroll, benefit coordination training); and information technology. **Founded:** 1996.

206 ■ ARC Analytics L.L.C.
2385 NW Executive Center Dr., Ste. 100
Boca Raton, FL 33431
Ph: (561)852-1936
Fax: (561)807-0084
Co. E-mail: arc@arcmg.com
URL: http://www.arcmg.com
Contact: Andrea Joyce Wagner, Partner
E-mail: ajwagner@arcmg.com
Scope: A consulting firm specializing in investment related disputes. Litigation support services include forensic accounting in securities litigation, portfolio analysis, and damage calculations. Brokerage firm experts in compliance, operations and trading. **Founded:** 2002. **Telecommunication Services:** customerservice@arcmg.com.

207 ■ Avery, Cooper & Co.
4918-50th St.
Yellowknife, NT, Canada X1A 2P2
Ph: (867)873-3441
Free: 800-661-0787

Fax: (867)873-2353
Co. E-mail: gerry@averyco.nt.ca
URL: http://www.averycooper.com
Contact: Bernie H. Bauhaus, Manager
E-mail: bernieb@averyco.nt.ca
Scope: Accounting and management consulting firm. **Founded:** 1969. **Seminars:** Sage Software Training. **Special Services:** ACCPAC Plus; Sage Accpac ERP.

208 ■ BAPTurnkey
12 Greenway Plz., Ste. 1100
Houston, TX 77046
Ph: (281)705-0427
Co. E-mail: CustomerCare@BAPTurnkey.com
URL: http://www.bapturnkey.com
Contact: Greg Businelle, Manager
Scope: A "turnkey" hardware, internet, and software best practices company. Provides partners and direct hire candidates. Specializes in several industries: industrial, information technology, engineering, finance, and accounting. Turnkey hardware solutions include maintenance and evaluation and support of hardware/network infrastructure. Suggest solutions to supplement current set-up. Turnkey internet solutions incorporate solid design principles. Turnkey software solutions include updating and patching software. **Founded:** 2000.

209 ■ Bowie Decimal Systems
719 N 81st St.
Seattle, WA 98103
Ph: (206)715-5261
Fax: (206)783-4236
Co. E-mail: paulinebowie@mac.com
Contact: Pauline Bowie, Principal
Scope: Assists with accounting system installation, conversion, set-up, training, and support for businesses. Works closely with clients' CPA s. Offers continuing on-site support as well as telephone assistance.

210 ■ BRB Business Solutions
80 Washington St.
Barre, VT 05641-4448
Ph: (802)479-0999
Contact: Richard Barton, Jr., Principal
Scope: Consultant offers book keeping and management assistance to businesses, including how to use MYOB accounting software. **Founded:** 2006.

211 ■ Steve Burns Inc.
Landmark Sq. II, 1708 Dolphin Ave., Ste. 806
Kelowna, BC, Canada V1Y 9S4
Ph: (250)763-4706
Free: 877-763-4022
Fax: (877)353-8608
Co. E-mail: steve@burnsinnovation.com
Contact: Steve Burns, Principal
E-mail: steve@burnsinnovation.com
Scope: A full-service accounting firm with experience in advising technology companies on a broad range of financing, accounting, and taxation issues. **Publications:** "Entrepreneurialism Okanagan Style," 2005; "Burns Business Builder Beyond the Box," 2005; "Overhauling Your Sales Effort," 2005; "The Inside/Outside Marketing Measurement System," 2005; "Overhauling Your Marketing Efforts," 2005. **Seminars:** Performance Management Seminar; Marketing Intelligence Part 1; Human Resource Planning/Policies; Four Ways To Grow Your Business; How To Effectively Recruit High Technology Personnel; How To Interview, Select And Hire High Technology Personnel; Making Your Business Really Fly.

212 ■ The Business Advisor
6 Main St.
Hamilton, ON, Canada L9S 1M8
Ph: (705)431-0511
Fax: (705)431-0522
Contact: Jacob M. Hoeppner, President
Scope: Assists in the preparation and implementation of efficient systems and procedures. Advises on business and management methods and procedures. Provides temporary interim management solutions for businesses requiring leadership to re-evaluate business direction and operations. Offers accounting and tax advice. Prepares for business succession. **Founded:** 2000.

213 ■ Capital Balance L.L.C.
1105 Berea Dr.
Boulder, CO 80305
Ph: (303)579-8893
Fax: (303)554-1555
Co. E-mail: toni@capitalbalance.com
URL: http://www.capitalbalance.com
Contact: Toni Frank, Principal
E-mail: toni@capitalbalance.com
Scope: Accounting system consultant specializing in MYOB installation and proper company set up; training; support by phone, email, or on site; month end and year end procedures, including tax prep; payroll, quarterly reports, and filing of federal and state taxes; implementation of safety programs for workman's compensation; and consulting for new business start up.

214 ■ CBIZ Inc.
6050 Oak Tree Blvd. S, Ste. 500
Cleveland, OH 44131-6951
Ph: (216)447-9000
Fax: (216)447-9007
URL: http://www.cbizinc.com
Contact: Jerome P. Grisko, President
URL(s): www.cbiz.com. **Scope:** A business consulting and tax services firm providing financial, consulting, tax and business services through seven groups: Financial management, tax advisory, construction and real estate, health-care, litigation support, capital resource and CEO outsource. **Founded:** 1996. **Publications:** "FAS 154: Changes in the Way We Report Changes," 2006; "Equity-Based Compensation: How Much Does it Really Cost Your Business," 2006; "Preventing Fraud - Tips for Nonprofit Organizations"; "Today's Workforce and Nonprofit Organizations: Meeting a Critical Need"; "IRS Highlights Top Seven Form 990 Errors". **Seminars:** Health Care - What the Future Holds; Consumer Driven Health Plans; Executive Plans; Health Savings Accounts; Healthy Wealthy and Wise; Legislative Update; Medicare Part D; Retirement Plans.

215 ■ R. Shane Chance
1000 W Aztec Blvd.
Aztec, NM 87410-1867
Ph: (505)334-4375
Fax: (505)334-1850
URL: http://www.chancecpa.com
Contact: R. Shane Chance, Owner
E-mail: shanechancecpa@qwest.net
Scope: Firm's services include accounting, tax preparation, financial statements and training on MYOB accounting software. Offers installation, setup and on-site customer support for software. **Founded:** 1994.

216 ■ CheckMark Software Inc.
724 Whalers Way, Bldg. H, Ste. 101
Fort Collins, CO 80525-7578
Ph: (970)225-0522
Free: 800-444-9922
Fax: (970)225-0611
Co. E-mail: info@checkmark.com
URL: http://www.checkmark.com
Contact: Jim Mathre, President
Scope: Developer of accounting software tools for small businesses and provides fast, easy to use, affordable accounting and payroll solutions to small and medium sized businesses. Provides payroll software and multiledger integrated accounting software. **Founded:** 1984. **Publications:** *Multi-Ledger*; *CheckMark Payroll for Macintosh*; *CheckMark Payroll for Windows*. **Special Services:** Multi-Ledger™; Payroll.

217 ■ T. L. Cramer Associates L.L.C.
1788 Broadstone Rd.
Grosse Pointe Woods, MI 48236
Ph: (313)332-0182
Co. E-mail: info@tlcramerassociates.com
URL: http://www.tlcramerassociates.com
Contact: Terry L. Cramer, Founder
E-mail: tlcramer@tlcramerassociates.com
Scope: Firm provides management advisory services to small and mid-sized businesses. Sessions include corporate structure; strategic and operational focus; financial management and issues, including accounting and cash flow; marketing and business develop-

ment; business planning and implementation; human resources and administrative issues; key management; information technology; and growth and profitability. **Publications:** "Biz Journals"; "Business Week for Small Business"; "Trade Pub".

218 ■ DacEasy Inc.—Sage Software Inc.
1715 N Brown Rd.
Lawrenceville, GA 30043
Free: 800-222-0505
Co. E-mail: sales@daceasy.com
URL: http://www.daceasy.com
Contact: Greg Hammermaster, President
URL(s): www.sagedaceasy.com. **Scope:** Develops an accounting system for small businesses that integrates accounting, invoicing, payroll, communications, and management software into a single package. **Founded:** 1981. **Seminars:** Tech Tuesday - Sage DacAccess Query and Publisher: Creating Basic Queries and Formatting, May, 2012; Tech Tuesday - Graphics Form Designer, Mar, 2012; Tech Tuesday - Year End Processes with Sage DacEasy; DacEasy Training.

219 ■ Richard Ditzler
826 Saint Helena Ave.
San Francisco, CA 95404
Ph: (415)661-6652
Co. E-mail: rditzler@pon.net
Contact: Richard Ditzler, Principal
Scope: Consultant specializes in providing installation, setup, training, support for MYOB accounting systems, and bookkeeping services. **Founded:** 1993.

220 ■ Emerald Alliance L.L.C.
3170 N Federal Hwy., Ste. 205B
Pompano Beach, FL 33064
Ph: (954)608-4302
Fax: (954)839-6213
Co. E-mail: info@myob-accounting.com
Contact: Julie Fitzpatrick, Principal
Scope: Performs business planning, accounting, and tax preparation for companies and individuals. Specializes in MYOB and Netsuite programs. Services include new business set up, conversion to MYOB from another accounting system, training, troubleshooting services, streamlining services and bookkeeping assistance. **Founded:** 1993.

221 ■ Fiscal Management Associates L.L.C.
440 Park Ave. S, 3rd Fl.
New York, NY 10016
Ph: (646)403-8040
Fax: (212)630-9922
Co. E-mail: info@fmaonline.net
URL: http://www.fmaonline.net
Contact: Dipty Jain, Director
E-mail: djain@fmaonline.net
Scope: Firm provides a range of fiscal consulting services to clients in the not-for-profit sector. Services include accounting, bookkeeping, audit preparation; budgeting, cost analysis, grants management; accounting software, FUND E-Z; defining fiscal staff roles and responsibilities; fiscal policies and procedures, internal controls; and fiscal training and coaching for staff and boards. Also provides fiscal management services to New York City charter schools. Supports school leaders through a training and audit support program in partnership. **Publications:** "The Evolution of Human Resources Directors' Responsibilities," The CPA Journal, Jul, 2009; "The Yin and the Yang of Strong Fiscal Infrastructures and Sound Programs," Apr, 2009; "A Countywide Non-profit Call to Action," The Register Star, Feb, 2009; "Fiscal Management: How Do Nonprofits Do It," New York Nonprofit Press, Sep, 2008; "What is the proper role of a nonprofit Chief Financial Officer," CPA Journal, Feb, 2008. **Seminars:** Building on Quality, Strengthening Financial Management Initiative Launch, Jul, 2009; Hands- 0n Tools for Managing through Tough Times, New York, May, 2009; Creating Investment Policies For Your Nonprofit, May, 2009; Seminars In Nonprofit Excellence, Apr, 2009; The Wallace Foundation Bidders Conference, Chicago, IL, Jan, 2009; The 2009 Nonprofit Economic Climate, Jan, 2009; Nonprofit Financial Management; Certified Nonprofit Accounting Professional (CNAP) Program; FUND E-Z Software; CPAmerica Technical.

222 ■ Arnold S. Goldin & Associates Inc.
5030 Champion Blvd., Ste. G-6231
Boca Raton, FL 33496
Ph: (561)994-5810
Fax: (561)994-5860
Co. E-mail: arnold@goldin.com
URL: http://www.goldin.com
Contact: Arnold S. Goldin, Principal
E-mail: arnold@goldin.com

Scope: An accounting and management consulting firm. Serves clients worldwide. Provides management services. Handles monthly write-ups and tax returns. **Founded:** 1978.

223 ■ Goldstein & Associates
8380 Waring Ave., Ste. 108
Los Angeles, CA 90069
Ph: (310)657-7161
Fax: (323)658-1034
Co. E-mail: dg90210@aol.com
Contact: David Goldstein, Owner

Scope: Firm provides temporary and permanent employment placement services. Offers career guidance and resume writing for job applicants. Also provides computer consulting to clients in the area of database applications, installation, training and support for small and medium business accounting systems. **Founded:** 1983.

224 ■ JLA Consulting
1013 N Causeway Blvd., Ste. 202
Metairie, LA 70001
Ph: (504)835-9639
Fax: (504)835-7850
Co. E-mail: jleonard@jlaconsulting.net
URL: http://www.jlaconsulting.net
Contact: John P. Leonard, Principal
E-mail: jleonard@jlaconsulting.net

Scope: Firm provides implementation of accounting software solutions for small to medium-size businesses. Helps companies evaluate, select and implement computer hardware and software solutions. Provides training and continuing support. Also offers Crystal Report writing and FRx Financial report writing consulting services.

225 ■ Job Finders Employment Service
1729 W Broadway, Ste. 4
Columbia, MO 65203-1190
Ph: (573)446-4250
Fax: (573)446-4257
URL: http://www.jobfindersusa.com
Contact: Anne Williams, President
E-mail: annew@jobfindersusa.com

Scope: Firm places professional, para professional and temporary associates. Offers direct, temp to hire, temporary, and contract positions. Placements range from administrative assistants to accounting personnel, to sales support, engineering, and software or web designers. **Founded:** 1986.

226 ■ Steven E. Kramer C.P.A.
8282 University Ave.
La Mesa, CA 91941-3821
Ph: (619)464-8183
Fax: (619)463-6256
Co. E-mail: talltax@ix.netcom.com
Contact: Steven E. Kramer, Owner

Scope: Provider of accounting and management services in the following areas: Estate and tax planning, income tax preparation, expert witness services, small business development, professional liability insurance, and professional practice management. **Founded:** 1975. **Seminars:** Starting Your Own CPA Firm; Protecting the Small CPA Firm Against Malpractice; Sole Practitioner's Conference; Loss Prevention Conference.

227 ■ McCallum & Kudravetz P.C.
250 E High St.
Charlottesville, VA 22902-5178
Ph: (434)293-8191

Fax: (434)296-9641
Co. E-mail: sreid@mkpc.com
URL: http://www.mkpc.com
Contact: Stacie H. Reid, Principal
E-mail: sreid@mkpc.com

Scope: Certified Public Accountant provides nonprofit tax preparation and general consulting on nonprofit accounting issues. **Founded:** 1982.

228 ■ Midwest Computer Group L.L.C. (MCG)
6060 Franks Rd.
House Springs, MO 63051
Ph: (314)954-1222
Co. E-mail: sales@mcgcomputer.com
URL: http://www.mcgcomputer.com
Contact: Leon Sanford, Jr., President
E-mail: leonjr@mcgcomputer.com

Scope: Specializes in helping businesses create accounting, marketing and business information systems; software development and database design and management. **Founded:** 1980.

229 ■ Nelson & Pickens
18383 Preston Rd., Ste. 350
Dallas, TX 75252-5476
Ph: (972)380-4096
Contact: Mark Pickens, President

Scope: A full service certified public accounting firm focused on selling, training, and supporting accounting software. **Founded:** 1989.

230 ■ Nonprofit Center of Milwaukee Inc.
2819 W Highland Blvd.
Milwaukee, WI 53208-3217
Ph: (414)344-3933
Fax: (414)344-7071
Co. E-mail: info@nonprofitcentermilwaukee.org
URL: http://www.nonprofitcentermilwaukee.org
Contact: Leigh Kunde, Executive Director
E-mail: lkunde@nonprofitcentermilwaukee.org

Scope: Mission is to promote excellence in financial management, offering a comprehensive mix of training, consulting, and contracted services. Consultation and administrative and management services include conference planning, conflict resolution, executive searches, nonprofit accounting, personnel policy review, and retreat and meeting facilitation. **Founded:** 1967. **Seminars:** Administrative Support Professionals Round table; Orientation to Starting a Nonprofit: To Be or Not To Be; Triad Leadership: How the Best Fund raising Teams Work; ED Leaders Circle; Learning Circle for Supervisors; Retirement Plans for 501(c)(3) Organizations: Maximizing the Value & Benefits-Minimizing the Costs and Administration.

231 ■ On-Q Software Inc.
13764 SW 11 St.
Miami, FL 33184
Ph: (305)553-2400
Free: 800-553-2862
Fax: (305)220-2666
Co. E-mail: info@on-qsoftware.com
URL: http://www.on-qsoftware.com
Contact: Hermenegildo Cajigas, Treasurer
E-mail: hcajigas@on-qsoftware.com

Scope: Provider of the small business community with simple to use, feature rich software. Provides software solutions including time and fixed fee billing, due date tracking and practice manager. **Founded:** 1987.

232 ■ Penny & Associates Inc.
2748 Bur Oak Ave., Unit 2
Markham, ON, Canada L6B 1K4
Ph: (905)985-0712
Free: 800-699-6190
Fax: (905)985-9461
Co. E-mail: mail@pennyinc.com
URL: http://www.pennyinc.com
Contact: Betty Penny, President
E-mail: betty@pennyinc.com

Scope: Accounting and management firm that offers accounting and business solutions. Assistance in preparation of financial reports, reconciliation of inter company accounts, foreign currency transactions, investment trades and auditor working paper files and assistance in developing accounting policies and procedures. Provides part-time controllers to prepare financial statements, cash flow management, credit

negotiations and give financial management advice or oversee accounting staff. **Founded:** 1994. **Seminars:** Quick Books, Aug, 2001; How to Stand Up to People Without Being a Jerk; How to Build Influence and Rapport With Almost Anyone; Dealing With Dissatisfied, Different and Difficult People; Effective Public Speaking; How to Incorporate Yourself; Company Perks: Attracting & Retaining Good People; FIRST AID. **Telecommunication Services:** info@pennyinc.com. **Special Services:** Quickbooks®.

233 ■ Professionals for NonProfits Inc.
515 Madison Ave., Ste. 1100
New York, NY 10022
Ph: (212)546-9091
Fax: (212)546-9094
Co. E-mail: info@nonprofitstaffing.com
URL: http://www.nonprofitstaffing.com
Contact: Gayle A. Brandel, President
E-mail: gbrandel@nonprofitstaffing.com

Scope: Firm provides temporary and permanent staff exclusively to non profits, including arts, social service and healthcare organizations, museums, universities, independent schools, cultural institutions, and international organizations. The Perm Division provides permanent staff on a contingency fee basis for senior executive and mid-level management positions as well as administrative and support positions. The Temp Division provides temporary staff and consultants with nonprofit experience in fundraising and special events, grants writing, accounting and book keeping, finance, information technology, administration and office support. **Founded:** 1996.

234 ■ PYA GatesMoore
33424 Peachtree Rd. NE, Monarch Twr., Ste. 700
Atlanta, GA 30326
Ph: (404)266-9876
Fax: (404)266-2669
Co. E-mail: info@pyagatesmoore.com
URL: http://www.pyagatesmoore.com
Contact: Ed Pershing, President
E-mail: epershing@pyapc.com

Scope: Firm provides management consulting and accounting services to medical practices, hospital owned practices, staff model managed care organizations, IPAs, MSOs, PO, and PHOs. Services include comprehensive operational assessments, managed care negotiations, practice start-ups and expansion, development of MSOs, strategic planning, mergers, cost accounting analysis, practice valuations, income division plans, medical record documentation and coding reviews, expert witness testimony, patient satisfaction surveys and corporate compliance planning. **Founded:** 1982. **Publications:** "Practicing Medicine in the 21st Century"; "Physicians, Dentists and Veterinarians"; "Insurance Portability and Accountability Act Privacy Manual"; "How To Guide for your Medical Practice and Health Insurance Portability and Accountability Act Security Manual"; "A How To Guide for your Medical Practice"; "Cost Analysis Made Simple: A Step by Step Guide to Using Cost Accounting to Ensure Practice Profitability"; "Cost Cutting Strategies for Medical Practices"; "Cost Cutting Strategies for Medical Practices"; "Getting the Jump on Year-End Tax Planning"; "New 401(k) Safe Harbor Option: Increased Opportunities for the Physician and Practice"; "Not All Tax News is Bad News"; "Shareholder Agreements: Identifying and Addressing Five Risk Areas"; "Surprise - Your Practice has a Deferred Income Tax Liability". **Seminars:** Documenting and Billing High Risk Codes, 2010; Current Challenges in Ob/Gyn Recruiting, 2010; Planning for Physician Wind-down & Retirement, 2010; HITECH "How To" - Opportunities & Risks, 2010; Pediatric Coding and Audits; Recruiting and Retaining Physicians; How to Prepare for the Recovery Audit Contractors - RAC, 2010; Meaningful Use Rule, 2010; The Revenue Stream in Practice, Apr, 2008; Improving Efficiencies in a Small Family Medicine Practice, Oct, 2007; Using Compensation Models to Improve Performance, Sep, 2007; The Financial Side of Personnel Management, Sep, 2007; Pay for Performance-Is it Really Contracting for Quality?, New York State Ophthalmological Society, Sep, 2007; Beyond the Class Action Settlement Payments-Looking Prospectively at Managed Care Companies Behavior, New York State Ophthalmological Society, Sep, 2007; Protecting your clients from Embezzlement, Jun, 2007; What P4P Means to Your Medical Practice, May, 2007; Finance for the Practicing Physician, May, 2007; Trashing, Dipping and Ghosts in Medical Practices: Protecting your clients from Embezzlement, Apr, 2006.

235 ■ RAFFA P.C.
1899 L St. NW, Ste. 900
Washington, DC 20036
Ph: (202)822-5000
Fax: (202)822-0669
Co. E-mail: info@raffa.com
URL: http://www.raffa.com
Contact: Thomas J. Raffa, President
E-mail: raffa@raffa.com
Scope: Firm provides a range of accounting, tax, technology, outsourcing, and business advisory services. Specific services include financial projections and forecasts; business valuations; budgeting and cash management; strategic planning; due diligence procedures; investment analysis, products and services; evaluation and structuring of business transactions, mergers, dispositions and reorganizations; establishment of new organizations, charter organizations, affiliates and for-profit and not-for-profit subsidiaries and ventures; grant and contract applications and administration; applications for the Combined Federal and United Way Campaigns; assistance in audits by granting, contracting and taxing authorities; establishment and reevaluation of indirect cost rates. Also provides high-level talent for short term emergencies or long term assignments with CFO, human resource directors, human resource consultants, benefit managers, controllers or bookkeepers, network administrators and web masters. **Founded:** 1984.

236 ■ Mary T. Rice
5623 Sugar Ridge Rd.
Crozet, VA 22932
Ph: (434)823-1882
Fax: (434)953-5788
Contact: Frederick T. Williamson, Owner
E-mail: f1w2@cville.net
Scope: Consultant assists nonprofits with QuickBooks accounting software setup, ongoing accounting operations and financial statements. Also offers training in office administration and management.

237 ■ Sphere Consulting Group L.L.C.
12901 Jefferson Hwy., Ste. 922
Baton Rouge, LA 70816
Ph: (225)751-0898
Co. E-mail: info@getsphere.com
URL: http://www.getsphere.com
Contact: Dennis J. Savoie, Managing Partner
E-mail: dennis.savoie@cox.net
Scope: A management consulting firm that provides management consulting in sales and marketing, engineering, information systems, finance, management, research and operations by combining strategies with products, services and technology. The firm's range of consulting services support products, services and technology include general management, finance and accounting, information systems, operations, engineering, research and technology, sales, marketing and customer service. **Founded:** 2005. **Seminars:** Total Statewide Interoperable Communication Methodology and Approach to a Solution, 2007; Sales Process The Key to Sales Productivity, 2006; Business Retention and Expansion, Business Attraction and Recruitment, and Entrepreneurship Economic Development Strategy Approach.

238 ■ Sterling Management Systems
350 W Arden Ave.
Glendale, CA 91203-1110
Ph: (818)241-1144
Free: 800-933-7538
Fax: (818)241-0271
Co. E-mail: info@sterling.us
URL: http://www.sterling-management.com
Contact: L. Ron Hubbard, Manager
Scope: Offers business consulting and management training for accountants and healthcare professionals. Offers on-site training and consulting. Designs an individualized program for clients to help them achieve their goals for their practice and to improve quality of life through precise application of Hubbard

technology. Creates an organization and an environment that promotes, supports and rewards people for their contribution and productivity. **Founded:** 1983. **Seminars:** How to Achieve Your Goals; How Staff Can Increase Sales in the Workplace; Handling Emotions in the Workplace; Successful Team Building; How to Be Happy, Winning and Successful as an Executive; The Secrets to Getting Great Products; Honesty and Integrity in the Workplace; How to Sell More Using the Tone Scale; Improving Business Through Communication; Successful Time Management; How to Be Happy, Winning and Successful; Increasing Productivity and Job Satisfaction.

239 ■ The Stillwater Group—Stillwater Consulting Group Inc.
920 E Shore Dr.
Stillwater, NJ 07875
Ph: (973)579-7080
Fax: (973)579-7970
Co. E-mail: education@stillwater.com
URL: http://www.stillwater.com
Contact: David Woodward, Chief Operating Officer
Scope: Provides strategic planning, budget and financial management, process improvement, organizational design and assessment, and college student services operations. **Founded:** 1993. **Publications:** "Integrated Resource Planning (Irp)," Business Officer Magazine, 2005; "The Economic Risk Conundrum," University Business Magazine; "Revenue Analysis and Tuition Strategy"; "Managing Advancement Services: Processes and Paper".

240 ■ John N. Zaremba—Zaremba Paxton P.S.
1314 N State St.
Bellingham, WA 98225
Ph: (360)671-1023
Fax: (360)671-3458
Co. E-mail: jackie@zarembacpa.com
URL: http://www.zarembacpa.com
Contact: John Zaremba, Principal
Scope: A full service public accounting office providing tax preparation services for individuals and businesses, financial statement preparation, and consultation regarding retirement planning and estate and gift tax issues. Also staffs certified MYOB software consultants and provides support services for many accounting software products. **Founded:** 2002.

241 ■ Zolfo Cooper L.L.C.
Grace Bldg., 1114 Ave. of the Americas, 41st Fl.
New York, NY 10036
Ph: (212)561-4000
Fax: (212)213-1749
Co. E-mail: rrandall@zolfocooper.com
URL: http://www.zolfocooper.com
Contact: Mark Cervi, Director
Scope: Provider of accounting consulting services to businesses. Specializes in restructuring and turnaround consulting; interim and crisis management; performance improvement; creditor advisory; cross-border restructuring and corporate finance. **Founded:** 1985.

FRANCHISES AND BUSINESS OPPORTUNITIES

242 ■ Accountants, Inc.
Select Appointments
111 Anza Blvd., No. 400
Burlingame, CA 94010
Ph: (650)579-1111
Free: 800-491-9411
Description: Placement for accounting & finance candidates. **No. of Franchise Units:** 16. **No. of Company-Owned Units:** 22. **Founded:** 1986.. **Franchised:** 1994. **Equity Capital Needed:** $144,400-$193,700 + franchise fee. **Franchise Fee:** $30,000. **Financial Assistance:** Yes. **Training:** Yes.

243 ■ CFO Today Inc.
545 E Tennessee St.
Tallahassee, FL 32308
Ph: (850)681-1941
Free: 888-643-1348

Fax: (850)561-1374
URL: http://www.cfotoday.com
Description: Offers regional franchise program through which a regional owner solicits local franchisees. Local franchisees operate an accounting and tax practice, utilizing special marketing techniques, in addition to operational and computer systems, to provide tax, record keeping and other services to clients. **No. of Franchise Units:** 103. **No. of Company-Owned Units:** 1. **Founded:** 1989.. **Franchised:** 1990. **Equity Capital Needed:** $24,400-$40,000. **Franchise Fee:** $24,000. **Royalty Fee:** 8%. **Training:** Provides 5 days training at corporate headquarters and 1 day onsite, with ongoing support.

244 ■ Ledgerplus
259 E 7th Ave.
Tallahassee, FL 32303
Ph: (888)643-1348
Description: Accounting, tax & consultation. **No. of Franchise Units:** 156. **No. of Company-Owned Units:** 5. **Founded:** 1989.. **Franchised:** 1991. **Equity Capital Needed:** $29,000. **Franchise Fee:** $16,000. **Financial Assistance:** Yes. **Training:** Yes.

245 ■ Liquid Capital Canada Corp.
5734 Yonge St., Ste. 400
Toronto, ON, Canada M2M 4E7
Ph: (416)342-8199
Free: 866-272-3704
Fax: (866)611-8886
URL: http://www.lcfranchise.com
Description: Operation of home-based B2B providing account receivable financing to small business. **No. of Franchise Units:** 27. **No. of Company-Owned Units:** 1. **Founded:** 1999.. **Franchised:** 2000. **Equity Capital Needed:** $200,000. **Franchise Fee:** $50,000. **Training:** Yes.

246 ■ Padgett Business Services
400 Blue Hill Dr., Ste. 201
Westwood, MA 02090
Free: 877-729-8725 x225
Co. E-mail: padgett@smallbizpros.com
URL: http://www.smallbizpros.com
Description: Padgett provides an array of services to small businesses, such as consulting, financial reporting, government compliance, payroll and tax preparation services. Padgett also offers credit card processing, pension and 125 plan administration, equipment financing and workers' compensation payment service. **No. of Franchise Units:** 435. **Founded:** 1966. **Franchised:** 1975. **Equity Capital Needed:** Total investment and net worth $105,955; liquid or cash $78,750. **Franchise Fee:** $56,000. **Financial Assistance:** Third party financing up to $75,000. Also enrolled in the SBA registry. **Training:** Initial training 12 days field visits, covering marketing, operations, and software. Ongoing training and support is provided through regular seminars in marketing, operations, tax, etc. Support is delivered through toll-free telephone and a wide range of information and material is provided via the company's web site.

247 ■ Sareen & Associates
10702 Vandor Ln.
Manassas, VA 20109
Ph: (703)366-3444
Fax: (703)366-3417
Description: Accounting, bookkeeping, taxes and payroll services. **No. of Company-Owned Units:** 5. **Founded:** 1993.. **Franchised:** 2006. **Equity Capital Needed:** $75,800-$145,000. **Franchise Fee:** $20,000. **Royalty Fee:** 15%.

248 ■ Webber Consulting Group, Inc.
3506 SW Sawgrass Pky.
Ankeny, IA 50023
Ph: (515)419-6122
Fax: (253)679-4351
Description: Franchise development and accounting service.

COMPUTERIZED DATABASES

249 ■ AICPA Online
1211 Avenue of the Americas
New York, NY 10036-8775
Ph: (212)596-6200

Free: 888-777-7077
Fax: (212)596-6213
Co. E-mail: service@aicpa.org
URL: http://www.aicpa.org
Contact: Barry C. Melancon, President
E-mail: bmelancon@aicpa.org
URL(s): www.aicpa.org/Pages/Default.aspx. **Entries include:** Contact information. Principal content of publication is a searchable collection of accounting information, including AICPA news and product information, a site tutorial with navigation tips, links to sites of interest to CPAs, and a students section offering information about the profession and research tips. **Database includes:** Organizations, colleges, and universities with accounting degree programs.

250 ■ Daily Tax Report
1801 S Bell St.
Arlington, VA 22202
Free: 800-372-1033
Co. E-mail: customercare@bna.com
URL: http://www.bna.com
Availability: Online: Bloomberg LP-Bloomberg BNA; Thomson Reuters - Westlaw. **Type:** Full-text.

251 ■ e-JEP
2014 Broadway, Ste. 305
Nashville, TN 37203
Ph: (615)322-2595
Fax: (615)343-7590
Co. E-mail: aeainfo@vanderbilt.edu
URL: http://www.vanderbilt.edu/AEA
Contact: Angus Deaton, President
Availability: Online: American Economic Association; Thomson Reuters - Westlaw. CD-ROM: American Economic Association. **Type:** Full-text.

252 ■ ProQuest Accounting & Tax™
789 E Eisenhower Pkwy.
Ann Arbor, MI 48106-1346
Ph: (734)761-4700
Free: 800-521-0600
Co. E-mail: info@il.proquest.com
URL: http://www.il.proquest.com
Contact: Matt Dunie, President
Availability: Online: ProQuest Co.; ProQuest LLC - Dialog; ProQuest LLC - Dialog. **Type:** Bibliographic.

253 ■ State Tax Notes®
400 S Maple Ave., Ste. 400
Falls Church, VA 22046
Ph: (703)533-4400
Free: 800-955-2444
Co. E-mail: cservice@tax.org
URL: http://www.taxanalysts.com
Availability: Online: LexisNexis Group. **Type:** Full-text.

254 ■ State Tax Today®
400 S Maple Ave., Ste. 400
Falls Church, VA 22046
Ph: (703)533-4400
Free: 800-955-2444
Co. E-mail: cservice@tax.org
URL: http://www.taxanalysts.com
Availability: Online: Tax Analysts. **Type:** Full-text.

255 ■ The Tax Directory®
400 S Maple Ave., Ste. 400
Falls Church, VA 22046
Ph: (703)533-4400
Free: 800-955-2444
Co. E-mail: cservice@tax.org
URL: http://www.taxanalysts.com
Availability: Online: LexisNexis Group. CD-ROM: Tax Analysts. **Type:** Directory.

256 ■ Tax Notes® Today
400 S Maple Ave., Ste. 400
Falls Church, VA 22046
Ph: (703)533-4400
Free: 800-955-2444
Co. E-mail: cservice@tax.org
URL: http://www.taxanalysts.com
Availability: Online: PricewaterhouseCoopers LLP; ProQuest LLC - Dialog; LexisNexis Group. **Type:** Full-text.

257 ■ Weekly Report
1801 S Bell St.
Arlington, VA 22202
Free: 800-372-1033
Co. E-mail: customercare@bna.com
URL: http://www.bna.com/tax-accounting-t5000
Availability: Online: The Bureau of National Affairs Inc. - Tax and Accounting Division; Thomson Reuters - Westlaw. **Type:** Full-text.

COMPUTER SYSTEMS/ SOFTWARE

258 ■ Accountant's Relief
140 Fell Ct.
Hauppauge, NY 11788
Ph: (888)999-1366
Free: 800-829-7354
Fax: (800)927-1283
Co. E-mail: contactus@accountantsworld.com
URL: http://www.accountantsworld.com
Description: Available for IBM computers and compatibles. System prepares 53 tax forms and schedules and calculates various personal and business taxes.

259 ■ BNA Estate and Gift Tax Planner
1801 S Bell St.
Arlington, VA 22202
Ph: (800)424-2938
Free: 800-424-2938
Fax: (703)341-2938
Co. E-mail: software@bna.com
URL: http://www.bnasoftware.com
Price: Contact BNA. **Description:** Available for IBM computers. System calculates federal and state taxes for the estates of spouses.

260 ■ BNA Fixed Asset Management System
1801 S Bell St.
Arlington, VA 20037
Ph: (800)424-2938
Free: 800-424-2938
Fax: (703)341-2938
Co. E-mail: software@bna.com
URL: http://www.bnasoftware.com
Price: Contact BNA. **Description:** Available for IBM computers and compatibles. System provides depreciation calculations for state and federal purposes.

261 ■ BNA Income Tax Planner
1801 S Bell St.
Arlington, VA 20037
Ph: (800)424-2938
Free: 800-424-2938
Fax: (703)341-2938
Co. E-mail: software@bna.com
URL: http://www.bnasoftware.com
Price: Contact BNA. **Description:** Available for IBM computers and compatibles. Calculates federal and state individual income taxes.

262 ■ CPA Client Master
2629 Redwing Rd.
Ft. Collins, CO 80527
Ph: (970)223-1530
Fax: (970)223-3004
URL: http://www.msifc.com
Description: Available for IBM computers and compatibles. System maintains client information for CPAs.

263 ■ FAS Fixed Asset Programs / Sage Software SB, Inc.
2325 Dulles Corner Blvd., Ste. 800
Herndon, VA 20171
Ph: (703)793-2700
Free: 800-368-2405
Fax: (703)793-2770
URL: http://www.sagenorthamerica.com
Description: Windows based. System calculates taxes and provides comparisons of tax liability over a certain number of years.

264 ■ TAX/PACK: Professional 1040
Division of Analytical Processes Corp.
737 S Townsend Ave.
Montrose, CO 81401

Ph: (805)525-1040
Free: 800-525-1040
Fax: (970)249-8511
Co. E-mail: info@taxpack.com
URL: http://www.alpinedata.com
Price: $410 (with laser), $245 (without laser). **Description:** Available for IBM computers and compatibles. Provides tax form preparation.

265 ■ Tax$imple
8 Emery Ave.
Randolph, NJ 07869
Ph: (973)989-8955
Free: 800-989-8955
Fax: (973)366-5877
Co. E-mail: support@taxsimple.com
URL: http://www.taxsimple.com/
Price: Contact TaxSimple for Pricing. **Description:** Available for IBM computers and compatibles. System for tax professionals offering tax form input, calculations, tables, schedules, and printing options.

LIBRARIES

266 ■ Brooklyn Public Library - Business Library
280 Cadman Plaza, W.
Tillary St.
Brooklyn, NY 11201
Ph: (718)623-7000
Co. E-mail: busref@brooklynpubliclibrary.org
URL: http://www.brooklynpubliclibrary.org/locations/business
Contact: Dionne Mack-Harvin, Executive Director
Scope: Accounting, advertising, business management, business procedure, career development and employment, finance, insurance, investment, public relations, small business, real estate. **Services:** Copying; Library open to the public. **Founded:** 1943. **Holdings:** 133,000 books; 730,000 microfiche; 22,000 reels of microfilm; 1000 directories; 120 videocassettes and DVDs; selective U.S. government documents depository. **Subscriptions:** 700 journals and other serials; 5 newspapers.

267 ■ Caixa Geral do Depositos SA - Mediateca e Centro de Informacao Europeia
Edificio-Sede da CGD, Av Joao XXI, 63
P-1000 Lisbon, Portugal
Co. E-mail: ana.monteiro@cgd.pt
URL: http://www.cgd.pt
Scope: Finance. **Services:** Centre open to the public. **Founded:** 1994. **Holdings:** 40,000 volumes. **Subscriptions:** 1000 journals and other serials.

268 ■ Canada Office of the Auditor General Knowledge Centre Library
240 Sparks St., 11th Fl. W.
Ottawa, ON, Canada K1A 0G6
Ph: (613)952-0213
Fax: (613)943-5485
Co. E-mail: joanne.hauckdemorest@oag-bvg.gc.ca
URL: http://www.oag-bvg.gc.ca/
Contact: Joanne Hauck DeMorest, Director
Scope: Accounting, auditing, public administration, finance, management. **Services:** Interlibrary loan; copying; SDI; Library open to the public by appointment. **Founded:** 1977. **Holdings:** 20,000 books; AV items. **Subscriptions:** 400 journals and other serials. **Telecommunication Services:** communications@oag-bvg.gc.ca.

269 ■ CMA Ontario - Member Services Centre
70 University Ave., Ste. 101
Toronto, ON, Canada M5J 2M4
Ph: (416)204-3142
Fax: (416)977-1365
Co. E-mail: msc@cma-ontario.org
Contact: Patricia Black, Manager, Member Services
Scope: Accounting, management, finance, strategy, taxation, investments. **Services:** Copying; SDI; Library not open to the public. **Founded:** 1990. **Holdings:** 2069 books; 267 videocassettes; 184 audiocassettes; 6 videodiscs. **Subscriptions:** 53 journals and other serials; 2 newspapers.

270 ■ Deloitte & Touche - Library
350 S. Grand Ave.
Los Angeles, CA 90071-3462
Ph: (213)688-0800
Fax: (213)688-0100
URL: http://www.deloitte.com
Scope: Auditing, taxation, management consultation, actuarial services, employee benefits, valuation consultation. **Services:** Library not open to the public. **Holdings:** Figures not available.

271 ■ Ernst & Young Center for Business Knowledge
155 N. Wacker Dr.
Chicago, IL 60606
Ph: (312)879-2000
Fax: (312)879-4000
URL: http://www.ey.com
Scope: Accounting, taxation, consulting, healthcare. **Services:** Interlibrary loan; library not open to the public. **Holdings:** 3000 books. **Subscriptions:** 500 journals and other serials.

272 ■ Ernst & Young Center for Business Knowledge
1 Victory Pk., Ste. 2000
2323 Victory Ave.
Dallas, TX 75219
Ph: (214)969-8000
Fax: (214)969-8587
URL: http://www.ey.com
Scope: Consulting, accounting, tax accounting, auditing. **Services:** Center open to the public at librarian's discretion.

273 ■ Ernst & Young Library
875 E. Wisconsin Ave.
Milwaukee, WI 53202
Ph: (414)273-5900
URL: http://www.ey.com
Scope: Taxation, tax law, accounting, auditing. **Services:** Performs searches on fee basis for clients only. **Holdings:** 1200 books. **Subscriptions:** 35 journals and other serials.

274 ■ Ernst & Young LLP Center for Business Knowledge
5 Times Sq.
New York, NY 10019
Ph: (212)773-3000
Fax: (212)773-6350
URL: http://www.ey.com/PH/en/OurLocations
Scope: Accounting and auditing, taxation, finance. **Services:** Interlibrary loan; copying; library open to clients and SLA members. **Founded:** 1953. **Holdings:** 3500 books. **Subscriptions:** 500 journals and other serials.

275 ■ Illinois CPA Society - Information & Research Center
550 W. Jackson, Ste. 900
Chicago, IL 60661-5716

Ph: (312)601-4613
Free: 800-993-0407
Fax: (312)906-8045
Co. E-mail: research@icpas.org
URL: http://www.icpas.org
Contact: Michele Courtney, Assistant Director
Scope: Accounting; auditing; taxation; business. **Services:** Research and book requests by phone or email. **Founded:** 1981. **Holdings:** 5000 books; 50 bound periodical volumes. **Subscriptions:** 100 journals and other serials.

276 ■ Institute of Management Accountants - McLeod Information Center
10 Paragon Dr., Ste. 1
Montvale, NJ 07645-1774
Ph: (201)573-9000, x1535
Free: 800-638-4427
URL: http://www.imanet.org/ima_home.aspx
Scope: Management and financial accounting, management and financial management. **Services:** Library open to members only. **Founded:** 1920. **Holdings:** 5000 books; 450 bound periodical volumes; 30 VF drawers. **Subscriptions:** 30 journals and other serials.

277 ■ KPMG - Research Centre
777 Dunsmuir St.
Vancouver, BC, Canada V7Y 1K3
Ph: (604)691-3000
Fax: (604)691-3031
URL: http://www.kpmg.ca
Scope: Accounting, tax, general business, stocks. **Services:** SDI; Library not open to the public. **Founded:** 1982. **Holdings:** 1000 books; 70 bound periodical volumes. **Subscriptions:** 50 journals and other serials; 6 newspapers.

278 ■ KPMG Resource Centre
160 Elgin St., Ste. 2000
Ottawa, ON, Canada K2P 2P8
Ph: (613)212-2844
Fax: (613)212-2896
Co. E-mail: hopebell@kpmg.ca
URL: http://www.kpmg.ca/en/
Contact: Hope A. Bell, Manager, Business Development
Scope: Economics, accounting, government. **Services:** Interlibrary loan; copying; Performs searches on fee basis. **Founded:** 1981. **Subscriptions:** 2 newspapers.

279 ■ PricewaterhouseCoopers - Research Centre
1250 Boul Rene-Levesque O
Bureau 2800
Montreal, QC, Canada H3B 2G4
Ph: (514)205-5000
Fax: (514)938-5709
URL: http://www.pwc.com/ca
Scope: Accounting, tax, management, business, finance. **Founded:** 1993. **Subscriptions:** 200 journals and other serials.

280 ■ Protape, Inc. Library
1540 Broadway
New York, NY 10036
Contact: Richard Sobelsohn
Scope: Accounting, law, real estate, English, math, insurance, travel, taxation, stock broker, medical billing, claims adjusting, private investigation, paralegal. **Services:** Library not open to the public. **Founded:** 1970. **Holdings:** 25,000 books; 250 bound periodical volumes. **Subscriptions:** 65 journals and other serials; 20 newspapers.

281 ■ U.S. Dept. of the Treasury - Treasury Library
1500 Pennsylvania Ave. NW, Rm. 1428
Washington, DC 20220
Ph: (202)622-0990
Fax: (202)622-6415
Co. E-mail: library.reference@do.treas.gov
URL: http://www.ustreas.gov/offices/management/privacy-records
Scope: Taxation, public finance, law, domestic and International economics, economic conditions and management. **Services:** Interlibrary loan within D.C.; copying; library open to the public by appointment for reference use only. **Founded:** 1789. **Holdings:** 70,000 books and bound periodical volumes; 500,000 microforms. **Subscriptions:** 300 journals and other serials; 6 newspapers.

282 ■ U.S. Tax Court Library
400 2nd St., NW
Washington, DC 20217
Ph: (202)521-4585
Fax: (202)521-4574
Co. E-mail: tclib@ustaxcourt.gov
URL: http://www.ustaxcourt.gov
Contact: Elsa B. Silverman, Librarian
Scope: Federal tax law - income, estate, and gift. **Services:** Interlibrary loan; library not open to the public. **Founded:** 1924. **Holdings:** 60,000 books; 9000 bound periodical volumes; Congressional Record, Federal Register, and federal tax legislation. **Subscriptions:** 200 journals and other serials.

283 ■ University of Kentucky - Business & Economics Information Center
B&E Info. Ctr., Rm. 116
335-BA Gatton College of Business & Economics
Lexington, KY 40506-0034
Ph: (859)257-8936
Fax: (859)257-1333
Co. E-mail: mrazeeq@pop.uk.edu
URL: http://www.uky.edu//Provost/academicprograms.html
Contact: Michael A. Razeeq, Librarian, Business
URL(s): gatton.uky.edu/. **Scope:** Business, economics, business management, marketing, finance, accounting. **Services:** Library open to the public for reference use only. **Founded:** 1993. **Telecommunication Services:** cber@uky.edu; klimar@pop.uky.edu; provost@email.uky.edu.

START-UP INFORMATION

284 ■ *"Caring Concern" in Small Business Opportunities (September 2010)*
Pub: Harris Publications Inc.
Description: Profile of Joshua Hoffman, founder and CEO of HomeWell Senior Care, Inc., provider of non-medical live-in and hourly personal care, companionship and homemaker services for seniors so they can remain in their own homes.

285 ■ *There's Someplace Like Home: Developing an Adult Day Care Center in Your Church*
Pub: Westminster John Knox Press
Ed: Donna T. Lott. **Released:** 1999. **Price:** $4.50.

ASSOCIATIONS AND OTHER ORGANIZATIONS

286 ■ **Assisted Living Federation of America (ALFA)**
1650 King St., Ste. 602
Alexandria, VA 22314-2747
Ph: (703)894-1805
Fax: (703)894-1831
Co. E-mail: rgrimes@alfa.org
URL: http://www.alfa.org
Contact: Richard Grimes, President
Description: Providers of assisted living, state associations of providers, and others interested or involved in the industry. Promotes the interests of the assisted living industry and works to enhance the quality of life for the population it serves. Provides a forum for assisted living providers to unite, exchange information, and interact. Encourages the development of high standards for the industry. Promotes the concept of assisted living facilities with public and private agencies and other professionals. Works to educate providers and the public and increase national awareness of assisted living. Sponsors speakers' bureau, conferences, educational opportunities, trade show, research & training products. **Founded:** 1990. **Publications:** *ALFA Alert* (Weekly); *Assisted Living Executive* (9/year); *Guide to Choosing an Assisted Living Residence*; *ALFA Executive Portfolio: Inside the Minds of the Leaders in Assisted Living and Senior Housing*. **Awards:** Hero Awards (Annual); Pioneer Award (Annual); Best of Home Architectural Design Award (Annual).

287 ■ **Little Brothers - Friends of the Elderly (LBFE)—Little Brothers of the Poor**
28 E Jackson Blvd., Ste. 405
Chicago, IL 60604
Ph: (312)829-3055
Fax: (312)829-3077
Co. E-mail: national@littlebrothers.org
URL: http://www.littlebrothers.org
Contact: Elisa T. Drew, Executive Director
Description: Seeks to combat the isolation and loneliness often experienced by elderly people by providing friendship and special assistance. Sponsors visitation programs, holiday and birthday parties,

and summer vacations. Provides transportation for shopping and doctor's visits, food packages, and other "special touches." Also offers information, referrals, and contacts with other public or private agencies. **Founded:** 1959. **Publications:** *Little Brothers Bulletin* (3/year).

288 ■ **National Adult Day Services Association**
1421 E Broad St., Ste. 425
Fuquay Varina, NC 27526
Free: 877-745-1440
Fax: (919)825-3945
Co. E-mail: nadsanews@gmail.com
URL: http://www.nadsa.org
Contact: Linda Alexander-Lieblang, Chairperson
Description: Adult daycare practitioners; health and social service planners; individuals involved in planning and providing services for older persons. (Daycare centers offer services in a group setting ranging from active rehabilitation to social and health care.) Promotes and enhances adult daycare programs; provides services and activities for disabled older persons on a long-term basis; provides training and technical assistance and consultation services for daycare personnel; organizes funding; develops standards and guidelines for adult daycare programs; encourages adult daycare centers to participate in local area health planning activities to heighten the effectiveness of adult daycare. Plans and conducts training events for annual meeting and related conferences; maintains annotated bibliography; lobbies for approved public policy positions; surveys state adult daycare regulations and legislation. **Founded:** 1979. **Educational Activities:** National Training Conference (Annual). **Awards:** Ruth Von Behren Award (Annual).

289 ■ **National Council on Aging (NCOA)**
1901 L St. NW, 4th Fl.
Washington, DC 20036
Ph: (202)479-1200
Free: 800-373-4906
Fax: (202)479-0735
Co. E-mail: info@ncoa.org
URL: http://www.ncoa.org
Contact: Richard Browdie, Chairman
Description: Serves as a national voice and powerful advocate on behalf of older Americans. Has developed programs such as Benefits CheckUp, Foster Grandparents and Family Friends. Works with thousands of its community organization members nationwide to provide needed services to the elderly. Members include senior centers, area agencies on aging, employment services, congregate meal sites, faith congregations, health centers and senior housing. Accredits senior centers nationally; provides consumer information for older Americans on health care and related programs and insurance; directs an intergenerational volunteer program that matches mature men and women with children and families at risk; Best Practices encompasses a series of research projects that have provided best practices for senior centers and other community based organizations in health care and other areas; administers two federal programs (Senior Community Service Em-

ployment Service and Senior Environmental Program), and the Maturity Works partnership that provide employment and training opportunities for mature adults through offices nationwide. **Founded:** 1950. **Publications:** *Abstracts in Social Gerontology* (Quarterly). **Awards:** Geneva Mathiasen Award; Ollie A. Randall Award; Arthur Flemming Award; Jack Ossofsky Award; Best Practices Award; Dorothy Bauer Award; Spirituality and Aging Award; NISC Founders Award; Public-Private Partnership Award; NISC Research Award; Arthur Flemming Award (Annual); Geneva Mathiasen Award (Annual); Jack Ossofsky Award (Annual); Ollie A. Randall Award (Annual); Molly Mettler Award for Leadership in Health Promotion; Anne H. McKinley Professional Leadership Award; Claude Pepper Award for Excellence in Community-Based Long-Term Care; Sid Spector Memorial Award for Excellence in Senior Housing Service.

REFERENCE WORKS

290 ■ *"$20M Aimed at Affordable Los Angeles Seniors Housing" in Commercial Property News (March 17, 2008)*
Pub: Nielsen Company
Description: Grand Plaza Apartments in Los Angeles, California will be renovated in order to maintain housing for over 400 low-income seniors. Details of plans are included.

291 ■ *"Advancing the Ball" in Inside Healthcare (Vol. 6, December 2010, No. 7, pp. 31)*
Pub: RedCoat Publishing Inc.
Ed: Michelle McNickle. **Description:** Profile of Medicalodges an elder-care specialty company that provides both patient care and technology development. President and CEO of the firm believes that hiring good employees is key to growth for any small business.

292 ■ *"Big Sell-Off At Sunwest" in The Business Journal-Portland (Vol. 25, July 25, 2008, No. 20, pp. 1)*
Pub: American City Business Journals, Inc.
Ed: Robin J. Moody. **Description:** Oregon's largest operator of assisted living facilities Sunwest Management Inc. is expected to sell 132 of its properties. The planned sale, which is believed to be worth more than $1 billion, will help Sunwest pay creditors and investors. Other views and information on the planned sale, as well as on Sunwest's services which include adult day care, are presented.

293 ■ *"Connecting the Dots Between Wellness and Elder Care" in Benefits and Compensation Digest (Vol. 47, August 2010, No. 8, pp. 18)*
Pub: International Foundation of Employee Benefit Plans
Contact: Richard Lyall, President
Ed: Sandra Timmermann. **Description:** Employees caring for aged and infirm parents deal with time and financial issues and other stresses. The connection

between health status of caregivers and employers' health care costs could be aided by linking programs and benefits with wellness and caregiving.

294 ■ *"Elder Care Costs Surge" in National Underwriter Life & Health (Vol. 114, November 8, 2020, No. 21, pp. 25)*
Pub: Summit Business Media
Ed: Trevor Thomas. **Description:** Nursing home and assisted living rates rose from 2009 to 2010, according to MetLife Mature Market Institute. Statistical data included.

295 ■ *"Elder Care, Rx Drugs Reforms Top Zoeller's Agenda" in Times (December 21, 2010)*
Pub: The Times
Ed: Sarah Tompkins. **Description:** Indiana Attorney General Greg Zoeller is hoping to develop a program in the state that will help regulate care for the elderly; freeze medical licenses for doctors involved in criminal investigations; address illegal drug use; and to establish a program to help individuals dispose of old prescription medications easily at pharmacies.

296 ■ *"Elder-Care Seminar to Teach Ways to Avoid Falls" in Virginian-Pilot (November 25, 2010)*
Pub: Virginian-Pilot
Ed: Amy Jeter. **Description:** ResCare HomeCare, a home health services firm, offers free seminars on helping to make residences safer for seniors prone to falling.

297 ■ *"EVMS Gets Grant to Train Providers for Elder Care" in Virginian-Pilot (October 29, 2010)*
Pub: Virginian-Pilot
Ed: Elizabeth Simpson. **Description:** Eastern Virginia Medical School received a federal grant to train health providers in elder care. Details of the program are provided.

298 ■ *"Face Issues if Elder Care, Unemployment Collide" in Atlanta Journal-Constitution (December 26, 2010, pp. G1)*
Pub: Atlanta Journal-Constitution
Ed: Amy Lindgren. **Description:** More issues arise during holiday for families with older members requiring care, including the issue of employment for those doing the caregiving.

299 ■ *"GeckoSystems Reduces Sensor Fusion Costs Due to Elder Care Robot Trials" in Internet Wire (December 14, 2010)*
Pub: Comtex
Description: GeckoSystems International Corporation has been able to reduce the cost of its sensor fusion system while maintaining reliability and performance. The firm's ongoing first in-home elder care robot trials have sparked interest regarding its business model, technologies available for licensing, and joint domestic and international ventures.

300 ■ *How to Start a Home-Based Senior Care Business: Check-in-Care, Transportation Services, Shopping and Cooking*
Pub: Globe Pequot Press
Ed: James L. Ferry. **Released:** January 1, 2010. **Price:** $18.95. **Description:** Information is provided to start a home-based senior care business.

301 ■ *National Directory of Adult Day Care Centers*
Pub: Health Resources Publishing
Contact: Rebekah McCallister, Editor

URL(s): www.healthresourcesonline.com/elderly_health/4dir.htm. **Released:** Irregular; latest edition 2002, 3rd edition. **Price:** $39.95, Individuals print; $995, Individuals database on CD. **Covers:** Over 3,200 centers and programs providing adult day care; 1,100 are described in detail. **Entries include:** Center or program name, address, phone, director or coordinator name; detailed listings include programs, providing sponsor information, geographic area served, fees, number of clients and staff, hours and days of operation, client eligibility criteria, services and activities offered. **Database includes:** Bibliography of resources; aging services suppliers' guide. **Arrangement:** Geographical. **Indexes:** Executive director, Alphabetical county, social models, medicals models.

302 ■ *"New Elder Care Center to Focus on Residents with Failing Memories" in Tulsa World (November 30, 2010)*
Pub: World Publishing
Ed: Robert Evatt. **Description:** People with Alzheimer's disease and other mental disorders require specialized care. Constant Care Management Company runs 'memory care' centers designed for the elderly with such conditions.

303 ■ *"Renewed Vision" in Hawaii Business (Vol. 54, August 2008, No. 2, pp. 49)*
Pub: Hawaii Business Publishing
Ed: Jason Ubay. **Description:** Saint Francis Healthcare System of Hawaii, ranked 81 in Hawaii's top 250 companies for 2008, has been rebranding to focus on senior community healthcare and sold some of its operations, which explains the decline in gross sales from $219.5M in 2006 to $122.7M in 2007. The system's senior services and home hospice service expansion are provided.

304 ■ *"Silver Dollars" in Small Business Opportunities (September 2008)*
Pub: Entrepreneur Media Inc.
Description: Profile of Always Best Care Senior Services, a franchise created by Michael Newman, which offers non-medical In-Home Care, Personal Emergency Response Systems, and Assisted Living Placement Services to seniors; the company offers franchisees the opportunity to fill what is oftentimes a void for the seniors and their families in the community.

305 ■ *"State Budget Woes Hurt Many Vendors, Senior Services" in Sacramento Business Journal (Vol. 25, August 15, 2008, No. 24, pp. 1)*
Pub: American City Business Journals, Inc.
Ed: Melanie Turner. **Description:** Delays in the passage of the California state budget have adversely affected the health care industry. The Robertson Adult Day Health Care had taken out loans to keep the business afloat. The state Legislature has reduced Medi-Cal reimbursement to health care providers by 10 percent.

STATISTICAL SOURCES

306 ■ *Adult Day Care in America: Summary of a National Survey*
Pub: National Council on the Aging
Contact: Dr. James P. Firman, President
E-mail: james.firman@ncoa.org
Ed: Ruth Van Behren. **Released:** 1986. **Price:** $5.95 (paper).

307 ■ *Adult Day Care: Findings From a National Survey*
Pub: Johns Hopkins University Press
Ed: William G. Weissert, Jennifer M. Elston, Elise J. Bolda, William N. Zelman, Elizabeth Mutran and Anne B. Magnum. **Released:** 1990.

TRADE PERIODICALS

308 ■ *Adult Day Services Letter*
Pub: Health Resources Publishing
Contact: Beth-Ann Kerber, Managing Editor
Released: Monthly. **Price:** $97, individuals. **Description:** Provides crucial management information and serves as a link between adult day programs across the country.

309 ■ *Clinical Gerontologist: The Journal of Aging and Mental Health*
Pub: Routledge Journals Taylor & Francis Group
URL(s): www.tandf.co.uk/journals/WCLI. **Ed:** Dolores Gallagher-Thompson, Larry W. Thompson. **Released:** Quarterly **Price:** $140, Individuals online; $156, Individuals print + online; $970, Institutions online only; $1078, Institutions print + online.

310 ■ *Homecare Administrative HORIZONS*
Pub: Beacon Health Corp.
Contact: Diane J. Omdahl, Editor-in-Chief
Released: Monthly. **Price:** $347, individuals. **Description:** Provides homecare agency management information on all kinds of business and personnel topics. Incorporates comprehensive how-to information, current regulatory requirements, and documentation strategies. Runs a series of articles, including how to move into managed care, how to manage and measure outcomes, how to survive scrutiny by medicare's fraud squad, strengthening agency/physician relationships, and personnel issues. Recurring features include columns titled Peaks & Valleys, Fine-tuning the Fundamentals, Clearing the Fog, and Higher Ground.

311 ■ *Homecare DIRECTION*
Pub: Beacon Health Corp.
Contact: Diane J. Omdahl, Editor-in-Chief
Released: Monthly. **Price:** $337. **Description:** Delivers timely regulatory information with how-to elements to apply to everyday care delivery. Equips agency patient care personnel with knowledge they need to deliver quality care and comply with medicare certification and reimbursement requirements. Offers valuable tips on interpreting medicare rules to justify care; how to create policies that reduce survey surprises, and documentation tips and examples. Recurring features include columns titled Documenting with Impact, Survey Sense, Looking for Direction, and From the Lamp Room.

VIDEOCASSETTES/ AUDIOCASSETTES

312 ■ *Art with the Elders in Long-Term Care*
Filmakers Library, Inc.
124 E. 40th St.
New York, NY 10016
Ph: (212)808-4980
Free: 800-555-9815
Fax: (212)808-4983
URL: http://www.filmakers.com
Released: 1985. **Description:** Filmed at Hillhaven Convalescent Hospital, this film describes the art program developed for people over 80 years old. **Availability:** VHS; 3/4 U.

313 ■ *Assessment & Intervention: The Confused Elderly*
Medcom Inc.
6060 Phyllis Dr.
Cypress, CA 90630
Free: 800-877-1443
Fax: (714)891-3140
Co. E-mail: customerservice@medcominc.com
URL: http://www.medcominc.com
Released: 1986. **Price:** $295.00. **Description:** Two different ways of dealing with older people who have grown confused are suggested for health care pros. **Availability:** VHS; 3/4 U.

TRADE SHOWS AND CONVENTIONS

314 ■ *Senior Housing South*
Merchandise Mart Properties Inc.
222 Merchandise Mart, Ste. 470
Chicago, IL 60654
Ph: (312)527-4141
Free: 800-677-6278
URL: http://www.merchandisemart.com
URL(s): www.seniorhousingshows.com. **Frequency:** Annual. **Principal Exhibits:** Equipment, supplies, and services for the planning, building, design and management of long-term care facilities.

FRANCHISES AND BUSINESS OPPORTUNITIES

315 ■ *Aging Excellence*
115 Middle St., Ste. 100
Portland, ME 04104
Ph: (207)771-0991

Fax: (207)771-0958

Description: Non-medical senior care services. **No. of Franchise Units:** 8. **Founded:** 1999.. **Franchised:** 2003. **Equity Capital Needed:** $61,600-$89,600 total investment. **Franchise Fee:** $35,000. **Royalty Fee:** 5%. **Financial Assistance:** Limited third party financing available. **Training:** Provides 1 week at headquarters, 2 days onsite with ongoing support.

316 ■ AristoCare
698 E Wetmore Rd., Ste. 200
Tucson, AZ 85715
Ph: (520)577-4825
Fax: (520)721-1915

Description: Senior care services. **No. of Franchise Units:** 2. **No. of Company-Owned Units:** 3. **Founded:** 1999.. **Franchised:** 2003. **Equity Capital Needed:** $148,900-$259,400. **Franchise Fee:** $36,000. **Royalty Fee:** 5-6%. **Training:** Yes.

317 ■ CareMinders Home Care Inc.
178 South Main St., Ste. 300
Alpharetta, GA 30009
Ph: (770)360-5554
Free: 855-757-2640
Fax: (770)360-5579
Co. E-mail: sales@careminders.com
URL: http://www.careminders.com

Description: Non-medical personal care for seniors & convalescing adults. **No. of Franchise Units:** 69. **No. of Company-Owned Units:** 3. **Founded:** 2004.. **Franchised:** 2004. **Equity Capital Needed:** $138,100-$199,000. **Franchise Fee:** $39,000. **Royalty Fee:** 3.75-5%. **Training:** 1 week training provided at headquarters, 2 days onsite and ongoing support.

318 ■ Caring Senior Service
Caring Senior Service Franchise Partnership, L.P.

Description: Cares for health and nutrition services to senior people. **No. of Franchise Units:** 32. **No. of Company-Owned Units:** 8. **Franchised:** 2002. **Equity Capital Needed:** $65,000. **Franchise Fee:** $35,000. **Financial Assistance:** Yes. **Training:** Yes.

319 ■ ComForcare Senior Services
ComForcare Healthcare Holdings Inc.
2510 Telegraph Rd., Ste. 100
Bloomfield Hills, MI 48302
Ph: (248)745-9700
Free: 800-886-4044
Fax: (248)745-9763
URL: http://www.ComForcare.com

Description: Franchise provides home health care for seniors. **No. of Franchise Units:** 150. **No. of Company-Owned Units:** 1. **Founded:** 1996.. **Franchised:** 2001. **Equity Capital Needed:** $105,000-$155,000 includes franchise fee. **Franchise Fee:** $39,500. **Training:** Yes.

320 ■ Homewatch CareGivers
7100 E Belleview Ave., Ste. 303
Greenwood Village, CO 80111
Ph: (303)953-6871
Free: 800-472-2290
Fax: (303)758-1724
Co. E-mail: franchise@homewatchcaregivers.com
URL: http://www.homewatchcaregivers.com

Description: Offers services to elderly people who want to stay at home. **No. of Franchise Units:** 193. **No. of Company-Owned Units:** 3. **Founded:** 1980.. **Franchised:** 1997. **Equity Capital Needed:** $58,500-$90,000 initial investment. **Franchise Fee:** $35,000. **Training:** Offers pre-training, initial training, and post training program.

321 ■ Passport Health, Inc.
921 E Fort Ave., Ste. 100
Baltimore, MD 21230
Ph: (410)727-0556
Fax: (410)727-0696

Description: Offers health and nutrition services along with senior care facilities. **No. of Franchise Units:** 215. **No. of Company-Owned Units:** 16. **Founded:** 1997.. **Franchised:** 1997. **Equity Capital Needed:** $100,000. **Franchise Fee:** $35,000. **Training:** Yes.

322 ■ Personal Training Institute
Personal Training Institute Franchises, LLC
500 N Broadway
Jericho, NY 11753
Ph: (516)342-9064
Fax: (516)342-9067

Description: Weight loss and fitness center. **No. of Franchise Units:** 24. **Founded:** 1987.. **Franchised:** 2005. **Equity Capital Needed:** $112,050-$221,500. **Franchise Fee:** $10,000- $20,000. **Royalty Fee:** 6%. **Financial Assistance:** Third party financing available. **Training:** Provides 2 weeks training at headquarters, 1 week onsite and ongoing support.

COMPUTERIZED DATABASES

323 ■ AgeLine®
10 Estes St.
Ipswich, MA 01938-2106
Ph: (978)356-6500
Free: 800-653-2726
Fax: (978)356-6565
Co. E-mail: information@ebscohost.com
URL: http://www.ebscohost.com
Contact: Tim Collins, President
E-mail: tcollins@ebscohost.com
Availability: Online: EBSCO Publishing. **Type:** Bibliographic.

324 ■ Consumer InSite<svs>
610 Opperman Dr.
Eagen, MN 55122
Free: 800-477-4300
Co. E-mail: gale.contentlicensing@cengage.com
URL: http://www.insite2.gale.com
Availability: Online: Cengage Learning Inc. - Gale - InSite2. **Type:** Full-text.

325 ■ Health & Wellness InSite<svs>
610 Opperman Dr.
Eagen, MN 55122
Free: 800-477-4300
Co. E-mail: gale.contentlicensing@cengage.com
URL: http://www.insite2.gale.com
Availability: Online: Cengage Learning Inc. - Gale - InSite2. **Type:** Full-text.

326 ■ State Health Care Regulatory Developments™
1801 S Bell St.
Arlington, VA 22202
Free: 800-372-1033
Co. E-mail: customercare@bna.com
URL: http://www.bna.com
Availability: Online: Bloomberg LP-Bloomberg BNA; Thomson Reuters - Westlaw. **Type:** Full-text.

LIBRARIES

327 ■ American College of Health Care Administrators - ACHCA Information Center
1321 Duke St., Ste. 400
Alexandria, VA 22314
Ph: (202)536-5120
Fax: (866)874-1585
Co. E-mail: mgrachek@achca.org
URL: http://www.achca.org
Scope: Long-term care, gerontology. **Services:** Center open to ACHCA members only. **Founded:** 1991. **Holdings:** 100 books; governmental statistical reports. **Subscriptions:** 125 journals and other serials.

328 ■ Philadelphia Corporation for Aging Library—PCA Library.
642 N. Broad St.
Philadelphia, PA 19130
Ph: (215)765-9000
Free: 888-482-9060
Fax: (215)765-9066
Co. E-mail: sspencer@pcaphl.org
URL: http://www.pcacares.org/
Contact: Scott Spencer, Librarian
Scope: Gerontology, gerontological literature, health and social services for the aging. **Services:** Interlibrary loan; copying; library open to the public for reference use only; collection of proposals for

services to elderly available for review by appointment only (photocopies not permitted). **Founded:** 1978. **Holdings:** 3700 books and reports; 154 periodical volumes on microfiche; 300 videos; 16 VF drawers of pamphlets and reports. **Subscriptions:** 100 journals and other serials.

329 ■ Pima Council on Aging Library
8467 E. Broadway Blvd.
Tucson, AZ 85710
Ph: (520)790-7262
Fax: (520)790-7577
Co. E-mail: help@pcoa.org
URL: http://pcoa.org/
Contact: Melissa S. Morgan, Librarian
Scope: Aging programs and services, gerontology, long-term care, public policy related to the elderly. **Services:** Interlibrary loan; copying; SDI; library open to the public by appointment. **Founded:** 1979. **Holdings:** 2000 books; 24 VF drawers; 20,000 other cataloged items. **Subscriptions:** 30 journals and other serials; 350 newsletters; 6 newspapers. **Telecommunication Services:** mmorgan@pcoa.org.

330 ■ Benjamin Rose Library
11900 Fairhill Rd., Ste. 300
Cleveland, OH 44120
Ph: (216)373-1682
Fax: (216)373-1813
Co. E-mail: kbensing@benrose.org
URL: http://www.benrose.org/Library/Library.cfm
Contact: Karen McNally Bensing, Librarian
Scope: Aged - research, home care, long-term care, nursing homes, social work, nursing, elder abuse. **Services:** Interlibrary loan; copying; library open to the public by appointment on a limited schedule. **Founded:** 1974. **Holdings:** 1500 books; 4 lateral file drawers of reports, papers, manuscripts. **Subscriptions:** 80 journals and other serials. **Telecommunication Services:** info@benrose.org.

331 ■ United Way 2-1-1 - Information & Referral Service
PO Box 7548
Madison, WI 53707-7548
Ph: (608)246-4350
Fax: (608)246-4367
Co. E-mail: sandye@uwdc.org
URL: http://www.unitedwaydanecounty.org
Contact: Sandy Erickson, Director
Scope: Geriatrics, medical care. **Services:** Community resource telephone line providing information and referral services for Dane County. **Founded:** 1982.

332 ■ Virginia Commonwealth University - Virginia Center on Aging - Information Resources Center
730 E. Broad St.
Theatre Row Building
Richmond, VA 23219
Ph: (804)828-1525
Fax: (804)828-7905
Co. E-mail: eansello@vcu.edu
URL: http://www.sahp.vcu.edu/vcoa
Contact: Dr. Edward F. Ansello, Director
Scope: Gerontology, mental health, sociology and the politics of aging, geriatrics, family relationships, long-term care, lifelong learning. **Services:** Library open to the public with restrictions (audio/visual materials available to Virginia residents only). **Founded:** 1978. **Holdings:** 1500 books; 4 archives; 120 AV items. **Subscriptions:** 6 journals and other serials.

333 ■ Western Illinois Area Agency on Aging - Greta J. Brook Elderly Living and Learning Facility—Elderly Living and Learning Facility (ELLF).
729 34th Ave.
Rock Island, IL 61201
Ph: (309)793-6800
Free: 800-322-1051

Fax: (309)793-6807
Co. E-mail: firststopforseniors@wiaaa.org
URL: http://www.wiaaa.org
Contact: Barbara Eskildsen, Executive Director
Scope: Gerontology, Senior Housing, Family Caregiving, Medicare, Medicaid, Social Security, Retirement Planning, Intergenerational Programs, Program Development. **Services:** Interlibrary loan; Senior Computer Center open to those fifty years of age or older; facility open to the public. **Founded:** 1988. **Holdings:** 1108 books; 260 videotapes; 130 audio/visual materials; 35 DVDs and CDs. **Subscriptions:** 2 journals and other serials, 12 periodicals. **Telecommunication Services:** jblaser@wiaaa.org.

RESEARCH CENTERS

334 ■ Brown University - Center for Gerontology and Health Care Research
121 S Main St., S-6
Providence, RI 02912
Ph: (401)863-3211
Fax: (401)863-3489
Co. E-mail: richard_besdine@brown.edu
URL: http://www.chcr.brown.edu
Contact: Dr. Richard W. Besdine, Director
Services: Data collection, database development and training. **Founded:** 1986. **Publications:** *Monograph Series.* **Educational Activities:** Biology of Aging Conference. **Awards:** Medical Student Gerontol-

ogy Prize; Faculty development fellowships; Graduate student research assistantships; Postdoctoral training grants. **Telecommunication Services:** info@brown.edu.

335 ■ Case Western Reserve University - Elderly Care Research Center (ECRC)
231B Mather Memorial Bldg.
10900 Euclid Ave.
Cleveland, OH 44106-7124
Ph: (216)368-2704
Fax: (216)368-1078
Co. E-mail: exk@case.edu
URL: http://www.case.edu/artsci/soci/ecrc
Contact: Dr. Eva Kahana, Director
Founded: 1968. **Publications:** *ECRC Brochure.* **Telecommunication Services:** ecrc@case.edu.

START-UP INFORMATION

336 ■ *The Small Business Owner's Manual: Everything You Need to Know to Start Up and Run Your Business*
Pub: Career Press, Incorporated
Ed: Joe Kennedy. **Released:** June 2005. **Price:** $19.99 (US), $26.95 (Canadian). **Description:** Comprehensive guide for starting a small business, focusing on twelve ways to obtain financing, business plans, selling and advertising products and services, hiring and firing employees, setting up a Web site, business law, accounting issues, insurance, equipment, computers, banks, financing, customer credit and collection, leasing, and more.

ASSOCIATIONS AND OTHER ORGANIZATIONS

337 ■ *Ad Complaints Report*
S Tower
175 Bloor St. E, Ste. 1801
Toronto, ON, Canada M4W 3R8
Ph: (416)961-6311
Fax: (416)961-7904
Co. E-mail: info@adstandards.com
URL: http://www.adstandards.com/en
Contact: John Coyne, Chairman
Released: Annual

338 ■ Advertising Club of New York (ACNY)
989 Ave. of the Americas, 7th Fl.
New York, NY 10018
Ph: (212)533-8080
Fax: (212)533-1929
Co. E-mail: gina@theadvertisingclub.org
URL: http://www.theadvertisingclub.org
Contact: Beth-Ann Eason, Chairwoman
Description: Professionals in advertising, publishing, marketing and business. Sponsors educational and public service activities, promotional and public relations projects and talks by celebrities and advertising persons. Conducts annual advertising and marketing course, which offers classes in copywriting, special graphics, verbal communication, advertising production, sale promotion, marketing and management. Sponsors competitions and charitable programs. **Founded:** 1906. **Publications:** *ACNY Membership Roster* (Annual); *Auction Catalogue and Program* (Annual); *ANDY Souvenir Journal* (Annual). **Awards:** ANDY Awards; ANDY Award (Annual); The Silver Medal Award (Annual).

339 ■ Advertising Council (AC)
815 2nd Ave., 9th Fl.
New York, NY 10017
Ph: (212)922-1500
Fax: (212)922-1676
Co. E-mail: info@adcouncil.org
URL: http://www.adcouncil.org
Contact: Andrew Robertson, Chairman
Description: Founded and supported by American business, media, and advertising sectors to conduct public service advertising campaigns. Encourages advertising media to contribute time and space and advertising agencies to supply creative talent and facilities to further timely national causes. Specific campaigns include: Drug Abuse Prevention; AIDS Prevention; Teen-Alcoholism; Child Abuse; Crime Prevention; Forest Fire Prevention. **Founded:** 1941. **Publications:** *PSA Bulletin* (Bimonthly). **Awards:** Public Service Award (Annual); Silver Bell Award (Annual); Public Service Award.

340 ■ Advertising and Marketing International Network (AMIN)
3587 Northshore Dr.
Wayzata, MN 55391
Ph: (952)457-1116
Fax: (952)471-7752
Co. E-mail: jsundby@aminworldwide.com
URL: http://www.aminworldwide.com
Contact: Janna Sperry Sundby, Manager, Member Services
Description: Comprised of cooperative worldwide network of non-competing independent advertising agencies organized to provide facilities and branch office services for affiliated agencies. **Founded:** 1932. **Educational Activities:** Advertising and Marketing International Network Seminar (Annual).

341 ■ Advertising Standards Canada (ASC)—Normes Canadiennes de la Publicite
S Tower
175 Bloor St. E, Ste. 1801
Toronto, ON, Canada M4W 3R8
Ph: (416)961-6311
Fax: (416)961-7904
Co. E-mail: info@adstandards.com
URL: http://www.adstandards.com/en
Contact: John Coyne, Chairman
Description: Committed to ensuring the integrity and viability of advertising through industry self-regulation. Administers the Canada Code of Advertising Standards, accepts and reviews complaints about advertising, and provides advertising pre-clearance services. **Founded:** 1957. **Publications:** *Ad Complaints Report* (Annual).

342 ■ Advertising Women of New York (AWNY)
25 W 45th St., Ste. 403
New York, NY 10036
Ph: (212)221-7969
Fax: (212)221-8296
Co. E-mail: awny@awny.org
URL: http://www.awny.org
Contact: Arlene Manos, President
E-mail: amanos@awny.org
Description: Women in advertising and related industries that provides a forum for professional growth, serves as catalyst for enhancement and advancement of women; promotes philanthropic endeavors. Conducts events of interest and benefit to members and non-members involved in the industry. Membership concentrated in the metropolitan New York area. **Founded:** 1912. **Awards:** Silver Medal Award; Advertising Woman of the Year (Annual); President's Award; Crystal Prism Award.

343 ■ American Academy of Advertising (AAA)
Florida International University
831 Langdon
831 Fearrington Post
Pittsboro, NC 27312
Ph: (786)393-3333
Free: 866-607-8512
Co. E-mail: director@aaasite.org
URL: http://www.aaasite.org
Contact: Patricia B. Rose, Executive Director
Description: Serves as a professional organization for college and university teachers of advertising and for industry professionals who wish to contribute to the development of advertising education. **Founded:** 1958. **Publications:** *Journal of Advertising* (Quarterly); *Journal of Interactive Advertising* (Semiannual); *Proceedings of the Conference of the American Academy of Advertising* (Annual); *Roster of Members* (Annual). **Awards:** Distinguished Service Award; Doctoral Dissertation Grant Competition; Distinguished Service Award (Periodic); Fellow of the American Academy of Advertising Award (Periodic); Journal of Advertising Best Article Award (Annual); Outstanding Contribution to Research Award (Periodic).

344 ■ American Advertising Federation (AAF)—AAF
1101 Vermont Ave. NW, Ste. 500
Washington, DC 20005-6306
Ph: (202)898-0089
Free: 800-999-2231
Fax: (202)898-0159
Co. E-mail: aaf@aaf.org
URL: http://www.aaf.org
Contact: James Edmund Datri, President
Description: Works to advance the business of advertising as a vital and essential part of the American economy and culture through government and public relations; professional development and recognition; community service, social responsibility and high standards; and benefits and services to members. Operates Advertising Hall of Fame, Hall of Achievement, and National Student Advertising Competition. Maintains speakers' bureau. **Founded:** 1967. **Publications:** *AAF Government Report*; *American Advertising Federation--Speakers Directory* (Annual); *Communicator* (Monthly); *Newsline* (Monthly); *American Advertising*; *American Advertising: The American Advertising Federation Magazine* (Quarterly). **Educational Activities:** National Advertising (Annual); American Advertising Federation Annual Conference (Annual). **Awards:** ADDY Awards (Annual); Barton A. Cummings Gold Medal Award (Annual); Betty Riehl Excellence in Service Award (Annual); Distinguished Advertising Educator Award (Annual); Silver Medal Award; Advertising Hall of Fame; Club Achievement Awards; Distinguished Advertising Educator Award; National Student Advertising Competition; Silver Medal; Advertising Hall of Achievement (Annual); James S. Fish Aid to Advertising Education Award. **Telecommunication Services:** acroot@aaf.org.

345 ■ American Association of Advertising Agencies (AAAA)
1065 Ave. of the Americas, 16th Fl.
New York, NY 10018
Ph: (212)682-2500
Fax: (212)682-8391
Co. E-mail: nhill@aaaa.org
URL: http://www.aaaa.org
Contact: Nancy Hill, President

Description: Fosters development of the advertising industry; assists member agencies to operate more efficiently and profitably. Sponsors member information and international services. Maintains 47 committees. Conducts government relations. **Scope:** advertising, marketing. **Services:** Interlibrary loan; primarily serves association members. **Founded:** 1917. **Holdings:** 2000 books; 300 VF drawers of clippings, reports, and pamphlets. **Subscriptions:** 250 journals and other serials. **Publications:** *AAAA Publications Catalog* (Periodic); *The Reporter* (Bimonthly); *Roster of Members* (Annual); *Cable Broadcast Traffic Guide*; *American Association of Advertising Agencies-- Roster and Organization* (Annual); *Advertising Agency Accounting/Finance/Collaboration Software Directory.* **Educational Activities:** American Association of Advertising Agencies Conference (Annual). **Awards:** O'Toole Agency Awards; O'Toole Award (Annual); Bill Bernbach Diversity Scholarships; Multicultural Advertising Intern Program; O'Toole Multicultural Advertising Award; O'Toole Public Service Award; AAAA Operation Jumpstart III Scholarships. **Telecommunication Services:** research@aaaa.org; webmaster@aaaa.org.

346 ■ American Photographic Artists (APA)
PO Box 725146
Atlanta, GA 31139
Free: 888-272-6264
Co. E-mail: ceo@apanational.com
URL: http://www.apanational.com
Contact: Theresa Raffetto, President

Description: Enhances dialogue among professional photographers and their clients. Suggests standards and business practices to improve the quality of professional photography; and acts as a forum for discussion of problems and solutions. Conducts discussion groups. **Founded:** 1981. **Publications:** *1999 APA National Photographer's Survey Report.*

347 ■ *Annual Fact Book*
1 Concorde Gate, Ste. 607
Don Mills, ON, Canada M3C 3N6
Ph: (416)391-2362
Fax: (416)441-4062
Co. E-mail: info@the-cma.org
URL: http://www.the-cma.org
Contact: John Gustavson, President
Released: Annual

348 ■ Association of National Advertisers (ANA)
708 3rd Ave., 33rd Fl.
New York, NY 10017-4270
Ph: (212)697-5950
Fax: (212)687-7310
Co. E-mail: info@ana.net
URL: http://www.ana.net
Contact: Robert D. Liodice, President

Description: Serves the needs of members by providing marketing and advertising industry leadership in traditional and e-marketing, legislative leadership, information resources, professional development and industry-wide networking. Maintains offices in New York City and Washington, DC. **Founded:** 1910. **Publications:** *The Advertiser* (Bimonthly). **Educational Activities:** Agency Relationship Forum (Annual). **Awards:** Multicultural Excellence Awards; Robert V. Goldstein Award (Annual).

349 ■ Canadian Advertising Research Foundation (CARF)—La Fondation Canadienne de Recherche en Publicite
160 Bloor St. E, Ste. 1005
Toronto, ON, Canada M4W 1B9
Ph: (416)413-3864

Fax: (416)413-3879
Co. E-mail: tjames@tvb.ca
URL: http://www.carf.ca
Contact: Tiffany James, Administrator
Description: Advertisers, advertising agencies, media outlets, research companies, and other firms with an interest in advertising and advertising research. Promotes growth and development in the fields of advertising research and media evaluation. Develops and publishes guidelines for communications research and studies; stimulates creation of new research techniques; serves as a forum for exchange of information on advertising and media research. Makes available services including media research and executive appraisals; offers reduced subscription rates to national and international advertising and media research publications. **Founded:** 1949. **Publications:** *CARF Newsletter* (Bimonthly); *CARF Update* (Periodic). **Awards:** Georgian College Award for Research (Annual); CARF Award in Memory of Arnold Acton (Annual).

350 ■ Canadian Marketing Association (CMA)—Association Canadienne du Marketing
1 Concorde Gate, Ste. 607
Don Mills, ON, Canada M3C 3N6
Ph: (416)391-2362
Fax: (416)441-4062
Co. E-mail: info@the-cma.org
URL: http://www.the-cma.org
Contact: John Gustavson, President
Description: Information-based marketing firms. Promotes growth and development in the information-based marketing industry. Facilitates communication and cooperation among members; serves as a clearinghouse on information-based marketing. **Founded:** 1967. **Publications:** *Annual Fact Book* (Annual); *E-Communicator* (10/year); *Canadian Marketing Association Membership Directory* (Annual).

351 ■ *CARF Newsletter*
160 Bloor St. E, Ste. 1005
Toronto, ON, Canada M4W 1B9
Ph: (416)413-3864
Fax: (416)413-3879
Co. E-mail: tjames@tvb.ca
URL: http://www.carf.ca
Contact: Tiffany James, Administrator
Released: Bimonthly **Price:** included in membership dues.

352 ■ *CARF Update*
160 Bloor St. E, Ste. 1005
Toronto, ON, Canada M4W 1B9
Ph: (416)413-3864
Fax: (416)413-3879
Co. E-mail: tjames@tvb.ca
URL: http://www.carf.ca
Contact: Tiffany James, Administrator
Released: Periodic

353 ■ Concerned Children's Advertisers (CCA)
885 Don Mills Rd., Ste. 301
Toronto, ON, Canada M3C 1V9
Ph: (416)484-0871
Fax: (416)484-6564
Co. E-mail: info@cca-arpe.ca
URL: http://www.cca-kids.ca
Contact: Bev Deeth, President
Description: Companies marketing their products to children. Seeks to combine effective children's advertising with the "social responsibility of caring for children". Promotes adherence by members to the Broadcast Code for Advertising for Children. Creates alliances between members, advertising producers, and government agencies to ensure creation of effective and socially responsible children's advertising. Conducts research and educational programs; produces television public service announcements on topics including substance abuse and healthy lifestyles. **Services:** Conducts educational programs. **Founded:** 1990.

354 ■ *E-Communicator*
1 Concorde Gate, Ste. 607
Don Mills, ON, Canada M3C 3N6

Ph: (416)391-2362
Fax: (416)441-4062
Co. E-mail: info@the-cma.org
URL: http://www.the-cma.org
Contact: John Gustavson, President
Released: 10/year

355 ■ Intermarket Agency Network (IAN)
c/o Cameron Green, Pres.
1938 Fairview Ave. E, Ste. 200
Seattle, WA 98102-3650
Ph: (206)447-4747
Fax: (206)447-9494
Co. E-mail: camg@greenrubino.com
URL: http://www.intermarketnetwork.com
Contact: Cam Green, President
Description: An active network of high-powered marketing/communications agencies in the United States, Canada, Central and South America, and Europe. **Founded:** 1967.

356 ■ International Advertising Association (IAA)
275 Madison Ave., Ste. 2102
New York, NY 10016
Ph: (212)557-1133
Fax: (212)983-0455
Co. E-mail: membership@iaaglobal.org
URL: http://www.iaaglobal.org
Contact: Luis Mendiola Codina, President

Description: Global network of advertisers, advertising agencies, the media and related services, spanning 99 countries. Demonstrates to governments and consumers the benefits of advertising as the foundation of diverse, independent media. Protects and advances freedom of commercial speech and consumer choice, encourages greater practice and acceptance of advertising self-regulation, provides a forum to debate emerging professional marketing communications issues and their consequences in the fast-changing world environment, and takes the lead in state-of-the-art professional development through education and training for the marketing communications industry of tomorrow. Conducts research on such topics as restrictions and taxes on advertising, advertising trade practices and related information, and advertising expenditures around the world. Sponsors IAA Education Program. Has compiled recommendations for international advertising standards and practices. **Scope:** advertising/marketing communications, regulatory issues affecting the industry. **Founded:** 1938. **Subscriptions:** audiovisuals books clippings monographs periodicals. **Publications:** *IAA Membership Directory* (Annual); *International Advertising Association--Membership Directory* (Continuous); *IAA National & World News*; *The Case for Advertising Self-Regulation*; *IAA Annual Report* (Annual); *IAA Membership Directory* (Annual); *International Advertising Association Membership Directory*; *IAA National & World News*. **Educational Activities:** World Advertising (Biennial); International Advertising Association - World Advertising Congress (Biennial). **Awards:** Samir Fares Award (Biennial). **Telecommunication Services:** iaa@iaaglobal.org.

357 ■ International Communications Agency Network (ICOM)
PO Box 490
Rollinsville, CO 80474-0490
Ph: (303)258-9511
Fax: (303)484-4087
Co. E-mail: info@icomagencies.com
URL: http://www.icomagencies.com
Contact: Mr. Gary Burandt, Executive Director

Description: Network of non-competing advertising agencies. Provides an interchange of management information, international facilities, and branch office service for partner agencies. Provides discounts on syndicated services and access to 1,000 computer databases. **Founded:** 1950. **Publications:** *Agency Client Lists* (Monthly); *Agency Client Lists* (Monthly); *The Globe* (Monthly); *Membership Roster* (Annual). **Educational Activities:** International Management Conference (Annual). **Awards:** Creative Award (Annual).

358 ■ Mailing and Fulfillment Service Association (MFSA)
1421 Prince St., Ste. 410
Alexandria, VA 22314-2806
Ph: (703)836-9200
Free: 800-333-6272
Fax: (703)548-8204
Co. E-mail: mfsa-mail@mfsanet.org
URL: http://www.mfsanet.org
Contact: Michael Kellogg, Chairman of the Board

Description: Commercial direct mail producers, letter shops, mailing list houses, fulfillment operations, and advertising agencies. Conducts special interest group meetings. Offers specialized education; conducts research programs. **Founded:** 1920. **Publications:** *Postscripts* (Monthly); *MFSA Wage Salary, and Fringe Benefit Survey* (Semiannual); *Performance Profiles: The Financial Ratios for the Mailing Service Industry* (Annual); *Who's Who: MASA's Buyers' Guide to Blue Ribbon Mailing Services* (Annual). **Educational Activities:** Mid-Winter Executive Conference (Annual). **Awards:** Leo G. Bill Bernheimer Award (Annual); Miles Kimball Medallion (Annual); Henry Hoke, Sr. Award; Miles Kimball Medallion; Mailing Industry Ingenuity Award; President's Plaque; John Howie Wright Cup; L.V. Luke Kaiser Educational Award (Annual); Robert M. Huse Chapter Achievement Award (Annual); Leo G. Bill Bernheimer, Jr. Award; L. U. "Luke" Kaiser Educational Award.

359 ■ Marketing and Advertising Global Network (MAGNET)
1017 Perry Hwy., Ste. 5
Pittsburgh, PA 15237
Ph: (412)366-6850
Fax: (412)366-6840
Co. E-mail: mxdirector@verizon.net
URL: http://www.magnetglobal.org
Contact: Cheri D. Gmiter, Executive Director

Description: Cooperative network of non-competing advertising, marketing, merchandising, and public relations agencies. Aims to bring about, through mutual cooperation, greater accomplishment and efficiency in the management of member advertising agencies. Other goals are: to raise standards of the advertising agency business through the exchange of information relative to agency management and all phases of advertising; to exchange information on all common problems, such as management, sales development, market studies, agency functions, and operations. Aims to inform the general public of current global marketing trends. **Founded:** 1946. **Publications:** *MAGNET Matters* (3/year); *This Week in MAGNET* (Weekly). **Educational Activities:** Marketing and Advertising Global Network Annual Meeting (Annual). **Awards:** Indie Awards Competition (Annual). **Telecommunication Services:** cheri@magnetglobal.org.

360 ■ National Advertising Review Board (NARB)
70 W 36th St., 13th Fl.
New York, NY 10018
Ph: (212)705-0114
Co. E-mail: bhopewell@asrcreviews.org
URL: http://www.asrcreviews.org/category/narb
Contact: Bruce Hopewell, Director

Description: Individuals from industry and the public. Sponsored by the National Advertising Review Council for the purpose of sustaining high standards of truth and accuracy in national advertising. Aims to maintain a self-regulatory mechanism that responds constructively to public complaints about national advertising and which significantly improves advertising performance and credibility. **Scope:** advertising disputes. **Founded:** 1971. **Subscriptions:** 84 reports. **Publications:** *NARB Panel Reports.*

361 ■ Sign Association of Canada (SAC)—Association Canadienne de l'enseigne
216 Chrislea Rd., Ste. 301
Woodbridge, ON, Canada L4L 8S5
Ph: (905)856-0000
Free: 877-470-9787
Fax: (905)856-0064
Co. E-mail: fred@sac-ace.ca
URL: http://www.sac-ace.ca
Contact: Fred Elkins, President

Description: Manufacturers of advertising signs; suppliers of sign components and services. Promotes increased use of signs in advertising. Represents members' interests. Facilitates communication and cooperation among members; conducts research and studies on advertising, sign technologies, and human resources. Sponsors competitions. **Services:** Sponsors competitions. **Founded:** 1955. **Publications:** *Signs Canada* (Bimonthly). **Educational Activities:** Sign Association of Canada Conference (Annual).

362 ■ Signs Canada
216 Chrislea Rd., Ste. 301
Woodbridge, ON, Canada L4L 8S5
Ph: (905)856-0000
Free: 877-470-9787
Fax: (905)856-0064
Co. E-mail: fred@sac-ace.ca
URL: http://www.sac-ace.ca
Contact: Fred Elkins, President
Released: Bimonthly

363 ■ Traffic Audit Bureau for Media Measurement (TAB)
271 Madison Ave., Ste. 1504
New York, NY 10016
Ph: (212)972-8075
Fax: (212)972-8928
Co. E-mail: larryhennessy@tabonline.com
URL: http://www.tabonline.com
Contact: Joseph C. Philport, President

Description: Advertisers, advertising agencies, operators of outdoor advertising plants, bus shelter advertising companies, and backlighted display and painted bulletin companies. Sets standard practices for the evaluation of circulation and visibility of outdoor advertising; issues statements on the circulation values of outdoor advertising plants. Encourages standardization of terminology and practices in the industry. Seeks to educate those involved in out-of-home media on ways of developing circulation data for advertising sites. Compiles statistics. **Founded:** 1933. **Publications:** *TABBriefs*; *Building Accountability for Out of Home Media*; *TAB Eyes On Out of Home*; *What You Should Know About the New TAB Audit.* **Educational Activities:** Conference and Marketing Expo (Annual); Traffic Audit Bureau for Media Measurement Out of Home Media Conference & Marketing Expo (Annual). **Telecommunication Services:** inquiry@tabonline.com.

364 ■ Transworld Advertising Agency Network (TAAN)
814 Watertown St.
Newton, MA 02465
Ph: (617)795-1706
Fax: (419)730-1706
Co. E-mail: peterg@taan.org
URL: http://www.taan.org
Contact: Mark Gale, Chairman of the Board

Description: Independently owned advertising agencies that cooperate for exchange of management education and information, reciprocal service, and personal local contact. Allows members to seek aid of other members in campaign planning, creative services, merchandising, public relations, publicity, media, research, and test facilities. Conducts annual expertise audit. **Founded:** 1936.

DIRECTORIES OF EDUCATIONAL PROGRAMS

365 ■ Who's Who in the Media and Communications
Pub: Marquis Who's Who L.L.C.
Contact: James A. Finkelstein, President
URL(s): www.marquiswhoswho.com. **Covers:** More than 18,500 professionals in print journalism, broadcasting, publishing, television, public relations, advertising, radio, telecommunications, interactive multimedia, and education. **Entries include:** Biographical data.

REFERENCE WORKS

366 ■ "10 Trends That Are Shaping Global Media Consumption" in Advertising Age (Vol. 81, December 6, 2010, No. 43, pp. 3)
Pub: Crain Communications, Inc.
Ed: Ann Marie Kerwin. **Description:** Ad Age offers the statistics from the TV penetration rate in Kenya to the number of World Cup watchers and more.

367 ■ "A&E Networks" in Brandweek (Vol. 49, April 21, 2008, No. 16, pp. SR9)
Pub: VNU Business Media, Inc.
Ed: Anthony Crupi. **Description:** Provides contact information for sales and marketing personnel for the A&E Networks as well as a listing of the station's top programming and an analysis of the current season and the target audience for those programs running in the current season. A&E has reinvented itself as a premium entertainment brand over the last five years and with its $2.5 million per episode acquisition of The Sopranos, the station signaled that it was serious about getting back into the scripted programming business. The acquisition also helped the network compete against other cable networks and led to a 20 percent increase in prime-time viewers.

368 ■ "Abacast, Citadel Strike Radio Ad Deal" in Business Journal Portland (Vol. 27, December 31, 2010, No. 44, pp. 3)
Pub: Portland Business Journal
Ed: Erik Siemers. **Description:** Software firm Abacast Inc. has partnered with Citadel Media to aid the latter's advertising sales. Citadel provides radio networks and syndicated programs to 4,200 affiliate stations.

369 ■ "ABC" in Brandweek (Vol. 49, April 21, 2008, No. 16, pp. SR6)
Pub: VNU Business Media, Inc.
Ed: John Consoli. **Description:** Provides contact information for sales and marketing personnel for the ABC network as well as a listing of the station's top programming and an analysis of the current season and the target audience for those programs running in the current season.

370 ■ "Ad Firms Stew Over Lost Car Biz; Diversifying Business Is Uphill Battle" in Crain's Detroit Business (Vol. 23, July 30, 2007, No. 31)
Pub: Crain Communications, Inc.
Ed: Jean Halliday. **Description:** Struggling Detroit automakers are breaking their tradition of loyalty and moving their advertising accounts to agencies in Los Angeles, San Francisco, and Boston; This has Detroit's advertising community very worried.

371 ■ "Advertisers Don't Party With CBS's Swingers" in Advertising Age (Vol. 79, July 7, 2008, No. 26, pp. 1)
Pub: Crain Communications, Inc.
Ed: Brian Steinberg. **Description:** Broadcast networks that are trying to air edgier programming such as CBS's 'Swingtown' but are running into problems with advertisers who are fearful of consumer complaints and backlash when running commercials during such fare.

372 ■ "Advertisers Hooked on Horns, their Playground" in Austin Business JournalInc. (Vol. 28, July 25, 2008, No. 19, pp. A1)
Pub: American City Business Journals
Ed: Sandra Zaragoza. **Description:** Renovation of the D.K. Royal-Texas Memorial Stadium has increased its advertising revenue from $570,000 in 1993 to $10 in 2008. Sponsorship has grown in the past years due to the revenue-sharing agreement, a ten-year contract through 2015 between the University of Texas and IMG College Sports.

373 ■ Advertising Age--Agencies Ranked by Gross Income Issue
Pub: Crain Communications Inc.
URL(s): chicagobusiness.com/. **Ed:** Craig Endicott. **Released:** Annual **Price:** $25, Individuals PDF; $45, Individuals Excel. **Covers:** More than 600 advertising

agencies. **Entries include:** For agencies with gross income over three million dollars: agency name, rank for two years, billing, gross income, and number of employees.

374 ■ "Advertising May Take a Big Hit in Southwest/AirTran Merger" in Baltimore Business Journal (Vol. 28, October 1, 2010, No. 21, pp. 1)
Pub: Baltimore Business Journal
Ed: Gary Haber. **Description:** Advertising on television stations and the publishing industry in Baltimore could drop as a result of the merger between rival discount airlines Southwest Airlines and AirTran Airways. Southwest is among the top advertisers in the U.S., spending $126 million in 2009. No local jobs are expected to be affected because neither airline uses a local advertising firm.

375 ■ "Africa Rising" in Harvard Business Review (Vol. 86, September 2008, No. 9, pp. 36)
Pub: Harvard Business School Press
Ed: John T. Landry. **Description:** Review of the book entitled, 'Africa Rising: How 900 Million African Consumers Offer More Than You Think' provides advice for marketing to those on the African continent.

376 ■ "The Agency Model Is Bent But Not Broken" in Advertising Age (Vol. 79, July 7, 2008, No. 26, pp. 17)
Pub: Crain Communications, Inc.
Ed: Stephen Fajen. **Description:** In the new-media environment, advertising agencies must change the way in which they do business and receive payment.

377 ■ "The Agency-Selection Process Needs Fixing Now" in Advertising Age (Vol. 79, July 7, 2008, No. 26, pp. 18)
Pub: Crain Communications, Inc.
Ed: Avi Dan. **Description:** Marketers are facing increased challenges in this sagging economic climate and must realize the importance of choosing the correct advertising agency for their company in order to benefit from a more-stable relationship that yields better business results. Advice for marketers regarding the best way to choose an agency is included.

378 ■ "The AHA Moment" in Hispanic Business (December 2010)
Pub: Hispanic Business
Ed: Rebecca Vallaneda. **Description:** An interview with Gisela Girard on how competitive market conditions push buttons. Girard stepped down from her 18-month position as chairwoman the Association of Hispanic Advertising Agencies. She has more than 20 years of experience in advertising and research marketing.

379 ■ "All Bundled Up" in Entrepreneur (Vol. 35, November 2007, No. 11, pp. 104)
Pub: Entrepreneur Media Inc.
Ed: Kim T. Gordon. **Description:** Bundling is a marketing strategy that combines a variety of features to present products and services as a whole. Tips on how to handle bundling are outlined.

380 ■ All You Need Is a Good Idea!: How to Create Marketing Messages that Actually Get Results
Pub: John Wiley and Sons, Inc.
Ed: Jay Heyman. **Released:** May 2008. **Price:** $24.95. **Description:** Advertising guru Jay Heyman offers advice to successfully market products and services. Heyman uses his years of experience and case histories to become creative with advertising campaigns.

381 ■ "Alliance Atlantis Takes a Cheekier Attitude to Life" in Globe & Mail (March 5, 2007, pp. B5)
Pub: CTVglobemedia Publishing Inc.
Ed: Keith McArthur. **Description:** Alliance Atlantis Communications Inc. is re-branding its human life ministry Life Network specialty channel as Slice. The new channel is being promoted with an advertising campaign.

382 ■ "Ampm Focus Has BP Working Overtime; New Convenience-Store Brand Comes to Chicago" in Crain's Chicago Business (April 28, 2008)
Pub: Crain Communications, Inc.
Ed: John T. Slania. **Description:** Britian's oil giant BP PLC is opening its ampm convenience stores in the Chicago market and has already begun converting most of its 78 Chicago-area gas stations to ampms. The company has also started to franchise the stores to independent operators. BP is promoting the brand with both traditional and unconventional marketing techniques such s real or simulated 3D snacks embedded in bus shelter ads and an in-store Guitar Hero contest featuring finalists from a recent contest at the House of Blues.

383 ■ "Anja Carroll; Media Director-McDonald's USA" in Advertising Age (Vol. 79, November 17, 2008, No. 34, pp. 6)
Pub: Crain Communications, Inc.
Ed: Emily Bryson York. **Description:** Profile of Anja Carroll who is the media director for McDonald's USA and has the challenge of choosing the right mix of media for the corporation.

384 ■ "App Time: Smartphone Applications Aren't Just for Fun and Games Anymore" in Inc. (Volume 32, December 2010, No. 10, pp. 116)
Pub: Inc. Magazine
Ed: Jason Del Rey. **Description:** Smart phone technology can help any small business market their products and services.

385 ■ "Apparel Apparatchic at Kmart" in Barron's (Vol. 88, March 17, 2008, No. 11, pp. 16)
Pub: Dow Jones & Company, Inc.
Description: Kmart began a nationwide search for women to represent the company in a national advertising campaign. Contestants need to upload their photos to Kmart's website and winners will be chosen by a panel of celebrity judges. The contest aims to reverse preconceived negative notions about the store's quality and service.

386 ■ "Are Offline Pushes Important to E-Commerce?" in DM News (Vol. 31, September 14, 2009, No. 23, pp. 10)
Pub: Haymarket Media, Inc.
Description: With the importance of Internet marketing and the popularity of ecommerce increasing experts debate the relevance of more traditional channels of advertising.

387 ■ "Art Attack 2007 Comes to Minneapolis" in Art Business News (Vol. 34, November 2007, No. 11, pp. 11)
Pub: Pfingsten Publishing, LLC
Description: Overview of Art Attack 2007, an open studio and gallery crawl in the Northeast Minneapolis Arts District which featured artists working in glass, ceramics, jewelry, mosaics, mixed media, photography, painting, pottery, sculpture, textiles and wood.

388 ■ "Ask Inc." in Inc. (October 2007, pp. 74)
Pub: Gruner & Jahr USA Publishing
Description: Promoting a new comedy club using television, radio and print advertising and tracking results is discussed.

389 ■ "At 5-Year Mark, News 9 Makes Presence Felt in Competition for Ad Dollars" in Business Review, Albany New York (October 5, 2007)
Pub: American City Business Journals, Inc.
Ed: Barbara Pinckney. **Description:** The 24-hour news channel Capital News 9 can be watched live by viewers on their cell phones beginning late 2007 or early 2008 as part of a deal between Time Warner Cable and Sprint Nextel Corporation to bring Sprint's Pivot technology. News 9 marked its fifth year and plans to continue expanding coverage and provide better services to viewers.

390 ■ "Attention, Please" in Entrepreneur (Vol. 36, April 2008, No. 4, pp. 52)
Pub: Entrepreneur Media, Inc.
Ed: Andrea Cooper. **Description:** Gurbaksh Chahal created his own company ClickAgents at the age of 16, and sold it two years later for $40 million to ValueClick. He then founded BlueLithium, an online advertising network on behavioral targeting, which Yahoo! Inc. bought in 2007 for $300 million. Chahal, now 25, talks about his next plans and describes how BlueLithium caught Yahoo's attention.

391 ■ Authenticity: What Consumers Really Want
Pub: Harvard Business School Press
Ed: James H. Gilmore. **Released:** September 24, 2007. **Price:** $26.95. **Description:** In today's marketplace, consumers tend to buy based on how authentic a company's offer appears. A company's identity is explored through case studies and advertising slogans. The authors write from the theory that most everything is artificial, manmade, and fake.

392 ■ "avVaa World Health Care Products Rolls Out Internet Marketing Program" in Health and Beauty Close-Up (September 18, 2009)
Pub: Close-Up Media
Description: avVaa World Health Care Products, Inc., a biotechnology company, manufacturer and distributor of nationally branded therapeutic, natural health care and skin products, has signed an agreement with Online Performance Marketing to launch of an Internet marketing campaign in order to broaden its presence online. The impact of advertising on the Internet to generate an increase in sales is explored.

393 ■ "Being all a-Twitter" in Canadian Business (Vol. 81, December 8, 2008, No. 21, pp. 22)
Pub: Rogers Media Ltd.
Ed: Andrew Wahl. **Description:** Marketing experts suggest that advertising strategies have to change along with new online social media. Companies are advised to find ways to incorporate social software because workers and customers are expected to continue its use.

394 ■ "Better ROI Or Your Money Back, Says Buzz Agency" in Advertising Age (Vol. 79, July 14, 2008, No. 7, pp. 1)
Pub: Crain Communications, Inc.
Ed: Michael Bush. **Description:** Word-of-mouth marketing is discussed as well as the impact on the advertising industry. Although many firms specializing in this form of marketing have opened over the past few years, many marketers are reluctant to try this route.

395 ■ "Better Than New" in Bellingham Business Journal (Vol. February 2010, pp. 16)
Pub: Sound Publishing Inc.
Ed: Ashley Mitchell. **Description:** Profile of family owned Better Than New clothing store that sells overstock items from department stores and clothing manufacturers. The stores location makes it easy to miss and its only advertising is a large sign posted outside. This is the sixth store owned by the couple, Keijeo and Sirba Halmekanqas.

396 ■ "Blue Bell Touts Non-Shrinkage" in Ice Cream Reporter (Vol. 21, July 20, 2008, No. 8, pp. 1)
Pub: Ice Cream Reporter
Description: Blue Bell Ice Cream is promoting its decision to keep their ice cream products in a full half-gallon container rather than downsizing the package. Thirty-second television ads contrast the move by other ice cream makers to offer less for the same money.

397 ■ BOOM: Marketing to the Ultimate Power Consumer-The Baby-Boomer Woman
Pub: American Management Association
Contact: Charles R. Craig, Chairman
Ed: Mary Brown; Carol Orsborn. **Released:** 2006. **Price:** $24.00.

398 ■ *"Branding Your Way"* in *Canadian Business (Vol. 80, February 12, 2007, No. 4, pp. 31)*
Pub: Rogers Media
Ed: Erin Pooley. **Description:** The trend in involving consumers in brand marketing by seeking their views through contests or inviting them to produce and submit commercials through Internet is discussed.

399 ■ *"Brands' Mass Appeal"* in *ADWEEK (Vol. 51, June 14, 2010, No. 24)*
Pub: Nielsen Business Media Inc.
Ed: Lisa Thorell, James Sherret. **Description:** Engineering/science crowdsourced projects tend to result from posting and/or publishing interim results as well as from other talents building upon those results to produce even better results. However, the author does not see the same results in the creative world.

400 ■ *"Brewing Up a Brand"* in *Canadian Business (Vol. 80, February 26, 2007, No. 5, pp. 68)*
Pub: Rogers Media
Ed: Clavin Leung. **Description:** The marketing strategies adopted by Molson Coors Brewing Company, to improve customer loyalty to the Coors Light brand, are presented.

401 ■ *Briefs for Building Better Brands: Tips, Parables and Insight into Market Leaders*
Pub: AGCD Brandspa Books
Ed: Allan Gorman. **Released:** September 2004. **Description:** In today's marketplace, a company needs to gain consumer trust in order to build a brand. By gaining trust, the brand gets sold by word-of-mouth publicity. The author calls this type of marketing: guerrilla marketing, and he believes it to be more effective than traditional advertising.

402 ■ *"Bright Lights, Big Impact: Why Digital Billboards are Growing in Popularity"* in *Inc. (March 2008, pp. 61-62)*
Pub: Gruner & Jahr USA Publishing
Ed: Sarah Goldstein. **Description:** Clear Channel provides high tech digital billboards which allow companies to change advertising as often as necessary during a contract period. The Outdoor Advertising Association of America predicts the growth of digital billboards at several hundred per year over the next few years. CEO of Magic Media believes all billboards will eventually go digital.

403 ■ *"Broadcast Commercial Acceptance"* in *MarketingMagazine (Vol. 115, September 27, 2010, No. 13, pp. 29)*
Pub: Rogers Publishing Ltd.
Description: Advertising rules for the broadcast commercial industry in Canada are reviewed.

404 ■ *"Business Forecast: Stormy and Successful"* in *Women In Business (Vol. 62, June 2010, No. 2, pp. 12)*
Pub: American Business Women's Association
Ed: Kathleen Leighton. **Description:** Stormy Simon, vice president of customer service at Overstock.com is a self-made career woman who started out as a temporary employee in the company in 2001. She was not able to attend college because she had two sons to care for after her divorce. Simon got involved in advertising and media buying and shares her love for business.

405 ■ *"Buying In"* in *Harvard Business Review (Vol. 86, September 2008, No. 9, pp. 36)*
Pub: Harvard Business School Press
Ed: Andrew O'Connell. **Description:** Review of the book entitled, 'Buying In: The Secret Dialogue between What We Buy and Who We Are' which offers tips that those in the field of marketing will find useful.

406 ■ *Buying In: The Secret Dialogue Between What We Buy and Who We Are*
Pub: Random House
Ed: Rob Walker. **Released:** 2008. **Price:** $25.00. **Description:** The book offers a look at the state of advertising today and shows why even those who

feel like they see through marketing feel attached to specific brands as a way to both project and foster their identities.

407 ■ *"Buzz Marketing for Movies"* in *Business Horizons (September-October 2007, pp. 395)*
Pub: Elsevier Technology Publications
Ed: Iris Mohr. **Description:** Application of buzz marketing through the context of movie differentiation strategies such as cosmetic movie features, differentiation to reach market segments, growing a movie segment, positioning to support the movie image, positioning to extend the movie image, and differentiation via non-traditional channels are all discussed.

408 ■ *Call Me Ted*
Pub: Grand Central Publishing
Ed: Ted Turner. **Released:** 2008. **Price:** $30.00. **Description:** Media mogul, Ted Turner's biography is full of personal and business details from his careers in advertising and broadcasting.

409 ■ *"Canadian Market Data"* in *MarketingMagazine (Vol. 115, September 27, 2010, No. 13, pp. 6)*
Pub: Rogers Publishing Ltd.
Description: Canadian marketing statistics are outlined.

410 ■ *"CBS"* in *Brandweek (Vol. 49, April 21, 2008, No. 16, pp. SR6)*
Pub: VNU Business Media, Inc.
Ed: John Consoli. **Description:** Provides contact information for sales and marketing personnel for the CBS network as well as a listing of the station's top programming and an analysis of the current season and the target audience for those programs running in the current season.

411 ■ *"CBS Television Distribution"* in *Brandweek (Vol. 49, April 21, 2008, No. 16, pp. SR13)*
Pub: VNU Business Media, Inc.
Ed: Marc Berman. **Description:** Provides contact information for sales and marketing personnel for CBS Television Distribution as well as a listing of the station's top programming and an analysis of the current season and the target audience for those programs running in the current season. Due to the unprecedented, decade-plus advantage of first-run leaders such as Wheel of Fortune, Oprah, Judge Judy and Entertainment Tonight, CBS is poised to remain a leader among the syndicates.

412 ■ *"Change Agent; What Peter Francese Says You Need to Know"* in *Advertising Age (Vol. 79, July 7, 2008, No. 26, pp. 13)*
Pub: Crain Communications, Inc.
Ed: Peter Francese. **Description:** Advice for marketers on how to deal effectively with a changing consumer base is given.

413 ■ *"Charlotte Pipe Launches Satirical Campaign"* in *Contractor (Vol. 57, January 2010, No. 1, pp. 6)*
Pub: Penton Media, Inc.
Description: Charlotte Pipe and Foundry Co. launched an advertising campaign that uses social media and humor to make a point about how it can be nearly impossible to determine if imported cast iron pipes and fittings meet the same quality standards as what is made in the U.S. The campaign features 'pipe whisperers' and also spoofs pipe sniffing dogs.

414 ■ *"Cheese Spread Whips Up a Brand New Bowl"* in *Brandweek (Vol. 49, April 21, 2008, No. 16, pp. 17)*
Pub: VNU Business Media, Inc.
Ed: Mike Beirne. **Description:** Mrs. Kinser's Pimento Cheese Spread is launching a new container for its product in order to attempt stronger brand marketing with a better bowl in order to win over the heads of households as young as in their 30s. The company also intends to begin distribution in Texas and the

West Coast. Mrs. Kinser's is hoping that the new packaging will provide a more distinct branding and will help consumers distinguish what flavor they are buying.

415 ■ *"Chief Boo Boo Officer"* in *Marketing to Women (Vol. 21, February 2008, No. 2, pp. 1)*
Pub: EPM Communications Inc.
Contact: Ira Mayer, President
E-mail: imayer@epmcom.com
Ed: Ellen Neuborne. **Description:** Pharmaceutical companies are reaching out to women through innovative marketing techniques.

416 ■ *"Clicks For Cash: Earning More From Your Website"* in *Inc. (December 2007, pp. 64-65)*
Pub: Gruner & Jahr USA Publishing
Ed: Michael Fitzgerald. **Description:** Ways to use a company's Website to generate revenue are discussed. Free services for placing ads include Google AdSense, AdBrite, AuctionAds, Chitkia eMiniMalls, Vizu Answers, and Value Click; profiles of each service are presented.

417 ■ *"CMO Nicholson Exits Pepsi as Share Declines"* in *Advertising Age (Vol. 79, July 7, 2008, No. 26, pp. 4)*
Pub: Crain Communications, Inc.
Ed: Natalie Zmuda. **Description:** Cie Nicholson, the chief marketing officer at Pepsi-Cola UK, is leaving the company at a time when its market share is down; the brand, which was known for its dynamic marketing, has diverted much of its attention from its core brands and shifted attention to the ailing Gatorade brand as well as Sobe Life Water and Amp.

418 ■ *"Comcast Networks"* in *Brandweek (Vol. 49, April 21, 2008, No. 16, pp. SR9)*
Pub: VNU Business Media, Inc.
Ed: Anthony Crupi. **Description:** Provides contact information for sales and marketing personnel for the Comcast networks as well as a listing of the station's top programming and an analysis of the current season and the target audience for those programs running in the current season. Experts believe Comcast will continue to acquire more stations into their portfolio.

419 ■ *"Commensurate with Experience"* in *Entrepreneur (Vol. 37, October 2009, No. 10, pp. 84)*
Pub: Entrepreneur Media, Inc.
Ed: Carol Tice. **Description:** RingRevenue, a firm that specializes in pay-per-call technology that allows affiliate networks and advertising agencies to track purchases, began a funding round in June 2009 which it closed quickly after obtaining $3.5 million in venture capital. The round was closed earlier than the projections of its owners due to their track record.

420 ■ *"Commercials Make Us Like TV More"* in *Harvard Business Review (Vol. 88, October 2010, No. 10, pp. 36)*
Pub: Harvard Business School Publishing
Ed: Leif Nelson. **Description:** Research indicates that people prefer commercial interruption over uninterrupted shows due to the break creating a reactivation of the initial pleasure when beginning a desirable activity.

421 ■ *The Complete Guide to Google Adwords: Secrets, Techniques, and Strategies You Can Learn to Make Millions*
Pub: Atlantic Publishing Company
Released: December 1, 2010. **Price:** $24.95. **Description:** Google AdWords, when it launched in 2002 signaled a fundamental shift in what the Internet was for so many individuals and companies. Learning and understanding how Google AdWords operates and how it can be optimized for maximum exposure, boosting click through rates, conversions, placement, and selection of the right keywords, can be the key to a successful online business.

422 ■ *"Congress Targets Ad Tracking"* in *Inc. (Vol. 33, November 2011, No. 9, pp. 30)*
Pub: Inc. Magazine
Ed: Issie Lapowsky. **Description:** Congressional bills dealing with behavioral tracking whereby advertising networks monitor people's online behavior and use

the date to tailor ads to people's interest propose Do Not Track measures which would allow consumers to turn off online behavior tracking by clicking a button.

423 ■ *"Connie Ozan; Founder, Design Director, Twist Creative, 37" in Crain's Cleveland Business (Vol. 28, November 19, 2007, No. 46)*
Pub: Crain Communications, Inc.
Ed: John Booth. **Description:** Profile of Connie Ozan, design director and founder of Twist Creative, an advertising agency that she runs with her husband, Michael; Ms. Ozan credits her husband's business sense in bringing a more strategic side to the company in which to complement her art direction.

424 ■ *"Contest Produce Ad Designs on a Dime" in San Diego Business Journal (Vol. 31, August 23, 2010, No. 31, pp. 1)*
Pub: San Diego Business Journal
Ed: Mike Allen. **Description:** San Diego-based Prova.fm runs design contests for clients such as the U.S. Postal Service. The client then chooses the best entry from the contest. Prova.fm relies on the Internet to deliver a range of possible graphic solutions and allowing the customer to make the right selection for its business through a process called crowdsourcing.

425 ■ *"Conversations Need to Yield Actions Measured in Dollars" in Advertising Age (Vol. 79, July 7, 2008, No. 26, pp. 18)*
Pub: Crain Communications, Inc.
Ed: Jonathan Salem Baskin. **Description:** New ways in which to market to consumers are discussed.

426 ■ *"Crain's Makes Ad Sales, Custom Marketing Appointments" in Crain's Chicago Business (Vol. 34, October 24, 2011, No. 42, pp. 13)*
Pub: Crain Communications Inc.
Description: Crain's Chicago Business announced key appointments in its sales department: David Denor has been named first director of custom marketing services and Kate Van Etten will succeed Denor as advertising director.

427 ■ *The Creative Business Guide to Running a Graphic Design Business*
Pub: W.W. Norton & Company, Incorporated
Ed: Cameron S. Foote. **Released:** April 2004. **Price:** $23.10. **Description:** Advice for running a graphic design firm, focusing on organizations, marketing, personnel and operations.

428 ■ *"The CW" in Brandweek (Vol. 49, April 21, 2008, No. 16, pp. SR8)*
Pub: VNU Business Media, Inc.
Ed: John Consoli. **Description:** Provides contact information for sales and marketing personnel for the CW network as well as a listing of the station's top programming and an analysis of the current season and the target audience for those programs running in the current season. Purchases of advertising feel that Warner Bros. and CBS made a mistake merging The WB and UPN into the new CW rather than folding UPN into the more-established WB; compared to last season ratings are down more than 20 percent across the board.

429 ■ *"Dana Anderson's Celebrity Rules for Digital Marketing" in Advertising Age (Vol. 81, December 6, 2010, No. 43, pp. 4)*
Pub: Crain Communications, Inc.
Ed: Kunur Patel. **Description:** Things that can be learned from Hollywood in terms of marketing strategy and communications are outlined.

430 ■ *"Datran Media Executives to Lead Industry Debates Across Q1 Conferences" in Internet Wire (January 22, 2010)*
Pub: Comtex News Network, Inc.
Description: Datran Media, an industry-leading digital marketing technology company, will be sending members of its management team to several conferences in the early part of the first quarter of 2010; discussions will include Internet marketing innovations, e-commerce and media distribution.

431 ■ *"Dear Customer: Managing E-Mail Campaigns" in Inc. (March 2008, pp. 58-59)*
Pub: Gruner & Jahr USA Publishing
Ed: Ryan Underwood. **Description:** Internet services that help firms manage their online business including email marketing, to manage subscriber lists, comply with spam regulations, monitor bouncebacks, and track potential customers are profiled. Constant Contact, MobileStorm Stun, Campaign Monitor, Pop Commerce, Emma, and StrongMail E-mail Server are among software and services highlighted.

432 ■ *Design and Launch Your Online Boutique in a Week*
Pub: Entrepreneur Press
Ed: Melissa Campanelli. **Released:** June 26, 2008. **Price:** $17.95. **Description:** Tips for starting an online boutique in a short amount of time are given. The books shows how to build the online boutique with designer goods or your own product, ways to create eye-catching content, online tools to handle payments and accept orders, marketing and advertising techniques, and customer service.

433 ■ *"Designer is Walking Ad for TIBI Line" in Charlotte Observer (February 5, 2007)*
Pub: Knight-Ridder/Tribune Business News
Ed: Crystal Dempsey. **Description:** Profile of Amy Smilovic, mother of two children, and clothing designer. Smilovic wears what she designs, making her a great marketing tool for her clothing line TIBI.

434 ■ *"A Direct Approach" in Business Journal-Portland (Vol. 24, November 9, 2007, No. 36, pp. 1)*
Pub: American City Business Journals, Inc.
Ed: Matthew Kish. **Description:** Respond 2 LLC's annual revenue has increased from $14.2 million in 2004 to almost $50 million in 2007. The growth is attributed to a $100 million contract with Vonage. The role of the popularity of infomercials on the success of the Portland-based marketing company is evaluated.

435 ■ *"Direct Marketing" in MarketingMagazine (Vol. 115, September 27, 2010, No. 13, pp. 74)*
Pub: Rogers Publishing Ltd.
Description: Direct marketing data is shared covering provinces in Canada.

436 ■ *"Discovery Networks" in Brandweek (Vol. 49, April 21, 2008, No. 16, pp. SR9)*
Pub: VNU Business Media, Inc.
Ed: Anthony Crupi. **Description:** Provides contact information for sales and marketing personnel for the Discovery networks as well as a listing of the station's top programming and an analysis of the current season and the target audience for those programs running in the current season. The networks flagship station returned to the top 10 in 2007, averaging 1.28 million viewers.

437 ■ *"Disney-ABC Domestic Television Distribution" in Brandweek (Vol. 49, April 21, 2008, No. 16, pp. SR13)*
Pub: VNU Business Media, Inc.
Ed: Marc Berman. **Description:** Provides contact information for sales and marketing personnel for Disney-ABC Domestic Television Distribution as well as a listing of the station's top programming and an analysis of the current season and the target audience for those programs running in the current season.

438 ■ *"Doyle: Domino's New Pizza Seasoned with Straight Talk" in Crain's Detroit Business (Vol. 26, January 11, 2010, No. 2, pp. 1)*
Pub: Crain Communications Inc.
Ed: Nathan Skid. **Description:** Interview with J. Patrick Doyle, the CEO of Domino's Pizza, Inc.; the company has launched a new marketing campaign that focuses on its bold new vision.

439 ■ *"Dramatic Results: Making Opera (Yes, Opera) Seem Young and Hip" in Inc. (October 2007, pp. 61-62)*
Pub: Gruner & Jahr USA Publishing
Description: Profile of Peter Gelb, who turned New York's Metropolitan Opera into one of the most media-savvy organizations in the country, using a multifaceted marketing strategy through the media. Gelb used streaming audio and simulcasts on satellite radio and movie theaters to promote a message that opera is hip.

440 ■ *Duct Tape Marketing: The World's Most Practical Small Business Marketing Guide*
Pub: Thomas Nelson Inc.
Ed: John Jantsch. **Released:** May 2008. **Price:** $14.99. **Description:** Small business owners are provided the tools and tactics necessary to market and grow a business.

441 ■ *e-Riches 2.0: Next-Generation Marketing Strategies for Making Million Online*
Pub: AMACOM
Ed: Scott Fox. **Released:** May 27, 2009. **Price:** $25.00. **Description:** Beginner's guide to using the Internet to help grow business, including the best ways to use email lists and newsletters, RSS feeds, online viral marketing, social networking, microblogging, online video and radio/podcasts, tele-seminars and webinars, search engine keyword advertising and affiliate program advertising.

442 ■ *EBay Income: How ANYONE of Any Age, Location, and/or Background Can Build a Highly Profitable Online Business with eBay*
Pub: Atlantic Publishing Company
Released: December 1, 2010. **Price:** $24.95. **Description:** A complete overview of eBay is given and guides any small company through the entire process of creating the auction and auction strategies, photography, writing copy, text and formatting, multiple sales, programming tricks, PayPal, accounting, creating marketing, merchandising, managing email lists, advertising plans, taxes and sales tax, best time to list items and for how long, sniping programs, international customers, opening a storefront, electronic commerce, buy-it now pricing, keywords, Google marketing and eBay secrets.

443 ■ *"Economic Crises Calls For Better Marketing Plans" in Entrepreneur (October 1, 2008)*
Pub: Entrepreneur Media Inc.
Ed: Tim Berry. **Description:** Revising one's business plan is essential, especially during times of economic crisis; sales and marketing plans should be reviewed, analyzed and changed in an attempt to survive the economic downturn.

444 ■ *"Economy Should Play Big Role When Presidential Spotlight Returns" in Business First-Columbus (November 9, 2007, pp. A1)*
Pub: American City Business Journals, Inc.
Ed: Jeff Bell. **Description:** Ohio leaders, including the president of Columbus Chamber, Ty Marsh, suggests that Ohio has benefited from past campaigns as candidates spend money on advertising along with the media exposure the state received. The significance of Ohio in determining the winner in the 2008 presidential elections is discussed.

445 ■ *"Elanco Challenges Bayer's Advantage, K9 Advantix Ad Claims" in Pet Product News (Vol. 64, November 2010, No. 11, pp. 11)*
Pub: BowTie Inc.
Description: Elanco Animal Health has disputed Bayer Animal Health's print and Web advertising claims involving its flea, tick, and mosquito control products Advantage and K9 Advantix. The National Advertising Division of the Council of Better Business Bureaus recommended the discontinuation of ads, while Bayer Animal Health reiterated its commitment to self-regulation.

446 ■ *"Entrepreneur Column" in Entrepreneur (September 24, 2009)*
Pub: Entrepreneur Media, Inc.
Ed: Allen Moon. **Description:** In an attempt to compete with Google, Microsoft and Yahoo have entered a partnership to merge their search services; advice on the best ways to get noticed on this new search engine entitled Bing, is provided.

447 ■ *"Every Little Bit Helps" in Black Enterprise (Vol. 38, November 2007, No. 4, pp. 102)*
Pub: Earl G. Graves Publishing Co. Inc.
Ed: Tennille M. Robinson. **Description:** After a career in the cosmetics industry, Tricialee Riley is marketing and advertising her new venture, the Polish Bar, a salon offering manicures, pedicures, makeup application, and waxing.

448 ■ *"Everyone Has a Story Inspired by Chevrolet" in Automotive News (Vol. 86, October 31, 2011, No. 6488, pp. S003)*
Pub: Crain Communications Inc.
Ed: Keith E. Crain. **Description:** Besides being a great ad slogan, 'Baseball, Hot Dogs, Apple Pie and Chevrolet', the brand conjures up memories for most everyone in our society. Louis Chevrolet had a reputation as a race car driver and lent his name to the car that has endured for 100 years.

449 ■ *"Far Out: Satellite Radio Finds New Way to Tally Listeners" in Globe & Mail (March 14, 2007, pp. B14)*
Pub: CTVglobemedia Publishing Inc.
Ed: Grant Robertson. **Description:** The marketing strategy adopted by satellite radio broadcasting firm XM Satellite Radio Inc. in Canada for increasing its subscriber based is discussed.

450 ■ *Financial Management 101: Get a Grip on Your Business Numbers*
Pub: Self-Counsel Press, Incorporated
Ed: Angie Mohr. **Released:** November 2007. **Price:** $16.95. **Description:** An overview of business planning, financial statements, budgeting and advertising for small businesses. s.

451 ■ *"First Mariner's New Ads No Passing Fancy" in Boston Business Journal (Vol. 29, September 16, 2011, No. 19, pp. 1)*
Pub: American City Business Journals Inc.
Ed: Gary Haber. **Description:** Baltimore, Maryland-based First Mariner Bank replaced Ed Hale, the bank's CEO and founder, as the pitchman for its television ads with Ravens quarterback Joe Flacco. Hales' exit from the advertisements is the result of First Mariner's struggle to raise money for re-capitalization.

452 ■ *"First the Merger: Then, The Culture Clash. How To Fix the Little Things That Can Tear a Company Apart" in Inc. (January 2008)*
Pub: Gruner & Jahr USA Publishing
Ed: Elaine Appleton Grant. **Description:** Ways three CEOs handled the culture classes that followed after company mergers; companies profiled include Fuel Outdoor, an outdoor advertising company; Nelson, an interior design and architecture firm; and Beber Silverstein, an ad agency.

453 ■ *"Fitter from Twitter" in Boston Business Journal (Vol. 30, December 17, 2010, No. 47, pp. 1)*
Pub: Boston Business Journal
Ed: Lisa van der Pool. **Description:** Small businesses are increasing their use of the Twitter microblogging platform to attract and retain customers. Lisa Johnson, who owns Modern Pilates studios, managed to raise awareness of her personal brand nationally through the social media platform.

454 ■ *"Fox" in Brandweek (Vol. 49, April 21, 2008, No. 16, pp. SR3)*
Pub: VNU Business Media, Inc.
Ed: John Consoli. **Description:** Provides contact information for sales and marketing personnel for the Fox network as well as a listing of the station's top programming and an analysis of the current season and the target audience for those programs running in the current season. In terms of upfront advertising dollars, it looks as if Fox will be competing against NBC for third place due to its success at courting the 18-49-year-old male demographic.

455 ■ *"Fox Cable Entertainment Networks" in Brandweek (Vol. 49, April 21, 2008, No. 16, pp. SR10)*
Pub: VNU Business Media, Inc.
Ed: Anthony Crupi. **Description:** Provides contact information for sales and marketing personnel for the Fox Cable Entertainment networks as well as a list-

ing of the station's top programming and an analysis of the current season and the target audience for those programs running in the current season.

456 ■ *"A Framework for Conceptual Contributions in Marketing" in Journal of Marketing (Vol. 75, July 2011, No. 4, pp. 136)*
Pub: American Marketing Association
Ed: Deborah J. MacInnis. **Description:** A look at a new framework for thinking about conceptualization in marketing is presented. Conceptual advances are essential to the vitality of the marketing discipline but recent writings indicate that advancement is slowing. The types of conceptual contributions are described, including their similarities and difference, and their importance to the field of marketing.

457 ■ *"Friendly" in Ice Cream Reporter (Vol. 21, August 20, 2008, No. 9, pp. 8)*
Pub: Ice Cream Reporter
Description: Advertising Age presented Friendly's with the award, 'Ad of the Day' for its television commercial depicting a Norman Rockwell-esque family transported to a psychedelic wonderland.

458 ■ *"From OTC Sellers to Surgeons, Healthcare Marketers Target Women to Achieve Growth" in Marketing to Women (February 2008)*
Pub: EPM Communications Inc.
Contact: Ira Mayer, President
E-mail: imayer@epmcom.com
Description: Healthcare companies are targeting women with ad campaigns, new product development and new technology in order to reach and develop brand loyalty.

459 ■ *"FTC Takes Aim At Foreclosure 'Rescue' Firm" in The Business Journal-Serving Greater Tampa Bay (Vol. 28, September 19, 2008, No. 39)*
Pub: American City Business Journals, Inc.
Ed: Michael Hinman. **Description:** United Home Savers LLP has been ordered to halt its mortgage foreclosure rescue services after the Federal Trade Commission accused it of deceptive advertising. The company is alleged to have charged customers $1,200 in exchange for unfulfilled promises to keep them in their homes.

460 ■ *"Funeral Directors Get Creative As Boomers Near Great Beyond" in Advertising Age (Vol. 79, October 13, 2008, No. 38, pp. 30)*
Pub: Crain Communications, Inc.
Ed: Lenore Skenazy. **Description:** Despite the downturn in the economy, the funeral business is thriving due to the number of baby boomers who realize the importance of making preparations for their death. Marketers are getting creative in their approach and many companies have taken into consideration the need for a more environmental friendly way to dispose of bodies and thus have created innovative businesses that reflect this need.

461 ■ *"Funny Business" in Canadian Business (Vol. 82, April 27, 2009, No. 7, pp. 27)*
Pub: Rogers Media
Ed: Rachel Pulfer. **Description:** Companies are advised to use humor in marketing to drive more revenue. IBM Canada, for example, commissioned Second City Communications for a marketing campaign that involved humor. While IBM Canada declined to give sales or traffic figures, firm executives rank the marketing campaign as an overall success.

462 ■ *"General Motors Can't Kick Incentives-But They Work" in Advertising Age (Vol. 79, July 7, 2008, No. 26, pp. 3)*
Pub: Crain Communications, Inc.
Ed: Jean Halliday. **Description:** General Motors Corp. was able to maintain their market share just as Toyota Motor Corp. was beginning to pass the manufacturer; GM lured in customers with a sales incentive that they heavily advertised and subsequently helped build demand; investors, however,

were not impressed and GM shares were hammered to their lowest point in 50 years after analysts speculated the company might go bankrupt.

463 ■ *"Get Real" in Entrepreneur (Vol. 36, April 2008, No. 4, pp. 86)*
Pub: Entrepreneur Media, Inc.
Ed: Kim T. Gordon. **Description:** Selling points of a product or service must show real benefits to women. Provide detailed information as women look at details more deeply before purchasing. Other tips on how to market products designed for women consumers are provided.

464 ■ *"Giants Now Admit They Roam Planet Earth; Time To Buy?" in Barron's (Vol. 88, March 31, 2008, No. 13, pp. 39)*
Pub: Dow Jones & Company, Inc.
Ed: Eric J. Savitz. **Description:** Oracle's third-quarter results showed that top-line growth fell short of expectations but the company is expected to fare better than most applications companies in the downturn. Google had a flat growth in the number of people who click their online ads. The time for investors in the tech sector with a long-term horizon has arrived.

465 ■ *"Global Imagery in Online Advertisements" in Business Communication Quarterly (December 2007, pp. 487)*
Pub: SAGE Publications USA
Contact: Blaise R. Simqu, President
Ed: Geraldine E. Hynes, Marius Janson. **Description:** Respondents from six countries were interviewed about their reactions to two online ads to determine cultural differences in understanding advertising elements. Universal appeals and cultural values determine the effectiveness of symbols in online advertising.

466 ■ *"Go Beyond Local Search With Hyper-Local" in Women Entrepreneur (October 30, 2008)*
Pub: Entrepreneur Media Inc.
Ed: Lena West. **Description:** According to Forrester Research, as much as $500 billion in local spending in 2007 was influenced by the Internet and industry analysts report that consumers spend approximately 80 percent of their income within 50 miles of their home. Discussion of ways in which to capitalize on the hyper-local trend that is being driven by greater Internet connectivity and use of the web to find information is provided.

467 ■ *"Google, MySpace Deal Hits Snag" in Globe & Mail (February 7, 2007, pp. B11)*
Pub: CTVglobemedia Publishing Inc.
Ed: Julia Angwin; Kevin J. Delaney. **Description:** MySpace's intention to partner with eBay which is delaying the finalization of its $900 million online advertising deal signed with Google Inc. is discussed.

468 ■ *"Got Slogan? Guidelines for Creating Effective Slogans" in Business Horizons (September-October 2007, pp. 415)*
Pub: Elsevier Technology Publications
Ed: Chiranjeev Kohli, Lance Leuthesser, Rajneesh Suri. **Description:** Relevant case studies of industry publications are considered to determine the creation and utilization of effective slogans. The importance of branding as well as factors that contribute to memory and recall are discussed.

469 ■ *Guerrilla Marketing During Tough Times*
Pub: Morgan James Publishing, LLC
Ed: Jay Conrad Levinson. **Released:** November 2005. **Price:** $14.00. **Description:** Ways to market a small business during slow economic times.

470 ■ *Guerrilla Marketing for the New Millennium*
Pub: Morgan James Publishing, LLC
Ed: Jay Conrad Levinson. **Released:** September 2005. **Price:** $14.00. **Description:** Steps to successfully market a small business on the Internet.

471 ■ *Guerrilla Marketing: Put Your Advertising on Steroids*
Pub: Morgan James Publishing, LLC
Ed: Jay Conrad Levinson. **Released:** December 2005. **Price:** $14.00. **Description:** Marketing concepts to successfully advertise any Internet business, featuring the ten most successful advertising campaigns of the 20th Century.

472 ■ *"Half of Canadian Firms to Boost Marketing Budgets" in Globe & Mail (January 22, 2007, pp. B1)*
Pub: CTVglobemedia Publishing Inc.
Ed: Keith McArthur. **Description:** The advertising and marketing spending plans of different companies are presented.

473 ■ *"Harley-Davidson Moves to Unconventional Marketing Plan" in Business Journal-Milwaukee (Vol. 28, November 26, 2010, No. 8, pp. A1)*
Pub: Milwaukee Business Journal
Ed: Rich Rovito. **Description:** Harley Davidson Inc. hired Boulder, Colorado-based Victors & Spoils, an agency that specializes in crowdsourcing, to implement a new creative marketing model. Under the plan, Harley Davidson will draw on the ideas of its brand enthusiasts to help guide the brand's marketing direction.

474 ■ *"Headwinds From the New Sod Slow Aer Lingus" in Barron's (Vol. 88, March 10, 2008, No. 10, pp. M6)*
Pub: Dow Jones & Company, Inc.
Ed: Sean Walters; Arindam Nag. **Description:** Aer Lingus faces a drop in its share prices with a falling US market, higher jet fuel prices, and lower long-haul passenger load factors. British media companies Johnston Press and Yell Group are suffering from weaker ad revenue and heavier debt payments due to the credit crunch.

475 ■ *"'Help Wanted' Meets 'Buy It Now': Why More Companies Are Integrating Marketing and Recruiting" in Inc. (November 2007, pp. 50-52)*
Pub: Gruner & Jahr USA Publishing
Ed: Ryan McCarthy. **Description:** Five tips to merge marketing and recruiting together include: thinking every help wanted ad as a marketing opportunity, treating every job candidate as a potential customer, involving the youngest employees in the interview process, look for way to promote recruiting events, and to sponsor community-oriented events.

476 ■ *"Herrell's Launches New Corporate Identity at Fancy Food Show" in Ice Cream Reporter (Vol. 23, July 20, 2010, No. 8, pp. 3)*
Pub: Ice Cream Reporter
Description: Herrell's ice cream introduced a new corporate branding at the Summer 2010 Fancy Food Show last summer. Slightly Mad Communications advertising agency developed the new brand to reflect the era of the early 1970s.

477 ■ *"High-Tech, Niche Options Change Sports Marketing" in Crain's Detroit Business (Vol. 24, March 17, 2008, No. 11, pp. 14)*
Pub: Crain Communications, Inc.
Ed: Leah Boyd. **Description:** Sports advertisers have an ever-increasing menu of high-tech or niche marketing options such as interactive campaigns through cell phones and electronic banners which can span arenas.

478 ■ *How to Advertise a Small Business: Step by Step Guide to Starting Your Own Business*
Pub: Lewis and Renn Associates
Ed: Leslie D. Renn; Jerre G. Lewis. **Released:** 2007. **Price:** $21.95. **Description:** Step-by-step guide to help small business owners advertise products and services.

479 ■ *"How to Attract Big-City Talent to Small Towns" in Advertising Age (Vol. 79, July 7, 2008, No. 26, pp. 24)*
Pub: Crain Communications, Inc.
Ed: Joe Erwin. **Description:** Advice concerning ways in which to attract talent to mid-market agencies is given and innovative techniques that have worked for some firms are discussed.

480 ■ *"How to Boost Your Super Bowl ROI" in Advertising Age (Vol. 80, December 7, 2009, No. 41, pp. 3)*
Pub: Crain's Communications
Ed: Abbey Klaassen. **Description:** Internet marketing is essential, even for the corporations that can afford to spend $3 million on a 30-second Super Bowl spot; last year, Super Bowl advertising reached an online viewership of 99.5 million while 98.7 million people watched the game on television validating the idea that public relations must go farther than a mere television ad campaign. Social media provides businesses with a longer shelf life for their ad campaigns. Advice is also given regarding ways in which to strategize a smart and well-thought plan for utilizing the online marketing options currently available.

481 ■ *How to Get Rich on the Internet*
Pub: Morgan James Publishing, LLC
Ed: Ted Ciuba. **Released:** August 2004. **Price:** $19.95. **Description:** Interviews with successful Internet entrepreneurs provide insight into marketing products and services online using minimal investment. The importance of a sound marketing ad campaign using the Internet is discussed; maintaining a database and Website will automatically carry out business transactions daily. Suggestions for various types of businesses to run online are given.

482 ■ *"How to Improve Your Mobile Marketing" in Contractor (Vol. 56, October 2009, No. 10, pp. 54)*
Pub: Penton Media, Inc.
Ed: Matt Michel. **Description:** Plumbers can improve their mobile advertising by making their logos as large as possible and positioning their logo on top of the truck so people can see it over traffic. They should also make the phone numbers small because people only take note of these when the truck is parked.

483 ■ *"How to Ramp Up Marketing in a Downturn" in Entrepreneur (Vol. 37, July 2009, No. 7, pp. 55)*
Pub: Entrepreneur Media, Inc.
Ed: Jeff Wuorio. **Description:** How businesses can save money while boosting their marketing efforts during a down economy is discussed. Using price-driven marketing, online social networks, and cause-driven marketing are among the suggested ways companies can attract more customers. Guarantees and warrantees, as well as contests, can also be used as marketing tools.

484 ■ *How to Start a Faux Painting or Mural Business, Second Edition*
Pub: Allworth Press
Ed: Rebecca Pittman. **Released:** October 1, 2010. **Price:** $24.95. **Description:** Updated and expanded to cover better ways to advertise, innovative supplies (such as Venetian plasters and stained cements), unique bidding and studio setups required for new plasters and varnishes.

485 ■ *How to Use the Internet to Advertise, Promote, and Market Your Business or Web Site: With Little or No Money*
Pub: Atlantic Publishing Company
Released: December 1, 2010. **Price:** $24.95. **Description:** Information is given to help build, promote, and make money from your Website or brick and mortar store using the Internet, with minimal costs.

486 ■ *Hug Your Customers*
Pub: Hyperion Books
Ed: Jack Mitchell. **Price:** $19.95. **Description:** The CEO of Mitchells/Roberts, two very successful clothing stores, professes his belief in showering customers with attention. His secrets for long-term business success include advice about attracting a good staff, lowering marketing costs, and maintaining higher gross margins and revenues.

487 ■ *"An Ice Boost in Revenue; Wings Score With Expanded Corporate Sales" in Crain's Detroit Business (Vol. 25, June 1, 2009, No. 22)*
Pub: Crain Communications Inc. - Detroit
Ed: Bill Shea. **Description:** Stanley Cup finals always boost business for the Detroit area, even during a recession. The Red Wings corporate office

reported corporate sponsorship revenue luxury suite rentals, Legends Club seats and advertising were up 40 percent this year over 2008.

488 ■ *Instant Income*
Pub: McGraw-Hill Inc.
Ed: Janet Switzer. **Released:** February 2007. **Price:** $30.95 (CND). **Description:** Book covers small business advertising techniques, marketing, joint ventures, and sales.

489 ■ *"Insurers No Longer Paying Premium for Advertising" in Brandweek (Vol. 49, April 21, 2008, No. 16, pp. SR3)*
Pub: VNU Business Media, Inc.
Ed: Eric Newman. **Description:** Insurance companies are cutting their advertising budgets after years of accelerated double-digit growth in spending due to the economic downturn, five years of record-breaking ad spend and a need to cut expenditures as claims costs rise and a competitive market keeps premiums in place. Statistical data included.

490 ■ *"Internet Marketing Agency .Com Marketing Wins National Awards for Web Design and SEO" in Marketing Weekly News (Jan. 2, 2010)*
Pub: Investment Weekly News
Description: Internet marketing agency .Com Marketing has won two bronze awards for its exceptional quality web services; the company is a full-service interactive marketing and advertising agency that specializes in a variety of online services including web design, social media marketing and press releases.

491 ■ *"Internet Marketing Agency .Com Marketing Wins National Awards for Web Design and SEO" in Marketing Weekly News (January 2, 2010)*
Pub: Investment Weekly News
Description: Internet marketing agency .Com Marketing has won two bronze awards for its exceptional quality web services; the company is a full-service interactive marketing and advertising agency that specializes in a variety of online services including web design, social media marketing and press releases.

492 ■ *"Internet Marketing and Social Media Knowledge Vital for SMBs" in Internet Wire (November 24, 2009)*
Pub: Comtex News Network, Inc.
Description: Small and medium-size businesses must learn to market themselves over the Internet in order to succeed and grow in today's marketplace. Web Marketing Today offers the largest source of the most important information concerning doing business on the Internet including e-commerce, email marketing and social networking opportunities.

493 ■ *"Irene Rosenfeld; Chairman and CEO, Kraft Foods Inc." in Crain's Chicago Business (Vol. 31, May 5, 2008, No. 18, pp. 31)*
Pub: Crain Communications, Inc.
Ed: David Sterrett. **Description:** Profile of Irene Rosenfeld who is the chairman and CEO of Kraft Foods Inc. and is entering the second year of a three-year plan to boost sales of well-known brands such as Oreo, Velveeta and Oscar Mayer while facing soaring commodity costs and a declining marketshare. Ms. Rosenfeld's turnaround strategy also entails spending more on advertising and giving managers more control over their budgets and product development.

494 ■ *"Israeli Spam Law May Have Global Impact" in Information Today (Vol. 26, February 2009, No. 2, pp. 28)*
Pub: Information Today, Inc.
Ed: David Mirchin. **Description:** Israels new law, called Amendment 40 of the Communications Law, will regulate commercial solicitations including those sent without permission via email, fax, automatic phone dialing systems, or short messaging technologies.

495 ■ *"It's Back to Business for the Ravens"* in Boston Business Journal (Vol. 29, July 29, 2011, No. 12, pp. 1)
Pub: American City Business Journals Inc.
Ed: Scott Dance. **Description:** The Baltimore Ravens football team has been marketing open sponsorship packages following the end of the National Football League lockout. Team officials are working to get corporate logos and slogans on radio and television commercials and online advertisements.

496 ■ *It's Not Who You Know - It's Who Knows You!: The Small Business Guide to Raising Your Profits by Raising Your Profile*
Pub: John Wiley & Sons, Inc.
Ed: David Avrin. **Released:** November 9, 2010. **Price:** $24.95. **Description:** When it comes to promoting a small business or a brand, it is essential to know how valuable high-profile attention can be. But for most small companies, the cost of hiring an outside firm to increase attention can be too expensive.

497 ■ *"Johnson's Taps Online Animation"* in Marketing to Women (Vol. 21, April 2008, No. 4, pp. 3)
Pub: EPM Communications Inc.
Contact: Ira Mayer, President
E-mail: imayer@epmcom.com
Description: Johnson's has launched a new integrated campaign for its baby lotion in an effort to appeal to the growing number of moms online.

498 ■ *"Kawasaki's New Top Gun"* in Brandweek (Vol. 49, April 21, 2008, No. 16, pp. 18)
Pub: VNU Business Media, Inc.
Description: Discusses Kawasaki's marketing plan which included designing an online brochure in which visitors could create a video by building their own test track on a grid and then selecting visual special effects and musical overlay. This engaging and innovative marketing technique generated more than 166,000 unique users within the first three months of being launched.

499 ■ *The King of Madison Avenue: David Ogilvy and the Making of Modern Advertising*
Pub: Palgrave Macmillan
Ed: Kenneth Roman. **Released:** 2009. **Price:** $27.95. **Description:** The rise and fall of David Ogilvy, once the leader on Madison Avenue, is discussed.

500 ■ *Lateral Marketing: New Techniques for Finding Breakthrough Ideas*
Pub: John Wiley & Sons, Incorporated
Ed: Philip Kotler, Fernando Trias de Bes. **Released:** September 2003. **Price:** $34.95. **Description:** Lateral marketing complements traditional marketing by allowing marketers develop a new product for a wider audience.

501 ■ *"LatinWorks Cozies Up to Chevy in Detroit"* in Austin Business Journal (Vol. 31, August 12, 2011, No. 23, pp. A1)
Pub: American City Business Journals Inc.
Ed: Sandra Zaragoza. **Description:** Hispanic marketing agency LatinWorks opened an office in Detroit to better serve its client Chevrolet and to potentially secure more contracts from its parent company General Motors, whose offices are located nearby.

502 ■ *"Leading Ohio Internet Marketing Firm Announces Growth in September"* in Marketing Weekly News (September 26, 2009, pp. 24)
Pub: Investment Weekly News
Description: Despite a poor economy, Webbed Marketing, a leading social media marketing and search engine optimization firm in the Midwest, has added five additional professionals to its fast-growing team. The company continues to win new business, provide more services and hire talented employees.

503 ■ *"Leapin' Lizards, Does SoBe Have Some Work To Do On Life Water"* in Brandweek (Vol. 49, April 21, 2008, No. 16, pp. 32)
Pub: VNU Business Media, Inc.
Ed: Amy Shea. **Description:** Discusses the competing marketing campaigns of both Vitaminwater, now owned by Coca-Cola, and SoBe Life Water which is owned by Pepsi; also looks at the repositioning of Life Water as a thirst-quencher, rather than a green product as well as the company's newest advertising campaign.

504 ■ *"LED Screen Technology Takes Centre Stage"* in Canadian Electronics (Vol. 23, June-July 2008, No. 4, pp. 17)
Pub: Action Communication Inc.
Ed: Ed Whitaker. **Description:** Display technologies based on light emitting diodes are becoming more popular due to their flexibility, versatility and reproducibility of displays. These are being increasingly used in different applications, such as advertising and concerts.

505 ■ *"Lifetime Networks"* in Brandweek (Vol. 49, April 21, 2008, No. 16, pp. SR10)
Pub: VNU Business Media, Inc.
Ed: Anthony Crupi. **Description:** Provides contact information for sales and marketing personnel for the ABC network as well as a listing of the station's top programming and an analysis of the current season and the target audience for those programs running in the current season. Lifetime will still produce its original signature movies but will now focus its emphasis more clearly on series development in order to appeal to a younger, hipper female demographic.

506 ■ *"Local Firm Snaps up 91 Area Pizza Huts"* in Orlando Business Journal (Vol. 26, January 8, 2010, No. 32, pp. 1)
Pub: American City Business Journals
Ed: Alexis Muellner, Anjali Fluker. **Description:** Orlando, Florida-based CFL Pizza LLC bought the 91 Orlando-area Pizza Hut restaurants for $35 million from parent company Yum! Brands Inc. CFL Pizza plans to distribute parts of the business to Central Florida vendors and the first business up for grabs is the advertising budget.

507 ■ *"Looking Out for the Little Guys"* in Black Enterprise (Vol. 38, October 2007, No. 3, pp. 58)
Pub: Earl G. Graves Publishing Co. Inc.
Ed: Kaylyn Kendall Dines. **Description:** Biz Tech-Connect is a Web portal that offers free online and social networking, along with four modules that help small businesses with marketing and advertising, communications and mobility, financial management, and customer relationship management.

508 ■ *"Lotteries Scratch Their Way to Billions"* in Saint Louis Business Journal (Vol. 31, August 19, 2011, No. 52, pp. 1)
Pub: Saint Louis Business Journal
Ed: Kelsey Volkmann. **Description:** Missouri Lottery reported $1 billion in sales in 2011. A six-fold increase in the lottery's advertising budget is seen to drive the revenue increase; a 4.5 percent rise in its scratch-off tickets and new sponsorships has also contributed to the development.

509 ■ *"Macy's Seeks Balance in All Things Ad-Related"* in Crain's Chicago Business (Vol. 31, March 31, 2008, No. 13, pp. 19)
Pub: Crain Communications, Inc.
Ed: Natalie Zmuda. **Description:** Macy's Inc. is seeking to balance its national television campaign with locally tailored promotions and products.

510 ■ *Made To Stick: Why Some Ideas Survive and Others Die*
Pub: Random House
Ed: Chip Heath; Dan Heath. **Released:** 2007. **Price:** $26.00. **Description:** Eight principles marketers can use to make their ideas and branding efforts resonate with consumers.

511 ■ *MadScam: Kick-Ass Advertising Without the Madison Avenue Price Tag*
Pub: Entrepreneur Press
Ed: George Parker. **Released:** January 2007. **Price:** $19.95. **Description:** Effective advertising plans for small to medium-sized business on a small budget.

512 ■ *MadScam: Kick-Ass Advertising Without the Madison Avenue Price Tag*
Pub: McGraw-Hill Ryerson Ltd.
Ed: George Parker. **Released:** November 2006. **Price:** $24.95. **Description:** Effective advertising strategies for small companies on a budget are presented.

513 ■ *Mail Order in the Internet Age*
Pub: Morgan James Publishing, LLC
Ed: Ted Ciuba. **Released:** May 2004. **Price:** $19.95. **Description:** Direct response market, or mail order, for marketing and selling a product or service is discussed, with emphasis on how direct marketing compares favorably to other methods in terms of speed, ease, profitability, and affordability. Advice is given for writing ads; seminars to attend; and newsletters, mailing lists and magazines in which to subscribe.

514 ■ *"Making Sense of Ambiguous Evidence"* in Harvard Business Review (Vol. 86, September 2008, No. 9, pp. 53)
Pub: Harvard Business School Press
Ed: Lisa Burrell. **Description:** Documentary filmmaker Errol Morris emphasizes the role of perception in portraying objective reality, and how investigation and analysis enhance the accuracy of that portrayal.

515 ■ *"Marketers Push for Mobile Tuesday as the New Black Friday"* in Advertising Age (Vol. 79, December 1, 2008, No. 44, pp. 21)
Pub: Crain Communications, Inc.
Ed: Natalie Zmuda. **Description:** Marketers are using an innovative approach in an attempt to stimulate business on the Tuesday following Thanksgiving by utilizing consumer's cell phones to alert them of sales or present them with coupons for this typically slow retail business day; with this campaign both advertisers and retailers are hoping to start Mobile Tuesday, another profitable shopping day in line with Black Friday and Cyber Monday.

516 ■ *"Marketing in the Digital World: Here's How to Craft a Smart Online Strategy"* in Black Enterprise (Vol. 40, July 2010, No. 12, pp. 47)
Pub: Earl G. Graves Publishing Co. Inc.
Ed: Sonya A. Donaldson. **Description:** Social media is an integral part of any small business plan in addressing marketing, sales, and branding strategies.

517 ■ *Marketing Outrageously: How to Increase Your Revenue by Staggering Amounts*
Pub: Bard Press
Ed: Jon Spoelstra. **Released:** July 25, 2001. **Price:** $24.95. **Description:** Creative marketing strategies are defined. The book shows how considering marketing problems as outrageously but consistently can benefit any small business. The author talks about his own experience when there were not adequate funds for marketing and advertising and the outrageous approach he created to promote sports teams.

518 ■ *"Marketing: 'Twill Be the Season"* in Entrepreneur (Vol. 35, October 2007, No. 10, pp. 108)
Pub: Entrepreneur Media Inc.
Ed: Kim T. Gordon. **Description:** Entrepreneurs should plan ahead in order to promote products for the holiday season, since it is peak sales time. They can unify their business theme, use customer incentives, advertise early using TV or radio, and reorganize the company Website. Other ways to market for the holiday season are provided.

519 ■ *Marketing in a Web 2.0 World - Using Social Media, Webinars, Blogs, and More to Boost Your Small Business on a Budget*
Pub: Atlantic Publishing Company
Ed: Peter VanRysdam. **Released:** June 1, 2010. **Price:** $24.95. **Description:** Web 2.0 technologies have leveled the playing field for small companies trying to boost their presence by giving them an equal voice against larger competitors. Advice is given to help target your audience using social networking hubs.

520 ■ *Marketing Without Money for Small and Midsize Businesses: 300 FREE and Cheap Ways to Increase Your Sales*
Pub: Halle House Publishing
Contact: Nicholas E. Bade, Publisher

Ed: Nicholas E. Bade. **Released:** July 2005. **Price:** $16.95. **Description:** Three hundred practical low-cost or no-cost strategies to increase sales, focusing on free advertising, free marketing assistance, and free referrals to the Internet.

521 ■ *Marketing Works: Unlock Big Company Strategies for Small Business*
Pub: Morgan James Publishing, LLC

Ed: Chris Lee; Daniele Lima. **Released:** May 2006. **Price:** $19.95. **Description:** Marketing strategies for any small business are outlined.

522 ■ *Marketing Your Small Business for Big Profits*
Pub: Morgan James Publishing, LLC

Released: September 2006. **Price:** $12.95. **Description:** Successful marketing tip to grow a small business are presented.

523 ■ *"Mars Advertising's Orbit Grows as Other Ad Segments Fall" in Crain's Detroit Business (Vol. 25, June 1, 2009, No. 22, pp. 10)*
Pub: Crain Communications Inc. - Detroit

Ed: Bill Shea. **Description:** An electrical fire burned at Mars Advertising's headquarters in Southfield, Michigan. The company talks about its plans for regrouping and rebuilding. The family firm specializes in in-store marketing that targets consumers already in the buying mode.

524 ■ *"McD's Warms Up For Olympics Performance" in Advertising Age (Vol. 79, July 7, 2008, No. 26, pp. 8)*
Pub: Crain Communications, Inc.

Description: Overview of McDonald's marketing plans for the company's sponsorship of the Olympics which includes a website, an alternate-reality game, names featured on U.S. athletes and on-the-ground activities.

525 ■ *"Medicine Men" in Canadian Business (Vol. 80, February 12, 2007, No. 4, pp. 19)*
Pub: Rogers Media

Ed: Joe Castaldo. **Description:** The effort of HPI Health Products' owners Dong Pedersen and Kent Pedersen to popularize their pain reliever product 'Lakota' is discussed.

526 ■ *"Mobile Marketing Grows With Size of Cell Phone Screens" in Crain's Detroit Business (Vol. 24, January 14, 2008, No. 2, pp. 13)*
Pub: Crain Communications Inc. - Detroit

Ed: Bill Shea. **Description:** Experts are predicting increased marketing for cell phones with the inception of larger screens and improved technology.

527 ■ *"Moet, Rivals Pour More Ad Bucks Into Bubbly" in Advertising Age (Vol. 88, September 3, 2007, No. 35, pp. 4)*
Pub: Crain Communications, Inc.

Ed: Jeremy Mullman. **Description:** In an attempt to revive sluggish sales, champagne companies are raising their advertising budgets, transforming themselves from light-spending seasonal players to year-round heavyweights in the advertising world.

528 ■ *"Moms Dis Super Bowl Ads" in Marketing to Women (Vol. 21, March 2008, No. 3, pp. 6)*
Pub: EPM Communications Inc.
Contact: Ira Mayer, President
E-mail: imayer@epmcom.com

Description: According to a survey by the Marketing to Moms Coalition, although 80 percent of moms tune into the Super Bowl most complain that the advertisements are not appropriate for a family sports viewing experience.

529 ■ *"Moms Rely on Coupons, Specials to Lower Grocery Bills" in Marketing to Women (Vol. 23, November 2010, No. 11, pp. 8)*
Pub: EPM Communications Inc.
Contact: Ira Mayer, President
E-mail: imayer@epmcom.com

Description: Eighty-four percent of moms surveyed reported using coupons when grocery shopping in order to lower costs. They are also purchasing less snack foods, fewer brand name items, alcoholic beverages, organic items, meat and fresh fruits and vegetables.

530 ■ *"Moosylvania Releases Latest XL Marketing Trends Report" in Wireless News (October 6, 2009)*
Pub: Close-Up Media

Description: Moosylvania, a digital promotion and branding agency that also has an on-site research facility, has released its 2nd XL Marketing Trends Report which focuses on digital video; the study defines the top digital video trends marketers must focus on now and well into the future and notes that in 2010, Mobile Web Devices, such as smart phones will outnumber computers in this country. Statistical data included.

531 ■ *"More Ad Shops Link Payment to Results" in Boston Business Journal (Vol. 30, November 12, 2010, No. 42, pp. 1)*
Pub: Boston Business Journal

Ed: Lisa van der Pool. **Description:** A growing number of advertising firms are proposing a 'value-based' payment scheme where they are paid a base fee plus a bonus if certain sales goals or other targets are met. The proposed shift in payment scheme is seen as reminiscent of the dot-com boom about ten years ago. Advertising firms are traditionally paid by the hour.

532 ■ *"More Leading Retailers Using Omniture Conversion Solutions to Boost Sales and Ecommerce Performance" in Internet Wire (Sept. 22,2009)*
Pub: Comtex News Network, Inc.

Description: Many retailers are utilizing Omniture conversion solutions to improve the performance of their ecommerce businesses; recent enhancements to Omniture Merchandising and Omniture Recommendations help clients drive increased conversion to their Internet ventures.

533 ■ *"More Leading Retailers Using Omniture Conversion Solutions to Boost Sales and Ecommerce Performance" in Internet Wire (Sept. 22,2009)*
Pub: Comtex News Network, Inc.

Description: Many retailers are utilizing Omniture conversion solutions to improve the performance of their ecommerce businesses; recent enhancements to Omniture Merchandising and Omniture Recommendations help clients drive increased conversion to their Internet ventures.

534 ■ *"More Sales Leads, Please: Or, What Happened When Frontline Selling Started Practicing What It Preaches" in Inc. (November 2007)*
Pub: Gruner & Jahr USA Publishing

Description: Frontline Selling located in Oakland, New Jersey helps train sales teams to generate and convert sales leads. The consulting firm doubled their marketing budget to increase their own sales.

535 ■ *"MTV Networks" in Brandweek (Vol. 49, April 21, 2008, No. 16, pp. SR10)*
Pub: VNU Business Media, Inc.

Ed: Anthony Crupi. **Description:** Provides contact information for sales and marketing personnel for the MTV networks as well as a listing of the station's top programming and an analysis of the current season and the target audience for those programs running in the current season. MTV networks include MTV, VH1, Nickelodeon and Comedy Central.

536 ■ *"Navigate to Better Direct Response Messaging Through Search Marketing" in DM*

News (Vol. 32, January 18, 2010, No. 2, pp. 26)
Pub: Haymarket Media, Inc.

Ed: Mark Simon. **Description:** Important lessons to apply when utilizing Internet marketing schemes include telling your customers you have what they want to buy, provide them with discounts or ways to save additional money and drive them to a customized destination like an Online store.

537 ■ *"NBC" in Brandweek (Vol. 49, April 21, 2008, No. 16, pp. SR6)*
Pub: VNU Business Media, Inc.

Ed: John Consoli. **Description:** Provides contact information for sales and marketing personnel for the NBC network as well as a listing of the station's top programming and an analysis of the current season and the target audience for those programs running in the current season. NBC also devised a new strategy of announcing its prime-time schedule 52 weeks in advance which was a hit for advertisers who felt this gave them a better opportunity to plan for product placement. Even with the station's creative sales programs, they could face a challenge from Fox in terms of upfront advertisement purchases.

538 ■ *"NBC Universal Cable" in Brandweek (Vol. 49, April 21, 2008, No. 16, pp. SR11)*
Pub: VNU Business Media, Inc.

Ed: Anthony Crupi. **Description:** Provides contact information for sales and marketing personnel for the NBC Universal Cable networks as well as a listing of the station's top programming and an analysis of the current season and the target audience for those programs running in the current season. The network's stations include USA, Sci Fi and Bravo. Ad revenue for the network grew 30 percent in the first quarter.

539 ■ *"NBC Universal Domestic Television Distribution" in Brandweek (Vol. 49, April 21, 2008, No. 16, pp. SR13)*
Pub: VNU Business Media, Inc.

Ed: Marc Berman. **Description:** Provides contact information for sales and marketing personnel for NBC Universal Domestic Television Distribution as well as a listing of the station's top programming and an analysis of the current season and the target audience for those programs running in the current season.

540 ■ *"Never Boring: Ad Agencies' Big Changes" in Business Courier (Vol. 24, February 8, 2008, No. 44, pp. 1)*
Pub: American City Business Journals, Inc.

Ed: Dan Monk. **Description:** Many changes are occurring in Cincinnati's advertising industry, including new clients, acquisitions, and market leaders, and an increase in employment. Bridge Worldwide passed Northlich LLC as the city's largest advertising agency.

541 ■ *"The New Basics of Marketing" in Inc. (February 2008, pp. 75-81)*
Pub: Gruner & Jahr USA Publishing

Ed: Leigh Buchanan. **Description:** New tools for marketing a business or service include updating or upgrading a Website, using email or texting, or advertising on a social Internet network.

542 ■ *"New King Top the Charts" in The Business Journal-Portland (Vol. 25, August 8, 2008, No. 22, pp. 1)*
Pub: American City Business Journals, Inc.

Ed: Andy Giegerich. **Description:** Spanish-language KRYP-FM station's spring 2008 ratings soared to 6.4 from 2.8 for the previous year. The station timing is flawless given the fact that one of every three new Portland-area residents between 2002 and 2007 were Latino.

543 ■ *"New Sony HD Ads Tout Digital" in Brandweek (Vol. 49, April 21, 2008, No. 16, pp. 5)*
Pub: VNU Business Media, Inc.

Description: Looking to promote Sony Electronics' digital imaging products, the company has launched another campaign effort known as HDNA, a play on the words high-definition and DNA; originally Sony focused the HDNA campaign on their televisions, the new ads will include still and video cameras as well and marketing efforts will consist of advertising in print, Online, television spots and publicity at various venues across the country.

544 ■ *"New TurnHere Survey Reveals Online Video Trends"* **in** *Internet Wire (October 22, 2009)*
Pub: Comtex News Network, Inc.
Description: TurnHere, Inc., the leading online video marketing services company, released the findings of its recent survey regarding current and future trends in online video among marketing agencies and brand recognition; the report found that online video has and will continue to play a prominent role in the realm of marketing edging out both search and email marketing campaigns. Additional highlights and statistical data included.

545 ■ *"A Nice Consistency"* **in** *Inc. (Vol. 31, January-February 2009, No. 1, pp. 94)*
Pub: Mansueto Ventures LLC
Ed: Jason Del Rey. **Description:** PJ Madison spent almost a quarter of its revenue promoting its latest product, organic ice cream. The Texas-based firm saw sales increase dramatically.

546 ■ *"No, Those Casino Rama Ads Aren't Running in NYC"* **in** *Globe & Mail (March 15, 2006, pp. B1)*
Pub: CTVglobemedia Publishing Inc.
Ed: Keith McArthur. **Description:** The reason Casino Rama did not advertise on New York Cabs is discussed.

547 ■ *"Nortel Makes Customers Stars in New Campaign"* **in** *Brandweek (Vol. 49, April 21, 2008, No. 16, pp. 8)*
Pub: VNU Business Media, Inc.
Ed: Mike Beirne. **Description:** Nortel has launched a new television advertising campaign in which the business-to-business communications technology provider cast senior executives in 30-second TV case studies that show how Nortel's technology helped their businesses innovate.

548 ■ *"Nowspeed and OneSource to Conduct Webinar"* **in** *Internet Wire (December 14, 2009)*
Pub: Comtex News Network, Inc.
Description: OneSource, a leading provider of global business information, and Nowspeed, an Internet marketing agency, will conduct a webinar titled 'How to Develop Social Media Content That Gets Results' in order to provide marketers insight into how to develop and optimize effective social media content to get consumer results that translate into purchases and lead generation.

549 ■ *"Nowspeed's David Reske to Speak at SolidWorks World 2010 in Anaheim"* **in** *Internet Wire (January 7, 2010)*
Pub: Comtex News Network, Inc.
Description: David Reske, managing director at Nowspeed, an Internet marketing agency based in the Boston area, will be presenting at SolidWorks World 2010; the convention's presentation will focus on proven methodologies, practical tips and real-world case studies in order to help attendees leverage the powerful Internet marketing innovations that are proving effective for businesses.

550 ■ *Obsessive Branding Disorder: The Illusion of Business and the Business of Illusion*
Pub: Public Affairs
Ed: Lucas Conley. **Released:** 2008. **Price:** $22.95. **Description:** The implications of brand-centric marketing shows how defenseless consumers are against advertising because they are assaulted with 3,000 to 5,000 ads and branding stratagems that subtly dictate all aspects of their lives.

551 ■ *"Old Spice Guy (Feb.-July 2010)"* **in** *Canadian Business (Vol. 83, August 17, 2010, No. 13-14, pp. 23)*
Pub: Rogers Media Ltd.
Ed: Andrew Potter. **Description:** Old Spice Guy was played by ex-football player and actor Isaiah Mustafa who made the debut in the ad for Old Spice Red Zone

body wash that was broadcast during Super Bowl XLIV in February 2010. Old Spice Guy has become one of social marketing success but was cancelled in July when online viewership started to wane.

552 ■ *"Omniture's Next Version of SearchCenter Delivers Landing Page Optimization"* **in** *Internet Wire (September 24, 2009)*
Pub: Comtex News Network, Inc.
Description: Omniture, Inc., a leading provider of online business optimization software, has announced a new release of Omniture SearchCenter; this latest version will allow search engine marketers to test landing pages across campaigns and ad groups.

553 ■ *"The One Thing You Must Get Right When Building a Brand"* **in** *Harvard Business Review (Vol. 88, December 2010, No. 12, pp. 80)*
Pub: Harvard Business School Publishing
Ed: Patrick Barwise, Sean Meehan. **Description:** Four uses for new media include: communicating a clearly defined customer promise, creating trust via delivering on the promise, regularly improving on the promise, and innovating past what is familiar.

554 ■ *"Online Marketing: Puppy Power: Using a New Tool Called a Widget To Boost Your Brand"* **in** *Inc. (November 2007, pp. 55-56)*
Pub: Gruner & Jahr USA Publishing
Ed: Dan Brody. **Description:** Widgets look like small television screens posted on Websites, blogs or desktops with a company's brand or logo. It can display any type of information or image, including sports scores, news headlines, weather reports, animated graphics, or a slide show. Profiles of CarDomain Network, Babystrology, DailyPuppy.com, AnchorBank and more are included.

555 ■ *"Our World with Black Enterprise"* **in** *Black Enterprise (Vol. 37, February 2007, No. 7, pp. 145)*
Pub: Earl G. Graves Publishing Co. Inc.
Description: Our World with Black Enterprise is a television broadcast that features roundtable discussions and interviews with important African American figures.

556 ■ *"Out to Draw Work, Talent"* **in** *Crain's Detroit Business (Vol. 24, April 14, 2008, No. 15, pp. 3)*
Pub: Crain Communications, Inc.
Ed: Bill Shea. **Description:** Profile of Southfield-based Kinetic Post Inc., a growing post-production house that offers video, audio, animation, print, online and related services to corporations and advertising agencies.

557 ■ *"Out-Of-Home and Transit"* **in** *MarketingMagazine (Vol. 115, September 27, 2010, No. 13, pp. 53)*
Pub: Rogers Publishing Ltd.
Description: Out-of-home and transit marketing data covering Canada is presented.

558 ■ *"Paper Tigers"* **in** *Conde Nast Portfolio (Vol. 2, June 2008, No. 6, pp. 84)*
Pub: Conde Nast Publications
Contact: David Carey, President
Ed: Roger Lowenstein. **Description:** Newspapers are losing their advertisers and readers and circulation today is equal to that of 1950, a time when the U.S. population was half its present size.

559 ■ *"Pet-Food Crisis a Boon to Organic Players"* **in** *Advertising Age (Vol. 78, April 9, 2007, No. 15, pp. 3)*
Pub: Crain Communications, Inc.
Ed: Jack Neff. **Description:** In the wake of the pet-food recall crisis, the natural-and-organic segment of the market is gaining recognition and sales; one such manufacturer, Blue Buffalo, has not only seen huge sale increases but also has witnessed a 50-60 percent increase in traffic to the brand's website which has led to the decision to move up the timetable for the brand's first national ad campaign.

560 ■ *"Planning Your Next Move in Ad Land"* **in** *Advertising Age (Vol. 81, January 4, 2009, No. 1, pp. 1)*
Pub: Crain's Communications
Description: Overview of the challenges that ad agencies face today and will face in the years to come; highlights include problems occurring in various industries, Internet marketing innovations and the social media landscape.

561 ■ *"Play By Play: These Video Products Can Add New Life to a Stagnant Website"* **in** *Black Enterprise (Vol. 41, December 2010, No. 5)*
Pub: Earl G. Graves Publishing Co. Inc.
Ed: Marcia Wade Talbert. **Description:** Web Visible, provider of online marketing products and services, cites video capability as the fastest-growing Website feature for small business advertisers. Profiles of various devices for adding video to a Website are included.

562 ■ *"Play It Safe"* **in** *Entrepreneur (Vol. 35, November 2007, No. 11, pp. 26)*
Pub: Entrepreneur Media Inc.
Ed: Gwen Moran. **Description:** U.S.-based toy manufacturers find opportunity from concerns regarding the recent recalls of toys that are made in China. The situation can provide better probability of parents buying toys made in the U.S. or Europe, where manufacturing standards are stricter.

563 ■ *"Political Ads Big Boost to Local Media"* **in** *Baltimore Business Journal (Vol. 28, October 22, 2010, No. 24, pp. 1)*
Pub: Baltimore Business Journal
Ed: Scott Dance. **Description:** Information about the intense demand for advertising time from political campaigns in Baltimore, Maryland is provided. The surge in political advertisement spending would mean big money for local broadcasters, because they see a surging demand for local advertising time for virtually any time of day.

564 ■ *"PopCap Games Achieves Significant Increase in Return on Ad Spend With Omniture SearchCenter"* **in** *Internet Wire (September 15, 2009)*
Pub: Comtex News Network, Inc.
Description: PopCap Games, a leading computer games provider, is using Omniture SearchCenter together with Omniture SiteCatalyst to increase revenue from its search engine marketing campaign. Omniture, Inc. is a leading provider of Internet business optimization software.

565 ■ *The Power of Nice: How to Conquer the Business World with Kindness*
Pub: Doubleday
Ed: Linda Kaplan Thaler; Robin Koval. **Released:** September 19, 2006. **Price:** $17.95. **Description:** The key principles to running a business through thoughtfulness and kindness are exhibited with the use of success stories.

566 ■ *"Prime-Time Exposure"* **in** *Inc. (March 2008, pp. 66, 68)*
Pub: Gruner & Jahr USA Publishing
Ed: Adam Bluestein. **Description:** Product placement in television shows has increase sales for many companies. Tips for placing products or services into TV shows are explained: consider hiring an agency, target efforts, dream up a plot point, be ready to go on short notice, and work the niches.

567 ■ *"Pro Teams Shift Ad Budgets; Naming Rights Deals Near $1 Billion"* **in** *Brandweek (Vol. 49, April 21, 2008, No. 16, pp. 18)*
Pub: VNU Business Media, Inc.
Ed: Barry Janoff. **Description:** More and more professional sports marketers are spending less of their advertising budgets on traditional media outlets such as television, print and radio; the growing trend in sports marketing is in utilizing new media venues such as the Internet in which innovative means are used to encourage interaction with fans.

568 ■ *"Promotions Create a Path to Better Profit"* in Pet Product News (Vol. 64, December 2010, No. 12, pp. 1)
Pub: BowTie Inc.
Ed: Joan Hustace Walker. **Description:** Pet store retailers can boost small mammal sales by launching creative marketing and promotions such as social networking and adoption days.

569 ■ *"Psst..Spread the Word"* in Boston Business Journal (Vol. 27, November 23, 2007, No. 43, pp. 1)
Pub: American City Business Journals Inc.
Ed: Lisa van der Pool. **Description:** More and more Boston companies are using word-of-mouth marketing to boost sales, and spending on it rose to $981 million in 2006. It is projected that spending on word-of-mouth marketing will reach $1.4 billion in 2007, and marketing companies using this type of method are getting higher funding. Trends in word-of-mouth marketing are discussed.

570 ■ *"Put Power in Your Direct Mail Campaigns"* in Contractor (Vol. 56, September 2009, No. 9, pp. 64)
Pub: Penton Media, Inc.
Ed: Matt Michel. **Description:** Advice on how members of the United States plumbing industry should manage direct mail marketing campaigns are offered. Determining the purpose of a campaign is recommended. Focusing on a single message, product or service is also encouraged.

571 ■ *"Quantivo Empowers Online Media Companies to Immediately Expand Audiences and Grow Online Profits"* in Internet Wire (Nov. 18, 2009)
Pub: Comtex News Network, Inc.
Description: Quantivo, the leader in on-demand Behavioral Analytics, has launched a new solution that includes 22 of the most critical Internet audience behavior insights as out-of-the-box reports; Internet marketers need to understand their audience, what they want and how often to offer it to them in order to gain successful branding and campaigns online.

572 ■ *"Quebecor Inc. Takes Hit on Slipping Ad Revenue"* in Globe & Mail (February 21, 2007, pp. B7)
Pub: CTVglobemedia Publishing Inc.
Ed: Catherine McLean. **Description:** Canada-based Quebecor Inc. has reported fourth quarter losses of $97.1 million with revenues of $847.8 million. Decreased advertisement revenues are said to be the key reason behind the loss.

573 ■ *"Reply! Grows at Unprecedented Rate, Rips Beta Off Its Marketplace"* in Marketing Weekly News (September 19, 2009, pp. 149)
Pub: Investment Weekly News
Description: Profile of Reply.com, a leader in locally-targeted Internet marketing, announced significant growth in terms of revenue, enhanced features and services and new categories since launching its beta Reply! Marketplace platform. Even in the face of an economic downturn, the company has posted over 50 percent revenue growth in the Real Estate and Automotive categories.

574 ■ *"Reportlinker Adds Report: Social Networks: Five Consumer Trends for 2009"* in Wireless News (October 23, 2009)
Pub: Close-Up Media
Description: 'Social Networks: Five Consumer Trends for 2009,' a new market research report by Reportlinker.com found that in the countries of Italy and Spain lag behind their European neighbors in Internet development. Since large numbers of consumers in these two countries remain offline, only a minimal portion of total advertising spending goes into Internet marketing, and those advertising campaigns are directed at the relatively young, affluent users. Statistical data included.

575 ■ *"Research and Markets Adds Report: The U.S. Mobile Web Market"* in Entertainment Close-Up (December 10, 2009)
Pub: Close-Up Media
Description: Highlights of the new Research and Markets report 'The U.S. Mobile Web Market: Taking Advantage of the iPhone Phenomenon' include:

mobile Internet marketing strategies; the growth of mobile web usage; the growth of revenue in the mobile web market; and a look at Internet business communications, social media and networking.

576 ■ *"Research and Markets Adds Report: USA - Internet Market - Analysis, Statistics and Forecasts"* in Wireless News (January 15, 2010)
Pub: Close-Up Media
Description: According to Research and Markets new report concerning the United State's Internet market, e-commerce and Online advertising are expected to recover strongly in 2010.

577 ■ *"Retailers Pull Out All Stops to Combat Poor Projections"* in Austin Business JournalInc. (Vol. 28, November 21, 2008, No. 36, pp. 1)
Pub: American City Business Journals
Ed: Jean Kwon. **Description:** Report from Wachovia Economics Group reports that holiday sales for 2008 are expected to decline by 2 percent and local retailers are planning to boost holiday sales through marketing efforts, which include giving freebies to early shoppers. Details on marketing strategies of several retailers are provided.

578 ■ *"The Return of the Infomercial"* in Canadian Business (Vol. 83, September 14, 2010, No. 15, pp. 19)
Pub: Rogers Media Ltd.
Ed: James Cowan. **Description:** Infomercials or direct response ads have helped some products succeed in the marketplace. The success of infomercials is due to the cheap advertising rates, expansion into retail stores and the products' oddball appeal. Insights into the popularity of infomercial products on the Internet and on television are given.

579 ■ *"Rich Returns: Media Master"* in Entrepreneur (Vol. 35, October 2007, No. 10, pp. 42)
Pub: Entrepreneur Media Inc.
Ed: Robert Kiyosaki. **Description:** Advertising is a powerful way of reaching clients, however, public relations is a less expensive method which is just as effective as advertising. Entrepreneurs must also be ready to try something new to be noticed by the public. Insights on how to master the use of media are given.

580 ■ *"Rise Interactive, Internet Marketing Agency, Now Offers Custom Google Analytics Installation"* in Internet Wire (September 29, 2009)
Pub: Comtex News Network, Inc.
Description: In order to optimize a client's return of investment, Rise Interactive, a full-service Internet marketing agency, now offers custom Google Analytics installation to its customers; the installation process includes identifying an Internet marketing campaign's unique key performance indicators, translating them to actions one will perform o n a website and configuring the analytical tool to ensure the customized advertising campaign goals are set and properly tracked.

581 ■ *"Rock Hall Shifts Advertising to 'Significant Markets' in Region"* in Crain's Cleveland Business (Vol. 28, July 23, 2007, No. 29, pp. 6)
Pub: Crain Communications, Inc.
Ed: John Booth. **Description:** Cleveland's Rock and Roll Hall of Fame and Museum is attempting a different marketing strategy this year with aims of reaching a broader audience in the Midwest and Great Lakes regions.

582 ■ *"ROIonline Announces Streaming Video Products"* in Marketing Weekly News (December 5, 2009, pp. 155)
Pub: Investment Weekly News
Description: ROIonline LLC, an Internet marketing firm serving business-to-business and the industrial marketplace, has added streaming video options to the Internet solutions it offers its clients; due to the huge increase of broadband connections, videos are now commonplace on the Internet and can often

convey a company's message in a must more efficient, concise and effective way that will engage a website's visitor thus delivering a high return on a company's investment.

583 ■ *"Ronald Taketa"* in Hawaii Business (Vol. 54, September 2008, No. 3, pp. 28)
Pub: Hawaii Business Publishing
Ed: Shara Enay. **Description:** Interview with Ronald Taketa of the Hawaii Carpenters Union who states that the economic downturn has affected the construction industry as 20 percent of the union's 7,800 members are unemployed. He shares his thoughts about the industry's economic situation, the union's advertisements, and his role as a leader of the union.

584 ■ *"Scripps Networks"* in Brandweek (Vol. 49, April 21, 2008, No. 16, pp. SR12)
Pub: VNU Business Media, Inc.
Ed: Anthony Crupi. **Description:** Provides contact information for sales and marketing personnel for the Scripps networks as well as a listing of the station's top programming and an analysis of the current season and the target audience for those programs running in the current season. Scripps networks include HGTV and the Food Network. HGTV boasts on of the industry's best commercial-retention averages, keeping nearly 97 percent of its viewers during advertising breaks.

585 ■ *"Search and Discover New Opportunities"* in DM News (Vol. 31, December 14, 2009, No. 29, pp. 13)
Pub: Haymarket Media, Inc.
Ed: Chantal Tode. **Description:** Although other digital strategies are gaining traction in Internet marketing, search marketing continues to dominate this advertising forum. Companies like American Greetings, which markets e-card brands online, are utilizing social networking sites and affiliates to generate a higher demand for their products.

586 ■ *The Secrets of Spiritual Marketing: A Complete Guide for Natural Therapists*
Pub: O Books
Ed: Lawrence Ellyard. **Released:** November 1, 2009. **Price:** $24.95. **Description:** Strategies for marketing and advertising a natural therapy business are examined.

587 ■ *"Seed Funding"* in Saint Louis Business Journal (Vol. 31, July 29, 2011, No. 49, pp. 1)
Pub: Saint Louis Business Journal
Ed: Kelsey Volkmann. **Description:** Monsanto kicked off a new campaign, 'St. Louis Grown' to show its commitment to the St. Louis, Missouri region after spending millions of dollars in recent years on national advertising campaigns. Monsanto had a marketing budget totaling $839 million in 2010 for both brand and corporate marketing.

588 ■ *The Seven Principles of WOM and Buzz Marketing: Crossing the Tipping Point*
Pub: Springer
Ed: Panos Mourdoukoulas, George J. Siomkos. **Released:** October 9, 2010. **Price:** $119.00. **Description:** An examination into the reasons for some word-of-mouth marketing campaigns being effective while other fail, with a discussion about which group of consumers should be targeted, and how to turn a word-of-mouth campaign into buzz.

589 ■ *"Shoestring-Budget Marketing"* in Women Entrepreneur (January 5, 2009)
Pub: Entrepreneur Media Inc.
Ed: Maria Falconer. **Description:** Pay-per-click search engine advertising is the traditional type of e-marketing that may not only be too expensive for certain kinds of businesses but also may not attract the quality customer base a business looking to grow needs to find. Social networking websites have become a mandatory marketing tool for business owners who want to see growth in their sales; tips are provided for utilizing these networking websites in order to gain more visibility on the Internet which can, in turn, lead to the more sales.

590 ■ "Show Me the Love" in Canadian Business (Vol. 79, November 6, 2006, No. 22, pp. 77)
Pub: Rogers Media
Ed: Jeannette Hanna. **Description:** The strategies to improve brand image with relation to success of Tim Horton's brand are presented.

591 ■ "Sick of Trends? You Should Be" in Brandweek (Vol. 49, April 21, 2008, No. 16, pp. 22)
Pub: VNU Business Media, Inc.
Ed: Eric Zeitoun. **Description:** Eric Zeitoun, the president of Dragon Rouge, a global brand consultancy, discusses the importance of macrotrends as opposed to microtrends which he feels are often irrelevant, create confusion and cause marketers to lose site of the larger picture of their industry. Macrotrends, on the other hand, create a fundamental, societal shift that influences consumer attitudes over a long period of time.

592 ■ "Sign, Sign, Everywhere a Sign: How I Did It: Richard Schaps" in Inc. (October 2007, pp. 128)
Pub: Gruner & Jahr USA Publishing
Ed: Stephanie Clifford. **Description:** Richard Schaps shares the story of selling his outdoor-advertising firm, Van Wagner for $170 million and sharing the wealth with his employees. Schaps then started another outdoor-sign company.

593 ■ The Small Business Bible: Everything You Need to Know to Succeed in Your Small Business
Pub: John Wiley and Sons, Inc.
Ed: Steven D. Strauss. **Released:** September 2008. **Price:** $19.95 (US), $28.99 (Canadian). **Description:** Comprehensive guide to starting and running a successful small business. Topics include bookkeeping and financial management, marketing, publicity, and advertising.

594 ■ The Social Media Bible: Tactics, Tools, and Strategies for Business Success
Pub: John Wiley & Sons, Inc.
Ed: Lon Safko, David Brake. **Released:** June 17, 2009. **Price:** $29.95. **Description:** Information is given to build or transform a business into social media, where customers, employees, and prospects connect, collaborate, and champion products and services in order to increase sales and to beat the competition.

595 ■ "Sony Pictures Television" in Brandweek (Vol. 49, April 21, 2008, No. 16, pp. SR13)
Pub: VNU Business Media, Inc.
Ed: Marc Berman. **Description:** Provides contact information for sales and marketing personnel for Sony Pictures Television Distribution as well as a listing of the station's top programming and an analysis of the current season and the target audience for those programs running in the current season.

596 ■ "Sorrell Digs Deep to Snag TNS" in Advertising Age (Vol. 79, July 14, 2008, No. 7, pp. 1)
Pub: Crain Communications, Inc.
Ed: Michael Bush. **Description:** Martin Sorrell's strategic vision for expansion in order to become the largest ad-agency holding company in the world is discussed.

597 ■ Start Your Own Fashion Accessories Business
Pub: Entrepreneur Press
Contact: Perlman Neil, President
Released: March 1, 2009. **Price:** $17.95. **Description:** Entrepreneurs wishing to start a fashion accessories business will find important information for setting up a home workshop and office, exploring the market, managing finances, publicizing and advertising the business and more.

598 ■ "Staying Power" in Canadian Business (Vol. 79, November 6, 2006, No. 22, pp. 73)
Pub: Rogers Media
Ed: John Gray. **Description:** The effects on brand image on customer choices are analyzed. The need of maintaining brand image is also emphasized.

599 ■ "Strength In Numbers" in Black Enterprise (Vol. 38, January 2008, No. 6, pp. 53)
Pub: Earl G. Graves Publishing Co. Inc.
Description: According to recent studies geared to advertisers, African Americans represent a demographic that drives style and consumer trends. The African American buying power is expected to increase to $1.1 trillion by 2011. Beyond Demographics helps clients identify ways to value and measure investments within the black community.

600 ■ "Stretch Your Advertising Dollars" in Women Entrepreneur (January 27, 2009)
Pub: Entrepreneur Media Inc.
Ed: Rosalind Resnick. **Description:** During such poor economic times, most businesses are having to cut their advertising budgets; tips for targeting your advertising dollars toward the customer base most likely to buy your product are given.

601 ■ "Success a Big Seller: N. Carolina, Duke Coaches Cash in as Marketers' Dreams" in Charlotte Observer (February 7, 2007)
Pub: Knight-Ridder/Tribune Business News
Ed: Ken Tysiac. **Description:** North Carolina sporting coaches are marketing goods and services in television commercials and print media.

602 ■ Success Secrets of Social Media Marketing Superstars
Pub: Entrepreneur Press
Contact: Perlman Neil, President
Ed: Mitch Meyerson. **Released:** June 1, 2010. **Price:** $21.95. **Description:** Provides access to the playbooks of social media marketers who reveal their most valuable strategies and tactics for standing out in the new online media environment.

603 ■ "Suits Keep Flying in Wireless Service Marketing Wars" in Globe & Mail (March 22, 2007, pp. B3)
Pub: CTVglobemedia Publishing Inc.
Ed: Catherine McLean. **Description:** The suit filed by Telus Corp. against BCE Mobile Communications Inc. over the latter's alleged misleading advertisement in the press is discussed.

604 ■ "Survey: More Buyers Expect to Spend Less in Most Media" in Advertising Age (Vol. 79, July 7, 2008, No. 26, pp. 3)
Pub: Crain Communications, Inc.
Ed: Megan McIlroy. **Description:** Marketers are decreasing their budgets for advertising in television, radio, newspaper and outdoor due to the economic downturn. Statistical data concerning advertising agencies and marketers included.

605 ■ "Survey Points to Big Jump in 2006 Ad Budgets" in Globe & Mail (January 23, 2006, pp. B3)
Pub: CTVglobemedia Publishing Inc.
Ed: Keith McArthur. **Description:** The findings of ICA Survey of Marketing Budgets on the advertising budgets of marketing executives, in 2006, are presented.

606 ■ "T3 Grows, Recovers Well After Losing Dell" in Austin Business JournalInc. (Vol. 28, September 19, 2008, No. 27)
Pub: American City Business Journals
Ed: Sandra Zaragoza. **Description:** T3 Inc. an Austin, Texas-based advertising company is recovering from losing its Dell Inc. account with the addition of new clients, such as Taco Bell, ConocoPhillips, Robbins Brothers, and Intel. The country is projected to earn capitalized billings of $313 million for 2008. Details on the company's plans to consolidate its offices are discussed.

607 ■ "Taco Bell; David Ovens" in Advertising Age (Vol. 79, November 17, 2008, No. 43, pp. S2)
Pub: Crain Communications, Inc.
Ed: Emily Bryson York. **Description:** Due to the addition of new products such as a low-calorie, low-fat Fresco menu; a fruity iced beverage; and a value initiative, Taco Bell now accounts for half of Yum

Brands' profits. The chain has also benefited from a new chief marketing officer, David Ovens, who oversees ad support.

608 ■ "Telemundo" in Brandweek (Vol. 49, April 21, 2008, No. 16, pp. SR8)
Pub: VNU Business Media, Inc.
Ed: John Consoli. **Description:** Provides contact information for sales and marketing personnel for the Telemundo network as well as a listing of the station's top programming and an analysis of the current season and the target audience for those programs running in the current season.

609 ■ "That Canadian Tire Couple Won't Be Annoying You Anymore" in Globe & Mail (March 10, 2006, pp. B3)
Pub: CTVglobemedia Publishing Inc.
Ed: Keith McArthur. **Description:** The details pertaining to the rolling out of new advertisements by Canadian Tire Corp. Ltd. are presented. The commercials have been made by Taxi Advertising and Design, which has redesigned the previous ad of the tire maker.

610 ■ "This Week: McD's Eyes Ad Plan, Shifts Breakfast Biz" in Crain's Chicago Business (Vol. 30, February 2007, No. 6, pp. 1)
Pub: Crain Communications, Inc.
Ed: Kate MacArthur. **Description:** McDonald's is moving its national breakfast ad account from DDB Chicago to Arnold Worldwide of Boston and Moroch of Dallas in an attempt to change its marketing strategy. It is also doing a study to keep abreast of consumer trends.

611 ■ "Thomas Morley; President, The Lube Stop Inc., 37" in Crain's Cleveland Business (Vol. 28, November 19, 2007, No. 46, pp. F-12)
Pub: Crain Communications, Inc.
Ed: David Bennett. **Description:** Profile of Thomas Morley, president of The Lube Stop Inc., who is dedicated to promoting the company's strong environmental record as an effective way to differentiate Lube Stop from its competition. Since Mr. Morley came to the company in 2004, Lube Stop has increased sales by 10 percent and has boosted its operating profits by 30 percent.

612 ■ "Ticket Tiff Erupts Over Fund Ads" in Globe & Mail (January 31, 2007, pp. B1)
Pub: CTVglobemedia Publishing Inc.
Description: The opposition of Cineplex Entertainment LP to Mackenzie Financial Corp.'s advertisement about high cost of movie ticket is discussed.

613 ■ "Tim Armstrong" in Canadian Business (Vol. 81, July 21, 2008, No. 11, pp. 10)
Pub: Rogers Media Ltd.
Ed: Calvin Leung. **Description:** Interview with Tim Armstrong who is the president of advertising and commerce department of Google Inc. for North America; the information technology company executive talked about the emerging trends and changes to YouTube made by the company since its acquisition in 2006.

614 ■ "Titan to Become New York's Largest Provider of Phone Kiosk Advertising" in Marketing Weekly News (September 11, 2010, pp. 150)
Pub: VerticalNews
Description: Titan will acquire from Verizon 1,900 payphones at 1,300 phone kiosk locations in New York City, New York. This transaction will triple the firm's inventory of New York Phone Kiosk media to over 5,000 advertising faces. Details are included.

615 ■ "To Catch Up, Colgate May Ratchet Up Its Ad Spending" in Advertising Age (Vol. 81, December 6, 2010, No. 43, pp. 1)
Pub: Crain Communications, Inc.
Ed: Jack Neff. **Description:** Colgate-Palmolive Company has been losing market share in the categories of toothpaste, deodorant, body wash, dish soap and pet food.

616 ■ *"The Top Mistakes of Social Media Marketing"* in *Agency Sales Magazine* (Vol. 39, November 2009, No. 9, pp. 42)
Pub: MANA
Ed: Pam Lontos; Maurice Ramirez. **Description:** One common mistake in social media marketing is having more than one image on the Internet because this ruins a business' credibility. Marketers need to put out messages that are useful to their readers and to keep messages consistent.

617 ■ *TRUTH: The New Rules for Marketing in a Skeptical World*
Pub: AMACOM
Ed: Lynn B. Upshaw. **Released:** August 8, 2007. **Price:** $24.95. **Description:** Because consumers are more informed today, small business owners must find new ways to market products and services.

618 ■ *"Turner Broadcasting System"* in *Brandweek* (Vol. 49, April 21, 2008, No. 16, pp. SR13)
Pub: VNU Business Media, Inc.
Ed: Anthony Crupi. **Description:** Provides contact information for sales and marketing personnel for the Turner Broadcasting System networks as well as a listing of the station's top programming and an analysis of the current season and the target audience for those programs running in the current season. Recent acquisitions are also discussed.

619 ■ *"Twentieth Television"* in *Brandweek* (Vol. 49, April 21, 2008, No. 16, pp. SR16)
Pub: VNU Business Media, Inc.
Ed: Marc Berman. **Description:** Provides contact information for sales and marketing personnel for Twentieth Television as well as a listing of the station's top programming and an analysis of the current season and the target audience for those programs running in the current season.

620 ■ *"The Twittering Class"* in *Entrepreneur* (Vol. 37, September 2009, No. 9, pp. 40)
Pub: Entrepreneur Media, Inc.
Ed: Mikal E. Belicove. **Description:** Advice on how entrepreneurs can use online social networks to promote their businesses is presented. Facebook offers applications and advertising solutions to promote Websites, products and services. Twitter, on the other hand, provides instant messaging, which can be done through computer or cell phone.

621 ■ *Twitterville: How Businesses Can Thrive in the New Global Neighborhoods*
Pub: Portfolio Hardcover
Ed: Shel Israel. **Price:** $23.95. **Description:** Twitter is the most rapidly adopted communication tool in history, going from zero to ten million users in just over two years. On Twitter, word can spread faster than wildfire. Companies no longer have the option of ignoring the conversation. Unlike other hot social media spaces, Twitterville is dominated by professionals, not students. And despite its size, it still feels like a small town. Twitter allows people to interact much the way they do face-to-face, honestly and authentically.

622 ■ *Ultimate Guide to Project Management*
Pub: Entrepreneurial Press
Ed: Sid Kemp. **Released:** October 2005. **Price:** $29.95 (US), $39.95 (Canadian). **Description:** Project management strategies including writing a business plan and developing a good advertising campaign.

623 ■ *The Ultimate Small Business Marketing Toolkit: All the Tips, Forms, and Strategies You'll Ever Need!*
Pub: McGraw-Hill Inc.
Ed: Beth Goldstein. **Released:** July 2007. **Price:** $27.95. **Description:** An all-in-one sales and marketing resource for entrepreneurs to grow a business.

624 ■ *"Univision"* in *Brandweek* (Vol. 49, April 21, 2008, No. 16, pp. SR8)
Pub: VNU Business Media, Inc.
Ed: John Consoli. **Description:** Provides contact information for sales and marketing personnel for the Univision network as well as a listing of the station's top programming and an analysis of the current

season and the target audience for those programs running in the current season. Univision is the No. 1 network on Friday nights in the 18-34 demographic, beating all English-language networks.

625 ■ *"Unleashing the Power of Marketing"* in *Harvard Business Review* (Vol. 88, October 2010, No. 10, pp. 90)
Pub: Harvard Business School Publishing
Ed: Beth Comstock, Ranjay Gulati, Stephen Liguori. **Description:** Chronicle of the development of General Electric's marketing framework that focused on three key factors: Principles, people and process. GE determined that successful marketing fulfills four functions: instigating, innovating, implementing, and integrating.

626 ■ *"Use Social Media to Enhance Brand, Business"* in *Contractor* (Vol. 56, December 2009, No. 12, pp. 14)
Pub: Penton Media, Inc.
Ed: Elton Rivas. **Description:** Advice on how plumbing contractors should use online social networks to increase sales is presented including such issues as clearly defining goals and target audience. An additional advantage to this medium is that advertisements can easily be shared with other users.

627 ■ *"Utah Technology Council: Social Media Is Here to Stay; Embrace It"* in *Wireless News* (December 14, 2009)
Pub: Close-Up Media
Description: Social media outlets such as Facebook and Twitter are blurring the lines between advertising, public relations, branding and marketing; businesses must stop thinking in terms of traditional marketing versus Internet marketing if they want to succeed in today's marketing climate.

628 ■ *"Warner Bros. Domestic Television Distribution"* in *Brandweek* (Vol. 49, April 21, 2008, No. 16, pp. SR16)
Pub: VNU Business Media, Inc.
Ed: Marc Berman. **Description:** Provides contact information for sales and marketing personnel for Warner Bros. Domestic Television Distribution as well as a listing of the station's top programming and an analysis of the current season and the target audience for those programs running in the current season.

629 ■ *"Web-Based Marketing Excites, Challenges Small Business Use"* in *Colorado Springs Business Journal* (January 20, 2010)
Pub: Dolan Media Co.
Ed: Becky Hurley. **Description:** Business-to-business and consumer-direct firms alike are using the fast-changing Web technologies to increase sales, leads and track consumer behavior but once a company commits to an Online marketing plan, experts believe, they must be prepared to consistently tweak and overhaul content and distribution vehicles in order to keep up.

630 ■ *"Web Traffic Numbers Facing Scrutiny"* in *Boston Business Journal* (Vol. 27, November 2, 2007, No. 40, pp. 1)
Pub: American City Business Journals Inc.
Ed: Jesse Noyes. **Description:** Interactive Advertising Bureau (IAB) held a summit meeting with major industry players in an effort to create more transparent standards for measuring Internet traffic. The terms at issue were registered users, unique visitors, time spent and retention.

631 ■ *"Webadvertising"* in *MarketingMagazine* (Vol. 115, September 27, 2010, No. 13, pp. 70)
Pub: Rogers Publishing Ltd.
Description: Website advertising in Canada is examined.

632 ■ *"Web.Preneuring: How Local TV Ads and Online Marketing Can Help You Win Big"* in *Small Business Opportunities* (January 2008)
Pub: Harris Publications Inc.
Ed: David Waxman. **Description:** Spot Runner, an Internet-based advertising agency offers low-cost local business television ads. The company secures the ad buy, places and tracks the ads, and analyzes viewership and demographics for clients.

633 ■ *"Welch's Uses Taste Strips in Ads"* in *Marketing to Women* (Vol. 21, April 2008, No. 4, pp. 3)
Pub: EPM Communications Inc.
Contact: Ira Mayer, President
E-mail: imayer@epmcom.com
Description: Welch's is positioning its 139-year-old brand in a new and inventive way with a new marketing campaign in which print ads will feature a tamper-evident flavor pouch that contains a dissolving taste strip flavored with Welch's grape juice.

634 ■ *"What Players in the Midmarket Are Talking About"* in *Mergers & Acquisitions: The Dealmaker's Journal* (March 1, 2008)
Pub: SourceMedia, Inc.
Description: Sports Properties Acquisition Corp. went public at the end of January; according to the company's prospectus, it is not limiting its focus to just teams, it is also considering deals for stadium construction companies, sports leagues, facilities, sports-related advertising and licensing of products, in addition to other related segments.

635 ■ *"What Women Watch on TV"* in *Marketing to Women* (Vol. 21, February 2008, No. 2, pp. 6)
Pub: EPM Communications Inc.
Contact: Ira Mayer, President
E-mail: imayer@epmcom.com
Description: According to BIGresearch, women are more likely to watch sports than they are soap operas. Statistical data included.

636 ■ *"Why Some Get Shaften By Google Pricing"* in *Advertising Age* (Vol. 79, July 14, 2008, No. 7, pp. 3)
Pub: Crain Communications, Inc.
Ed: Abbey Klaassen. **Description:** Google's search advertising is discussed as well as the company's pricing structure for these ads.

637 ■ *"Why You Need a New-Media 'Ringmaster"* in *Harvard Business Review* (Vol. 88, December 2010, No. 12, pp. 78)
Pub: Harvard Business School Publishing
Ed: Patrick Spenner. **Description:** The concept of ringmaster is applied to brand marketing. This concept includes integrative thinking, lean collaboration skills, and high-speed decision cycles.

638 ■ *"With Traffic Jam in Super Bowl, Can Any Auto Brand Really Win?"* in *Advertising Age* (Vol. 81, December 6, 2010, No. 43, pp. 1)
Pub: Crain Communications, Inc.
Ed: Rupal Parekh, Brian Steinberg. **Description:** Car marketers are doubling down for Super Bowl XLV in Arlington, Texas and asking their ad agencies to craft commercials unique enough to break through the clutter and to capture viewers' attention.

639 ■ *"Women See Special Interest, Review Sites as Most Brand-Friendly"* in *Marketing to Women* (Vol. 23, November 2010, No. 11, pp. 4)
Pub: EPM Communications Inc.
Contact: Ira Mayer, President
E-mail: imayer@epmcom.com
Description: Rather focusing on specific demographics, marketing and ad agencies should focus on women's core needs such as mom versus mom or Gen X versus Baby Boomer.

640 ■ *Work at Home Now*
Pub: Career Press, Inc.
Ed: Christine Durst, Michael Haaren. **Released:** October 9, 2010. **Price:** $14.99. **Description:** There are legitimate home-based jobs and projects that can be found on the Internet, but trustworthy guidance is scarce. There is a 58 to 1 scam ratio in work at-home advertising filled with fraud.

641 ■ *"XM Burning Through Cash to Catch Sirius"* in *Globe & Mail* (April 17, 2007, pp. B5)
Pub: CTVglobemedia Publishing Inc.
Ed: Grant Robertson. **Description:** The effort of XM Satellite Radio Holdings Inc. to spend about $45 million to increase sale of its radio in Canada is discussed.

642 ■ *"Yahoo! - Microsoft Pact: Alive Again?"* in *Barron's* (Vol. 89, July 27, 2009, No. 30, pp. 8)

Pub: Dow Jones & Co., Inc.

Ed: Mark Veverka. **Description:** Yahoo! reported higher than expected earnings in the second quarter of 2009 under CEO Carol Bartz who has yet to articulate her long-term vision and strategy for turning around the company. The media reported that Yahoo! and Microsoft are discussing an advertising-search partnership which should benefit both companies.

643 ■ *"You Lost Me at Hello"* in *Entrepreneur* (Vol. 35, November 2007, No. 11, pp. 136)

Pub: Entrepreneur Media Inc.

Ed: John Jantsch. **Description:** Managing your marketing materials by making them more informational is an effective tool to educate consumers about your product. Information that should be included in your marketing kit are outlined.

644 ■ *"Your Big Give"* in *Small Business Opportunities* (September 2008)

Pub: Entrepreneur Press

Contact: Perlman Neil, President

Ed: Michael Guld. **Description:** Cause related marketing is beneficial to businesses as well as the communities they inhabit; three small businesses that are elevating their standing in the community while at the same time increasing their customer base are profiled.

645 ■ *YouTube and Video Marketing: An Hour a Day*

Pub: Sybex

Ed: Greg Jarboe. **Released:** August 10, 2009. **Price:** $29.99. **Description:** The importance of online video marketing for businesses is stressed. Tips for developing and implementing video marketing are outlined.

SOURCES OF SUPPLY

646 ■ *Business Marketing Association--Membership & Resource Directory*

Business Marketing Association

Contact: Rick Kean, Executive Director

URL(s): marketing.org/i4a/pages/index.cfm?pageid=1. **Released:** Annual; January. **Covers:** Over 4,500 member business communications professionals in fields of advertising, marketing communications, and marketing; their service and supply companies are listed in the "Marketing Resources" section. **Entries include:** For individuals--Name, title, company with which affiliated, address, phone. For companies--Name, address, phone, contact, description of products or services. **Arrangement:** Individuals are alphabetical within chapter; companies are classified by product or service. **Indexes:** Alpha, company, chapter.

STATISTICAL SOURCES

647 ■ *RMA Annual Statement Studies*

Pub: Risk Management Association

Contact: Kevin M. Blakey, President

Released: Annual. **Price:** $175.00 2006-07 edition, $105.00. **Description:** Contains composite balance sheets and income statements for more than 360 industries, including the accounting, auditing, and bookkeeping industries. Also contains five years of comparative historical data for discerning trends. Includes 16 commonly used ratios, computed for most of the size groupings for nearly every industry.

648 ■ *Standard & Poor's Industry Surveys*

Pub: Standard & Poor's Corp.

Released: Annual. **Price:** $3633.00. **Description:** Two-volume book that examines the prospects for specific industries, including trucking. Also provides analyses of trends and problems, statistical tables and charts, and comparative company analyses.

TRADE PERIODICALS

649 ■ *AAF Government Report*

Pub: American Advertising Federation

Contact: James Edmund Datri, President

Ed: Bob Kohlmeyer, Editor. **Released:** 10/year. **Description:** Supplies information on federal and state legislative and regulatory issues that affect the advertising industry. **Remarks:** Available online only.

650 ■ *Advertising Compliance Service*

Pub: JL Com Publishing Company L.L.C.

Contact: John Lichtenberger, Editor-in-Chief

Released: Semimonthly. **Price:** $595, individuals. **Description:** Functions as the only comprehensive reference source for information regarding advertising compliance requirements and issues. Subscription includes: 24 issues annually, 6 special reports, and a three- volume based volume (1,500 plus pages) for initial subscribers only.

651 ■ *Adweek/New England*

Pub: Adweek L.P.

URL(s): www.adweek.com. **Released:** Weekly **Price:** $299, Individuals print and online; $149, Individuals digital access only; $24.95, Individuals monthly, print + online; $19.95, Individuals monthly, online only.

652 ■ *IAA National & World News*

Pub: International Advertising Association

Contact: Luis Mendiola Codina, President

Ed: Pamela Yaeger, Editor, pamela@iaaglobal.org. **Released:** Quarterly. **Price:** $50, Included in membership. **Description:** Supplies information on Association policies and activities. Includes reviews of publications and reports from the 62 chapters worldwide.

653 ■ *Journal of Advertising Research*

Pub: Advertising Research Foundation

Contact: Robert Barocci, President

E-mail: bb@thearf.org

URL(s): www.jar.warc.com/. **Released:** Quarterly; Bimonthly **Price:** $215, Individuals; €430, Individuals with enhanced online; $110, /year in U.S.; $140, /year outside U.S.

654 ■ *PROMO: Ideas. Connections. Brands*

Pub: Penton

Contact: Raymond E. Maloney, President

URL(s): promomagazine.com/. **Released:** Monthly

655 ■ *Promotional Products Business*

Contact: Tina Berres Filipski, Editor

E-mail: tinaf@ppa.org

URL(s): www.ppbmag.com/. **Ed:** Tina Berres Filipski. **Released:** Monthly **Price:** $48, Members; $60, Canada and Mexico members; $65, Other countries members; $62, Members for prospective members in U.S.; $74, Canada and Mexico for prospective members in Canada and Mexico; $79, Other countries for prospective members in other countries.

656 ■ *Topline*

Pub: MSW Research

Contact: Harold Spielman, Owner

Ed: Paula Kay Pierce, Editor. **Released:** Quarterly. **Price:** Free. **Description:** Contains advertising research findings and analysis. Covers trends in advertising.

VIDEOCASSETTES/AUDIOCASSETTES

657 ■ *Ad Campaigns That Work*

Instructional Video

2219 C St.

Lincoln, NE 68502

Ph: (402)475-6570

Free: 800-228-0164

Fax: (402)475-6500

Co. E-mail: feedback@insvideo.com

URL: http://www.insvideo.com

Released: 19??. **Price:** $89.95. **Description:** Three successful ad agency executives furnish information on successful ad campaigns and why they were successful. Covers principles of successful advertising. **Availability:** VHS.

658 ■ *Advertising: The Hidden Language*

First Light Video Publishing

2321 Abbot Kinney Blvd.

Venice, CA 90291

Ph: (310)577-8581

Free: 800-262-8862

Fax: (310)574-0886

Co. E-mail: sale@firstlightvideo.com

URL: http://www.firstlightvideo.com

Released: 19??. **Description:** Features Dr. Phillip Bell as he demostrates how successful ads grab the consumer and make them want to purchase the product. **Availability:** VHS.

659 ■ *Advertising Tricks Without the Gimmicks*

Instructional Video

2219 C St.

Lincoln, NE 68502

Ph: (402)475-6570

Free: 800-228-0164

Fax: (402)475-6500

Co. E-mail: feedback@insvideo.com

URL: http://www.insvideo.com

Released: 19??. **Price:** $79.00. **Description:** Offers an overview and practical hints on the basics of advertising. **Availability:** VHS.

660 ■ *Promotion: Polishing the Apple*

RMI Media

1365 N. Winchester St.

Olathe, KS 66061-5880

Ph: (913)768-1696

Free: 800-745-5480

Fax: (800)755-6910

Co. E-mail: actmedia@act.org

URL: http://www.actmedia.com

Released: 1991. **Price:** $89.95. **Description:** Presents promotional mixes developed by Apple Computers for the Apple IIc, the Macintosh, and the Macintosh Office to demonstrate successful uses of print and television advertising. **Availability:** VHS.

CONSULTANTS

661 ■ *Black Eagle Consulting 2000 Inc.—Black Eagle Executive Search*

451 Barclay Cres.

Oakville, ON, Canada L6J 6H8

Ph: (905)842-3010

Fax: (905)842-9586

Co. E-mail: info@blackeagle.ca

URL: http://www.blackeagle.ca

Contact: Richard L. Simms, President

E-mail: rsimms@blackeagle.ca

Scope: Business firm offers services in outplacement and career counseling career review and personal assessment, Myers-Briggs type instrument practitioner, resume review and revision, interview coaching, job search techniques, job offer counsel, strategic planning and corporate reviews business plan analysis, corporate vision, mission and values definition, goals and objectives, strengths, weaknesses, opportunities, threats (swot) analysis, merger and acquisition strategy; facilitator, strategic planning meetings (agenda preparation, on topic/on time, meeting assessment); organizational structure review (requirements for growth, succession planning); executive coaching; and marketing and sales (analysis of the company's product line, pricing, packaging, merchandising, and advertising programs, market research, assessment of current sales organization/compensation issues). **Founded:** 2000. **Special Services:** Myers-Briggs Type Instrument®.

662 ■ *The Center for Technical Communication—Bob Bly Copywriter*

590 Delcina Dr.

River Vale, NJ 07675

Ph: (201)505-9451

Fax: (201)385-1138

Co. E-mail: rwbly@bly.com

URL: http://www.bly.com

Contact: Bob Bly, President

E-mail: rwbly@bly.com

Scope: An independent consultant and copywriter specializing in business-to-business, industrial, hi-tech, and direct response advertising, marketing, publicity, and promotion. Writes marketing plans, ad campaigns, sales brochures, publicity materials, direct response ads, sales letters, and direct mail packages for clients nationwide. Industries served: publishing, business-to-business products or services, software or computers, electronics, financial, healthcare, medical equipment, industrial equipment, chemicals, consulting, and professional services. **Founded:** 1982. **Publications:** "The Bulletproof Book Proposal "; "Finding A Good Idea For Your Book"; "A Fine Position to Be In"; "What to Do When Your Book Goes Out of Print"; "How To Write a Good Advertisement"; "31 -derfully Simple Ways To Make Your Ads Generate More Inquiries"; "On Target Advertising"; "How to Write More Effective Product Brochures "; "Classy Outfit...Classy Brochure?"; "Improving Your Listening Skills"; "Improving Your Interpersonal Skills"; "10 Ways To Get More Done in Less Time"; "How to Give a Successful Presentation". **Seminars:** Active Listening; Become an Instant Guru; Get More Done In Less Time: How To Double Your Personal Productivity; How To Write A Nonfiction Book And Get It Published; How To Succeed as a Freelance Writer; The 1-Hour E-Zine Writing Formula; World's Best-Kept Copywriting Secrets; What's Working in Direct Mail Today; What's Working in E-Mail Marketing Today; Copywriting for Non-Copywriters; Effective Business Writing; Effective Technical Writing; How To Write Copy That Sells; Selling Your Services.

663 ■ Ideas To Go Inc.
1 Main St. SE, 5th Fl.
Minneapolis, MN 55414
Ph: (612)331-1570
Fax: (612)331-1602
Co. E-mail: inquiries@ideastogo.com
URL: http://www.ideastogo.com
Contact: Charlie Hartwell, President
E-mail: chartwell@ideastogo.com
Scope: Offers creative process consultation and facilitation, in the context of creative problem-solving, long-range planning, new product development, team building, marketing and advertising issues. Serves private industries as well as government agencies. **Founded:** 1980. **Seminars:** Pennsylvania Manufacturing Confectioners' Association, Feb, 2010; Custom-designed creativity training; Creative Problem Solving Institute facilitator training; Received focus group moderator training, RIVA Institute. **Special Services:** Forness®; E-deation®; Concentrated Concept Development; Claimstorming; Creative Ethnography.

664 ■ IMC Consulting & Training
901 McHenry Ave., Ste. A
Modesto, CA 95350
Ph: (209)572-2271
Fax: (209)572-2862
Co. E-mail: info@imc-1.net
URL: http://www.imc-1.net
Contact: Michael J. Loschke, President
E-mail: michael@imc-1.net
Scope: Helps businesses and professionals identify, develop and market their selling proposition to increase profits. Services include B-to-B surveys, direct marketing, media relations, planning and strategy, sales management, training and leadership coaching. **Founded:** 1994. **Publications:** "Consultant Earns Advanced Certificate," Hccsc Business Review, Dec, 2004; "Adapting to Change - the New Competitive Advantage," Business Journal, Jul, 2004; "Loyalty Marketing Can Divide New Business," Jun, 2004; "Eleven Major Marketing Mistakes," Jul, 2003; "Planning to Win or Racing to Fail," Jun, 2003. **Seminars:** Negotiating High Profit Sales; How to Write Winning Proposals, Modesto Chamber of Commerce, Oct, 2007; Winning the 2nd Half: A 6-month Plan to Score New Customers and Profits. **Telecommunication Services:** imcinfo@imc-1.net.

665 ■ ReCourses Inc.
6101 Stillmeadow Dr.
Nashville, TN 37211-6518
Ph: (615)831-2277
Free: 888-476-5884
Fax: (615)831-2212
Co. E-mail: info@recourses.com
URL: http://www.recourses.com
Contact: Julie Warren, Manager
Scope: A management consulting firm that works exclusively with small service providers in the com-

munications industry, including public relations firms, advertising agencies, interactive companies and design studios. Services include Total Business Review, a complete examination of your business starting with an on site examination or discussion, followed by written recommendations and then supplemented with six months of implementation guidance. Areas reviewed include positioning, marketing, management, personnel, structure, finance, retirement, technology and specific growth issues. **Founded:** 1994. **Publications:** "Managing (Right) for the First Time"; "Financial Management of a Marketing Firm". **Seminars:** 10th Annual New Business Summit , Jan, 2013; Event - TEDx Nashville: Success from the Inside Out--Alignment & Engagement , Apr, 20163; Event - AIGA Brand Academy (Emory Executive Education @ Goizueta Business School) , Apr, 2013; Measuring Economic Performance: Measuring and Enhancing Performance in a Marketing Firm, Dec, 2012; Managing Client Relationships: Being Indispensable, Growing the Account, Making Money, Nov, 2012; The Business of Design Oct, 2012; Getting a Good Start in Your Creative Career, Nov, 2011; Research and Insights, Nov, 2011; Managing Client Relationships; Research and Strategy; Financial Management: Measuring and Enhancing Performance in a Marketing Firm, Sep, 2009; Building and Leading a Staff: The When, How, and What of Growth and Culture, Sep, 2009; Doing Effective Work: Adding Significance to the Strategic Portion of Your Work for Clients, Sep, 2009; Resourcing the Creative Process: Managing Pricing, Deadlines, Budgets, Quality, and Capacity, Apr, 2009. **Special Services:** ReCourses®.

FRANCHISES AND BUSINESS OPPORTUNITIES

666 ■ AllOver Media
6901 E Fish Lake Rd., Ste. 180
Maple Grove, MN 55369
Ph: (800)525-8762
Fax: (763)424-1836
Co. E-mail: infor@allovermedia.com
URL: http://www.allovermedia.com
Description: Indoor print, gas pump and electric LCD advertising. **No. of Franchise Units:** 27. **No. of Company-Owned Units:** 1. **Founded:** 2002.. **Franchised:** 2002. **Equity Capital Needed:** $37,300-$124,800 total investment; $75,000 net worth, $35,000 liquidity. **Franchise Fee:** $30,000. **Royalty Fee:** 6%. **Financial Assistance:** Limited third party financing available. **Training:** Provides 40 hours at headquarters and 40 hours onsite with ongoing support.

667 ■ American Town Mailer
4638 E Ingram
Mesa, AZ 85205
Ph: (480)649-0344
Fax: (480)641-9988
Description: Direct-mail advertising. **No. of Franchise Units:** 3. **Founded:** 1976.. **Franchised:** 2000. **Equity Capital Needed:** $23,900-$37,200 total investment; $25,000 net worth, $25,000 cash liquidity. **Franchise Fee:** $20,000. **Training:** Provides 1 week at headquarters, 1 week onsite with ongoing support.

668 ■ AmeriCare Franchise Ltd.
225 Laura Dr.
Addison, IL 60101
Ph: (630)458-1990
Free: 800-745-6191
Fax: (630)458-1994
Description: Offers restroom sanitation and air-freshening services. **No. of Franchise Units:** 20. **No. of Company-Owned Units:** 5. **Founded:** 1964.. **Franchised:** 1968. **Equity Capital Needed:** $90,000. **Franchise Fee:** $50,000. **Royalty Fee:** 15%. **Training:** Provides 2 weeks at headquarters, 1 week+ with ongoing support.

669 ■ Best Coupon Book
260 Maitland Ave., Ste. 2000
Altamonte Springs, FL 32701

Ph: (407)571-3713
Description: Direct mail advertising. **No. of Franchise Units:** 3. **No. of Company-Owned Units:** 1. **Founded:** 1997.. **Franchised:** 2005. **Equity Capital Needed:** $50,000. **Franchise Fee:** $35,000. **Training:** Yes.

670 ■ Billboard Connection
2121 Vista Pky.
West Palm Beach, GA 33416
Ph: (561)868-1355
Fax: (561)478-4340
Co. E-mail: franchise@billboardconnection.com
URL: http://www.billboardconnection.com
Description: Advertising agency specializing in out-of-home media. We consult with clients & place their ads on billboards, buses, taxis, airport dioramas, mall kiosks, movie theaters and more. **No. of Franchise Units:** 89. **Founded:** 1997.. **Franchised:** 2003. **Equity Capital Needed:** $41,000. **Franchise Fee:** $24,500. **Financial Assistance:** Yes. **Training:** Offers 2 week training program and ongoing support.

671 ■ Bride and Groom Planner
Bride & Groom Planner Licensing Corp.
5330B Wooster Pike
Cincinnati, OH 45227
Free: 888-515-3095
Description: Wedding Planner Book. **Founded:** 2001.. **Franchised:** 2005. **Equity Capital Needed:** $49,000-$86,000, includes franchise fee. **Franchise Fee:** $15,000-$30,000. **Training:** Yes.

672 ■ City Publications
City Publications Franchise Group, Inc.
Interstate North Pky. SE
Atlanta, GA 30339
Ph: (770)951-0441
Fax: (770)951-0437
Description: Sale of advertising for direct mail. **No. of Franchise Units:** 65. **Founded:** 2002.. **Franchised:** 2002. **Equity Capital Needed:** $89,000; $40,000 start-up. **Franchise Fee:** $50,000. **Financial Assistance:** Yes. **Training:** Yes.

673 ■ Kwik Kopy Business Centers
Kwik Kopy Business Centers, Inc. Kwik Kopy Business Centers
12715 Telge Rd.
Cypress, TX 77429
Free: 888-638-8722
Fax: (281)256-4178
Co. E-mail: franchisedevelopment@iced.net
URL: http://www.iced.net
Description: Offers business advertisement aids and printing and copying services. **No. of Franchise Units:** 16. **No. of Company-Owned Units:** 1. **Founded:** 2001.. **Franchised:** 2001. **Equity Capital Needed:** $65,000 liquid capital; $250,000 net worth. **Franchise Fee:** $35,000. **Financial Assistance:** Yes. **Training:** Owners attend classroom and field training, as well as ongoing training through workshops and conferences.

674 ■ Money Mailer, Inc.
12131 Western Ave.
Garden Grove, CA 92841
Free: 800-508-6663
Description: Offers direct mail advertising services to local and national businesses and professionals, whose ads are combined and mailed in the same envelope to residences in the franchisees exclusive market between regions, local franchisees, and the corporate office with regional conferences and newsletters. **No. of Franchise Units:** 183. **Founded:** 1979.. **Franchised:** 1980. **Equity Capital Needed:** $20,000 above franchise fee. **Franchise Fee:** $37,500. **Financial Assistance:** Yes. **Training:** 5 weeks of classroom and in-field training is provided for regional owners. Local franchisees receive a mandatory 2 week training course that includes 1 week of classroom training and 1 week of field training in their local areas.

675 ■ Monthly Coupons Franchising
Monthly Coupons Franchising, Inc.
7231 Boulder Ave.
Highland, CA 92346
Ph: (909)386-0550

Fax: (909)425-5989

Description: Advertising/direct mail coupons. **No. of Franchise Units:** 45. **No. of Company-Owned Units:** 6. **Founded:** 2001.. **Franchised:** 2007. **Equity Capital Needed:** $33,700. **Franchise Fee:** $25,000. **Financial Assistance:** Yes. **Training:** Yes.

676 ■ Our Town America, A Franchising Corp.
Our Town, Inc.
3845 Gateway Centre Blvd., Ste. 300
Pinellas Park, FL 33782
Ph: (727)345-0811
Free: 800-497-8360
Fax: (727)345-0338

Description: Direct mail. **No. of Franchise Units:** 40. **Founded:** 1972.. **Franchised:** 2005. **Equity Capital Needed:** $74,800-$105,450. **Franchise Fee:** $47,500. **Training:** Offers classroom training at headquarters followed with up to 2 weeks field training with a Franchise Training Manager who will be your ongoing sales support.

677 ■ RSVP Publications
6730 W Linebaugh Ave., Ste. 201
Tampa, FL 33625
Ph: (813)960-7787
Fax: (877)725-0621
Co. E-mail: rsvp@rsvppublications.com
URL: http://www.rsvppublications.com

Description: 'Direct mail to the upscale,' is ideal for sales or marketing professionals. **No. of Franchise Units:** 96. **Founded:** 1985.. **Franchised:** 1986. **Equity Capital Needed:** $49,499-$180,599. **Franchise Fee:** $30,000-$120,000. **Royalty Fee:** 7%. **Financial Assistance:** In-house assistance available with franchise fee. **Training:** Offers 7 days training and ongoing support.

678 ■ Sign Biz, Inc.
24681 La Plaza, Ste. 270
Dana Point, CA 92629
Ph: (949)234-0408
Free: 800-633-5580
Fax: (949)234-0426
URL: http://www.signbiz.com

Description: Visual communication stores developing digital sign making. **No. of Franchise Units:** 185. **Founded:** 1989.. **Franchised:** 1990. **Equity Capital Needed:** $45,000-$50,000 liquid. **Franchise Fee:** None. **Training:** 2 weeks initial training at corporate office and 1-2 week home study program.

679 ■ SuperCoups
Valassis
350 Revolutionary Dr.
East Taunton, MA 02718
Ph: (508)977-2000
Free: 866-855-2525
Fax: (508)977-0644

Description: Cooperative direct mail. **No. of Franchise Units:** 136. **No. of Company-Owned Units:** 22. **Founded:** 1982.. **Franchised:** 1984. **Equity Capital Needed:** $50,000. **Franchise Fee:** $17,000-$26,000. **Training:** Provides 1 week training at headquarters, 1 week at franchisee's location, and ongoing support.

680 ■ Valpak Direct Marketing Systems Inc.
8065 Largo Lakes Dr.
Largo, FL 33773
Ph: (727)399-3091
Free: 800-237-6266
Fax: (727)392-0049
Co. E-mail: todd_leiser@valpak.com.com
URL: http://www.valpakfranchising.com

Description: Valpak is a direct mail franchisor and contains money-savings coupons from a variety of businesses, which are mailed via Canada post. **No. of Franchise Units:** 9. **No. of Company-Owned Units:** 2. **Founded:** 1968.. **Franchised:** 1988. **Equity Capital Needed:** $75,000 and up Canadian. **Franchise Fee:** $15,000 Canadian. **Training:** Offers 6-8 days training and ongoing.

COMPUTERIZED DATABASES

681 ■ *Advertising Age*
1155 Gratiot Ave.
Detroit, MI 48207
Ph: (313)446-6000
Free: 800-678-2427
Fax: (313)446-1616
Co. E-mail: info@crain.com
URL: http://www.crain.com

Availability: Online: ProQuest LLC - Dialog; ProQuest LLC - Dialog; Crain Communications Inc. **Type:** Full-text.

682 ■ *Advertising Red Books™*
PO Box 1514
Summit, NJ 07902
Free: 800-908-5395
Co. E-mail: info@redbooks.com
URL: http://www.redbooks.com

Availability: Online: Red Books LLC. **Type:** Directory; Numeric.

683 ■ *Big Yellow: Yellow Pages on the Web*
2200 W Airfield Dr.
Dallas, TX 75261
Ph: (972)453-7000
Free: 800-555-4833
Fax: (888)839-4480
Co. E-mail: info@supermedia.com
URL: http://www.supermedia.com
Contact: Peter Mcdonald, President

Availability: Online: SuperMedia LLC. **Type:** Directory.

684 ■ *MultiAd® Builder*
1720 W Detweiller Dr.
Peoria, IL 61615
Ph: (309)692-1530
Fax: (309)692-6566
Co. E-mail: info@multiad.com
URL: http://www.multiad.com

Availability: Online: MultiAd Inc. CD-ROM: MultiAd Inc. **Type:** Image.

LIBRARIES

685 ■ Advertising Research Foundation Information Center
432 Park Ave. S., 6th Fl.
New York, NY 10016-8013
Ph: (212)751-5656
Fax: (212)319-5265
Co. E-mail: mihui@thearf.org
URL: http://www.thearf.org
Contact: Jill Peled

Scope: Market research, advertising, research methods, media research. **Services:** Library open to members. **Founded:** 1952. **Holdings:** 3000 volumes; 2000 vertical files of clippings, reports, surveys. **Subscriptions:** 110 journals and other serials.

686 ■ DDB Chicago Library
200 E. Randolph
Chicago, IL 60601
Ph: (312)552-6000
Fax: (312)552-2379
URL: http://www.ddb.com
Contact: Peter McGuinness, Chief Executive Officer

Scope: Advertising, marketing research, business. **Services:** Interlibrary loan; SDI; full reference service; Center not open to the public except for prearranged student group tours. **Founded:** 1948. **Holdings:** 5000 books; 200 VF drawers of pictures and print advertisements; 300 VF drawers of subject clippings; 150 VF drawers of corporation files and Annual reports; 100 pamphlet boxes of consumer analysis material. **Subscriptions:** 450 journals and other serials; 6 newspapers.

687 ■ DDB Worldwide Information Center
437 Madison Ave.
New York, NY 10022
Ph: (212)415-2000

Fax: (212)415-3414
Co. E-mail: pat.sloan@ddb.com
URL: http://www.ddb.com
Contact: Pat Sloan, Director, Public Affairs

Scope: Advertising, marketing. **Services:** Interlibrary loan; Center not open to the public. **Founded:** 1962. **Holdings:** 9000 books; 100 bound periodical volumes; 50 VF drawers of pictures; 150 VF drawers of subject files. **Subscriptions:** 304 journals and other serials.

688 ■ Draft/FCB Worldwide Information Center
101 E. Erie
Chicago, IL 60611
Ph: (312)425-5000
Co. E-mail: info@draftfcb.com
URL: http://www.draftfcb.com/
Contact: Michael Fassnacht, President

Scope: Advertising and marketing. **Services:** Library not open to the public. **Founded:** 1977. **Holdings:** 1000 books; 100 subject files. **Subscriptions:** 20 journals and other serials; 6 newspapers. **Telecommunication Services:** inquiries@dfcbx.com.

689 ■ Hanley-Wood, LLC Library
426 S. Westgate St.
Addison, IL 60101-4546
Ph: (630)543-0870
Fax: (630)543-3112
URL: http://www.hanleywood.com

Scope: Concrete, cement, masonry, construction, home building. **Services:** Interlibrary loan; copying. **Founded:** 1971. **Holdings:** 3000 books; 120 bound periodical volumes. **Subscriptions:** 100 journals and other serials.

690 ■ International Advertising Association - World Service Center
275 Madison Ave., Ste. 2102
New York, NY 10016
Ph: (212)557-1133
Fax: (212)983-0455
Co. E-mail: iaa@iaaglobal.org
URL: http://www.iaaglobal.org
Contact: Nubia Martinez, Administrator

Scope: Advertising and marketing. **Services:** Service Center open to members only. **Founded:** 1938. **Holdings:** General reference books; foreign advertising and marketing periodicals; reports; archives. **Subscriptions:** 25 journals and other serials; 10 newspapers.

691 ■ Leo Burnett Detroit - Information Resource Center
3310 W. Big Beaver, Ste. 107
Troy, MI 48084
Ph: (248)458-8300
URL: http://www.leoburnett.com/
Contact: Beth Callahan, Director

Scope: Marketing, advertising. **Services:** Copying (limited). **Founded:** 1952. **Holdings:** 3000 books; 200,000 pictures. **Subscriptions:** 150 journals and other serials; 8 newspapers.

692 ■ McCann-Erickson Advertising of Canada Ltd. Information Centre
10 Bay St., Ste. 1012
Toronto, ON, Canada M5J 2S3
Ph: (416)594-6400
Fax: (416)594-6272
Co. E-mail: contact@mccann.com
URL: http://www.mccann.com/
Contact: Valerie Walton, Manager

Scope: Advertising, marketing, business, industry. **Services:** Center not open to the public. **Founded:** 1960. **Holdings:** 1000 books. **Subscriptions:** 90 journals and other serials.

693 ■ Noble and Associates Library
2155 W. Chesterfield Blvd.
Springfield, MO 65807

Ph: (417)875-5000
Co. E-mail: julie.tumy@noble.net
URL: http://www.noble.net
Contact: Julie Tumy, President
Scope: Food, food service, advertising, construction, agriculture. **Services:** Interlibrary loan; copying; SDI; Library not open to the public. **Holdings:** 500 books; 1000 reports. **Subscriptions:** 300 journals and other serials; 5 newspapers.

694 ■ Television Bureau of Canada Library—Bureau de la Television du Canada - Bibliotheque.
160 Bloor St. E., Ste. 1005
Toronto, ON, Canada M4W 1B9

Ph: (416)923-8813
Free: 800-231-0051
Fax: (416)413-3879
Co. E-mail: tvb@tvb.ca
URL: http://www.tvb.ca
Contact: Duncan Robertson, Manager
Scope: Television, advertising. **Services:** Copying; library open to members of the advertising industry. **Founded:** 1962. **Holdings:** 50 books; 500 bound periodical volumes; 500 reports; 2 archives. **Subscriptions:** 50 journals and other serials; 4 newspapers. **Telecommunication Services:** drobertson@tvb.ca.

695 ■ J. Walter Thompson Canada - Information Services
160 Bloor St., E.
Toronto, ON, Canada M4W 3P7
Ph: (416)926-7300
Fax: (416)926-7375
Co. E-mail: susan.varney@jwt.com
URL: http://www.jwt.com/
Contact: Michelle Bouzide
Scope: Marketing, advertising, economics, industry, communication, mass media, finance. **Services:** Services not open to the public. **Founded:** 1975. **Holdings:** Information and picture file. **Subscriptions:** 33 journals and other serials; 3 newspapers.

ASSOCIATIONS AND OTHER ORGANIZATIONS

696 ■ Automotive Service Association (ASA)
PO Box 929
Bedford, TX 76095-0929
Ph: (817)283-6205
Free: 800-272-7467
Fax: (817)685-0225
Co. E-mail: asainfo@asashop.org
URL: http://www.asashop.org
Contact: Ron Pyle, President
Description: Automotive service businesses including body, paint, and trim shops, engine rebuilders, radiator shops, brake and wheel alignment services, transmission shops, tune-up services, and air conditioning services; associate members are manufacturers and wholesalers of automotive parts, and the trade press. Represents independent business owners and managers before private agencies and national and state legislative bodies. Promotes confidence between consumer and the automotive service industry, safety inspection of motor vehicles, and better highways. **Founded:** 1951. **Publications:** *AutoInc.* (Monthly). **Educational Activities:** Congress of Automotive Repair and Service (Annual); International Autobody Congress and Exposition (Annual); International Autobody Congress and Exposition - NACE (Annual).

REFERENCE WORKS

697 ■ *Air Bag Technology, 1999*
Pub: Society of Automotive Engineers
Contact: Thomas W. Ryan, III, President
Ed: Powell. **Released:** 1999. **Price:** $95.00.

698 ■ *SAE Online Roster*
Pub: Society of Automotive Engineers International
Contact: David L. Schutt, Chief Executive Officer
E-mail: david.schutt@sae.org
URL(s): www.sae.org. **Released:** Continuous **Publication includes:** List of 121,000 members concerned with self-propelled ground, air, and space vehicles worldwide. **Entries include:** For members--Member name, company name, address, job title. **Arrangement:** Alphabetical by member name. **Indexes:** Members by company name, product.

TRADE PERIODICALS

699 ■ *The Auto Parts Report*
Pub: Automotive Parts International
Ed: Ron Demarnes, Editor, itsron@bellatlantic.net. **Released:** Semimonthly. **Description:** Provides news and information on auto parts.

700 ■ *AutoInc.*
Pub: Automotive Service Association
Contact: Ron Pyle, President
URL(s): www.autoinc.org. **Ed:** Leona Dalavai Scott. **Released:** Monthly **Price:** included in membership dues; $35, Individuals; $65, Two years; $95, Other countries; $175, Other countries two years; $40, Canada and Mexico; $70, Canada and Mexico two years.

701 ■ *Automotive Litigation Reporter*
Pub: Thomson West
Contact: Kathryn M. Downing, President
Ed: Nick Sullivan, Editor. **Released:** Semimonthly. **Price:** $2,683.56, individuals. **Description:** Covers significant federal and state lawsuits, including pretrial, trial, and appeal proceedings, settlements, and class action suits. Offers complete texts of key decisions and pleadings.

702 ■ *Motor Vehicle Regulation*
Pub: Wakeman/Walworth Inc.
Ed: Keyes Walworth, Editor. **Released:** 48/year. **Price:** $245, individuals. **Description:** Covers state laws and regulations regarding vehicle safety, inspections, tages, fees and taxes, emissions standards, drunken driving laws, motorist licensing, insurance and education, and school bus regulation.

TRADE SHOWS AND CONVENTIONS

703 ■ Dayton Auto Show
Dayton Area Auto Dealers Association
655 Metro Pl. S., Ste. 270
Dublin, OH 43017
Ph: (937)222-4911
Free: 800-686-9100
Fax: (614)766-9600
Co. E-mail: webmaster@oada.com
URL: http://www.daada.org
URL(s): www.daytonautoshow.com. **Price:** $7, adults. **Frequency:** Annual. **Audience:** General public. **Principal Exhibits:** Automobiles and automotive equipment, supplies, and services.

704 ■ Massachusetts International Auto Show
Telegram & Gazette
100 Front St.
Worcester, MA 01615-0012
Ph: (508)793-9100
Co. E-mail: info@telegram.com
URL: http://www.telegram.com
URL(s): www.worcesterautoshow.com/auto_show/index.html. **Price:** $6, for adults; children under 12 are free. **Frequency:** Annual. **Audience:** General public and trade professionals. **Principal Exhibits:** New automobiles, trucks, vans, and related equipment, supplies, and services. **Dates and Locations:** , Centrum. **Telecommunication Services:** info@expomanage.com.

705 ■ Montreal International Auto Show
Montreal International Auto Show, Ltd.
2335 Guenette St.
Montreal, QC, Canada H4R 2V4
Ph: (514)331-6571
Fax: (514)331-2045
Co. E-mail: c.vachon@ccam.qc.ca
URL: http://www.ccam.qc.ca/en/salon-de-lauto-de-montreal/
URL(s): www.montrealautoshow.com. **Price:** $15, Onsite general admission; $13, Onsite "Access Montreal" card; $5, Onsite Children 6-12, must have parent; $10, Onsite Students and 65 years and older (with ID). **Frequency:** Annual. **Audience:** General public. **Principal Exhibits:** New cars, light trucks, and vehicle accessories/services. **Dates and Locations:** , Olympic Stadium. **Telecommunication Services:** communications@ccam.qc.ca.

COMPUTERIZED DATABASES

706 ■ *ALLDATA® Online*
9650 W Taron Dr., Ste. 100
Elk Grove, CA 95757
Ph: (916)684-5200
Free: 800-859-3282
Fax: (916)684-5225
Co. E-mail: marketing@alldata.com
URL: http://www.alldata.com
Contact: Jeffery Lagges, President
Availability: Online: ALLDATA L.L.C. **Type:** Image; Full-text.

LIBRARIES

707 ■ U.S. National Highway Traffic Safety Administration - Technical Information Services
1200 New Jersey Ave., SE
Washington, DC 20590
Ph: (888)327-4236
Fax: (202)493-2833
Co. E-mail: tis@nhtsa.dot.gov
URL: http://www.nhtsa.dot.gov/cars/problems/trd/?name=
Contact: Shirlene D. Ball, Analyst
Scope: Motor vehicle safety, highway traffic safety, alcohol countermeasures for driving safety, vehicle occupant protection, emergency medical services. **Services:** Copying; TIS open to the public. **Founded:** 1967. **Holdings:** 200 books; 52,000 agency and related publications and reports; 920,000 microfiche. **Subscriptions:** 40 journals and other serials.

RESEARCH CENTERS

708 ■ Center for Auto Safety (CAS)
1825 Connecticut Ave. NW, Ste. 330
Washington, DC 20009-5708
Ph: (202)328-7700
Fax: (202)387-0140
URL: http://www.autosafety.org
Contact: Clarence Ditlow, Executive Director
Services: Safety research service. **Founded:** 1970. **Publications:** *Impact* (Bimonthly); *Lemon Times* (Quarterly). **Awards:** CAS Internships.

709 ■ Insurance Institute for Highway Safety (IIHS)
1005 N Glebe Rd., Ste. 800
Arlington, VA 22201
Ph: (703)247-1500

Fax: (703)247-1588
URL: http://www.iihs.org
Contact: Adrian Lund, President
Founded: 1959. **Publications:** *IIHS Annual Report*, *Status Report*.

ASSOCIATIONS AND OTHER ORGANIZATIONS

710 ■ *Air Line Pilot*
360 Albert St., Ste. 1715
Ottawa, ON, Canada K1R 7X7
Ph: (613)569-5668
Fax: (613)569-5681
Co. E-mail: humanresources@alpa.org
URL: http://www.alpa.org
Contact: Capt. John Prater, President
Released: Quarterly **Price:** $50, /year in U.S.; C$65, /year outside U.S.; C$37, /year for students.

711 ■ Air Line Pilots Association International - Canada (ALPA)—Association Canadienne des Pilotes de Ligne Internationale
360 Albert St., Ste. 1715
Ottawa, ON, Canada K1R 7X7
Ph: (613)569-5668
Fax: (613)569-5681
Co. E-mail: humanresources@alpa.org
URL: http://www.alpa.org
Contact: Capt. John Prater, President
Description: Commercially licensed pilots. Promotes safety and efficiency in air transportation. Collects and distributes information on professional problems and concerns. Negotiates collective employment agreements with airlines. **Founded:** 1931. **Publications:** *Air Line Pilot* (Quarterly).

712 ■ Air Transport Association of Canada (ATAC)
255 Albert St., Ste. 700
Ottawa, ON, Canada K1P 6A9
Ph: (613)233-7727
Fax: (613)230-8648
Co. E-mail: atac@atac.ca
URL: http://www.atac.ca
Contact: John McKenna, President
Description: Air transport companies. Promotes a business climate beneficial to members. Represents' members interests before government agencies. Conducts research and educational programs; compiles industry statistics. **Services:** Conducts educational programs; compiles industry statistics. **Founded:** 1934. **Publications:** *Flightplan* (Semiannual). **Educational Activities:** ATAC Spring Reception (Annual); ATA ACI-NA Deicing Conference (Annual); ATAC's Annual General Meeting and Tradeshow (Annual). **Awards:** Life Membership (Periodic); Paul Mulrooney Memorial Award of Excellence (Annual).

713 ■ Aircraft Owners and Pilots Association (AOPA)
421 Aviation Way
Frederick, MD 21701
Ph: (301)695-2000
Free: 800-872-2672

Fax: (301)695-2375
Co. E-mail: aopahq@aopa.org
URL: http://www.aopa.org
Contact: Phil Boyer, President
Description: Represents general aviation pilots and owners, 60 percent of U.S. are members, as are three-quarters of the nation's general aviation aircraft owners. Works to make flying safer, less expensive, and more fun. **Founded:** 1939. **Publications:** *AOPA Pilot* (Monthly); *AOPA Flight Training* (Monthly); *AOPA Flight Training Magazine* (Monthly); *AOPA Pilot* (Monthly); *AOPA's Airport Directory*; *AOPA's Airport Directory: The Pilot and FBO Flight Planning Guide* (Biennial); *AOPA Pilot--General Aviation Aircraft Directory Issue*; *AOPA's Aviation U.S.A.* (Semiannual). **Educational Activities:** AOPA Aviation Summit - Aircraft Owners and Pilots Association (Annual). **Awards:** Laurence P. Sharples Perpetual Award (Annual); Joseph B. Hartranft Award; Laurence P. Sharples Perpetual Award; Joseph B. Hartranft, Jr. "Doc" Award (Annual); Max Karant Awards for Excellence in Aviation Journalism (Annual).

714 ■ *Airline/Interline Club Newsletter*
c/o International Air Transport Association
PO Box 113
Montreal, QC, Canada H4Z 1M1
Ph: (514)874-0202
Fax: (514)874-1753
Co. E-mail: info@waca.org
URL: http://www.waca.org
Contact: Maga Ramasamy, President
Released: 3/year **Price:** C$0.50.

715 ■ Airlines for America (A4A)
1301 Pennsylvania Ave. NW, Ste. 1100
Washington, DC 20004-7017
Ph: (202)626-4000
Free: 800-497-3326
Fax: (202)626-4264
Co. E-mail: a4a@airlines.org
URL: http://www.airlines.org
Contact: Nicholas E. Calio, President
URL(s): www.air-transport.org. **Description:** Airlines engaged in transporting persons, goods and mail by aircraft between fixed terminals on regular schedules. **Scope:** Transportation, civil aviation history. **Services:** Interlibrary loan; copying; Library open to the public by appointment. **Founded:** 1936. **Holdings:** 12,000 volumes; 12 VF drawers of pamphlets and Annual reports; 350 reels of microfilm; 3 drawers of microfiche; 500 report files. **Subscriptions:** 120 journals and other serials; 10 newspapers. **Publications:** *Air Transport*; *Air Transport* (Annual); *Economic* (Annual). **Educational Activities:** Air Transport Association Engineering, Maintenance and Material Forum. **Telecommunication Services:** ata@airlines.org; pubs@airlines.org; ata@air-lines.org.

716 ■ Airport Minority Advisory Council (AMAC)
2345 Crystal Dr., Ste. 902
Arlington, VA 22202
Ph: (703)414-2622

Fax: (703)414-2686
Co. E-mail: amac.info@amac-org.com
URL: http://www.amac-org.com
Contact: Gene Roth, Executive Director
Description: Advocates for equal opportunity for minorities and women in airport contracting and employment. **Founded:** 1998. **Publications:** *AMAC-ESP Informational Brochure*. **Educational Activities:** Airport Business Diversity (Annual). **Awards:** Airport AEC Award (Annual); Airport Concessions Award (Annual); Award of the Organization (Annual); Hall of Fame Award (Annual).

717 ■ Canadian Business Aviation Association (CBAA)
955 Green Valley Crescent, Ste. 155
Ottawa, ON, Canada K2C 3V4
Ph: (613)236-5611
Fax: (613)236-2361
Co. E-mail: info@cbaa.ca
URL: http://www.cbaa-acaa.ca
Contact: Frank Burke, Chairman
Description: Companies operating or supporting business aviation. Promotes business aviation; encourages safety and efficiency; makes recommendations to regulatory agencies. **Founded:** 1962. **Educational Activities:** Canadian Business Aviation Association Convention (Annual). **Awards:** Award of Merit; National Safety Awards; Honorary Lifetime Membership Award; CBAA Award of Merit (Annual); Honorary Lifetime Membership Award (Annual).

718 ■ Flight Safety Foundation
601 Madison St., Ste. 300
Alexandria, VA 22314-1756
Ph: (703)739-6700
Fax: (703)739-6708
Co. E-mail: aarp1@aol.com
URL: http://www.flightsafety.org
Contact: William R. Voss, President
E-mail: voss@flightsafety.org
Description: Aerospace manufacturers, domestic and foreign airlines, insurance companies, fuel and oil companies, schools and miscellaneous organizations having an interest in the promotion of safety in flight. Sponsors safety audits. Compiles statistics. **Scope:** aviation safety. **Services:** Information clearinghouse on flight safety. **Founded:** 1945. **Subscriptions:** 1000 archival material articles audiovisuals books periodicals reports. **Publications:** *Human Factors and Aviation Medicine*; *Accident Prevention* (Monthly); *Airport Operations* (Bimonthly); *Cabin Crew Safety* (Bimonthly); *European Aviation Mechanics Bulletin* (Bimonthly); *Flight Safety Digest* (Monthly); *Helicopter Safety* (Bimonthly); *Human Factors and Aviation Medicine* (Bimonthly); *Accident Prevention* (Monthly); *Flight Safety Digest* (Monthly); *Human Factors and Aviation Medicine* (Bimonthly); *Flight Safety Digest* (Monthly); *Pilots Safety Exchange*; *Flight Safety Foundation--Directory of Members*; *Aviation Mechanics Bulletin* (Bimonthly). **Educational Activities:** Corporate Aviation Safety Seminar (Annual); International Air Safety Seminar (Annual); FSF Conferences and workshops; Corporate Aviation Safety Seminar (Annual); European air safety seminar; European Air Safety Seminar

(Annual); International Air Safety Seminar (Annual); International Air Safety Seminar (Annual). **Awards:** Laura Taber Barbour Air Safety Award; Cecil A. Brownlow Publication Award (Annual); Business Aviation Meritorious Service Award; Admiral Luis de Florez Flight Safety Award (Annual); Business Aviation Meritorious Service Award (Annual); Heroism Award (Annual); Honeywell Bendix Trophy for Aviation Safety (Annual); Joe Chase Award (Annual); Laura Taber Barbour Air Safety Award (Annual); Professionalism Award (Annual); Richard Teller Crane Founder's Award (Annual); Brownlow Award; De Florez Award; Distinguished Service Award; Heroism Award; Joe Chase Award; Meritorious Service Award; Joe M. Chase Award; Aviation Week and Space Technology Distinguished Service Award; Aviation Week and Space Technology Distinguished Service Award (Annual). **Telecommunication Services:** fsf@radix.net; wahdan@flightsafety.org.

719 ■ Flightplan
255 Albert St., Ste. 700
Ottawa, ON, Canada K1P 6A9
Ph: (613)233-7727
Fax: (613)230-8648
Co. E-mail: atac@atac.ca
URL: http://www.atac.ca
Contact: John McKenna, President
Released: Semiannual

720 ■ Helicopter Association International (HAI)
1635 Prince St.
Alexandria, VA 22314-2818
Ph: (703)683-4646
Free: 800-435-4976
Fax: (703)683-4745
Co. E-mail: questions@rotor.com
URL: http://www.rotor.com
Contact: Matt Zuccaro, President
E-mail: matt.zuccaro@rotor.com
Description: Owners, operators, helicopter enthusiasts, and affiliated companies in the civil helicopter industry. Receives and disseminates information concerning the use, operation, hiring, contracting, and leasing of helicopters. Maintains a collection of current helicopter service bulletins and technical data; organizes safety seminars, continuing education courses, and helicopter operator management courses; and maintains a maintenance malfunction information database. **Founded:** 1948. **Publications:** Heliport Directory (Biennial); Operations and Management, Guide/Safety Manual; The Helicopter Annual (Annual); HAI Heliport Directory (Quarterly); Helicopter Association International--The Helicopter Annual (Annual); Heliport/Vertiport Development Guide; Helicopter Annual (Annual); Heliport Directory (Biennial); Heliport/Vertiport Development Guide (Periodic); Operations Update (Monthly); Rotorgram (Quarterly); ROTOR (Quarterly); Rotor: By the Industry - For the Industry (Quarterly). **Educational Activities:** Heli-Expo (Annual); HELI-EXPO - Helicopter Association International Annual Meeting and Industry Exposition (Annual). **Awards:** Aviation Maintenance Technician Safety Award (Annual); Operator Safety Award (Annual); Pilot Safety Award (Annual); Salute to Excellence (Annual); Lawrence D. Bell Memorial Award; AgustaWestland Community Service Award; Excellence in Communications Award; Joe Mashman Safety Award; Eurocopter Golden Hour Award; Pilot of the Year Award; Pilot Safety Award; Robert E. Trimble Memorial Award; Igor Sikorsky Award for Humanitarian Service; Rolls-Royce Excellence in Helicopter Maintenance Award; W. A. (Dub) Blessing Certified Flight Instructor of the Year.

721 ■ IBAC Update
999 Rue University, Ste. 16-33
Montreal, QC, Canada H3C 5J9
Ph: (514)954-8054
Fax: (514)954-6161
Co. E-mail: info@ibac.org
URL: http://www.ibac.org
Contact: Donald D. Spruston, Director General
Released: Quarterly

722 ■ ICAO Journal
999 University St.
Montreal, QC, Canada H3C 5H7

Ph: (514)954-8219
Fax: (514)954-6077
Co. E-mail: icaohq@icao.int
URL: http://www.icao.int
Contact: Mr. Roberto Kobeh Gonzalez, President
Released: 9/year

723 ■ International Business Aviation Council
999 Rue University, Ste. 16-33
Montreal, QC, Canada H3C 5J9
Ph: (514)954-8054
Fax: (514)954-6161
Co. E-mail: info@ibac.org
URL: http://www.ibac.org
Contact: Donald D. Spruston, Director General
Description: International business aircraft associations; national and regional business aviation organizations or subgroups. Aims to provide information on all aspects of international business aircraft operations; ensure that the interests of international business aviation are brought to the attention of and understood by authorities; improve the safety, efficiency and economic use of business aircraft operating internationally. Stresses the importance of business aviation to the economy and to the well-being of all nations. Maintains liaison with international aviation organizations to ensure safe and orderly growth of international business aviation throughout the world. Compiles statistics. **Publications:** IBAC Update (Quarterly).

724 ■ International Civil Aviation Organization (ICAO)—Organisation de l'Aviation Civile Internationale
999 University St.
Montreal, QC, Canada H3C 5H7
Ph: (514)954-8219
Fax: (514)954-6077
Co. E-mail: icaohq@icao.int
URL: http://www.icao.int
Contact: Mr. Roberto Kobeh Gonzalez, President
Description: National government representatives. Seeks to develop the standards and procedures in international air navigation and to foster the planning and development of international air transport so as to insure safe and orderly growth of international civil aviation. Carries out activities in air navigation, air transport, and legal matters. Provides advice, assistance, and training. Compiles statistics. **Founded:** 1944. **Publications:** ICAO Journal (9/year); ICAO Designators for Aircraft Operating Agencies, Aeronautical Authorities and Services (Quarterly); ICAO Location Indicators: Doc 7910/114 (Quarterly); ICAO Aeronautical Chart Catalogue; Aeronautical Information Services Provided by States: Doc 7383 (Annual); Aeronautical Chart Manual: Doc 8697; The ICAO Journal: Magazine of the International Civil Aviation Organization (Bimonthly). **Awards:** Edward Warner Award; Edward Warner Award (Annual).

725 ■ National Air Carrier Association (NACA)
1000 Wilson Blvd., Ste. 1700
Arlington, VA 22209
Ph: (703)358-8060
Fax: (703)358-8070
Co. E-mail: obrooks@naca.cc
URL: http://www.naca.cc
Contact: A. Oakley Brooks, President
Description: Represents U.S. certificated airlines specializing in low-cost scheduled and air charter operations. Assists members in the promotion of air transportation and serves as a liaison between members and U.S. government bodies that regulate air transportation. **Founded:** 1962.

726 ■ National Air Transportation Association (NATA)
4226 King St.
Alexandria, VA 22302
Ph: (703)845-9000
Free: 800-808-6282

Fax: (703)845-8176
Co. E-mail: rmulholland@nata.aero
URL: http://www.nata.aero
Contact: James K. Coyne, President
Description: Represents the interests of aviation businesses nationwide. Provides vital aviation services to the airlines, the military, and business/corporate/individual aircraft owners and operators; services includes fueling, maintenance, and flight instruction. **Scope:** aviation. **Founded:** 1940. **Subscriptions:** archival material. **Publications:** National Air Transportation Association Official Membership Directory; NATAnews (Monthly); Wage and Salary Handbook (Annual). **Educational Activities:** FBO Leadership (Annual). **Awards:** Airport Executive Partnership Award (Annual); Distinguished Service Award (Annual); FAA Customer Service Excellence Award (Annual); William A. "Bill" Ong Memorial Award (Annual); Distinguished Service Award; Aviation Journalism Award (Annual); General Aviation Service Technician Award; Excellence in Pilot Training Award (Annual); NATA Aviation Maintenance Technician Employer Recognition Award (Annual).

727 ■ National Business Aviation Association (NBAA)
1200 18th St. NW, Ste. 400
Washington, DC 20036-2527
Ph: (202)783-9000
Free: 800-394-6222
Fax: (202)331-8364
Co. E-mail: info@nbaa.org
URL: http://www.nbaa.org
Contact: Edward M. Bolen, President
Description: Companies owning and operating aircraft for business use, suppliers, and maintenance and air fleet service companies. Compiles statistics; provides literature for researchers and students. **Scope:** business aircraft operations. **Founded:** 1947. **Subscriptions:** articles books reports video recordings. **Publications:** Maintenance and Operations Bulletin (Semiannual); Management Guide; National Business Aircraft Association--Membership Directory (Periodic); NBAA Update (Weekly); NBAA Directory of Member Companies and Aircraft (Annual). **Educational Activities:** National Business Aviation Association Annual Meeting & Convention (Annual); NBAA Annual Meeting and Convention (Annual). **Awards:** Gold Wing Award; American Spirit Award; Doswell Award (Annual); Flying Safety Award (Annual); Gold Wing Award (Annual); Meritorious Service Award (Annual); Platinum Wing Award (Annual); Silk Scarf Award (Annual); Staff Lifetime Achievement Award (Periodic); Janice K. Barden Aviation Scholarships; Alan H. Conklin Business Aviation Management Scholarships; Corporate Aviation Management Scholarships; William M. Fanning Maintenance Scholarships; Flight Attendants/Flight Technician Scholarships; Lawrence Ginocchio Aviation Scholarships; Maintenance Technical Reward and Career Scholarships; Scheduler and Dispatchers Scholarships; Schedulers and Dispatchers Outstanding Achievement and Leadership Award (Annual); Donald A. Baldwin Sr. Business Aviation Management Scholarships; Exxon Mobil Aviation and the Avitats International Operators Scholarships; NORDAM Dee Howard/Etienne Fage Scholarships; U.S. Aircraft Insurance Group Professional Development Program (USAIG PDP) Scholarships.

728 ■ World Airlines Clubs Association (WACA)
c/o International Air Transport Association
PO Box 113
Montreal, QC, Canada H4Z 1M1
Ph: (514)874-0202
Fax: (514)874-1753
Co. E-mail: info@waca.org
URL: http://www.waca.org
Contact: Maga Ramasamy, President
Description: Airline/interline clubs in 50 countries representing 3,000 employees of the civil and commercial airline industry. Promotes airline transportation as a mode of travel and works to provide better service to the traveling public. Seeks to increase public awareness of the contribution of the airlines to world of the contribution of the airlines to world understanding and to extend, promote, and publicize

the airline/interline clubs movement; advises on and coordinates the activities of member clubs worldwide. Promotes economic and social programs for the betterment of airlines and the community and country that the club serves. Fosters discussion on civil and commercial aviation; organizes annual and ongoing projects in the field; sponsors charitable programs and conducts sports tournaments. **Scope:** memorabilia. **Founded:** 1966. **Subscriptions:** archival material. **Publications:** *Airline/Interline Club Newsletter* (3/year). **Awards:** Certifications of Appreciation (Periodic).

DIRECTORIES OF EDUCATIONAL PROGRAMS

729 ■ *Directory of Private Accredited Career Schools and Colleges of Technology*
Pub: Accrediting Commission of Career Schools and Colleges of Technology
Contact: Michale S. McComis, Executive Director
Released: On web page. **Price:** Free. **Description:** Covers 3900 accredited post-secondary programs that provide training programs in business, trade, and technical fields, including various small business endeavors. Entries offer school name, address, phone, description of courses, job placement assistance, and requirements for admission. Arrangement is alphabetical.

REFERENCE WORKS

730 ■ *Minnesota Airport Directory & Travel Guide*
Pub: Minnesota Department of Transportation, Office of Aeronautics
Contact: Raymond J. Rought, Director
E-mail: larry.myking@dot.state.mn.us
URL(s): www.dot.state.mn.us/aero. **Released:** Annual **Price:** Free. **Covers:** Airports and public seaplane bases in Minnesota. **Entries include:** Address and telephone number. **Database includes:** Information on approaches, ditches, lights, nearby rivers, elevation, latitude and longitude, storage facilities and repair potential.

731 ■ *National Air Transportation Association--Aviation Resource and Membership Directory*
Pub: National Air Transportation Association
URL(s): www.nata.aero. **Released:** Annual; Latest edition 2008. **Price:** $50, Nonmembers; $25, Members. **Covers:** More than 1,000 regular, associate, and affiliate members; regular members include airport service organizations, air taxi operators, and commuter airlines. **Entries include:** Company name, address, phone, fax number, name and title of contact. **Arrangement:** Regular members are classified by service; associate and affiliate members are alphabetical in separate sections. **Indexes:** Geographical.

STATISTICAL SOURCES

732 ■ *RMA Annual Statement Studies*
Pub: Risk Management Association
Contact: Kevin M. Blakey, President
Released: Annual. **Price:** $175.00 2006-07 edition, $105.00. **Description:** Contains composite balance sheets and income statements for more than 360 industries, including the accounting, auditing, and bookkeeping industries. Also contains five years of comparative historical data for discerning trends. Includes 16 commonly used ratios, computed for most of the size groupings for nearly every industry.

733 ■ *Standard & Poor's Industry Surveys*
Pub: Standard & Poor's Corp.
Released: Annual. **Price:** $3633.00. **Description:** Two-volume book that examines the prospects for specific industries, including trucking. Also provides analyses of trends and problems, statistical tables and charts, and comparative company analyses.

TRADE PERIODICALS

734 ■ *99NEWS Magazine*
Pub: The Ninety-Nines Inc.
Released: Bimonthly. **Price:** $20, nonmembers within the U.S.; $30, nonmembers in Canada and other.

Description: Includes material of interest to the members of The Ninety-Nines, Inc., an international organization of women pilots. Recurring features include interviews, news of research, letters to the editor, news of educational opportunities, a calendar of events, and columns titled President's and Careers.

735 ■ *Air Medical Journal*
Pub: Mosby Inc.
URL(s): journals.elsevierhealth.com/periodicals/ymam. **Ed:** Jacqueline C. Stocking, Eric R. Swanson. **Released:** Bimonthly **Price:** $125, Individuals online and print; $177, Canada and Mexico online and print; $177, Other countries online and print.

736 ■ *Aviation Medical Bulletin*
Pub: Harvey W. Watt & Company Inc.
Released: Monthly. **Price:** $19.95, U.S. and Canada. **Description:** Provides the latest medical information for those working in the aviation field. Recurring features include news of research.

737 ■ *Aviation Monthly*
Pub: Peter Katz Productions Inc.
URL(s): www.aviationmonthly.comwww.newsletteraccess.com/display.php?id=2986. **Ed:** Peter Katz. **Released:** Monthly **Price:** $39, Individuals; $20, Individuals air mail.

TRADE SHOWS AND CONVENTIONS

738 ■ *AOPA Aviation Summit - Aircraft Owners and Pilots Association*
Aircraft Owners and Pilots Association (AOPA)
421 Aviation Way
Frederick, MD 21701
Ph: (301)695-2000
Free: 800-872-2672
Fax: (301)695-2375
Co. E-mail: aopahq@aopa.org
URL: http://www.aopa.org
Contact: Phil Boyer, President
URL(s): www.aopa.org/summit/. **Frequency:** Annual. **Audience:** Pilots, aircraft owners, suppliers, and used aircraft trade. **Principal Exhibits:** Single-engine and multi-engine aircraft, avionics, airframes, power plant and equipment, financing information, and related equipment, supplies, and services. **Telecommunication Services:** aopahq@aopa.org.

739 ■ *Aviation Industry Expo*
Cygnus Business Media
801 Cliff Rd., Ste. 201
Burnsville, MN 55337
Ph: (952)894-8007
Free: 800-827-8009
Fax: (952)894-8252
Co. E-mail: info@farmshows.com
URL: http://www.cygnusb2b.com
URL(s): cygnusaviationexpo.com/. **Price:** $25, On-site. **Frequency:** Annual. **Audience:** Air cargo dealers, aircraft dealers, flight schools, ground handlers, manufacturers, military. **Principal Exhibits:** General aviation products and services; fixed base operation and air charter products and services.

740 ■ *HELI-EXPO - Helicopter Association International Annual Meeting and Industry Exposition*
Helicopter Association International (HAI)
1635 Prince St.
Alexandria, VA 22314-2818
Ph: (703)683-4646
Free: 800-435-4976
Fax: (703)683-4745
Co. E-mail: questions@rotor.com
URL: http://www.rotor.com
Contact: Matt Zuccaro, President
E-mail: matt.zuccaro@rotor.com
URL(s): www.heliexpo.com. **Price:** $155, Pre-registered, members 3-day registration, early bird; $240, Pre-registered, non-members 3-day registration, early bird. **Frequency:** Annual. **Audience:** Helicopter operators. **Principal Exhibits:** Helicopter

airframes, engines, accessories, avionics, communications equipment, and insurance information. **Telecommunication Services:** questions@rotor.com.

CONSULTANTS

741 ■ *AVITAS Inc.*
14520 Avion Pkwy., Ste. 300
Chantilly, VA 20151
Ph: (703)476-2300
Fax: (703)860-5855
Co. E-mail: info@avitas.com
URL: http://www.avitas.com
Contact: John W. Vitale, President
E-mail: john.vitale@avitas.com
Scope: A full service consulting company providing advisory and technical services to airlines, aircraft manufacturers, industry suppliers, maintenance providers, aircraft lessors and financiers, legal council and government entities. **Founded:** 1985. **Publications:** "Bluebook of Jet Aircraft Values"; "Bluebook of Commercial Turboprop Aircraft Values"; "Bluebook of Jet Engine Values"; "BlueBook of Flight Simulator Values"; "Aircraft Block Hour Operating Costs and Operations Guide"; "SAVI - Scenario Analysis & Value Index". **Special Services:** AVITAS Analyst; Online Aircraft Appraisal Service; Online Portfolio Monitoring Service; Online Engine Appraisal Service; Online Flight Distance Calculator.

742 ■ *CAROPAM Corp.*
20125 Stewart Airlines Hangar X37
Spring, TX 77379
Ph: (281)355-8182
Free: 888-926-7645
Fax: (281)355-8182
URL: http://www.caropam.com
Contact: John F. Dyer, President
E-mail: johndyer@caropam.com
Scope: Offers services to the aviation industry including industrial relations, flight training and airline management. **Founded:** 1982.

COMPUTERIZED DATABASES

743 ■ *AvData Air Carrier File*
101 First St., 2nd Fl.
Utica, NY 13501
Ph: (315)797-4420
Free: 800-553-8638
Fax: (315)797-4798
URL: http://www.avdatainc.com
Availability: Online: McGraw-Hill Companies Inc. - Aviation Week Group. **Type:** Directory.

744 ■ *Aviation Daily*
1200 G St. NW, Ste. 922
Washington, DC 20005
Ph: (202)383-2403
Free: 800-525-5003
Fax: (202)383-2346
URL: http://www.aviationweek.com
Availability: Online: ProQuest LLC - Dialog; LexisNexis Group; McGraw-Hill Companies Inc. - Aviation Week Group. **Type:** Full-text.

745 ■ *History of Aviation*
553 N Ave.
New Rochelle, NY 10801
Ph: (914)235-4340
Free: 800-866-6434
Fax: (914)235-4367
Co. E-mail: multied@multied.com
URL: http://www.multieducator.com
Availability: CD-ROM: MultiEducator Inc. **Type:** Full-text; Image; Video.

746 ■ *Jane's Aero-Engines*
Sentinel House
163 Brighton Rd.
Surrey
Coulsdon CR5 2YH, United Kingdom
Ph: 20 8700 3700

Fax: 20 8763 1006
Co. E-mail: info.uk@janes.com
URL: http://www.janes.com
Availability: Online: IHS Global Ltd.-IHS Jane's:
Defense & Security Intelligence & Analysis. **Type:**
Full-text; Directory; Image.

747 ■ Jane's Aircraft Upgrades
Sentinel House
163 Brighton Rd.
Surrey
Coulsdon CR5 2YH, United Kingdom
Ph: 20 8700 3700
Fax: 20 8763 1006
Co. E-mail: info.uk@janes.com
URL: http://www.janes.com
Availability: Online: IHS Global Ltd.-IHS Jane's:
Defense & Security Intelligence & Analysis. **Type:**
Full-text; Directory; Image.

**748 ■ Jane's Airports and Handling Agents
Library**
Sentinel House
163 Brighton Rd.
Surrey
Coulsdon CR5 2YH, United Kingdom
Ph: 20 8700 3700
Fax: 20 8763 1006
Co. E-mail: info.uk@janes.com
URL: http://www.janes.com
Availability: Online: IHS Global Ltd.-IHS Jane's:
Defense & Security Intelligence & Analysis. **Type:**
Directory; Full-text.

**749 ■ Jane's Helicopter Markets and
Systems**
Sentinel House
163 Brighton Rd.
Surrey
Coulsdon CR5 2YH, United Kingdom
Ph: 20 8700 3700
Fax: 20 8763 1006
Co. E-mail: info.uk@janes.com
URL: http://www.janes.com
Availability: Online: IHS Global Ltd.-IHS Jane's:
Defense & Security Intelligence & Analysis. **Type:**
Full-text; Directory; Image.

**750 ■ Jane's Unmanned Aerial Vehicles and
Targets**
Sentinel House
163 Brighton Rd.
Surrey
Coulsdon CR5 2YH, United Kingdom
Ph: 20 8700 3700
Fax: 20 8763 1006
Co. E-mail: info.uk@janes.com
URL: http://www.janes.com
Availability: Online: IHS Global Ltd.-IHS Jane's:
Defense & Security Intelligence & Analysis. **Type:**
Full-text; Directory; Image.

751 ■ Jane's World Airlines
Sentinel House
163 Brighton Rd.
Surrey
Coulsdon CR5 2YH, United Kingdom
Ph: 20 8700 3700
Fax: 20 8763 1006
Co. E-mail: info.uk@janes.com
URL: http://www.janes.com
Availability: Online: IHS Global Ltd.-IHS Jane's:
Defense & Security Intelligence & Analysis. **Type:**
Directory; Full-text.

LIBRARIES

752 ■ Aircraft Technical Publishers Library
101 S. Hill Dr.
Brisbane, CA 94005
Ph: (415)330-9500
Free: 800-227-4610
Fax: (415)468-1596
Co. E-mail: sales@atp.com
URL: http://www.atp.com
Scope: Aviation maintenance, avionics, aviation
regulations. **Services:** Center not open to the public.
Founded: 1973. **Holdings:** 4 million pages of avia-
tion information.

**753 ■ Boeing Company - Integrated Defense
Systems - Business Information Center**
2201 Seal Beach Blvd., 110-SB72
Seal Beach, CA 90740
Ph: (562)797-4239
Fax: (562)797-5050
Co. E-mail: gathmann@boeing.com
URL: http://www.boeing.com/bds/
Scope: Military/aircraft, defense electronics, space,
communications, marketing. **Services:** Library not
open to the public. **Holdings:** Figures not available.

**754 ■ British Columbia Institute of
Technology - Aerospace and Technology
Campus Library**
3800 Cessna Dr.
Richmond, BC, Canada V7B 0A1
Ph: (778)333-3708
Free: 866-434-1610
Fax: (604)207-8437
Co. E-mail: bill_nadiger@bcit.ca
URL: http://www.lib.bcit.ca/
Contact: Bill Nadiger, Librarian, Reference
Scope: Aeronautics. **Services:** Interlibrary loan;
library open to the public with restrictions (upon
purchase of a membership card). **Holdings:** 4000
books; 900 videos. **Subscriptions:** 50 journals and
other serials.

755 ■ Flight Safety Foundation Library
801 N. Fairfax St., Ste. 400
Alexandria, VA 22314
Ph: (703)739-6700

Fax: (703)739-6708
Co. E-mail: setze@flightsafety.org
URL: http://www.flightsafety.org/home.html
Contact: Patricia Setze, Librarian
Scope: Aviation safety. **Services:** Library open to the
public for reference use only. **Holdings:** 1000 books,
audio/visuals, periodicals, and archival materials.
Subscriptions: 150 journals and other serials. **Tele-
communication Services:** wahdan@flightsafety.org.

**756 ■ Honeywell, Inc. - Air Transport
Systems Engineering Library**
21111 N. 19th Ave.
Phoenix, AZ 85027
Ph: (602)436-0272
Fax: (602)436-1500
URL: http://honeywell.com/
Scope: Electronic engineering, computer sciences,
flight instrumentation. **Services:** Interlibrary loan;
copying. **Founded:** 1960. **Holdings:** 3000 books;
1000 technical reports. **Subscriptions:** 150 journals
and other serials.

**757 ■ International Association for Air Travel
Couriers Library**
PO Box 31279
Omaha, NE 68132
Ph: (402)218-1982
Co. E-mail: inforeq@iaatc.org
URL: http://www.courier.org
Contact: Kathy Craig, President
Scope: Air courier industry. **Services:** Library open
to the public for reference use only. **Founded:** 1989.
Holdings: 2100 books and maps. **Subscriptions:**
18 journals and other serials.

**758 ■ Transport Canada - Aircraft Services
Directorate - Technical Library, AAFBAA**
275 Slater St., 6th Fl.
Ottawa, ON, Canada K1A 0N5
Ph: (613)998-5128
Fax: (613)954-4731
Co. E-mail: library-bibliotheque@tc.gc.ca
URL: http://www.tc.gc.ca/eng/corporate-services/
    library-menu.htm
Scope: Transportation. **Services:** Library open to the
public. **Holdings:** 75,000 books; 2000 technical
manuals; 8000 technical drawings. **Subscriptions:**
175 journals and other serials.

**759 ■ U.S. Federal Aviation Administration -
Mike Monroney Aeronautical Center
Library—FAA - Mike Monroney Aeronautical
Center Library.**
Academy Bldg. Rm. 114
6500 S. MacArthur Blvd.
Oklahoma City, OK 73169
Ph: (405)954-2665
Fax: (405)954-4742
URL: http://www.faa.gov/about/office_org/
    headquarters_offices/arc/programs/academy
Scope: Aeronautics, airplanes, mathematics, avion-
ics, electronics, management. **Services:** Interlibrary
loan; Library open to the public with restrictions.
Founded: 1962. **Holdings:** 12,000 volumes; books;
periodicals; 15,000 technical reports. **Subscriptions:**
65 journals and other serials.

ASSOCIATIONS AND OTHER ORGANIZATIONS

760 ■ Air Conditioning Contractors of America (ACCA)
2800 Shirlington Rd., Ste. 300
Arlington, VA 22206
Ph: (703)575-4477
Free: 888-290-2220
Fax: (703)575-4449
Co. E-mail: info@acca.org
URL: http://www.acca.org
Contact: Paul T. Stalknecht, President
E-mail: paul.stalknecht@acca.org
Description: Contractors involved in installation and service of heating, air conditioning, and refrigeration systems. Associate members are utilities, manufacturers, wholesalers, and other market-oriented businesses. Monitors utility competition and operating practices of HVAC manufacturers and wholesalers. Provides consulting services, technical training, and instructor certification program; offers management seminars. Operates annual educational institute. **Scope:** load calculation, HVAC system design, duct design, residential and commercial equipment selection, psychometrics. **Founded:** 1969. **Subscriptions:** 13 software. **Publications:** *Air Conditioning Contractors of America--Membership Directory* (Annual); *ACCA Technical Bulletin* (Monthly); *Air Conditioning Contractors of America Membership Directory* (Annual); *Air Conditioning Contractors of America Quality Contractor's Catalog of Products and Services* (Annual). **Educational Activities:** Air Conditioning Contractors of America Conference (Annual); ACCA Annual Conference and Indoor Air Expo; Air Conditioning Contractors of America Annual Conference (Annual). **Awards:** ACCA Spirit of Independence Award (Periodic); Distinguished Service Award (Periodic); Quality Contractor of the Year (Annual); Small Contractor of the Year (Annual); Spirit of Federation Award (Periodic). **Telecommunication Services:** media@acca.org.

761 ■ Air-Conditioning Heating and Refrigeration Institute (AHRI)
2111 Wilson Blvd., Ste. 500
Arlington, VA 22201
Ph: (703)524-8800
Fax: (703)562-1942
Co. E-mail: ahri@ahrinet.org
URL: http://www.ahrinet.org
Contact: Stephen Yurek, President

Description: Manufacturers of air conditioning, refrigeration and heating products and components. Develops and establishes equipment and application standards and certifies performance of certain industry products; provides credit and statistical services to members. Provides representation and technical assistance to government entities in federal, state and local legislative matters; provides public relations, consumer education and promotional programs for the industry. **Founded:** 1953. **Publications:** *ARI Curriculum Guide*; *Minuteman* (Monthly).

762 ■ American Society of Heating, Refrigerating and Air-Conditioning Engineers (ASHRAE)
1791 Tullie Cir. NE
Atlanta, GA 30329
Ph: (404)636-8400
Free: 800-527-4723
Fax: (404)321-5478
Co. E-mail: ashrae@ashrae.org
URL: http://www.ashrae.org
Contact: Thomas E. Watson, President
E-mail: twatson@ashrae.org
URL(s): wwwe.ashrae.org. **Description:** Represents Technical society of heating, ventilating, refrigeration, and air-conditioning engineers. Sponsors numerous research programs in cooperation with universities, research laboratories, and government agencies on subjects such as human and animal environmental studies, effects of air-conditioning, quality of inside air, heat transfer, flow, and cooling processes. Conducts professional development seminars. Writes method of test standards and other standards addressing energy conservation in buildings, indoor air quality, and refrigerants. Publishes extensive literature and electronic products. **Founded:** 1894. **Publications:** *ASHRAE Insights* (Monthly); *IAQ Applications* (Quarterly); *International Journal of HUAC&R Research* (Quarterly); *Duct Fitting Database*; *American Society of Heating, Refrigerating, and Air-Conditioning Engineers-Membership Roster*; *ASHRAE Journal* (Monthly); *ASHRAE Transactions*; *HVAC&R Research* (Bimonthly). **Educational Activities:** International Air Conditioning, Heating, Refrigerating Exposition (Annual). **Awards:** F. Paul Anderson Award; Award for Distinguished Public Service; Homer Addams Award; Technology Award/Award of Engineering Excellence; ASHRAE Fellow; ASHRAE Journal Paper Award; Symposium Paper Award; Technical Paper Award; Willis H. Carrier Award; Andrew T. Boggs Service Award; Lincoln Bouillon Award; E. K. Campbell Award of Merit; William J. Collins, Jr. Research Promotion Award; Distinguished Fifty-Year Member Award; Distinguished Service Award; Crosby Field Award; Louise and Bill Holladay Distinguished Fellow Award; Honorary Member; John F. James International Award; Ralph G. Nevins Physiology and Human Environment Award; Milton W. Garland Commemorative Refrigeration Award for Project Excellence; Student Design Project Competition; Hall of Fame; Standards Achievement Award; Henry Adams Scholarships; American Society of Heating, Refrigerating, and Air-Conditioning Memorial Scholarships; American Society of Heating, Refrigerating, and Air-Conditioning Undergraduate Scholarships; Willis H. Carrier Scholarships; Frank M. Coda Scholarships; Duane Hanson Scholarships; Alwin B. Newton Scholarships; Donald E. Nichols Scholarships; Reuben Trane Scholarships.

763 ■ Associated Specialty Contractors (ASC)
3 Bethesda Metro Ctr., Ste. 1100
Bethesda, MD 20814
Co. E-mail: dgw@necanet.org
URL: http://www.assoc-spec-con.org
Contact: D. L. Smith, Chairman
Description: Works to promote efficient management and productivity. Coordinates the work of

specialized branches of the industry in management information, research, public information, government relations and construction relations. Serves as a liaison among specialty trade associations in the areas of public relations, government relations, and with other organizations. Seeks to avoid unnecessary duplication of effort and expense or conflicting programs among affiliates. Identifies areas of interest and problems shared by members, and develops positions and approaches on such problems. **Founded:** 1955. **Publications:** *Contract Documents*.

764 ■ Evaporative Cooling Institute (ECI)
MSC 3ECI - NMSU
Las Cruces, NM 88003-8001
Ph: (505)646-1846
Fax: (505)646-3841
Co. E-mail: moreinfo@evapcooling.org
URL: http://www.evapcooling.org
Description: Represents manufacturers of evaporative apparatus; designers, specifiers, and users of heating, ventilating, and air conditioning systems; sales representatives; representatives of educational and governmental agencies; interested individuals. Seeks to advance the art and science of evaporative air cooling and air conditioning by: promoting the technology and industry; collecting and publishing information on applying, installing, operating, and maintaining evaporative systems; disseminating information on codes, standards, and certification programs; identifying and encouraging research; maintaining contact with related trade associations, professional societies, government agencies, and customers. **Scope:** evaporative and desiccant cooling. **Founded:** 1989. **Subscriptions:** 150 books clippings periodicals. **Publications:** *Membership Services Directory* (Annual); *Evaporative Air-conditioning Applications for Environmentally Friendly Cooling*. **Awards:** Honorary Life Membership Award.

765 ■ Heating, Refrigeration and Air Conditioning Institute of Canada (HRAI)
2800 Skymark Ave., Bldg. 1, Ste. 201
Mississauga, ON, Canada L4W 5A6
Ph: (905)602-4700
Free: 800-267-2231
Fax: (905)602-1197
Co. E-mail: hraimail@hrai.ca
URL: http://www.hrai.ca
Contact: Warren Heeley, President
E-mail: warren.heeley@hrai.ca

Description: Corporations engaged in the heating, refrigeration, air-conditioning, ventilation, and related industries. Seeks to advance the techniques and technologies available to members, and the heating and cooling industries as a whole. Conducts educational programs; compiles statistics. **Scope:** A nonprofit trade association of manufacturers, whole sellers and contractors in the Canadian heating, ventilation, air conditioning and refrigeration (HVACR) industry. Organization's mission includes educating and training industry members and facilitating industry solutions. **Founded:** 1968. **Subscriptions:** books. **Educational Activities:** CMX - CIPHEX National Tradeshow and Learning Forum (Biennial). **Awards:** Orvil L. Davie Bursary (Semiannual). **Seminars:**

SkillTech Academy Training and Education; Refrigeration Controls Training; Building Automation Systems; Pneumatic Controls System.

766 ■ Home Ventilating Institute (HVI)

1000 N Rand Rd., Ste. 214
Wauconda, IL 60084
Ph: (847)416-7257
Fax: (480)559-9722
Co. E-mail: hvi@hvi.org
URL: http://www.hvi.org
Contact: Jacki Donner, Executive Director

Description: Aims to serve consumers and members by advancing residential ventilation. Provides a forum for industry to meet and discuss common issues. **Founded:** 1955. **Publications:** *Home Ventilating Guide* (Periodic).

767 ■ IAPMO—IAPMO Research and Testing Inc.

5001 E Philadelphia St.
Ontario, CA 91761-2816
Ph: (909)472-4100
Free: 800-854-2766
Fax: (909)472-4150
Co. E-mail: iapmo@iapmo.org
URL: http://www.iapmo.org
Contact: Dan Daniels, President

Description: Government agencies, administrative officials, sales representatives, manufacturers, associations, and members of associations related to the plumbing field. Sponsors and writes Uniform Plumbing Codes; also sponsors Uniform Mechanical Code. Sponsors speakers' bureau. **Founded:** 1926. **Publications:** *Official Magazine* (Bimonthly); *Drinking Water & Backflow Prevention*; *Directory of Listed Plumbing Products* (Bimonthly); *Directory of Manufactured Housing/RV Research Recommendations* (Bimonthly); *Official* (Bimonthly); *Directory of Listed Plumbing Products for Mobile Homes and Recreational Vehicles* (Bimonthly); *Directory of Listed Plumbing Products* (Weekly); *Directory of Listed Plumbing Products for Mobile Homes and Recreational Vehicles* (Bimonthly); *Uniform Mechanical Illustrated Training Manual* (Periodic); *Uniform Plumbing Code Illustrated Training Manual*. **Awards:** American Flag Award (Annual); Government Person of the Year (Annual); Industry Person of the Year (Annual); George Kauffman Lifetime Achievement Award (Annual); Joseph Kneidinger Green Contractor of the Year (Annual).

768 ■ International District Energy Association (IDEA)

24 Lyman St., Ste. 230
Westborough, MA 01581-2841
Ph: (508)366-9339
Fax: (508)366-0019
Co. E-mail: idea@districtenergy.org
URL: http://www.districtenergy.org
Contact: Rob P. Thornton, President
E-mail: rob.idea@districtenergy.org

Description: Suppliers of space heating by means of steam and hot water, and air conditioning by means of steam and chilled water, via piping systems from a central station to groups of buildings. **Founded:** 1909. **Publications:** *International District Energy Association--Membership Directory* (Annual); *District Energy* (Quarterly); *District Energy Now* (Quarterly); *International District Energy Association--Membership Directory* (Annual); *Manual of District Heating*; *District Energy*. **Educational Activities:** International District Energy Association Conference (Annual); International District Energy Association Annual Conference and Trade Show (Annual). **Awards:** Environmental Champion Award; Unsung Hero Award; Norman R. Taylor Award; System of the Year Award; IDEA Unsung Hero Award (Annual); Norman R. Taylor Award (Annual); Public Sector Leadership Award (Annual); System of the Year Award (Annual).

769 ■ International Ground Source Heat Pump Association (IGSHPA)

1201 S Innovation Way Lot 400
Stillwater, OK 74074-1583
Ph: (405)744-5175
Free: 800-626-4747

Fax: (405)744-5283
Co. E-mail: igshpa@okstate.edu
URL: http://www.igshpa.okstate.edu
Contact: Jim Bose, Executive Director

Description: Manufacturers, distributors, and contractors in the ground source heat pump systems and products industry. Seeks to educate the public about ground source heat pump systems and promote their use as economical energy saving systems. (The system consists of a water source heat pump connected to a plastic pipe buried in the ground in which the earth supplies energy for space heating, domestic water heating, and a place to waste excess heat during cooling cycles.) Sponsors teleconferences, exhibits at trade show, and conducts training workshops. **Founded:** 1987. **Publications:** *The Source* (Bimonthly); *Closed-Loop Ground-Source Heat Pump Systems Installation Guide*; *Grouting Procedures for Ground Source Heat Pump Systems*; *Installation Guide*. **Educational Activities:** May Tech (Annual); International Ground Source Heat Pump Association Conference and Exposition (Annual).

770 ■ Masonry Heater Association of North America (MHA)

2180 S Flying Q Ln.
Tucson, AZ 85713
Ph: (520)883-0191
Fax: (480)371-1139
Co. E-mail: execdir@mha-net.org
URL: http://www.mha-net.org
Contact: Richard Smith, Executive Director

Description: Represents builders, manufacturers and retailers of masonry heaters. Seeks to promote the industry, sponsor research and development, shape regulations, standards and codes, inform and educate the public and further the expertise and professionalism of its membership. **Founded:** 1981. **Publications:** *Masonry Heaters - The Intelligent Choice*.

771 ■ Mechanical Contractors Association of America (MCAA)

1385 Piccard Dr.
Rockville, MD 20850-4340
Ph: (301)869-5800
Fax: (301)990-9690
Co. E-mail: mcaainfo@mcaa.org
URL: http://www.mcaa.org
Contact: John R. Gentille, Chief Executive Officer

Description: Represents firms involved in heating, air conditioning, refrigeration, plumbing, piping, and mechanical service. Provides educational materials and programs to help members attain the highest level of managerial and technical expertise. **Founded:** 1889. **Publications:** *MCAA National Update* (Weekly); *MCAA Reporter* (Bimonthly); *MCAA Membership Directory and Buyers' Guide* (Annual). **Educational Activities:** Mechanical Contractors Association of America Convention (Annual). **Awards:** Affiliated Association Best Practices Awards (Annual); Distinguished Service Award (Annual); Educator of the Year (Annual); Foster McCarl Jr. Philanthropy Award (Periodic); Safety Awards (Annual); E. Robert Kent Award for Management Innovation (Periodic).

772 ■ Mobile Air Conditioning Society

225 S Broad St.
Lansdale, PA 19446
Ph: (215)631-7020
Fax: (215)631-7017
Co. E-mail: info@macsw.org
URL: http://www.imaca.org
Contact: Elvis L. Hoffpauir, President
E-mail: elvis@macsw.org

Description: Distributors, service specialists, installers, manufacturers, and suppliers of automotive and truck air conditioners and parts. Works to disseminate information and develop specialized education. **Scope:** automotive and truck air conditioners. **Publications:** *Shop Talk* (Monthly); *Action* (8/year); *International Mobile Air Conditioning Association--Membership/Industry Contact Directory*; *MACS Service Reports* (Monthly). **Educational Activities:** Mobile Air Conditioning Society Worldwide Convention (Annual). **Awards:** Mobile A/C Pioneer Award (Annual); Simon Oulouhojian Achievement Award (Annual).

773 ■ National Association of Plumbing, Heating, Cooling Contractors (PHCC)

180 S Washington St.
Falls Church, VA 22046
Ph: (703)237-8100
Free: 800-533-7694
Fax: (703)237-7442
URL: http://www.phccweb.org
Contact: Keith Bienvenu, President

Description: Federation of state and local associations of plumbing, heating, and cooling contractors. Seeks to advance sanitation, encourage sanitary laws, and generally improve the plumbing, heating, ventilating, and air conditioning industries. Conducts apprenticeship training programs, workshops, seminars, political action committee, educational and research programs. **Founded:** 1883. **Publications:** *Who's Who in the Plumbing-Heating-Cooling Contracting Business* (Annual). **Awards:** Chapter Excellence Award (Annual).

774 ■ National Environmental Balancing Bureau (NEBB)

8575 Grovemont Cir.
Gaithersburg, MD 20877
Ph: (301)977-3698
Free: 866-497-4447
Fax: (301)977-9589
Co. E-mail: info@nebb.org
URL: http://www.nebb.org
Contact: William C. Neudorfer, President

Description: Qualified heating, ventilation, and air-conditioning contractors specializing in the fields of air and hydronic systems balancing, sound vibration measuring, testing of heating and cooling systems, building systems commissioning, and testing of clean rooms. Seeks to establish and maintain industry standards, procedures, and specifications for testing, adjusting, and balancing work; certify those firms that meet the qualification requirements; establish educational programs to provide competent management and supervision of Testing and Balancing (TAB) work. Establishes professional qualifications for TAB supervisors. Maintains chapters in Australia and Canada. **Founded:** 1971. **Publications:** *Procedural Standards for TAB Environmental Systems*; *Procedural Standards for the Measurement and Assessment of Sound and Vibration*. **Educational Activities:** National Environmental Balancing Bureau Seminar; National Environmental Balancing Bureau Meeting and Educational Conference (Annual). **Telecommunication Services:** karen@nebb.org.

775 ■ Refrigerating Engineers and Technicians Association (RETA)

PO Box 1819
Salinas, CA 93902
Ph: (831)455-8783
Fax: (831)455-7856
Co. E-mail: info@reta.com
URL: http://www.reta.com
Contact: Don Tragethon, Executive Director

Description: Focuses on the professional development of industrial refrigeration operators and technicians. Offers self-study and on-line training courses on industrial refrigeration. Offers a nationally-recognized certification program for operators and technicians on two levels of understanding and knowledge. **Founded:** 1910. **Publications:** *RETA Breeze* (Bimonthly). **Educational Activities:** Refrigerating Engineers and Technicians Association Convention (Annual).

776 ■ Refrigeration Service Engineers Society (RSES)

1666 Rand Rd.
Des Plaines, IL 60016-3552
Ph: (847)297-6464
Free: 800-297-5660
Co. E-mail: bruceirma@aol.com
URL: http://www.rses.org
Contact: Lawrence R. Donaldson, President

Description: Persons engaged in refrigeration, air-conditioning and heating installation, service, sales and maintenance. Conducts training courses and certification testing. Maintains a hall of fame and a speakers' bureau. **Scope:** heating AC programs for chapter use. **Founded:** 1933. **Subscriptions:** 1000

SMALL BUSINESS PROFILES

archival material audiovisuals books clippings periodicals. **Publications:** *Service Application Manuals.* **Awards:** Distinguished Service (Annual); Educator of the Year (Annual); Rising Star Award (Annual); Speaker of the Year (Annual).

777 ■ Sheet Metal and Air Conditioning Contractors' National Association (SMACNA)
4201 Lafayette Center Dr.
Chantilly, VA 20151-1209
Ph: (703)803-2980
Fax: (703)803-3732
Co. E-mail: info@smacna.org
URL: http://www.smacna.org
Contact: Vincent R. Sandusky, Chief Executive Officer
E-mail: vsandusky@smacna.org
Description: Ventilation, air handling, warm air heating, architectural and industrial sheet metal, kitchen equipment, testing and balancing, siding, and decking and specialty fabrication contractors. Prepares standards and codes; sponsors research and educational programs on sheet metal duct construction and fire damper (single and multi-blade) construction. Engages in legislative and labor activities; conducts business management and contractor education programs. **Scope:** technical and safety issues related to sheet metal and air conditioning industry. **Founded:** 1943. **Subscriptions:** 40 books. **Educational Activities:** Sheet Metal and Air-Conditioning Contractors National Association Convention/Exhibition Forum (Annual); SMACNA Convention and Exhibition (Annual). **Awards:** Sheet Metal And Air Conditioning Contractors' National Association College of Fellows Scholarships.

DIRECTORIES OF EDUCATIONAL PROGRAMS

778 ■ *Directory of Private Accredited Career Schools and Colleges of Technology*
Pub: Accrediting Commission of Career Schools and Colleges of Technology
Contact: Michale S. McComis, Executive Director
Released: On web page. **Price:** Free. **Description:** Covers 3900 accredited post-secondary programs that provide training programs in business, trade, and technical fields, including various small business endeavors. Entries offer school name, address, phone, description of courses, job placement assistance, and requirements for admission. Arrangement is alphabetical.

REFERENCE WORKS

779 ■ *"Adventures at Hydronicahh"* in Contractor (Vol. 56, September 2009, No. 9, pp. 52)
Pub: Penton Media, Inc.
Ed: Mark Eatherton. **Description:** Installation of the heating system of a lakeview room are described. The room's radiant windows are powered by electricity from a solar PV array and a propane-powered hydrogen fuel cell. The system will be programmed to use the most energy available.

780 ■ *"Adventures at Hydronicahh"* in Contractor (Vol. 56, November 2009, No. 11, pp. 36)
Pub: Penton Media, Inc.
Ed: Mark Eatherton. **Description:** Part 6 of the installation of a five stage ground-source heat pump for a hydronic heating system is discussed. The heat exchanger will be bidirectional in the plan described.

781 ■ *"Adventures at Hydronicahh"* in Contractor (Vol. 56, October 2009, No. 10, pp. 42)
Pub: Penton Media, Inc.
Ed: Mark Eatherton. **Description:** Design and installation of a solar thermal system for a hydronic heating project is described. This portion has two 32-square feet of flat plate glazed solar collectors that are tied to a 120-gallon reverse indirect DHW heater.

782 ■ *Air Conditioning Contractors of America--Membership Directory*
Pub: Air Conditioning Contractors of America
Contact: Paul T. Stalknecht, President
E-mail: paul.stalknecht@acca.org
URL(s): www.acca.org. **Released:** Annual; summer.
Covers: Member air conditioning and heating contractors, manufacturers, vocational technical schools. **Entries include:** Company name, address, phone, fax, names and titles of key personnel, description of fields, and types of work performed. **Arrangement:** Geographical. **Indexes:** Alphabetical.

783 ■ *Air Conditioning, Heating & Refrigeration News--Directory Issue: The News HVACR Directory and Source Guide*
Pub: BNP Media
Contact: Al Reser, President
URL(s): www.achrnews.com. **Released:** Annual; Latest edition 2011. **Publication includes:** Lists of about 2,086 manufacturers, 4,383 wholesalers and factory outlets, 1,667 HVACR products, exporters specializing in the industry; related trade organizations; manufacturers representatives, consultants, services; videos and software. **Entries include:** For manufacturers--Company Name, address, phone, fax, e-mail, URL, names of key personnel, brand names, list of products; similar information for other categories. **Arrangement:** Manufacturers and exporters are alphabetical; wholesalers and representatives are geographical. **Indexes:** Product, trade name.

784 ■ *"Alternative Energy Calls for Alternative Marketing"* in Indoor Comfort Marketing (Vol. 70, June 2011, No. 6, pp. 8)
Pub: Industry Publications Inc.
Ed: Richard Rutigliano. **Description:** Advice for marketing solar energy products and services is given.

785 ■ *American Supply Association--Membership Directory: Resource Guide*
Pub: American Supply Association
Contact: Scott Weaver, President
URL(s): www.asa.net/Membership/MemberDirectory/tabid/65/Default.aspx. **Released:** Annual **Price:** $25, Members; $299, Nonmembers; $1125, Individuals electronic; $225, Nonmembers diskette; $145, Members print and diskette; $265, Nonmembers print and diskette. **Covers:** 4,000 member wholesalers handling plumbing, heating, and cooling materials and supplies. **Entries include:** Company name, address, phone, names of executives, list of products or services, fax numbers, email and website. **Arrangement:** Geographical and alphabetical. **Indexes:** Special interest divisions.

786 ■ *"AREE Meets in Atlantic City"* in Indoor Comfort Marketing (Vol. 70, June 2011, No. 6, pp. 28)
Pub: Industry Publications Inc.
Description: Highlights of the Atlantic Region Energy Expo are provided.

787 ■ *"Art Institute of Chicago Goes Green"* in Contractor (Vol. 56, July 2009, No. 7, pp. 1)
Pub: Penton Media, Inc.
Ed: Candace Roulo. **Description:** Art Institute of Chicago's Modern Wing museum addition will receive a certification that makes them one of the most environmentally sound museum expansions in the U.S. A modified variable-air-volume system is being used to meet temperature and humidity requirements in the building and it also has a double curtain wall to capture summer heat.

788 ■ *"Be Proactive - Closely Review Contracts"* in Contractor (Vol. 56, July 2009, No. 7, pp. 19)
Pub: Penton Media, Inc.
Ed: Al Schwartz. **Description:** Contract disputes can make subcontractors suffer big financial losses or even cause a new subcontractor to fail. Subcontractors should scour the plans and specifications for any references to work that might remotely come under their scope and to cross out any line in the contract that does not accurately reflect the work that they agreed to.

789 ■ *"Be Wary of Dual-Flush Conversion Kits"* in Contractor (Vol. 56, September 2009, No. 9, pp. 66)
Pub: Penton Media, Inc.
Ed: John Koeller; Bill Gauley. **Description:** Recommendation of untested dual-flush conversion devices for tank-type toilets in the United States have been questioned. The products are being advertised as having the ability to convert single-flush to a dual-flush toilet. No evidence of water conservation from using such devices has been recorded.

790 ■ *"Bigger is Definitely Not Better When It Comes to Cooling"* in Indoor Comfort Marketing (Vol. 70, May 2011, No. 5, pp. 49)
Pub: Industry Publications Inc.
Ed: Eugene Silberstein. **Description:** Efficiency is more important when installing air conditioning equipment over size of the unit. Details are provided.

791 ■ *"Bioheat - Alternative for Fueling Equipment"* in Indoor Comfort Marketing (Vol. 70, May 2011, No. 5, pp. 14)
Pub: Industry Publications Inc.
Ed: Gary Hess. **Description:** Profile of Worley and Obetz, supplier of biofuels used as an alternative for fueling industry equipment.

792 ■ *"Bold Goals Will Require Time"* in Contractor (Vol. 56, October 2009, No. 10, pp. S2)
Pub: Penton Media, Inc.
Ed: Ted Lower. **Description:** Offering a broad range of courses is the Radiant Panel Association (RPA), an organization that holds education as its top priority. The RPA must lead the industry by raising the educational bar for future installers.

793 ■ *"Burner Handles Everything From #2 to B100"* in Indoor Comfort Marketing (Vol. 70, May 2011, No. 5, pp. 24)
Pub: Industry Publications Inc.
Description: A new oil burner being offered by AMERIgreen Energy is profiled.

794 ■ *"Canadian Hydronics Businesses Promote 'Beautiful Heat"* in Indoor Comfort Marketing (Vol. 70, September 2011, No. 9, pp. 20)
Pub: Industry Publications Inc.
Description: Canadian hydronics companies are promoting their systems as beautiful heat. Hydronics is the use of water as the heat-transfer medium in heating and cooling system.

795 ■ *"Cash for Appliances Targets HVAC Products, Water Heaters"* in Contractor (Vol. 56, October 2009, No. 10, pp. 1)
Pub: Penton Media, Inc.
Ed: Candace Roulo. **Description:** States and territories would need to submit a full application that specifies their implementation plans if they are interested in joining the Cash for Appliances program funded by the American Recovery and Reinvestment Act. The Department of Energy urges states to focus on heating and cooling equipment, appliances and water heaters since these offer the greatest energy savings potential.

796 ■ *"Certified Technicians can Increase Bottom Line"* in Contractor (Vol. 56, September 2009, No. 9, pp. 37)
Pub: Penton Media, Inc.
Ed: Ray Isaac. **Description:** Certified technicians increase the value of HVAC firms, a survey by Service Round Table reported. The increased value has been attributed to fewer callbacks, less warranty work and greater ability to educate consumers. Meanwhile, consumers are willing to pay more for the services of certified technicians.

797 ■ *"The Challenges of Commercial Work"* in Indoor Comfort Marketing (Vol. 70, May 2011, No. 5, pp. 14)
Pub: Industry Publications Inc.
Ed: Matt Spink. **Description:** The challenges faced by heating, ventilation, cooling small businesses expanding into commercial accounts are discussed.

798 ■ *"Changing Fuel Compositions: What It Means To You and Your Business"* in *Indoor Comfort Marketing (Vol. 70, June 2011, No. 6, pp. 30)*
Pub: Industry Publications Inc.
Ed: Paul Nazzaro. **Description:** Biofuels are outlined and the way it is changing the HVAC/R industry are discussed.

799 ■ *"Chicago Public School District Builds Green"* in *Contractor (Vol. 56, October 2009, No. 10, pp. 5)*
Pub: Penton Media, Inc.
Ed: Candace Roulo. **Description:** Chicago Public Schools district has already built six U.S. Green Building Council LEED certified schools and one addition in five years and will continue to build new green buildings. The district has an Environmental Action Plan that strives to reduce energy usage, improve indoor air quality, and reduce contribution to climate change.

800 ■ *"Climate Right Systems Provides Pre-Assembled Equipment Packages"* in *Contractor (Vol. 56, July 2009, No. 7, pp. 1)*
Pub: Penton Media, Inc.
Description: Climate Right Systems offers completely engineered, assembled, and tested equipment packages for hydronic heating and cooling. This package does away with the need to custom fabricate on-site and lets mechanical and plumbing contractors expand their offerings without added overhead and risk.

801 ■ *"Combo Dorm-Field House Built to Attain LEED Gold"* in *Contractor (Vol. 56, September 2009, No. 9, pp. 1)*
Pub: Penton Media, Inc.
Ed: Candace Roulo; Robert P. Mader. **Description:** North Central College in Illinois has built a new dormitory that is expected to attain Leadership in Energy and Environmental Design Gold certification from the United States Green Building Council. The structure features a geo-exchange heat pump system and radiant floor heat. A description of the facility is also provided.

802 ■ *"Contractors Can't Do It Alone, PHCC's Pfeffer Says"* in *Contractor (Vol. 56, October 2009, No. 10, pp. 3)*
Pub: Penton Media, Inc.
Ed: Robert P. Mader. **Description:** President Herbert 'Skip' Pfeffer of the Plumbing-Heating-Cooling Contractors National Association says lobbying and education are the services that the association offers that a contractor cannot do individually. Pfeffer says the dues for the association are set up in a manner that allows members to pay monthly.

803 ■ *"A Day Late and a Dollar Short"* in *Indoor Comfort Marketing (Vol. 70, March 2011, No. 3, pp. 30)*
Pub: Industry Publications Inc.
Ed: Philip J. Baratz. **Description:** A discussion involving futures options and fuel oil prices is presented.

804 ■ *"Design Programs for HVAC Sizing Solutions"* in *Contractor (Vol. 57, January 2010, No. 1, pp. 44)*
Pub: Penton Media, Inc.
Ed: William Feldman; Patti Feldman. **Description:** Rhvac 8 is an HVAC design program that lets users calculate peak heating and cooling load requirements for rooms, zones, systems, and entire buildings. The HVAC Pipe Sizer software for the iPhone enables quick sizing of a simple piping system.

805 ■ *Directory of Certified Unitary Air-Conditioners, Unitary Air-Source Heat Pumps and Sound-Rated Outdoor Unitary Equipment*
Pub: Air-Conditioning and Refrigeration Institute
URL(s): www.ari.org. **Released:** Semiannual; January and July. **Price:** $10, plus $5 shipping; payment with order. **Publication includes:** List of about 65 manufacturers of air- and coil-heating and cooling

units, and air-to-air heat pumps. **Entries include:** Manufacturer name, address. **Arrangement:** Alphabetical. **Indexes:** Trade name.

806 ■ *"Do the Right Thing"* in *Contractor (Vol. 56, December 2009, No. 12, pp. 16)*
Pub: Penton Media, Inc.
Ed: Robert P. Mader. **Description:** Applewood Plumbing, Heating and Electric has won Contractor magazine's 2009 Contractor of the Year Award. The company has ranked eighth among more than 300 service companies in the United States. A brief history of the company is also provided.

807 ■ *"DOE Proposes New Water Heater Efficiency Standards"* in *Contractor (Vol. 57, January 2010, No. 1, pp. 3)*
Pub: Penton Media, Inc.
Ed: Robert P. Mader. **Description:** U.S. Department of Energy is proposing higher efficiency standards for gas and electric water heaters which will not take effect until 2015. The proposal calls for gas-fired storage water heaters less than 60 gallons to have an Energy Factor of 0.675 and those larger than 60 gallons to have an Energy Factor of 0.717.

808 ■ *"Eco Smart Home Will Showcase Green Technology"* in *Contractor (Vol. 56, September 2009, No. 9, pp. 3)*
Pub: Penton Media, Inc.
Ed: Steve Spaulding. **Description:** Eco Smart World Wide is building the Eco Smart Demonstration House to promote the latest in sustainable, renewable and high-efficiency practices and products. The company will use insulated concrete forms in the construction of the building. Features and dimensions of the structure are also presented.

809 ■ *"Energy Is Put to Good Use in Antarctica"* in *Contractor (Vol. 56, July 2009, No. 7, pp. 32)*
Pub: Penton Media, Inc.
Ed: Carol Fey. **Description:** Recapturing waste heat is an important part of the heating system at the McMurdo Station in Antarctica. The radiators of generators are the heat source and this is supplemented by modular boilers when seasonal demands for heat increase. Waste heat is also used to make 55,000 gallons of fresh water a day.

810 ■ *"EPA to Tighten Energy Star Standards for 2011"* in *Contractor (Vol. 56, September 2009, No. 9, pp. 6)*
Pub: Penton Media, Inc.
Description: United States Environmental Protection Agency will tighten standards for its Energy Star for Homes program in 2011. The green trend in the construction industry has been cited as reason for the plan. The agency is adding requirements for energy-efficient equipment and building techniques.

811 ■ *"Expect Action on Health Care and the Economy"* in *Contractor (Vol. 57, January 2010, No. 1, pp. 30)*
Pub: Penton Media, Inc.
Ed: Kevin Schwalb. **Description:** The Plumbing-Heating-Cooling Contractors National Association is working to solidify its standing in the public policy arena as the legislative agenda will focus on health care reform, estate tax and immigration reform, all of which will impact the industries.

812 ■ *"Explore New Avenues to Success..Boldly!"* in *Indoor Comfort Marketing (Vol. 70, May 2011, No. 5, pp. 18)*
Pub: Industry Publications Inc.
Ed: Rich Rutigliano. **Description:** Strategies to help fuel companies succeed in today's market are explored.

813 ■ *"Fix-It Career: Jobs in Repair"* in *Occupational Outlook Quarterly (Vol. 54, Fall 2010, No. 3, pp. 26)*
Pub: U.S. Bureau of Labor Statistics
Ed: Elka Maria Torpey. **Description:** Auto mechanics and HVAC technician occupations require repair skills. Advantages for individuals with proper skills are outlined.

814 ■ *"Get Online Quick in the Office Or in the Field"* in *Contractor (Vol. 56, October 2009, No. 10, pp. 47)*
Pub: Penton Media, Inc.
Ed: William Feldman; Patti Feldman. **Description:** Contractors can set up a web site in minutes using the www.1and1.com website. Verizon's Novatel MIFI 2372 HSPA personal hotspot device lets contractors go online in the field. The StarTech scalable business management system helps contractors manage daily operations.

815 ■ *"Getting the Bioheat Word Out"* in *Indoor Comfort Marketing (Vol. 70, September 2011, No. 9, pp. 32)*
Pub: Industry Publications Inc.
Description: Ways to market advanced liquid fuels to the public are outlined.

816 ■ *"Gray, Gray, & Gray: a Difficult Year for Oilheat"* in *Indoor Comfort Marketing (Vol. 70, September 2011, No. 9, pp. 30)*
Pub: Industry Publications Inc.
Description: According to the 20th Annual Oilheat Industry Survey, 2011 will be another dismal year for the industry sector.

817 ■ *"Growing Your Business Through BPI Certification"* in *Indoor Comfort Marketing (Vol. 70, May 2011, No. 5, pp. 12)*
Pub: Industry Publications Inc.
Ed: Scott Vadino. **Description:** Profile of the Building Performance Institute and the ways BPI certification will help grow a heating, ventilation, cooling firm.

818 ■ *"Harness the Internet to Boost Equipment Sales"* in *Indoor Comfort Marketing (Vol. 70, July 2011, No. 7, pp. 24)*
Pub: Industry Publications Inc.
Ed: Richard Rutigliano. **Description:** Advice is given to increase HVAC/R equipment sales using the Internet.

819 ■ *"Help Customers Choose Full Service Over Discount"* in *Indoor Comfort Marketing (Vol. 70, September 2011, No. 9, pp. 10)*
Pub: Industry Publications Inc.
Ed: Richard Rutigliano. **Description:** Marketing strategies for HVAC/R firms to use in 2011 and 2012 heating seasons are outlined, focusing on oil heat.

820 ■ *"Housing Slide Picks Up Speed"* in *Crain's Chicago Business (Vol. 31, April 21, 2008, No. 16, pp. 2)*
Pub: Crain Communications, Inc.
Ed: Eddie Baeb. **Description:** According to Tracy Cross & Associates Inc., a real estate consultancy, sales of new homes in the Chicago area dropped 61 percent from the year-earlier period which is more bad news for homebuilders, contractors and real estate agents who are eager for an indication that market conditions are improving.

821 ■ *"How Good Advice 'Online' Can Attract Customers"* in *Indoor Comfort Marketing (Vol. 70, August 2011, No. 8, pp. 20)*
Pub: Industry Publications Inc.
Ed: Richard Rutigilano. **Description:** Online marketing tips for heating and cooling small businesses are explained.

822 ■ *"How to Keep a US Naval Destroyer Warm"* in *Indoor Comfort Marketing (Vol. 70, April 2011, No. 4, pp. 34)*
Pub: Industry Publications Inc.
Ed: George R. Carey. **Description:** Boiler facts regarding US Naval destroyers are discussed.

823 ■ *HPAC Engineering--Info-Dex*
Pub: Penton Media Inc.
URL(s): directory.hpac.com/Main/DirectoryHome.aspxwww.penton.com. **Released:** Annual; Latest edition 2008-2009. **Publication includes:** Listing of over 2,000 manufacturers in the heating/piping/air conditioning industry, and associations and government agencies concerned with standards for the industry. **Entries include:** Company or organization name, address, phone, fax, URL and product codes. Listings for advertisers also show key personnel and

branch and representatives' offices. **Arrangement:** Separate alphabetical sections for manufacturers, associations, and advertisers. **Indexes:** Product, trade name.

824 ■ *"HVAC/R Evolution"* in *Indoor Comfort Marketing (Vol. 70, March 2011, No. 3, pp. 14)*
Pub: Industry Publications Inc.
Ed: Gene Bartholomew. **Description:** Tools and techniques for heating, ventilation, air conditioning and refrigeration are examined.

825 ■ *"IAPMO Seeks Group Participants"* in *Contractor (Vol. 56, September 2009, No. 9, pp. 37)*
Pub: Penton Media, Inc.
Description: International Association of Plumbing and Mechanical Officials is accepting applications for task groups that will develop its Uniform Plumbing Code and Uniform Mechanical Code. The codes are developed using American National Standards Institute accredited consensus process. Task groups are assigned to address a specific topic or problem.

826 ■ *"If the Opportunity is There, Move Boldly"* in *Indoor Comfort Marketing (Vol. 70, March 2011, No. 3, pp.)*
Pub: Industry Publications Inc.
Ed: Rich Rutigliano. **Description:** Suggestions are offered to help improve air conditioning sales.

827 ■ *"Illinois Residential Building Legislation Includes New HVAC Requirements"* in *Contractor (Vol. 56, July 2009, No. 7, pp. 3)*
Pub: Penton Media, Inc.
Ed: Candace Ruolo. **Description:** Illinois' Energy Efficient Building Act will require all new buildings and houses to conform to the International Energy Conservation Code. The code includes a duct leakage requirement followed by a post-construction test to verify leakage rates and requires programmable thermostats on all houses.

828 ■ *"Independence Station Utilizes Sustainable Technologies"* in *Contractor (Vol. 56, September 2009, No. 9, pp. 3)*
Pub: Penton Media, Inc.
Ed: Candace Ruolo. **Description:** Independence Station building in Oregon is seen to receive the most LEED points ever awarded by the United States Green Building Council. The building will use an ice-based cooling storage system, biofuel cogeneration system and phovoltaic system. Other building features and dimensions are also supplied.

829 ■ *"Indoor Air Quality - a Tribute to Efficiency"* in *Indoor Comfort Marketing (Vol. 70, August 2011, No. 8, pp. 8)*
Pub: Industry Publications Inc.
Ed: Matthew Maleske. **Description:** Efficiency of new HVAC/R equipment has helped improve indoor air quality.

830 ■ *"Interested in 12 Billion Dollars?"* in *Indoor Comfort Marketing (Vol. 70, March 2011, No. 3, pp. 18)*
Pub: Industry Publications Inc.
Ed: Matthew Maleske. **Description:** Trends in the indoor quality industry are cited, with insight into expanding an existing indoor heating and cooling business.

831 ■ *"It's Always 55 Degrees F"* in *Contractor (Vol. 56, September 2009, No. 9, pp. 38)*
Pub: Penton Media, Inc.
Ed: Carol Fey. **Description:** Geothermal-exchange heating and cooling systems can save businesses up to 60 percent on energy costs for heating and cooling. Geothermal systems get heat from the earth during winter. Design, features and installation of geothermal systems are also discussed.

832 ■ *"It's New or Improved, But Does It Work?"* in *Contractor (Vol. 57, January 2010, No. 1, pp. 22)*
Pub: Penton Media, Inc.
Ed: Al Schwartz. **Description:** There is a place for skepticism in the HVAC and plumbing industry as not all new products that are specified may not always perform. The tradesman has the responsibility of integrating new technology into the field.

833 ■ *"Know the Facts About Natural Gas!"* in *Indoor Comfort Marketing (Vol. 70, August 2011, No. 8, pp. 26)*
Pub: Industry Publications Inc.
Description: AEC Activity Update is presented on the American Energy Coalition's Website.

834 ■ *"Large Homes can be Energy Efficient Too"* in *Contractor (Vol. 56, October 2009, No. 10, pp. 5)*
Pub: Penton Media, Inc.
Ed: Candace Roulo. **Description:** Eco Estate at Briggs Chaney subdivision in Silver Spring, Maryland has model houses that use sustainable technologies and products and the homes that will be built on the subdivision will feature some of the technologies featured on the model home. The energy efficient HVAC system of the model homes are discussed.

835 ■ *"The Latest on E-Verify"* in *Contractor (Vol. 56, September 2009, No. 9, pp. 58)*
Pub: Penton Media, Inc.
Ed: Susan McGreevy. **Description:** United States government has required federal contractors to use its E-Verify program to verify the eligibility of incoming and existent employees. The use of the program is seen to eliminate Social Security mismatches.

836 ■ *"Legislation Introduced"* in *Indoor Comfort Marketing (Vol. 70, July 2011, No. 7, pp. 6)*
Pub: Industry Publications Inc.
Description: New industry legislation is examined by the National Oilheat Research Alliance.

837 ■ *"Manufacturers Become Part of Coalition"* in *Contractor (Vol. 56, July 2009, No. 7, pp. 40)*
Pub: Penton Media, Inc.
Description: Bradford White Water Heaters, Rheem Water Heating, Rinnai America Corp., and A.O. Smith Water Heaters have joined the Consortium for Energy Efficiency in the Coalition for Energy Star Water Heaters. The coalition seeks to increase the awareness of Energy Star water heaters.

838 ■ *"The Many Hats and Faces of NAOHSM"* in *Indoor Comfort Marketing (Vol. 70, May 2011, No. 5, pp. 8)*
Pub: Industry Publications Inc.
Description: Profile of the National Association of Oil Heating Service Managers, and its role in the industry, is presented.

839 ■ *"Minnesota State Park Building Exemplifies Sustainability"* in *Contractor (Vol. 56, November 2009, No. 11, pp. 5)*
Pub: Penton Media, Inc.
Ed: Candace Ruolo. **Description:** Camden State Park's newly remodeled information/office building in Lynd, Minnesota features a 10 kw wind turbine which is capable of offsetting most of the facility's electricity and a geothermal heat pump system. The heat pump is a 4-ton vertical closed-loop ground source heat pump by ClimateMaster.

840 ■ *"A Necessary Balancing Act: Bookkeeping"* in *Contractor (Vol. 56, November 2009, No. 11, pp. 22)*
Pub: Penton Media, Inc.
Ed: Al Schwartz. **Description:** Pros and cons of getting a bookkeeper or a certified public accountant for the subcontractor are discussed. A bookkeeper can help a subcontractor get new accounting software up and running while an accountant will more than likely keep after the books at regular intervals throughout the year.

841 ■ *"A New Day is Dawning"* in *Indoor Comfort Marketing (Vol. 70, August 2011, No. 8, pp. 18)*
Pub: Industry Publications Inc.
Ed: Paul Nazzaro. **Description:** New trends in the HVAC/R industry regarding biofuels and bioheat are explored.

842 ■ *"New Hydronic Heating Technologies Work"* in *Contractor (Vol. 57, January 2010, No. 1, pp. 58)*
Pub: Penton Media, Inc.
Ed: Carol Fey. **Description:** Technology behind hydronic heating systems is reviewed. These technologies include radiant and geothermal hydronic heating. System requirements for installing these greener forms of heating are discussed.

843 ■ *"Nexstar Super Meeting Breaks Business Barriers"* in *Contractor (Vol. 56, November 2009, No. 11, pp. 3)*
Pub: Penton Media, Inc.
Ed: Candace Roulo. **Description:** Around 400 Nexstar members met to discuss the trends in the HVAC industry and the economic outlook for 2010. Former lead solo pilot John Foley for the Blue Angels made a presentation on how a business can increase overall productivity based on the culture of the Blue Angels. Some breakout sessions tackled how to optimize workflow and marketing.

844 ■ *"OHC Aids Long Island Family"* in *Indoor Comfort Marketing (Vol. 70, May 2011, No. 5, pp. 45)*
Pub: Industry Publications Inc.
Ed: Judy Garber. **Description:** Ways Community Oil Heat helped a customer living in Long Island heat their home during desperate times.

845 ■ *"Oilheating Delivery Issues"* in *Indoor Comfort Marketing (Vol. 70, September 2011, No. 9, pp. 14)*
Pub: Industry Publications Inc.
Ed: John Levey. **Description:** Tools and techniques for delivery heating oil to customers this season are discussed.

846 ■ *"Overheating Taking Place? Pay Attention to Details.."* in *Indoor Comfort Marketing (Vol. 70, March 2011, No. 3, pp.)*
Pub: Industry Publications Inc.
Ed: George R. Carey. **Description:** Boiler facts are outlined to help the small HVAC company when servicing customers.

847 ■ *"PHCC Convention, Show Gets High Marks"* in *Contractor (Vol. 56, December 2009, No. 12, pp. 1)*
Pub: Penton Media, Inc.
Ed: Robert P. Mader. **Description:** Plumbing-Heating-Cooling Contractors National Association has held its first convention and trade show in New Orleans, Louisiana. Attendees were treated to a variety of seminars and exhibitors during the event. Comments from event organizers are also given.

848 ■ *"Phoenix Conference Reveals Opportunities are Coming"* in *Indoor Comfort Marketing (Vol. 70, March 2011, No. 3, pp. 24)*
Pub: Industry Publications Inc.
Ed: Paul J. Nazzaro. **Description:** Advanced liquid fuels were spotlighted at the Phoenix conference revealing the opportunities for using liquid fuels.

849 ■ *"Plumbing, Heating Products Shine at Greenbuild Expo"* in *Contractor (Vol. 56, December 2009, No. 12, pp. 1)*
Pub: Penton Media, Inc.
Ed: Robert P. Mader. **Description:** Greenbuild Show held in Phoenix, Arizona has showcased the latest in plumbing and heating products. Zurn displayed its EcoVantage line of fixtures and valves during the event. Meanwhile, Sloan Valve offered its washdown 1-pint/flush Alphine urinal.

850 ■ *PM Directory & Reference Issue: Plumbers Buyers Guide*
Pub: BNP Media
Contact: Al Reser, President
URL(s): www.pmmag.com. **Ed:** Steve Smith. **Released:** Annual; Latest edition 2010. **Covers:** Manufacturers, wholesalers, products, consultants, and manufacturers' representatives in the industries of plumbing, piping, and hydronic heating. **Entries include:** Contact name, company, address, phone, fax, and product descriptions. **Arrangement:** Alphabetical. **Indexes:** By products.

851 ■ *"Portland Home Is First in U.S. to Use Variable Speed 'Inverter' Technology"* in Contractor (Vol. 56, December 2009, No. 12, pp. 5)
Pub: Penton Media, Inc.
Description: Daikin Altherma heat pump with inverter drive has been installed in a Portland, Oregon home. The heat pump provides a high coefficient of performance while delivering hydronic and domestic hot water functionality. Other product features and dimensions are also supplied.

852 ■ *"Positive Transformational Change"* in Indoor Comfort Marketing (Vol. 70, April 2011, No. 4, pp. 30)
Pub: Industry Publications Inc.
Ed: Blaine Fox. **Description:** Management changes taking place at Shark Bites HVAC firm are discussed.

853 ■ *"PPC's Major Commitment to Biofuel Infrastructure"* in Indoor Comfort Marketing (Vol. 70, April 2011, No. 4, pp. 6)
Pub: Industry Publications Inc.
Description: Petroleum Products Corporation's commitment to the biofuel infrastructure is outlined.

854 ■ *"Programs Provide Education and Training"* in Contractor (Vol. 56, September 2009, No. 9, pp. 56)
Pub: Penton Media, Inc.
Ed: William Feldman; Patti Feldman. **Description:** Opportunity Interactive's Showroom v2 software provides uses computer graphics to provide education and training on HVAC equipment and systems. It can draw heat pump balance points for a specific home. Meanwhile, Simutech's HVAC Training Simulators provide trainees with 'hands-on' HVACR training.

855 ■ *"Proposal Ruffles Builders"* in Austin Business JournalInc. (Vol. 29, November 20, 2009, No. 37, pp. 1)
Pub: American City Business Journals
Ed: Jacob Dirr. **Description:** A proposal that requires heating, ventilation and cooling equipment checking for a new commercial building having an area of at least 10,000 square feet might cost 25 cents to 50 cents per square foot for the owners. This may lead to higher housing costs. Both the Building and Fire Code Board of Appeals and the Mechanical Plumbing and Solar Board have recommended the plan.

856 ■ *"Put Your Heating Cap On.."* in Indoor Comfort Marketing (Vol. 70, September 2011, No. 9, pp. 26)
Pub: Industry Publications Inc.
Ed: George Carey. **Description:** Tools and techniques for HVAC/R technicians servicing boilers are outlined.

857 ■ *"A Quick Guide to NATE"* in Indoor Comfort Marketing (Vol. 70, February 2011, No. 2, pp. 12)
Pub: Industry Publications Inc.
Description: Guide for training and certification in the North American Technician Excellence award.

858 ■ *"Radiant - the Hottest Topic in .. Cooling"* in Indoor Comfort Marketing (Vol. 70, February 2011, No. 2, pp. 8)
Pub: Industry Publications Inc.
Description: Examination of radiant cooling systems, a new trend in cooling homes and buildings.

859 ■ *"Rehab Center Slashes Energy Bills By Going Tankless"* in Contractor (Vol. 56, December 2009, No. 12, pp. 3)
Pub: Penton Media, Inc.
Description: Melburne Health and Rehabilitation Center in Florida has reduced its energy bills by installing a tankless hot water system. Sun Plumbing was selected to install the system. The system was installed on a mechanical room that housed the old tank-type heaters.

860 ■ *"Route Optimization Impacts the Bottom Line"* in Contractor (Vol. 56, November 2009, No. 11, pp. 48)
Pub: Penton Media, Inc.
Ed: Dave Beaudry. **Description:** Plumbing and HVAC businesses can save a significant amount of money from route optimization. The process begins

with gathering information on a fleet and a routing software tool can determine the effectiveness of current route configurations and identify preferable route plans.

861 ■ *"RPA Preps for Building Radiant Conference, Show"* in Contractor (Vol. 57, January 2010, No. 1, pp. 5)
Pub: Penton Media, Inc.
Description: Radiant Panel Association is accepting registrations for its Building Radiant 2010 Conference and Trade Show. The conference will discuss radiant heating as well as insurance and other legal matters for mechanical contractors.

862 ■ *"Safety Managers Need to Be Safety Experts"* in Indoor Comfort Marketing (Vol. 70, May 2011, No. 5, pp. 10)
Pub: Industry Publications Inc.
Ed: Mike Hodge. **Description:** It is imperative to have a good safety manager in place for all heating and cooling firms.

863 ■ *"Selling a Job When There's Buyer's Remorse"* in Contractor (Vol. 56, December 2009, No. 12, pp. 37)
Pub: Penton Media, Inc.
Ed: H. Kent Craig. **Description:** Advice on how contractors should manage low-profit jobs in the United States are presented. Efforts should be made to try and find at least one quality field foreman or superintendent. Contractors should also try to respectfully renegotiate the terms of the job.

864 ■ *"Software Solutions from Trane and Carrier"* in Contractor (Vol. 56, July 2009, No. 7, pp. 38)
Pub: Penton Media, Inc.
Ed: William Feldman; Patti Feldman. **Description:** Trane Trace 700 software helps HVAC contractors optimize the design of a building's HVAC system and aids in the evaluation of various key energy-saving concepts, including daylighting, high-performance glazing, and other optimization strategies. Carrier's E20-II family of software programs lets contractors increase the accuracy of an HVAC system estimate.

865 ■ *"Solar Choices"* in Contractor (Vol. 56, October 2009, No. 10, pp. 32)
Pub: Penton Media, Inc.
Ed: Tom Scheel. **Description:** Price, performance, and ease of installation of a flat plate versus an evacuated tube collector for a plumbing and heating job are compared. The better choice with regards to weight, aesthetics, efficiency in warm or cool climates, year round load, and space heating is discussed.

866 ■ *"Start Connecting Today"* in Indoor Comfort Marketing (Vol. 70, May 2011, No. 5, pp. 34)
Pub: Industry Publications Inc.
Ed: Paul Nazzaro. **Description:** An in-depth discussion regarding the use of biofuels on bioheat use and dealership.

867 ■ *"Tracking Your Fleet Can Increase Bottom Line"* in Contractor (Vol. 56, November 2009, No. 11, pp. 26)
Pub: Penton Media, Inc.
Ed: Candace Roulo. **Description:** GPS fleet management system can help boost a contractor's profits, employee productivity, and efficiency. These are available as a handheld device or a cell phone that employees carry around or as a piece of hardware installed in a vehicle. These lets managers track assets and communicate with employees about jobs.

868 ■ *"Trade Craft: Take Pride in Your Trade, Demand Excellence"* in Contractor (Vol. 56, October 2009, No. 10, pp. 24)
Pub: Penton Media, Inc.
Ed: Al Schwartz. **Description:** There is a need for teaching, developing, and encouraging trade craft. An apprentice plumber is not only versed in the mechanical aspects of the trade but he also has a working knowledge of algebra, trigonometry, chemistry, and thermal dynamics. Contractors should be demanding on their personnel regarding their trade craft and should only keep and train the very best people they can hire.

869 ■ *"Two Field Service Management Solutions"* in Contractor (Vol. 56, November 2009, No. 11, pp. 37)
Pub: Penton Media, Inc.
Ed: William Feldman; Patti Feldman. **Description:** Bella Solutions Field Service Software v. 4.2 is a web based solution for HVAC service contractors that enables scheduling of emergency, one-time, multi-visit or periodically recurring jobs with drag and drop appointments. VaZing is another web based solution that costs $99 per month for contractors. It can handle line-item discounting and invoices aside from scheduling.

870 ■ *"UA Turns Ann Arbor Green"* in Contractor (Vol. 56, September 2009, No. 9, pp. 5)
Pub: Penton Media, Inc.
Ed: Robert P. Mader. **Description:** Instructors at the United Association of Plumbers and Steamfitters have studied the latest in green and sustainable construction and service at the Washtenaw Community College in Michigan. Classes included building information modeling, hydronic heating and cooling and advanced HVACR troubleshooting. The UA is currently focusing on green training.

871 ■ *"The Ultimate Comfort System"* in Contractor (Vol. 56, July 2009, No. 7, pp. 30)
Pub: Penton Media, Inc.
Ed: Mark Eatherton. **Description:** Retrofitting of a hydronic heating system to an existing home is presented. The project approaches near net-zero energy production.

872 ■ *"Ultra Green Energy Services Opens NJ Biodiesel Transload Facility"* in Indoor Comfort Marketing (Vol. 70, June 2011, No. 6, pp. 35)
Pub: Industry Publications Inc.
Description: Profile of Ultra Green Energy Services and the opening of their new biodiesel facility in New Jersey is discussed.

873 ■ *"Ultra Low Sulfur Diesel: The Promise and the Reality"* in Indoor Comfort Marketing (Vol. 70, July 2011, No. 7, pp. 22)
Pub: Industry Publications Inc.
Ed: Ed Kitchen. **Description:** Impacts of ultra low sulfur diesel are examined.

874 ■ *"University Data Center Goes Off-Grid, Is Test Bed"* in Contractor (Vol. 57, February 2010, No. 2, pp. 1)
Pub: Penton Media, Inc.
Ed: Candace Roulo. **Description:** Syracuse University's Green Data Center has gone off-grid through the use of natural gas fired turbines. It is expected to use 50 percent less energy than a typical computer center. The center's heating and cooling system setup is also discussed.

875 ■ *"Warm Floors Make Warm Homes"* in Contractor (Vol. 56, October 2009, No. 10, pp. S18)
Pub: Penton Media, Inc.
Ed: Lisa Murton Beets. **Description:** Three award winning radiant floor-heating installations are presented. The design and the equipment used for these systems are discussed.

876 ■ *"Water Efficiency Bill Move Through Congress"* in Contractor (Vol. 56, July 2009, No. 7, pp. 20)
Pub: Penton Media, Inc.
Ed: Kevin Schwalb. **Description:** National Association, a plumbing-heating-cooling contractor, was instrumental in drafting the Water Advanced Technologies for Efficient Resource Use Act of 2009 and they are also backing the Water Accountability Tax Efficiency Reinvestment Act. The first bill promotes WaterSense-labeled products while the other promotes water conservation through tax credits.

877 ■ *"Web-Based Solutions Streamline Operations"* in Contractor (Vol. 56, December 2009, No. 12, pp. 28)
Pub: Penton Media, Inc.
Ed: William Feldman; Patti Feldman. **Description:** Sage Project Lifecycle Management is a Web-based service platform for plumbing and HVAC contractors.

It enables effective workflow and document management. Projectmates, on the other hand, is a Web-based enterprise-wide solution for managing both commercial plumbing and HVAC projects.

878 ■ *"What Is a Geothermal Heat Pump" in Indoor Comfort Marketing (Vol. 70, August 2011, No. 8, pp. 14)*
Pub: Industry Publications Inc.

Ed: George Carey. **Description:** Examination of geothermal heat pumps is provided, citing new trends in the industry.

879 ■ *"Where the Future is Made" in Indoor Comfort Marketing (Vol. 70, May 2011, No. 5, pp. 48)*
Pub: Industry Publications Inc.

Description: Research being performed at Brookhaven National Laboratory, located in Upton, New York, is discussed, focusing on new energy sources for our nation.

880 ■ *"Yates Helps Turn Log Home Green" in Contractor (Vol. 56, December 2009, No. 12, pp. 40)*
Pub: Penton Media, Inc.

Description: Upgrading and greening of a log home's HVAC system in Pennsylvania is discussed. F. W. Behler Inc. president Dave Yates was chosen to manage the project. A large coil of R-flex was used to connect the buffer tank to the garage's radiant heat system.

881 ■ *"Yates Helps Turn Log Home Green" in Contractor (Vol. 56, November 2009, No. 11, pp. 1)*
Pub: Penton Media, Inc.

Description: Dave Yates of F.W. Behler Inc. helped homeowners from James Creek, Pennsylvania achieve energy efficiency on the heating system of their log cabin. The mechanical system installed on the cabin had high-temp 'THW' water-to-water geothermal system by ClimateMaster, two twin-coil indirect water heaters, and several pre-assembled, pre-engineered Hydronex panels by Watts Radiant.

882 ■ *"Yates Turns Log Home Green - Part Three" in Contractor (Vol. 57, January 2010, No. 1, pp. 5)*
Pub: Penton Media, Inc.

Description: Dave Yates of F.W. Behler Inc. discusses remodeling a log home's HVAC system with geo-to-radiant heat and thermal-solar systems. The solar heater's installation is discussed.

883 ■ *"You Can't Fix It If You Don't Face It!" in Indoor Comfort Marketing (Vol. 70, June 2011, No. 6, pp. 14)*
Pub: Industry Publications Inc.

Ed: John Levey. **Description:** Tips for avoiding repeat customer calls when installing or servicing HVAC/R equipment are provided.

SOURCES OF SUPPLY

884 ■ *Appliance--Appliance Industry Purchasing Section Issue*
Dana Chase Publications Inc.

URL(s): www.appliancemagazine.com. **Ed:** David Chase. **Released:** Annual; January. **Publication includes:** Suppliers to manufacturers of consumer, commercial, and business appliances. Membership directories for the following associations: Air-Conditioning and Refrigeration Institute, Association of Home Appliance Manufacturers, Commercial Refrigerator Manufacturers Association, Computer and Business Equipment Manufacturers Association, Consumer Electronics Group/Electronic Industries Association, Gas Appliance Manufacturers Association, Cookware Manufacturers Association, National Association of Food Equipment Manufacturers, National Housewares Manufacturers Association, Power Tool Institute, and Vacuum Cleaner Manufacturers Association. **Entries include:** Company name, address, phone, fax, and products. **Arrangement:** Classified by product. **Indexes:** Manufacturer, product heading.

885 ■ *The Wholesaler--Directory of Manufacturers Representatives Issue*
Trend Publishing

URL(s): www.plumbingengineer.comwww.thewholesaler.com. **Released:** Annual; Latest edition 2009. **Price:** $50, Individuals hardcopy or CD-ROM. **Publication includes:** 2,000 manufacturers' representatives handling plumbing, heating, piping, air conditioning, and refrigeration products. **Entries include:** Representative's name or firm name, address, phone, fax, territory, and lines carried. **Arrangement:** Geographical by territory (Central States, North Pacific, etc.).

STATISTICAL SOURCES

886 ■ *RMA Annual Statement Studies*
Pub: Risk Management Association
Contact: Kevin M. Blakey, President

Released: Annual. **Price:** $175.00 2006-07 edition, $105.00. **Description:** Contains composite balance sheets and income statements for more than 360 industries, including the accounting, auditing, and bookkeeping industries. Also contains five years of comparative historical data for discerning trends. Includes 16 commonly used ratios, computed for most of the size groupings for nearly every industry.

TRADE PERIODICALS

887 ■ *Alabama Contractor*
Pub: Associated Plumbing Heating & Cooling

URL(s): www.alphccapprentice.org/. **Released:** Annual **Price:** Free.

888 ■ *Contracting Business: Helping HVACR Contractors Improve Life, Comfort & Safety*
Pub: Penton Media Inc.

URL(s): contractingbusiness.com/. **Released:** Monthly

889 ■ *Heating/Piping/Air Conditioning Engineering: The Magazine of Mechanical Systems Engineering (HPAC)*
Pub: Penton Media Inc.

URL(s): hpac.com/. **Released:** Monthly

890 ■ *Heating-Plumbing-Air Conditioning Magazine (HPAC)*
Pub: Business Information Group
Contact: Bruce Creighton, President

URL(s): www.hpacmag.com. **Ed:** Kerry Turner. **Released:** 7/yr.

891 ■ *Indiana Contractor: Air Conditioning, Heating, Plumbing, Refrigeration, Sheet Metal*
Pub: Indiana Association of Plumbing, Heating, Cooling Contractors

URL(s): www.iaphcc.com/Membership/IndianaContractorMagazine/tabid/75/Default. **Released:** Quarterly

892 ■ *MACS Service Reports*
Pub: Mobile Air Conditioning Society Worldwide

Ed: Elvis Hoffpauir, Editor, elvis@macsw.org. **Released:** Monthly. **Price:** $70. **Description:** Serves as the technical information publication of the Mobile Air Conditioning Society Worldwide. Recurring features include news of research, news of educational opportunities, and How to and technical articles.

893 ■ *MCAA Reporter*
Pub: Mechanical Contractors Association of America Inc.

Contact: Stephanie Mills, Managing Editor

Ed: Adrienne Breedlove, Editor. **Released:** Monthly, except in February and August. **Price:** Included in membership; $50, nonmembers. **Description:** Covers labor issues and government affairs as they affect mechanical contractors in the plumbing, pipefitting, air conditioning, refrigeration, fire protection, and high-purity piping industries. Recurring features include reports on the activities of the Association and notices of pertinent seminars and meetings.

894 ■ *Snips Magazine*
Pub: BNP Media
Contact: Al Reser, President
URL(s): www.snipsmag.com/. **Ed:** Michael McConnell. **Released:** Monthly **Price:** Free.

TRADE SHOWS AND CONVENTIONS

895 ■ AHR Expo - International Air-Conditioning, Heating, Refrigerating Exposition
Air-Conditioning, Heating, and Refrigeration Institute
2111 Wilson Blvd., Ste. 500
Arlington, VA 22201
Ph: (703)524-8800
Fax: (703)562-1942
Co. E-mail: ahri@ahrinet.org
URL: http://www.ahrinet.org/
Contact: Stephen R. Yurek, President
E-mail: wgsutton@ari.org
URL(s): www.ahrexpo.com. **Price:** $20, Onsite; Pre-registered free. **Frequency:** Annual. **Audience:** Air conditioning, heating, refrigeration, and ventilation industry and related industries professionals; contractors; engineers, distributors, reps, OEMs. **Principal Exhibits:** Industrial, commercial, and residential heating, refrigeration, air conditioning, and ventilation equipment and components. **Telecommunication Services:** jmarshall@ashrae.org.

896 ■ North Carolina Association of Plumbing, Heating, and Cooling Contractors Annual Trade Show
North Carolina Association of Plumbing, Heating, and Cooling Contractors
5540 McNeely Dr., Ste. 202
Raleigh, NC 27612
Ph: (919)532-0522
Fax: (919)532-0523
URL: http://www.ncaphcc.org
Contact: Jim Pendergrass, Executive Director
E-mail: jim@phccnc.org
URL(s): www.phccnc.org. **Price:** $30, Members; $50, Non-members. **Frequency:** Annual. **Audience:** Plumbing, heating, and cooling contractors; architects; engineers; and general public. **Principal Exhibits:** Plumbing, heating, and cooling equipment, supplies, and services.

897 ■ Sheet Metal and Air-Conditioning Contractors National Association Convention/ Exhibition Forum
Sheet Metal and Air Conditioning Contractors' National Association (SMACNA)
4201 Lafayette Center Dr.
Chantilly, VA 20151-1209
Ph: (703)803-2980
Fax: (703)803-3732
Co. E-mail: info@smacna.org
URL: http://www.smacna.org
Contact: Vincent R. Sandusky, Chief Executive Officer
E-mail: vsandusky@smacna.org
URL(s): www.smacna.org. **Frequency:** Annual. **Audience:** Owners of sheet metal and air-conditioning contracting firms. **Principal Exhibits:** Limited to table tops only. **Telecommunication Services:** info@smacna.org.

898 ■ Southeast Roofing and Sheet Metal Spectacular Trade Exposition
Florida Roofing, Sheet Metal, and Air Conditioning Contractors Association FRSA
4111, Metric Dr., Ste. 6
Winter Park, FL 32792
Ph: (407)671-3772
Fax: (407)679-0010
Co. E-mail: frsa@floridaroof.com
URL: http://www.floridaroof.com
URL(s): www.floridaroof.com. **Frequency:** Annual. **Audience:** Roofing, and sheet metal, contractors, architects, specifiers, and building officials. **Principal Exhibits:** Roofing and sheet metal supplies, products and services. **Telecommunication Services:** lisapate@floridaroof.com.

CONSULTANTS

899 ■ Ben Briskin Associates Inc.
5434 Claridge Ln.
West Bloomfield, MI 48322-3862
Ph: (248)851-2114
Contact: Ben Briskin, President
E-mail: bbriskin@hotmail.com
Scope: Consultants in the design and analysis of heating, air conditioning, ventilating and piping systems. Emphasis is on air conditioning design, energy use, and energy audit studies. Additional expertise in areas of research and development labs and paint spray booths. Industries served: Construction, pharmaceutical laboratories, research labs and government agencies. **Founded:** 1960.

900 ■ Calmac Manufacturing Corp.
3-00 Banta Pl.
Fair Lawn, NJ 07410
Ph: (201)797-1511
Fax: (201)797-1522
Co. E-mail: info@calmac.com
URL: http://www.calmac.com
Contact: Mark M. Mac Cracken, President
E-mail: mmaccracken@calmac.com
Scope: The company specializes in the product design and manufacture of Off-Peak Cooling (OPC) systems, which utilize Thermal Energy Storage (TES) to air condition buildings. Other solutions include clever designs of heating pads for hospitals. **Founded:** 1947. **Publications:** "Intelligent Building Series, Volume 1: Large Commercial Buildings," EPRI; "Energy Storage is the Answer to Looming Power Shortages, Frost and Sullivan"; "Thermal Energy Storage- Btu's in the Land of the kWh's," IEEE; "Market Evaluation for Energy Storage in the United States," KEMA; "The Future of the Electric Grid," MIT; "2020 Strategic Analysis of Energy Storage in California"; "Energy Storage Providing for a Low Carbon Future," ASHRAE Journal. **Telecommunication Services:** calmac@calmac.com.

901 ■ Environmental & Engineering Services Inc.
687 NW 5th St.
Corvallis, OR 97330
Ph: (541)754-1062
Fax: (541)753-3948
Co. E-mail: kelly.guenther@eesinet.com
URL: http://www.eesinet.com
Contact: Steve Barney, Principal
Scope: Provider of mechanical, electrical engineering and commissioning services, with a special emphasis in renovation and energy upgrades. Offers a wide range of HVAC, electrical and controls engineering services including feasibility assessments, master planning, budgeting, cost analysis, design, computer aided drafting, energy use modeling, facility management and construction management. **Founded:** 1979.

902 ■ Fanning, Fanning & Associates Inc.—FFA Inc.
2555 74th St.
Lubbock, TX 79423
Ph: (806)745-2533
Fax: (806)745-3596
Co. E-mail: nfanning@fanningfanning.com
URL: http://www.fanningfanning.com
Contact: William White, Manager
E-mail: bwhite@fanningfanning.com
Scope: Specializes in engineering services including mechanical, electrical, plumbing design and plant layout, HVAC, energy conservation and management, utilities, fire protection and alarms, central heating and cooling plants and communications for institutional, commercial and industrial buildings. Offers design services for drawings, specifications and bid documents, master planning, engineering reports, estimates, analysis, feasibility studies and construction phase services.

903 ■ GHT Ltd.
1010 N Glebe Rd., Ste. 200
Arlington, VA 22201-4749
Ph: (703)243-1200

Fax: (703)276-1376
Co. E-mail: ght@ghtltd.com
URL: http://www.ghtltd.com
Contact: Robert M. Menuet, Principal
E-mail: rmenuet@ghtltd.com
Scope: Provider of design services in mechanical engineering. Offers telecommunications and security engineering services. Provides life safety engineering services and utilities planning services. Provides estimates of life expectancy and replacement or upgrade costs for mechanical and electrical equipment and systems. **Founded:** 1965. **Publications:** "Critical spaces keep the pace of business humming," May, 2004; "To avoid staticlater, hire right telecom consultant," Oct, 2007. **Special Services:** LEED®.

904 ■ GPD P.C.
524 First Ave. S
Great Falls, MT 59401
Ph: (406)452-9558
Fax: (406)727-9720
Co. E-mail: gpd-info@gpdinc.com
URL: http://www.gpdinc.com
Contact: Dana Lund, Manager
E-mail: dlund@gpdinc.com
Scope: Mechanical and electrical engineers offering counsel on heating; ventilation; air conditioning; refrigeration; air pollution control; plumbing; construction management; site, design and build utilities; fire protection; temperature control; incineration; lighting; power distribution; communications; airports; energy conservation; and lifecycle costing.

905 ■ Greacen Consulting Engineers Inc.
919 Old Hwy. 8 NW, Ste. 200
Saint Paul, MN 55112
Ph: (651)633-1318
Fax: (651)633-1885
Contact: Ed Greacen, Principal
Scope: Specializes in plumbing, heating, ventilating, air conditioning and project management. Designs domestic water and water treatment systems, fire protection, fuel and gas piping, humidification and de-humidification systems, variable air volume (VAV), fan-powered VAV, and retrofit systems for Indoor Air Quality (IAQ). **Founded:** 1999.

906 ■ Lundquist, Killeen, Potvin and Bender Inc.—LKPB Engineers Inc.
1935 W County Road B2, Ste. 300
Saint Paul, MN 55113-2722
Ph: (651)633-1223
Fax: (651)633-1355
Co. E-mail: nbart@lkpb.com
URL: http://www.lkpb.com
Contact: Allen V. Theisen, Manager
Scope: Provider of services in heating, ventilation, plumbing, piping, refrigeration, air conditioning, fire protection, lighting design and fixture selection, communications, electrical power distribution, security, life safety system design, energy conservation analysis, design and implementation. **Founded:** 1969.

907 ■ Lawrence G. Spielvogel Inc.—L. G. Spielvogel Inc.
190 Presidential Blvd., Ste. 310
Bala Cynwyd, PA 19004-1151
Ph: (610)783-6350
Fax: (610)783-6349
Co. E-mail: spielvogel@comcast.net
URL: http://www.lspielvogel.com
Contact: Lawrence G. Spielvogel, President
E-mail: spielvogel@comcast.net
Scope: Technical consultant in energy management and mechanical and electrical engineering for buildings. Areas of activities include energy procurement, heating, ventilating, and air conditioning and plumbing, system design, energy studies, feasibility studies, reports, appraisals, trouble-shooting, heat recovery and computer applications. Serves consulting engineers, contractors, government agencies, architects and owners. Provides expert legal testimony in relevant cases. **Founded:** 1970.

908 ■ Stueven Engineering Consultants
140 W 3rd Ave.
Escondido, CA 92025
Ph: (760)735-8577

Fax: (760)735-8578
Co. E-mail: sb@stueven-engineering.com
URL: http://www.stueven-engineering.com
Contact: Harold J. Stueven, President
E-mail: hjs@stueven-engineering.com
Scope: Provider of services in professional engineering, planning, design, and construction support services for mechanical and plumbing systems. **Founded:** 1994.

909 ■ Robert G. Thomas Jr.
1417 Sadler Rd., Ste. 269
Fernandina Beach, FL 32034
Ph: (904)343-2365
Co. E-mail: rgt@rgthomas.com
URL: http://www.eifs.com
Contact: Robert G. Thomas, Manager
Scope: Provider of insulation, weatherproofing and a finished surface in a single integrated product. **Founded:** 1980. **Publications:** "EIFS Design Handbook"; "EIFS New Construction Inspection Guide"; "EIFS Existing Construction Inspection Maintenance and Repair Guide"; "EIFS Homeowners Guide".

FRANCHISES AND BUSINESS OPPORTUNITIES

910 ■ Aire Serv Heating and Air Conditioning
The Dwyer Group
1020 N University Parks Dr.
Waco, TX 76707
Free: 800-583-2662
Fax: (800)378-9480
Description: National heating, ventilating and air conditioning franchise organization, focused on the residential and light commercial service and replacement market. Franchisees typically professional, state-licensed HVAC contractors. **No. of Franchise Units:** 176. **No. of Company-Owned Units:** 101. **Founded:** 1992.. **Franchised:** 1992. **Equity Capital Needed:** $64,300-$183,900 capital required. **Franchise Fee:** $28,000. **Financial Assistance:** Yes. **Training:** training is provided throughout the year with 4 national conferences, each focused on a topic of concern to the HVAC contractor.

911 ■ One Hour Heating & Air
50 Central Ave., Ste. 920
Sarasota, FL 34236
Ph: (941)552-5100
Free: 800-574-1725
Fax: (941)552-5130
Description: HVAC replacement and services. **No. of Franchise Units:** 223. **No. of Company-Owned Units:** 48. **Founded:** 1999. **Franchised:** 2003. **Equity Capital Needed:** $42,015-$535,870. **Franchise Fee:** $25,000-$150,500. **Royalty Fee:** 5%. **Financial Assistance:** Limited in-house and third party financing available. **Training:** Provides 3 days training at headquarters, at model centers and training school, Internet training, onsite with ongoing support.

LIBRARIES

912 ■ International Union of Operating Engineers - Training Center - Local 68, 68A, 68B Library
14 Fairfield Pl.
West Caldwell, NJ 07006
Ph: (973)227-6426
URL: http://www.iuoe-68.org/index1.cfm
Contact: Thomas P. Giblin, Business Manager
Scope: Refrigeration, welding, heating, ventilation, air conditioning, labor, occupational health and safety. **Services:** Copying; SDI; Library open to the public by appointment. **Holdings:** 1000 books; 2000 VF materials; 15 operator's manuals; 40 equipment manuals; 95 AV programs. **Subscriptions:** 15 journals and other serials.

913 ■ Refrigeration Service Engineers Society Library
1911 Rohlwing Rd., Ste. A
Rolling Meadows, IL 60008-1397
Ph: (847)297-6464
Free: 800-297-5660
Fax: (847)297-5038
Co. E-mail: mlowry@rses.org
URL: http://www.rses.org
Contact: Renee Tomlinson, Director
Scope: Refrigeration, air conditioning, heating, heat pumps, HVAC controls, ventilation, indoor air quality,

electricity. **Services:** Copying; library open to members. **Founded:** 1933. **Holdings:** 500 books; 1000 bound periodical volumes; reports; manuscripts. **Subscriptions:** 35,000 journals and other serials.

RESEARCH CENTERS

914 ■ American Society of Heating, Refrigerating and Air-Conditioning Engineers Research Program (ASHRAE)
1791 Tullie Cir. NE
Atlanta, GA 30329
Ph: (404)636-8400

Free: 800-527-4723
Fax: (404)321-5478
Co. E-mail: ashrae@ashrae.org
URL: http://www.ashrae.org
Contact: Jeff Littleton, Executive Vice President
Founded: 1894. **Publications:** *ASHRAE Handbook* (Annual); *ASHRAE Transactions* (Semiannual); *HVAC&R RESEARCH* (Bimonthly). **Awards:** Grants-in-aid (Annual), to 20 graduate students.

915 ■ University of California - California Institute for Energy and Environment (CIEE)
2087 Addison St., 2nd Fl.

Berkeley, CA 94704-1103
Ph: (510)643-1440
Fax: (510)643-9324
Co. E-mail: blumstei@berkeley.edu
URL: http://uc-ciee.org
Contact: Dr. Carl Blumstein, Director

Founded: 1989. **Publications:** *CIEE Technical reports*. **Educational Activities:** Project workshops (Annual), on global climate change, demand response, and transmission research. **Telecommunication Services:** ciee@uc-ciee.org.

ASSOCIATIONS AND OTHER ORGANIZATIONS

916 ■ Allergy/Asthma Information Association (AAIA)—Association d'information sur l'allergie et l'asthme
295 The West Mall, Ste. 118
Toronto, ON, Canada M9C 4Z4
Ph: (416)621-4571
Free: 800-611-7011
Fax: (416)621-5034
Co. E-mail: admin@aaia.ca
URL: http://www.aaia.ca
Contact: Mary Allen, Chief Executive Officer
Description: Seeks to develop societal awareness of the seriousness of allergic disease, including asthma, and to enable allergic individuals, their families, and caregivers to increase control over allergy symptoms. Provides leadership in information, education, and advocacy through partnership with healthcare professionals, businesses, industry, and government. Maintains speakers' bureau. **Founded:** 1964. **Subscriptions:** books clippings periodicals. **Publications:** *Awareness and Info Allergie* (Quarterly). **Awards:** Distinguished Volunteer Service Award (Annual); Riva Cohen Award (Annual); Distinguished Volunteer Service Award; Riva Cohen Award.

917 ■ *Awareness and Info Allergie*
295 The West Mall, Ste. 118
Toronto, ON, Canada M9C 4Z4
Ph: (416)621-4571
Free: 800-611-7011
Fax: (416)621-5034
Co. E-mail: admin@aaia.ca
URL: http://www.aaia.ca
Contact: Mary Allen, Chief Executive Officer
Released: Quarterly

REFERENCE WORKS

918 ■ *"Chicago Public School District Builds Green"* in Contractor (Vol. 56, October 2009, No. 10, pp. 5)
Pub: Penton Media, Inc.
Ed: Candace Roulo. **Description:** Chicago Public Schools district has already built six U.S. Green Building Council LEED certified schools and one addition in five years and will continue to build new green buildings. The district has an Environmental Action Plan that strives to reduce energy usage, improve indoor air quality, and reduce contribution to climate change.

919 ■ *"San Diego Museum Receives LEED Certification"* in Contractor (Vol. 57, January 2010, No. 1, pp. 14)
Pub: Penton Media, Inc.
Description: San Diego Natural History Museum received an LEED certification for existing buildings. The certification process began when they committed to displaying the Dead Sea Scrolls in 2007 and they had to upgrade their buildings' air quality and to

control for air moisture, temperature, and volume. They reduced their energy consumption by upwards of 20 percent.

TRADE PERIODICALS

920 ■ *The Air Pollution Consultant*
Pub: Aspen Publishers, Inc.
Contact: Robert Becker, President
URL(s): www.aspenpublishers.com/PDF/SS10586628.pdf. **Released:** 7/yr. **Price:** $775, Individuals.

921 ■ *Air Pollution Monitoring and Sampling Newsletter*
Pub: McIlvaine Co.
Ed: Christine Hennig, Editor, chennig@mail.mcilvaine.com. **Released:** Monthly. **Price:** $270, U.S.; $300. **Description:** Provides current information on air pollution monitoring and sampling equipment and service. Includes 'product comparisons, trends, conference reports, coverage of new products, new orders, a calendar of events, and informed analysis.'.

VIDEOCASSETTES/AUDIOCASSETTES

922 ■ *Air Pollution: Indoor*
Films for the Humanities & Sciences
132 West 31st Street
New York, NY 10001
Ph: (609)671-1000
Free: 800-257-5126
Fax: (609)671-0266
Co. E-mail: custserv@films.com
URL: http://www.films.com
Released: 1989. **Description:** This tape explores indoor air pollution, particularly pollutants introduced in homes from painting, thermal insulation and other energy saving improvements, and water-proofing devices. **Availability:** VHS; 3/4 U.

CONSULTANTS

923 ■ Pathogen Control Associates Inc.
270 Scientific Dr., Ste. 3
Norcross, GA 30092
Ph: (770)446-0540
Free: 866-728-4266
Fax: (770)446-0610
URL: http://www.pathcon.com
Contact: Brian G. Shelton, President
E-mail: bshelton@pathcon.com
Scope: Applied microbiology problems: microbiological/air quality issues, sick building syndrome, Legionella and air quality testing, prevention and control of food-related pathogens diseases, hazard analysis, prevention strategies, medical, epidemiological, public health evaluations, seminars, courses, laboratory evaluations and expert witness testimony. Industries served: buildings indoor air quality, heating/air conditioning, poultry industry and government agencies. **Founded:** 1986. **Publications:** "Microbes

in the Indoor Environment"; "Legionellosis: Is there a National Preventing Strategy". **Seminars:** Micro Organisms in Indoor Air: Health Complaints Associated With Environmental and Occupational Settings; Environmental Hazards in HealthCare Settings; Moisture and Engineering Design; Mold Remediation; Sampling Strategy; Airborne Bacteria; Legionella.

FRANCHISES AND BUSINESS OPPORTUNITIES

924 ■ Coit Cleaning and Restoration Services
897 Hinckley Rd.
Burlingame, CA 94010
Ph: (800)243-8797
Fax: (650)692-8397
Co. E-mail: franchise@coit.com
URL: http://www.coit.com
Description: Coit is a multi-service cleaning company, offering drapery cleaning, carpet cleaning, upholstery cleaning, area rug cleaning, air duct cleaning and more. **No. of Franchise Units:** 42. **No. of Company-Owned Units:** 8. **Founded:** 1950.. **Franchised:** 1962. **Equity Capital Needed:** $50,000-$145,000. **Franchise Fee:** $24,000-$40,000. **Financial Assistance:** Yes. **Training:** Includes 10 days in corporate office.

925 ■ Ductmedic
Ductmedic International, Inc.
2939 Cornhusker Hwy., Ste. A
Lincoln, NE 68504
Ph: (402)435-3828
Free: 800-700-9877
Fax: (402)467-2561
Description: Air duct cleaning/indoor air quality. **No. of Franchise Units:** 2. **No. of Company-Owned Units:** 1. **Founded:** 1994.. **Franchised:** 2004. **Equity Capital Needed:** $50,000-$90,000; $10,000-$20,000 area fee. **Franchise Fee:** $9,500. **Financial Assistance:** Yes. **Training:** Yes.

LIBRARIES

926 ■ Cadwalader, Wickersham & Taft Library
700 6th St., N.W.
Washington, DC 20001
Ph: (202)862-2200
Fax: (202)862-2400
Co. E-mail: jane.platt-brown@cwt.com
URL: http://www.cadwalader.com
Contact: Jane Platt-Brown, Director, Library Services
Scope: Law - antitrust, corporate, securities, taxation, business fraud. **Services:** Interlibrary loan; library open to the public by appointment (with restrictions). **Holdings:** 15,000 volumes; microforms; CD-ROM. **Telecommunication Services:** cwtdclibrary@cwt.com.

927 ■ California Environmental Protection Agency Library
1001 I St.
Sacramento, CA 95814

Ph: (916)327-0635
Fax: (916)327-4494
Co. E-mail: calepalibrary@arb.ca.gov
URL: http://www.calepa.ca.gov/Library/
Contact: Gerhard Achtelik, Manager
Scope: The environment, air and water pollution, climate change, solid hazardous waste management, pesticide application. **Services:** Interlibrary loan; copying; Library open to the public. **Founded:** 1972. **Holdings:** 30,000 books, reports, documents, journals, and other reference materials. **Subscriptions:** 310 journals and other serials; 13 newspapers. **Telecommunication Services:** gchen@dtsc.ca.gov.

928 ■ URS Library
Crown Corporate Center
2870 Gateway Oaks Dr., Ste. 150
Sacramento, CA 95833-4308
Ph: (916)679-2000
Fax: (916)679-2900
URL: http://www.urscorp.com
Scope: Environment, air quality, hazardous waste. **Services:** Interlibrary loan; Library not open to the public. **Founded:** 1986. **Holdings:** 5000 books;

technical and government reports; government agency rules and regulations. **Subscriptions:** 75 journals and other serials.

929 ■ Washington University - Center for Air Pollution Impact and Trend Analysis Library
Campus Box 1124
St. Louis, MO 63130
Ph: (314)935-6099
Fax: (314)935-6145
Co. E-mail: rhusar@me.wustl.edu
URL: http://capita.wustl.edu/capita/people/sfalke/
SFalkeCV.htm
Contact: Rudolf B. Husar, Director
Scope: Air pollution. **Holdings:** 1000 reports. **Subscriptions:** 10 journals and other serials; 2 newspapers.

RESEARCH CENTERS

930 ■ Northeastern University - Center for Nano and Microcontamination Control (CMC)
Egan Research Ctr.
360 Huntington Ave.
Boston, MA 02115-5000

Ph: (617)373-6012
Fax: (617)373-3266
Co. E-mail: busnaina@coe.neu.edu
URL: http://www.cmc.neu.edu
Contact: Prof. Ahmed A. Busnaina, Director

Services: Consulting. **Founded:** 1986. **Publications:** CMC Newsletter; Research conference report (Biennial). **Educational Activities:** Technical conference (Annual); CMC Short courses (Annual); Industrial Advisory Board Meeting (Biennial).

931 ■ University of California, Davis - Air Quality Group
Crocker Nuclear Laboratory
1 Shields Ave.
Davis, CA 95616
Ph: (530)752-1460
Fax: (530)752-0952
Co. E-mail: flocchini@crocker.ucdavis.edu
URL: http://crocker.ucdavis.edu/research_aqg.php
Contact: Robert G. Flocchini, Director

ASSOCIATIONS AND OTHER ORGANIZATIONS

932 ■ American Ambulance Association
8201 Greensboro Dr., Ste. 300
Mc Lean, VA 22102
Ph: (703)610-9018
Free: 800-523-4447
Fax: (703)610-0210
Co. E-mail: stephenw@emsa.net
URL: http://www.the-aaa.org
Contact: Stephen Williamson, President
Description: Represents private suppliers of ambulance service. Aims to: aid in developing private enterprise pre-hospital emergency medical treatment and medical transportation services as a viable cost-effective alternative to publicly-operated services; promote improved patient care; develop efficient medical transportation at a reasonable cost; improve personnel and equipment standards; work with organizations offering medical transportation; encourage high standards of ethics and conduct. Acts as an information clearinghouse; informs members of developments in the industry. Offers advice on federal statutes and regulations related to the medical transportation industry, such as insurance and antitrust regulations. Holds four regional seminars per year on topics such as training requirements, insurance systems, Medicare reimbursement, and local, state, and federal legislation and regulations. Conducts quarterly emergency medical services management seminar. **Publications:** *Ambulance Industry Journal* (Quarterly); *American Ambulance Association*; *Medicare Reference* (Annual).

TRADE PERIODICALS

933 ■ *Emergency Medicine Alert / Practical Summary and Acute Care Report*
Pub: American Health Consultants
Contact: Donald R. Johnson, Publisher
Ed: Richard A. Harrigan, M.D., Editor. **Released:** Monthly. **Price:** $299, U.S. **Description:** Provides information on developments and improvements in emergency medicine.

VIDEOCASSETTES/ AUDIOCASSETTES

934 ■ *Advanced Skills for the EMT*
Emergency Training
Emory University
Dobbs University Center - 5th Floor
1440 Clifton Rd., N.E
Fairlawn, OH 44334
Ph: (404)727-3853
Fax: (404)727-5667
Released: 1988. **Price:** $620.00. **Description:** A video series desinged to supplement the teachings of an EMT Intermediate course. **Availability:** VHS.

935 ■ *AIDS, Hepatitis and the Emergency Responder*
Emergency Film Group
Detrick Lawrence Corp.
Edgartown, MA 02539
Ph: (508)627-8844
Free: 800-842-0999
Fax: (508)627-8863
Co. E-mail: info@efilmgroup.com
URL: http://www.efilmgroup.com
Released: 1988. **Price:** $250.00. **Description:** The tape shows how an emergency worker can better help victims and reduce his own risk of getting a disease. **Availability:** VHS; 3/4 U; Special order formats.

936 ■ *Anonymous Hero*
Pyramid Media
PO Box 1048/WEB
Santa Monica, CA 90406
Ph: (310)398-6149
Free: 800-421-2304
Fax: (310)398-7869
Co. E-mail: info@pyramedia.com
URL: http://www.pyramidmedia.com
Released: 1989. **Price:** $195.00. **Description:** This program teaches emergency medical dispatchers about anxious callers, medical interrogation, and telephone treatment sequences for common emergencies. **Availability:** VHS; 3/4 U.

COMPUTERIZED DATABASES

937 ■ *State Health Care Regulatory Developments™*
1801 S Bell St.
Arlington, VA 22202
Free: 800-372-1033
Co. E-mail: customercare@bna.com
URL: http://www.bna.com
Availability: Online: Bloomberg LP-Bloomberg BNA; Thomson Reuters - Westlaw. **Type:** Full-text.

RESEARCH CENTERS

938 ■ University of California, San Francisco - San Francisco Injury Center (SFIC)
San Francisco General Hospital
Department of Surgery, Ward 3A, Box 0807
1001 Potrero Ave.
San Francisco, CA 94110
Ph: (415)206-4623
Fax: (415)206-5484
Co. E-mail: pknudson@sfghsurg.ucsf.edu
URL: http://sfic.surgery.ucsf.edu
Contact: Prof. M. Margaret Knudson, Director
Founded: 1989. **Telecommunication Services:** marks@sfghsurg.ucsf.edu.

ASSOCIATIONS AND OTHER ORGANIZATIONS

939 ■ **American Amusement Machine Association (AAMA)**
450 E Higgins Rd., Ste. 201
Elk Grove Village, IL 60007
Ph: (847)290-9088
Co. E-mail: information@coin-op.org
URL: http://www.coin-op.org
Contact: John Schultz, President

Description: Manufacturers and distributors of coin machines; parts suppliers and others interested in promoting and protecting the amusement machine industry. Seeks solutions to the problem of copyright infringement by foreign manufacturers, and legislative and regulatory problems facing the industry and manufacturers. Works to improve the image of the coin-operated amusement industry. Presents views to governmental decision-makers. Operates American Amusement Machine Charitable Foundation. **Founded:** 1981. **Educational Activities:** Amusement Showcase International (Annual).

REFERENCE WORKS

940 ■ *"Boots Treat Street Rolls Out Trolley Dash App on Androis and iPhone OS" in Entertainment Close-Up (October 24, 2011)*
Pub: Close-Up Media

Description: Shoppers using Boots Treat Street can now download the Trolley Dash app game, available from the Apple Store and the Android Market, and enjoy the pastel colored street featuring favorite retailers such as eBay, New Look and Play.com collecting prizes while avoiding hazards.

941 ■ *"Boxing, Tech Giants Team to Help Teens" in Hispanic Business (January-February 2009, pp. 44)*
Pub: Hispanic Business

Ed: Daniel Soussa. **Description:** Microsoft and Oscar de la Hoya are providing teens a head start for careers in the sciences by offering a competition in the categories of photography, short films or Web-based games.

942 ■ *"Cineplex Sees Past the Big Picture" in Globe & Mail (February 8, 2007, pp. B9)*
Pub: CTVglobemedia Publishing Inc.

Ed: Shirley Won. **Description:** Cineplex Entertainment LP reported $4.6 million profit in the final quarter of 2006. The movie chain is introducing video-game tournaments and live rock concerts to improve sales.

943 ■ *"Game Changer" in Canadian Business (Vol. 83, June 15, 2010, No. 10, pp. 52)*
Pub: Rogers Media Ltd.

Ed: Jordan Timm. **Description:** Ubisoft chose Ontario to be the site for its new development studio and it has appointed Jade Raymond as its managing director. Raymond was born in Montreal in 1975 and

studied computer science at McGill. Raymond is said to possess the understanding of the game industry's technical, art, and business components.

944 ■ *The Game Makers*
Pub: Harvard Business School Press

Ed: Philip E. Orbanes. **Released:** November 2003. **Price:** $29.95. **Description:** Profile of game expert and president of a specialty game company, author of books about games, Monopoly championship judge, senior vice president of research and development at Parker Brothers, and inventor of board and card games in highlighted.

945 ■ *"Games Gone Wild: City's Newest Public Company Aims for the Sky" in Business Courier (Vol. 27, September 24, 2010, No. 21, pp. 1)*
Pub: Business Courier

Ed: Dan Monk. **Description:** Video game company Zoo Entertainment Inc., which is based in Norwood near Cincinnati, Ohio aims to build a strong company and to position itself for future growth. The company reported $27.6 million in revenue for the first half of 2010 and analysts project $100 million in sales for 2011.

946 ■ *"Great Canadian's President Folds His Cards" in Globe & Mail (February 21, 2006, pp. B4)*
Pub: CTVglobemedia Publishing Inc.

Ed: Peter Kennedy. **Description:** The reasons behind the resignation of Anthony Martin as president of Great Canadian Gaming Corp. are presented.

947 ■ *How to Get Rich*
Pub: Ebury Press

Ed: Felix Dennis. **Released:** 2008. **Price:** $25.95. **Description:** Publisher of Maxim, The Week, and Stuff magazines, discusses the mistakes he made running his companies. He didn't understand that people who buy computer gaming magazines wanted a free game with each copy, as one of his rivals was offering. And he laments not diversifying into television and exploiting the Internet.

948 ■ *"Kiosk Outfit ecoATM Now Recycling Video Games" in San Diego Union-Tribune (October 7, 2010)*
Pub: San Diego Union-Tribune

Ed: Mike Freeman. **Description:** ecoATM makes automated kiosks to buy back cell phones will now include video games as part of their recycling business.

949 ■ *"Lighter Than Air" in Game Developer (Vol. 18, November 1, 2011, No. 10, pp. 38)*
Pub: Think Services

Ed: Andy Firth. **Description:** Floating point performance tips and tricks are outlined. Floating point allows freedom of representation when implementing algorithms and is both intuitive to set up and simple to work with; hardware is also improved so that it is faster to use floating point math as opposed to integer in many environments.

950 ■ *"Our Gadget of the Week: Balancing Act" in Barron's (Vol. 88, March 31, 2008, No. 13, pp. 40)*
Pub: Dow Jones & Company, Inc.

Ed: Naureen S. Malik. **Description:** Wii Fit gives users the experience of a virtual personal trainer and workouts that become progressively harder. The device turns the typical fitness regimes into fun exercises and users can choose workouts in four categories including yoga, balance, strength-training and, low impact aerobics.

951 ■ *"Public Media Works to Launch DVD Kiosk Operations in Toronto, Canada" in Internet Wire (November 15, 2010)*
Pub: Comtex

Description: Public Media Works Inc. along with its EntertainmentXpress Inc., have partnered with Spot Venture Distribution Inc. and Signifi Solutions Inc., both headquartered in Toronto, Canada, to manage and expand the Spot DVD movie and game kiosk business in greater Toronto and other Canadian locations.

952 ■ *The Race for a New Game Machine: Creating the Chips Inside the Xbox 360 and the PlayStation 3*
Pub: Citadel Press
Contact: Steven Zacharius, President
E-mail: szacharius@kensingtonbooks.com

Ed: David Shippy, Mickie Phipps. **Released:** 2009. **Price:** $21.95. **Description:** The story of Microsoft and Sony's race to deliver the goods for the Xbox 360 and Playstation 3 is explored.

953 ■ *"Silverdome Bidders Bring New Proposals" in Crain's Detroit Business (Vol. 24, March 17, 2008, No. 11, pp. 23)*
Pub: Crain Communications, Inc.

Ed: Daniel Duggan. **Description:** Discusses the seven plans which have been proposed as part of the third round of bidding for the Pontiac Silverdome; proposals range from Global Baseball Inc., a baseball league that would pit a team from every country against one another, to an Indian casino, a musical 'hall of fame', a convention center, a horse track, a hotel and an indoor water park.

954 ■ *"Tony Hawk Carves a New Niche" in Entrepreneur (Vol. 37, October 2009, No. 10, pp. 26)*
Pub: Entrepreneur Media, Inc.

Ed: Gary Cohn. **Description:** Professional skateboarder Tony Hawk discusses the growth of Birdhouse, the skateboard company he founded. He is excited about the release of Tony Hawk Ride, a videogame with a skateboard controller.

955 ■ *Vending Times--Buyers Guide and Directory Issue*
Pub: Vending Times Inc.
Contact: Alicia Lavay-Kertes, President
E-mail: alicia@vendingtimes.net

URL(s): www.vendingtimes.com. **Released:** Annual; Latest edition 2012. **Price:** $40, Individuals includes shipping and handling. **Publication includes:** Lists of manufacturers and suppliers of equipment and products used by vending machine industry operators, including product venders, juke boxes, pinball and other games; industry trade associations. **Entries include:** Company name, address, phone, names of key personnel, description of products. **Database includes:** Specifications of major vending machines. **Arrangement:** Classified by product or service.

956 ■ *"Work for Play: Careers in Video Game Development" in Occupational Outlook Quarterly (Vol. 55, Fall 2011, No. 3, pp. 2)*
Pub: U.S. Bureau of Labor Statistics
Ed: Drew Liming, Dennis Vilorio. **Description:** Game developers make a living creating the games the public enjoys playing. The video gaming industry reported sales over $10 billion in 2009 and employed 32,000 people in 34 states. Career options in video game development are featured.

TRADE PERIODICALS

957 ■ *RePlay Magazine*
Pub: RePlay Magazine
URL(s): www.replaymag.com/. **Ed:** Steve White. **Released:** Monthly **Price:** $65, Individuals; $90, Canada and Mexico; $230, Other countries airmail; $120, Two years; $170, Canada and Mexico 2 years; $420, Other countries 2 years.

TRADE SHOWS AND CONVENTIONS

958 ■ Amusement and Music Operators Association Convention
Amusement and Music Operators Association
600 Spring Hill Ring Rd., Ste. 111
West Dundee, IL 60118
Ph: (847)428-7699
Free: 800-937-2662
Fax: (847)428-7719
Co. E-mail: amoa@amoa.com
URL: http://www.amoa.com
Contact: Jack Kelleher, Executive Vice President
E-mail: jackamoa@aol.com
URL(s): www.amusementexpo.org. **Frequency:** Annual. **Audience:** Trade professionals. **Principal Ex-**

hibits: Coin-operated arcade, video and gaming machines, games, jukeboxes, stuffed toys, records, and jewelry. **Telecommunication Services:** info@amusementexpo.org.

959 ■ FUN Expo
Reed Exhibitions North American Headquarters
383 Main Ave.
Norwalk, CT 06851
Ph: (203)840-4800
Fax: (203)840-5805
Co. E-mail: inquiry@reedexpo.com
URL: http://www.reedexpo.com
URL(s): www.funexpo.com. **Price:** $20, Pre-registered, members; $40, Pre-registered, non-members; $65, Onsite registered, members; $90, Onsite registered, non-members. **Frequency:** Annual. **Principal Exhibits:** Amusement and recreation products for family and location based entertainment centers, small amusement parks and family oriented businesses such as bowling centers, skating rinks, sports parks, miniature golf courses, golf driving ranges, family restaurants, resorts and other entertainment/recreation businesses.

960 ■ Pinball Expo
Pinball Expo / Flip Out Pinball Tournament
c/o Robert Berk
1085 Eagle Trace Rd.
Warren, OH 44484
Ph: (330)369-1192
Free: 800-323-3547
Fax: (330)369-1087
Co. E-mail: brkpinball@aol.com
URL: http://www.pinballexpo.net
Contact: Robert Berk, Chairman of the Board
URL(s): www.pinballexpo.net. **Price:** $145, Pre-registered without banquet; $160, Pre-registered with banquet; $155, Onsite without banquet; $170, Onsite with banquet. **Frequency:** Annual. **Audience:** Trade personnel, collectors, distributors and suppliers of related products. **Principal Exhibits:** Pinball machines and related supplies. **Dates and Locations:** Ramada Inn.

CONSULTANTS

961 ■ Erin Services Inc.
111 Travelers Way
Saint Simons Island, GA 31522-5632
Ph: (912)638-9916
Fax: (912)638-5701
Co. E-mail: dennisd@ns.technonet.com
Contact: Dennis J. Donnelly, III, President
E-mail: dennis179@yahoo.com

Scope: Offers assistance in technical proposal production, marketing, and research. Industries served: Food service, janitorial, landscaping, hospitality and lodging, parks, and recreational. **Founded:** 1990.

FRANCHISES AND BUSINESS OPPORTUNITIES

962 ■ Monkey Joe's Party And Play
Raving Brands
1718 Peachtree St. NW, Ste. 1070
Atlanta, GA 30309
Ph: (404)351-3500
URL: http://www.monkeyjoes.com

Description: Interactive indoor party center filled with an array of giant air-filled play structures, jumps, slides, thrilling obstacle courses, development games and fun party rooms. For the parents, there's comfortable seating, flatscreen TVs and high-speed internet. **No. of Franchise Units:** 56. **No. of Company-Owned Units:** 1. **Founded:** 2004. **Franchised:** 2005. **Equity Capital Needed:** $500,000 net worth; $150,000 liquid. **Franchise Fee:** $25,000. **Training:** Raving Brands University classroom and onsite training provided. From register operation to food preparation, from hiring staff to accounting procedures, you'll improve your management skills, setup back office and develop a sales and marketing plan.

START-UP INFORMATION

963 ■ *"Noah's Park: $150M Project Eyed in Ky."* in *Business Courier (Vol. 27, November 19, 2010, No. 29, pp. 1)*
Pub: Business Courier

Ed: Lucy May. **Description:** Grant County, Kentucky has been abuzz with speculation about a $150M Noah's Ark-themed project being planned for Williamstown, Kentucky. The theme park's planned location is halfway between Cincinnati, Ohio and Louisville, Kentucky and about 40 minutes south of the Answers in Genesis Creation Museum in Petersburg.

ASSOCIATIONS AND OTHER ORGANIZATIONS

964 ■ **Amusement Industry Manufacturers and Suppliers International (AIMS)—AIMS International**
3026 S Orange
Santa Ana, CA 92707
Ph: (714)425-5747
Fax: (714)276-9666
Co. E-mail: info@aimsintl.org
URL: http://www.aimsintl.org
Contact: Mike Gutknecht, President
Description: Represents manufacturers and suppliers of amusement riding devices and equipment used by amusement parks, carnivals, and traveling amusement companies. Exchanges information on safety, maintenance, state laws, transportation, and credit. Works to develop safety programs and codes at the federal and state levels; carries out public relations activities; and cooperates with the ASTM to develop voluntary standards for amusement rides and devices. **Founded:** 1994. **Publications:** *Full List of AIMS Members.* **Educational Activities:** Safety Seminar (Annual); Safety Seminar (Annual). **Awards:** Safety Awards (Annual).

965 ■ **Canadian Association of Fairs and Exhibitions (CAFE)—Association Canadienne des Foires et Expositions**
Box 13161
Ottawa, ON, Canada K2K 1X4
Ph: (613)233-0012
Free: 800-663-1714
Fax: (613)233-1154
Co. E-mail: info@canadian-fairs.ca
URL: http://www.canadian-fairs.ca
Contact: Mavis Hanna, Executive Director
Description: Exhibition and fair operators. Seeks to advance the exhibition industry. Represents members' interests before trade organizations, government agencies, and the public. **Founded:** 1924.

966 ■ **International Association of Amusement Parks and Attractions (IAAPA)**
1448 Duke St.
Alexandria, VA 22314
Ph: (703)836-4800

Fax: (703)836-6742
Co. E-mail: pressoffice@iaapa.org
URL: http://www.iaapa.org
Contact: Rob Norris, President
E-mail: rob@seabreeze.com
Description: Operators of amusement parks, theme parks, tourist attractions, water parks, zoos, aquariums, museums, miniature golf courses and family entertainment centers; manufacturers and suppliers of amusement equipment and services. Conducts research programs; compiles statistics; hosts annual convention and trade show; publishes periodicals. **Scope:** amusement industry. **Founded:** 1918. **Publications:** *Funworld* (Monthly); *Funworld; Funworld* (11/year); *International Association of Amusement Parks and Attractions International Directory and Buyers' Guide; International Directory and Buyer's Guide* (Annual); *Year in Review* (Annual); *International Association of Amusement Parks and Attractions--International Directory and Buyer's Guide; International Directory and Buyer's Guide: D & G* (Annual). **Educational Activities:** Asian Attractions Expo (Annual); Euro Attractions Show (Annual); Asian Attractions Expo (Annual); Association of Amusement Parks Convention and Trade Show; Euro Attractions Show (Annual); International Association of Amusement Parks and Attractions Annual Convention and Trade Show (Annual). **Awards:** Service Awards (Annual); Big-E Awards (Annual); Brass Ring Award (Annual); Hall of Fame Award (Annual); Spirit of Excellence Award (Annual). **Telecommunication Services:** ccleary@iaapa.org; convention@iaapa.org.

967 ■ **Outdoor Amusement Business Association (OABA)**
1035 S Semoran Blvd., Ste. 1045A
Winter Park, FL 32792
Ph: (407)681-9444
Free: 800-517-OABA
Fax: (407)681-9445
Co. E-mail: oaba@oaba.org
URL: http://www.oaba.org
Contact: Robert W. Johnson, President
Description: Represents executives and employees of carnivals and fairs; ride owners; independent food and games concessionaires; manufacturers and suppliers of equipment. Promotes and lobbies on behalf of the interests of the outdoor amusement industry; provides a center for dissemination of information. **Founded:** 1965. **Publications:** *Midway Marquee* (Annual).

968 ■ **World Waterpark Association (WWA)**
8826 Santa Fe Dr., Ste. 310
Overland Park, KS 66212
Ph: (913)599-0300
Fax: (913)599-0520
Co. E-mail: wwamemberinfo@waterparks.org
URL: http://www.waterparks.org
Contact: Rick Root, President
E-mail: rroot@waterparks.org
Description: Water leisure amusement facilities; suppliers of products and services. Provides a forum for the discussion of information related to the water amusement park industry. Furthers safety and profitability in the water leisure industry through educa-

tional conferences and publications. Maintains placement service; compiles statistics. **Founded:** 1980. **Publications:** *Considerations for Operating Safety; Splash & Spray* (9/year); *World Waterpark* (10/year); *World Waterpark Association--Buyer's Guide.* **Educational Activities:** World Waterpark Association Symposium and Tradeshow (Annual). **Awards:** SWIM Awards (Annual); WWA Executive Board Award (Annual); WWA Media Award (Annual). **Telecommunication Services:** memberservices@waterparks.org.

REFERENCE WORKS

969 ■ *"Cedar Fair to Solicit Bids for Geauga Lake"* in *Crain's Cleveland Business (Vol. 28, October 8, 2007, No. 40, pp. 1)*
Pub: Crain Communications, Inc.

Ed: Stan Bullard. **Description:** Cedar Fair Entertainment Co. plans to seek sealed bids for the redevelopment of nearly 540 acres of their amusement park site in southwest Geauga County and northwest Portage County.

970 ■ *"Legoland Florida Theme Park Construction to Start in May"* in *Orlando Business Journal (Vol. 26, January 29, 2010, No. 35, pp. 1)*
Pub: American City Business Journals

Ed: Richard Bilbao. **Description:** Merlin Entertainments Group purchased the closed Cypress Garden theme park in Winter Haven, Florida for $22.3 million and plans to spend a reported $100 million or more to begin transforming it into the world's largest Legoland. Winter Haven businesses are expecting a windfall from the theme park's constructions workers.

971 ■ *"Legoland Plans Could Tumble After State's Modesa Denial"* in *Business Journal-Serving Metropolitan Kansas City (November 16, 2007)*
Pub: American City Business Journals, Inc.

Ed: Jim Davis. **Description:** RED Development LLC's officials are not giving up after the Missouri Department of Economic Development said RED could not exploit the Missouri Downtown and Rural Economic Stimulus Act (Modesa) for the Legoland theme park development in Lee's Summit. Legoland's proposed site southeast of Interstate 470 and U.S. Highway 50 does not fit the Modesa because it is outside Lee's Summit.

972 ■ *Promising Practices: Progress Toward the Goals (1998): Lessons from the States*
Pub: DIANE Publishing Co.

Ed: Emily Wurtz. **Released:** 1999. **Price:** $15.00.

973 ■ *"Schlitterbahn Broadens"* in *Austin Business JournalInc. (Vol. 28, September 19, 2008, No. 27, pp. A1)*
Pub: American City Business Journals

Ed: Kate Harrington. **Description:** Schlitterbahn is planning to introduce a Christmas-themed event this winter 2008 in its water amusement park that will keep it open from November to January. The company is also constructing its first out-of-Texas park, which is a $170 million, 376-acre project in Kansas City, Missouri. Other details about Schlitterbahn's expansion are discussed.

974 ■ *"Silverdome Bidders Bring New Proposals" in Crain's Detroit Business (Vol. 24, March 17, 2008, No. 11, pp. 23)*
Pub: Crain Communications, Inc.
Ed: Daniel Duggan. **Description:** Discusses the seven plans which have been proposed as part of the third round of bidding for the Pontiac Silverdome; proposals range from Global Baseball Inc., a baseball league that would pit a team from every country against one another, to an Indian casino, a musical 'hall of fame', a convention center, a horse track, a hotel and an indoor water park.

975 ■ *"Theme Park Sale has Vendor Upside" in Tampa Bay Business Journal (Vol. 29, October 23, 2009, No. 44, pp. 1)*
Pub: American City Business Journals
Ed: Margie Manning. **Description:** Private equity firm The Blackstone Group has concluded its $2.7 billion purchase of Busch Entertainment Corporation. Aside from enhanced business opportunities in Florida's Tampa Bay area, new attractions might be built in the Busch Gardens and Adventure Island properties that will be acquired by Blackstone. Blackstone's other plans are also discussed.

976 ■ *"Up In the Air" in The Business Journal-Serving Greater Tampa Bay (Vol. 28, July 18, 2008, No. 30, pp. 1)*
Pub: American City Business Journals, Inc.
Ed: Margie Manning. **Description:** Views and information on Busch Gardens and its future, are presented. The park's 3,769 employees worry for their future, after tourism industry experts have expressed concerns on possible tax cuts and other cost reductions. The future of the park, which ranks number 19 as the most visited park in the world, is expected to have a major impact on the tourism industry.

977 ■ *"Water Park, Convention Center Plan Matures" in Austin Business JournalInc. (Vol. 28, July 18, 2008, No. 18, pp. 1)*
Pub: American City Business Journals
Ed: Kate Harrington. **Description:** Plans for the proposed water park in Cedar Park in Austin, Texas is moving forward as it grows in size from 40 to 90 acres, with first phase of construction to begin in early 2009.

STATISTICAL SOURCES

978 ■ *The Amusement and Theme Parks Industry Market*
Pub: Rector Press, Ltd.
Contact: Lewis Skolnick, President
Released: 2009. **Price:** Contact Rector Press.

979 ■ *RMA Annual Statement Studies*
Pub: Risk Management Association
Contact: Kevin M. Blakey, President
Released: Annual. **Price:** $175.00 2006-07 edition, $105.00. **Description:** Contains composite balance sheets and income statements for more than 360 industries, including the accounting, auditing, and bookkeeping industries. Also contains five years of comparative historical data for discerning trends. Includes 16 commonly used ratios, computed for most of the size groupings for nearly every industry.

TRADE PERIODICALS

980 ■ *Splash Magazine*
Pub: Splash Magazine
URL(s): www.lasplash.com. **Ed:** Barbara Keer, Beverly Cohn. **Released:** Monthly **Price:** Free.

TRADE SHOWS AND CONVENTIONS

981 ■ **FUN Expo**
Reed Exhibitions North American Headquarters
383 Main Ave.
Norwalk, CT 06851

Ph: (203)840-4800
Fax: (203)840-5805
Co. E-mail: inquiry@reedexpo.com
URL: http://www.reedexpo.com

URL(s): www.funexpo.com. **Price:** $20, Pre-registered, members; $40, Pre-registered, non-members; $65, Onsite registered, members; $90, Onsite registered, non-members. **Frequency:** Annual. **Principal Exhibits:** Amusement and recreation products for family and location based entertainment centers, small amusement parks and family oriented businesses such as bowling centers, skating rinks, sports parks, miniature golf courses, golf driving ranges, family restaurants, resorts and other entertainment/recreation businesses.

982 ■ **International Association of Amusement Parks and Attractions Annual Convention and Trade Show**
International Association of Amusement Parks and Attractions (IAAPA)
1448 Duke St.
Alexandria, VA 22314
Ph: (703)836-4800
Fax: (703)836-6742
Co. E-mail: pressoffice@iaapa.org
URL: http://www.iaapa.org
Contact: Rob Norris, President
E-mail: rob@seabreeze.com

URL(s): www.iaapa.org/. **Price:** $109, Members early bird; $209, Non-members early bird; $169, Onsite registered, members; $309, Onsite registered, non-members. **Frequency:** Annual. **Audience:** Trade professionals. **Principal Exhibits:** Amusement, leisure, recreation, and family entertainment-related products and services. **Telecommunication Services:** exhibitsales@iaapa.org.

983 ■ **International Association of Fairs and Expositions Trade Show**
International Association of Fairs and Expositions (IAFE)
3043 E. Cairo St.
Springfield, MO 65802
Ph: (417)862-5771
Free: 800-516-0313
Fax: (417)862-0156
Co. E-mail: iafe@fairsandexpos.com
URL: http://www.fairsandexpos.com
Contact: Jim Tucker, Chief Executive Officer
E-mail: jimt@fairsandexpos.com

URL(s): www.fairsandexpos.com. **Frequency:** Annual. **Audience:** Fair managers, staffs, and board members; carnival owners and staffs; concessionaires; talent and other agencies related to the fair industry. **Principal Exhibits:** Talent agencies, concessionaires, novelties, amusement devices, insurance, ribbons, plaques, attractions, and equipment. Products and services for the fair industry. **Dates and Locations:** , Hilton Hotel. **Telecommunication Services:** iafe@fairsandexpos.com.

CONSULTANTS

984 ■ **Frank Barnes & Associates**
PO Box 241806
Los Angeles, CA 90024-9606
Ph: (213)388-5800
Fax: (213)388-2221
Co. E-mail: barnes@crpoa.org
Contact: Edgar Tom, President
Scope: Provider of transit, park-and-ride, traffic control, and parking operations planning for special events and activities involving the movement of large numbers of people and vehicles at stadiums, theaters, convention centers, arenas, shopping centers and amusement parks. Services are provided to both government and private clients. **Founded:** 1982.

985 ■ **Dennis G. Glore Inc. (DGG)**
120 S Virginia Eureka
Eureka, MO 63025-2003
Ph: (636)938-7887

Fax: (636)938-6590
Co. E-mail: mike.glore@dgg-inc.com
URL: http://www.dgg-inc.com
Contact: Michael Gore, President
Scope: Offers counsel on the design of food service facilities for hotels, motels, hospitals, office buildings, restaurants, cafeterias, amusement parks and any commercial operation. **Founded:** 1971. **Telecommunication Services:** mike.key@dgg-inc.com.

986 ■ **Erin Services Inc.**
111 Travelers Way
Saint Simons Island, GA 31522-5632
Ph: (912)638-9916
Fax: (912)638-5701
Co. E-mail: dennisd@ns.technonet.com
Contact: Dennis J. Donnelly, III, President
E-mail: dennis179@yahoo.com
Scope: Offers assistance in technical proposal production, marketing, and research. Industries served: Food service, janitorial, landscaping, hospitality and lodging, parks, and recreational. **Founded:** 1990.

987 ■ **KZF Design Inc.**
700 Broadway St.
Cincinnati, OH 45202-6010
Ph: (513)621-6211
Fax: (513)621-6530
Co. E-mail: natascha.grody@kzf.com
URL: http://www.kzf.com
Contact: William H. Wilson, President
E-mail: bill.wilson@kzf.com
Scope: Provider of design and counsel in the fields of architecture, engineering, space planning, interior design and planning. Skilled in all aspects of design and planning for industry, institutions, commercial, corporations and public sector. Offers civil and transportation engineering for highways, bridges and storm and waste water systems. Also offers city, regional and land development planning. **Founded:** 1956. **Publications:** "The art of grieving," Oct, 2008; "Cincinnati Enquirer," 2008; "KZF Design moving Downtown," Feb, 2008; "Cincinnati Business Courier," Feb, 2008; "Tampa Bay Business Journal," Feb, 2008; "Work life strategy". **Special Services:** LEED®.

988 ■ **Lougheed Resource Group Inc. (LRG)**
17608 Deer Isle Cir.
Winter Garden, FL 34787
Ph: (407)654-1212
Fax: (407)654-5419
Co. E-mail: info@lrgconstruction.com
URL: http://www.lrgconstruction.com
Contact: Karen Lougheed, Owner
E-mail: karen@lrgmanagement.com
Scope: Construction consultants specializing in project strategies, scope preparation, contract negotiation, project management, document and code evaluation, peer reviews, scheduling/estimates, dispute resolution, and forensic analysis expert testimony. **Founded:** 1987.

989 ■ **Nikki Safety Consultants**
333 Elmer St.
Trenton, NJ 08611-1512
Ph: (609)599-1345
Contact: Nick Valli, Jr., President
Scope: Inspects amusement rides and consults on codes governing amusement rides. Also involves in the area of fire protection, crime prevention, and security inspection. Industries served: manufacturing, investigations, accidents, safety and security, crime prevention, amusement rides, hotel and restaurant management, engineering, and electrical. **Founded:** 1978.

990 ■ **Nyikos Associates Inc.**
18219A Flower Hill Way
Gaithersburg, MD 20879-5331
Ph: (240)683-9530
Fax: (240)683-9532
Co. E-mail: nyikassoc@aol.com
URL: http://www.nyikosassociates.com
Contact: Amanda Nyikos, Manager
Scope: Independent professional design/consulting organization specializing in commercial food service and laundry facilities for hospitals, hotels, restaurants,

schools, universities, employee cafeterias, correctional facilities, convention centers, nursing homes, ski resorts, amusement parks and sports stadiums. Firm also offers management consulting for marketing and feasibility purposes. **Founded:** 1988. **Publications:** "Maryland State Department of Education School Food and Nutrition Design Manual," Jan, 1995.

991 ■ Turner Consulting Group Inc.
306 Florida Ave. NW
Washington, DC 20001-1804
Ph: (202)986-5533
Fax: (202)986-5532
Co. E-mail: info@tcg.com
URL: http://www.tcg-inc.com
Contact: Daniel A. Turner, President
URL(s): www.tcg.com. **Scope:** Provider of IT and management consulting services. **Founded:** 1994.

ASSOCIATIONS AND OTHER ORGANIZATIONS

992 ■ Alpaca Breeders of the Rockies (ABR)
PO Box 1965
Estes Park, CO 80517
Ph: (970)586-5589
Free: 888-993-9898
Co. E-mail: president@alpacabreeders.org
URL: http://www.alpacabreeders.org
Contact: Denise Haines, President
Description: Breeders of Alpacas (an Alpaca is a close relative of the Llama); processors and distributors of Alpaca products. Promotes public awareness of Alpacas; seeks to advance the Alpaca industries. Facilitates communication and cooperation among members; conducts marketing campaigns. Participates in agricultural fairs; sponsors parades and other social activities. **Founded:** 1994. **Awards:** Hummdinger (Annual).

993 ■ American Border Leicester Association (ABLA)
PO Box 500
Cuba, IL 61427
Ph: (309)785-5058
Fax: (309)785-5050
Co. E-mail: baaewe1@yahoo.com
URL: http://www.ablasheep.com
Contact: Barb Hintzsche, President
Description: Owners and admirers of Border Leicester sheep. Promotes Border Leicesters as a source of wool and meat. Sets breed standards and confers certification; maintains breed registry. Sponsors competitions; conducts educational programs. **Founded:** 1973. **Publications:** *American Border Leicester Association Quarterly News* (Quarterly). **Educational Activities:** Maryland Sheep and Wool Festival (Annual); The National Border Leicester Sale. **Awards:** Junior Shepherd Award (Annual).

994 ■ American Brahmousin Council (ABC)
PO Box 88
Whitesboro, TX 76273
Ph: (903)564-3995
URL: http://www.brahmousin.org
Contact: Bob Cummins, Director (Interim)
Description: Breeders of Brahmousin cattle.

995 ■ American Cat Fanciers Association (ACFA)
PO Box 1949
Nixa, MO 65714-1949
Ph: (417)725-1530
Fax: (417)725-1533
Co. E-mail: acfa@aol.com
URL: http://www.acfacat.com
Contact: Jim Mendenhall, President
Description: Breeders and exhibitors of purebred cats; individuals interested in educating the public regarding the health and welfare of domesticated cats. Maintains studbook registry and licenses cat shows and cat judges. Registers pedigreed cats. Sponsors charitable program; compiles statistics. **Founded:** 1955. **Publications:** *ACFA Bulletin* (7/

year); *AFCA Parade of Royalty* (Annual); *Clerking Manual*; *Breeder's Directory* (Annual); *Robinson's Genetics for Cat Breeders and Veterinarians* (Periodic). **Educational Activities:** American Cat Fanciers Association Board meeting (Semiannual). **Awards:** Inter-American (Annual); Legacy of Achievement (Annual); Legacy of Excellence (Annual); Regional Inter-American.

996 ■ American Kennel Club (AKC)
8051 Arco Corporate Dr., Ste. 100
Raleigh, NC 27617
Ph: (919)233-9767
Fax: (212)696-8299
Co. E-mail: communications@akc.org
URL: http://www.akc.org
Contact: Dennis B. Sprung, President
Description: All-breed, specialty breed, obedience, and field trial dog clubs. Maintains stud book registry and pedigree records; approves standards for judging breeds eligible for registration; adopts and enforces rules governing shows, obedience trials, hunting tests, and field trials. Supervises a public and children's education program promoting responsible dog ownership. Provides free information to the public. Offers judging education; compiles statistics. **Founded:** 1884. **Publications:** *Puppies* (Annual); *Pure-Bred Dogs - American Kennel Gazette* (Monthly); *AKC Family Dog* (Bimonthly); *American Kennel Club Awards* (Monthly); *AKC Afield* (Monthly); *American Kennel Club Gazette: The Official Journal for the Sport of Purebred Dogs* (Monthly); *AKC Gazette--List of Clubs Issue* (Annual); *Complete Dog Book*; *The Stud Book Register* (Monthly); *AKC Dog Care and Training*. **Awards:** Awards for Canine Excellence (Annual); Breeder of the year Award (Annual); Awards for Canine Excellence; Breeder of the Year Award; Lifetime Achievement Awards.

997 ■ Ayrshire Breeders' Association of Canada (ABAC)—Association des Eleveurs Ayrshire du Canada
4865, boul. Laurier O
St.-Hyacinthe, QC, Canada J2S 3V4
Ph: (450)778-3535
Fax: (450)778-3531
Co. E-mail: info@ayrshire-canada.com
URL: http://www.ayrshire-canada.com
Contact: Linda Ness, Executive Director
Description: Breeders of Ayrshire cattle. Promotes improvement of the Ayrshire breed; seeks to advance the dairy industry. Maintains breed registry; provides support and assistance to Ayrshire breeders. **Founded:** 1901. **Publications:** *Canadian Ayrshire Review*. **Awards:** Ayrshire Award of Merit (Annual); Master Breeder (Annual).

998 ■ *Breeders' News*
PO Box 172
Rexdale, ON, Canada M9W 5L1
Ph: (416)675-3602
Fax: (416)675-9405
Co. E-mail: cthsont@idirect.com
URL: http://www.cthsont.com
Contact: Sue Leslie, President
Released: Quarterly

999 ■ *Canadian Ayrshire Review*
4865, boul. Laurier O
St.-Hyacinthe, QC, Canada J2S 3V4
Ph: (450)778-3535
Fax: (450)778-3531
Co. E-mail: info@ayrshire-canada.com
URL: http://www.ayrshire-canada.com
Contact: Linda Ness, Executive Director
Released: six times a year. **Price:** C$35, /year.

1000 ■ Canadian Cat Association (CCA)—Association Feline Canadienne (AFC)
5045 Orbitor Dr., Bldg. 12, Ste. 102
Mississauga, ON, Canada L4W 4Y4
Ph: (905)232-3481
Fax: (289)232-9481
Co. E-mail: office@cca-afc.com
URL: http://www.cca-afc.com
Contact: Sandra Dawes, Executive Director
Description: Cat breeders and fanciers. Promotes responsible pet care; seeks to improve the bloodlines of purebred cats. Serves as a clearinghouse on purebred cats; maintains breed registries; sponsors competitions.

1001 ■ Canadian Kennel Club (CKC)—Club Canin Canadien
200 Ronson Dr., Ste. 400
Etobicoke, ON, Canada M9W 5Z9
Ph: (416)675-5511
Free: 800-250-8040
Fax: (416)675-6506
Co. E-mail: information@ckc.ca
URL: http://www.ckc.ca
Contact: Michael Shoreman, Chairman
Description: Dog owners, breeders, and enthusiasts. Promotes responsible pet ownership; seeks to improve the bloodlines of pedigreed dogs. Sponsors educational programs for dogs and dog owners; maintains breed registries; sets breed standards; holds competitions. **Founded:** 1888. **Publications:** *Dogs in Canada* (Monthly).

1002 ■ Canadian Thoroughbred Horse Society (CTHS)
PO Box 172
Rexdale, ON, Canada M9W 5L1
Ph: (416)675-3602
Fax: (416)675-9405
Co. E-mail: cthsont@idirect.com
URL: http://www.cthsont.com
Contact: Sue Leslie, President
Description: Owners and breeders of thoroughbred horses; providers of services to horse racing and the thoroughbred horse industry. Promotes a viable future for the thoroughbred industry in Canada. Serves as a clearinghouse on thoroughbred breeding, provides support and services to members including remote naming and live foal reporting. Lobbies government agencies to secure tax legislation more favorable to the industry. Operates Thoroughbred Improvement Programs, in conjunction with the provincial governments. Sponsors stakes races; compiles statistics. **Founded:** 1906. **Publications:** *Breeders' News* (Quarterly). **Awards:** Breeders' Awards (Annual).

1003 ■ Cat Fanciers' Association (CFA)
260 E Main St.
Alliance, OH 44601-2423
Ph: (330)680-4070
Fax: (330)680-4633
Co. E-mail: cfa@cfa.org
URL: http://www.cfainc.org
Contact: Jerold Hamza, President
URL(s): www.cfa.org. **Description:** Federation of all-breed and specialty cat clubs. Promotes the welfare of cats, register pedigrees, and license shows held under association rules. **Founded:** 1906. **Publications:** *Show Rules; Show Standards Booklet; CFA Complete Cat Book.* **Educational Activities:** Cat Fanciers' Association Meeting (Annual). **Awards:** National Award Winner (Annual).

1004 ■ Cat Fanciers' Federation (CFF)
PO Box 661
Gratis, OH 45330
Ph: (937)787-9009
Fax: (937)787-9009
Co. E-mail: cffinc@live.com
URL: http://www.cffinc.org
Contact: Ken Staples, President
Description: Federation of local clubs of persons who own, breed, and exhibit cats and who are interested in the general welfare of cats. Maintains records on the ancestry of cats; encourages the holding of shows; trains judges; creates and promulgates rules and standards for judging cats, holding shows, and recording ancestry. Local clubs hold annual cat shows under federation rules, usually for the benefit of humane organizations. **Founded:** 1919. **Publications:** *CFF Newsletter* (Quarterly). **Awards:** Parade of Perfection Award (Annual).

1005 ■ *Dogs in Canada*
200 Ronson Dr., Ste. 400
Etobicoke, ON, Canada M9W 5Z9
Ph: (416)675-5511
Free: 800-250-8040
Fax: (416)675-6506
Co. E-mail: information@ckc.ca
URL: http://www.ckc.ca
Contact: Michael Shoreman, Chairman
Released: Monthly **Price:** C$25, /year; C$45, /2 years.

1006 ■ Field Spaniel Society of America (FSSA)
351 E Kerley Corners Rd.
Tivoli, NY 12583
Ph: (845)756-2595
Co. E-mail: maxinereed@frontiernet.net
URL: http://fieldspaniels.org
Contact: Jane Chopson, Postmaster General
Description: Owners and admirers of field spaniels. Promotes responsible breeding and pet ownership; seeks to increase public awareness and appreciation of field spaniels. Maintains breed registry; conducts educational and public relations activities. **Founded:** 1972. **Publications:** *Field Spaniel Fancier* (Quarterly).

1007 ■ International Generic Horse Association (IGHA)
PO Box 6778
San Pedro, CA 90734-6778
Co. E-mail: volunteer@equinerescue.net
URL: http://www.igha.org/index1.html
Description: Owners and breeders of horses. Promotes "a better understanding, appreciation, and development of all equine types and breeds without prejudice or fault due to any known or unknown origin, lineage or breeding." Maintains registry of horses of unknown or crossbreeding; collects data relevant to the well-being of crossbred horses. **Founded:** 1975. **Publications:** *IGHA/HA Catalog* (Periodic); *IHG/HA Informational Brochure* (Periodic).

1008 ■ International Jumper Futurity (IJF)
PO Box 1445
Georgetown, KY 40324
Ph: (502)535-6787

Fax: (502)535-4412
Co. E-mail: yjcoffice@youngjumpers.com
URL: http://youngjumpers.com/yjcblog/
Description: Owners, breeders, and trainers of sport horses. Promotes interest and participation in show jumping and other equestrian events; seeks to improve sport horse bloodlines. Serves as a clearing-house on North American sport horses; recognizes outstanding equestrian riders, trainers, and breeders. **Founded:** 1989.

1009 ■ International Sporthorse Registry (ISR)
517 DeKalb Ave.
Sycamore, IL 60178
Ph: (815)899-7803
Fax: (815)899-7823
Co. E-mail: isreg@aol.com
URL: http://www.isroldenburg.org
Description: Owners and breeders of sport horses. Seeks to improve sport horse bloodlines. Formulates and enforces standards of breed conformance; maintains breed registry. **Founded:** 1983. **Publications:** *Breeders Guide* (Annual). **Awards:** Champion Foal Award (Annual); Champion Mare Award (Annual); Premium Awards for Mares; USDF All Breed Award (Annual).

1010 ■ International Spotted Horse Registry Association (ISHR)
PO Box 412
Anderson, MO 64831-0412
Ph: (417)475-6273
Free: 866-201-3098
Co. E-mail: ishrppa@aol.com
URL: http://spottedhorses.tripod.com/index.html
Contact: Rebecca Rogers, President
Description: Color registry for any/all types of spotted horses. Drafts to miniatures, grade to purebred, champion to family pet. Spots from Paints to Pintaloosas; each horse gets a permanent registration number. Conducts several programs for members and horses for year-end awards and rewards. **Founded:** 1990. **Publications:** *Rainbow Connection* (3/year); *Foundation Stallions, Foundation Broodmares* (Annual). **Educational Activities:** Open Horse Show (Annual). **Awards:** Special Year End Awards (Annual); ROM Year End High Point Trophies (Annual).

1011 ■ National Chincoteague Pony Association (NCPA)
2595 Jensen Rd.
Bellingham, WA 98226
Ph: (360)671-8338
Co. E-mail: gfreder426@aol.com
URL: http://www.pony-chincoteague.com
URL(s): www.pony-chincoteague.org. **Description:** Admirers of Chincoteague ponies, a rare breed of horse which developed on Chincoteague Island off the coast of Virginia. Promotes responsible horse ownership; seeks to improve the Chincoteague pony. Facilitates communication and cooperation among members; maintains breed registry; establishes standards required for breed conformation; arranges Chincoteague pony sales. **Founded:** 1985.

1012 ■ Navajo-Churro Sheep Association (NCSA)
PO Box 1994
El Prado, NM 87529
Ph: (575)751-3767
Co. E-mail: churrosheep@mac.com
URL: http://www.navajo-churrosheep.com
Contact: Connie Taylor, Registrar
Description: Owners and breeders of Navajo-Churro sheep; fiber artists and collectors of textiles. Promotes preservation the Navajo-Churro breed of sheep. Facilitates breeding of Navajo-Churro sheep and maintains breed registry. **Founded:** 1986. **Publications:** *Catch Pen* (Quarterly); *Flockbook* (Annual).

1013 ■ Norwegian Forest Cat Breed Council
260 E Main St.
Alliance, OH 44601
Ph: (330)680-4070

Fax: (330)680-4633
Co. E-mail: dawn@skogeier.com
URL: http://www.nfcbc.org
Contact: Dawn M. Shiley, Secretary
Description: Breeders and owners of Norwegian Forest Cats. Works to promote healthy and beautiful cats. **Founded:** 1985. **Awards:** Paddy Trophy (Semi-annual).

1014 ■ Oldenburg Registry N.A. (OLD NA)
517 DeKalb Ave.
Sycamore, IL 60178
Ph: (815)899-7803
Fax: (815)899-7823
Co. E-mail: isreg@aol.com
URL: http://www.isroldenburg.org
Description: Owners and breeders of modern sport horses used as dressage, hunter/jumpers, and performance horses. Seeks to improve sport horse bloodlines. Maintains breed registry; formulates and enforces standards of breed conformance. **Scope:** copies of Breeders Guide. **Founded:** 1983. **Awards:** Champion Foal Award (Annual); Champion Mare Award (Annual); USDF All Breed Award (Annual).

1015 ■ Professional Handlers' Association (PHA)
17017 Norbrook Dr.
Olney, MD 20832-2623
Ph: (301)924-0089
Co. E-mail: kathy@phadoghandlers.com
URL: http://www.phadoghandlers.com
Contact: Ollie Click, President
Description: Seeks to promote the interests of individuals who show purebred dogs at dog shows as a profession. Enhances the stature of professional dog handling. Provides information on purebred dogs to interested persons. Sponsors seminars and lectures. **Founded:** 1926.

1016 ■ Traditional Cat Association (TCA)
PO Box 178
Heisson, WA 98622-0178
Co. E-mail: info@traditionalcats.com
URL: http://www.traditionalcats.com
Contact: Diana Fineran, Founder
Description: Breeders and fanciers of traditional cats. Promotes, preserves, protects, and perpetuates the traditional cat. Operates kitten referral services. Conducts educational, charitable, and research programs. Sponsors competitions and shows; compiles statistics. Maintains registry, placement services, hall of fame, and museum. **Founded:** 1987. **Awards:** National Champion Award (Annual).

1017 ■ United Kennel Club (UKC)
100 E Kilgore Rd.
Kalamazoo, MI 49002-5584
Ph: (269)343-9020
Fax: (269)343-7037
Co. E-mail: registration@ukcdogs.com
URL: http://www.ukcdogs.com
Contact: Wayne R. Cavanaugh, President
Description: Registry for purebred dogs. Maintains records and pedigrees and establishes rules for events. Promotes improvement of dog breeds; sponsors events to test merit and quality of individual dogs. Awards championships for outstanding dogs. Conducts seminars for show judges, masters of hounds, and for training and handling of dogs. Compiles statistics. Maintains computerized records. **Founded:** 1898. **Publications:** *Bloodlines* (Monthly); *Coonhound Bloodlines* (Monthly); *Hunting Retriever Magazine* (Bimonthly). **Awards:** Hunting Retriever Champion.

REFERENCE WORKS

1018 ■ *Cat Fanciers' Association--Yearbook*
Pub: Cat Fanciers' Association Inc.
Contact: Pam Delabar, President
URL(s): www.cfa.org/client/pubspublications.aspx.
Released: Annual; Latest edition 2013. **Price:** $59.99, Individuals. **Publication includes:** List of cat clubs, cat breeders. **Entries include:** Name, address.

1019 ■ *"No-Shed Dogs Lead the Way to Big Growth"* in Business Courier (Vol. 26, January 8, 2010, No. 38, pp. 1)
Pub: American City Business Journals, Inc.
Ed: Lucy May. **Description:** Ed Lukacevic of Grant County, Kentucky is developing Dinovite, a dietary supplement that minimizes shedding and scratching in dogs. Statistical data included.

1020 ■ *QuickBooks for the New Bean Counter: Business Owner's Guide 2006*
Pub: Wheatmark
Ed: Joseph L. Catallini. **Released:** July 2006. **Price:** $21.95. **Description:** Profile of QuickBooks software, offering insight into using the software's accounting and bookkeeping functions.

1021 ■ *"Shear Profit"* in Crain's Cleveland Business (Vol. 28, October 29, 2007, No. 43, pp. 3)
Pub: Crain Communications, Inc.
Ed: David Bennett. **Description:** Alpaca farms are becoming a very profitable business for a number of Northeast Ohio entrepreneurs due to the high return on initial investments, tax incentives and the rise in demand for the animals. Ohio leads the country in the number of alpaca farms with roughly one-third located in Northeast Ohio.

1022 ■ *"VC Boosts WorkForce; Livonia Software Company to Add Sales, Marketing Staff"* in Crain's Detroit Business (March 24, 2008)
Pub: Crain Communications, Inc.
Ed: Tom Henderson. **Description:** WorkForce Software Inc., a company that provides software to manage payroll processes and oversee compliance with state and federal regulations and with union rules, plans to use an investment of $5.5 million in venture capital to hire more sales and marketing staff.

TRADE PERIODICALS

1023 ■ *ACFA Bulletin*
Pub: American Cat Fanciers Association Inc.
Released: 7/year. **Description:** Contains Association news, show schedules, news about the officers and judges, and articles of interest to cat fanciers.

1024 ■ *American Salers*
Pub: American Salers Association
Contact: Sherry Doubet, Executive Vice President
URL(s): www.salersusa.org/index.php?option=com_content&view=article&id=85&lt emid=76. **Released:** Quarterly

1025 ■ *Charolais Journal*
Pub: American-International Charolais Association
Contact: Harlin Hecht, President
URL(s): www.charolaisusa.com/charolaisjournal.html.
Ed: Kori Conley. **Released:** Monthly **Price:** $75, Individuals U.S.; $100, Individuals 1st class; $125, Other countries first class; $100, Other countries.

1026 ■ *Feed-Lot*
Pub: Feed-Lot Magazine
URL(s): www.feedlotmagazine.com/. **Ed:** Robert Strong. **Released:** Bimonthly **Price:** $50, Other countries; Free qualified U.S. recipients.

1027 ■ *Miniature Donkey Talk: The Talk of the Donkey World*
Pub: Pheasant Meadow Farm
URL(s): www.qis.net/~minidonk/mdt.htmwww.webdonkeys.com/index.php. **Ed:** Bonnie Gross. **Released:** Bimonthly **Price:** $40, By mail 1st class; $75, Two years mailed 1st class.

1028 ■ *Palmetto Poultry Life*
Pub: South Carolina Poultry Federation
Contact: Connie Smith, President
URL(s): www.scpoultry.org/. **Released:** Quarterly

1029 ■ *The Rottweiler Quarterly*
Pub: Print It Design and Publishing, Inc.
URL(s): www.411web.com/R/ROTTQUARTER/Product.htm?F=. **Released:** Quarterly **Price:** $40, Individuals; $60, Individuals first class; $75, Two years; $55, Individuals outside U.S.; $100, Individuals via airmail.

1030 ■ *The Royal Spaniels*
Pub: Premiere Publications
URL(s): www.the-royal-spaniels.com/. **Ed:** Holly Cornwell. **Released:** Quarterly **Price:** $45, Individuals; $55, Canada; $80, Other countries airmail.

1031 ■ *Sheltie Pacesetter*
Pub: Sheltie Pacesetter
URL(s): www.sheltie.com. **Ed:** Nancy Lee Cathcart. **Released:** Quarterly **Price:** $61.95, Individuals; $109.20, Individuals first class mail; $77.70, Canada and Mexico; $124.95, Canada and Mexico first class mail; $82.95, Other countries surface mail; $145.95, Other countries first class mail; $21, Single issue; $25.73, Single issue first class mail; $22.05, Single issue Canada.

1032 ■ *Terrier Type*
Pub: Dan Kiedrowski Co.
URL(s): www.terriertype.com/. **Ed:** Shawn Nichols. **Released:** Monthly **Price:** $45, Individuals regular/surface; $75, Individuals first class; $75, Canada first/class airmail.

VIDEOCASSETTES/ AUDIOCASSETTES

1033 ■ *Dog Showmanship: The Winning Edge*
ESPN Inc.
ESPN Plz.
Bristol, CT 06010
Ph: (860)766-2000
Free: 888-549-3776
Fax: (860)766-2213
Co. E-mail: espnpr@espn.com
URL: http://espn.go.com
Contact: Steven M. Bornstein, President
Released: 198?. **Price:** $39.95. **Description:** Is your dog good enough to show? This video demonstrates grooming and nutrition, as well as gaiting, ring patterns, and stacking. Also includes advice from top breeders. **Availability:** VHS.

1034 ■ *The Westminster Kennel Club Dog Care Guide*
Paramount Home Video
5555 Melrose Ave.
Los Angeles, CA 90038
Ph: (323)956-5000
URL: http://www.paramount.com
Released: 1989. **Price:** $19.95. **Description:** A high-pedigree instructional tape explaining how to select, care for and properly train a dog. **Availability:** VHS.

LIBRARIES

1035 ■ **American Kennel Club Library**
260 Madison Ave., 4th Fl.
New York, NY 10016
Ph: (212)696-8234
Fax: (212)696-8252
Co. E-mail: jxc@akc.org
URL: http://www.akc.org/about/library/index.cfm
Contact: Barbara Kolk, Librarian
Scope: Dogs - breeds, training, health, literature, art. **Services:** Copying; Library open to the public by appointment. **Founded:** 1934. **Holdings:** 18,000 volumes; VF drawers of clippings; videocassettes; fine art collection; 5 dissertations. **Subscriptions:** 300 journals and other serials.

1036 ■ **Bloodstock Research Information Services, Inc. Library**
801 Corporate Dr., 3rd Fl.
Lexington, KY 40544-4097
Ph: (859)223-4444
Free: 800-354-9206
Fax: (859)223-7024
Co. E-mail: brisinfo@brisnet.com
URL: http://www.brisnet.com
Scope: Thoroughbred horses, horse breeding, horse racing, horse and farm management. **Services:** Library not open to the public. **Founded:** 1972. **Holdings:** 1000 bound volumes. **Subscriptions:** 20 journals and other serials. **Telecommunication Services:** bristech@brisnet.com.

1037 ■ **Cleveland Public Library - Science and Technology Department**
Louis Stokes Wing, 3rd Fl.
325 Superior Ave.
Cleveland, OH 44114-1271
Ph: (216)623-2932
Fax: (216)623-7029
Co. E-mail: scitech@cpl.org
URL: http://www.cpl.org/thelibrary/subjectscollections/sciencetechnology.aspx
Contact: Maureen Mullin, Manager
Scope: Engineering, science, metallurgy, aeronautics, mechanics, chemistry, geology, environment, agriculture, history of science and technology, natural history, handicrafts, photography, car and truck repair. **Services:** Interlibrary loan; copying; department open to the public. **Founded:** 1869. **Holdings:** 347,249 volumes; 380 VF drawers; 1239 CD-ROMs; 21,322 microfiche; 795 reels of microfilm.

1038 ■ **Glendale Public Library - Special Collections Room**
222 E. Harvard St.
Glendale, CA 91205
Ph: (818)548-2037
Fax: (818)548-7225
Co. E-mail: centlibref@ci.glendale.ca.us
URL: http://glendalepubliclibrary.org
Contact: Cindy Cleary, Director, Library Services
Scope: Glendale and area history, California history, cats and cat genealogy. **Services:** Copying; room open to the public for reference use only (call for open hours or appointments). **Founded:** 1906. **Holdings:** 400 bound periodical volumes; city departmental reports; archives; microfilm, clippings file. **Subscriptions:** 11 current journals and other serials.

1039 ■ **National Animal Control Association - Research Library**
101 N Church St.
Olathe, KS 66061
Ph: (913)768-1319
Fax: (913)768-1378
Co. E-mail: naca@nacanet.org
URL: http://www.nacanet.org
Contact: John Mays, Executive Director
Scope: Animal control, bites and attacks, rabies, euthanasia, humane education, officer training. **Services:** Copying; library open to the public. **Founded:** 1978. **Holdings:** 85 books; 50 bound periodical volumes; 10,000 reports; videocassettes. **Subscriptions:** 15 journals and other serials; 1 newspaper.

1040 ■ **Oregon Thoroughbred Breeders Association Library**
PO Box 17248
Portland, OR 97217
Ph: (503)285-0658
Fax: (503)285-0659
Co. E-mail: info@oregontoba.com
URL: http://www.oregontoba.com
Contact: Wendie Hayes-Pounds, Executive Director
Scope: Thoroughbreds - life, breeding, racing. **Services:** Copying; library open to the public. **Founded:** 1980. **Holdings:** 200 books; 3 bound periodical volumes; 50 reports; microfiche; CD-ROMs. **Subscriptions:** 15 journals and other serials; 2 newspapers. **Telecommunication Services:** wendie@oregontoba.com.

1041 ■ **Second Chance Animal Center Library**
PO Box 620
Shaftsbury, VT 05262-0620
Ph: (802)375-2898
Fax: (802)375-0235
Co. E-mail: secondchance@wildblue.net
URL: http://www.2ndchanceanimalcenter.org/
Scope: Animals - welfare, rights, farm, dog and cat care. **Services:** Library open to the public. **Founded:** 1990. **Holdings:** 600 books; videocassettes. **Subscriptions:** 14 journals and other serials; 3 newspapers.

1042 ■ U.S. Dept. of Defense - Central Repository for Military Working Dog Records Archives
DOD Dog Center
Lackland AFB, TX 78236-5000
Ph: (512)671-3402

Scope: Military working dogs - training, working assignments, veterinary records.

1043 ■ Voice for Animals Library
PO Box 120095
San Antonio, TX 78212
Ph: (210)737-3138
Co. E-mail: voice@voiceforanimals.org
URL: http://www.voiceforanimals.org/

Scope: Animal rights; vegetarianism. **Services:** Library not open to the public. **Founded:** 1987. **Holdings:** 200 books; newsletters; videocassettes.

RESEARCH CENTERS

1044 ■ University of California, Davis - Veterinary Genetics Laboratory (VGL)
School of Veterinary Medicine
1 Shields Ave.
Davis, CA 95616-8744
Ph: (530)752-2211
Fax: (530)752-3556
Co. E-mail: karnelson@ucdavis.edu
URL: http://www.vgl.ucdavis.edu
Contact: Karen Nelson, Manager
Founded: 1955.

START-UP INFORMATION

1045 ■ *"Elanco Challenges Bayer's Advantage, K9 Advantix Ad Claims" in Pet Product News (Vol. 64, November 2010, No. 11, pp. 11)*

Pub: BowTie Inc.

Description: Elanco Animal Health has disputed Bayer Animal Health's print and Web advertising claims involving its flea, tick, and mosquito control products Advantage and K9 Advantix. The National Advertising Division of the Council of Better Business Bureaus recommended the discontinuation of ads, while Bayer Animal Health reiterated its commitment to self-regulation.

ASSOCIATIONS AND OTHER ORGANIZATIONS

1046 ■ **American Animal Hospital Association (AAHA)**

12575 W Bayaud Ave.
Lakewood, CO 80228
Ph: (303)986-2800
Free: 800-883-6301
Fax: (303)986-1700
Co. E-mail: info@aahanet.org
URL: http://www.aahanet.org
Contact: Kate S. Knutson, President

Description: Represents veterinary care providers who treat companion animals. Accredits veterinary hospitals throughout the U.S. and Canada. Conducts stringent accreditation process that covers patient care, client service and medical protocols. **Founded:** 1933. **Publications:** *Journal of the American Animal Hospital Association* (Bimonthly); *NEWStat* (Biweekly); *TRENDS Magazine* (Bimonthly); *Journal of the American Animal Hospital Association* (Bimonthly); *TRENDS Magazine; Career Choices for Veterinary Technicians: Opportunities for Animal Lovers.* **Educational Activities:** American Animal Hospital Association Annual Conference. **Awards:** AAHA Award; Practitioner-of-the-Year Award (Annual); AAHA Award; Royal Canin Veterinary Diet Award.

1047 ■ **American Veterinary Medical Association (AVMA)**

1931 N Meacham Rd., Ste. 100
Schaumburg, IL 60173-4360
Ph: (847)925-8070
Free: 800-248-2862
Fax: (847)925-1329
Co. E-mail: avmainfo@avma.org
URL: http://www.avma.org
Contact: Douglas Aspros, President

Description: Professional society of veterinarians. Conducts educational and research programs. Provides placement service. Sponsors American Veterinary Medical Association Foundation and Educational Commission for Foreign Veterinary Graduates. Compiles statistics. Accredits veterinary medical education programs and veterinary technician education programs. **Founded:** 1863. **Publications:** *American Journal of Veterinary Research*

(Monthly); *Vaccines and Sarcomas; Methicillin-resistant Staphylococcus Aureus; Welfare Implications of Deer Velvet; American Journal of Veterinary Research* (Monthly); *Journal of the American Veterinary Medical Association* (Semimonthly); *Programs in Veterinary Technology* (Semiannual); *Journal of the American Veterinary Medical Association* (Semimonthly); *Canine Parvoviris; Pet Euthanasia; External Parasites; When Your Animal Dies; Selecting an Amphibian; Toxoplasmosis Pamphlet; Veterinarians; BSE: Bovine Spongiform Encephalopathy; Facts About CWD: Chronic Wasting Disease; What You Should Know About Rabies; Today's Veterinarian; What You Should Know About Toxoplasmosis; What You Should Know About Vaccinations; The Veterinary Health Care Team; A Career in Veterinary Technology; African Horse Sickness; African Swine Fever; Anthrax, VMA; Avian Influenza; Bluetongue; BSE; Brucellosis; Canine Influenza; Chronic Wasting Disease; Classical Swine Fever, Equine Influenza; Equine Piroplasmosis; Exotic Newcastle Disease; Foot and Mouth Disease; Glanders and Melioidosis; Monkeypox; Plague, VMA; Q Fever, Swine Influenza; Tularemia, VMA; Vesicular Stomatitis; Viral Encephalitis; Welfare Implications of Castration of Cattle; Care for Animals; Cancer in Animals; Canine Distemper, AVMA Directory; AVMA Disaster Preparedness and Response Guide; AVMA Membership Directory and Resource Manual* (Annual); *Economic Report on Veterinarians and Veterinary Practices* (Semiannual); *American Veterinary Medical Association--Directory and Resource Manual: AVMA Membership Directory and Resource Manual* (Annual); *AVMA Placement Service Bulletin; What You Should Know About Buying a Horse; What You Should Know About Internal Parasites in Horses; What You Should Know About Selecting a Pet Ferret; What You Should Know About Selecting a Pet Rabbit; What You Should Know About Selecting a Reptile; What You Should Know About Selecting a Pet Rodent; What You Should Know About Canine Parvovirus; What You Should Know About Selecting a Bird; What You Should Know About Traveling with Your Pet; Treating Pain in Your Dog: Keeping Your Best Friend Active, Safe and Pain Free; Colleges of Veterinary Medicine Accredited by American Veterinary Medical Association* (Semiannual); *What You Should Know About Cancer in Animals; What You Should Know About Canine Distemper; What You Should Know About Choosing a Veterinarian for Your Pet; What You Should Know About Dog Bite Prevention; How Do I Know It Is Time? Equine Euthanasia; What You Should Know About External Parasites; What You Should Know About Feline Lower Urinary Tract Disease; What You Should Know About Feline Panleukopenia; What You Should Know About Heartworm Disease; What You Should Know About Household Hazards to Pets; What You Should Know About Internal Parasites In Cats and Dogs; What You Should Know About Internal Parasites in Horses; How Do I Know It Is Time? Pet Euthanasia; What You Should Know About Selecting a Cat; What You Should Know About Selecting a Dog; What You Should Know About Spaying and Neutering; What You Should Know About West Nile Virus; Understanding Your Feelings of Loss When Your Animal Dies; Welfare Implications of Dehorning and Disbudding of Cattle; Welfare Implica-*

tions of Tail Docking of Dairy Cattle; U.S. Pet Ownership and Demographic Sourcebook (Semiannual). **Educational Activities:** American Veterinary Medical Association Annual Convention (Annual). **Awards:** AVMA Advocacy Award (Annual); Meritorious Service Award (Annual); AVMA Award; Charles River Prize; Royal Canin Award; Humane Award; Practitioner Research Award; Public Service Award; International Veterinary Congress Prize; Animal Welfare Award; Bustad Companion Animal Veterinarian of the Year Award; American Kennel Club Career Achievement Award in Canine Research; American Kennel Club Excellence in Research Awards.

1048 ■ **Animal Health Institute (AHI)**

1325 G St. NW, Ste. 700
Washington, DC 20005-3127
Ph: (202)637-2440
Fax: (202)393-1667
Co. E-mail: rphillips@ahi.org
URL: http://www.ahi.org
Contact: Alexander S. Mathews, President

Description: Represents manufacturers of animal health products (vaccines, pharmaceuticals, and feed additives used in modern food production; and medicines for household pets). Works with government agencies and legislators; prepares position papers; and compiles and disseminates information. Sponsors AHI Foundation. **Founded:** 1941. **Publications:** *AHI Newsletter.*

1049 ■ *Canadian Journal of Veterinary Research*

339 Booth St.
Ottawa, ON, Canada K1R 7K1
Ph: (613)236-1162
Fax: (613)236-9681
Co. E-mail: admin@cvma-acmv.org
URL: http://canadianveterinarians.net/index.aspx
Contact: Mr. Jost Am Rhyn, Executive Director
Released: Quarterly

1050 ■ *Canadian Veterinary Journal*

339 Booth St.
Ottawa, ON, Canada K1R 7K1
Ph: (613)236-1162
Fax: (613)236-9681
Co. E-mail: admin@cvma-acmv.org
URL: http://canadianveterinarians.net/index.aspx
Contact: Mr. Jost Am Rhyn, Executive Director
Released: Monthly

1051 ■ **Canadian Veterinary Medical Association (CVMA)—Association Canadienne des Medecins Veterinaires (ACMV)**

339 Booth St.
Ottawa, ON, Canada K1R 7K1
Ph: (613)236-1162
Fax: (613)236-9681
Co. E-mail: admin@cvma-acmv.org
URL: http://canadianveterinarians.net/index.aspx
Contact: Mr. Jost Am Rhyn, Executive Director

Description: Veterinarians in Canada. Encourages excellence in the field of veterinary medicine; seeks to increase awareness of the importance of animals;

represents the interests of members. **Founded:** 1948. **Publications:** *Canadian Journal of Veterinary Research* (Quarterly); *Canadian Veterinary Journal* (Monthly); *CVMA Directory* (Annual). **Awards:** CVMA Industry Award (Annual); Hill's Public Relations Award (Annual); President's Award (Annual); RVL Walker Award (Annual); Schering Veterinary Award (Annual); Small Animal Practitioner Award (Annual); Small Animal Practitioner Award; President's Award; R.V.L. Walker Award; Intervet Schering-Plough Award; Humane Award; CVMA Award; CVMA Award (Annual); CVMA Humane Award (Annual); CVMA Pet Food Certification Nutrition Award (Annual). **Telecommunication Services:** jamrhyn@cvma-acmv.org.

1052 ■ Cornell Feline Health Center
College of Veterinary Medicine
Ithaca, NY 14853
Ph: (607)253-3414
Fax: (607)253-3419
Co. E-mail: kmm8@cornell.edu
URL: http://www.vet.cornell.edu/fhc
Contact: Dr. Colin R. Parrish, Director

Description: Professionals devoted to cats. Seeks to unravel the mysteries of feline health, nutrition, and behavior. Works to educate veterinarians and cat owners, and to aid veterinarians when new or unknown diseases occur. Provides educational programs. **Founded:** 1975. **Publications:** *CatWatch* (Monthly); *Dog Watch*; *Pre-Veterinary* (Bimonthly); *Feline Health Topics*; *The Cornell Book of Cats, Second Edition*. **Telecommunication Services:** cvmerm@cornell.edu.

1053 ■ *CVMA Directory*
339 Booth St.
Ottawa, ON, Canada K1R 7K1
Ph: (613)236-1162
Fax: (613)236-9681
Co. E-mail: admin@cvma-acmv.org
URL: http://canadianveterinarians.net/index.aspx
Contact: Mr. Jost Am Rhyn, Executive Director
Released: Annual

1054 ■ Vaccine and Infectious Disease Organization - International Vaccine Centre (VIDO-InterVac)
University of Saskatchewan
120 Veterinary Rd.
Saskatoon, SK, Canada S7N 5E3
Ph: (306)966-7465
Fax: (306)966-7478
Co. E-mail: info@vido.org
URL: http://www.vido.org
Contact: Dr. Andrew Potter, Chief Executive Officer

Description: Promotes animal health through diagnosis and prevention of production-limiting diseases. Conducts research focusing on development of new vaccines to better treat infectious diseases and the discovery and application of biotechnologies. Serves as a clearinghouse on commercial veterinary diagnosis and treatment techniques; makes available laboratory and field study services. Makes available educational and extension services. **Scope:** immunology, virology, bacteriology, biotechnology. **Founded:** 1975. **Subscriptions:** articles books periodicals.

REFERENCE WORKS

1055 ■ *American Veterinary Medical Association--Directory and Resource Manual: AVMA Membership Directory and Resource Manual*
Pub: American Veterinary Medical Association
Contact: Douglas Aspros, President

URL(s): www.avma.orgwww.avma.org/Professional Development/Education/Specialties/Pages/abvs-procedures-viii.aspx. **Released:** Annual; January; Latest edition 2008-2009. **Price:** $150, Nonmembers in USA and their territories; $175, Nonmembers other countries. **Covers:** AVMA members; code of ethics, AVMA bylaws. **Entries include:** Name, spouse's name, address, email, phones and codes for practice activity, type of employer, institution granting degree, and year received. **Database includes:** Extensive

list of veterinary medical and related associations, veterinary schools, related government agencies. **Arrangement:** Geographical and alphabetical. **Indexes:** Alphabetical.

1056 ■ *"Best In Show" in Pet Product News (Vol. 64, November 2010, No. 11, pp. 20)*
Pub: BowTie Inc.

Ed: Lizett Bond. **Description:** Cherrybrook Premium Pet Supplies offers an expanded array of quality holistic products and is staffed by people who possess wide knowledge of these products. Aside from receiving the Outstanding Holistic Approach award, Cherrybrook has opened three stores in New Jersey. How a holistic approach to service kept customers coming back is discussed.

1057 ■ *"Capture New Markets" in Pet Product News (Vol. 64, December 2010, No. 12, pp. 12)*
Pub: BowTie Inc.

Ed: Ethan Mizer. **Description:** Flea and tick treatments are among the product categories that can be offered in order to clinch new markets. With the help of manufacturers, pet store retailers are encouraged to educate themselves about these products considering that capturing markets involves variations in customer perceptions. Retailers would then be deemed as resources and sources for these products.

1058 ■ *"Experts Strive to Educate on Proper Pet Diets" in Pet Product News (Vol. 64, November 2010, No. 11, pp. 40)*
Pub: BowTie Inc.

Ed: John Hustace Walker. **Description:** Pet supply manufacturers have been bundling small mammal food and treats with educational sources to help retailers avoid customer misinformation. This action has been motivated by the customer's quest to seek proper nutritional advice for their small mammal pets.

1059 ■ *"Food as Nature Intended" in Pet Product News (Vol. 64, November 2010, No. 11, pp. 30)*
Pub: BowTie Inc.

Ed: Nikki Moustaki. **Description:** Dog owners have been extending their health-consciousness to their pets by seeking natural products that will address their pets' raw food diet. Retailers response to this trend are outlined.

1060 ■ *"Must Work for Food" in Pet Product News (Vol. 64, November 2010, No. 11, pp. 24)*
Pub: BowTie Inc.

Ed: Wendy Bedwell-Wilson. **Description:** Pet supply retailers can benefit from stocking foods and treats that address obesity, which according to the American Veterinary Medical Association, has become the most prevalent nutritional disorder in dogs. With the rise in dog obesity, products like work-for-their food toys have been sought by dog owners.

1061 ■ *"No-Shed Dogs Lead the Way to Big Growth" in Business Courier (Vol. 26, January 8, 2010, No. 38, pp. 1)*
Pub: American City Business Journals, Inc.

Ed: Lucy May. **Description:** Ed Lukacevic of Grant County, Kentucky is developing Dinovite, a dietary supplement that minimizes shedding and scratching in dogs. Statistical data included.

1062 ■ *"Online Pet Medication Store Supports Free Vaccinations for Cats" in Internet Wire (August 31, 2010)*
Pub: Comtex

Description: Pethealth Inc., The Petango Store will help to support The Humane Society of Tampa Bay's efforts by offering free feline vaccinations for the cat's entire lifetime that is adopted between September 1, 2010 and February 28, 2010. The cat must be one year or older at time of adoption.

1063 ■ *"Pet Kiosk Offers Search Options" in Times-News (October 14, 2010)*
Pub: Times-News Publishing Company

Ed: Roselee Papandrea. **Description:** Chameleon Pet Kiosk located at the Spay and Neuter Clinic of Alamance County in Burlington, North Carolina allows users to see and read about animals available for adoption at the center.

1064 ■ *"Solutions for the Frustrating Feline" in Pet Product News (Vol. 64, November 2010, No. 11, pp. 46)*
Pub: BowTie Inc.

Ed: Lori Luechtefeld. **Description:** Products that can help customers deal with problematic cat behaviors, such as out-of-the-box urination and scratching are described. Information on such products including litter box deodorants and disposable scratchers is provided. Feline territorial behaviors can also be addressed by pheromone products that can calm hyperactive cats.

1065 ■ *"Supplements Mix Nutrition With Convenience" in Pet Product News (Vol. 64, November 2010, No. 11, pp. 44)*
Pub: BowTie Inc.

Ed: Karen Shugart. **Description:** Pet supply manufacturers have been making supplements and enhanced foods that improve mineral consumption, boost bone density, and sharpen appetite in herps. Customers seem to enjoy the convenience as particular herps demands are being addressed by these offerings. Features of other supplements and enhanced foods for herps are described.

1066 ■ *"Sustaining Health" in Pet Product News (Vol. 64, November 2010, No. 11, pp. 28)*
Pub: BowTie Inc.

Ed: Angela Pham. **Description:** How pet supply retailers have responded to dog owners' interest in health supplements and their ingredients is discussed. Dog owners are showing interest in the ingredients inside the supplements and are reading labels. Retailers must now prove the beneficial effects of these ingredients in order to make the sale.

1067 ■ *"Tapping the 'Well' in Wellness" in Pet Product News (Vol. 64, November 2010, No. 11, pp. 1)*
Pub: BowTie Inc.

Ed: Wendy-Bedwell Wilson. **Description:** Healthy food and treats are among the leading wellness products being sought by customers from specialty retailers to keep their pets healthy. With this demand for pet wellness products, retailers suggest making sure that staff know key ingredients to emphasize to customers. Other insights into this trend and ways to engage customers are discussed.

TRADE PERIODICALS

1068 ■ *AHI Newsletter*
Pub: Animal Health Institute
Contact: Alexander S. Mathews, President

Released: 4/year. **Price:** Free. **Description:** Discusses developments of significance to animal health, livestock, and veterinary industries. Includes legislative and regulatory updates and news of research.

1069 ■ *American Journal of Veterinary Research*
Pub: American Veterinary Medical Association
Contact: Douglas Aspros, President

URL(s): https://www.avma.org/News/Journals/Pages/default.aspx. **Ed:** Bruce G. McLaughlin. **Released:** Monthly **Price:** $255, Nonmembers; $265, Other countries; $40, Students.

1070 ■ *Animal News*
Pub: Morris Animal Foundation
Contact: David Haworth, President

Ed: Carissa Lester, Editor, clester@morrisanimalfoundation.org. **Released:** 3/year. **Price:** Included in membership; Free. **Description:** Contains articles about Morris Animal Foundation's work to ensure a healthier tomorrow for animals.

1071 ■ *AVMA Members' Magazine*
Pub: Alberta Veterinary Medical Association

Ed: Midge Landals, Editor, midge.landals@avma.ab.ca. **Released:** Bimonthly. **Price:** Included in membership. **Description:** Features, letters to the editor, a calendar of events, reports of meetings, news of educational opportunities, and job listings.

1072 ■ *Canadian Veterinary Journal*
Contact: Heather Broughton, Managing Editor
URL(s): canadianveterinarians.net/publications-journal-issue.aspx. **Released:** Monthly **Price:** $170, Canada; $180, Other countries.

1073 ■ *CVO Update*
Pub: College of Veterinarians of Ontario
Contact: Beth Ready, Assistant
E-mail: bready@cvo.org
Released: Quarterly. **Price:** Free. **Description:** Covers veterinary-related issues.

1074 ■ *Feline Health Topics*
Pub: Cornell Feline Health Center
Contact: Dr. Colin R. Parrish, Director
Released: Quarterly. **Price:** $30, U.S.; $1, single issue; $35. **Description:** Focuses on diseases of cats, examining particular diseases in depth in each issue. Provides news of disease outbreaks, recommendations for treatment, and news of research. Publishes news and activities of the Center, and social issues pertaining to veterinarians.

1075 ■ *Humane News*
Pub: Associated Humane Societies
Contact: Roseann Trezza, Executive Director
Ed: Roseann Trezza, Editor. **Released:** Monthly. **Price:** Included in membership. **Description:** Reports on news of the programs and activities of humane societies seeking to assist wild and domestic animals. Provides legislative updates on bills supporting animal welfare.

1076 ■ *Journal of the American Animal Hospital Association*
Pub: American Animal Hospital Association
Contact: Kate S. Knutson, President
URL(s): www.jaaha.org. **Released:** Bimonthly **Price:** $107, Institutions and non-members; $107, Institutions, Canada and non-members; $107, Institutions, other countries and non-members.

1077 ■ *Journal of the American Veterinary Medical Association*
Pub: American Veterinary Medical Association
Contact: Douglas Aspros, President
URL(s): https://www.avma.org/News/Journals/Pages/default.aspx. **Ed:** Dr. Bruce G. McLaughlin. **Released:** Semimonthly **Price:** $210, Nonmembers; $230, Other countries; $25, Single issue; $30, Single issue foreign.

1078 ■ *Miniature Donkey Talk: The Talk of the Donkey World*
Pub: Pheasant Meadow Farm
URL(s): www.qis.net/~minidonk/mdt.htmwww.webdonkeys.com/index.php. **Ed:** Bonnie Gross. **Released:** Bimonthly **Price:** $40, By mail 1st class; $75, Two years mailed 1st class.

1079 ■ *Protecting Animals*
Pub: American Humane
Released: Quarterly. **Description:** Covers animal control and sheltering issues. Reports on ideas, technologies, and procedures to enhance and expand shelter programs and animal care.

1080 ■ *TRENDS Magazine*
Pub: American Animal Hospital Association
Contact: Kate S. Knutson, President
URL(s): www.aahanet.org/publications/trendsmagazine.aspxtrends.aahanet.org/eweb/. **Ed:** Constance Hardesty. **Released:** 6-8/yr. **Price:** $60, U.S. and Canada; $70, Other countries; $20, Single issue.

1081 ■ *Veterinary Clinics of North America: Equine Practice*
Pub: Elsevier
URL(s): www.elsevier.com/wps/find/journaldescription.cws_home/623253/descrip tion#description. **Ed:** Prof. Simon A. Turner. **Released:** 3/yr. **Price:** $496, Institutions, other countries; $346, Other countries; $172, Students, other countries; $397, Institutions; $126, Students; $299, Canada; $257, Individuals; $496, Institutions, Canada.

1082 ■ *Your Dog*
Pub: Tufts University
Contact: Linda Ross, Editor-in-Chief
Ed: Gloria Parkinson, Editor. **Released:** Monthly. **Price:** $20, individuals. **Description:** Publishes medical and behavioral advice and tips on dogs by veterinarians. Recurring features include columns titled My Dog and Chewing It Over.

TRADE SHOWS AND CONVENTIONS

1083 ■ American Veterinary Medical Association Annual Convention
American Veterinary Medical Association (AVMA)
1931 N Meacham Rd., Ste. 100
Schaumburg, IL 60173-4360
Ph: (847)925-8070
Free: 800-248-2862
Fax: (847)925-1329
Co. E-mail: avmainfo@avma.org
URL: http://www.avma.org
Contact: Douglas Aspros, President
URL(s): www.avma.org. **Price:** $475, Members; $700, Non-members; $75, veterinary student. **Frequency:** Annual. **Audience:** Veterinarians. **Principal Exhibits:** Products, materials, equipment, data, and services for veterinary medicine. **Telecommunication Services:** avmainfo@avma.org.

1084 ■ Florida Veterinary Medical Association Annual Meeting
Florida Veterinary Medical Association
7131 Lake Ellenor Dr.
Orlando, FL 32809
Ph: (407)851-3862
Free: 800-992-3862
Fax: (407)240-3710
Co. E-mail: info@fvma.com
URL: http://www.fvma.com
Contact: James A. Kanzler, President
URL(s): www.fvma.com. **Frequency:** Annual. **Audience:** Veterinarians and technicians. **Principal Exhibits:** Scientific drugs and equipment related to veterinary medicine. **Telecommunication Services:** info@fvma.com.

1085 ■ GEOTECH EXPO 2013
Artenergy Publishing
Via Antonio Gramsci, 57
20032 Cormano, Italy
Ph: 39 2 66306866
Fax: 39 2 66305510
Co. E-mail: info@artenergypublishing.com
URL: http://www.artenergy.it/
URL(s): www.geotechexpo.eu/. **Frequency:** Biennial. **Audience:** Energy, water, and utility companies; mining companies; contractors; engineers; government agencies; environmental and civil protection agencies. **Principal Exhibits:** Platforms and equipment for onsite geotechnical investigations, perforation for deep foundations and horizontal directions, instrumentation and equipment for environmental analysis, land monitoring and restoration.

1086 ■ Missouri Veterinary Medical Association Annual Convention
Missouri Veterinary Medical Association
2500 Country Club Dr.
Jefferson City, MO 65109
Ph: (573)636-8612
Fax: (573)659-7175
Co. E-mail: mvma@movma.org
URL: http://www.mvma.us
Contact: Richard Antweiler, Executive Director
URL(s): www.movma.org. **Price:** $155, Pre-registered, members; $180, Onsite registered, members; $230, Pre-registered, non-members; $255, Onsite registered, non-members. **Frequency:** Annual. **Audience:** Veterinarians; veterinary medicine students, spouses, and veterinary technicians. **Principal Exhibits:** Veterinary instruments, surgical equipment, pharmaceuticals, dog food, publications, and animal care products.

1087 ■ Ohio Veterinary Medical Association/ Midwest Veterinary Conference
Ohio Veterinary Medical Association
3168 Riverside Dr.
Columbus, OH 43221
Ph: (614)486-7253
Free: 800-662-OVMA
Fax: (614)486-1325
Co. E-mail: ohiovma@ohiovma.org
URL: http://www.ohiovma.org
Contact: Linda Lord, President
URL(s): www.mvcinfo.org. **Frequency:** Annual. **Audience:** Veterinarians, technicians, students, and suppliers of veterinary medicine, hospital staff, spouses, hospital managers. **Principal Exhibits:** Veterinary supplies. **Dates and Locations:** Ohio Center. **Telecommunication Services:** info@mvcinfo.org.

1088 ■ Western Veterinary Conference
Western Veterinary Conference (WVC)
2425 E Oquendo Rd.
Las Vegas, NV 89120
Ph: (702)739-6698
Free: 866-800-7326
Fax: (702)739-6420
Co. E-mail: carolyn@wvc.org
URL: http://www.wvc.org
Contact: James E. Creed, President
URL(s): www.wvc.org/. **Price:** $425, veterinarian; $315, veterinary technician, practice manager, admin. staff. **Frequency:** Annual. **Audience:** Veterinarians, veterinary technicians, and veterinary hospital management. **Principal Exhibits:** Veterinary equipment, supplies, and services, including drugs. **Dates and Locations:** , Hilton Riviera.

1089 ■ Wisconsin Veterinary Medical Association Annual Convention
Wisconsin Veterinary Medical Association
2801 Crossroads Dr., Ste. 1200
Madison, WI 53718
Ph: (608)257-3665
Fax: (608)257-8989
Co. E-mail: wvma@wvma.org
URL: http://www.wvma.org
Contact: Kim Brown, Executive Director
URL(s): www.wvma.org. **Frequency:** Annual. **Audience:** Veterinarians, certified veterinary technicians, veterinary students, veterinary practice managers, spouses. **Principal Exhibits:** Veterinary supplies, pharmaceuticals, pet food, business systems, and record-keeping equipment.

CONSULTANTS

1090 ■ Thinnes & Dutton P.C.
121 W Locust St., Ste. 304
Davenport, IA 52803-2827
Ph: (563)323-6622
Fax: (563)323-1232
Contact: Teresa A. Thinnes, President
Scope: Practice management consultant for physicians, dentists, osteopathic physicians, and veterinarians. Services are adapted to each client's individual needs and desires. **Founded:** 1964.

COMPUTER SYSTEMS/ SOFTWARE

1091 ■ *DentalWare*
9645 Granite Ridge Dr., Ste. 230
San Diego, CA 92123
Ph: (858)514-0300
Free: 800-875-0480
Fax: (858)514-1210
Co. E-mail: sale@e-dsi.com
URL: http://www.e-dsi.com/
Description: Available for IBM computers and MS-DOS compatibles. Software contains a series of programs for veterinary office management, including billing, posting payments and charges, and statements and insurance forms.

1092 ■ *VetLogic*
9645 Granite Ridge Ste. 230
San Diego, CA 92123

Ph: (858)514-0300
Free: 800-875-0480
Fax: (858)514-0318
Co. E-mail: sale@e-dsi.com
URL: http://www.e-dsi.com/
Price: $2000.00. **Description:** Available for IBM computers and MS-DOS compatibles. System providing management reports, accounts receivable, patient data storage, and other functions.

LIBRARIES

1093 ■ Animal Medical Center Library
510 E. 62nd St.
New York, NY 10021
Ph: (212)838-8100
Fax: (212)832-9630
Co. E-mail: info@amcny.org
URL: http://www.amcny.org
Scope: Veterinary medicine, medicine. **Services:** Interlibrary loan; medical editing; library open to the public by appointment. **Holdings:** 1000 books; 1000 bound periodical volumes; 500 periodical volumes on microfiche. **Subscriptions:** 75 journals and other serials.

1094 ■ Auburn University - Charles Allen Cary Veterinary Medical Library
College of Veterinary Medical Complex
101 Greene Hall
Auburn University, AL 36849
Ph: (334)844-1749
Fax: (334)844-1758
Co. E-mail: vmedlib@auburn.edu
URL: http://www.lib.auburn.edu/vetmed/
Contact: Bob Buchanan, Librarian
Scope: Veterinary medicine. **Services:** Interlibrary loan; copying; Library open to the public. **Founded:** 1971. **Holdings:** 30,000 volumes. **Subscriptions:** 120 active paper serials; 7000 online journals and other serials. **Telecommunication Services:** buchara@auburn.edu.

1095 ■ District of Columbia Public Library - Technology and Science Division
Martin Luther King Memorial Library
901 G St., NW, Rm. 220
Washington, DC 20001
Ph: (202)727-1175
Fax: (202)727-1129
Co. E-mail: commentssuggestions.dcpl@dc.gov
URL: http://www.dclibrary.org
Contact: Diane Henry, Assistant Director
Scope: Automobile and appliance repair, botany, cookery, general science, geology, genetics, manufacturing, nutrition, paleontology, pet care, printing, zoology, mathematics, computer science, biology, domestic arts, earth science, chemistry and chemical technology, physics, engineering, agriculture, gardening, medicine, psychiatry, astronomy, consumer information, health, veterinary science, physical anthropology. **Services:** Interlibrary loan; copying; free Wi-Fi access; library open to the public. **Founded:** 1907. **Holdings:** 92,127 books; 2500 bound periodical volumes; 5755 microforms; 65 VF drawers. **Subscriptions:** 300 journals and other serials. **Telecommunication Services:** mlkjrlibrary@dc.gov.

1096 ■ Massachusetts Society for the Prevention of Cruelty to Animals - Angell Memorial Animal Hospital Veterinary Library
350 S. Huntington Ave.
Boston, MA 02130-4803
Ph: (617)522-7282
Fax: (617)522-4885
Co. E-mail: angellquestions@mspca.org
URL: http://www.mspca.org/
Scope: Veterinary medicine, conservation, zoology, pet care, humane education, animal welfare, animal rights. **Services:** Library open to the public by appointment. **Founded:** 1963. **Holdings:** 2000 volumes. **Subscriptions:** 50 journals and other serials.

1097 ■ National Animal Control Association - Research Library
101 N Church St.
Olathe, KS 66061

Ph: (913)768-1319
Fax: (913)768-1378
Co. E-mail: naca@nacanet.org
URL: http://www.nacanet.org
Contact: John Mays, Executive Director
Scope: Animal control, bites and attacks, rabies, euthanasia, humane education, officer training. **Services:** Copying; library open to the public. **Founded:** 1978. **Holdings:** 85 books; 50 bound periodical volumes; 10,000 reports; videocassettes. **Subscriptions:** 15 journals and other serials; 1 newspaper.

1098 ■ Ross University - School of Veterinary Medicine - Stanley Mark Dennis Veterinary Library
630 U.S. Hwy. 1
North Brunswick, NJ 08902
Free: 855-ROSS-VET
Co. E-mail: phsmith@rossvet.edu.kn
URL: http://www.rossu.edu/veterinary-school/learning-resource-center/Library.cfm
Contact: Phillip Smith, Director, Library Services
Scope: Veterinary medicine. **Services:** Interlibrary loan; copying; library open to the public with restrictions (closed weekends and two weeks prior to finals). **Founded:** 1995. **Holdings:** 6000 volumes. **Subscriptions:** 107 journals and other serials.

1099 ■ Second Chance Animal Center Library
PO Box 620
Shaftsbury, VT 05262-0620
Ph: (802)375-2898
Fax: (802)375-0235
Co. E-mail: secondchance@wildblue.net
URL: http://www.2ndchanceanimalcenter.org/
Scope: Animals - welfare, rights, farm, dog and cat care. **Services:** Library open to the public. **Founded:** 1990. **Holdings:** 600 books; videocassettes. **Subscriptions:** 14 journals and other serials; 3 newspapers.

1100 ■ Voice for Animals Library
PO Box 120095
San Antonio, TX 78212
Ph: (210)737-3138
Co. E-mail: voice@voiceforanimals.org
URL: http://www.voiceforanimals.org/
Scope: Animal rights; vegetarianism. **Services:** Library not open to the public. **Founded:** 1987. **Holdings:** 200 books; newsletters; videocassettes.

RESEARCH CENTERS

1101 ■ Cornell University - Baker Institute for Animal Health
College of Veterinary Medicine
Hungerford Hill Rd.
Ithaca, NY 14853
Ph: (607)256-5600
Fax: (607)256-5608
Co. E-mail: jaa2@cornell.edu
URL: http://bakerinstitute.vet.cornell.edu
Contact: Judith A. Appleton, Director
Founded: 1950. **Publications:** *Baker Institute for Animal Health Annual report*; Brochures on Research Topics (Periodic). **Educational Activities:** Scientific conference (Annual); Tuesday Noon Seminar Series, Thaw lecture theater. **Telecommunication Services:** baker_institute@cornell.edu.

1102 ■ Cornell University - Cornell Feline Health Center
College of Veterinary Medicine
Hungerford Hill Rd.
Ithaca, NY 14853
Ph: (607)253-3414
Free: 800-548-8937
Fax: (607)253-3419
URL: http://www.vet.cornell.edu/fhc
Contact: Colin R. Parrish, Director
Services: Camuti Consultation and Diagnostic Service: which aids veterinarians and cat owners. **Founded:** 1974. **Publications:** *Cornell Feline Health Center Annual report*; Cat Watch (Monthly); Feline Health Topics for Veterinarians (Quarterly); Feline Information Bulletin (Periodic). **Educational Activi-**

ties: Continuing Education Program, on feline diseases for feline practitioners and cat owners; Feline Specialist Seminar (Annual), for veterinarians.

1103 ■ Iowa State University of Science and Technology - Institute for International Cooperation in Animal Biologics (IICAB)
2160 College of Veterinary Medicine
Ames, IA 50011
Ph: (515)294-7189
Fax: (515)294-8259
Co. E-mail: iicab@iastate.edu
URL: http://www.cfsph.iastate.edu/IICAB
Contact: James A. Roth, Director
Services: Technology transfer: from the Center to industry. **Founded:** 1987. **Publications:** *IICAB Annual Report* (Annual). **Educational Activities:** Veterinary Biologies Training Program (Annual), for biologics industry and government regulatory officials; every May. **Telecommunication Services:** jaroth@iastate.edu.

1104 ■ Iowa State University of Science and Technology - Veterinary Diagnostic Laboratory (VDL)
College of Veterinary Medicine
1600 S 16th St.
Ames, IA 50011-1250
Ph: (515)294-1950
Fax: (515)294-3564
Co. E-mail: isuvdlv@iastate.edu
URL: http://vetmed.iastate.edu/diagnostic-lab
Contact: Patrick G. Halbur, Executive Director
Services: Diagnostic services and consultation: to livestock and pet owners. **Founded:** 1947. **Publications:** *VDL Annual Reports*; Scientific journal articles. **Educational Activities:** Continuing education and scientific presentations, 8-15 per year. **Telecommunication Services:** pghalbur@iastate.edu.

1105 ■ Oklahoma State University - Surgical Laser Laboratory
Department of Veterinary Clinical Sciences
Veterinary Teaching Hospital
College of Veterinary Medicine
Stillwater, OK 74078
Ph: (405)744-8689
Fax: (405)744-6265
Co. E-mail: kebart@okstate.edu
Contact: Dr. Kenneth E. Bartels, Director
Services: Clinical treatment using laser modalities for large and small animals (Weekly). **Founded:** 1989. **Educational Activities:** Didactic classes (Occasionally), on basic laser surgery.

1106 ■ University of California, Davis - Center for Companion Animal Health (CCAH)
School of Veterinary Medicine
1 Shields Ave.
Davis, CA 95616-8782
Ph: (530)752-7295
Fax: (530)752-7701
Co. E-mail: ncpedersen@ucdavis.edu
URL: http://www.vetmed.ucdavis.edu/ccah
Contact: Prof. Niels C. Pedersen, Director
Founded: 1976. **Educational Activities:** Annual Canine or Feline Health Seminars; Research Educational Meeting (Annual). **Awards:** CCAH Research fellowships.

1107 ■ University of Wyoming - Wyoming State Veterinary Laboratory (WSVL)
1174 Snowy Range Rd.
Laramie, WY 82070
Ph: (307)766-9925
Free: 800-442-8331
Fax: (307)721-2051
Co. E-mail: montgome@uwyo.edu
URL: http://www.uwyo.edu/wyovet
Contact: Prof. Donald L. Montgomery, Director
Founded: 1947. **Publications:** *WSVL Annual report*; WSVL Newsletter.

1108 ■ Utah State University - Central Utah Veterinary Diagnostic Laboratory
PO Box 80
Nephi, UT 84648-0080
Ph: (435)623-1402
Fax: (435)623-1548
URL: http://www.usu.edu/uvdl/
Founded: 1944.

1109 ■ Virginia Polytechnic Institute and State University - Marion Du Pont Scott Equine Medical Center
PO Box 1938
Leesburg, VA 20177
Ph: (703)771-6800
Free: 800-436-2911
Fax: (703)771-6810
Co. E-mail: nawhite2@vt.edu

URL: http://equinemedicalcenter.net
Contact: Prof. Nathaniel A. White, II, Director

Services: Clinical service to horses. **Founded:** 1984. **Educational Activities:** Continuing education programs; Veterinary professional curriculum, residency training programs, graduate studies program; Tuesday Talks, in winter session. **Awards:** Rotating internships. **Telecommunication Services:** emc@vt.edu.

ASSOCIATIONS AND OTHER ORGANIZATIONS

1110 ■ American Hatpin Society
c/o Cathy Miller, VP
2505 Indian Creek Rd.
Diamond Bar, CA 91765-3307
Ph: (909)861-4267
Co. E-mail: info@americanhatpinsociety.com
URL: http://www.americanhatpinsociety.com
Contact: Jodi Lenocker, President
Description: Collectors of hatpins. Promotes collection, preservation, and restoration of hatpins and related fashion accessories. Serves as a clearinghouse on hatpins and their history; facilitates exchange of information among members; conducts educational programs. **Founded:** 1989. **Publications:** *American Hatpin Society Newsletter.*

1111 ■ Antiquarian Booksellers' Association of Canada (ABAC)—Association de la Librairie Ancienne du Canada
368 Dalhousie St., Ste. 301
Ottawa, ON, Canada K1N 7G3
Co. E-mail: info@abac.org
URL: http://www.abac.org
Contact: Liam McGahern, President
Description: Bookselling firms and dealers in rare books and manuscripts. Promotes adherence to high standards of ethics and practice in the trade of antiquarian books. Serves as liaison between members and book collectors and as a clearinghouse on antiquarian books and their trade. **Founded:** 1966.

1112 ■ Appraisers Association of America (AAA)
386 Park Ave. S, 20th Fl., Ste. 2000
New York, NY 10016
Ph: (212)889-5404
Fax: (212)889-5503
Co. E-mail: aaa@appraisersassoc.org
URL: http://www.appraisersassoc.org
Contact: Nancy Harrison, President
Description: Professional society of appraisers of personal property such as: Americana; antiques; armor; art objects; bibelot; books; bronzes; china and porcelain; clocks and watches; coins; crystal and glass; curios; diamonds and jewelry; enamels; etchings; fine art; firearms; furniture; furs; graphic art; guns; household furnishings; ivories; leather goods; lighting fixtures; linens and lace; miniatures; music; musical instruments; oriental art; paintings; pewter; pianos; primitive art; prints; rugs; sculpture; Sheffield plate; silver and silverware; stamps; steins and tankards; taxes; and woodcarvings. **Scope:** personal property, auction records. **Founded:** 1949. **Subscriptions:** books periodicals. **Publications:** *The Appraiser* (Quarterly); *Appraisers Association of America--Membership Directory* (Biennial).

1113 ■ Art and Antique Dealers League of America (AADLA)
Lennox Hill Sta.
New York, NY 10021
Ph: (212)879-7558
Fax: (212)772-7197
Co. E-mail: secretary@artantiquedealersleague.com
URL: http://www.artantiquedealersleague.com
Contact: Clinton Howell, President
Description: Represents retailers and wholesalers of antiques and art objects. Convention/Meeting: none. **Founded:** 1926.

1114 ■ Cracker Jack Collectors Association (CJCA)
c/o Linda Farris, Membership Chair
4908 N Holborn Dr.
Muncie, IN 47304
Co. E-mail: lindajfarris@comcast.net
URL: http://www.crackerjackcollectors.com
Contact: Nancy Schultz, President
Description: Collectors of Cracker Jack prizes and related items. Promotes collection and preservation of Cracker Jack memorabilia. Gathers and disseminates information on Cracker Jack collectibles and their availability; facilitates exchange of information and promotes good fellowship among members. **Founded:** 1993.

1115 ■ Fostoria Glass Collectors (FGC)
PO Box 826
Moundsville, WV 26041
Ph: (304)845-9188
URL: http://www.fostoriacollectors.org
Contact: Jim Davis, President
Description: Collectors and admirers of handmade American glassware. Promotes appreciation of handmade American glass products. Serves as a clearinghouse on handmade American glassware and its collection; sponsors research and educational programs; participates in charitable activities; maintains museum. **Founded:** 1990. **Educational Activities:** Fostoria Glass Collectors Meeting (Monthly). **Awards:** Gift (Annual).

1116 ■ Foundation for the Study of the Arts and Crafts Movement at Roycroft (FSA/CM)
46 Walnut St.
East Aurora, NY 14052-2330
Ph: (716)652-3333
Fax: (716)655-0562
Co. E-mail: info@roycroftshops.com
URL: http://www.roycroft.org/foundation
Contact: Kitty Turgeon, Executive Director
Description: Represents individuals interested in getting information about and collecting mission, prairie, and other arts and crafts pieces from the arts and crafts era (1895-1930). Studies the works of William Morris, Elbert Hubbard and Roycrofters, furniture designer Gustav Stickley, and architects Frank Lloyd Wright and Greene & Greene. Encourages the collecting of antiques from the Craftsman era and the Roycroft shops. Operates speakers' bureau. Sponsors educational programs. Group is currently expanding with Elderhostel and higher visibility. **Founded:** 1989. **Publications:** *Annual Issue* (Annual); *Craftsman Homeowner.* **Educational Activities:** Arts and Crafts - California Symposium (Annual). **Awards:** Mary Roelofs Stott Fund (Semiannual).

1117 ■ International League of Antiquarian Booksellers (ILAB)
c/o Tom Congalton, Pres.
35 W Maple Ave.
Merchantville, NJ 08109-5141
Ph: (856)665-2284
Fax: (856)665-3639
Co. E-mail: mail@betweenthecovers.com
URL: http://www.ilab.org
Contact: Tom Congalton, President
Description: Represents national associations of antiquarian booksellers around the world. Organizes professional training courses for members. Sponsors book fairs. **Founded:** 1947. **Educational Activities:** International League of Antiquarian Booksellers Congress (Biennial). **Awards:** Bibliographic Award (Periodic); Breslauer Prize for Bibliography.

1118 ■ International Paperweight Society (IPS)
410 S Michigan Ave., Ste. No. 207
Chicago, IL 60605
Ph: (312)583-1177
Free: 800-538-0766
Co. E-mail: lselman@got.net
URL: http://www.paperweight.com
Contact: Larry Selman, President
Description: Promotes paperweight collecting. Conducts educational programs. Runs a speakers' bureau. **Founded:** 1993.

1119 ■ National Antique & Art Dealers Association of America Inc. (NAADAA)
220 E 57th St.
New York, NY 10022
Ph: (212)826-9707
Fax: (212)832-9493
Co. E-mail: paulh@naada.org
URL: http://www.naadaa.org
Contact: James McConnaughy, President
Description: Art and antique dealers who handle antiques and works of art of the highest quality. Safeguards the interests of those who buy, sell, and collect antiques and works of art. Sponsors periodic exhibitions; maintains speakers' bureau. **Scope:** antiques, arts. **Founded:** 1954. **Publications:** *National Antique & Art Dealers Association of America Membership Directory*; *National Antique & Art Dealers Association of America--Membership Directory* (Continuous). **Telecommunication Services:** inquiries@naadaa.org.

1120 ■ National Shaving Mug Collectors Association (NSMCA)
366 Lake Shore Dr.
Hewitt, NJ 07421
URL: http://www.nsmca.net
Contact: Don Allain, Treasurer
Description: Collectors of shaving mugs and other shaving equipment. Promotes collection of shaving paraphernalia as a hobby. Facilitates communication and trading among members; gathers and disseminates information on shaving mugs and related equipment. **Founded:** 1980.

REFERENCE WORKS

1121 ■ Appraisers Association of America--Membership Directory
Pub: Appraisers Association of America Inc.
Contact: Roslym Goldman, President
URL(s): www.appraisersassoc.org. **Released:** Biennial; Even years. **Covers:** 800 member appraisers of fine art, antiques, and personal property. **Entries include:** Name, address, phone, specialties. **Arrangement:** Geographical. **Indexes:** Alphabetical, specialty.

1122 ■ "Echo Vintage Clothing Fundraiser Set July 24" in Tri-City Herald (July 22, 2010)
Pub: McClatchy-Tribune
Description: Bicentennial Echo Vintage Clothing Show and Tea was held July 24, 2010 at the Echo City Hall Ballroom in Echo, Oregon. The event is held every two years to fund project in Echo and to maintain the vintage clothing collection.

1123 ■ How to Buy and Sell Antiques
Pub: Parkwest Publications, Incorporated
Ed: Fiona Shoop. **Released:** August 2006. **Price:** $28.50. **Description:** Fiona Shoop shares twenty years experience to train individuals to become successful antiques dealers.

1124 ■ National Antique & Art Dealers Association of America--Membership Directory
Pub: National Antique & Art Dealers Association of America Inc.
Contact: James McConnaughy, President
URL(s): www.naadaa.org. **Released:** Continuous **Covers:** 46 member dealers. **Entries include:** Firm name, address, phone, names of one or more principal executives, cable address, specialties, and areas of expertise. **Arrangement:** Alphabetical.

1125 ■ Old-Stuff--Directory of Shops Section
Pub: VBM Printers Inc.
Contact: Ron Miller, Publisher
E-mail: ron@oldstuffnews.com
URL(s): oldstuffnews.com. **Ed:** Donna Miller. **Released:** 6 times a year. **Price:** $20, Individuals yearly subscription; $5.50, Single issue; $35, Two years; $35, Canada. **Publication includes:** List of approximately 900 antiques shops in the northwestern United States. **Entries include:** Shop name, address, phone. **Database includes:** Calendar of events. **Arrangement:** Geographical. **Indexes:** Shops, alphabetical by city.

1126 ■ "Prime Time for Vintage" in Daily Variety (Vol. 308, August 23, 2010, No. 35, pp. 12)
Pub: Reed Business Information Inc.
Ed: Cynthia Littleton. **Description:** The week of August 23 starts the busy season for owners of Los Angeles' vintage couture shops due to Emmy-related events.

1127 ■ "Shop Around" in Houston Chronicle (December 7, 2010, pp. 3)
Pub: Houston Chronicle
Ed: Tara Dooley. **Description:** Profile of Diana Candida and Maria Martinez who partnered to open Beatniks, a shop carrying vintage clothing, art from various artists, dance shoes, and jewelry.

1128 ■ Warman's Antiques & Collectibles Price Guide
Pub: Krause Publications Inc.
Contact: Roger Case, President
URL(s): www.krausebooks.comwww.collect.com. **Released:** Annual; latest edition 2013. **Price:** $12, Individuals Paperback. **Covers:** Over 50,000 antiques and collectibles, plus listings for collector's clubs. **Entries include:** Description, price. **Database includes:** 1,500 color photos.

SOURCES OF SUPPLY

1129 ■ Collectibles Market Guide & Price Index
Collectors Information Bureau
Contact: Linda Kruger, Director
E-mail: lkruger@pioneermagazines.com
URL(s): www.treasuresmagazine.com. **Released:** Annual; latest edition 20th. **Price:** $24.95, Individuals

suggested retail; $10, Individuals sales price. **Publication includes:** List of manufacturers of limited edition collectible plates, figurines, bells, graphics, ornaments, dolls, and steins; related associations and museums; price guide to secondary market values of limited edition collectibles. **Entries include:** Company name and address, history, current projects, values of retired editions. **Arrangement:** Membership organization. Editorial restricted to member companies. **Indexes:** Price index of collectibles. Biographies of collectibles artists; collectibles price index; feature articles; glossary; directory of secondary market dealers.

TRADE PERIODICALS

1130 ■ Antique Bottle and Glass Collector
Pub: Antique Bottle and Glass Collector
URL(s): www.glswrk-auction.com. **Ed:** Ralph Finch. **Released:** Monthly **Price:** $32, Individuals 2nd class; $47, Individuals 1st class; $54, Individuals CAN; $95, Other countries by airmail.

1131 ■ Antique Trader Weekly: America's Weekly Antiques & Collectibles Marketplace
Pub: Krause Publications Inc.
Contact: Roger Case, President
URL(s): www.antiquetrader.com. **Ed:** Karen Knapstein. **Released:** Weekly **Price:** $26, Individuals; $115.98, Canada; $165.98, Other countries.

1132 ■ Antiques and the Arts Weekly
Pub: Bee Publishing Company Inc.
URL(s): antiquesandthearts.com/. **Ed:** Scudder R. Smith. **Released:** Weekly **Price:** $81, Individuals print & web access; $143, Two years print & web access.

1133 ■ Antiques & Collecting Magazine
Pub: Lightner Publishing Corp.
URL(s): www.acmagazine.com/. **Released:** Monthly **Price:** $38, Individuals; $66, Two years.

1134 ■ Collectors News: Serving Coolectors for 50 Years
Pub: Pioneer Communications Inc.
Contact: Jim Miller, President
E-mail: jmiller@thepioneergroup.com
URL(s): collectors-news.com. **Released:** Monthly **Price:** $26.95, Individuals.

1135 ■ Country Home
Pub: Meredith Corp.
URL(s): www.countryhome.com. **Released:** Monthly; 10/yr. **Price:** $4.95, Individuals newstand; $21.97, Two years.

1136 ■ Discover Mid-America
Pub: Discovery Publications Inc.
URL(s): www.discoverypub.com. **Released:** Monthly

1137 ■ The Magazine Antiques
Pub: Brant Publications Inc.
Contact: Evanly Schindler, President
URL(s): www.themagazineantiques.com/. **Released:** Monthly **Price:** $29.95, Individuals; $79.95, Canada; $95, Other countries.

1138 ■ The New England Antiques Journal
Pub: Turley Publications
Contact: Patrick Turley, President
URL(s): www.antiquesjournal.com. **Released:** Monthly **Price:** $15.95, Individuals; $25.95, Two years; $15.95, Individuals gift subscription; $25.95, Two years two years gift subscription; $32, Canada; $63, Individuals European (surface price); $142, Individuals European (air mail); $54, Canada two years.

1139 ■ Uncoverings: The Research Papers of the American Quilt Study Group
Pub: American Quilt Study Group
Contact: Mary G. Persyn, President
URL(s): www.americanquiltstudygroup.org/publications.asp. **Ed:** Laurel Horton. **Released:** Annual **Price:** $20, Single issue.

VIDEOCASSETTES/ AUDIOCASSETTES

1140 ■ Hidden Treasures: A Collector's Guide to Antique and Vintage Jewelry of the 19th and 20th Centuries
S.I. Video Sales Group
PO Box 63745
Philadelphia, PA 19147
Ph: (267)519-2222
Co. E-mail: stann@sivideo.com
URL: http://www.sivideo.com
Released: 1992. **Price:** $24.95. **Description:** A tour through the decades highlights the popular jewelry of the day and how to distinguish the real articles through workmanship, materials, motif, and other signs of authenticity, age, and value. Also provides a visual price guide. **Availability:** VHS.

1141 ■ Inside Tips on Discovering Antiques
Curtis, Inc.
105 Western Ave.
Cincinnati, OH 45203
Ph: (513)621-8895
Free: 800-733-2878
Fax: (513)621-0942
Co. E-mail: info@curtisinc.com
URL: http://www.curtisinc.com
Released: 1992. **Price:** $19.95. **Description:** Learn how to buy and sell antiques with confidence and discover secrets on finding treasures in the trash, reviving old wood without stripping, and finding antiques at affordable prices. **Availability:** VHS.

TRADE SHOWS AND CONVENTIONS

1142 ■ The Winter Olympia Fine Art and Antiques Fair
Clarion Events Ltd.
Earls Court Exhibition Centre
Warwick Rd.
London SW5 9TA, United Kingdom
Ph: 44 20 7370 8139
URL: http://www.clarionevents.com
Contact: Simon Kimble, Chief Executive Officer
URL(s): www.olympia-antiques.com/. **Frequency:** Annual. **Audience:** Trade and general public. **Principal Exhibits:** Antiques including fine, oak, garden, and country furniture; rugs; paintings; ceramics; clocks; sculptures; jewelry, silver, and bronzes. **Telecommunication Services:** olympia-antiques@eco.co.uk.

LIBRARIES

1143 ■ California University of Pennsylvania - Louis L. Manderino Library - Special Collections
250 University Ave., Rm. 435
California, PA 15419
Ph: (724)938-5926
Fax: (724)938-5901
Co. E-mail: pokol@calu.edu
URL: http://library.calu.edu
Contact: Alber Pokol, Archivist Librarian, Special Collections
Scope: Rare books, art, music. **Services:** Interlibrary loan; Library open to the public by appointment.

1144 ■ Dunham Tavern Museum Library
6709 Euclid Ave.
Cleveland, OH 44103
Ph: (216)431-1060
Co. E-mail: dunhamtavern@sbcglobal.net
URL: http://dunhamtavern.org
Contact: William Ruper, President
Scope: Antique collecting; history of Cleveland and Ohio. **Services:** Library open to members only. **Holdings:** 1000 books.

1145 ■ Houston Museum of Decorative Arts Library
201 High St.
Chattanooga, TN 37403

Ph: (423)267-7176
Fax: (423)267-7177
Co. E-mail: houston@chattanooga.net
URL: http://www.thehoustonmuseum.com
Contact: Amy H. Frierson, Director
Scope: Hand-blown antique glass, porcelain, pottery, ceramics, early American furniture, decorative art. **Founded:** 1961. **Holdings:** 300 books; 750 unbound reports; unbound periodical volumes; archival files of articles pertaining to the collection.

1146 ■ Hunter Museum of American Art Library
10 Bluff View St.
Chattanooga, TN 37403-1197
Ph: (423)267-0968
Fax: (423)267-9844
Co. E-mail: esimak@huntermuseum.org
URL: http://www.huntermuseum.org
Contact: Ellen Simak, Curator
Scope: American art, antiques, architecture, biography, abstract art, arts and crafts. **Services:** Library not open to the public. **Founded:** 1958. **Holdings:** 800 books; 13 VF drawers of sales and auction catalogs; 17 VF drawers of museum and exhibition catalogs. **Subscriptions:** 38 journals and other serials.

1147 ■ Karpeles Manuscript Library - Buffalo Museum
North Hall
220 North St.
Buffalo, NY 14201
Ph: (716)885-4139
Co. E-mail: kmuseumbuf@aol.com
URL: http://www.rain.org/~karpeles/
Contact: Christopher Kelly, Director
Scope: Special manuscripts. **Services:** Library open to the public. **Founded:** 1998. **Holdings:** 30,000 books; 1.1 million manuscripts.

1148 ■ Karpeles Manuscript Library - Charleston Museum
68 Spring St.
Charleston, SC 29403
Ph: (843)853-4651
Co. E-mail: kmuseumchr@aol.com
URL: http://www.rain.org/~karpeles/
Contact: Dr. Stephen J. White, Director
Scope: Special manuscripts. **Services:** Library open to the public. **Founded:** Holdings: Figures not available.

1149 ■ Karpeles Manuscript Library - Collections
21 W. Anapamu St.
Santa Barbara, CA 93101
Ph: (805)962-5322
Co. E-mail: kmuseumsb@aol.com
URL: http://www.rain.org/~karpeles
Contact: Norm Cohan, Director
Scope: Historical manuscripts from all periods in world history. **Founded:** 1983. **Holdings:** 1 million manuscripts.

1150 ■ Karpeles Manuscript Library - Jacksonville Museum
101 W. 1st St.
Jacksonville, FL 33206
Ph: (904)356-2992
URL: http://www.rain.org/~karpeles/jax.html
Contact: Richard Minor, Director
Scope: Rare manuscripts. **Services:** Library open to the public. **Founded:** 1993. **Holdings:** 200 books; manuscripts.

1151 ■ Karpeles Manuscript Library - Santa Barbara Museum
21 W. Anapamu St.
Santa Barbara, CA 93101
Ph: (805)962-5322

Fax: (805)962-5322
Co. E-mail: kmuseumsba@aol.com
URL: http://www.rain.org/~karpeles/sb.html
Contact: Norman Cohan, Director
Scope: Special manuscripts. **Services:** Library open to the public. **Founded:** 1986. **Holdings:** 1 million manuscripts; patents; archives.

1152 ■ Karpeles Manuscript Library - Tacoma Museum
407 S. G St.
Tacoma, WA 98405
Ph: (253)383-2575
Co. E-mail: kmuseumtaq@aol.com
URL: http://www.rain.org/~karpeles/taqfrm.html
Contact: Thomas M. Jutilla, Director
Scope: Rare manuscripts. **Services:** Library open to the public. **Founded:** 1991. **Holdings:** Figures not available.

1153 ■ Miami University - Southwest Ohio Regional Depository
4200 E. University Blvd.
Middletown, OH 45052
Ph: (513)727-3475
Co. E-mail: lipscope@muohio.edu
URL: http://www.sword.org
Contact: Pam Lipscomb, Manager
URL(s): www.lib.muohio.edu/policies/sword. **Scope:** Rare books. **Services:** Interlibrary loan; copying; Library open to the public by appointment. **Founded:** 1994. **Holdings:** 1,990,618 volumes.

1154 ■ Niagara University Library - Rare Book Room Collection
5795 Lewiston Rd.
Niagara Falls, NY 14109
Ph: (716)286-8001
Fax: (716)286-8030
Co. E-mail: schoen@niagara.edu
URL: http://library.niagara.edu/about/special-collections/rare-book-collection/
Contact: David Schoen, Director, Library Services
Scope: Rare books, 1473-1800. **Services:** Library open to the public by appointment. **Founded:** 1850. **Holdings:** 2000 books; manuscripts.

1155 ■ Ohio Wesleyan University - L.A. Beeghly Library - Archives/Special Collections
43 Rowland Ave.
Delaware, OH 43015
Ph: (740)368-3285
Fax: (740)368-3222
Co. E-mail: aoum@owu.edu
URL: http://lis.owu.edu/spcindex.htm
Contact: Carol Holliger, Archivist
Scope: Ohio Wesleyan University history, Methodism in Ohio, rare books. **Services:** Interlibrary loan; Library open to the public by appointment. **Holdings:** 480,000 items. **Subscriptions:** 1000 journals and other serials.

1156 ■ Winfred L. and Elizabeth C. Post Foundation - Post Memorial Art Reference Library
300 S. Main St.
Joplin, MO 64801-2384
Ph: (417)782-7678
Co. E-mail: lsimpson@postlibrary.org
URL: http://www.postlibrary.org
Contact: Leslie Simpson, Director
Scope: Visual arts, antiques, architecture, photography, historic preservation, heraldry. **Services:** Copying; monthly art exhibits; library open to the public. **Founded:** 1981. **Holdings:** 3600 books; 245 bound periodical volumes; 16 VF drawers of pictures, articles, pamphlets; 1000 slides. **Subscriptions:** 31 journals and other serials.

1157 ■ Shelburne Museum Research Library
6000 Shelburne Rd.
Shelburne, VT 05482
Ph: (802)985-3346
Fax: (802)985-2331
Co. E-mail: library@shelburnemuseum.org
URL: http://www.shelburnemuseum.org
Contact: Polly Darnell, Archivist Librarian
Scope: American folk art, decorative arts, fine art, and design. **Services:** Copying; library open to the public by appointment. **Founded:** 1947. **Holdings:** 7000 books; 400 lin.ft. archives; 450 manuscript items. **Subscriptions:** 30 journals and other serials. **Telecommunication Services:** info@shelburnemuseum.org.

1158 ■ Society of Inkwell Collectors Library
P.O. Box 447
Fort Madison, IA 52627-0447
Ph: (319)372-0881
Fax: (319)372-0882
Co. E-mail: sam@pendemonium.com
URL: http://www.soic.com/Librarian.html
Contact: Sam Fiorella, Librarian
Scope: Inkwells, bottles, and pens; history of writing; repair and cleaning techniques. **Services:** Library open to the public for reference use only. **Founded:** 2004. **Holdings:** 75 books; periodicals; clippings; audio/visuals. **Telecommunication Services:** soic@soic.com.

1159 ■ Bayard Taylor Memorial Library
216 E. State St.
Kennett Square, PA 19348-3112
Ph: (610)444-2702
Co. E-mail: dmurray@ccls.org
URL: http://www.bayardtaylor.org
Contact: Donna Murray, Director, Library Services
Scope: Antiques, arts, social sciences, history, gardening. **Services:** Interlibrary loan; copying; library open to the public. **Founded:** 1895. **Holdings:** 50,000 fiction and nonfiction books; 1000 books on tape; 2000 feature films; 150 periodical titles. **Subscriptions:** 150 journals and other serials; 8 newspapers. **Telecommunication Services:** psapko@ccls.org.

1160 ■ Villanova University - Falvey Memorial Library - Special Collections
Villanova, PA 19085
Ph: (610)519-4290
Fax: (610)519-6000
Co. E-mail: bente.polites@villanova.edu
URL: http://www.library.villanova.edu
Contact: Bente Polites, Librarian, Special Collections
Scope: Augustiniana, early printed books and general rare books, Irish history, James Joyce. **Services:** Interlibrary loan; copying; library open to the public. **Founded:** 1842. **Holdings:** 15,000 items. **Telecommunication Services:** michael.foight@villanova.edu; laura.bang@villanova.edu.

1161 ■ Western Maryland Public Libraries - Regional Library
100 S. Potomac St.
Hagerstown, MD 21740
Ph: (301)739-3250
Fax: (301)739-5839
Co. E-mail: jthompson@washcolibrary.org
URL: http://www.westmdlib.info
Contact: Joe Thompson, Associate Director
Scope: Small business; antiques and collectibles; Civil Service and vocational tests; small scale farming. **Services:** Interlibrary loan; copying; library open to the public with restrictions. **Founded:** 1968. **Holdings:** 62,000 books; 2500 audiovisuals. **Subscriptions:** 3 newspapers.

TRADE PERIODICALS

1162 ■ *Apartment Management Magazine*
Pub: Apartment News Publications Inc.
URL(s): www.aptmags.com. **Ed:** David Gale. **Released:** Monthly **Price:** $15, Individuals Southern California only; $24, Out of area; $69, Out of area.

1163 ■ *Building Business & Apartment Management*
Pub: Building Industry Association of Southeastern Michigan
Contact: Susan Adler-Shanteau, Vice President, Communications
URL(s): www.builders.org/bbam-magazine.php. **Ed:** Susan Adler Shanteau. **Released:** Monthly **Price:** $48, Individuals.

VIDEOCASSETTES/AUDIOCASSETTES

1164 ■ *Apartment For Rent*
Cambridge Educational
c/o Films Media Group
132 West 31st Street, 17th Floor
Ste. 124
New York, NY 10001
Free: 800-257-5126
Fax: (609)671-0266
Co. E-mail: custserve@films.com
URL: http://www.cambridgeol.com
Released: 1991. **Price:** $89.00. **Description:** Follows three individuals on their quests for apartments. Introduces terms and questions that should be asked before signing a lease. Outlines basic considerations to be explored by the individual, including size needs, cost effectiveness, etc. **Availability:** VHS.

1165 ■ *Finding That First Apartment*
Cambridge Educational
c/o Films Media Group
132 West 31st Street, 17th Floor
Ste. 124
New York, NY 10001
Free: 800-257-5126
Fax: (609)671-0266
Co. E-mail: custserve@films.com
URL: http://www.cambridgeol.com
Released: 1991. **Price:** $79.00. **Description:** Outlines the basic needs that should be considered when apartment hunting, explains what to look for in ads, how to make a budget, and deposit fees. Also debates buying and renting furniture. **Availability:** VHS.

TRADE SHOWS AND CONVENTIONS

1166 ■ American Real Estate Society Annual Meeting
American Real Estate Society
5353 Parkside Dr.
Cleveland State Univ.
Coll. of Bus.
Dept. of Finance, UC513
Jupiter, FL 33458
Ph: (561)799-8664
Fax: (561)799-8535
Co. E-mail: dcooper@fau.edu
URL: http://www.aresnet.org
Contact: Stephen A. Pyhrr, Executive Director
E-mail: spyhrr@kennedywilson.com
URL(s): www.aresnet.org. **Frequency:** Annual. **Audience:** College and university professors; high-level practicing professionals involved in all aspects real estate. **Principal Exhibits:** Exhibits relating to decision-making within real estate finance, real estate market analysis, investment, valuation, development, and other areas related to real estate in the private sector. Data providers, book publishers, etc. **Dates and Locations:** , Mauna Lani Bay Hotel.

1167 ■ Canadian Real Estate Association Annual Conference and Trade Show
Canadian Real Estate Association
Canada Bldg.
200 Catherine St., 6th Fl.
Ottawa, ON, Canada K2P 2K9
Ph: (613)237-7111
Free: 800-842-2732
Fax: (613)234-2567
Co. E-mail: info@crea.ca
URL: http://www.crea.ca
URL(s): crea.ca. **Price:** $425, Pre-registered, members. **Frequency:** Annual. **Audience:** Real estate professionals, brokers, managers, corporate representatives from real estate boards across the country. **Principal Exhibits:** Real Estate, financial, printing, and computer business equipment.

1168 ■ Old House/New House Home Show
Kennedy Productions, Inc.
1208 Lisle Pl.
Lisle, IL 60532-2262
Ph: (630)515-1160
Fax: (630)515-1165
Co. E-mail: kp@core.com
URL: http://www.kennedyproductions.com
Contact: Joanne Kennedy, Manager
URL(s): www.kennedyproductions.com. **Frequency:** Semiannual. **Audience:** Trade professionals and general public. **Principal Exhibits:** Products and services for home remodeling, improvement, enhancement, decorating, landscaping and more. Hundreds of ideas to improve and beautify every home. **Dates and Locations:** Pleasant Run Resorts Mega Center.

1169 ■ Philadelphia Home Show
dmg world media inc.
200 Haddonfield-Berlin Rd., Ste. 302
High Ridge Commons
Gibbsboro, NJ 08026
Ph: (856)784-4774
Free: 800-756-5692
Fax: (856)435-5920
URL: http://www.dmgworldmedia.com
URL(s): www.phillyhomeshow.com. **Frequency:** Annual. **Audience:** Home owners and apartment dwellers. **Principal Exhibits:** House and apartment products, supplies, and services.

1170 ■ South Dakota Association of Realtors Convention
South Dakota Association of Realtors
204 N. Euclid Ave.
Pierre, SD 57501
Ph: (605)224-0554
Free: 800-227-5877
Fax: (605)224-8975
Co. E-mail: sdar@sdrealtor.org
URL: http://www.sdrealtor.org
Contact: Cartor Carlson, President
URL(s): www.sdrealtor.org/realtorconventionofthedakotas. **Price:** $190, REALTOR members, state/board AE and staff; $150, affiliate or board association. **Frequency:** Annual. **Audience:** Industry professionals. **Principal Exhibits:** Real estate. **Telecommunication Services:** convention@2013blackhills.com.

1171 ■ Texas Apartment Association Annual Education Conference and Lone Star Expo
Texas Apartment Association, Inc.
1011 San Jacinto Blvd., Ste. 600
Austin, TX 78701-1951
Ph: (512)479-6252
Fax: (512)479-6291
Co. E-mail: communications@taa.org
URL: http://www.taa.org
URL(s): www.taa.org/member/eduandconf. **Frequency:** Annual. **Audience:** Owners and management company reps of multi-housing communities from Texas. **Principal Exhibits:** Goods and services geared to multi-housing professionals, including software, soft goods, and property supplies.

CONSULTANTS

1172 ■ Rental Relocation Inc. (RRI)
281 S Atlanta St.
Roswell, GA 30075
Ph: (770)641-8393
Free: 800-641-7368
Fax: (770)641-8607
Co. E-mail: ahlsinfo@rentalrelocation.com
URL: http://www.rentalrelocation.com
Contact: Christopher Bliss, President
E-mail: cbliss@rentalrelocation.com
Scope: Relocation firm offering services in corporate housing, rentals, free metro Atlanta apartment locating service, property management, house and condo rental relocation tours. **Founded:** 1989.

COMPUTERIZED DATABASES

1173 ■ *Claritas Update Demographics*
770 Broadway
New York, NY 10003-9595
URL: http://www.claritas.com/sitereports/default.jsp
Availability: Online: The Nielsen Co. - Nielsen SiteReports. CD-ROM: The Nielsen Co. - Nielsen SiteReports. **Type:** Statistical.

1174 ■ *Colorado Economic and Demographic Information System (CEDIS)*
1313 Sherman St., Rm. 500
Denver, CO 80203
Ph: (303)866-4904
Fax: (303)866-4077
Co. E-mail: dola.helpdesk@state.co.us
URL: http://dola.colorado.gov
Availability: Online: Colorado Department of Local Affairs. **Type:** Time Series.

1175 ■ *Psychoanalytic Dialogues*
27 Church Rd.
Hove
East Sussex BN3 2FA, United Kingdom
Ph: 20 7017 7747
Fax: 20 7017 6717
URL: http://www.psychoanalysisarena.com
Availability: Online: Informa UK Ltd.-Taylor & Francis Group-Routledge Mental Health-Psychoanalysis Arena. **Type:** Full-text.

RESEARCH CENTERS

1176 ■ Harvard University - Joint Center for Housing Studies (JCHS)
1033 Massachusetts Ave., 5th Fl.
Cambridge, MA 02138
Ph: (617)495-7908

Fax: (617)496-9957
Co. E-mail: chris_herbert@harvard.edu
URL: http://www.jchs.harvard.edu
Contact: Chris Herbert, Director, Research
Founded: 1959. **Publications:** *JCHS Newsletter* (Semiannual); *State of the Nation's Housing Report* (Annual); *JCHS Working Papers* (10/year). **Educational Activities:** Lunchtime lecture series; John T. Dunlop lecture in Housing Studies (Annual). **Awards:** JCHS Summer fellowships, for emerging leaders in community development. **Telecommunication Services:** jchs@harvard.edu.

1177 ■ National Housing Law Project (NHLP)
703 Market St., Ste. 2000
San Francisco, CA 94103
Ph: (415)546-7000
Fax: (415)546-7007
Co. E-mail: nhlp@nhlp.org
URL: http://www.nhlp.org
Contact: Marcia Rosen, Executive Director
Services: Case assistance: to legal services lawyers and housing development corporations. **Founded:** 1968. **Publications:** *Housing Law Bulletin* (Bimonthly). **Educational Activities:** NHLP Conferences (Periodic), on low-income housing issues. **Telecommunication Services:** mrosen@nhlp.org.

1178 ■ San Francisco Planning and Urban Research Association (SPUR)
654 Mission St.
San Francisco, CA 94105-4015

Ph: (415)781-8726
Fax: (415)781-7291
Co. E-mail: rmandel@rci.rutgers.edu
URL: http://www.spur.org
Contact: Ruth B. Mandel, Director
Founded: 1959. **Publications:** *SPUR Newsletter* (11/year). **Educational Activities:** SPUR Annual conference; SPUR Forums, 12 per month, on topics including transportation, housing, urban planning, etc. **Awards:** Silver SPUR Awards (Annual), for long-term contribution to the civic life of the city. **Telecommunication Services:** info@spur.org.

1179 ■ University of California, Berkeley - Fisher Center for Real Estate and Urban Economics (FCREUE)
Gerson Baker Faculty Bldg., F602
Haas School of Business, MC 6105
Berkeley, CA 94720-6105
Ph: (510)643-6105
Fax: (510)643-7357
Co. E-mail: creue@haas.berkeley.edu
URL: http://groups.haas.berkeley.edu/realestate
Contact: Nancy Wallace, Co-Chairperson
Founded: 1950. **Publications:** *FCREUE Newsletter*; *Reprints*; *FCREUE Working papers*. **Educational Activities:** Executive education conferences (Annual); Professional conferences; FCREUE Public lectures; FCREUE Seminars. **Awards:** Graduate student scholarships and fellowships (Annual). **Telecommunication Services:** wallace@haas.berkeley.edu.

START-UP INFORMATION

1180 ■ *"Stockerts Open Repair Business" in Dickinson Press (July 13, 2010)*
Pub: Dickinson Press

Ed: Ashley Martin. **Description:** Ed Stockert is opening his new appliance repair firm in Dickinson, North Dakota with his wife Anna.

ASSOCIATIONS AND OTHER ORGANIZATIONS

1181 ■ Appliance Parts Distributors Association (APDA)
3621 N Oakley Ave.
Chicago, IL 60618
Ph: (773)230-9851
Fax: (888)308-1423
Co. E-mail: ro@apda.com
URL: http://www.apda.com
Contact: Bruce Swane, President

Description: Wholesale distributors of appliance parts, supplies and accessories. Promotes the sale of appliance parts through independent parts distributors. **Founded:** 1937.

1182 ■ Association of Home Appliance Manufacturers (AHAM)
1111 19th St. NW, Ste. 402
Washington, DC 20036
Ph: (202)872-5955
Fax: (202)872-9354
Co. E-mail: info@aham.org
URL: http://www.aham.org
Contact: Robert P. Scaglione, Chairman of the Board

Description: Companies manufacturing major and portable appliances; supplier members provide products and services to the appliance industry. Major areas of activity include: market research and reporting of industry statistics; development of standard methods for measuring appliance performance and certification of certain characteristics of room air conditioners, refrigerators, freezers, humidifiers, dehumidifiers, and room air cleaners; public relations and press relations. Represents the appliance industry before government at the federal, state, and local levels. **Scope:** appliance industry. **Founded:** 1967. **Subscriptions:** archival material audiovisuals books clippings periodicals. **Publications:** *AHAM Membership Directory* (Annual); *Directory of Certified Dehumidifiers* (Semiannual); *Directory of Certified Humidifiers* (Semiannual); *Directory of Certified Refrigerators and Freezers* (Semiannual); *AHAM Major Home Appliance Industry Factbook.* **Awards:** Hail Award (Annual).

1183 ■ International Housewares Association (IHA)
6400 Shafer Ct., Ste. 650
Rosemont, IL 60018
Ph: (847)292-4200
Fax: (847)292-4211
Co. E-mail: showteam@housewares.org
URL: http://www.housewares.org
Contact: Phil J. Brandl, President
E-mail: pbrandl@housewares.org

Description: Manufacturers and distributors of housewares and small appliances. Conducts annual market research survey of the housewares industry. Manages the international housewares show. **Founded:** 1939. **Publications:** *IHA Membership Directory* (Annual); *BusinessWatch* (Monthly); *Housewares MarketWatch* (Quarterly); *IHA Reports* (Bimonthly); *January Exhibitors Directory* (Annual); *NHMA Reports Newsletter* (Bimonthly); *NHMA Export Interest Directory*; *Exhibitors' Directory to the International Housewares Exposition* (Annual). **Educational Activities:** International Housewares Association Show (Annual); International Home & Housewares Show (Annual). **Awards:** National Student Design Competition Award (Annual). **Telecommunication Services:** pbrandl@housewares.org.

1184 ■ National Appliance Parts Suppliers Association (NAPSA)
4015 W Marshall Ave.
Longview, TX 75604
Ph: (903)759-3983
Co. E-mail: board06@napsaweb.org
URL: http://www.napsaweb.org
Contact: Jim Bossman, President
E-mail: jim@apcntr.com

Description: Wholesale distributors of replacement parts for major home appliance. Promotes and supports good relations among groups in the supply and distribution of appliance service parts. Sponsors Young Executives Society of NAPSA to prepare younger generations for leadership in the appliance parts wholesale and distribution industry and to handle problems characteristic of family businesses. **Founded:** 1966. **Publications:** *National Appliance Parts Suppliers Association--Results* (Quarterly); *National Appliance Parts Suppliers Association--Membership Roster* (Annual). **Educational Activities:** National Appliance Parts Suppliers Association Annual Convention (Annual). **Telecommunication Services:** board11@napsaweb.org.

1185 ■ National Appliance Service Association (NASA)
PO Box 2514
Kokomo, IN 46904
Ph: (765)453-1820
Fax: (765)453-1895
Co. E-mail: nasahq@sbcglobal.net
URL: http://www.nasa1.org
Contact: Carrie Giannakos, Executive Director

Description: Owners of factory-authorized portable appliance repair centers servicing small electrical appliances and commercial food equipment. Promotes the interests and welfare of the commercial-domestic appliance service industry. **Founded:** 1949. **Publications:** *NASA News* (Monthly). **Educational Activities:** National Appliance Service Association Annual Convention (Annual).

REFERENCE WORKS

1186 ■ *Appliance--Appliance Industry Purchasing Section Issue*
Pub: Dana Chase Publications Inc.

URL(s): www.appliancemagazine.com. **Ed:** David Chase. **Released:** Annual; January. **Publication includes:** Suppliers to manufacturers of consumer, commercial, and business appliances. Membership directories for the following associations: Air-Conditioning and Refrigeration Institute, Association of Home Appliance Manufacturers, Commercial Refrigerator Manufacturers Association, Computer and Business Equipment Manufacturers Association, Consumer Electronics Group/Electronic Industries Association, Gas Appliance Manufacturers Association, Cookware Manufacturers Association, National Association of Food Equipment Manufacturers, National Housewares Manufacturers Association, Power Tool Institute, and Vacuum Cleaner Manufacturers Association. **Entries include:** Company name, address, phone, fax, and products. **Arrangement:** Classified by product. **Indexes:** Manufacturer, product heading.

1187 ■ *"A Call for Common Sense with WaterSense" in Contractor (Vol. 56, July 2009, No. 7, pp. 42)*
Pub: Penton Media, Inc.

Ed: Dave Yates. **Description:** Instillation of a shower that is supposed to protect bathers from being scalded is presented. Plumbers should be aware that the WaterSense shower heads still have a 50/50 chance of scalding their users.

1188 ■ *"Cash for Appliances Targets HVAC Products, Water Heaters" in Contractor (Vol. 56, October 2009, No. 10, pp. 1)*
Pub: Penton Media, Inc.

Ed: Candace Roulo. **Description:** States and territories would need to submit a full application that specifies their implementation plans if they are interested in joining the Cash for Appliances program funded by the American Recovery and Reinvestment Act. The Department of Energy urges states to focus on heating and cooling equipment, appliances and water heaters since these offer the greatest energy savings potential.

1189 ■ *"Consumers Like Green, But Not Mandates" in Business Journal-Milwaukee (Vol. 28, December 10, 2010, No. 10, pp. A1)*
Pub: Milwaukee Business Journal

Ed: Sean Ryan. **Description:** Milwaukee, Wisconsin consumers are willing to spend more on green energy, a survey has revealed. Respondents also said they will pay more for efficient cars and appliances. Support for public incentives for homeowners and businesses that reduce energy use has also increased.

1190 ■ *Electrical Appliance and Utilization Equipment Directory*
Pub: Underwriters Laboratories
Contact: Keith E. Williams, President

URL(s): www.ul.com. **Released:** Annual; latest edition 2010. **Price:** $150, Individuals. **Covers:** Companies that have qualified to use the UL listing mark or classification marking on or in connection with products that have been found to be in compliance with UL's requirements. Coverage includes foreign companies that manufacture for distribution in the United States. **Entries include:** Company name, city, ZIP code, UL file number, and type of product. **Database includes:** Section listing a limited number of trade names or trademarks authorized to use UL certification without mention of company name. **Arrangement:** Classified by type of product. **Indexes:** Company name.

1191 ■ *"The Final Piece; Lowe's to Fill Last Big Parcel Near Great Lakes Crossing" in Crain's Detroit Business (March 10, 2008)*
Pub: Crain Communications, Inc.

Ed: Daniel Duggan. **Description:** Silverman Development Co. is developing a Lowe's home-improvement store on the last major retail parcel near the intersection of I-75 and Joslyn Road, an area which was once desolate but is now home to several restaurants and other retail facilities.

1192 ■ *"Life's Work" in Harvard Business Review (Vol. 88, July-August 2010, No. 7-8, pp. 172)*
Pub: Harvard Business School Publishing

Ed: Alison Beard. **Description:** The founder of appliance company Dyson Ltd. discusses the role of making mistakes in learning and innovation, and emphasizes the importance of hands-on involvement to make a company successful.

1193 ■ National Appliance Parts Suppliers Association--Membership Roster
Pub: National Appliance Parts Suppliers Association
Contact: Jim Bossman, President
E-mail: jim@apcntr.com

URL(s): www.napsaweb.org/search.cfm. **Released:** Annual **Covers:** Over 100 wholesale distributors of appliance parts operating in 250 locations, about 80 manufactures of replacement parts for major home appliances and service providers, over 20 manufacturer's representatives. **Entries include:** Company name, address, phone, name of principal executive. **Arrangement:** Alphabetical. **Indexes:** Geographical.

1194 ■ *"A Switch in the Kitchen" in Barron's (Vol. 88, March 24, 2008, No. 12, pp. 17)*
Pub: Dow Jones & Company, Inc.

Description: Men are doing more kitchen duties, with 18 percent of meals at home being made by men in 2007 compared to 11 percent four years previously. Young wives, however, choose to forgo work and stay at home.

1195 ■ *"War Veteran Hit Payoff with Repair Business" in Tulsa World (July 28, 2010)*
Pub: Tulsa World

Ed: Tim Stanley. **Description:** Profile of Sam Melton, Korean War veteran and retired Air Force staff sergeant, launched appliance repair stores in the Tulsa, Oklahoma area 50 years ago.

1196 ■ *"A Wireless Makes 8 Store-In-Store Kiosk Acquisitions" in Wireless News (October 16, 2010)*
Pub: Close-Up Media Inc.

Description: A Wireless, a retailer for Verizon Wireless has acquired eight of Verizon's retail kiosks that are positioned in home appliance and electronics stores.

1197 ■ *"Your Turn in the Spotlight" in Inc. (Volume 32, December 2010, No. 10, pp. 57)*
Pub: Inc. Magazine

Ed: John Brandon. **Description:** Examples of three video blogs created by entrepreneurs to promote their businesses and products are used to show successful strategies. Wine Library TV promotes a family's wine business; SHAMA.TV offers marketing tips and company news; and Will It Blend? promotes sales of a household blender.

STATISTICAL SOURCES

1198 ■ RMA Annual Statement Studies
Pub: Risk Management Association
Contact: Kevin M. Blakey, President
Released: Annual. **Price:** $175.00 2006-07 edition, $105.00. **Description:** Contains composite balance sheets and income statements for more than 360 industries, including the accounting, auditing, and bookkeeping industries. Also contains five years of comparative historical data for discerning trends. Includes 16 commonly used ratios, computed for most of the size groupings for nearly every industry.

1199 ■ Standard & Poor's Industry Surveys
Pub: Standard & Poor's Corp.
Released: Annual. **Price:** $3633.00. **Description:** Two-volume book that examines the prospects for specific industries, including trucking. Also provides analyses of trends and problems, statistical tables and charts, and comparative company analyses.

TRADE PERIODICALS

1200 ■ Appliance Design
Pub: BNP Media
Contact: Al Reser, President
URL(s): www.appliancedesign.com. **Released:** Monthly **Price:** Free.

1201 ■ Appliance: Serving the Appliance Industry Worldwide
Pub: Dana Chase Publications Inc.
URL(s): appliancemagazine.com. **Ed:** Tim Somheil. **Released:** Monthly **Price:** $30, Individuals print copy domestic; $35, Individuals print copy foreign; $40, Individuals; $45, Individuals print copy; $85, Individuals print copy domestic; $95, Individuals print copy foreign; $137, Individuals print copy domestic; $154, Individuals print copy foreign; $190, Individuals print copy domestic; $214, Individuals print copy foreign.

TRADE SHOWS AND CONVENTIONS

1202 ■ National Appliance Parts Suppliers Association Annual Convention
National Appliance Parts Suppliers Association (NAPSA)
4015 W Marshall Ave.
Longview, TX 75604
Ph: (903)759-3983
Co. E-mail: board06@napsaweb.org
URL: www.napsaweb.org
Contact: Jim Bossman, President
E-mail: jim@apcntr.com
URL(s): www.napsaweb.org. **Frequency:** Annual. **Principal Exhibits:** Exhibits for wholesale distributors of replacement parts of major home appliances. **Telecommunication Services:** info@napsaweb.org.

FRANCHISES AND BUSINESS OPPORTUNITIES

1203 ■ Corbeil Appliances
6783 blvd. Leger
Montreal Nord, QC, Canada H1G 6H8
Ph: (514)322-7726
Fax: (514)322-8051
Co. E-mail: developpement@corbeilelectro.com
URL: http://www.corbeilelectro.com
Description: Specialty retailer of quality and innovative home appliance products and services. **No. of Franchise Units:** 18. **No. of Company-Owned Units:** 15. **Founded:** 1949.. **Franchised:** 1997. **Equity Capital Needed:** $150,000-$200,000. **Franchise Fee:** $35,000-$85,000. **Training:** Provides 3 weeks training.

COMPUTERIZED DATABASES

1204 ■ Consumer Buying Power™
770 Broadway
New York, NY 10003-9595
URL: http://www.claritas.com/sitereports/default.jsp
Availability: Online: The Nielsen Co. - Nielsen SiteReports. **Type:** Statistical.

ASSOCIATIONS AND OTHER ORGANIZATIONS

1205 ■ American Society of Appraisers (ASA)
11107 Sunset Hills Rd, Suite 310
Reston, VA 20190
Ph: (703)478-2228
Free: 800-ASA-VALU
Fax: (703)742-8471
Co. E-mail: asainfo@appraisers.org
URL: http://www.appraisers.org/ASAHome.aspx
Contact: Jim Hirt, Chief Executive Officer
Description: Professional appraisal educator, testing, and accrediting society. Sponsors mandatory recertification program for all members. Offers a consumer information service to the public. **Scope:** appraisal. **Founded:** 1952. **Publications:** *ASA Professional Magazine* (Quarterly); *Business Valuation Review* (Quarterly); *Directory of Professional Appraisal Services* (Annual); *Personal Property Journal* (Quarterly); *Real Property Journal* (3/year). **Educational Activities:** International Appraisal Conference (Annual).

1206 ■ Appraisal Institute
200 W Madison St., Ste. 1500
Chicago, IL 60606
Ph: (312)335-4401
Free: 888-756-4624
Fax: (312)335-4415
Co. E-mail: aiservice@appraisalinstitute.org
URL: http://www.appraisalinstitute.org
Contact: Sara W. Stephens, President
Description: General appraisers who hold the MAI designation, and residential members who hold the SRA designation. Enforces Code of Professional Ethics and Standards of Professional Appraisal Practice. Confers one general designation, the MAI, and one residential designation, the SRA. Provides training in valuation of residential and income properties, market analysis, and standards of professional appraisal practice. Sponsors courses in preparation for state certification and licensing; offers continuing education programs for designated members. **Scope:** real estate appraisal. **Founded:** 1935. **Subscriptions:** 1800 books monographs periodicals. **Publications:** *The Appraisal Journal* (Quarterly); *Valuation* (Quarterly); *The Appraisal Journal* (Quarterly); *Appraiser News in Brief* (8/year); *Appraisal Institute--Directory of Designated Members*; *The Dictionary of Real Estate Appraisal, 4th Edition.* **Educational Activities:** Appraisal Institute Annual Meeting (Annual). **Awards:** Appraisal Institute Education Trust Scholarship; Minority and Women Scholarships.

1207 ■ Appraisers Association of America (AAA)
386 Park Ave. S, 20th Fl., Ste. 2000
New York, NY 10016
Ph: (212)889-5404
Fax: (212)889-5503
Co. E-mail: aaa@appraisersassoc.org
URL: http://www.appraisersassoc.org
Contact: Nancy Harrison, President
Description: Professional society of appraisers of personal property such as: Americana; antiques; armor; art objects; bibelot; books; bronzes; china and porcelain; clocks and watches; coins; crystal and glass; curios; diamonds and jewelry; enamels; etchings; fine art; firearms; furniture; furs; graphic art; guns; household furnishings; ivories; leather goods; lighting fixtures; linens and lace; miniatures; music; musical instruments; oriental art; paintings; pewter; pianos; primitive art; prints; rugs; sculpture; Sheffield plate; silver and silverware; stamps; steins and tankards; taxes; and woodcarvings. **Scope:** personal property, auction records. **Founded:** 1949. **Subscriptions:** books periodicals. **Publications:** *The Appraiser* (Quarterly); *Appraisers Association of America--Membership Directory* (Biennial).

1208 ■ International Society of Appraisers (ISA)
303 W Madison St., Ste. 2650
Chicago, IL 60606
Ph: (312)981-6778
Fax: (312)265-2908
Co. E-mail: isa@isa-appraisers.org
URL: http://www.isa-appraisers.org
Contact: Todd W. Sigety, President
Description: Represents personal property appraisers. Seeks to provide the public with a network of appraisal specialists who have been pre-screened by ISA. Conducts educational opportunities for members, the consumer public and other affinity groups. Offers Certified Appraiser of Personal Property Program, education, testing and certification program. Compiles statistics; maintains speakers' bureau. Offers free appraisal referral service in the U.S. and Canada. **Founded:** 1979. **Publications:** *ISA Professional Appraisers Information Exchange.* **Awards:** Media Award; Media Award (Annual).

1209 ■ Jewelers' Security Alliance (JSA)
6 E 45th St.
New York, NY 10017
Ph: (212)687-0328
Free: 800-537-0067
Fax: (212)808-9168
Co. E-mail: jsa2@jewelerssecurity.org
URL: http://www.jewelerssecurity.org
Contact: John J. Kennedy, President
Description: Advocates for crime prevention in the jewelry industry. Provides crime information and assistance to the jewelry industry and law enforcement. **Founded:** 1883. **Publications:** *JSA Manual of Jewelry Security* (Biennial); *Annual Report on Crime Against the Jewelry Industry in U.S.* (Annual). **Educational Activities:** Security Seminar and Expo for Retail Jewelry Chains (Annual). **Awards:** Gold and Silver Shield Awards (Annual).

1210 ■ National Association of Independent Fee Appraisers (NAIFA)
330 N Wabash Ave., Ste. 2000
Chicago, IL 60611
Ph: (312)321-6830
Fax: (312)673-6652
Co. E-mail: info@naifa.com
URL: http://www.naifa.com
Contact: Charles E. Blau, President
Description: Appraisers for real estate groups, savings and loan associations, title insurance groups, governmental agencies, and related industries. Raises the standards of the appraisal profession. Sponsors career training and professional development programs. Conducts general and applied research in real estate and related fields. **Scope:** real estate appraisal. **Founded:** 1961. **Publications:** *Appraiser-Gram* (Quarterly); *Technical Manual* (Periodic); *National Association of Independent Fee Appraisers--National Membership Directory* (Annual); *NAIFA Membership Directory* (Annual); *Appraisal Review: Official Journal of the National Association of Independent Fee Appraisers (NAIFA)* (Quarterly). **Educational Activities:** NAIFA National Convention (Annual). **Awards:** Appraiser of the Year Award.

1211 ■ National Association of Jewelry Appraisers (NAJA)
PO Box 18
Rego Park, NY 11374-0018
Ph: (718)896-1536
Fax: (718)997-9057
Co. E-mail: office@najaappraisers.com
URL: http://www.najaappraisers.com
Contact: Ms. Gail Brett Levine, Executive Director
Description: Gem and jewelry appraisers, jewelers, importers, brokers, manufacturers, gemological students, and others professionally interested in jewelry appraisal. Seeks to recognize and make available to the public the services of highly qualified, experienced, independent, and reliable jewelry appraisers. Conducts seminars on jewelry appraisal techniques, methods, and pricing for members and the public. Supports legislation to establish minimum standards of competency and licensing of jewelry appraisers; maintains code of professional ethics. Operates appraiser referral program; sponsors ongoing public relations campaign. Offers equipment discounts, new appraisal forms, travel discounts, insurance, and professional aids for members only. Compiles statistics. **Founded:** 1981. **Publications:** *National Association of Jewelry Appraisers Membership Directory* (Annual); *The Jewelry Appraiser.*

1212 ■ National Association of Real Estate Appraisers (NAREA)
810 N Farrell Dr.
Palm Springs, CA 92262
Ph: (760)327-5284
Free: 877-815-4172
Fax: (760)327-5631
Co. E-mail: info@narea-assoc.org
URL: http://www.narea-assoc.org
Description: Real estate appraisers. Aims to make available the services of the most highly qualified real estate appraisers. Offers certification to members. **Scope:** real estate. **Founded:** 1966. **Subscriptions:** 752 books. **Publications:** *NAREA Real Estate Appraisal Newsletter* (Bimonthly). **Educational Activities:** National Association of Real Estate Appraisers Annual Conference (Annual). **Awards:** Appraiser of the Year (Annual). **Telecommunication Services:** support@assoc-hdqts.org.

REFERENCE WORKS

1213 ■ *Appraisers Association of America--Membership Directory*
Pub: Appraisers Association of America Inc.
Contact: Roslym Goldman, President
URL(s): www.appraisersassoc.org. **Released:** Biennial; Even years. **Covers:** 800 member appraisers of

fine art, antiques, and personal property. **Entries include:** Name, address, phone, specialties. **Arrangement:** Geographical. **Indexes:** Alphabetical, specialty.

1214 ■ *Directory of the Association of Machinery and Equipment Appraisers*
Pub: Association of Machinery and Equipment Appraisers
URL(s): www.amea.org. **Ed:** Mary Flynn Boener. **Released:** Annual; January. **Price:** Free. **Covers:** Nearly 300 member certified machinery appraisers. **Entries include:** Firm name, address, phone, name and title of contact, geographic territory covered, professional designation. **Arrangement:** Alphabetical. **Indexes:** Geographical.

1215 ■ *Gems & Jewelry Appraising: Techniques of Professional Practice*
Pub: GemStone Press
Ed: Anna M. Miller; Gail Brett Levine. **Released:** August 28, 2008. **Price:** $39.99 paperback. **Description:** Comprehensive book for practicing appraisers, would-be appraisers; provides extension information about the profession.

1216 ■ *Institute of Business Appraisers--Directory*
Pub: Institute of Business Appraisers
Contact: Chris M. Mellen, Principal
URL(s): www.go-iba.org. **Price:** $20, Members; $20, Nonmembers. **Covers:** Listing of members and certified business appraisers.

1217 ■ *National Association of Independent Fee Appraisers--National Membership Directory*
Pub: National Association of Independent Fee Appraisers
Contact: Charles E. Blau, President
URL(s): www.naifa.com. **Released:** Annual; January. **Covers:** 4,300 independent real estate appraisers. **Entries include:** Name, address, phone, level of membership. **Arrangement:** Geographical.

TRADE PERIODICALS

1218 ■ *The Appraiser*
Pub: The Appraisal Institute of American Inc.
Ed: Hermine Chivian-Cobb, Editor. **Released:** Quarterly. **Price:** $90. **Description:** Covers topics of interest to personal property appraisers. Recurring features include a calendar of events, book reviews, and news of educational opportunities.

1219 ■ *The Appraisers Standard*
Pub: New England Appraisers Association
Released: Quarterly **Price:** $20, Individuals; $25, Canada; $30, Other countries.

1220 ■ *Canadian Property Valuation*
Pub: Appraisal Institute of Canada
Contact: Keith Lancastle, Chief Executive Officer
E-mail: keithl@aicanada.ca
URL(s): www.aicanada.ca/cmsPage.aspx?id=168. **Released:** Quarterly **Price:** $20, Individuals.

1221 ■ *IBA News*
Pub: Institute of Business Appraisers
Ed: Raymond C. Miles, Editor. **Released:** Bimonthly. **Price:** Included in membership. **Description:** Directed toward business appraising and supplies news

of the Institute. Recurring features include news of research, a calendar of events, reports of meetings, book reviews, and notices of publications available.

1222 ■ *The Jewelry Appraiser*
Pub: National Association of Jewelry Appraisers
Contact: Ms. Gail Brett Levine, Executive Director
Ed: Gail Breit Leving, Editor. **Released:** Quarterly. **Price:** Included in membership. **Description:** Provides information on jewelry and gem appraising. Carries items on current appraisal practices and standards, and a wholesale price guide titled the Price Reporter. Recurring features include editorials, news of research, letters to the editor, news of new products, news of members, book reviews, a calendar of events, and columns titled News and Views, Industry News, and Association News.

TRADE SHOWS AND CONVENTIONS

1223 ■ **American Society of Appraisers - International Appraisal Conference**
American Society of Appraisers
11107 Sunset Hills Rd., Ste. 310
Reston, VA 20190
Ph: (703)478-2228
Free: 800-ASA-VALU
Fax: (703)742-8471
Co. E-mail: asainfo@appraisers.org
URL: http://www.appraisers.org
URL(s): www.appraisers.org. **Frequency:** Annual. **Principal Exhibits:** Exhibits for professional appraisers. **Telecommunication Services:** asainfo@appraisers.org.

1224 ■ **Appraisal Institute Annual Meeting**
Appraisal Institute
200 W Madison St., Ste. 1500
Chicago, IL 60606
Ph: (312)335-4401
Free: 888-756-4624
Fax: (312)335-4415
Co. E-mail: aiservice@appraisalinstitute.org
URL: http://www.appraisalinstitute.org
Contact: Sara W. Stephens, President
URL(s): www.appraisalinstitute.org. **Frequency:** Annual. **Audience:** Real estate appraisers, and valuation professionals. **Principal Exhibits:** Exhibits for general appraisers who hold the MAI, SRPA or designations and residential members who hold the SRA or RM designations. **Telecommunication Services:** aiservice@appraisalinstitute.org.

CONSULTANTS

1225 ■ **Artemis Inc.**
4715 Crescent St.
Bethesda, MD 20816
Ph: (301)229-2058
Fax: (301)229-2186
Contact: Sandra J. Tropper, Owner
E-mail: sjtropper@aol.com
Scope: Fine art appraiser, consultation on art purchases decoration, framing and presentation.It also provides Auction Services. **Founded:** 1990.

FRANCHISES AND BUSINESS OPPORTUNITIES

1226 ■ **Auto Appraisal Network Inc.**
19 Spectrum Pointe Dr.
Lake Forest, CA 92630
Ph: (949)387-7774
Fax: (949)387-7775
Description: Vehicle appraisal services. **No. of Franchise Units:** 23. **No. of Company-Owned Units:** 5. **Founded:** 1989.. **Franchised:** 2007. **Equity Capital Needed:** $26,700-$64,275. **Franchise Fee:** $12,000-$30,000. **Royalty Fee:** $95/appraisal. **Financial Assistance:** Financial assistance available for franchise fee. **Training:** Offers 5-6 days training at headquarters and ongoing support.

1227 ■ **Business America**
Business America Assoc., Inc.
2120 Greentree Rd.
Pittsburgh, PA 15220
Ph: (412)276-7701
Description: Sells businesses and franchise appraisal. **No. of Franchise Units:** 4. **Founded:** 1984.. **Franchised:** 1985. **Equity Capital Needed:** $10,000. **Franchise Fee:** $7,995. **Training:** Yes.

1228 ■ **Property Damage Appraisers, Inc.**
PO Box 471909
Ft. Worth, TX 76147
Ph: (817)731-5555
Fax: (817)731-5550
Description: Appraising company. Automobile damage appraising experience is a pre-requisite. Provides automobile and property appraisal services for insurance companies and the self-insured. **No. of Franchise Units:** 256. **Founded:** 1963.. **Franchised:** 1963. **Equity Capital Needed:** $9,250-$24,050. **Franchise Fee:** None. **Training:** Yes.

COMPUTER SYSTEMS/ SOFTWARE

1229 ■ *Building Cost Analysis*
330 New Brunswick Ave.
Fords, NJ 08863
Ph: (732)738-8500
Free: 800-673-0366
Fax: (732)738-9603
Co. E-mail: info@datamaticsinc.com
URL: http://www.datamaticsinc.com

LIBRARIES

1230 ■ **Appraisal Institute - Y.T. and Louise Lee Lum Library**
200 W. Madison, Ste. 1500
Chicago, IL 60606
Ph: (312)335-4467
Fax: (312)335-4486
Co. E-mail: ailibrary@appraisalinstitute.org
URL: http://www.appraisalinstitute.org/profession/ lumlibry.aspx
Contact: Eric B. Goodman, Manager
Scope: Real estate appraisal, real estate market analysis, real estate finance. **Services:** Library open to members, nonmember appraisers, and allied real estate professionals. **Founded:** 1992. **Holdings:** 2500 books. **Subscriptions:** 35 journals and other serials.

START-UP INFORMATION

1231 ■ *"Add Aquatics to Boost Business" in Pet Product News (Vol. 64, December 2010, No. 12, pp. 20)*

Pub: BowTie Inc.

Ed: David Lass. **Description:** Pet stores are encouraged to add aquatics departments to increase profitability through repeat sales. This goal can be realized by sourcing, displaying, and maintaining high quality live fish. Other tips regarding the challenges associated with setting up an aquatics department are presented.

1232 ■ *"Aquatic Medications Engender Good Health" in Pet Product News (Vol. 64, November 2010, No. 11, pp. 47)*

Pub: BowTie Inc.

Ed: Madelaine Heleine. **Description:** Pet supply manufacturers and retailers have been exerting consumer education and preparedness efforts to help aquarium hobbyists in tackling ornamental fish disease problems. Aquarium hobbyists have been also assisted in choosing products that facilitate aquarium maintenance before disease attacks their pet fish.

1233 ■ *"Foods for Thought" in Pet Product News (Vol. 64, December 2010, No. 12, pp. 16)*

Pub: BowTie Inc.

Ed: Maddy Heleine. **Description:** Manufacturers have been focused at developing species-specific fish foods due to consumer tendency to assess the benefits of the food they feed their fish. As retailers stock species-specific fish foods, manufacturers have provided in-store items and strategies to assist in efficiently selling these food products. Trends in fish food packaging and ingredients are also discussed.

ASSOCIATIONS AND OTHER ORGANIZATIONS

1234 ■ **Canadian Association of Aquarium Clubs (CAOAC)**

908-373 Front St. W
Toronto, ON, Canada M5V 3R7
Ph: (416)883-0571
Co. E-mail: robert.j.l.wright@sympatico.ca
URL: http://www.caoac.ca
Contact: Bob Wright, President

Description: Represents aquarium owners and other aquaculture hobbyists in Canada. Promotes effective care and breeding of aquatic plants and animals; encourages participation in the hobby of aquaculture. Conducts educational programs. **Founded:** 1959. **Publications:** *CAOAC Newsletter* (10/year). **Educational Activities:** Canadian Association of Aquarium Clubs Convention (Annual). **Awards:** Breeders' Award; Competition Awards; Hobbyist of the Year; Aquatic Horticulturist Award; Junior Hobbyist of the Year; Scientist Award.

1235 ■ **CAOAC Newsletter**

908-373 Front St. W
Toronto, ON, Canada M5V 3R7
Ph: (416)883-0571
Co. E-mail: robert.j.l.wright@sympatico.ca
URL: http://www.caoac.ca
Contact: Bob Wright, President

Released: 10/year **Price:** included in membership dues.

1236 ■ **World Pet Association (WPA)**

135 W Lemon Ave.
Monrovia, CA 91016-2809
Ph: (626)447-2222
Free: 800-999-7295
Fax: (626)447-8350
Co. E-mail: info@wpamail.org
URL: http://www.worldpetassociation.org/files/homepage/index.html
Contact: Ruth Jeffers, Chairman of the Board

Description: Manufacturers, retailers and distributors of pet food and services and of avian, aquarium and companion animal care products, equipment and services. Seeks to advance the economic interests of members; promotes responsible pet ownership. Conducts trade shows, certificate training courses and seminars for pet shop retailers, grooming establishments and veterinary clinics. **Founded:** 1951. **Educational Activities:** Super Zoo (Annual).

TRADE PERIODICALS

1237 ■ *Tropical Fish Hobbyist*

Pub: T.F.H. Publications Inc.
Contact: Glen Axelrod, President
URL(s): www.tfhmagazine.com. **Released:** Monthly **Price:** $28, Individuals; $48, Canada; $53, Other countries; $49, Two years.

RESEARCH CENTERS

1238 ■ **Auburn University - International Center for Aquaculture and Aquatic Environments (ICAAE)**

203 Swingle Hall
Department of Fisheries & Allied Aquacultures
Auburn, AL 36849
Ph: (334)844-4786
Fax: (334)844-9208
Co. E-mail: fish@auburn.edu
URL: http://www.ag.auburn.edu/fish/international/academic-exchanges/
Contact: Prof. Bryan L. Duncan, Director

Services: Provides information on relevant technical subjects. **Founded:** 1971. **Publications:** *ICAAE Abstracts*; *ICAAE Newsletter* (Quarterly). **Awards:** Minigrants for purposes consistent with ICAAE objectives. **Telecommunication Services:** duncabl@auburn.edu.

ASSOCIATIONS AND OTHER ORGANIZATIONS

1239 ■ Archery Range and Retailers Organization (ARRO)
156 N Main, Ste. D
Oregon, WI 53575
Ph: (608)835-9060
Free: 800-234-7499
Fax: (608)835-9360
Co. E-mail: lynn@archeryretailers.com
URL: http://www.archeryretailers.com
Contact: John Larsen, Sr., President
Description: Owners of archery retail shops and/or indoor archery lanes. Functions as a cooperative buying group. Sanctions indoor archery leagues; provides national cash awards. **Founded:** 1981. **Educational Activities:** Bowhunting Show; Shot Show.

1240 ■ National Field Archery Association (NFAA)
800 Archery Ln.
Yankton, SD 57078
Ph: (605)260-9279
Free: 800-811-2331
Fax: (605)260-9280
URL: http://www.NFAAarchery.com
Contact: Bruce Cull, President
Description: Field archers and bowhunters. Sponsors field archery schools, three national tournaments, and 16 sectional tournaments; works toward conservation of game and its natural habitat. **Founded:** 1939. **Educational Activities:** National Field Archery Association Conference (Annual). **Awards:** Bowfisher of the Year (Annual); Diamond Buck Award (Annual); Memorial Scholarship (Annual).

1241 ■ National Rifle Association of America
11250 Waples Mill Rd.
Fairfax, VA 22030
Free: 800-672-3888
Co. E-mail: info@nraila.org
URL: http://www.nrahq.org
Description: Target shooters, hunters, gun collectors, gunsmiths, police officers, and others interested in firearms. Promotes rifle, pistol, and shotgun shooting, hunting, gun collecting, home firearm safety, and wildlife conservation. Encourages civilian marksmanship. Educates police firearms instructors. Maintains national and international records of shooting competitions; sponsors teams to compete in world championships. Also maintains comprehensive collection of antique and modern firearms. Administers the NRA Political Victory Fund. Compiles statistics; sponsors research and education programs; maintains speakers' bureau and museum. Lobbies on firearms issues. **Publications:** *American Rifleman* (Monthly); *American Hunter* (Monthly); *American Rifleman* (Monthly); *America's 1st Freedom* (Monthly); *InSights: NRA News for Young Shooters* (Monthly); *National Rifle Association Collegiate Shooting Sports Directory* (Triennial). **Awards:** Defender of Freedom Award; National Police Shooting Championships; National Championships.

1242 ■ National Sporting Clays Association (NSCA)
5931 Roft Rd.
San Antonio, TX 78253
Ph: (210)688-3371
Free: 800-877-5338
Fax: (210)688-3014
Co. E-mail: mhampton@nssa-nsca.com
URL: http://www.mynsca.com
Contact: Michael Hampton, Executive Director
Description: Promotion of shooting sports. Acts as the governing body of sporting clays and has an Advisory Council composed of range owners, shooters, and industry persons. Sanctions registered tournaments for member clubs, and uses registered scores to create an impartial classification system for competition. Operates national league and sweepstakes. Conducts championship competitions. Offers Instructor Certification Program to members. **Founded:** 1989. **Publications:** *Sporting Clays Magazine* (Monthly); *Rule Book*. **Educational Activities:** National Delegate Meeting (Annual); National Sporting Clays Championships. **Awards:** NSSA/NSCA Collegiate Scholarships.

REFERENCE WORKS

1243 ■ Guns Illustrated
Pub: Krause Publications Inc.
Contact: Roger Case, President
URL(s): www.krausebooks.com/product/guns-illustrated-2011/firearms. **Released:** Annual; Latest edition 43rd; 2011. **Price:** $17.81, Individuals softcover. **Publication includes:** Lists of national and international firearms associations; manufacturers, importers, and distributors of firearms, shooting equipment, and services. **Entries include:** For associations--Name, address, phone, area of interest. For manufacturers and distributors--Name, address, phone, product or service provided. Principal content of publication is articles on hunting, handloading, ammunition, ballistics, collecting, gunsmithing, and customizing, as well as other related information. **Database includes:** 1,500 black and white photos. **Arrangement:** Alphabetical.

TRADE PERIODICALS

1244 ■ American Rifleman
Pub: National Rifle Association of America
URL(s): www.americanrifleman.org/. **Ed:** Brian Sheetz. **Released:** Monthly **Price:** $10, Individuals.

1245 ■ Bow and Arrow Hunting: America's Bow Hunting Authority
Pub: Y-Visionary Publishing L.P.
URL(s): www.bowhunting.net/bow&arrow/default. htm#topwww.bowandarrowhunting.com/. **Ed:** Joe Bell. **Released:** 9/yr. **Price:** $19.95, Individuals.

1246 ■ Guns & Ammo
Pub: PRIMEDIA Los Angeles
URL(s): www.gunsandammo.com/. **Ed:** Jim Bequette. **Released:** Monthly **Price:** $14, Individuals; $15, Two years; $27, Canada; $41, Canada 2 years; $29, Other countries; $45, Other countries 2 years.

1247 ■ Precision Shooting
Pub: Precision Shooting Inc.
URL(s): www.precisionshooting.com/. **Released:** Monthly **Price:** $70, Two years; $39, Individuals; $64, Canada; $72, Individuals Europe; $77, Other countries.

1248 ■ Rifle: The Sporting Firearms Journal
Pub: Wolfe Publishing Co.
Contact: Mark Harris, President
URL(s): www.riflemagazine.com. **Released:** Bimonthly **Price:** $19.97, Individuals; $51, Individuals combo; $11.99, Individuals military; $19.97, Individuals online.

1249 ■ Shooting Industry
Pub: Publishers Development Corp.
URL(s): www.shootingindustry.com. **Ed:** Russ Thurman. **Released:** Monthly **Price:** $45, Other countries.

1250 ■ Shooting Times
Pub: PRIMEDIA Los Angeles
URL(s): www.shootingtimes.com. **Ed:** Joseph von Benedikt. **Released:** Monthly **Price:** $12, Individuals; $15, Two years; $25, Canada; $41, Canada 2 years; $27, Other countries; $45, Other countries 2 years.

1251 ■ Skeet Shooting Review
Pub: National Skeet Shooting Association
Contact: Don Snyder, Executive Director
E-mail: dsnyder@nssa-nsca.com
URL(s): www.mynssa.com/CMS/NSSADisplayPage. aspx?ContentID=96&PageTitle=SSR%2 0Magazine. **Ed:** Susie Fluckiger. **Released:** Monthly **Price:** $24, Individuals; $60, Canada and Mexico; $92, Other countries; $45, Two years.

1252 ■ The Tab
Pub: Bowhunters of North America
Ed: Adrian Jacobs, Editor. **Released:** 2/year. **Price:** Included in membership. **Description:** Provides articles intended to promote the sport of bowhunting. Discusses such topics as improving hunter-landowner relations and increasing the understanding of bowhunting among the non-hunting public. Recurring features include news of members, announcements of new products, and articles on bowhunting techniques.

TRADE SHOWS AND CONVENTIONS

1253 ■ JAGEN UND FISCHEN - International Exhibition for Hunters, Fishermen and Marksmen
Kallman Worldwide, Inc.
4 North St., Ste. 800
Waldwick, NJ 07463-1842
Ph: (201)251-2600
Fax: (201)251-2760
Co. E-mail: info@kallman.com
URL: http://www.kallman.com
URL(s): www.jagenundfischen.deComment2. **Principal Exhibits:** Equipment, supplies, and services for hunters, fishermen, and marksmen. **Telecommunication Services:** newsline@messe-muenchen.de.

1254 ■ The Shooting, Hunting, and Outdoor Trade Show (SHOT SHOW)
Reed Exhibitions Contemporary Forums
6377 Clark Ave., Ste. 200
Dublin, CA 94568
Ph: (925)828-7100
Fax: (800)329-9923
Co. E-mail: info@cforums.com
URL: http://www.contemporaryforums.com
URL(s): www.shotshow.org. **Audience:** Federally licensed firearms dealers and legitimate sporting goods dealers. **Principal Exhibits:** Shooting and hunting equipment and products; sports accessories, clothing, and supplies. **Telecommunication Services:** nbogdanski@reedexpo.com.

LIBRARIES

1255 ■ National Rifle Association of America - NRA Technical Library
11250 Waples Mill Rd.
Fairfax, VA 22030
Ph: (703)267-1000
Fax: (703)267-3971
Co. E-mail: mbussard@nrahq.org
Contact: Michael Bussard, Editor

Scope: Firearms, ammunition, military ordnance, antique arms, ballistics, handloading, collecting, history. **Services:** Library not open to the public. **Founded:** 1946. **Holdings:** 1700 books. **Subscriptions:** 25 journals and other serials.

ASSOCIATIONS AND OTHER ORGANIZATIONS

1256 ■ Canadian Centre for Architecture (CCA)—Centre Canadien d'Architecture
1920, rue Baile
Montreal, QC, Canada H3H 2S6
Ph: (514)939-7026
Co. E-mail: info@cca.qc.ca
URL: http://www.cca.qc.ca/en
Contact: Mr. Mirko Zardini, Director
Description: Study center and museum devoted to the art of architecture, past and present. Provides access to research collections, exhibitions, publications, colloquia, educational and cultural programs, as well as family programs. **Scope:** architecture, landscape design, urban planning. **Founded:** 1979. **Subscriptions:** 215000 audiovisuals books periodicals archival material. **Publications:** *Sense of the City*; *Money Matters: A Critical Look at Bank Architecture*.

1257 ■ *Money Matters: A Critical Look at Bank Architecture*
1920, rue Baile
Montreal, QC, Canada H3H 2S6
Ph: (514)939-7026
Co. E-mail: info@cca.qc.ca
URL: http://www.cca.qc.ca/en
Contact: Mr. Mirko Zardini, Director

1258 ■ *RAIC Bulletin*
330-55 rue Murray St.
Ottawa, ON, Canada K1N 5M3
Ph: (613)241-3600
Fax: (613)241-5750
Co. E-mail: info@raic.org
URL: http://www.raic.org
Contact: David Craddock, President
Released: Monthly

1259 ■ Royal Architectural Institute of Canada (RAIC)—Institut Royal d'Architecture du Canada
330-55 rue Murray St.
Ottawa, ON, Canada K1N 5M3
Ph: (613)241-3600
Fax: (613)241-5750
Co. E-mail: info@raic.org
URL: http://www.raic.org
Contact: David Craddock, President
Description: Registered architects in Canada united to further develop the quality of architecture. **Scope:** architecture. **Founded:** 1907. **Publications:** *RAIC Bulletin* (Monthly); *Update* (Bimonthly); *Building the West*. **Educational Activities:** Royal Architectural Institute of Canada Conference (Annual). **Awards:** Andre Francou Legacy; Allied Arts Medal; Gold Medal; Student Medal; Arthur Buckwell Memorial Scholarship; Ernest Wilby Memorial Scholarship.

1260 ■ Royal Oak Foundation (ROF)
35 W 35th St., Ste. 1200
New York, NY 10001-2205
Ph: (212)480-2889
Free: 800-913-6565
Fax: (212)785-7234
Co. E-mail: general@royal-oak.org
URL: http://www.royal-oak.org
Contact: Mr. Sean E. Sawyer, Executive Director
Description: Professionals, students, and laypeople who are interested in architecture, nature conservation, and historic preservation areas. Seeks to further the preservation and understanding of Anglo-American cultural and architectural heritage. Conducts symposia; presents lecture series and special lectures given by foreign speakers visiting the U.S.; sponsors exhibits emphasizing historic preservation. Maintains charitable program. **Founded:** 1973.

1261 ■ *Sense of the City*
1920, rue Baile
Montreal, QC, Canada H3H 2S6
Ph: (514)939-7026
Co. E-mail: info@cca.qc.ca
URL: http://www.cca.qc.ca/en
Contact: Mr. Mirko Zardini, Director

1262 ■ *Update*
330-55 rue Murray St.
Ottawa, ON, Canada K1N 5M3
Ph: (613)241-3600
Fax: (613)241-5750
Co. E-mail: info@raic.org
URL: http://www.raic.org
Contact: David Craddock, President
Released: Bimonthly

DIRECTORIES OF EDUCATIONAL PROGRAMS

1263 ■ *The Encyclopedia of Associations and Information Sources for Architects, Designers, and Engineers*
Pub: M.E. Sharpe Inc.
Contact: Myron E. Sharpe, President
URL(s): mesharpe.com. **Price:** $176.95, Individuals available to all countries. **Covers:** 5,000 U.S. and Canadian resources such as journals, online databases, CD-ROMs, testing laboratories, government sources, web sites and more for architects, designers, and engineers. **Entries include:** Contact information, web addresses.

REFERENCE WORKS

1264 ■ *"$100 Million Plan for Jefferson Arms"* in Saint Louis Business Journal (Vol. 32, October 14, 2011, No. 7, pp. 1)
Pub: Saint Louis Business Journal
Ed: Evan Binns. **Description:** Teach for America is planning a $100 million renovation project of the former Jefferson Arms hotel in St. Louis, Missouri. The organization has signed a letter of intent to occupy the space. Financing of the project will be mainly through tax credits.

1265 ■ *"2010: Important Year Ahead for Waterfront"* in Bellingham Business Journal (Vol. March 2010, pp. 2)
Pub: Sound Publishing Inc.
Ed: Isaac Bonnell. **Description:** A tentative timeline has been established for the environmental impact statement (EIS) slated for completion in May 2010. The plan for the Waterfront District includes detailed economic and architectural analysis of the feasibility of reusing remaining structures and retaining some industrial icons.

1266 ■ *"Advertisers Hooked on Horns, their Playground"* in Austin Business JournalInc. (Vol. 28, July 25, 2008, No. 19, pp. A1)
Pub: American City Business Journals
Ed: Sandra Zaragoza. **Description:** Renovation of the D.K. Royal-Texas Memorial Stadium has increased its advertising revenue from $570,000 in 1993 to $10 in 2008. Sponsorship has grown in the past years due to the revenue-sharing agreement, a ten-year contract through 2015 between the University of Texas and IMG College Sports.

1267 ■ *"Annapolis Seeks City Market Vendors"* in Boston Business Journal (Vol. 29, June 10, 2011, No. 5, pp. 3)
Pub: American City Business Journals Inc.
Ed: Daniel J. Sernovitz. **Description:** The city of Annapolis, Maryland is planning to revive the historical landmark Market House and it is now accepting bids from vendors until June 10, 2011. The city hopes to reopen the facility by July 2011 for a six-month period after which it will undergo renovations.

1268 ■ *"Bridging the Ingenuity Gap"* in Canadian Business (Vol. 79, November 6, 2006, No. 22, pp. 12)
Pub: Rogers Media
Ed: Rachel Pulfer. **Description:** The views of Patrick Whitney, director of Illinois Institute of Technology's Institute of design, on globalization and business design methods are presented.

1269 ■ *"Can This Duo be Saved? Renovating 2 Tallest Edifices Downtown Will Be Costly, Owner Says"* in Charlotte Observer (February 4, 2007)
Pub: Knight-Ridder/Tribune Business News
Ed: Jefferson George. **Description:** Gastonia, North Carolina city leaders are making plans to renovate the Lawyers Building and the Commercial Building in an effort to revitalize the downtown area.

1270 ■ *"Firm Takes 'Local' Worldwide"* in Hispanic Business (July-August 2007, pp. 48)
Pub: Hispanic Business
Ed: Keith Rosenblum. **Description:** Willy A. Bermello tells how he has expanded his architectural, engineering and construction firm globally.

1271 ■ *"First the Merger: Then, The Culture Clash. How To Fix the Little Things That Can Tear a Company Apart"* in Inc. (January 2008)
Pub: Gruner & Jahr USA Publishing
Ed: Elaine Appleton Grant. **Description:** Ways three CEOs handled the culture classes that followed after company mergers; companies profiled include Fuel

Outdoor, an outdoor advertising company; Nelson, an interior design and architecture firm; and Beber Silverstein, an ad agency.

1272 ■ *"'Groundhog Day' B & B Likely Will Be Converted Into One In Real Life"* in *Chicago Tribune (October 21, 2008)*
Pub: McClatchy-Tribune Information Services
Ed: Carolyn Starks. **Description:** Everton Martin and Karla Stewart Martin have purchased the Victorian house that was featured as a bed-and-breakfast in the 1993 hit move 'Groundhog Day'; the couple was initially unaware of the structure's celebrity status when they purchased it with the hope of fulfilling their dream of owning a bed-and-breakfast.

1273 ■ *"Historic Glenview Homes Could Be Torn Down"* in *Chicago Tribune (September 25, 2008)*
Pub: McClatchy-Tribune Information Services
Ed: Courtney Flynn. **Description:** Leaders of the Glenview New Church would like to see a buyer emerge who would move and restore two historic homes sitting on the church's property. If a buyer does not come forward the church plans to demolish the homes to make room for condominiums and the expansion of their school.

1274 ■ *"Historic Tax Credit Plan Gains Support"* in *Baltimore Business Journal (Vol. 27, January 8, 2010, No. 36, pp. 1)*
Pub: American City Business Journals
Ed: Heather Harlan Warnack. **Description:** Maryland Governor Martin O'Malley plans to push legislation in the General Assembly to extend for three more years the tax credit program for rehabilitation of obsolete buildings. The Maryland Heritage Structure Rehabilitation Tax Credit Program has declined from almost $75 million in expenses in 2001 to roughly $5 million in 2010 fiscal year. Details on the projects that benefited from the program are explored.

1275 ■ *"Honcoop Honored as BIAWC's Builder of the Year"* in *Bellingham Business Journal (Vol. February 2010, pp. 17)*
Pub: Sound Publishing Inc.
Description: Gary Honcoop, co-owner and president of Roosendaal-Honcoop Construction Inc. was honored by the Building Industry Association of Whatcom County as Builder of the Year. The construction company was founded in 1979.

1276 ■ *"Hospital to Get $72M Makeover"* in *Austin Business JournalInc. (Vol. 29, January 15, 2010, No. 45, pp. 1)*
Pub: American City Business Journals
Ed: Sandra Zaragoza. **Description:** St. David's South Austin Medical Center, formerly St. David's South Austin Hospital, is undertaking an expansion and renovation project worth $72 million. Meanwhile, CEO Erol Akdamar has resigned to serve as CEO of Medical City Hospital in Dallas, Texas. A new CEO and a general contractor for the project are yet to be chosen by the hospital.

1277 ■ *How to Open and Operate a Financially Successful Redesign, Redecorating, and Home Staging Business: With Companion CD-ROM*
Pub: Atlantic Publishing Group, Inc.
Ed: Mary Larsen; Teri B. Clark. **Released:** January 2008. **Price:** $39.95 paperback. **Description:** Questions are asked to help individuals determine if they should launch their own redesign or real estate staging firm.

1278 ■ *"Innovation Can Be Imperative for Those in Hands-On Trades"* in *Crain's Cleveland Business (Vol. 28, November 12, 2007, No. 45)*
Pub: Crain Communications, Inc.
Ed: Harriet Tramer. **Description:** Discusses the importance of networking and innovative marketing concerning those in art and restoration trades.

1279 ■ *"Investors Eye Old Buildings"* in *Business Journal-Portland (Vol. 24, October 19, 2007, No. 34, pp. 1)*
Pub: American City Business Journals, Inc.
Ed: Wendy Culverwell. **Description:** Office vacancy rates in downtown Portland has dipped to around five percent, causing brokers and investors to search for

older buildings in the Class B and Class C categories where the rent is also cheaper. Some notable older and cheaper buildings will be renovated for use.

1280 ■ *"Muirhead Farmhouse B & B Owners Get Hospitality Right"* in *Chicago Tribune (July 31, 2008)*
Pub: McClatchy-Tribune Information Services
Ed: Glenn Jeffers. **Description:** Profile of the Muirhead Farmhouse, a bed-and-breakfast owned by Mike Petersdorf and Sarah Muirhead Petersdorf; Frank Lloyd Wright designed the historic farmhouse which blends farm life and history into a unique experience that is enhanced by the couple's hospitality.

1281 ■ *"N.H. Near the LEED in Green Space"* in *New Hampshire Business Review (Vol. 33, March 25, 2011, No. 6, pp. 30)*
Pub: Business Publications Inc.
Description: New Hamphire's architects, contractors and suppliers are among the leaders with LEED-certified space per capita.

1282 ■ *"Not Enough Room"* in *Austin Business JournalInc. (Vol. 29, November 13, 2009, No. 36, pp. A1)*
Pub: American City Business Journals
Ed: Jacob Dirr. **Description:** Hotel and convention business in downtown Austin, Texas lost nearly $5.3 million when Dell Inc. relocated its annual convention to Las Vegas. However, lack of capital caused the postponement of various hotel projects which need to be finished in order to attract well-attended conventions. Makeover projects on Austin's Waller Creek and Sixth Street are discussed.

1283 ■ *"P&L Building Owner Nears Start of $157M Condo Plan"* in *Business Journal-Serving Metropolitan Kansas City (November 23, 2007)*
Pub: American City Business Journals, Inc.
Ed: Jim Davis. **Description:** The owner of Power and Light Building is ready to begin a $157 million plan to refurbish the Kansas City landmark and redevelop a property right next to it after receiving tax increment refinancing for the project.

1284 ■ *"The Power of Fun"* in *Canadian Business (Vol. 79, November 6, 2006, No. 22, pp. 58)*
Pub: Rogers Media
Ed: Zena Olijnyk. **Description:** The creative efforts of Phillippe Starck in designing condos are analyzed.

1285 ■ *"Restoring Grandeur"* in *Business Courier (Vol. 26, December 4, 2009, No. 32, pp. 1)*
Pub: American City Business Journals, Inc.
Ed: Dan Monk. **Description:** Eagle Realty Group intends to spend more than $10 to restore the historic 12-story Phelps apartment building in Lytle Park in Cincinnati. Its president, Mario San Marco, expressed the need to invest in the building in order to maintain operations. The building could be restored into a hotel catering to executives and consultants.

1286 ■ *"Stone Company Slated to Expand Here"* in *Austin Business JournalInc. (Vol. 28, September 12, 2008, No. 26, pp. 1)*
Pub: American City Business Journals
Ed: Jean Kwon. **Description:** Architectural Granite & Marble Inc. has a $6 million investment that moved the company from 2,500 square feet of space to a 10,000 square foot office in Southwest Austin, Texas. The investment will also provide for the company's expansion in Nashville, Tennessee and San Antonio, Texas.

1287 ■ *"Texas State Poised for Boom"* in *Austin Business JournalInc. (Vol. 29, January 29, 2010, No. 47, pp. 1)*
Pub: American City Business Journals
Ed: Sandra Zaragoza. **Description:** Texas State University, San Marcos has seen its student population grow to 30,800 and the university is set for $633 million in construction projects to address demand for

student housing and building expansions and renovations. Details on the buildings and student housing plans for the projects are provided.

1288 ■ *"This Just In"* in *Crain's Detroit Business (Vol. 25, June 22, 2009, No. 25, pp. 1)*
Pub: Crain Communications Inc. - Detroit
Description: Yamasaki Associates, an architectural firm has been sued for non payment of wages to four employees. Yamasaki spokesperson stated the economy has affected the company and it is focusing marketing efforts on areas encouraged by recovery funding.

1289 ■ *"USF Plans $30M Sports Complex"* in *Tampa Bay Business Journal (Vol. 29, October 23, 2009, No. 44, pp. 1)*
Pub: American City Business Journals
Ed: Jane Meinhardt. **Description:** University of South Florida (USF) is going to build a new sports complex with the aid of a $30 million loan from BB&T. The project, which is also comprised of new and renovated athletic facilities on USF's Tampa campus, is projected to create more than $37 million in revenue in its first year. Revenues from the said facilities are expected to achieve an annual growth of at least four percent.

1290 ■ *"Vegas in the D; Local Architects Collaborate On MGM Grand"* in *Crain's Detroit Business (Vol. 23, October 1, 2007, No. 40, pp. 1)*
Pub: Crain Communications Inc. - Detroit
Ed: Daniel Duggan. **Description:** Local Detroit architects, Smith Group and Hamilton Anderson Associates are among the contractors vying for subcontracted architecture, construction and consulting contracts for the new MGM Grand Detroit casino and hotel.

1291 ■ *"Vernon Revamp"* in *Business Courier (Vol. 26, October 9, 2009, No. 24, pp. 1)*
Pub: American City Business Journals, Inc.
Ed: Dan Monk. **Description:** Al Neyer Inc. will redevelop the Vernon Manor Hotel as an office building for the Cincinnati Children's Hospital Medical Center. The project will cost $35 million and would generate a new investment vehicle for black investors who plan to raise $2.7 million in private offerings to claim majority ownership of the property after its renovations.

TRADE PERIODICALS

1292 ■ *AppendX*
Pub: Appendx
URL(s): www.appendx.org. **Released:** Annual

1293 ■ *Azure Magazine*
Pub: Azure Publishing Inc.
URL(s): www.azuremagazine.com/. **Ed:** Nelda Rodger. **Released:** 8/yr. **Price:** C$32.95, Individuals; C$54.95, Two years; $32.95, Individuals; $54.95, Two years; $48, Other countries; $78, Other countries 2 years.

1294 ■ *Downtown Idea Exchange*
Pub: Alexander Communications Group Inc.
Contact: Margaret DeWitt, Publisher
Ed: Paul Felt, Editor. **Released:** Monthly. **Price:** $227, individuals; $227, elsewhere. **Description:** Focuses on revitalizing central business districts, including planning, design, development, preservation, parking, transit, traffic, funding, and organization.

1295 ■ *Journal of the Society of Architectural Historians (JSAH)*
Pub: Society of Architectural Historians
Contact: Pauline Saliga, Executive Director
URL(s): www.sah.org/index.php?submenu=Publications&src=gendocs&ref=JSAH&category=Publications. **Ed:** Prof. Hilary Ballon, Prof. David Brownlee. **Released:** Quarterly

1296 ■ *Municipal Art Society Newsletter*
Pub: Municipal Art Society
Released: 6/year. **Price:** Included in membership.
Description: Provides updates on advocacy efforts, exhibitions, and programming on urban issues. Recurring features include a calendar of events and tour schedule.

1297 ■ *Timber Framing: Journal of the Timber Framers Guild*
Pub: Timber Framers Guild
Contact: Joel McCarty, Executive Director
URL(s): www.timberframersguild.org/pubpg.html. **Ed:** Ken Rower. **Released:** Quarterly **Price:** $25, Free with membership; $25, Nonmembers.

CONSULTANTS

1298 ■ Glenn Acomb Associates Inc.
1024 NE 5th St.
Gainesville, FL 32601
Ph: (352)392-6098
Fax: (352)372-6233
Co. E-mail: ufadvisor06@flasla.org
Contact: Glenn A. Acomb, President
E-mail: gaafl@aol.com
Scope: Offers planning and design services for downtown revitalization, CRA/development, master plans, historic design, waterfronts, parks and plazas. **Founded:** 1978. **Publications:** "Implications of the Physical Plan," 2006; "Low Impact Design and Development Techniques," May, 2005; "New Towns and New Urbanism: A Critique from a Landscape Perspective," 2000. **Seminars:** Downtown Revitalization; Planning Your Streetscape; Livable Communities; Sustainable Communities.

1299 ■ ALSA Architecture L.L.C.
570 7th Ave., Ste. 1206
New York, NY 10018-1603
Ph: (212)302-2180
Fax: (212)391-2148
Co. E-mail: mail@alsaarchitecture.com
URL: http://www.alsaarchitecture.com
Contact: Roy Sokoloski, President
E-mail: roy@alsaarchitecture.com
Scope: Architectural and engineering design firm that provides consulting expertise in construction contract documents, construction administration and facilities management. The firm has a preservation department specializing in exterior and interior building rehabilitation, including landmark properties restoration. Offers comprehensive services including architectural, mechanical, plumbing, electrical, fire and life safety design. Industries served: Academic, industrial, financial, government, health care, housing, corporate and retail. **Founded:** 1963.

1300 ■ Beckett and Raeder Inc.—BRI Inc.
535 W William St., Ste. 101
Ann Arbor, MI 48103
Ph: (734)663-2622
Fax: (734)663-6759
Co. E-mail: info@bria2.com
URL: http://www.bria2.com
Contact: Connie Pulcipher, Manager
E-mail: conniep@bria2.com
Scope: Provider of exceptional and innovative professional service to a variety of municipal governments, state and federal agencies, institution and private sector clients. **Founded:** 1966.

1301 ■ Building Conservation Associates Inc.
44 E 32nd St.
New York, NY 10016
Ph: (212)777-1300
Fax: (212)777-1606
Co. E-mail: info@bcausa.com
URL: http://www.bcausa.com
Contact: Raymond Pepi, President
Scope: A consulting firm that specializes in both the technical and historical aspects of restoring buildings and works of art. Assists clients in the preparation of federal rehabilitation tax credit applications. Combines field documentation, archival research, materials testing and scientific research. **Founded:** 1985. **Publications:** "Journal of the American Institute foe Conservation".

1302 ■ Jonathan Cohen and Associates, Architects and Planners (JC&A)
65 Acacia Ave.
Berkeley, CA 94708-1201
Ph: (510)558-8154
Fax: (510)558-8054
Co. E-mail: info@jcarchitects.com
URL: http://www.jcarchitects.com
Contact: Jonathan Cohen, Principal
E-mail: jonathan@jcarchitects.com
Scope: Offers a full range of architectural, planning and urban design services including programming, master planning, feasibility studies; design, rehabilitation and restoration; materials research; working drawings and specifications; construction administration; post construction evaluation; and seismic and disabled access retrofit. Expertise in the application of information technology used in the design, construction, and operations of buildings. Expert testimony and dispute consultation is also provided to the construction and design industries. **Founded:** 1987. **Publications:** "The New Architect: Keeper of Knowledge and Rules," The Architect's Handbook of Professional Practice, John Wiley and Sons, 2004; "Participatory Design with the Internet," Architectural Record, Aug, 2003; "Communication and Design with the Internet"; "Secrets to a Fulfilling Life". **Seminars:** Project Information Managers: The New Master Builders, Zweig White AEC Technology Strategies, Washington, DC, Jun, 2003; Web-based Design Communication, Fisher Center for Information Technology & Marketplace Transformation, Haas School of Business, UC Berkeley, Apr, 2003; Web Development for Architects, AIA Minnesota annual convention, Nov, 2002; Geographic Information Systems for Architects, AEC Systems, Anaheim, CA, Jun, 2002; The Internet in Architectural Practice and Web Authoring for Architects; Ontario Association of Architects annual convention: Changing Practice, Practicing Change, Niagara Falls, Ontario, Canada, May, 2002; Architect at the Center: A Radical Proposal for the Building Industry, AIA Professional Practice Conference, Washington, DC, Apr, 2002; Networked Design Organizations and the Project Information Manager, Build Boston Nov, 2001; Architecture in the Net Economy, Form, Function, Future, AIA Professional Practice Conference, Portland, OR, Oct, 2000; Healing a Fragmented Industry: New Opportunities for the Architectural Profession, Association of Collegiate Schools of Architecture Technology Conference, MIT, Jul, 2000; Owning the Project Information: An Opportunity for Architects, Greenwich 2000 Symposium on Digital Creativity, Virtual Design/Build Organizations and the Project Information Manager; University of Greenwich, London, UK, Jan, 2000; Intra nets and Web Portals for Collaboration and Knowledge Management; Virtual Design/Build Organizations and the Project Information Manager; Web Sites for Participatory Programming and Design; Geographic Information Systems; Cool Software Tools for Designers; Participatory Design and Planning with the Internet Case Study; Intra nets and Web Portals for Collaboration and Knowledge Management; Virtual Design/Build Organizations and the Project Information Manager.

1303 ■ Cox Graae + Spack Architects
2909 M St. NW
Washington, DC 20007-3714
Ph: (202)965-7070
Fax: (202)965-7144
URL: http://www.cgsarchitects.com
Contact: Ed Foley, Manager
E-mail: efoley@cgsarchitects.com
Scope: Services include architecture, historic preservation, planning, programming, space planning, interior design, building codes, design guidelines, ADA, waterfront development, rehabilitation technology, restoration and public transportation. **Founded:** 1981.

1304 ■ Cropsey and Associates Inc.
800 W Taylor St.
Griffin, GA 30224-2722
Ph: (770)229-1100
Fax: (770)229-1326
Contact: Paul A. Cropsey, President
Scope: General practice architectural design firm experienced in rehabilitating historic buildings in ac-

cordance with the Secretary of the Interior's guidelines for Historic Preservation and ISTEA funding. **Founded:** 1991.

1305 ■ DANTH Inc.
83-85 116th St., Ste. 3D
Kew Gardens, NY 11418
Ph: (718)805-9507
Fax: (718)805-2656
Co. E-mail: danth@danth.com
URL: http://www.danth.com
Contact: N. David Milder, President
E-mail: danthinc@yahoo.com
Scope: Provider of economic revitalization consulting to downtown, commercial district and local government organizations. Focuses on the development of comprehensive retail and office revitalization policies and programs. **Founded:** 1977. **Publications:** "MAKING MEMBERSHIP BUY-INS EASY," Downtown Idea Exchange, Oct, 2004. **Seminars:** Niche Development and Marketing; Reconnaissance and Action Plan; Retail Revitalization Strategy and Action Plan. **Telecommunication Services:** danth@yahoo.com.

1306 ■ Roger du Toit Architects Ltd.—Du Toit Allsop Hillier
50 Park Rd.
Toronto, ON, Canada M4W 2N5
Ph: (416)968-7908
Fax: (416)968-0687
Co. E-mail: admin@dtah.com
URL: http://www.dtah.com
Contact: Adam Nicklin, Manager
Scope: Architects, landscape architects, urban designers, and planners specializing in facilities for educational, institutional, recreation land commercial/retail uses; barrier-free design, design for the elderly; housing; renovation/restoration; streets-capes; and waterfronts. Services: include master plans, feasibility studies, site analysis, design, working drawings, specifications, and contract administration. **Founded:** 1975. **Publications:** "Designs for second Bow Bridge unveiled," Sep, 2009; "Waterfront on a roll with classy Wave Deck," Jun, 2009; "Skate parks, promenades and plazas," Jun, 2009; "Evergreen Brick Works"; "Toronto Central Waterfront".

1307 ■ Gove Lumber Co.
80 Colon St.
Beverly, MA 01915
Ph: (978)922-0921
Fax: (978)921-4522
Co. E-mail: info@govelumber.com
URL: http://www.govelumber.com
Contact: Bruce Gove, President
Scope: Specializes in wood doors and windows for historic preservation. Supplies mill work in mahogany, cypress, oak and ships in the United States and abroad. Areas of expertise include: Adaptive reuse, architectural historic preservation, design guidelines, rehabilitation technology, and restoration. **Founded:** 1910.

1308 ■ Halstead Architects
1139 Shelby St.
Indianapolis, IN 46203-1165
Ph: (317)684-1431
Fax: (317)684-1433
Co. E-mail: mikeh@halstead-architects.com
URL: http://www.halstead-architects.com
Contact: Lauren Furry, Manager
E-mail: lfurry@halstead-architects.com
Scope: Offers architectural expertise in planning, libraries, community based projects, historic preservation, residential, entertainment, religious, educational, and interiors in the United States. **Founded:** 1993. **Publications:** "Coffee, snacks ahead for canal walkers," Indianapolis Star, Oct, 2003; "Canal-side Church Building to Get Makeover," Indiana Business Journal.

1309 ■ Hemmler + Camayd Architects
409 Lackawanna Ave., Ste. 400
Scranton, PA 18503-1432
Ph: (570)961-1302

Fax: (570)961-3919
Co. E-mail: info@hc-architects.com
URL: http://www.hc-architects.com
Contact: Richard J. Leonari, Partner
Scope: Provider of comprehensive architectural, interior design and planning services to corporate, government, education, health/elderly care and religious sectors in the mid-Atlantic states, primarily Pennsylvania. Offers services for creative design of new buildings, renovation and alteration of existent buildings and adaptive reuse, restoration and preservation of historic structures. Also provides feasibility studies, existing conditions evaluations, master planning, facility planning, interior space planning and FF and E (furniture, fixtures, and equipment)planning and construction observation services. **Founded:** 1978.

1310 ■ Historic Exterior Paint Colors Consulting—Historic House Colors
3661 Waldenwood Dr.
Ann Arbor, MI 48105
Ph: (734)668-0298
Co. E-mail: robs@umich.edu
URL: http://www.historichousecolors.com
Contact: Robert Schweitzer, Owner
E-mail: robs@umich.edu
Scope: Provider of exterior paint color consulting services. Provides services for historic, contemporary, new, commercial and residential services; museums. **Publications:** "Proof that Paint Color Lends Detail," Arts and Crafts Homes, 2006; "Bungalow Colors-Exteriors," Gibbs-Smith Publishers, 2002; "Color Scheming," Design NJ, 2002; "Colonial Revival Homes," Victorian Homes, Feb, 2003; "America's Favorite Homes"; "Color a New World," 60s Ranch Color Makeover, Romantic Homes, Aug, 2001; "How Shall I Paint my House," American Bungalow, 1999; "Color Concepts and Bungalow Basics," Cottages & Bungalows.

1311 ■ Hoisington Koegler Group Inc. (HKGI)
123 N 3rd St., Ste. 100
Minneapolis, MN 55401
Ph: (612)338-0800
Fax: (612)338-6838
Co. E-mail: blc@hkgi.com
URL: http://www.hkgi.com
Contact: Mark Koegler, President
E-mail: mkoegler@hkgi.com
Scope: Planners and landscape architects provide the technical and strategic expertise needed to develop innovative solutions that respond to the natural environment and to the needs of the community. Emphasizes sustainability and integration of the natural landscape and historic resources. Areas of expertise include city planning, landscape architecture, urban planning, community development, and group facilitation. **Founded:** 1982.

1312 ■ Integrated Conservation Resources Inc. (ICR)
41 E 11th St., 3rd Fl.
New York, NY 10003
Ph: (212)947-4499
Fax: (212)947-7766
Co. E-mail: info@icr-icc.com
URL: http://www.icr-icc.com
Contact: Glenn Boornazian, President
E-mail: gboornazian@icr-icc.com
Scope: Assists design professionals by providing specialized expertise on historic building materials. Services span the full spectrum of architectural conservation services. **Founded:** 1987.

1313 ■ Karl Kardel Consultancy
4926 E 12th St.
Oakland, CA 94601
Ph: (510)261-4149
Fax: (510)436-7486
Co. E-mail: karl@kardelconsultancy.com
URL: http://www.kardelconsultancy.com
Contact: Kaj Kardel, Manager
E-mail: kaj@kardelconsultancy.com
Scope: Provider of consultation in water invasion in windows, wall systems and membranes. Offers problem resolution in finishes and coatings and forensic analysis in building failures. Specializes in

historic conservation, architectural finishes, water invasion, windows, curtain walls and stucco. Gives analysis for managed case cost controls. **Founded:** 1959.

1314 ■ Karn Charuhas Chapman & Twohey (KCCT)
1120 Connecticut Ave. NW, Ste. 1250
Washington, DC 20036
Ph: (202)659-5600
Fax: (202)659-5605
Co. E-mail: info@kcct.com
URL: http://www.kcct.com
Contact: Paul Phillips, Manager
Scope: Consultants for architecture, urban design and planning. Specialists in transportation design, building renovation, and historic preservation. **Founded:** 1983.

1315 ■ Leeds Clark Inc.
3010 Shady Grove Rd.
Midlothian, TX 76065
Ph: (972)775-3843
Fax: (972)725-3263
Co. E-mail: info@leedsclark.com
URL: http://www.leedsclark.com
Contact: Tom Clark, Owner
E-mail: tomclark@leedsclark.com
Scope: Provider of historic preservation consulting, condition assessment and inspections, proforma cost estimating, historic window surveys, duplication and retrofit. **Founded:** 1982. **Seminars:** Historic Building Condition Assessment; Main Street Training and Lead Paint Abatement on Windows; Selecting and working with contractors; Specification writing and code compliance; Project planning.

1316 ■ John Leeke
26 Higgins St.
Portland, ME 04103
Ph: (207)773-2306
Fax: (207)773-2306
Co. E-mail: johnleeke@historichomeworks.com
URL: http://www.historichomeworks.com
Contact: John Leeke, Consultant
Scope: Assists owners, trades people, contractors and professionals understand and maintain their historic and older buildings. **Publications:** "Window Restoration". **Seminars:** Save Your Wood Windows; Exterior Wood and Paint; Restore Omaha, Nov, 2006; The Business Side of Preservation Vermont, Nov, 2006; Save Your Wood Windows, May, 2007; Exterior Woodwork: Repairs and Painting, Jun, 2007; Windows: Small Shop Business, 2007. **Special Services:** Historic HomeWorks™.

1317 ■ Jan Rubin Associates Inc.
2022 Chancellor St.
Philadelphia, PA 19103-5605
Ph: (215)564-5956
Fax: (215)564-1939
Co. E-mail: jra@jragroup.com
URL: http://www.jragroup.org
Contact: Jan Rubin, Owner
E-mail: janrubin@jragroup.org
Scope: Specializes in structuring and developing low income housing and historic tax credits, HOPE VI, CDBG or HOME transactions for public and private organizations. **Founded:** 1987.

1318 ■ Schrager Lighting Design L.L.C.
412 Main St., Ste. H
Ridgefield, CT 06877
Ph: (203)438-1188
Fax: (203)438-2299
Co. E-mail: sspublic@schragerlightingdesign.com
Contact: Sara Schrager, Principal
Scope: Provides consulting services in architectural lighting design, with experience in lighting museums, academic and religious institutions, historic preservation, public atriums, corporate interiors, exterior lighting for landscapes and hard capes, art collections, restaurants and fine homes and estates. **Founded:** 2008.

1319 ■ Shakespeare Composites & Electronics
19845 US Hwy. 76
Newberry, SC 29108

Ph: (803)276-5504
Free: 800-800-9008
Fax: (803)276-8940
Co. E-mail: composites@skp-cs.com
URL: http://www.skp-cs.com
Contact: J. Wayne Merck, President
Scope: Specializes in fiberglass reinforced composites design, engineering and manufacturing. **Founded:** 1897.

1320 ■ Richard Sharpe Associates P.C.
30 Connecticut Ave.
Norwich, CT 06360-1502
Ph: (860)889-7314
Fax: (860)889-3940
Co. E-mail: rsa-arch@snet.net
Contact: William C. Clapet, Manager
Scope: Design consultants providing architectural design, interior design, urban and regional design, project analysis, space analysis and planning, and graphic design services. Special expertise in historic rehabilitation, industrial, corporate planning, courthouses, and schools. Industries served: state, federal government, municipalities, and the private sector in the northeast region U.S. **Founded:** 1956. **Seminars:** Local Fire Code; Americans with Disabilities Act (ADA); Innovations in Lighting; Various Window Solutions; Standing Seam Metal Roofs. **Telecommunication Services:** rsa-arch@99main.com. **Special Services:** Auto CAD Release 2000.

1321 ■ Brenda Spencer
10150 Onaga Rd.
Wamego, KS 66547-9584
Ph: (785)456-9857
Fax: (785)456-9857
Contact: Mike Boatwright, Manager
Scope: Specializes in main street revitalization and historic preservation.

1322 ■ Uptown Shelby Association Inc.
211 S Trade St.
Shelby, NC 28150
Ph: (704)484-3100
Fax: (704)484-3934
Co. E-mail: info@uptownshelby.org
URL: http://www.uptownshelby.org
Contact: Jay Gragg, President
Scope: Consults on a number of downtown issues addressing virtually any aspect of design, organization, promotion, economic restructuring and historic preservation, board training, strategic planning, technical assistance or resource teams and problem solving on specific issues. **Founded:** 1982. **Publications:** "Help Save Historic Rogers Theatre".

1323 ■ Vertical Systems Analysis Inc.
307 W 36th St., 8th Fl.
New York, NY 10018
Ph: (212)989-5525
Fax: (212)989-6860
Co. E-mail: bisufi@vsaconsulting.com
URL: http://www.vsaconsulting.com
Contact: Jose Romero, Chief Executive Officer
Scope: Elevator and escalator engineering and consulting firm. Works with residential and commercial buildings of all sizes. Firm evaluates elevators and escalators for modernization and restoration projects. Prepares and creates specifications and plans for all elevator and escalator applications. Also evaluates elevators to ensure that proper maintenance is being provided. Industries served: real estate, hospital, hotel, engineering, legal, universities and schools, cooperatives and condominiums, architectural and state facilities, and government agencies. **Founded:** 1986. **Publications:** "Owners Guide to Better Elevator Service". **Telecommunication Services:** info@vsaconsulting.com.

1324 ■ Walter Sedovic Architects
1 Bridge St., Ste. 1
Irvington, NY 10533
Ph: (914)591-1900

Fax: (914)591-1999
Co. E-mail: wsa@modernruins.com
URL: http://www.modernruins.com
Contact: Walter Sedovic, Chief Executive Officer
E-mail: gibrwalter@modernruins.com
Scope: Dedicated to all aspects of historic preservation and contextual design. Specializes in acquisition planning, condition assessments and problem solving and scope of work recommendation. **Founded:** 1987. **Publications:** "What Replacement Windows Can't Replace," Association for Preservation Technology International, 2005; "Helping Main Street Thrive," Traditional Building, May, 2002; "Traditional Bldgs," Feb, 2002.

1325 ■ W.J. Whatley Inc.—Whatley, W J Inc.
3550 Odessa Way, Ste. A
Aurora, CO 80011
Ph: (303)287-8053
Free: 877-959-7678
Fax: (303)286-7216
Co. E-mail: sales@whatley.com
URL: http://www.whatley.com
Contact: George Maybee, President
Scope: A composite lamp post company offering coordinated luminaries and accessories. Specialist in custom designs and historic replicas. **Founded:** 1981. **Special Services:** XTREME.

1326 ■ Howard L. Zimmerman Architects P.C. (HLZA)
11 W 30th St.
New York, NY 10001
Ph: (212)564-9393
Fax: (212)564-9032
Co. E-mail: info@hlzimmerman.com
URL: http://www.hlzimmerman.com
Contact: Howard L. Zimmerman, President
E-mail: howard@hlzimmerman.com
Scope: Offers evaluation of building restoration and preventive maintenance to building owners. Services include exterior restoration, historic preservation, capital improvement, forensic investigation and interior design services. Technical services include facade investigation, materials testing, analysis and evaluation, due diligence evaluations, building systems analysis, pre-purchase inspections, inspection reports, local law reports, CAD services, building code analysis and interpretation, building alteration reviews and peer reviews. Provides expert legal testimony. Specializes in the design of commercial spaces, restaurants, luxury apartments and adaptive re-use of buildings. **Founded:** 1978. **Publications:** "Forensic Architecture: The Art of Understanding a Buildings Unwritten History".

LIBRARIES

1327 ■ City College of City University of New York - Art Visual Resources Library
Compton-Goethals, Rm. 245A
160 Convent Ave.
New York, NY 10031
Ph: (212)650-7175
Fax: (212)650-7604
Co. E-mail: artimage@ccny.cuny.edu
URL: http://www1.ccny.cuny.edu/library/art_resources/index.cfm
Contact: Ching-Jung Chen, Curator
Scope: Art, architecture, design. **Services:** Library not open to the public. **Holdings:** 100,000 slides. **Telecommunication Services:** cchen@ccny.cuny.edu.

1328 ■ Tri-County Heritage Society Reference Library
PO Box 352
Morgantown, PA 19543
Ph: (610)286-7477
Co. E-mail: tchs@dejazzd.com
URL: http://www.tricountyheritage.org/reflibrary.html
Contact: Rebecca Leamy, Librarian
Scope: History - state, local; architectural research; genealogy. **Services:** Library open to the public for reference use only. **Founded:** 1970. **Holdings:** 1500 books; 500 bound periodical volumes; 70 cubic feet archival materials; 25 reels of microfilm; maps; warrants; surveys; magazines; journals; photographs. **Subscriptions:** 12 journals and other serials; 4 newspapers.

1329 ■ University of Nevada, Las Vegas - Architecture Studies Library
Box 454049
4505 Maryland Pkwy.
Las Vegas, NV 89154-4049
Ph: (702)895-1959
Fax: (702)895-1975
Co. E-mail: caroline.smith@unlv.edu
URL: http://www.library.unlv.edu/arch/index.html
Contact: Caroline Smith, Director
Scope: Architecture - history, design, theory, and criticism; landscape architecture; interior design; construction; urban planning. **Services:** Interlibrary loan; copying; scanners; Library open to the public. **Founded:** 1997. **Holdings:** 25,000 volumes; 600 videos/DVDs; archives; microfiche and microfilm. **Subscriptions:** 150 journals and other serials.

RESEARCH CENTERS

1330 ■ College of William and Mary - Center for Archaeological Research
PO Box 8795
Williamsburg, VA 23187-8795
Ph: (757)221-1581
Fax: (757)221-2564
Co. E-mail: jbjone@wm.edu
URL: http://web.wm.edu/wmcar
Contact: Joseph B. Jones, Director
Services: Artifact identification and analysis, zooarchaeological analysis, and material excavation of archaeological ceramics; Preparation of cultural resource planning overviews and reports for inclusion in Environmental Impact Statements; Professional assistance to both public and private agencies and organizations in the area of cultural resource management. **Founded:** 1988. **Publications:** Occasional Papers in Archaeology; Technical Report Series. **Educational Activities:** Internships in public archaeology for graduate and undergraduate students of anthropology, history, and American studies. **Awards:** CRM internship (Biennial), 1 per semester for qualified Anthropology Department graduate students.

1331 ■ Cornell University - Program in International Studies in Planning
106 W Sibley Hall
Ithaca, NY 14853-3901
Ph: (607)255-4331
Fax: (607)255-1971
Co. E-mail: wwg2@cornell.edu
URL: http://www.aap.cornell.edu/crp/programs/grad/mrp.cfm
Contact: Prof. William Goldsmith, Chairperson
Founded: 1972. **Educational Activities:** Courses abroad; Program in International Studies in Planning Seminars; Program in International Studies in Plan-

ning Seminars, held Fridays with visiting lecturers in the spring; Annual one-semester lecture series; Program in International Studies in Planning Student travel grants.

1332 ■ Frank Lloyd Wright Preservation Trust Research Center
931 Chicago Ave.
Oak Park, IL 60302
Ph: (708)848-1976
Fax: (708)848-1248
Co. E-mail: research@gowright.org
URL: http://www.gowright.org/research.html
Contact: Brian Reis, President
Founded: 1974. **Publications:** Frank Lloyd Wright Preservation Trust Research Center Journal (Quarterly); Frank Lloyd Wright Preservation Trust Research Center Newsletter (Monthly). **Telecommunication Services:** info@gowright.org.

1333 ■ The Getty Conservation Institute (GCI)
1200 Getty Ctr. Dr., Ste. 700
Los Angeles, CA 90049-1684
Ph: (310)440-7325
Fax: (310)440-7702
Co. E-mail: gciweb@getty.edu
URL: http://www.getty.edu/conservation
Contact: Timothy P. Whalen, Director
Founded: 1985. **Publications:** Conservation Perspectives Newsletter (Semiannual); Symposium proceedings and preprints; Research in Conservation Series, Tools for Conservation Series. **Educational Activities:** Conservation Guest Scholars Program (Annual); Seminars, meetings, and workshops. **Awards:** GCI Research fellowship.

1334 ■ Mississippi State University - Carl Small Town Center (CSTC)
College of Architecture, Art, & Design
Mississippi State, MS 39762
Ph: (662)325-2207
Fax: (662)325-0723
Co. E-mail: cstcinfo@caad.msstate.edu
URL: http://www.carlsmalltowncenter.org
Contact: Prof. John Poros, Director
Founded: 1979. **Telecommunication Services:** jporos@caad.msstate.edu.

1335 ■ University of Mary Washington - Center for Historic Preservation (CHP)
1301 College Ave.
Fredericksburg, VA 22401
Ph: (540)654-1041
Fax: (540)654-1068
Co. E-mail: msanford@umw.edu
URL: http://www.umw.edu/chp
Contact: Dr. Douglas Sanford, Director
Services: Cultural resource management. **Founded:** 1980. **Publications:** Cultural resource management reports; Historic Preservation at Mary Washington College Newsletter. **Educational Activities:** Lectures, conferences, workshops.

1336 ■ University of Texas at Austin - Center for American Architecture and Design (CAAD)
Battle Hall, Ste. 100
School of Architecture
1 University Station, B7500
Austin, TX 78712-0222
Ph: (512)471-9890
Fax: (512)471-7033
Co. E-mail: caad@austin.utexas.edu
URL: http://soa.utexas.edu/caad
Contact: Prof. Michael L. Benedikt, Director
Founded: 1982. **Publications:** CENTER: Architecture and Design in America. **Educational Activities:** Exhibitions and symposia, open to the public. **Telecommunication Services:** mbenedikt@mail.utexas.edu.

ASSOCIATIONS AND OTHER ORGANIZATIONS

1337 ■ Art Dealers Association of America (ADAA)
205 Lexington Ave., Ste. 901
New York, NY 10016
Ph: (212)488-5550
Fax: (646)688-6809
Co. E-mail: lmitchem@artdealers.org
URL: http://www.artdealers.org
Contact: Lucy Mitchell-Innes, President
Description: Art dealers united to promote the highest standards of connoisseurship, scholarship, and ethical practice within the profession and to increase public awareness of the role and responsibilities of reputable art dealers. Works with museums and scholars on activities and problems of mutual concern; cooperates with domestic and international government agencies on art matters and offers assistance and expertise to these agencies; advises on legislation and other governmental activity regarding the fine arts; seeks to identify and remove fake works of art from the marketplace. Appraises, for tax purposes only, works of art donated to nonprofit institutions. **Founded:** 1962. **Publications:** *Art Dealers Association of America--Directory* (Annual); *Art Dealers Association of America Directory* (Annual).

1338 ■ Association of International Photography Art Dealers (AIPAD)
2025 M St. NW, Ste. 800
Washington, DC 20036
Ph: (202)367-1158
Fax: (202)367-2158
Co. E-mail: info@aipad.com
URL: http://www.aipad.com
Contact: Stephen Bulger, President
Description: Galleries and private dealers in fine art and photography, who have been in business for at least 5 years. Promotes a greater understanding of photography as an art form. Fosters communication within the photographic community. Encourages public support of art photography. Seeks to increase the public's confidence in responsible photography dealers. **Founded:** 1979. **Publications:** *AIPAD Membership Directory and Illustrated Catalogue* (Annual); *On Collecting Photographs*. **Educational Activities:** The Photography Show New York (Annual).

1339 ■ *Canadian Arctic Multimedia Information Kit*
2081 Merivale Rd.
Ottawa, ON, Canada K2G 1G9
Ph: (613)224-8189
Free: 800-830-3293
Fax: (613)224-2907
Co. E-mail: iaf@inuitart.org
URL: http://www.inuitart.org
Contact: Marybelle Mitchell, Executive Director
Price: C$295, /copy.

1340 ■ Inuit Art Foundation (IAF)
2081 Merivale Rd.
Ottawa, ON, Canada K2G 1G9

Ph: (613)224-8189
Free: 800-830-3293
Fax: (613)224-2907
Co. E-mail: iaf@inuitart.org
URL: http://www.inuitart.org
Contact: Marybelle Mitchell, Executive Director
Description: Promotes appreciation of and demand for Inuit art. Offers professional development opportunities to Canadian Inuit artists. Organizes research and educational programs; operates Inuit artists' shop. **Scope:** Inuit art. **Founded:** 1985. **Subscriptions:** books periodicals. **Publications:** *Inuit Art Quarterly* (Quarterly); *Canadian Arctic Multimedia Information Kit*; *Inuit Art Quarterly* (Quarterly). **Awards:** Inuit Curatorial Scholarship (Annual); Virginia J. Watt Award.

1341 ■ *Inuit Art Quarterly*
2081 Merivale Rd.
Ottawa, ON, Canada K2G 1G9
Ph: (613)224-8189
Free: 800-830-3293
Fax: (613)224-2907
Co. E-mail: iaf@inuitart.org
URL: http://www.inuitart.org
Contact: Marybelle Mitchell, Executive Director
Released: Quarterly

REFERENCE WORKS

1342 ■ *"Arario Gallery Opens First American Space"* in Art Business News (Vol. 34, November 2007, No. 11, pp. 14)
Pub: Pfingsten Publishing, LLC
Description: Opening a new space in New York's Chelsea gallery district is Arario Gallery, a leader in the field of Asian contemporary art; the gallery will feature new works by Chinese artists at its opening.

1343 ■ *Art Dealers Association of America--Directory*
Pub: Art Dealers Association of America
Contact: Lucy Mitchell-Innes, President
URL(s): www.artdealers.org. **Released:** Annual; Fall. **Covers:** About 160 members of the ADAA. **Entries include:** Company name, address, phone, fax, names and titles of key personnel, and descriptions of areas of specialization. **Arrangement:** Alphabetical.

1344 ■ *"Art Miami Comes to Miami's Wynwood Art District"* in Art Business News (Vol. 34, November 2007, No. 11, pp. 18)
Pub: Pfingsten Publishing, LLC
Description: In December, The Art Group will hold its Art Miami fair in the Wynwood Art District; the exhibitors range from painting, sculpture, video and works on paper.

1345 ■ *Art Now Gallery Guides*
Pub: Art Now Inc.
URL(s): www.artinfo.com/galleryguide. **Released:** Monthly; 10/year. **Price:** $35, Individuals; $77, Other countries. **Covers:** in 'Art Now Gallery Guide--International Edition' current exhibitions in over 1,800

museums and galleries. Separate regional editions cover metropolitan New York, Boston and New England, the Philadelphia area, the southeast, Chicago and the midwest, the southwest, California and the northwest, Latin America, and Europe. Listings are paid. **Entries include:** Gallery or museum name, address, phone, days and hours of operation, artist's name or name of the exhibit, medium, and dates of showing. **Arrangement:** International and regional editions are geographical.

1346 ■ *"Artexpo Celebrates 30th Anniversary"* in Art Business News (Vol. 34, November 2007, No. 11, pp. 18)
Pub: Pfingsten Publishing, LLC
Description: In honor of its 30th anniversary Artexpo New York 2008 will be an unforgettable show offering a collection of fine-art education courses for both trade and consumer attendees and featuring a variety of artists working in all mediums.

1347 ■ *"An Artwork in Progress"* in Hawaii Business (Vol. 53, March 2008, No. 9, pp. 45)
Pub: Hawaii Business Publishing
Ed: Jolyn Okimoto Rosa. **Description:** Art galleries in Honolulu, Hawaii holds the First Friday Gallery Walk and other special events, which draw crowd to and increase sales activities in the city's downtown. The district also advocates for the reintroduction of Honolulu's Chinatown to the people. Details regarding the art galleries' Chinatown revival and its local economic impact are discussed.

1348 ■ *"Creative Cluster Paints Business Success"* in Business Journal Serving Greater Tampa Bay (Vol. 30, October 29, 2010, No. 45, pp. 1)
Pub: Tampa Bay Business Journal
Ed: Jane Meinhardt. **Description:** How Tom Gaffney, a cofounder of the private equity firm The Anderson Group realized the great return on investment in the 600 block of Central Avenue in St. Petersburg, Florida is discussed. Focusing on long-term value rather than short-term profitability and exit, Gaffney purchased this block in 2008 for $2.3 million and cultivated arts businesses as tenants.

1349 ■ *"Gallery Street Launches ArtCandy"* in Art Business News (Vol. 34, November 2007, No. 11, pp. 8)
Pub: Pfingsten Publishing, LLC
Description: Fine-art reproduction house Gallery Street recently launched its new division, ArtCandy Editions; the division was created in order to help a network of artists expand the distribution of their work.

1350 ■ *How to Market and Sell Your Art, Music, Photographs, and Handmade Crafts Online*
Pub: Atlantic Publishing Group, Inc.
Ed: Lee Rowley. **Released:** May 2008. **Price:** $24.95. **Description:** The book provides all the basics for starting and running an online store selling arts,

crafts, photography or music. There are more than 300 Websites listed to help anyone market and promote their arts and/or crafts online.

1351 ■ *Institute of Museum & Library Services--Annual Report*
Pub: Institute of Museum & Library Services
Contact: Susan Hildreth, Director
E-mail: shildreth@imls.gov
URL(s): www.imls.gov. **Released:** Annual; fall; Latest edition 2006. **Covers:** more than 1,000 museums and libraries receiving federal support. **Entries include:** Museum or library name, city, state, grant amount. **Arrangement:** Classified by type of funding received. **Indexes:** Institution name, museum discipline, size of budget.

1352 ■ *"Let the Light Shine" in Retail Merchandiser (Vol. 51, July-August 2011, No. 4, pp. 74)*
Pub: Phoenix Media Corporation
Description: For over 25 years, The Thomas Kinkade Company has been producing art that is collected by both old and young, and is the only company that publishes Thomas Kinkade art.

1353 ■ *Rogues' Gallery: The Secret Story of the Lust, Lies, Greed, and Betrayals That Made the Metropolitan Museum of Art*
Pub: Crown Business Books
Ed: Michael Gross. **Released:** May 11, 2010. **Price:** $16.99. **Description:** Michael Gross, leading chronicler of the American rich, looks at the saga of the nation's largest museum, the Metropolitan Museum of Art.

1354 ■ *Seven Days in the Art World*
Pub: W.W. Norton & Company
Ed: Sarah Thornton. **Released:** 2009. **Price:** $24.95. **Description:** A sociologist renders the interplay among buyers, critics, curators and makers of contemporary art.

1355 ■ *"Show Dates" in Art Business News (Vol. 34, November 2007, No. 11, pp. 18)*
Pub: Pfingsten Publishing, LLC
Description: Listing of conferences, trade shows and gallery openings for artists and those in the art industry.

1356 ■ *"A Vegas Sensation Inaugural Artexpo Las Vegas" in Art Business News (Vol. 34, November 2007, No. 11, pp. 1)*
Pub: Pfingsten Publishing, LLC
Ed: Jennifer Dulin. **Description:** Overview of the first Artexpo Las Vegas which featured exhibitors, artists and buyers and was a wonderful place for networking.

TRADE PERIODICALS

1357 ■ *ARTnews Magazine*
Pub: ARTnews L.L.C.
Contact: Steva Barnes, Manager
URL(s): artnews.com. **Ed:** Milton Esterow. **Released:** Monthly **Price:** $39.95, Canada; $99.95, Other countries; $19.95, Individuals.

1358 ■ *The ARTnewsletter*
Pub: ARTnews L.L.C.
Contact: Steva Barnes, Manager
Ed: Eileen Kinsella, Editor. **Released:** Semimonthly. **Price:** $279, individuals $279/year, U.S.; $309 elsewhere; $309 Canada and other. **Description:** Presents reviews of forthcoming auctions, analyses of prices, attribution controversies, ownership squabbles, and case histories of thievery, forgery, and fraud. Discusses the impact of museum exhibitions on the art market, the latest IRS rulings, import and export regulations, legislative hearings, debates and acts, print tax shelters, art insurance, and appraisals. Recurring features include interviews with dealers, auctioneers, curators, and collectors.

1359 ■ *Artsfocus*
Pub: Colorado Springs Fine Arts Center
Released: Quarterly. **Price:** Included in membership. **Description:** Notifies of upcoming art exhibitions and other related events. Covers museum acquisitions.

Gives updates on traveling exhibitions. Visual art exhibitions, live theatre performances and Bemis school of Art classes for adults and children. Lectures, tours, permanent collection and pre collection of Southwestern and Native American art. a calendar of events, reports of meetings, news of educational opportunities, and notices of publications available.

1360 ■ *ARTWEEK*
Pub: ARTWEEK
URL(s): www.artweek.com. **Released:** Monthly **Price:** $64, Two years; $38, Institutions; $60, Canada; $80, Other countries.

1361 ■ *Azure Magazine*
Pub: Azure Publishing Inc.
URL(s): www.azuremagazine.com/. **Ed:** Nelda Rodger. **Released:** 8/yr. **Price:** C$32.95, Individuals; C$54.95, Two years; $32.95, Individuals; $54.95, Two years; $48, Other countries; $78, Other countries 2 years.

1362 ■ *CAA News*
Pub: College Art Association
Contact: Linda Downs, Executive Director
Ed: Christopher Howard, Editor. **Released:** Bimonthly. **Price:** Included in membership. **Description:** Features news of the Association as well as activities, achievements, funding opportunities, conferences, programs, exhibitions, and legislation in the arts field. Recurring features include news of research, a calendar of events, reports of meetings, news of educational opportunities, notices of publications available, and columns titled From the Executive Director, People in the News, Grants, Awards & Honors, Conferences & Symposia, and Opportunities.

1363 ■ *CityArt Magazine: A Contemporary Review of the Visual Arts*
Pub: Fleisher Fine Arts Inc.
URL(s): www.artfocustoronto.presspublisher.us/. **Released:** 3/yr. **Price:** $15, Canada 7% GST.

1364 ■ *Country Home*
Pub: Meredith Corp.
URL(s): www.countryhome.com. **Released:** Monthly; 10/yr. **Price:** $4.95, Individuals newstand; $21.97, Two years.

1365 ■ *Musea*
Pub: Tom Hendricks
Ed: Art S. Revolutionary, Editor. **Released:** Monthly. **Price:** $10, individuals; Free. **Description:** A zine opposed to the Corporate Art 10, and for the best of 'indie' arts.

1366 ■ *National Association of Women Artists, Inc. News*
Pub: National Association of Women Artists
Contact: Sonia Stark, President
Released: Semiannual. **Price:** Included in membership. **Description:** Presents news of women in the art field. Recurring features include a calendar of events, news of educational opportunities, juried shows, workshops, exhibits, and a column titled President's Letter. (This is a members only newsletter).

1367 ■ *NSS News Bulletin*
Pub: National Sculpture Society
Contact: Gwen Pier, Executive Director
Ed: Patricia, Delahanty, Editor. **Released:** Bimonthly. **Price:** Included in membership. **Description:** Covers sculpture competitions, awards, grants, exhibitions, and commissions. Reports members' works and activities. Recurring features include news of research, a calendar of events, reports of meetings, news of educational opportunities, job listings, notices of publications available, and Seeking and Offering.

1368 ■ *The Photograph Collector*
Pub: The Photograph Collector
Ed: Stephen Perloff, Editor, sperloff@libertynet.org. **Released:** Monthly. **Price:** $149.95, individuals in North America; $169.95, elsewhere. **Description:** Carries in-depth coverage of topics such as print prices, archival techniques, dealer activities, major acquisitions, and the international photography

market. Recurring features include statistics, book reviews, news of research, and columns titled Gallery Row, Auction News, and Publishers Row.

VIDEOCASSETTES/ AUDIOCASSETTES

1369 ■ *David Armstrong Paints*
Karol Media
Hanover Industrial Estates
375 Stewart Rd.
Wilkes Barre, PA 18773-7600
Ph: (570)822-8899
Free: 800-526-4773
Co. E-mail: sales@karolmedia.com
URL: http://www.karolmedia.com
Released: 1997. **Price:** $29.95. **Description:** Portrays the artist and his work. **Availability:** VHS.

1370 ■ *Maya Collection*
Tapeworm Video Distributors
25876 The Old Road #141
Stevenson Ranch, CA 91381
Ph: (661)257-4904
Fax: (661)257-4820
Co. E-mail: sales@tapeworm.com
URL: http://www.tapeworm.com
Released: 19??. **Description:** Ten volume collection documents the art and philosophy of Mayan Culture. **Availability:** VHS.

1371 ■ *Windows to a View: Chris Reis*
Karol Media
Hanover Industrial Estates
375 Stewart Rd.
Wilkes Barre, PA 18773-7600
Ph: (570)822-8899
Free: 800-526-4773
Co. E-mail: sales@karolmedia.com
URL: http://www.karolmedia.com
Released: 1997. **Price:** $29.95. **Description:** Portrays the artist and his work. **Availability:** VHS.

TRADE SHOWS AND CONVENTIONS

1372 ■ The Winter Olympia Fine Art and Antiques Fair
Clarion Events Ltd.
Earls Court Exhibition Centre
Warwick Rd.
London SW5 9TA, United Kingdom
Ph: 44 20 7370 8139
URL: http://www.clarionevents.com
Contact: Simon Kimble, Chief Executive Officer
URL(s): www.olympia-antiques.com/. **Frequency:** Annual. **Audience:** Trade and general public. **Principal Exhibits:** Antiques including fine, oak, garden, and country furniture; rugs; paintings; ceramics; clocks; sculptures; jewelry, silver, and bronzes. **Telecommunication Services:** olympia-antiques@eco.co.uk.

CONSULTANTS

1373 ■ Lawrence Jeppson Associates
9004 Honeybee Ln.
Bethesda, MD 20817-6927
Ph: (301)365-7400
Fax: (301)365-7409
Contact: Lawrence S. Jeppson, Owner
Scope: Provider of counseling service in art investment, authentication, appraising and marketing of art and art objects and in the publishing of editions of multiple-original art. **Founded:** 1952.

COMPUTERIZED DATABASES

1374 ■ *Art on Screen Database™*
200 Willoughby Ave.
Brooklyn, NY 11205-3817
Ph: (718)399-4506

Fax: (718)399-4507
Co. E-mail: info@artfilm.org
URL: http://www.artfilm.org
Availability: Online: Program for Art on Film Inc.
Type: Directory.

1375 ■ Bibliography of the History of Art (BHA)
1200 Getty Ctr. Dr.
Los Angeles, CA 90049-1679
Ph: (310)440-7300
Fax: (310)440-7716
Co. E-mail: info@getty.edu
URL: http://www.getty.edu
Availability: Online: ProQuest LLC - Dialog; J. Paul Getty Trust; Wolters Kluwer Health - Ovid. **Type:** Bibliographic.

1376 ■ The Getty Provenance Index® Databases
1200 Getty Ctr. Dr.
Los Angeles, CA 90049-1679
Ph: (310)440-7300
Fax: (310)440-7716
Co. E-mail: info@getty.edu
URL: http://www.getty.edu
Availability: Online: J. Paul Getty Trust. CD-ROM: J. Paul Getty Trust. **Type:** Directory.

1377 ■ Gordon's Print Prices Database
610 E Bell Rd., Ste. 2-163
Phoenix, AZ 85022
Ph: (602)253-6948
Free: 800-892-4622
Fax: (602)253-2104
Co. E-mail: office@gordonsart.com
URL: http://www.gordonsart.com
Availability: Online: LTB Gordonsart Inc. CD-ROM: LTB Gordonsart Inc. **Type:** Directory.

1378 ■ A Survey of Western Art
1601 N Sepulveda Blvd., Ste. 374
Manhattan Beach, CA 90267
Ph: (310)406-1803
Fax: (310)406-0833
Co. E-mail: contact@tdcinteractive.com
URL: http://www.tdcinteractive.net
Availability: CD-ROM: Technology Dynamics Corp. - TDC Interactive. **Type:** Full-text; Image.

LIBRARIES

1379 ■ Abbaye Saint-Benoit - Bibliotheque
1 Main St.
St. Benoit du Lac, QC, Canada J0B 2M0
Ph: (819)843-4080
Fax: (819)868-1861
Co. E-mail: abbaye@st-benoit-du-lac.com
URL: http://www.st-benoit-du-lac.com/
Scope: Religion, theology, philosophy, history, art, church science. **Services:** Bibliotheque open to the public at librarian's discretion to men only. **Founded:** 1912. **Holdings:** Figures not available.

1380 ■ Art Gallery of Greater Victoria Library
1040 Moss St.
Victoria, BC, Canada V8V 4P1
Ph: (205)384-4171
Fax: (250)361-3995
Co. E-mail: mjhughes@aggv.bc.ca
URL: http://www.aggv.ca
Contact: Mary Jo Hughes, Curator
Scope: Art - Canadian, Asian; British Columbia artists. **Services:** Library currently only available to in-house staff and volunteers due to lack of staff. **Founded:** 1951. **Holdings:** 10,000 volumes.

1381 ■ Beaverbrook Art Gallery Library
703 Queen St.
Fredericton, NB, Canada E3B 5A6
Ph: (506)458-8545

Fax: (506)459-7450
Co. E-mail: bag@beaverbrookartgallery.org
URL: http://beaverbrookartgallery.org
Contact: Terry Graff, Curator Deputy Director
Scope: Art, humanities, culture. **Services:** Copying; library open by permission only. **Founded:** 1959. **Holdings:** 4000 books and videos. **Subscriptions:** 15 journals and other serials; 2 newspapers.

1382 ■ California University of Pennsylvania - Louis L. Manderino Library - Special Collections
250 University Ave., Rm. 435
California, PA 15419
Ph: (724)938-5926
Fax: (724)938-5901
Co. E-mail: pokol@calu.edu
URL: http://library.calu.edu
Contact: Alber Pokol, Archivist Librarian, Special Collections
Scope: Rare books, art, music. **Services:** Interlibrary loan; Library open to the public by appointment.

1383 ■ Carnegie Library of Pittsburgh - Music Department
4400 Forbes Ave.
Pittsburgh, PA 15213
Ph: (412)622-3105
Fax: (412)687-8982
Co. E-mail: musicdept@carnegielibrary.org
URL: http://www.clpgh.org/locations/music
Contact: Kathryn Logan, Department Head
Scope: Music, art, architecture, interior design, collectibles, dance. **Services:** Reference and reader's assistance; department open to the public. **Founded:** 1938. **Holdings:** 110,000 music books and scores; 63,000 art books; 1500 dance books; 30,000 sound recordings; 1200 videocassettes; 280,000 mounted pictures; 54,000 slides; 69 VF drawers; 1700 videos and DVDs. **Subscriptions:** 320 journals and other serials.

1384 ■ Colby College - Bixler Art and Music Library
5660 Mayflower Hill
Waterville, ME 04901
Ph: (207)859-5660
Fax: (207)859-5105
Co. E-mail: mrpukkil@colby.edu
URL: http://libguides.colby.edu/bixler
Contact: Marilyn R. Pukkila
Scope: Art, Music, Photography. **Services:** Interlibrary loan; copying; Apple computer lab; in-house listening and video viewing stations; Library open to the public for reference use only. **Founded:** 1959. **Holdings:** 33,000 books and bound periodical volumes; 10,000 music scores; 11,000 sound recordings; 1200 videos; 450 CD-ROMs. **Subscriptions:** 90 journals and other serials. **Telecommunication Services:** refbix@colby.edu.

1385 ■ Craigdarroch Castle
1050 Joan Crescent
Victoria, BC, Canada V8S 3L5
Ph: (250)592-5323
Fax: (250)799-1099
Co. E-mail: info@thecastle.ca
URL: http://www.thecastle.ca
Contact: Bruce Davies, Curator
Scope: Nineteenth Century European and North American domestic material. **Services:** Library open by appointment to serious researchers only. **Founded:** 1959. **Holdings:** Photographs; documents; memorabilia; graphic materials; moving images; sound recordings; textual records.

1386 ■ Drury University - F.W. Olin Library - Art & Architecture Slide Library
900 N. Benton Ave.
Springfield, MO 65802
Ph: (417)873-7337
Fax: (417)873-7432
Co. E-mail: jtygart@drury.edu
URL: http://library.drury.edu/services-info/collections/slide-library/
Contact: Jacqueline Tygart, Curator
Scope: Architecture, art, photography, textiles, ceramics. **Services:** Library open to the public. **Holdings:** 60,000 35mm slides.

1387 ■ Edinboro University - Baron-Forness Library - Special Collections
200 Tartan Rd., 7th Fl.
Edinboro, PA 16444
Ph: (814)732-2415
Fax: (814)732-2883
Co. E-mail: obringer@edinboro.edu
URL: http://www.edinboro.edu/departments/library/archives/page_one.dot
Contact: Prof. David Obringer
Scope: Music, art, education, Pennsylvania history, Civil War regimental history, rare books. **Services:** Interlibrary loan; tutoring; Library open to the public with restrictions. **Founded:** 1860. **Holdings:** 3000 volumes; prints.

1388 ■ Emmanuel College - Cardinal Cushing Library
400 The Fenway
Boston, MA 02115
Ph: (617)735-9927
Co. E-mail: tuohyc@emmanuel.edu
URL: http://www1.emmanuel.edu/library/
Contact: Dr. Susan von Daum Tholl, Director
Scope: Theology, pastoral ministry, religious history, women's studies, arts, humanities, education. **Services:** Interlibrary loan; library open to the public. **Founded:** 1964. **Holdings:** 130,000 volumes. **Subscriptions:** 2000 journals and other serials.

1389 ■ Hardin-Simmons University - Rupert and Pauline Richardson Library
2341 Hickory St.
Abilene, TX 79698
Ph: (325)670-1236
Fax: (325)677-8351
Co. E-mail: aspecht@hsutx.edu
URL: http://hsutx.edu/library
Contact: Belinda Norvell
Scope: Hardin-Simmons University history, government records. **Founded:** 1891. **Holdings:** 150 online databases. **Telecommunication Services:** hsuref@hsutx.edu.

1390 ■ Hillwood Museum & Gardens - Art Research Library
4155 Linnean Ave., NW
Washington, DC 20008
Ph: (202)243-3953
Fax: (202)966-7846
Co. E-mail: plynagh@hillwoodmuseum.org
URL: http://www.hillwoodmuseum.org/research-resources/art-research-library
Contact: Pat Lynagh, Assistant Librarian
Scope: Art - decorative, French, Russian; Russian imperial history; interior design. **Services:** Copying; library open to the public by appointment. **Founded:** 1960. **Holdings:** 30,000 volumes; 16,000 auction catalogs; pamphlets. **Subscriptions:** 30 journals and other serials.

1391 ■ Juilliard School - Lila Acheson Wallace Library
60 Lincoln Center Plaza
New York, NY 10023-6588
Ph: (212)799-5000, x-265
Fax: (212)724-0263
Co. E-mail: library@juilliard.edu
URL: http://www.juilliard.edu/library/index.php
Contact: Jane Gottlieb, Associate Vice President
Scope: Music, drama, dance. **Services:** Interlibrary loan; library open to public for reference use by arrangement only. **Founded:** 1945. **Holdings:** 23,000 books; 75,000 music performance, study scores; 25,000 sound recordings; 2500 videos. **Subscriptions:** 200 journals and other serials.

1392 ■ Menil Collection Library
1515 Sul Ross St.
Houston, TX 77006
Ph: (713)525-9400
Fax: (713)525-9444
Co. E-mail: info@menil.org
URL: http://www.menil.org/home.html
Contact: Anne Adler
Scope: Modern art, medieval art, classical antiquities, tribal art. **Services:** Interlibrary loan; copying; Library open to the public by appointment. **Founded:**

1986. **Holdings:** 30,000 books, periodicals and auction catalogs. **Subscriptions:** 100 journals and other serials. **Telecommunication Services:** library@menil.org.

1393 ■ Musee McCord d'histoire Canadienne - Archives and Documentation Centre
690, rue Sherbrooke ouest
Montreal, QC, Canada H3A 1E9
Ph: (514)398-7100, x249
Fax: (514)398-5045
Co. E-mail: info@mccord.mcgill.ca
URL: http://www.musee-mccord.qc.ca/en/services/archives/
Contact: Francois Cartier
Scope: Art, Canadian history, photography, ethnology. **Services:** Copying; library open to the public by appointment. **Founded:** 1921. **Holdings:** 9108 books; 2000 rare books; 200 meters of archives; 95 reels of microfilm; 1 million photographs; electronic records; graphic materials; textual records. **Subscriptions:** 180 journals and other serials. **Telecommunication Services:** nora.hague@mccord.mcgill.ca.

1394 ■ St. Cloud State University - Learning Resource Services - University Archives and Special Collections
720 4th Ave., S.
Miller Center 314
St. Cloud, MN 56301-4442
Ph: (320)308-4755
Co. E-mail: archives@stcloudstate.edu
URL: http://lrts.stcloudstate.edu/library/special/archives/default.asp
Contact: Tom Steman, Archivist
Scope: Art, theater, literature, Sinclair Lewis. **Founded:** 1977. **Telecommunication Services:** askref@stcloudstate.edu.

1395 ■ St. Norbert Arts Centre Archives
PO Box 175
Winnipeg, MB, Canada R3V 1L6
Ph: (204)269-0564
Fax: (204)261-1927
Co. E-mail: snac@snac.mb.ca
URL: http://www.snac.mb.ca
Contact: Louise May, Director
Scope: Art - visual art, music, theater, and dance. **Services:** Archives open to the public. **Founded:** 1996. **Holdings:** Graphic materials; textual records.

1396 ■ San Francisco Public Library - Bernard Osher Foundation - Art, Music & Recreation Center
100 Larkin St., 4th Fl.
San Francisco, CA 94102
Ph: (415)557-4525
Fax: (415)557-4524
Co. E-mail: info@sfpl.org
URL: http://www.sfpl.org
Contact: Mark Hall, Manager
URL(s): sfpl.org/index.php?pg=0200001401. **Scope:** Arts - visual, graphic; sports and recreation; photography; architecture; arts and crafts; performing arts; music - orchestral, chamber, opera, popular, folk, jazz. **Services:** Center open to the public. **Holdings:** Books; serials; scores. **Telecommunication Services:** artmusicrec@sfpl.org.

1397 ■ Santa Clara University - de Saisset Museum Library
500 El Camino Real
Santa Clara, CA 95053-0550
Ph: (408)554-4528
Fax: (408)554-7840
Co. E-mail: rschapp@scu.edu
URL: http://www.scu.edu/deSaisset
Contact: Rebecca Schapp, Director
Scope: Art publications. **Services:** Library not open to the public. **Founded:** 1955. **Holdings:** Art magazines, art catalogs from the de Saisset Museum and

other institutions. **Subscriptions:** 9 journals and other serials. **Telecommunication Services:** desaissetmuseum@scu.edu.

1398 ■ Allen Sapp Gallery Archives
1 Railway Ave.
North Battleford, SK, Canada S9A 2Y6
Ph: (306)445-1760
Fax: (306)445-1694
Co. E-mail: sapp@accesscomm.ca
URL: http://www.allensapp.com
Contact: Robin Dyck, Manager, Administration
Scope: Cree artist Allan Sapp. **Services:** Library open to the public with restrictions. **Founded:** 1989. **Holdings:** Graphic materials; moving images; textual records; reports; archives; film videos. **Telecommunication Services:** sapp2@accesscomm.ca; sapp3@accesscomm.ca.

1399 ■ Sculptors' Society of Canada - Canadian Sculpture Centre Archives
500 Church St.
Toronto, ON, Canada M4Y 2C8
Ph: (647)435-5858
Co. E-mail: gallery@cansculpt.org
URL: http://www.cansculpt.org
Contact: Judi Michelle Young, President
Scope: Sculpture. **Services:** Archive open to the public by appointment. **Founded:** 1928. **Holdings:** Photographs; slides; files.

1400 ■ Sweet Briar College - Martin C. Shallenberger Book Arts Library
134 Chapel Rd.
Sweet Briar, VA 24595
Ph: (434)381-6139
Fax: (434)381-6173
Co. E-mail: jgjaffe@sbc.edu
URL: http://library.sbc.edu
Contact: John Jaffe, Director
Scope: Book arts, rare books, archives. **Services:** Interlibrary loan. **Holdings:** 14,000.

1401 ■ Tom Thomson Art Gallery Archives
840 1st Ave., W.
Owen Sound, ON, Canada N4K 4K4
Ph: (519)376-1932
Fax: (519)376-3037
Co. E-mail: ttag@e-owensound.com
URL: http://www.tomthomson.org
Contact: Virginia Eichhorn, Director
Scope: Art. **Services:** Library open to the public by appointment. **Founded:** 1967. **Holdings:** Textual records; archives. **Subscriptions:** 1 journal.

1402 ■ University of California, San Diego - The Arts Libraries
Geisel Bldg.
9500 Gilman Dr., 0175Q
La Jolla, CA 92093-0175
Ph: (858)534-8074
Co. E-mail: labrams@ucsd.edu
URL: http://libraries.ucsd.edu/locations/arts/
Contact: Leslie Abrams, Director
Scope: Western art history from prehistory to contemporary with strength in post 1950 art movements; art criticism and aesthetics; art and literature; ethnic and tribal arts; Latin American, pre-Columbian and Asian art; photography as fine art; documentary photography; landscape architecture; architectural history and theory; decorative arts; music theory; folk music; jazz music. **Services:** Library open to the public. **Founded:** 1992. **Holdings:** 101,000 volumes; 4900 CDs; 308,000 slides; 5000 factual film archive; 64,000 sound recordings; 49,000 pieces of music. **Subscriptions:** 305 journals and other serials. **Telecommunication Services:** voriordan@ucsd.edu.

1403 ■ University of North Carolina School of the Arts - Semans Library
UNC School of the Arts
1533 S. Main St.
Winston-Salem, NC 27127

Ph: (336)770-3270
Fax: (336)770-3271
Co. E-mail: rebeccab@uncsa.edu
URL: http://www.uncsa.edu/library
Contact: Christia Thomason
Scope: Music, art and design, theater, film, dance, humanities. **Services:** Interlibrary loan; Library open to the public. **Founded:** 1965. **Holdings:** 111,000 books; 9000 bound periodical volumes; 50,000 music scores; 45,000 sound recordings; 5200 DVDs and videos. **Subscriptions:** 470 journals and other serials; 25 newspapers.

1404 ■ University of Saskatchewan - Art Collection - Kenderine Art Gallery Archive
University of Saskatchewan
107 Administration Pl.
Saskatoon, SK, Canada S7N 5A2
Ph: (306)966-4571
Fax: (306)978-8340
Co. E-mail: kent.archer@usask.ca
URL: http://www.usask.ca/kenderine
Contact: Kent Archer, Director
URL(s): www.art.usask.ca. **Scope:** Art. **Services:** Gallery open to the public. **Founded:** 1911. **Holdings:** Graphic materials; textual records.

1405 ■ Andy Warhol Museum - Archives Study Center
117 Sandusky St.
Pittsburgh, PA 15212-5890
Ph: (412)237-8300
Fax: (412)237-8340
Co. E-mail: wrbicanm@warhol.org
URL: http://www.warhol.org/collections/archives.html
Contact: Matt Wrbican, Archivist
Scope: Andy Warhol, pop art movement, journalism, rock music, celebrity culture, fashion. **Services:** Archives is open to researchers by appointment. **Founded:** 1994. **Holdings:** Business records; scrapbooks; photographs; audiocassettes; videotapes; published materials; books; art work; clothing; posters; correspondence; personal objects; 4000 audio tapes. **Telecommunication Services:** information@warhol.org.

1406 ■ Watkins College of Art, Design, & Film Library
2298 Rosa L. Parks Blvd.
Nashville, TN 37228
Ph: (615)277-7427
Fax: (615)383-4849
Co. E-mail: library@watkins.edu
URL: http://www.watkins.edu/library
Contact: Lisa Williams, Director, Library Services
Scope: Film, fine arts, interior design, graphic design, photography. **Services:** Interlibrary loan; Library open to the public for reference use only. **Holdings:** 11,600 books; 1200 videotapes and films. **Subscriptions:** 50 journals and other serials; 11 newspapers. **Telecommunication Services:** lwilliams@watkins.edu.

RESEARCH CENTERS

1407 ■ New York University - Conservation Center
Stephen Chan House
14 E 78th St.
New York, NY 10075
Ph: (212)992-5848
Fax: (212)992-5851
Co. E-mail: conservation.program@nyu.edu
URL: http://www.nyu.edu/gsas/dept/fineart/conservation/index.htm
Contact: Judy Steinhardt, Chairperson
Services: Consultation: to museums. **Founded:** 1959. **Publications:** *Conservation Center Newsletter*. **Educational Activities:** Conservation Center Lecture series; Summer sessions, for museum professionals; Conservation Center Symposia; Conservation Center Workshops. **Awards:** Fellowships and internships. **Telecommunication Services:** hannelore.roemich@nyu.edu.

ASSOCIATIONS AND OTHER ORGANIZATIONS

1408 ■ Art and Creative Materials Institute (ACMI)
PO Box 479
Hanson, MA 02341-0479
Ph: (781)293-4100
Fax: (781)294-0808
Co. E-mail: debbief@acminet.org
URL: http://www.acminet.org
Contact: Douglas Hopper, President
Description: Manufacturers of art and creative materials; sponsors certification program to ensure that art materials are non-toxic or affixed with health warning labels where appropriate. Works with ASTM International and the American National Standards Institute to develop and maintain chronic hazard labeling standards and performance standards. Sponsors annual Youth Art Month in March to emphasize the value of art education for all children and to encourage public support for quality school art programs; publicizes value of art and art education in newspapers and magazines. **Scope:** safety of art materials, list of certified products, how to celebrate Youth Art Month. **Founded:** 1936. **Subscriptions:** 3. **Publications:** *What You Need to Know About the Safety of Art and Craft Materials.*

1409 ■ National Art Materials Trade Association (NAMTA)—International Art Materials Trade Association
20200 Zion Ave.
Cornelius, NC 28031
Ph: (704)892-6244
Free: 800-746-2682
Fax: (704)892-6247
Co. E-mail: info@namta.org
URL: http://www.namta.org
Contact: Eric Zelenko, President
E-mail: ezelenko@plazaart.com
Description: Domestic and international retailers, distributors, manufacturers, publishers, and importers of fine art and creative materials. Provides useful business education and services, including research programs. Maintains the art materials industry's Hall of Fame. **Founded:** 1950. **Publications:** *Who's Who in Art Materials* (Annual); *Art Materials Retailer* (Quarterly); *NAMTA's Annual Convention Directory; National Art Materials Trade Association--News and*

Views (Monthly); *Who's Who in Art Materials* (Annual); *National Art Materials Trade Association's Annual Convention Directory* (Annual); *NAMTA's Annual Convention Directory; Who's Who in Art Materials/ NAMTA Membership Directory* (Annual). **Educational Activities:** National Art Materials Trade Association Convention (Annual); National Art Materials Trade Association (Annual). **Awards:** NAMTA Scholarship (Annual).

REFERENCE WORKS

1410 ■ "Creative Cluster Paints Business Success" in Business Journal Serving Greater Tampa Bay (Vol. 30, October 29, 2010, No. 45, pp. 1)
Pub: Tampa Bay Business Journal
Ed: Jane Meinhardt. **Description:** How Tom Gaffney, a cofounder of the private equity firm The Anderson Group realized the great return on investment in the 600 block of Central Avenue in St. Petersburg, Florida is discussed. Focusing on long-term value rather than short-term profitability and exit, Gaffney purchased this block in 2008 for $2.3 million and cultivated arts businesses at tenants.

TRADE PERIODICALS

1411 ■ CityArt Magazine: A Contemporary Review of the Visual Arts
Pub: Fleisher Fine Arts Inc.
URL(s): www.artfocustoronto.presspublisher.us/. **Released:** 3/yr. **Price:** $15, Canada 7% GST.

1412 ■ Country Home
Pub: Meredith Corp.
URL(s): www.countryhome.com. **Released:** Monthly; 10/yr. **Price:** $4.95, Individuals newstand; $21.97, Two years.

1413 ■ Needlework Retailer
Pub: Yarn Tree Design Inc.
URL(s): yarntree.comneedleworkretailer.com/. **Released:** Bimonthly

VIDEOCASSETTES/ AUDIOCASSETTES

1414 ■ Piet Mondrian: Mr. Boogie-Woogie Man
Crystal Productions
1812 Johns Dr.
Box 2159
Glenview, IL 60025-6519

Ph: (847)657-8144
Free: 800-255-8629
Fax: (847)657-8149
Co. E-mail: custserv@crystalproductions.com
URL: http://www.crystalproductions.com
Released: 1998. **Price:** $39.95. **Description:** Details the painter's development of a new art and his experiments with Symbolism, Fauvism, and Cubism. **Availability:** VHS.

1415 ■ Vermeer: Light, Love, and Silence
Home Vision Cinema
c/o Image Entertainment
20525 Nordhoff St., Ste. 200
Chatsworth, CA 91311
Co. E-mail: inquiries@image-entertainment.com
URL: http://www.homevision.com
Released: 1998. **Price:** $39.95. **Description:** Explores the social, economic, scientific, and political context of the painter's work. **Availability:** VHS.

TRADE SHOWS AND CONVENTIONS

1416 ■ The Winter Olympia Fine Art and Antiques Fair
Clarion Events Ltd.
Earls Court Exhibition Centre
Warwick Rd.
London SW5 9TA, United Kingdom
Ph: 44 20 7370 8139
URL: http://www.clarionevents.com
Contact: Simon Kimble, Chief Executive Officer
URL(s): www.olympia-antiques.com/. **Frequency:** Annual. **Audience:** Trade and general public. **Principal Exhibits:** Antiques including fine, oak, garden, and country furniture; rugs; paintings; ceramics; clocks; sculptures; jewelry, silver, and bronzes. **Telecommunication Services:** olympia-antiques@eco.co.uk.

FRANCHISES AND BUSINESS OPPORTUNITIES

1417 ■ Marad Fine Art International
66 Glenbrook Rd., Ste. 3327
Stamford, CT 06902
Ph: (203)912-8402
Description: Artwork supplies business. **No. of Franchise Units:** 3. **No. of Company-Owned Units:** 1. **Founded:** 1938.. **Franchised:** 2000. **Equity Capital Needed:** $49,000-$70,000. **Franchise Fee:** $39,000. **Training:** Yes.

ASSOCIATIONS AND OTHER ORGANIZATIONS

1418 ■ **American College of Health Care Administrators (ACHCA)**
1321 Duke St., Ste. 400
Alexandria, VA 22314
Ph: (202)536-5120
Free: 888-882-2422
Fax: (866)874-1585
Co. E-mail: mgrachek@achca.org
URL: http://www.achca.org
Contact: Marianna Kern Grachek, President
Description: Persons actively engaged in the administration of long-term care facilities, such as nursing homes, retirement communities, assisted living facilities, and sub-acute care programs. Administers professional certification programs for assisted living, sub-acute and nursing home administrators. Works to elevate the standards in the field and to develop and promote a code of ethics and standards of education and training. Seeks to inform allied professions and the public that good administration of long-term care facilities calls for special formal academic training and experience. Encourages research in all aspects of geriatrics, the chronically ill, and administration. Maintains placement service. Holds special education programs; facilitates networking among administrators. **Scope:** long-term care administration, geriatrics, gerontology. **Founded:** 1962. **Subscriptions:** 500 books papers periodicals. **Publications:** *ACHCA E-News* (Biweekly); *Balance: The Source for Administrators in Long-Term Health Care*; *Continuum*. **Educational Activities:** Winter Marketplace (Annual); ACHCA Annual Winter Marketplace (Annual); American College of Health Care Administrators (Annual). **Awards:** Distinguished Administrator Award (Annual); Education Award (Annual); Journalism Award (Annual); New Administrator Award (Annual); Richard L. Thorpe Fellowship (Annual); Abbott Nutrition Award for Distinguished Service to ACHCA (Annual); Phillip McConnell Student Scholarship Fund (Annual). **Telecommunication Services:** mtn@achca.org; meetings@achca.org; info@achca.org.

1419 ■ **Assisted Living Federation of America (ALFA)**
1650 King St., Ste. 602
Alexandria, VA 22314-2747
Ph: (703)894-1805
Fax: (703)894-1831
Co. E-mail: rgrimes@alfa.org
URL: http://www.alfa.org
Contact: Richard Grimes, President
Description: Providers of assisted living, state associations of providers, and others interested or involved in the industry. Promotes the interests of the assisted living industry and works to enhance the quality of life for the population it serves. Provides a forum for assisted living providers to unite, exchange information, and interact. Encourages the development of high standards for the industry. Promotes the concept of assisted living facilities with public and private agencies and other professionals. Works to

educate providers and the public and increase national awareness of assisted living. Sponsors speakers' bureau, conferences, educational opportunities, trade show, research & training products. **Founded:** 1990. **Publications:** *ALFA Alert* (Weekly); *Assisted Living Executive* (9/year); *Guide to Choosing an Assisted Living Residence*; *ALFA Executive Portfolio: Inside the Minds of the Leaders in Assisted Living and Senior Housing.* **Awards:** Hero Awards (Annual); Pioneer Award (Annual); Best of Home Architectural Design Award (Annual).

REFERENCE WORKS

1420 ■ *"Advancing the Ball"* in *Inside Healthcare (Vol. 6, December 2010, No. 7, pp. 31)*
Pub: RedCoat Publishing Inc.
Ed: Michelle McNickle. **Description:** Profile of Medicalodges an elder-care specialty company that provides both patient care and technology development. President and CEO of the firm believes that hiring good employees is key to growth for any small business.

1421 ■ *"Big Sell-Off At Sunwest"* in *The Business Journal-Portland (Vol. 25, July 25, 2008, No. 20, pp. 1)*
Pub: American City Business Journals, Inc.
Ed: Robin J. Moody. **Description:** Oregon's largest operator of assisted living facilities Sunwest Management Inc. is expected to sell 132 of its properties. The planned sale, which is believed to be worth more than $1 billion, will help Sunwest pay creditors and investors. Other views and information on the planned sale, as well as on Sunwest's services which include adult day care, are presented.

1422 ■ *"Connecting the Dots Between Wellness and Elder Care"* in *Benefits and Compensation Digest (Vol. 47, August 2010, No. 8, pp. 18)*
Pub: International Foundation of Employee Benefit Plans
Contact: Richard Lyall, President
Ed: Sandra Timmermann. **Description:** Employees caring for aged and infirm parents deal with time and financial issues and other stresses. The connection between health status of caregivers and employers' health care costs could be aided by linking programs and benefits with wellness and caregiving.

1423 ■ *"Elder Care Costs Surge"* in *National Underwriter Life & Health (Vol. 114, November 8, 2020, No. 21, pp. 25)*
Pub: Summit Business Media
Ed: Trevor Thomas. **Description:** Nursing home and assisted living rates rose from 2009 to 2010, according to MetLife Mature Market Institute. Statistical data included.

1424 ■ *"Elder Care, Rx Drugs Reforms Top Zoeller's Agenda"* in *Times (December 21, 2010)*
Pub: The Times
Ed: Sarah Tompkins. **Description:** Indiana Attorney General Greg Zoeller is hoping to develop a program

in the state that will help regulate care for the elderly; freeze medical licenses for doctors involved in criminal investigations; address illegal drug use; and to establish a program to help individuals dispose of old prescription medications easily at pharmacies.

1425 ■ *"Elder-Care Seminar to Teach Ways to Avoid Falls"* in *Virginian-Pilot (November 25, 2010)*
Pub: Virginian-Pilot
Ed: Amy Jeter. **Description:** ResCare HomeCare, a home health services firm, offers free seminars on helping to make residences safer for seniors prone to falling.

1426 ■ *"EVMS Gets Grant to Train Providers for Elder Care"* in *Virginian-Pilot (October 29, 2010)*
Pub: Virginian-Pilot
Ed: Elizabeth Simpson. **Description:** Eastern Virginia Medical School received a federal grant to train health providers in elder care. Details of the program are provided.

1427 ■ *"Face Issues if Elder Care, Unemployment Collide"* in *Atlanta Journal-Constitution (December 26, 2010, pp. G1)*
Pub: Atlanta Journal-Constitution
Ed: Amy Lindgren. **Description:** More issues arise during holiday for families with older members requiring care, including the issue of employment for those doing the caregiving.

1428 ■ *"GeckoSystems Reduces Sensor Fusion Costs Due to Elder Care Robot Trials"* in *Internet Wire (December 14, 2010)*
Pub: Comtex
Description: GeckoSystems International Corporation has been able to reduce the cost of its sensor fusion system while maintaining reliability and performance. The firm's ongoing first in-home elder care robot trials have sparked interest regarding its business model, technologies available for licensing, and joint domestic and international ventures.

1429 ■ *"New Elder Care Center to Focus on Residents with Failing Memories"* in *Tulsa World (November 30, 2010)*
Pub: World Publishing
Ed: Robert Evatt. **Description:** People with Alzheimer's disease and other mental disorders require specialized care. Constant Care Management Company runs 'memory care' centers designed for the elderly with such conditions.

1430 ■ *"Prime Site Lands Retirement Center"* in *Business Courier (Vol. 24, November 2, 2008, No. 29, pp. 1)*
Pub: American City Business Journals, Inc.
Ed: Laura Baverman. **Description:** Erickson Retirement Communities plans to build a $220 million campus on 65 acres of land between Evendale and Glendale. The project will depend on votes casted by village councils in Evendale and Glendale, expected

to take place in December 2007. Both areas must sign on and alter zoning rules before the development can proceed.

1431 ■ "Silver Dollars" in Small Business Opportunities (September 2008)
Pub: Entrepreneur Media Inc.
Description: Profile of Always Best Care Senior Services, a franchise created by Michael Newman, which offers non-medical In-Home Care, Personal Emergency Response Systems, and Assisted Living Placement Services to seniors; the company offers franchisees the opportunity to fill what is oftentimes a void for the seniors and their families in the community.

1432 ■ "Small Is Best, Says Housing Officials" in Business First Buffalo (November 16, 2007, pp. 1)
Pub: American City Business Journals, Inc.
Ed: Tracey Drury. **Description:** Nonprofit organizations in some parts of the U.S. are moving senior citizens from larger institutions into smaller housing. The benefits of smaller housing for the elderly are evaluated.

1433 ■ "Sunwest Vies To Stave Off Bankruptcy" in The Business Journal-Portland (Vol. 25, August 15, 2008, No. 23, pp. 1)
Pub: American City Business Journals, Inc.
Ed: Robin J. Moody. **Description:** Sunwest Management Inc. is teetering on the edge of bankruptcy as creditors start foreclosure on nine of their properties. This could potentially displace residents of the assisted living operator. Sunwest is trying to sell smaller packages of properties to get a $100 million bridge loan to maintain operations.

1434 ■ "They've Fallen, But They Can Get Up" in Barron's (Vol. 88, March 10, 2008, No. 10, pp. 43)
Pub: Dow Jones & Company, Inc.
Ed: Kopin Tan. **Description:** Shares of senior housing companies present buying opportunities to investors because of their low prices. Companies such as Brookdale Senior Living are not as dependent on housing prices but have suffered declines in share prices.

TRADE PERIODICALS

1435 ■ AHCA Notes
Pub: American Health Care Association
Contact: Mark Parkinson, President
Ed: Nathan Childs, Editor, nchilds@ahca.org. **Released:** Monthly; Monthly, 12/year. **Price:** Included in membership.; included in membership dues; Included in membership. **Description:** Presents information on nursing homes, assisted living, and residential care facilities. Covers legislation on prescription drug prices, nurse assistant training, certification enforcement, Medicare/Medicaid and long term care requirements, and legal activities.

1436 ■ The Capsule Newsletter
Pub: Children of Aging Parents
Contact: Lenore Sherman, Executive Director
Ed: Lorraine Sailor, Editor. **Released:** Bimonthly. **Price:** Included in membership; Free; $100. **Description:** Contains articles and informational notices on the concerns and issues of elderly persons and those who care for them. Provides organizations, resources, and services to help caregivers of elderly.

1437 ■ Home Health Care Services Quarterly
Pub: Routledge Journals Taylor & Francis Group
URL(s): www.tandf.co.uk/journals/WHHC. **Ed:** Maria Aranda. **Released:** Quarterly **Price:** $125, Individuals online; $134, Individuals print & online.

1438 ■ Housing for Seniors Report
Pub: CD Publications
Ed: Marcella Kogan, Editor. **Released:** Monthly. **Price:** $297/year. **Description:** Provides news and practical suggestions concerning the production, management, marketing and other business aspects of housing for the elderly. Coverage includes nursing

homes, apartment projects, and retirement communities; also government-operated programs. Recurring features include news of research.

1439 ■ National Hispanic Council on Aging --News
Pub: National Hispanic Council on Aging
Contact: Ms. Yanira L. Cruz, President
Released: Quarterly. **Price:** Included in membership; Free. **Description:** Publicizes the activities of the Council, which fosters the well-being of the Hispanic elderly through research, policy analysis, projects, development of educational resources, and training. Also provides a network for organizations and community groups interested in the Hispanic elderly. Recurring features include a calendar of events, legislative updates, and notices of publications available.

TRADE SHOWS AND CONVENTIONS

1440 ■ California Association of Homes and Services for the Aging Annual Meeting and Exhibition
Aging Services of California (CAHSA)
1315 I St., Ste. 100
Sacramento, CA 95814-2912
Ph: (916)392-5111
Fax: (916)428-4250
Co. E-mail: jhandy@aging.org
URL: http://www.aging.org
Contact: Joanne Handy, President
E-mail: jhandy@aging.org
URL(s): www.aging.org. **Frequency:** Annual. **Audience:** Administrators of retirement homes, nurses, executives of multihome corporations (nonprofit), activities directors, and dieticians. **Principal Exhibits:** Food services, medical and financial record systems, industrial cleaning and maintenance equipment, architectural services, interior design materials, medical equipment, computers, software, insurance services, employee benefit services and accounting services.

LIBRARIES

1441 ■ Albany Medical College - Schaffer Library of Health Sciences
43 New Scotland Ave.
Albany, NY 12208
Ph: (518)262-5586
Co. E-mail: library@mail.amc.edu
URL: http://www.amc.edu/Academic/Schaffer/index.html
Contact: Enid Geyer, Director
Scope: Medicine, pre-clinical sciences, nursing. **Services:** Interlibrary loan; copying; document delivery; library open to allied health personnel. **Founded:** 1928. **Holdings:** 150,000 volumes; 98,597 bound periodical volumes; 2700 audio/visual programs. **Subscriptions:** 4950 journals and other serials.

1442 ■ American Association of Occupational Health Nurses Library
7794 Grow Dr.
Pensacola, FL 32514
Ph: (850)474-6963
Free: 800-241-8014
Fax: (850)484-8762
Co. E-mail: aaohn@aaohn.org
URL: http://www.aaohn.org
Contact: Kay Campbell, Executive Director
Scope: Occupational and environmental health nursing, occupational medicine. **Services:** Library not open to the public. **Founded:** 1965. **Holdings:** 1200 books; 24 bound periodical volumes; 1050 pamphlets. **Subscriptions:** 54 journals and other serials; 6 newspapers. **Telecommunication Services:** editor@aaohn.org; jon.dancy@dancyamc.com.

1443 ■ American Nurses Association Library Information Center
8515 Georgia Ave., Ste. 400
Silver Spring, MD 20910-3492

Ph: (301)628-5000
Co. E-mail: info@ana.org
URL: http://www.nursingworld.org
Contact: Richard J. Barry, Librarian
Scope: Nurses, nursing, healthcare. **Services:** Library not open to the public. **Founded:** 1952. **Holdings:** 180 books; 1275 reports. **Subscriptions:** 30 journals and other serials.

1444 ■ Deaconess Hospital Health Science Library
600 Mary St.
Evansville, IN 47747
Ph: (812)450-3384
Fax: (812)450-7255
Co. E-mail: julia_esparza@deaconess.com
URL: http://www.deaconess.com/body.cfm?id=81
Contact: Julia Esparza, Librarian, Science
Scope: Nursing, clinical medicine, consumer health, healthcare management, business management, allied health sciences, clinical pastoral care. **Services:** Interlibrary loan; copying; current awareness; library open to laypersons. **Founded:** 1969. **Holdings:** 2000 books; 200 audio/visual programs. **Subscriptions:** 135 journals and other serials; 2 newspapers.

1445 ■ El Camino Hospital - Health Library and Resource Center
Main Bldg., 1st Fl.
2500 Grant Rd.
Mountain View, CA 94040
Ph: (650)940-7210
Fax: (650)940-7174
Co. E-mail: healthlib@elcaminohospital.org
URL: http://www.elcaminohospital.org/Patient_Services/Health_Library
Contact: Jack Black, Librarian, Medical Science
Scope: Medicine, nursing, healthcare administration, caregiving, elder care. **Services:** Interlibrary loan; copying; library open to the public. **Founded:** 1986. **Holdings:** 5500 books and videotapes. **Subscriptions:** 150 journals and other serials; 3 newspapers.

1446 ■ Health Occupations Center - Learning Resource Center
9368 Oakbourne Rd.
Santee, CA 92071
Ph: (619)596-3676
Fax: (619)579-4779
Co. E-mail: johnsonk@guhsd.net
Contact: Kathleen A. Johnson
Scope: Nursing, medicine, dentistry. **Services:** Copying; Center open to the public for reference use only. **Holdings:** 2100 books. **Subscriptions:** 30 journals and other serials.

1447 ■ Jefferson College of Health Sciences Learning Resource Center
101 Elm Ave., SE
Roanoke, VA 24013
Ph: (540)985-9828
Free: 888-985-8483
Co. E-mail: rhthiss@jcarilionclinic.org
URL: http://www.jchs.edu/page.php/prmID/611
Contact: Ramona Thiss, Director, Library Services
Scope: Nursing, allied health, respiratory care, physical therapy assistant, occupational therapy assistant, emergency health services, physicians' assistant, radiologic science, biology. **Services:** Interlibrary loan; copying; Center open to the public for reference use only. **Holdings:** 11,000 books; 1704 bound periodical volumes. **Subscriptions:** 370 journals and other serials.

1448 ■ Kaiser-Permanente Medical Center Health Sciences Library
2425 Geary Blvd.
San Francisco, CA 94115
Ph: (415)833-2000
URL: http://www.kaiserpermanente.org
Scope: Clinical sciences. **Services:** Interlibrary loan; Library not open to the public. **Founded:** 1955. **Holdings:** 3800 books; 11,000 bound periodical volumes; 50 pamphlets. **Subscriptions:** 190 journals and other serials.

1449 ■ Loma Linda University - Del E. Webb Memorial Library
11072 Anderson St.
Loma Linda, CA 92350-1704
Ph: (909)558-4550
Fax: (909)558-4188
Co. E-mail: libwebeditor@llu.edu
URL: http://www.llu.edu/llu/library
Contact: Carlene Drake, Director

Scope: Medicine, nursing, dentistry, religion, health, allied health professions. **Services:** Interlibrary loan; copying; Library open to qualified users. **Founded:** 1907. **Holdings:** 186,719 books; 121,609 bound periodical volumes; 62,318 microforms; 6265 tapes and phonograph records; 8130 filmstrips, films, slides; 1160 feet of archival materials. **Subscriptions:** 1411 journals and other serials; 7 newspapers.

1450 ■ Los Angeles County/Harbor-UCLA Medical Center - A.F. Parlow Library of the Health Sciences
1000 W. Carson St.
Box 18
Torrance, CA 90502
Ph: (310)222-2372
Fax: (310)212-5542
Co. E-mail: libref@labiomed.org
URL: http://www.humc.edu
Contact: Mary Ann Berliner, Director, Library Services

URL(s): harborucla.org/library. **Scope:** Medicine, nursing, patient education, administration. **Services:** Interlibrary loan; copying; Library open to the public with restrictions. **Founded:** 1946. **Holdings:** 35,000 books; 45,000 bound periodical volumes; 1700 AV programs. **Subscriptions:** 866 journals and other serials. **Telecommunication Services:** mberliner@labiomed.org; library@humc.edu.

1451 ■ McMaster University - Health Sciences Library
1280 Main St., W. HSC 2B
Hamilton, ON, Canada L8N 3Z5
Ph: (905)525-9140
Fax: (905)528-3733
Co. E-mail: bayleyl@mcmaster.ca
URL: http://hsl.mcmaster.ca
Contact: Liz Bayley, Director

Scope: Basic medical sciences, clinical medicine, nursing, allied health sciences, history of medicine.

Services: Interlibrary loan; copying; Library open to the public for reference use only. **Founded:** 1967. **Holdings:** 61,777 (volumes) books; 93,330 bound periodical volumes; 1717 multimedia resources, including 879 videotapes; 828 audiocassettes; 284 computer software programs. **Subscriptions:** 2600 journals and other serials. **Telecommunication Services:** hslib@mcmaster.ca.

1452 ■ Spectrum Health Sciences Libraries
A-level, West Bldg.
100 Michigan St., NE
Grand Rapids, MI 49503-2560
Ph: (616)391-1655
Fax: (616)391-3527
Co. E-mail: diane.hummel@spectrumhealth.org
URL: http://www.spectrumhealth.org/spectrumhealth-libraries
Contact: Diane Hummel, Manager

Scope: Medicine, surgery, medical/surgical specialties, nursing. **Services:** Copying; document delivery; Library open to the public. **Founded:** 1948. **Holdings:** 6000 books; bound periodical volumes; audio and videocassettes; microfiche; microfilm. **Subscriptions:** 500 periodicals.

ASSOCIATIONS AND OTHER ORGANIZATIONS

1453 ■ AMC Institute (AMCi)—Association Management Companies Institute
100 N 20th St., 4th Fl.
Philadelphia, PA 19103-1443
Ph: (215)564-3484
Fax: (215)564-2175
Co. E-mail: info@amcinstitute.org
URL: http://www.amcinstitute.org
Contact: Susan Cabrera, Director
E-mail: susan@mgmtresources.org
URL(s): www.iaamc.org. **Description:** Management companies serving a number of associations on a professional basis (but not executives serving more than one association in an employee relationship). Membership employs nearly 3,000 association management professionals and serves over 1,200 associations with annual budgets exceeding 960 million dollars and serving nearly 1.7 million members. **Founded:** 1964. **Publications:** *Association Management Companies Institute--Directory*. **Educational Activities:** AMC Institute Meeting (Annual). **Awards:** G.W. Bostrum Award for Service Quality & Excellence (Annual). **Telecommunication Services:** info@iaamc.org.

1454 ■ American Society of Association Executives (ASAE)—The Center for Association Leadership
1575 I St. NW
Washington, DC 20005-1103
Ph: (202)371-0940
Free: 888-950-2723
Fax: (202)371-8315
Co. E-mail: asaeservice@asaecenter.org
URL: http://www.asaecenter.org
Contact: John H. Graham, IV, President
URL(s): www.asaecenter.org. **Description:** Professional society of paid executives of international, national, state, and local trade, professional, and philanthropic associations. Seeks to educate association executives on effective management, including: the proper objectives, functions, and activities of associations; the basic principles of association management; the legal aspects of association activity; policies relating to association management; efficient methods, procedures, and techniques of association management; the responsibilities and professional standards of association executives. Maintains information resource center. Conducts resume, guidance, and consultation services; compiles statistics in the form of reports, surveys, and studies; carries out research and education. Maintains ASAE Services Corporation to provide special services and ASAE Foundation to do future-oriented research and make grant awards. Offers executive search services and insurance programs. Provides CEO center for chief staff executives. Conducts Certified Association Executive (CAE) program. **Scope:** Association management specialists providing training for those who manage nonprofit voluntary membership organizations. Typical client or target audience association

executives and their staffs. **Founded:** 1920. **Subscriptions:** 1400. **Publications:** "Guide to the Newest Irs Form 990"; "Spring 2009 Catalog"; "The Power of Partnership: Principles and Practices for Creating Strategic Relationships"; "Put Your Data to Work: 52 Tips and Techniques for Effectively Managing Your Database"; "Association Executive Compensation and Benefits Study"; "Turbulent Change: Every Working Person's Survival Guide"; "Reinventing Your Board: A Step-By-Step Guide to Implementing Policy Governance"; "International Legal Issues for Non profit Organizations"; "Strategic Planning for Association Executives"; "Net Worth: Shaping Markets When Customers Make the Rules"; "1001 Ways to Market Your Books"; "199 Ideas: Membership Recruitment and Retention"; "2008-2009 Blue Chip Association Executive Compensation & Benefits Study"; "2009 Associations Now Volunteer Leadership Issue Magazine"; "2010-2011 Blue Chip Association Executive Compensation & Benefits Study"; "2010-2011GW Area & Nat'l Compensation & Benefits Study Set"; "50 Ways to Motivate Your Board: A Guide for Nonprofit Executives"; "7 Measures of Success Implementation Guide and Assessment Tool"; "70 Suggestions and More for a Shorter, Smarter Job Hunt"; "Achieving Goals: Making Your Mark as a Board Member". "Achieving Sponsorship Success". **Educational Activities:** Strategic Leadership Forum (Annual); ASAE Annual Meeting & Exposition (Annual); Management and Technology Conferences - ASAE Annual Meeting (Annual); Springtime Expo (Annual). **Awards:** Key Awards; ASAE Fellow; Academy of Leaders Award; Gold Circle Awards; Academy of Leaders Awards; ASAE Fellows; Associations Advance America Awards (Annual); Banff Centre Scholarship Award; Key Award; Sentinel Award (Periodic); Associations Advance America Award of Excellence; Associations Make A Better World Award; Diversity Executive Leadership Program Scholarships; Associations Make a Better World Awards (Annual). **Seminars:** Nation's Capital Distinguished Speakers Series. **Telecommunication Services:** infocentral@asaenet.org.

1455 ■ *Association*
10 King St. E, Ste. 1100
Toronto, ON, Canada M5C 1C3
Ph: (416)363-3555
Free: 800-461-3608
Fax: (416)363-3630
Co. E-mail: manderson@csae.com
URL: http://www.csae.com
Contact: Michael Anderson, President
Released: Bimonthly

1456 ■ *The Association Agenda*
10 King St. E, Ste. 1100
Toronto, ON, Canada M5C 1C3
Ph: (416)363-3555
Free: 800-461-3608
Fax: (416)363-3630
Co. E-mail: manderson@csae.com
URL: http://www.csae.com
Contact: Michael Anderson, President
Released: Periodic

1457 ■ Canadian Society of Association Executives (CSAE)
10 King St. E, Ste. 1100
Toronto, ON, Canada M5C 1C3
Ph: (416)363-3555
Free: 800-461-3608
Fax: (416)363-3630
Co. E-mail: manderson@csae.com
URL: http://www.csae.com
Contact: Michael Anderson, President
Description: CEO, presidents, executive directors and managers working for non-profit associations operating in Canada. Promotes efficient operation of non-profit associations; facilitates continued professional advancement of members. Serves as a forum for exchange of ideas and information among members; conducts educational and training programs. **Scope:** best practices, non dues revenues, association management. **Founded:** 1951. **Subscriptions:** 264. **Publications:** *Association* (Bimonthly); *The Association Agenda* (Periodic). **Educational Activities:** Canadian Society of Association Executives Conference (Annual). **Awards:** Chapter of the Year Award (Annual); John Griner Award (Biennial); John Griner Award; Pinnacle Award (Annual); John Griner Award; Pinnacle Award; Award for Excellence in Association Leadership (Annual); Donna Mary Shaw Award. **Telecommunication Services:** csae@csae.com.

1458 ■ DMA Nonprofit Federation (DMANF)
1615 L St. NW, Ste. 1100
Washington, DC 20036
Ph: (202)861-2410
Co. E-mail: cquinn@the-dma.org
URL: http://www.nonprofitfederation.org
Contact: Christopher Quinn, Executive Director
Description: Trade and lobbying group for non-profit organizations that use direct and online marketing to raise funds and communicate with members. Sponsors professional development conferences and seminars, lobbies on state and federal legislation, regulation, and standards related to direct marketing and related issues. Provides information about and participants in litigation affecting non-profits. Promotes the overall welfare of non-profits. Represents health care charities, social service agencies, religious groups, colleges and universities and fraternal organizations. **Founded:** 1982. **Publications:** *Journal of the DMA Nonprofit Federation* (Quarterly); *News Update* (Biweekly). **Educational Activities:** New York Nonprofit Conference (Annual); Washington Nonprofit Conference (Annual). **Awards:** Max L. Hart Nonprofit Advancement Award (Annual); Nonprofit Organization of the Year (Annual).

1459 ■ Society for Nonprofit Organizations (SNPO)
PO Box 510354
Livonia, MI 48151
Ph: (734)451-3582
Fax: (734)451-5935
Co. E-mail: info@snpo.org
URL: http://www.snpo.org
Contact: Katie Burnham Laverty, President
E-mail: kburnham@snpo.org
Description: Brings together those who serve in the nonprofit world in order to build a strong network of

professionals throughout the country; provides a forum for the exchange of information, knowledge, and ideas on strengthening and increasing productivity within nonprofit organizations and among their leaders. Mission is accomplished through the publication of Nonprofit World magazine, educational programs offered by the Learning Institute, and other communications with its members. **Scope:** nonprofit management, board governance, fundraising, strategic planning, resource development, social entrepreneurship. **Founded:** 1983. **Subscriptions:** 21 archival material articles audio recordings books periodicals video recordings. **Publications:** Funding Alert (Monthly); Nonprofit World (Bimonthly); Resource Center Product Catalog; Nonprofit World: The National Bi-Monthly Nonprofit Leadership and Management Journal; Nonprofit World--National Directory of Product and Service Providers (Bimonthly).

REFERENCE WORKS

1460 ■ Association Management Companies Institute--Directory
Pub: AMC Institute
Contact: Susan Cabrera, Director
E-mail: susan@mgmtresources.org
URL(s): www.amcinstitute.org. **Released:** Latest edition 2010-2011. **Covers:** 200 members representing 4,000 associations. **Entries include:** Management company name, address, phone, fax, e-mail, URL address, member and title. **Arrangement:** Alphabetical. **Indexes:** Association name, member name, city, state.

1461 ■ Association Management--Convention Center & Convention Bureau Directory
Pub: American Society of Association Executives
Contact: John H. Graham, IV, President
URL(s): www.asaecenter.org. **Ed:** Debra Popovich.
Released: Annual; February. **Price:** Free Online version. **Publication includes:** List of convention halls, centers, auditoriums, arenas, and convention and visitors bureaus in the United States, Canada, and abroad. **Entries include:** Name of hall or CVB, phone, fax, and exhibit space available. **Arrangement:** Geographical. **Telecommunication Services:** Email: mhallin@asaenet.org.

1462 ■ Encyclopedia of Associations: National Organizations of the U.S.
Pub: Cengage Learning Inc.
Contact: Ronald Dunn, President
URL(s): www.gale.cengage.com. **Released:** Annual **Price:** $778, Individuals. **Covers:** Approximately 25,000 nonprofit U.S. Membership organizations of national scope divided into 18 classifications: trade, business, and commercial; environmental and agricultural; legal, governmental, public administration, and military; engineering, technological, and natural and social science; educational; cultural; social welfare; health and medical; public affairs; fraternal, nationality, and ethnic; religious organizations; veterans, hereditary, and patriotic; hobby and avocational; athletic and sports; labor unions, associations, and federations; chambers of commerce and trade and tourism; Greek and non-Greek letter societies, associations, and federations; fan clubs. **Entries include:** Organization name, address, phone, fax, name of executive officer, staff size, date founded, number of members, membership dues, annual budget, description of objectives, activities, committees, publications, computer and telecommunications services, historical information, convention dates and locations; publications, including title, description, ISSN, circulation, whether advertising is accepted, alternate formats, and former or alternate name(s) of publication. **Arrangement:** By subject keyword within classifications cited above. **Indexes:** Organization name/keyword (including references to organizations listed in International Organizations; also includes addresses and phone numbers after each association's primary reference); separate volume includes geographical and executive indexes (including organization name, address, phone, and name of chief executive in both arrangements).

1463 ■ National Trade and Professional Associations of the U.S.
Pub: Columbia Books and Information Services
Contact: Debra Mayberry, President
E-mail: dmayberry@columbiabooks.com
URL(s): www.columbiabooks.com. **Released:** Annual; Latest edition 2013, published November 2012.

Price: $269, Individuals standing order; $299, Individuals mailing list; per thousand; minimum order $269. **Covers:** Approximately 7,800 trade associations, professional societies and labor unions. **Entries include:** Name, year established, name of chief executive and other senior staff, address, phone, toll free, fax, e-mail & internet addresses; number of staff members, budget, size of membership; date, expected attendance, and location of annual meeting; publications; historical and descriptive data. Title formerly included '. and Canada and Labor Unions'; Canadian coverage was dropped beginning with 1982 edition, but American labor unions are still included. **Arrangement:** Alphabetical. **Indexes:** Geographical, subject, budget, acronym, executive.

1464 ■ State & Regional Associations of the United States
Pub: Columbia Books and Information Services
Contact: Debra Mayberry, President
E-mail: dmayberry@columbiabooks.com
URL(s): www.columbiabooks.com/State-and-Regional-Associations-Directory. **Released:** Annual; Latest edition 2011. **Price:** $199, Individuals. **Covers:** 8,800 state and regional trade associations, professional societies, and labor unions. **Entries include:** Organization name, address, toll-free phone, fax, e-mail & internet addresses; year established, name of chief executive and select senior staff, number of members, financial data, staff size, requirements for membership, services, publications, annual meetings. **Arrangement:** Geographical, alphabetical within state. **Indexes:** Subject, budget, executive, acronym.

1465 ■ Who's Who in Association Management: Membership Directory & Buyer's Guide
Pub: American Society of Association Executives
Contact: John H. Graham, IV, President
URL(s): www.asaenet.org/buyers_guide. **Released:** Annual; Latest edition 2007. **Price:** $70, Members; $160, Nonmembers. **No. of Listings:** 20,000. **Covers:** Paid executives who are members of the association; suppliers of products and services to associations; supplier listings are paid. **Entries include:** For members--Name, address, phone, association represented. For suppliers--Company name, address, phone, contact name, description of products and services. **Arrangement:** Members are alphabetical; suppliers are classified by product or service. **Indexes:** Association, geographical, personal name, membership category.

STATISTICAL SOURCES

1466 ■ Association Meeting Trends
American Society of Association Executives
Contact: John H. Graham, IV, President
Released: 2004. **Price:** $107.95 (paper) ($86.95 for members). **Description:** Study containing statistics on association conventions, expositions, board and committee meetings, and educational seminars. Includes more than 100 tables.

TRADE PERIODICALS

1467 ■ ASAE Membership Developments
Pub: Membership Section
Contact: Meggan Freedman, Section Chief
E-mail: mharrison@asaenet.org
Released: Monthly. **Price:** Included in membership. **Description:** Emphasizes direct mail, telemarketing, surveys, and member recruitment and retention. Recurring features include news of the Society.

1468 ■ Association Meetings: The Independent Voice of the Association Industry
Pub: Primedia Business Magazines & Media
URL(s): meetingsnet.com/associationmeetings/. **Ed:** Sue Pelletier, Barbara Scofidio. **Released:** Bimonthly **Price:** $65, Canada; $98, Other countries.

1469 ■ Association News
Pub: Schneider Publishing Company Inc.
Ed: Ann Shepphird, Editor, ann.shepphird@schneiderpublishing.com. **Released:** Monthly. **Price:** Free. **Description:** Provides timely independent

information on association management, meeting planning, and convention business. Seeks to provide a medium for information and news, and offers a communications link among the various nonprofit organizations and the commercial entities servicing them. Recurring features include editorials, commentary, news of industry organizations, and articles in the areas of association management and meeting planning.

1470 ■ Association Trends
Pub: Martineau Corp.
URL(s): www.associationtrends.comwww.assntrends. com. **Released:** Monthly **Price:** $165, Individuals standard class; $189, Individuals 1st class; $189, Individuals library; $189, Canada standard class.

1471 ■ Communication News
Pub: American Society of Association Executives
Contact: John H. Graham, IV, President
Ed: LaRonda Famodu, Editor, lfamodu@asaenet.org. **Released:** Monthly. **Price:** Included in membership. **Description:** Focuses on public relations, writing and editing, publications management, postal rates and regulations, advertising sales, censorship, and printing and typography. Advises readers on how to improve their publications and alerts them to pertinent legal and legislative action and upcoming conventions and courses.

1472 ■ Government Relations
Pub: Government Relations Section
Contact: Tamara Faggen, Associate Editor
Released: Monthly. **Price:** Included in membership. **Description:** Carries updates on government legislation affecting associations and practical information and suggestions on lobbying techniques. Recurring features include news of Section programs and activities.

1473 ■ Meetings & Incentive Travel
Pub: Business Information Group
Contact: Bruce Creighton, President
URL(s): www.meetingscanada.com/. **Released:** 6/yr.

TRADE SHOWS AND CONVENTIONS

1474 ■ Holiday Showcase
Association Forum of Chicagoland
10 S Riverside Plaza, Ste. 800
Chicago, IL 60606
Ph: (312)924-7000
Fax: (312)924-7100
Co. E-mail: info@associationforum.org
URL: http://www.associationforum.org
Contact: Christie A. Tarantino, President
URL(s): www.holidayshowcase.org. **Frequency:** Annual. **Audience:** Association executives. **Principal Exhibits:** Hotel, airline, and convention center information; printers; insurance and accounting services, banking, technology.

1475 ■ Management and Technology Conferences - ASAE Annual Meeting
American Society of Association Executives (ASAE)
1575 I St. NW
Washington, DC 20005-1103
Ph: (202)371-0940
Free: 888-950-2723
Fax: (202)371-8315
Co. E-mail: asaeservice@asaecenter.org
URL: http://www.asaecenter.org
Contact: John H. Graham, IV, President
URL(s): www.technologyconference.org. **Price:** $895, Members early bird; $1095, Non-members early bird; $995, Onsite registered, members; $1195, Onsite registered, non-members. **Frequency:** Annual. **Audience:** Association executives and meeting planners. **Principal Exhibits:** Equipment, supplies, and services for associations. **Telecommunication Services:** mbrdev@asaecenter.org.

COMPUTERIZED DATABASES

1476 ■ Associations Canada
555 Richmond St. W, Ste. 301
Toronto, ON, Canada M5V 3B1
Ph: (416)644-6479
Free: 866-433-4739

Fax: (416)644-1904
Co. E-mail: info@greyhouse.ca
URL: http://www.greyhouse.ca
Availability: Online: Grey House Publishing - Grey House Publishing Canada Inc. **Type:** Directory.

LIBRARIES

1477 ■ American Society of Association Executives - The Center for Association

Leadership - Knowledge Center
1575 I St., NW
Washington, DC 20005
Ph: (202)326-9559
Fax: (202)842-1109
Co. E-mail: knowledgecenter@asaecenter.org
URL: http://www.asaecenter.org/Resources/Knowl-edgeCenter.cfm?navItemNumber=14973
Scope: Association management - law, communications, human resources, conventions, education, vol-untarism, finance, membership promotion, government relations, International affair chapter relations, marketing. **Services:** Library open to the public by appointment. **Founded:** 1954. **Holdings:** 2000 books and research publications; 20 VF drawers containing samples of association management materials. **Subscriptions:** 60 journals and other serials.

START-UP INFORMATION

1478 ▪ *202 Things You Can Buy and Sell for Big Profits*
Pub: Entrepreneur Press
Ed: James Stephenson; Jason R. Rich. **Released:** July 2008. **Price:** $19.95. **Description:** Become an entrepreneur at selling new and used products. This handbook will help individuals cash in on the boom in reselling new and used products online. A new section defines ways to set realistic goals while distinguishing between 'get-rich schemes' and long term, viable businesses. A discussion about targeting and reaching the right customer base is included, along with finding and obtaining the service support needed for starting a new business.

1479 ▪ *"Auction Company Grows with Much Smaller Sites" in Automotive News (Vol. 86, October 31, 2011, No. 6488, pp. 23)*
Pub: Crain Communications Inc.
Ed: Arlena Sawyers. **Description:** Auction Broadcasting Company has launched auction sites and is expanding into new areas. The family-owned business will provide auctions half the size traditionally used. The firm reports that 40 percent of the General Motors factory-owned vehicles sold on consignment were purchased by online buyers, up 30 percent over 2010.

1480 ▪ *Complete Idiot's Guide to Starting an Ebay Business*
Pub: Penguin Books USA Inc.
Ed: Barbara Weltman, Malcolm Katt. **Released:** February 2008. **Price:** $19.95 (US), $29.00 (Canadian). **Description:** Guide for starting an eBay business includes information on products to sell, how to price merchandise, and details for working with services like PayPal, and how to organize fulfillment services.

1481 ▪ *eBay Business the Smart Way*
Pub: AMACOM
Ed: Joseph T. Sinclair. **Released:** June 6, 2007. **Price:** $17.95. **Description:** eBay commands ninety percent of all online auction business. Computer and software expert and online entrepreneur shares information to help online sellers get started and move merchandise on eBay. Tips include the best ways to build credibility, find products to sell, manage inventory, create a storefront Website, and more.

1482 ▪ *EBay Business Start-up Kit: 100s of Live Links to All the Information and Tools You Need*
Pub: NOLO
Ed: Richard Stim. **Released:** July 2008. **Price:** $24.99. **Description:** Interactive kit that connects user directly to EBay is presented.

1483 ▪ *EBay Income: How ANYONE of Any Age, Location, and/or Background Can Build a Highly Profitable Online Business with eBay*
Pub: Atlantic Publishing Company
Released: December 1, 2010. **Price:** $24.95. **Description:** A complete overview of eBay is given and guides any small company through the entire process

of creating the auction and auction strategies, photography, writing copy, text and formatting, multiple sales, programming tricks, PayPal, accounting, creating marketing, merchandising, managing email lists, advertising plans, taxes and sales tax, best time to list items and for how long, sniping programs, international customers, opening a storefront, electronic commerce, buy-it now pricing, keywords, Google marketing and eBay secrets.

1484 ▪ *"Power Up" in Entrepreneur (Vol. 35, November 2007, No. 11, pp. 140)*
Pub: Entrepreneur Media Inc.
Ed: Amanda C. Kooser. **Description:** PowerSeller is a status in the Internet company eBay, wherein sellers average at least $1,000 in sales per month for three consecutive months. There are five tiers in the PowerSeller status, which ranges from Bronze to Titanium. Launching startups at eBay can help entrepreneurs pick up a wide customer base, but getting and maintaining PowerSeller status is a challenge.

1485 ▪ *Start Your Own Business on eBay, 2nd Edition*
Pub: Entrepreneur Press
Ed: Jacquelyn Lynn. **Released:** May 2007. **Price:** $19.95. **Description:** Tips for starring a new online business on eBay are shared.

1486 ▪ *Starting an Ebay Business for Canadians for Dummies*
Pub: John Wiley & Sons, Incorporated
Ed: Marsha Collier; Bill Summers. **Released:** February 2007. **Price:** $35.99. **Description:** Tips for turning a hobby into a successful online eBay company.

ASSOCIATIONS AND OTHER ORGANIZATIONS

1487 ▪ **Livestock Marketing Association (LMA)**
10510 NW Ambassador Dr.
Kansas City, MO 64153
Ph: (816)891-0502
Free: 800-821-2048
Fax: (816)891-7926
Co. E-mail: lmainfo@lmaweb.com
URL: http://www.lmaweb.com
Contact: David Macedo, President
URL(s): www.lmaauctions.com. **Description:** Livestock marketing businesses and livestock dealers. Sponsors annual World Livestock Auctioneer Championships. Offers management and promotional services. **Founded:** 1947.

1488 ▪ **National Auctioneers Association (NAA)**
8880 Ballentine St.
Overland Park, KS 66214
Ph: (913)541-8084
Fax: (913)894-5281
Co. E-mail: support@auctioneers.org
URL: http://www.auctioneers.org
Contact: Christie King, President
E-mail: cking@ckingbenefits.com
Description: Professional auctioneers. Provides continuing education classes for auctioneers, pro-

motes use of the auction method of marketing in both the private and public sectors. Encourages the highest ethical standards for the profession. **Founded:** 1949. **Publications:** *IAL Auction Newsletter | Auctionier; The Auctioneer; Auctioneer--Directory Issue* (Annual). **Educational Activities:** National Auctioneers Association National Convention (Annual). **Awards:** Marketing Competition; International Auctioneers Championship; Hall of Fame Award. **Telecommunication Services:** aucmktinst@aol.com.

1489 ▪ **National Auto Auction Association (NAAA)**
5320 Spectrum Dr., Ste. D
Frederick, MD 21703
Ph: (301)696-0400
Fax: (301)631-1359
Co. E-mail: naaa@naaa.com
URL: http://www.naaa.com
Contact: Charlotte Pyle, President
Description: Owners/operators of wholesale automobile and truck auctions; associate members are car and truck manufacturers, insurers of checks and titles, car and truck rental companies, publishers of auto price guide books, and others connected with the industry. Maintains hall of fame. **Founded:** 1948. **Publications:** *National Auto Auction Association--Membership Directory* (Annual); *On the Block* (Quarterly). **Educational Activities:** Convention and Equipment and Services Exposition (Annual); National Auto Auction Association Annual Convention and Equipments and Services Exposition (Annual). **Awards:** Hall of Fame (Annual).

REFERENCE WORKS

1490 ▪ *"3.4 Million Votes Cast in 2011 eBay Motors People's Pick Poll - Winners Announced at SEMA Show" in Benzinga.com (, 2011)*
Pub: Benzinga.com
Ed: Benzinga Staff. **Description:** eBay Motors sponsored the 2011 People's Picks survey, an annual poll inviting car enthusiasts to vote on their favorite auto thing, ranging from the best camshaft, favorite ignition, to favorite muscle car. More than 3.4 million votes were counted this year. A complete profile of eBay Motors is also provided.

1491 ▪ *"Antwerpen Takes on Chrysler Financial Over Foreclosure Sales" in Baltimore Business Journal (Vol. 28, July 30, 2010, No. 12, pp. 1)*
Pub: Baltimore Business Journal
Ed: Gary Haber. **Description:** Antwerpen Motorcars Ltd. aims to fight the scheduled foreclosure sale of real estate it leases in Baltimore County, including the showroom for its Hyundai dealership on Baltimore National Pike in Catonsville, Maryland. The company is planning to file papers in court to stop the scheduled August 11, 2010 auction sought by Chrysler Financial Services Americas LLC.

1492 ▪ *"Auction-Rate Cash Frees Up" in The Business Journal-Portland (Vol. 25, August*

15, 2008, No. 23, pp. 1)
Pub: American City Business Journals, Inc.
Ed: Aliza Earnshaw. Description: FEI Co. and Radi-Sys Corp. have received notices that UBS AG will buy back the auction-rate securities that were sold to them in around two years from 2008. FEI had $110.1 million invested in auction-rate securities while Radi-Sys holds $62.8 million of these securities.

1493 ■ *Auctioneer--Directory Issue*
Pub: National Auctioneers Association
Contact: Christie King, President
E-mail: cking@ckingbenefits.com
URL(s): www.auctioneers.org. Released: Annual; February. Publication includes: List of about 6,000 auctioneers. Entries include: Name, address, phone, fax, e-mail, website, specialization. Arrangement: Geographical and alphabetical.

1494 ■ *"Auctions and Bidding: a Guide for Computer Scientists" in ACM Computing Surveys (Vol. 43, Summer 2011, No. 2, pp. 10)*
Pub: Association for Computing Machinery
Ed: Simon Parsons, Juan A. Rodriguez-Aguilar, Mark Klein. Description: There are various actions: single dimensional, multi-dimensional, single-sided, double-sided, first-price, second-price, English, Dutch, Japanese, sealed-bid, and these have been extensively discussed and analyzed in economics literature. This literature is surveyed from a computer science perspective, primarily from the viewpoint of computer scientists who are interested in learning about auction theory, and to provide pointers into the economics literature for those who want a deeper technical understanding. In addition, since auctions are an increasingly important topic in computer science, the article also looks at work on auctions from the computer science literature. The aim is to identify what both bodies of work tell us about creating electronic auctions.

1495 ■ *"B-N Pawn Shop Auctions Off Jimmy Hoffa's Rifle" in Pantagraph (September 14, 2010)*
Pub: The Pantagraph
Ed: Ryan Denham. Description: Midwest Exchange pawn shop located in IAA Drive in Bloomington, Illinois auctioned a rifle once belonging to Jimmy Hoffa.

1496 ■ *"Boots Treat Street Rolls Out Trolley Dash App on Androis and iPhone OS" in Entertainment Close-Up (October 24, 2011)*
Pub: Close-Up Media
Description: Shoppers using Boots Treat Street can now download the Trolley Dash app game, available from the Apple Store and the Android Market, and enjoy the pastel colored street featuring favorite retailers such as eBay, New Look and Play.com collecting prizes while avoiding hazards.

1497 ■ *"Brief: US-Business/eBay Earnings Rise 31 Per Cent" in Denver Post (July 21, 2011)*
Pub: The Denver Post
Ed: Andy Goldberg. Description: eBay's strong performance in second quarter 2011 is being attributed to Paypal online payments division. eBay's online auction sites reported gross merchandise volume up 34 percent. Statistical data included.

1498 ■ *"The Business Case for Mobile Content Acceleration" in Streaming Media (November 2011, pp. 78)*
Pub: Information Today Inc.
Ed: Dan Rayburn. Description: Last holiday season, eBay became a mobile commerce (m-commerce) giant when sales rose by 134 percent, as most online retailers offered customers the ability to purchase items using their mobile devices.

1499 ■ *"Cash in Your Attic: Is Your Junk Someone Else's Treasure?" in Black Enterprise (Vol. 37, November 2006, No. 4, pp. 156)*
Pub: Earl G. Graves Publishing Co. Inc.
Ed: Angela P. Moore-Thorpe. Description: Selling items accumulated over the years or purchased at auctions or garage sales can be a lucrative way to make extra cash. Advice and resources on auctions, collecting, and consignment shops included.

1500 ■ *"Channelside On the Blocks" in The Business Journal-Serving Greater Tampa Bay (Vol. 28, August 29, 2008, No. 36, pp. 1)*
Pub: American City Business Journals, Inc.
Ed: Michael Hinman. Description: In a bankruptcy auction for The Place, one of the more visible condominium projects at Channelside, the lowest bid is just below $73 a square foot. KeyBank National Association, the Key Developers Group LLC's lender, leads the auction planned for October 15, 2008. The reason behind the low minimum bid required to participate in the said action is discussed.

1501 ■ *"Coastal Luxury Management Reports Los Angeles Food and Wine Tickets On Sale" in Food & Beverage Close-Up (August 24, 2011)*
Pub: Close-Up Media
Description: Wolfgang Puck's Sunday Brunch and Charity Auction will raise money for Saint Vincent Meals on Wheels program.

1502 ■ *"Condo Markdown" in Boston Business Journal (Vol. 27, November 30, 2007, No. 44, pp. 1)*
Pub: American City Business Journals Inc.
Ed: Michelle Hillman. Description: Boston real estate market is softening, and condominium developers such as Beacon Communities LLC are sending out various incentives like markdowns and unit upgrades. Developers have also held auctions and even offered brand new cars to lure buyers. Other perks being offered by various Boston developers are discussed.

1503 ■ *"The Data Drivers" in Canadian Business (Vol. 81, September 15, 2008, No. 14-15, pp. 1)*
Pub: Rogers Media Ltd.
Ed: Andrew Wahl. Description: Canadian regulators hope that an auction of telecommunications companies will inject more competition into the industry; however, newcomers may not be able to rely on lower prices in order to gain market share from the three major telecommunications companies that already have a stronghold on the market. Analysts feel that providing additional data service is the key to surviving market disruptions.

1504 ■ *"Dollar General Selects GSI Commerce to Launch Its eCommerce Business" in Benzinga.com (October 29, 2011)*
Pub: Benzinga.com
Ed: Benzinga Staff. Description: Dollar General Corporation chose GSI Commerce, a leading provider of ecommerce and interactive marketing solutions, to launch its online initiative. GSI Commerce is an eBay Inc. company.

1505 ■ *"eBay Business Looking Up" in Zacks (July 26, 2011)*
Pub: Comtex News Network Inc.
Ed: Sejuti Banerjea. Description: eBay reported solid revenue growth for 2011 second quarter, keeping in line with the Zacks Consensus Estimate, and third quarter earnings are expected to be higher. eBay's new strategy is to direct traffic to bigger sellers with improved customer service, making this good for eBay businesses.

1506 ■ *"EBay Finally Gaining Traction in China" in San Jose Mercury News (October 26, 2011)*
Pub: San Jose Mercury News
Ed: John Boudreau. Description: eBay has developed a new strategy in China that allows exporters of every type of merchandise to sell directly to eBays 97 million overseas users.

1507 ■ *"eBay Inc. Completes Acquisition of Zong" in Benzinga.com (October 29, 2011)*
Pub: Benzinga.com
Ed: Benzinga Staff. Description: eBay Inc. acquired Zong, a provider of payments through mobile carrier billing. Terms of the agreement are outlined.

1508 ■ *"eBay Introduces Open Commerce Ecosystem" in Entertainment Close-Up (October 24, 2011)*
Pub: Close-Up Media
Description: eBay's new X.commerce is an open commerce ecosystem that will arm developers and merchants with the technology tools required to keep pace with the ever-changing industry. X.commerce brings together the technology assets and developer communities of eBay, PayPal, Magento and partners to expand on eBays vision for enabling commerce.

1509 ■ *"eBay and Jonathan Adler Team to Launch 'The eBay Inspiration Shop" in Entertainment Close-Up (October 25, 2011)*
Pub: Close-Up Media
Description: Designer Jonathan Adler partnered with eBay to create a collection of new must-have merchandise for the fall season. Top trendsetters, including actors, designers, bloggers, stylists, editors, photographers, models and musicians helped curate the items being featured in the windows by sharing their shopping wish lists with users.

1510 ■ *The Ebay Seller's Tax and Legal Answer Book*
Pub: AMACOM
Ed: Cliff Ennico. Released: April 30, 2007. Price: $19.95. Description: Helps sellers using Ebay to file taxes properly, while saving money.

1511 ■ *Ebay the Smart Way: Selling, Burying, and Profiting on the Web's Number One Auction Site*
Pub: AMACOM
Ed: Joseph T. Sinclair. Released: May 2007. Price: $17.95. Description: Resource to help individuals sell, buy and profit using the Internet auction site Ebay.

1512 ■ *"Facebook, Adobe, Kenshoo, Outright and Cignex Datamatics Sign On to X.commerce" in Entertainment Close-Up (October 24, 2011)*
Pub: Close-Up Media
Description: Facebook, Adobe, Kenshoo, Outright and Cignex Datamatics have all partnered with X.commerce's ecosystem, where developers build and merchants can come to shop for new technologies and services.

1513 ■ *"Fifty Percent of Global Online Retail Visits Were to Amazon, eBay and Alibaba in June 2011" in Benzinga.com (October 29, 2011)*
Pub: Benzinga.com
Ed: Benzinga Staff. Description: Current statistics and future forecasts through the year 2015 for Amazon, eBay and Alibaba are explored.

1514 ■ *"Former Schaefer and Strohminger Dealerships to Hit Auction Block" in Baltimore Business Journal (Vol. 28, September 10, 2010)*
Pub: Baltimore Business Journal
Ed: Gary Haber. Description: Maryland's real estate developers have a chance to vie for almost 11 acres of prime Baltimore County real estate that are on the auction block. The five properties were once home to Schaefer and Strohminger car dealerships and were located in the county's busiest areas. Other potential uses for the properties are also discussed.

1515 ■ *"Get Sold On eBay" in Entrepreneur (Vol. 36, March 2008, No. 3, pp. 94)*
Pub: Entrepreneur Media Inc.
Ed: Marcia Layton Turner. Description: Entrepreneurs are increasingly using eBay to sell products. Some tips to start selling products through eBay include: starting with used items, developing a niche to sell specific products, and researching product pricing. Other tips with regard to starting an eBay business are covered.

1516 ■ *"Hedge-Fund Titan Cohen Plans Bid for Dodgers" in Wall Street Journal Eastern*

Edition (November 25 , 2011, pp. C3)
Pub: Dow Jones & Company Inc. Enterprise Media Group
Contact: Clare Hart, President

Ed: Matthew Futterman, Gregory Zuckerman. **Description:** Steven A. Cohen, the founder and head of hedge-fund SAC Capital Advisors LLC is looking to make an offer at the bankruptcy auction for the financially-troubled Los Angeles Dodgers baseball team.

1517 ■ *"HER's: the Future is Free" in Benzinga.com (October 29, 2011)*
Pub: Benzinga.com

Ed: Benzinga Staff. **Description:** In order to create and maintain electronic health records that connects every physician and hospital it is essential to create a reliable, easy-to-use, certified Web-based ambulatory ERH using an ad-supported model. eBay seems to be the company showing the most potential for improving services to physicians and consumers, but requires sellers to pay fees based upon sales price.

1518 ■ *"High-End Jeweler Loses Street Sparkle" in Houston Business Journal (Vol. 40, November 27, 2009, No. 29, pp. 1)*
Pub: American City Business Journals

Ed: Allison Wollam. **Description:** High-end jeweler Bailey Banks & Biddle's 7,000 square foot prototype store in Houston, Texas' CityCentre will be ceasing operations despite its parent company's filing for Chapter 11 protection from creditors. According to the bankruptcy filing, parent company Finlay Enterprises Inc. of New York intends to auction off its business and assets. Finlay has 67 Bailey Banks locations throughout the US.

1519 ■ *"Luxe Hotels on a Budget" in Inc. (Volume 32, December 2010, No. 10, pp. 60)*
Pub: Inc. Magazine

Ed: Adam Baer. **Description:** Off & Away Website allows users to vie for discounted hotel rooms at more than 100 luxury properties. To compete, uses buy $1 bids and each time an individual bids the price of the room goes up by 10 cents.

1520 ■ *National Auto Auction Association--Membership Directory*
Pub: National Auto Auction Association
Contact: Charlotte Pyle, President

URL(s): www.naaa.com. **Released:** Annual; Latest edition 2011. **Price:** $15; $15, Members; $35, Nonmembers. **Covers:** 25,446 automobile auction firms. **Entries include:** Company name, address, names and phone numbers of auction personnel; pick up, delivery, and reconditioning services available. **Arrangement:** Geographical.

1521 ■ *"Online Reverse Auctions: Common Myths Versus Evolving Reality" in Business Horizons (September-October 2007, pp. 373)*
Pub: Elsevier Technology Publications

Ed: Tobias Schoenherr, Vincent A. Mabert. **Description:** Common misconceptions about online reverse auctions are examined based on the data obtained from 30 case study companies. Strategies for maintaining a good buyer-supplier relationship and implications for firms and supply managers are presented.

1522 ■ *"The Open Mobile Summit Opens in San Francisco Today: John Donahoe CEO eBay to Keynote" in Benzinga.com (November 2, 2011)*
Pub: Benzinga.com

Ed: Benzinga Staff. **Description:** eBay's CEO, John Donahoe was keynote speaker at the 4th Annual Open Mobile Summit held in San Francisco, California. eBay is one of the 130 companies participating as speakers at the event.

1523 ■ *"Points of Light Sells MissionFish to eBay" in Non-Profit Times (Vol. 25, May 15,*

2011, No. 7, pp. May 15, 2011)
Pub: NPT Publishing Group Inc.
Contact: John McIlquham, President

Description: eBay purchased MissionFish, a subsidiary of Points of Light Institute for $4.5 million. MissionFish allows eBay sellers to give proceeds from sales to their favorite nonprofit organization and helps nonprofits raise funds by selling on eBay.

1524 ■ *"Pro Livestock Launches Most Comprehensive Virtual Sales Barn for Livestock and Breed Stock" in Benzinga.com (October 29, 2011)*
Pub: Benzinga.com

Ed: Benzinga Staff. **Description:** Pro Livestock Marketing launched the first online sales portal for livestock and breed stock. The firm has designed a virtual sales barn allowing individuals to purchase and sell cattle, swine, sheep, goats, horses, rodeo stock, show animals, specialty animals, semen and embryos globally. It is like an eBay for livestock and will help ranchers and farmers grow.

1525 ■ *"Ritchie Bros. Breaks Record for Internet Sales at Fort Worth Site During Multi-Million Dollar Unreserved Auction" in Canadian Corporate News*
Pub: Comtex News Network Inc.

Description: Ritchie Bros. Auctioneers, the world's largest auctioneer of trucks and industrial equipment, conducted a large unreserved auction at its permanent auction facility in Fort Worth, Texas, in which the company broke the record for Internet sales with bidders using the company's online bidding service, rbauctionBid-Live. Internet bidders purchased more than 440 lots in the auction.

1526 ■ *The Secret of Exiting Your Business Under Your Terms!*
Pub: Outskirts Press, Incorporated

Ed: Gene H. Irwin. **Released:** August 2005. **Price:** $29.95. **Description:** Topics include how to sell a business for the highest value, tax laws governing the sale of a business, finding the right buyer, mergers and acquisitions, negotiating the sale, and using a limited auction to increase future value of a business.

1527 ■ *Selling Online: Canada's Bestselling Guide to Becoming a Successful E-Commerce Merchant*
Pub: John Wiley and Sons Canada Ltd.

Ed: Jim Carroll; Rick Broadhead. **Released:** September 6, 2002. **Description:** Helps individuals build online retail enterprises; this updated version includes current tools, information and success strategies, how to launch an online storefront, security, marketing strategies, and mistakes to avoid.

1528 ■ *"Shoppes of Kenwood Files Chap. 11" in Business Courier (Vol. 26, December 18, 2009, No. 34, pp. 1)*
Pub: American City Business Journals, Inc.

Ed: Jon Newberry. **Description:** Shoppes of Kenwood filed for Chapter 11 reorganization in US Bankruptcy Court just as the property was scheduled to be offered at a sheriff's auction. Details of the filing are included.

1529 ■ *"Tim Tebow Foundation to Hold Pink 'Cleats for a Cure' Auction" in Travel & Leisure Close-Up (October 20, 2011)*
Pub: Close-Up Media

Description: Tim Tebow Foundation partnered with XV Enterprises to hold the 'Cleats for a Cure' auction on eBay. Tebow is auctioning off a pair of pink cleans he wore during the Denver Broncos vs. Tennessee Titans game October 3, 2010. All funds will go toward finding a cure for breast cancer.

1530 ■ *Titanium EBay: A Tactical Guide to Becoming a Millionaire PowerSeller*
Pub: Penguin Group Incorporated

Ed: Skip McGrath. **Released:** June 2006. **Price:** $24.95. **Description:** Advice is given to help anyone selling items on eBay to become a Power Seller, an award presented based on monthly gross merchandise sales.

1531 ■ *"Treasuries Rally Despite Huge Supply" in Barron's (Vol. 89, July 13, 2009, No. 28, pp. M10)*
Pub: Dow Jones & Co., Inc.

Ed: Randall W. Forsyth. **Description:** Prices of U.S. Treasuries were sent higher and their yields lower despite four auctions of coupon securities because of the strong appetite for government securities around the world. The reopening of the 10-year note in the week ending July 10, 2009 drew the strongest bidding since 1995.

1532 ■ *"Understanding Persuasive Online Sales Messages from eBay Auctions" in Business Communication Quarterly (December 2007, pp. 482)*
Pub: SAGE Publications USA
Contact: Blaise R. Simqu, President

Ed: Barbara Jo White, Daniel Clapper, Rita Noel, Jenny Fortier, Pierre Grabolosa. **Description:** eBay product listings were studied to determine the requirements of persuasive sales writing. Potential sellers should use the proper keywords and make an authentic description with authentic photographs of the item being auctioned.

1533 ■ *"Young Entrepreneur Gets Some Recognition and Some Help for College" in Philadelphia Inquirer (August 30, 2010)*
Pub: Philadelphia Inquirer

Ed: Susan Snyder. **Description:** Profile of Zachary Gosling, age 18, who launched an online auction Website from his bedroom, using advertising and sponsorship funds rather than charging fees to users.

TRADE PERIODICALS

1534 ■ *The Auctioneer*
Pub: National Auctioneers Association
Contact: Christie King, President
E-mail: cking@ckingbenefits.com
URL(s): www.auctioneers.org/advertise. **Released:** 10/yr.

1535 ■ *IAL Auction Newsletter / Auctionier*
Pub: National Auctioneers Association
Contact: Christie King, President
E-mail: cking@ckingbenefits.com

Ed: Ann Wood, Editor. **Released:** Quarterly. **Price:** Included in membership. **Description:** Promotes the educational activities of the Institute. Carries miscellaneous items of interest to member auctioneers and for candidates for membership. Recurring features include notices of courses and seminars.

TRADE SHOWS AND CONVENTIONS

1536 ■ *National Auctioneers Association National Convention*
National Auctioneers Association (NAA)
8880 Ballentine St.
Overland Park, KS 66214
Ph: (913)541-8084
Fax: (913)894-5281
Co. E-mail: support@auctioneers.org
URL: http://www.auctioneers.org
Contact: Christie King, President
E-mail: cking@ckingbenefits.com
URL(s): www.auctioneers.org. **Frequency:** Annual. **Principal Exhibits:** Auctioneering equipment, supplies, and services.

FRANCHISES AND BUSINESS OPPORTUNITIES

1537 ■ *Certigard*
Petro Canada
2489 N Sheridan Way
Mississauga, ON, Canada L5K 1A8
Free: 888-541-7632
Fax: (905)804-4898
Co. E-mail: hupponen@petro-canada.ca
URL: http://www.petro-canada.ca
Description: Offers car repair franchise. **No. of Franchise Units:** 105. **Founded:** 1987.. **Equity Capital Needed:** $75,000 minimum, business development fee 2%, warranty fee 0.2%. **Franchise Fee:** $25,000. **Training:** Yes.

ASSOCIATIONS AND OTHER ORGANIZATIONS

1538 ■ Association of Automotive Aftermarket Distributors/Parts Plus (AAAD)
3085 Fountainside Dr., No. 210
Germantown, TN 38138
Free: 800-727-8112
Fax: (901)682-9098
Co. E-mail: info@networkhq.org
URL: http://www.partsplus.com
Contact: Bob Barstow, Liaison
Description: Represents the independent automotive warehouse distributors. Purchases and markets automotive replacement parts through wholesale/retail auto parts stores. Conducts marketing activities. **Founded:** 1977. **Publications:** *Network*; *Parts Plus Magazine* (Bimonthly); *Car Care Center*.

1539 ■ Auto International Association (AIA)
7101 Wisconsin Ave., Ste. 1300
Bethesda, MD 20814
Ph: (301)654-6664
Fax: (301)654-3299
Co. E-mail: aia@aftermarket.org
URL: http://aftermarket.org/Segments/AIA
Contact: Stephen Bearden, Chairman
Description: Manufacturers/importers, distributors/retailers, subcontractors and manufacturers' representatives supporting the import automotive aftermarket products industry. Works to promote and protect the interests of the import auto and accessories industry. Offers Import Parts Specialist certification program for sales personnel. Produces annual AIA World Auto Parts Conference. Compiles statistics. **Founded:** 1983. **Publications:** *AIA Facts* (Biweekly). **Educational Activities:** Auto International Association Show (Annual); World Auto Parts.

1540 ■ Auto Suppliers Benchmarking Association (ASBA)
4606 FM 1960 W, Ste. 250
Houston, TX 77069-9949
Ph: (281)440-5044
Fax: (281)440-6677
URL: http://www.asbabenchmarking.com
Description: Automotive supplier firms with an interest in benchmarking. Promotes the use of benchmarking, wherein businesses compare their processes with those of their competitors, as a means of improving corporate efficiency and profitability. Facilitates exchange of information among members; conducts target operations, procurement, development, and maintenance studies; identifies model business practices. **Founded:** 1996.

1541 ■ Automotive Service Association (ASA)
PO Box 929
Bedford, TX 76095-0929
Ph: (817)283-6205
Free: 800-272-7467
Fax: (817)685-0225
Co. E-mail: asainfo@asashop.org
URL: http://www.asashop.org
Contact: Ron Pyle, President
Description: Automotive service businesses including body, paint, and trim shops, engine rebuilders, radiator shops, brake and wheel alignment services, transmission shops, tune-up services, and air conditioning services; associate members are manufacturers and wholesalers of automotive parts, and the trade press. Represents independent business owners and managers before private agencies and national and state legislative bodies. Promotes confidence between consumer and the automotive service industry, safety inspection of motor vehicles, and better highways. **Founded:** 1951. **Publications:** *AutoInc.* (Monthly). **Educational Activities:** Congress of Automotive Repair and Service (Annual); International Autobody Congress and Exposition (Annual); International Autobody Congress and Exposition - NACE (Annual).

1542 ■ Automotive Warehouse Distributors Association
7101 Wisconsin Ave., Ste. 1300
Bethesda, MD 20814
Ph: (301)654-6664
Fax: (301)654-3299
Co. E-mail: info@awda.org
Contact: Kathleen Schmatz, President
Description: Warehouse distributors of automotive parts and supplies; manufacturers of automotive parts and suppliers; jobbers, business services, major program groups. **Scope:** aftermarket management resources. **Publications:** *Aftermarket Insider* (Bimonthly); *Facts*; *AAIA SmartBrief* (Biweekly); *Leadership Directory* (Annual); *Aftermarket Insider*; *APAA Who's Who* (Annual); *Foreign Buyers Directory* (Annual); *Life in the Fast Lane: Careers in the Automotive Aftermarket*. **Educational Activities:** Automotive Aftermarket Products Expo (Annual). **Awards:** AVI Scholarships; Florida Automotive Industry Scholarships; Industry Leadership Award (Annual); Automotive Leader of the Year (Annual); Martin Fromm Lifetime Achievement Award (Annual); Memorial Scholarship Award (Annual); Pursuit of Excellence Awards (Annual); Tom Babcox Memorial Scholarships; Richard Cossette/Gale Memorial Scholarships; APSAIL's Ralph Silverman Memorial Scholarships; Sloan Northwood University Heavy-Duty Scholarships. **Telecommunication Services:** info@aftermarket.org; aaia@aftermarket.org.

1543 ■ Motor and Equipment Manufacturers Association (MEMA)
10 Laboratory Dr.
Research Triangle Park, NC 27709
Ph: (919)549-4800
Fax: (919)406-1465
Co. E-mail: info@mema.org
URL: http://www.mema.org
Contact: Robert E. McKenna, President
Description: Manufacturers of automotive and heavy-duty original equipment and aftermarket components, maintenance equipment, chemicals, accessories, refinishing supplies, tools, and service equipment united for research into all aspects of the automotive and heavy-duty markets. Provides manufacturer-oriented services and programs including marketing consultation for the automotive industry; federal and state legal, safety, and legislative representation and consultation; personnel services; manpower development workshops; international information. **Founded:** 1904. **Publications:** *Market Analysis* (Bimonthly); *Automotive Industry Status Report* (Annual); *Car Maintenance in the U.S.A.*; *Credit and Sales Reference Directory* (3/year); *Sales Force Compensation and Benefits Practice* (Annual); *AAPEX Export Interest Directory: 2008*; *International Buyers Guide of U.S. Automotive and Heavy Duty Products for Export* (Biennial). **Educational Activities:** Heavy Duty Dialogue Conference (Biennial); Motor and Equipment Manufacturers Association Seminar (Biennial). **Awards:** Triangle Award; Triangle Award (Periodic).

1544 ■ National Truck Equipment Association (NTEA)
37400 Hills Tech Dr.
Farmington Hills, MI 48331-3414
Ph: (248)489-7090
Free: 800-441-6832
Fax: (248)489-8590
Co. E-mail: info@ntea.com
URL: http://www.ntea.com
Contact: Steven Sill, President
E-mail: ssill@aspeneq.com
Description: Serves as a trade group for commercial truck, truck body, truck equipment, trailer and accessory manufacturers and distributors. Advises members of current federal regulations affecting the manufacturing and installation of truck bodies and equipment; works to enhance the professionalism of management and improve profitability in the truck equipment business. **Scope:** commercial truck industry, fleet and utility, association industries. **Founded:** 1964. **Subscriptions:** periodicals. **Publications:** *Excise Tax Bulletin* (Periodic); *Membership Roster and Product Directory* (Annual); *NTEA News* (Monthly); *Truck Equipment Handbook*; *NTEA Technical Report* (Periodic); *Membership Roster and Product Directory* (Annual); *NTEA News* (Monthly); *National Truck Equipment Association--Market Resource Guide* (Annual). **Educational Activities:** The Work Truck Show and Annual NTEA Convention (Annual).

1545 ■ Specialty Equipment Market Association (SEMA)
1575 S Valley Vista Dr.
Diamond Bar, CA 91765-0910
Ph: (909)396-0289
Fax: (909)860-1709
Co. E-mail: sema@sema.org
URL: http://www.sema.org
Contact: Chris Kersting, President
E-mail: chrisk@sema.org
Description: Manufacturers, retailers, sales representatives, distributors, motorsports sanctioning groups and other firms related to the automotive high performance and custom vehicle industry. Represents the industry to governmental agencies and consumer groups. Coordinates and conducts research; assists

in writing of regulations and codes; collects and disseminates information; compiles statistics. **Founded:** 1963. **Publications:** *SEMA News*; *Fast Facts* (Monthly); *SEMA News* (Monthly); *SEMA News.* **Educational Activities:** Australian Automotive Trade Fair (AATF) (Annual); The Hot Rod and Restoration Trade Show; SEMA International Auto Salon (Annual); SEMA Show (Annual). **Awards:** Loan Forgiveness Scholarships; Specialty Equipment Market Association Scholarships; Manufacturers' Representative of the Year (Annual); Person of the Year (Annual); SEMA Hall of Fame Award (Annual); Warehouse Distributor of the Year (Annual).

REFERENCE WORKS

1546 ■ "3.4 Million Votes Cast in 2011 eBay Motors People's Pick Poll - Winners Announced at SEMA Show" in Benzinga.com (, 2011)
Pub: Benzinga.com
Ed: Benzinga Staff. **Description:** eBay Motors sponsored the 2011 People's Picks survey, an annual poll inviting car enthusiasts to vote on their favorite auto thing, ranging from the best camshaft, favorite ignition, to favorite muscle car. More than 3.4 million votes were counted this year. A complete profile of eBay Motors is also provided.

1547 ■ "All Revved Up" in Barron's (Vol. 90, September 13, 2010, No. 37, pp. 18)
Pub: Barron's Editorial & Corporate Headquarters
Ed: Christopher C. Williams. **Description:** Shares of Advance Auto Parts has returned 55 percent in a span of three years and the stock could still reach the mid-60s by 2011 from its price of 46.07 in the second week of September 2010. The shares are trading at just 13 times the 2011 earnings.

1548 ■ "American Axle Sues to Force Steelmaker to Resume Suspended Parts Shipment" in Crain's Detroit Business (Vol. 25, June 15, 2009)
Pub: Crain Communications Inc. - Detroit
Ed: Robert Sherefkin. **Description:** American Axle & Manufacturing Holdings Inc. is facing a shutdown if a Michigan court does not force Republic Engineered Products Inc., a specialty steelmaker, to ship parts. If the parts are not shipped, it could cause assembly plants to shutdown.

1549 ■ "Auto Bankruptcies Could Weaken Defense" in Crain's Detroit Business (Vol. 25, June 8, 2009, No. 23, pp. 1)
Pub: Crain Communications Inc. - Detroit
Ed: Chad Halcom. **Description:** Bankruptcy and supplier consolidation of General Motors Corporation and Chrysler LLC could interfere with the supply chains of some defense contractors, particularly makers of trucks and smaller vehicles.

1550 ■ Automotive Warehouse Distributors Association--Membership Directory
URL(s): www.aftermarket.org/Segments/awda.aspx.
Released: Annual; March. **Covers:** Over 200 automotive parts distributors, 300 manufacturers of automotive parts, and marketing associations, manufacturer representatives, and affiliate members. **Entries include:** Company name, address, phone, names of key personnel, products distributed or manufactured, territories served, number and location of branches. **Arrangement:** Alphabetical. **Indexes:** Geographical.

1551 ■ "Detroit 3's Fall Would Be a Big One in Ohio" in Business First Columbus (Vol. 25, November 28, 2008, No. 14, pp. A1)
Pub: American City Business Journals
Ed: Dan Eaton. **Description:** Ohio's economy will suffer huge negative effects in the event of a failure of one or more of the automotive companies, General Motors Corporation, Ford Motor Company, or Chrysler LLC. The state is home to 97,900 jobs in the automotive industry and is a vital link to the industry's supply network.

1552 ■ Directory of Automotive Aftermarket Suppliers
Pub: Chain Store Guide
Contact: Lisa Patterson, President
URL(s): www.csgis.com/csgis-frontend. **Ed:** Arthur Rosenberg. **Released:** Annual; October. **Price:** $365,

Individuals. **Covers:** Approximately 1,900 Auto Aftermarket retailers/jobbers; over 1,000 auto parts warehouse distributors; and 100 marine retailers in the United States and Canada, with annual sales of at least $250,000. Included retailers operate approximately 29,500 stores. **Entries include:** For retailers only--fax number, company e-mail address, sales by customer type, percentage of products installed, total selling square footage, total units, units by trade name, projected openings and remodeling, and average number of checkouts. For distributors only--services provided. For retailers and distributors--company name; physical address; mailing address; company web site address; Internet order processing indicator; listing type; trading areas; distribution center locations; programmed distribution group name and location; year founded; public company indicator; parent company name and location; regional, divisional, and branch office locations; and key personnel with titles. **Arrangement:** Geographical. **Indexes:** Product line, alphabetical.

1553 ■ "Greening the Auto Industry" in Business Journal-Serving Phoenix & the Valley of the Sun (Vol. 30, July 23, 2010, No. 46, pp. 1)
Pub: Phoenix Business Journal
Ed: Patrick O'Grady. **Description:** Thermo Fluids Inc. has been recycling used oil products since 1993 and could become Arizona's first home for oil filter recycling after retrofitting its Phoenix facility to include a compaction machine. The new service could help establish Thermo Fluids as a recycling hub for nearby states.

1554 ■ "Japan-Brand Shortages Will Linger Into '12" in Automotive News (Vol. 86, October 31, 2011, No. 6488, pp. 1)
Pub: Crain Communications Inc.
Ed: Amy Wilson, Mark Rechtin. **Description:** Floods in Thailand and the tsunami in Japan have caused shortages of Japanese-brand vehicle parts. These shortages are expected to linger into 2012.

1555 ■ "Local Auto Suppliers Upbeat as Detroit 3's Prospects Trend Up" in Crain's Cleveland Business (Vol. 30, June 8, 2009, No. 22, pp. 1)
Pub: Crain Communications, Inc.
Ed: Dan Shingler. **Description:** According to the Center for Automotive Research located in Ann Arbor, Michigan, if Detroit automakers can hold their market share, they will end up producing more vehicles as the market recovers.

1556 ■ "Local Dealers Fear Shortages in Car Supply" in Boston Business Journal (Vol. 29, May 13, 2011, No. 1, pp. 1)
Pub: American City Business Journals Inc.
Ed: Scott Dance. **Description:** The earthquake and tsunami in Japan are seen to impact the automobile dealers in Baltimore, Maryland. Automobile supply in the area is seen to decrease dramatically during the summer sales season. Shortage of transmission parts and paint colors is also forecasted.

1557 ■ "On a Roll" in Canadian Business (Vol. 79, Winter 2006, No. 24, pp. 49)
Pub: Rogers Media
Ed: Thomas Watson. **Description:** The efforts of the Canadian automobile spare parts manufacturer, Magna International Inc., to expand into the the Russian market, are described.

1558 ■ "Reply! Grows at Unprecedented Rate, Rips Beta Off Its Marketplace" in Marketing Weekly News (September 19, 2009, pp. 149)
Pub: Investment Weekly News
Description: Profile of Reply.com, a leader in locally-targeted Internet marketing, announced significant growth in terms of revenue, enhanced features and services and new categories since launching its beta Reply! Marketplace platform. Even in the face of an economic downturn, the company has posted over 50 percent revenue growth in the Real Estate and Automotive categories.

1559 ■ "Research Reports: How Analysts Size Up Companies" in Barron's (Vol. 88, July 14, 2008, No. 28, pp. M13)
Pub: Dow Jones & Co., Inc.
Ed: Anita Peltonen. **Description:** Shares of Bankrate and AutoZone both get a 'Buy' rating from analysts while Zions Bancorporation's shares are downgraded from 'Outperform' to 'Neutral'. The shares of Jet Blue Airline and Deckers Outdoor, a manufacturer of innovative footwear, are also rated and discussed. Statistical data included.

1560 ■ "Shifting Gears" in Business Journal-Serving Phoenix & the Valley of the Sun (Vol. 31, November 12, 2010, No. 10, pp. 1)
Pub: Phoenix Business Journal
Ed: Patrick O'Grady. **Description:** Automotive parts recyclers in Arizona are benefiting from the challenging national economic conditions as well as from the green movement. Recyclers revealed that customers prefer recycled parts more because they are cheaper and are more environmentally friendly. Other information about the automotive parts recycling industry is presented.

1561 ■ "Slimmer Interiros Make Small Cars Seem Big" in Automotive News (Vol. 86, October 31, 2011, No. 6488, pp. 16)
Pub: Crain Communications Inc.
Ed: David Sedgwick. **Description:** Cost-conscious buyers want luxury car amenities in their smaller vehicles, so automakers are rethinking interiors. Style, efficiency and value could be the next trend in vehicles.

1562 ■ "Steering Toward Profitability" in Black Enterprise (Vol. 41, December 2010, No. 5, pp. 72)
Pub: Earl G. Graves Publishing Co. Inc.
Ed: Alan Hughes. **Description:** Systems Electro Coating LLC had to make quick adjustments when auto manufacturers were in a slump. The minority father-daughter team discuss their strategies during the auto industry collapse.

1563 ■ "Suppliers May Follow Fiat" in Crain's Detroit Business (Vol. 25, June 15, 2009, No. 24, pp. 1)
Pub: Crain Communications Inc. - Detroit
Ed: Ryan Beene. **Description:** Italian suppliers to Fiat SpA are looking toward Detroit after the formation of Chrysler Group LLC, the Chrysler-Fiat partnership created from Chrysler's bankruptcy. The Italian American Alliance for Business and Technology is aware of two Italy-based powertrain component suppliers that are considering a move to Detroit.

1564 ■ Tire Review--Performance Tire and Custom Wheel Guide
Pub: Babcox
URL(s): www.babcox.com/magintro.htm#tr. **Ed:** Jim Smith. **Released:** Annual; March. **Publication includes:** List of about 15 custom wheel and performance tire manufacturers and marketers. **Entries include:** Manufacturer name, address, phone, names and titles of key personnel, wheel types and sizes, wheel accessories, email and web addresses.

1565 ■ "Wheatfield First Choice for Canadian Manufacturer" in Business First Buffalo (November 23, 2007, pp. 1)
Pub: American City Business Journals, Inc.
Ed: James Fink. **Description:** Niagara County Industrial Development Agency is preparing an enticement program that would lure automotive parts manufacturer Pop & Lock Corporation to shift manufacturing operations to Wheatfield, Niagara County, New York. The package includes job-training grants and assistance for acquiring new machinery. Details of the plan are included.

1566 ■ "ZF Revving Up Jobs, Growth" in Business Courier (Vol. 26, November 6, 2009, No. 28, pp. 1)
Pub: American City Business Journals, Inc.
Ed: Jon Newberry. **Description:** Proposed $96 million expansion of German-owned automotive supplier ZF Steering systems LLC is anticipated to generate

299 jobs in Boone County, Kentucky. ZF might invest $90 million in equipment, while the rest will go to building and improvements.

SOURCES OF SUPPLY

1567 ■ *Truck Cover and Tarp Association Membership Directory*

Industrial Fabrics Association International
Contact: Stephen M. Warner, Chief Executive Officer
E-mail: smwarner@ifai.com
URL(s): www.ifai.comwww.truckcover-tarp.org. **Released:** Annual; October. **Price:** Free. **Publication includes:** Listings of member companies that manufacture and supply material, equipment or services to the truck cover and tarpaulin industry. **Entries include:** name, address, phone, fax of company and names and titles of key personnel, along with descriptions of services and products. **Arrangement:** Geographical. **Indexes:** Alphabetical.

1568 ■ *Undercar Digest--Buyer's Guide Issue: The Sourcebook*

MD Publications Inc.
URL(s): www.mdpublications.com/md/mdproducts. htmwww.undercardigest.com. **Ed:** James R. Wilder. **Released:** Annual; Latest edition 2013. **Price:** $10, Individuals. **Publication includes:** List of automotive aftermarket manufacturers and suppliers of mufflers, exhaust pipes, brakes, chassis, steering, suspension, driveline, shop equipment and tools, and other products. **Entries include:** Company name, address, phone, fax, name and title of contact, products. **Arrangement:** Alphabetical. **Indexes:** Product, warehouse distributors, franchise headquarters.

STATISTICAL SOURCES

1569 ■ *The Motor Vehicle Parts Aftermarket*

Pub: Business Trend Analysts, Inc.
Released: 2005-2006. **Price:** $2195.00. **Description:** Profiles the motor vehicle parts aftermarket, covering tires, batteries, engines, brakes, cooling systems, and other replacement parts. Provides information on pricing, factors affecting demand, advertising, foreign trade, and distribution channels. Also contains profiles of leading marketers.

1570 ■ *RMA Annual Statement Studies*

Pub: Risk Management Association
Contact: Kevin M. Blakey, President
Released: Annual. **Price:** $175.00 2006-07 edition, $105.00. **Description:** Contains composite balance sheets and income statements for more than 360 industries, including the accounting, auditing, and bookkeeping industries. Also contains five years of comparative historical data for discerning trends. Includes 16 commonly used ratios, computed for most of the size groupings for nearly every industry.

1571 ■ *Standard & Poor's Industry Surveys*

Pub: Standard & Poor's Corp.
Released: Annual. **Price:** $3633.00. **Description:** Two-volume book that examines the prospects for specific industries, including trucking. Also provides analyses of trends and problems, statistical tables and charts, and comparative company analyses.

TRADE PERIODICALS

1572 ■ *Aftermarket Insider*

Pub: Automotive Warehouse Distributors Association
Contact: Kathleen Schmatz, President
Ed: Jennifer Ortiz, Editor. **Released:** BIM. **Price:** Included in membership. **Description:** Provides Association members with news of developments affecting the warehouse distribution of automotive parts and supplies. Supplies operations tips and articles on marketing and sales techniques. Concentrates on news of members, Association sponsored events and activities, awards, and conferences. Recurring features include news of research, news of educational opportunities, and a calendar of events.

1573 ■ *Automotive Plastics Newsletter*

Pub: Market Search Inc.
Released: Biweekly. **Price:** $498, individuals. **Description:** Reports on news of the automotive and plastics industry. Also includes forecasts.

1574 ■ *Body Language*

Pub: Automotive Body Parts Association
Contact: Stan Rodman, Executive Director
Released: Monthly, 10-12 times/year. **Price:** $90, individuals; $120, elsewhere. **Description:** Reports news impacting the aftermarket body parts industry, industry trends, and Association news. Recurring features include meeting reports and a calendar of events.

1575 ■ *Consumer Electronics Vision*

Pub: Consumer Electronics Association
Contact: Gary Shapiro, President
E-mail: gshapiro@ce.org
Ed: Robert MacMillan, Editor, cstevens@ce.org. **Released:** Quarterly, 6/year. **Price:** Free. **Description:** Provides news and information concerning mobile electronics, audio, radar, security, and cellular communications. Examines the manufacture, market trends, and installation of mobile electronics. Covers legislative and regulatory issues at the state and federal levels with particular emphasis on business, manufacturing, and insurance issues. Recurring features include a monthly series of retail management information and news of the Association.

1576 ■ *Counterman: Dedicated to Successful Parts Distribution*

Pub: Babcox
URL(s): www.babcox.com/site/our-brands/countermanwww.counterman.com/. **Ed:** Mark Phillips. **Released:** Monthly **Price:** Free.

1577 ■ *Import Automotive Parts & Accessories*

Pub: Meyers Publishing
URL(s): www.meyerspublishing.com/ IAPA%20Home%20Page_6.hlmcms. **Ed:** Steve Relyea. **Released:** Monthly **Price:** $75, Canada and Mexico; $105, Other countries; $55, Individuals; $10, Single issue; $25, Individuals import industry sourcebook; $35, Individuals import industry sourcebook outside the U.S.; $20, Single issue outside the U.S.

1578 ■ *ImportCar: The Complete Import Service Magazine*

Pub: Babcox
URL(s): www.import-car.comwww.babcox.com/site/ our-brands/importcar. **Ed:** Mary DellaValle. **Released:** Monthly **Price:** Free.

1579 ■ *SEMA News*

Pub: Specialty Equipment Market Association
Contact: Chris Kersting, President
E-mail: chrisk@sema.org
Released: Monthly. **Price:** Included in membership. **Description:** Covers the automotive specialty, performance equipment, and accessory sectors. Recurring features include news of government and legislative actions, new products, international markets, and member and Association activities.

1580 ■ *Specialty Automotive Magazine*

Pub: Meyers Publishing
URL(s): www.meyerspublishing.com/ SAM%20Home_18.hlmcms. **Ed:** Steve Relyea. **Released:** Bimonthly **Price:** $40, Individuals U.S.; $25, Individuals specialty and performance industry sourcebook; $60, Canada and Mexico; $95, Other countries; $35, Other countries; $10, Single issue; $20, Single issue outside the U.S.

TRADE SHOWS AND CONVENTIONS

1581 ■ Florida RV Supershow

Florida RV Trade Association
10510 Gibsonton Dr.
Riverview, FL 33578
Ph: (813)741-0488
Fax: (813)741-0688
Co. E-mail: info@frvta.org
URL: http://www.frvta.org
Contact: Lance Wilson, Executive Director
E-mail: lancewilson@frvta.org
URL(s): www.frvta.org/supershow.asp. **Price:** $10, adults; kids ages 16 and under. **Frequency:** Annual. **Audience:** First time buyers as well as current owners. **Principal Exhibits:** Recreational vehicle supplies and accessories.

1582 ■ International Big R Show

Automotive Parts Remanufacturers Association (APRA)
4215 Lafayette Center Dr., Ste. 3
Chantilly, VA 20151-1243
Ph: (703)968-2772
Fax: (703)968-2878
Co. E-mail: membership@buyreman.com
URL: http://www.apra.org
Contact: William C. Gager, President
URL(s): www.bigrshow.com. **Frequency:** Annual. **Audience:** Rebuilders of automotive and truck parts and suppliers to rebuilders. **Principal Exhibits:** Cleaning machines for rebuilt parts; test equipment; new and remanufactured products, including alternators, starters, regulators, water pumps, brakes, carburetors, transmissions, cv joints, steering systems, and axles; component parts for rebuilders. **Telecommunication Services:** gager@buyreman.com.

1583 ■ International Midas Dealers Association Annual Conference

International Midas Dealers Association
c/o David Scott Levaton, Executive Director & Legal Counsel
4831 Las Virgenes Rd., Ste. 159
Calabasas, CA 91302
Ph: (877)543-6203
Fax: (847)647-8940
URL: http://www.imdaonline.org
Contact: David Scott Levaton
E-mail: david@franchiselegalsupport.com
URL(s): www.imdaonline.org. **Frequency:** Annual. **Audience:** Owners of Midas shops. **Principal Exhibits:** Exhibits for Midas muffler and brake shops franchisees.

1584 ■ Minneapolis International Motorcycle Show

Advanstar Communications
641 Lexington Ave., 8th Fl.
New York, NY 10022
Ph: (212)951-6600
Free: 800-346-0085
Fax: (212)951-6793
Co. E-mail: info@advanstar.com
URL: http://www.advanstar.com
Contact: Robert Krakoff, President
URL(s): www.motorcycleshows.com. **Audience:** Public: Motorcycle, watercraft and ATV enthusiasts. **Principal Exhibits:** A marketplace where manufacturers and retailers can display and sell their products such as motorcycles, all-terrain vehicles (ATV), scooters, watercraft, apparel, parts and accessories.

1585 ■ Service Specialists Association Annual Convention

Service Specialists Association
c/o Wade & Partners
160 Symphony Way
Elgin, IL 60120
Ph: (330)725-7160
Free: 800-763-5717
Fax: (330)722-5638
Co. E-mail: trucksvc@aol.com
URL: http://www.truckservice.org
URL(s): truckservice.org. **Frequency:** Annual. **Audience:** Trade-Heavy Duty Aftermarket. **Principal Exhibits:** Exhibits related to truck repair operations, rebuilding departments, individuals who have maintained shop equipment such as hydraulic press or heat treating furnace.

1586 ■ Undercar Expo - Showpower-Transmission Expo

MD Publications Inc.
3057 E. Cairo
Springfield, MO 65802
Ph: (417)866-3917
Free: 800-274-7890
Fax: (417)866-2781
Co. E-mail: showmanager@showpowerexpo.com
URL: http://www.mdpublications.com
Contact: Carol Langsford, President
E-mail: clangsford@mdpublications.com
URL(s): www.showpowerexpo.com. **Price:** $10, Pre-registered, members; $20, Onsite registered, members. **Frequency:** Annual. **Audience:** Persons

included in the under-the-car and transmission segment of the automotive aftermarket. **Principal Exhibits:** Equipment, supplies, and services for the under-the-car segment of the automotive aftermarket and the transmission aftermarket. **Telecommunication Services:** showpower@mdpublications.com.

CONSULTANTS

1587 ■ **ASC Retail Consulting**
10 Iverness Center Pky., Ste. 320
Birmingham, AL 35242
Ph: (205)995-5300
Free: 800-633-4767
Fax: (205)995-5360
Co. E-mail: martincic@hoffman.ds.adp.com
URL: http://www.ascconsulting.com
Contact: Mark Martincic, Director
E-mail: martincic@hoffman.ds.adp.com

Scope: Offers management consulting for auto dealers, distributors and manufacturers specializing in service, parts and body shop departments. Industries served automotive retail, wholesale and manufacturers. **Founded:** 1971. **Publications:** "Competitive and Profitable"; "Controlling Service Expense". **Special Services:** Applied Service Management; Extended

Service Performance; Process Reengineering; Applied Body Shop Management; Customized Solutions.

FRANCHISES AND BUSINESS OPPORTUNITIES

1588 ■ **Batteries Plus**
925 Walnut Ridge Dr.
Hartland, WI 53029
Free: 800-274-9155
Fax: (262)912-3100
Co. E-mail: franchising@batteriesplus.com
URL: http://www.batteriesplus.com

Description: Serves both retail and commercial customers. Program incorporates a unique and recognizable store design, coordinated graphics, color scheme, signage and product brands. **No. of Franchise Units:** 380. **No. of Company-Owned Units:** 25. **Founded:** 1988.. **Franchised:** 1992. **Equity Capital Needed:** $250,000 minimum. **Franchise Fee:** $37,500. **Training:** 3 weeks training at corporate headquarters plus 10 days at franchisee's store. Training covers successful company philosophies, store operations and product knowledge.

1589 ■ **Top Value Car & Truck Service Centers**
International Top Value Automotive, L.L.C.
36887 Schoolcraft Rd.
Livonia, MI 48150
Ph: (734)462-3633
Free: 800-860-8258
Fax: (734)462-1088
Description: Offers automobile products and services. **No. of Franchise Units:** 34. **No. of Company-Owned Units:** 6. **Founded:** 1977.. **Franchised:** 1980. **Equity Capital Needed:** $102,500-$158,200, including franchise fee and working capital. **Franchise Fee:** $17,500. **Financial Assistance:** Yes. **Training:** Yes.

COMPUTERIZED DATABASES

1590 ■ *Tire Business*
1155 Gratiot Ave.
Detroit, MI 48207
Ph: (313)446-6000
Free: 800-678-2427
Fax: (313)446-1616
Co. E-mail: info@crain.com
URL: http://www.crain.com
Availability: Online: Crain Communications Inc. **Type:** Full-text; Numeric.

TRADE PERIODICALS

1591 ■ *Automotive Plastics Newsletter*
Pub: Market Search Inc.
Released: Biweekly. **Price:** $498, individuals. **Description:** Reports on news of the automotive and plastics industry. Also includes forecasts.

1592 ■ *ImportCar: The Complete Import Service Magazine*
Pub: Babcox
URL(s): www.import-car.comwww.babcox.com/site/our-brands/importcar. **Ed:** Mary DellaValle. **Released:** Monthly **Price:** Free.

1593 ■ *Professional Carwashing & Detailing*
Pub: National Trade Publications Inc.
Contact: Mike Perkins, Director
E-mail: mperkins@ntpinc.com
URL(s): www.carwash.com/. **Ed:** Deb Gorgos. **Released:** Monthly

1594 ■ *Restoration*
Pub: International Society for Vehicle Preservation
URL(s): www.aztexcorp.com/root/isvp.html. **Released:** Semiannual **Price:** $20, Members; $3, Single issue.

1595 ■ *Underhood Service*
Pub: Babcox
URL(s): www.underhoodservice.comwww.babcox.com/site/our-brands/underhood-service. **Ed:** Edward Sunkin. **Released:** Monthly

VIDEOCASSETTES/ AUDIOCASSETTES

1596 ■ *SMART Body Shop Talk: Paint Tips*
Karol Media
Hanover Industrial Estates
375 Stewart Rd.
Wilkes Barre, PA 18773-7600
Ph: (570)822-8899
Free: 800-526-4773
Co. E-mail: sales@karolmedia.com
URL: http://www.karolmedia.com
Released: 1991. **Price:** $9.95. **Description:** A guide to the wide variety of paint products available and how to properly use them. **Availability:** VHS.

1597 ■ *Tune Up America: Detailing*
Morris Video
12881 Knott St.
Garden Grove, CA 92841
Ph: (310)533-4800
Fax: (310)320-3171
Released: 1986. **Price:** $19.95. **Description:** The steps you'll need to revitalize and maintain car interiors, exteriors, trim areas, and engine compartments are covered. **Availability:** VHS.

TRADE SHOWS AND CONVENTIONS

1598 ■ AAPEX
William T. Glasgow, Inc.
10070 W. 190th Pl.
Mokena, IL 60448
Ph: (708)226-1300
Co. E-mail: info@wtglasgow.com
URL: http://www.wtglasgow.com
URL(s): www.aapexshow.com. **Frequency:** Annual. **Audience:** Retailers, wholesalers, jobbers, manufacturers of the automotive aftermarket. **Principal Exhibits:** Automotive repair parts, tools, equipment, accessories and related services. **Dates and Locations:** Sands Expo and Convention Center. **Telecommunication Services:** bill.glasgow@aapexshow.com.

1599 ■ Service Specialists Association Annual Convention
Service Specialists Association
c/o Wade & Partners
160 Symphony Way
Elgin, IL 60120
Ph: (330)725-7160
Free: 800-763-5717
Fax: (330)722-5638
Co. E-mail: trucksvc@aol.com
URL: http://www.truckservice.org
URL(s): truckservice.org. **Frequency:** Annual. **Audience:** Trade-Heavy Duty Aftermarket. **Principal Exhibits:** Exhibits related to truck repair operations, rebuilding departments, individuals who have maintained shop equipment such as hydraulic press or heat treating furnace.

FRANCHISES AND BUSINESS OPPORTUNITIES

1600 ■ Aero-Colours Inc.
Aero-Colours, Inc.
128 S Tryon St., Ste. 900
Charlotte, NC 28202
Free: 800-275-5200
URL: http://www.aerocolours.com
Description: Mobile paint touch-up process used to repair nicks, chips, scratches and other blemishes in painted surfaces. Service is provided to car dealers, fleet owners, insurance companies and retail customers. Aero-Colours employs a very sophisticated system for paint mixing, matching, application and blending. Each franchisee is granted the right to use the Aero-Colours process in an exclusive territory. **No. of Franchise Units:** 218. **Founded:** 1985.. **Franchised:** 1993. **Equity Capital Needed:** $66,400-$175,400. **Franchise Fee:** $25,000. **Financial Assistance:** Yes. **Training:** Provides 2 weeks classroom/hands-on and 2 weeks onsite training with dealer account development in your exclusive territory.

1601 ■ Altracolor Systems
Aftermarket Appearance Industries Inc.
111 Phlox Ave. 0162
Metairie, LA 70001-4537
Ph: (504)456-1714
Free: 800-727-6567
Fax: (504)456-1714
Co. E-mail: altra@altracolor.com
URL: http://www.altracolor.com
Description: Mobile auto painting and plastic repair. **No. of Franchise Units:** 60. **Founded:** 1989.. **Franchised:** 1991. **Equity Capital Needed:** $37,500-$53,950 total investment. **Franchise Fee:** $8,000-$19,950. **Royalty Fee:** $95/week. **Financial Assistance:** Limited in-house financing available. **Training:** Yes.

1602 ■ CARSTAR Automotive Canada, Inc.
1460 Stonechurch Rd. E
Hamilton, ON, Canada L8W 3V3
Ph: (905)388-4720
Fax: (905)388-1124
URL: http://www.carstarcanada.ca
Description: Quality collision service. **No. of Franchise Units:** 160. **Founded:** 1974.. **Franchised:** 1994. **Equity Capital Needed:** $30,000-$250,000. **Franchise Fee:** Based on market. **Training:** Full menu of support services.

1603 ■ Colors on Parade
Total Car Franchising Inc.
642 Century Cir.
Conway, SC 29526
Free: 800-726-5677
URL: http://www.colorsfranchise.com
Description: Onsite automotive painting and body restoration. **No. of Franchise Units:** 270. **No. of Company-Owned Units:** 3. **Founded:** 1989. **Franchised:** 1991. **Equity Capital Needed:** $15,000. **Franchise Fee:** $5,000. **Financial Assistance:** Yes. **Training:** Provides 2 weeks training at headquarters, 3 months at franchisee's location, and ongoing support.

1604 ■ The Ding King Training Institute
The Ding King Training Institute Inc.
1280 Bison Ave., Ste. B-9
Newport Beach, CA 92660
Ph: (714)775-9450
Free: 800-304-3464
Fax: (714)775-9454
Co. E-mail: todd@dingking.com
URL: http://www.dingking.com
Description: Auto reconditioning includes paint less dent removal, paint blemish repair, windshield repair, gold plating, window tinting, odor removal and Patented Chip Magic system. **No. of Franchise Units:** 1,345. **Founded:** 1991.. **Franchised:** 1993. **Equity Capital Needed:** $100,000. **Franchise Fee:** None. **Training:** Includes training at company headquarters and onsite with ongoing support.

1605 ■ Dr. Vinyl & Associates, Ltd.
201 NW Victoria Dr.
Lee's Summit, MO 64086
Ph: (800)531-6600

Fax: (816)525-6333

Description: Mobile repair, reconditioning and after-market sales and services to auto dealers and other commercial accounts, such as vinyl, leather, velour, fabric, bumper, windshield, plastic and paint less dent repair, application of striping, body moldings, deck racks, graphics, gold plating, etc. **No. of Franchise Units:** 253. **No. of Company-Owned Units:** 2. **Founded:** 1972.. **Franchised:** 1981. **Equity Capital Needed:** $55,000-$85,000. **Franchise Fee:** $38,950. **Financial Assistance:** Yes. **Training:** (Missouri for combined classroom and field training and 4-5 days in franchisees territory). Training also available for franchisees employees or sub-contractors.

1606 ■ Fibrenew
Site 16, RR8
Box 33
Calgary, AB, Canada T2J 2T9
Ph: (403)278-7818
Free: 800-345-2951
Fax: (403)278-1434
Description: Mobile interior reconditioning and repair. **No. of Franchise Units:** 93. **Founded:** 1985.. **Franchised:** 1995. **Equity Capital Needed:** $75,000. **Franchise Fee:** $59,500. **Training:** Yes.

1607 ■ Line-X Protective Coatings
Line-X Franchise Development Corp.
1862 Sparkman Dr
Huntsville, AL 35816
Free: 877-330-1331
Co. E-mail: sales@line-x.com
URL: http://line-x.com
Description: Spray-on truck bed liners for truck dealers and retail customers. **No. of Franchise Units:** 360. **Founded:** 1994.. **Franchised:** 1999. **Equity Capital Needed:** $68,000-$147,000. **Franchise Fee:** $20,000. **Training:** Provides 3 weeks of in-house technical, business operations and onsite application training and onging training and support from Operations team.

1608 ■ Maaco Franchising, Inc.
Maaco Enterprises Inc.
610 Freedom Business Ctr., Ste. 200
King of Prussia, PA 19406
Ph: (610)265-6606
Free: 800-521-6282
Fax: (610)337-6154
Co. E-mail: info@maaco.com
URL: http://www.maaco.com
Description: Maaco Auto Painting & Bodyworks Centers are complete production auto paint and body repair centers. No prior automotive experience necessary. **No. of Franchise Units:** 459. **Founded:** 1972.. **Franchised:** 1972. **Equity Capital Needed:** $90,000 minimum cash required. **Franchise Fee:** $40,000. **Financial Assistance:** Yes. **Training:** 4 weeks formal training at corporate headquarters, continuing operational support thereafter. Assistance in financing, site selection and installation of equipment.

1609 ■ Maaco Systems Canada Inc.
Maaco Collision Repair and Auto Painting
8400 Lawson Rd., Ste. 1
Milton, ON, Canada L9T 0A4
Ph: (905)875-1248
Free: 800-387-6780
Fax: (905)875-0105
Co. E-mail: maaco@maaco.com
URL: http://www.maaco.ca
Description: Auto painting and body repair. **No. of Franchise Units:** 34. **No. of Operating Units:** 534. **Founded:** 1972.. **Franchised:** 1974. **Equity Capital Needed:** $299,000-$330,000 investment required; $75,000-$85,000 SBL. **Franchise Fee:** $30,000. **Training:** Provides 4 weeks in U.S. and 3 man weeks onsite with ongoing support.

1610 ■ The Shine Factory
Shine Factory Systems Inc.
75 Akerley Blvd.
Dartmouth, NS, Canada B3B 1R7
Ph: (902)405-3171
Fax: (902)405-3484
Co. E-mail: info@shinefactory.com
URL: http://www.shinefactory.com
Description: Canada's automotive and polishing franchise. **No. of Franchise Units:** 16. **Founded:** 1981. **Franchised:** 1981. **Equity Capital Needed:** $100,000+. **Franchise Fee:** $25,000 depending upon market area study. **Training:** Training conducted in Halifax, NS.

1611 ■ Sprayglo Auto Refinishing & Body Repair
Sprayglo USA Inc.
340 Smith Street
Clayton, GA 30525
Ph: (877)677-7294
Fax: (877)677-7294
Co. E-mail: info@sprayglo.com
URL: http://www.sprayglo.com
Description: Automotive painting and body repair. **No. of Franchise Units:** 8. **No. of Company-Owned Units:** 13. **Founded:** 1986.. **Franchised:** 1995. **Equity Capital Needed:** $216,800-$296,000. **Franchise Fee:** $20,000. **Royalty Fee:** 6%. **Training:** 30 days at training facilities, and 2 weeks at site location. All paint, materials, and equipment available from franchisor.

1612 ■ Ziebart
Ziebart International Corp.
1290 E Maple Rd.
Troy 48083-2817
Ph: (248)588-4100
Fax: (248)588-2513
Co. E-mail: info@ziebart.com
URL: http://www.ziebart.com
Description: Automotive application of detailing-accessories and protection services. **No. of Franchise Units:** 400. **No. of Company-Owned Units:**

14. **Founded:** 1954.. **Franchised:** 1962. **Equity Capital Needed:** $100,000-$250,000. **Franchise Fee:** $25,000. **Financial Assistance:** Yes. **Training:** Yes.

COMPUTER SYSTEMS/ SOFTWARE

1613 ■ *Auto Detailing*
Entrepreneur, Inc.
2445 McCabe Way
Irvine, CA 92614
Ph: (949)261-2325
Free: 800-421-2300
Fax: (949)261-7729
URL: http://www.entrepreneur.com

Price: $69.00. **Description:** Software designed to help operate an auto detailing business.

LIBRARIES

1614 ■ Max S. Hayes Vocational School Library
4600 Detroit Ave.
Cleveland, OH 44102
Ph: (216)631-1528
Fax: (216)634-2175
URL: http://www.maxshayes.com/
Contact: Tony Ascota, Librarian

Scope: Automotive trades, metalwork, machine shop work, vocational education, construction, textile fabrication. **Services:** Interlibrary loan; copying; Library open to the public by appointment. **Founded:** 1958. **Holdings:** 12,000 volumes; U.S. and foreign car shop manuals, 1965 to present. **Subscriptions:** 85 journals and other serials.

1615 ■ Phoenix Public Library - Burton Barr Central Library - Vehicle and Appliance Repair Collection—Burton Barr Central Library - Vehicle and Appliance Repair Collection.
1221 N. Central, 2nd Fl.
Phoenix, AZ 85004
Ph: (602)262-4636
URL: http://www.phoenixpubliclibrary.org/pageView. jsp?id=6029

Contact: Jennifer M. Orf, Library Assistant

Scope: Vehicle and motor repair - flat rate, interchange; electronic data and schematics for computers, appliances, transistor and ham radios. **Services:** Interlibrary loan; collection open to the public. **Holdings:** 3500 books; 10,000 schematics and 400 volumes of SAMS photofact publications as well as peripheral publications; DVDs; CDs. **Subscriptions:** 17 journals and other serials.

ASSOCIATIONS AND OTHER ORGANIZATIONS

1616 ■ American Automotive Leasing Association (AALA)
675 N Washington St., Ste. 410
Alexandria, VA 22314-1939
Ph: (703)548-0777
Fax: (703)548-1925
Co. E-mail: sederholm@aalafleet.com
URL: http://www.aalafleet.com
Contact: Mike Pitcher, President
Description: Represents the commercial automotive fleet leasing and management industry. **Founded:** 1955.

1617 ■ Automotive Fleet and Leasing Association (AFLA)
1000 Westgate Dr., Ste. 252
St. Paul, MN 55114
Ph: (651)203-7247
Fax: (651)290-2266
Co. E-mail: info@aflaonline.com
URL: http://www.aflaonline.org
Contact: Theresa Belding, President
Description: New car dealers, fleet administrators, leasing companies, drive-away companies, auto manufacturers, and consultants. Provides a forum for the exchange of information between related segments of the fleet and leasing industry. Seeks to build working relationships with professionals in all phases of the industry, develop new ideas that will help the industry continue to grow, and help the industry find ways to operate more efficiently and profitably. **Founded:** 1969. **Publications:** *The Forum* (Quarterly). **Awards:** Professional Fleet Manager of the Year, McGarvey Award (Annual).

1618 ■ NAFA Fleet Management Association (NAFA)
125 Village Blvd., Ste. 200
Princeton, NJ 08540
Ph: (609)720-0882
Fax: (609)452-8004
Co. E-mail: info@nafa.org
URL: http://www.automotive-fleet.com
Contact: Charles A. Gibbens, Jr., President
E-mail: gib03@co.henrico.va.us
URL(s): www.nafa.org. **Description:** Persons responsible for the administration of a motor vehicle fleet of 25 or more units for a firm not commercially engaged in the sale, rental, or lease of motor vehicles. Compiles statistics. Maintains placement service and speakers' bureau; conducts research programs. Operates Fleet Information Resource Center. Sponsors professional Certified Automotive Fleet Manager certification. **Scope:** fleet management. **Founded:** 1957. **Publications:** *Fleet Solutions* (Bimonthly); *FleetFocus* (Biweekly); *NAFA Roster* (Annual); *NAFA's Fleet Executive* (Monthly); *NAFA Annual Reference Book*; *NAFA Fleet Executive: The Magazine for Vehicle Management*; *National Association of Fleet Administrators--Annual Reference Book* (Annual); *NAFA Annual Reference Book*. **Educational**

Activities: Institute and Expo (Annual). **Awards:** Distinguished Service Award (Annual); Excellence in Education Award (Annual); Outstanding Chapter Service Award (Annual); Larry Goill Memorial Quality Fleet Management Idea Award (Annual).

1619 ■ National Truck Leasing System (NTLS)
1S450 Summit Ave., Ste. 300
Oakbrook Terrace, IL 60181-3990
Ph: (630)925-7710
Free: 800-729-6857
Fax: (630)953-0040
Co. E-mail: passwords@nationalease.com
URL: http://www.ntls.com
Contact: Doug Clark, President
Description: Franchiser of independent companies. Provides full-service truck leasing. Promotes simplification of operating practices. Sponsors seminars. **Founded:** 1944. **Publications:** *NationaLease Newsletter* (Weekly). **Educational Activities:** National Truck Leasing System Meeting (Annual).

1620 ■ National Vehicle Leasing Association (NVLA)
7250 Pkwy. Dr., Ste. 510
Hanover, MD 21076
Ph: (410)782-2342
Free: 800-225-6852
Fax: (410)712-4038
Co. E-mail: info@nvla.org
URL: http://www.nvla.org
Contact: Ben Carfrae, President
Description: Companies that lease vehicles. Provides education and information services. Lobbies on behalf of members. Maintains speakers' bureau; offers placement services; compiles statistics. **Founded:** 1968. **Publications:** *Lifeline* (Bimonthly); *Vehicle Leasing Today* (Bimonthly; Quarterly); *National Guide to Vehicle Leasing Suppliers and Services* (Annual). **Educational Activities:** National Vehicle Leasing Association Conference (Annual). **Telecommunication Services:** nvla@ix.netcom.com.

1621 ■ Recreation Vehicle Rental Association (RVRA)
3930 University Dr.
Fairfax, VA 22030-2515
Ph: (703)591-7130
Fax: (703)359-0152
Co. E-mail: info@rvda.org
URL: http://www.rvra.org
Description: Dealers involved in the rental of recreation vehicles such as folding trailers, travel trailers, and motor homes. Works to improve the professionalism of the RV rental dealer through educational programs and promote the use of rentals by disseminating information. Compiles statistics; conducts seminars. **Founded:** 1982.

1622 ■ Truck Renting and Leasing Association (TRALA)
675 N Washington St., Ste. 410
Alexandria, VA 22314
Ph: (703)299-9120

Fax: (703)299-9115
Co. E-mail: smurray@trala.org
URL: http://www.trala.org
Contact: Tom James, President
E-mail: tjames@trala.org
URL(s): trala.org. **Description:** Truck and trailer rental and leasing companies and systems; suppliers to the industry. Seeks to encourage and promote a favorable climate and sound environment conducive to the renting and leasing of trucks, tractors, and trailers, and dedicated contract carriage. **Founded:** 1978. **Publications:** *The TRALA Vehicle* (Annual); *EnRoute* (Biweekly); *Inside TRALA* (Quarterly); *Truck Renting and Leasing Association--News Digest* (Quarterly); *Weekly Wire* (Weekly); *inside TRALA*. **Educational Activities:** National Leadership Conference (Annual). **Awards:** Larry Miller Memorial Scholarship (Annual); TRALA Scholarship Program. **Telecommunication Services:** tjames@trala.org.

REFERENCE WORKS

1623 ■ *"Credit Crunch Gives, Takes Away"* in The Business Journal-Serving Metropolitan Kansas City (Vol. 27, October 17, 2008, No. 5, pp. 1)
Pub: American City Business Journals, Inc.
Ed: Suzanna Stagemeyer. **Description:** Although many Kansas City business enterprises have been adversely affected by the U.S. credit crunch, others have remained relatively unscathed. Examples of how local businesses are being impacted by the crisis are provided including: American Trailer & Storage Inc., which declared bankruptcy after failing to pay a long-term loan; and NetStandard, a technology firm who, on the other hand, is being pursued by prospective lenders.

1624 ■ *Rent-A-Wreck Worldwide Directory*
Pub: Rent-A-Wreck of America Inc.
URL(s): www.rentawreck.com/citypages.html. **Ed:** Lori Shaffron. **Released:** Annual; August. **Price:** Free. **Covers:** Nearly 500 franchise locations worldwide. **Entries include:** Name, address, phone. **Arrangement:** Geographical.

1625 ■ *"Transportation Enterprise"* in Advertising Age (Vol. 79, June 9, 2008, No. 23, pp. S10)
Pub: Crain Communications, Inc.
Ed: Jean Halliday. **Description:** Overview of Enterprise rent-a-car's plan to become a more environmentally-friendly company. The family-owned business has spent $1 million a year to plant trees since 2006 and has added more fuel-efficient cars, hybrids and flex-fuel models.

STATISTICAL SOURCES

1626 ■ *RMA Annual Statement Studies*
Pub: Risk Management Association
Contact: Kevin M. Blakey, President
Released: Annual. **Price:** $175.00 2006-07 edition, $105.00. **Description:** Contains composite balance sheets and income statements for more than 360

industries, including the accounting, auditing, and bookkeeping industries. Also contains five years of comparative historical data for discerning trends. Includes 16 commonly used ratios, computed for most of the size groupings for nearly every industry.

TRADE PERIODICALS

1627 ■ Automotive Fleet
Pub: Bobit Business Media
Contact: Ty Bobit, President
URL(s): www.automotive-fleet.com/. **Released:** Monthly **Price:** Free.

1628 ■ Automotive Fleet and Leasing Association--Forum
Pub: Automotive Fleet and Leasing Association
Ed: Rose Finch, Editor, rose@bobit.com. **Released:** Quarterly. **Price:** Included in membership. **Description:** Seeks to keep automotive fleet dealers and leasing agencies updated on important events, membership news, new legislation, and government programs. Recurring features include editorials and letters to the editor.

1629 ■ inside TRALA
Pub: Truck Renting and Leasing Association
Contact: Tom James, President
E-mail: tjames@trala.org
Ed: Mary S. Payne, Editor, mpayne@trala.org. **Released:** Quarterly. **Price:** Included in membership; Free. **Description:** Publishes news and activities of TRALA members and suppliers. Addresses federal and state legislation and regulatory issues affecting the industry.

1630 ■ The Latest Scoop
Pub: Latest Scoop Publishing
Contact: Tracey Ellis, Publisher
E-mail: scoopautoevents@aol.com
Released: 9/year. **Price:** $15, individuals; $30, Canada. **Description:** Provides current information on car-related events taking place in the Rocky Mountain Region, including auctions, autocross, off-road, parades, races, rallies, rod runs/cruises/tours, swap meets, and shows. Recurring features include a calendar of events and columns titled Club Meetings and The Latest Scoop on. . .

TRADE SHOWS AND CONVENTIONS

1631 ■ Great American Trucking Show (GATS)
Sellers Expositions
222 Pearl St., Ste. 300
New Albany, IN 47150
Ph: (812)949-9200
Free: 800-558-8767
Fax: (812)949-9600
URL: http://www.sellersexpo.com
Contact: Warren Sellers, Chief Executive Officer
E-mail: wss315@aol.com
URL(s): www.gatsonline.com. **Audience:** Truck owners and operators, exempt haulers, company drivers and truck drivers for hire, aftermarket parts purchasers, purchasing agents, mechanics, fleet owner. **Principal Exhibits:** Trucks and related equipment, supplies, and services.

1632 ■ Service Specialists Association Annual Convention
Service Specialists Association
c/o Wade & Partners
160 Symphony Way
Elgin, IL 60120
Ph: (330)725-7160
Free: 800-763-5717
Fax: (330)722-5638
Co. E-mail: trucksvc@aol.com
URL: http://www.truckservice.org
URL(s): truckservice.org. **Frequency:** Annual. **Audience:** Trade-Heavy Duty Aftermarket. **Principal Exhibits:** Exhibits related to truck repair operations, rebuilding departments, individuals who have maintained shop equipment such as hydraulic press or heat treating furnace.

FRANCHISES AND BUSINESS OPPORTUNITIES

1633 ■ Active Green + Ross
580 Evans Ave.
Toronto, ON, Canada M8W 2W1
Ph: (416)255-5581
Fax: (416)255-4793
Co. E-mail: info@activegreenross.com
URL: http://www.activegreenross.com
Description: This is one of the largest independent groups of tire and automotive service centres in Canada. It is located in Toronto and the surrounding area. **No. of Franchise Units:** 67. **No. of Company-Owned Units:** 8. **Founded:** 1982.. **Equity Capital Needed:** $115,000-$200,000. **Franchise Fee:** $25,000. **Training:** Training provided for up to 2 months.

1634 ■ Bates International Motor Home Rental Systems, Inc.
Bates Motor Home Rental Network, Inc.
3690 S Eastern Ave., Ste. 220
Las Vegas, NV 89169
Ph: (702)737-9050
Free: 800-732-2283
Fax: (702)737-9149
Co. E-mail: headquarters@batesintl.com
Description: Motor home rentals. **No. of Franchise Units:** 16. **Founded:** 1973.. **Franchised:** 1995. **Equity Capital Needed:** $17,000. **Franchise Fee:** $35,000-$50,000. **Training:** Yes.

1635 ■ Budget Brake & Muffler Distributors Ltd
200-185 Golden Dr.
Coquitlam, BC, Canada V3K 6T1
Ph: (604)464-1239
Free: 800-746-9659
Fax: (604)464-1426
Co. E-mail: info@budgetbrake.com
URL: http://www.budgetbrake.com
Description: Provides retail automotive service specializing in brakes, exhaust, shocks and associated work. **No. of Franchise Units:** 33. **Founded:** 1969.. **Franchised:** 1972. **Equity Capital Needed:** $185,000-$225,000. **Franchise Fee:** $25,000. **Training:** Provides 2 weeks.

1636 ■ Dollar Rent A Car
Dollar Systems, Inc.
PO Box 33167
Tulsa, OK 74153
Ph: (918)669-3103
Description: Daily rental car. **No. of Franchise Units:** 1,300. **No. of Company-Owned Units:** 30. **Founded:** 1967.. **Equity Capital Needed:** Dependent on fleet size. **Franchise Fee:** minimum $12,500. **Financial Assistance:** Yes. **Training:** Yes.

1637 ■ Eaglerider Motorcycle Rental
Eaglerider, Inc.
11860 S La Cienga Blvd.
Los Angeles, CA 90250
Ph: (310)536-6777
Free: 800-501-TOUR
Fax: (310)536-6770
Description: Motorcycle rental and guide tour company specializing in Harley-Davidson motorcycles. **No. of Franchise Units:** 65. **No. of Company-Owned Units:** 16. **No. of Operating Units:** 83. **Founded:** 1992.. **Franchised:** 1999. **Equity Capital Needed:** $48,783-$179,496. **Franchise Fee:** $20,000-$30,000. **Royalty Fee:** 10%. **Financial Assistance:** Third party financing available and assistance with franchise fee. **Training:** Provides 6 days at headquarters, 2 days onsite, and ongoing support.

1638 ■ Payless Car Rental
Avalon Global Group, Inc.
2350 N 34th St. N
St. Petersburg, FL 33713
Ph: (800)729-5255

Fax: (727)322-6540
Description: Automobile rental and sales. **No. of Franchise Units:** 83. **Founded:** 1971.. **Franchised:** 1971. **Equity Capital Needed:** Minimum $500,000 net worth. **Franchise Fee:** $20,000-$500,000. **Training:** Yes.

1639 ■ Thrifty Rent-A-Car System, Inc.
Dollar Thrifty Automotive Group
5310 E 31st St.
Tulsa, OK 74135
Ph: (918)669-2219
Fax: (918)669-2061
Description: Over 90% of retail outlets are owned by independent businesses under the company's trade name. **No. of Franchise Units:** 545. **No. of Company-Owned Units:** 3. **Founded:** 1962. **Franchised:** 1962. **Equity Capital Needed:** minimum PNW $650,000 unencumbered, $120,000 minimum working capital. **Franchise Fee:** Varies. **Financial Assistance:** Yes. **Training:** Yes.

1640 ■ Wheelchair Getaways, Inc.
PO Box 1098
Mukilteo, WA 98275
Ph: (800)536-5518
Fax: (425)355-6159
Co. E-mail: info@wheelchairgetaways.com
Description: Provides rental of speciallyconverted vans on a daily basis to people using wheelchairs. **No. of Franchise Units:** 43. **Founded:** 1988.. **Franchised:** 1989. **Equity Capital Needed:** $40,000-$108,000. **Franchise Fee:** $27,500. **Training:** Yes.

COMPUTERIZED DATABASES

1641 ■ Consumer InSite<svs>
610 Opperman Dr.
Eagen, MN 55122
Free: 800-477-4300
Co. E-mail: gale.contentlicensing@cengage.com
URL: http://www.insite2.gale.com
Availability: Online: Cengage Learning Inc. - Gale - InSite2. **Type:** Full-text.

1642 ■ Highway Vehicles Safety Database
400 Commonwealth Dr.
Warrendale, PA 15096-0001
Ph: (724)776-4841
Free: 877-606-7323
Fax: (724)776-0790
Co. E-mail: CustomerService@sae.org
URL: http://www.sae.org
Availability: Online: SAE International. CD-ROM: SAE International. **Type:** Bibliographic.

COMPUTER SYSTEMS/ SOFTWARE

1643 ■ Black Book, Inc.
PO Box 758
Gainesville, GA 30503
Ph: (770)532-4111
Free: 800-554-1026
Fax: (800)357-3444
URL: http://www.blackbookusa.com
Description: Available for IBM computers and MS-DOS compatibles. System provides including cost and retail, options, and finance and lease payments. pricing information on cars and light trucks, including cost and retail, options, and finance and lease payments.

LIBRARIES

1644 ■ Alabama Department of Transportation - Research & Development Bureau - Research Library
1409 Coliseum Blvd.
Montgomery, AL 36110
Ph: (334)253-6940

Fax: (334)264-2042
Co. E-mail: brownje@dot.state.al.us
URL: http://www.dot.state.al.us/rdweb/Index.htm
Contact: Jeffrey W. Brown
Scope: Transportation. **Services:** Interlibrary loan; Library not open to the public. **Founded:** 1953. **Holdings:** 1000 books; 5000 reports. **Subscriptions:** 8 journals and other serials.

1645 ■ California State Department of Motor Vehicles - Licensing Operations Division - Research and Development Branch - Traffic Safety Research Library
2415 1st Ave., MS F-126
Sacramento, CA 95818
Ph: (916)657-3079
Free: 800-368-4327
Fax: (916)657-8589
Co. E-mail: dluong@dvm.ca.gov
Contact: Douglas Luong, Analyst
Scope: Automobile transportation. **Services:** Copying; library not open to the public. **Holdings:** 500 books; 10,000 bound periodical volumes; reports; manuscripts. **Subscriptions:** 20 journals and other serials.

1646 ■ ConnDOT Library and Information Center
2800 Berlin Tpke.
Newington, CT 06111-4116
Ph: (860)594-2000
Fax: (860)594-3039
Co. E-mail: drew.coleman@ct.gov
URL: http://www.ct.gov/dot/site/default.asp
Contact: Betty Ambler, Librarian
Scope: Transportation. **Services:** Interlibrary loan; copying; library open to the public by appointment. **Founded:** 1983. **Holdings:** 10,000 books; 10,000 reports; videos.

1647 ■ Kansas Department of Transportation Library—KDOT Library.
700 SW Harrison St.
Eisenhower State Office Bldg., 4th Fl. W.
Topeka, KS 66603-3745
Ph: (785)291-3854
Fax: (785)291-3717
Co. E-mail: library@ksdot.org
Contact: Marie Manthe, Librarian
Scope: Transportation. **Services:** Interlibrary loan; Library open to the public. **Founded:** 1963. **Holdings:** 3000 books; 20,000 reports; 175 CD-ROMs; 100 videos. **Subscriptions:** 100 journals and other serials.

1648 ■ Kentucky Transportation Center Library
University of Kentucky
176 Raymond Bldg.
Lexington, KY 40506-0281
Ph: (859)257-2155
Free: 800-432-0719
Fax: (859)257-1815
Co. E-mail: lwhayne@engr.uky.edu
URL: http://www.kyt2.com/
Contact: Laura Whayne, Librarian
Scope: Transportation. **Services:** Interlibrary loan; copying; Library open to the public. **Founded:** 1980.

Holdings: 6000 books; 9000 reports; 800 videotapes. **Subscriptions:** 300 journals and other serials. **Telecommunication Services:** vbrock@engr.uky.edu.

1649 ■ Missouri Highway and Transportation Department - Division of Materials Library
105 W. Capitol Ave.
Jefferson City, MO 65102-0270
Ph: (573)751-6735
Free: 888-275 6636
Fax: (573)526-5636
Co. E-mail: michael.meyerhoff@mail.modot.state.mo.us
URL: http://www.modot.org/
Contact: Mona Scott
Scope: Transportation. **Services:** Library not open to the public. **Holdings:** Figures not available.

1650 ■ Montana Department of Transportation Library
2701 Prospect Ave.
Helena, MT 59620-1001
Ph: (406)444-6338
Free: 800-335-7592
Fax: (406)444-6204
Co. E-mail: ssillick@mt.gov
URL: http://www.mdt.mt.gov/research/unique/services.shtml
Contact: Susan Sillick
Scope: Transportation. **Services:** Interlibrary loan; copying. **Holdings:** 10,000 items; reports; CD-ROMs; video. **Subscriptions:** 10 journals and other serials. **Telecommunication Services:** mdtresearch@mt.gov.

1651 ■ New Jersey Department of Transportation Research Library
1035 Parkway Ave.
Trenton, NJ 08625-0600
Ph: (609)530-5289
Fax: (609)530-2052
Co. E-mail: library@dot.state.nj.us
URL: http://www.state.nj.us/transportation/refdata/library/
Contact: Carol Paszamant, Librarian
Scope: Transportation. **Services:** Interlibrary loan; copying; library open to the public by appointment. **Founded:** 1962. **Holdings:** 300 books; 11,000 reports. **Subscriptions:** 50 journals and other serials.

1652 ■ North Carolina Department of Transportation, Research and Development Library
PO Box 25201
Raleigh, NC 27611
Ph: (919)715-2463
Fax: (919)715-0137
Co. E-mail: rhhall@dot.state.nc.us
URL: http://www.ncdot.org/
Contact: Bob Hall
Scope: Transportation. **Services:** Interlibrary loan; copying; Library open to the public for reference use only. **Holdings:** 11,209 books; 20,021 reports; 132 videos. **Subscriptions:** 57 journals and other serials.

1653 ■ North Dakota Department of Transportation - Materials and Research Division Library
608 East Blvd.
Bismarck, ND 58505-0700
Ph: (701)328-2500
Free: 855-637-6237
Fax: (701)328-0310
Co. E-mail: gweisger@nd.gov
URL: http://www.dot.nd.gov
Contact: Gerri Weisgerber, Manager, Administration
Scope: Transportation. **Services:** Library not open to the public. **Founded:** 1970. **Holdings:** 6600 reports. **Subscriptions:** 5 journals and other serials.

1654 ■ South Carolina Department of Transportation Library
955 Park St., Rm. 110
Columbia, SC 29202
Ph: (803)737-9897
Free: 855-467-2368
Fax: (803)737-0824
Co. E-mail: adcockda@dot.state.sc.us
URL: http://www.dot.state.sc.us
Contact: Ann Adcock, Manager
Scope: Transportation, engineering, mass transit. **Services:** Interlibrary loan; transportation related research; library open to the public. **Founded:** 1998. **Holdings:** 5500 books; 90 bound periodical volumes; 1900 reports; 250 videos. **Subscriptions:** 41 journals and other serials; 10 newspapers. **Telecommunication Services:** SCDOT_contact@scdot.org.

1655 ■ Vermont Agency of Transportation, Policy and Planning Division Library
1 National Drive
c, VT 05633-0001
Ph: (802)828-3960
Fax: (802)828-3983
URL: http://www.aot.state.vt.us
Contact: Sandy Aja
Scope: Transportation. **Holdings:** Figures not available.

RESEARCH CENTERS

1656 ■ Automotive Market Research Council (AMRC)
PO Box 13966
Research Triangle Park, NC 27709-3966
Ph: (919)549-4800
Fax: (919)549-4824
Co. E-mail: info@amrc.org
URL: http://www.amrc.org
Contact: Otto Szalavari, President
Description: Represents manufacturers of automotive service equipment, automotive parts, components, subassemblies, accessories as original or replacement equipment, and employees whose principal responsibility is market research analysis and business planning. Promotes more complete, prompt, and accurate gathering and dissemination of marketing data; seeks to increase the reliability of forecasts of demand in the industry; works to improve the professional abilities of market analysis. Works with government agencies to improve collection of statistics. **Founded:** 1966. **Publications:** *The Researcher* (Quarterly).

REFERENCE WORKS

1657 ■ *"Babynut.com to Shut Down" in Bellingham Business Journal (Vol. February 2010, pp. 3)*
Pub: Sound Publishing Inc.
Description: Saralee Sky and Jerry Kilgore, owners of Babynut.com will close their online store. The site offered a free online and email newsletter to help mothers through pregnancy and the first three years of their child's life. Products being sold at clearance prices include organic and natural maternity and nursing clothing, baby and toddler clothes, books on pregnancy, and more.

1658 ■ *"Baby's Room Franchisee Files Bankruptcy" in Crain's Detroit Business (Vol. 25, June 22, 2009, No. 25, pp. 15)*
Pub: Crain Communications Inc. - Detroit
Ed: Gabe Nelson. **Description:** Emery L, a franchisee of USA Baby Inc. and ran the franchised Baby's Room Nursery Furniture stores in the area has filed for bankruptcy. Details of the bankruptcy are included.

1659 ■ *"Consignment Shop Offers Children's Clothes, Products" in Frederick News-Post (August 19, 2010)*
Pub: Frederick News-Post
Ed: Ed Waters Jr. **Description:** Sweet Pea Consignments for Children offers used items for newborns to pre-teens. The shop carries name brand clothing as well as toys, books and baby products.

1660 ■ *"Delaware Diaper Maker Wanting To Expand Less Than a Year After Move" in Business First-Columbus (December 7, 2007, pp. A6)*
Pub: American City Business Journals, Inc.
Ed: Dan Eaton. **Description:** Duluth, Georgia-based Associated Hygienic Products LLC is planning to expand its production operations by 20 percent and hire new workers. The diaper maker was awarded state incentives to facilitate its transfer from Marion to Delaware. Details are included.

1661 ■ *"King of the Crib: How Good Samaritan Became Ohio's Baby HQ" in Business Courier (Vol. 27, June 18, 2010, No. 7, pp. 1)*
Pub: Business Courier
Ed: James Ritchie. **Description:** Cincinnati's Good Samaritan hospital had 6,875 live births in 2009, which is more than any other hospital in Ohio. They specialize in the highest-risk pregnancies and deliveries and other hospitals are trying to grab Good Samaritan's share in this niche.

1662 ■ *"Procter & Gamble Boosts Bet on Exclusive Brands" in Business Courier (Vol. 27, July 9, 2010, No. 10, pp. 1)*
Pub: Business Courier
Ed: Jon Newberry. **Description:** Procter & Gamble is creating more special versions of its brands such as Pringles and Pampers exclusively for retail partners such as Tesco in the U.K. The greater push towards this direction is seen as a way to regain market share.

1663 ■ *"Retail Briefs - Dollar Store Opens in Long Leaf Mall" in Star-News (November 5, 2010)*
Pub: Star-News Media
Ed: Judy Royal. **Description:** Dollar Delight$ opened a new shop in Long Leaf Mall in Wilmington, North Carolina. The store will carry gift bags, balloons, party supplies, greeting cards, school supplies, health and beauty products, hardware, baby items, toys, Christmas goods, crafts, housewares and jewelry in its inventory.

1664 ■ *"What's In That Diaper?" in Inc. (November 2007, pp. 126)*
Pub: Gruner & Jahr USA Publishing
Ed: Nitasha Tiku. **Description:** Profile of Jason and Kimberly Graham-Nye, inventors of the gDiaper, consisting of a washable cotton elastine outer pant and an insert made of fluffed wood pulp and viscose rayon, both harvested from trees certified by the Sustainable Forestry Initiative.

SOURCES OF SUPPLY

1665 ■ *Toys & Games--Buyer's Guide Issue*
Chelsie Communications Inc.
URL(s): www.toysandgamesmag.com. **Released:** Annual; Latest edition 2008. **Publication includes:** List of about 400 Canadian manufacturers and distributors of toys and games for children; trade associations, trade show organizers, and licensors. **Entries include:** For manufacturers and distributors--Company name, address, phone, key officials, branches, name of firm represented, key to line of business. For associations--Name, address, phone, contact name, property/show represented. **Arrangement:** Alphabetical. **Indexes:** Product, brand name.

VIDEOCASSETTES/ AUDIOCASSETTES

1666 ■ *Baby Massage*
Leslie T. McClure
PO Box 1223
Pebble Beach, CA 93953
Ph: (831)656-0553
Fax: (831)656-0555
Co. E-mail: leslie@411videoinfo.com
URL: http://www.411videoinfo.com
Released: 1998. **Price:** $29.95. **Description:** Instructs how to give a complete massage to your baby. **Availability:** VHS.

TRADE SHOWS AND CONVENTIONS

1667 ■ *Denver Apparel and Accessory Market*
Denver Merchandise Mart
451 E. 58th Ave., Ste. 4270
Denver, CO 80216-8470
Ph: (303)292-6278
Free: 800-289-6278

Fax: (303)297-8473
Co. E-mail: info@denvermart.com
URL: http://www.denvermart.com
URL(s): www.denvermart.com. **Frequency:** 5/year. **Audience:** Retailers of women's, children's, and men's apparel and accessories. **Principal Exhibits:** Women's, men's, and children's apparel and accessories. **Dates and Locations:** Merchandise Mart. **Telecommunication Services:** info@denvermart. com.

1668 ■ *International Juvenile Product Show*
Juvenile Products Manufacturers Association
15000 Commerce Pkwy., Ste. C
Mount Laurel, NJ 08054
Ph: (856)638-0420
Fax: (856)439-0525
Co. E-mail: jpma@jpma.org
URL: http://www.jpma.org
Contact: Robert Waller, Jr., President
E-mail: wmacmillan@ahint.com
Frequency: Annual. **Audience:** Manufacturers, retailers, reps, wholesalers, importers, and other trade professionals. **Principal Exhibits:** Juvenile products, including furniture, toys, infant accessories, and soft goods. **Dates and Locations:** , International Apparel Mart.

1669 ■ *Just Kidstuff - A Division of the New York International Gift Fair*
George Little Management, LLC
1133 Westchester Ave., Ste. N136
White Plains, NY 10606
Ph: (914)421-3200
Free: 800-272-SHOW
Co. E-mail: cathy_steel@glmshows.com
URL: http://www.glmshows.com
URL(s): www.nyigf.com. **Frequency:** Semiannual. **Audience:** Buyers from specialty and department stores, giftshops, jewelry stores, interior designers, importers and distributors of home products, mail order catalogs. **Principal Exhibits:** Presents a wide variety of upscale products for children of all ages, including bedding, furniture, dolls, toys and games, gifts, clothes, books and educational products and accessories. **Telecommunication Services:** deborah_hilfman@glmshows.com.

1670 ■ *Just Kidstuff - A Division of the San Francisco International Gift Fair*
George Little Management, LLC
1133 Westchester Ave., Ste. N136
White Plains, NY 10606
Ph: (914)421-3200
Free: 800-272-SHOW
Co. E-mail: cathy_steel@glmshows.com
URL: http://www.glmshows.com
URL(s): www.sfigf.com. **Frequency:** February and August. **Audience:** Specialty and department stores, gift shops, jewelry stores, interior designers, importers and distributors of home products, mail order catalogs, museums, etc. **Principal Exhibits:** Upscale products for children of all ages, including bedding, furniture, dolls, toys and games, gifts, clothes, books,

and educational products and accessories. **Dates and Locations:** Moscone Convention Center. **Telecommunication Services:** sfigf@glmshows.com.

1671 ■ Women's and Children's Apparel and Accessories Mart
Dallas Market Center Co.
2100 Stemmons Fwy.
Dallas, TX 75207
Ph: (214)655-6100
Free: 800-DAL-MKTS
Co. E-mail: lvillarreal@dmcmail.com
URL: http://www.dallasmarketcenter.com/
Audience: Apparel and accessories and home furnishings retailers. **Principal Exhibits:** Regional Merchandising Mart servicing department and specialty store buyers nationwide.

FRANCHISES AND BUSINESS OPPORTUNITIES

1672 ■ Children's Lighthouse Franchise Co.
101 S Jennings Ave., Ste. 209
Fort Worth, TX 76104
Ph: (888)338-4466
Fax: (817)338-2716
Co. E-mail: info@ChildrensLighthouse.com
URL: http://childrenslighthouse.com
Description: Childcare franchise. **No. of Franchise Units:** 24. **No. of Company-Owned Units:** 8. **Founded:** 1997.. **Franchised:** 1999. **Equity Capital Needed:** $501,500-$3,351,000 total investment. **Franchise Fee:** $60,000. **Royalty Fee:** 7%. **Financial Assistance:** Third party financing available. **Training:** Available at headquarters for 4 weeks, 4 weeks at franchisee's location, unlimited training for the first year and unlimited support.

1673 ■ Stork News
Stork News of America Inc.
1305 Hope Mills Rd., Ste. A
Fayetteville, NC 28304
Ph: (910)426-1357
Free: 800-633-6395
Fax: (910)426-2473
Description: Provides announcement services to newborn. **No. of Franchise Units:** 140. **No. of Company-Owned Units:** 1. **Founded:** 1983.. **Franchised:** 1985. **Equity Capital Needed:** $2,000, not including franchise fee. **Franchise Fee:** $10,800 plus. **Training:** Yes.

LIBRARIES

1674 ■ Art Institute of Philadelphia Library
1610 Chestnut St.
Philadelphia, PA 19103
Ph: (215)405-6402
Co. E-mail: rschachter@aii.edu
URL: http://www.artinstitutes.edu/philadelphia
Contact: Ruth Schachter, Director
URL(s): www.artinstitutes.edu/philadelphia/studentlife/library.aspx. **Scope:** Visual communications, interior design, industrial design, animation, fashion marketing, fashion design, visual merchandising, photography, website design, multimedia. **Services:** Interlibrary loan; copying; library not open to the public (circulation services provided for students and faculty). **Founded:** 1974. **Holdings:** 31,000 volumes; 2000 videocassettes; audiocassettes. **Subscriptions:** 180 print subscriptions and other serials.

1675 ■ Bauder College Library
384 Northyards Blvd. NW, Ste. 190 and 400
Atlanta, GA 30313
Ph: (404)237-7573
Free: 800-935-1857
Fax: (404)237-1619
URL: http://atlanta.bauder.edu
Scope: Fashion design and merchandising, interior design, information technology, business administration, graphic design, criminal justice. **Services:** Library not open to the public. **Founded:** 1967. **Hold-ings:** 7800 books; 500 videotapes; 6500 slide sets; 100 filmstrips. **Subscriptions:** 160 journals and other serials; 6 newspapers.

1676 ■ Fashion Institute of Design & Merchandising - Cyril Magnin Resource and Research Center
55 Stockton St., 5th Fl.
San Francisco, CA 94108-5829
Ph: (415)675-5200
Free: 800-422-3436
Fax: (415)296-7299
URL: http://fidm.edu
Contact: Jim Glenny, Director, Library Services
Scope: Fashion design and merchandising, interior design, apparel manufacturing, advertising, merchandising, marketing. **Services:** Center not open to the public. **Founded:** 1977. **Holdings:** 4000 books; 800 AV programs; 1000 newspaper clipping files; 4000 videos, DVDs, and slides. **Subscriptions:** 200 journals and other serials.

1677 ■ Fashion Institute of Technology - Gladys Marcus Library
7th Ave. at 27th St.
E-Bldg. E502
New York, NY 10001-5992
Ph: (212)217-4340
Fax: (212)217-4371
Co. E-mail: greta_earnest@fitnyc.edu
URL: http://www.fitnyc.edu/library.asp
Contact: Prof. N.J. Wolfe, Director, Library Services
Scope: Costume, fashion, interior design, management engineering technology, fashion buying and merchandising, textiles, toy design, packaging design, advertising. **Services:** Interlibrary loan; copying; library open to the public for reference use only by appointment. **Founded:** 1944. **Holdings:** 130,260 books; 113,265 nonprint units; 20,637 bound periodical volumes; 125,000 fashion slides; 4712 reels of microfilm; 438 CD-ROM serials and digital monographs. **Subscriptions:** 4000 journals and other serials. **Telecommunication Services:** nj_wolfe@fitnyc.edu.

START-UP INFORMATION

1678 ■ *How to Bake a Business: Recipes to Turn Your Bright Idea Into a Successful Enterprise*
Pub: Allen & Unwin

Ed: Julia Bickerstaff. **Released:** May 10, 2010. **Price:** $17.95. **Description:** Guide to starting and running a successful baker are offered in a purse-size handbook.

ASSOCIATIONS AND OTHER ORGANIZATIONS

1679 ■ **American Bakers Association (ABA)**
1300 I St. NW, Ste. 700 W
Washington, DC 20005
Ph: (202)789-0300
Fax: (202)898-1164
Co. E-mail: rmackie@americanbakers.org
URL: http://americanbakers.org
Contact: Robb MacKie, President

Description: Manufacturers and wholesale distributors of bread, rolls, and pastry products; suppliers of goods and services to bakers. Conducts seminars and expositions. **Founded:** 1897.

REFERENCE WORKS

1680 ■ *"The Ultimate Vending Machine" in Benzinga.com (August 15, 2011)*
Pub: Benzinga.com

Ed: Benzinga Staff. **Description:** Louis Hecht, a baker from Hombourg-Haut, France is selling fresh-baked bread in vending machines. Each machine holds 90 pre-cooked loaves which are warmed before being delivered to the customer.

SOURCES OF SUPPLY

1681 ■ *Baking/Snack Directory & Buyer's Guide*
Sosland Publishing Co.

URL(s): www.sosland.com. **Released:** Annual; Latest edition 2010. **Price:** $205, Individuals S&H for ea. additional copy is $2 reg., $16 prior. **Covers:** Wholesale bakers of bread, cake, cookies, crackers, pasta; manufacturers of snack foods, mixes, and frozen dough; licensors of proprietary brands; manufacturers of equipment and products and suppliers of services used in wholesale baking. For bakers-- Company name, address, phone, principal headquarters and plant personnel, principal products, sales volume, production method, and number of employees. For manufacturers--Company name, address, phone, name and title of contact. **Entries include:** Company name, address, phone, executive name. **Arrangement:** Bakers are classified by product type; manufacturers are alphabetical. **Indexes:** Executive name, plant (bakers); product (manufacturers and suppliers).

TRADE PERIODICALS

1682 ■ *Baker's Rack*
Pub: The Retailer's Bakery Association

Ed: Anna Allen, Editor, sesh@rbanet.com. **Released:** Monthly. **Price:** Included in membership. **Description:** Examines trends and issues in the bakery industry. Features items on bakery production, marketing, business management, and other topics of interest. Recurring features include news of research, meeting reports, a calendar of events, and various columns.

1683 ■ *Baking Buyer*
Pub: Sosland Publishing Co.

URL(s): www.bakingbuyer.com. **Ed:** L. Joshua Sosland. **Released:** Monthly **Price:** $80, Other countries.

1684 ■ *Baking & Snack*
Pub: Sosland Publishing Co.

URL(s): www.sosland.comwww.sosland.com/mediakits.asp. **Ed:** Dan Malovany. **Released:** Monthly; (except January). **Price:** $72, Other countries print; $36, Individuals.

1685 ■ *Dairy-Deli-Bake Digest*
Pub: International Dairy-Deli-Bakery Association
Contact: Steve Beekhuizen, President

Ed: Carol L. Christison, Editor, cchristison@iddba.org. **Released:** Monthly. **Price:** Included in membership. **Description:** Supports the Association, which seeks to increase supermarket dairy-deli-bakery business. Focuses on issues of concern to manufacturers, retailers, brokers, distributors, businesses, and organizations involved with the dairy-deli-bakery industry. Recurring features include research news, reports of meetings, news of educational opportunities and industrial trends, and notices of publications available.

1686 ■ *Milling & Baking News*
Pub: Sosland Publishing Co.

URL(s): www.bakingbusiness.com. **Ed:** Josh Sosland. **Released:** Weekly (Tues.) **Price:** $135, U.S. and Canada; $210, U.S. and Canada 2 years; $290, U.S. and Canada 3 years; $190, Out of country; $320, Out of country 2 years; $455, Out of country 3 years.

1687 ■ *Modern Baking*
Pub: Penton Media Inc.
Contact: John French, President

URL(s): modern-baking.com. **Released:** Monthly

TRADE SHOWS AND CONVENTIONS

1688 ■ **Dairy-Deli-Bake Seminar and Expo**
International Dairy-Deli-Bakery Association (IDDBA)
PO Box 5528
Madison, WI 53705-0528
Ph: (608)310-5000

Fax: (608)238-6330
Co. E-mail: iddba@iddba.org
URL: http://www.iddba.org
Contact: Steve Beekhuizen, President

URL(s): www.iddba.org. **Frequency:** Annual. **Audience:** Retailers, wholesalers, distributors, brokers, and manufacturers of the dairy, deli, and bakery industry. **Principal Exhibits:** Dairy, deli, and bakery products, packaging, and equipment.

FRANCHISES AND BUSINESS OPPORTUNITIES

1689 ■ **Bagel Patch**
Bagel Patch, Inc.
c/o Marketing Resources Group
83-26 Lefferts Blvd.
Kew Gardens, NY 11415
Ph: (718)261-8882

Description: Bagel shop. **No. of Franchise Units:** 9. **No. of Company-Owned Units:** 1. **Founded:** 1980.. **Franchised:** 1994. **Equity Capital Needed:** $120,000-$146,000, including franchise fee. **Franchise Fee:** $15,000. **Training:** Yes.

1690 ■ **Between Rounds Bakery Sandwich Cafe**
Between Rounds Franchise Corp.
19A John Fitch Blvd.
South Windsor, CT 06074
Ph: (860)291-0323
Fax: (860)289-2732

Description: Bagels and other baked goods. **No. of Franchise Units:** 1. **No. of Company-Owned Units:** 3. **Founded:** 1990.. **Franchised:** 1994. **Equity Capital Needed:** $300,000 liquid. **Franchise Fee:** $65,000-$175,000. **Training:** Yes.

1691 ■ **Big Apple Bagels**
BAB, Inc.
500 Lake Cook Rd., Ste. 475
Deerfield, IL 60015
Ph: (847)948-7520
Fax: (847)405-8140
Co. E-mail: tcervini@babcorp.com
URL: http://www.babcorp.com

Description: A bakery style cafe featuring our three brands, made from scratch daily Big Apple Bagels and My Favorite Muffin, and freshly roasted Brewster's Coffee. Product offering includes made to order gourmet sandwiches, salads, soups, and espresso beverages. **No. of Franchise Units:** 102. **Founded:** 1992. **Franchised:** 1993. **Equity Capital Needed:** $252,300-$374,800. **Franchise Fee:** $25,000. **Training:** Extensive training covers all aspects of operations and management, combines hands-on experience at our corporate store training facility with classroom presentations by management and key note vendors.

1692 ■ **Big Town Hero**
Hero Systems, Inc.
333 SW Taylor St., Ste. 200
Portland, OR 97204
Ph: (503)228-4376

Fax: (503)228-8778
Description: Sandwiches, salads, soups, fresh bread and baked goods from scratch. Fast and friendly. **No. of Franchise Units:** 34. **Founded:** 1983.. **Franchised:** 1989. **Equity Capital Needed:** $75,000-$175,000. **Franchise Fee:** $20,000. **Training:** Yes.

1693 ■ Blue Chip Cookies
BDGS, LLC
210 Harrison St.
Loveland, OH 45140
Ph: (513)697-6610
Free: 800-888-9866
Fax: (513)697-2783
Co. E-mail: bluechipcookies@fuse.net
URL: http://www.bluechipcookies.com
Description: Cookies, bakery items, ice cream, coffees, depending on model and site. **No. of Franchise Units:** 5. **No. of Company-Owned Units:** 3. **Founded:** 1983.. **Franchised:** 1986. **Equity Capital Needed:** $150,000-$250,000. **Franchise Fee:** $25,000. **Training:** Offers 2 weeks of training.

1694 ■ Breadsmith
Breadsmith Franchising, Inc.
409 E Silver Spring Dr.
Whitefish Bay, WI 53217
Ph: (414)962-1965
Fax: (414)431-5789
Description: Specialty European artisan bakery. **No. of Franchise Units:** 34. **No. of Company-Owned Units:** 2. **Founded:** 1992.. **Franchised:** 1993. **Equity**

Capital Needed: $242,500-$324,000. **Franchise Fee:** $30,000. **Training:** Yes.

1695 ■ Bruegger's
159 Bank St.
Burlington, VT 05401
Free: 886-660-4104
Fax: (802)660-4034
Co. E-mail: franchise@brueggers.com
URL: http://www.brueggers.com
Description: Bakery style cafe serving bagels, sandwiches, breads, and fresh salads. **No. of Franchise Units:** 99. **No. of Company-Owned Units:** 148. **Founded:** 1983.. **Franchised:** 1993. **Equity Capital Needed:** $100,000 liquid; $200,000 net worth. **Franchise Fee:** $30,000. **Training:** Up to 8 weeks of on-the-job training.

1696 ■ Canada Bread Company, Limited
10 Four Seasons Pl.
Etobicoke, ON, Canada M9B 6H7
Ph: (416)641-4521
Fax: (416)626-7506
URL: http://www.cbfranchise.ca
Description: Bread, rolls, bagels, etc. **No. of Franchise Units:** 985. **No. of Company-Owned Units:** 65. **Founded:** 1960.. **Equity Capital Needed:** Initial investment ranges from $50,000-$200,000 Canadian. **Franchise Fee:** $5,000 Canadian. **Training:** Yes.

1697 ■ Lox of Bagels
11801 Prestwick Rd., Ste. 301
Potomac, MD 20854

Ph: (301)299-8523
Description: Bagels and gourmet coffee. **No. of Franchise Units:** 12. **Founded:** 1983.. **Franchised:** 1998. **Equity Capital Needed:** $50,000 in equity with typical cost of $150,000-$200,000 per unit. **Franchise Fee:** $9,500. **Training:** Yes.

1698 ■ Perfecto's Caffe
Perfecto's Caffe Development LLC
79 N Main St.
Andover, MA 01810
Ph: (978)749-7022
Fax: (978)749-9433
Description: Bagels, muffins, coffee, wraps, salads, and cookies. **No. of Franchise Units:** 2. **No. of Company-Owned Units:** 2. **Founded:** 1993.. **Franchised:** 2005. **Equity Capital Needed:** $175,000-$275,000, initial investment. **Franchise Fee:** $20,000. **Training:** Yes.

LIBRARIES

1699 ■ American Society of Baking - Information Service and Library
PO Box 336
Swedesboro, NJ 08085
Free: 800-713-0462
Fax: (888)315-2612
Co. E-mail: kvanamburg@asbe.org
URL: http://www.asbe.org
Contact: Kent Van Amburg, Executive Director
Scope: Baking and allied subjects. **Holdings:** 10,000 references. **Telecommunication Services:** info@asbe.org.

REFERENCE WORKS

1700 ■ *"Convictions Under the Fisheries Act"*
in Canadian Corporate News (May 16, 2007)
Pub: Comtex News Network Inc.
Description: Fisheries and Oceans Canada is
mandated to protect and conserve marine resources
and thus released a list of fishers fined for various offences under the Fisheries Act in March and April.

TRADE PERIODICALS

1701 ■ *Fishing Tackle Retailer*
Pub: BASS/ESPN
URL(s): sports.espn.go.com/outdoors/bassmaster/
news/story?page=bass_media_fi shing_retailer. **Ed:**
Dave Ellison. **Released:** 11/yr.

VIDEOCASSETTES/
AUDIOCASSETTES

1702 ■ *Advanced Walleye Systems I*
The In-Fisherman
7819 Highland Scenic Rd.
Baxter, MN 56425-8011
Ph: (218)829-1648
Free: 800-260-6397
Fax: (218)829-2371
Co. E-mail: customerservice@imoutdoors.com
URL: http://www.in-fisherman.com
Released: 19??. **Description:** Covers rigging tech-
niques, hot locations in rivers, beating the postspawn
slowdown, and more. **Availability:** VHS.

1703 ■ *Advanced Walleye Systems II*
The In-Fisherman
7819 Highland Scenic Rd.
Baxter, MN 56425-8011
Ph: (218)829-1648
Free: 800-260-6397
Fax: (218)829-2371
Co. E-mail: customerservice@imoutdoors.com
URL: http://www.in-fisherman.com
Released: 19??. **Description:** Provides step-by-step
instructions for locating and successfully catching
walleye. **Availability:** VHS.

1704 ■ *Advanced Walleye Systems III*
The In-Fisherman
7819 Highland Scenic Rd.
Baxter, MN 56425-8011
Ph: (218)829-1648
Free: 800-260-6397
Fax: (218)829-2371
Co. E-mail: customerservice@imoutdoors.com
URL: http://www.in-fisherman.com
Released: 19??. **Description:** Presents veteran
anglers as they combine fishing techniques and boat
control maneuvers to catch more fish. **Availability:**
VHS.

1705 ■ *Advanced Walleye Trolling Tactics*
The In-Fisherman
7819 Highland Scenic Rd.
Baxter, MN 56425-8011
Ph: (218)829-1648
Free: 800-260-6397
Fax: (218)829-2371
Co. E-mail: customerservice@imoutdoors.com
URL: http://www.in-fisherman.com
Released: 19??. **Description:** Covers boat rigging,
bait selection, leadcore line fishing, and more. **Avail-
ability:** VHS.

1706 ■ *Bass Tackle: How to Buy & Save*
Bennett Marine Video
2321 Abbot Kinney Blvd., Top Fl.
Venice, CA 90291
Ph: (310)827-8064
Free: 800-733-8862
Fax: (310)827-8074
Co. E-mail: questions@bennettmarine.com
URL: http://www.bennettmarine.com
Contact: Michael Bennett, President
Released: 1988. **Price:** $29.99. **Description:** This is
a guide to fishing tackle, with an emphasis on looking
for bargains. **Availability:** VHS.

1707 ■ *The Big Catfish Connection*
The In-Fisherman
7819 Highland Scenic Rd.
Baxter, MN 56425-8011
Ph: (218)829-1648
Free: 800-260-6397
Fax: (218)829-2371
Co. E-mail: customerservice@imoutdoors.com
URL: http://www.in-fisherman.com
Released: 19??. **Description:** Covers pre-spawn
staging locations, rigging right, summer hot spots,
and how to find wintering holes. **Availability:** VHS.

1708 ■ *The Big Catfish Connection II*
The In-Fisherman
7819 Highland Scenic Rd.
Baxter, MN 56425-8011
Ph: (218)829-1648
Free: 800-260-6397
Fax: (218)829-2371
Co. E-mail: customerservice@imoutdoors.com
URL: http://www.in-fisherman.com
Released: 19??. **Description:** Provides information
on night cats, high-water cats, bobber cats, and light-
line cats. **Availability:** VHS.

1709 ■ *Big Fish Ontario*
The In-Fisherman
7819 Highland Scenic Rd.
Baxter, MN 56425-8011
Ph: (218)829-1648
Free: 800-260-6397
Fax: (218)829-2371
Co. E-mail: customerservice@imoutdoors.com
URL: http://www.in-fisherman.com
Released: 19??. **Description:** Explains locations
and techniques for successful fishing in Ontario.
Availability: VHS.

1710 ■ *Big Walleye Presentations*
The In-Fisherman
7819 Highland Scenic Rd.
Baxter, MN 56425-8011
Ph: (218)829-1648
Free: 800-260-6397
Fax: (218)829-2371
Co. E-mail: customerservice@imoutdoors.com
URL: http://www.in-fisherman.com
Released: 19??. **Description:** Covers live bait, soft
plastics, rod selection, rigging methods, spinners,
and drift socks. **Availability:** VHS.

1711 ■ *Big Water Catfish*
The In-Fisherman
7819 Highland Scenic Rd.
Baxter, MN 56425-8011
Ph: (218)829-1648
Free: 800-260-6397
Fax: (218)829-2371
Co. E-mail: customerservice@imoutdoors.com
URL: http://www.in-fisherman.com
Released: 19??. **Description:** Offers tips on anchor-
ing and setting lines and hints on finding the best
places to fish. **Availability:** VHS.

1712 ■ *Catfish Fever*
The In-Fisherman
7819 Highland Scenic Rd.
Baxter, MN 56425-8011
Ph: (218)829-1648
Free: 800-260-6397
Fax: (218)829-2371
Co. E-mail: customerservice@imoutdoors.com
URL: http://www.in-fisherman.com
Released: 19??. **Description:** Covers methods and
equipment for catching catfish. **Availability:** VHS.

1713 ■ *Crappie Tactics for Lakes and
Reservoirs*
The In-Fisherman
7819 Highland Scenic Rd.
Baxter, MN 56425-8011
Ph: (218)829-1648
Free: 800-260-6397
Fax: (218)829-2371
Co. E-mail: customerservice@imoutdoors.com
URL: http://www.in-fisherman.com
Released: 19??. **Description:** Covers methods and
equipment for catching crappies. **Availability:** VHS.

1714 ■ *Fly Fishing for Pike*
The In-Fisherman
7819 Highland Scenic Rd.
Baxter, MN 56425-8011
Ph: (218)829-1648
Free: 800-260-6397
Fax: (218)829-2371
Co. E-mail: customerservice@imoutdoors.com
URL: http://www.in-fisherman.com
Released: 19??. **Description:** Covers rigging tech-
niques, and how, when, and where to catch pike with
a fly rod. **Availability:** VHS.

1715 ■ Ice Fishing Secrets I
The In-Fisherman
7819 Highland Scenic Rd.
Baxter, MN 56425-8011
Ph: (218)829-1648
Free: 800-260-6397
Fax: (218)829-2371
Co. E-mail: customerservice@imoutdoors.com
URL: http://www.in-fisherman.com
Released: 19??. **Description:** Covers jigging methods, tip-ups, and terminal rigs. **Availability:** VHS.

1716 ■ Northern Pike: The Water World
The In-Fisherman
7819 Highland Scenic Rd.
Baxter, MN 56425-8011
Ph: (218)829-1648
Free: 800-260-6397
Fax: (218)829-2371
Co. E-mail: customerservice@imoutdoors.com
URL: http://www.in-fisherman.com
Released: 19??. **Description:** Al Lindner explains where to catch pike, what lures to use, trolling patterns, and more. **Availability:** VHS.

1717 ■ Panfish Patterns
The In-Fisherman
7819 Highland Scenic Rd.
Baxter, MN 56425-8011
Ph: (218)829-1648
Free: 800-260-6397
Fax: (218)829-2371
Co. E-mail: customerservice@imoutdoors.com
URL: http://www.in-fisherman.com
Released: 19??. **Description:** Covers methods and equipment for catching panfish. **Availability:** VHS.

1718 ■ Pike in the Dead Zone
The In-Fisherman
7819 Highland Scenic Rd.
Baxter, MN 56425-8011
Ph: (218)829-1648
Free: 800-260-6397
Fax: (218)829-2371
Co. E-mail: customerservice@imoutdoors.com
URL: http://www.in-fisherman.com
Released: 19??. **Description:** Covers floats, rods, dead bait triggers for early season pike, and more. **Availability:** VHS.

1719 ■ Prime Time Walleye Locations
The In-Fisherman
7819 Highland Scenic Rd.
Baxter, MN 56425-8011
Ph: (218)829-1648
Free: 800-260-6397
Fax: (218)829-2371
Co. E-mail: customerservice@imoutdoors.com
URL: http://www.in-fisherman.com
Released: 19??. **Description:** Includes information on shallow water walleyes, night fishing, speed control, lure choice, and equipment selection. **Availability:** VHS.

1720 ■ River Walleye Location Secrets
The In-Fisherman
7819 Highland Scenic Rd.
Baxter, MN 56425-8011
Ph: (218)829-1648
Free: 800-260-6397
Fax: (218)829-2371
Co. E-mail: customerservice@imoutdoors.com
URL: http://www.in-fisherman.com
Released: 19??. **Description:** Presents prespawn, summer, and fall techniques. **Availability:** VHS.

1721 ■ River Walleye Presentation Secrets
The In-Fisherman
7819 Highland Scenic Rd.
Baxter, MN 56425-8011
Ph: (218)829-1648
Free: 800-260-6397
Fax: (218)829-2371
Co. E-mail: customerservice@imoutdoors.com
URL: http://www.in-fisherman.com
Released: 19??. **Description:** Covers bait options, rod and reel types, depth control , and setting the hook. **Availability:** VHS.

1722 ■ Secrets of the Walleye Trail
The In-Fisherman
7819 Highland Scenic Rd.
Baxter, MN 56425-8011
Ph: (218)829-1648
Free: 800-260-6397
Fax: (218)829-2371
Co. E-mail: customerservice@imoutdoors.com
URL: http://www.in-fisherman.com
Released: 19??. **Description:** Covers wind fishing, leadcore trolling, advanced bottom bouncing, jigging spoons, and shallow water fishing techniques. **Availability:** VHS.

1723 ■ Smallmouth Bass: America's Greatest Sportfish
The In-Fisherman
7819 Highland Scenic Rd.
Baxter, MN 56425-8011
Ph: (218)829-1648
Free: 800-260-6397
Fax: (218)829-2371
Co. E-mail: customerservice@imoutdoors.com
URL: http://www.in-fisherman.com
Released: 19??. **Description:** Covers location keys and sight fishing, rattle baits, lures, chuggers, and more. **Availability:** VHS.

1724 ■ Stream Trout Tactics
The In-Fisherman
7819 Highland Scenic Rd.
Baxter, MN 56425-8011
Ph: (218)829-1648
Free: 800-260-6397
Fax: (218)829-2371
Co. E-mail: customerservice@imoutdoors.com
URL: http://www.in-fisherman.com
Released: 19??. **Description:** Covers methods and equipment for catching stream trout. **Availability:** VHS.

1725 ■ Trophy Lake Trout Tactics
The In-Fisherman
7819 Highland Scenic Rd.
Baxter, MN 56425-8011
Ph: (218)829-1648
Free: 800-260-6397
Fax: (218)829-2371
Co. E-mail: customerservice@imoutdoors.com
URL: http://www.in-fisherman.com
Released: 19??. **Description:** Covers methods and equipment for catching lake trout. **Availability:** VHS.

1726 ■ The World's Greatest Walleye Lure
The In-Fisherman
7819 Highland Scenic Rd.
Baxter, MN 56425-8011
Ph: (218)829-1648
Free: 800-260-6397
Fax: (218)829-2371
Co. E-mail: customerservice@imoutdoors.com
URL: http://www.in-fisherman.com
Released: 19??. **Description:** Discusses presentation, triggering, snap jigging, and specialty jigs. **Availability:** VHS.

TRADE SHOWS AND CONVENTIONS

1727 ■ Cincinnati Travel, Sports, and Boat Show
Hart Productions, Inc.
322 E. Main St.
Batavia, OH 45103
Ph: (513)797-7900
Free: 877-704-8190
Fax: (513)797-1013
URL: http://www.hartproductions.com
URL(s): www.hartproductions.com. **Price:** $11, Onsite. **Frequency:** Annual. **Audience:** General public. **Principal Exhibits:** Showcasing a world of travel and recreation featuring vacation travel exhibits, boats, sporting goods, fishing and hunting equipment and seminars. **Dates and Locations:** , Dr. Albert B. Sabin Convention Center. **Telecommunication Services:** chip@hartproductions.com.

1728 ■ Cleveland Sport, Travel & Outdoor Show
Expositions Inc.
PO Box 550, Edgewater Br.
Cleveland, OH 44107-0550
Ph: (216)529-1300
Fax: (216)529-0311
Co. E-mail: showinfo@expoinc.com
URL: http://www.expoinc.com
URL(s): www.sportandtravel.com/cleveland/. **Frequency:** Annual. **Principal Exhibits:** Sport fishing. **Telecommunication Services:** cmfassnacht@gmail.com.

1729 ■ Detroit Boat Show
Michigan Boating Industries Association
32398 5 Mile Rd.
Livonia, MI 48154-6109
Ph: (734)261-0123
Free: 800-932-2628
Fax: (734)261-0880
Co. E-mail: boatmichigan@mbia.org
URL: http://www.mbia.org
Contact: John J. Ropp, President
E-mail: jropp@mbia.org
URL(s): www.mbia.org. **Price:** $12, adult; children ages 12 & under. **Frequency:** Annual. **Audience:** Trade professionals and general public. **Principal Exhibits:** Boats, fishing equipment, boat-related accessories, charter rentals, nautical attire, trailer and outboard motors, and personal watercraft. **Dates and Locations:** , Cobo Conference and Exhibition Center.

1730 ■ Eastern Fishing and Outdoor Exposition
Eastern Fishing and Outdoor Exposition Inc.
750 Central Ave., Ste. R
Dover, NH 03820
Ph: (603)431-4315
Fax: (603)431-1971
Co. E-mail: info@sportshows.com
URL: http://www.sportshows.com
URL(s): www.sportshows.com/. **Price:** $9. **Frequency:** Annual. **Audience:** Metro Boston/Worcester Market. **Principal Exhibits:** Fishing and outdoor sports. **Telecommunication Services:** info@sportshows.com.

1731 ■ World Fishing and Outdoor Exposition
Eastern Fishing and Outdoor Exposition Inc.
750 Central Ave., Ste. R
Dover, NH 03820
Ph: (603)431-4315
Fax: (603)431-1971
Co. E-mail: info@sportshows.com
URL: http://www.sportshows.com
URL(s): www.sportshows.com/suffern/index.html. **Frequency:** Annual. **Audience:** Metro New York City Market. **Principal Exhibits:** Fishing and outdoor sports. **Telecommunication Services:** info@sportshows.com.

FRANCHISES AND BUSINESS OPPORTUNITIES

1732 ■ Cinnzeo
Cinnaroll Bakeries Ltd.
2140 Pegasus Rd., NE
Calgary, AB, Canada T2E 8G8
Ph: (403)255-4556
Free: 877-246-6036
Fax: (403)259-5124
Description: Quick service cinnamon roll bakery. **No. of Franchise Units:** 20. **No. of Company-Owned Units:** 4. **Founded:** 1987. **Franchised:** 1998. **Equity Capital Needed:** $214,000-$621,000. **Franchise Fee:** $15,000. **Royalty Fee:** 7%. **Training:** Offers 3 weeks at headquarters, 2 weeks at franchise's location with ongoing support.

1733 ■ Desert Moon Fresh Mexican Grill
Desert Moon Franchise LLC
Description: Specializes in Mexican food delicacies. **No. of Franchise Units:** 15. **No. of Company-Owned Units:** 3. **Founded:** 1992. **Franchised:** 1999. **Equity Capital Needed:** $350,000. **Franchise Fee:** $25,000. **Financial Assistance:** Yes. **Training:** Yes.

1734 ■ White Hen Pantry, Inc.
Clark Retail Enterprises Inc.
1722 Routh St., Ste. 1000
Dallas, TX 75201
Ph: (630)366-3100
Fax: (630)366-3447

Description: Convenience food store of approximately 2,500 square feet. Up-front parking for 10-15 cars. Stores are usually open 24 hours (some operate a lesser number of hours) for 365 days a year. Product line includes a service deli, fresh bakery, fresh produce and a wide variety of staples. **No. of Franchise Units:** 260. **Founded:** 1965.. **Franchised:** 1965. **Equity Capital Needed:** $40,000-$45,000, not including franchise fee. **Franchise Fee:** $25,000. **Financial Assistance:** Yes. **Training:** 3 weeks of classroom and in-store training precede store opening. Follow-up training provided after taking over store. Detailed operations manuals provided.

LIBRARIES

1735 ■ International Game Fish Association - E.K. Harry Library of Fishes
IGFA Fishing Hall of Fame and Museum, 2nd Fl.
300 Gulf Stream Way
Dania Beach, FL 33004
Ph: (954)927-2628
Fax: (954)924-4299
Co. E-mail: hq@igfa.org
URL: http://www.igfa.org/Museum/IGFA-MUSEUM-LIBRARY.aspx
Contact: Gail M. Morchower, Museum Director

Scope: Fish, sport fishing. **Services:** Library open to the public for reference use only. **Founded:** 1973. **Holdings:** 15,000 books; fishing club yearbooks and newsletters; 2100 fishing videos; stamps; photographs; angling artifacts. **Subscriptions:** 150 journals

and other serials. **Telecommunication Services:** cdiaz@igfa.org.

1736 ■ Virginia Institute of Marine Science - William J. Hargis, Jr. Library
College of William and Mary
School of Marine Science
Gloucester Point, VA 23062-1346
Ph: (804)684-7114
Fax: (804)684-7113
Co. E-mail: coughlin@vims.edu
URL: http://web.vims.edu/library/
Contact: Carol Coughlin, Director, Library Services
Scope: Marine and estuarine biology and ecology, oceanography, aquaculture, Chesapeake Bay. **Services:** Interlibrary loan; copying; library open to the public. **Founded:** 1947. **Holdings:** 29,511 book titles; 30,149 bound periodical volumes; 5007 maps; 51,000 serial volumes. **Subscriptions:** 685 journals and other serials.

START-UP INFORMATION

1737 ■ *"Hand-Held Heaven: Smallcakes Cupcakery"* *in Tulsa World (February 15, 2011)*
Pub: McClatchy Company

Description: Franchisee Carolyn Archer displays her products at Smallcakes Cupcakery, a Jenks shop that's the first to be co-branded with FreshBerry under the Beautiful Brands International banner. The shop's launch is part of a franchise deal between BBI and Jeff and Brandy Martin, co-owners of Smallcakes; twelve concepts have been developed and marketed already by Tulsa-based BBI.

1738 ■ *How to Bake a Business: Recipes to Turn Your Bright Idea Into a Successful Enterprise*
Pub: Allen & Unwin

Ed: Julia Bickerstaff. **Released:** May 10, 2010. **Price:** $17.95. **Description:** Guide to starting and running a successful baker are offered in a purse-size handbook.

1739 ■ *How to Open a Financially Successful Bakery: With a Companion CD-ROM*
Pub: Atlantic Publishing Company

Ed: Sharon Fullen, Douglas R. Brown. **Released:** July 18, 2009. **Price:** $39.95. **Description:** Expert tips, tricks and information is offered to help start and run a bakery.

1740 ■ *My Life From Scratch: A Sweet Journey of Starting Over, One Cake at a Time*
Pub: Broadway Books
Contact: David Drake, Manager
E-mail: ddrake@randomhouse.com

Released: June 8, 2010. **Price:** $14.00. **Description:** Lively account of Old World recipes, Bullock-Prado, a former Hollywood film developer and sister to actress Sandra Bullock, recounts the joys and heartbreak of running her own patisserie in Montpelier, Vermont. Having fled Los Angeles with her husband, Ray for the simpler pleasures of a small town near the Green Mountains, she opened her own bake shop, Gesine Confectionary in 2004, mostly on the fame of the macaroons she refashioned from her German mother's favorite almond treat, mandelhoernchen (and the casual mention of her sister in an interview). Her memoir follows one day in a busy baker's life, from waking at 3 a.m. to prepare the batter and bake her croissants, scones, and sticky buns, before opening her shop at 7 a.m., through the hectic lunch, and 3 p.m. tea time.

1741 ■ *The Specialty Shop: How to Create Your Own Unique and Profitable Retail Business*
Pub: AMACOM

Ed: Dorothy Finell. **Released:** February 27, 2007. **Price:** $21.95. **Description:** Advise to start retail businesses, including bakeries, gift shops, toy stores, book shops, tea houses, clothing boutiques, and other unique stores.

1742 ■ *"Try a Little Piece of Heaven at this Suffolk Cupcakery"* *in Virginia-Pilot (February 13, 2011)*
Pub: McClatchy Company

Ed: Hattie Brown Garrow. **Description:** Profile of Tanya West, owner of the new startup called Divine Creations Cupcakery and Desserts located in Suffolk, Virginia. West is a full-time baker and mother of three children.

ASSOCIATIONS AND OTHER ORGANIZATIONS

1743 ■ **AIB International**
1213 Bakers Way
Manhattan, KS 66505-3999
Ph: (785)537-4750
Free: 800-633-5137
Fax: (785)537-1493
Co. E-mail: aibmarketing@aibonline.org
URL: http://www.aibonline.org
Contact: James Munyon, President
E-mail: jmunyon@aibonline.org

Description: Baking research and educational center. Conducts basic and applied research, educational and hands-on training, and in-plant sanitation and worker safety audits. Maintains museum. Provides bibliographic and reference service. Serves as registrar for ISO-9000 quality certification. **Scope:** Offers consulting services in the fields of applied research and product development, food bakery plant equipment and engineering, food defense/security, food product nutritional labeling, bakery product nutrition, food safety audits, and general bakery production consultation. Also provides education, research, product development, technical assistance and management services to domestic and international food related industries. **Founded:** 1919. **Subscriptions:** 11350 archival material books periodicals reports. **Publications:** "Baking Technology - Laminated Dough Systems," 1996; "Baking Technology-Controlled Baking," 1995; "Technology of Food Product Development," 1994; "Cookie and Cracker Technology," 1992; "Chemistry and Technology of Cereals as Food and Feed," 1991; "Bakery Technology," 1989; "Baker's Math"; "Baking Science and Technology"; "Formulating and Processing Dietetic Foods"; "Baker's Math"; "Baking Science and Technology Vol 1: Fundamentals and Ingredients". **Awards:** AIB Scholarship (Annual), for maintenance engineering and baking science and technology resident courses. **Seminars:** Principles of Inspecting and Auditing Food Plants, Atlanta, Nov, 2009; Reportable Food Registry - An Executive Briefing and Discussion, Nov, 2009; Maintenance Management for Food Plants, Manhattan, Nov, 2009; All About Baking, Manhattan, Feb, 2009; Food Plant GMP/Sanitation Workshop, Phoenix, Feb, 2009; Hands-On Programmable Controllers, Manhattan, Feb, 2009; GMP Workshop for Packaging Suppliers, Louisville, Jun, 2008; Advanced Bread and Roll Production, Manhattan, May, 2008; Food Plant GMP/Sanitation Workshop, Portland, Apr, 2008; Maintenance Engineering, Manhattan, Mar, 2008; An Integrated Quality System for the Food Industry, San Antonio, Feb, 2008; Freezing Technology, Huntersville, Feb, 2008. **Telecommunication Services:** membership@aibonline.org.

1744 ■ **American Bakers Association (ABA)**
1300 I St. NW, Ste. 700 W
Washington, DC 20005
Ph: (202)789-0300
Fax: (202)898-1164
Co. E-mail: rmackie@americanbakers.org
URL: http://americanbakers.org
Contact: Robb MacKie, President

Description: Manufacturers and wholesale distributors of bread, rolls, and pastry products; suppliers of goods and services to bakers. Conducts seminars and expositions. **Founded:** 1897.

1745 ■ **American Society of Baking**
PO Box 336
Swedesboro, NJ 08085
Free: 800-713-0462
Fax: (888)315-2612
Co. E-mail: info@asbe.org
URL: http://www.asbe.org
Contact: Mike Elenz, Chairman

Description: Professional organization of persons engaged in bakery production; chemists, production supervisors, engineers, technicians, and others from allied fields. Maintains information service and library references to baking and related subjects. **Scope:** baking industry. **Founded:** 1924.

1746 ■ **Baking Association of Canada (BAC)—Association Canadienne de la Boulangerie**
7895 Tranmere Dr., Ste. 202
Mississauga, ON, Canada L5S 1V9
Ph: (905)405-0288
Free: 888-674-2253
Fax: (905)405-0993
Co. E-mail: info@baking.ca
URL: http://www.bakingassoccanada.com
Contact: Paul Hetherington, President

Description: Bakeries. Promotes growth and development of the domestic baking industries. Represents the interests of bakers (retail, wholesale, in-store, food service) before industrial and labor organizations, government agencies, and the public. **Founded:** 1997. **Publications:** *The Bulletin* (10/year). **Educational Activities:** Baking Association of Canada Tradeshow (Biennial).

1747 ■ *The Bulletin*
7895 Tranmere Dr., Ste. 202
Mississauga, ON, Canada L5S 1V9
Ph: (905)405-0288
Free: 888-674-2253
Fax: (905)405-0993
Co. E-mail: info@baking.ca
URL: http://www.bakingassoccanada.com
Contact: Paul Hetherington, President

Released: 10/year **Price:** included in membership dues.

1748 ■ Independent Bakers Association (IBA)
PO Box 3731
Washington, DC 20007
Ph: (202)333-8190
Fax: (202)337-3809
Co. E-mail: independentbaker@yahoo.com
URL: http://www.independentbaker.net/independent-bakersassociation
Contact: Len Amoroso, Chairman

Description: Trade association representing small-medium wholesale bakers and allied trade members. Represents independent wholesale bakers on federal legislative and regulatory issues. Offers annual Smith-Schaus-Smith internships. **Founded:** 1968. **Publications:** *The Independent* (Annual); *News Release* (Biweekly). **Educational Activities:** Independent Bakers Association Meeting (Annual).

1749 ■ Retail Bakers of America (RBA)
202 Village Cir., Ste. 1
Slidell, LA 70458
Ph: (985)643-6504
Free: 800-638-0924
Fax: (985)643-6929
Co. E-mail: info@rbanet.com
URL: http://www.retailbakersofamerica.org
Contact: Kenneth Downey, Sr., President

Description: Independent and in-store bakeries, food service, specialty bakeries, suppliers of ingredients, tools and equipment; other. Provides information, management, production, merchandising and small business services. **Scope:** retail baking. **Founded:** 1918. **Subscriptions:** books. **Publications:** *The Business Owner* (Bimonthly).

REFERENCE WORKS

1750 ■ "At This Bakery, Interns' Hope Rises Along With the Bread" in Chicago Tribune (October 31, 2008)
Pub: McClatchy-Tribune Information Services

Ed: Mary Schmich. **Description:** Profile of Sweet Miss Givings Bakery and its diverse founder, interns and employees; the bakery was founded by Stan Sloan, an Episcopal priest who started the business to help fund his ministry; Sloan saw a need for jobs for those living with HIV and other disabilities and through the bakery the interns learn the skills needed to eventually find work elsewhere.

1751 ■ "Baxter Baker Wins in Hot Finale of 'Cupcake Wars"' in Fort Mill Times (September 13, 2011)
Pub: McClatchy Company

Ed: Jenny Overmann. **Description:** Heather McDonnell, owner of Cupcrazed Cakery, and her assistant Debbie McDonnell, vied for a chance to win $10,000 on the cable network show called 'Cupcake Wars', and to serve cupcakes at the album release party for country singer Jennette McCurdy. At the end of the show, the sisters-in-law won the top prize.

1752 ■ "Blue Hill Tavern to Host Baltimore's First Cupcake Camp" in Daily Record (August 10, 2011)
Pub: Dolan Company

Ed: Rachel Bernstein. **Description:** Cities joining the trend to host cupcake camps are listed. The camps are open to all individuals wishing to share and eat cupcakes in an open environment.

1753 ■ "Breadwinner Tries on Designer Jeans" in Houston Business Journal (Vol. 40, December 18, 2009, No. 32, pp. 1)
Pub: American City Business Journals

Ed: Allison Wollam. **Description:** Chuck Cain, the franchisee who introduced Panera Bread to Houston, Texas has partnered with tax accountant Jim Jacobsen to introduce custom-make Tattu Jeans. As more Tattu Jeans outlets are being planned, Cain is using entrepreneurial lessons learned from Panera Bread in the new venture. Both Panera Bread and Tattu Jeans were opened by Cain during economic downturns.

1754 ■ "Canada's Largest Bakery Officially Opened Today" in Ecology,Environment & Conservation Business (October 15, 2011, pp. 7)
Pub: HighBeam Research

Description: Maple Leaf Foods opened Canada's largest commercial bakery in Hamilton, Ontario. The firm's 385,000 square foot Trillium bakery benefits from efficient design flow and best-in-class technologies.

1755 ■ "Cold Stone Creamery Offers New Eight-Layer Ice Cream Cakes" in Ice Cream Reporter (Vol. 23, October 20, 2010, No. 11, pp. 2)
Pub: Ice Cream Reporter

Description: Cold Stone Creamery is introducing a new line of eight-layer ice cream cakes, which are crafted with three layers of ice cream, three layers of cake and two mid-layers of mix-ins and finished with frosting and a creative design.

1756 ■ "Cupcake Craze" in Mail Tribune (March 2, 2011)
Pub: Southern Oregon Media Group

Ed: Sarah Lemon. **Description:** Gourmet cupcake shops are sprouting up in large cities in Oregon. The Cupcake Company, a family business, is profiled.

1757 ■ "Cupcake Eating Contest Draws World-Class Competitors" in Waterloo Courier (April 14, 2011)
Pub: Lee Enterprises

Ed: Amie Steffen. **Description:** World Cupcake Eating Championships were held at the Isle Casino Hotel Waterloo, Iowa, April 23, 2011. Major League Eating reports this to be the first time they've held a cupcake eating contest.

1758 ■ "Cupcake Maker Explains Tricks of the Trade" in Chattanooga Times/Free Press (September 6, 2011)
Pub: Chattanooga Publishing Company

Ed: Holly Leber. **Description:** Sunny Burden, head baker at Whipped Cupcakes in Chattanooga, Tennessee creates themed cupcakes as well as traditional ones. Burden finds baking therapeutic.

1759 ■ "Cupcake Maker Grabs Outpost" in Crain's New York Business (Vol. 27, August 15, 2011, No. 33, pp. 16)
Pub: Crain Communications, Inc.

Ed: Jermaine Taylor. **Description:** Family-owned miniature cupcake maker, Baked by Melissa, singed a ten-year lease, expanding their stores to five. The business was started three years ago by advertising executive Melissa Bushell.

1760 ■ "'Cupcake Wars' TV Show Returns to Hampton Roads" in Virginian-Pilot (September 11, 2011)
Pub: McClatchy Company

Ed: Carolyn Shapiro. **Description:** Virginia Beach, Virginia sweet shop called Just Cupcakes and Carolina Cupcakery will compete for prizes on cable TV's Food Network Channel. Carla Hesseltine, owner of Just Cupcakes made it to the final rounds.

1761 ■ "Dunkin' Donuts Franchise Looking Possible for 2011" in Messenger-Inquirer (January 2, 2010)
Pub: Messenger-Inquirer

Ed: Joy Campbell. **Description:** Dunkin' Donuts has approved expansion of their franchises in the Owensboro, Kentucky region.

1762 ■ "GoodNews.com and the Little Cupcake Shoppe Support Calgary Food Bank With Unique $1.00 Deal" in Marketwire Canada (March 9, 2011)
Pub: Marketwire Canada

Description: Socially-conscious group-buying Website, GoodNews.com has partnered with The Little Cupcake Shoppe in Calgary, to raise funds for the Inter-Faith Food Bank. The fundraiser will feature a half dozen, pre-packaged assorted miniature cupcakes for $1.00. The entire amount is donated to the Calgary Food Bank.

1763 ■ "Hostess Reveals Grand Prize Winner of 'CupCake Jackpot' Promotion" in Entertainment Close-Up (August 19, 2011)
Pub: Close-Up Media

Description: Tricia Botbyl was the grand prize winner of the Hostess 'CupCake Jackpot' promotion that asked consumers to 'spin' online to win $10,000. Consumers were asked to vote for their favorite Hostess Brand cupcake flavor.

1764 ■ "How Sweet It Is: a Health Hardship Leads to Cupcake Commerce" in Black Enterprise (Vol. 41, August 2010, No. 1, pp. 56)
Pub: Earl G. Graves Publishing Co. Inc.

Ed: Tamara E. Holmes. **Description:** Profile of Andra Hall, entrepreneur who started her cupcake business when her one-year-old daughter suffered from sleep apnea and wanted the flexibility to be with her baby. Hall and her husband refinanced their home in order to start the bakery.

1765 ■ "It's all Kosher at Downtown Eatery/ Bakery" in AZ Daily Star (July 10, 2008)
Pub: Arizona Daily Star

Ed: Valerie Vinyard. **Description:** Rabbi James Botwright and partner Wayne Anderson are profiled. Details of how the partners opened their bakery and eatery in Tucson, Arizona. Botwright, who attended culinary school in San Francisco, learned much from his grandfather who was a pastry chef.

1766 ■ "Katie's Cupcakes to Celebrate One-Year Anniversary" in Bellingham Business Journal (Vol. March 2010, pp. 3)
Pub: Sound Publishing Inc.

Description: Katie Swanson, owner of Katie's Cupcakes, celebrated her firm's one-year anniversary with a fundraiser for the Whatcom Humane Society by offering free specialty cupcakes and other special events to the public. The specialty cupcakes will feature either a paw or bone and will be available throughout the month of March.

1767 ■ "Lux Coffees, Breads Push Chains to React" in Advertising Age (Vol. 77, June 26, 2006, No. 26, pp. S14)
Pub: Crain Communications, Inc.

Ed: Kate MacArthur. **Description:** Fast-food giants such as McDonald's, Burger King, Dunkin' Donuts and Subway have adjusted their menus in order to become more competitive with gourmet coffee shops and bakeries like Panera Bread and Starbucks which have taken a large share in the market. Statistical data included.

1768 ■ "Nation of Islam Businessman Who Became Manager for Muhammad Ali Dies" in Chicago Tribune (August 28, 2008)
Pub: McClatchy-Tribune Information Services

Ed: Trevor Jensen. **Description:** Profile of Jabir Herbert Muhammad who died on August 25, after heart surgery; Muhammad lived nearly all his life on Chicago's South Side and ran a number of small businesses including a bakery and a dry cleaners before becoming the manager to famed boxer Mohammad Ali.

1769 ■ "New Zealand Natural Co-Branding with Mrs. Fields" in Ice Cream Reporter (Vol. 23, November 20, 2010, No. 12, pp. 2)
Pub: Ice Cream Reporter

Description: Mrs. Fields has partnered with a New Zealand firm to co-brand ice cream and cookies in Australian markets.

1770 ■ "Red Velvet Cupcake Bites" in CandyIndustry (Vol. 176, September 2011, No. 9, pp. RC4)
Pub: BNP Media
Contact: Al Reser, President

Description: Taste of Nature's Cookie Dough Bites has launched a new candy called, Red Velvet Cupcake Bites. The new product will feature a cupcake center covered in red frosting; ingredients are listed.

1771 ■ *"Toughen Up, Cupcake: You Know Who Plays for Keeps These Days? Cupcake Makers" in Inc (Vol. 33, May 2011, No. 4, pp. 100)*

Pub: Inc. Magazine

Ed: Burt Helm. **Description:** Cupcake shops are sprouting up everywhere across the nation and Washington, DC seems to be the epicenter for the trend. Profile of a new bakery called Sprinkles, that offers cupcake creations, is featured.

1772 ■ *"Two Local Bakers Winners of TV's 'Cupcake Wars" in Toledo Blade (July 6, 2011)*

Pub: Toledo Times

Description: Winners of cable network Food Channel's Cupcake Wars, Lori Jacobs and Dana Iliev own Cake in a Cup in Toledo, Ohio. The partners shop features creative cupcakes with names such as Monkey Business, Pretty in Pink, and Tropical Getaway.

1773 ■ *"The Ultimate Vending Machine" in Benzinga.com (August 15, 2011)*

Pub: Benzinga.com

Ed: Benzinga Staff. **Description:** Louis Hecht, a baker from Hombourg-Haut, France is selling fresh-baked bread in vending machines. Each machine holds 90 pre-cooked loaves which are warmed before being delivered to the customer.

STATISTICAL SOURCES

1774 ■ *The Market Outlook for Bakery Products*

Business Trend Analysts, Inc. Industry Studies

Released: 2005-2006. **Price:** $2195.00. **Description:** Profiles markets for bread, rolls, cakes, pies, cookies, crackers, other sweets, and pretzels. Provides information on consumption patterns, distribution trends, pricing, new products, and advertising strategies. Also contains profiles of leading marketers.

1775 ■ *RMA Annual Statement Studies*

Pub: Risk Management Association

Contact: Kevin M. Blakey, President

Released: Annual. **Price:** $175.00 2006-07 edition, $105.00. **Description:** Contains composite balance sheets and income statements for more than 360 industries, including the accounting, auditing, and bookkeeping industries. Also contains five years of comparative historical data for discerning trends. Includes 16 commonly used ratios, computed for most of the size groupings for nearly every industry.

1776 ■ *The U.S. Bread Market*

Pub: MarketResearch.com

Released: 1998. **Price:** $2062.50. **Description:** This report from Packaged Facts analyzes the $21 billion U.S. market for packaged, fresh and frozen bread products, focusing on the increasing diversity of the consumer base and the products marketed.

TRADE PERIODICALS

1777 ■ *American Institute of Baking Technical Bulletin*

Pub: American Institute of Baking Research Dept.

URL(s): https://www.aibonline.org/onlinecatalog/products/bulletins/technical/indexh tml. **Released:** Monthly **Price:** $100, U.S.; $125, Other countries; $20, Single issue plus shipping; $20, Single issue via email and fax.

1778 ■ *Baker's Rack*

Pub: The Retailer's Bakery Association

Ed: Anna Allen, Editor, sesh@rbanet.com. **Released:** Monthly. **Price:** Included in membership. **Description:** Examines trends and issues in the bakery industry. Features items on bakery production, marketing, business management, and other topics of interest. Recurring features include news of research, meeting reports, a calendar of events, and various columns.

1779 ■ *Baking & Snack*

Pub: Sosland Publishing Co.

URL(s): www.sosland.comwww.sosland.com/mediak-its.asp. **Ed:** Dan Malovany. **Released:** Monthly; (except January). **Price:** $72, Other countries print; $36, Individuals.

1780 ■ *IDDBA Legis-Letter*

Pub: International Dairy-Deli-Bakery Association

Contact: Steve Beekhuizen, President

Ed: Carol L. Christison, Editor, cchristison@iddba. org. **Price:** Included in membership. **Description:** Reports on legislative activity concerning the supermarket dairy-deli-bakery industry.

1781 ■ *Milling & Baking News*

Pub: Sosland Publishing Co.

URL(s): www.bakingbusiness.com. **Ed:** Josh Sosland. **Released:** Weekly (Tues.) **Price:** $135, U.S. and Canada; $210, U.S. and Canada 2 years; $290, U.S. and Canada 3 years; $190, Out of country; $320, Out of country 2 years; $455, Out of country 3 years.

1782 ■ *Pastry Art & Design*

Pub: Haymarket Group Ltd.

URL(s): www.pastryartanddesign.com/. **Ed:** Tish Boyle. **Released:** Bimonthly **Price:** $50, Individuals; $100, Two years; $60, Canada; $120, Canada for two years; $60, Other countries; $120, Other countries for two years.

1783 ■ *WrapUp*

Pub: International Dairy-Deli-Bakery Association

Contact: Steve Beekhuizen, President

Ed: Carol L Christison, Editor, cchristison@iddba.org. **Released:** Quarterly. **Price:** Included in membership. **Description:** Reports on news, activities, and topics of interest to the Association.

VIDEOCASSETTES/ AUDIOCASSETTES

1784 ■ *A Baker's Dozen: 13 European Concepts, 144 Great Ideas!*

International Dairy-Deli-Bakery Association (IDDBA)
PO Box 5528
Madison, WI 53705-0528
Ph: (608)310-5000
Fax: (608)238-6330
Co. E-mail: iddba@iddba.org
URL: http://www.iddba.org
Contact: Steve Beekhuizen, President
Released: 19??. **Price:** $100.00. **Description:** Merchandising and training video. **Availability:** VHS.

1785 ■ *Bakery High Notes from Europe*

International Dairy-Deli-Bakery Association (IDDBA)
PO Box 5528
Madison, WI 53705-0528
Ph: (608)310-5000
Fax: (608)238-6330
Co. E-mail: iddba@iddba.org
URL: http://www.iddba.org
Contact: Steve Beekhuizen, President
Released: 19??. **Price:** $100.00. **Description:** Merchandising and training video. **Availability:** VHS.

1786 ■ *Bakery Merchandising 101*

International Dairy-Deli-Bakery Association (IDDBA)
PO Box 5528
Madison, WI 53705-0528
Ph: (608)310-5000
Fax: (608)238-6330
Co. E-mail: iddba@iddba.org
URL: http://www.iddba.org
Contact: Steve Beekhuizen, President
Released: 19??. **Price:** $50.00. **Description:** Discusses ways for successful promotion and product appeal to help increase bakery sales. **Availability:** VHS.

1787 ■ *Bakery Merchandising Certificate Program*

International Dairy-Deli-Bakery Association (IDDBA)
PO Box 5528
Madison, WI 53705-0528
Ph: (608)310-5000

Fax: (608)238-6330
Co. E-mail: iddba@iddba.org
URL: http://www.iddba.org
Contact: Steve Beekhuizen, President
Released: 19??. **Price:** $160.00. **Description:** Examines the benefits of suggestive selling, sampling, displays, and event merchandising. **Availability:** VHS.

1788 ■ *Cake Decorating for All Occasions*

Cambridge Educational
c/o Films Media Group
132 West 31st Street, 17th Floor
Ste. 124
New York, NY 10001
Free: 800-257-5126
Fax: (609)671-0266
Co. E-mail: custserve@films.com
URL: http://www.cambridgeol.com
Released: 1987. **Price:** $49.95. **Description:** Just about anyone can learn how to make a beautifully decorated cake by watching this program. Available as two half hour tapes or one 60 minute program. **Availability:** VHS.

1789 ■ *More Knowledge, More Sales*

International Dairy-Deli-Bakery Association (IDDBA)
PO Box 5528
Madison, WI 53705-0528
Ph: (608)310-5000
Fax: (608)238-6330
Co. E-mail: iddba@iddba.org
URL: http://www.iddba.org
Contact: Steve Beekhuizen, President
Released: 19??. **Price:** $160.00. **Description:** Bakery product knowledge training video. **Availability:** VHS.

1790 ■ *Path to Profit*

International Dairy-Deli-Bakery Association (IDDBA)
PO Box 5528
Madison, WI 53705-0528
Ph: (608)310-5000
Fax: (608)238-6330
Co. E-mail: iddba@iddba.org
URL: http://www.iddba.org
Contact: Steve Beekhuizen, President
Released: 19??. **Price:** $160.00. **Description:** Analyzes strategies for increasing bakery impulse sales and bottom-line profitability. Discusses how to control shrink and effectively schedule labor. **Availability:** VHS.

1791 ■ *Puff Pastry Dough*

Culinary Institute of America (CIA)
1946 Campus Dr.
Hyde Park, NY 12538
Ph: (845)452-9430
Free: 800-285-4627
Co. E-mail: admissions@culinary.edu
URL: http://www.ciachef.edu
Contact: Rachel Birchwood, Director, Admissions
Released: 1988. **Price:** $100.00. **Description:** Two different ways of making this type of dough are demonstrated. **Availability:** VHS; 3/4 U.

1792 ■ *Service That Sells*

International Dairy-Deli-Bakery Association (IDDBA)
PO Box 5528
Madison, WI 53705-0528
Ph: (608)310-5000
Fax: (608)238-6330
Co. E-mail: iddba@iddba.org
URL: http://www.iddba.org
Contact: Steve Beekhuizen, President
Released: 19??. **Price:** $160.00. **Description:** Bakery customer service training video. **Availability:** VHS.

1793 ■ *Sit-Up Shaped Cakes*

Cine-Video West
112 Annandale Rd.
Pasadena, CA 91105-1406
Ph: (626)792-0842
Released: 1988. **Description:** A video course in creating special party cakes shaped like upright seated figures, such as clowns. **Availability:** VHS.

1794 ■ Stay Clean, Stay Safe
International Dairy-Deli-Bakery Association (IDDBA)
PO Box 5528
Madison, WI 53705-0528
Ph: (608)310-5000
Fax: (608)238-6330
Co. E-mail: iddba@iddba.org
URL: http://www.iddba.org
Contact: Steve Beekhuizen, President
Released: 19??. **Price:** $160.00. **Description:** Bakery food safety training course. **Availability:** VHS.

1795 ■ Successful Food Demonstration & Sampling
International Dairy-Deli-Bakery Association (IDDBA)
PO Box 5528
Madison, WI 53705-0528
Ph: (608)310-5000
Fax: (608)238-6330
Co. E-mail: iddba@iddba.org
URL: http://www.iddba.org
Contact: Steve Beekhuizen, President
Released: 19??. **Price:** $100.00. **Description:** Presents ways supermarket dairy, deli, bakery and food-service employees can sell more through food demonstrations and sampling. **Availability:** VHS.

TRADE SHOWS AND CONVENTIONS

1796 ■ Dairy-Deli-Bake Seminar and Expo
International Dairy-Deli-Bakery Association (IDDBA)
PO Box 5528
Madison, WI 53705-0528
Ph: (608)310-5000
Fax: (608)238-6330
Co. E-mail: iddba@iddba.org
URL: http://www.iddba.org
Contact: Steve Beekhuizen, President
URL(s): www.iddba.org. **Frequency:** Annual. **Audience:** Retailers, wholesalers, distributors, brokers, and manufacturers of the dairy, deli, and bakery industry. **Principal Exhibits:** Dairy, deli, and bakery products, packaging, and equipment.

CONSULTANTS

1797 ■ Isaksen Foodservice Consultants Inc.
11228 Georgia Ave.
Silver Spring, MD 20902-2712
Ph: (301)933-2100
Fax: (301)933-2101
Co. E-mail: isaksen@erols.com
Contact: Ron Isaksen, Manager
Scope: Consultants to architects, developers, and owners regarding layout and design of food service equipment for health care, elder care, country clubs, bakeries, hotels, hospitals, restaurants, nursing homes, schools, prisons and other institutions, as well as government agencies. Also space planning, lighting and acoustic design, laundry layout and design and food service area construction and installation supervision services. **Founded:** 1982. **Publications:** "Contemporary Long Term Care," Oct, 1997; "Pantries Take on Non-Institutional Look"; "Hospitality Profiles," Nov, 1994; "Interview: Ron Isak sen of Isak sen Food services Strategies"; "Food service Equipment and Supplies Specialist," Sep, 1991; "Winning Kitchens Show Their Metal"; "Food service Equipment and Supplies Specialist," Jun, 1991; "Isak sen, Others Devote Time to Charity," Restaurants and Institutions, Feb, 1991; "Nothing Fishy About Proper Seafood Refrigeration," Food service Equipment and Supplies Specialist, Oct, 1990; "Seven Great Kitchen Design Ideas". **Seminars:** Recipe for Success: New Concepts in Nutrition for the Aging; Integration of Food Delivery Systems with Decentralized Cluster Concepts.

FRANCHISES AND BUSINESS OPPORTUNITIES

1798 ■ Atlanta Bread Company, Intl.
1200 Wilson Way SE., Ste. A
Smyrna, GA 30082
Ph: (770)432-0933
Fax: (770)444-1991
Description: Bakery and cafe. **No. of Franchise Units:** 110. **No. of Company-Owned Units:** 4. **Franchised:** 1995. **Equity Capital Needed:** $629,700-$831,300. **Franchise Fee:** $40,000. **Training:** Yes.

1799 ■ Blue Chip Cookies
BDGS, LLC
210 Harrison St.
Loveland, OH 45140
Ph: (513)697-6610
Free: 800-888-9866
Fax: (513)697-2783
Co. E-mail: bluechipcookies@fuse.net
URL: http://www.bluechipcookies.com
Description: Cookies, bakery items, ice cream, coffees, depending on model and site. **No. of Franchise Units:** 5. **No. of Company-Owned Units:** 3. **Founded:** 1983. **Franchised:** 1986. **Equity Capital Needed:** $150,000-$250,000. **Franchise Fee:** $25,000. **Training:** Offers 2 weeks of training.

1800 ■ Bojangles' Chicken 'n Biscuits
Bojangles Restaurants Inc.
9432 Southern Pine Blvd.
Charlotte 28273
Ph: (704)527-2675
Fax: (704)523-6803
Co. E-mail: contact@bojangles.com
URL: http://www.bojangles.com
Description: Fast-service chicken and biscuits restaurant. **No. of Franchise Units:** 310. **No. of Company-Owned Units:** 201. **Founded:** 1977. **Franchised:** 1979. **Equity Capital Needed:** $500,000 liquid assets; $1,000,000 net worth. **Franchise Fee:** $25,000. **Training:** Offers an 5 week training program at as well as a one week training program at Bojangles University.

1801 ■ Breadsmith
Breadsmith Franchising, Inc.
409 E Silver Spring Dr.
Whitefish Bay, WI 53217
Ph: (414)962-1965
Fax: (414)431-5789
Description: Specialty European artisan bakery. **No. of Franchise Units:** 34. **No. of Company-Owned Units:** 2. **Founded:** 1992. **Franchised:** 1993. **Equity Capital Needed:** $242,500-$324,000. **Franchise Fee:** $30,000. **Training:** Yes.

1802 ■ Cinnzeo
Cinnaroll Bakeries Ltd.
2140 Pegasus Rd., NE
Calgary, AB, Canada T2E 8G8
Ph: (403)255-4556
Free: 877-246-6036
Fax: (403)259-5124
Description: Quick service cinnamon roll bakery. **No. of Franchise Units:** 20. **No. of Company-Owned Units:** 4. **Founded:** 1987. **Franchised:** 1998. **Equity Capital Needed:** $214,000-$621,000. **Franchise Fee:** $15,000. **Royalty Fee:** 7%. **Training:** Offers 3 weeks at headquarters, 2 weeks at franchise's location with ongoing support.

1803 ■ Coffee Time Donuts Inc.
77 Progress Ave.
Toronto, ON, Canada M1P 2Y7
Ph: (416)288-8515
Fax: (416)288-8895
Co. E-mail: franchising@coffeetime.ca
URL: http://www.coffeetime.ca
Description: The menu includes donuts, muffins, croissants, pastries and gourmet blend coffee, soups, chili, salads, sandwiches and various hot and cold beverages. store, serving customers in a warm and efficient manner and fostering good employee relationships. **No. of Franchise Units:** 184. **No. of Company-Owned Units:** 16. **Founded:** 1982. **Franchised:** 1986. **Equity Capital Needed:** $100,000-$360,000. **Training:** Yes.

1804 ■ Einstein Bros. Bagels
Einstein Noah Restaurant Group Inc.
555 Zang St., Ste. 300
Lakewood, CO 80228-1013
Ph: (303)568-8000
Free: 800-859-3090
Fax: (303)568-8039
URL: http://www.newworldrestaurantgroup.com
Description: Quick casual bakery segment that offers cuisine at breakfast, lunch or anytime. **No. of Franchise Units:** 22. **No. of Company-Owned Units:** 345. **Founded:** 1995. **Franchised:** 2006. **Equity Capital Needed:** $2,500,000 net worth; $1,000,000 liquid. **Franchise Fee:** $35,000. **Training:** Solid corporate infrastructure at headquarters, complete training materials, R&D and local support.

1805 ■ Fuddruckers, Inc.
Magic Restaurants
5700 Mopac Expy. S, Ste. C300
Austin, TX 78749
Ph: (512)275-0421
Fax: (512)275-0670
Description: Upscale restaurant that serves fresh ground beef patties from on-premises butcher shop and freshly baked buns from on-premises bakery. Breast of chicken, fish fillet, hot dogs, salads, fries, onion rings, fresh cookies, brownies, pies, milk shakes and beverages with unlimited refills are also available. **No. of Franchise Units:** 99. **No. of Company-Owned Units:** 113. **Founded:** 1980. **Franchised:** 1983. **Equity Capital Needed:** $740,000-$1,500,000 total investment; $1,500,000 net worth; $550,000 cash liquidity. **Franchise Fee:** $50,000. **Royalty Fee:** 5%. **Training:** Provides 6 week training program with ongoing support.

1806 ■ Great American Cookies
Global Franchise Group
1346 Oakbrook Dr., Ste. 170
Norcross, GA 30093
Ph: (880)524-6444
Fax: (770)514-4903
URL: http://www.theathletesfoot.com
Description: Franchises chocolate chip cookie stores, located in shopping centers. **No. of Franchise Units:** 285. **Founded:** 1977. **Franchised:** 1978. **Equity Capital Needed:** $185,150-$288,950. **Franchise Fee:** $25,000. **Royalty Fee:** 6%. **Financial Assistance:** Third party financing available. **Training:** Franchisor offers 5 days training at headquarters with ongoing support.

1807 ■ Great Harvest Franchising, Inc.
Great Harvest Franchising Inc.
28 S Montana St.
Dillon, MT 59725-2434
Ph: (406)683-6842
Free: 800-442-0424
Fax: (406)683-5537
Co. E-mail: kateo@greatharvest.com
URL: http://www.greatharvest.com
Description: Retail premium bread bakeries, specializing in whole wheat products. **No. of Franchise Units:** 229. **Founded:** 1976. **Franchised:** 1978. **Equity Capital Needed:** $121,624-$569,248. **Franchise Fee:** $35,000. **Training:** Yes.

1808 ■ House of Bread
299 Marsh St.
San Luis Obispo, CA 93401
Ph: (805)801-4853
Fax: (805)542-0257
Co. E-mail: bread@houseofbread.com
URL: http://www.houseofbread.com
Description: Specialty bread bakery. **No. of Franchise Units:** 7. **No. of Company-Owned Units:** 1. **Founded:** 1996. **Franchised:** 2000. **Equity Capital Needed:** $100,000 liquid; $300,000 net worth. **Franchise Fee:** $32,000. **Financial Assistance:** Yes. **Training:** Offers 3 weeks of hands-on training and ongoing support.

1809 ■ Insomnia Cookies Franchising LLC
650 5th Ave., 31st Fl.
New York, NY 10019
Ph: (212)286-2403
Fax: (866)422-8402
Description: Cookies & baked goods stores/late-night delivery. **No. of Company-Owned Units:** 14. **Founded:** 2002. **Franchised:** 2006. **Equity Capital Needed:** $65,600-$111,400. **Franchise Fee:** $25,000. **Royalty Fee:** 6%. **Training:** Offer 2-3

weeks training at headquarters, 2-3 weeks at franchisee's location, at other franchisee/corporate locations as needed and ongoing support.

1810 ■ Jo To Go Coffee
Jo to Go America, Inc.
1263 Main St., Ste. 228
Green Bay, WI 54302
Free: 866-568-6461
Fax: (920)482-5623
Description: Drive-thru specialty coffee, smoothies and bakery. **No. of Franchise Units:** 12. **No. of Company-Owned Units:** 6. **Founded:** 1998.. **Franchised:** 2001. **Equity Capital Needed:** $133,000-$409,000. **Franchise Fee:** $25,000. **Royalty Fee:** 7%. **Financial Assistance:** Third party financing available. **Training:** Provides 1 week at headquarters, 1 week at franchisee's location, 1 week at a corporate store and ongoing support.

1811 ■ Kolache Factory, Inc.
23240 Westheimer Pkwy.
Katy, TX 77494
Ph: (218)829-6188
Fax: (281)829-6813
Description: Bakery/cafe specializing in kolaches. **No. of Franchise Units:** 20. **No. of Company-Owned Units:** 21. **Founded:** 1982.. **Franchised:** 2000. **Equity Capital Needed:** $150,000 liquid; $500,000 net. **Franchise Fee:** $35,000. **Financial Assistance:** Yes. **Training:** Yes.

1812 ■ Lamar's Donuts
Donut Holdings, Inc.
6950 E Belleview, Ste. 200
Greenwood Village, CO 80111
Ph: (402)420-0203
Free: 800-533-7489
Fax: (402)420-0209
Description: Donuts, specialties and gourmet coffee. **No. of Franchise Units:** 28. **No. of Company-Owned Units:** 4. **Founded:** 1960.. **Franchised:** 1993. **Equity Capital Needed:** $290,000-$390,000. **Franchise Fee:** $28,500. **Training:** Yes.

1813 ■ Michel's Baguette Bakery Cafe
mmmuffins Canada Corp.
7880 Keele St., Ste. 101
Vaughan, ON, Canada L4K 4G7
Ph: (905)482-7300
Free: 877-434-3223
Fax: (905)482-7330
Co. E-mail: franchise@threecaf.com
URL: http://www.mmmuffins.com
Description: International experienced bakers, where international breads, pastries, salads, sandwiches and entrees are prepared around the clock, fresh every day. **No. of Franchise Units:** 9. **No. of Company-Owned Units:** 5. **Founded:** 1980.. **Franchised:** 1994. **Equity Capital Needed:** $400,000-$650,000 investment required; $200,000 minimum start-up capital required. **Franchise Fee:** $40,000 plus applicable taxes. **Training:** Provides 3 week training program.

1814 ■ mmmuffins
Threecaf Brands Canada Inc.
7880 Keele St., Ste. 101
Vaughan, ON, Canada L4K 4G7
Ph: (905)482-7300
Free: 877-434-3223
Fax: (905)482-7330
Co. E-mail: franchise@threecaf.com
URL: http://www.mmmuffins.com
Description: mmmuffins products are freshly baked onsite, every day, served with freshly roasted coffee. With our extensive library of recipes, we can customize your menu to suit customer preferences. **No. of Franchise Units:** 22. **No. of Company-Owned Units:** 3. **Founded:** 1979.. **Franchised:** 1980. **Equity Capital Needed:** $300,000-$400,000 investment required. **Franchise Fee:** $25,000 plus applicable taxes. **Training:** Provides 3 weeks training.

1815 ■ Mrs. Field's Original Cookies Inc.—Mrs. Field's CookiesMrs Fields; Mrs. Fields Gifts Inc.;
1141 W 2400 S
Salt Lake City, UT 84104-3236

Ph: (801)736-5600
Free: 800-343-5377
URL: http://www.mrsfields.com
Contact: Debbi Fields, President
Description: Fresh baked cookies and more. **No. of Franchise Units:** 378. **No. of Company-Owned Units:** 147. **Founded:** 1977. **Franchised:** 1990. **Equity Capital Needed:** $200,000 net worth; $150,000 liquid. **Franchise Fee:** $30,000. **Training:** Yes.

1816 ■ Nestle Toll House Cafe by Chip
Crest Foods, Inc.
101 W Renner Rd., Ste. 240
Richardson, TX 75082
Ph: (214)495-9533
Fax: (214)853-5347
Description: The franchise offers fresh baked cookies, baked goods, coffee, ice cream and smoothies. **No. of Franchise Units:** 99. **No. of Company-Owned Units:** 1. **Founded:** 2000.. **Franchised:** 2000. **Equity Capital Needed:** $157,500-$425,400. **Franchise Fee:** $30,000. **Royalty Fee:** 6%. **Financial Assistance:** Limited third party financing available. **Training:** Offers 12 days at headquarters and ongoing support.

1817 ■ PJ's Coffee of New Orleans
Raving Brands
109 New Camellia Blvd., Ste. 201
Covington, LA 70433
Ph: (404)351-3500
URL: http://www.pjscoffee.com
Description: Founded in New Orleans, PJ's has been brewing its distinguished brand of signature roasts for over 25 years. Our beans are hand-selected, hand-roasted and brewed to perfection. PJ's also offers a variety of gourmet pastries and deserts. **No. of Franchise Units:** 107. **No. of Company-Owned Units:** 1. **Founded:** 1978.. **Franchised:** 1989. **Equity Capital Needed:** $400,000 net worth; $100,000 liquid assets. **Franchise Fee:** $25,000. **Training:** Raving Brands University classroom and onsite training provided. From register operation to food preparation, from hiring staff to accounting procedures, you'll improve your management skills, setup your back office and develop an airtight sales and marketing plan.

1818 ■ Robin's Donuts
Robin's Foods, Inc.
77 Progress Ave.
Toronto, ON, Canada M1P 2Y7
Ph: (416)646-0987
Fax: (807)637-7745
Description: Coffee house, deli, donuts, pastry, and pies. **No. of Franchise Units:** 130. **No. of Company-Owned Units:** 10. **Founded:** 1975.. **Franchised:** 1977. **Equity Capital Needed:** $130,000. **Franchise Fee:** $25,000. **Training:** Yes.

1819 ■ Saint Cinnamon Bake Shoppe
Saint Cinnamon Bakery Ltd.
350 Esna Park Dr.
Markham, ON, Canada L3R 1H5
Ph: (905)470-1517
Free: 877-490-5916
Fax: (905)470-8112
Co. E-mail: markh@saintcinnamon.com
URL: http://www.saintcinnamon.com
Description: Freshly-baked cinnamon rolls made in front of the customer and served immediately from the oven. Served with quality coffees in a kiosk or in-line concept. **No. of Franchise Units:** 97. **No. of Company-Owned Units:** 3. **Founded:** 1986.. **Franchised:** 1986. **Equity Capital Needed:** $144,050-$264,700, approximate total investment. **Franchise Fee:** $25,000. **Training:** Franchisee is provided with both local and national assistance in the format of both master franchisee and franchisor.

1820 ■ Southern Maid Donuts
Southern Maid Donut Flour Co.
3615 Cavalier Dr.
Garland, TX 75042
Ph: (972)272-6425
Free: 800-936-6887

Fax: (972)276-3549
Description: Makes and sells donuts, muffins and other delectable items, as well as coffee, juices and soda drinks. **No. of Franchise Units:** 90. **Founded:** 1937.. **Franchised:** 1939. **Equity Capital Needed:** Approximately $50,000. **Franchise Fee:** $5,000. **Training:** Yes.

1821 ■ Tim Hortons
T.H.D. Donut, Delaware, Inc.
4150 Tuller Rd., Ste. 236
Dublin, OH 43017
Ph: (614)791-4200
Description: Retail coffee, donut and specialty baked goods chain, with over 800 stores across Canada and the US. Franchisee purchases a turn-key operation, the right to use Tim Horton's trademarks and trade names, as well as a comprehensive 7-8 week training program and ongoing operational and marketing support. **No. of Franchise Units:** 1,763. **No. of Company-Owned Units:** 130. **Founded:** 1964. **Franchised:** 1965. **Equity Capital Needed:** $300,000-$734,900, includes franchise fee. **Franchise Fee:** $35,000. **Training:** A 7-8 week training program is conducted at principal offices in Oakville, ON, Canada. Cost incurred while in training (accommodations, meals, etc.) are the responsibility of the franchisee.

LIBRARIES

1822 ■ American Institute of Baking - Information Services Department - Ruth Emerson Library
1213 Bakers Way
Manhattan, KS 66502-3999
Ph: (785)537-4750
Free: 800-633-5137
Fax: (785)537-1493
Co. E-mail: information@aibonline.org
URL: http://www.aibonline.org
Scope: Baking science and technology, food chemistry, nutrition. **Services:** Interlibrary loan; copying; library open to the public for reference use only. **Founded:** 1925. **Holdings:** 7000 books; 2500 reference and non-circulating volumes; 3500 bound periodical volumes; 80 VF drawers of unbound material on baking and nutrition. **Subscriptions:** 350 journals and other serials.

1823 ■ American Institute of Food Distribution, Inc. - Information and Research Center—The Food Institute.
1 Broadway Plaza, 2nd Fl.
Elmwood Park, NJ 07407
Ph: (201)791-5570
Fax: (201)791-5222
Co. E-mail: jkastrinsky@foodinstitute.com
URL: http://www.foodinstitute.com/
Contact: Brian Todd, President
Scope: Food industry. **Services:** Center open to the public on fee basis. **Founded:** 1928. **Subscriptions:** 400 journals and other serials. **Publications:** *Food Business Mergers and Acquisitions.* **Telecommunication Services:** food1@foodinstitute.com.

1824 ■ American Society of Baking - Information Service and Library
PO Box 336
Swedesboro, NJ 08085
Free: 800-713-0462
Fax: (888)315-2612
Co. E-mail: kvanamburg@asbe.org
URL: http://www.asbe.org
Contact: Kent Van Amburg, Executive Director
Scope: Baking and allied subjects. **Holdings:** 10,000 references. **Telecommunication Services:** info@asbe.org.

1825 ■ Noble and Associates Library
2155 W. Chesterfield Blvd.
Springfield, MO 65807
Ph: (417)875-5000
Co. E-mail: julie.tumy@noble.net
URL: http://www.noble.net
Contact: Julie Tumy, President
Scope: Food, food service, advertising, construction, agriculture. **Services:** Interlibrary loan; copying; SDI;

Library not open to the public. **Holdings:** 500 books; 1000 reports. **Subscriptions:** 300 journals and other serials; 5 newspapers.

RESEARCH CENTERS

1826 ■ **American Institute of Baking (AIB)**
PO Box 3999
Manhattan, KS 66505-3999
Ph: (785)537-4750

Free: 800-633-5137
Fax: (785)537-1493
Co. E-mail: info@aibonline.org
URL: http://www.aibonline.org
Contact: James Munyon, President
Services: Food Safety/Security Audits and Consulting; ISO 9000 registration; Technical assistance group. **Founded:** 1919. **Publications:** *AIB Update* (Quarterly); *AIB Newsletter* (Monthly); *Technical bulletins* (Monthly). **Educational Activities:** Correspon-

dence and CD-Rom courses, in applied baking, food safety, and maintenance engineering; AIB Courses, in baking and maintenance engineering; Training and professional education, for bakers, food safety auditors, and employee safety personnel; Worldwide seminars, in baking, food safety, nutrition, technology transfer. **Awards:** AIB Scholarship (Annual), for maintenance engineering and baking science and technology resident courses.

START-UP INFORMATION

1827 ■ *"Thirsty Lion on the Prowl" in Business Journal Portland (Vol. 27, November 5, 2010, No. 36, pp. 1)*
Pub: Portland Business Journal

Ed: Wendy Culverwell. **Description:** Concept Entertainment Inc.'s impending launch of the Thirsty Lion Pub and Grill at the Washington Square in downtown Portland, Oregon is part of its West Coast expansion plan. A discussion of the planning involved in realizing Thirsty Lion is discussed, along with pub offerings that are expected to be enjoyed by customers.

ASSOCIATIONS AND OTHER ORGANIZATIONS

1828 ■ Beverage Network (BN)
44 Pleasant St., Ste. 110
Watertown, MA 02472
Ph: (617)231-8800
Fax: (617)812-7740
Co. E-mail: jcraven@bevnet.com
URL: http://www.bevnet.com
Contact: John Craven, Chief Executive Officer

Description: Beverage distributors dealing primarily in "new wave specialty non-alcoholic" products and some specialty food items. Serves as a forum for the exchange of information among members. Assists members in identifying new products. **Founded:** 1986.

1829 ■ Distilled Spirits Council of the United States (DISCUS)
1250 Eye St. NW, Ste. 400
Washington, DC 20005
Ph: (202)628-3544
Fax: (202)682-8888
Co. E-mail: press@discus.org
URL: http://www.discus.org
Contact: Dr. Peter H. Cressy, President

Description: Serves as national trade association of producers and marketers of distilled spirits sold in the U.S. Provides statistical and legal data for industry and the public and serves as public information source; conducts educational programs. **Scope:** alcohol abuse, alcoholism, liquor industry, prohibition. **Founded:** 1973. **Subscriptions:** 3500 periodicals. **Publications:** *Summary of State Laws and Regulations Relating to Distilled Spirits* (Biennial); *Distilled Spirit, Wine and Beer Directories* (Biennial).

REFERENCE WORKS

1830 ■ *"$100 Million Complex To Be Built..On a Bridge" in Business Courier (Vol. 27, November 12, 2010, No. 28, pp. 1)*
Pub: Business Courier

Ed: Lucy May. **Description:** A development firm closed a deal with the Newport Southbank Bridge Company for a $100M entertainment complex that

will be built on tope of the Purple People Bridge. The proposed project will cover 150,000 square feet with attractions such as restaurants, a boutique hotel, and pubs.

1831 ■ *"Bars, Restaurants to Offer Prix Fixe Menus, Space to Race Patrons" in Boston Business Journal (Vol. 29, July 22, 2011, No. 11, pp. 1)*
Pub: American City Business Journals Inc.

Ed: Alexander Jackson. **Description:** Restaurants and bar owners in Baltimore, Maryland have changed the way they do business as the Baltimore Grand Prix approaches. Owners have gone so far as to offering new services or renting out their entire restaurants to companies for the three-day event in September.

1832 ■ *"Beer Stocks Rally on Anheuser, InBev Report" in Globe & Mail (February 16, 2007, pp. B3)*
Pub: CTVglobemedia Publishing Inc.

Ed: Keith McArthur. **Description:** The stock prices of beer manufacturing industries have increased considerably after impressive profit reports from Anheuser Busch Cos Inc. and InBev SA. Complete analysis in this context is presented.

1833 ■ *Beverage Industry--Annual Manual Issue*
Pub: BNP Media
Contact: Al Reser, President

URL(s): directories.bevindustry.com/manual. **Released:** Annual; Latest edition 2010. **Publication includes:** List of over 1,700 companies supplying equipment and materials to the soft drink, beer, wine, bottled water, and juice industries; industry associations; bottling and supply franchise companies; beer importers distributors; manufacturers' representatives; soft drink distributors. **Entries include:** For suppliers--Company name, address, phone, code to indicate products. For associations--Name, address, phone, name of president; some association listings also include meeting date and location and names of other executives. For franchise companies--Name, address, phone, names and titles of executives, number of plants, number of franchised plants, products, foreign involvement. For beer importers and distributors--Name, address, phone, names and titles of key executives, brands handled. For manufacturers' representatives--Name, address, phone, names of contacts, market areas, products represented. **Database includes:** Statistics and industry surveys. **Arrangement:** State associations and supplier associations are geographical; other listings are alphabetical. **Indexes:** Trade name, product/service.

1834 ■ *Beverage World--Buyers Guide Issue*
Pub: Beverage World
Contact: Lisa Adams, Director, Sales
E-mail: leoguenther@bellsouth.net

URL(s): www.beverageworld.com. **Released:** Annual; Latest edition June 2008. **Publication includes:** List of suppliers to the beverage industry. **Entries include:** Company name, address. **Arrangement:** Classified by product.

1835 ■ *"Big Gains Brewing at Anheuser-Busch InBev" in Barron's (Vol. 90, August 30, 2010, No. 35, pp. 34)*
Pub: Barron's Editorial & Corporate Headquarters

Ed: Christopher C. Williams. **Description:** Anheuser-Busch InBev is realizing cost synergies and it posted better than expected returns two years after the merger that formed the company. One analyst believes its American depositary receipt could be worth as much as 72 in a year.

1836 ■ *"Booze Makers Battle Over Turkey Day" in Advertising Age (Vol. 78, October 29, 2007, No. 43, pp. 4)*
Pub: Crain Communications, Inc.

Ed: Jeremy Mullman. **Description:** Beer and wine marketers are jockeying for position in regards to the Thanksgiving holiday.

1837 ■ *"Canada's New Government Introduces Amendments to Deny Work Permits to Foreign Strippers" in Canadian Corporate News (May 16, 2007)*
Pub: Comtex News Network Inc.

Description: Honourable Diane Finley, Minister of Citizenship and Immigration, introduced amendments to the Immigration and Refugee Protection Act (IRPA) to help prevent the exploitation and abuse of vulnerable foreign workers, such as strippers.

1838 ■ *"Closures Pop Cork on Wine Bar Sector Consolidation" in Houston Business Journal (Vol. 40, January 22, 2010, No. 37, pp. A2)*
Pub: American City Business Journals

Ed: Allison Wollam. **Description:** Wine bar market in Houston, Texas is in the midst of a major shift and heads toward further consolidation due to the closure of pioneering wine bars that opened in the past decade. The Corkscrew owner, Andrew Adams, has blamed the creation of competitive establishments to the closure which helped wear out his concept.

1839 ■ *"Counting on Cornhole: Popular Bean Bag Game Brings Crowds to Bars" in Boston Business Journal (Vol. 29, July 15, 2011, No. 10, pp. 1)*
Pub: American City Business Journals Inc.

Ed: Alexander Jackson. **Description:** Cornhole game is being used by bars to spur business as the games hikes beer and food sales on slow weekdays. The game is played with two cornhole boards facing each other and is played with one or two people on one team who try to place a bag on the board.

1840 ■ *"A Crystal Ball" in Business Journal Portland (Vol. 27, December 31, 2010, No. 44, pp. 1)*
Pub: Portland Business Journal

Ed: Wendy Culverwell. **Description:** McMenamins Pubs and Breweries has resumed construction of its Crystal Hotel project. The company has been working to convert a former bath house into a 51-room hotel. The hotel is expected to open in 2011.

1841 ■ *"Deals Still Get Done at Drake's Coq d'Or"* in *Crain's Chicago Business (Vol. 31, November 17, 2008, No. 46, pp. 35)*

Pub: Crain Communications, Inc.

Ed: Shia Kapos. **Description:** Chicago's infamous Coq d'Or, a restaurant and lounge located at the Drake Hotel, is still a favorite establishment for noted executives but the eatery is now trying to cater to younger professionals through marketing and offering new beverages that appeal to that demographic. Many find it the perfect environment in which to close deals, relax or network.

1842 ■ *"Discount Beers Take Fizz Out Of Molson"* in *Globe & Mail (February 10, 2006, pp. B3)*

Pub: CTVglobemedia Publishing Inc.

Ed: Omar El Akkad. **Description:** The reasons behind the decline in profits by 60 percent for Molson Coors Brewing Co., during fourth quarter 2005, are presented.

1843 ■ *"Eat, Drink and Be a Success"* in *Entrepreneur (Vol. 37, August 2009, No. 8, pp. 70)*

Pub: Entrepreneur Media, Inc.

Ed: Joel Holland. **Description:** Profile of Fritz Brogan, who is a full time student but also runs a successful bar and restaurant named Gin & Tonic and Kitchen. The bar was built with their target audience in mind which happens to be Brogan's college friends.

1844 ■ *"Executive Decision: Damn the Profit Margins, Sleeman Declares War on Buck-a-Beer Foes"* in *Globe & Mail (January 28, 2006, pp. B3)*

Pub: CTVglobemedia Publishing Inc.

Ed: Andy Hoffman. **Description:** The cost savings plans of chief executive officer John Sleeman of Sleeman Breweries Ltd. are presented.

1845 ■ *"Fair Exchange"* in *Food and Drink (Winter 2010, pp. 84)*

Pub: Schofield Media Group

Ed: Don Mardak. **Description:** Bartering can assist firms in the food and beverage industry to attract new customers, maximize resources, and reduce cash expenses.

1846 ■ *"Grape Expectations"* in *Canadian Business (Vol. 80, March 12, 2007, No. 6, pp. 55)*

Pub: Rogers Media

Ed: Andrea Jezvovit. **Description:** The emergence of Nova Scotia as one of the leading wine-making places in Canada, in view of its favorable climate for growing grapes, is discussed.

1847 ■ *"Hike in Md.'s Alcohol Tax May Be Hard For Lawmakers to Swallow"* in *Baltimore Business Journal (Vol. 28, November 19, 2010, No. 28)*

Pub: Baltimore Business Journal

Ed: Emily Mullin. **Description:** Maryland's General Assembly has been reluctant to support a dime-per-drink increase in alcohol tax that was drafted in the 2009 bill if the tax revenue goes into a separate fund. The alcohol tax increase is considered unnecessary by some lawmakers and business leaders due to impending federal spending boosts.

1848 ■ *"Homes, Not Bars, Stay Well Tended"* in *Advertising Age (Vol. 79, January 28, 2008, No. 4, pp. 8)*

Pub: Crain Communications, Inc.

Ed: Jeremy Mullman. **Description:** Due to the downturn in the economy, consumers are drinking less at bars and restaurants; however, according to the Distilled Spirits Council of the United States, they are still purchasing expensive liquor to keep in their homes.

1849 ■ *"I Love L.A."* in *Canadian Business (Vol. 81, December 8, 2008, No. 21, pp. S22)*

Pub: Rogers Media Ltd.

Ed: Rachel Pulfer. **Description:** Los Angeles-based Standard Downtown, which was built in the 1950s, has a bar that remains popular to Hollywood celebrities. The Standard L.A., which used to house the former headquarters of Superior Oil, offers Devon's Bourbon Sour.

1850 ■ *"Imports Frothing Up Beer Market"* in *Globe & Mail (February 16, 2006, pp. B4)*

Pub: CTVglobemedia Publishing Inc.

Ed: Andy Hoffman. **Description:** The reasons behind the rise in market share of beer imports, in Canada, are presented.

1851 ■ *"Labatt to Swallow Lakeport"* in *Globe & Mail (February 2, 2007, pp. B1)*

Pub: CTVglobemedia Publishing Inc.

Ed: Keith McArthur. **Description:** The decision of Labatt Brewing Company Ltd. to acquire Lakeport Brewing Income Fund for $201.4 million is discussed.

1852 ■ *"Lawyers Cash In On Alcohol"* in *Business Journal Portland (Vol. 27, November 19, 2010, No. 38, pp. 1)*

Pub: Portland Business Journal

Ed: Andy Giegerich. **Description:** Oregon-based law firms have continued to corner big business on the state's growing alcohol industry as demand for their services increased. Lawyers, who represent wine, beer and liquor distillery interests, have seen their workload increased by 20 to 30 percent in 2009.

1853 ■ *"Lee's Launches With Focus on Liqueur-based Ice Creams"* in *Ice Cream Reporter (Vol. 23, August 20, 2010, No. 9, pp. 6)*

Pub: Ice Cream Reporter

Description: Lee's Cream Liqueur Ice Cream Parlors launched their grand opening in Old Town Scottsdale in July, featuring premium liqueurs to create adult-only ice creams that can be served on their own or blended into exotic drinks.

1854 ■ *"Little Cheer in Holiday Forecast for Champagne"* in *Advertising Age (Vol. 88, November 17, 2008, No. 43, pp. 6)*

Pub: Crain Communications, Inc.

Ed: Jeremy Mullman. **Description:** Due to a weak economy that has forced consumers to trade down from the most expensive alcoholic beverages as well as a weak U.S. dollar that has driven already lofty Champagne prices higher, makers of the French sparkling wine are anticipating a brutally slow holiday season.

1855 ■ *"Moet, Rivals Pour More Ad Bucks Into Bubbly"* in *Advertising Age (Vol. 88, September 3, 2007, No. 35, pp. 4)*

Pub: Crain Communications, Inc.

Ed: Jeremy Mullman. **Description:** In an attempt to revive sluggish sales, champagne companies are raising their advertising budgets, transforming themselves from light-spending seasonal players to year-round heavyweights in the advertising world.

1856 ■ *National Conference of State Liquor Administrators--Official Directory*

Pub: National Conference of State Liquor Administrators

URL(s): www.ncsla.org. **Released:** Annual **Covers:** State alcohol beverage control administrators in 36 jurisdictions in the United States, Puerto Rico, District of Columbia, and Guam. **Entries include:** Name, office address and phone. **Arrangement:** Geographical.

1857 ■ *"A New Flavor for Second Street: Lamberts Chef Backs New Restaurant"* in *Austin Business JournalInc. (Vol. 28, January 2, 2009)*

Pub: American City Business Journals

Ed: Sandra Zaragoza. **Description:** Chef Larry McGuire has teamed up with the Icon Group to develop the La Condesa restaurant and the Malverde lounge in the Second Street district. The La Condesa restaurant will be a Mexico City-inspired restaurant, while the Malverde lounge atop the La Condesa will host DJs and live music.

1858 ■ *"Nighttime Shuttle to Connect Detroit, Ferndale, Royal Oak"* in *Crain's Detroit Business (Vol. 24, October 6, 2008, No. 40, pp. 24)*

Pub: Crain Communications, Inc.

Ed: Nancy Kaffer. **Description:** With hopes of bridging the social gap between the cities and suburbs, Chris Ramos has launched The Night Move, a new shuttle service that will ferry passengers between Royal Oak, Ferndale and downtown Detroit. The cost for a round trip ticket is $12.

1859 ■ *"Plan B Saloon Opened New Year's Eve"* in *Bellingham Business Journal (Vol. February 2010, pp. 7)*

Pub: Sound Publishing Inc.

Description: Plan B Saloon, located in Bellingham, Washington, opened New Year's Eve 2010. The bar/restaurant will feature classic American food consisting of sandwiches and burgers and will host local musicians on Friday and Saturday nights.

1860 ■ *"The Price Is Right: What You Can Learn From the Wine Industry"* in *Advertising Age (Vol. 88, February 11, 2008, No. 6, pp. 14)*

Pub: Crain Communications, Inc.

Ed: Lenore Skenazy. **Description:** In California a wine study was conducted in which participants' brains were hooked up to an MRI so researchers could watch what was happening in both the taste centers as well as the pleasure centers; the participants were given three different wines but were told that the samples were from a variety of wines that differed radically in price; surprisingly, the differences did not affect the taste centers of the brain, however, when the participants were told that a sample was more expensive, the pleasure centers were greatly affected.

1861 ■ *"Startup to Serve Bar Scene"* in *Austin Business JournalInc. (Vol. 29, December 18, 2009, No. 41, pp. 1)*

Pub: American City Business Journals

Ed: Christopher Calnan. **Description:** Startup ATX Innovation Inc. of Austin, Texas has developed a test version of TabbedOut, a Web-based tool that would facilitate mobile phone-based restaurant and bar bill payment. TabbedOut has been tested by six businesses in Austin and will be available to restaurant and bar owners for free. Income would be generated by ATX through a 99-cent convenience charge per transaction.

1862 ■ *"To Live and Thrive in L.A."* in *Canadian Business (Vol. 81, October 13, 2008, No. 17, pp. 78)*

Pub: Rogers Media Ltd.

Ed: Rachel Pulfer. **Description:** Toronto entrepreneur Shereen Arazm thrived in Los Angeles, California as the queen of nightlife. Arazm holds or has held ownership stakes in bars, nightspots and restaurants that include the Geisha House, Concorde, Shag, Parc and Central, and Terroni L.A.

1863 ■ *"The Traveling Godfather: Beam Global Spirits & Wine Inc."* in *Canadian Business (Vol. 81, October 13, 2008, No. 17, pp. S10)*

Pub: Rogers Media Ltd.

Ed: Andy Holoway. **Description:** Dan Tullio, director of Canadian Club, is seen as a godfather because he gets to be asked a lot of favors. Tullio gets to immerse himself into other cultures because of his employment as global ambassador of Beam Global Spirits & Wine Inc. Tullio's views, as well as information about him are presented.

1864 ■ *"Union, Uneven But Imaginative, Works"* in *Crain's Chicago Business (Vol. 34, September 12, 2011, No. 37, pp. 30)*

Pub: Crain Communications Inc.

Ed: Alison Neumer Lara. **Description:** Japanese restaurant, Union Sushi & Barbecue Bar opened in Chicago this year. Union is a hip and urban place for business and leisure diners.

1865 ■ *"Waite, Cancer Survivor, Readies Sch'dy 'Big House' after Long Delay"* in

Business Review, Albany New York (October 26, 2007)
Pub: American City Business Journals, Inc.
Ed: Michael DeMasi. **Description:** Stephen Waite, owner of Big House Brewing Company, will be opening its new nightclub called Big House Underground. The nightclub is part of a $3.25 million project Waite started in 2005, which was delayed due to his battle with tonsil cancer. Details of turning the building into a restaurant, bar and nightclub are provided.

1866 ■ *"What'll You Have Tonight?" in Barron's (Vol. 88, July 4, 2008, No. 28, pp. 22)*
Pub: Dow Jones & Co., Inc.
Ed: Neil A. Martin. **Description:** Shares of Diageo could rise by 30 percent a year from June 2008 after it slipped due to U.S. sales worries. The company also benefits from the trend toward more premium alcoholic beverage brands worldwide especially in emerging markets.

SOURCES OF SUPPLY

1867 ■ *Beverage Marketing Directory*
Beverage Marketing Corp.
Contact: Michael C. Bellas, Chief Executive Officer
E-mail: mbellas@beveragemarketing.com
URL(s): www.beveragemarketing.com/?service=publications&section=directory. **Released:** Annual; Latest edition 33rd; 2011. **Price:** $1435, Individuals softcover or in PDF format; $5495, Individuals database on CD-ROM; $5495, Canada database on CD-ROM. **Covers:** Over 25,500 beer wholesalers, wine and spirits wholesalers, soft drink bottlers and franchisors, breweries, wineries, distilleries, alcoholic beverage importers, bottled water companies; and trade associations, government agencies, micro breweries, juice, coffee, tea, milk companies, and others concerned with the beverage and bottling industries; coverage includes Canada. **Entries include:** Beverage and bottling company listings contain company name, address, phone, names of key executives, number of employees, brand names, and other information, including number of franchisees, number of delivery trucks, sales volume. Suppliers and related companies and organizations listings include similar but less detailed information. **Arrangement:** Geographical. **Indexes:** Personnel, supplier's product, company name.

STATISTICAL SOURCES

1868 ■ *RMA Annual Statement Studies*
Pub: Risk Management Association
Contact: Kevin M. Blakey, President
Released: Annual. **Price:** $175.00 2006-07 edition, $105.00. **Description:** Contains composite balance sheets and income statements for more than 360 industries, including the accounting, auditing, and bookkeeping industries. Also contains five years of comparative historical data for discerning trends. Includes 16 commonly used ratios, computed for most of the size groupings for nearly every industry.

TRADE PERIODICALS

1869 ■ *Cheers: The Beverage Magazine for Full Service Restaurants and Bars*
Pub: Adams Business Media
URL(s): www.cheersmagazine.com/ME2/. **Released:** Bimonthly **Price:** $35, Individuals print version only; $50, Canada and Mexico print version only; $130, Other countries print version only; $45, Individuals print & digital; $60, Canada and Mexico print & digital; $140, Other countries print & digital.

1870 ■ *Cocktails Magazine*
Pub: Destiny Productions for Print, Radio & Cable Promotions
URL(s): www.cocktail.com/. **Released:** Monthly

1871 ■ *The Food & Beverage Journal*
Pub: Journal Publications Inc.
URL(s): www.fbworld.com. **Ed:** Ellen Walsh, Jason Barlow. **Released:** Bimonthly **Price:** $30, Individuals; $40, Two years.

1872 ■ *Modern Brewery Age*
Pub: Business Journals, Inc.
Contact: Britton Jones, President
E-mail: brittonj@busjour.com
URL(s): www.breweryage.com. **Ed:** Peter V.K. Reid. **Released:** Bimonthly **Price:** $125, Individuals.

VIDEOCASSETTES/ AUDIOCASSETTES

1873 ■ *Art of the Cocktail, Part 1*
Tapeworm Video Distributors
25876 The Old Road #141
Stevenson Ranch, CA 91381
Ph: (661)257-4904
Fax: (661)257-4820
Co. E-mail: sales@tapeworm.com
URL: http://www.tapeworm.com
Released: 19??. **Price:** $29.95. **Description:** Offers instruction on cocktail mixing and preparation. **Availability:** VHS.

1874 ■ *Art of the Cocktail, Part 2*
Tapeworm Video Distributors
25876 The Old Road #141
Stevenson Ranch, CA 91381
Ph: (661)257-4904
Fax: (661)257-4820
Co. E-mail: sales@tapeworm.com
URL: http://www.tapeworm.com
Released: 19??. **Price:** $29.95. **Description:** Offers instruction on cocktail mixing and preparation. **Availability:** VHS.

1875 ■ *Mr. Boston's Official Video Bartender's Guide*
MGM/UA
MGM
10250 Constellation Blvd.
Los Angeles, CA 90067
Ph: (310)449-3000
URL: http://www.mgm.com
Released: 1985. **Price:** $14.98. **Description:** In a bar-hopping romp across the U.S.A. the Glenmore Distillery people offer step-by-step instructions for preparing the world's most popular cocktails and punches. **Availability:** VHS.

1876 ■ *100 Fabulous Cocktails*
Tapeworm Video Distributors
25876 The Old Road #141
Stevenson Ranch, CA 91381
Ph: (661)257-4904
Fax: (661)257-4820
Co. E-mail: sales@tapeworm.com
URL: http://www.tapeworm.com
Released: 1997. **Price:** $19.95. **Description:** Professional bartenders instruct how to prepare and order drinks. **Availability:** VHS.

TRADE SHOWS AND CONVENTIONS

1877 ■ *Nightclub & Bar/Beverage Retailer/ Food and Beverage Convention & Tradeshow*
Oxford Publishing Inc.
307 W Jackson Ave.
Oxford, MS 38655-2154
Free: 800-247-3881
Fax: (662)236-5541
Co. E-mail: info@oxpub.com
URL: http://www.nightclub.com
URL(s): www.nightclub.com. **Frequency:** Semiannual. **Audience:** Owners and managers of bars, clubs, and restaurants; corporate executives and food/beverage managers of hotels, resorts, state buyers, retailers. **Principal Exhibits:** Equipment, supplies, and services for nightclubs, restaurants, bars, hotels, casinos, and retailers of alcoholic beverages.

CONSULTANTS

1878 ■ *GEC Consultants Inc.*
4604 Birchwood Ave.
Skokie, IL 60076-3835
Ph: (847)674-6310
Fax: (847)674-3946
Co. E-mail: experts@gecconsultants.com
URL: http://www.gecconsultants.com
Contact: Lloyd M. Gordon, President
E-mail: legal@gecconsultants.com
Scope: Consulting in all areas of bar and restaurant operations. Restaurant manager development appraises existing locations or sites. Studies the feasibility of projects. Develop new concepts. Assist in expanding, existing food operations, marketing, expert witness (legal) for hospitality/restaurant industry. **Founded:** 1963. **Publications:** "How You Can Fight Back to Minimize This Recession!"; "New Thoughts On Leases"; "The Use of Job Analysis to Actually Reduce Payroll Costs"; "Do You Need a Feasibility Study?"; "Combat Negative Hospitality"; "How To Run A Successful Night club"; "Are Capitalists In Your Cabinet?"; "Marketing For The 21st Century"; "Profitability In The Banquet Industry"; "Starting a Restaurant, Bar or Catering Business"; "How To Find And Retain Suitable Employees"; "26 Things To Do To Plan A Restaurant"; "Wall Fabric or Paint: Decor Magic It's Your Call"; "The Art of Cafe Ambiance"; "Why You Need A Consultant". **Telecommunication Services:** legal@gecconsultants.com.

FRANCHISES AND BUSINESS OPPORTUNITIES

1879 ■ *Bevinco*
505 Consumers Rd., Ste. 510
Toronto, ON, Canada M2J 4V8
Ph: (416)490-6266
Fax: (416)490-6899
Co. E-mail: info@bevinco.com
URL: http://www.bevinco.com
Description: Liquor inventory control system for bars, restaurants, hotels, clubs, etc. **No. of Franchise Units:** 250. **No. of Company-Owned Units:** 1. **Founded:** 1987.. **Franchised:** 1991. **Equity Capital Needed:** $40,000. **Franchise Fee:** $40,000. **Financial Assistance:** Yes. **Training:** 7 days corporate training in Toronto, 5-10 days regional training with state master franchise.

1880 ■ *Boston Bartenders School of America*
Boston Bartenders School Associates, Inc.
64 Enterprise Rd.
Hyannis, MA 02601
Free: 800-357-3210
Fax: (508)771-1165
Description: Program in mixology and alcohol awareness. **No. of Franchise Units:** 10. **No. of Company-Owned Units:** 3. **Founded:** 1968.. **Franchised:** 1994. **Equity Capital Needed:** $50,000. **Franchise Fee:** $10,000. **Financial Assistance:** Yes. **Training:** Yes.

1881 ■ *Bridge Business and Property Brokers Inc.*
60 Knickerbocker Ave.
Bohemia, NY 11716-3143
Free: 888-614-6592
Fax: (888)605-5727
URL: http://www.bridgebrokers.com
Contact: Raymond Barton, President
Description: Specialize in bringing together buyers and sellers of businesses to provide a seamless transfer of ownership. Expertise extends into franchise and business consulting, commercial real estate brokerage, helping find commercial insurance and acquiring loans. **No. of Franchise Units:** 4. **No. of Company-Owned Units:** 19. **Founded:** 2004. **Franchised:** 2005. **Equity Capital Needed:** $38,000-$63,000. **Franchise Fee:** $25,000. **Royalty Fee:** 6%. **Training:** Offers training program designed to expedite the process of making your employees proficient in the art of business brokering.

1882 ■ *Cartoon Cuts*
5501 NW 21st Ave., Ste. 410
Ft. Lauderdale, FL 33309
Ph: (954)653-2887
Free: 800-701-2887

Fax: (954)653-9074

Description: Hair salons for children. **No. of Company-Owned Units:** 19. **Founded:** 1991.. **Franchised:** 2001. **Equity Capital Needed:** $97,000-$216,000. **Franchise Fee:** $25,000. **Training:** Yes.

1883 ■ Dooley's

795 Main St., Ste. 200
Moncton, NB, Canada E1C 8P9
Ph: (506)857-8050
URL: http://franchisedirectory.ca

Description: Each Dooly's features a comfortable atmosphere with a fireplace, cozy sofas, lounge area and of course, first-class billiard tables. **No. of Franchise Units:** 90. **Founded:** 1993. **Equity Capital Needed:** $350,000-$450,000 total investment; $150,000 minimum cash liquidity. **Training:** Extensive training, both in operations and marketing are provided. Field representatives will help with hiring and training your manager and staff with ongoing training and support through workshops and annual meetings.

1884 ■ Old Chicago Pizza

Rock Bottom Restaurants, Inc.
248 Centennial Pky.
Louisville, CO 80027
Ph: (303)664-4200

Fax: (303)664-4007

Description: Pizza restaurant with a large high energy bar. **No. of Franchise Units:** 22. **No. of Company-Owned Units:** 58. **Founded:** 1976.. **Equity Capital Needed:** $3,000,000 net worth; $750,000 available for investment. **Franchise Fee:** $15,000 area $40,000 fee. **Training:** Yes.

LIBRARIES

1885 ■ Anheuser-Busch Companies, Inc. - Corporate Library

1 Busch Pl.
St. Louis, MO 63118
Ph: (314)577-2000
Free: 800-342-5283
URL: http://www.anheuser-busch.com
Contact: Ann Lauenstein, Librarian

Scope: Brewing chemistry, fermentation technology, food and beverage industries, alcohol and alcoholism, yeast, business and industrial management. **Services:** Interlibrary loan. **Founded:** 1852. **Holdings:** 50,000 books; 60,000 bound periodical volumes; 100 pamphlet boxes of Annual reports; 25 VF drawers of U.S. and foreign patents; 70 pamphlet boxes of clippings. **Subscriptions:** 1000 journals and other serials.

1886 ■ Coca-Cola Company - The INFOSOURCE

PO Box 1734
Atlanta, GA 30301
Ph: (404)515-4636
Fax: (404)253-4575
Co. E-mail: koinfo@na.ko.com
URL: http://www.coca-cola.com
Contact: Barbara Kahn-Aitken

Scope: Business, Legal, Marketing, Technical - including beverages, soft drinks, fruit juices, food technology, nutrition, chemistry, engineering. **Founded:** 1967. **Telecommunication Services:** coca-cola@na.ko.com.

1887 ■ Distilled Spirits Council of the U.S. Library

1250 Eye St. NW, Ste. 400
Washington, DC 20005
Ph: (202)628-3544
Fax: (202)682-8877
URL: http://www.discus.org/

Scope: Distilled spirits industry, prohibition, temperance movement, alcoholism, liquor laws, alcohol and health/safety issues, moderate drinking, drinking customs. **Services:** Interlibrary loan; copying; library open to researchers with prior approval. **Founded:** 1974. **Holdings:** 3500 volumes; 72 VF drawers of information on subjects and organizations. **Subscriptions:** 225 journals and other serials.

ASSOCIATIONS AND OTHER ORGANIZATIONS

1888 ■ American Health and Beauty Aids Institute (AHBAI)
PO Box 19510
Chicago, IL 60619-0510
Ph: (708)633-6328
Fax: (708)633-6329
Co. E-mail: ahbai1@sbcglobal.net
URL: http://www.ahbai.org
Contact: Clyde Hammond, Chairman

Description: Minority-owned companies engaged in manufacturing and marketing health and beauty aids for the black consumer. Represents the interests of members and the industry before local, state, and federal governmental agencies. Assists with business development and economic progress within the minority community by providing informational and educational resources. Maintains speakers' bureau. Conducts annual Proud Lady Beauty Show. **Founded:** 1981. **Awards:** Fred Luster, Sr. Education Foundation Cosmetology Scholarship (Annual); Fred Luster, Sr. Education Foundation Scholarship Fund (Annual).

1889 ■ Cosmetic Industry Buyers and Suppliers (CIBS)
c/o Rafael Cruz
830 Terry Rd.
Hauppauge, NY 11788
Co. E-mail: cibsmail@cibsonline.com
URL: http://www.cibsonline.com
Contact: Charles Marchese, President

Description: Buyers and suppliers of essential oils, chemicals, packaging, and finished goods relative to the cosmetic industry. Enhances growth, stability, prosperity, and protection of the American cosmetic industry through close personal contact and the exchange of ideas and experiences. **Founded:** 1948.

1890 ■ International Aloe Science Council (IASC)
8630 Fenton St., Ste. 918
Silver Spring, MD 20910
Ph: (301)588-2420
Fax: (301)588-1174
Co. E-mail: info@iasc.org
URL: http://www.iasc.org
Contact: Santiago Rodriguez, Chairman

Description: Manufacturers and marketers of foods, drugs and cosmetics containing gel of the aloe vera plant. Aims to provide scientific research for support of product claims. Educates members on the plant and its products and uses. Acts as a liaison for government agency regulations on aloe vera business. **Scope:** research in aloe. **Founded:** 1981. **Subscriptions:** 500 articles. **Educational Activities:** International Aloe Science Council Conference (Annual). **Awards:** Reviewed Scientific Article (Annual); Yun Ho Lee Scientific Award (Annual).

1891 ■ NAGMR
c/o Jim Lewis
15038 SE Fairwood Blvd.
Renton, WA 98058-8505
Ph: (425)271-4506
Fax: (425)271-0864
Co. E-mail: jnlsales@aol.com
URL: http://nagmr.com
Contact: Ken Laner, President

Description: Consumer products brokers specializing in selling drug, health, beauty aids, and nonfood products to food chains and the same products and grocery items to the nonfood market. **Founded:** 1948. **Educational Activities:** NAGMR Convention (Annual). **Awards:** NAGMR Award of Excellence (Annual).

1892 ■ Personal Care Product Council
1101 17th St. NW, Ste. 300
Washington, DC 20036-4702
Ph: (202)331-1770
Fax: (202)331-1969
Co. E-mail: membership@personalcarecouncil.org
URL: http://www.personalcarecouncil.org
Contact: Lezlee Westine, President

Description: Manufacturers and distributors of finished cosmetics, fragrances, and personal care products; suppliers of raw materials and services. Provides scientific, legal, regulatory, and legislative services. Coordinates public service, educational, and public affairs activities. **Founded:** 1894. **Publications:** *CTFA News* (Biweekly); *International Color Handbook*; *International Resource Manual*.

1893 ■ Professional Beauty Association (PBA) - National Cosmetology Association
15825 N 71st St., Ste. 100
Scottsdale, AZ 85254
Ph: (480)281-0424
Free: 800-468-2274
Fax: (480)905-0708
Co. E-mail: info@probeauty.org
URL: http://www.probeauty.org
Contact: Max Wexler, Chairman

Description: Manufacturers and manufacturers' representatives of beauty and barber products, cosmetics, equipment, and supplies used in or resold by beauty salons or barbershops. Promotes the beauty industry; works to ensure product safety; disseminates information. Holds educational seminars; organizes charity events. **Founded:** 1985. **Publications:** *PBA Progress* (3/year). **Educational Activities:** Cosmoprof North America; Cosmoprof North America; International Salon & Spa Expo (Annual); Pro Termal (Annual); Professional Beauty Africa (Annual). **Awards:** Sally Beauty Scholarships for High School Graduates.

REFERENCE WORKS

1894 ■ "avVaa World Health Care Products Rolls Out Internet Marketing Program" in
Health and Beauty Close-Up (September 18, 2009)
Pub: Close-Up Media

Description: avVaa World Health Care Products, Inc., a biotechnology company, manufacturer and distributor of nationally branded therapeutic, natural health care and skin products, has signed an agreement with Online Performance Marketing to launch of an Internet marketing campaign in order to broaden its presence online. The impact of advertising on the Internet to generate an increase in sales is explored.

1895 ■ "Cross Atlantic Commodities Launches National Internet Marketing Programs" in Manufacturing Close-Up (September 8, 2009)
Pub: Close-Up Media

Description: Profile of the Internet campaign recently launched by Cross Atlantic Commodities, Inc., a manufacturer of specialty beauty and health products.

1896 ■ "Freeman Beauty Labs" in Retail Merchandiser (Vol. 51, September-October 2011, No. 5, pp. 74)
Pub: Phoenix Media Corporation

Description: Profile of Freeman Beauty Labs, the family owned beauty product developer supplying retailers and salons with quality products. The firm promotes its bath, foot care, hair care, and skincare brands as a whole, not as individual products.

1897 ■ "In the Raw: Karyn Calabrese Brings Healthy Dining to a New Sophisticated Level" in Black Enterprise (Vol. 41, September 2010)
Pub: Earl G. Graves Publishing Co. Inc.

Ed: Sonia Alleyne. **Description:** Profile of Karyn Calabrese whose businesses are based in Chicago, Illinois. Calabrese has launched a complete line of products (vitamins and beauty items), services (spa, chiropractic, and acupuncture treatments), and restaurants to bring health dining and lifestyles to a better level.

1898 ■ Lessons of a Lipstick Queen: Finding and Developing the Great Idea That Can Change Your Life
Pub: Simon and Schuster Inc.
Contact: Carolyn Reidy, President
E-mail: carolyn.reidy@simonandschuster.com

Ed: Poppy King. **Released:** May 1, 2009. **Price:** $14.00. **Description:** Poppy King tells how she started her lipstick brand at age eighteen. She reveals how she managed to launch her business using a good idea and finding financing, marketing the product and how she became successful.

1899 ■ The Perfect Scent: A Year Inside the Perfume Industry in Paris and New York
Pub: Henry Holt and Co.
Contact: Michael Naumann, President

Ed: Chandler Burr. **Released:** 2009. **Price:** $25.00. **Description:** An insiders glimpse at the development of two new fragrances from Hermes and Coty.

1900 ■ *"Retail Briefs - Dollar Store Opens in Long Leaf Mall' in Star-News (November 5, 2010)*

Pub: Star-News Media

Ed: Judy Royal. **Description:** Dollar Delight$ opened a new shop in Long Leaf Mall in Wilmington, North Carolina. The store will carry gift bags, balloons, party supplies, greeting cards, school supplies, health and beauty products, hardware, baby items, toys, Christmas goods, crafts, housewares and jewelry in its inventory.

1901 ■ *"Scream Therapy: A Chain of New York City Beauty Stores Perfect Halloween Pop-Ups" in Inc. (Vol. 33, October 2011, No. 8, pp. 99)*

Pub: Inc. Magazine

Ed: Amy Barrett. **Description:** Ricky's Halloween stores will open 30 temporary stores for about two months, 28 of which are permanent beauty supply shops the rest of the year.

1902 ■ *"White Cat Media Tells You Where to Get a Bargain. Now It's Shopping for $1.5 Million" in Inc. (March 2008, pp. 48)*

Pub: Gruner & Jahr USA Publishing

Ed: Athena Schindelheim. **Description:** Profile of White Cat Media which runs two shopping Websites: SheFinds.com for fashion and beauty items, and MomFinds.com for mothers. The New York City firm reported revenues for 2007 at $400,000 and is looking for funding capital in the amount of $1.7 million.

1903 ■ *"Women Prioritize Luxury Spending" in Marketing to Women (Vol. 22, July 2009, No. 7, pp. 8)*

Pub: EPM Communications Inc.

Contact: Ira Mayer, President

E-mail: imayer@epmcom.com

Description: In 2008, women spent 7 percent less on luxury items than in the previous year, according to Unity Marketing. Some luxury items, such as facial care products, are faring better than others. Statistical data included.

STATISTICAL SOURCES

1904 ■ *RMA Annual Statement Studies*

Pub: Risk Management Association

Contact: Kevin M. Blakey, President

Released: Annual. **Price:** $175.00 2006-07 edition, $105.00. **Description:** Contains composite balance sheets and income statements for more than 360 industries, including the accounting, auditing, and bookkeeping industries. Also contains five years of comparative historical data for discerning trends. Includes 16 commonly used ratios, computed for most of the size groupings for nearly every industry.

1905 ■ *The Skincare Market*

Pub: Rector Press, Ltd.

Contact: Lewis Sckolnick, President

Released: 2009. **Price:** Contact Rector Press. and rankings for both mass-market and limited.

1906 ■ *Standard & Poor's Industry Surveys*

Pub: Standard & Poor's Corp.

Released: Annual. **Price:** $3633.00. **Description:** Two-volume book that examines the prospects for specific industries, including trucking. Also provides analyses of trends and problems, statistical tables and charts, and comparative company analyses.

1907 ■ *Suncare - U.S. Report*

Pub: MarketResearch.com

Released: 2008. **Price:** $3995.00. **Description:** This report addresses all the key issues affecting the suncare market, such as the combining of suncare and skincare products, the difficulty attracting teens to suncare products, and how consumer education continues to impact sales.

TRADE PERIODICALS

1908 ■ *Cosmetics & Toiletries: The International Magazine of Cosmetic*

Technology

Contact: Jane Evison, Account Manager

E-mail: jane-evison@btconnect.com

URL(s): www.cosmeticsandtoiletries.com. **Released:** Monthly **Price:** $98, Individuals; $137, Canada; $189, Other countries; $169, Two years; $231, Canada two years; $330, Other countries two years.

1909 ■ *Skin Inc.: Professional Skin Care*

Contact: Melinda Taschetta-Millane, Editor-in-Chief

E-mail: taschetta_millane@allured.com

URL(s): www.skininc.com/. **Released:** Monthly **Price:** $49, Individuals; $57, Canada; $98, Other countries.

TRADE SHOWS AND CONVENTIONS

1910 ■ American Association of Cosmetology Schools Annual Conference - AACS Annual Convention & Expo

American Association of Cosmetology Schools (AACS)

9927 E Bell Rd., Ste. 110

Scottsdale, AZ 85260

Ph: (480)281-0431

Free: 800-831-1086

Fax: (480)905-0993

Co. E-mail: jim@beautyschools.org

URL: http://www.beautyschools.org

Contact: Jim Cox, Executive Director

E-mail: jim@beautyschools.org

URL(s): www.beautyschools.org. **Price:** $500, Members online registration; $500, Non-members online registration. **Frequency:** Annual. **Audience:** School owners. **Principal Exhibits:** Beauty supplies and products, and cosmetology services. **Telecommunication Services:** dilsah@beautyschools.org.

FRANCHISES AND BUSINESS OPPORTUNITIES

1911 ■ Beauty Supply Outlet

6465 Millcreek Dr., Ste. 210

Mississauga, ON, Canada L5N 5R6

Ph: (905)363-4105

Fax: (952)995-3403

Co. E-mail: franchiseleads@regiscorp.com

URL: http://www.regisfranchise.com

Description: Retails professional hair care and beauty products, professional hair and beauty tools and trendy and elegant accessories. **No. of Franchise Units:** 37. **Founded:** 1993.. **Equity Capital Needed:** $100,000 in liquid; $300,000 networth. **Franchise Fee:** $25,000. **Training:** New franchisee training and ongoing support.

1912 ■ Chatters Salon

271 Burnt Park Dr.

Red Deer County, AB, Canada T4S 2L4

Ph: (403)342-5055

Free: 888-944-5055

Fax: (403)347-7759

Co. E-mail: franchise@chatters.ca

URL: http://www.chatters.ca

Description: Hair salon and beauty supply full salon services with extensive retail component. **No. of Franchise Units:** 68. **No. of Company-Owned Units:** 22. **Founded:** 1988.. **Franchised:** 1991. **Equity Capital Needed:** $400,000-$700,000. **Franchise Fee:** $40,000.

1913 ■ Facelogic

200 W State Hwy. 6, Ste. 225

Woodway, TX 76712

Ph: (254)757-1554

Fax: (254)751-9034

Description: Skin care. **No. of Franchise Units:** 43. **Founded:** 2005.. **Franchised:** 2005. **Equity Capital Needed:** $212,700-$355,600. **Franchise Fee:** $34,900. **Royalty Fee:** 4%. **Training:** 3 days training provided at headquarters, 5 days onsite and ongoing support.

1914 ■ Glamour Secrets

Glamour Secrets Franchising, Inc.

101 Jevlan Dr.

Woodbridge, ON, Canada L4L 8C2

Free: 866-713-7487

Fax: (905)264-2779

Description: Retail stores selling exclusive salon beauty products. **No. of Franchise Units:** 31. **No. of Company-Owned Units:** 15. **Founded:** 1990.. **Franchised:** 1990. **Equity Capital Needed:** $175,000-$400,000. **Franchise Fee:** $25,000. **Financial Assistance:** Yes. **Training:** Yes.

1915 ■ The Woodhouse Day Spa

1 O'Connor Plaza., 12th Fl.

Victoria, TX 77901

Ph: (361)570-7772

Free: 877-570-7772

Fax: (361)578-7116

Co. E-mail: info@woodhousespas.com

URL: http://www.woodhousespas.com

Description: Day spa services, bath and body retail products. **No. of Franchise Units:** 24. **No. of Company-Owned Units:** 2. **Founded:** 2001.. **Franchised:** 2003. **Equity Capital Needed:** $420,250-$522,200. **Franchise Fee:** $45,000. **Royalty Fee:** 6%. **Financial Assistance:** Limited third party financing available. **Training:** Offers 2-3 weeks training and an additional 1-2 days with ongoing support.

LIBRARIES

1916 ■ Avon Products, Inc. Research Library

777 Third Ave.

New York, NY 10017

Ph: (212)282-7000

Free: 800-445-2866

Fax: (914)369-2803

Co. E-mail: dearavon@avon.com

URL: http://www.avoncompany.com/

Scope: Cosmetics, packaging, toxicology, dermatology, pharmacology, chemistry, engineering, microbiology. **Services:** Interlibrary loan; SDI; library open to the public for reference use only on request. **Founded:** 1934. **Holdings:** 6500 books; 5000 bound periodical volumes; 6000 U.S. and foreign patents. **Subscriptions:** 300 journals and other serials.

1917 ■ Johnson and Johnson - Consumer and Personal Products Worldwide Library

199 Grandview Rd.

Skillman, NJ 08558

Free: 866-565-2229

URL: http://www.jnj.com/connect/

Contact: Susan Gleckner, Director, Library Services

URL(s): www.johnsonsbaby.com/. **Scope:** Infant care, health and beauty aids, toiletries, chemistry, pharmaceuticals, oral care, wound care, skin care, dermatology, women's health. **Holdings:** 2000 books; 1500 bound periodical volumes. **Subscriptions:** 400 journals and other serials.

1918 ■ Mary Kay Inc. Information Resources

16251 N. Dallas Pkwy.

Addison, TX 75001

Ph: (972)687-5527

Fax: (972)687-1643

Co. E-mail: cecilia.armas@mkcorp.com

Contact: Lynn F. Johnson

Scope: Cosmetics, dermatology, toxicology, chemistry, business, marketing. **Services:** Interlibrary loan. **Founded:** 1976. **Holdings:** 2000 books; 500 bound periodical volumes. **Subscriptions:** 250 journals and other serials.

1919 ■ Revlon Research Center Library

2121 Rte. 27

Edison, NJ 08818

Ph: (732)287-1400

Fax: (732)287-7270

URL: http://www.revlon.com/

Contact: Ann Van Dine, Librarian

Scope: Cosmetics, soaps, chemistry, perfumery, dermatology, pharmacology, microbiology, aerosols. **Services:** Interlibrary loan; copying; SDI; library open to the public by appointment for reference only. **Founded:** 1955. **Holdings:** 11,000 books; 4000 bound periodical volumes. **Subscriptions:** 100 journals and other serials.

START-UP INFORMATION

1920 ■ *How to Start and Run a B&B: All You Need to Know to Build a Successful Enterprise*

Pub: How To Books

Ed: David Weston; Louise Weston. **Released:** December 2006. **Price:** $24.75. **Description:** Advice is offered for starting and running a Bed and Breakfast operation. Topics include information on planning, budgeting, pricing, regulation and compliance, accounting and taxation, and defining a market.

REFERENCE WORKS

1921 ■ *"B&B to Hit SoCo Next Month" in Austin Business JournalInc. (Vol. 28, September 5, 2008, No. 25, pp. 1)*

Pub: American City Business Journals

Ed: Sandra Zaragoza. **Description:** The KimberModern bed and breakfast will opening Austin's trendy South Congress neighborhood on October 10, 2008. The establishment will have a secured gate instead of a front desk and will let guests enjoy their breakfasts at their leisure unlike hotels that close their early morning breakfasts to guests at a set time.

1922 ■ *"B&B Hopes to Appeal to Fiat Execs" in Crain's Detroit Business (Vol. 25, June 15, 2009, No. 24, pp. 21)*

Pub: Crain Communications Inc. - Detroit

Ed: Daniel Duggan. **Description:** Cobblestone Manor, a ten-room bed and breakfast in Auburn Hills, Michigan is hoping to provide rooms for Fiat executives. The owners have been working with travel organizations to promote the castle-like bed and breakfast which appeals to European visitors.

1923 ■ *Best Places to Stay in New England*

Pub: Houghton Mifflin Books

Contact: Stephen Tapp, President

URL(s): www.houghtonmifflinbooks.com. **Ed:** Christina Tree, Kimberly Grant. **Released:** Biennial **Price:** $19, Individuals trade paperback. **Covers:** Over 350 bed and breakfast homes, inns, hotels, farms, and other accommodations; coverage includes Connecticut, Maine, Massachusetts, New Hampshire, Rhode Island, and Vermont. **Entries include:** Hotel or inn name, owner, address, rates, credit cards accepted, whether children or pets are allowed, description. **Database includes:** Maps. **Arrangement:** Classified by type of location (lakeside, beach, farm, etc.), then geographical. **Indexes:** Alphabetical, geographical.

1924 ■ *Buying and Running a Guesthouse or Small Hotel*

Pub: Hot To Books Ltd.

Ed: Dan Marshall. **Released:** December 2007. **Price:** $30.00. **Description:** Teaches how to build and enjoy a lifestyle while running a guesthouse or small hotel.

1925 ■ *"'Groundhog Day' B & B Likely Will Be Converted Into One In Real Life" in*

Chicago Tribune (October 21, 2008)

Pub: McClatchy-Tribune Information Services

Ed: Carolyn Starks. **Description:** Everton Martin and Karla Stewart Martin have purchased the Victorian house that was featured as a bed-and-breakfast in the 1993 hit move 'Groundhog Day'; the couple was initially unaware of the structure's celebrity status when they purchased it with the hope of fulfilling their dream of owning a bed-and-breakfast.

1926 ■ *How to Open a Financially Successful Bed & Breakfast or Small Hotel*

Pub: Atlantic Publishing Company

Ed: Lora Arduser; Douglas R. Brow. **Released:** May 1, 2004. **Price:** $39.95. **Description:** Handbook with CD ROM demonstrates ways to set up, operate and manage a financially successful bed-and-breakfast or small hotel.

1927 ■ *How to Open and Operate a Bed & Breakfast, 8th Edition*

Pub: Globe Pequot Press

Ed: Jan Stankus. **Released:** January 1, 2007 (paperback). **Price:** $18.95 (paperback). **Description:** Handbook outlines how to set up and run a bed and breakfast, whether using a spare room of a home or a small inn.

1928 ■ *How to Start and Operate Your Own Bed-and-Breakfast: Down-To-Earth Advice from an Award-Winning B&B Owner*

Pub: Owl Books

Ed: Martha W. Murphy. **Released:** May 15, 1994. **Price:** $18.00. **Description:** Bed and breakfast owner shares tip for running a successful business.

1929 ■ *INNside Scoop: Everything You Ever Wanted to Know About Bed & Breakfast Inns*

Pub: The B&B and Country Inn Marketplace

Ed: Maxine Pinson. **Released:** December 2002. **Description:** Guide for running a successful bread and breakfast inn.

1930 ■ *"Muirhead Farmhouse B & B Owners Get Hospitality Right" in Chicago Tribune (July 31, 2008)*

Pub: McClatchy-Tribune Information Services

Ed: Glenn Jeffers. **Description:** Profile of the Muirhead Farmhouse, a bed-and-breakfast owned by Mike Petersdorf and Sarah Muirhead Petersdorf; Frank Lloyd Wright designed the historic farmhouse which blends farm life and history into a unique experience that is enhanced by the couple's hospitality.

1931 ■ *"Sleep It Off In a Silo B & B" in Chicago Tribune (December 14, 2008)*

Pub: McClatchy-Tribune Information Services

Ed: Bill Daley. **Description:** Profile of Oregon's Abbey Road Farm bed-and-breakfast which is located on an 82-acre working farm; guests stay in shiny metal farm silos which have been converted into luxury rooms with views of the farm.

1932 ■ *So, You Want to Be an Innkeeper*

Pub: Chronicle Books LLC

Ed: JoAnn M. Bell; Susan Brown, Mary Davies; Pat Hardy. **Released:** March 2004. **Description:** Provides information for aspiring innkeepers, includes information on cottages, luxury properties, and spa services.

1933 ■ *"South Lake Tahoe B & B Blocks Out Neveda's Neon" in Chicago Tribune (May 18, 2008)*

Pub: McClatchy-Tribune Information Services

Ed: Randall Weissman. **Description:** Profile of the Black Bear Inn, a small bed-and-breakfast in South Lake Tahoe owned by Jerry Birdwell and Kevin Chandler; the welcoming ambience is a delightful departure from ski resort hotel rooms. Pricing and further details of the various rooms are described.

1934 ■ *Start and Run a Profitable Bed and Breakfast*

Pub: Self-Counsel Press Inc.

Ed: Monica Taylor, Richard Taylor. **Released:** October 1999. **Description:** Information for starting and running a successful bed and breakfast is presented.

1935 ■ *Upstart Guide to Owning and Managing a Bed and Breakfast*

Pub: Kaplan Publishing

Ed: Lisa Angowski Rogak. **Released:** November 1, 1994. **Description:** Guide for running a profitable bed and breakfast.

TRADE PERIODICALS

1936 ■ *innkeeping*

Pub: Professional Association of Innkeepers International

Ed: Pat Hardy, Editor, ph@paii.org. **Released:** Monthly. **Price:** $95, individuals. **Description:** Addresses topics of interest to innkeepers who own and operate bed and breakfast operations. Recurring features include letters to the editor, news of research, news of educational opportunities, and notices of publications available.

1937 ■ *The Place: Southern California's Visitors Guide*

Pub: Inn Room Visitors Magazine

Released: Monthly

1938 ■ *Southern Festivals: The South's Festival Newspaper*

Pub: Southern Festivals

URL(s): www.southfest.com/festival_list/georgia.html. **Released:** Bimonthly

COMPUTERIZED DATABASES

1939 ■ *Food Code - Recommendations of the United States Public Health Service Food and Drug Administration*

10903 New Hampshire Ave.

Silver Spring, MD 20993-0002

Free: 888-INFO-FDA

URL: http://www.fda.gov

Availability: CD-ROM: U.S. Department of Commerce - Technology Administration - National Technical Information Service. **Type:** Full-text.

ASSOCIATIONS AND OTHER ORGANIZATIONS

1940 ■ American Beekeeping Federation (ABF)
3525 Piedmont Rd., Bldg. 5, Ste. 300
Atlanta, GA 30305
Ph: (404)760-2875
Co. E-mail: info@abfnet.org
URL: http://www.abfnet.org
Contact: George Hansen, President

Description: Commercial and avocational beekeepers, suppliers, bottlers, packers, and others affiliated with the honey industry. Promotes the industry and serves as an representative before legislative bodies; makes recommendations and helps secure appropriations for research programs. Operates the Honey Defense Fund, which works to insure the purity of honey marketed in the U.S. Sponsors American Honey Queen Program. **Founded:** 1943. **Publications:** *Bee Culture* (Monthly). **Awards:** ABF President's Award (Annual).

1941 ■ Apiary Inspectors of America (AIA)
Minnesota Department of Agriculture
32736 180th St.
Starbuck, MN 56381
Ph: (320)239-4725
Free: 800-967-2474
Fax: (320)239-4725
Co. E-mail: don.hopkins@ncagr.gov
URL: http://www.apiaryinspectors.org
Contact: Don Hopkins, President

Description: State and provincial apiarists; individuals interested in beekeeping and bee research are associate members. Seeks to promote and protect the beekeeping industry of North America. Participates in research meetings at United States Department of Agriculture-Science and Educational Administration laboratories. **Founded:** 1926.

1942 ■ Eastern Apicultural Society of North America (EAS)
142 Cemetery Rd.
Mocksville, NC 27028
Ph: (336)998-2975
Co. E-mail: chairman@easternapiculture.org
URL: http://www.easternapiculture.org
Contact: Jim Bobb, Chairman of the Board

Description: Hobbyist beekeepers and producers of honey; supporting members are manufacturers of beekeeping equipment and packers of honey. Provides an educational program for hobbyist beekeepers and the public on the science of apiculture (beekeeping). **Founded:** 1955. **Awards:** DiVelbiss Award (Annual); EAS Student Apiculture Award (Annual); James I. Hambleton Award (Annual); Roger A. Morse Outstanding Teaching/Extension Service/Regulatory Award (Annual); J. I. Hambleton Award; Roger A. Morse Outstanding Teaching/Extension Service/Regulatory Award.

1943 ■ National Honey Packers and Dealers Association (NHPDA)
3301 Rte. 66, Ste. 205, Bldg. C
Neptune, NJ 07753
Ph: (732)922-3008
Fax: (732)922-3590
Co. E-mail: info@nhpda.org
URL: http://www.nhpda.org

Description: Represents cooperative and independent processors, packers, and dealers of honey at either the wholesale or retail level. Offers members information on testing facilities for honey analysis. Consults with Department of Agriculture on research programs in the field of honey marketing. **Founded:** 1950.

REFERENCE WORKS

1944 ■ *Bee Culture--Who's Who in Apiculture Issue: The Magazine of American Beekeeping*
Pub: The A.I. Root Co.

URL(s): www.beeculture.com. **Ed:** Kim Flottum. **Released:** Annual; April; Latest edition 2008. **Price:** $23.50, U.S. one year; $38.50, Individuals foreign surface; $83.50, Individuals foreign airmail. **Publication includes:** List of United States and Canadian government agencies concerned with apiculture, including university, extension and apiary inspectors, and other groups concerned with apiculture. **Entries include:** For government agencies--Agency name, address; names, titles, phone numbers, e-mail and webpage of key personnel. For associations and other groups--Name, address, name and title of contact. **Arrangement:** Geographical.

1945 ■ *"A Busy Little Parasite" in Hawaii Business (Vol. 53, March 2008, No. 9, pp. 1)*
Pub: Hawaii Business Publishing

Ed: Jason Ubay. **Description:** Bee mites were first sighted in Hawaii by Michael Kliks on April 6, 2007 and have since been a cause of concern for the beekeeping industry and pollinated-dependent crop industry. Hawaii's agricultural industry estimates that the losses due to bee mites may amount to between $42 million and $62 million. Steps taken to address the issue are discussed.

1946 ■ *"Buzz Kill" in Canadian Business (Vol. 83, August 17, 2010, No. 13-14, pp. 24)*
Pub: Rogers Media Ltd.

Ed: Rachel Mendleson. **Description:** Beekeeping industry has been plagued by a massive wave of honeybee deaths since 2006, which pushed upward the cost of per hive-rental. The death of honeybees has put the food supply at risk since it jeopardized the growth of pumpkins, as well as other crops in large acreage. Insights on the Colony Collapse Disorder are outlined.

TRADE PERIODICALS

1947 ■ *American Bee Journal*
Pub: Dadant and Sons Inc.
Contact: Timothy Dadant, President
URL(s): www.americanbeejournal.com. **Ed:** Joe Graham. **Released:** Monthly **Price:** $27, Individuals;

$51, Two years; $41, Canada; $79, Canada 2 years; $50, Other countries; $96, Other countries 2 years; $61, Canada airmail; $80, Other countries airmail.

1948 ■ *American Beekeeping Federation--News Letter*
Pub: American Beekeeping Federation Inc.
Contact: Troy Fore, Executive Director
Ed: Troy H. Fore, Jr., Editor, troyfore@abfnet.org. **Released:** Bimonthly. **Price:** $35, individuals. **Description:** Discusses Federation activities and national problems of the beekeeping industry. Also covers related legislation, regulations, and marketing and production information. Recurring features include news of research, book reviews, and columns titled President's Page, Washington Update, and Honey Queen Program Activities.

1949 ■ *Hive Lights*
Pub: Canadian Honey Council
Ed: Heather Clay, Editor. **Released:** Quarterly. **Price:** Included in membership; $25, nonmembers Canada; $30, nonmembers U.S.; $25. **Description:** Cover topics related to the beekeeping and honey industry. Recurring features include letters to the editor, news of research, a calendar of events, reports of meetings, news of educational opportunities, and job listings.

1950 ■ *Manitoba Beekeeper*
Pub: Manitoba Beekeepers' Association
Ed: Heather Laird, Editor, hlaird@mb.sympatico.ca. **Released:** Quarterly. **Price:** Included in membership; $20, nonmembers. **Description:** Furnishes information about beekeeping. Recurring features include news of research, a calendar of events, reports of meetings, and honey market news.

1951 ■ *The Speedy Bee: The Beekeeper's Newspaper*
Pub: The Speedy Bee
URL(s): thespeedybee.com/. **Ed:** Troy H. Fore, Jr. **Released:** Quarterly **Price:** $17.25, Individuals.

1952 ■ *The Sting*
Pub: Ontario Beekeepers' Association
Contact: Pat Westlake, Administrator
Released: Bimonthly. **Price:** Included in membership. **Description:** Provides news and information for beekeepers in the Ontario area and beyond. Recurring features include letters to the editor, news of research, a calendar of events, reports of meetings, news of educational opportunities, and job listings.

VIDEOCASSETTES/ AUDIOCASSETTES

1953 ■ *Bee Breeding: The Search for the Perfect Honeybee*
Bullfrog Films, Inc.
PO Box 149
Oley, PA 19547
Ph: (610)779-8226
Free: 800-543-3764

Fax: (610)370-1978
Co. E-mail: video@bullfrogfilms.com
URL: http://bullfrogfilms.com
Released: 1988. **Price:** $250.00. **Description:** A look at the work and genetic advances in bee breeding by Brother Adam, a 90-year-old English monk who stands as the world's foremost bee-breeder. **Availability:** VHS; 3/4 U.

TRADE SHOWS AND CONVENTIONS

1954 ■ American Beekeeping Federation Convention
American Beekeeping Federation
3525 Piedmont Rd., Bldg. 5, Ste. 300
Atlanta, GA 30305
Ph: (404)760-2875
Fax: (404)240-0998
Co. E-mail: info@abfnet.org
URL: http://www.abfnet.org
URL(s): www.abfnet.org. **Frequency:** Annual. **Audience:** Trade and general public. **Principal Exhibits:** Products to benefit beekeeping/honey industry; gift packs, equipment, packaging, and bee items. **Telecommunication Services:** info@abfnet.org.

LIBRARIES

1955 ■ Bee Biology and Systematics Laboratory - Library
Utah State University
UMC 5310
Logan, UT 84322

Ph: (435)797-2524
URL: http://uaes.usu.edu
URL(s): uaes.usu.edu/htm/farms-and-facilities/usda-bee-biology-and-systematics-laboratory/. **Scope:** Bees, pollination, crops, systematics, biology, management and control. **Services:** Library not open to the public. **Founded:** 1946. **Holdings:** 17,000 volumes.

1956 ■ Florida Department of Agriculture and Consumer Services - Division of Plant Industry Library
1911 SW 34th St.
Gainesville, FL 32608-1268
Ph: (352)372-3505, x-131
Fax: (352)955-2301
Co. E-mail: popeb@doacs.state.fl.us
URL: http://www.neflin.org/dpi/default.html
Contact: Beverly Pope, Librarian
Scope: Entomology, apiary, plant pathology, plant inspection, nematology. **Services:** Interlibrary loan; copying; library open to the public for reference use only. **Founded:** 1915. **Holdings:** 17,000 volumes; 124 microfiche; photographs; clippings; maps; manuscripts . **Subscriptions:** 417 journals and other serials. **Telecommunication Services:** dpilib@doacs.state.fl.us; sandera@doacs.state.fl.us.

1957 ■ Michigan State University - Special Collections Library
366 W. Circle Dr.
East Lansing, MI 48824
Ph: (517)884-6471

Fax: (517)353-5069
Co. E-mail: berg@msu.edu
URL: http://specialcollections.lib.msu.edu
Contact: Randall Scott, Librarian
Scope: American radicalism; history of French monarchy and revolution; Italian Risorgimento history; English 18th-century studies; comic art; popular fiction; early works in criminology, fencing, agriculture, botany, entomology, toxicology, cookery. **Services:** Interlibrary loan; copying; Library open to the public with required identification. **Founded:** 1962. **Holdings:** 450,000 volumes; facsimile editions of illuminated manuscripts. **Subscriptions:** 150 journals and newspapers. **Telecommunication Services:** scottr@msu.edu.

1958 ■ University of California, Davis - University Libraries - Special Collections
100 NW Quad
Shields Library, 1st Fl.
Davis, CA 95616-5292
Ph: (530)752-1621
Fax: (916)754-5758
Co. E-mail: dmorrison@ucdavis.edu
URL: http://www.lib.ucdavis.edu/dept/specol/
Contact: Liz Phillips
Scope: Reference. **Services:** Copying; collections open to the public for reference use only. **Founded:** 1966. **Holdings:** 129,500 books; 18,700 lin.ft. of archives and manuscripts. **Subscriptions:** 40 journals and other serials; 2 newspapers. **Telecommunication Services:** speccoll@ucdavis.edu.

ASSOCIATIONS AND OTHER ORGANIZATIONS

1959 ■ *Advisor*
24 Olive St., Unit 10
Grimsby, ON, Canada L3M 2B6
Ph: (905)309-0224
Free: 800-896-1054
Fax: (905)309-0225
Co. E-mail: info@camx.ca
URL: http://www.camx.ca/call-center/index_ang.cfm
Contact: Linda Osip, Executive Director
Released: Bimonthly

1960 ■ Canadian Call Management Association (CAM-X)
24 Olive St., Unit 10
Grimsby, ON, Canada L3M 2B6
Ph: (905)309-0224
Free: 800-896-1054
Fax: (905)309-0225
Co. E-mail: info@camx.ca
URL: http://www.camx.ca/call-center/index_ang.cfm
Contact: Linda Osip, Executive Director
Description: Call centers and message exchanges. Promotes excellence in the handling of voice and electronic messages. Represents members' interests; facilitates technical advancement in the field of telecommunications. **Founded:** 1964. **Publications:** *Advisor* (Bimonthly). **Awards:** Award of Excellence; Call Centre Award of Distinction.

1961 ■ PCIA - The Wireless Infrastucture Association (PCIA)
901 N Washington St., Ste. 600
Alexandria, VA 22314
Ph: (703)535-7518
Free: 800-759-0300
Fax: (703)836-1608
Co. E-mail: membership@pcia.com
URL: http://www.pcia.com
Contact: Dave Mayo, Director
Description: Promotes the wireless infrastructure, tower and siting industry through advocacy, education, programs, a trade show and other marketplace initiatives. **Scope:** personal communications services. **Founded:** 1949. **Subscriptions:** books papers periodicals reports. **Publications:** *The Bulletin* (Bimonthly); *PICA Bulletin: News and Analysis for the Personal Communication Industry; PCIA Zoning Field Guide: Information and Resources for Tower Siting.* **Educational Activities:** PCIA GlobalXChange (Annual); PCIA Wireless Infrastructure Show (Annual); PCIA Wireless Infrastructure Conference and Expo (Annual). **Awards:** PCIA Industry Awards (Annual); PCIA Marketing Awards (Annual); Eugene C. Bowler Award (Annual); Eugene C. Bowler Scholarship (Annual). **Telecommunication Services:** nancy.touhill@pcia.com; consumerinfo@pica.com; ebrahiml@pcia.com.

RESEARCH CENTERS

1962 ■ Virginia Polytechnic Institute and State University - Center for Wireless Telecommunications (CWT)
466 Whittemore Hall
Virginia Tech
Blacksburg, VA 24061-0111
Ph: (540)231-5096
Fax: (540)231-3004
Co. E-mail: bostian@vt.edu
URL: http://www.cwt.vt.edu
Contact: Charles W. Bostian, Director
Services: Analysis and consulting services; Engineering and business planning development. **Founded:** 1993. **Publications:** *CWT Newsletter* (Semiannual). **Educational Activities:** Wireless opportunities workshop. **Awards:** Wireless Entrepreneur of the Year. **Telecommunication Services:** cwt@vt.edu.

ASSOCIATIONS AND OTHER ORGANIZATIONS

1963 ■ Adventure Cycling Association
150 E Pine St.
Missoula, MT 59807
Ph: (406)721-1776
Free: 800-755-2453
Fax: (406)721-8754
Co. E-mail: info@adventurecycling.org
URL: http://www.adventurecycling.org
Contact: Jeffrey Miller, President

Description: Originally founded to develop the TransAmerica Coast-to-Coast Bicycle Trail (4450 miles) that was inaugurated in 1976 during the 200th birthday celebration of the U.S. Focuses on the research, maintenance, and mapping of over 20,000 miles of bicycle touring and mountain biking routes. Efforts are aimed at promoting bicycle adventure travel and educating the public in bicycle usage and safety. **Publications:** *Adventure Cyclist* (9/year); *Cyclists' Yellow Pages* (Annual).

1964 ■ Bicycle Product Suppliers Association (BPSA)
PO Box 187
Montgomeryville, PA 18936
Ph: (215)393-3144
Fax: (215)893-4872
Co. E-mail: bpsa@bpsa.org
URL: http://bpsa.org
Contact: Chris Speyer, President

Description: Wholesalers of bicycles, bicycle parts, and accessories; vendor members are manufacturers and suppliers. Affiliate members supply services and products to bicycle retailers. Offers educational programs; compiles statistics and safety information. **Founded:** 1912. **Publications:** *Statistical Report* (Annual).

1965 ■ League of American Bicyclists
1612 K St. NW, Ste. 510
Washington, DC 20006-2849
Ph: (202)822-1333
Fax: (202)822-1334
Co. E-mail: bikeleague@bikeleague.org
URL: http://www.bikeleague.org
Contact: Andy D. Clarke, President

Description: Bicyclists and bicycle clubs. Promotes bicycling for fun, fitness, and transportation, and works through advocacy and education for a bicycle-friendly America. Represents members' interests. Seeks to bring better bicycling to all communities. **Founded:** 1880. **Publications:** *American Bicyclist* (Quarterly); *BikeLeague News* (Bimonthly); *Almanac, Tour Finder, and Ride Guide: Tour Finder and Ride Guide* (Annual); *TourFinder: Almanac of Cyclists, Tourfinder, and Ride Guide* (Annual). **Educational Activities:** National Bike Summit (Annual); Rally and Membership Consortium (Annual). **Awards:** Dr. Paul Dudley White Award (Annual).

1966 ■ National Bicycle Dealers Association (NBDA)
3176 Pullman St., No. 117
Costa Mesa, CA 92626
Ph: (949)722-6909
Fax: (949)722-1747
Co. E-mail: info@nbda.com
URL: http://nbda.com
Contact: Dan Thornton, President

Description: Represents independent retail dealers who sell and service bicycles. Sponsors workshops and provides programs. **Founded:** 1946. **Publications:** *Outspokin'*; *Outspokin'*.

1967 ■ National Bicycle League (NBL)
1000 Creekside Plz., Ste. 300
Gahanna, OH 43230
Ph: (480)961-1903
Free: 800-886-BMX1
Fax: (480)961-1842
Co. E-mail: administration@nbl.org
URL: http://www.nbl.org
Contact: B.A. Anderson, Chief Executive Officer

Description: BMX racers. (BMX stands for bicycle motocross, a race of unmotorized bicycles on a tight course of 600 to 1,000 ft. over natural terrain that includes steep hills, sharp turns, and jumps.) Aims to establish rules and regulations for BMX races. Sponsors national competitions; distributes number plates to be earned by the top 40 racers. Maintains file on points earned by members in local races; licenses racers according to age class and proficiency. **Founded:** 1974. **Publications:** *BMX Today* (Monthly). **Educational Activities:** Competition Congress (Annual). **Awards:** Bob Warnicke Scholarship Fund (Annual).

1968 ■ National Center for Bicycling and Walking (NCBW)—Pro Bike
1612 K St. NW, Ste. 802
Washington, DC 20006
Ph: (202)223-3621
Co. E-mail: mark@bikewalk.org
URL: http://www.bikewalk.org
Contact: Mark Plotz, Program Manager

Description: Promotes bicycling for transportation and recreation; encourages increased quality and number of local bicycling programs; facilitates communication within the bicycle community. Disseminates information and provides technical assistance to community bicycle activists and city officials involved in bicycle programs. Designs and manages national bicycle promotion campaigns. Studies liability issues; develops guidelines for community bicycle programs; sponsors training seminars and programs for safety and planning professionals; conducts workshops on bicycle safety. Plans to offer advocacy and promotion services to government, industry, consumers, and organizations. **Founded:** 1977. **Publications:** *NCBW Forum* (Quarterly); *Pro Bike News* (Monthly); *Pro Bike Proceedings* (Biennial); *NCBW Pro Bike Directory* (Periodic).

1969 ■ United States Cycling Federation (USCF)
210 USA Cycling Point, Ste. 100
Colorado Springs, CO 80919-2215
Ph: (719)434-4200
Fax: (719)434-4300
Co. E-mail: membership@usacycling.org
URL: http://www.usacycling.org
Contact: Steve Johnson, Chief Executive Officer

Description: National governing body for cycling in the United States. Supervises and controls all elite and amateur bicycle championships, including road, track, mountain bike, BMX, and cyclo-cross; Compiles national bicycle racing records. Conducts development camps, coaching education, mechanics and officials training. **Founded:** 1921. **Publications:** *NORBA Newsletter* (Periodic); *Take the Lead*; *U.S.A. Cycling Magazine* (Bimonthly); *Rule Book* (Annual).

REFERENCE WORKS

1970 ■ Achieving Planned Innovation: A Proven System for Creating Successful New Products and Services
Pub: Simon and Schuster
Ed: Frank R. Bacon. **Released:** August 2007. **Price:** $16.95. **Description:** Planned innovation is a disciplined and practical step-by-step sequence of procedures for reaching the intended destination point: successful products. This easy-to-read book explains the system along with an action-oriented program for continuous success in new-product innovations. Five steps outlined include: a disciplined reasoning process; lasting market orientation; proper selection criteria that reflect both strategic and tactical business objectives and goals along with dynamic matching of resources to present and future opportunities, and positive and negative requirements before making major expenditures; and proper organizational staffing. The author explains what to do and evaluating the potential of any new product or service, ranging from ventures in retail distribution to the manufacture of goods as diverse as bicycles, motorcycles, aerospace communication and navigation equipment, small business computers, food packaging, and medical products.

1971 ■ Cyclists' Yellow Pages
Pub: Adventure Cycling Association
Contact: Jeffrey Miller, President
URL(s): www.adventurecycling.org/. Ed: Michael Deme. **Released:** Annual **Price:** included in membership dues; Free. **Covers:** Sources of bicycle maps, books, routes, clubs, tour operators, and organizations in the United States, Canada, and foreign countries. **Entries include:** For sources--Name of agency or organization, address, phone, e-mail, web sites. For publications--Title, name and address of publisher, description, price. For organizations and shops--Name, address, phone, e-mail, description of activities, interests, or offerings. **Database includes:** Advocacy resources; tips on transporting your bicycle, getting in shape, best places to go mountain biking, etc. **Arrangement:** Most sections are geographical; others are classified by topic or line of business.

1972 ■ *"Riding High" in Small Business Opportunities (November 2008)*
Pub: Entrepreneur Press
Contact: Perlman Neil, President
Ed: Stan Roberts. **Description:** Profile of David Sanborn who found a way to turn his passion for biking into a moneymaking opportunity by opening his own bicycle shops; Sanborn's goal is to become the largest independent bike retailer in the United States.

STATISTICAL SOURCES

1973 ■ *RMA Annual Statement Studies*
Pub: Risk Management Association
Contact: Kevin M. Blakey, President
Released: Annual. **Price:** $175.00 2006-07 edition, $105.00. **Description:** Contains composite balance sheets and income statements for more than 360 industries, including the accounting, auditing, and bookkeeping industries. Also contains five years of comparative historical data for discerning trends. Includes 16 commonly used ratios, computed for most of the size groupings for nearly every industry.

TRADE PERIODICALS

1974 ■ *Adventure Cyclist*
Pub: Adventure Cycling Association
Contact: Jeffrey Miller, President
URL(s): www.adventurecycling.org/mag/index.cfm.
Ed: Daniel D'Ambrosio, Editor. **Released:** 9/year

Price: included in membership dues. **Description:** Magazine for members of Adventure Cycling Assn.

1975 ■ *Bicycling*
Pub: Bicycling
URL(s): www.bicycling.com. **Released:** 11/yr. **Price:** $11, Individuals plus free delivery; $22, Two years plus free delivery.

1976 ■ *Mountain Bike Magazine: World's Best-Selling Mountain Bike Magazine*
Pub: Mountain Bike Magazine
URL(s): www.bicycling.com/mountainbikecom. **Released:** 11/yr. **Price:** $11, U.S.; $22, Two years.

1977 ■ *Outspokin'*
Pub: National Bicycle Dealers Association
Contact: Dan Thornton, President
Ed: John Francis, Editor. **Released:** 10/year. **Price:** Included in membership. **Description:** Offers bicycle retailing and management tips, and provides consumer survey results. Recurring features include Association and industry news.

TRADE SHOWS AND CONVENTIONS

1978 ■ Interbike
VNU Expo
310 Broadway
Laguna Beach, CA 92651

Ph: (946)376-6200
Free: 800-486-2701
Fax: (949)497-5290
Co. E-mail: interbike@wyoming.com
URL: http://www.vnuexpo.com

URL(s): www.interbike.com. **Price:** $25, Onsite late retailer registration; $200, Onsite industry affiliate. **Frequency:** Annual. **Audience:** Owners and managers of cycling and specialty sports retail store. **Principal Exhibits:** Cycling hard goods, gear and accessories. **Telecommunication Services:** andy.tompkins@nielsen.com.

RESEARCH CENTERS

1979 ■ **Cornell University - Cornell BioRobotics and Locomotion Laboratory**
306 Kimball Hall
Department of Theoretical & Applied Mechanics
Ithaca, NY 14853
Ph: (607)255-7108
Co. E-mail: ruina@cornell.edu
URL: http://ruina.tam.cornell.edu/research/index.php

Services: Recycling services for old bicycles. **Publications:** *Cornell BioRobotics and Locomotion Laboratory Journal* articles.

START-UP INFORMATION

1980 ■ *"Pocket Change?" in Inc. (Vol. 30, December 2008, No. 12, pp. 28)*
Pub: Mansueto Ventures LLC
Ed: Ryan McCarthy. **Description:** Owner of a chain of nine retail billiard showrooms grew his business by starting to deliver pool tables for Sears. The company, consisting of seven retail locations and two warehouses, is now for sale. Details are included.

ASSOCIATIONS AND OTHER ORGANIZATIONS

1981 ■ **Billiard and Bowling Institute of America (BBIA)**
PO Box 6573
Arlington, TX 76005
Ph: (817)385-8120
Free: 800-343-1329
Fax: (817)633-2940
Co. E-mail: answer@billiardandbowling.org
URL: http://www.billiardandbowling.org
Contact: Bill Supper, Executive Director
Description: Represents distributors and manufacturers of billiard and bowling equipment. **Founded:** 1940. **Educational Activities:** Billiard and Bowling Institute of America Convention (Annual). **Awards:** Industry Service Award (Annual).

1982 ■ **Billiard Congress of America (BCA)**
12303 Airport Way, Ste. 140
Broomfield, CO 80021
Ph: (719)264-8300
Free: 866-852-0999
Fax: (719)264-0900
Co. E-mail: marketing@bca-pool.com
URL: http://www.bca-pool.com
Contact: Rob Johnson, Chief Executive Officer
E-mail: rob@bca-pool.com
Description: Develops rules for pocket billiards. Serves as national clearinghouse for billiard activities. Compiles statistics. **Founded:** 1948. **Publications:** *BCA Break* and *BCA Open Table* (Quarterly); *Official Rules and Records Book* (Annual). **Educational Activities:** International Billiard and Home Recreation Expo (Annual); Billiard Congress of America Trade Expo (Annual). **Awards:** Billiard Hall of Fame Award (Annual). **Telecommunication Services:** rob@bca-pool.com; carrie@bca-pool.com.

TRADE PERIODICALS

1983 ■ **BBIA enews**
Pub: Billiards and Bowling Institute of America
Ed: Sebastian Dicasoli, Editor. **Released:** Monthly, 3/year. **Price:** Free. **Description:** Serves as an update on the Institute's programs for manufacturers, distributors, and retailers of billiard and bowling supplies and equipment. Monitors executive changes, special promotions, new products, and trade show activities. Recurring features include member news.

1984 ■ **Billiards Digest**
Contact: Nicholas Leider, Managing Editor
E-mail: nickl@billiardsdigest.com
URL(s): www.billiardsdigest.comwww.lubypublishing.com/bd. **Released:** Monthly **Price:** $48, Individuals; $80, Two years; $115, Other countries for two years; $115, Individuals three years.

VIDEOCASSETTES/ AUDIOCASSETTES

1985 ■ **Billiard Basics**
MNTEX Entertainment, Inc.
500 Kirts Blvd.
Troy, MI 48084-5225
Ph: (248)362-4400
Free: 800-786-8777
Released: 1989. **Description:** A comprehensive guide toward the mastery of billiards. **Availability:** VHS.

1986 ■ **Billiards for All Age Groups**
School-Tech Inc.
745 State Cir.
Ann Arbor, MI 48106
Free: 800-521-2832
Fax: (800)654-4321
Co. E-mail: service@school-tech.com
URL: http://www.schoolmasters.com
Released: 1990. **Price:** $12.95. **Description:** Pool legend Willie Mosconi demonstrates proper hand position and strategies for making those near-impossible shots. **Availability:** VHS.

1987 ■ **Pool 1: Pool School**
ESPN Inc.
ESPN Plz.
Bristol, CT 06010
Ph: (860)766-2000
Free: 888-549-3776
Fax: (860)766-2213
Co. E-mail: espnpr@espn.com
URL: http://espn.go.com
Contact: Steven M. Bornstein, President
Released: 1988. **Price:** $39.95. **Description:** Champions Jim Rempe and Loree Jon Jones offer techniques for beginner to intermediate pool skills. **Availability:** VHS.

1988 ■ **Pool 2: Power Pool**
ESPN Inc.
ESPN Plz.
Bristol, CT 06010
Ph: (860)766-2000
Free: 888-549-3776
Fax: (860)766-2213
Co. E-mail: espnpr@espn.com
URL: http://espn.go.com
Contact: Steven M. Bornstein, President
Released: 1988. **Price:** **Description:** Learn control of the cueball via tip position, jumping the ball and other advanced techniques with Jim Rempe and Loree Jon Jones. **Availability:** VHS.

1989 ■ **Pool 3: Trick Shots**
ESPN Inc.
ESPN Plz.
Bristol, CT 06010
Ph: (860)766-2000
Free: 888-549-3776
Fax: (860)766-2213
Co. E-mail: espnpr@espn.com
URL: http://espn.go.com
Contact: Steven M. Bornstein, President
Released: 1988. **Price:** $39.95. **Description:** Six of the game's greatest show you their signature shots and teach you how to perform them. Hosted by Jim Rempe and Loree Jon Jones. **Availability:** VHS.

TRADE SHOWS AND CONVENTIONS

1990 ■ **Billiard Congress of America Trade Expo**
Billiard Congress of America (BCA)
12303 Airport Way, Ste. 140
Broomfield, CO 80021
Ph: (719)264-8300
Free: 866-852-0999
Fax: (719)264-0900
Co. E-mail: marketing@bca-pool.com
URL: http://www.bca-pool.com
Contact: Rob Johnson, Chief Executive Officer
E-mail: rob@bca-pool.com
URL(s): www.bcaexpo.com. **Price:** $free, Pre-registered, members if ordered before deadline; $50, Pre-registered, non-members if ordered before deadline; $25, Non-members children 12-17; children 11 and under. **Frequency:** Annual. **Principal Exhibits:** Billiards and pocket billiards equipment, supplies, and services. **Telecommunication Services:** expo@bca-pool.com.

FRANCHISES AND BUSINESS OPPORTUNITIES

1991 ■ **American Poolplayers Association, Inc.**
1000 Lake St. Louis Blvd., Ste. 325
Lake St. Louis, MO 63367
Ph: (636)625-8611
Free: 800-372-2536
Fax: (636)625-2975
URL: http://www.poolplayers.com
Description: Governing body of amateur pool; sanctions weekly league play for over 120,000 members through a nationwide franchising network. **No. of Franchise Units:** 296. **No. of Company-Owned Units:** 5. **Founded:** 1981. **Franchised:** 1982. **Equity Capital Needed:** $17,080-$24,150. **Franchise Fee:** $10,000-$20,150. **Royalty Fee:** $2.50 plus/team/wk. **Training:** Yes.

1992 ■ **Dooley's**
795 Main St., Ste. 200
Moncton, NB, Canada E1C 8P9

Ph: (506)857-8050
URL: http://franchisedirectory.ca
Description: Each Dooly's features a comfortable atmosphere with a fireplace, cozy sofas, lounge area and of course, first-class billiard tables. **No. of Franchise Units:** 90. **Founded:** 1993. **Equity Capital Needed:** $350,000-$450,000 total investment; $150,000 minimum cash liquidity. **Training:** Extensive training, both in operations and marketing

are provided. Field representatives will help with hiring and training your manager and staff with ongoing training and support through workshops and annual meetings.

1993 ■ West Side Charlie's Bar and Billiards
Churchill Square
St. John's, NL, Canada A1B 4J9
Ph: (709)738-4747

Fax: (709)726-4849
Co. E-mail: franchise@westsidecharlies.com
URL: http://www.westsidecharlies.com
Description: Offers customers with an upscale billiard room experience. **No. of Franchise Units:** 13. **Founded:** 1996.. **Franchised:** 1996. **Equity Capital Needed:** $150,000-$300,000. **Franchise Fee:** $20,000. **Training:** Offers 1 week and ongoing support.

ASSOCIATIONS AND OTHER ORGANIZATIONS

1994 ■ Asphalt Institute (AI)
2696 Research Park Dr.
Lexington, KY 40511-8480
Ph: (859)288-4960
Fax: (859)288-4999
Co. E-mail: info@asphaltinstitute.org
URL: http://www.asphaltinstitute.org
Contact: Peter T. Grass, President
Description: Composed of petroleum asphalt/bitumen producers, manufacturers and affiliated businesses. Promotes the use, benefits, and quality performance of petroleum asphalt through environmental marketing, research, engineering, and technical development, and through the resolution of issues affecting the industry. **Scope:** asphalt. **Founded:** 1919. **Publications:** *MS-4: The Asphalt Handbook*; *Asphalt*; *Catalog of Asphalt Institute Publications*.

1995 ■ International Slurry Surfacing Association (ISSA)
3 Church Cir.
PMB 250
Annapolis, MD 21401
Ph: (410)267-0023
Fax: (410)267-7546
Co. E-mail: krissoff@slurry.org
URL: http://www.slurry.org
Contact: Doug Ford, President
Description: Dedicated to the interests, education, and success of slurry surfacing professionals and corporations around the world. Promotes ethics and quality. Provides members with information, technical assistance, and ongoing opportunities for networking and professional development. **Scope:** pavement preservation. **Founded:** 1963. **Subscriptions:** audiovisuals. **Educational Activities:** World Congress (Annual). **Awards:** President's Award (Annual).

1996 ■ National Asphalt Pavement Association (NAPA)
5100 Forbes Blvd.
Lanham, MD 20706
Ph: (301)731-4748
Free: 888-468-6499
Fax: (301)731-4621
Co. E-mail: napa@hotmix.org
URL: http://www.hotmix.org
Contact: Mike Acott, President
E-mail: macott@hotmix.org
URL(s): www.ownyourroad.com. **Description:** Manufacturers and producers of scientifically proportioned Hot Mix Asphalt for use in all paving, including highways, airfields, and environmental usages. Membership includes hot mix producers, paving contractors, equipment manufacturers, engineering consultants, and others. Supports research and publishes information on: producing, stockpiling, and feeding of the aggregate to the manufacturing facility; drying; methods of screening, storing, and proportioning in the manufacturing facility; production of the hot mix asphalt; transporting mix to paver; lay down procedure and rolling; general workmanship; and related construction practices and materials. Commits to product quality, environmental control, safety and health, and energy conservation. Conducts training programs on a variety of technical and managerial topics for industry personnel. Maintains speakers' bureau and Hot Mix Asphalt Hall of Fame. **Scope:** asphalt pavement technology. **Founded:** 1955. **Subscriptions:** 2000 articles books periodicals. **Publications:** *National Asphalt Pavement Association-- Publications Catalog* (Annual); *HMAT*. **Educational Activities:** World of Asphalt Show and Conference (Annual). **Awards:** Quality in Construction Award (QIC); Community Involvement Awards (Annual); Hot Mix Asphalt Hall of Fame (Annual); Quality in Construction Awards; Sheldon G. Hayes Award (Annual).

REFERENCE WORKS

1997 ■ Asphalt Emulsion Manufacturers Association--Membership Directory
Pub: Asphalt Emulsion Manufacturers Association
Contact: Mike Krissoff, Executive Director
URL(s): www.aema.org. **Ed:** Michael R. Krissoff. **Released:** Biennial; Latest edition 2010-2011. **Covers:** About 100 member manufacturers and their plants and suppliers to the industry; international coverage. **Entries include:** Company name, address, phone, names and titles of representatives. Plant listings include address and phone. **Arrangement:** Classified by membership type, then alphabetical. Plants are geographical. **Indexes:** Personal name, company name.

1998 ■ Asphalt Paving Technologists
Pub: Association of Asphalt Paving Technologists
Contact: Reynaldo Roque, Director
URL(s): www.asphalttechnology.org. **Ed:** Eugene L. Skok, Jr. **Released:** Annual; Latest edition 2010. **Price:** $25, Members; $100, Nonmembers. **Covers:** About 850 member engineers and chemists engaged in paving or related fields, such as paving materials and construction equipment; international coverage. **Entries include:** Name, affiliation, address, phone. **Arrangement:** Alphabetical.

1999 ■ Asphalt Recycling & Reclaiming Association--Membership Directory
Pub: Asphalt Recycling and Reclaiming Association
Contact: Bill Garrity, President
E-mail: bill.garrity@garrityasphalt.com
URL(s): www.arra.org. **Released:** Annual; June. **Covers:** About 200 contractors, manufacturers, consulting engineers, and public works officials involved in asphalt reclaiming and recycling. **Entries include:** Name of company, address, phone; key personnel; type of organization or company; product line, or contact person. **Arrangement:** By type of membership, then alphabetical. **Indexes:** Personal name, geographical.

2000 ■ *"Bridging the Bay" in Business Journal Serving Greater Tampa Bay (Vol. 30, November 5, 2010, No. 46, pp. 1)*
Pub: Tampa Bay Business Journal
Ed: Mark Holan. **Description:** The Florida Department of Transportation has launched a study to design the proposed addition to the Howard Frankland Bridge. The bridge would be designed to accommodate more than personal vehicles.

2001 ■ *"Contracting Firm Sees Timing Right for Expansion" in Tampa Bay Business Journal (Vol. 29, November 13, 2009, No. 47, pp. 1)*
Pub: American City Business Journals
Ed: Janet Leiser. **Description:** Construction management company Moss & Associates LLC of Fort Lauderdale, Florida has launched its expansion to Tampa Bay. Moss & Associates has started the construction of the Marlins stadium in Miami, Florida's Little Havana section. It also plans to diversify by embarking on other government development, such as health care facilities and airports.

2002 ■ *"Contractors Scramble for Jobs" in Business Journal Portland (Vol. 26, December 18, 2009, No. 41, pp. 1)*
Pub: American City Business Journals Inc.
Ed: Andy Giegerich. **Description:** Contractors in Portland area are expected to bid for capital construction projects that will be funded by municipalities in the said area. Contracts for companies that work on materials handling, road improvement, and public safety structure projects will be issued.

2003 ■ *"Downtown Light Rail Plans Up in the Air" in Business Journal Serving Greater Tampa Bay (Vol. 30, October 22, 2010, No. 44, pp. 1)*
Pub: Tampa Bay Business Journal
Ed: Mark Holan. **Description:** Construction of Tampa's $2 billion light rail transit is suspended pending the result of the November 2, 2010 referendum. The routes, usage, and financing of the light rail project will be decided on the referendum. Whether the light rail will be elevated is also discussed.

2004 ■ *"Giant Garages Could Rise Up Downtown" in Business Courier (Vol. 27, October 22, 2010, No. 25, pp. 1)*
Pub: Business Courier
Ed: Dan Monk. **Description:** More than 2,500 new parking spaces could rise up to the eastern edge of downtown Cincinnati, Ohio as public and private investors collect resources for new garage projects. These projects are expected to accommodate almost 1,500 monthly parkers who will lose access at Broadway Commons due to the construction of Harrah's casino.

2005 ■ *"Port Authority Taking Heat in Kenwood Mess" in Business Courier (Vol. 26, September 18, 2009, No. 21, pp. 1)*
Pub: American City Business Journals, Inc.
Ed: Dan Monk. **Description:** Port of Greater Cincinnati Development Authority is being criticized for not requiring payment and performance bonds to ensure that contractors would be paid. The criticism occurred

after the general contractor for the project to build a parking garage at Kenwood Towne Plaza stopped paying its subcontractors.

2006 ■ "A Second Chance at Road Dollars" in Orlando Business Journal (Vol. 26, February 5, 2010, No. 36, pp. 1)
Pub: American City Business Journals
Ed: Bill Orben. **Description:** Nearly $10 million worth of construction projects in Central Florida would give construction companies that missed the initial round of federal stimulus-funded local road building projects another opportunity. Cost savings in the initial round of road projects enabled Orange, Osceola, and Seminole Counties to secure additional projects.

SOURCES OF SUPPLY

2007 ■ Better Roads--Annual Winter Maintenance Equipment & Materials Issue: Federal State County Township Road & Municipalities
James Informational Media Inc.
URL(s): www.betterroads.com. **Released:** Annual; June. **Price:** $95, Individuals per year prepaid. **Publication includes:** List of manufacturers of equipment and suppliers of materials and services for winter roads maintenance. Also features information on road agencies, construction/maintenance, and safety. **Entries include:** Company name, address. **Arrangement:** Alphabetical. **Indexes:** Product/service.

2008 ■ Parking Products & Services Directory: Parking Magazine
National Parking Association
Contact: Christine Banning, President
E-mail: christinebanning@npapark.org
URL(s): www.npapark.org. **Released:** Annual; Latest edition 2008. **Price:** $25, Members; $45, Nonmembers. **Covers:** About 300 firms supplying products and services to the parking industry, including about 52 parking consultants. **Entries include:** Company name, address, phone, fax, product/service descriptions. **Arrangement:** Classified by product/service. **Indexes:** Product/service, trade name.

TRADE PERIODICALS

2009 ■ The Asphalt Contractor
Pub: The Asphalt Contractor
URL(s): www.forconstructionpros.com/magazine/acon. **Ed:** Gregory Udelhofen. **Released:** Monthly

TRADE SHOWS AND CONVENTIONS

2010 ■ National Pavement Maintenance Exposition and Conference
Sellers Expositions
222 Pearl St., Ste. 300
New Albany, IN 47150
Ph: (812)949-9200
Free: 800-558-8767
Fax: (812)949-9600
URL: http://www.sellersexpo.com
Contact: Warren Sellers, Chief Executive Officer
E-mail: wss315@aol.com
URL(s): www.nationalpavementexpo.com. **Frequency:** Annual. **Audience:** Pavement contractors, distributors, and dealers of pavement maintenance products and equipment, and property owners and managers. **Principal Exhibits:** Pavement maintenance equipment, supplies, and services.

LIBRARIES

2011 ■ Asphalt Institute Research Library
2696 Research Park Dr.
Lexington, KY 40511-8480
Ph: (859)288-4960
Fax: (859)288-4999
Co. E-mail: info@asphaltinstitute.org
URL: http://www.asphaltinstitute.org
Scope: Asphalt - technology, history, industry. **Services:** Copying; library open to serious students by advance application. **Founded:** 1919. **Holdings:** 1000 volumes; 288 boxes of fugitive literature. **Subscriptions:** 20 journals and other serials.

2012 ■ Golden Bear Oil Specialties - QC/R & D Library
24152 Park Casino
Calabasas, CA 91302-2538
Ph: (661)393-7110
Fax: (661)392-8584
Contact: Euthene Snell, Librarian
Scope: Petroleum refining, lubricants, asphalt pavements, rubber, emulsions, instrumental analyses. **Services:** Library not open to the public. **Founded:** 1948. **Holdings:** 2200 books; 670 bound periodical volumes; 5 catalogs; 5 VF drawers of internal technical reports; preprints; reprints; instrumental scans; 5 VF drawers of patents, technical documents, product development information; 5 VF drawers of government and industry specifications, qualifications, and contracts. **Subscriptions:** 47 journals and other serials.

2013 ■ National Asphalt Pavement Association - Charles R. Foster Technical Library
5100 Forbes Blvd.
Lanham, MD 20706-4413
Ph: (301)731-4748
Free: 888-468-6499
Fax: (301)731-4621
Co. E-mail: napa@hotmix.org
URL: http://www.hotmix.org
Contact: Judy Hornung
Scope: Hot mix asphalt technology and applications, highway engineering. **Services:** Library not open to the public. **Founded:** 1976. **Holdings:** Manuals; selected reports (Transportation Research Board, Federal Highway Administration, Federal Aviation Administration, Transport and Road Research Laboratory); selected proceedings; foreign asphalt association publications; 30 VF drawers. **Subscriptions:** 75 journals and other serials. **Telecommunication Services:** jhornung@hotmix.org; webmaster@hotmix.org.

2014 ■ Saskatchewan Highways and Transportation Library
1855 Victoria Ave., 11th Fl.
Regina, SK, Canada S4P 3V5
Ph: (306)787-4800
Fax: (306)787-8700
Co. E-mail: library@highways.gov.sk.ca
URL: http://www.highways.gov.sk.ca/
Scope: Highway and traffic engineering, transportation, management, traffic safety, rail and air transport; asphalt construction. **Services:** Interlibrary loan; copying; SDI; library open to the public for reference use only. **Founded:** 1957. **Holdings:** 15,000 books. **Subscriptions:** 150 journals and other serials.

2015 ■ U.S. Army Engineer Research and Development Center - Airfields, Pavements, and Mobility Information Analysis Center
3909 Halls Ferry Rd.
Vicksburg, MS 39180-6199
Ph: (601)634-2955
Fax: (601)634-3139
Co. E-mail: gsl-info@erdc.usace.army.mil
URL: http://gsl.erdc.usace.army.mil/lgiacs.html
Contact: Gary Anderton, Director
Scope: Soil trafficability, mobility, pavements, terrain evaluation. **Services:** Interlibrary loan; copying. **Holdings:** Center is supported by the collection of holdings in the Research Library.

2016 ■ U.S. Army Engineer Research and Development Center - Research Library
3909 Halls Ferry Rd.
Bldg. 1000
Vicksburg, MS 39180-6199
Ph: (601)634-2355
Fax: (601)634-2542
Co. E-mail: library-ms@erdc.usace.army.mil
URL: http://itl.erdc.usace.army.mil
Contact: Debbie Carpenter, Librarian
Scope: Hydraulics, soil mechanics, concrete, weapons effects, mobility of vehicles, environmental studies, explosive excavation, pavements, geology, computer science. **Services:** Interlibrary loan; copying; SDI; center open to the public with restrictions. **Founded:** 1933. **Holdings:** 545,100 volumes, including microforms. **Subscriptions:** 1494 journals and other serials. **Telecommunication Services:** itl-web@usace.army.mil.

RESEARCH CENTERS

2017 ■ Auburn University - National Center for Asphalt Technology (NCAT)
277 Technology Pky.
Auburn, AL 36830
Ph: (334)844-6228
Fax: (334)844-6248
Co. E-mail: westran@auburn.edu
URL: http://www.ncat.us
Contact: Randy West, Director
Founded: 1986. **Educational Activities:** Asphalt Technology (3/year), training course covering asphalt mix design, production and control, construction, pavement design.

2018 ■ Oregon State University - Kiewit Center for Infrastructure and Transportation
220 Owen Hall
Corvallis, OR 97331-3212
Ph: (541)737-4273
Fax: (541)737-3052
Co. E-mail: scott.ashford@oregonstate.edu
URL: http://kiewit.oregonstate.edu
Contact: Prof. Scott A. Ashford, Director
Founded: 1962. **Publications:** Biennial report. **Educational Activities:** Northwest Transportation Conference; Kiewit Center for Infrastructure and Transportation Short courses, as part of a continuing education program sponsored by the Oregon Traffic Safety Division; Transportation seminars. **Awards:** Kiewit Center for Infrastructure and Transportation Fellowships, available through the U.S. Department of Transportation's University Transportation Centers Advanced Institute Program. **Telecommunication Services:** kiewit.center@oregonstate.edu.

2019 ■ Texas A&M University - Texas Transportation Institute (TTI)
3135 TAMU
College Station, TX 77843-3135
Ph: (979)845-1713
Fax: (979)845-9356
Co. E-mail: dennis-c@tamu.edu
URL: http://tti.tamu.edu
Contact: Dr. Dennis L. Christiansen, Director
Services: Contributes to the Texas Transportation Technology Transfer Program. **Founded:** 1950. **Publications:** Texas Transportation Researcher (Quarterly). **Educational Activities:** Short courses in highway engineering; Traffic engineering schools; Transportation Certificate Program, awarded through Texas A&M University; Transportation Conferences; Undergraduate and graduate instruction in highway, traffic, transportation engineering, and structural mechanics. **Awards:** SWUTC Advanced Institute Fellowships.

2020 ■ University of Texas at Austin - Center for Transportation Research (CTR)
1616 Guadalupe St., Ste. 4.202, MC D9300
Austin, TX 78701
Ph: (512)232-3100
Fax: (512)232-3153
Co. E-mail: rbm@mail.utexas.edu
URL: http://www.utexas.edu/research/ctr
Contact: Dr. Randy Machemehl, Director
Founded: 1963. **Publications:** CTR Annual report. **Educational Activities:** Annual Texas Department of Transportation Symposium, in April, open to the public. **Awards:** Fellowships and internships, offered through its affiliate, the Advanced Institute. **Telecommunication Services:** ctrlib@uts.cc.utexas.edu.

2021 ■ Western Research Institute (WRI)
365 N 9th St.
Laramie, WY 82072-3380
Ph: (307)721-2011
Free: 888-463-6974
Fax: (307)721-2345
Co. E-mail: don.collins@uwyo.edu

URL: http://www.westernresearch.org
Contact: Donald W. Collins, Chief Executive Officer

Founded: 1983. **Educational Activities:** WRI Workshops and conferences; Annual Asphalt Meeting, in July. **Awards:** Internships to University of Wyoming students.

ASSOCIATIONS AND OTHER ORGANIZATIONS

2022 ■ Home Fashion Products Association (HFPA)
355 Lexington Ave., Ste. 1500
New York, NY 10017-6603
Ph: (212)297-2122
Fax: (212)370-9047
Co. E-mail: contactus@hfpaonline.org
URL: http://www.homefashionproducts.com
Contact: Katie Goshgarian, Executive Director
Description: Manufacturers of curtains, draperies, bedding, rugs and related products. Sponsors annual scholarship for students attending accredited schools in home textiles. **Founded:** 1968. **Awards:** Scholarship (Annual).

2023 ■ International Furnishings and Design Association (IFDA)
610 Freedom Business Ctr. Dr., Ste. 110
King of Prussia, PA 19406
Ph: (610)535-6422
Fax: (610)535-6423
Co. E-mail: info@ifda.com
URL: http://www.ifda.com
Contact: Martha Heinze, Executive Director
Description: Represents individuals engaged in design, production, distribution, education, promotion and editorial phases of the interior furnishings industry and related fields. Founded IFDA Educational Foundation in 1968. Conducts charitable programs; maintains speakers' bureau. **Founded:** 1947. **Publications:** *IFDA Directory* (Annual); *IFDA Network* (Quarterly). **Awards:** Fellow Recognition Award; Honorary Recognition Award; Trailblazer Award; IFDA Fellow (Annual); National Honorary Recognition Award (Annual); Trailblazer Award (Annual); International Furnishings and Design Association Educational Foundation Student Scholarships; International Furnishings and Design Association Part-time Student Scholarships; Charles D. Mayo Student Scholarships.

2024 ■ Window Covering Manufacturers Association (WCMA)
355 Lexington Ave., 15th Fl.
New York, NY 10017

Ph: (212)297-2122
URL: http://www.wcmanet.org
Contact: Ralph Vasami, Executive Director
Description: Represents corporations engaged in the manufacture or assembly of Venetian blinds, vertical blinds, pleated shades, or their components. Promotes the use, utility, image, and attractiveness of the products and services offered by the window covering industry. **Founded:** 1979. **Awards:** Product Innovation Awards (Annual).

REFERENCE WORKS

2025 ■ *Draperies & Window Coverings--Directory & Buyer's Guide Issue: 2005*
Pub: L.C. Clark Publishing Company Inc.
URL(s): www.dwcinternational.comwww.dwconline.com/Directory/index.html. **Ed:** Howard Shingle. **Released:** Annual; fall. **Publication includes:** List of about 2,000 manufacturers and distributors of window coverings and other products used in the window coverings and interior fashions industry. **Entries include:** Company name, address, phone, key executives, brand names carried. **Arrangement:** Alphabetical. **Indexes:** Product/service.

FRANCHISES AND BUSINESS OPPORTUNITIES

2026 ■ Blind Man of America
Keller Corp.
606 Fremont Cir.
Colorado Springs, CO 80919
Free: 800-547-9889
Fax: (719)272-4105
Description: Mobile window coverings. **No. of Franchise Units:** 9. **No. of Company-Owned Units:** 1. **Founded:** 1991.. **Franchised:** 1996. **Equity Capital Needed:** $45,500-$69,100. **Franchise Fee:** $15,000. **Royalty Fee:** 4.3%. **Training:** Provides 2 weeks at headquarters with ongoing support.

2027 ■ Budget Blinds
Home Franchise Concepts, Inc.
1927 N Glassell St.
Orange, CA 92865

Free: 800-258-7079
Description: Custom window coverings. **No. of Franchise Units:** 710. **No. of Operating Units:** 794. **Founded:** 1992.. **Franchised:** 1994. **Equity Capital Needed:** $89,240-$174,070. **Franchise Fee:** $14,950. **Royalty Fee:** Varies. **Training:** Provides 2 weeks at headquarters and ongoing training and support.

2028 ■ Coit Cleaning and Restoration Services
897 Hinckley Rd.
Burlingame, CA 94010
Ph: (800)243-8797
Fax: (650)692-8397
Co. E-mail: franchise@coit.com
URL: http://www.coit.com
Description: Coit is a multi-service cleaning company, offering drapery cleaning, carpet cleaning, upholstery cleaning, area rug cleaning, air duct cleaning and more. **No. of Franchise Units:** 42. **No. of Company-Owned Units:** 8. **Founded:** 1950.. **Franchised:** 1962. **Equity Capital Needed:** $50,000-$145,000. **Franchise Fee:** $24,000-$40,000. **Financial Assistance:** Yes. **Training:** Includes 10 days in corporate office.

LIBRARIES

2029 ■ Arizona State University - Architectural and Environmental Design Library
College of Architecture
Tempe, AZ 85287-1705
Ph: (480)965-6400
Co. E-mail: deborah.koshinsky@asu.edu
URL: http://www.asu.edu
Contact: Annmarie Leonard
URL(s): lib.asu.edu/architecture/. **Scope:** Architecture, city planning, landscape architecture, industrial design, interior design, graphic design. **Services:** Interlibrary loan; copying; Library open to the public; special collections open to the public by appointment. **Founded:** 1960. **Holdings:** 50,000 volumes; 150 cassette and tape recordings; 563 titles on microfilm; 125 films and videocassettes; archives; microfiche; CD-ROMs. **Subscriptions:** 140 journals and other serials.

START-UP INFORMATION

2030 ■ *"Franchises with an Eye on Chicago"*
in Crain's Chicago Business (Vol. 34, March
14, 2011, No. 11, pp. 20)
Pub: Crain Communications Inc.
Description: Profiles of franchise companies seeking franchisees for the Chicago area include: Extreme Pita, a sandwich shop; Hand and Stone, offering massage, facial and waxing services; Molly Maid, home-cleaning service; Primrose Schools, private accredited schools for children 6 months to 6 hears and after-school programs; Protect Painters, residential and light-commercial painting contractor; and Wingstop, a restaurant offering chicken wings in nine flavors, fries and side dishes.

ASSOCIATIONS AND OTHER ORGANIZATIONS

2031 ■ **Cosmetic Industry Buyers and Suppliers (CIBS)**
c/o Rafael Cruz
830 Terry Rd.
Hauppauge, NY 11788
Co. E-mail: cibsmail@cibsonline.com
URL: http://www.cibsonline.com
Contact: Charles Marchese, President
Description: Buyers and suppliers of essential oils, chemicals, packaging, and finished goods relative to the cosmetic industry. Enhances growth, stability, prosperity, and protection of the American cosmetic industry through close personal contact and the exchange of ideas and experiences. **Founded:** 1948.

2032 ■ **International Spa Association (ISPA)**
2365 Harrodsburg Rd., Ste. A325
Lexington, KY 40504
Ph: (859)226-4326
Free: 888-651-4772
Fax: (859)226-4445
Co. E-mail: ispa@ispastaff.com
URL: http://www.experienceispa.com
Contact: Ms. Lynne Walker McNees, President
Description: Professional association and voice of the spa industry. Forms and maintains alliances that educate, set standards, provide resources, influence policy and build coalitions for the industry. Raises awareness of the spa industry and educates the public and industry professionals about the benefits of the spa experience. **Founded:** 1991. **Publications:** *LiveSpa*; *Pulse* (Bimonthly). **Educational Activities:** International Spa Association Conference (Annual). **Awards:** Mary Tabacchi Scholarship (Annual).

2033 ■ **Personal Care Product Council**
1101 17th St. NW, Ste. 300
Washington, DC 20036-4702
Ph: (202)331-1770
Fax: (202)331-1969
Co. E-mail: membership@personalcarecouncil.org
URL: http://www.personalcarecouncil.org
Contact: Lezlee Westine, President
Description: Manufacturers and distributors of finished cosmetics, fragrances, and personal care products; suppliers of raw materials and services. Provides scientific, legal, regulatory, and legislative services. Coordinates public service, educational, and public affairs activities. **Founded:** 1894. **Publications:** *CTFA News* (Biweekly); *International Color Handbook*; *International Resource Manual*.

REFERENCE WORKS

2034 ■ *Avon: Building the World's Premier Company for Women*
Pub: John Wiley & Sons, Incorporated
Ed: Laura Klepacki. **Released:** May 2006. **Price:** $16.95. **Description:** Profile of Avon and how it grew from a small business selling door-to-door to one of the largest cosmetics companies in the world.

2035 ■ *Business as Usual*
Pub: HarperBusiness
Ed: Anita Roddick. **Released:** 2005. **Price:** $12.95. **Description:** Founder of The Body Shop shares her story and gives her opinion on everything from cynical cosmetic industry to destructive consultants.

2036 ■ *Cosmetics & Toiletries--Cosmetic Bench Reference*
Contact: Janet Ludwig, President
URL(s): store.yahoo.com/allured/itoma.htmlwww.allured.com/ct, allured.stores.yahoo.net/cobere20.html.
Ed: Linda Knott. **Released:** Annual **Price:** $199, Individuals. **Publication includes:** List of cosmetic ingredient suppliers. **Entries include:** Supplier name, address, phone, fax, chemicals, trade names. Principal content of publication is data on cosmetic ingredients, with label names, trade names, functions, EINECS, INCI names, and CAS numbers. **Arrangement:** Alphabetical by chemical name (includes trade names).

2037 ■ *"Every Little Bit Helps"* in *Black Enterprise (Vol. 38, November 2007, No. 4, pp. 102)*
Pub: Earl G. Graves Publishing Co. Inc.
Ed: Tennille M. Robinson. **Description:** After a career in the cosmetics industry, Tricialee Riley is marketing and advertising her new venture, the Polish Bar, a salon offering manicures, pedicures, makeup application, and waxing.

2038 ■ *"First: Package Deal"* in *Entrepreneur (Vol. 35, October 2007, No. 10, pp. 114)*
Pub: Entrepreneur Media Inc.
Ed: Nichole L. Torres. **Description:** Unique packaging of Me! Bath's products proved to be an effective marketing strategy for the company, which has over $3 million dollar sales yearly. Their ice cream-looking bath products have become popular and are much appreciated by vendors. Details of how packaging can affect sales are presented.

2039 ■ *Fragrance and Olfactory Dictionary*
Pub: The Fragrance Foundation Inc.
Contact: Rochelle R. Bloom, President
E-mail: rbloom@fragrance.org
URL(s): www.fragrance.org/publications_books.php.
Released: Irregular **Price:** $5, for members; $7, for nonmembers. **Description:** Principal content of publication definitions of fragrance and olfactory terms. **Arrangement:** Alphabetical.

2040 ■ *"Greening the Manscape"* in *Canadian Business (Vol. 81, October 13, 2008, No. 17, pp. S19)*
Pub: Rogers Media Ltd.
Ed: David Lackie. **Description:** Buyer's guide of environmentally friendly grooming products for men is provided. Improved formulations have solved the problems of having synthetic ingredients in grooming products. Details about a face scrub, after shave conditioner, and a nourishing cream made of 91 percent organic ingredients are given, including prices.

2041 ■ *"How I Did It: It Just Came Naturally"* in *Inc. (November 2007, pp. 110-112)*
Pub: Gruner & Jahr USA Publishing
Ed: Athena Schindelheim. **Description:** Profile of Bobbi Brown, CEO and founder of Bobbi Brown Cosmetics, designed to highlight a woman's natural look. Brown opened her first freestanding retail store recently that houses a makeup artistry school in the back.

2042 ■ *"How to Keep Your Cool and Your Friends in a Heat Wave"* in *Canadian Business (Vol. 83, August 17, 2010, No. 13-14, pp. 79)*
Pub: Rogers Media Ltd.
Ed: Angelina Chapin. **Description:** A buyer's guide of menswear clothing for businessmen is presented. The products include an antiperspirant and deodorant, men's dress shorts, shoes and bamboo fabric undershirt.

2043 ■ *"Identify and Conquer"* in *Black Enterprise (Vol. 38, December 2007, No. 5, pp. 76)*
Pub: Earl G. Graves Publishing Co. Inc.
Ed: Tennille M. Robinson. **Description:** Twenty-two-year-old entrepreneur wants to expand her wholesale body oil and skincare products business.

2044 ■ *"In the Raw: Karyn Calabrese Brings Healthy Dining to a New Sophisticated Level"* in *Black Enterprise (Vol. 41, September 2010)*
Pub: Earl G. Graves Publishing Co. Inc.
Ed: Sonia Alleyne. **Description:** Profile of Karyn Calabrese whose businesses are based in Chicago, Illinois. Calabrese has launched a complete line of products (vitamins and beauty items), services (spa, chiropractic, and acupuncture treatments), and restaurants to bring health dining and lifestyles to a better level.

2045 ■ *"Ivorydale Looks to Clean Up"* in *Business Courier (Vol. 26, January 15, 2010, No. 39, pp. 1)*
Pub: American City Business Journals, Inc.
Ed: Jon Newberry. **Description:** Cincinnati-based St. Bernard Soap Company plans to focus on new services such as product development and logistics and to continue growth and put excess capacity to

work. The unit of Ontario, Canada-based Trillium Health Care Products Inc. is the largest contract manufacturer of bar soap in North America.

2046 ■ Lessons of a Lipstick Queen: Finding and Developing the Great Idea That Can Change Your Life
Pub: Simon and Schuster Inc.
Contact: Carolyn Reidy, President
E-mail: carolyn.reidy@simonandschuster.com
Ed: Poppy King. **Released:** May 1, 2009. **Price:** $14.00. **Description:** Poppy King tells how she started her lipstick brand at age eighteen. She reveals how she managed to launch her business using a good idea and finding financing, marketing the product and how she became successful.

2047 ■ "Natural Attraction: Bath and Body Products Maker Delivers Wholesome Goodness" in Black Enterprise (Vol. 38, November 2007, No. 4)
Pub: Earl G. Graves Publishing Co. Inc.
Ed: Kaylyn Kendall Dines. **Description:** Profile of Dawn Fitch, creator of Pooka Inc., manufacturer of handmade bath and body products that contain no preservatives. Sales are expected to reach $750,000 for 2007.

2048 ■ "New Year's Resolutions: How Three Companies Came Up With Their 2008 Growth Strategies" in Inc. (January 2008, pp. 47-49)
Pub: Gruner & Jahr USA Publishing
Ed: Martha C. White. **Description:** Three companies share 2008 growth strategies; companies include a candle company, a voice mail and text messaging marketer, and hotel supplier of soap and shampoo.

2049 ■ "Old Spice Guy (Feb.-July 2010)" in Canadian Business (Vol. 83, August 17, 2010, No. 13-14, pp. 23)
Pub: Rogers Media Ltd.
Ed: Andrew Potter. **Description:** Old Spice Guy was played by ex-football player and actor Isaiah Mustafa who made the debut in the ad for Old Spice Red Zone body wash that was broadcast during Super Bowl XLIV in February 2010. Old Spice Guy has become one of social marketing success but was cancelled in July when online viewership started to wane.

2050 ■ "P&G to Mine E-Commerce Potential" in Business Courier (Vol. 26, September 18, 2009, No. 21, pp. 1)
Pub: American City Business Journals, Inc.
Ed: Lisa Biank Fasig. **Description:** Procter & Gamble (P&G) is looking to turn the hits to the company's Websites into increased sales. The program will include a shop now option to track all emerging sales.

2051 ■ The Perfect Scent: A Year Inside the Perfume Industry in Paris and New York
Pub: Henry Holt and Co.
Contact: Michael Naumann, President
Ed: Chandler Burr. **Released:** 2009. **Price:** $25.00. **Description:** An insiders glimpse at the development of two new fragrances from Hermes and Coty.

2052 ■ "Private Equity Firm Links First Arizona Deal" in Business Journal-Serving Phoenix and the Valley of the Sun (November 2, 2007)
Pub: American City Business Journals, Inc.
Ed: Chris Cassacchia. **Description:** Pacific Investment Partners and Your Source Financial launched a $10 million fund and signed their first deal. The two companies acquires a minority stake in Dreambrands Inc. for $3 million. Dreambrands is using the capital to market its personal lubricant product Carrageenana.

2053 ■ "A Team Sport" in Business Courier (Vol. 26, October 2, 2009, No. 23, pp. 1)
Pub: American City Business Journals, Inc.
Ed: Lisa Biank Fasig. **Description:** Procter & Gamble (P&G) revised the way it works with marketing, design and public relations firms. Creative discussions will be managed by only two representatives, the franchise leader and the brand agency leader in order for P&G to simplify operations as it grows larger and more global.

2054 ■ "To Catch Up, Colgate May Ratchet Up Its Ad Spending" in Advertising Age (Vol. 81, December 6, 2010, No. 43, pp. 1)
Pub: Crain Communications, Inc.
Ed: Jack Neff. **Description:** Colgate-Palmolive Company has been losing market share in the categories of toothpaste, deodorant, body wash, dish soap and pet food.

2055 ■ "Vitabath: Sweet Smell of Success" in Retail Merchandiser (Vol. 51, September-October 2011, No. 5, pp. 82)
Pub: Phoenix Media Corporation
Description: After taking over at Vitabath, Rich Brands developed new scents and products and while discovering new channels to distribute these items.

2056 ■ "Want a Facial With That Steak?" in Charlotte Observer (February 5, 2007)
Pub: Knight-Ridder/Tribune Business News
Ed: Jen Aronoff. **Description:** Profile of Burke Myotherapy Massage & Spa and Schell's Bistro. Lynn Shell moved her massage therapy business into a 106-year old home that had been used as a restaurant. She opened her own eatery on the first floor and offers massage therapy upstairs.

2057 ■ "Zit Zapper Lands New Funding" in Houston Business Journal (Vol. 40, November 27, 2009, No. 29, pp. 1)
Pub: American City Business Journals
Ed: Mary Ann Azevedo. **Description:** Tyrell Inc. of Houston, Texas generated $20 million in funds for making a cheaper version of its acne-removing Zeno device. The upcoming product, Zeno Mini, will be targeted to a mass market with a price tag of about $89. In 2005, the original Zeno acne treatment device could only be bought through medical offices and spas at about $225.

TRADE PERIODICALS

2058 ■ Cosmetics & Toiletries: The International Magazine of Cosmetic Technology
Contact: Jane Evison, Account Manager
E-mail: jane-evison@btconnect.com
URL(s): www.cosmeticsandtoiletries.com. **Released:** Monthly **Price:** $98, Individuals; $137, Canada; $189, Other countries; $169, Two years; $231, Canada two years; $330, Other countries two years.

2059 ■ Flavour and Fragrance Journal
Pub: John Wiley & Sons Inc.
Contact: Stephen M. Smith, President
URL(s): onlinelibrary.wiley.com/journal/10.1002/(-ISSN)1099-1026. **Ed:** Daniel Joulain. **Released:** Bimonthly **Price:** $2328, Institutions print only; $2678, Institutions print & online.

2060 ■ The Rose Sheet
Pub: Elsevier Business Intelligence
URL(s): www.therosesheet.com/fdc/weekly/rose/toc.htm. **Released:** Weekly (Mon.) **Price:** $1395, Individuals print & online.

2061 ■ Skin Inc.: Professional Skin Care
Contact: Melinda Taschetta-Millane, Editor-in-Chief
E-mail: taschetta_millane@allured.com
URL(s): www.skininc.com/. **Released:** Monthly **Price:** $49, Individuals; $57, Canada; $98, Other countries.

TRADE SHOWS AND CONVENTIONS

2062 ■ Beauty Fair
The Finnish Fair Corp.
PO Box 21
FIN-00521 Helsinki, Finland
Ph: 358 40 4503250
Fax: 358 9 142358
Co. E-mail: info@finnexpo.fi
URL: http://web.finnexpo.fi/en/Yritys/finnishfair/Pages/default.aspx
URL(s): www.finnexpo.fi. **Frequency:** Annual. **Audience:** General public. **Principal Exhibits:** Beauty and fashion, cosmetics and services; hair products and services; clothing, showes, bags, accessories, jewelry, education, and publications.

2063 ■ Extracts - A Division of New York International Gift Fair
George Little Management, LLC
1133 Westchester Ave., Ste. N136
White Plains, NY 10606
Ph: (914)421-3200
Free: 800-272-SHOW
Co. E-mail: cathy_steel@glmshows.com
URL: http://www.glmshows.com
URL(s): www.extractsny.com. **Frequency:** Semiannual. **Audience:** Specialty, chain and department stores, gift and drug stores, mail order catalog houses, cosmetic companies, home furnishings/decorative accessory retailers. **Principal Exhibits:** Personal care products, aromatherapy products, body lotions, bath and shower gels, soaps, fragrances, botanicals, potpourri, candles, home fragrance products, bath accessories, and small appliances. **Telecommunication Services:** customerrelations@glmshows.com.

FRANCHISES AND BUSINESS OPPORTUNITIES

2064 ■ Fruits & Passion
21 Paul-Gaugin
Candiac, QC, Canada J5R 3X8
Ph: (450)638-2212
Fax: (450)638-2430
Co. E-mail: info@fruits-passion.com
URL: http://www.fruits-passion.com
Description: Offers natural body care products, home ambiance and gourmet specialties based on the curative and regenerative properties of fruit with award-winning, high-quality products. **No. of Franchise Units:** 36. **No. of Company-Owned Units:** 53. **Founded:** 1992.. **Equity Capital Needed:** $174,000-$400,000. **Franchise Fee:** $25,000. **Training:** Initial and ongoing.

2065 ■ Women's Health Boutique
Women's Health Boutique Franchise System, Inc.
12715 Telge Rd.
Cypress, TX 77429
Free: 888-708-9982
Fax: (281)256-4100
Co. E-mail: w-h-bsales@w-h-b.com
URL: http://www.w-h-b.com
Description: Products and services related to pre and postnatal care, post-mastectomy, compression therapy, hair loss, incontinence, and skin care. **No. of Franchise Units:** 13. **Founded:** 1991.. **Franchised:** 1994. **Equity Capital Needed:** $49,000 minimum start-up cash. **Training:** Yes.

COMPUTERIZED DATABASES

2066 ■ Pharmaceutical News Index® (PNI)
789 E Eisenhower Pkwy.
Ann Arbor, MI 48106-1346
Ph: (734)761-4700
Free: 800-521-0600
Co. E-mail: info@il.proquest.com
URL: http://www.il.proquest.com
Contact: Matt Dunie, President
Availability: Online: ProQuest Co.; ProQuest LLC - Dialog; ProQuest LLC - Dialog. **Type:** Bibliographic.

LIBRARIES

2067 ■ Avon Products, Inc. Research Library
777 Third Ave.
New York, NY 10017
Ph: (212)282-7000
Free: 800-445-2866
Fax: (914)369-2803
Co. E-mail: dearavon@avon.com
URL: http://www.avoncompany.com/
Scope: Cosmetics, packaging, toxicology, dermatology, pharmacology, chemistry, engineering, microbiology. **Services:** Interlibrary loan; SDI; library open to the public for reference use only on request. **Founded:** 1934. **Holdings:** 6500 books; 5000 bound periodical volumes; 6000 U.S. and foreign patents. **Subscriptions:** 300 journals and other serials.

2068 ■ Clairol Research Library
1 Blachley Rd.
Stamford, CT 06922
Free: 800-252-4765
URL: http://www.clairol.com
Scope: Chemistry and technology of cosmetics, hair dyes and dyeing, personal care. **Services:** Library open to the public with restrictions. **Holdings:** 10,000 books; 6000 bound periodical volumes; 30 titles on microfilm. **Subscriptions:** 350 journals and other serials.

2069 ■ Colgate Palmolive Company Technology Information Center
909 River Rd.
Piscataway, NJ 08854
Ph: (732)878-7574
Fax: (732)878-7128
URL: http://www.colgate.com
Contact: Miranda D. Scott, Associate
Scope: Soaps and detergents, fats and oils, dentifrices, cosmetics, perfumes and essential oils, environmental pollution, foods, chemistry. **Services:**

Interlibrary loan; copying; SDI. **Founded:** 1936. **Holdings:** 20,000 books; 10,000 bound periodical volumes; 16,000 periodical volumes on 4000 reels of microfilm; 250 VF drawers of internal reports; 10 VF drawers of archival materials. **Subscriptions:** 300 journals and other serials.

2070 ■ Johnson and Johnson - Consumer and Personal Products Worldwide Library
199 Grandview Rd.
Skillman, NJ 08558
Free: 866-565-2229
URL: http://www.jnj.com/connect/
Contact: Susan Gleckner, Director, Library Services
URL(s): www.johnsonsbaby.com/. **Scope:** Infant care, health and beauty aids, toiletries, chemistry, pharmaceuticals, oral care, wound care, skin care, dermatology, women's health. **Holdings:** 2000 books; 1500 bound periodical volumes. **Subscriptions:** 400 journals and other serials.

2071 ■ Mary Kay Inc. Information Resources
16251 N. Dallas Pkwy.
Addison, TX 75001

Ph: (972)687-5527
Fax: (972)687-1643
Co. E-mail: cecilia.armas@mkcorp.com
Contact: Lynn F. Johnson
Scope: Cosmetics, dermatology, toxicology, chemistry, business, marketing. **Services:** Interlibrary loan. **Founded:** 1976. **Holdings:** 2000 books; 500 bound periodical volumes. **Subscriptions:** 250 journals and other serials.

2072 ■ Revlon Research Center Library
2121 Rte. 27
Edison, NJ 08818
Ph: (732)287-1400
Fax: (732)287-7270
URL: http://www.revlon.com/
Contact: Ann Van Dine, Librarian
Scope: Cosmetics, soaps, chemistry, perfumery, dermatology, pharmacology, microbiology, aerosols. **Services:** Interlibrary loan; copying; SDI; library open to the public by appointment for reference only. **Founded:** 1955. **Holdings:** 11,000 books; 4000 bound periodical volumes. **Subscriptions:** 100 journals and other serials.

START-UP INFORMATION

2073 ■ *How to Start and Run a Small Book Publishing Company: A Small Business Guide to Self-Publishing and Independent Publishing*

Pub: HCM Publishing

Ed: Peter I. Hupalo. **Released:** August 30, 2002. **Price:** $18.95. **Description:** The book teaches all aspects of starting and running a small book publishing company. Topics covered include: inventory accounting in the book trade, just-in-time inventory management, turnkey fulfillment solutions, tax deductible costs, basics of sales and use tax, book pricing, standards in terms of the book industry, working with distributors and wholesalers, cover design and book layout, book promotion and marketing, how to select profitable authors to publish, printing process, printing on demand, the power of a strong backlist, and how to value copyright.

ASSOCIATIONS AND OTHER ORGANIZATIONS

2074 ■ **About Books Inc. (ABI)**
1001 Taurus Dr.
Colorado Springs, CO 80906
Ph: (719)632-8226
Free: 800-548-1876
Fax: (719)471-2182
Co. E-mail: infoabi@about-books.com
URL: http://www.about-books.com
Contact: Debi Flora, President
Description: Information clearinghouse on self-publishing and marketing of books. Provides educational programs; maintains speakers' bureau. Provides audiotape programs and books on the subject.
Scope: Full service writing and publishing consultants organized to assist corporations, organizations and individuals in the writing, editing, producing and marketing of books. Also develop sponsored and premium books. **Founded:** 1977. **Publications:** "Molding Young Athletes," Purington Press. **Telecommunication Services:** deb@about-books.com.

2075 ■ *ACP Update*
174 Spadina Ave., Ste. 306
Toronto, ON, Canada M5T 2C2
Ph: (416)487-6116
Fax: (416)487-8815
Co. E-mail: admin@canbook.org
URL: http://publishers.ca
Contact: Carolyn Wood, Executive Director
Released: Biweekly **Price:** for members only.

2076 ■ *AECB News*
1 Nicholas St., Ste. 504
Ottawa, ON, Canada K1N 7B7
Ph: (613)562-2324
Fax: (613)562-2329
Co. E-mail: info@livrescanadabooks.com
URL: http://www.livrescanadabooks.com
Contact: Francois Charette, Executive Director
Released: Periodic **Price:** free for Canadian publishers.

2077 ■ **American Book Producers Association (ABPA)**
151 W 19th St., 3rd Fl.
New York, NY 10011-4116
Ph: (917)741-1919
Fax: (212)675-1364
Co. E-mail: office@abpaonline.org
URL: http://www.abpaonline.org
Contact: Richard Rothschild, President
Description: Book producing companies that develop the concepts for books and, based on a contractual agreement with a publisher, may produce finished books or production-ready film, camera-ready mechanicals, finished manuscripts, art and layouts. Aims to increase the book industry's awareness of members' capabilities and the state of the book producers' art. Facilitates exchange of information for the purpose of improving business and establishing trade standards. **Founded:** 1980. **Publications:** *American Book Producers Association--Newsletter* (Monthly); *American Book Producers Association--Directory of Members* (Annual).

2078 ■ **American Booksellers Association (ABA)**
200 White Plains Rd., Ste. 600
Tarrytown, NY 10591
Ph: (914)591-2665
Free: 800-637-0037
Fax: (914)591-2720
Co. E-mail: info@bookweb.org
URL: http://www.bookweb.org
Contact: Becky Anderson, President
Description: Seeks to meet the needs of members, independently owned bookstores with storefront locations, through education, information dissemination, and advocacy. Supports free speech, literacy, and programs that encourage reading. **Founded:** 1900. **Publications:** *Bookselling this Week*; *ABA Electronic Book Buyer's Handbook*; *ABACUS* (Annual); *Bookselling this Week* (Weekly); *ABA Book Buyer's Handbook*; *ABA Bookselling This Week* (Weekly); *Bookselling This Week*; *American Bookseller: The Official Magazine of The American Booksellers Association* (Monthly). **Educational Activities:** BookExpo America (Annual); BookExpo America (Annual). **Awards:** Indies Choice Book Award; Book Sense Book of the Year Award (Annual).

2079 ■ **Association of American Publishers (AAP)**
71 5th Ave., 2nd Fl.
New York, NY 10003-3004
Ph: (212)255-0200
Fax: (212)255-7007
Co. E-mail: amyg@publishers.org
URL: http://www.publishers.org
Contact: Tom Allen, President
E-mail: tallen@publishers.org
Description: Represents the major commercial publishers in the United States as well as smaller and non-profit publishers, university presses and scholarly societies. Helps in the protection of intellectual property rights in all media. Promotes reading and literacy and the freedom to publish at home and abroad. Conducts seminars and workshops on various publishing topics including rights and permission, sales, and educational publishing. Compiles statistics. **Founded:** 1970. **Publications:** *AAP Monthly Report* (Monthly); *Association of American Publishers--College Textbook Publishers Greenbook* (Annual); *Who's Who (Internationally) at American Booksellers Association Annual Convention*; *Exhibits Directory*. **Educational Activities:** Professional and Scholarly Publishers Meeting (Annual); Smaller and Independent Publishers Meeting (Annual). **Awards:** Mary McNulty Award (Periodic); R.R. Hawkins Award (Annual); AAP Honors (Annual); Jeri Laber International Freedom to Publish Award (Annual); Miriam Bass Award for Creativity in Independent Publishing (Annual); Curtis G. Benjamin Award for Creative Publishing; Jeri Laber International Freedom to Publish Award; Miriam Bass Award for Creativity in Independent Publishing. **Telecommunication Services:** info@publishers.org.

2080 ■ **Association of American University Presses (AAUP)**
28 W 36th St., Ste. 602
New York, NY 10018
Ph: (212)989-1010
Fax: (212)989-0275
Co. E-mail: info@aaupnet.org
URL: http://www.aaupnet.org
Contact: MaryKatherine Callaway, President
E-mail: mcallaway@aaupnet.org
Description: Helps university presses do their work more economically, creatively, and effectively through its own activities in education-training, fundraising and development, statistical research and analysis, and community and institutional relations. **Founded:** 1937. **Publications:** *AAUP Directory* (Annual); *Exchange* (Quarterly); *AAUP Directory* (Annual); *Association of American University Presses--Directory* (Annual); *Advertising and Publicity Resources for Scholarly Books*. **Educational Activities:** Association of American University Presses Annual Meeting (Annual). **Awards:** Constituency Award (Annual); Book, Jacket and Journal Design Show.

2081 ■ **Association of Canadian Publishers (ACP)**
174 Spadina Ave., Ste. 306
Toronto, ON, Canada M5T 2C2
Ph: (416)487-6116
Fax: (416)487-8815
Co. E-mail: admin@canbook.org
URL: http://publishers.ca
Contact: Carolyn Wood, Executive Director
Description: Canadian-owned book publishers. Supports the development of a vibrant domestic publishing industry. Encourages writing, publishing, distribution, and promotion of Canadian books. Conducts industry research, including salary surveys, book sales analyses, and accounting modifications; facilitates communication among members; makes available promotion, public relations, and marketing services. Serves as a clearinghouse on Canadian writing and publishing; sponsors lobbying activities. **Founded:** 1976. **Publications:** *ACP Update* (Biweekly).

2082 ■ Association of Catholic Publishers (ACP)
4725 Dorsey Hall Dr., Ste. A
PMB No. 709
Ellicott City, MD 21042
Ph: (410)988-2926
Fax: (410)571-4946
Co. E-mail: tbrown@cbpa.org
URL: http://www.catholicpublishers.org
Contact: Therese Brown, Executive Director
URL(s): www.catholicsread.org. **Description:** Facilitates the sharing of professional information, networking, cooperation, and friendship among those involved in Catholic publishing in the United States and abroad. **Founded:** 1987. **Publications:** *The Catholic Book Publishers Association Directory* (Annual); *CBPA Newsletter; The Spirit of Books* (Semiannual). **Educational Activities:** Professional Skills Workshops (Annual). **Awards:** Outstanding Service Award (Annual).

2083 ■ Authors and Publishers Association (APA)
25661 Field Store Rd.
Waller, TX 77484-5930
Co. E-mail: info@authorsandpublishers.org
URL: http://www.authorsandpublishers.org
Contact: Ron Kaye, President (Acting)
Description: Authors, aspiring authors, editors, artists, printers and publishers, marketers, distributors, booksellers, and other corporations and individuals with an interest in the book trade. Seeks to assist writers, authors, and publishers to "keep the literary craft alive". Serves as a clearinghouse on the book publishing industry; provides employment and other information to writers; facilitates networking among members.

2084 ■ Bay Area Independent Publishers Association (BAIPA)
PO Box E
Corte Madera, CA 94976
Ph: (415)456-0247
Free: 866-622-1325
Co. E-mail: board@baipa.org
URL: http://www.baipa.org
Contact: Judy Baker, President
Description: Promotes authors interested in independent publishing as an alternative to the commercial publishing system; printers, artists, typists, and others in allied fields. Aims to become a comprehensive source of self-publishing information and to develop knowledge and expertise to better assist members in promoting, marketing, and publishing their works. Acts as a liaison and clearinghouse of information and provides guidance in all aspects of self-publishing, including copy preparation, book production, and marketing and sales. **Founded:** 1979. **Publications:** *SPEX; SPEX* (Monthly). **Awards:** Jack Mason Award (Annual). **Telecommunication Services:** info@baipa.net.

2085 ■ Book Industry Study Group (BISG)
370 Lexington Ave., Ste. 900
New York, NY 10017
Ph: (646)336-7141
Fax: (646)336-6214
Co. E-mail: info@bisg.org
URL: http://www.bisg.org
Contact: Scott Lubeck, Executive Director
Description: Represents publishers, manufacturers, suppliers, wholesalers, retailers, librarians, and other engaged in the business of print and electronic media. **Founded:** 1975. **Publications:** *Book Industry TRENDS* (Annual); *Book Industry Trends* (Annual); *BISG Research Reports* (Quarterly); *Trends Update; Student Attitudes Toward Content in Higher Education* (Semiannual). **Educational Activities:** BISG Seminars and conferences (Annual), for discussion of implications of statistical information on the book industry. **Telecommunication Services:** scott@bisg.org.

2086 ■ Book Manufacturers' Institute (BMI)
Two Armand Beach Dr., Ste. 1B
Palm Coast, FL 32137-2612
Ph: (386)986-4552

Fax: (386)986-4553
Co. E-mail: info@bmibook.com
URL: http://www.bmibook.com
Contact: Jac B. Garner, Chairman
Description: Represents the trade association for manufacturers of books. **Founded:** 1920. **Awards:** Distinguished Master Bookman Award (Annual); Gutenberg Award (Annual); Signature Award (Annual).

2087 ■ Book and Periodical Council (BPC)
192 Spadina Ave., Ste. 107
Toronto, ON, Canada M5T 2C2
Ph: (416)975-9366
Fax: (416)975-1839
Co. E-mail: info@thebpc.ca
URL: http://www.thebpc.ca
Contact: Anne McClelland, Executive Director
Description: Associations representing writers, editors, and publishers of books and periodicals and manufacturers, distributors, and sellers and lenders of printed materials. Promotes improved market conditions for Canadian publications and seeks to insure availability of a representative range of Canadian books and periodicals. Works to strengthen book and periodical distribution systems; supports development of new and existing Canadian-owned publishing companies; serves as a forum for discussion of industry issues. **Founded:** 1975.

2088 ■ *Books on Canada*
1 Nicholas St., Ste. 504
Ottawa, ON, Canada K1N 7B7
Ph: (613)562-2324
Fax: (613)562-2329
Co. E-mail: info@livrescanadabooks.com
URL: http://www.livrescanadabooks.com
Contact: Francois Charette, Executive Director
Released: Annual

2089 ■ Canadian Children's Book Centre (CCBC)
40 Orchard View Blvd., Ste. 217
Toronto, ON, Canada M4R 1B9
Ph: (416)975-0010
Fax: (416)975-8970
Co. E-mail: info@bookcentre.ca
URL: http://www.bookweek.ca
Contact: Todd Kyle, President
URL(s): www.bookcentre.ca. **Description:** Promotes the reading, writing, illustrating and publishing of Canadian books for young readers. Offers programs, publications and resources to help teachers, librarians, booksellers and parents to select the best books for young readers. **Scope:** children's fiction, non-fiction. **Founded:** 1976. **Subscriptions:** 8000 books. **Publications:** *Canadian Children's Book News* (Quarterly); *Our Choice* (Annual). **Awards:** TD Canadian Children's Literature Award (Annual); Geoffrey Bilson Award for Historical Fiction (Annual); Norma Fleck Award for Non-Fiction (Annual).

2090 ■ *Canadian Children's Book News*
40 Orchard View Blvd., Ste. 217
Toronto, ON, Canada M4R 1B9
Ph: (416)975-0010
Fax: (416)975-8970
Co. E-mail: info@bookcentre.ca
URL: http://www.bookweek.ca
Contact: Todd Kyle, President
Released: Quarterly **Price:** free for members.

2091 ■ Canadian Copyright Institute (CCI)
192 Spadina Ave., Ste. 107
Toronto, ON, Canada M5T 2C2
Ph: (416)975-1756
Fax: (416)975-1839
Co. E-mail: info@thecci.ca
URL: http://www.canadiancopyrightinstitute.ca
Contact: Anne McClelland, Administrator
Description: Creators, producers, and distributors of copyrighted works. Encourages a more complete understanding of copyright laws among members and the public. Consults with government and judicial bodies regarding reform of copyright laws. Conducts and sponsors research on copyright laws worldwide. Works with organizations pursuing similar goals to

improve copyright legislation and enforcement. **Founded:** 1965. **Publications:** *Copyright Reform Legislation Reporting Service* (Periodic).

2092 ■ Canadian Publishers' Council (CPC)
250 Merton St., Ste. 203
Toronto, ON, Canada M4S 1B1
Ph: (416)322-7011
Fax: (416)322-6999
Co. E-mail: jhushion@pubcouncil.ca
URL: http://www.pubcouncil.ca
Contact: Jacqueline Hushion, Executive Director
Description: English-language publishers. Seeks to advance the domestic book publishing industry; encourages publication of Canadian authors. Facilitates communication and cooperation among members; represents members' interests before trade organizations, government agencies, and the public. **Scope:** book publishing, literature. **Founded:** 1910. **Subscriptions:** articles books periodicals.

2093 ■ Center for the Book (CBLC)
Library of Congress
101 Independence Ave. SE
Washington, DC 20540-4920
Ph: (202)707-5221
Fax: (202)707-0269
Co. E-mail: glam@loc.gov
URL: http://www.read.gov/cfb
Contact: John Y. Cole, Director
Description: Uses resources and prestige of Library of Congress to stimulate public interest in books, reading, literacy, and libraries, and encourage the study of books and the printed word. Sponsors lectures, symposia, reading promotion projects, and publications. Develops partnerships with state center for the book affiliates and national organizations. **Founded:** 1977.

2094 ■ *Copyright Reform Legislation Reporting Service*
192 Spadina Ave., Ste. 107
Toronto, ON, Canada M5T 2C2
Ph: (416)975-1756
Fax: (416)975-1839
Co. E-mail: info@thecci.ca
URL: http://www.canadiancopyrightinstitute.ca
Contact: Anne McClelland, Administrator
Released: Periodic **Price:** C$650, /year for members; C$750, /year for nonmembers.

2095 ■ Evangelical Christian Publishers Association (ECPA)
9633 S 48th St., Ste. 140
Phoenix, AZ 85044
Ph: (480)966-3998
Fax: (480)966-1944
Co. E-mail: info@ecpa.org
URL: http://www.ecpa.org
Contact: Mark W. Kuyper, President
E-mail: mkuyper@ecpa.org
Description: Companies that primarily publish Christian religious literature. Conducts annual sales and operation survey, and a series of educational seminars and trade shows. **Founded:** 1974. **Publications:** *Monday Rush* (Weekly); *Evangelical Christian Publishers Association--Membership Directory.* **Awards:** Christian Book Awards; Book Cover Award; Jordon Lifetime Achievement Award; Pinnacle Award; Chairperson Award (Annual); Christian Book Awards (Annual); Christian Book of the Year Award (Annual); Lifetime Achievement Award (Annual); Press Book Cover Award (Annual); Gold/Platinum/Diamond Book Awards; Gold/Platinum/Diamond Book Awards (Periodic).

2096 ■ Independent Book Publishers Association (IBPA)
1020 Manhattan Beach Blvd., Ste. 204
Manhattan Beach, CA 90266
Ph: (310)546-1818
Fax: (310)546-3939
Co. E-mail: info@ibpa-online.org
URL: http://www.pma-online.org
Contact: Terry Nathan, Executive Director
URL(s): www.ibpa-online.org. **Description:** Entrepreneurial publishers of trade books and video and audio cassette tapes. Aims to assist independent publishers in the marketing and sale of their titles to

bookstores, libraries, and specialty markets. Holds marketing and educational programs. **Founded:** 1983. **Publications:** *PMA Resource Directory* (Annual); *PMA Independent*; *IBPA Independent*. **Educational Activities:** American Library Association Annual Conference 2013 (Annual). **Awards:** Benjamin Franklin Awards; Benjamin Franklin Award (Annual). **Telecommunication Services:** info@pma-online. org.

2097 ■ Literary Press Group of Canada (LPG)
501-192 Spadina Ave.
Toronto, ON, Canada M5T 2C2
Ph: (416)483-1321
Fax: (416)483-2510
Co. E-mail: jack@lpg.ca
URL: http://www.lpg.ca
Contact: Jack Illingworth, Executive Director
Description: Canadian owned and controlled literary book publishers. Promotes growth and development of members. Makes available cooperative sales and marketing services. **Founded:** 1975.

2098 ■ Livres Canada Books
1 Nicholas St., Ste. 504
Ottawa, ON, Canada K1N 7B7
Ph: (613)562-2324
Fax: (613)562-2329
Co. E-mail: info@livrescanadabooks.com
URL: http://www.livrescanadabooks.com
Contact: Francois Charette, Executive Director
Description: Helps Canadian publishers develop foreign markets and promote export sales of books. Provides financial assistance and market intelligence. Organizes collective Canada stands at major international book fairs. **Scope:** publishing, international trade. **Founded:** 1972. **Subscriptions:** books periodicals. **Publications:** *AECB News* (Periodic); *Books on Canada* (Annual); *Rights Canada* (Semiannual).

2099 ■ National Information Standards Organization (NISO)
1 N Charles St., Ste. 1905
Baltimore, MD 21201
Ph: (301)654-2512
Free: 866-957-1593
Fax: (410)685-5278
Co. E-mail: nisohq@niso.org
URL: http://www.niso.org
Contact: Todd Carpenter, Executive Director
Description: Identifies, develops, maintains, and publishes technical standards to manage information in the changing environment used by libraries, publishers, and information services. Supports open access to NISO standards. Standards available at website. **Founded:** 1939. **Publications:** *Information Standards Quarterly* (Quarterly); *Newsline* (Monthly); *Technical Report* (Periodic); *Information Standards Quarterly*; *Information Standards Quarterly: News About Library, Information Sciences, and Publishing Standards*.

2100 ■ Our Choice
40 Orchard View Blvd., Ste. 217
Toronto, ON, Canada M4R 1B9
Ph: (416)975-0010
Fax: (416)975-8970
Co. E-mail: info@bookcentre.ca
URL: http://www.bookweek.ca
Contact: Todd Kyle, President
Released: Annual **Price:** included in membership dues.

2101 ■ Periodical and Book Association of America (PBAA)
481 8th Ave., Ste. 526
New York, NY 10001
Ph: (212)563-6502
Fax: (212)563-4098
Co. E-mail: lisawscott@hotmail.com
URL: http://www.pbaa.net
Contact: Lisa W. Scott, Executive Director
Description: Magazine and paperback publishers concerned with single copy or newsstand sales. Carries out concerted action in areas of publishing, production, and sales. **Founded:** 1965. **Awards:** Publishing Leader of the Year (Annual).

2102 ■ *Rights Canada*
1 Nicholas St., Ste. 504
Ottawa, ON, Canada K1N 7B7
Ph: (613)562-2324
Fax: (613)562-2329
Co. E-mail: info@livrescanadabooks.com
URL: http://www.livrescanadabooks.com
Contact: Francois Charette, Executive Director
Released: Semiannual

2103 ■ Small Publishers Association of North America (SPAN)
PO Box 9725
Colorado Springs, CO 80932-0725
Ph: (719)924-5534
Fax: (719)213-2602
Co. E-mail: brad@spannet.org
URL: http://www.spannet.org
Contact: Brad Poulson, Executive Director
Description: For self-publishers, authors and small presses. Works to advance the image and profits of independent publishers through education and marketing. Offers continuing education, co-op buying power and sales and networking opportunities, plus discounts on many products and services. Publishes monthly newsletter. **Founded:** 1996. **Telecommunication Services:** span@spannet.org.

2104 ■ Society for Scholarly Publishing (SSP)
10200 W 44th Ave., Ste. 304
Wheat Ridge, CO 80033
Ph: (303)422-3914
Fax: (303)422-8894
Co. E-mail: info@sspnet.org
URL: http://www.sspnet.org
Contact: Carol Anne Meyer, President
E-mail: cmeyer@crossref.org
Description: Individuals, including librarians, booksellers, publishers, printers, authors, and editors interested in scholarly publication; organizations. Serves as an educational forum. **Founded:** 1978. **Publications:** *Society for Scholarly Publishing--Membership Directory* (Annual). **Educational Activities:** Society for Scholarly Publishing Seminar.

2105 ■ Special Libraries Association (SLA)
331 S Patrick St.
Alexandria, VA 22314-3501
Ph: (703)647-4900
Fax: (703)647-4901
Co. E-mail: janice@sla.org
URL: http://www.sla.org
Contact: Janice R. Lachance, Chief Executive Officer
E-mail: janice@sla.org
Description: International association of information professionals who work in specialized information environments such as business, research, government, universities, newspapers, museums, and institutions. Seeks to advance the leadership role of information professionals through learning, networking and advocacy. Offers consulting services to organizations that wish to establish or expand a library or information services. Conducts strategic learning and development courses, public relations, and government relations programs. Provides employment services. Operates knowledge exchange on topics pertaining to the development and management of special libraries. **Founded:** 1909. **Publications:** *Information Outlook* (8/year); *SLA Connections* (Monthly); *SpeciaList* (Monthly); *Information Outlook* (Monthly); *Information Outlook* (Monthly); *Directory of Catalogers in the Special Libraries Association*; *Who's Who in Special Libraries* (Annual). **Educational Activities:** Winter Education Conference (Annual); Special Libraries Association Information Revolution (Annual). **Awards:** Diversity Leadership Development Program Award (Annual); Factiva Leadership Award (Annual); Honorary Member Award (Annual); John Cotton Dana Award (Annual); President's Award; Professional Award; SLA Scholarship (Annual); Steven I. Goldspeil Memorial Research Fund (Annual); Fellow of the Special Libraries Association; Hall of Fame; Honorary Member; John Cotton Dana Award; Professional Award; H. W. Wilson Company Award; Affirmative Action Scholarships; Mary Adeline Conner Professional Development

Scholarships; Institute for Scientific Information Scholarships (ISI); Plenum Scholarships; Special Libraries Association Scholarships (SLA); J.J. Keller Innovations in Technology Award. **Telecommunication Services:** sla@sla.org.

2106 ■ Women's National Book Association (WNBA)
PO Box 237
New York, NY 10150
Ph: (615)386-6760
Fax: (212)208-4629
Co. E-mail: info@wnba-books.org
URL: http://www.wnba-books.org
Contact: Mary Grey James, President
Description: Women and men who work with and value books. Exists to promote reading and to support the role of women in the book community. **Founded:** 1917. **Publications:** *The Bookwoman*; *The Bookwoman* (3/year). **Awards:** Lucile Micheels Pannell Award (Annual); Women's National Book Association Award; Ann Heidbreder Eastman Grant (Annual); The WNBA Award (Biennial); WNBA Eastman Grants. **Telecommunication Services:** sandy@sk-passociates.com.

EDUCATIONAL PROGRAMS

2107 ■ Managing the Publications Department
EEI Communications
8945 Guilford Rd., Ste. 145
Columbia, MD 21046
Ph: (410)309-8200
Free: 888-253-2762
Fax: (410)630-3980
Co. E-mail: train@eeicom.com
URL: http://www.eeicom.com/eei-training-services
Price: $745.00. **Description:** Covers the role of the publications manager, techniques for managing multiple projects, standardizing and organizing the publications process, creating productivity standards and quality control procedures, using new technology, and working effectively with peers, subordinates, and superiors. **Dates and Locations:** Alexandria, VA.

2108 ■ Production Techniques and Technology
EEI Communications
8945 Guilford Rd., Ste. 145
Columbia, MD 21046
Ph: (410)309-8200
Free: 888-253-2762
Fax: (410)630-3980
Co. E-mail: train@eeicom.com
URL: http://www.eeicom.com/eei-training-services
Price: $745.00. **Description:** Seminar for editors, writers, designers, and graphic artists; covers the print production process within the publishing industry, including processes and principles of graphic production, pre-press, and printing; basics of design, typography, and layout; electronic advances on the desktop and in the printing plant; working with vendors; and the basics of scheduling, estimating, and quality control. **Dates and Locations:** Alexandria, VA.

2109 ■ Quality Control in Publications
EEI Communications
8945 Guilford Rd., Ste. 145
Columbia, MD 21046
Ph: (410)309-8200
Free: 888-253-2762
Fax: (410)630-3980
Co. E-mail: train@eeicom.com
URL: http://www.eeicom.com/eei-training-services
Price: $425.00. **Description:** Covers the process of publication, including planning and quality control systems, error detection processes, effectively using software, and dealing with print vendors. **Dates and Locations:** Alexandria, VA.

REFERENCE WORKS

2110 ■ *"Africa Rising" in Harvard Business Review (Vol. 86, September 2008, No. 9, pp. 36)*
Pub: Harvard Business School Press
Ed: John T. Landry. **Description:** Review of the book entitled, 'Africa Rising: How 900 Million African Consumers Offer More Than You Think' provides advice for marketing to those on the African continent.

2111 ■ *"ALA: Hot Topics for Librarianship" in Information Today (Vol. 28, September 2011, No. 8, pp. 17)*
Pub: Information Today, Inc.
Ed: Barbara Brynko. **Description:** Highlights from the American Library Association Annual Conference and Exhibition are listed. Thousands of attendees sought out services, displays, demos, new product rollouts, and freebies. Emerging technology for librarians, staff development, gray literature, interlibrary loans, and next-generation interfaces were among the topics discussed.

2112 ■ *Association of American University Presses--Directory*
Pub: Association of American University Presses
Contact: MaryKatherine Callaway, President
E-mail: mcallaway@aaupnet.org
URL(s): www.aaupnet.org. **Released:** Annual; Latest edition 2012. **Price:** $30, Individuals. **Covers:** 124 presses and affiliates worldwide. **Entries include:** Press name, address, phone, e-mail, URL; titles and names of complete editorial and managerial staffs; editorial program; mailing, warehouse, printing, and/or customer service addresses; other details. **Arrangement:** Classified by press affiliation, alphabetical by press name. **Indexes:** Personal name.

2113 ■ *"Back Talk with Chris Gardner" in Black Enterprise (Vol. 37, January 2007, No. 6, pp. 112)*
Pub: Earl G. Graves Publishing Co. Inc.
Ed: Kenneth Meeks. **Description:** Profile of with Chris Gardner and his Chicago company, Gardner Rich L.L.C., a multimillion-dollar investment firm. During an interview, Gardner discusses his rise from homelessness. His story became a book, The Pursuit of Happyness and was recently released as a film starring Will Smith.

2114 ■ *"Because Kids Need To Be Heard: Tina Wells: Buzz Marketing Group: Voorhees, New Jersey" in Inc. (Volume 32, December 2010)*
Pub: Inc. Magazine
Ed: Tamara Schweitzer. **Description:** Profile of Tina Wells, founder and CEO of Buzz Marketing Group, who writes a tween book series called Mackenzie Blue to reach young girls.

2115 ■ *Book Dealers Dropship Directory*
Pub: North American Bookdealers Exchange
Contact: Russ von Hoelscher, Director
URL(s): www.bookmarketingprofits.com/DSDirectory.html. **Released:** Irregular; Latest edition 2005-2006. **Price:** $15, Individuals with free shipping in USA and Canada. **Covers:** More than 300 dealers and distributors who ship individual copies of books to customers for publishers and mail order companies. **Entries include:** Company name, address, titles or types of books handled. **Arrangement:** Alphabetical.

2116 ■ *Book Fairs: An Exhibiting Guide for Publishers*
Pub: Para Publishing
Contact: Daniel F. Poynter, Owner
E-mail: danpoynter@parapublishing.com
URL(s): www.parapublishing.com. **Released:** Irregular **Price:** $7.95, Individuals plus shipping charges. **Publication includes:** List of about 30 major book fairs; display equipment suppliers, exhibition services: associations, periodicals, consultants, seminars; international coverage. **Entries include:** For fairs--Fair name, sponsoring organization name and address. For suppliers--Firm name, address, name of contact, product or service. Principal content is author's advice on taking part in book exhibits and fairs. **Arrangement:** Each list is alphabetical.

2117 ■ *"The Book On Indigo" in Canadian Business (Vol. 81, July 22, 2008, No. 12-13, pp. 29)*
Pub: Rogers Media Ltd.
Ed: Thomas Watson. **Description:** Indigo Books & Music Inc. reported record sales of $922 million resulting in a record net profit of $52.8 million for the 2008 fiscal year ended March 29, 2008. Earnings per share were $2.13, greater than Standard & Poor's expected $1.70 per share. Additional information concerning Indigo Books is presented.

2118 ■ *"Book Publishing is Growing" in Information Today (Vol. 28, October 2011, No. 9, pp. 10)*
Pub: Information Today, Inc.
Ed: Paula J. Hane. **Description:** U.S. book publishing industry is reporting growth in its sector, despite the poor economy. BookStats, a comprehensive statistical survey conducted on the modern publishing industry in the U.S. reported Americans are reading in all print and digital formats. In 2011, 114 million ebooks were sold and now account for 13.6 percent of revenue from adult fiction. In contrast, 603 million trade hardcover books (fiction and nonfiction) were sold in 2011, a 5.8 percent increase over 2008.

2119 ■ *Books in Print*
Pub: R.R. Bowker
URL(s): www.bowker.com/www.greyhouse.com/bowk_bip.htm. **Released:** Annual; Latest edition 2009-2010. **Price:** $995, Individuals hardcover; 7 volumes. **Description:** Over 2.8 million entries covering books published and distributed in the U.S. **Entries include:** For publishers--Company name, address. For books--Authors, title, price, publisher, other bibliographic information as available. The material in "Books in Print" is also available in subject-classified form in "Subject Guide to Books in Print," published as a five-volume set, annually in September. **Arrangement:** Publishers, authors, and titles are alphabetical in separate sections.

2120 ■ *"Bridging the Worlds" in Academy of Management Journal (Vol. 50, No. 5, October 2007, pp. 1043)*
Pub: Academy of Management
Contact: Ming-Jer Chen, President
Ed: Lise Saari. **Description:** Need to transfer human resource research information published in journals to practitioners and organizations is investigated, along with suggestions on ways of achieving this goal.

2121 ■ *"Buying In" in Harvard Business Review (Vol. 86, September 2008, No. 9, pp. 36)*
Pub: Harvard Business School Press
Ed: Andrew O'Connell. **Description:** Review of the book entitled, 'Buying In: The Secret Dialogue between What We Buy and Who We Are' which offers tips that those in the field of marketing will find useful.

2122 ■ *Children's Books in Print*
Pub: R.R. Bowker L.L.C.
URL(s): www.bowker.com/index.php/component/content/article/17. **Released:** Annual; Latest edition 2009. **Price:** $455, Individuals 2-vol. set. **Entries include:** Book entries--Title, subtitle, author(s), editor(s), illustrator(s), publishing date, edition, price, binding, ISBN, LC number, publisher; Publisher entries--Name, address, phone, ISBN prefix. The material in "Children's Books in Print" is also available in subject-classified form in "Subject Guide to Children's Books in Print," also published in December. **Arrangement:** Alphabetical within each index. **Indexes:** Author, title, illustrator, award or prize, publisher.

2123 ■ *"Copyright Clearance Center (CCC) Partnered with cSubs" in Information Today (Vol. 28, November 2011, No. 10, pp. 14)*
Pub: Information Today, Inc.
Description: Copyright Clearance Center (CCC) partnered with cSubs to integrate CCC's point-of-content licensing solution RightsLink Basic directly into cSubs workflow. The partnership will allow cSubs'

customers a user-friendly process for obtaining permissions. Csubs is a corporate subscription management service for books, newspapers, and econtent.

2124 ■ *Directory of Small Press--Magazine Editors and Publishers*
Pub: Dustbooks
Contact: Len Fulton, Publisher
E-mail: lenfulton@dustbooks.com
URL(s): www.dustbooks.com/de.htm. **Ed:** Len Fulton. **Released:** Annual; Latest edition 42nd; 2011-2012. **Price:** $49.95, Individuals online; $21, Individuals CD-ROM. **Covers:** About 7,500 publishers and editors. **Entries include:** Individual name, title of press or magazine, address and phone number. **Arrangement:** Alphabetical.

2125 ■ *"EBSCO Adds New Features to EBSCOhost Content Viewer" in Information Today (Vol. 26, February 2009, No. 2, pp. 31)*
Pub: Information Today, Inc.
Description: EBSCOhost Content Viewer historical digital archive collection provides a visual overview of a displayed document, highlighting search keywords on the page as well as providing a document map that shows the number of times a given keyword is mentioned in a periodical, monograph, article, or other document. For periodical content, the viewer lets users browse multiple issues in a volume without leaving the interface; features include zoom and pan technology similar to online maps.

2126 ■ *The Entrepreneurial Author*
Pub: Morgan James Publishing, LLC
Ed: David L. Hancock. **Released:** October 2009. **Price:** $17.95. **Description:** Handbook to help entrepreneurs author and publish a book based on their expertise in their chosen field.

2127 ■ *"Etextbook Space Heats Up" in Information Today (Vol. 28, November 2011, No. 10, pp. 10)*
Pub: Information Today, Inc.
Ed: Paula J. Hane. **Description:** The use of etextbooks is expected to grow with the use of mobile devices and tablets. A new group of activists is asking students, faculty members and others to sign a petition urging higher education leaders to prioritize affordable textbooks or free ebooks over the traditional, expensive new books required for classes.

2128 ■ *"Etextbooks: Coming of Age" in Information Today (Vol. 28, September 2011, No. 8, pp. 1)*
Pub: Information Today, Inc.
Ed: Amanda Mulvihill. **Description:** National average for textbooks costs was estimated at $1,137 annually at a 4-year public college for the 2010-2011 school year. Amazon reported selling 105 etextbooks for every 100 print books, while Barnes and Noble announced that their etextbooks were outselling print 3 to 1.

2129 ■ *"Ex Libris Rosetta Hits the Market" in Information Today (Vol. 26, February 2009, No. 2, pp. 30)*
Pub: Information Today, Inc.
Description: Ex Libris Rosetta, the latest version of the Ex Libris Group's Digital Preservation System supports the acquisition, validation, ingest, storage, management, preservation, and dissemination of digital objects, allowing libraries the infrastructure and technology to preserve and facilitate access to digital collections. The firm's Ex Libris Rosseta Charter Program helps users develop strategic collaboration between Ex Libris and its customers to improve the product.

2130 ■ *"Ex-MP? Ex-con? Exactly!" in Canadian Business (Vol. 83, October 12, 2010, No. 17, pp. 16)*
Pub: Rogers Media Ltd.
Ed: James Cowan. **Description:** British author Jeffrey Archer's novels could be made into movies. Archer sold 250 million books in 63 countries, which include political thrillers, spy novels, and crime capers.

2131 ■ *"Facebook Purchased Push Pop Press"* in *Information Today* (Vol. 28, October 2011, No. 9, pp. 12)

Pub: Information Today, Inc.

Description: Facebook purchased Push Pop Press, a digital publishing company that developed a multi-touch interface for ebook publishing on the iPad.

2132 ■ *First Editions, a Guide to Identification: Statements of Selected North American, British Commonwealth, and Irish Publishers on Their Methods of Designating First Editions*

Pub: Spoon River Press

Contact: Linda Verkler, Editor

URL(s): www.spoonriverpress.com/Page1.html. **Ed:** Edward N. Zempel, Linda A. Verkler. **Released:** Latest edition 4th. **Price:** $60, Individuals hardcover, plus $3.50, postage for U.S. delivery. **Covers:** 4,200 English language publishers and their methods of designating first editions. **Entries include:** Publisher name, method of designation.

2133 ■ *"Five More Great Books on Entrepreneurship"* in *Entrepreneur* (Vol. 37, July 2009, No. 7, pp. 19)

Pub: Entrepreneur Media, Inc.

Description: 800-CEO-Read founder, Jack Covert, and president, Todd Sattersten, share five books that would have been included in the book, 'The 100 Business Books of All Time' if space was not an issue. 'You Need to Be a Little Crazy,' 'Oh, the Places You'll Go!,' 'Founders at Work,' 'The Innovator's Dilemma,' and 'Purple Cow' are highly recommended for entrepreneurs.

2134 ■ *From Entrepreneur to Infopreneur: Make Money with Books, E-Books, and Other Information Products*

Pub: John Wiley & Sons, Incorporated

Ed: Stephanie Chandler. **Released:** November 2006. **Price:** $19.95. **Description:** Infopreneurs sell information online in the forms of books, e-books, special reports, audio and video products, seminars, and more.

2135 ■ *"A Good Book Is Worth a Thousand Blogs"* in *Barron's* (Vol. 88, July 14, 2008, No. 28, pp. 42)

Pub: Dow Jones & Co., Inc.

Ed: Gene Epstein. **Description:** Nine summer book suggestions on economics are presented. The list includes 'The Revolution' by Ron Paul, 'The Forgotten Man' by Amity Shales, 'The Commitments of Traders Bible' by Stephen Briese, and 'Economic Facts and Fallacies' by Thomas Sowell.

2136 ■ *"Guide to Carbon Footprinting"* in *American Printer* (Vol. 128, June 1, 2011, No. 6)

Pub: Penton Media Inc.

Description: PrintCity Alliance published its new report, 'Carbon Footprint & Energy Reduction for Graphic Industry Value Chain.' The report aims to help improve the environmental performance of printers, converters, publishers, brand owners and their suppliers.

2137 ■ *Guild of Book Workers--Supplies and Services Directory*

Pub: Guild of Book Workers Inc.

Contact: Andrew Huot, President

E-mail: vicepresident@guildofbookworkers.allmail.net

URL(s): www.guildofbookworkers.org/resources/supply/search.php. **Ed:** Bernadette G. Callery, Susan B. Martin. **Released:** Irregular; Latest edition November 2008. **Price:** $15, Individuals 2001 issue. **Covers:** More than 250 manufacturers and suppliers of products used in bookbinding, calligraphy, and repair and conservation of documents and books; coverage includes Canada. **Entries include:** Name of firm, address, phone, products or services, minimum order requirements, shipping restrictions, whether catalog or samples are available. **Arrangement:** Geographical, then by product or service. **Indexes:** Alphabetical.

2138 ■ *"Harlequin Leads the Way"* in *Marketing to Women* (Vol. 22, July 2009, No. 7, pp. 1)

Pub: EPM Communications Inc.

Contact: Ira Mayer, President

E-mail: imayer@epmcom.com

Description: Although the publishing industry has been slow to embrace new media options, the Internet is now a primary source for reaching women readers. Harlequin has been eager to court their female consumers over the Internet and often uses women bloggers in their campaigns strategies.

2139 ■ *"Health Care Leads Sectors Attracting Capital"* in *Hispanic Business* (March 2008, pp. 14-16, 18)

Pub: Hispanic Business

Ed: Scott Williams. **Description:** U. S. Hispanic healthcare, media, and food were the key industries in the U.S. gaining investors in 2007.

2140 ■ *"Hit the Books"* in *Black Enterprise* (Vol. 38, July 2008, No. 12, pp. 42)

Pub: Earl G. Graves Publishing Co. Inc.

Ed: Mellody Hobson. **Description:** Four books that deal with investing are discussed as is the idea that reading even 15 minutes a day from one of these books will give you tools that far exceed what you can learn from magazines and the business section of your daily newspaper.

2141 ■ *"Hitting the E-Books"* in *Inc.* (Vol. 33, September 2011, No. 7, pp. 36)

Pub: Inc. Magazine

Ed: Shivani Vora. **Description:** Textbooks may be getting cheaper for college students now that they can use electronic textbooks that can be read on a laptop or tablet. The market is growing about 50 percent annually. Statistical data included.

2142 ■ *"Ideas at Work: Total Communicator"* in *Business Strategy Review* (Vol. 21, Autumn 2010, No. 3, pp. 10)

Pub: Blackwell Publishers Ltd.

Ed: Stuart Crainer. **Description:** Vittorio Colao has been chief executive of Vodafone Group for two years. He brings to the company special experience as CEO of RCS MediaGroup in Milan, which publishes newspapers, magazines and books in Italy, Spain and France. Prior to RCS, he held other positions within Vodafone. Colao shares his views on business, the global economy and leading Vodafone.

2143 ■ *"In It For the Long Run"* in *Business Journal-Serving Phoenix & the Valley of the Sun* (Vol. 30, August 20, 2010, No. 50, pp. 1)

Pub: Phoenix Business Journal

Ed: Angela Gonzales. **Description:** Cancer survivor Helene Neville has finished a record-breaking 2,520-mile run in 93 days and then celebrated her 50th birthday despite being diagnosed with Hodgkins' lymphoma in 1991. Neveille, who is also a Phoenix area registered nurse, made stops along the way to promote her book, 'Nurses in Shape'. Neville also discusses how she fought her cancer through running.

2144 ■ *International Directory of Little Magazines and Small Presses*

Pub: Dustbooks

Contact: Len Fulton, Publisher

E-mail: lenfulton@dustbooks.com

URL(s): www.dustbooks.com/d.htm. **Ed:** Len Fulton. **Released:** Annual; Latest edition 47th; 2011-2012. **Price:** $65, Individuals CD-ROM (3 directories); $49.95, Individuals online; $30, Individuals CD-ROM. **Covers:** Over 4,000 small, independent magazines, presses, and papers. **Entries include:** Name, address, size, circulation, frequency, price, type of material used, number of issues or books published annually, and other pertinent data. **Arrangement:** Alphabetical. **Indexes:** Subject, regional.

2145 ■ *"Lafley Gives Look At His Game Plan"* in *Business Courier* (Vol. 24, March 21, 2008, No. 50, pp. 1)

Pub: American City Business Journals, Inc.

Ed: Lisa Biank Fasig. **Description:** Overview of A.G. Lafley's book entitled 'The Game-Changer', is presented. Lafley, Procter & Gamble Co.'s chief execu-

tive officer, documented his philosophy and strategy in his book. His work also includes Procter & Gamble's hands-on initiatives such as mock-up grocery stores and personal interviews with homeowners.

2146 ■ *Library and Book Trade Almanac*

Pub: Information Today Inc.

Contact: Thomas H. Hogan, President

E-mail: ctuthill@infotoday.com

URL(s): books.infotoday.com. **Released:** Annual; Latest edition 57th; June 2012. **Price:** $249, Individuals hardbound; plus $17 shipping and handling charges; $224.10, Individuals first time standing order. **Publication includes:** Lists of accredited library schools; scholarships for education in library science; library organizations; library statistics; publishing and bookselling organizations. **Entries include:** Directory listings give name of institution, address, phone, fax, name of officer or contact, publications; scholarship listings include requirements, value of grant, contact name. Principal content is articles and special reports on topics of interest to those in library/information science and publishers; international reports; annual reports from federal agencies and libraries and from national associations; information on legislation, funding, etc. **Database includes:** Lists of notable books, best-sellers, literary prize winners; library and trade statistics; calendar of events. **Arrangement:** Topical. **Indexes:** Organization; subject.

2147 ■ *Literary Market Place: The Directory of the American Book Publishing Industry*

Pub: Information Today Inc.

Contact: Thomas H. Hogan, President

E-mail: ctuthill@infotoday.com

URL(s): books.infotoday.com. **Released:** Annual; Latest edition 2012. **Price:** $339, Individuals 2-volume set/softbound plus $25 shipping/handling; $305.10, Individuals first time standing order. **Covers:** Over 12,500 firms or organizations offering services related to the publishing industry, including book publishers in the United States and Canada who issued three or more books during the preceding year, plus a small press section of publishers who publish less than three titles per year or those who are self-published. Also included: book printers and binders; book clubs; book trade and literary associations; selected syndicates, newspapers, periodicals, and radio and TV programs that use book reviews or book publishing news; translators and literary agents. **Entries include:** For publishers--Company name, address, phone, address for orders, principal executives, editorial directors, and managers, date founded, number of titles in previous year, number of backlist titles in print, types of books published, ISBN prefixes, representatives, imprints, and affiliations. For suppliers, etc.--Listings usually show firm name, address, phone, executives, services, etc. **Arrangement:** Classified by line of business. **Indexes:** Principal index is 35,000-item combined index of publishers, publications, and personnel; several sections have geographical and/or subject indexes; translators are indexed by source and target language.

2148 ■ *"Negotiating Tips"* in *Black Enterprise* (Vol. 37, December 2006, No. 5, pp. 70)

Pub: Earl G. Graves Publishing Co. Inc.

Description: Sekou Kaalund, head of strategy, mergers & acquisitions at Citigroup Securities & Fund Services, states that 'Negotiation skills are paramount to success in a business environment because of client, employee, and shareholder relationships'. He discusses how the book by George Kohlrieser, Hostage at the Table: How Leaders Can Overcome Conflict, Influence Others, and Raise Performance, has helped him negotiate more powerfully and enhance his skills at conflict-resolution.

2149 ■ *"New Approach to Mechanical Binding"* in *American Printer* (Vol. 128, July 1, 2011, No. 7)

Pub: Penton Media Inc.

Description: EcoBinder coil binding system from Kugler-Womako eliminates traditional plastic combs or wire spiral with the use of 22-mm wide printable paper rings.

2150 ■ *"New Book Takes Alternate View on Ontario's Wind Industry"* in CNW Group (September 19, 2011)
Pub: CNW Group
Contact: Carolyn McGill-Davidson, President
Description: Dirty Business: The Reality Behind Ontario's Rush to Wind Power, was written by editor and health care writer Jane Wilson of Ottawa, Ontario, Canada along with contributing editor Parker Gallant. The book contains articles and papers on the wind business, including information on illnesses caused from the environmental noise.

2151 ■ *"Online Book Sales Surpass Bookstores"* in Information Today (Vol. 28, September 2011, No. 8, pp. 11)
Pub: Information Today, Inc.
Ed: Cindy Martine. **Description:** Online book sales outpaced bookstore purchases in the United States, signaling a shift in the US book industry. Statistical data included.

2152 ■ *"Online Self-Publishing Services"* in Black Enterprise (Vol. 37, November 2006, No. 4, pp. 90)
Pub: Earl G. Graves Publishing Co. Inc.
Description: Profiles of five online self-publishing services.

2153 ■ *Publishers' Catalogues*
Pub: Northern Lights Internet Solutions Ltd.
URL(s): www.lights.ca. **Released:** Continuous updates. **Price:** Free. **Covers:** Publishing companies worldwide. **Entries include:** Company name, address, phone, fax, titles. **Arrangement:** Geographical by country, then alphabetical.

2154 ■ *Publishers Directory*
Pub: Cengage Learning Inc.
Contact: Ronald Dunn, President
URL(s): www.gale.cengage.com. **Released:** Annual; Latest edition 37th; March, 2012. **Price:** $756, Individuals. **Covers:** Over 20,000 new and established, commercial and nonprofit, private and alternative, corporate and association, government and institution publishing programs and their distributors; includes producers of books, classroom materials, prints, reports, and databases. **Entries include:** Firm name, address, phone, fax, company e-mail address, URL, year founded, ISBN prefix, Standard Address Number, whether firm participates in the Cataloging in Publication program of the Library of Congress, names of principal executives, personal e-mail addresses, number of titles in print, description of firm and its main subject interests, discount and returns policies, affiliated and parent companies, mergers and amalgamations, principal markets, imprints and divisions, alternate formats products are offered; distributors also list firms for which they distribute, special services, terms to publishers and regional offices. **Arrangement:** Alphabetical; distributors listed separately. **Indexes:** Subject, geographical, publisher, imprints, and distributor. **Availability:** Online: Cengage Learning Inc.; LexisNexis Group. **Type:** Directory.

2155 ■ *Publishers, Distributors, and Wholesalers of the United States*
Pub: R.R. Bowker L.L.C.
URL(s): www.bowker.com. **Released:** Annual; latest edition 2010. **Price:** $500, Individuals in 2 volumes; hard cover. **Covers:** Over 196,066 publishers, distributors, and wholesalers; includes associations, museums, software producers and manufacturers, and others not included in 'Books in Print'. **Entries include:** Publisher name, editorial and ordering addresses, e-mail, websites, phone, Standard Address Numbers (SANs), International Standard Book Number prefix. **Arrangement:** Alphabetical; distributors and wholesalers are listed separately. **Indexes:** ISBN prefix, abbreviation, type of business, imprint name, geographical, inactive and out of business company name, toll-free phone and fax, wholesaler and distributor.

2156 ■ *The Publishing Game: Publish a Book in 30 Days*
Pub: Peanut Butter and Jelly Press LLC
Ed: Fern Reiss. **Released:** January 31, 2003. **Price:** $19.95. **Description:** Excellent resource for individuals wanting to write a book and become their own publisher.

2157 ■ *"Publishing Technology Introduces IngentaConnect Mobile"* in Information Today (Vol. 26, February 2009, No. 2, pp. 33)
Pub: Information Today, Inc.
Description: College undergraduates will find Publishing Technology's newest publisher product, IngentaConnect Mobile helpful. The product allows users to read articles and abstracts on mobile devices. According to a recent study, 73 percent of young adults with wireless hand-held devices use them to access non-voice data on any given day.

2158 ■ *"Reducing the Book's Carbon Footprint"* in American Printer (Vol. 128, July 1, 2011, No. 7)
Pub: Penton Media Inc.
Description: Green Press Initiative's Book Industry Environmental Council is working to achieve a 20 percent reduction in the book industry's carbon footprint by 2020. The Council is made up of publishers, printers, paper suppliers, and non-governmental organizations.

2159 ■ *"SAGE Publications Announced a Partnership with Which Medical Device"* in Information Today (Vol. 28, November 2011, No. 10, pp. 15)
Pub: Information Today, Inc.
Description: SAGE Publications has partnered with Which Medical Device to offer insights, tutorials, and reviews of medical devices.

2160 ■ *"Savvy Solutions"* in Black Enterprise (Vol. 41, November 2010, No. 4, pp. 42)
Pub: Earl G. Graves Publishing Co. Inc.
Ed: Tennile M. Robinson. **Description:** Society of Children's Book Writers and Illustrators offers members many benefits, including directories of agencies looking for new writers of books.

2161 ■ *"Scientific American Builds Novel Blog Network"* in Information Today (Vol. 28, September 2011, No. 8, pp. 12)
Pub: Information Today, Inc.
Ed: Kurt Schiller. **Description:** Scientific American launched a new blog network that joins a diverse lineup of bloggers cover various scientific topics under one banner. The blog network includes 60 bloggers providing insights into the ever-changing world of science and technology.

2162 ■ *"The Seat-Of-The-Pants School of Marketing"* in Brandweek (Vol. 49, April 21, 2008, No. 16, pp. 24)
Pub: VNU Business Media, Inc.
Ed: David Vinjamuri. **Description:** Excerpt from the book 'Accidental Branding: How Ordinary People Build Extraordinary Brands,' by David Vinjamuri, discusses six shared principles for creating a brand that is unique and will be successful over the long-term.

2163 ■ *The Self-Publishing Manual: How To Write, Print, and Sell Your Own Book*
Pub: Para Publishing
Ed: Dan Poynter. **Released:** 2007. **Price:** $19.95. **Description:** The book provides a complete course in writing, publishing, marketing, promoting, and distributing books. Poynter offers a step-by-step study of the publishing industry and explains various book-marketing techniques.

2164 ■ *"Serials Solutions Launches 360 Resource Manager Consortium Edition"* in Information Today (Vol. 26, February 2009, No. 2, pp. 32)
Pub: Information Today, Inc.
Description: Serials Solutions new Serials Solutions 360 Resource Manager Consortium Edition helps consortia, groups and member libraries with their e-resource management services. The products allows users to consolidate e-resource metadata and acquisition information into one place, which enables groups to manage holdings, subscriptions, licensing, contacts, and cost information and to streamline delivery of information to members.

2165 ■ *Society for Scholarly Publishing--Membership Directory*
Pub: Society for Scholarly Publishing
Contact: Carol Anne Meyer, President
E-mail: cmeyer@crossref.org
URL(s): www.sspnet.org. **Released:** Annual **Database covers:** More than 1,000 librarians, publishers, printers, authors, and editors interested in scholarly publication; related organizations. **Database includes:** Name, title, address, phone, organization. **Arrangement:** Alphabetical.

2166 ■ *"Spotlight; 'Classroom Focus' at Encyclopaedia Britannica"* in Crain's Chicago Business (Vol. 34, October 24, 2011, No. 42, pp. 6)
Pub: Crain Communications Inc.
Ed: Paul Merrion. **Description:** Profile of Gregory Healy, product officer for Encyclopaedia Britannica is presented. Healy took the position in May 2010 and is focused on online offerings of their publication and to make them more useful to teachers.

2167 ■ *"Swedes Swoop In To Save Time4"* in Advertising Age (Vol. 78, January 29, 2007, No. 5, pp. 4)
Pub: Crain Communications, Inc.
Ed: Nat Ives. **Description:** Overview of Stockholm's Bonnier Group, a family-owned publisher that is looking to expand its U.S. presence; Bonnier recently acquired a number of Time Inc. magazines.

2168 ■ *"Traits that Makes Blogs Attractive to Book Publishers"* in Marketing to Women (Vol. 22, July 2009, No. 7, pp. 1)
Pub: EPM Communications Inc.
Contact: Ira Mayer, President
E-mail: imayer@epmcom.com
Description: Book publishers are finding a beneficial relationship between themselves and women bloggers on the Internet. A high visitor count, frequent updates and active readership are criteria for identifying the blogs with the most clout and therefore providing the greatest benefit to publishers.

2169 ■ *"University Book Store Inc.: an Act of Independence"* in Retail Merchandiser (Vol. 51, September-October 2011, No. 5, pp. 68)
Pub: Phoenix Media Corporation
Ed: Lori Sichtermann. **Description:** University Book Store Inc. is a campus bookstore located at the University of Washington, in Seattle. The book store provides more than $1 million in UW customer rebates and discounts annually and donated more than $800,000 in UW student scholarships.

2170 ■ *"An Updated Ranking of Academic Journals in Economics"* in Canadian Journal of Economics (Vol. 44, November 2011, No. 4, pp. 1525)
Pub: Blackwell Publishers Ltd.
Ed: Pantelis Kalaitzidakis, Theofanis P. Mamuneas, Thanasis Stengos. **Description:** An updated list showing the ranking of economic journals (2003) is presented; however this present study differs methodologically from an earlier study by using a rolling window of years between 2003 and 2008, for each year counting the number of citations of articles published in the previous ten years.

2171 ■ *"The Way I Work: Kim Kleeman"* in Inc. (October 2007, pp. 110-112, 114)
Pub: Gruner & Jahr USA Publishing
Ed: Leigh Buchanan. **Description:** Profile of Kim Kleemna, founder and president of ShakespeareSquared, a firm that develops educational materials, including lesson plans, teacher guides, activity workbooks, and discussion guides for large publishers. Kleeman talks about the challenges she faces running her nearly all-women company while maintaining a balance with her family.

2172 ■ *"Why Women Blog and What They Read"* in Marketing to Women (Vol. 22, July 2009, No. 7, pp. 8)
Pub: EPM Communications Inc.
Contact: Ira Mayer, President
E-mail: imayer@epmcom.com
Description: Listing of topics that are visited the most by female Internet users. Statistical data included.

2173 ■ *"Wikinomics: The Sequel' in Business Strategy Review (Vol. 21, Summer 2010, No. 2, pp. 64)*
Pub: Blackwell Publishers Ltd.
Description: Ever optimistic Don Tapscott and Anthony Willis, co-authors of Wikinomics (Atlantic Books 2008) as well as various other books that study the Internet and its relationship to society are now working on a new book, one for which they are using the Internet to determine its title.

2174 ■ *"Wikinomics: The Sequel' in Business Strategy Review (Vol. 21, Summer 2010, No. 2, pp. 64)*
Pub: Wiley-Blackwell
Description: Ever-optimistic Don Tapscott and Anthony Williams, coauthors of Wikinomics and individually, of a number of other books that study the Internet and its relation to society, are now working on a new book, one for which they're using the Internet to determine its title.

2175 ■ *"Women Prefer Cookbooks Over Word-Of-Mouth for Recipe Suggestions" in Marketing to Women (Vol. 23, November 2010, No. 11, pp. 6)*
Pub: EPM Communications Inc.
Contact: Ira Mayer, President
E-mail: imayer@epmcom.com
Description: Sixty-five percent of women surveyed enjoy a sit-down dinner at least five times a week according to Martha Steward Omni-media. Cookbooks, recipe Websites, food-focused magazines, and TV cooking shows are their primary source for new recipes.

STATISTICAL SOURCES

2176 ■ *Book Industry Trends*
Pub: Book Industry Study Group
Contact: Scott Lubeck, Executive Director
Ed: Compiled by Statistical Service Center staff. **Released:** 2009. **Price:** $875.00 (paper).

2177 ■ *RMA Annual Statement Studies*
Pub: Risk Management Association
Contact: Kevin M. Blakey, President
Released: Annual. **Price:** $175.00 2006-07 edition, $105.00. **Description:** Contains composite balance sheets and income statements for more than 360 industries, including the accounting, auditing, and bookkeeping industries. Also contains five years of comparative historical data for discerning trends. Includes 16 commonly used ratios, computed for most of the size groupings for nearly every industry.

2178 ■ *Standard & Poor's Industry Surveys*
Pub: Standard & Poor's Corp.
Released: Annual. **Price:** $3633.00. **Description:** Two-volume book that examines the prospects for specific industries, including trucking. Also provides analyses of trends and problems, statistical tables and charts, and comparative company analyses.

2179 ■ *U.S. Book Publishing Industry*
Business Trend Analysts, Inc. Industry Studies
Released: 2007. **Price:** $149.00. **Description:** The Book Publishing Industry report features 2008 current and 2009 forecast estimates on the size of the industry (sales, establishments, employment) nationally and for all 50 U.S. States and over 900 metro areas.

TRADE PERIODICALS

2180 ■ *AAP Monthly Report*
Pub: Association of American Publishers Inc.
Ed: Judith Platt, Editor, jplatt@publishers.org. **Released:** Monthly. **Price:** Included in membership. **Description:** Examines subjects of interest to publishers, including copyright issues, First Amendment issues, Washington legislation, and programs and activities of the Association. Recurring features include reports of meetings, and notices of publications available.

2181 ■ *Book Marketing Update*
Pub: Open Horizons
Ed: John Kremer, Editor, johnkremer@bookmarket.com. **Released:** Semimonthly. **Price:** $297, U.S. and Canada; $337, elsewhere. **Description:** Surveys resources for publishers interested in marketing their books to bookstores, libraries, wholesalers, catalogs, book clubs, and other special markets.

2182 ■ *The Bookwoman*
Pub: Women's National Book Association
Contact: Mary Grey James, President
Ed: Ellen Myrick, Editor, ellenmyrick@ingrambook.com. **Released:** 3/year. **Price:** $10, nonmembers in U.S.; $12, nonmembers elsewhere. **Description:** Covers major topics of interest to publishers, librarians, educators, writers, and agents in the book world. Recurring features include editorials, letters to the editor, book reviews, and news of members, articles, essays, profiles of woman-owned presses, and news of the bookworld and WNBA chapters.

2183 ■ *Fiction Writer's Guideline*
Pub: Fiction Writer's Connection
Contact: Blythe Camenson, Director
E-mail: bcamenson@aol.com
Released: Enewsletter. **Description:** Offers practical advice and support on writing and getting published. Recurring features include interviews, book reviews, and Advice From agents and editors and Writing Tips.

2184 ■ *Guild of Book Workers Newsletter*
Pub: Guild of Book Workers Inc.
Contact: Andrew Huot, President
E-mail: vicepresident@guildofbookworkers.allmail.net
Ed: Margaret Johnson, Editor. **Released:** Bimonthly, Every 2 months. **Price:** Included in membership. **Description:** Covers issues in book arts, binding, book conservation, calligraphy, and printing. Recurring features include letters to the editor, interviews, news of research, a calendar of events, reports of meetings, news of educational opportunities, job listings, book reviews, and notices of publications available.

2185 ■ *The Horn Book Magazine: About Books for Children and Young Adults*
Pub: The Horn Book Inc.
Contact: Anne Quirk, Director
URL(s): www.hbook.com/magazine/. **Released:** Bimonthly **Price:** $49, Individuals; $66, Canada and Mexico; $70, Other countries.

2186 ■ *How To Be Your Own Publisher Update*
Pub: Bibliotheca Press
Ed: A. Doyle, Editor. **Released:** Annual. **Price:** $12.95, U.S.; $15.95, Canada; $19.95, other countries. **Description:** Acts as a reference for self publishers. Distributed by Prosperity & Profits Unlimited Distribution Services, PO Box 416, Denver, CO, 80201.

2187 ■ *Independent Publisher Online: The Voice of The Independent Publishing Industry*
Pub: Jenkins Group Inc.
Contact: James J. Kalajian, President
E-mail: jjk@bookpublishing.com
URL(s): www.independentpublisher.com/. **Released:** Monthly **Price:** Free.

2188 ■ *Journal of Scholarly Publishing*
Pub: University of Toronto Press-Journal Div.
URL(s): www.utpjournals.com/Journal-of-Scholarly-Publishing.html. **Ed:** Tom Radko. **Released:** Quarterly **Price:** $55, Individuals print; $155, Institutions print only; $45, Members print only; $45, Canada print.

2189 ■ *Kirkus Reviews*
Pub: Nielsen Business Media
Contact: Anne Larsen, Executive Editor
E-mail: larsenx13@aol.com
Released: Semimonthly. **Price:** $355, institutions libraries according to book budget. **Description:** Publishes book reviews on current titles of both fiction and nonfiction for adults and children. Also provides author, publisher, price, and page count.

2190 ■ *Laughing Bear Newsletter*
Pub: Laughing Bear Press
Ed: Tom Person, Editor, editor@laughingbear.com. **Released:** Monthly. **Price:** $15, U.S.; $17.50, Canada; $25, elsewhere. **Description:** Reviews small press and business publications; provides information and resources on publishing, designs, and planning techniques for self-published books. Contains news and commentary on independent publishing and related services.

2191 ■ *PMA Independent*
Pub: Independent Book Publishers Association
Contact: Terry Nathan, Executive Director
Ed: Jan Nathan, Editor. **Released:** Monthly. **Price:** $12, members; $40, nonmembers others. **Description:** Informs member entrepreneurial book publishers about upcoming marketing programs and other Association activities aimed at helping independent publishers succeed. Also carries articles on topics such as desktop publishing and typesetting systems. Recurring features include member, committee, and research news, notices of educational and cooperative marketing opportunities, a calendar of events, and columns titled News from the "Net" and From the Director's Desk.

2192 ■ *Professional Publishing Report*
Pub: SIMBA Information Inc.
Contact: Jason W. Fuchs, Specialist
Released: Monthly. **Price:** $749 USA and Canada. **Description:** Features news on the publishing industry, including company figures, mergers, industry trends, revenue comparisons, and more.

2193 ■ *Publishers Weekly: The International voice for Book Publishing and Bookselling*
Pub: Publishers Weekly
URL(s): www.publishersweekly.com. **Released:** Weekly **Price:** $249.99, Individuals; $299.99, Canada; $399.99, Other countries air delivery.

2194 ■ *Publishing Executive: Creative, Production and Work Flow at Digital Speed*
Pub: North American Publishing Co.
Contact: Ned S. Borowsky, President
URL(s): www.napco.comwww.pubexec.com. **Ed:** Brian Howard. **Released:** 10/yr.

2195 ■ *Publishing Poynters*
Pub: Para Publishing
Ed: Dan Poynter, Editor, DanPoynter@ParaPublishing.com. **Released:** Semimonthly, 2/month. **Description:** Contains publishing industry news as well as management and marketing suggestions. Recurring features include news of research, news of educational opportunities, book reviews, and notices of publications available.

2196 ■ *The Russ von Hoelscher Direct Response Profit Report*
Pub: Publishers Media
Contact: Teri Apodaca
Ed: Russ von Hoelscher, Editor. **Released:** 8/year. **Price:** $36 1 year; $60 2 years. **Description:** Provides marketing advice for independent publishers and small presses, with special emphasis given to the non-bookstore market. Recurring features include letters to the editor, interviews, news of research, and book reviews, plus how to sell by mail and on the internet.

2197 ■ *Sell More Books! Newsletter*
Pub: Florida Publishers Association
Ed: Betsy Wright-Lampe, Editor. **Released:** Bimonthly. **Price:** Included in membership. **Description:** Reports on news, events, and updates of the Florida Publishers Association. Also focuses on publishing companies, book successes, and useful tips.

2198 ■ *SPEX*
Pub: Bay Area Independent Publishers Association
Contact: Judy Baker, President
Released: Monthly. **Description:** Discusses opportunities and changes in the field of publishing. Reviews members' books. Publicizes meetings, seminars, and other information of importance to small publishers. Recurring features include letters to

the editor, interviews, news of research, a calendar of events, news of members, and a column titled the President's Message.

VIDEOCASSETTES/ AUDIOCASSETTES

2199 ■ *Inside Business Today*
GPN Educational Media
1550 Executive Drive
Elgin, IL 60123
Ph: (402)472-2007
Free: 800-228-4630
Fax: (800)306-2330
Co. E-mail: askgpn@smarterville.com
URL: http://www.shopgpn.com
Released: 1989. **Description:** Leaders in business and industry tell their success stories in this extensive series. **Availability:** VHS; 3/4 U.

TRADE SHOWS AND CONVENTIONS

2200 ■ Bologna Children's Book Fair - Fiera Del Libro Per Ragazzi
Bologna Fiere
Via della Fiera 20
40128 Bologna, Italy
Ph: 39 51 282111
Fax: 39 51 6374004
Co. E-mail: segreteria.generale@bolognafiere.it
URL: http://www.bolognafiere.it
URL(s): www.bookfair.bolognafiere.it. **Frequency:** Annual. **Principal Exhibits:** Children's and juvenile books, text books and electronic books. **Telecommunication Services:** bookfair@bolognafiere.it.

2201 ■ Special Libraries Association Information Revolution
Special Libraries Association (SLA)
331 S Patrick St.
Alexandria, VA 22314-3501
Ph: (703)647-4900
Fax: (703)647-4901
Co. E-mail: janice@sla.org
URL: http://www.sla.org
Contact: Janice R. Lachance, Chief Executive Officer
E-mail: janice@sla.org
Frequency: Annual. **Audience:** Information managers and librarians. **Principal Exhibits:** Library equipment, supplies, and services, including computers and software, Database information.

CONSULTANTS

2202 ■ About Books Inc. (ABI)
1001 Taurus Dr.
Colorado Springs, CO 80906
Ph: (719)632-8226
Free: 800-548-1876
Fax: (719)471-2182
Co. E-mail: infoabi@about-books.com
URL: http://www.about-books.com
Contact: Debi Flora, President
Description: Information clearinghouse on self-publishing and marketing of books. Provides educational programs; maintains speakers' bureau. Provides audiotape programs and books on the subject. **Scope:** Full service writing and publishing consultants organized to assist corporations, organizations and individuals in the writing, editing, producing and marketing of books. Also develop sponsored and premium books. **Founded:** 1977. **Publications:** "Molding Young Athletes," Purington Press. **Telecommunication Services:** deb@about-books.com.

2203 ■ Editorial Code and Data Inc. (ECDI)
814 Wolverine Dr., Ste. 2
Walled Lake, MI 48390
Ph: (248)926-5187

Fax: (248)926-6047
Co. E-mail: monique.magee@gmail.com
URL: http://www.marketsize.com
Contact: Monique D. Magee, President
E-mail: monique@marketsize.com
Scope: Provider of data and computer services primarily to the publishing industry, with specialization in statistical data drawn from government sources. Services include data acquisition, analysis, formatting, and typesetting, archiving of computer data on CD-ROM, custom data display, search, and printing software, information brokering services, and related services such as design, writing, and data processing design. Industries served: publishing, in-house printing, non-profit organizations, government agencies, utilities, and manufacturing. **Founded:** 1990. **Publications:** "Market Share Reporter"; "Encyclopedia of Products & Industries"; "Economic Indicators Handbook"; "American Salaries and Wages Survey"; "Dun and Bradstreet & Gale: Industrial Handbook"; "Reference American Cost of Living Survey".

2204 ■ J. S. Eliezer Associates Inc. (JSEA)
300 Atlantic St., 7th Fl.
Stamford, CT 06901-3513
Ph: (203)658-1300
Fax: (203)658-1301
Contact: Judah S. Eliezer, President
E-mail: jeliezer@jseliezer.com
Scope: Management and market research consultants offering design and implementation of manufacturing strategy, feasibility analysis and systems analysis, as well as management information systems and prepress systems; manufacturing proposals analysis, negotiations and contracts; paper purchasing strategy and contract negotiations; catalog distribution effectiveness analysis. Serves the publishing and catalog industries. **Founded:** 1964.

2205 ■ Leon Gelfond & Associates
17266 Boca Club Blvd., Apt. 1606
Boca Raton, FL 33487-1279
Ph: (561)995-0865
Contact: Leon Gelfond, President
Scope: Consultants offering services in mail order, fulfillment, data processing, shipping and warehousing, printing, and book packaging. Primarily serving the publishing industry. Also has the capabilities and facilities for providing clients with a complete mail order package, from the creation to the printing and mailing of the promotion. Serves government also. **Founded:** 1986.

2206 ■ Harian Creative Enterprises—Harian Creative Books
47 Hyde Blvd.
Ballston Spa, NY 12020
Ph: (518)885-6699
Fax: (518)885-7397
Contact: Shirley Garrett, Director
Description: Description: Publishes fiction, poetry and monographs on writing, the arts, education and culture. Offers conferences, workshops, lecturing, and teaching. Accepts solicited manuscripts only. Reaches market through direct mail, trade sales and wholesalers and distributors. Does not accept unsolicited manuscripts. **Scope:** Literary service for writers and publishers, offering counsel on the writing and completion of literary projects, including titling, book and jacket design and editorial work. Industries served: Education, culture, and art and entertainment. **Founded:** 1967. **Seminars:** The Workshop Under the Sky.

2207 ■ Heidelberg Graphics (HG)
2 Stansbury Ct.
Chico, CA 95928
Ph: (530)342-6582
Fax: (530)342-6582
Co. E-mail: service@heidelberggraphics.com
URL: http://www.heidelberggraphics.com
Contact: Jennifer Rowe, Manager
Description: Description: Publishes books on fiction, poetry, biography and history. Reaches market through Internet, direct mail, reviews and listings and wholesalers and distributors. Does not accept unsolicited manuscripts. **Scope:** Offers services including scans, disc conversions, layouts, editing and printing for books, catalogs and magazines. Provides the

codes on paper, disk, film, embedded in designs, or in variable labeling and personalized printing. Serves private industries as well as government agencies. **Founded:** 1972. **Publications:** "Chronicles of the Clandestine Knights: Hyacinth Blue," 2003; "A Book of Thoughts II," 2001; "Historic Shot Glasses: The pre-Prohibition," 1992; "After the War," 1981; "Phantasm," 1980.

2208 ■ The Live Oak Press L.L.C.
445 Burgess Dr.
Menlo Park, CA 94306-0036
Ph: (650)853-0197
Fax: (815)366-8205
URL: http://www.liveoakpress.com
Contact: David M. Hamilton, President
E-mail: mhamilton@liveoakpress.com
Scope: Manages design and implementation of publishing programs. Also offers complete book and magazine preparation and publishing consulting, including web resources, advertising, concept development, manuscript, design, development and production through finished product. Specializes in high-technology clients and electronic publishing. **Founded:** 1970. **Publications:** "The Tools of My Trade"; "To the Yukon with Jack London"; "Earthquakes and Young Volcanoes"; "The Lost Cement Mine"; "Inner Voyage"; "Studies in the Development of Consciousness"; "Dialectical Realism: Studies on a Philosophy of Growth"; "Mammoth Lakes Sierra"; "Deepest Valley"; "Mammoth Gold"; "Old Mammoth". **Seminars:** Internet publishing Seminar.

2209 ■ Martin Cook Associates Ltd.
353 Strawtown Rd.
New City, NY 10956
Ph: (914)639-5316
Fax: (914)639-5318
Contact: Martin H. Cook, President
E-mail: mcanewcity@aol.com
Scope: Provider of book and print production and design management to publishers, foundations, and corporations. Offers allied graphic services, including copy editing, proofreading, design and typography of books, jackets and print materials, typesetting, color separations, printing, binding, warehousing, and distribution. Also conducts budgeting, scheduling, and sourcing of foreign and domestic suppliers based on cost, schedule, and quality requirements. **Founded:** 1977.

2210 ■ Edward F. McCartan Publishing Consultant
220 E 54th St.
New York, NY 10022
Ph: (212)421-2641
Fax: (212)421-4115
Co. E-mail: edmccartan@aol.com
Scope: Advises potential author or authors with unpublished manuscripts on content, style, and form by written evaluation. Edits manuscripts for spelling, grammar, punctuation, and consistency. **Founded:** 1984.

2211 ■ Moseley Associates Inc.
6 Bart Bull Rd.
Middletown, NY 10941
Ph: (845)673-5955
Co. E-mail: pwadams@consultmoseley.com
URL: http://www.consultmoseley.com
Contact: Peter W. Adams, President
E-mail: pwadams@consultmoseley.com
Scope: Provider of management consulting services. It is also engaged in appraisals of books, magazines, and learning materials. **Founded:** 1971. **Publications:** "Is This the End of Publishing? As We Know It," Jun, 2007; "US School Publishing," Apr, 2001; "A Century of Progress," Jun, 2006; "Technology in Publishing: A Century of Progress," Against the Grain, May, 2001; "Why I Don't Read Electronic Journals: An Iconoclast Speaks Out," Sep, 1997; "Post-Traumatic Shock Syndrome, Or, Surviving the Merger," Jun, 2009; "Familiar and Unfamiliar Quotations," Apr, 2009.

2212 ■ nSight Inc.
1 Van de Graaff Dr., Ste. 202
Burlington, MA 01803-5171
Ph: (781)273-6300

Fax: (781)273-6301
Co. E-mail: sales@nsightworks.com
URL: http://www.nsightworks.com
Contact: Thomas E. Leblanc, President
E-mail: tleblanc@nsightworks.com
Scope: Provider of complete communications and publications support and training through its four divisions. Temporary and Permanent Placement Division assigns tested publications professionals to companies. Consulting offers consulting services such as publications evaluation and Internet strategies. Industries served: Computer industry, management and environmental consulting firms, book publishers, banks and government agencies. **Founded:** 1982. **Seminars:** Business Writing: Grammar and Usage; XML: An Introduction; XML: DTD Design; Writing and Editing for the Web; Writing for Public Relations; Editing for an International Audience; Creating Effective PowerPoint Presentations; Instructional Design for Blended Learning: A Practical Approach, Apr, 2008; Project Management for Publishing Writers and Editors, Mar, 2008; Online Editing with MS Word and Adobe Acrobat, Mar, 2008; Copyediting for Technical Documentation, Mar, 2008; Advanced Copyediting for Technical Documentation, Mar, 2008; Business Writing: Grammar and Usage, Mar, 2008; Copyediting for BioTech/Medical Documentation, Feb, 2008; Copyediting Fundamentals, Feb, 2008; Editing International Documents, Feb, 2008; Creating Corporate Style Guides, Feb, 2008; Creating a Web Content Style Guide, Feb, 2008; Design for Non-Designers, Feb, 2008; HTML 4.01 Web Authoring Basic, Jan, 2008; Indexing Technical Documentation, Jan, 2008; Polishing Your Writing through Self-Editing, Jan, 2008; Proofreading essentials, Jan, 2008; Substantive and Developmental Editing, Jan, 2008. **Special Services:** EDIT EXPRESS™.

2213 ■ James Peter Associates Inc.
PO Box 772
Tenafly, NJ 07670
Ph: (201)568-0760
Fax: (201)568-2959
Contact: Herbert F. Holtje, Principal
E-mail: bholtje@attmail.com
Scope: Consults with publishers and industry on such projects for total book production from conception through writing, design and illustration to camera-ready copy, video tapes and programmed instruction. Also works with businesses and non-profit organizations to develop books and periodical publications. **Founded:** 1971.

2214 ■ Stillman H. Publishers Inc.
21405 Woodchuck Ln.
Boca Raton, FL 33428
Ph: (561)482-6343
Contact: Herbert Stillman, President
Scope: Offers consulting services in the following areas: management, start ups, profit maximization, world wide negotiating, interim management, corporate debt resolution. **Founded:** 1984.

2215 ■ Donald Wigal
4 Park Ave., Ste. 8M
New York, NY 10016
Ph: (212)683-3478
Fax: (212)683-8064
Co. E-mail: donwigal@ix.netcom.com
URL: http://www.dwigal.com
Contact: Don Wigal, President
Scope: Offers services and products to businesses and individuals. Newsgroup and web searching consulting services include database searching, ad copy, a-presentations, career guidance and niche marketing. Other services include manuscript preparation, editing, copy editing, abstracting and indexing. **Founded:** 1979. **Publications:** "The Cicero Project: A Celebration of Old Age by Common Bonders," 2009; "1000 Beromda Konstverk," 2007; "1000 Genialnich Obrazu," 2007; "Faszination des Opiums in Geschichte und Kunst, Die," Parkstone International, 2004; "Who's Who in the East".

FRANCHISES AND BUSINESS OPPORTUNITIES

2216 ■ FinderBinder/SourceBook Directories
5173 Waring Rd., Ste. 8
San Diego, CA 92120

Ph: (619)582-8500
Description: Current news media directories for specific areas. $20,000-$25,000. **No. of Franchise Units:** 20. **No. of Company-Owned Units:** 1. **Founded:** 1974. **Franchised:** 1978. **Equity Capital Needed:** $20,000-$25,000. **Franchise Fee:** $2,000. **Training:** Franchisor provides a field representative to assist franchise for a minimum of 8 hours and for further time as deemed necessary by the franchisor. Supervisory assistance is available at the discretion of the franchisor.

2217 ■ The Little Black Book For Every Busy Woman
LBB LLC
PO Box 21466
Charleston, SC 29413
Free: 866-958-8600
Fax: (843)853-0771
Description: Publish a directory for women. **No. of Franchise Units:** 7. **No. of Company-Owned Units:** 1. **Founded:** 1999.. **Franchised:** 2003. **Equity Capital Needed:** $22,000-$47,000, includes franchise fee. **Franchise Fee:** $12,000-$22,000. **Training:** Yes.

COMPUTERIZED DATABASES

2218 ■ Book Review Index Online (BRI)
10650 Toebben Dr.
Independence, KY 41051
Free: 800-354-9706
Fax: (800)487-8488
Co. E-mail: investors@cengage.com
URL: http://www.gale.cengage.com
Contact: Ronald Dunn, President
Availability: Online: Cengage Learning Inc. **Type:** Bibliographic.

2219 ■ BooksInPrint.com® Professional (BIP)
630 Central Ave.
New Providence, NJ 07974
Ph: (908)268-1090
Free: 888-269-5372
Fax: (908)665-3528
Co. E-mail: customerservice@bowker.com
URL: http://www.bowker.com
Availability: Online: ProQuest LLC - Dialog; Colorado Alliance of Research Libraries; R.R. Bowker LLC. CD-ROM: R.R. Bowker LLC. **Type:** Bibliographic.

2220 ■ LC MARC: Books All
101 Independence Ave. SE
Washington, DC 20541-4912
Ph: (202)707-6100
Fax: (202)707-1334
Co. E-mail: cdsinfo@loc.gov
URL: http://www.loc.gov/cds
Availability: Online: ProQuest LLC - Dialog; U.S. Library of Congress - Cataloging Distribution Service. **Type:** Bibliographic.

LIBRARIES

2221 ■ American Booksellers Association Information Service Center
200 White Plains Rd. Ste. 600
Tarrytown, NY 10591
Free: 800-637-0037
Fax: (914)591-2720
Co. E-mail: info@bookweb.org
URL: http://www.bookweb.org
Contact: Oren Teicher, Chief Executive Officer
Scope: Book selling and publishing. **Founded:** 1989. **Holdings:** 5000 volumes; 1000 bound periodical volumes; 100 newsletters; 11 VF drawers; 2000 publishers catalogs. **Telecommunication Services:** oren@bookweb.org.

2222 ■ Cleveland Public Library - Literature Department
Main Bldg., 2nd Fl.
325 Superior Ave.
Cleveland, OH 44114-1271

Ph: (216)623-2881
Co. E-mail: literature@cpl.org
URL: http://www.cpl.org/thelibrary/subjectscollections/literature.aspx
Contact: Amy Dawson, Manager
Scope: Fiction, drama and theater, film, radio, television, poetry, essays, humor, oratory and public speaking, craft of writing, literary criticism and biography, classical Greek and Latin, linguistics, journalism, book trade, printing, publishing, Library and information science. **Services:** Department open to the public. **Founded:** 1869. **Holdings:** 500,000 volumes; 11,368 bound periodical volumes; 23,000 theater programs and playbills; 16,000 titles of microform editions of plays and miscellanea; 190 vertical files. **Subscriptions:** 825 journals and other serials.

2223 ■ Free Library of Philadelphia - Social Science & History Department
1901 Vine St.
Philadelphia, PA 19103
Ph: (215)686-5396
Fax: (215)563-3628
URL: http://www.freelibrary.org
Contact: Jim DeWalt, Director
Scope: History, biography, social sciences, law, travels and geography, archeology, anthropology, sports and games. **Services:** Interlibrary loan. **Founded:** 1953. **Holdings:** 228,000 volumes; 53,900 pamphlets; 35 VF drawers of clippings. **Subscriptions:** 610 journals and other serials.

2224 ■ Grolier Club of New York Library
47 E. 60th St.
New York, NY 10022
Ph: (212)838-6690
Fax: (212)838-2445
Co. E-mail: ejh@grolierclub.org
URL: http://www.grolierclub.org
Contact: Eric Holzenberg, Director
Scope: Bibliography, history of printing, book-collecting, bookselling, arts of the book. **Services:** Library open to the public with restrictions. **Founded:** 1884. **Holdings:** 100,000 volumes; 5000 prints and portraits; bookplates. **Subscriptions:** 100 journals and other serials. **Telecommunication Services:** fpena@grolierclub.org; mconstantinou@grolierclub.org.

2225 ■ Hanley-Wood, LLC Library
426 S. Westgate St.
Addison, IL 60101-4546
Ph: (630)543-0870
Fax: (630)543-3112
URL: http://www.hanleywood.com
Scope: Concrete, cement, masonry, construction, home building. **Services:** Interlibrary loan; copying. **Founded:** 1971. **Holdings:** 3000 books; 120 bound periodical volumes. **Subscriptions:** 100 journals and other serials.

2226 ■ Houghton Mifflin Company - School Division Research Center
222 Berkeley St.
Boston, MA 02116
Ph: (617)351-5275
Fax: (617)351-3546
Co. E-mail: april-baglole@hmco.com
URL: http://www.hmco.com
Contact: April Baglole, Librarian
Scope: Publishing, education, textbooks. **Services:** Interlibrary loan; research. **Founded:** 1966. **Holdings:** 8000 books. **Subscriptions:** 15 journals and other serials.

2227 ■ The McGraw-Hill Companies, Inc. - Business Information Center
1221 Ave. of the Americas, 48th Fl.
New York, NY 10020
Ph: (212)512-4001
Fax: (212)512-4646
Co. E-mail: bic_bic@mcgraw-hill.com
Contact: Susan Gormley, Manager
Scope: Finance, education, communications, publishing. **Services:** Library not open to the public. **Founded:** 1925. **Holdings:** 800 volumes; archives. **Subscriptions:** 42 journals and other serials.

2228 ■ Omohundro Institute of Early American History and Culture - Kellock Library
College of William and Mary
400 Landrum Dr.
Williamsburg, VA 23187-8781
Ph: (757)221-1114
Fax: (757)221-1047
Co. E-mail: azimmerli@wm.edu
URL: http://oieahc.wm.edu
Contact: Adam Zimmerli, Archivist Librarian
Scope: Early American history, book publishing. **Services:** Interlibrary loan; library open to outside users with permission of director. **Founded:** 1966. **Holdings:** 8650 books; 942 bound periodical volumes; 2000 reels of microfilm. **Subscriptions:** 54 journals and other serials.

2229 ■ Reed Business Information - Frederic G. Melcher Library
360 Park Ave., S.
New York, NY 11010
Ph: (646)746-6845
Fax: (646)746-6689
Co. E-mail: meredith.king@reedbusiness.com
URL: http://www.reedbusiness.co.uk/rb2_home/rb2_home.htm
Contact: Gary Ink, Librarian
Scope: Book industries and trade, Library science. **Services:** Library not open to the public. **Founded:** 1963. **Holdings:** 4000 books; 700 bound periodical volumes; 130 VF drawers. **Subscriptions:** 200 journals and other serials.

2230 ■ Science Associates/International, Inc. Library
6 Hastings Rd.
Marlboro, NJ 07746-1313
Ph: (908)536-7673
Free: 800-721-1080
Fax: (908)536-7673
Contact: Roxy Bauer, Librarian
Scope: Information science, library science, documentation, publishing, computer science. **Services:** Library not open to the public. **Founded:** 1965. **Holdings:** 2000 books; 750 library and information science reports; 100 newsletters. **Subscriptions:** 100 journals and other serials.

2231 ■ Silver Burdett & Ginn - Editorial Library
299 Jefferson Rd.
Parsippany, NJ 07054
Ph: (973)739-8000
Fax: (973)898-0114
Scope: General education, publishing, market research. **Services:** Library not open to the public. **Holdings:** 10,000 books. **Subscriptions:** 150 journals and other serials.

2232 ■ Simmons College - Graduate School of Library and Information Science Library
300 The Fenway
Boston, MA 02115
Ph: (617)521-2824
Fax: (617)521-3192
Co. E-mail: gslisadm@simmons.edu
URL: http://www.simmons.edu/gslis
Contact: Linda H. Watkins, Librarian
Scope: Library and information science, publishing, media resources and study, Library management. **Services:** Interlibrary loan; copying; Library open to the public for reference use only by appointment. **Founded:** 1902. **Holdings:** 24,258 books; 7537 bound periodical volumes; 4935 microfiche; 911 reels of microfilm; 34 VF drawers; School of Library Science doctoral field studies; information files on 100 library-related subjects; doctoral dissertations on microfilm. **Subscriptions:** 560 journals and other serials. **Telecommunication Services:** watkins@simmons.edu.

2233 ■ John Wiley and Sons Information Center
111 River St.
Hoboken, NJ 07030
Ph: (201)748-6000
Free: 800-225-5945
Fax: (201)748-6088
Co. E-mail: info@wiley.com
URL: http://as.wiley.com/WileyCDA/Section/index.html
Scope: Publishing, business and management, higher education. **Services:** Center not open to the public. **Founded:** 1982. **Holdings:** 200 books; 9 VF drawers of clippings. **Subscriptions:** 25 journals and other serials.

RESEARCH CENTERS

2234 ■ Simon Fraser University - Canadian Centre for Studies in Publishing (CCSP)
Harbor Ctr.
515 W Hastings St.
Vancouver, BC, Canada V6B 5K3
Ph: (778)782-5242
Fax: (778)782-5239
Co. E-mail: lorimer@sfu.ca
URL: http://tkbr.ccsp.sfu.ca
Contact: Prof. Rowland Lorimer, Director
Services: Consulting: for specialized professional development. **Founded:** 1987. **Publications:** *CCSP Articles* (Occasionally); *CCSP Books*; *Canadian Journal of Communication* (Quarterly); *CCSP Reports* (Occasionally); *Scholarly and Research Communication* (3/year). **Educational Activities:** Master of Publishing Program (Annual), attended by graduate students from Canada and around the world; CCSP Seminars and conferences; Summer Publishing Workshops; Writing and Publishing Program (Occasionally), for specialized professional development. **Telecommunication Services:** ccsp-info@sfu.ca.

ASSOCIATIONS AND OTHER ORGANIZATIONS

2235 ■ Binders' Guild (BG)
2925 Powell St.
Eugene, OR 97405
Ph: (541)485-6527
Co. E-mail: editor@bindersguild.org
URL: http://www.bindersguild.org
Description: Amateur and professional hand book-binders and other interested persons. Facilitates exchange of information among members concerning techniques and sources of supplies. **Founded:** 1977.

2236 ■ Binding Industries Association International (BIA)
200 Deer Run Rd.
Sewickley, PA 15143
Ph: (412)741-6860
Free: 800-9104283
Fax: (412)741-2311
Co. E-mail: printing@printing.org
URL: http://www.gain.net
Contact: Justin Goldstein, Manager
Description: Represents trade binders and loose-leaf manufacturers united to conduct seminars, hold conventions, and formulate and maintain standards. **Founded:** 1955. **Publications:** *Binders Bulletin* (Monthly). **Educational Activities:** Binding Industries Association International Annual Convention (Annual). **Awards:** Product of Excellence (Annual).

2237 ■ Book Manufacturers' Institute (BMI)
Two Armand Beach Dr., Ste. 1B
Palm Coast, FL 32137-2612
Ph: (386)986-4552
Fax: (386)986-4553
Co. E-mail: info@bmibook.com
URL: http://www.bmibook.com
Contact: Jac B. Garner, Chairman
Description: Represents the trade association for manufacturers of books. **Founded:** 1920. **Awards:** Distinguished Master Bookman Award (Annual); Gutenberg Award (Annual); Signature Award (Annual).

2238 ■ Center for Book Arts (CBA)
28 W 27th St., 3rd Fl.
New York, NY 10001
Ph: (212)481-0295
Fax: (212)481-9853
Co. E-mail: info@centerforbookarts.org
URL: http://www.centerforbookarts.org
Contact: Alexander Campos, Executive Director
Description: Dedicated to the preservation of the traditional crafts of bookmaking, as well as encouraging contemporary interpretations of the book as an art object. Organizes exhibitions related to the art of the book and offers an extensive selection of educational courses, workshops and seminars in traditional and contemporary bookbinding, letterpress printing, fine press publishing, and other associated arts. Other programs include Artist-in-Residence, Broadsides Reading Series, and the Poetry Chapbook Competition. Supported by local businesses, various foundations including the Lenrow Fund, the Milton and Sally Avery Arts Foundation, the NY State Council on the Arts, the National Endowment for the Arts, and its members. **Founded:** 1974. **Awards:** Poetry Chapbook Competition, Artist Residency Program (Annual).

2239 ■ Guild of Book Workers Inc. (GBW)
521 5th Ave.
New York, NY 10175-0038
Ph: (212)757-6454
Co. E-mail: secretary@guildofbookworkers.org
URL: http://www.guildofbookworkers.org
Contact: Andrew Huot, President
E-mail: vicepresident@guildofbookworkers.allmail.net
Description: Amateur and professional workers in the handbook crafts such as bookbinding, calligraphy, illuminating, fine presswork, and decorative paper-making. Works to improve standards by the sponsorship of exhibitions, field trips, lectures, workshops, and discussion groups. **Scope:** bookcrafts. **Founded:** 1906. **Subscriptions:** 1500 books video recordings. **Publications:** *Guild of Book Workers Newsletter; Guild of Book Workers--Membership Directory* (Annual); *Guild of Book Workers--Newsletter* (Bimonthly); *Supply Directory; Guild of Book Workers--Membership Directory* (Annual); *Guild of Book Workers--Membership List; Directory of Study Opportunities List* (Irregular); *Guild of Book Workers Membership List; Directory of Study Opportunities; Guild of Book Workers--Supplies and Services Directory* (Irregular); *Guild of Book Workers Newsletter; Directory of Study Opportunities.*

2240 ■ Library Binding Institute (LBI)
4440 PGA Blvd., Ste. 600
Palm Beach Gardens, FL 33410
Ph: (561)745-6821
Fax: (561)472-8401
Co. E-mail: dnolan@lbibinders.org
URL: http://www.lbibinders.org
Contact: Jack Tolbert, President
Description: Firms and certified library binders doing library binding in accordance with LBI Standard for Library Binding, including rebinding of worn volumes, prebinding of new volumes, initial hardcover binding of periodicals, and other binding principally for libraries and schools; associate members are suppliers and manufacturers of library binding materials and equipment. Certifies qualified binding companies after examination of work and investigation of experience, insurance for protection of customers' property, and examination of bank and library references. Conducts research on materials used in library binding. Conducts statistical surveys of unit production, operating statement data, and wage data. **Founded:** 1935. **Educational Activities:** Library Binding Institute Conference (Annual).

DIRECTORIES OF EDUCATIONAL PROGRAMS

2241 ■ Directory of Private Accredited Career Schools and Colleges of Technology
Pub: Accrediting Commission of Career Schools and Colleges of Technology
Contact: Michale S. McComis, Executive Director
Released: On web page. **Price:** Free. **Description:** Covers 3900 accredited post-secondary programs that provide training programs in business, trade, and technical fields, including various small business endeavors. Entries offer school name, address, phone, description of courses, job placement assistance, and requirements for admission. Arrangement is alphabetical.

REFERENCE WORKS

2242 ■ Guild of Book Workers--Supplies and Services Directory
Pub: Guild of Book Workers Inc.
Contact: Andrew Huot, President
E-mail: vicepresident@guildofbookworkers.allmail.net
URL(s): www.guildofbookworkers.org/resources/supply/search.php. **Ed:** Bernadette G. Callery, Susan B. Martin. **Released:** Irregular; Latest edition November 2008. **Price:** $15, Individuals 2001 issue. **Covers:** More than 250 manufacturers and suppliers of products used in bookbinding, calligraphy, and repair and conservation of documents and books; coverage includes Canada. **Entries include:** Name of firm, address, phone, products or services, minimum order requirements, shipping restrictions, whether catalog or samples are available. **Arrangement:** Geographical, then by product or service. **Indexes:** Alphabetical.

2243 ■ Study Opportunities List
Pub: Guild of Book Workers Inc.
Contact: Andrew Huot, President
E-mail: vicepresident@guildofbookworkers.allmail.net
URL(s): www.guildofbookworkers.org/resources/studyopp.php. **Released:** Irregular; Latest edition 2011. **Price:** $15, Individuals 1995 issue. **Covers:** About 130 teachers, schools, and centers offering hand bookbinding and calligraphic services; international coverage. **Entries include:** Craftsperson's name, address, special interests, source of expertise, whether apprentices are desired; also includes (for schools and other centers) names and addresses of instructors and courses offered. **Arrangement:** Geographical.

STATISTICAL SOURCES

2244 ■ Book Industry Trends
Pub: Book Industry Study Group
Contact: Scott Lubeck, Executive Director
Ed: Compiled by Statistical Service Center staff. **Released:** 2009. **Price:** $875.00 (paper).

TRADE PERIODICALS

2245 ■ Guild of Book Workers Newsletter
Pub: Guild of Book Workers Inc.
Contact: Andrew Huot, President
E-mail: vicepresident@guildofbookworkers.allmail.net
Ed: Margaret Johnson, Editor. **Released:** Bimonthly, Every 2 months. **Price:** Included in membership. **Description:** Covers issues in book arts, binding, book conservation, calligraphy, and printing. Recurring features include letters to the editor, interviews, news

of research, a calendar of events, reports of meetings, news of educational opportunities, job listings, book reviews, and notices of publications available.

2246 ■ MCBA Newsletter
Pub: Minnesota Center for Book Arts
Ed: Lori Brink, Editor. **Released:** 3/year (always March, July, and December). **Price:** $40, Included in membership; $15, nonmembers. **Description:** Focuses on the field of book arts, including letterpress printing, bookbinding, and papermaking. Reviews current and future Center exhibitions and announces classes available at the Center. Recurring features include book reviews and news of educational opportunities.

VIDEOCASSETTES/ AUDIOCASSETTES

2247 ■ Papermaking & Bookbinding
Crystal Productions
1812 Johns Dr.
Box 2159
Glenview, IL 60025-6519
Ph: (847)657-8144
Free: 800-255-8629
Fax: (847)657-8149
Co. E-mail: custserv@crystalproductions.com
URL: http://www.crystalproductions.com
Released: 1991. **Price:** $89.50. **Description:** Desktop publishing the old-fashioned way. Learn how to make paper using ordinary household materials. The making of both hard and soft covers is also covered. A teacher's guide is included. **Availability:** VHS.

CONSULTANTS

2248 ■ Davis Consultants Library—W. F. Davis Consultants
179 Voelbel Rd.
Hightstown, NJ 08520-2807
Ph: (609)448-0161
Contact: William F. Davis, Owner
Scope: Offers counsel to corporations on planning, manufacturing, product development, product conception, special purpose machinery development, production methodology, profit enhancement, and manufacturing systems. Clients include paper, printing, publication, graphic arts machinery, disposable products, textile, consumer products, machine tool and instrumentation industries. **Founded:** 1953.

LIBRARIES

2249 ■ Book Club of California - Albert Sperisen Library
312 Sutter St., Ste. 510
San Francisco, CA 94108-4320
Ph: (415)781-7532
Free: 800-869-7656
Fax: (415)781-7537
Co. E-mail: bland@bccbooks.org
URL: http://www.bccbooks.org
Contact: Barbara Jane Land, Librarian
Scope: Printing, bookbinding, typography, books, papermaking, private presses, history of printing and

printing methods; California and Western history. **Services:** Library open to the public (on written application). **Founded:** 1912. **Holdings:** 8300 volumes; ephemera from private presses. **Subscriptions:** 10 journals and other serials. **Telecommunication Services:** library@bccbooks.org.

2250 ■ Canadian Bookbinders & Book Artists Guild Library
80 Ward St., Ste. 207
Toronto, ON, Canada M6H 4A6
Ph: (416)581-1071
Co. E-mail: cbbag@cbbag.ca
URL: http://www.cbbag.ca
Contact: Mary McIntyre, President
Scope: Bookbinding, fine printing, book arts. **Services:** Copying; library open to the public by appointment. **Founded:** 1985. **Holdings:** Figures not available. **Subscriptions:** 500 journals and other serials.

2251 ■ Grolier Club of New York Library
47 E. 60th St.
New York, NY 10022
Ph: (212)838-6690
Fax: (212)838-2445
Co. E-mail: ejh@grolierclub.org
URL: http://www.grolierclub.org
Contact: Eric Holzenberg, Director
Scope: Bibliography, history of printing, book-collecting, bookselling, arts of the book. **Services:** Library open to the public with restrictions. **Founded:** 1884. **Holdings:** 100,000 volumes; 5000 prints and portraits; bookplates. **Subscriptions:** 100 journals and other serials. **Telecommunication Services:** fpena@grolierclub.org; mconstantinou@grolierclub.org.

2252 ■ Guild of Book Workers Library
Emory University Libraries
540 Asbury Circle
Atlanta, GA 30322
Ph: (404)727-0307
Co. E-mail: ann.frellsen@emory.edu
URL: http://www.lib.uiowa.edu/spec-coll/gbw/gbw1.html
Contact: Nancy Baker, Librarian
URL(s): www.lib.uiowa.edu/news/archives/newsletter/24-2.pdf. **Scope:** Bookbinding, history of the book, calligraphy, printing, paper making. **Services:** Library open to members only. **Founded:** 1958. **Holdings:** 700 books; videotapes; DVDs. **Telecommunication Services:** sid-huttner@uiowa.edu.

2253 ■ Mills College - F.W. Olin Library - Special Collections
5000 MacArthur Blvd.
Oakland, CA 94613
Ph: (510)430-2385
Fax: (510)430-2278
Co. E-mail: jbraun@mills.edu
URL: http://www.mills.edu/academics/library/index.php
Contact: Janice Braun, Librarian, Special Collections
Scope: English and American literature, printing, dance, Shakespeare, women's history, bookbinding, book arts. **Services:** Copying; collections open to the public for reference use only. **Founded:** 1852. **Hold-

ings:** 12,000 books; 10,000 manuscripts. **Subscriptions:** 12 journals and other serials. **Telecommunication Services:** library@mills.edu.

2254 ■ Newark Public Library - Special Collections Division
5 Washington St.
Newark, NJ 07101-0630
Ph: (973)733-7745
Fax: (973)733-5648
Co. E-mail: wgrey@npl.org
URL: http://www.npl.org/Pages/Collections/special-collections1.html
Contact: William Grey, Director
Scope: Graphic arts, commercial art and design, original fine prints, rare books, fine art, artist's book movement, original lithographs, etchings, serigraphs and mixed media, book illustration, and the history of fine printing. **Services:** Division open to the public by appointment. **Founded:** 1889. **Holdings:** 10,000 books; about 100 lin. ft. of vertical files on artists in collections, printing history, and art and music topics. **Subscriptions:** 15 journals and other serials. **Telecommunication Services:** reference@npl.org; specialcollections@npl.org.

2255 ■ Rochester Institute of Technology - Melbert B. Cary, Jr. Graphic Arts Collection
Wallace Memorial Library
90 Lomb Memorial Dr.
Rochester, NY 14623-5604
Ph: (585)475-2408
Fax: (585)475-6900
Co. E-mail: ahfwml@rit.edu
URL: http://library.rit.edu/cary
Contact: Steven K. Galbraith, Curator
Scope: Printing history, type specimens, typography, book arts, press books, calligraphy, papermaking, graphic arts, bookbinding. **Services:** Copying (limited); collection open to the public. **Founded:** 1969. **Holdings:** 50,000 books; 20 VF drawers of clippings; ephemera; pamphlets; 50 boxes of posters, broadsides, drawings; 400 boxes of correspondence and manuscript material. **Subscriptions:** 20 journals and other serials. **Telecommunication Services:** skgtwc@rit.edu; circwml@rit.edu.

2256 ■ Yale University - Arts Library - Special Collections
Robert B. Haas Family Arts Library, Lower Level
180 York St.
New Haven, CT 06520-8318
Ph: (203)432-4439
Fax: (203)432-0549
Co. E-mail: jae.rossman@yale.edu
URL: http://www.library.yale.edu/arts/specialcollections
Contact: Jae Jennifer Rossman, Assistant Director
Scope: Typography, book illustration and design, bookbinding, papermaking, bookplates, private presses, artists' books, conceptual books, and fine printing. **Services:** Collection open to the public. **Founded:** 1967. **Holdings:** 20,000 books; prints and broadsides; type specimens; archive of student printing, including masters' theses from School of Graphic Design and School of Photography at Yale; 1 million bookplates; Japanese prints; stage and costume designs. **Subscriptions:** 20 journals and other serials.

ASSOCIATIONS AND OTHER ORGANIZATIONS

2257 ■ **Canadian Institute of Chartered Accountants (CICA)—L'Institut Canadien des comptables agrees - Institut Canadien des Comptables Agrees**
277 Wellington St. W
Toronto, ON, Canada M5V 3H2
Ph: (416)977-3222
Free: 800-268-3793
Fax: (416)977-8585
Co. E-mail: member.services@cica.ca
URL: http://www.cica.ca
Contact: Kevin J. Dancey, President
E-mail: kevin.dancey@cica.ca
Description: Sets national accounting, auditing, and financial reporting standards. Maintains an active professional development program for its members. Represents the profession's viewpoint on federal legislation issues and matters of national concern. Confers with other national organizations to achieve worldwide harmonization of accounting and auditing standards. **Founded:** 1902. **Publications:** *Directory of Canadian Chartered Accountants* (Periodic); *Directory of Canadian Chartered Accountants* (Periodic); *Directory of Canadian Chartered Accountants* (Biennial); *CA Magazine: For Canada's Chartered Accountants.* **Telecommunication Services:** jan.burns@cica.ca.

2258 ■ **Canadian Institute of Quantity Surveyors (CIQS)—Institut Canadien des Economistes en Construction**
90 Nolan Ct., Unit 19
Markham, ON, Canada L3R 4L9
Ph: (905)477-0008
Free: 866-345-1168
Fax: (905)477-6774
Co. E-mail: info@ciqs.org
URL: http://www.ciqs.org
Contact: Roy Lewis, President
Description: Quantity surveyors and construction estimators. Establishes and maintains standards for certification and provides through advice to members relating to construction costs, management and administration of construction projects. Conducts continuing professional development programs for members. **Founded:** 1959. **Publications:** *The Construction Economist* (Quarterly). **Awards:** Buster Vermeulen Memorial Award (Annual); Frank Helyar Memorial Award (Annual); Buster Vermeulen Memorial Award; Frank Helyar Memorial Award. **Telecommunication Services:** president@ciqs.org.

2259 ■ *The Construction Economist*
90 Nolan Ct., Unit 19
Markham, ON, Canada L3R 4L9
Ph: (905)477-0008
Free: 866-345-1168
Fax: (905)477-6774
Co. E-mail: info@ciqs.org
URL: http://www.ciqs.org
Contact: Roy Lewis, President
Released: Quarterly

2260 ■ *Directory of Canadian Chartered Accountants*
277 Wellington St. W
Toronto, ON, Canada M5V 3H2
Ph: (416)977-3222
Free: 800-268-3793
Fax: (416)977-8585
Co. E-mail: member.services@cica.ca
URL: http://www.cica.ca
Contact: Kevin J. Dancey, President
E-mail: kevin.dancey@cica.ca
Released: Periodic

2261 ■ *Professional Accountant*
250 Consumers Rd., Ste. 1007
Toronto, ON, Canada M2J 4V6
Ph: (416)350-8145
Free: 877-515-4447
Fax: (416)350-8146
Co. E-mail: president@professionalaccountant.org
URL: http://www.professionalaccountant.org
Contact: Mr. John Singer, Vice President
Released: Quarterly

2262 ■ **Society of Professional Accountants of Canada (SPAC)—La societe des comptables professionnels du Canada**
250 Consumers Rd., Ste. 1007
Toronto, ON, Canada M2J 4V6
Ph: (416)350-8145
Free: 877-515-4447
Fax: (416)350-8146
Co. E-mail: president@professionalaccountant.org
URL: http://www.professionalaccountant.org
Contact: Mr. John Singer, Vice President
Description: Professional accountants and individuals working to pass qualifying accountancy examinations. Promotes ongoing professional education among accountants; encourages students to enter the accounting field; works to advance the profession of accounting. Gathers and disseminates information on accounting; sponsors educational programs; conducts professional accountancy qualifying examinations. **Founded:** 1978. **Publications:** *Professional Accountant* (Quarterly).

REFERENCE WORKS

2263 ■ *"2011 Tax Information of Interest"* in *Business Owner (Vol. 35, November-December 2011, No. 6, pp. 10)*
Pub: DL Perkins Company
Description: Compilation of 2011 tax information to help small business take advantage of all tax incentives.

2264 ■ *"Accrual vs. Cash Accounting, Explained"* in *Business Owner (Vol. 35, July-August 2011, No. 4, pp. 13)*
Pub: DL Perkins Company
Description: Cash method versus accrual accounting methods are examined, using hypothetical situations.

2265 ■ *"Adler Blanchard & Freeman Reports New SmartKeeper Bookkeeping Service"* in *Professional Services Close-Up (March 24, 2011)*
Pub: Close-Up Media
Description: Profile of Adler Blanchard & Freeman (AB&F) accountants and business advisors. The firm has expanded its client offerings to include their new SmartKeeper Business and Personal Bookkeeping Service for small to mid-sized companies and individuals.

2266 ■ *"Attend To Your Corporate Housekeeping"* in *Women Entrepreneur (December 4, 2008)*
Pub: Entrepreneur Media Inc.
Ed: Nina Kaufman. **Description:** Business owners can lose all the benefits and privileges of the corporate form if they do not follow proper corporate formalities such as holding an annual meeting, electing officers and directors and adopting or passing corporate resolutions. Creditors are able to take from one's personal assets if such formalities have not been followed.

2267 ■ *"Battling Back from Betrayal"* in *Harvard Business Review (Vol. 88, December 2010, No. 12, pp. 130)*
Pub: Harvard Business School Publishing
Ed: Daniel McGinn. **Description:** Stephen Greer's scrap metal firm, Hartwell Pacific, lost several million dollars due to a lack of efficient and appropriate inventory audits, accounting procedures, and new-hire reference checks for his foreign operations. Greer believes that balancing growth with control is a key component of success.

2268 ■ *Beat the Taxman: Easy Ways to Tax Save in Your Small Business*
Pub: John Wiley & Sons, Incorporated
Ed: Stephen Thompson. **Released:** May 2008. **Price:** $26.95. **Description:** Concise tax planner to help entrepreneurs take advantage of current tax laws.

2269 ■ *"A Bigger Deal"* in *Crain's Cleveland Business (Vol. 28, November 12, 2007, No. 45, pp. 1)*
Pub: Crain Communications, Inc.
Ed: Shawn A. Turner. **Description:** In an attempt to boost its revenue CBiz Inc., a provider of accounting and business services, is looking to balance its acquisitions of smaller companies with larger ones as part of its overall growth strategy.

2270 ■ *"Bookkeeping Service Opens First Sacramento Franchise"* in *Sacramento Bee (April 13, 2011)*
Pub: Sacramento Bee
Ed: Mark Glover. **Description:** Franchise bookkeeping service called BookKeeping Express opened its new office in Roseville, California; its first shop in the area.

2271 ■ *"Cautions On Loans With Your Business"* in *Business Owner (Vol. 35,*

July-August 2011, No. 4, pp. 5)
Pub: DL Perkins Company
Description: Caution must be used when borrowing from or lending to any small business. Tax guidelines for the borrowing and lending practice are also included.

2272 ■ *"Changing the Rules of the Accounting Game" in Canadian Business (Vol. 81, December 8, 2008, No. 21, pp. 19)*
Pub: Rogers Media Ltd.
Ed: Al Rosen. **Description:** Interference from world politicians in developing accounting standards is believed to have resulted in untested rules that are inferior to current standards. European lawmakers have recently asked to change International Financial Reporting Standards.

2273 ■ *"Channeling for Growth" in The Business Journal-Serving Greater Tampa Bay (Vol. 28, July 11, 2008, No. 29, pp. 1)*
Pub: American City Business Journals, Inc.
Ed: Margie Manning. **Description:** HSN Inc., one of the largest employers in Tampa Bay, Florida, is expected to spend an additional $9.7 million annually as it plans to hire more accounting, internal audit, legal, treasury and tax personnel after its spin-off to a public company. Details on the company's sales growth are provided.

2274 ■ *"Convergence Collaboration: Revising Revenue Recognition" in Management Accounting Quarterly (Vol. 12, Spring 2011, No. 3, pp. 18)*
Pub: Management Accounting Quarterly
Ed: Jack T. Ciesielski, Thomas R. Weirich. **Description:** While revenue recognition is critical, regulations have been developed on an ad hoc basis until now. The joint FASB/IASB proposed accounting standard on revenue recognition is a meaningful convergence of standards that will require a major adjustment for financial statement preparers. The proposal is a radical departure from the way revenue has been recognized by the U.S. GAAP. For industries such as consulting, engineering, construction, and technology, it could dramatically change revenue recognition, impacting the top line. The new proposed standard, its potential impact, and the critical role that contracts play is examined thoroughly.

2275 ■ *Deduct It!: Lower Your Small Business Taxes*
Pub: NOLO
Ed: Stephen Fishman. **Released:** November 2009. **Price:** $34.99. **Description:** Ways to make the most of tax deductions for any small business are covered. The book is organized into categories featuring common deductions, start-up expenses, health deductions, entertainment, travel, inventory, equipment and more. Current tax laws and numbers for 2008 are included.

2276 ■ *"DHS Finalizes Rules Allowing Electronic I-9s" in HR Specialist (Vol. 8, September 2010, No. 9, pp. 5)*
Pub: Capitol Information Group Inc.
Description: U.S. Department of Homeland Security issued regulations that give employers more flexibility to electronically sing and store I-9 employee verification forms.

2277 ■ *Directory of Global Professional Accounting and Business Certifications*
Pub: John Wiley & Sons, Incorporated
Ed: Lal Balkaran. **Released:** February 9, 2007. **Price:** $35.00. **Description:** Resource for international accounting, auditing, and business professions.

2278 ■ *"Do Fair Value Adjustments Influence Dividend Policy?" in Accounting and Business Research (Vol. 41, Spring 2011, No. 2, pp. 51)*
Pub: American Institute of Certified Public Accountants
Contact: Barry C. Melancon, President
E-mail: bmelancon@aicpa.org
Ed: Igor Goncharov, Sander van Triest. **Description:** The impact of positive fair value adjustments on corporate distributions is examined using a Russian

setting that requires disclosure of unrealized fair value adjustments in income. It was found that there is no rise in dividends due to positive fair value adjustments and that on the contrary, a negative relationship exists between adjustments and dividend changes.

2279 ■ *"Economic Crisis and Accounting Evolution" in Accounting and Business Research (Vol. 41, Summer 2011, No. 3, pp. 2159)*
Pub: American Institute of Certified Public Accountants
Contact: Barry C. Melancon, President
E-mail: bmelancon@aicpa.org
Ed: Gregory Waymire, Sudipta Basu. **Description:** Financial reporting changes at the face of economic crises are studied using a punctuated equilibrium evolution. Findings show that financial reporting has a minor impact but may amplify economic crises. Attempts to enhance accounting amid economic crises may not be as beneficial as planned.

2280 ■ *"Economic Crisis and Accounting Evolution" in Accounting and Business Research (Vol. 41, Summer 2011, No. 3, pp. 2159)*
Pub: Routledge
Ed: Gregory Waymire, Sudipta Basu. **Description:** Financial reporting changes at the face of economic crises are studied using a punctuated equilibrium evolution. Findings show that financial reporting has a minor impact but may amplify economic crises. Attempts to enhance accounting and economic crises may not be as beneficial as planned.

2281 ■ *Electronic Commerce: Technical, Business, and Legal Issues*
Pub: Prentice Hall PTR
Ed: Oktay Dogramaci; Aryya Gangopadhyay; Yelena Yesha; Nabil R. Adam. **Released:** August 1998. **Description:** Provides insight into the goals of using the Internet to grow a business in the areas of networking and telecommunication, security, and storage and retrieval; business areas such as marketing, procurement and purchasing, billing and payment, and supply chain management; and legal aspects such as privacy, intellectual property, taxation, contractual and legal settlements.

2282 ■ *"Finally, Justice" in Canadian Business (Vol. 82, April 27, 2009, No. 7, pp. 12)*
Pub: Rogers Media
Ed: John Gray. **Description:** Former investment adviser Alex Winch feels that he was vindicated with the Canadian Court's ruling that Livent Inc. founders Garth Drabinsky and Myron Gottlieb were guilty of fraud. Drabinsky filed a libel case on Winch over Winch's letter that complained over Livent's accounting procedures. Winch also criticized the inconsistent accounting during Drabinsky's term as chief executive of another firm.

2283 ■ *Finance & Accounting: How to Keep Your Books and Manage Your Finances with an MBA, a CPA, or a Ph.D*
Pub: Adams Media Corporation
Ed: Suzanne Caplan. **Price:** $19.95.

2284 ■ *"Furniture Making May Come Back--Literally" in Business North Carolina (Vol. 28, March 2008, No. 3, pp. 32)*
Pub: Business North Carolina
Description: Due to the weak U.S. dollar and the fact that lumber processors never left the country, foreign furniture manufacturers are becoming interested in moving manufacturing plants to the U.S.

2285 ■ *"Give Until It Works" in Hispanic Business (Vol. 30, March 2008, No. 3, pp. 26)*
Pub: Hispanic Business
Ed: Rick Munarriz. **Description:** Donating to qualified charities and non-profit organizations for maximizing tax advantage to be availed on the income tax bill is examined. The amount that can be deducted from the total taxable amount is usually less then the actual amount donated and must be made during that calendar year.

2286 ■ *"Handle With Care" in Hawaii Business (Vol. 53, October 2007, No. 5, pp. 66)*
Pub: Hawaii Business Publishing
Ed: Kenneth Sheffield. **Description:** Discusses a fiduciary, who may be a board member, business owner, or a trustee, and is someone who supervises and manages the affairs and the resources of a principal. Fiduciary duties, which include accounting, cost review and risk management, must be served with the benefit of the principal as the priority. Ways of breaching fiduciary duties and how to avoid them are discussed.

2287 ■ *"The Hidden Tax" in Canadian Business (Vol. 81, April 14, 2008, No. 6, pp. 28)*
Pub: Rogers Media
Ed: Al Rosen. **Description:** Accounting fraud could take out a sizable sum from one's retirement fund when computed over a long period of time. The much bigger tax on savings is the collective impact of the smaller losses that do not attract the attention they deserve. Ensuring that investors are not unnecessarily taxed 2 percent of their total investments every year outweighs the benefit of a 2 percent reduction in personal tax rates.

2288 ■ *How to Start an Internet Sales Business*
Pub: Lulu.com
Ed: Dan Davis. **Released:** August 2005. **Price:** $19.95. **Description:** Small business guide for launching an Internet sales company. Topics include business structure, licenses, and taxes.

2289 ■ *"How To: Manage Your Cash Better" in Inc. (Volume 32, December 2010, No. 10, pp. 69)*
Pub: Inc. Magazine
Description: A monthly guide to policies, procedures and practices for managing cash for a small business.

2290 ■ *"IFRS Monopoly: the Pied Piper of Financial Reporting" in Accounting and Business Research (Vol. 41, Summer 2011, No. 3, pp. 291)*
Pub: American Institute of Certified Public Accountants
Contact: Barry C. Melancon, President
E-mail: bmelancon@aicpa.org
Ed: Shyam Sunder. **Description:** The disadvantages of granting monopoly to the international financial reporting standards (IFRS) are examined. Results indicate that an IFRS monopoly removes the chances for comparing alternative practices and learning from them. An IFRS monopoly also eliminates customization of financial reporting to fit local differences in governance, business, economic, and legal conditions.

2291 ■ *"IRS Announces New Standards for Tax Preparers" in Bellingham Business Journal (Vol. February 2010, pp. 9)*
Pub: Sound Publishing Inc.
Ed: Isaac Bonnell. **Description:** A new oversight plan was announced by the Internal Revenue Services (IRS) that will require tax professionals to pass a competency test and register with the government in order to ensure greater accountability in the industry.

2292 ■ *"It's Time to Take Full Responsibility" in Harvard Business Review (Vol. 88, October 2010, No. 10, pp. 42)*
Pub: Harvard Business School Publishing
Ed: Rosabeth Moss Kanter. **Description:** A case for corporate responsibility is cited, focusing on long-term impact and the effects of public accountability.

2293 ■ *"Kaboom!" in Canadian Business (Vol. 81, November 10, 2008, No. 19, pp. 18)*
Pub: Rogers Media Ltd.
Ed: Al Rosen, Mark Rosen. **Description:** International Financial Reporting Standards (IFRS) is a good idea in theory but was implemented in a hurry and had poor quality standards from the beginning.

2294 ■ *"Know Your Numbers" in Inc. (Volume 32, December 2010, No. 10, pp. 39)*
Pub: Inc. Magazine

Ed: Norm Brodsky. **Description:** Ways to maximize profit and minimize tax burden are presented.

2295 ■ *"Living in a 'Goldfish Bowl'" in WorkingUSA (Vol. 11, June 2008, No. 2, pp. 277)*
Pub: Blackwell Publishers Ltd.

Ed: John Lund. **Description:** Recent changes in laws, regulations and even the reporting format of labor organization annual financial reports in both the U.S. and Australia have received surprisingly little attention, yet they have significantly increased the amount of information available both to union members and the public in general, as reports in both countries are available via government Websites. While such financial reporting laws are extremely rare in European countries, with the exception of the UK and Ireland, the U.S. and Australian reporting systems have become among the most detailed in the world. After reviewing these changes in financial reporting and the availability of these reports, as well as comparing and contrasting the specific reporting requirements of each country, this paper then examines the cost-benefit impact of more detailed financial reporting.

2296 ■ *"Merger Mania: Regional Snaps Up HVS" in The Business Journal-Serving Greater Tampa Bay (Vol. 28, September 26, 2008, No. 40, pp. 1)*
Pub: American City Business Journals, Inc.

Ed: Alexis Muellner. **Description:** It was reported that Harper Van Scoik & Co. LLP has finalized a merger with Carr Riggs & Ingram LLC. The agreement, effective October 1, 2008, is a merger of HVS assets into CRI. Bill Carr, a managing partner, revealed that HVS' $5 million in revenue will take CRI from $78 million to $82 million in revenue.

2297 ■ *"My Favorite Tool for Managing Expenses" in Inc. (Volume 32, December 2010, No. 10, pp. 60)*
Pub: Inc. Magazine

Ed: J.J. McCorvey. **Description:** Web-based service called Expensify is outlined. The service allows companies to log expenses while away from the office using the service's iPhone application.

2298 ■ *"A Necessary Balancing Act: Bookkeeping" in Contractor (Vol. 56, November 2009, No. 11, pp. 22)*
Pub: Penton Media, Inc.

Ed: Al Schwartz. **Description:** Pros and cons of getting a bookkeeper or a certified public accountant for the subcontractor are discussed. A bookkeeper can help a subcontractor get new accounting software up and running while an accountant will more than likely keep after the books at regular intervals throughout the year.

2299 ■ *"New Century's Fall Has a New Culprit" in Barron's (Vol. 88, March 31, 2008, No. 13, pp. 20)*
Pub: Dow Jones & Company, Inc.

Ed: Jonathan R. Laing. **Description:** Court examiner Michael Missal reports that New Century Financial's auditor contributed to New Century's demise by its negligence in permitting improper and imprudent practices related to New Century's accounting processes. New Century's bankruptcy filing is considered the start of the subprime-mortgage crisis.

2300 ■ *"New Institutional Accounting and IFRS" in Accounting and Business Research (Vol. 41, Summer 2011, No. 3, pp. 309)*
Pub: American Institute of Certified Public Accountants

Contact: Barry C. Melancon, President

E-mail: bmelancon@aicpa.org

Ed: Peter Wysocki. **Description:** A new framework for institutional accounting research is presented. It has five fundamental components — efficient versus inefficient results, interdependencies, causation, level

of analysis, and institutional structure. The use of the framework for evaluation accounting institutions such as the international financial reporting standards is discussed.

2301 ■ *"New Institutional Accounting and IFRS" in Accounting and Business Research (Vol. 41, Summer 2011, No. 3, pp. 309)*
Pub: Routledge

Ed: Peter Wysocki. **Description:** A new framework for institutional accounting research is presented. It has five fundamental components: efficient versus inefficient results, interdependencies, causation, level of analysis, and institutional structure. The use of the framework for evaluation accounting institutions such as the international financial reports standards (IFRS) is discussed.

2302 ■ *"Paperless Bookkeeping Program" in Fleet Owner Online (February 15, 2011)*
Pub: Penton Business Media Inc.

Description: TruckTax launched its new paperless bookkeeping system to help manage bookkeeping tasks, accounting and business tax information and filings for truckers.

2303 ■ *"Privacy Concern: Are 'Group' Time Sheets Legal?" in HR Specialist (Vol. 8, September 2010, No. 9, pp. 4)*
Pub: Capitol Information Group Inc.

Description: Under the Fair Labor Standards Act (FLSA) employers are required to maintain and preserve payroll or other records, including the number of hours worked, but it does not prescribe a particular order or form in which these records must be kept.

2304 ■ *"Proposed Accounting Changes Could Complicate Tenant's Leases" in Baltimore Business Journal (Vol. 28, July 2, 2010, No. 8, pp. 1)*
Pub: Baltimore Business Journal

Ed: Daniel J. Sernovitz. **Description:** The Financial Accounting Standards Board has proposed that companies must indicate the value of real estate leases as assets and liabilities on balance sheets instead of expenses. The proposals could cause some companies to document millions of dollars in charges on their books or find difficulty in getting loans.

2305 ■ *"Prosecutors Dish Sordid AIPC Story" in The Business Journal-Serving Metropolitan Kansas City (Vol. 27, September 19, 2008, No. 1)*
Pub: American City Business Journals, Inc.

Ed: Suzanna Stagemeyer. **Description:** Prosecutors in the American Italian Pasta Co.'s accounting fraud case have revealed evidence on the schemes used by then-officers of the company to commit fraud. District attorney John Wood has dubbed the case as the largest corporate fraud lawsuit in the history of the district of Missouri. How AIPC fell from being an industry leader is also discussed.

2306 ■ *QuickBooks All-in-One Desk Reference for Dummies*
Pub: John Wiley & Sons, Incorporated

Ed: Stephen L. Nelson. **Released:** January 2007. **Price:** $29.99 (US), $42.99 (Canadian). **Description:** Compilation of nine self-contained minibooks to get the most from QuickBooks accounting software. Companion Web site with sample business plan workbook and downloadable profit-volume cost analysis workbook included.

2307 ■ *QuickBooks Simple Start for Dummies*
Pub: John Wiley and Sons, Inc.

Ed: Stephen L. Nelson. **Released:** October 2004. **Price:** $21.99. **Description:** Profile of Intuits new accounting software geared to micro businesses. Advice is offered on daily, monthly, and yearly accounting activities covering records, sales tax, and reports.

2308 ■ *Reading Financial Reports for Dummies*
Pub: John Wiley and Sons, Inc.

Ed: Lita Epstein. **Released:** January 2009. **Price:** $21.99. **Description:** This second edition contains more new and updated information, including new

information on the separate accounting and financial reporting standards for private/small businesses versus public/large businesses; updated information reflecting 2007 laws on international financial reporting standards; new content to match SEC and other governmental regulatory changes over the last three years; new information about how the analyst-corporate connection has changed the playing field; the impact of corporate communications and new technologies; new examples that reflect the current trends; and updated Websites and resources.

2309 ■ *"Reform or Perish" in Canadian Business (Vol. 82, April 27, 2009, No. 7, pp. 20)*
Pub: Rogers Media

Ed: Al Rosen. **Description:** It is believed that Canada needs to fix its financial regulatory framework in order to provide more oversight on accounting procedures that is often left up to auditors. While the U.S. has constantly rebuilt its regulatory framework, Canada has not instituted reforms on its regulations. Canada entered the recession with a strong system but needs to build more substance into it.

2310 ■ *Sarbanes-Oxley for Dummies, 2nd Ed.*
Pub: John Wiley and Sons, Inc.

Ed: Jill Gilbert Welytok. **Released:** February 2008. **Price:** $21.99. **Description:** Provides the latest Sarbanes-Oxley (SOX) legislation with procedures to safely and effectively reduce compliance costs. Topics include way to: establish SOX standards for IT professionals, minimize compliances costs for every aspect of a business, survive a Section 404 audit, avoid litigation under SOX, anticipate future rules and trends, create a post-SOX paper trail, increase a company's standing and reputation, work with SOX in a small business, meet new SOX standards, build a board that can't be bought, and to comply with all SOX management mandates.

2311 ■ *"SEC Extends Small Business Deadline for SOX Audit Requirement" in HRMagazine (Vol. 53, August 2008, No. 8, pp. 20)*
Pub: Society for Human Resource Management

Contact: Henry G. Jackson, President

E-mail: hjackson@shrm.org

Description: Securities and Exchange Commission has approved a one-year extension of the compliance date for smaller public companies to meet the Section 404(b) auditor attestation requirement of the Sarbanes-Oxley Act.

2312 ■ *Self-Employed Tax Solutions: Quick, Simple, Money-Saving, Audit-Proof Tax and Recordkeeping Basics*
Pub: The Globe Pequot Press

Ed: June Walker. **Released:** January 1, 2009. **Price:** $17.95. **Description:** A simple system for maintaining tax records and filing tax forms for any small business is explored.

2313 ■ *The Small Business Bible: Everything You Need to Know to Succeed in Your Small Business*
Pub: John Wiley and Sons, Inc.

Ed: Steven D. Strauss. **Released:** September 2008. **Price:** $19.95 (US), $28.99 (Canadian). **Description:** Comprehensive guide to starting and running a successful small business. Topics include bookkeeping and financial management, marketing, publicity, and advertising.

2314 ■ *"Spotlight on Principles-based Financial Reporting" in Business Horizons (September-October 2007, pp. 359)*
Pub: Elsevier Technology Publications

Ed: Laureen A. Maines. **Description:** Employment of principles-based standards in order to generate reliable financial reporting and to reduce misrepresentations is discussed. Rules-based standards are distinguished from principles-based standards.

2315 ■ *"Staffing Firm Grows by Following Own Advice-Hire a Headhunter" in Crain's Detroit Business (Vol. 24, October 6, 2008,*

No. 40, pp. 1)
Pub: Crain Communications, Inc.

Ed: Sherri Begin. **Description:** Profile of Venator Holdings L.L.C., a staffing firm that provides searches for companies in need of financial-accounting and technical employees; the firm's revenue has increased from $1.1 million in 2003 to a projected $11.5 million this year due to a climate in which more people are exiting the workforce than are coming in with those particular specialized skills and the need for a temporary, flexible workforce for contract placements at companies that do not want to take on the legacy costs associated with permanent employees. The hiring of an external headhunter to find the right out-of-state manager for Venator is also discussed.

2316 ■ *"Surviving an IRS Audit: Tips for Small Businesses" in Agency Sales Magazine (Vol. 39, July 2009, No. 7, pp. 52)*
Pub: MANA

Ed: Joshua D. Mosshart. **Description:** It is a good idea to enlist the services of a tax professional even if an audit is expected to go smoothly since the IRS is likely to scrutinize the unreported income and personal as well as business expenses of a small business during an audit.

2317 ■ *"Test Your Structural Integrity" in Entrepreneur (Vol. 37, August 2009, No. 8, pp. 60)*
Pub: Entrepreneur Media, Inc.

Ed: Jennifer Lawler. **Description:** Tax considerations can be important when choosing a business structure. For example, profits are taxed to the corporation in a C corp while profits are taxed only once at an S corp or a limited liability company. Meeting a tax professional should be done prior to switching to a different structure.

2318 ■ *"Throughput Metrics Meet Six Sigma" in Management Accounting Quarterly (Vol. 12, Spring 2011, No. 3, pp. 12)*
Pub: Management Accounting Quarterly

Ed: Shaun Aghili. **Description:** Throughput accounting (TA) metrics can be combined with six sigma's DMAIC methodology and various time-related analysis and measurement tools for added effectiveness in resolving resource constraint issues. The goal is to optimize not only the output of a specific department but that of the entire system, by implementing a cost accounting system that is conducive to system optimization while increasing product quality, process integrity, or ideally, both.

2319 ■ *"ValienteHernandez Acquired" in The Business Journal-Serving Greater Tampa Bay (Vol. 28, September 12, 2008, No. 38, pp. 1)*
Pub: American City Business Journals, Inc.

Ed: Alexis Muellner. **Description:** Minnesota accounting firm LarsonAllen LLP has acquired Florida-based ValienteHernandez PA, creating a company with 35 employees to be based in ValienteHernandez's newly built office in Tampa Bay Area. Other details about the merger are provided.

2320 ■ *"Welcome Back" in Canadian Business (Vol. 82, April 27, 2009, No. 7, pp. 25)*
Pub: Rogers Media

Ed: Sarka Halas. **Description:** Some Canadian companies such as Gennum Corporation have taken advantage of corporate sale-leasebacks to raise money at a time when credit is hard to acquire. Corporate sale-leasebacks allow companies to sell their property assets while remaining as tenants of the building. Sale-leasebacks allow firms to increase capital while avoiding the disruptions that may result with moving.

2321 ■ *"Where Women Work" in Marketing to Women (Vol. 21, April 2008, No. 4, pp. 8)*
Pub: EPM Communications Inc.

Contact: Ira Mayer, President
E-mail: imayer@epmcom.com

Description: According to the U.S. Census Bureau, 60 percent of America's professional tax preparers are women. Also features additional trends concerning women in the workplace. Statistical data included.

2322 ■ *Working Papers, Chapters 1-14 for Needles/Powers/Crosson's Financial and Managerial Accounting*
Pub: Cengage South-Western

Ed: Belverd E. Needles, Marian Powers, Susan V. Crosson. **Released:** May 10, 2010. **Price:** $62.95. **Description:** Appropriate accounting forms for completing all exercises, problems and cases in the text are provided for financial management of a small company.

TRADE SHOWS AND CONVENTIONS

2323 ■ Business & Technology Solutions Show
Illinois Certified Public Accounting Society
550 W Jackson, Ste. 900
Chicago, IL 60661-5716
Ph: (312)933-0407
Free: 800-993-0407
Fax: (312)993-9954
URL: http://www.icpas.org
Contact: Teresa Bates, Coordinator, Conferences

URL(s): www.icpas.org. **Frequency:** Annual. **Audience:** Certified public accountants and their clients, business owners and managers, and others from the financial and business community. **Principal Exhibits:** Computers, office equipment, software publishing and educational supplies, and financial services. **Dates and Locations:** , Donald E. Stephens Convention Center.

2324 ■ Institute of Management Accountants Conference
Institute of Management Accountants, Inc.
10 Paragon Dr.
Montvale, NJ 07645-1718
Ph: (201)573-9000
Free: 800-638-4427
Fax: (201)474-1600
Co. E-mail: ima@imanet.org
URL: http://www.imanet.org

URL(s): www.imanet. **Price:** $770, Pre-registered; $1000, Onsite; $1000, Non-members; $1300, Onsite registered, non-members. **Frequency:** Annual. **Audience:** Management accountants. **Principal Exhibits:** Management accounting equipment, supplies, and services. Review courses, shipping companies, software companies, and risk management consultants.

2325 ■ New Jersey Accounting, Business & Technology Show & Conference
Flagg Management, Inc.
353 Lexington Ave.
New York, NY 10016
Ph: (212)286-0333
Fax: (212)286-0086
Co. E-mail: flaggmgmt@msn.com
URL: http://www.flaggmgmt.com

URL(s): www.flaggmgmt.com/nj. **Frequency:** Annual. **Audience:** CPAs, accounting professionals, business and financial executives of New Jersey, Fortune 1000 corporations, business owners and managers, IT managers. **Principal Exhibits:** Information and technology, financial and business services, computer accounting systems, software, tax preparation, accounting, audit, practice management software - windows, and computer and business systems. Banking, insurance, financial and business software. Internet, online systems and middle market software and investment services. **Telecommunication Services:** flaggmgmt@msn.com.

CONSULTANTS

2326 ■ On-Q Software Inc.
13764 SW 11 St.
Miami, FL 33184
Ph: (305)553-2400
Free: 800-553-2862

Fax: (305)220-2666
Co. E-mail: info@on-qsoftware.com
URL: http://www.on-qsoftware.com
Contact: Hermenegildo Cajigas, Treasurer
E-mail: hcajigas@on-qsoftware.com

Scope: Provider of the small business community with simple to use, feature rich software. Provides software solutions including time and fixed fee billing, due date tracking and practice manager. **Founded:** 1987.

FRANCHISES AND BUSINESS OPPORTUNITIES

2327 ■ CFO Today Inc.
545 E Tennessee St.
Tallahassee, FL 32308
Ph: (850)681-1941
Free: 888-643-1348
Fax: (850)561-1374
URL: http://www.cfotoday.com

Description: Offers regional franchise program through which a regional owner solicits local franchisees. Local franchisees operate an accounting and tax practice, utilizing special marketing techniques, in addition to operational and computer systems, to provide tax, record keeping and other services to clients. **No. of Franchise Units:** 103. **No. of Company-Owned Units:** 1. **Founded:** 1989.. **Franchised:** 1990. **Equity Capital Needed:** $24,400-$40,000. **Franchise Fee:** $24,000. **Royalty Fee:** 8%. **Training:** Provides 5 days training at corporate headquarters and 1 day onsite, with ongoing support.

2328 ■ Ledgers Professional Services
17665 Leslie St., Ste. 39
Newmarket, ON, Canada L3Y 3E3
Ph: (905)953-1268
Co. E-mail: sales@ledgers.com
URL: http://www.ledgers.com

Description: Provides a comprehensive suite of services to small businesses, including bookkeeping, payroll and personal income taxes to corporate financial statement preparation and tax returns. **No. of Franchise Units:** 50. **No. of Company-Owned Units:** 1. **Founded:** 1994.. **Franchised:** 1996. **Equity Capital Needed:** $10,000. **Franchise Fee:** $20,000. **Training:** Provides 5 days training.

LIBRARIES

2329 ■ Defense Finance & Accounting Service - Denver Center - Learning Center
6760 E. Irvington Pl.
Denver, CO 80279-5000
Ph: (303)676-7053
Fax: (303)676-7052
URL: http://www.dfas.mil
Contact: Harvey Reynolds, Librarian

Scope: Computers, accounting, finance, management. **Services:** Library not open to the public. **Founded:** 1950. **Holdings:** 7000 books. **Subscriptions:** 450 journals and other serials; 20 newspapers.

2330 ■ Deloitte Services LLP Information Center
50 S. 6th St., Ste. 2800
Minneapolis, MN 55402-1538
Ph: (612)397-4342
Co. E-mail: marcollins@deloitte.com
Contact: Marsha Collins, Manager

Scope: Accounting, auditing, taxation, healthcare, consulting. **Services:** Library not open to the public. **Founded:** 1976. **Holdings:** 3000 books; 178 bound periodical volumes. **Subscriptions:** 300 journals and other serials; 5 newspapers.

2331 ■ Deloitte & Touche - Library and Information Center
2800 - 1055 Dunsmuir St.
4 Bentall Ctr.
Vancouver, BC, Canada V7X 1P4
Ph: (604)669-4466

Fax: (604)685-0395
URL: http://www.deloitte.com
Scope: Accounting, auditing, taxation, industry. **Services:** Interlibrary loan; copying; Library open to the public with restrictions. **Holdings:** 2000 books; stock, exchange rate, and dividend records. **Subscriptions:** 65 journals and other serials; 6 newspapers.

2332 ■ Deloitte & Touche - Research Center
111 S. Wacker Dr., Ste. 24
Chicago, IL 60606
Ph: (312)486-1000
URL: http://deloitte.com/view/en_US/us/index.htm

Contact: Barbara Dolmon, Manager
Scope: Accounting, auditing, taxation, business and finance, management, electronic data processing/information technology. **Services:** Interlibrary loan; copying; Library open to the public by appointment. **Holdings:** 2500 books. **Subscriptions:** 250 journals and other serials; 15 newspapers.

2333 ■ District of Columbia Public Library - Business, Economics and Vocations Division
Martin Luther King Memorial Library
901 G St. NW, Rm. 107
Washington, DC 20001
Ph: (202)727-0321
Co. E-mail: mlkjrlibrary@dc.gov
URL: http://www.dclibrary.org/
Contact: David Robinson, Division Manager
Scope: Business; statistics, economics, vocations, investment, real estate, import, export, accounting, taxation, business report writing, organizational behavior, commerce, management, marketing, labor, transportation. **Services:** Interlibrary loan; copying; division open to the public. **Founded:** 1907. **Holdings:** 55,639 books; 1150 bound periodical volumes; 471 business directories; 6000 pamphlets; 508 telephone directories; 5521 reels of microfilm; 88 microcards; 7268 microfiche. **Subscriptions:** 428 journals and other serials; 35 newspapers and financial services. **Telecommunication Services:** david.robinson@dc.gov.

2334 ■ Ernst & Young Center for Business Knowledge
1 Victory Pk., Ste. 2000
2323 Victory Ave.
Dallas, TX 75219
Ph: (214)969-8000
Fax: (214)969-8587
URL: http://www.ey.com
Scope: Consulting, accounting, tax accounting, auditing. **Services:** Center open to the public at librarian's discretion.

2335 ■ Howard University - School of Business Library
2600 6th St., NW
Washington, DC 20059
Ph: (202)806-1561
Fax: (202)986-4780
Co. E-mail: lsmiley@howard.edu
URL: http://www.howard.edu/businesslibrary
Contact: Lucille B. Smiley, Librarian
Scope: Business administration, health services administration, management, accounting, real estate, insurance, marketing, finance, computer-based management information systems, hospitality management, International business. **Services:** Interlibrary loan; copying; Library open to the public for reference use only. **Founded:** 1970. **Holdings:** 80,000 books; 10,500 bound periodical volumes; 25,000 reels of microfilm; 500,000 10K reports on microfiche. **Subscriptions:** 1372 journals and other serials; 35 newspapers.

2336 ■ KPMG LLP Library
355 S. Grand Ave., Ste. 2000
Los Angeles, CA 90071-1568
Ph: (213)972-4000
Fax: (213)622-1217
URL: http://www.kpmg.com/us/en/pages/default.aspx
Scope: Accounting, taxation, business management, auditing, economics. **Services:** Interlibrary loan; copying; Library open to the public. **Holdings:** 2500 books; 100 bound periodical volumes. **Subscriptions:** 636 journals and other serials; 2 newspapers.

2337 ■ KPMG L.L.P. Resource Centre
Ste. 2700, Bow Valley Sq. 2
205-5th Ave., SW
Calgary, AB, Canada T2P 4B9
Ph: (403)691-8000
Fax: (403)691-8008
URL: http://www.kpmg.com/ca/en/Pages/Default.aspx
Scope: Accounting, taxation, oil and gas. **Services:** Interlibrary loan; copying; services open to clients. **Founded:** 1982. **Holdings:** 900 books; 900 Annual reports. **Subscriptions:** 50 journals and other serials; 6 newspapers.

2338 ■ KPMG - Research Centre
777 Dunsmuir St.
Vancouver, BC, Canada V7Y 1K3
Ph: (604)691-3000
Fax: (604)691-3031
URL: http://www.kpmg.ca
Scope: Accounting, tax, general business, stocks. **Services:** SDI; Library not open to the public. **Founded:** 1982. **Holdings:** 1000 books; 70 bound periodical volumes. **Subscriptions:** 50 journals and other serials; 6 newspapers.

2339 ■ Price Waterhouse Library
1300 SW 5th Ave., Ste. 3100
Portland, OR 97201-5638
Ph: (971)544-4000
Fax: (971)544-4100
URL: http://www.pwc.com
Contact: Lynne Trueblood, Librarian
Scope: Tax law, accounting, auditing, management consulting. **Services:** Interlibrary loan; copying; SDI; library open to the public by appointment. **Founded:** 1979. **Holdings:** Figures not available. **Subscriptions:** 80 journals and other serials; 7 newspapers.

2340 ■ PricewaterhouseCoopers - North Toronto Research Centre—PwC - Toronto - Metro North.
1900-5700 Yonge St.
North York, ON, Canada M2M 4K7
Ph: (416)218-1500
Fax: (416)218-1499
URL: http://www.pwc.com/ca/en/office-location/index.jhtml
Contact: Catherine Southwell, Specialist
Scope: Taxation, GST/Commodity tax, real estate, estate administration, tax law. **Services:** Interlibrary loan; centre not open to the public. **Founded:** 1995. **Holdings:** 1200 books. **Subscriptions:** 100 journals and other serials; 3 newspapers.

RESEARCH CENTERS

2341 ■ Connecticut Society of Certified Public Accountants - Education and Research Foundation
845 Brook St., Bldg. 2
Rocky Hill, CT 06067-3405
Ph: (860)258-4800
Free: 800-232-2232
Fax: (860)258-4859
Co. E-mail: artr@cs-cpa.org
URL: http://www.cs-cpa.org
Contact: Arthur J. Renner, Executive Director
Services: Consultation. **Founded:** 1908. **Publications:** *Education and Research Foundation Newsletter* (10/year). **Educational Activities:** Colloquium (Annual); Seminars, conferences, and technical sessions. **Awards:** Postdoctoral support; Support for final year PhD students. **Telecommunication Services:** cpe@cs-cpa.org.

2342 ■ Credit Research Foundation (CRF)
1812 Baltimore Blvd., Ste. H
Westminster, MD 21157
Ph: (443)821-3000
Fax: (443)821-3627
URL: http://www.crfonline.org
Contact: Terry Callahan, President
Founded: 1949. **Publications:** *Annual Collection Productivity Report*; *Credit Executives Handbook*; *CRF News* (Quarterly); *National Summary of Domestic Trade Receivables* (Quarterly); *Quarterly Credit and Financial Management Review*; *Net Bad-Debt*

Writeoffs and Allowance for Uncollectibles (Annual). **Educational Activities:** CRF Credit and Accounts Receivable Forums (3/year), held in various cities around America; CRF Online Classroom, online training for credit personnel.

2343 ■ Financial Executives Research Foundation (FERF)
W Twr., 7th Fl.
1250 Headquarters Plz.
Morristown, NJ 07960
Ph: (973)765-1000
Fax: (973)765-1023
Co. E-mail: mhollein@financialexecutives.org
URL: http://www.financialexecutives.org/eweb/DynamicPage.aspx?Site=_fei&Webcode=ferf_home
Contact: Marie Hollein, President
Founded: 1944. **Publications:** *Executive reports* (Monthly); *Issue alerts* (Quarterly); *FERF Newsletters* (Quarterly). **Educational Activities:** Professional development presentations (Monthly); Association, research, leadership meetings (Quarterly).

2344 ■ New York University - Salomon Center for the Study of Financial Institutions
Stern School of Business
44 W 4th St., Ste. 9-160
New York, NY 10012
Ph: (212)998-0700
Fax: (212)995-4220
Co. E-mail: mrichar0@stern.nyu.edu
URL: http://w4.stern.nyu.edu/salomon
Contact: Prof. Matthew Richardson, Director
Services: Associates Program: which encourages participation of interested business organizations. **Founded:** 1972. **Publications:** *Instruments and Markets* (5/year); *Journal of Derivatives* (Quarterly); *Journal of Financial Institutions*; *Journal of International Financial Management and Accounting* (Quarterly); *Salomon Center for the Study of Financial Institutions Newsletter* (Annual); *Occasional Papers in Business and Finance* (Occasionally); *Working Paper Series*. **Educational Activities:** Salomon Center for the Study of Financial Institutions Short courses (3/year), on advanced topics in finance; Salomon Center for the Study of Financial Institutions Workshops; Conferences and forums. **Awards:** Doctoral awards; Faculty grants; Salomon Center for the Study of Financial Institutions Research assistantships (3/year). **Telecommunication Services:** salomon@stern.nyu.edu.

2345 ■ Shippensburg University of Pennsylvania - Office of Extended Studies
Horton Hall 111
1871 Old Main Dr.
Shippensburg, PA 17257
Ph: (717)477-1502
Fax: (717)477-4050
Co. E-mail: extended@ship.edu
URL: http://www.ship.edu/extended
Services: Provides speakers for professional meetings; Research and data collection services. **Founded:** 1976. **Publications:** *Working Paper Series*. **Educational Activities:** Annual Small Business Management Series, open to small business owners or managers; Tax Institute Small Business Management Seminar. **Telecommunication Services:** aswint@ship.edu.

2346 ■ University of Iowa - RSM McGladrey Institute of Accounting Education and Research
108 John Pappajohn Business Bldg.
Henry B. Tippie College of Business
Iowa City, IA 52242-1994
Ph: (319)335-0958
Fax: (319)335-1956
Co. E-mail: ramji-balakrishnan@uiowa.edu
URL: http://tippie.uiowa.edu/accounting/mcgladrey/index.cfm
Contact: Prof. Ramji Balakrishnan, Director
Founded: 1981. **Publications:** *RSM McGladrey Institute of Accounting Education and Research Working papers* (Occasionally). **Educational Activities:** National Speaker series; PriceWaterhouseCoopers Accounting Research Workshop; Sidney G. Winter lecture series. **Telecommunication Services:** mcg-inst@uiowa.edu.

2347 ■ University of Rhode Island - Research Center in Business and Economics (RCBE)
College of Business Administration
7 Lippitt Rd.

Kingston, RI 02881
Ph: (401)874-2549
Fax: (401)874-4825
Co. E-mail: rcbe@etal.uri.edu

URL: http://www.cba.uri.edu/research/rcbe/
Contact: Jerri Paquin, Associate Director
Founded: 1965.

START-UP INFORMATION

2348 ■ *How to Open and Operate a Financially Successful Bookstore on Amazon and Other Web Sites: With Companion CD-ROM*
Pub: Atlantic Publishing Company
Released: December 1, 2010. **Price:** $39.95. **Description:** This book was written for every used book aficionado and bookstore owner who currently wants to take advantage of the massive collection of online resources available to start and run your own online bookstore business.

2349 ■ *The Specialty Shop: How to Create Your Own Unique and Profitable Retail Business*
Pub: AMACOM
Ed: Dorothy Finell. **Released:** February 27, 2007. **Price:** $21.95. **Description:** Advise to start retail businesses, including bakeries, gift shops, toy stores, book shops, tea houses, clothing boutiques, and other unique stores.

ASSOCIATIONS AND OTHER ORGANIZATIONS

2350 ■ **American Booksellers Association (ABA)**
200 White Plains Rd., Ste. 600
Tarrytown, NY 10591
Ph: (914)591-2665
Free: 800-637-0037
Fax: (914)591-2720
Co. E-mail: info@bookweb.org
URL: http://www.bookweb.org
Contact: Becky Anderson, President
Description: Seeks to meet the needs of members, independently owned bookstores with storefront locations, through education, information dissemination, and advocacy. Supports free speech, literacy, and programs that encourage reading. **Founded:** 1900. **Publications:** *Bookselling this Week*; *ABA Electronic Book Buyer's Handbook*; *ABACUS* (Annual); *Bookselling this Week* (Weekly); *ABA Book Buyer's Handbook*; *ABA Bookselling This Week* (Weekly); *Bookselling This Week*; *American Bookseller: The Official Magazine of The American Booksellers Association* (Monthly). **Educational Activities:** BookExpo America (Annual); BookExpo America (Annual). **Awards:** Indies Choice Book Award; Book Sense Book of the Year Award (Annual).

2351 ■ **Antiquarian Booksellers Association of America (ABAA)**
20 W 44th St., Ste. 507
New York, NY 10036-6604
Ph: (212)944-8291
Fax: (212)944-8293
Co. E-mail: hq@abaa.org
URL: http://www.abaa.org
Contact: John Thomson, President
Description: Dealers and appraisers of fine, rare and out-of-print books, manuscripts, and related materials. Sponsors two annual regional international

book fairs and four biennial regional international book fairs. Promotes ethical standards in the industry. Sponsors educational programs for members, librarians, archivists, and the public. Administers the Antiquarian Booksellers' Benevolent Fund. **Founded:** 1949.

2352 ■ **Antiquarian Booksellers' Association of Canada (ABAC)—Association de la Librairie Ancienne du Canada**
368 Dalhousie St., Ste. 301
Ottawa, ON, Canada K1N 7G3
Co. E-mail: info@abac.org
URL: http://www.abac.org
Contact: Liam McGahern, President
Description: Bookselling firms and dealers in rare books and manuscripts. Promotes adherence to high standards of ethics and practice in the trade of antiquarian books. Serves as liaison between members and book collectors and as a clearinghouse on antiquarian books and their trade. **Founded:** 1966.

2353 ■ **Book Industry Study Group (BISG)**
370 Lexington Ave., Ste. 900
New York, NY 10017
Ph: (646)336-7141
Fax: (646)336-6214
Co. E-mail: info@bisg.org
URL: http://www.bisg.org
Contact: Scott Lubeck, Executive Director
Description: Represents publishers, manufacturers, suppliers, wholesalers, retailers, librarians, and other engaged in the business of print and electronic media. **Founded:** 1975. **Publications:** *Book Industry TRENDS* (Annual); *Book Industry Trends* (Annual); *BISG Research Reports* (Quarterly); *Trends Update*; *Student Attitudes Toward Content in Higher Education* (Semiannual). **Educational Activities:** BISG Seminars and conferences (Annual), for discussion of implications of statistical information on the book industry. **Telecommunication Services:** scott@bisg.org.

2354 ■ *Canadian Bookseller*
1255 Bay St., Ste. 902
Toronto, ON, Canada M5R 2A9
Ph: (416)467-7883
Free: 866-788-0790
Fax: (416)467-7886
Co. E-mail: enquiries@cbabook.org
URL: http://www.cbabook.org
Contact: Mark Lefebvre, President
Released: Bimonthly **Price:** C$24, for members in Canada; $42, for members in U.S.; C$65, for members overseas.

2355 ■ **Canadian Booksellers Association (CBA)**
1255 Bay St., Ste. 902
Toronto, ON, Canada M5R 2A9
Ph: (416)467-7883
Free: 866-788-0790

Fax: (416)467-7886
Co. E-mail: enquiries@cbabook.org
URL: http://www.cbabook.org
Contact: Mark Lefebvre, President
Description: Represents the interests of Canadian booksellers from coast to coast to government, media, suppliers and other industry stakeholders. Works to improve the status of the book trade. Fosters communication among members. **Founded:** 1952. **Publications:** *CBA Sourcebook*; *Canadian Bookseller* (Bimonthly). **Awards:** Author of the Year Award; Bookseller of the Year Award; Campus Bookseller of the Year Award; Specialty Bookseller of the Year Award; Publisher of the Year Award; Distributor of the Year Award; Sales Representative of the Year Award; Lifetime Achievement Award; Fiction Book of the Year Award; Non-Fiction Book of the Year Award; Editor of the Year Award; CBA Libris Awards (Annual); Small Press Publisher of the Year Award. **Telecommunication Services:** lefebvr@mcmaster.ca.

2356 ■ **CBA**
PO Box 62000
Colorado Springs, CO 80962-2000
Ph: (719)265-9895
Free: 800-252-1950
Fax: (719)272-3510
Co. E-mail: info@cbaonline.org
URL: http://www.cbaonline.org
Contact: Jim Powell, President
E-mail: jp@ctaintl.com
Description: Serves as trade association for retail stores selling Christian books, Bibles, gifts, and Sunday school and church supplies. Compiles statistics; conducts specialized education programs. **Founded:** 1950. **Publications:** *CBA Retailers@ PLSResources*; *CBA International Market Directory*; *Christian Booksellers Association--Suppliers Directory* (Annual); *Current Christian Books* (Annual). **Educational Activities:** International Christian Retail Show (Annual); Christian Booksellers Association International Convention (Annual); International Christian Retail Show (Annual). **Awards:** Store of the Year (Annual); Supplier of the Year (Annual). **Telecommunication Services:** info@cba-intl.org.

2357 ■ **Great Lakes Independent Booksellers Association (GLiBA)**
PO Box 901
Grand Haven, MI 49417
Ph: (616)847-2460
Free: 800-745-2460
Fax: (616)842-0051
Co. E-mail: info@gliba.org
URL: http://www.gliba.org
Contact: Deb Leonard, Executive Director
URL(s): www.books-gliba.org. **Description:** Booksellers. Supports bookstores and promotes excellence in publishing, distribution, promotion and selling of books. Provides a forum for information exchange; fosters a sense of community among booksellers; provides information and services for the advancement of members; promotes literacy; and supports the First Amendment rights of members. **Founded:** 1989. **Publications:** *Great Lakes Bookseller* (Bi-

monthly); *Directory and Handbook* (Annual); *Books for Holiday Giving* (Annual). **Awards:** Great Lakes Book Awards (Annual). **Telecommunication Services:** info@books-glba.org.

2358 ■ Institute of Communication Agencies (ICA)
2300 Yonge St., Ste. 3002
Toronto, ON, Canada M4P 1E4
Ph: (416)482-1396
Free: 800-567-7422
Fax: (416)482-1856
Co. E-mail: ica@icacanada.ca
URL: http://www.icacanada.ca
Contact: Jani Yates, President
Description: Aims to represent advertising agencies in a wide variety of beneficial activities. **Scope:** advertising, marketing. **Founded:** 1905.

2359 ■ International League of Antiquarian Booksellers (ILAB)
c/o Tom Congalton, Pres.
35 W Maple Ave.
Merchantville, NJ 08109-5141
Ph: (856)665-2284
Fax: (856)665-3639
Co. E-mail: mail@betweenthecovers.com
URL: http://www.ilab.org
Contact: Tom Congalton, President
Description: Represents national associations of antiquarian booksellers around the world. Organizes professional training courses for members. Sponsors book fairs. **Founded:** 1947. **Educational Activities:** International League of Antiquarian Booksellers Congress (Biennial). **Awards:** Bibliographic Award (Periodic); Breslauer Prize for Bibliography.

2360 ■ National Association of College Stores (NACS)
500 E Lorain St.
Oberlin, OH 44074
Ph: (440)775-7777
Free: 800-622-7498
Fax: (440)775-4769
Co. E-mail: webteam@nacs.org
URL: http://www.nacs.org
Contact: Danny A. Key, President
E-mail: dkey@wingate.edu
Description: Institutional, private, leased, and cooperative college stores selling books, supplies, and other merchandise to college students, faculty, and staff; associate members include publishers and suppliers. Seeks to effectively serve higher education by providing educational research, advocacy and other to college stores and their suppliers. Maintains NACSCORP, Inc., a wholly owned subsidiary corporation, which distributes trade and mass market books and educational software. Sponsors seminars. Conducts manager certification, specialized education, and research programs. Maintains College Stores Research and Educational Foundation which provides grants for educational programs and conducts research. **Founded:** 1923. **Publications:** *NACS Book Buyers Manual* (Annual); *Campus Marketplace* (Weekly); *The College Store* (Bimonthly); *NACS Book Buyers Manual* (Annual); *NACS Directory of Colleges and College Stores* (Annual); *NACS Directory of Publishers* (Biennial); *Instructional Resources for Faculty* (Biennial); *Schedule of College and University Dates* (Annual); *The College Store--Buyers' Guide Issue* (Annual). **Educational Activities:** CAMEX (Annual); National Association of College Stores Annual Meeting and Campus Market Expo (Annual). **Telecommunication Services:** info@nacs.org; service@nacscorp.com; thecollege@nacs.org.

2361 ■ Women's National Book Association (WNBA)
PO Box 237
New York, NY 10150
Ph: (615)386-6760
Fax: (212)208-4629
Co. E-mail: info@wnba-books.org
URL: http://www.wnba-books.org
Contact: Mary Grey James, President
Description: Women and men who work with and value books. Exists to promote reading and to support the role of women in the book community.

Founded: 1917. **Publications:** *The Bookwoman*; *The Bookwoman* (3/year). **Awards:** Lucile Micheels Pannell Award (Annual); Women's National Book Association Award; Ann Heidbreder Eastman Grant (Annual); The WNBA Award (Biennial); WNBA Eastman Grants. **Telecommunication Services:** sandy@sk-passociates.com.

REFERENCE WORKS

2362 ■ "Africa Rising" in Harvard Business Review (Vol. 86, September 2008, No. 9, pp. 36)
Pub: Harvard Business School Press
Ed: John T. Landry. **Description:** Review of the book entitled, 'Africa Rising: How 900 Million African Consumers Offer More Than You Think' provides advice for marketing to those on the African continent.

2363 ■ Book Dealers Dropship Directory
Pub: North American Bookdealers Exchange
Contact: Russ von Hoelscher, Director
URL(s): www.bookmarketingprofits.com/DSDirectory.html. **Released:** Irregular; Latest edition 2005-2006. **Price:** $15, Individuals with free shipping in USA and Canada. **Covers:** More than 300 dealers and distributors who ship individual copies of books to customers for publishers and mail order companies. **Entries include:** Company name, address, titles or types of books handled. **Arrangement:** Alphabetical.

2364 ■ "The Book On Indigo" in Canadian Business (Vol. 81, July 22, 2008, No. 12-13, pp. 29)
Pub: Rogers Media Ltd.
Ed: Thomas Watson. **Description:** Indigo Books & Music Inc. reported record sales of $922 million resulting in a record net profit of $52.8 million for the 2008 fiscal year ended March 29, 2008. Earnings per share were $2.13, greater than Standard & Poor's expected $1.70 per share. Additional information concerning Indigo Books is presented.

2365 ■ "Book Publishing is Growing" in Information Today (Vol. 28, October 2011, No. 9, pp. 10)
Pub: Information Today, Inc.
Ed: Paula J. Hane. **Description:** U.S. book publishing industry is reporting growth in its sector, despite the poor economy. BookStats, a comprehensive statistical survey conducted on the modern publishing industry in the U.S. reported Americans are reading in all print and digital formats. In 2011, 114 million ebooks were sold and now account for 13.6 percent of revenue from adult fiction. In contrast, 603 million trade hardcover books (fiction and nonfiction) were sold in 2011, a 5.8 percent increase over 2008.

2366 ■ Books in Print
Pub: R.R. Bowker
URL(s): www.bowker.com/www.greyhouse.com/bowk_bip.htm. **Released:** Annual; Latest edition 2009-2010. **Price:** $995, Individuals hardcover; 7 volumes. **Description:** Over 2.8 million entries covering books published and distributed in the U.S. **Entries include:** For publishers--Company name, address. For books--Authors, title, price, publisher, other bibliographic information as available. The material in "Books in Print" is also available in subject-classified form in "Subject Guide to Books in Print," published as a five-volume set, annually in September. **Arrangement:** Publishers, authors, and titles are alphabetical in separate sections.

2367 ■ "Boom and Bust in the Book Biz" in Canadian Business (Vol. 83, August 17, 2010, No. 13-14, pp. 16)
Pub: Rogers Media Ltd.
Ed: Jordan Timm. **Description:** Electronic book marketplace is booming with Amazon.com's e-book sales for the Kindle e-reader exceeding the hardcover sales. Kobo Inc. has registered early success with its Kobo e-reader and has partnered with Hong Kong telecom giant on an e-book store.

2368 ■ "Borders Previews New Web Site" in Crain's Detroit Business (Vol. 23, October 8,

2007, No. 41, pp. 4)
Pub: Crain Communications Inc. - Detroit
Ed: Sheena Harrison. **Description:** Borders Group Inc. previewed its new Website that allows customers to buy items that include the Magic Shelf, a virtual bookcase that displays available recommended books, movies and music.

2369 ■ "Burdened by Debt, Borders Group Suspends Dividends, May Be Sold" in Crain's Detroit Business (Vol. 24, March 24, 2008, No. 12)
Pub: Crain Communications, Inc.
Ed: Nancy Kaffer. **Description:** Ann Arbor-based Borders Group Inc. is exploring its options and may put itself up for sale due to its declining stock price and mounting debt. The company's fiscal year was capped by poor holiday sales and Borders does not have the cash on hand to meet the 2009 goals set in its strategic plan.

2370 ■ "Buying In" in Harvard Business Review (Vol. 86, September 2008, No. 9, pp. 36)
Pub: Harvard Business School Press
Ed: Andrew O'Connell. **Description:** Review of the book entitled, 'Buying In: The Secret Dialogue between What We Buy and Who We Are' which offers tips that those in the field of marketing will find useful.

2371 ■ Children's Books in Print
Pub: R.R. Bowker L.L.C.
URL(s): www.bowker.com/index.php/component/content/article/17. **Released:** Annual; Latest edition 2009. **Price:** $455, Individuals 2-vol. set. **Entries include:** Book entries--Title, subtitle, author(s), editor(s), illustrator(s), publishing date, edition, price, binding, ISBN, LC number, publisher; Publisher entries--Name, address, phone, ISBN prefix. The material in "Children's Books in Print" is also available in subject-classified form in "Subject Guide to Children's Books in Print," also published in December. **Arrangement:** Alphabetical within each index. **Indexes:** Author, title, illustrator, award or prize, publisher.

2372 ■ "Consignment Shop Offers Children's Clothes, Products" in Frederick News-Post (August 19, 2010)
Pub: Federick News-Post
Ed: Ed Waters Jr. **Description:** Sweet Pea Consignments for Children offers used items for newborns to pre-teens. The shop carries name brand clothing as well as toys, books and baby products.

2373 ■ "Copyright Clearance Center (CCC) Partnered with cSubs" in Information Today (Vol. 28, November 2011, No. 10, pp. 14)
Pub: Information Today, Inc.
Description: Copyright Clearance Center (CCC) partnered with cSubs to integrate CCC's point-of-content licensing solution RightsLink Basic directly into cSubs workflow. The partnership will allow cSubs' customers a user-friendly process for obtaining permissions. Csubs is a corporate subscription management service for books, newspapers, and econtent.

2374 ■ "Gadget Makers Aim for New Chapter in Reading" in Crain's Cleveland Business (Vol. 28, October 22, 2007, No. 42, pp. 20)
Pub: Crain Communications, Inc.
Ed: Jennifer McKevitt. **Description:** Although e-books and e-audiobooks are becoming more popular, e-readers, devices that display digital books, still haven't caught on with the public. Experts feel that consumers, many of whom have to look at a computer screen all day for work, still like the feel of a real book in their hands.

2375 ■ "A Good Book Is Worth a Thousand Blogs" in Barron's (Vol. 88, July 14, 2008, No. 28, pp. 42)
Pub: Dow Jones & Co., Inc.
Ed: Gene Epstein. **Description:** Nine summer book suggestions on economics are presented. The list includes 'The Revolution' by Ron Paul, 'The Forgot-

ten Man' by Amity Shales, 'The Commitments of Traders Bible' by Stephen Briese, and 'Economic Facts and Fallacies' by Thomas Sowell.

2376 ■ *"A Gripping Read: Bargains & Noble" in Barron's (Vol. 88, March 17, 2008, No. 11, pp. 20)*
Pub: Dow Jones & Company, Inc.
Ed: Jonathan R. Laing. **Description:** Barnes & Noble's earnings forecast for the fiscal year ending in January, 2008 to be $1.70 to $1.90 per share which is way lower than the $2.12 analyst consensus. The company also said that sales at stores one-year old or older dropped 0.5 percent in the fourth quarter. However, the shares are now cheap at 4.9 times enterprise value with some analysts putting a price target of 41 per share.

2377 ■ *"Hit the Books" in Black Enterprise (Vol. 38, July 2008, No. 12, pp. 42)*
Pub: Earl G. Graves Publishing Co. Inc.
Ed: Mellody Hobson. **Description:** Four books that deal with investing are discussed as is the idea that reading even 15 minutes a day from one of these books will give you tools that far exceed what you can learn from magazines and the business section of your daily newspaper.

2378 ■ *"Interactive Stores a Big Part of Borders' Turnaround Plan" in Crain's Detroit Business (Vol. 24, February 18, 2008, No. 7, pp. 4)*
Pub: Crain Communications Inc. - Detroit
Description: Borders Group Inc. is using digital technology and interactive media as a part of the firm's turnaround plan. The digital store will allow shoppers to create CDs, download audio books, publish their own works, print photos and search family genealogy.

2379 ■ *"Lafley Gives Look At His Game Plan" in Business Courier (Vol. 24, March 21, 2008, No. 50, pp. 1)*
Pub: American City Business Journals, Inc.
Ed: Lisa Biank Fasig. **Description:** Overview of A.G. Lafley's book entitled 'The Game-Changer', is presented. Lafley, Procter & Gamble Co.'s chief executive officer, documented his philosophy and strategy in his book. His work also includes Procter & Gamble's hands-on initiatives such as mock-up grocery stores and personal interviews with homeowners.

2380 ■ *"Last Founder Standing" in Conde Nast Portfolio (Vol. 2, June 2008, No. 6, pp. 124)*
Pub: Conde Nast Publications
Contact: David Carey, President
Ed: Kevin Maney. **Description:** Interview with Amazon CEO Jeff Bezos in which he discusses the economy, the company's new distribution center and the hiring of employees for it, e-books, and the overall vision for the future of the firm.

2381 ■ *Library and Book Trade Almanac*
Pub: Information Today Inc.
Contact: Thomas H. Hogan, President
E-mail: ctuthill@infotoday.com
URL(s): books.infotoday.com. **Released:** Annual; Latest edition 57th; June 2012. **Price:** $249, Individuals hardbound; plus $17 shipping and handling charges; $224.10, Individuals first time standing order. **Publication includes:** Lists of accredited library schools; scholarships for education in library science; library organizations; library statistics; publishing and bookselling organizations. **Entries include:** Directory listings give name of institution, address, phone, fax, name of officer or contact, publications; scholarship listings include requirements, value of grant, contact name. Principal content is articles and special reports on topics of interest to those in library/information science and publishers; international reports; annual reports from federal agencies and libraries and from national associations; information on legislation, funding, etc. **Database includes:** Lists of notable books, best-sellers, literary prize winners; library and trade statistics; calendar of events. **Arrangement:** Topical. **Indexes:** Organization; subject.

2382 ■ *"Negotiating Tips" in Black Enterprise (Vol. 37, December 2006, No. 5, pp. 70)*
Pub: Earl G. Graves Publishing Co. Inc.
Description: Sekou Kaalund, head of strategy, mergers & acquisitions at Citigroup Securities & Fund Services, states that 'Negotiation skills are paramount to success in a business environment because of client, employee, and shareholder relationships'. He discusses how the book by George Kohlrieser, Hostage at the Table: How Leaders Can Overcome Conflict, Influence Others, and Raise Performance, has helped him negotiate more powerfully and enhance his skills at conflict-resolution.

2383 ■ *"New Book Takes Alternate View on Ontario's Wind Industry" in CNW Group (September 19, 2011)*
Pub: CNW Group
Contact: Carolyn McGill-Davidson, President
Description: Dirty Business: The Reality Behind Ontario's Rush to Wind Power, was written by editor and health care writer Jane Wilson of Ottawa, Ontario, Canada along with contributing editor Parker Gallant. The book contains articles and papers on the wind business, including information on illnesses caused from the environmental noise.

2384 ■ *"Online Book Sales Surpass Bookstores" in Information Today (Vol. 28, September 2011, No. 8, pp. 11)*
Pub: Information Today, Inc.
Ed: Cindy Martine. **Description:** Online book sales outpaced bookstore purchases in the United States, signaling a shift in the US book industry. Statistical data included.

2385 ■ *Publishers Directory*
Pub: Cengage Learning Inc.
Contact: Ronald Dunn, President
URL(s): www.gale.cengage.com. **Released:** Annual; Latest edition 37th; March, 2012. **Price:** $756, Individuals. **Covers:** Over 20,000 new and established, commercial and nonprofit, private and alternative, corporate and association, government and institution publishing programs and their distributors; includes producers of books, classroom materials, prints, reports, and databases. **Entries include:** Firm name, address, phone, fax, company e-mail address, URL, year founded, ISBN prefix, Standard Address Number, whether firm participates in the Cataloging in Publication program of the Library of Congress, names of principal executives, personal e-mail addresses, number of titles in print, description of firm and its main subject interests, discount and returns policies, affiliated and parent companies, mergers and amalgamations, principal markets, imprints and divisions, alternate formats products are offered; distributors also list firms for which they distribute, special services, terms to publishers and regional offices. **Arrangement:** Alphabetical; distributors listed separately. **Indexes:** Subject, geographical, publisher, imprints, and distributor. **Availability:** Online: Cengage Learning Inc.; LexisNexis Group. **Type:** Directory.

2386 ■ *"SAGE Publications Announced a Partnership with Which Medical Device" in Information Today (Vol. 28, November 2011, No. 10, pp. 15)*
Pub: Information Today, Inc.
Description: SAGE Publications has partnered with Which Medical Device to offer insights, tutorials, and reviews of medical devices.

2387 ■ *"The Seat-Of-The-Pants School of Marketing" in Brandweek (Vol. 49, April 21, 2008, No. 16, pp. 24)*
Pub: VNU Business Media, Inc.
Ed: David Vinjamuri. **Description:** Excerpt from the book 'Accidental Branding: How Ordinary People Build Extraordinary Brands,' by David Vinjamuri, discusses six shared principles for creating a brand that is unique and will be successful over the long-term.

2388 ■ *"University Book Store Inc.: an Act of Independence" in Retail Merchandiser (Vol.*

51, September-October 2011, No. 5, pp. 68)*
Pub: Phoenix Media Corporation
Ed: Lori Sichtermann. **Description:** University Book Store Inc. is a campus bookstore located at the University of Washington, in Seattle. The book store provides more than $1 million in UW customer rebates and discounts annually and donated more than $800,000 in UW student scholarships.

2389 ■ *"An Updated Ranking of Academic Journals in Economics" in Canadian Journal of Economics (Vol. 44, November 2011, No. 4, pp. 1525)*
Pub: Blackwell Publishers Ltd.
Ed: Pantelis Kalaitzidakis, Theofanis P. Mamuneas, Thanasis Stengos. **Description:** An updated list showing the ranking of economic journals (2003) is presented; however this present study differs methodologically from an earlier study by using a rolling window of years between 2003 and 2008, for each year counting the number of citations of articles published in the previous ten years.

2390 ■ *"What Slump? Davis Likely to Fill Borders Gap Quickly" in Sacramento Business Journal (Vol. 28, July 29, 2011, No. 22, pp. 1)*
Pub: Sacramento Business Journal
Ed: Kelly Johnson. **Description:** The nationwide shutdown of Borders bookstores worry most cities, but not Davis, California, which is experiencing a relatively low retail vacancy rate of 6.3 percent.

STATISTICAL SOURCES

2391 ■ *Book Industry Trends*
Pub: Book Industry Study Group
Contact: Scott Lubeck, Executive Director
Ed: Compiled by Statistical Service Center staff. **Released:** 2009. **Price:** $875.00 (paper).

2392 ■ *RMA Annual Statement Studies*
Pub: Risk Management Association
Contact: Kevin M. Blakey, President
Released: Annual. **Price:** $175.00 2006-07 edition, $105.00. **Description:** Contains composite balance sheets and income statements for more than 360 industries, including the accounting, auditing, and bookkeeping industries. Also contains five years of comparative historical data for discerning trends. Includes 16 commonly used ratios, computed for most of the size groupings for nearly every industry.

TRADE PERIODICALS

2393 ■ *Book Dealers World*
Pub: North American Bookdealers Exchange
Contact: Russ von Hoelscher, Director
URL(s): www.bookmarketingprofits.com/BDWAdRates2.html. **Released:** Quarterly **Price:** $45, Individuals; $5, Single issue.

2394 ■ *Bookselling This Week*
Pub: American Booksellers Association
Contact: Becky Anderson, President
Ed: Dan Cullen, Editor, dcullen@bookweb.org. **Released:** Weekly. **Price:** $49.99, individuals; $5, single issue. **Description:** Contains information on book selling.

2395 ■ *CBA Marketplace: The No. 1 Resource for Christian Retailers and Suppliers*
Pub: CBA Service Corp.
Released: Monthly; 12/year. **Price:** $59.95, Nonmembers.

2396 ■ *College Store Executive: The National News and Merchandising Magazine of the College Store Industry*
Pub: Executive Business Media Inc.
URL(s): ebmpubs.com/CSE/index.asp. **Released:** 8/yr. **Price:** $35, Individuals; $60, Two years; $87, Other countries mail.

2397 ■ *Forecast*
Pub: Baker & Taylor
URL(s): www.btol.com/ps_details.cfm?id=11. **Released:** Monthly

2398 ■ *The New York Review of Books*
Pub: The New York Review of Books
Contact: Diane Seltzer, Manager
URL(s): www.nybooks.com. **Ed:** Robert B. Silvers. **Released:** 20/yr. **Price:** $69, Individuals; $109, Other countries; $89, Canada.

2399 ■ *The New York Times Book Review*
Pub: The New York Times Co.
Contact: Janet L. Robinson, President
URL(s): www.nytimes.com/pages/books. **Released:** Weekly **Price:** $65, U.S. 52 weeks; $98.80, Canada 52 weeks; $119.60, Other countries 52 weeks.

2400 ■ *Publishers Weekly: The International voice for Book Publishing and Bookselling*
Pub: Publishers Weekly
URL(s): www.publishersweekly.com. **Released:** Weekly **Price:** $249.99, Individuals; $299.99, Canada; $399.99, Other countries air delivery.

2401 ■ *Sell More Books! Newsletter*
Pub: Florida Publishers Association
Ed: Betsy Wright-Lampe, Editor. **Released:** Bi-monthly. **Price:** Included in membership. **Description:** Reports on news, events, and updates of the Florida Publishers Association. Also focuses on publishing companies, book successes, and useful tips.

TRADE SHOWS AND CONVENTIONS

2402 ■ BookExpo America
Reed Exhibitions Contemporary Forums
6377 Clark Ave., Ste. 200
Dublin, CA 94568
Ph: (925)828-7100
Fax: (800)329-9923
Co. E-mail: info@cforums.com
URL: http://www.contemporaryforums.com
URL(s): www.bookexpoamerica.com. **Frequency:** Annual. **Audience:** Book retailers and wholesalers, librarians, literacy agents, and scouts. **Principal Exhibits:** Books and related products. **Telecommunication Services:** inquiry@bookexpoamerica.com.

2403 ■ Christian Booksellers Association International Convention
CBA
PO Box 62000
Colorado Springs, CO 80962-2000
Ph: (719)265-9895
Free: 800-252-1950

Fax: (719)272-3510
Co. E-mail: info@cbaonline.org
URL: http://www.cbaonline.org
Contact: Jim Powell, President
E-mail: jp@ctaintl.com
URL(s): www.christianretailshow.com. **Frequency:** Annual. **Audience:** Christian bookstore trade. **Principal Exhibits:** Christian bookstore merchandise, including literature, music, gifts, cards, jewelry, and curricula. **Telecommunication Services:** info@cbaonline.org.

COMPUTERIZED DATABASES

2404 ■ *Books in Print ON DISC™ - Canadian Edition*
630 Central Ave.
New Providence, NJ 07974
Ph: (908)268-1090
Free: 888-269-5372
Fax: (908)665-3528
Co. E-mail: customerservice@bowker.com
URL: http://www.bowker.com
Availability: CD-ROM: R.R. Bowker LLC. **Type:** Bibliographic.

2405 ■ *BooksInPrint.com® Professional (BIP)*
630 Central Ave.
New Providence, NJ 07974
Ph: (908)268-1090
Free: 888-269-5372
Fax: (908)665-3528
Co. E-mail: customerservice@bowker.com
URL: http://www.bowker.com
Availability: Online: ProQuest LLC - Dialog; Colorado Alliance of Research Libraries; R.R. Bowker LLC. CD-ROM: R.R. Bowker LLC. **Type:** Bibliographic.

2406 ■ *ChildrensBooksInPrint.com™*
630 Central Ave.
New Providence, NJ 07974
Ph: (908)268-1090
Free: 888-269-5372
Fax: (908)665-3528
Co. E-mail: customerservice@bowker.com
URL: http://www.bowker.com
Availability: Online: R.R. Bowker LLC. **Type:** Bibliographic.

2407 ■ *LC MARC: Books All*
101 Independence Ave. SE
Washington, DC 20541-4912
Ph: (202)707-6100
Fax: (202)707-1334
Co. E-mail: cdsinfo@loc.gov
URL: http://www.loc.gov/cds
Availability: Online: ProQuest LLC - Dialog; U.S. Library of Congress - Cataloging Distribution Service. **Type:** Bibliographic.

2408 ■ *The Title Source™ III*
2550 W Tyvola Rd., Ste. 300
Charlotte, NC 28217
Ph: (704)998-3100
Free: 800-775-1800
Co. E-mail: btinfo@btol.com
URL: http://www.btol.com
Availability: Online: Baker & Taylor Inc. **Type:** Bibliographic; Numeric.

LIBRARIES

2409 ■ American Booksellers Association Information Service Center
200 White Plains Rd. Ste. 600
Tarrytown, NY 10591
Free: 800-637-0037
Fax: (914)591-2720
Co. E-mail: info@bookweb.org
URL: http://www.bookweb.org
Contact: Oren Teicher, Chief Executive Officer
Scope: Book selling and publishing. **Founded:** 1989. **Holdings:** 5000 volumes; 1000 bound periodical volumes; 100 newsletters; 11 VF drawers; 2000 publishers catalogs. **Telecommunication Services:** oren@bookweb.org.

2410 ■ Grolier Club of New York Library
47 E. 60th St.
New York, NY 10022
Ph: (212)838-6690
Fax: (212)838-2445
Co. E-mail: ejh@grolierclub.org
URL: http://www.grolierclub.org
Contact: Eric Holzenberg, Director
Scope: Bibliography, history of printing, book-collecting, bookselling, arts of the book. **Services:** Library open to the public with restrictions. **Founded:** 1884. **Holdings:** 100,000 volumes; 5000 prints and portraits; bookplates. **Subscriptions:** 100 journals and other serials. **Telecommunication Services:** fpena@grolierclub.org; mconstantinou@grolierclub.org.

2411 ■ Villanova University - Falvey Memorial Library - Special Collections
Villanova, PA 19085
Ph: (610)519-4290
Fax: (610)519-6000
Co. E-mail: bente.polites@villanova.edu
URL: http://www.library.villanova.edu
Contact: Bente Polites, Librarian, Special Collections
Scope: Augustiniana, early printed books and general rare books, Irish history, James Joyce. **Services:** Interlibrary loan; copying; library open to the public. **Founded:** 1842. **Holdings:** 15,000 items. **Telecommunication Services:** michael.foight@villanova.edu; laura.bang@villanova.edu.

ASSOCIATIONS AND OTHER ORGANIZATIONS

2412 ■ **International Bottled Water Association (IBWA)**
1700 Diagonal Rd., Ste. 650
Alexandria, VA 22314
Ph: (703)683-5213
Free: 800-WATER-11
Fax: (703)683-4074
Co. E-mail: ibwainfo@bottledwater.org
URL: http://www.bottledwater.org
Contact: Philippe Caradec, Chairman
Description: Bottled water plants; distributors; manufacturers of bottled water supplies; international bottlers, distributors and suppliers. Conducts seminars and technical research. **Publications:** *IBWA Audit Handbook*; *IBWA Membership Roster* (Annual); *Bottled Water Reporter* (Bimonthly); *International Bottled Water Association--Membership Directory* (Annual). **Educational Activities:** International Bottled Water Association Convention and Trade Show (Annual). **Awards:** Bottled Water Hall of Fame; Aqua Awards (Annual).

REFERENCE WORKS

2413 ■ *"CEO Tapped for Perrier, Poland Springs"* **in** *Black Enterprise* **(Vol. 38, February 2008, No. 7, pp. 30)**
Pub: Earl G. Graves Publishing Co. Inc.
Ed: Brenda Porter. **Description:** John J. Harris, newly appointed CEO, is hoping to increase market share of Nestle's bottled water products.

2414 ■ *"Eco-Preneuring"* **in** *Small Business Opportunities* **(Jan. 2008)**
Pub: Harris Publications Inc.
Description: Iceland Naturally is a joint marketing effort among tourism and business interests hoping to increase demand for Icelandic products including frozen seafood, bottled water, agriculture, and tourism in North America.

2415 ■ *"A Precious Resource: Investing In the Fate of Fresh Water"* **in** *Black Enterprise* **(Vol. 38, February 2008, No. 7, pp. 44)**
Pub: Earl G. Graves Publishing Co. Inc.
Ed: Charles Keenan. **Description:** Despite rising oil prices, water may become the most precious commodity in years to come because the world's supply of drinkable water is dwindling.

2416 ■ *"Pulque with Flavor"* **in** *Canadian Business* **(Vol. , pp.)**
Pub: Rogers Media Ltd.
Ed: Augusta Dwyer. **Description:** Mexico-based Pulque Poliqhui, which has exported 20,000 bottles of Pulque into Canada in March 2008, plans to distribute in Ontario and Quebec. Pulque Poliqhui is introducing Cool Passion, a fruit-flavored version of pulque in Canada.

2417 ■ *"Thirsty? Now There's a Water Cooler to Suit Every Taste"* **in** *Inc.* **(Vol. 33, October 2011, No. 8, pp. 43)**
Pub: Inc. Magazine
Ed: John Brandon. **Description:** Brita's Hydration Station is a wall-mounted unit with a touch-free sensor for dispensing water. This water cooler cuts down on landfill waste and offers special features.

STATISTICAL SOURCES

2418 ■ *The Bottled Water Market*
Pub: Business Trend Analysts, Inc.
Released: 2005-2006 Edition. **Price:** $2195.00. **Description:** An in-depth examination of the size and projected growth (to 2014) of the bottled water market, covering both domestic and imported products.

TRADE PERIODICALS

2419 ■ *Bottled Water Reporter*
Pub: International Bottled Water Association
Contact: Philippe Caradec, Chairman
URL(s): www.bottledwater.org. **Released:** Bimonthly **Price:** $50, Nonmembers U.S. & Canada; $100, Other countries; Free for members.

2420 ■ *Hot Springs, Mineral Waters*
Pub: Bibliotheca Press
Ed: A. Doyle, Editor. **Released:** Irregular. **Price:** $7. 95, U.S.. **Description:** Lists hot springs and mineral water locations for tourists.

TRADE SHOWS AND CONVENTIONS

2421 ■ **International Bottled Water Association Convention and Trade Show**
International Bottled Water Association (IBWA)
1700 Diagonal Rd., Ste. 650
Alexandria, VA 22314
Ph: (703)683-5213
Free: 800-WATER-11
Fax: (703)683-4074
Co. E-mail: ibwainfo@bottledwater.org
URL: http://www.bottledwater.org
Contact: Philippe Caradec, Chairman
URL(s): www.bottledwater.org. **Frequency:** Annual.
Audience: Bottled water company executives and suppliers to the industry. **Principal Exhibits:** Bottled water industry supplies and equipment. **Telecommunication Services:** ibwainfo@bottledwater.org.

FRANCHISES AND BUSINESS OPPORTUNITIES

2422 ■ **Purified Water Store**
11566 24 St. SE, Unit 214
Calgary, AB, Canada T2Z 3J3
Ph: (403)261-7873
Free: 800-976-9283

Fax: (403)720-6020
Co. E-mail: info@purifiedwaterstore.com
URL: http://www.purifiedwaterstore.com
Description: Offers reverse osmosis bottled water production facilities. Retail show rooms marketing coolers, crocks and purified water accessories are provided. In-home filtration systems and water conditioning equipment is also offered. **No. of Franchise Units:** 23. **No. of Company-Owned Units:** 1. **Founded:** 1999.. **Franchised:** 2000. **Equity Capital Needed:** $154,000. **Franchise Fee:** $20,000. **Training:** 1 week corporate training program, 1 week onsite, and follow up on store opening.

2423 ■ **Water Depot**
92 Commerce Park Dr. Unit 2
Barrie, ON, Canada L4N 8W8
Ph: (705)735-6642
Fax: (705)792-5157
Co. E-mail: info@waterdepotinc.com
URL: http://www.waterdepotinc.com
Description: Supplies bottled water and water treatment products to consumers. **No. of Franchise Units:** 20. **No. of Company-Owned Units:** 1. **Founded:** 1989.. **Franchised:** 2001. **Franchise Fee:** $25,000. **Training:** Ongoing Water Depot College and University courses, seminars, question and answer Sessions and events.

2424 ■ **World of Water International Ltd.**
326 Keewatin St.
Winnipeg, MB, Canada R2X 2R9
Ph: (204)774-7770
Free: 866-749-1146
Fax: (204)772-5051
Co. E-mail: info@worldofwater.ca
URL: http://www.worldofwater.ca
Description: Producer and marketer of Dewdrop steam distilled water and franchisor of retail bottled water stores. The retail stores cater to retail as well as home and office delivery customers through our franchise stores. **No. of Franchise Units:** 18. **Founded:** 1976.. **Franchised:** 1976. **Equity Capital Needed:** $145,000. **Franchise Fee:** $25,000. **Training:** Yes.

COMPUTERIZED DATABASES

2425 ■ *WATERNET Bibliographic Database*
6666 W Quincy Ave.
Denver, CO 80235-3098
Ph: (303)794-7711
Free: 800-926-7337
Fax: (303)347-0804
URL: http://www.awwa.org
Contact: David B. LaFrance, Executive Director
Availability: CD-ROM: American Water Works Association. **Type:** Bibliographic.

LIBRARIES

2426 ■ **Coca-Cola Company - The INFOSOURCE**
PO Box 1734
Atlanta, GA 30301

Ph: (404)515-4636
Fax: (404)253-4575
Co. E-mail: koinfo@na.ko.com
URL: http://www.coca-cola.com

Contact: Barbara Kahn-Aitken
Scope: Business, Legal, Marketing, Technical - including beverages, soft drinks, fruit juices, food

technology, nutrition, chemistry, engineering. **Founded:** 1967. **Telecommunication Services:** coca-cola@na.ko.com.

ASSOCIATIONS AND OTHER ORGANIZATIONS

2427 ■ **Billiard and Bowling Institute of America (BBIA)**
PO Box 6573
Arlington, TX 76005
Ph: (817)385-8120
Free: 800-343-1329
Fax: (817)633-2940
Co. E-mail: answer@billiardandbowling.org
URL: http://www.billiardandbowling.org
Contact: Bill Supper, Executive Director
Description: Represents distributors and manufacturers of billiard and bowling equipment. **Founded:** 1940. **Educational Activities:** Billiard and Bowling Institute of America Convention (Annual). **Awards:** Industry Service Award (Annual).

2428 ■ **Bowling Proprietors' Association of America (BPAA)**
621 Six Flags Dr.
Arlington, TX 76011
Ph: (817)649-5105
Free: 800-343-1329
Fax: (817)633-2940
Co. E-mail: steve@bpaa.com
URL: http://www.bpaa.com
Contact: Steve Johnson, Executive Director
Description: Represents proprietors of bowling establishments. **Founded:** 1932. **Publications:** *Bowling Center Management* (Monthly); *Talking Human Resources.* **Educational Activities:** International Bowl Expo (Annual). **Awards:** V. A. Wapensky Award; Victor Lerner Memorial Medal; President's Medal.

2429 ■ **Bowling Proprietors' Association of Canada (BPAC)**
250 Shields Ct., Unit 10-A
Markham, ON, Canada L3R 9W7
Ph: (905)479-1560
Fax: (905)479-8613
Co. E-mail: info@bowlcanada.ca
URL: http://www.bowlcanada.ca
Contact: Paul Oliveira, Executive Director
Description: Owners of bowling alleys. Promotes increased participation in recreational and competitive bowling. Represents members' interests before business and labor organizations, government agencies, and the public. Conducts promotional activities.

2430 ■ **The National Bowling Association (TNBA)**
9944 Reading Rd.
Evendale, OH 45241-3106
Ph: (513)769-1985
Fax: (513)769-3596
Co. E-mail: nationaloffice@tnbainc.org
URL: http://www.tnbainc.org
Contact: Dr. Michael L. Boykins, President
Description: Seeks to: foster good sportsmanship, fellowship, and friendship; increase the interests, talents, and skills of adult and youth bowlers; create national awareness and interest in civic and community programs. Participates in and promotes bowling tournaments and other activities. Sponsors fundraising programs for sickle cell anemia and the United Negro College Fund. Bestows bowling awards, annual special bowling and service awards, and annual national and local scholarship awards. Maintains hall of fame; compiles statistics. **Founded:** 1939. **Publications:** *Bowler* (Quarterly); *Souvenir Yearbook* (Annual); *NBA History Book.*

2431 ■ **Professional Bowlers Association of America (PBA)**
719 2nd Ave., Ste. 701
Seattle, WA 98104-1747
Ph: (206)332-9688
Fax: (206)332-9722
Co. E-mail: membership@pba.com
URL: http://www.pba.com
Contact: Tom Clark, Commissioner
Description: Professional bowlers. Works to promote the status of the qualified bowler to the rank of professional; also promotes bowling as a major sport. Sponsors tournaments; assists the American Bowling Congress in enforcing its rules and regulations; has established code of ethics. Promotes better understanding between professional bowlers and bowling proprietors, bowling manufacturers, and the communications media. Maintains placement service, hall of fame, school, and insurance programs for members. Compiles statistics. **Founded:** 1958. **Awards:** Hall of Fame; Senior Player of the Year; Senior Rookie of the Year; Chris Schenkel Player of the Year; Harry Golden Rookie of the Year.

2432 ■ **United States Bowling Congress (USBC)**
621 Six Flags Dr.
Arlington, TX 76011
Ph: (414)321-8310
Free: 800-514-2695
Fax: (414)321-8356
Co. E-mail: bowlinfo@bowl.com
URL: http://www.bowl.com
Contact: Andrew Cain, President
Description: Aims to be the unified organization of choice focused on the growth of bowling. Ensures the integrity and protects the future of the sport, provides programs and services and enhances the bowling experience. **Founded:** 1895. **Publications:** *US Bowler* (Quarterly); *Bowling Magazine: Official Publication of American Bowling Congress* (Bimonthly). **Awards:** US Bowler Writing Competition (Annual); Media Awards Competition.

EDUCATIONAL PROGRAMS

2433 ■ **Vincennes University**
1002 N 1st St.
Vincennes, IN 47591
Ph: (812)888-4313
Free: 800-742-9198
Fax: (812)888-5707
Co. E-mail: vuadmit@vinu.edu
URL: http://www.vinu.edu
Contact: Richard E. Helton, President
Description: Two-year college offering a program in business administration; small business management classes; and bowling lane management and technology. **Founded:** 1801.

STATISTICAL SOURCES

2434 ■ **RMA Annual Statement Studies**
Pub: Risk Management Association
Contact: Kevin M. Blakey, President
Released: Annual. **Price:** $175.00 2006-07 edition, $105.00. **Description:** Contains composite balance sheets and income statements for more than 360 industries, including the accounting, auditing, and bookkeeping industries. Also contains five years of comparative historical data for discerning trends. Includes 16 commonly used ratios, computed for most of the size groupings for nearly every industry.

TRADE PERIODICALS

2435 ■ **BBIA enews**
Pub: Billiards and Bowling Institute of America
Ed: Sebastian Dicasoli, Editor. **Released:** Monthly, 3/year. **Price:** Free. **Description:** Serves as an update on the Institute's programs for manufacturers, distributors, and retailers of billiard and bowling supplies and equipment. Monitors executive changes, special promotions, new products, and trade show activities. Recurring features include member news.

2436 ■ **Bowlers Journal**
Contact: Keith Hamilton, President
URL(s): www.bowlersjournal.com/. **Released:** Monthly **Price:** $32, Individuals; $44, Two years; $54, Individuals three years; $57, Other countries.

2437 ■ **Bowling-Golfing News**
Pub: Master Associates
Ed: E.C. Townsend, Editor, edwardctownsend@hotmail.com. **Released:** Weekly. **Description:** Provides news and information on bowling and golf.

TRADE SHOWS AND CONVENTIONS

2438 ■ **FUN Expo**
Reed Exhibitions North American Headquarters
383 Main Ave.
Norwalk, CT 06851
Ph: (203)840-4800
Fax: (203)840-5805
Co. E-mail: inquiry@reedexpo.com
URL: http://www.reedexpo.com
URL(s): www.funexpo.com. **Price:** $20, Preregistered, members; $40, Pre-registered, nonmembers; $65, Onsite registered, members; $90, Onsite registered, non-members. **Frequency:** Annual. **Principal Exhibits:** Amusement and recreation products for family and location based entertainment centers, small amusement parks and family oriented businesses such as bowling centers, skating rinks, sports parks, miniature golf courses, golf driving ranges, family restaurants, resorts and other entertainment/recreation businesses.

2439 ■ International Bowl Expo
Bowling Proprietors Association of America
621 Six Flags Dr.
Arlington, TX 76011
Ph: (800)343-1329

Fax: (817)633-2940
URL: http://www.bpaa.com
Contact: Steve Johnson, Executive Director
E-mail: steve@bpaa.com
URL(s): www.bowlexpo.com. **Frequency:** Annual.
Audience: Bowling center owners/operators billiard

center owners, Bowling Pro Shop Owners. **Principal Exhibits:** Equipment, supplies, and services for the bowling industry, , Awards and Promotional Products, Financial and Insurance Services, Redemption Products. **Telecommunication Services:** leeann@bpaa.com.

START-UP INFORMATION

2440 ■ *Brewing Up a Business: Adventures in Entrepreneurship from the Founder of Dogfish Head Craft*
Pub: John Wiley and Sons, Inc.
Ed: Sam Calagione. **Released:** October 2006. **Price:** $16.95. **Description:** Author shares nontraditional success secrets. Calgione began his business with a home brewing kit and grew it into Dogfish Head Craft Beer, the leading craft brewery in the U.S.

ASSOCIATIONS AND OTHER ORGANIZATIONS

2441 ■ **American Beverage Institute (ABI)**
1090 Vermont Ave. NW, Ste. 800
Washington, DC 20005
Ph: (202)463-7110
URL: http://www.abionline.org
Contact: Sarah Longwell, Managing Director
Description: Provides public information regarding the consumption of adult beverages. Offers research and educational programs. **Founded:** 1991.

2442 ■ **American Breweriana Association (ABA)**
PO Box 595767
Fort Gratiot, MI 48059-5767
Ph: (810)385-7101
Fax: (810)385-7121
Co. E-mail: jseelow@americanbreweriana.org
URL: http://www.americanbreweriana.org
Contact: Larry Bowden, President
Description: Promotes the interest of collectors of brewery advertising and antiques, brewery historians, breweries, beer distributors and retailers, industrial workers, and beer workers. Promotes increased public knowledge of brewing history. Serves collectors and historians. Preserves the memories and artifacts of historic breweries in the U.S. Aims to restore the former brewery at Potosi, WI, into a National Brewery Museum. Provides an exchange service allowing collectors of beer labels, coasters, crown caps, openers, and printed material to exchange duplicates with other members. Assists members with research regarding brewery history and the industry. **Founded:** 1982. **Publications:** *American Breweriana Journal* (Bimonthly); *Directory of the American Breweriana Association* (Annual). **Educational Activities:** American Breweriana Association Convention (Annual). **Awards:** Excellence in Literature (Annual).

2443 ■ **Beer Institute**
122 C St., Ste. 350
Washington, DC 20001-2109
Ph: (202)737-2337
Fax: (202)737-7004
Co. E-mail: info@beerinstitute.org
URL: http://www.beerinst.org
Contact: Susan Haney, Director
E-mail: shaney@beerInstitute.org
Description: Brewers, importers, and suppliers to the industry. Committed to the development of public policy and to the values of civic duty and personal responsibility. **Publications:** *Brewing Industry in the U.S.: Brewers Almanac* (Annual); *Brewers Almanac; Beer Institute Bulletin* (Quarterly); *Membership.* **Educational Activities:** Beer Institute Meeting (Annual).

2444 ■ **Brewers Association of Canada (BAC)—L'Association des Brasseurs du Canada - Association des Brasseurs du Canada**
100 Queen St., Ste. 650
Ottawa, ON, Canada K1P 1J9
Ph: (613)232-9601
Fax: (613)232-2283
Co. E-mail: info@brewers.ca
URL: http://www.brewers.ca
Contact: Mr. Ian Faris, President
Description: Independent breweries operating in Canada. Promotes operation of microbreweries; seeks growth and development of the brewing industry. Represents members' interests; conducts educational programs; makes available promotional services to members. **Scope:** brewing. **Founded:** 1943. **Subscriptions:** books. **Publications:** *On Tap* (Bimonthly); *Statistical Bulletin* (Annual).

2445 ■ **Brewing and Malting Barley Research Institute (BMBRI)**
1510 One Lombard Pl.
Winnipeg, MB, Canada R3B 0X3
Ph: (204)927-1407
Fax: (204)947-5960
Co. E-mail: info@bmbri.ca
URL: http://www.bmbri.ca
Contact: Dr. Michael Brophy, President
Description: Supports the development and evaluation of new malting barley varieties in Canada on behalf of member companies. **Scope:** brewing, malting. **Founded:** 1948. **Subscriptions:** archival material business records clippings periodicals.

2446 ■ **Fermenters International Trade Association (FITA)**
c/o Dee Roberson, Sec.-Treas.
PO Box 1373
Valrico, FL 33595
Ph: (813)685-4261
Fax: (813)681-5625
Co. E-mail: droberson1@verizon.net
URL: http://www.fermentersinternational.org
Contact: John Pastor, President
Description: Manufacturers, wholesalers, retailers, authors, and editors having a commercial interest in the home beer-making and winemaking trade. Promotes the development and growth of home brewing, home winemaking, and associated trades. Sponsors wine competition. **Founded:** 1979. **Awards:** HWBTA Service Award (Annual).

2447 ■ **Master Brewers Association of the Americas (MBAA)**
3340 Pilot Knob Rd.
St. Paul, MN 55121-2055
Ph: (651)454-7250
Fax: (651)454-0766
Co. E-mail: mbaa@mbaa.com
URL: http://www.mbaa.com
Contact: Michael Sutton, President
Description: Provides opportunity for brewing professionals to interact with other fermentation industry professionals and to learn practical solutions, resourceful safeguards, and innovative technologies. **Founded:** 1887. **Publications:** *MBAA Technical Quarterly* (Quarterly). **Awards:** William A. Hipp Scholarships.

2448 ■ *On Tap*
100 Queen St., Ste. 650
Ottawa, ON, Canada K1P 1J9
Ph: (613)232-9601
Fax: (613)232-2283
Co. E-mail: info@brewers.ca
URL: http://www.brewers.ca
Contact: Mr. Ian Faris, President
Released: Bimonthly

2449 ■ *Statistical Bulletin*
100 Queen St., Ste. 650
Ottawa, ON, Canada K1P 1J9
Ph: (613)232-9601
Fax: (613)232-2283
Co. E-mail: info@brewers.ca
URL: http://www.brewers.ca
Contact: Mr. Ian Faris, President
Released: Annual

REFERENCE WORKS

2450 ■ *"Beer Drinkers Wanted More. The Brewer Had No Room to Expand. How Could It Keep the Taps Flowing?"* in *Inc.* (October 2007, pp. 65-66)
Pub: Gruner & Jahr USA Publishing
Ed: Alex Salkever. **Description:** Profile of John McDonald, founder of Boulevard, the second-largest beer company located in Kansas City, Missouri. McDonald tells how he was able to expand his turn-of-the-century brick building he had imported from Bavaria by developing a 70,000-square-foot building on four acres adjacent to his existing location rather move to a suburb.

2451 ■ *"Beer Sales 'Foament' a Dispute"* in *Philadelphia Business Journal* (Vol. 28, October 9, 2009, No. 34, pp. 1)
Pub: American City Business Journals
Ed: Peter van Allen. **Description:** Malt Beverages Distributors Association of Pennsylvania filed a case against the Liquor Control Board (LCB) at the Pennsylvania Supreme Court in order to further restrict store sales. The dispute stems from the supermarket chains circumventing the liquor law with the blessings of LCB.

2452 ■ *"Big Gains Brewing at Anheuser-Busch InBev"* in *Barron's* (Vol. 90, August 30, 2010, No. 35, pp. 34)
Pub: Barron's Editorial & Corporate Headquarters
Ed: Christopher C. Williams. **Description:** Anheuser-Busch InBev is realizing cost synergies and it posted better than expected returns two years after the

merger that formed the company. One analyst believes its American depositary receipt could be worth as much as 72 in a year.

2453 ■ *"Black Lotus Brewing Co." in Crain's Detroit Business (Vol. 23, October 1, 2007, No. 40, pp. 13)*
Pub: Crain Communications Inc. - Detroit
Ed: Leah Boyd. **Description:** Profile of Black Lotus Brewing Company and owner, Mike Allan who converted a drug store location into a brewery while restoring the building's original architecture.

2454 ■ *"Coors Execs Listen to Milwaukee Pitch" in Business Journal-Milwaukee (Vol. 25, November 2, 2007, No. 5, pp. A1)*
Pub: American City Business Journals, Inc.
Ed: Rich Rovito. **Description:** Coors Brewing Company officials met with Wisconsin Governor Jim Doyle and Milwaukee Mayor Tom Barnett about putting the MillerCoors corporate headquarters in Milwaukee. The city is competing with Denver, Colorado for the headquarters of the joint venture.

2455 ■ *"A Crystal Ball" in Business Journal Portland (Vol. 27, December 31, 2010, No. 44, pp. 1)*
Pub: Portland Business Journal
Ed: Wendy Culverwell. **Description:** McMenamins Pubs and Breweries has resumed construction of its Crystal Hotel project. The company has been working to convert a former bath house into a 51-room hotel. The hotel is expected to open in 2011.

2456 ■ *"Denver Will Put Up Fight for MillerCoors HQ" in Business Journal-Milwaukee (Vol. 25, October 19, 2007, No. 3, pp. A1)*
Pub: American City Business Journals, Inc.
Ed: Rich Rovito. **Description:** A contention exists between Milwaukee and Denver over which city will become the new location of the Miller Brewing Company (Milwaukee) and Coors Brewing Company (Colorado) joint venture MillerCoors. Leaders of the breweries since the announcement of the merger, have contended frantically to prepare strategies to back up their own cities. The advantages and disadvantages of both cities are presented.

2457 ■ *"Harding Brews Success at Anheuser-Busch" in Black Enterprise (Vol. 37, February 2007, No. 7, pp. 1)*
Pub: Earl G. Graves Publishing Co. Inc.
Ed: Mashaun D. Simon. **Description:** Profile of Michael S. Harding, president and CEO of Anheuser-Busch packaging group. Harding oversees five business units, 15 facilities, and over 2,300 workers.

2458 ■ *"I Fought the Law: a Brewery Comes Out on Top" in Inc. (Vol. 33, November 2011, No. 9, pp. 28)*
Pub: Inc. Magazine
Ed: Darren Dahl. **Description:** Profile of Omar Ansari, founder of Surly Brewing is presented. Ansari credits fans on Facebook and Twitter for contacting legislators with phone calls and emails to allow him to sell his beer to customers on site.

2459 ■ *The King of Vodka: The Story of Pyotr Smirnov and the Upheaval of an Empire*
Pub: HarperCollins Publishers
Ed: Linda Himelstein. **Released:** 2009. **Price:** $29.99. **Description:** Biography of Pyotr Smirnov and how his determination took him from serf to the head of Smirnov Vodka. Smirnov's marketing techniques are defined and show how he expanded the drink worldwide.

2460 ■ *"Lawyers Cash In On Alcohol" in Business Journal Portland (Vol. 27, November 19, 2010, No. 38, pp. 1)*
Pub: Portland Business Journal
Ed: Andy Giegerich. **Description:** Oregon-based law firms have continued to corner big business on the state's growing alcohol industry as demand for their services increased. Lawyers, who represent wine, beer and liquor distillery interests, have seen their workload increased by 20 to 30 percent in 2009.

2461 ■ *North American Brewers Resource Directory*
Pub: Brewers Publications
Contact: Paul Gatza, Director
URL(s): www.brewerspublications.com/browse-our-books. **Released:** Biennial; latest edition 2011-2012. **Price:** $59, Members; $125, Nonmembers. **Covers:** Manufacturers, suppliers, publications, associations, institutions, and breweries concerned with the beer microbrewing industry. **Entries include:** Organization, company, or institution name, address, phone, contact name, products or services, laws, publications. **Arrangement:** Classified by line of business. **Indexes:** Trade name, product/service (suppliers only), geographical.

2462 ■ *"SABMiller Deal Hit by Tax Ruling" in Wall Street Journal Eastern Edition (November 21 , 2011, pp. B9)*
Pub: Dow Jones & Company Inc.
Ed: David Fickling, Simon Zekaria. **Description:** SABMiller PLC, the giant brewer in the United Kingdom, is acquiring Australian beer icon Foster's Group Ltd. for US$9.9 billion, but will have to come up with another A$582 million following a tax ruling by the Australian Taxation Office in order that shareholders of Foster's don't lose.

2463 ■ *"South Park Draws Brewers, Vintners" in Puget Sound Business Journal (Vol. 29, August 29, 2008, No. 19, pp. 1)*
Pub: American City Business Journals
Ed: Heidi Dietrich. **Description:** Craft breweries and wineries are moving into Seattle, Washington's South Park neighborhood due to the area's low rents, convenience, and ample equipment space. These industries bring a more upscale flavor to the heavily industrial area and the tastings and festivals draw people from throughout the Seattle region.

2464 ■ *Star Spangled Beer: A Guide to America's New Microbreweries and Brewpubs*
Pub: Jack Erickson
URL(s): www.realbeer.com/redbrickpress/bookord.html. **Price:** $13.95, Individuals. **Covers:** 100 microbreweries and brewpubs; coverage includes Canada. **Entries include:** Company name, address, phone, products. **Arrangement:** Geographical. **Indexes:** Company name.

2465 ■ *"They're Hopping Mad" in Canadian Business (Vol. 80, October 22, 2007, No. 21, pp. 20)*
Pub: Rogers Media
Description: Alberta Review Panel is calling for a 20 percent increase in oil and gas development taxes. SABMiller and Molson Coors Brewing Company combined its U.S. and Puerto Rican operations, though the deal is still subject to regulatory approvals. Montreal Exchange Inc. filed for approval of the trade of Montreal Climate Exchange futures contracts.

2466 ■ *"The Traveling Godfather: Beam Global Spirits & Wine Inc." in Canadian Business (Vol. 81, October 13, 2008, No. 17, pp. S10)*
Pub: Rogers Media Ltd.
Ed: Andy Holoway. **Description:** Dan Tullio, director of Canadian Club, is seen as a godfather because he gets to be asked a lot of favors. Tullio gets to immerse himself into other cultures because of his employment as global ambassador of Beam Global Spirits & Wine Inc. Tullio's views, as well as information about him are presented.

2467 ■ *"Troy Brewer Opens Own Bottling Operation" in Business Review, Albany New York (Vol. 34, November 16, 2007, No. 33, pp. 3)*
Pub: American City Business Journals, Inc.
Ed: Michael DeMasi. **Description:** Brown Brewing Company's owner Peter Martin invested in $100,000 worth of bottling equipment and has now doubled his production capacity to 3,000 barrels. Davidson Brothers, another brewery that bottles its own beer, sells 3,000 to 5,000 cases of beer annually. Industry sales of draft breweries are presented.

STATISTICAL SOURCES

2468 ■ *The Microbreweries Market*
Pub: Rector Press, Ltd.
Contact: Lewis Sckolnick, President
Released: 2009. **Price:** Contact Rector Press.

2469 ■ *Outlook for the American Beer Market*
Pub: Business Trend Analysts, Inc.
Released: 2004-2005. **Price:** $1895.00. **Description:** Analyzes the U.S. beer market. Covers the influence of new imports and the Canadian beer market through 1991. Profiles companies such as Anheuser-Busch, Coors, Heilemann, Philip Morris, and Stroh. Profiles include financial news, marketing strategies, and brand performance.

2470 ■ *Standard & Poor's Industry Surveys*
Pub: Standard & Poor's Corp.
Released: Annual. **Price:** $3633.00. **Description:** Two-volume book that examines the prospects for specific industries, including trucking. Also provides analyses of trends and problems, statistical tables and charts, and comparative company analyses.

TRADE PERIODICALS

2471 ■ *Ale Street News*
Pub: Tuscarora Inc.
Contact: Anthony Forder, President
URL(s): www.alestreetnews.com/. **Released:** Bimonthly **Price:** $20, Individuals.

2472 ■ *Cocktails Magazine*
Pub: Destiny Productions for Print, Radio & Cable Promotions
URL(s): www.cocktail.com/. **Released:** Monthly

2473 ■ *Modern Brewery Age*
Pub: Business Journals, Inc.
Contact: Britton Jones, President
E-mail: brittonj@busjour.com
URL(s): www.breweryage.com. **Ed:** Peter V.K. Reid. **Released:** Bimonthly **Price:** $125, Individuals.

2474 ■ *Modern Brewery Age Tabloid Edition*
Pub: Business Journals, Inc.
Contact: Britton Jones, President
E-mail: brittonj@busjour.com
URL(s): www.breweryage.com/tabloid/. **Ed:** Peter Reid. **Released:** Weekly **Price:** $95, Individuals via email.

VIDEOCASSETTES/ AUDIOCASSETTES

2475 ■ *How It's Made*
Lucerne Media
37 Ground Pine Rd.
Morris Plains, NJ 07950
Free: 800-341-2293
Fax: (973)538-0855
Co. E-mail: lucernemedia@optonline.net
URL: http://www.lucernemedia.com
Released: 1988. **Price:** $95.00. **Description:** The entire process of the beer industry is distilled into these three programs, plus a look at how bottle caps are made. **Availability:** VHS; 3/4 U.

TRADE SHOWS AND CONVENTIONS

2476 ■ **National Beer Wholesalers Association Convention and Exposition**
National Beer Wholesalers Association
1101 King St., Ste. 600
Alexandria, VA 22314-2944
Ph: (703)683-4300
Free: 800-300-6417
Fax: (703)683-8965
Co. E-mail: info@nbwa.org
URL: http://www.nbwa.org
Contact: Craig A. Purser, President
URL(s): www.nbwa.org. **Frequency:** Biennial. **Audience:** Beer distributors and wholesalers. **Principal Exhibits:** Brewery software and hardware, trucking,

beer cleaning equipment, and related equipment, supplies, and services. **Telecommunication Services:** info@nbwa.org.

2477 ■ Wine and Spirits Wholesalers of America Convention and Exposition

Wine and Spirits Wholesalers of America
805 15th St. NW, Ste. 430
Washington, DC 20005
Ph: (202)371-9792
Fax: (202)789-2405
Co. E-mail: juanita.duggan@wswa.org
URL: http://www.wswa.org
Contact: Craig Wolf, President

URL(s): wswa.org/meetings.php?EventID=10. **Frequency:** Annual. **Audience:** Wine and spirits wholesalers; suppliers of any product of service distributed or utilized by wholesalers. **Principal Exhibits:** Producers of spirits, wine, beer, mixes, bottled water; freight routing/forwarding companies; computer hardware/software; point of sale products vendors; warehouse equipment producers; forklifts, security systems, conveyor and packing systems; scanners.

CONSULTANTS

2478 ■ Bio-Technical Resources L.P. (BTR)

1035 S 7th St.
Manitowoc, WI 54220-5301
Ph: (920)684-5518
Fax: (920)684-5519
Co. E-mail: info@biotechresources.com
URL: http://www.biotechresources.com
Contact: Tom Jerrell, President

Scope: Services include strain improvement, process development and metabolic engineering. Solutions are also offered for the development of biotechnology products and processes through contract services in research and development, bio process scale-up, pilot scale manufacturing, technology and economic assessments. Target audience: pharmaceutical, biotechnology, chemical and food and feed industries. Client base may be global leaders as well as small companies and startups. **Founded:** 1962. **Publications:** "A Novel Fungus for the Production of Efficient Cellulases and Hemi-Cellulases," Jun, 2009; "Linoleic Acid Isomerase from Propionibacterium acnes: Purification, Characterization, Molecular Cloning, and Heterologous Expression," 2007; "Purification and Characterization of a Membrane-Bound Linoleic Acid Isomerase from Clostridium sporogenes," 2007; "Metabolic Engineering of Sesquiterpene Metabolism in Yeast," 2007; "Purification and Characterization of a Membrane-Bound Linoleic Acid Isomerase from Clostridium sporogenes," 2007; "Reduction of Background Interference in the Spectrophotometric Assay of Mevalonate Kinase," 2006; "A Soluble Form of Phosphatase in Saccharomyces cerevisiae Capable of Converting Farnesyl Diphosphate to E, E-Farnesol," 2006; "Ascorbate Biosynthesis: A Diversity of Pathways," BIOS Scientific Publishers, 2004; "The Biotechnology of Ascorbic Acid Manufacture," BIOS Scientific Publishers, 2004; "Detection of Farnesyl Diphosphate Accumulation in YeastERG9 Mutants," 2003; "Reverse Two-Hybrid System: Detecting Critical Interaction Domains and Screening for Inhibitors," Eaton Publishing, 2000. **Seminars:** Metabolic Engineering for Industrial Production of Glucosamine and N-Acetylglucosamine, Aug, 2003; Metabolic Engineering of E. coli for the Industrial Production of Glucosamine, Apr, 2003.

LIBRARIES

2479 ■ Anheuser-Busch Companies, Inc. - Corporate Library

1 Busch Pl.
St. Louis, MO 63118
Ph: (314)577-2000
Free: 800-342-5283
URL: http://www.anheuser-busch.com
Contact: Ann Lauenstein, Librarian

Scope: Brewing chemistry, fermentation technology, food and beverage industries, alcohol and alcoholism, yeast, business and industrial management. **Services:** Interlibrary loan. **Founded:** 1852. **Holdings:** 50,000 books; 60,000 bound periodical volumes; 100 pamphlet boxes of Annual reports; 25 VF drawers of U.S. and foreign patents; 70 pamphlet boxes of clippings. **Subscriptions:** 1000 journals and other serials.

2480 ■ Brewers Association of Canada Library

45 O'Connor St.,Ste. 650
Ottawa, ON, Canada K1P 1A4
Ph: (613)232-9601
Fax: (613)232-2283
Co. E-mail: info@brewers.ca
URL: http://www.brewers.ca
Contact: Edwin P. Gregory, Director, Research Policy Director

Scope: Brewing process (technical), legislation, control policies in Canada and abroad, beer and health, beer statistics (domestic and international).

Services: Interlibrary loan; copying; library open to the public by appointment only. **Founded:** 1970. **Holdings:** 500 books; 500 papers on use and abuse of alcohol. **Subscriptions:** 25 journals and other serials.

2481 ■ Coors Brewing Company Technical Library

PO Box 4030
Golden, CO 80401
Free: 800-642-6116
URL: http://www.coors.com/
Contact: Stephen Boss, Librarian

Scope: Brewing, microbiology, chemistry, law, engineering. **Services:** Copying; library open to the public by appointment with restrictions. **Founded:** 1972. **Holdings:** 7000 books; 40,000 internal reports; patents; clippings; pamphlets. **Subscriptions:** 400 journals and other serials; 15 newspapers.

2482 ■ Miller Brewing Company - Scientific and Technical Information Facility

3939 W. Highland Blvd.
Milwaukee, WI 53208
Ph: (414)931-3640
Fax: (414)931-2818
Co. E-mail: langley.emily@mbco.com
URL: http://www.millerbrewing.com
Contact: Emily A. Langley, Specialist

Scope: Brewing, chemistry, microbiology, chemical engineering, genetics, enzymology. **Services:** Interlibrary loan; facility open to the public with restrictions. **Founded:** 1979. **Holdings:** 3000 books; 1500 bound periodical volumes; 10,000 patents; 80 reels of microfilm; 4000 microfiche; 1500 research reports. **Subscriptions:** 200 journals and other serials.

2483 ■ University of California, Davis - University Libraries - Special Collections

100 NW Quad
Shields Library, 1st Fl.
Davis, CA 95616-5292
Ph: (530)752-1621
Fax: (916)754-5758
Co. E-mail: dmorrison@ucdavis.edu
URL: http://www.lib.ucdavis.edu/dept/specol/
Contact: Liz Phillips

Scope: Reference. **Services:** Copying; collections open to the public for reference use only. **Founded:** 1966. **Holdings:** 129,500 books; 18,700 lin.ft. of archives and manuscripts. **Subscriptions:** 40 journals and other serials; 2 newspapers. **Telecommunication Services:** speccoll@ucdavis.edu.

START-UP INFORMATION

2484 ■ *How to Open and Operate a Financially Successful Wedding Consultant and Planning Business: With Companion CD-ROM*
Pub: Atlantic Publishing Group, Inc.
Ed: John N. Peragine. **Released:** May 2008. **Price:** $39.95 paperback. **Description:** Consumers are spending a record $46 billion on weddings annually, with the average wedding costing around $32,000. Wedding consultants and planners provide information, ideas and contacts for brides along with guidance on etiquette, invitations, planning and directing the rehearsal and ceremony, and even arranging transportation and accommodations.

2485 ■ *Start Your Own Wedding Consultant Business*
Pub: Entrepreneur Press
Ed: Eileen Figure Sandlin. **Released:** December 2003. **Description:** Advice for starting and running a wedding consulting business.

ASSOCIATIONS AND OTHER ORGANIZATIONS

2486 ■ American Society of Wedding Professionals (ASWP)
26 Roden Way
Closter, NJ 07624
Ph: (201)244-5969
Free: 800-274-3350
Fax: (973)574-7626
Co. E-mail: info@localtrafficbuilder.com
URL: http://www.localtrafficbuilder.com
Contact: Brian D. Lawrence, Executive Officer
Description: Professionals in the wedding industry. Promotes the wedding professional and educates brides on the experience of working with a consultant. Provides trends, etiquette, marketing, consulting information, directory listing, referrals, networking, and co-op advertising. Offers local forums for information exchange among members. Compiles statistics and conducts educational programs and seminars. **Scope:** general business, marketing, wedding planning, wedding etiquette, international weddings, wedding industry, bridal statistics. **Founded:** 1992. **Subscriptions:** audio recordings books clippings periodicals. **Publications:** *WedPro News* (Monthly).

2487 ■ Association of Bridal Consultants
56 Danbury Rd., Ste. 11
New Milford, CT 06776
Ph: (860)355-7000
Fax: (860)354-1404
Co. E-mail: office@bridalassn.com
URL: http://www.bridalassn.com
Contact: David M. Wood, III, President
Description: Represents independent bridal and wedding consultants; persons employed by companies in wedding-related businesses and novices looking to get into the business. Strives to improve professionalism and recognition of bridal and wedding

consultants. Offers professional development program, startup manual and seminars. Provides advertising, publicity, referrals and information services. Operates speakers' bureau; compiles statistics. **Scope:** weddings, business management, consulting. **Founded:** 1955. **Subscriptions:** 75 audiovisuals books. **Publications:** *ABC Dialogue* (Bimonthly); *Retail Resource Directory* (Semiannual); *Weddings As A Business*; *Retail Resource Directory* (Semiannual); *ABC Dialogue*; *Ethnic and Specialty by Wedding Guide* (Periodic); *Association of Bridal Consultants--Retail Resource Directory* (Semiannual). **Educational Activities:** Business of Brides Annual Conference (Annual). **Awards:** "Miss Dorothy" Heart (Annual); "Miss Dorothy" Scholarship (Annual).

2488 ■ Association for Wedding Professionals International (AFWPI)
6700 Freeport Blvd., Ste. 202
Sacramento, CA 95822
Ph: (916)392-5000
Free: 800-242-4461
Fax: (916)392-5222
Co. E-mail: richard@afwpi.com
URL: http://www.afwpi.com
Contact: Richard Markel, Director
Description: Professionals working in the wedding industry. Promotes adherence to high standards of ethics and practice by members; seeks to advance members' professional standing. Serves as a network linking members; offers member discounts on business services, insurance, and advertising; sponsors educational programs. **Founded:** 1995. **Publications:** *Professional Connection* (Quarterly). **Educational Activities:** Christmas Party; Monthly Networking Mixer (Monthly); Regionals (Annual). **Awards:** Wedding Professional of the Year (Annual).

2489 ■ Bridal Association of America (BAOA)
531 H St.
Bakersfield, CA 93304
Ph: (661)633-9200
Free: 866-699-3334
Fax: (661)633-9199
Co. E-mail: kyle@bridalassociationofamerica.com
URL: http://www.bridalassociationofamerica.com
Contact: Mr. Kyle Brown, Executive Director
Description: Provides free and accessible information on wedding planning and on how to adjust on living life as a couple. Provides a forum for wedding professionals to express their own approaches and styles when it comes to their own wedding products and services. **Scope:** weddings. **Founded:** 1999. **Subscriptions:** 1. **Publications:** *The Wedding Book* (Annual).

2490 ■ Wedding and Event Videographers Association International (WEVA)
8499 S Tamiami Trail
PMB 208
Sarasota, FL 34238
Ph: (941)923-5334
Fax: (941)921-3836
Co. E-mail: info@weva.com
URL: http://www.weva.com
Contact: Roy Chapman, Chairman Founder
URL(s): www.wevaexpo.com. **Description:** Professional wedding and event videographers. Serves as

a trade organization representing members' commercial interests. Provides educational programs and resources to wedding and event videographers. **Founded:** 1995. **Publications:** *Wedding and Event Videography Resource Guide*; *The Business of Wedding and Special Event Videography*. **Awards:** Creative Excellence Award (Annual).

2491 ■ Wedding and Portrait Photographers International (WPPI)
c/o Nielsen Expositions
6255 Sunset Blvd., 19th Fl.
Los Angeles, CA 90028-7420
Ph: (323)817-3500
URL: http://www.wppionline.com/index.shtml
Contact: Steven Sheanin, President
URL(s): www.wppionline.com. **Description:** Represents wedding portrait and digital photographers and photographers employed at general photography studios. Promotes high artistic and technical standards in wedding photography. Serves as a forum for the exchange of technical knowledge and experience; makes available the expertise of top professionals in the field of photographic arts and technology, advertising, sales promotion, marketing, public relations, accounting, business management, tax, and profit planning. Members are offered the opportunity to purchase special products and services. **Founded:** 1973. **Publications:** *Rangefinder*; *Wedding Photographer* (Monthly); *WPPI Photography Monthly* (Monthly); *Marketing and Technical Manual* (Quarterly). **Educational Activities:** Wedding and Portrait Photographers International Competition (Semiannual); Wedding and Portrait Photographers International Convention (Semiannual). **Awards:** Accolade Program (Semiannual); Print Competitions (Annual); Awards of Excellence.

REFERENCE WORKS

2492 ■ *"2011 Summer Wedding and Party Tips and Must Have's" in Benzinga.com (June 17, 2011)*
Pub: Benzinga.com
Ed: Benzinga Staff. **Description:** Tips for hosting garden parties and get-togethers, but focusing on wedding receptions are provided.

2493 ■ *"Carnival Cruise Lines Hosts First-Ever Wedding at Charleston's Annual 10K Cooper River Bridge Run" in Benzinga.com (April 4, 2011)*
Pub: Benzinga.com
Ed: Benzinga Staff. **Description:** Carnival Cruise Lines hosted a post-race wedding ceremony after the Cooper River Bridge Run in South Carolina.

2494 ■ *"Chesapeake Beach Resort and Spa Announces Dream Waterfront Wedding Giveaway" in Benzinga.com (October 29, 2011)*
Pub: Benzinga.com
Ed: Benzinga Staff. **Description:** Chesapeake Beach Resort and Spa will give away a Dream Waterfront Wedding to a lucky bride and groom in order to promote their resort as a wedding venue.

2495 ■ *"CPI Corporation Acquires Assets of Bella Pictures"* in *Benzinga.com (January 28, 2011)*
Pub: Benzinga.com
Ed: Benzinga Staff. **Description:** CPI Corporation acquired assets of Bella Pictures Inc., a leading provider of branded wedding photography services. Details of the acquisition are explained.

2496 ■ *"Destination Wedding Giveaway!"* in *Benzinga.com (October 29, 2011)*
Pub: Benzinga.com
Ed: Benzinga Staff. **Description:** Eden Condominiums in Perdido Key, Florida will award a beach wedding to a couple in 2012. The event is a marketing tool to draw attention brides as a perfect wedding venue.

2497 ■ *"Discover the Wedding Location of Your Dreams"* in *Benzinga.com (December 24, 2011)*
Pub: Benzinga.com
Ed: Benzinga Staff. **Description:** Ritz Carlton Hotel Company helps couples choose from their 70 wedding locations worldwide with wedding advisors to assist in planning.

2498 ■ *"Esencia Estate to Host 'The Esencia Experience for Upscale Wedding Planners"* in *Benzinga.com (October 29, 2011)*
Pub: Benzinga.com
Ed: Benzinga Staff. **Description:** Esencia Estate located in the Riviera Maya, Mexico is reintroducing the estate as a premier wedding venue. They are hosting an event to help wedding planners envision plans at the estate.

2499 ■ *"Fairfax Announces Acquisition of William Ashley"* in *Benzinga.com (August 16, 2011)*
Pub: Benzinga.com
Ed: Benzinga Staff. **Description:** Fairfax Financial Holdings Limited acquired the family-owned William Ashley China company, leader within the dinnerware and wedding registry industries and was the first company in North America to introduce a computerized wedding registry system.

2500 ■ *"Finally, a Unique Solution to Meet All Wedding Planning Needs"* in *Benzinga.com (September 29, 2011)*
Pub: Benzinga.com
Ed: Benzinga Staff. **Description:** WEDdeals.ca, a Canadian-based firm, lists up to 90 percent discounts on wedding vendor services in a particular area to help couples plan their weddings.

2501 ■ *"Freelance Writer Creates L.I. Bridal Blog"* in *Long Island Business News (September 10, 2010)*
Pub: Dolan Media Newswires
Ed: Gregory Zeller. **Description:** Profile of Claudia Copquin, freelance journalist who created a blog for brides on the Internet.

2502 ■ *"Grand Bohemian Hotel in Orlando, Fla. Takes Lead in Wedding Planning"* in *Benzinga.com (August 4, 2011)*
Pub: Benzinga.com
Ed: Benzinga Staff. **Description:** MAD-Marketing launched a newly-designed Website for the Grand Bohemian Hotel in Orlando, Florida. The site features the hotel's wedding vanity site to help target prospective couples planning their weddings.

2503 ■ *"Host Your Dream Wedding at the Minneapolis Marriott Southwest"* in *Benzinga.com (June 6, 2011)*
Pub: Benzinga.com
Ed: Benzinga Staff. **Description:** Minneapolis Marriott Southwest is helping engaged couples plan their wedding destination at their property. Details of wedding reception options are outlined.

2504 ■ *"International Monetary Barter Helps Discretionary Industry"* in *Benzinga.com (January 24, 2011)*
Pub: Benzinga.com
Ed: Benzinga Staff. **Description:** International Monetary Systems Limited, a business-to-business bartering firm, is helping wedding and event planners close deals with customers with bartering solutions.

2505 ■ *"Markel American Insurance Company Announces Wedding and Special Event Insurance for Consumers"* in *Benzinga.com (February 16, 2011)*
Pub: Benzinga.com
Ed: Benzinga Staff. **Description:** Markel American Insurance Company, headquartered in Waukesha, Wisconsin has launched its new special event insurance and wedding insurance to protect both liabilities and cancellations associated with these events.

2506 ■ *"Memphis Marriott Downtown Offers Wedding Reception Discounts to Soon-To-Be Newlyweds"* in *Benzinga.com (June 23, 2011)*
Pub: Benzinga.com
Ed: Benzinga Staff. **Description:** Memphis Marriott Downtown in Memphis, Tennessee is offering wedding reception discounts to couples planning their weddings.

2507 ■ *"Military Brides Can Get Free Wedding Gowns"* in *Virginian-Pilot (November 10, 2010)*
Pub: The Virginia-Pilot
Ed: Jamesetta Walker. **Description:** Seventy-five designer wedding gowns will be given to military brides on a first-come, first-served basis at Maya Couture through the Brides Across America's wedding gown giveaway program. Gowns are valued between $500 to $3,000 and are donated by designers Maggie Sottero, Pronovias and Essense of Australia.

2508 ■ *"Modern Bride Unveiled Exclusively at JCPenney"* in *Benzinga.com (February 3, 2011)*
Pub: Benzinga.com
Ed: Benzinga Staff. **Description:** JCPenney created its new Modern Bride concept in its bridal find jewelry departments. The new shopping experience is a collaboration between the retailer and Conde Nast catering to the bridal customer.

2509 ■ *"More Brides, Grooms Say 'I Do' to Interracial Marriage"* in *Black Enterprise (Vol. 41, August 2010, No. 1, pp. 36)*
Pub: Earl G. Graves Publishing Co. Inc.
Description: According to a recent survey conducted by Pew Research Center, a record 14.6 percent of all new marriages in the U.S. in 2008 were interracial. Statistical data included.

2510 ■ *"New York City-Based New Street Realty Advisors has Secured a New Flagship for David's Bridal"* in *Chain Store Age (August 2008)*
Pub: Chain Store Age
Description: New York City-based New Street Realty Advisors secured a new flagship store for David's Bridal in the Chelsea district of Manhattan. David's Bridal will occupy 12,800 square feet on two floors in a retail condominium development.

2511 ■ *"On Your Marks, American Airlines, Now Vote!"* in *Benzinga.com (, 2011)*
Pub: Benzinga.com
Ed: Benzinga Staff. **Description:** Wedding planner, Aviva Samuels, owner of Kiss the Planner boutique wedding and event planning agency in Florida, says that winning this contest would help her increase her knowledge base and provide in-depth, personal experience offering more destination wedding destinations.

2512 ■ *"Online Security Crackdown: Scanning Service Oversees Site Security at David's Bridal"* in *(Vol. 84, July 2008, No. 7, pp. 46)*
Pub: Chain Store Age
Ed: Samantha Murphy. **Description:** Online retailers are beefing up security on their Websites. Cyber thieves use retail systems in order to gain entry to consumer data. David's Bridal operates over 275 bridal showrooms in the U.S. and has a one-stop wedding resource for new brides planning weddings.

2513 ■ *"Party Animals"* in *Business Review, Albany New York (Vol. 34, November 16, 2007, No. 33, pp. 1)*
Pub: American City Business Journals, Inc.
Ed: Donna Abbott Viahos. **Description:** Total Events LLC, an event planning firm founded by Richard Carrier, generated sales from $13,000 to $1.5 million in eight years. Fine Affairs Inc. generates more than a million of revenues a year. Both companies provide party planning, organizing and decorating, wedding, galas, bar mitzvahs and other event planning.

2514 ■ *"Peacocks Launches Its First Wedding Dress"* in *Benzinga.com (July 1, 2011)*
Pub: Benzinga.com
Ed: Benzinga Staff. **Description:** Peacocks, a leading fashion retailer in the United Kingdom launched its first wedding dress available for sale in August 2011.

2515 ■ *"Plan Your Next Event at Newport News Marriott at City Center"* in *Benzinga.com (July 29, 2011)*
Pub: Benzinga.com
Ed: Benzinga Staff. **Description:** Newport News Marriott at City Center is promoting itself as the premier venue for business meetings, conventions and weddings.

2516 ■ *"Plan Your Wedding with Cleveland Airport Marriott's Certified Event Planners"* in *Benzinga.com (February 2, 2011)*
Pub: Benzinga.com
Ed: Benzinga Staff. **Description:** Cleveland's Airport Marriott makes wedding planning easy with its venue spaces and a full team of wedding planners.

2517 ■ *"Planning a Wedding Fit for a Royal? Read This First, Urge Legal and General"* in *Benzinga.com (April 21, 2011)*
Pub: Benzinga.com
Ed: Benzinga Staff. **Description:** When planning a wedding, the author suggests checking life insurance to be sure you are covered for any situations that may arise.

2518 ■ *"The Power of Commitment: Mere Motivation Is Often Not Enough To Achieve Your Goals"* in *Black Enterprise (November 2007)*
Pub: Earl G. Graves Publishing Co. Inc.
Ed: Tamara E. Holmes. **Description:** Profile of Michelle Tucker Kirk who opened her bridal shop in 2006. Kirk explains how her commitment and determination were keys to the company's success. Five signs to help any would-be entrepreneur discover if they are truly committed to a business idea are listed.

2519 ■ *"Renren Partners With Recruit to Launch Social Wedding Services"* in *Benzinga.com (June 7, 2011)*
Pub: Benzinga.com
Ed: Benzinga Staff. **Description:** Renren Inc. and Recruit Company Ltd. partnered to build a wedding social media catering to engaged couples and newlyweds in China. The platform will integrate online wedding related social content and offline media such as magazine and wedding exhibitions.

2520 ■ *"Renren Partnership With Recruit to Launch Social Wedding Services"* in *Benzinga.com (June 7, 2011)*
Pub: Benzinga.com
Ed: Benzinga Staff. **Description:** Renren Inc., the leading real name social networking Internet platform in China has partnered with Recruit Company Limited, Japan's largest human resource and classified media group to form a joint venture to build a wedding social media catering to the needs of engaged couples and newlyweds in China.

2521 ■ *"Research and Markets: Wedding Statistics and Industry Reports"* in *Benzinga.com (June 24, 2011)*
Pub: Benzinga.com
Ed: Benzinga Staff. **Description:** The latest trends and statistics regarding weddings and the wedding industry are spotlighted.

2522 ■ *"Style Me Pretty on My Wedding Day - Final Chance to Enter" in Benzinga.com (October 29, 2011)*
Pub: Benzinga.com
Ed: Benzinga Staff. **Description:** Style Me Pretty and Christian Dior have partnered to award one bride the chance to have a personal Dior makeup artist for their wedding day.

2523 ■ *"Sylvie Collection Offers a Feminine Perspective and Voice in Male Dominated Bridal Industry" in Benzinga.com (October 29, 2011)*
Pub: Benzinga.com
Ed: Benzinga Staff. **Description:** Bridal jewelry designer Sylvie Levine has created over 1,000 customizable styles of engagement rings and wedding bands and is reaching out to prospective new brides through a new Website, interactive social media campaign and monthly trunk show appearances.

2524 ■ *"TLC's 'Jumping the Broom' Red Carpet Wedding Contest" in Benzinga.com (March 30, 2011)*
Pub: Benzinga.com
Ed: Benzinga Staff. **Description:** The Learning Channel's 'Jumping the Broom' Red Carpet Wedding Contest provides couples the chance to marry or renew vows at the star-studded Hollywood premier of the new film.

2525 ■ *"TripIt Itineraries Show Labor Day is the Most Popular Weekend for Wedding Travel" in Benzinga.com (August 26, 2011)*
Pub: Benzinga.com
Ed: Benzinga Staff. **Description:** According to TripIt, the leading mobile trip organizer, Labor Day is the most popular weekend to travel for weddings between the months of April and August.

2526 ■ *"Trousseaus of Memories Trail Behind Wedding Gowns" in Oregonian (September 4, 2010)*
Pub: The Oregonian
Ed: Anne Saker. **Description:** Readers are asked to share stories about their wedding gowns and what that garment meant to them at the time and now.

2527 ■ *"Wedding Bells on a Budget: Have Your Cake and Eat It Too" in Benzinga.com (June 11, 2011)*
Pub: Benzinga.com
Ed: Benzinga Staff. **Description:** Typical American weddings cost about $24,000 with most couples spending between $18,000 to $30,000; a checklist and budget are critical. Nine ideas to help couples plan for their big day are outlined.

2528 ■ *"Wedding Present Shopping - What to Get the Couple Who Have Everything" in Benzinga.com (April 19, 2011)*
Pub: Benzinga.com
Ed: Benzinga Staff. **Description:** Tips for purchasing the perfect wedding gift are outlined.

2529 ■ *"Wedding: Style Gowns Ready to Go" in Houston Chronicle (June 3, 2010)*
Pub: Houston Chronicle
Ed: Molly Glentzer. **Description:** Wedding gowns with slender silhouettes travel well for destination weddings. Amsale, Oscar del la Renta and Monique Lhuillier dresses are highlighted.

2530 ■ *"WeddingChannel.com Reviews Tops More than 200,000 Wedding Reviews" in Benzinga.com (June 23, 2011)*
Pub: Benzinga.com
Ed: Benzinga Staff. **Description:** WeddingChannel. com is the leading wedding and gift registry Website for soon-to-be brides with search and review information on over 130,000 of the wedding industry's top vendors and even allows vendors to interact with the prospective brides.

TRADE PERIODICALS

2531 ■ *ABC Dialogue*
Pub: Association of Bridal Consultants
Contact: David M. Wood, III, President
Ed: Gerard J. Monaghan, Editor. **Released:** Bimonthly, 6/year. **Price:** Included in membership. **Description:** Explores the various aspects of wedding consulting, including bridal attire, jewelry, food, photography, and business management and advertising. Recurring features include business tips and profiles of members.

2532 ■ *Cincinnati Wedding*
Pub: Cincinnati Magazine Inc.
URL(s): www.cincinnatimagazinewedding.com/. **Ed:** Kara Hagerman. **Released:** Semiannual

2533 ■ *Modern Bride*
Pub: Conde Nast Publications
Contact: David Carey, President
URL(s): www.brides.com/about/modern-bridewww. condenast.com/. **Released:** Monthly **Price:** $16.95, Individuals 12 issues; $28, Two years 24 issues.

2534 ■ *New England Bride*
Pub: New England Bride Inc.
URL(s): www.nebride.com. **Released:** Monthly **Price:** $36, Individuals.

2535 ■ *Vows: The Bridal and Wedding Business Journal*
Pub: Grimes and Associates
Contact: Karl Nazarro, Director
E-mail: karl@vowsmagazine.com
URL(s): www.vowsmagazine.com. **Released:** Bimonthly **Price:** $30, Individuals; $52, Two years; $55, Elsewhere.

VIDEOCASSETTES/ AUDIOCASSETTES

2536 ■ *Planning a Wedding to Remember*
Cambridge Educational
c/o Films Media Group
132 West 31st Street, 17th Floor
Ste. 124
New York, NY 10001
Free: 800-257-5126
Fax: (609)671-0266
Co. E-mail: custserve@films.com
URL: http://www.cambridgeol.com
Released: 1990. **Price:** $19.95. **Description:** Wedding authority Beverly Clark covers all facets involved in planning a wedding. **Availability:** VHS.

2537 ■ *Planning Your Wedding, Vol. 1: Selecting Your Formal Wear*
Leslie T. McClure
PO Box 1223
Pebble Beach, CA 93953
Ph: (831)656-0553
Fax: (831)656-0555
Co. E-mail: leslie@411videoinfo.com
URL: http://www.411videoinfo.com
Released: 1998. **Price:** $29.95. **Description:** Part of a ten-volume series for brides- and grooms-to-be that follows the steps taken by a typical couple, Jeff and Lisa, in their preparation for the big event. **Availability:** VHS.

2538 ■ *Planning Your Wedding, Vol. 2: A Visit to Your Caterer*
Leslie T. McClure
PO Box 1223
Pebble Beach, CA 93953
Ph: (831)656-0553
Fax: (831)656-0555
Co. E-mail: leslie@411videoinfo.com
URL: http://www.411videoinfo.com
Released: 1998. **Price:** $29.95. **Description:** Part of a ten-volume series for brides- and grooms-to-be that follows the steps taken by a typical couple, Jeff and Lisa, in their preparation for the big event. **Availability:** VHS.

2539 ■ *Planning Your Wedding, Vol. 3: Selecting Your Wedding Cake*
Leslie T. McClure
PO Box 1223
Pebble Beach, CA 93953
Ph: (831)656-0553

Fax: (831)656-0555
Co. E-mail: leslie@411videoinfo.com
URL: http://www.411videoinfo.com
Released: 1998. **Price:** $29.95. **Description:** Part of a ten-volume series for brides- and grooms-to-be that follows the steps taken by a typical couple, Jeff and Lisa, in their preparation for the big event. **Availability:** VHS.

2540 ■ *Planning Your Wedding, Vol. 4: Selecting Your Photographer*
Leslie T. McClure
PO Box 1223
Pebble Beach, CA 93953
Ph: (831)656-0553
Fax: (831)656-0555
Co. E-mail: leslie@411videoinfo.com
URL: http://www.411videoinfo.com
Released: 1998. **Price:** $29.95. **Description:** Part of a ten-volume series for brides- and grooms-to-be that follows the steps taken by a typical couple, Jeff and Lisa, in their preparation for the big event. **Availability:** VHS.

2541 ■ *Planning Your Wedding, Vol. 5: Visiting Your Travel Agent*
Leslie T. McClure
PO Box 1223
Pebble Beach, CA 93953
Ph: (831)656-0553
Fax: (831)656-0555
Co. E-mail: leslie@411videoinfo.com
URL: http://www.411videoinfo.com
Released: 1998. **Price:** $29.95. **Description:** Part of a ten-volume series for brides- and grooms-to-be that follows the steps taken by a typical couple, Jeff and Lisa, in their preparation for the big event. **Availability:** VHS.

2542 ■ *Planning Your Wedding, Vol. 6: Meeting with Your Financial Advisor*
Leslie T. McClure
PO Box 1223
Pebble Beach, CA 93953
Ph: (831)656-0553
Fax: (831)656-0555
Co. E-mail: leslie@411videoinfo.com
URL: http://www.411videoinfo.com
Released: 1998. **Price:** $29.95. **Description:** Part of a ten-volume series for brides- and grooms-to-be that follows the steps taken by a typical couple, Jeff and Lisa, in their preparation for the big event. **Availability:** VHS.

2543 ■ *Planning Your Wedding, Vol. 7: Visiting with Your Jeweler*
Leslie T. McClure
PO Box 1223
Pebble Beach, CA 93953
Ph: (831)656-0553
Fax: (831)656-0555
Co. E-mail: leslie@411videoinfo.com
URL: http://www.411videoinfo.com
Released: 1998. **Price:** $29.95. **Description:** Part of a ten-volume series for brides- and grooms-to-be that follows the steps taken by a typical couple, Jeff and Lisa, in their preparation for the big event. **Availability:** VHS.

2544 ■ *Planning Your Wedding, Vol. 8: Meeting with Your Minister*
Leslie T. McClure
PO Box 1223
Pebble Beach, CA 93953
Ph: (831)656-0553
Fax: (831)656-0555
Co. E-mail: leslie@411videoinfo.com
URL: http://www.411videoinfo.com
Released: 1998. **Price:** $29.95. **Description:** Part of a ten-volume series for brides- and grooms-to-be that follows the steps taken by a typical couple, Jeff and Lisa, in their preparation for the big event. **Availability:** VHS.

2545 ■ *Planning Your Wedding, Vol. 9: Selecting Your Flowers*
Leslie T. McClure
PO Box 1223
Pebble Beach, CA 93953
Ph: (831)656-0553
Fax: (831)656-0555
Co. E-mail: leslie@411videoinfo.com
URL: http://www.411videoinfo.com
Released: 1998. **Price:** $29.95. **Description:** Part of a ten-volume series for brides- and grooms-to-be that follows the steps taken by a typical couple, Jeff and Lisa, in their preparation for the big event. **Availability:** VHS.

2546 ■ *Planning Your Wedding, Vol. 10: Meeting with Your Bridal Consultant*
Leslie T. McClure
PO Box 1223
Pebble Beach, CA 93953
Ph: (831)656-0553
Fax: (831)656-0555
Co. E-mail: leslie@411videoinfo.com
URL: http://www.411videoinfo.com
Released: 1998. **Price:** $29.95. **Description:** Part of a ten-volume series for brides- and grooms-to-be that follows the steps taken by a typical couple, Jeff and Lisa, in their preparation for the big event. **Availability:** VHS.

TRADE SHOWS AND CONVENTIONS

2547 ■ Haus-Garten-Freizeit
Leipziger Messe GmbH
Messe-Allee 1
04356 Leipzig, Germany
Ph: 0341 6 78-0
Fax: 0341 6 78-8762
Co. E-mail: info@leipziger-messe.de
URL: http://www.leipziger-messe.de
Contact: Dr. Arend Oetker, Director
URL(s): www.leipziger-messe.de. **Frequency:** Annual. **Audience:** General public. **Principal Exhibits:** Cooking, eating, housekeeping, home and furnishing, textiles, jewellery, cosmetics, arts and crafts, health, fitness, pets.

2548 ■ National Bridal Market
Modern Bride
249 W 17th St.
New York, NY 10011
Ph: (212)645-0067
Fax: (212)337-7129
URL(s): www.nationalbridalmarket.com/. **Frequency:** and October. **Audience:** Retailers. **Principal Exhibits:** Bridal gowns, special occasion gowns, tuxedos, and related accessories. **Dates and Locations:** , Merchandise Mart.

2549 ■ Wedding Wishes/Formal Fair
Thunder Bay Chamber of Commerce
200 Syndicate Ave. S, Ste. 102
Thunder Bay, ON, Canada P7E 1C9
Ph: (807)624-2626
Fax: (807)622-7752
Co. E-mail: chamber@tbchamber.ca
URL: http://www.tb-chamber.on.ca
Contact: Nancy Milani, Coordinator, Events
E-mail: nancy@tbchamber.ca
URL(s): www.tb-chamber.on.ca. **Frequency:** Annual. **Principal Exhibits:** Wedding related supplies and services. **Dates and Locations:** , Valhalla Inn. **Telecommunication Services:** chamber@tbchamber.ca.

FRANCHISES AND BUSINESS OPPORTUNITIES

2550 ■ Sweet Beginnings
1037 W Broadway, Ste. 105
Vancouver, BC, Canada V6H 1E3
Ph: (604)738-9552
Fax: (604)876-6460
Description: Wedding & event planning, decorating and chair covers. **No. of Franchise Units:** 2. **No. of Company-Owned Units:** 2. **Founded:** 1997.. **Franchised:** 2004. **Equity Capital Needed:** $29,100-$44,700. **Franchise Fee:** $10,000-$20,000. **Royalty Fee:** $300/month. **Financial Assistance:** Limited third party financing available. **Training:** Provides 5 days training and 3 days onsite.

ASSOCIATIONS AND OTHER ORGANIZATIONS

2551 ■ American Institute of Inspectors (AII)
PO Box 7243
South Lake Tahoe, CA 96158
Ph: (530)577-1407
Free: 800-877-4770
Co. E-mail: tahoeinspector@sbcglobal.net
URL: http://www.inspection.org
Contact: Perry Hawkins, President
Description: Certified home inspectors. Works to set standards for impartial evaluations of residential properties. Certifies members in four areas: residential homes, mobile homes, mechanics, and earthquake hazard reduction. Maintains speakers' bureau. **Scope:** electromagnetic fields, construction materials. **Founded:** 1989. **Subscriptions:** books video recordings.

2552 ■ Canadian Association of Home and Property Inspectors (CAHPI)—Association Canadienne des Inspecteurs de Biens Immobiliers
PO Box 13715
Ottawa, ON, Canada K2K 1X6
Ph: (902)890-0710
Free: 888-748-2244
Fax: (866)876-9877
Co. E-mail: info@cahpi.ca
URL: http://www.cahpi.ca
Contact: Blaine Swan, President
Description: Home inspectors. Promotes professional advancement of members. Seeks to insure adherence to high standards of ethics and practice among home inspectors. Represents members' collective interests. **Founded:** 1982. **Publications:** *The Canadian Home Inspector* (3/year). **Awards:** President's Award; President's Award (Annual); Stephen Greenford Award (Annual); Stephen Greenford Award. **Telecommunication Services:** president@cahpi.ca.

2553 ■ *The Canadian Home Inspector*
PO Box 13715
Ottawa, ON, Canada K2K 1X6
Ph: (902)890-0710
Free: 888-748-2244
Fax: (866)876-9877
Co. E-mail: info@cahpi.ca
URL: http://www.cahpi.ca
Contact: Blaine Swan, President
Released: 3/year **Price:** $15, /issue.

2554 ■ Canadian Institute of Professional Home Inspectors (CIPHI)
c/o WITCO
999 W Broadway, Ste. 720
Vancouver, BC, Canada
Ph: (604)732-0617
Co. E-mail: info@edwitzke.com
URL: http://www.edwitzke.com
Description: Home inspectors. Seeks to advance the profession of home inspection; promotes adherence to high standards of ethics and practice among

members. Serves as a forum for the exchange of information among members; sponsors educational and training programs. **Founded:** 1965. **Publications:** *Complete Canadian Home Inspection Guide.*

2555 ■ *Chapter Specifiers*
120 Carlton St., Ste. 312
Toronto, ON, Canada M5A 4K2
Ph: (416)777-2198
Free: 800-668-5684
Fax: (416)777-2197
Co. E-mail: info@csc-dcc.ca
URL: http://www.csc-dcc.ca
Contact: Bruce Gillham, President
Released: 10/year

2556 ■ *Construction Canada*
120 Carlton St., Ste. 312
Toronto, ON, Canada M5A 4K2
Ph: (416)777-2198
Free: 800-668-5684
Fax: (416)777-2197
Co. E-mail: info@csc-dcc.ca
URL: http://www.csc-dcc.ca
Contact: Bruce Gillham, President
Released: Bimonthly

2557 ■ Construction Specifications Canada (CSC)
120 Carlton St., Ste. 312
Toronto, ON, Canada M5A 4K2
Ph: (416)777-2198
Free: 800-668-5684
Fax: (416)777-2197
Co. E-mail: info@csc-dcc.ca
URL: http://www.csc-dcc.ca
Contact: Bruce Gillham, President
Description: Construction companies, workers, engineers, and writers of building standards and specifications. Promotes continuing professional development of members; seeks to insure adherence to high standards of practice in the building industries. Conducts educational programs; makes available vocational training courses. Develops industry standards. Represents members' interests before industry organizations and government agencies; advises government agencies responsible for promulgating building codes and construction specifications. Makes available discount insurance and vehicle leasing programs to members. **Founded:** 1954. **Publications:** *Construction Specifications Canada--Directory* (Annual); *Chapter Specifiers* (10/year); *Construction Canada* (Bimonthly); *News in Brief* (Semiannual); *National Master Specification (NMS)*. **Awards:** Award of Merit; Chapter Certificate of Appreciation (Periodic); President's Award (Annual); Lloyd Boddy Chapter of the Year Award.

2558 ■ *News in Brief*
120 Carlton St., Ste. 312
Toronto, ON, Canada M5A 4K2
Ph: (416)777-2198
Free: 800-668-5684

Fax: (416)777-2197
Co. E-mail: info@csc-dcc.ca
URL: http://www.csc-dcc.ca
Contact: Bruce Gillham, President
Released: Semiannual

REFERENCE WORKS

2559 ■ *International Conference of Building Officials--Membership Directory*
Pub: International Code Council
Contact: William D. Dupler, President
URL(s): www.iccsafe.org/membership/. **Covers:** government agencies and officials, primarily in the United States, responsible for preparing and publishing building construction standards and the Uniform Building Code, to be used as a basis for regulations concerning materials and types of construction. **Entries include:** Name, company name, address, phone. **Arrangement:** Alphabetical.

TRADE PERIODICALS

2560 ■ *The Appraisers Standard*
Pub: New England Appraisers Association
Released: Quarterly **Price:** $20, Individuals; $25, Canada; $30, Other countries.

2561 ■ *The Construction Specifier: Solutions for the Construction Industry*
Pub: The Construction Specifications Institute
URL(s): www.csinet.org/www.constructionspecifier.com/. **Released:** Monthly

CONSULTANTS

2562 ■ AEP Associates Inc.
53 Notch Rd.
West Paterson, NJ 07424-1953
Ph: (973)256-7575
Fax: (973)890-7848
Contact: Stanley John Lacz, President
E-mail: stl@aepassoc.com
Scope: Provider of comprehensive professional services in the following areas: Architectural-building, programming, cost analysis, construction documents, construction inspection, and interior design; landscape architecture; engineering-site plans, energy studies, storm drainage, foundations, structures, plumbing, water supply, heating, air conditioning, electrical lighting, and land subdivisions; planning-master plan studies, zoning ordinance, variances, application to government agencies; governmental approvals-stream encroachment, wet lands. Clients include leading corporations; municipal, county, state, and federal governmental agencies; various developers; organizations and individuals for mercantile, educational, and medical projects; and homeowners. **Founded:** 1965.

2563 ■ American Forensic Engineers
34 Sammis Ln.
White Plains, NY 10605
Ph: (914)949-5978

Fax: (914)949-0350
Co. E-mail: gusmundel@aol.com
Contact: August B. Mundel, President
E-mail: gusmundel@aol.com
Scope: Provider of industrial, safety, and forensic consulting services. Services include relevant engineering studies, sampling, statistical studies, quality and reliability efforts, industrial hygiene, human factors analysis, industrial experimentation, product safety analysis and product liability causes in the electrical, electronic, electro-chemical, chemical, mechanical, and battery industrial areas. Also offers building inspection services. Serves private industries as well as government agencies in the U.S. **Founded:** 1975. **Publications:** "Ethics in Quality," Marcell Dekker.

2564 ■ American Roofing Consultants Inc.
785 Briggs Rd.
Salisbury, NC 28147-9539
Ph: (704)637-0370
Free: 800-455-6207
Fax: (704)630-0774
Contact: F. Lee Russell, President
Scope: Provider of investigative roof surveys; on-site roof construction inspection; nuclear, infrared, capacitance moisture surveys; roof maintenance schedules; plan and specification reviews; and specialty roof seminars. Also serves as expert witness. **Founded:** 1972.

2565 ■ Applied Fire Protection Engineering Inc.
14401 Sweitzer Ln., Ste. 40
Laurel, MD 20707
Ph: (301)931-3330
Free: 800-331-6373
Fax: (301)931-6412
Co. E-mail: nfse@mindspring.com
URL: http://www.nfse.com
Contact: Dennis A. Sullivan, President
E-mail: dennis@nfsa.com
Scope: Provider of comprehensive consulting services in the field of fire protection (including building and fire code analysis for new construction and renovations; existing building inspections and analysis; fire alarm system design; and automatic sprinkler system design) as well as annual testing and maintenance of fire alarm systems, fire pumps and sprinkler systems. **Founded:** 1986. **Telecommunication Services:** info@afpengineering.net.

2566 ■ Architectural Consultants Ltd.
500 W Central Rd., Ste. 208
Mount Prospect, IL 60056-2381
Ph: (847)577-5777
Fax: (847)577-5784
Contact: Edward S. Busche, President
Scope: Professional activities include forensic services for all types of building and/or construction-related problems; architectural services for the renovation, restoration and expansion of buildings; due diligence studies to determine the condition of buildings and the cost of restoring them to an acceptable condition. Services are provided by a multidisciplinary team of architects, structural, electrical and mechanical engineers with broad experience in building design, construction and restoration. **Founded:** 1981.

2567 ■ Architecture, Building Codes & Inspection
0310 Crystal Country Cir.
Carbondale, CO 81623
Ph: (970)963-8209
Fax: (970)963-8209
Contact: Jack Dysart, Principal
E-mail: dysart@rof.net
Scope: Architect, building inspector, construction inspector, and contractor who offers forensic support of litigation concerning building design, codes and construction. Recent experience with the Americans with Disabilities Act facilities compliance, architecture, and residential buildings. Industries served building and corporate owners, single family homeowners, realtors, banks lenders, attorneys, insurance companies, architects and contractors, and city building departments. **Founded:** 1977. **Publications:** "Ibc International Building Code Research & Critiques";

"Building Code Compliance Checklists"; "Aia "Masterspec" Master Specifications Contributor, American Institute of Architects"; "Cost Estimating Computer Programs for Cmc College Lectures & Private Practice".

2568 ■ Breen & Associates Inc.
PO Box 120424
Arlington, TX 76012
Ph: (817)275-4711
Fax: (817)275-4711
Co. E-mail: jbreen504@aol.com
Contact: James E. Breen, President
E-mail: jbreen504@aol.com
Scope: Building construction consultants offering complete inspection services of residential and commercial structures (includes structural, equipment and systems). Clients include real estate brokers, investors (real estate) and builders/developers. **Founded:** 1978.

2569 ■ Foit-Albert Associates
763 Main St.
Buffalo, NY 14203-1395
Ph: (716)856-3933
Fax: (716)856-3961
Co. E-mail: info@foit-albert.com
URL: http://www.foit-albert.com
Contact: Dr. Beverly Foit-Albert, President
E-mail: bfa@foit-albert.com
Scope: Full architectural/engineering surveying Consulting firm specializing in Historic Preservation, Educational Facilities, Full-Time Construction Inspection and Engineering Coordination, Grant Writing Services available. **Founded:** 1977.

2570 ■ N.R. Goldstein & Associates
1200US Highway 130
Trenton, NJ 08691
Ph: (609)426-1888
Fax: (609)426-1230
Contact: Norman R. Goldstein, Owner
Scope: Provider of forensic safety services regarding slips and falls, machine guarding, construction, and building codes. Primarily serves attorneys and insurance carriers. **Founded:** 1987.

2571 ■ The Hall Partnership Architects L.L.P.
42 E 21st St.
New York, NY 10010-7216
Ph: (212)777-2090
Fax: (212)979-2217
Co. E-mail: info@hallarchitect.com
URL: http://www.hallarchitect.com
Contact: William A. Hall, Partner
E-mail: thall@hallarchitect.com
Scope: Offers full range of architectural and planning consulting services. Serves private industries as well as government agencies. **Founded:** 1959.

2572 ■ InspectAmerica Engineering P.C.
3 School St.
White Plains, NY 10606-1408
Ph: (914)682-9090
Fax: (845)661-5183
Co. E-mail: comments@inspectamerica.com
URL: http://www.inspectamerica.com
Contact: Edwin M. Frank, President
E-mail: inspectionsvc@aol.com
Scope: Provider of engineering inspection services for pre-purchase purposes, condominium and co-operative conversions and inspections to analyze and design remedies for problems in homes and buildings. Services encompass both commercial and residential properties. Industries served: real estate, lawyers, bankers, property management, landlords, investors, and government agencies. **Founded:** 1974. **Publications:** "Home Inspectors Check for Termites"; "Structural Inspection"; "Healthy Home Inspection". **Special Services:** Home Inspection SuperSite™; Home Inspection TechTalk™; InspectAmerica®.

2573 ■ Kohn Engineering
4220 Mountain Rd.
Macungie, PA 18062
Ph: (610)967-4766

Fax: (610)967-6468
Co. E-mail: don@kohnengineering.com
URL: http://www.kohnengineering.com
Contact: Don Kohn, Principal
E-mail: don@kohnengineering.com
Scope: Offers fire protection consulting. Provides a wide range of fire protection consulting services that includes design, code interpretation, expert witness, project management, fire safety program development, and hazard identification. Provides cost effective solutions to fire protection problems. **Founded:** 1995. **Seminars:** Fire Protection in Nuclear Power Plants.

2574 ■ Middle Department Inspection Agency Inc.
101 N Meadows Dr., Ste. 130
Wexford, PA 15090
Ph: (724)935-1558
Fax: (724)935-7480
Co. E-mail: radmdia@comcast.net
URL: http://www.mdia.net
Contact: Glenn G. Beaver, President
Scope: Offers building, electrical, fire protection and plumbing inspections. Serves private industries as well as government agencies, such as municipalities and counties. **Founded:** 1883. **Special Services:** IBC®; IRC®; ICC®; CABO®; BOCA®.

2575 ■ Professional Engineering Inspections Inc.
PO Box 859
Friendswood, TX 77549
Ph: (713)664-1264
Fax: (281)619-8166
Co. E-mail: mail@profengineering.com
URL: http://www.profengineering.com
Contact: Paul Vinson, Manager
Scope: Specializes in residential inspections, commercial inspections and consulting, structural inspection-mechanical and electrical, pools and spas foundation, roof- energy loss, quality of construction-condition of property, and capital reserve studies-special inspections. **Founded:** 1980.

2576 ■ Harvey Toub Engineering
6145 Barfield Rd. NE, Ste. 220
Atlanta, GA 30328
Ph: (404)843-1192
Fax: (404)256-9780
Contact: Harvey Toub, President
Scope: Engineering consulting firm which provides HVAC, plumbing and electrical design services for new buildings and for modifications/additions to existing buildings. Also offers boiler testing, energy efficiency studies and design, boiler operator training, building inspection/reports, industrial design for ventilation, electrical installations and preventive maintenance planning. Industries served: Foundry, pharmaceutical, boiler, manufacturing, institutional and government agencies. **Founded:** 1982.

2577 ■ Trendzitions Inc.
25691 Atlantic Ocean, Ste. B13
Lake Forest, CA 92630-8842
Ph: (949)727-9100
Free: 800-266-2767
Fax: (949)727-3444
Co. E-mail: ctooker@trendzitions.com
URL: http://www.trendzitions.com
Contact: Christian Tooker, President
E-mail: ctooker@trendzitions.com
Scope: Provider of services in the areas of communications consulting, project management, construction management, and furniture procurement. Offers information on spatial uses, building codes, ADA compliance and city ordinances. Also offers budget projections. **Founded:** 1986.

FRANCHISES AND BUSINESS OPPORTUNITIES

2578 ■ Amerispec Home Inspection Service
ServiceMaster
3839 Forest Hill Irene Rd.
Memphis, TN 38125
Free: 800-338-6833

Fax: (901)820-7580
Co. E-mail: sales@amerispec.net
URL: http://www.amerispecfranchise.com
Description: Home inspection franchise which sells independently-owned and operated businesses to entrepreneurs in exclusive territories. Owners use a proprietary software program to generate a narrative report and/or an onsite report to clients. Large or small area franchises available-priced accordingly. **No. of Franchise Units:** 305. **Founded:** 1987.. **Franchised:** 1988. **Equity Capital Needed:** $41,350-$72,400. **Franchise Fee:** $25,900-$35,900. **Financial Assistance:** Yes. **Training:** Yes.

2579 ■ AmeriSpec Inspection Service
ServiceMaster
5462 Timberlea Blvd.
Mississauga, ON, Canada L4W 2T7
Ph: (905)670-0000
Free: 800-263-5928
Fax: (905)670-0077
Co. E-mail: thould@smclean.com
URL: http://www.amerispec.ca
Description: Home inspection franchise in North America. **No. of Franchise Units:** 84. **Founded:** 1988.. **Franchised:** 1988. **Equity Capital Needed:** $30,000-$60,000; start-up capital required $40,000. **Franchise Fee:** $24,000-$34,900. **Training:** Yes.

2580 ■ The BrickKicker
RonLen Enterprises Inc.
849 N Ellsworth St.
Naperville, IL 60563
Free: 888-339-5425
Fax: (630)420-2270
Co. E-mail: linda@brickkicker.com
URL: http://www.brickkicker.com
Description: Building inspection service. **No. of Franchise Units:** 152. **Founded:** 1989.. **Franchised:** 1995. **Equity Capital Needed:** $15,000-$40,000. **Franchise Fee:** $9,000-$40,000. **Financial Assistance:** Yes. **Training:** Yes.

2581 ■ Home-Alyze
3740B 11A St. NE, Ste. 201
Calgary, AB, Canada T2E 6M6
Ph: (403)730-9986
Free: 800-831-6272
Fax: (403)274-4821
Co. E-mail: info@homealyze.com
URL: http://www.homealyzefranchise.com
Description: Home-Alyze offers home inspection services. **No. of Franchise Units:** 9. **Founded:** 1978.. **Franchised:** 1999. **Equity Capital Needed:** $60,000. **Franchise Fee:** $24,900. **Training:** Initial basic orientation plus industry courses.

2582 ■ The Hometeam Inspection Services, Inc.
575 Chamber Dr.
Milford, OH 45150
Ph: (800)598-5297
Fax: (513)831-6010
Co. E-mail: sales@hometeaminspection.com
URL: http://www.hometeaminspection.com
Description: National franchisor of home inspections. **No. of Franchise Units:** 163. **Founded:** 1991.. **Franchised:** 1992. **Equity Capital Needed:** $10,000-$71,000 start-up cash; $39,000-$71,000 total investment. **Franchise Fee:** $9,800. **Financial Assistance:** Yes. **Training:** 14 day comprehensive training program at corporate office.

2583 ■ Housemaster, Home Inspections, Done Right
426 Vosseller Ave.
Bound Brook, NJ 08805

Ph: (732)823-4087
URL: http://www.housemaster.com
Description: Home inspections for home buyers and sellers. **No. of Franchise Units:** 365. **Founded:** 1971.. **Franchised:** 1979. **Equity Capital Needed:** Net $80,000; liquid $45,000. **Franchise Fee:** $42,500. **Training:** Offers 2-5 weeks of initial training.

2584 ■ Inspect-It 1st LLC
Inspect-It 1st Franchising Corp.
7100 E Pleasant Valley Rd., Ste. 300
Independence, OH 44131
Free: 877-392-6278
Fax: (216)674-0650
Co. E-mail: administrator@inspectit1st.com
URL: http://www.inspectit1st.com
Description: Offers home inspection service. **No. of Franchise Units:** 39. **Founded:** 1991.. **Franchised:** 1998. **Equity Capital Needed:** $34,400-$53,400. **Franchise Fee:** $26,900. **Royalty Fee:** $200-$400/month. **Financial Assistance:** In-house financing available with limited third party financing. **Training:** Provides 10 days in Phoenix with ongoing support.

2585 ■ Lighthouse Inspections Canada
2400 Dundas St. W, Unit 6
Mississauga, ON, Canada L5K 2R8
Ph: (905)278-7887
Fax: (905)278-9582
Co. E-mail: franchise@lighthouseinspections.com
URL: http://www.lighthouseinspections.com
Description: Offers lighthouse inspection service. **No. of Franchise Units:** 19. **No. of Company-Owned Units:** 1. **Founded:** 1999.. **Franchised:** 2000. **Franchise Fee:** $20,000. **Training:** Minimum 3 weeks initial training, ongoing support, seminars and re-certification.

2586 ■ National Property Inspections
9375 Burt St., Ste. 201
Omaha, NE 68114
Ph: (402)333-9807
Fax: (800)933-2508
Co. E-mail: npi@npiweb.com
URL: http://www.npiweb.com
Description: NPI offers a home inspection franchise opportunity with exclusive, protected territories and a turn-key start-up package, complete with the training and equipment needed for your business. NPI's support goes beyond training. You'll also receive continual technical assistance & education for both residential and commercial inspections, as well as marketing programs to help you build your business year after year. **No. of Franchise Units:** 283. **Founded:** 1987. **Franchised:** 1987. **Equity Capital Needed:** Working capital of $5,000 or more (not including franchise fee). **Franchise Fee:** $24,900. **Financial Assistance:** Yes. **Training:** 2 weeks of training at our home office, plus a third optional week in the field with a veteran NPI inspector in our mentor program.

2587 ■ Pillar to Post Inc.
14502 N Dale Mabry Hwy., Ste. 200
Tampa, FL 33618
Ph: (877)963-3129
Co. E-mail: tampa@pillartopost.com
URL: http://www.pillartopost.com
Description: Home inspection service. **No. of Franchise Units:** 500. **Founded:** 1994.. **Franchised:** 1994. **Equity Capital Needed:** $24,500-$54,500. **Franchise Fee:** $19,900-$45,900. **Training:** Yes.

2588 ■ Pillar to Post Inc.
5805 Whittle Rd., Ste. 211
Mississauga, ON, Canada L4Z 2J1
Ph: (905)568-8608

Fax: (905)568-8137
Co. E-mail: franchise.development@pillartopost.com
URL: http://www.pillartopost.com
Description: Qualified home inspection franchise. **No. of Franchise Units:** 88. **No. of Operating Units:** 349. **Founded:** 1994.. **Franchised:** 1994. **Equity Capital Needed:** $30,700-$42,750. **Franchise Fee:** $14,900-$29,900. **Royalty Fee:** 7%. **Financial Assistance:** In-house and third party assistance available with franchise fee. **Training:** Offers 2 weeks of training and ongoing support.

2589 ■ Prospection
7100 E Pleasant Valley Rd., Ste. 300
Independence, OH 44131
Free: 866-328-7720
Fax: (216)674-0652
Description: Professional home inspection service. **No. of Franchise Units:** 28. **Founded:** 2003.. **Franchised:** 2003. **Equity Capital Needed:** $6,000-$12,000. **Training:** Yes.

2590 ■ Service One Janitorial
1180 Spring Centre S. Blvd., Ste. 208
Altamonte, FL 32714
Ph: (407)261-1300
Free: 866-502-1162
Fax: (800)846-3992
URL: http://www.service1janitorial.com
Description: Commercial janitorial business. **No. of Franchise Units:** 420. **Founded:** 1967.. **Franchised:** 1985. **Equity Capital Needed:** $10,000. **Franchise Fee:** $9,000. **Royalty Fee:** 8-15%.

2591 ■ Sharkey's Cuts For Kids, Franchising Co., LLC
37 Highland Rd.
Westport, CT 06880
Ph: (203)637-8911
Fax: (203)637-0386
Co. E-mail: info@sharkeycutsforkids.com
URL: http://www.sharkeyscutsforkids.com
Description: Kids' salon, including Flat Screen/Fun Chairs/PS2, Gamecube, X-box/Rides/Pinball/Glamour Parties/Party Favors, and Karaoke Parties for Moms. **No. of Franchise Units:** 19. **Founded:** 2001. **Franchised:** 2004. **Equity Capital Needed:** $100,000 turnkey. **Franchise Fee:** None. **Financial Assistance:** Yes. **Training:** Yes.

2592 ■ Snip-Its
The Snip-Its Franchise Co.
6409 City West Pkwy., Ste. 205
Eden Prairie, MN 55344
Ph: (508)651-7052
Free: 800-651-7063
Fax: (508)651-0549
Co. E-mail: mmerrigan@snipits.com
URL: http://www.snipits.com
Description: Children's haircuts. **No. of Franchise Units:** 62. **No. of Company-Owned Units:** 1. **Founded:** 1995.. **Franchised:** 2003. **Equity Capital Needed:** $141,189-$273,731 Salon, $127,775-$187,850 Express Salon. **Franchise Fee:** $25,000. **Training:** Yes.

2593 ■ WIN Home Inspection
9238 Madison Blvd., Ste. 750
Madison, AL 35758
Ph: (206)728-8100
Free: 800-967-8127
Fax: (206)441-3655
Co. E-mail: joinwin@wini.com
URL: http://www.winfranchise.com
Description: Performs home inspection. **No. of Franchise Units:** 168. **Founded:** 1993.. **Franchised:** 1994. **Equity Capital Needed:** $42,300-$56,650 (alternate)/$52,300-$65,500 (std). **Franchise Fee:** $30,000-$40,000. **Training:** Yes.

START-UP INFORMATION

2594 ■ "Legendary Success" in Small Business Opportunities (November 2010)
Pub: Harris Publications Inc.
Description: Von Schrader is famous in the cleaning industry and more than 50,000 individuals have started their own professional cleaning service businesses using the company's air cell technology cleaning systems along with their proven business systems. This is a perfect business for anyone wishing to start and run it from their home.

ASSOCIATIONS AND OTHER ORGANIZATIONS

2595 ■ Building Service Contractors Association International (BSCAI)
401 N Michigan Ave., Ste. 2200
Chicago, IL 60611-4267
Ph: (312)321-5167
Free: 800-368-3414
Fax: (312)673-6735
Co. E-mail: info@bscai.org
URL: http://www.bscai.org
Contact: Taylor Bruce, President
Description: Firms and corporations in 40 countries engaged in contracting building maintenance services including the provision of labor, purchasing materials and janitorial cleaning and maintenance of a building or its surroundings; associate members are manufacturers of cleaning supplies and equipment. Seeks to provide a unified voice for building service contractors and to promote increased recognition by government, property owners and the general business and professional public. Conducts continuing study and action, through committees and special task groups on areas such as public affairs, costs and ratios, uniform accounting, industrial relations and personnel, marketing and sales, contract improvement, research and planning, materials and supplies sources, group insurance, management training, statistics collection, safety and insurance costs. Has developed a certification program for building service executives and a registration program for building service managers. **Founded:** 1965. **Publications:** *SmartBrief* (Weekly). **Awards:** BSCAI Awards and Recognition (Annual).

2596 ■ Canadian Association of Environmental Management (CAEM)—Association Canadienne de Gestion Environnementale
Aberdeen Hospital
835 E River Rd.
New Glasgow, NS, Canada B2G 3S6
Ph: (902)725-7600
Fax: (902)755-3975
Co. E-mail: rosemary.gillis-bowers@pcha.nshealth.ca
URL: http://www.thecanadiangroup.com/caha/index.htm
Contact: Rosemary Gillis-Bowers, President (Acting) Secretary Treasurer
Description: Environmental managers. Seeks to advance the environmental (housekeeping) profession; promotes adherence to high standards of ethics and practice by members. Represents members' interests; facilitates communication and cooperation among members. **Founded:** 1971. **Publications:** *The Quarterly* (Quarterly). **Awards:** CAH Certification (Annual).

2597 ■ Cleaning Management Institute (CMI)
19 British American Blvd. W
Latham, NY 12110
Ph: (518)640-3159
Fax: (518)783-1386
Co. E-mail: cmi@ntpinc.com
URL: http://www.cminstitute.net
Contact: W. Marion Ivey, Director
E-mail: wmivey@comcast.net
Description: Represents individuals and organizations active in cleaning maintenance and management, including contract cleaner firms. Develops home study educational courses and publications to promote professional certification, self-improvement, and efficient work methods. **Scope:** building maintenance. **Founded:** 1964. **Subscriptions:** 120 articles books software video recordings. **Publications:** *Cleaning and Maintenance Management Magazine: The Magazine for Today's Building Cleaning Maintenance/Housekeeping Executive* (Monthly). **Educational Activities:** Cleaning and Maintenance Conference and Exposition (Annual). **Telecommunication Services:** mgallinger@ntpmedia.com.

2598 ■ Facility Management Journal
46 Falcon St.
Toronto, ON, Canada M4S 2P5
Ph: (416)346-4729
Fax: (866)461-6469
Co. E-mail: admin@ifma-toronto.org
URL: http://www.ifma-toronto.org
Contact: Jane Rowbotham, President
Released: Bimonthly

2599 ■ IFMA Membership Services Directory
46 Falcon St.
Toronto, ON, Canada M4S 2P5
Ph: (416)346-4729
Fax: (866)461-6469
Co. E-mail: admin@ifma-toronto.org
URL: http://www.ifma-toronto.org
Contact: Jane Rowbotham, President
Released: Periodic

2600 ■ IFMA News
46 Falcon St.
Toronto, ON, Canada M4S 2P5
Ph: (416)346-4729
Fax: (866)461-6469
Co. E-mail: admin@ifma-toronto.org
URL: http://www.ifma-toronto.org
Contact: Jane Rowbotham, President
Released: Monthly

2601 ■ International Facility Management Association - Toronto Chapter
46 Falcon St.
Toronto, ON, Canada M4S 2P5
Ph: (416)346-4729
Fax: (866)461-6469
Co. E-mail: admin@ifma-toronto.org
URL: http://www.ifma-toronto.org
Contact: Jane Rowbotham, President
Description: Facilities management professionals. Promotes professionalism in the practice of facilities management; encourages professional advancement of members. Conducts continuing professional development courses; formulates and enforces standards of practice and ethics in facilities management. Conducts research; makes available job referral services; facilitates communication among members. **Scope:** facilities management. **Founded:** 1982. **Subscriptions:** books periodicals. **Publications:** *Facility Management Journal* (Bimonthly); *IFMA News* (Monthly); *Toronto News*; *IFMA Membership Services Directory* (Periodic). **Educational Activities:** World Workplace (Annual).

2602 ■ International Sanitary Supply Association (ISSA)
7373 N Lincoln Ave.
Lincolnwood, IL 60712-1799
Ph: (847)982-0800
Free: 800-225-4772
Fax: (847)982-1012
Co. E-mail: info@issa.com
URL: http://www.issa.com
Contact: John Garfinkel, Executive Director
URL(s): www.issafoundation.org. **Description:** Manufacturers, distributors, wholesalers, manufacturer representatives, publishers, and associate members of cleaning and maintenance supplies, chemicals, and equipment used by janitors, custodians, and maintenance workers in all types of industrial, commercial, and institutional buildings. Represents members in 83 countries. Produces videos and other educational materials. Offers specialized education seminars. **Scope:** application techniques to general management and sales training. **Founded:** 1923. **Subscriptions:** audio recordings books video recordings. **Publications:** *ISSA Today* (Bimonthly); *Legislative and Regulatory Update* (Monthly).

2603 ■ The Quarterly
Aberdeen Hospital
835 E River Rd.
New Glasgow, NS, Canada B2G 3S6
Ph: (902)725-7600
Fax: (902)755-3975
Co. E-mail: rosemary.gillis-bowers@pcha.nshealth.ca
URL: http://www.thecanadiangroup.com/caha/index.htm
Contact: Rosemary Gillis-Bowers, President (Acting)
Released: Quarterly **Price:** free for members; C$20, /year for nonmembers.

2604 ■ Sanitary Supply Wholesaling Association (SSWA)
PO Box 98
Swanton, OH 43558
Ph: (419)825-3055

Fax: (419)825-1815
Co. E-mail: info@sswa.com
URL: http://www.sswa.com
Contact: Lane Crosser, Vice President
Description: Wholesalers and manufacturers of janitorial supplies and/or paper products. Seeks to create integrity and recognition of wholesale distribution in the sanitary supply industry. **Founded:** 1980. **Awards:** Stanley E. Friedman Award of Merit (Periodic).

2605 ■ *Toronto News*
46 Falcon St.
Toronto, ON, Canada M4S 2P5
Ph: (416)346-4729
Fax: (866)461-6469
Co. E-mail: admin@ifma-toronto.org
URL: http://www.ifma-toronto.org
Contact: Jane Rowbotham, President

EDUCATIONAL PROGRAMS

2606 ■ Air Conditioning and Refrigeration (Onsite)
American Trainco, Inc.
9785 S Maroon Cir., Ste. 300
Englewood, CO 80112
Free: 877-978-7246
Fax: (303)531-4565
Co. E-mail: Sales@AmericanTrainco.com
URL: http://www.americantrainco.com
Price: $990.00. **Description:** A two-day course for building, plant, and facility maintenance personnel. Covers understanding principles, components and systems, maintenance, troubleshooting, and operating efficiency. **Dates and Locations:** Cities throughout the United States.

2607 ■ Basic Electricity for the Non Electrician (Onsite) (In-House Training)
American Trainco, Inc.
9785 S Maroon Cir., Ste. 300
Englewood, CO 80112
Free: 877-978-7246
Fax: (303)531-4565
Co. E-mail: Sales@AmericanTrainco.com
URL: http://www.americantrainco.com
Price: $990.00. **Description:** A two-day hands on training course for building, plant, and facility maintenance personnel. **Dates and Locations:** Cities throughout the United States.

2608 ■ Boiler Operation, Maintenance and Safety (Onsite) (In-House Training)
American Trainco, Inc.
9785 S Maroon Cir., Ste. 300
Englewood, CO 80112
Free: 877-978-7246
Fax: (303)531-4565
Co. E-mail: Sales@AmericanTrainco.com
URL: http://www.americantrainco.com
Price: $990.00. **Description:** A two-day training course for everyday building, plant, and facility maintenance. **Dates and Locations:** Cities throughout the United States.

2609 ■ Electric Motors, Drives and Control Circuits (In-House Training)
American Trainco, Inc.
9785 S Maroon Cir., Ste. 300
Englewood, CO 80112
Free: 877-978-7246
Fax: (303)531-4565
Co. E-mail: Sales@AmericanTrainco.com
URL: http://www.americantrainco.com
Price: $990.00. **Description:** A practical course for maintenance personnel working in industrial plants, public facilities, and commercial buildings. **Dates and Locations:** Cities throughout the United States.

2610 ■ HVAC Controls and Air Distribution (Onsite)
American Trainco, Inc.
9785 S Maroon Cir., Ste. 300
Englewood, CO 80112
Free: 877-978-7246

Fax: (303)531-4565
Co. E-mail: Sales@AmericanTrainco.com
URL: http://www.americantrainco.com
Price: $990.00. **Description:** A two-day course that teaches how to maximize HVAC comfort and efficiency. **Dates and Locations:** Cities throughout the United States.

2611 ■ Maintenance Welding (Onsite)
American Trainco, Inc.
9785 S Maroon Cir., Ste. 300
Englewood, CO 80112
Free: 877-978-7246
Fax: (303)531-4565
Co. E-mail: Sales@AmericanTrainco.com
URL: http://www.americantrainco.com
Price: $990.00. **Description:** Covers the fundamental, practical applications, and best practices of maintenance welding. **Dates and Locations:** Cities throughout the United States.

2612 ■ National College of Appraisal and Property Management
Professional Career Development Institute
430 Technology Pky.
Norcross, GA 30092
Ph: (770)729-8400
Free: 800-224-7234
Fax: (770)729-0961
URL: http://www.pcdi.com
Description: Home study course on property management. I.

2613 ■ Pumps and Pump Systems
American Trainco, Inc.
9785 S Maroon Cir., Ste. 300
Englewood, CO 80112
Free: 877-978-7246
Fax: (303)531-4565
Co. E-mail: Sales@AmericanTrainco.com
URL: http://www.americantrainco.com
Price: $990.00. **Description:** A comprehensive course designed to benefit mechanics, operators, consulting and design engineers, and multi-craft maintenance technicians. **Dates and Locations:** Cities throughout the United States.

2614 ■ Total Productive Maintenance and 5S (Onsite) (In-House Training)
American Trainco, Inc.
9785 S Maroon Cir., Ste. 300
Englewood, CO 80112
Free: 877-978-7246
Fax: (303)531-4565
Co. E-mail: Sales@AmericanTrainco.com
URL: http://www.americantrainco.com
Price: $990.00. **Description:** A two-day seminar designed to help reduce breakdowns, stoppages, and lower costs. **Dates and Locations:** Cities throughout the United States.

2615 ■ Toubleshooting Mechanical Drive Systems and Rotating Equipment (Onsite)
American Trainco, Inc.
9785 S Maroon Cir., Ste. 300
Englewood, CO 80112
Free: 877-978-7246
Fax: (303)531-4565
Co. E-mail: Sales@AmericanTrainco.com
URL: http://www.americantrainco.com
Price: $990.00. **Description:** A practical course designed for building facility and industrial plant maintenance technicians. **Dates and Locations:** Cities throughout the United States.

2616 ■ Understanding and Troubleshooting Hydraulics (Onsite)
American Trainco, Inc.
9785 S Maroon Cir., Ste. 300
Englewood, CO 80112
Free: 877-978-7246
Fax: (303)531-4565
Co. E-mail: Sales@AmericanTrainco.com
URL: http://www.americantrainco.com
Price: $990.00. **Description:** A two-day training course for everyday building, plant, and facility maintenance, including systems and components and identifying and fixing common problems. **Dates and Locations:** Cities throughout the United States.

DIRECTORIES OF EDUCATIONAL PROGRAMS

2617 ■ *Directory of Private Accredited Career Schools and Colleges of Technology*
Pub: Accrediting Commission of Career Schools and Colleges of Technology
Contact: Michale S. McComis, Executive Director
Released: On web page. **Price:** Free. **Description:** Covers 3900 accredited post-secondary programs that provide training programs in business, trade, and technical fields, including various small business endeavors. Entries offer school name, address, phone, description of courses, job placement assistance, and requirements for admission. Arrangement is alphabetical.

REFERENCE WORKS

2618 ■ *"ABM Janitorial Services Receives Service Excellence Award from Jones Lang LaSalle" in Investment Weekly News (July 16, 2011, pp. 75)*
Pub: NewsRX
Description: ABM Janitorial Services was awarded the 2010 Jones Lang LaSalle Distinction award in the category of Service Excellence. LaSalle is a leading financial and professional services firm that specializes in real estate services and investment management. The program recognizes supplier partners who play a vital role in LaSalle's aim to provide the highest quality of services, value and innovation to clients.

2619 ■ *"As Tradesmen Age, New Workers In Short Supply" in Boston Business Journal (Vol. 27, November 9, 2007, No. 41, pp. 1)*
Pub: American City Business Journals Inc.
Ed: Jackie Noblett. **Description:** It is becoming more difficult to find young people who have the skills for installation and maintenance businesses. Some businesses are unable to complete contracts on time due to lack of staff. Unions are making efforts to address the expected shortfall of laborers in the coming years through apprenticeship programs.

2620 ■ *"Brief: Janitorial Company Must Pay Back Wages" in Buffalo News (September 24, 2011)*
Pub: The Buffalo News
Ed: Jonathan D. Epstein. **Description:** Knights Facilities Management, located in Michigan, provides grounds maintenance and janitorial services at the Ralph Wilson Stadium in Buffalo, New York. The US Department of Labor ordered the firm to pay $22,000 in back wages and damages to 26 employees for overtime and minimum wage compensation. Details of the company's violation of the Fair Labor Standards Act are included.

2621 ■ *"Bringing Charities More Bang for Their Buck" in Crain's Chicago Business (Vol. 34, May 23, 2011, No. 21, pp. 31)*
Pub: Crain Communications Inc.
Ed: Lisa Bertagnoli. **Description:** Marcy-Newberry Association connects charities with manufacturers in order to use excess items such as clothing, janitorial and office supplies.

2622 ■ *"Butane Heated Pressure Washer Offers Diverse Cleaning Options" in Product News Network (March 8, 2011)*
Pub: Product News Network
Description: Profile of the Super Max (TM) 6000B power sprayer the can clean with cold or heated water and wet steam. Daimer Industries, provider of janitorial supplies, announced the availability of the machine that offers a variety of cleaning options for a range of applications.

2623 ■ *"Jacksonville-based Interline Expanding in Janitorial-Sanitation Market" in Florida Times-Union (May 10, 2011)*
Pub: Florida Times-Union
Ed: Mark Basch. **Description:** Interline Brands Inc., located in Jacksonville, Florida, aims to grow its business with two recent acquisitions of firms that

distribute janitorial and sanitation products. Interline markets and distributes maintenance, repair and operations products.

2624 ■ "Janitorial Equipment and Supplies US Market" in PR Newswire (October 24, 2011)
Pub: PR Newswire
Description: United States demand for janitorial equipment and supplies (excluding chemical products) is predicted to rise 2.4 percent per year to $7.6 billion in 2013. New product development will lead to increased sales of higher-value goods in the industry.

2625 ■ "Knox County Schools Debate Outsourcing Janitorial Services" in (March 29, 2011)
Pub: Knoxville News Sentinel
Ed: Lola Alapo. **Description:** Custodial services of Knox County Schools in Tennessee may be outsourced in move to save money for the school district. Details of the proposed program are included.

2626 ■ "Our Company is Dedicated to the Environment, But We Work With Vendors that Aren't" in Inc. (March 2008, pp. 78)
Pub: Gruner & Jahr USA Publishing
Ed: Myra Goodman. **Description:** Insight into working with vendors, such as construction and janitorial contractors, to comploy with your company's environmental policies is given.

2627 ■ "Pride Lands Janitorial Work at New Terminal" in Sacramento Business Journal (Vol. 28, June 10, 2011, No. 15, pp. 1)
Pub: Sacramento Business Journal
Ed: Kelly Johnson. **Description:** Pride Industries Inc. won the five-year $9.4 million contract to clean the Sacramento International Airport's new Terminal B, which will open in fall 2011. The nonprofit organization posts a revenue of $191 million for 2011 and currently employs more than 2,400 people with disabilities. The contract is expected to provide savings of over $3 million a year to the airport.

2628 ■ Sanitary Maintenance--Buyers' Guide Issue
Pub: Trade Press Media Group
Contact: Todd Kotlarek, Director
E-mail: todd.kotlarek@tradepress.com
URL(s): www.tradepress.comwww.cleanlink.com/ buyersguide. **Released:** Annual; Latest edition 2008. **Publication includes:** List of manufacturers and suppliers of equipment and products for the sanitary and janitorial supplies and building service contractors industry. **Entries include:** Companyname, address, phone, fax, trade and brand names, products or services. **Database includes:** Lists of brand names and related trade associations. **Arrangement:** Alphabetical. **Indexes:** Product/service.

2629 ■ "Staples Advantage Receives NJPA National Contract for Janitorial Supplies" in Professional Services Close-Up (April 22, 2011)
Pub: Close-Up Media
Description: Staples Advantage, the business-to-business division of Staples Inc. was awarded a contract for janitorial supplies to members of the National Joint Powers Alliance (NJPA). NJPA is a member-owned buying cooperative serving public and private schools, state and local governments, and nonprofit organizations.

2630 ■ "U Overhauling Its Janitorial Program, but Custodians Taking Exception" in Saint Paul Pioneer Press (August 20, 2011)
Pub: McClatchy-Tribune Regional News
Ed: Mila Koumpilova. **Description:** University of Minnesota developed a new team cleaning approach for its campus. The new custodian program will save $3.1 million annually while providing a cleaner campus. The union representing the custodians questions both claims.

STATISTICAL SOURCES

2631 ■ RMA Annual Statement Studies
Pub: Risk Management Association
Contact: Kevin M. Blakey, President
Released: Annual. **Price:** $175.00 2006-07 edition, $105.00. **Description:** Contains composite balance

sheets and income statements for more than 360 industries, including the accounting, auditing, and bookkeeping industries. Also contains five years of comparative historical data for discerning trends. Includes 16 commonly used ratios, computed for most of the size groupings for nearly every industry.

TRADE PERIODICALS

2632 ■ American Window Cleaner Magazine: TheVoice of the Professional Window Cleaner
Pub: American Window Cleaner Magazine
URL(s): www.awcmag.com. **Released:** Bimonthly **Price:** $45, U.S.; $50, Canada; $70, Other countries overseas; $80, U.S. two years; $90, Canada two years; $130, Other countries overseas.

2633 ■ Contracting Profits
Pub: Trade Press Media Group
Contact: Todd Kotlarek, Director
E-mail: todd.kotlarek@tradepress.com
URL(s): www.cleanlink.com/cp/www.tradepress.com. **Released:** 10/yr.

2634 ■ Maintenance Management Newsletter
Pub: Springfield Resources
Ed: Joel Levitt, Editor, jdl@maintrainer.com. **Released:** Monthly. **Price:** Free. **Description:** Provides information of interest to maintenance professionals and plant engineers. Recurring features include interviews, a calendar of events, book reviews, news of educational opportunities, and notices of publications available. **Remarks:** Available online only.

2635 ■ Services: The Magazine for the Building Service Contracting Industry
Pub: Building Service Contractors Association Int'l.
URL(s): www.servicesmag.org/. **Ed:** Lisa Kopochinski. **Released:** Bimonthly **Price:** $24, Members; $30, Nonmembers; $48, Other countries members; $54, Other countries non-members.

VIDEOCASSETTES/AUDIOCASSETTES

2636 ■ School Housekeeping
AMS Distributors, Inc.
PO Box 658
Lady Lake, FL 32158
Free: 800-424-3464
Fax: (352)750-5635
Co. E-mail: orders@vpats.com
URL: http://www.vpats.com
Released: 1989. **Price:** $1980.00. **Description:** Learn to keep all areas of your school from looking dingy through the techniques illustrated in this series.
Availability: VHS; 3/4 U.

2637 ■ Supervisory Series
AMS Distributors, Inc.
PO Box 658
Lady Lake, FL 32158
Free: 800-424-3464
Fax: (352)750-5635
Co. E-mail: orders@vpats.com
URL: http://www.vpats.com
Released: 1986. **Description:** A series training custodial supervisors in staff management. **Availability:** VHS; 3/4 U.

CONSULTANTS

2638 ■ Cleaning Consultant Services Inc. (CCS)
3693 E Marginal Way S
Seattle, WA 98134
Ph: (206)682-9748
Fax: (206)622-6876
Co. E-mail: wgriffin@cleaningconsultants.com
URL: http://www.cleaningbusiness.com
Contact: William R. Griffin, President
E-mail: wgriffin@cleaningconsultants.com
URL(s): www.cleaningbusiness.com. **Description:** Description: Publishes books on floor care, carpet care, self-employment, window washing, custodial training and many other areas related to the cleaning industry. Reaches market through direct mail, reviews

and listings, telephone sales, ads, catalogs and trade shows. **Scope:** Provider of engineering and consulting services. It deals with claim and dispute resolution, program and material development, and cleaning services. **Founded:** 1973. **Publications:** "Raising the Bar with Science, Training and Upward Mobility," Jan, 2010; "Technology Revolutionizes the Cleaning Process "Cleaning for Health" is the New Mantra," Distribution Sales and Management Magazine, May, 2003; "Bill Griffin's Crystal Balls-Cleaning Trends in the Usa 2001," Floor Care is Hot in 2001," Mar, 2001; "Inclean Magazine (Australia), Feb, 2001; "Maintaining Swimming Pools, Spas, Whirlpool Tubs and Saunas," Executive House keeping, Feb, 2001; "Whats New with Floor Care," 2001. **Seminars:** Stone Maintenance Technician (SMT) IICRC Certification Course; Carpet Cleaning Technician; Apprentice/Basic Skills; Organizing Custodial Operations for Maximum Efficiency: How to Sell & Price Contract Cleaning; Starting a House cleaning Business; Rugs & Carpet Cleaning; How to Start and Operate a Successful Cleaning Business; Cleaning Schools in the 2000and Beyond; Bringing About and Working Through Change; Organizing Custodial Operations for Maximum Efficiency; Floor Care Technician (FCT)11 CPC Certified Course; Administering Cleaning Service Contracts. **Telecommunication Services:** ccs@cleaningconsultants.com; marketing@cleaningconsultants.com.

2639 ■ Erin Services Inc.
111 Travelers Way
Saint Simons Island, GA 31522-5632
Ph: (912)638-9916
Fax: (912)638-5701
Co. E-mail: dennisd@ns.technonet.com
Contact: Dennis J. Donnelly, III, President
E-mail: dennis179@yahoo.com
Scope: Offers assistance in technical proposal production, marketing, and research. Industries served: Food service, janitorial, landscaping, hospitality and lodging, parks, and recreational. **Founded:** 1990.

FRANCHISES AND BUSINESS OPPORTUNITIES

2640 ■ 1-800-Got-Junk?
887 Great Northern Way, No. 301
Vancouver, BC, Canada V5T 2E9
Free: 866-255-5668
Fax: (514)370-4625
Co. E-mail: franopps@1800gotjunk.com
URL: http://www.1800gotjunk.com
Description: Junk removal service. **No. of Franchise Units:** 180. **No. of Company-Owned Units:** 1. **Founded:** 1989.. **Franchised:** 1999. **Equity Capital Needed:** Minimum of $90,000. **Franchise Fee:** $16,000+. **Financial Assistance:** Yes. **Training:** Yes.

2641 ■ 360Clean
3032 W Montague Ave., Ste. 103
Charleston, SC 29418
Ph: (888)241-4865
Fax: (843)552-0116
Co. E-mail: barry@360clean.com
URL: http://www.360cleanfranchise.com
Description: Commercial cleaning. **No. of Franchise Units:** 40. **Founded:** 2004.. **Franchised:** 2008. **Equity Capital Needed:** $10,000. **Franchise Fee:** $8,500 single; from $29,500 master. **Financial Assistance:** Yes. **Training:** Yes.

2642 ■ Aerowest Restroom Deodorizing Service
West Sanitation Services, Inc.
3882 Del Amo Blvd., Ste. 602
Torrance, CA 90503
Ph: (310)793-4242
Fax: (310)793-4250
Description: Restroom deodorizing dispenser service. **No. of Franchise Units:** 49. **No. of Company-Owned Units:** 41. **Founded:** 1983.. **Franchised:** 1983. **Equity Capital Needed:** $10,000. **Franchise Fee:** $2,000. **Financial Assistance:** Yes. **Training:** Yes.

2643 ■ Aire-Master of America, Inc.
PO Box 2310
Nixa, MO 65714-2310
Ph: (800)525-0957
Fax: (417)725-5737
Description: Room deodorizing, restroom deodorizing and disinfecting service. **No. of Franchise Units:** 83. **No. of Company-Owned Units:** 4. **Founded:** 1958.. **Franchised:** 1976. **Equity Capital Needed:** $35,500 start-up cash, $35,000-$88,500 total investment. **Franchise Fee:** $31,500. **Financial Assistance:** Yes. **Training:** Yes.

2644 ■ A All Animal Control
108 Roxalana Business Park Dr.
Dunbar, WV 25064
Ph: (866)380-9453
Fax: (304)345-2448
Description: wildlife management. **No. of Franchise Units:** 36. **Founded:** 1995.. **Franchised:** 2000. **Equity Capital Needed:** $10,750-$41,615. **Franchise Fee:** $5,000. **Training:** Extensive 5 day training program includes operations, marketing, sales and field experience followed by ongoing monthly webinars and an Annual Franchise Owners Convention.

2645 ■ American Restoration Services
22 Rutgers Rd.
Pittsburgh, PA 15215
Ph: (800)245-1617
Description: General restoration of homes and commercial structures, using a unique line of cleaning and sealing products. **No. of Franchise Units:** 262. **No. of Company-Owned Units:** 1. **Founded:** 1970.. **Franchised:** 1976. **Equity Capital Needed:** $22,500, includes franchise fees. **Franchise Fee:** $12,500 (U.S.F.). **Financial Assistance:** Yes. **Training:** Yes.

2646 ■ Anago Franchising, Inc.
Anago Cleaning Systems, Inc.
1100 Park Central Blvd., Ste. 1200
Pompano Beach, FL 33064
Free: 800-213-5857
Fax: (954)752-1200
URL: http://www.anagousa.com
Description: Janitorial service. **No. of Franchise Units:** 2,239. **Founded:** 1989.. **Franchised:** 1991. **Equity Capital Needed:** $100,000. **Franchise Fee:** $39,000. **Training:** Yes.

2647 ■ Bonus Building Care
Bonus of America
PO Box 300
Indianola, OK 74442
Ph: (918)823-4990
Free: 800-931-1102
Fax: (918)823-4994
Co. E-mail: franchisees@bonusbuildingcare.com
URL: http://www.bonusbuildingcare.com
Description: Commercial cleaning. **No. of Franchise Units:** 1,259. **No. of Company-Owned Units:** 1. **Founded:** 1996.. **Franchised:** 1996. **Equity Capital Needed:** $1,000. **Franchise Fee:** $7,500. **Financial Assistance:** Yes. **Training:** Intensive initial training, extended training and special services training all included at no additional cost. Flexible, onsite training coupled with comprehensive written guides gets you up and running.

2648 ■ BuildingStars Inc.
11489 Page Service Dr.
St. Louis, MO 63146
Free: 866-991-3356
URL: http://www.buildingstars.com
Description: Commercial cleaning services. **No. of Franchise Units:** 376. **Founded:** 1994.. **Franchised:** 2000. **Equity Capital Needed:** $2,195-$52,795. **Franchise Fee:** $995-$38,595. **Royalty Fee:** 10%. **Financial Assistance:** Limite in-house financial assistance available. **Training:** 1 week at corporate headquarters with ongoing support.

2649 ■ Certapro Painters
The Franchise Company
150 Green Tree Rd.
Oaks, PA 19456
Free: 800-689-7494

Fax: (610)650-9997
Description: Residential and commercial painting franchise. **No. of Franchise Units:** 325. **Founded:** 1992.. **Franchised:** 1992. **Equity Capital Needed:** $129,000-$156,000. **Franchise Fee:** $50,000. **Training:** 2 weeks of training prior to start-up; quarterly training in field. Advance training is also provided.

2650 ■ Chemstation International Inc.
3400 Encrete Ln.
Dayton, OH 45439
Ph: (937)297-8265
Fax: (937)534-0426
Description: Manufactures and distributes detergents in bulk. **No. of Franchise Units:** 49. **No. of Company-Owned Units:** 2. **Founded:** 1979.. **Franchised:** 1981. **Equity Capital Needed:** $500,000-$600,000. **Franchise Fee:** $45,000. **Financial Assistance:** Yes. **Training:** Yes.

2651 ■ City Wide Maintenance Franchise Co.
8460 Nieman Rd.
Lenexa, KS 66214
Ph: (866)887-4029
Fax: (913)888-5151
Description: Maintenance services. **No. of Franchise Units:** 31. **No. of Company-Owned Units:** 1. **Founded:** 1959.. **Franchised:** 2001. **Equity Capital Needed:** $102,325-$225,700. **Franchise Fee:** $50,000. **Royalty Fee:** 5%. **Financial Assistance:** Financial assistance available with franchise fee. **Training:** Offers 2 weeks at headquarters, 2 weeks at franchisee's location, annual training meeting with ongoing support.

2652 ■ Clean & Happy Windows
10019 Des Moines Memorial Dr.
Seattle, WA 98168
Ph: (866)762-7617
Fax: (206)762-7637
Description: Franchise offers maintenance and cleaning of windows. **No. of Franchise Units:** 2. **Founded:** 1990.. **Franchised:** 1999. **Equity Capital Needed:** $1,000-$3,000. **Franchise Fee:** $4,000. **Training:** Yes.

2653 ■ Clean Living Specialists
2742 Joseph Blvd., Ste. 10
Orleans, ON, Canada K1C 1G5
Ph: (613)860-0436
Free: 866-244-4434
Fax: (613)830-9445
Co. E-mail: admin@cleanliving.net
URL: http://www.cleanliving.net
Description: Clean living specialists offer residential cleaning services. **No. of Franchise Units:** 11. **No. of Company-Owned Units:** 14. **Founded:** 1988.. **Equity Capital Needed:** $20,000-$25,000; $150,000 master franchise. **Training:** Provides 2 weeks in Kanata, Ontario, 1 month in new business, followed by ongoing support. **Telecommunication Services:** sales@cleanliving.net.

2654 ■ The Cleaning Authority
7230 Lee Deforest Dr.
Columbia, MD 21046
Ph: (410)740-1900
Free: 877-504-6221
URL: http://www.thecleaningauthority.com
Description: Cleaning service. **No. of Franchise Units:** 160. **No. of Company-Owned Units:** 1. **Founded:** 1978.. **Franchised:** 1996. **Equity Capital Needed:** $90,000 -$110,000. **Franchise Fee:** $30,000-$50,000. **Training:** 2 week home office training; onsite visits, quarterly newsletter, ongoing training sessions.

2655 ■ Cleaning Consultant Services Inc.
PO Box 1273
Seattle, WA 98111
Ph: (206)682-9748
Description: Support services to those who own, manage and/or supervise cleaning operations. **No. of Franchise Units:** 2. **No. of Company-Owned Units:** 3. **Founded:** 1976.. **Franchised:** 1978. **Equity Capital Needed:** $7,500. **Franchise Fee:** $2,500. **Training:** 2-3 days at out training site in Seattle, WA.

2656 ■ Cleannet USA, Inc.
9861 Broken Land Pky., Ste. 208
Columbia, MD 21046
Ph: (301)621-8838
Fax: (410)720-5307
Description: Commercial facility cleaning services. **No. of Franchise Units:** 3,338. **No. of Company-Owned Units:** 464. **Founded:** 1987.. **Franchised:** 1988. **Equity Capital Needed:** $1,500-$100,000 for a master franchise. **Franchise Fee:** $3,200-$200,000. **Financial Assistance:** Yes. **Training:** Yes.

2657 ■ Clintar Groundskeeping Services
Truserve Groundcare Inc.
70 Esna Park Dr., Unit 1
Markham, ON, Canada L3R 1E3
Ph: (905)943-9530
Free: 800-361-3542
Fax: (905)943-9529
Co. E-mail: info@clintar.com
URL: http://www.clintar.com
Description: Grounds keeping services including landscape maintenance, snow and ice control, power sweeping, light construction, tree care and irrigation maintenance. **No. of Franchise Units:** 21. **Founded:** 1973.. **Franchised:** 1984. **Equity Capital Needed:** $100,000-$125,000; $50,000-$60,000 cash. **Franchise Fee:** $40,000. **Training:** Yes.

2658 ■ Coustic-Glo
CGI International Inc.
7111 Ohms Ln.
Minneapolis, MN 55439
Ph: (800)333-8523
Fax: (952)835-1395
Co. E-mail: cgiinc@aol.com
URL: http://www.cousticglo.com
Description: Offers a unique opportunity for an individual to pursue financial independence in a virtually untapped industry. The need for ceiling and wall cleaning and restoration is everywhere. Coustic-Glo franchisees are provided with all of the equipment, products, cleaning solutions and the training necessary to prosper in the field. Assistance with field problems, technical questions, etc. Complete test reports on all products are provided, with updating as necessary. A very aggressive national advertising campaign is pursued. Local ad mats and all product identification are provided. **No. of Franchise Units:** 100. **No. of Company-Owned Units:** 1. **Founded:** 1978.. **Franchised:** 1988. **Equity Capital Needed:** $18,000-$32,000. **Franchise Fee:** $15,000-$25,000. **Financial Assistance:** Yes. **Training:** Provided with a very intensive 2-3 day training program that takes place in his/her respective exclusive area, under the direct supervision of an experienced franchisee that is brought in form his/her area to assist in the establishment of the new franchisees business. Also available to the new franchisee is the option of a training course provided at the home office under the direct supervision of home office personnel.

2659 ■ Coverall Health-Based Cleaning System
Description: One of the nation's leading commercial cleaning franchise companies with more than 9,000 Franchise Owners worldwide. Franchisees are provided with training, equipment, billing and collection services, a quality control program, and a customer base. Ranked as the fastest growing commercial cleaning franchise in the nation by Entrepreneur's 22nd Annual 'Franchise 500'. **No. of Franchise Units:** 9,137. **Founded:** 1985. **Franchised:** 1985. **Equity Capital Needed:** $12,683-$37,160. **Franchise Fee:** $9,120-$30,643. **Training:** Coverall supports its Franchise Owners through comprehensive training, an initial customer base, billing and collection, services and a global network of 90 Support Centers, plus the unique benefits of the Health-Based Cleaning System Program.

2660 ■ Executive Business Maintenance Franchise
5931 Stanley Ave., Ste. S-6
Carmichael, CA 95608
Free: 877-326-8787

Fax: (916)484-3854

Description: Janitorial contract brokerage services. **Founded:** 1996. **Franchised:** 2006. **Equity Capital Needed:** $59,000-$89,000. **Franchise Fee:** $35,000. **Royalty Fee:** 8%. **Training:** Offers 5 business days at headquarters, 5 business days at franchisee's location and ongoing support.

2661 ■ Fibreclean Supplies Ltd.
3750 19th St. NE, Ste. 101
Calgary, AB, Canada T2E 6V2
Ph: (403)291-3991
Free: 800-661-8548
Fax: (403)291-2295
Co. E-mail: kbrown@fibreclean.com
URL: http://www.fibreclean.com

Description: Distributes specialty wholesale supplies to the cleaning industry. One of the soft fibre suppliers in Canada. **No. of Franchise Units:** 1. **No. of Company-Owned Units:** 4. **Founded:** 1977.. **Equity Capital Needed:** $70,000-$100,000 minimum investment. **Franchise Fee:** Varies by territory. **Training:** 2 weeks initial and ongoing support.

2662 ■ Fish Window Cleaning
200 Enchanted Pky.
Manchester, MO 63021
Ph: (877)707-3474
Fax: (636)530-7856
Co. E-mail: info@fishwindowcleaning.com
URL: http://www.fishwindowcleaning.com

Description: Residential and commercial low-rise window cleaning. **No. of Franchise Units:** 220. **No. of Company-Owned Units:** 1. **Founded:** 1978.. **Franchised:** 1998. **Equity Capital Needed:** $59,900-$127,000. **Franchise Fee:** $19,900-$49,900. **Financial Assistance:** Yes. **Training:** Intensive 10 day training in St. Louis followed by 4 days in franchisee territory. On-going support included.

2663 ■ Goodbye Graffiti Inc.
950 Powell St.
Vancouver, BC, Canada V6A 1H9
Free: 877-684-4747
Fax: (604)684-4547
Co. E-mail: amaddison@goodbyegraffiti.com
URL: http://www.goodbyegraffiti.com

Description: The company is into graffiti removal and abatement franchises. Specializes in environmentally friendly graffiti removal from all surfaces and long-term maintenance. **No. of Franchise Units:** 11. **Founded:** 1997.. **Franchised:** 2000. **Equity Capital Needed:** $60-$100,000. **Franchise Fee:** $27,000. **Training:** 2 weeks and ongoing support provided.

2664 ■ International Master Care Janitorial Franchising Inc.
555-6 St., Ste. 327
New Westminster, BC, Canada V3L 5H1
Ph: (604)525-8221
Free: 800-889-2799

Description: Commercial cleaning service. **No. of Franchise Units:** 95. **No. of Company-Owned Units:** 1. **Founded:** 1987.. **Franchised:** 1987. **Equity Capital Needed:** $10,000-$150,000. **Franchise Fee:** $6,000-$120,000. **Training:** Yes.

2665 ■ Jani-King International, Inc.
16885 Dallas Pky.
Addison, TX 75001
Ph: (972)991-0900
Fax: (972)239-7706
Co. E-mail: info@janiking.com
URL: http://www.janiking.com

Description: Offers entrepreneurs a proven system for operating a business involved in the cleaning of office buildings, retail, medical and other facilities. Franchisees in this growth industry are owner/operators of their own businesses who also have access to regional support centers. **No. of Franchise Units:** 10,500. **No. of Company-Owned Units:** 32. **Founded:** 1969.. **Franchised:** 1974. **Equity Capital Needed:** $8,200-$33,550 and up. **Franchise Fee:** $5,500-$15,750 and up. **Training:** Training covers cleaning, personnel, client relations, proposals and sales.

2666 ■ Jantize America
8801 JM Keynes Dr., Ste. 450
Charlotte, NC 28262
Ph: (888)540-0001
Fax: (704)405-5989

Description: Commercial cleaning. **No. of Franchise Units:** 247. **Founded:** 1988. **Franchised:** 1988. **Equity Capital Needed:** $29,650-$171,500. **Franchise Fee:** $29,650-$150,500. **Royalty Fee:** 4%. **Financial Assistance:** Limited in-house and third party financing available. **Training:** Includes 3 days training at headquarters, 2 days at franchisee's location and ongoing support.

2667 ■ JDI Cleaning Systems Inc.
3380 S Service Rd.
Burlington, ON, Canada L7N 3J5
Ph: (905)634-5228
Free: 800-597-5091
Fax: (905)634-8790
URL: http://www.jdicleaning.com

Description: Janitorial franchise. **No. of Franchise Units:** 100. **No. of Company-Owned Units:** 1. **Founded:** 1992.. **Franchised:** 1992. **Equity Capital Needed:** Varies dependent on program chosen. **Franchise Fee:** $10,000 plus (local); $50,000 plus (master). **Training:** 5 days and on the job training provided.

2668 ■ KCS Applications Inc.
4955 Creaser Rd.
Westmoreland, NY 13490
Ph: (315)853-4805
Fax: (315)853-4805
Co. E-mail: kcsapplications@aol.com
URL: http://www.kcs1.com

Description: Asphalt maintenance service. **No. of Franchise Units:** 16. **Founded:** 1992.. **Franchised:** 1994. **Equity Capital Needed:** $15,650. **Franchise Fee:** $15,000. **Royalty Fee:** $450/year. **Training:** 2 days at corporate headquarters, 1 day at franchisee's location and ongoing support provided.

2669 ■ Master Care
555 6 St., Ste. 327
New Westminster, BC, Canada V3L 5H1
Ph: (604)525-8221
Free: 800-889-2799
Fax: (604)526-2235
Co. E-mail: info@mastercare.com
URL: http://www.mastercare.com

Description: The franchise system is in search of associate master franchisee's for metropolitan areas. Provides training in commercial building cleaning. **No. of Franchise Units:** 159. **No. of Company-Owned Units:** 1. **Founded:** 1987.. **Franchised:** 1987. **Equity Capital Needed:** $18,000. **Franchise Fee:** $18,000. **Training:** Provides 3 weeks training and ongoing support.

2670 ■ Octoclean
Octoclean Franchising Systems
5225 Canyon Crest Dr., Ste. 71-339
Riverside, CA 92507
Ph: (951)683-5859
Free: 866-OCT-OCLN
Fax: (951)779-0270
Co. E-mail: chuck@octoclean.com
URL: http://www.octoclean.com

Description: Maintenance and cleaning services are provided. **No. of Franchise Units:** 196. **Founded:** 1983.. **Franchised:** 2000. **Financial Assistance:** Yes. **Training:** Provides hands on training and ongoing support.

2671 ■ Office Pride Commercial Cleaning Services
Office Pride, Inc.
170 N Jackson St.
Franklin, IN 46131
Free: 888-641-2310
Fax: (800)863-8708
URL: http://www.officepride.com

Description: Commercial cleaning service. **No. of Franchise Units:** 121. **Founded:** 1992.. **Franchised:** 1996. **Equity Capital Needed:** $14,900-$59,000. **Franchise Fee:** $9,000-$29,900. **Financial As-**

sistance: Yes. **Training:** 5 days of classroom training at corporate headquarters, follow-up training, and ongoing support.

2672 ■ Omex Office Maintenance Experts
Omex International, Inc.
205 House Ave.
Camp Hill, PA 17011
Ph: (717)737-7311
Free: 800-827-6639
Fax: (717)737-9271

Description: Cleaning services. **No. of Franchise Units:** 21. **No. of Company-Owned Units:** 1. **Founded:** 1979.. **Franchised:** 1994. **Equity Capital Needed:** $40,400-$70,600. **Franchise Fee:** $15,000-$25,000. **Training:** Yes.

2673 ■ Openworks
O.P.E.N. America, Inc.
4742 N 24th St., Ste. 300
Phoenix, AZ 85016
Ph: (602)224-0440
Free: 800-777-6736
Fax: (602)468-3788

Description: Offers maintenance and cleaning services. **No. of Franchise Units:** 316. **No. of Company-Owned Units:** 5. **Founded:** 1983.. **Franchised:** 1983. **Equity Capital Needed:** $16,450-$119,950. **Franchise Fee:** $14,000 and up. **Royalty Fee:** 10%. **Financial Assistance:** Yes. **Training:** Offers training at headquarters and 2 weeks at franchisee's location and ongoing support.

2674 ■ Rainbow International
The Dwyer Group
1020 N University Parks Dr.
Waco, TX 76707
Ph: (866)696-1504
Free: 800-280-9963
Fax: (800)209-7621
URL: http://www.rainbowintl.com

Description: Building Maintenance/Cleaning Service/Custodial Service. **No. of Franchise Units:** 294. **Founded:** 1981. **Franchised:** 1981. **Equity Capital Needed:** $115,675-$189,000; includes franchise fee, equipment package, and start-up costs. **Franchise Fee:** $28,000. **Financial Assistance:** Yes. **Training:** Ongoing support begins with a 2 week program, followed by field mentoring and seminars. Marketing concepts, operations, and the technical A, B, C's are taught. Experienced systems managers monitor the progress and are available for daily contact.

2675 ■ Scrubway
217 Ravenwood Rd.
Exton, PA 19341
Ph: (610)650-8270
Free: 800-355-3000
Fax: (610)650-3268
Co. E-mail: scrubway@comcast.net
URL: http://www.scrubway.com

Description: Commercial restroom hygiene franchise. **No. of Franchise Units:** 6. **No. of Company-Owned Units:** 1. **Founded:** 1994.. **Franchised:** 1994. **Equity Capital Needed:** $50,000-$75,000. **Franchise Fee:** $25,000-$35,000. **Training:** Yes.

2676 ■ Service-Tech Corporation
7589 First Pl.
Oakwood Village, OH 44146
Ph: (800)992-9302
Fax: (440)735-1433

Description: Indoor air quality remediation and industrial cleaning services. Opportunity to join 33 years of experience in solving the growing concerns associated with indoor air pollution. The list of cleaning services offered includes air duct systems, industrial exhaust systems, industrial ovens, overhead structural steel, restaurant hood exhaust systems, laboratory hood exhaust systems, computer room sub-floors, laundry and restroom exhaust systems. **No. of Franchise Units:** 2. **No. of Company-Owned Units:** 2. **Founded:** 1960.. **Franchised:** 1990. **Equity Capital Needed:** $13,000-$20,000 working capital, van lease and miscellaneous. **Franchise Fee:** $19,000 plus equipment. **Training:** 14 days training schedule conducted at the corporate training center, with hands-on field instruction at job sites. Training in marketing, sales, field operations, accounting, personnel and management trainings.

2677 ■ Steamatic, Inc.

BMS Enterprises, Inc.
3333 Quorum Dr., Ste. 280
Ft. Worth, TX 76137
Ph: (817)332-1575
Free: 800-527-1295
Fax: (817)332-5349
Description: Provides water, fire and storm insurance restoration (disaster recovery services); indoor environmental services, air duct and coil cleaning; carpet cleaning; furniture cleaning; drapery cleaning; deodorizing; wood restoration; document restoration; corrosion control; ceiling and wall cleaning. and 24-hour toll-free numbers. **No. of Franchise Units:** 391. **Founded:** 1948.. **Franchised:** 1968. **Equity Capital Needed:** $95,000-$165,960. **Franchise Fee:** $7,000-$24,000. **Training:** Yes.

2678 ■ Swisher Hygiene Franchise Corp.

Swisher International
4725 Piedmont Row Dr., No. 400
Charlotte, NC 28210
Ph: (704)364-7707
Free: 800-444-4138
Description: Provides restroom sanitation and other cleaning services. **No. of Franchise Units:** 31. **No. of Company-Owned Units:** 42. **Founded:** 1983.. **Franchised:** 1990. **Equity Capital Needed:** $83,300-$173,900. **Franchise Fee:** $45,000-$75,000. **Royalty Fee:** 6%. **Training:** Provides 1 week at headquarters, 1 week at franchisee's location, and ongoing support.

2679 ■ System4

4700 Rockside Rd., Ste. 610
Independence, OH 44131
Ph: (216)524-6100

Fax: (216)524-6117
Description: Commercial cleaning. **No. of Franchise Units:** 1,392. **No. of Company-Owned Units:** 2. **Founded:** 2003.. **Franchised:** 2003. **Equity Capital Needed:** $6,156-$37,750. **Franchise Fee:** $4,400-$32,000. **Royalty Fee:** 5%. **Financial Assistance:** Limited in-house financing available. **Training:** Training includes 3 days at franchisees location, 1 day each seminars and ongoing support.

2680 ■ Vacuvent Air Duct Cleaning

Vacuvent Franchising Inc.
13537 US Hwy 1, Ste. 106
Sebastian, FL 32958
Free: 800-690-7292
Fax: (800)690-7295
Description: Air duct cleaning. **No. of Franchise Units:** 5. **No. of Company-Owned Units:** 5. **Founded:** 2003.. **Franchised:** 2004. **Equity Capital Needed:** $3,500. **Franchise Fee:** $2,500. **Training:** Yes.

2681 ■ Vanguard Cleaning Systems Inc.

655 Mariners Island Blvd., Ste. 303
San Mateo, CA 94404
Ph: (650)287-2414
Fax: (650)591-1545
URL: http://www.vanguardcleaning.com
Contact: Doug Mousley, Chief Executive Officer
Description: Cleaning services. **No. of Franchise Units:** 2,200. **No. of Company-Owned Units:** 3. **Founded:** 1984. **Franchised:** 1984. **Equity Capital Needed:** $250,000. **Franchise Fee:** $100,000-$400,000. **Training:** Initial training at headquarters followed by onsite training.

2682 ■ Window Brigade

Window Brigade, Inc.
4907 Hollenden Dr., Ste. 208
Raleigh, NC 27616
Ph: (919)834-8215
Free: 866-587-6243

Fax: (919)834-7630
Description: Residential & commercial window cleaning. **No. of Franchise Units:** 7. **No. of Company-Owned Units:** 1. **Founded:** 1989.. **Franchised:** 2003. **Equity Capital Needed:** $36,500-$125,000. **Franchise Fee:** $6,000-$55,500. **Financial Assistance:** Yes. **Training:** Yes.

2683 ■ Window Genie

FOR Franchising, LLC
800 E Ross Ave.
Cincinnati, OH 45207
Free: 800-700-0022
URL: http://www.windowgenie.com
Description: Window cleaning service. **No. of Franchise Units:** 146. **Founded:** 1994.. **Franchised:** 1998. **Equity Capital Needed:** $60,700-$128,600. **Franchise Fee:** $19,500-$57,000. **Royalty Fee:** 7%. **Financial Assistance:** Limited third party financing available. **Training:** Offers 5 days at headquarters, 5 days at franchisees location with ongoing support.

2684 ■ Window King

Window King, Inc.
40 West Littleton Blvd. Ste. 210-202
Littleton, CO 80120
Ph: (720)283-8002
Fax: (719)487-9702
Description: Window cleaning services. **No. of Franchise Units:** 28. **No. of Company-Owned Units:** 2. **Founded:** 1997.. **Franchised:** 1998. **Equity Capital Needed:** $15,000-$30,000. **Franchise Fee:** $7,000. **Training:** Yes.

2685 ■ Wood Re New

220 S Dysart
Springfield, MO 65802
Ph: (417)865-3665
Fax: (417)833-5479
Description: Wood Re New offers maintenance and cleaning services. **No. of Franchise Units:** 22. **Founded:** 1993.. **Franchised:** 2001. **Equity Capital Needed:** $60,000. **Franchise Fee:** $30,000. **Training:** Yes.

REFERENCE WORKS

2686 ▪ *Computer Industry Almanac*
Pub: Computer Industry Almanac Inc.
Contact: Dr. Egil Juliussen, President
E-mail: ej@c-i-a.com
URL(s): www.c-i-a.com. **Released:** Annual **Price:**
$53, Individuals paperback; $63, Individuals hardcover. **Covers:** Over 3,000 firms involved in the
computer industry in the U.S. **Entries include:**
Company Name, address, phone, fax, products,
sales, number of employees, names and titles of key
personnel, e-mail addresses, websites. **Database
includes:** Lists of firms in various categories; industry
overview; lists of trade shows, associations, publications, market research companies, high-tech PR
companies.

TRADE PERIODICALS

2687 ▪ *DCLNews*
Pub: Data Conversion Laboratory
Contact: Mark Gross, President
Released: Monthly. **Price:** Included in membership;.
Description: E-journal providing you insider informa-
tion on XML and SGML, along with the latest technol-
ogy and e-publishing news.

2688 ▪ *Media Computing*
Pub: Dreamscape Productions
Ed: Sheridan Tatsuno, Editor, statsuno@aol.com.
Released: Monthly. **Price:** $495, institutions in the
U.S. and Canada; $550, institutions elsewhere. **De-
scription:** Supplies analysis of multimedia, internet,
intranet, and web computing issues. Recurring
features include interviews and reports of meetings.

2689 ▪ *Spotlights*
Pub: Internet/Media Strategies Inc.
Released: Weekly. **Description:** Analyzes business
opportunities on the Internet and other technologies.

CONSULTANTS

2690 ▪ Law Offices of Robert J. Keller P.C.
Farragut Sta.
Washington, DC 20033-3428
Ph: (202)223-2100
Fax: (202)223-2121
Co. E-mail: rjk@telcomlaw.com
URL: http://www.telcomlaw.com
Contact: Robert J. Keller, Chief Executive Officer
E-mail: rjk@telcomlaw.com
Scope: Specializes in telecommunications law,
policy, and regulation, with particular emphasis on
wireless telecommunications, new and emerging
technologies, transactions involving FCC-regulated
entities and licensees, and the special legal and
regulatory issues relating to toll free telephone
numbers. Experience in representing clients before
the Federal Communications Commission, federal
courts, and state and federal regulatory agencies.
Founded: 1994.

LIBRARIES

2691 ▪ Gartner IRC
56 Top Gallant Rd.
Stamford, CT 06904
Ph: (203)964-0096
Fax: (203)316-6480
Co. E-mail: inquiry@gartner.com
URL: http://www.gartner.com
Contact: Karen Laughlin
Scope: Information technology, computers, system
design, telecommunications. **Services:** SDI; center
not open to the public (client research only).
Founded: 1979. **Holdings:** 3000 items. **Subscrip-
tions:** 1200 journals and other serials. **Telecom-
munication Services:** info@amstock.com.

2692 ▪ International Data Corp. - IDC Library
2131 Landings Dr.
Mountain View, CA 94043
Ph: (650)962-6481
Fax: (650)691-0518
Co. E-mail: slake@idc.com
URL: http://www.idc.com
Contact: Sara Lake, Director, Library Services
Scope: Information technology. **Services:** Center not
open to the public. **Founded:** 1990. **Holdings:** 350
books; 250 subject files. **Subscriptions:** 70 journals
and other serials.

RESEARCH CENTERS

**2693 ▪ University of Minnesota - Charles
Babbage Institute for the History of
Information Technology (CBI)**
211 Andersen Library
222 21st Ave. S
Minneapolis, MN 55455
Ph: (612)624-5050
Fax: (612)625-8054
Co. E-mail: tmisa@umn.edu
URL: http://www.cbi.umn.edu
Contact: Thomas J. Misa, Director
Services: Advises corporations, institutions, and
individuals on record management and historical
archives development. **Founded:** 1977. **Publications:** *Charles Babbage Institute Newsletter* (Semiannual). **Educational Activities:** CBI Conferences and
workshops; CBI Lecture series. **Awards:** Arthur Norb-
erg travel grant to collections (Annual); Erwin and
Adelle Tomash fellowship in the history of information
processing (Annual). **Telecommunication Services:**
cbi@umn.edu.

START-UP INFORMATION

2694 ■ *EBay Business Start-up Kit: 100s of Live Links to All the Information and Tools You Need*
Pub: NOLO
Ed: Richard Stim. **Released:** July 2008. **Price:** $24.99. **Description:** Interactive kit that connects user directly to EBay is presented.

ASSOCIATIONS AND OTHER ORGANIZATIONS

2695 ■ Broker Management Council (BMC)
PO Box 150229
Arlington, TX 76015
Ph: (682)518-6008
Fax: (682)518-6476
Co. E-mail: assnhqtrs@aol.com
URL: http://www.bmcsales.com
Contact: Pamela L. Bess, Executive Director
Description: Foodservice sales and marketing companies specializing in institutional and restaurant food and allied products. Aims to: facilitate communication and exchange of management information; increase efficiency and reduce the cost of doing business; promote a favorable image of brokers in order to enhance their acceptance. Compiles statistics; conducts specialized education program. **Founded:** 1980. **Educational Activities:** FEDA (Monthly).

2696 ■ NAGMR
c/o Jim Lewis
15038 SE Fairwood Blvd.
Renton, WA 98058-8505
Ph: (425)271-4506
Fax: (425)271-0864
Co. E-mail: jnlsales@aol.com
URL: http://nagmr.com
Contact: Ken Laner, President
Description: Consumer products brokers specializing in selling drug, health, beauty aids, and nonfood products to food chains and the same products and grocery items to the nonfood market. **Founded:** 1948. **Educational Activities:** NAGMR Convention (Annual). **Awards:** NAGMR Award of Excellence (Annual).

2697 ■ Printing Brokerage/Buyers Association International (PB/BA)—PBBA International Inc.
1530 Locust St., Mezanine 124
Philadelphia, PA 19102
Ph: (215)821-6581
Free: 877-585-7141
Fax: (215)359-1577
Co. E-mail: contactus@pbba.org
URL: http://www.pbba.org
Contact: Vincent Mallardi, President
E-mail: vince@pbba.org
Description: Printing buyers/brokers/distributors, printers, typographers, binders, envelope and book manufacturers, packagers, color separation houses, pre-press service organizations, and related companies in the graphic arts industry. Promotes understanding, cooperation, and interaction among members while obtaining the highest standard of professionalism in the graphic arts industry. Gathers information on current technology in the graphic communications industry. Sponsors seminars for members to learn how to work with buyers, brokers and printers; also conducts technical and management seminars. Maintains referral service; compiles statistics. Conducts charitable programs. **Scope:** Printing and publishing marketing and corporate development specialists, whose services include start ups, joint ventures, acquisitions, mergers, contract negotiation, international trade, seminars, workshops, facilities planning, and cost reduction programs. Serves private industries as well as government agencies. **Founded:** 1985. **Subscriptions:** 500 books. **Publications:** "Hot Markets for 2007-2008," Jan, 2005. **Awards:** Printing Broker of the Year (Annual); Vendor of the Year (Annual). **Seminars:** How to Sell Printing Effectively; Sales Compensation and Management; How to Buy Printing Effectively; Hot Markets; International Priority Commerce. **Special Services:** Findprint®; Salesort®.

REFERENCE WORKS

2698 ■ *"Bartering Takes Businesses Back to Basics: Broker's Exchange Helps Members to Reach New Customers"* in Buffalo News (July 9, 2010)
Pub: The Buffalo News
Ed: Dino Grandoni. **Description:** Bartering clubs can help small businesses reach new customers and to expand their business.

2699 ■ *"Cyberwise"* in Black Enterprise (Vol. 41, September 2010, No. 2, pp. 49)
Pub: Earl G. Graves Publishing Co. Inc.
Ed: Marcia Wade Talbert. **Description:** Advice is given to assist in selling an online store called theupscalegaragesale.com. A listing of business brokers specializing in the sale of Internet businesses is included.

2700 ■ *The Ebay Seller's Tax and Legal Answer Book*
Pub: AMACOM
Ed: Cliff Ennico. **Released:** April 30, 2007. **Price:** $19.95. **Description:** Helps sellers using Ebay to file taxes properly, while saving money.

2701 ■ *Merger and Acquisition Sourcebook: 2008*
Pub: NVST Inc.
Contact: Walter Jurek, President
URL(s): www.nvst.com/pubs/masource07-pub_pre. asp. **Ed:** Nancy Rothlein. **Released:** Annual; latest edition 2008. **Price:** $315, Single issue discounted price. **Publication includes:** Profiles of companies most active in mergers and acquisitions in the previous year. **Entries include:** Company name, address, phone, financial data, history of transactions. Principal content of publication is summary and analysis of merger, acquisition, and divestiture activity in the previous year; company reorganizations; and terminated financial transactions. **Arrangement:** Classified by Standard Industrial Classification (SIC) code.

2702 ■ *"The Neighborhood Watch"* in Hawaii Business (Vol. 53, March 2008, No. 9, pp. 36)
Pub: Hawaii Business Publishing
Ed: David K. Choo. **Description:** OahuRe.com offers information on Hawaii real estate market, with spreadsheets and comparative market analysis page, which shows properties that are active, sold, or in escrow. Other details about OahuRe.com are discussed. A list of other top real estate websites in Hawaii and in the U.S. in general is provided.

2703 ■ *"Power Up"* in Entrepreneur (Vol. 35, November 2007, No. 11, pp. 140)
Pub: Entrepreneur Media Inc.
Ed: Amanda C. Kooser. **Description:** PowerSeller is a status in the Internet company eBay, wherein sellers average at least $1,000 in sales per month for three consecutive months. There are five tiers in the PowerSeller status, which ranges from Bronze to Titanium. Launching startups at eBay can help entrepreneurs pick up a wide customer base, but getting and maintaining PowerSeller status is a challenge.

2704 ■ *"Risky Business"* in Canadian Business (Vol. 79, October 23, 2006, No. 21, pp. 153)
Pub: Rogers Media
Ed: C.J. Burton. **Description:** Tips for Canadian managers on how to handle business risks are presented.

2705 ■ *"With New Listings, Business Brokers See Hope"* in Business Courier (Vol. 27, September 3, 2010, No. 18, pp. 1)
Pub: Business Courier
Ed: Lucy May. **Description:** Business brokers in Cincinnati, Ohio are expecting better prices in view of the strengthening economy.

2706 ■ *World M&A Network*
Pub: NVST Inc.
Contact: Walter Jurek, President
URL(s): www.worldm-anetwork.comwww.nvst.com/ pubs/worldma-pub.asp. **Ed:** John W. Bailey. **Released:** Monthly; Quarterly; Updated monthly online. **Price:** $395, U.S.; $425, Out of country; $395, Members annual membership; $39.50, Members month-to-month membership. **Covers:** Over 2,000 merger and acquisition leads for companies with annual revenues over $1 million. **Entries include:** company, size, geographic region and sales. **Arrangement:** Classified by Standard Industrial Classification (SIC) code.

TRADE PERIODICALS

2707 ■ *Barron's: The Dow Jones Business and Financial Weekly*
Pub: Dow Jones & Company Inc.
URL(s): online.barrons.com/public/mainwww.dow-jones.com. **Ed:** Edwin A. Finn, Jr. **Released:** Weekly (Mon.) **Price:** $149, Individuals print & online; $99, Individuals print only; $79, Individuals online only.

2708 ■ *Better Investing*
Pub: National Association of Investors Corp.
URL(s): www.betterinvesting.org/Public/MediaCenter/MediaCenter/BetterInvesti ng+Magazine/default.htm.
Ed: Adam Ritt. **Released:** Monthly **Price:** $19, Individuals.

2709 ■ *Business Opportunities Journal*
Pub: Business Service Corp.
URL(s): www.boj.com. **Ed:** Mark Adkins. **Released:** Monthly

2710 ■ *Computerized Investing*
Pub: American Association of Individual Investors
Contact: James B. Cloonan, Chairman
URL(s): www.aaii.com. **Released:** Bimonthly **Price:** $20, Members; $35, Members other countries, international; $40, Nonmembers U.S.; $45, Nonmembers other countries, international.

2711 ■ *Dow Theory Forecasts*
Pub: Horizon Publishing Company L.L.C.
URL(s): www.dowtheory.com/index.asp. **Ed:** Richard Moroney, Charles Carlson. **Released:** Weekly

2712 ■ *Futures Magazine*
Pub: Futures Magazine, Inc.
URL(s): www.futuresmag.com. **Ed:** Steve Zwick. **Released:** Monthly **Price:** $78, Individuals U.S.; $121, Other countries.

2713 ■ *Institutional Investor*
Pub: Institutional Investor
URL(s): www.institutionalinvestor.com. **Released:** Monthly **Price:** $549, Individuals silver; $1200, Individuals gold; $1600, Individuals platinum.

2714 ■ *Investment Advisor Magazine*
Pub: Investment Advisor Group
URL(s): www.investmentadvisor.com/directories/. **Released:** Monthly **Price:** $99, Canada; $139, Out of country.

2715 ■ *The Journal of Futures Markets: Futures, Options, and other Derivative Products*
Pub: John Wiley & Sons Inc.
Contact: Stephen M. Smith, President
URL(s): onlinelibrary.wiley.com/journal/10.1002/(-ISSN)1096-9934. **Ed:** Robert I. Webb. **Released:** Monthly **Price:** $2520, Institutions print only; $2640, Institutions, Canada and Mexico print only; $2742, Institutions, other countries print only; £1723, Institutions print with online; $2899, Institutions print with online; $3019, Institutions, Canada and Mexico print with online; $3121, Institutions, other countries print with online.

2716 ■ *The Journal of Portfolio Management*
Pub: Institutional Investor
URL(s): www.iijournals.com/toc/jpm/current. **Ed:** Frank J. Fabozzi, Peter Bernstein. **Released:** Quarterly **Price:** $960, Individuals; $1632, Two years.

2717 ■ *Money*
Pub: Time Inc.
Contact: Wayne Powers, President
URL(s): money.cnn.com. **Released:** Monthly **Price:** $14.95, Individuals; $29.90, Two years; $44.82, Individuals 3 years.

2718 ■ *Official Summary of Security Transactions and Holdings*
Pub: U.S. Government Printing Office
URL(s): bookstore.gpo.gov/actions/GetPublication.do?stocknumber=746-001-0001 4-2. **Released:** Monthly **Price:** $30, Single issue; $42, Other countries.

VIDEOCASSETTES/AUDIOCASSETTES

2719 ■ *Anatomy of a Leveraged Buyout*
Chesney Communications
2302 Martin St., Ste. 125
Irvine, CA 92612
Ph: (949)263-5500
Free: 800-223-8878
Fax: (949)263-5506
Co. E-mail: videocc@aol.com
URL: http://www.videocc.com
Released: 1989. **Price:** $49.95. **Description:** Now everyone can pull off a leveraged buyout, because Terry Greve, a man who has been involved with eight of them, tells his secrets in this video. **Availability:** VHS; 3/4 U.

2720 ■ *Private Placements and Other Private Financings*
Practising Law Institute (PLI)
810 7th Ave., 21st Fl.
New York, NY 10019-5818
Ph: (212)824-5700
Free: 800-260-4754
Co. E-mail: info@pli.edu
URL: http://www.pli.edu
Contact: Victor J. Rubino, President
E-mail: vrubino@pli.edu
Released: 1988. **Price:** $245.00. **Description:** This program focuses on the legal aspects of business finance. **Availability:** VHS.

CONSULTANTS

2721 ■ Allen Business Investments (ABI)—Abi Business Brokers & Appraisers
125 Ryan Industrial Ct., Ste. 100
San Ramon, CA 94583
Ph: (925)838-8150
Fax: (925)838-8173
URL: http://www.abi-bizbrkrs.com
Contact: Ron Johnson, President
E-mail: ron@abi-ma.com
Scope: Offers expertise on all phases of business opportunity valuations, and buyers and sellers of any type of business. Provides counsel on business frauds and expert witness services in superior and United States bankruptcy court valuations work for goodwill values; loss revenues; estate planning and dissolution of marriages. **Founded:** 1984. **Publications:** "Caution Small Business Owners - Be Wary of Companies That Want to Value and Help You Sell Your Business, for an Up-Front "Valuation" Fee"; "Wanted Considered Dangerous Known for Separating Business Owners From Their Money"; "Allocation of Purchase Price"; "Selling Your Business - a Quick Overview".

2722 ■ Associated Management Systems Inc.
1000 Elwell Ct., Ste. 234
Palo Alto, CA 94303-4306
Ph: (650)852-9041
Fax: (650)967-9992
Co. E-mail: amsn@rcn.com
Contact: M. A. Quraishi, President
Scope: The firm's entrepreneurial and professional expertise includes corporate management, investment banking, finance, strategic planning, risk evaluation, due diligence studies and management audits. Also assists with mergers and acquisitions, and provides management for turnaround situations. Undertakes project packaging, plant relocations, capital restructuring and funding. Industries served: Agriculture, real estate, insurance, computers, communications, retail/wholesale, electronics/instruments, paper/printing, food processing, furniture/home products, travel, transportation, recreation, heavy industry, pharmaceuticals, and government agencies. **Founded:** 1966.

2723 ■ Associated Marketers
10 E Hartshorn Dr.
Short Hills, NJ 07078
Ph: (973)376-3835
Contact: Lauren K. Hagaman, President
Scope: Consulting services limited to area of mergers and acquisitions through a network of associates. Active in serving manufacturing, distributing and service businesses seeking new corporate homes, acquiring additional businesses, or divesting divisions or subsidiaries. Fields served include appliances, house wares, advertising, industrial, publishing, building materials, printing and graphic arts, banking, insurance, apparel and textiles, automotive, transportation, home furnishings, food and confectionary

products, leisure products, mail order, natural resources, plastics, packaging, and service businesses and retailing. **Founded:** 1959.

2724 ■ Boice Dunham Group
30 W 13th St., Ste. 3C
New York, NY 10011-7912
Ph: (212)752-5550
Fax: (212)752-7055
Contact: Craig K. Boice, President
E-mail: bdgbusdevl@msn.com
Scope: Specialized business development service offering identification, assessment and positioning of new business opportunities; acquisition of new corporate resources and business plan implementation for new ventures based on innovative technologies and growing markets. **Founded:** 1983. **Seminars:** Methods of Market Transformation: Breakout from the Niche, Apr, 2007; How will Utilities Grow?, Denver, May, 2006; New Tools and New Strategies to build active Customer Relationships: The State of the Art, Miami, Dec, 2005; Technology management, Decision-making, and business planning; The Role of AMR in Demand Response and Reliability.

2725 ■ Bullitt-Hutchins Inc.
5555 West Loop S, Ste. 255
Bellaire, TX 77401-2112
Ph: (713)464-7705
Fax: (713)464-9578
Contact: Kevin O'Connor, President
Scope: Provides counseling and appraisal services to commercial, industrial and multi-family real estate in both urban and suburban settings. Specializes in providing negotiations for the acquisition and disposition of properties. **Founded:** 1969.

2726 ■ Business Team
1901 S Bascom Ave., Ste. 400
Campbell, CA 95008
Ph: (408)246-1102
Fax: (408)246-2219
Co. E-mail: sanjose@business-team.com
URL: http://www.business-team.com
Contact: William L. Kramer, Vice President
Scope: Business consulting services offered to companies looking for buyers. Specializes in mergers and acquisitions, business brokerage, and valuations. **Founded:** 1980. **Seminars:** Business Valuation Enhancing the Value of Your Company.

2727 ■ Federated Business Agencies
15 Hunter Dr.
Eastchester, NY 10709-5205
Ph: (914)793-2220
Fax: (914)793-2524
Contact: Nathan Papell, President
E-mail: papell@msn.com
Scope: Business brokers and real estate brokers actively involved with acquisitions and mergers; real estate; purchases and sales of various business entities; new business ventures; special situations; business expansion and diversification; management consultation and financing. **Founded:** 1931.

FRANCHISES AND BUSINESS OPPORTUNITIES

2728 ■ Business America
Business America Assoc., Inc.
2120 Greentree Rd.
Pittsburgh, PA 15220
Ph: (412)276-7701
Description: Sells businesses and franchise appraisal. **No. of Franchise Units:** 4. **Founded:** 1984. **Franchised:** 1985. **Equity Capital Needed:** $10,000. **Franchise Fee:** $7,995. **Training:** Yes.

2729 ■ Empire Business Brokers
PO Box 129
Buffalo, NY 14225
Ph: (716)240-2544
Fax: (610)535-2544
Co. E-mail: nickgug1@aol.com
URL: http://www.empirebb.com
Description: Assist sellers of existing business opportunities in finding buyers. **No. of Franchise Units:** 66. **No. of Company-Owned Units:** 1. **Founded:**

1981. **Franchised:** 1989. **Equity Capital Needed:** $20,000-$30,000 total investment. **Franchise Fee:** $17,500. **Royalty Fee:** 5%. **Training:** 5 days at company Headquarters by the country's foremost business broker, ongoing Seminars and conventions. Manuals, forms and tapes provided.

2730 ■ The Entrepreneur's Source

TES Franchising LLC
900 Main St. S, Bldg. 2
Southbury, CT 06488
Ph: (908)236-2264
Free: 800-289-0086
Fax: (203)264-3516
Co. E-mail: sstilwell@FranchiseSource.com
URL: http://www.franchisesearch.com
Description: Franchising consulting, coaching, placement/selection, and development firm providing services to prospective and existing franchisees and franchisors. **No. of Franchise Units:** 215. **Founded:** 1984.. **Franchised:** 1998. **Equity Capital Needed:** $67,200-$77,050. **Franchise Fee:** $45,000. **Training:** Initial and ongoing.

2731 ■ Executive Business Maintenance Franchise

5931 Stanley Ave., Ste. S-6
Carmichael, CA 95608
Free: 877-326-8787
Fax: (916)484-3854
Description: Janitorial contract brokerage services. **Founded:** 1996. **Franchised:** 2006. **Equity Capital Needed:** $59,000-$89,000. **Franchise Fee:** $35,000. **Royalty Fee:** 8%. **Training:** Offers 5 business days at headquarters, 5 business days at franchisee's location and ongoing support.

2732 ■ Murphy Business & Financial Corp.

513 N Belcher Rd.
Clearwater, FL 33765
Ph: (888)561-3243
Fax: (727)725-8090
Description: Business & franchise brokerage/commercial real estate. **No. of Franchise Units:** 141. **No. of Company-Owned Units:** 1. **Founded:** 1994.. **Franchised:** 2006. **Equity Capital Needed:** $45,750-$113,600. **Franchise Fee:** $35,000-$50,000. **Royalty Fee:** 10%. **Financial Assistance:** In-house financial assisstance available for franchise fee.

2733 ■ Realty World

Realty World America, Inc.
1600 Sunflower Ave. Ste. 100
Costa Mesa, CA 92626
Free: 800-685-4984
Description: Real estate brokerage. **No. of Franchise Units:** 216. **Founded:** 1973.. **Franchised:** 1973. **Equity Capital Needed:** $54,500-$227,000. **Franchise Fee:** $12,500-$50,000. **Royalty Fee:** Varies. **Training:** Provides 1 week training at headquarters, and ongoing support.

2734 ■ Sunbelt Business Brokers

2821 Riverside Dr.
Ottawa, ON, Canada K1V 8N4
Ph: (613)731-9140
Free: 800-905-3557
Fax: (613)526-0997
Co. E-mail: ottawa@sunbeltnetwork.com
URL: http://www.sunbeltnetwork.com
Description: Business brokerage company. **No. of Franchise Units:** 29. **Founded:** 2002.. **Franchised:** 2002. **Equity Capital Needed:** $100,000. **Franchise Fee:** $25,000. **Training:** Provides training and ongoing support.

COMPUTERIZED DATABASES

2735 ■ ABI/INFORM®

789 E Eisenhower Pkwy.
Ann Arbor, MI 48106-1346
Ph: (734)761-4700
Free: 800-521-0600
Co. E-mail: info@il.proquest.com
URL: http://www.il.proquest.com
Contact: Matt Dunie, President
Availability: Online: ProQuest Co.; ProQuest LLC-Dialog; ProQuest LLC - Dialog; LexisNexis Group; STN International; Wolters Kluwer Health - Ovid. **Type:** Full-text; Bibliographic; Image.

2736 ■ American Banker Financial Publications

1 State St. Plz., 27th Fl.
New York, NY 10004
Ph: (212)803-8200
Free: 800-221-1809
Fax: (212)843-9600
Co. E-mail: custserv@AmericanBanker.com
URL: http://www.americanbanker.com
Availability: Online: ProQuest LLC - Dialog. **Type:** Full-text.

2737 ■ Best's Statement File - Life/Health - United States

1 Ambest Rd.
Oldwick, NJ 08858-7000
Ph: (908)439-2200
Fax: (908)439-3296
Co. E-mail: customer_service@ambest.com
URL: http://www.ambest.com
Contact: James Peavy, President
Availability: CD-ROM: A.M. Best Company Inc. **Type:** Numeric; Directory.

2738 ■ Best's Statement File - Property/Casualty - United States

1 Ambest Rd.
Oldwick, NJ 08858-7000
Ph: (908)439-2200
Fax: (908)439-3296
Co. E-mail: customer_service@ambest.com
URL: http://www.ambest.com
Contact: James Peavy, President
Availability: CD-ROM: A.M. Best Company Inc. **Type:** Numeric; Directory.

2739 ■ Dial-Data™

95 Rockwell Pl.
Brooklyn, NY 11217
Ph: (718)522-7373
Free: 800-367-5968
Co. E-mail: info@trackdata.com
URL: http://www.trackdata.com
Availability: Online: Track Data Corp. **Type:** Numeric.

2740 ■ Dialog Finance and Banking Newsletters

2250 Perimeter Park Dr., Ste. 300
Morrisville, NC 27560
Ph: (919)804-6400
Free: 800-334-2564
Fax: (919)804-6410
Co. E-mail: contact@dialog.com
URL: http://www.dialog.com
Availability: Online: ProQuest LLC - Dialog. **Type:** Full-text.

2741 ■ Dividend Record

55 Water St.
New York, NY 10041
Ph: (212)438-2000
Free: 800-523-4534
Fax: (212)438-7375
Co. E-mail: questions@standardandpoors.com
URL: http://www.standardandpoors.com
Availability: Online: The McGraw-Hill Cos., Inc.-Standard & Poor's Financial Services LLC. **Type:** Numeric.

2742 ■ EIU ViewsWire

26 Red Lion Sq.
London WC1R 4HQ, United Kingdom
Ph: 20 7576 8181
Fax: 20 7576 8476
Co. E-mail: london@eiu.com
URL: http://www.eiu.com
Availability: Online: LexisNexis Group; Financial Times Ltd.; The Economist Group - Economist Intelligence Unit Ltd. **Type:** Full-text; Numeric.

2743 ■ Mergers Unleashed People Database

1 State St. Plz., 27th Fl.
New York, NY 10004
Ph: (212)803-8200
Free: 800-221-1809
Co. E-mail: custserv@sourcemedia.com
URL: http://www.sourcemedia.com
Availability: Online: Investcorp International Inc. - SourceMedia Inc. **Type:** Directory.

2744 ■ Quarterly Financial Report (QFR)

60 E 42nd St.
New York, NY 10165
Ph: (212)986-9300
Fax: (212)986-5857
Co. E-mail: data@haver.com
URL: http://www.haver.com
Availability: Online: Haver Analytics - HaverSelect. **Type:** Time Series.

2745 ■ SNL Financial Banks & Thrifts Module

One SNL Plz.
Charlottesville, VA 22902
Ph: (434)977-1600
Fax: (434)977-4466
Co. E-mail: support@snl.com
URL: http://www.snl.com
Availability: Online: SNL Financial LC. **Type:** Full-text; Directory; Numeric; Statistical.

2746 ■ SNL Financial North American Real Estate Module

One SNL Plz.
Charlottesville, VA 22902
Ph: (434)977-1600
Fax: (434)977-4466
Co. E-mail: support@snl.com
URL: http://www.snl.com
Availability: Online: SNL Financial LC. **Type:** Directory; Numeric; Statistical.

2747 ■ Value Line Electronic Convertibles

220 E 42nd St.
New York, NY 10017-5806
Ph: (212)907-1500
Free: 800-654-0508
Fax: (212)818-9747
Co. E-mail: vlcr@valueline.com
URL: http://www.valueline.com
Contact: Howard A. Brecher, President
Availability: Online: Value Line Inc. **Type:** Numeric.

START-UP INFORMATION

2748 ■ *How to Start a Home-Based Consulting Business: Define Your Specialty Build a Client Base Make Yourself Indispensable*
Pub: Globe Pequot Press
Ed: Bert Holtje. **Released:** January 10, 2010. **Price:** $18.95. **Description:** Everything needed for starting and running a successful consulting business from home.

2749 ■ *Starting and Running a Coaching Business*
Pub: How To Books
Ed: Aryanne Oade. **Released:** August 9, 2010. **Price:** $26.00. **Description:** Guide for the comprehensive, practical and personalized process of starting and running a coaching business is presented.

2750 ■ *Starting Up On Your Own: How to Succeed as an Independent Consultant or Freelance*
Pub: FT Press
Ed: Mike Johnson. **Released:** February 1, 2010. **Price:** $24.99. **Description:** Concise guide for anyone wanting to start their own consulting firm is provided.

ASSOCIATIONS AND OTHER ORGANIZATIONS

2751 ■ **Association of Consulting Engineering Companies - Canada (ACEC)—Association des Ingenieurs-Conseils du Canada**
130 Albert St., Ste. 420
Ottawa, ON, Canada K1P 5G4
Ph: (613)236-0569
Free: 800-565-0569
Fax: (613)236-6193
Co. E-mail: info@acec.ca
URL: http://www.acec.ca
Contact: John D. Gamble, President
E-mail: jgamble@acec.ca
Description: Promotes the interests of independent consulting engineers; represents electrical, civil, environmental, geotechnical, metallurgical, cultural, and other engineering fields. Standardizes forms of agreement, contracts, and guidelines for consulting engineers; acts as clearinghouse. **Scope:** A national association of consulting firms that provides engineering and other technology-based intellectual services. Promotes and safeguards the business and professional interests of the Canadian consulting engineering industry in Canada and abroad. **Founded:** 1925. **Subscriptions:** articles books periodicals reports. **Publications:** "There is a Best Practice for Hiring Engineering Firms"; "The Budget 2009 Infrastructure Stimulus Package: Maximizing Benefits to Canadians"; "Foreign Policy Statement: A Ray of Hope for Infrastructure Investments"; "Infrastructure Recovery: National Planning and the Right Engineering

Needed". **Awards:** Beaubien Award; Awards of Excellence; Schreyer Award; Merit Award (Annual). **Seminars:** Understanding Public Private Partnerships in Canada.

2752 ■ **Association for Corporate Growth - Toronto Chapter (ACG)—Canadian Angus Association**
720 Spadina Ave., Ste. 202
Toronto, ON, Canada M5S 2T9
Ph: (416)868-1881
Fax: (416)391-3633
Co. E-mail: acgtoronto@acg.org
URL: http://www.acg.org/toronto/default.aspx
Contact: Stephen B. Smith, President
Description: Professionals with a leadership role in strategic corporate growth. Seeks to facilitate the professional advancement of members, and the practice of corporate growth management. Fosters communication and cooperation among members; conducts continuing professional education programs. **Founded:** 1973. **Publications:** *Mergers & Acquisitions - The Dealmaker's Journal* (Monthly). **Educational Activities:** Association for Corporate Growth - Toronto Chapter Board meeting (Monthly); Capital Connection (Annual). **Awards:** Toronto Chapter Leadership Award (Annual).

2753 ■ **Association of Independent Consultants (AIC)**
15 Wilson St.
Markham, ON, Canada L3P 1M9
Ph: (416)410-8163
Fax: (905)669-5233
Co. E-mail: info1@aiconsult.ca
URL: http://www.aiconsult.ca/en
Contact: Lawrence Fox, President
Description: Independent consultants. Promotes professional advancement of members. Facilitates communication and cooperation among members; makes available volume discounts to members. Conducts business education courses; maintains speakers' bureau. **Founded:** 1989. **Publications:** *Thrive-on-Line*. **Educational Activities:** Association of Independent Consultants Meeting (Monthly). **Telecommunication Services:** president1@aiconsult.ca.

2754 ■ **Canadian Association of International Development Consultants (CAIDC)—Regroupement des consultants canadiens en developpement internationale**
260 St. Patrick St., Ste. 101
Ottawa, ON, Canada K1N 5K5
Ph: (613)244-1050
Fax: (613)244-8315
Co. E-mail: caidcrccdi@gmail.com
URL: http://www.caidc-rccdi.ca
Contact: Richard Beattie, President
Description: Aims to provide services for, and to represent the interests of, Canadian international development consultants. **Founded:** 1993.

2755 ■ *Canadian Consulting Engineer*
130 Albert St., Ste. 420
Ottawa, ON, Canada K1P 5G4
Ph: (613)236-0569

Free: 800-565-0569
Fax: (613)236-6193
Co. E-mail: info@acec.ca
URL: http://www.acec.ca
Contact: John D. Gamble, President
E-mail: jgamble@acec.ca
Released: Bimonthly **Price:** C$46.95, /year in Canada; $75.95, /year outside Canada.

2756 ■ *Communique*
130 Albert St., Ste. 420
Ottawa, ON, Canada K1P 5G4
Ph: (613)236-0569
Free: 800-565-0569
Fax: (613)236-6193
Co. E-mail: info@acec.ca
URL: http://www.acec.ca
Contact: John D. Gamble, President
E-mail: jgamble@acec.ca
Released: Monthly

2757 ■ *Electronic International Journal for Time Use Research*
c/o Dr. Kimberly Fisher, Sec.
University of Oxford
Dept. of Sociology
Manor Road Bldg.
Manor Rd.
Oxford OX1 3UQ, United Kingdom
Co. E-mail: kimberly.fisher@sociology.ox.ac.uk
URL: http://iatur.timeuse.org
Contact: Prof. Michael Bittman, President
Released: Annual

2758 ■ *Fifteenth Reunion of the International Association for Time Use Research Amsterdam*
c/o Dr. Kimberly Fisher, Sec.
University of Oxford
Dept. of Sociology
Manor Road Bldg.
Manor Rd.
Oxford OX1 3UQ, United Kingdom
Co. E-mail: kimberly.fisher@sociology.ox.ac.uk
URL: http://iatur.timeuse.org
Contact: Prof. Michael Bittman, President
Released: Periodic

2759 ■ **International Association for Time Use Research (IATUR)**
c/o Dr. Kimberly Fisher, Sec.
University of Oxford
Dept. of Sociology
Manor Road Bldg.
Manor Rd.
Oxford OX1 3UQ, United Kingdom
Co. E-mail: kimberly.fisher@sociology.ox.ac.uk
URL: http://iatur.timeuse.org
Contact: Prof. Michael Bittman, President
Description: The International Association for Time Use Research (IATUR) facilitates exchange of ideas, methodology, and data collection techniques among researchers and compilers of official statistics on the patterns of daily activities and changes in people's behaviours over time. **Scope:** time use, unpaid work,

leisure time, women's work, work time, exposure, health, exercise. **Founded:** 1970. **Subscriptions:** 5200 articles periodicals books archival material monographs papers. **Publications:** *Fifteenth Reunion of the International Association for Time Use Research Amsterdam* (Periodic); *Time Use Methodology: Towards Consensus*; *Electronic International Journal for Time Use Research* (Annual).

2760 ■ *Mergers & Acquisitions - The Dealmaker's Journal*
720 Spadina Ave., Ste. 202
Toronto, ON, Canada M5S 2T9
Ph: (416)868-1881
Fax: (416)391-3633
Co. E-mail: acgtoronto@acg.org
URL: http://www.acg.org/toronto/default.aspx
Contact: Stephen B. Smith, President
Released: Monthly **Price:** included in membership dues.

2761 ■ *Thrive-on-Line*
15 Wilson St.
Markham, ON, Canada L3P 1M9
Ph: (416)410-8163
Fax: (905)669-5233
Co. E-mail: info1@aiconsult.ca
URL: http://www.aiconsult.ca/en
Contact: Lawrence Fox, President
Price: free for members.

2762 ■ *Time Use Methodology: Towards Consensus*
c/o Dr. Kimberly Fisher, Sec.
University of Oxford
Dept. of Sociology
Manor Road Bldg.
Manor Rd.
Oxford OX1 3UQ, United Kingdom
Co. E-mail: kimberly.fisher@sociology.ox.ac.uk
URL: http://iatur.timeuse.org
Contact: Prof. Michael Bittman, President

REFERENCE WORKS

2763 ■ *"Achieving Greatness"* in *Black Enterprise* (Vol. 38, January 2008, No. 6, pp. 50)
Pub: Earl G. Graves Publishing Co. Inc.
Description: Randall Pinkett, winner of a reality show on television and chairman of BCT Partners, insists that a business cannot survive by doing just enough or more of the same. Pinkett's New Jersey company provides management, technology and consulting to other firms.

2764 ■ *"Altegrity Acquires John D. Cohen, Inc."* in *(November 19, 2009, pp. 14)*
Pub: Investment Weekly News
Description: John D. Cohen, Inc., a contract provider of national security policy guidance and counsel to the federal government, was acquired by Altegrity, Inc., a global screening and security solutions provider; the company will become part of US Investigations Services, LLC and operate under the auspices of Altegrity's new business, Altegrity Security Consulting.

2765 ■ *"The Art of War for Women"* in *Hawaii Business* (Vol. 54, July 2008, No. 1, pp. 23)
Pub: Hawaii Business Publishing
Description: Business consultant Chi-Ning Chu talks about her new book 'The Art of War for Women: Sun Tzu's Ancient Strategies and Wisdom for Winning at Work', which discusses how women can more effectively win in business. She also shares her thoughts about the advantages that women have, which they can use in businesses decisions.

2766 ■ *"BDC Launches New Online Business Advice Centre"* in *Internet Wire* (July 13, 2010)
Pub: Comtex
Description: The Business Development Bank of Canada (BDC) offers entrepreneurs the chance to use their new online BDC Advice Centre in order to

seek advice regarding the challenges of entrepreneurship. Free online business tools and information to help both startups and established firms are also provided.

2767 ■ *"Best Foot Forward"* in *Canadian Business* (Vol. 80, October 22, 2007, No. 21, pp. 115)
Pub: Rogers Media
Ed: Jeremy Shinewald. **Description:** Jeremy Shinewald's mbaMission admissions consulting business helps prospective MBA students with essay writing, mock interview preparation and school selection. The consulting fee for application to one school is $2,250. Details of the business schools' MBA programs and tuition fees are explored.

2768 ■ *"Brite-Strike Tactical Launches New Internet Marketing Initiatives"* in *Internet Wire* (September 15, 2009)
Pub: Comtex News Network, Inc.
Description: Brite-Strike Tactical Illumination Products, Inc. has enlisted the expertise of Internet marketing guru Thomas J. McCarthy to help revamp the company's Internet campaign. An outline of the Internet marketing strategy is provided.

2769 ■ *"Designing Events Updates Online Suite"* in *Wireless News* (October 25, 2009)
Pub: Close-Up Media
Description: Designing Events, an outsourcing and consulting firm for conferences and meetings, announced the release of an update to its Designing Events Online suite of web-based management and marketing tools; features include enhanced versions of online registration and collaboration, content management, session development, social media and conference websites.

2770 ■ *"The End of Clock-Punching"* in *Canadian Business* (Vol. 83, September 14, 2010, No. 15, pp. 96)
Pub: Rogers Media Ltd.
Ed: Lyndsie Bourgon. **Description:** Workplace consultant Peter Hadwen is pushing for the transformation of Canada's government departments into results-only work environments (ROWE). ROWE does not require employees to show up to work at a certain time as long as they are meeting goals and achieving results in their jobs. Details of studies regarding ROWE in US companies are examined.

2771 ■ *"Federal Fund Valuable Tool For Small-Biz Innovators"* in *Crain's Detroit Business* (Vol. 24, September 29, 2008, No. 39, pp. 42)
Pub: Crain Communications Inc.
Ed: Nancy Kaffer. **Description:** Grants from the Small Business Innovation Research Program, or SBIR grants, are federal funds that are set aside for 11 federal agencies to allocate to tech-oriented small-business owners. Firms such as Biotechnology Business Consultants help these companies apply for SBIR grants.

2772 ■ *"Five Low-Cost Home Based Startups"* in *Women Entrepreneur* (December 16, 2008)
Pub: Entrepreneur Media Inc.
Ed: Lesley Spencer Pyle. **Description:** During tough economic times, small businesses have an advantage over large companies because they can adjust to economic conditions more easily and without having to go through corporate red tape that can slow the implementation process. A budding entrepreneur may find success by taking inventory of his or her skills, experience, expertise and passions and utilizing those qualities to start a business. Five low-cost home-based startups are profiled. These include starting an online store, a virtual assistant service, web designer, sales representative and a home staging counselor.

2773 ■ *Franchise: Freedom or Fantasy*
Pub: iUniverse
Ed: Mitchell York. **Released:** June 22, 2009. **Price:** $13.95. **Description:** Successful franchisee and professional certified coach guides individuals through the many steps involved in deciding whether or not to buy a franchise and how to do it correctly.

2774 ■ *"Hire Power"* in *Entrepreneur* (Vol. 35, November 2007, No. 11, pp. 105)
Pub: Entrepreneur Media Inc.
Ed: Mark Henricks. **Description:** Companies with big resources may hire human resource (HR) consultants to help with writing manuals, drafting policies and designing benefits for employees. HR consultants may also be hired to assist with specific functions or other strategic aspects.

2775 ■ *"Interbrand's Creative Recruiting"* in *Business Courier* (Vol. 27, November 12, 2010, No. 28, pp. 1)
Pub: Business Courier
Ed: Dan Monk. **Description:** Global brand consulting firm Interbrand uses a creative recruitment agency to attract new employees into the company. Interbrand uses themed parties to attract prospective employees. The 'Alice In Wonderland' tea party for example, allowed the company to hire five new employees.

2776 ■ *"International Growth"* in *Black Enterprise* (Vol. 38, July 2008, No. 12, pp. 64)
Pub: Earl G. Graves Publishing Co. Inc.
Ed: Marcia A. Reed-Woodard. **Description:** Becoming an increasingly smaller portion of the global business environment is the U.S. economy. Christopher Catlin, an associate with Booz Allen Hamilton, a technology management and strategy-consulting firm, shares what he has learned about the global market.

2777 ■ *"Into the Groove: Fine-Tune Your Biz By Getting Into the Good Habit Groove"* in *Small Business Opportunities* (Spring 2008)
Pub: Harris Publications Inc.
Description: Profile of Ty Freyvogel and his consulting firm Freyvogel Communications. Freyvogel serves the telecommunications need of Fortune 500 and mid-sized businesses.

2778 ■ *"Leadership: The Couch in the Corner Office: Surveying the Landscape of the CEO Psyche"* in *Inc.* (January 2008, pp. 33-34)
Pub: Gruner & Jahr USA Publishing
Description: Profile of Leslie G. Mayer, founder of the Leadership Group, a firm that provides assistance to CEOs of firms by offering a deep understanding of the relationships, insecurities, and blind spots that can weaken strong leadership.

2779 ■ *"Managing the Facebookers; Business"* in *The Economist* (Vol. 390, January 3, 2009, No. 8612, pp. 10)
Pub: Economist Newspaper Ltd.
Description: According to a report from PricewaterhouseCoopers, a business consultancy, workers from Generation Y, also known as the Net Generation, are more difficult to recruit and integrate into companies that practice traditional business acumen. 61 percent of chief executive managers say that they have trouble with younger employees who tend to be more narcissistic and more interested in personal fulfillment with a need for frequent feedback and an overprecise set of objectives on the path to promotion which can be hard for managers who are used to a different relationship with their subordinates. Older bosses should prepare to make some concessions to their younger talent since some of the issues that make them happy include cheaper online ways to communicate and additional coaching, both of which are good for business.

2780 ■ *"Meet Rebecca. She's Here to Fire You"* in *Inc.* (November 2007, pp. 25-26)
Pub: Gruner & Jahr USA Publishing
Ed: Max Chafkin. **Description:** Amid liability concerns as well as CEO guilt, more and more firms are using consulting companies to fire workers. These outsourced firms help small companies structure severance and document information in order to limit legal liability when firing an employee.

2781 ■ *The Mirror Test: How to Breathe New Life Into Your Business*
Pub: Grand Central Publishing
Ed: Jeffrey W. Hayzlett. **Released:** May 10, 2010. **Price:** $24.99. **Description:** Consultant and author, Jeffrey Hayzlett, explains why a business is not doing well and asks the questions that most business managers are afraid to ask.

2782 ■ *"Montgomery & Barnes: a Service-Disabled, Veteran-Owned Small Business" in Underground Construction (Vol. 65, October 2010, No. 10)*
Pub: Oildom Publishing Company of Texas Inc.
Description: Gary Montgomery, chairman of Montgomery and Barnes announced that President Wendell (Buddy) Barnes is now majority owner, thus making the Houston-based civil engineering and consulting services firm, eligible to quality as a Service-Disabled Veteran-Owned Small Business (SDVOSB).

2783 ■ *"More Sales Leads, Please: Or, What Happened When Frontline Selling Started Practicing What It Preaches" in Inc. (November 2007)*
Pub: Gruner & Jahr USA Publishing
Description: Frontline Selling located in Oakland, New Jersey helps train sales teams to generate and convert sales leads. The consulting firm doubled their marketing budget to increase their own sales.

2784 ■ *"Nampa Police Department: Electronic Systems Just One Tool in Business Security Toolbox" in Idaho Business Review (October 29, 2010)*
Pub: Dolan Media Newswires
Ed: Brad Carlson. **Description:** Police departments and private security firms can help small businesses with hard security and business consultants can assist with internal audit security and fraud prevention.

2785 ■ *"New Database Brings Doctors Out of the Dark" in Business Courier (Vol. 26, October 23, 2009, No. 26, pp. 1)*
Pub: American City Business Journals, Inc.
Ed: James Ritchie. **Description:** A database created by managed care consulting firm Praesentia allows doctors in Cincinnati to compare average reimbursements from health insurance companies to doctors in different areas. Specialist doctors in the city are paid an average of $172.25 for every office consultation.

2786 ■ *"Nothing But Net: Fran Harris Offers Advice On Winning the Game of Business" in Black Enterprise (Vol. 38, March 2008, No. 8, pp. 50)*
Pub: Earl G. Graves Publishing Co. Inc.
Ed: Chana Garcia. **Description:** Fran Harris, certified life coach, business consultant, and CEO of her business, a multimedia development company, reveals five tips to ensure entrepreneurial success.

2787 ■ *"On Hire Ground" in Entrepreneur (Vol. 36, February 2008, No. 2, pp. 19)*
Pub: Entrepreneur Media Inc.
Description: ADP Small Business Services, an economic consulting firm, showed that small businesses had increased employment rates in 2007 and added 77,000 jobs in November 2007. Entrepreneurial employment and data showing the contribution of small businesses to job growth are presented.

2788 ■ *"Outplacement Services" in Black Enterprise (Vol. 38, March 2008, No. 8, pp. 60)*
Pub: Earl G. Graves Publishing Co. Inc.
Ed: Marcia Reed Woodard. **Description:** Tips to use while in career-transition are offered. Many times outplacement services are provided as part of a severance package to employees.

2789 ■ *"Plan Your Next Event at Newport News Marriott at City Center" in Benzinga.com (July 29, 2011)*
Pub: Benzinga.com
Ed: Benzinga Staff. **Description:** Newport News Marriott at City Center is promoting itself as the premier venue for business meetings, conventions and weddings.

2790 ■ *PPC's Guide to Small Business Consulting Engagements*
Pub: Practitioners Publishing Company
Released: March 2004. **Price:** $226.00. **Description:** Technical guide for conducting consulting engagements for small business.

2791 ■ *PPC's Guide to Small Business Consulting Engagements, Vol. 2*
Pub: Practitioners Publishing Company
Released: March 2004. **Description:** Second volume of the technical guide for conducting consulting engagements for small business.

2792 ■ *PPC's Guide to Small Business Consulting Engagements, Vol. 3*
Pub: Practitioners Publishing Company
Released: March 2004. **Description:** Third volume of the technical guide for conducting consulting engagements for small business.

2793 ■ *"Reduce the Risk of Failed Financial Judgments" in Harvard Business Review (Vol. 86, July-August 2008, No. 8, pp. 24)*
Pub: Harvard Business School Press
Ed: Robert G. Eccles; Edward J. Fiedl. **Description:** Utilization of business consultants, evaluators, appraisers, and actuaries to decrease financial management risks is discussed.

2794 ■ *"Restoring Grandeur" in Business Courier (Vol. 26, December 4, 2009, No. 32, pp. 1)*
Pub: American City Business Journals, Inc.
Ed: Dan Monk. **Description:** Eagle Realty Group intends to spend more than $10 to restore the historic 12-story Phelps apartment building in Lytle Park in Cincinnati. Its president, Mario San Marco, expressed the need to invest in the building in order to maintain operations. The building could be restored into a hotel catering to executives and consultants.

2795 ■ *"Risky Business" in Canadian Business (Vol. 79, October 23, 2006, No. 21, pp. 153)*
Pub: Rogers Media
Ed: C.J. Burton. **Description:** Tips for Canadian managers on how to handle business risks are presented.

2796 ■ *"The Secret Life of a Serial CEO" in Inc. (January 2008, pp. 80-88)*
Pub: Gruner & Jahr USA Publishing
Ed: David H. Freedman. **Description:** Profile of Bob Cramer, who has lead six successful companies and is now searching for a new business venture and thinks he's found it. Cramer shares his journey from wooing venture capital, handling founders and his hunt for his newest venture.

2797 ■ *"Seven Ways to Fail Big" in Harvard Business Review (Vol. 86, September 2008, No. 9, pp. 82)*
Pub: Harvard Business School Press
Ed: Paul B. Carroll; Chunka Mui. **Description:** Seven factors involved in business failures are identified, and ways to avoid them are described. These factors include flawed financial engineering, hurrying into consolidation, and investing in technology that is not a good fit.

2798 ■ *The Sticking Point Solution: 9 Ways to Move Your Business from Stagnation to Stunning Growth in Tough Economic Times*
Pub: Vanguard Press
Contact: Bill Smith, Director
E-mail: bill.smith@perseusbooks.com
Ed: Jay Abraham. **Released:** May 10, 2010. **Price:** $25.95. **Description:** Renowned business consultant, Jay Abraham, reveals the nine ways even successful businesses get stuck, hit plateaus, and fail to achieve their dreams and he explains how to get unstuck and create exponential growth.

2799 ■ *"Think Disruptive! How to Manage In a New Era of Innovation" in Strategy & Leadership (Vol. 38, July-August 2010, No. 4, pp. 5-10)*
Pub: Emerald Inc.
Ed: Brian Leavy, John Sterling. **Description:** The views expressed by Scott Anthony, president of an innovation consultancy Innosight, on the need for corporate leaders to apply disruptive innovation in a recessionary environment are presented. His suggestion that disruptive innovation is the only way to survive during the economic crisis is discussed.

2800 ■ *"Trend: Tutors to Help You Pump Up the Staff" in Business Week (September 22, 2008, No. 4100, pp. 45)*
Pub: McGraw-Hill Companies, Inc.
Ed: Reena Janaj. **Description:** High-level managers are turning to innovation coaches in an attempt to obtain advice on how to better sell new concepts within their companies. Individuals as well as consulting firms are now offering this service.

2801 ■ *"Your Booming Business: How You Can Align Sales and Marketing for Dynamic Growth" in Small Business Opportunities (Spring 2008)*
Pub: Harris Publications Inc.
Ed: Voss W. Graham. **Description:** Voss Graham, founder and CEO of Inneractive Consulting Group Inc., works with companies to develop and hire successful sales teams. A checklist from the American Bankers Association to help write a business plan is included.

TRADE PERIODICALS

2802 ■ *The GreenMoney Journal & Online Guide*
Pub: The Greenmoney Journal
Contact: Cliff Feigenbaum, Editor
E-mail: cliff@greenmoney.com
Released: Bimonthly. **Price:** $50, individuals; $50, Canada plus $10 postage; $50, elsewhere plus $20. **Description:** Encourages and promotes the awareness of socially and environmentally responsible business, investing and consumer resources in publications and online. Our goal is to educate and empower individuals and businesses to make informed financial decisions through aligning their personal, corporate and financial principles. Recurring features include a calendar.

2803 ■ *Make It A Winning Life*
Pub: Wolf Rinke Associates,Inc.
Ed: Wolf J. Rinke, Ph.D., Editor, wolfrinke@aol.com. **Released:** Bimonthly. **Price:** Free. **Description:** Features ideas and strategies to help individuals succeed faster and improve the quality of their life. Remarks: America Online, Inc.

VIDEOCASSETTES/ AUDIOCASSETTES

2804 ■ *Building a Profitable Consulting Practice Series*
Instructional Video
2219 C St.
Lincoln, NE 68502
Ph: (402)475-6570
Free: 800-228-0164
Fax: (402)475-6500
Co. E-mail: feedback@insvideo.com
URL: http://www.insvideo.com
Released: 19??. **Description:** Two-part business educational series by Howard Shenson offers tips on how to build a profitable consulting practice. Covers consulting opportunities, market strategies, proposal writing, contracting strategies, fee setting, disclosure, and collection techniques. **Availability:** VHS.

2805 ■ *Exceeding Customer Expectations*
Service Quality Institute
9201 E. Bloomington Fwy.
Minneapolis, MN 55420-3437
Ph: (952)884-3311
Free: 800-548-0538
Fax: (952)884-8901
URL: http://www.customer-service.com
Released: 19??. **Price:** $149.95. **Description:** Teaches good customer interaction and how to treat co-workers as internal customers. **Availability:** VHS.

2806 ■ *Managing the Emerging Company*
Leslie T. McClure
PO Box 1223
Pebble Beach, CA 93953
Ph: (831)656-0553

Fax: (831)656-0555
Co. E-mail: leslie@411videoinfo.com
URL: http://www.411videoinfo.com
Released: 1997. Price: $990.00. Description: Ten-volume set deals with the functions of developing and running a business. Availability: VHS.

CONSULTANTS

2807 ■ Allen Business Investments (ABI)—Abi Business Brokers & Appraisers
125 Ryan Industrial Ct., Ste. 100
San Ramon, CA 94583
Ph: (925)838-8150
Fax: (925)838-8173
URL: http://www.abi-bizbrkrs.com
Contact: Ron Johnson, President
E-mail: ron@abi-ma.com
Scope: Offers expertise on all phases of business opportunity valuations, and buyers and sellers of any type of business. Provides counsel on business frauds and expert witness services in superior and United States bankruptcy court valuations work for goodwill values; loss revenues; estate planning and dissolution of marriages. Founded: 1984. Publications: "Caution Small Business Owners - Be Wary of Companies That Want to Value and Help You Sell Your Business, for an Up-Front "Valuation" Fee"; "Wanted Considered Dangerous Known for Separating Business Owners From Their Money"; "Allocation of Purchase Price"; "Selling Your Business - a Quick Overview".

2808 ■ The Alliance Management Group Inc.
38 Old Chester Rd., Ste. 300
Gladstone, NJ 07934
Ph: (908)234-2344
Fax: (908)234-0638
Co. E-mail: kathy@strategicalliance.com
URL: http://www.strategicalliance.com
Contact: Gene Slowinski, Director
E-mail: gene@strategicalliance.com
Scope: The firm enables leading companies to maximize the value of their strategic alliances, mergers and acquisitions. Offers services in partner evaluation process, a planning and negotiating program, mergers and acquisition integration, management issues, the turnaround or termination of poorly performing alliances, and a competitive strategic analysis program. Publications: "Effective Practices For Sourcing Innovation," Jan-Feb, 2009; "Intellectual Property Issues in Collaborative Research Agreements," Nov-Dec, 2008; "Building University Relationships in China," Sep-Oct, 2008; "Reinventing Corporate Growth: Implementing the Transformational Growth Model"; "The Strongest Link"; "Allocating Patent Rights in Collaborative Research Agreements"; "Protecting Know-how and Trade Secrets in Collaborative Research Agreements," Aug, 2006; "Sourcing External Technology for Innovation," Jun, 2006. Special Services: "Want, Find, Get, Manage" Model®; "Want, Find, Get, Manage" Framework®; WFGM Framework®; The Alliance Implementation Program®; WFGM Paradigm®; WFGM Model®; "Want, Find, Get, Manage" Paradigm®, Transformational Growth®; T-growth®.

2809 ■ Alliance Management International Ltd.
PO Box 470691
Cleveland, OH 44147-0691
Ph: (440)838-1922
Co. E-mail: bob@bgruss.com
Contact: Ashok Vasudevan, Director
Scope: A consulting company that helps to form national and international strategic alliances. Handles alliances between companies forming joint ventures. Staff specialized in small company-large company alliance, alliance assessment and analysis, and alliance strategic planning. Seminars: Joint Business Planning; Developing a Shared Vision; Current and New/Prospective Partner Assessment; Customer Service; Sales Training; Leader and Management Skills.

2810 ■ Allin Corp.
381 Mansfield Ave.
Pittsburgh, PA 15220-2751

Ph: (412)928-8800
Fax: (412)928-0887
URL: http://www.allin.com
Contact: Richard W. Talarico, President
Scope: A information technology consulting company that teams with businesses to help them transform the promise of the Internet into practical business realities through five interrelated solution areas: Information Technology Infrastructure, Business Operations, Knowledge Management, Electronic Business and Interactive Media. Founded: 1996. Seminars: Automate Business Processes using XML, Microsoft's new InfoPath 2003 and K2.net 2003.

2811 ■ Alternative Services Inc.
32625 7 Mile Rd., Ste. 10
Livonia, MI 48152
Ph: (248)471-4880
Fax: (248)471-5230
URL: http://www.asi-mi.org
Contact: Arthur Mack, President
Scope: Provider of social services management support to group homes for the mentally disabled. Also offers marketing, training, and financial services to businesses and nonprofit organizations. Founded: 1978.

2812 ■ Ambler Growth Strategy Consultants Inc.
3432 Reading Ave.
Hammonton, NJ 08037-8008
Ph: (609)567-9669
Free: 888-253-6662
Fax: (609)567-3810
Co. E-mail: thegrowthstrategist@ambler.com
URL: http://www.ambler.com
Contact: Aldonna R. Ambler, Chief Executive Officer
E-mail: aldonna@ambler.com
Scope: Growth strategies, strategic assessments, CEO coaching. Founded: 1979. Publications: "A joint venture can deliver more than growth"; "Achieving competitive advantage"; "Achieving resilience for your business during difficult times"; "Achieving resilient growth during challenging times"; "Acquisitions: A growth strategy to consider"; "Attracting and retaining longterm corporate sponsors"; "Celebrate Selling: The Consultative Relationship Way"; "A Joint Venture Can Deliver More Than Growth"; "Achieving Competitive Advantage"; "Achieving Resilience for Your Business During Difficult Times"; "Balancing Revenue Growth with Growth of a Business"; "Capture Your Competitive Advantage"; "Ease Succession Planning"; "Games Employees Play"; "How to Spark Innovation in an Existing Company"; "Managers demands must change with growth"; "Motivating Generation employees"; "Knowing when to hire ratios provide answers"; "Better customer service can bring black ink". Seminars: Strategic Leadership; Managing Innovation; Breaking Through Classic Barriers to Growth; Energize Your Enterprise; Capture Your Competitive Advantage; Four Entrepreneurial Styles; Perservance and Resilience; Real-Time Strategic Planning/RO1. Special Services: The Growth Strategist™.

2813 ■ American English Academy (AEA)—American English College
111 N Atlantic Blvd., Ste. 112
Monterey Park, CA 91754
Ph: (626)457-2800
Fax: (626)457-2808
Co. E-mail: admission@aea-usa.com
URL: http://www.aea-usa.com
Contact: Charles Policky, President
Scope: Specializes in providing on-site English language and communication development for corporations and individuals. Also develops and delivers training in speaking, writing, pronunciation, grammar, and idioms with an emphasis on business communication. Offers individual, small group, intensive, and long-distance learning. Programs tailor-made for each client. Founded: 1983. Telecommunication Services: info@aec.edu.

2814 ■ Association of Home-Based Women Entrepreneurs (HBWE)
PO Box 31561
Saint Louis, MO 63131-1561
Ph: (314)805-9519

Fax: (314)909-8179
Co. E-mail: aschaefer@advbizsol.com
URL: http://www.hbwe.org
Contact: Louise Wiedermann, President
E-mail: lw@projektek.com
Scope: Organization dedicated to women working from home-based offices. Focuses on the needs and interests of women doing their own business. It also focuses on business-related programs and issues, networking, leads and mentoring for professional growth in a dynamic and friendly atmosphere. Founded: 1998. Publications: "Taking Your Business International"; "Dressing For Success"; "Web 2.0 The Future of the Internet"; "Assertiveness Skills for Women in Business". Seminars: Making Connections, Jul, 2008; One Inch Wide, One Mile Deep, Jun, 2008; Accelerating Your Business, May, 2008; Change is Good, Apr, 2008; Pyro Marketing, Jan, 2007; Twenty Five Key Steps To Maintaining A Successful Home-Based Business, Nov, 2006.

2815 ■ Aurora Management Partners Inc.
4485 Tench Rd., Ste. 340
Suwanee, GA 30024
Ph: (770)904-5209
Fax: (770)904-5226
Co. E-mail: rturcotte@auroramp.com
URL: http://www.auroramp.com
Contact: William A. Barbee, Director
E-mail: abarbee@auroramp.com
Scope: Specializes in turnaround management and reorganization consulting. Firm develop strategic initiatives, organize and analyze solutions, deal with creditor issues, review organizational structure and develop time frames for decision making. Turnaround services offered include Recovery plans and their implementation, Viability analysis, Crisis management, Financial restructuring, Corporate and organizational restructuring, Facilities rationalization, Liquidation management, Loan workout, Litigation support and Expert testimony, Contract renegotiation, Sourcing loan refinancing and Sourcing equity investment. Founded: 2005. Publications: "TMA Turnaround of the Year Award, Small Company, Honorable Mention," Nov, 2005; "Back From The Brink - Bland Farms," Progressive Farmer, Oct, 2004; "New Breed of Turnaround Managers," Catalyst Magazine, Aug, 2004; "Key Performance Drivers - Bland Farms," The Produce News, Apr, 2004; "Corporate Governance: Averting Crisis's Before They Happen," ABJ journal, Feb, 2004.

2816 ■ Melvin E. Barnette & Associates Inc.
805 Hopkins Ave.
Pendleton, SC 29670
Ph: (864)646-7622
Fax: (626)296-5113
Co. E-mail: melvin@mbarnette.com
URL: http://www.mbarnette.com
Contact: Melvin E. Barnette, President
Scope: Management consulting firm specializing in higher education and public sector consulting services. Offers services including higher education administrative, business and financial operations studies; structuring of upper-level management organizations; state government operations; legislative liaison; personnel evaluation; crisis resolution and management; and management training. Founded: 1986.

2817 ■ Beacon Management - Management Consultants
1000 W McNab Rd.
Pompano Beach, FL 33069
Ph: (954)782-1119
Free: 800-771-8721
Fax: (954)969-2566
Co. E-mail: md@beaconmgmt.com
URL: http://www.beaconmgmt.com
Contact: Joyce Slencak, Manager
Scope: Specializes in change management, organized workplaces, multicultural negotiations and dispute resolutions and internet based decision making. Founded: 1985. Publications: "Sun-Sentinel Article," Oct, 2012.

2818 ■ Beeline Learning Solutions (BLS)
14911 Quorum Dr., Ste. 120
Dallas, TX 75254

Ph: (972)813-0465
Fax: (972)386-8667
Co. E-mail: info@consultingpartners.com
URL: http://www.beeline.com
Contact: Dominic Nagy, Manager
E-mail: dominic.nagy@consultingpartners.com
Scope: Consulting firm offering technology, content, and services addressing recruitment and sourcing, talent management, and learning and performance optimization. Solutions offered include contingent workforce solutions, vendor management software, talent management solutions, recruitment process outsourcing, performance management, applicant tracking, learning management and eLearning. **Founded:** 1990. **Special Services:** Beeline®.

2819 ■ **Benchmark Consulting Group Inc.—Benchmark Advisors**
283 Franklin St., Ste. 400
Boston, MA 02110-3100
Ph: (617)482-7661
Fax: (617)423-2158
Contact: Walter E. Robb, III, President
E-mail: werobb35@aol.com
Scope: Provides financial and management services to companies. Helps companies grow through debt, equity sourcing and restructuring, business valuation, acquisition and divestiture, computer information systems and improved operation profitability. **Founded:** 1978.

2820 ■ **Bio-Technical Resources L.P. (BTR)**
1035 S 7th St.
Manitowoc, WI 54220-5301
Ph: (920)684-5518
Fax: (920)684-5519
Co. E-mail: info@biotechresources.com
URL: http://www.biotechresources.com
Contact: Tom Jerrell, President
Scope: Services include strain improvement, process development and metabolic engineering. Solutions are also offered for the development of biotechnology products and processes through contract services in research and development, bio process scale-up, pilot scale manufacturing, technology and economic assessments. Target audience: pharmaceutical, biotechnology, chemical and food and feed industries. Client base may be global leaders as well as small companies and startups. **Founded:** 1962. **Publications:** "A Novel Fungus for the Production of Efficient Cellulases and Hemi-Cellulases," Jun, 2009; "Linoleic Acid Isomerase from Propionibacterium acnes: Purification, Characterization, Molecular Cloning, and Heterologous Expression," 2007; "Purification and Characterization of a Membrane-Bound Linoleic Acid Isomerase from Clostridium sporogenes," 2007; "Metabolic Engineering of Sesquiterpene Metabolism in Yeast," 2007; "Purification and Characterization of a Membrane-Bound Linoleic AcidIsomerase from Clostridium sporogenes," 2007; "Reduction of Background Interference in the Spectrophotometric Assay of Mevalonate Kinase," 2006; "A Soluble Form of Phosphatase in Saccharomyces cerevisiae Capable of Converting Farnesyl Diphosphate to E, E-Farnesol," 2006; "Ascorbate Biosynthesis: A Diversity of Pathways," BIOS Scientific Publishers, 2004; "The Biotechnology of Ascorbic Acid Manufacture," BIOS Scientific Publishers, 2004; "Detection of Farnesyl Diphosphate Accumulation in YeastERG9 Mutants," 2003; "Reverse Two-Hybrid System: Detecting Critical Interaction Domains and Screening for Inhibitors," Eaton Publishing, 2000. **Seminars:** Metabolic Engineering for Industrial Production of Glucosamine and N-Acetylglucosamine, Aug, 2003; Metabolic Engineering of E. coli for the Industrial Production of Glucosamine, Apr, 2003.

2821 ■ **BioChem Technology Inc.**
3620 Horizon Dr., Ste. 200
King of Prussia, PA 19406
Ph: (610)768-9360
Fax: (610)768-9363
Co. E-mail: sales@biochemtech.com
URL: http://www.biochemtech.com
Contact: George Lee, President
Scope: A process consultation firm specializing in the monitoring, optimization and control of wastewater treatment processes. The technological optimization services include assessment of treatment capacities,

facility re-rating, optimization services, de-bottlenecking services, flow dynamics/mixing pattern analysis. **Founded:** 1979. **Publications:** "Process Evaluation Provides Optimization and Energy Reduction"; "Effect of Ionic Strength on Ion Selective Electrodes in the Activated Sludge Process"; "DO Control Based on On-line Ammonia Measurement"; "Energy Savings at Phoenix 23rd Avenue Wastewater Treatment Plant Using Feed-Forward Process Control"; "A Novel Approach for Monitoring and Control of Denitrification in a Biological Nutrient Removal Facility," Oct, 1999; "A Unique Approach for Assessing the Capacity of a Biological Nutrient Removal Facility," Oct, 1999; "Enhancing Competitiveness of an Operations Staff: Five Years Experience with a BNR Wastewater Treatment Facility," Oct, 1998; "Optimization of Nitrification Process By On-Line Monitoring of Nitrification Time," Jun, 1997; "Monitoring and Control of the Nitrification Process Marine Park Water Reclamation Facility, City of Vancouver, WA," Oct, 1997; "Operational Improvements in a Biological Nutrient Removal Facility Using an Innovative Biological Activity Meter," May, 1996; "Operator Education and an Innovative Monitoring Technology Improve Performance of a Biological Nutrient Removal Facility," Oct, 1996; "Performance Enhancement of a BNR Wastewater Treatment Facility Utilizing a Microcosm Reactor Equipped With a Biological Activity Meter," Oct, 1996; "Optimization of Biological Denitrification Through Biological Activity Monitoring: System Development," Jun, 1995. **Seminars:** A Five Year Case Study of a Feed Forward Nitrogen Reduction Process Control System, Jun, 2009; Alternate DO Control Based on On-line Ammonia Measurement, Jun, 2009.

2822 ■ **BioSciCon Inc.**
14905 Forest Landing Cir.
Rockville, MD 20850
Ph: (301)610-9130
Fax: (301)610-7662
Co. E-mail: info@bioscicon.com
URL: http://www.bioscicon.com
Contact: Nenad Markovic, President
Scope: Sponsoring development of the technology of the Pap test accuracy via introduction of a new bio-marker that enhances visibility of abnormal cells on Pap smears or mono-layers of cervical cells obtained in solution. Conducts clinical trials for assessment of the test efficacy and safety, manufactures research tools for conduct of trials, and markets IP to license manufacturing, marketing, sales and distribution rights of the new technology line of products. **Founded:** 1996. **Publications:** "Cervical Acid Phosphates: A Biomarker of Cervical Dysplasia and Potential Surrogate Endpoint for Colposcopy," 2004; "Enhancing Pap test with a new biological marker of cervical dysplasia," 2004; "A cytoplasmic biomarker for liquid-based Pap," The FACEB Journal Experimental Biology, 2004; "Pap test and new biomarker-based technology for enhancing visibility of abnormal cells," 2004. **Special Services:** Mark-Pap®; PreservCyt®.

2823 ■ **Birchfield Jacobs Foodsystems Inc.**
519 N Charles St., Ste. 350A
Baltimore, MD 21201-5022
Ph: (410)528-8700
Fax: (410)528-6060
URL: http://www.birchfieldjacobs.com
Contact: Robert Jacobs, Owner Principal
E-mail: rjacobs@birchfieldJacobs.com
Scope: Food facilities design consultants for colleges; universities; schools; healthcare facilities; government; military; correctional; country clubs and restaurants. Services include facilities design; feasibility studies; operations analysis and master planning. **Founded:** 1979.

2824 ■ **C. Clint Bolte & Associates**
809 Philadelphia Ave.
Chambersburg, PA 17201
Ph: (717)263-5768
Fax: (717)263-8954
Co. E-mail: clint@clintbolte.com
URL: http://www.clintbolte.com
Contact: C. Clint Bolte, Principal
E-mail: cbolte3@comcast.net
Scope: Provider of management consulting services to firms involved with the printing industry. Services

include outsourcing studies, graphics supply chain management studies, company and equipment valuations, plant layout services, litigation support, fulfillment warehouse consulting and product development services. **Founded:** 1989. **Seminars:** How to compete with the majors.

2825 ■ **BPT Consulting Associates Ltd.**
12 Parmenter Rd., Ste. B-6
Londonderry, NH 03053
Ph: (603)437-8484
Free: 888-278-0030
Fax: (603)434-5388
Contact: John Kuczynski, Managing Director
Scope: Provides management consulting expertise and resources to cross-industry clients with services for: Business Management consulting, People/Human Resources Transition and Training programs, and a full cadre of multi-disciplined Technology Computer experts. Virtual consultants with expertise in e-commerce, supply chain management, organizational development, and business application development consulting. **Founded:** 1991.

2826 ■ **Business Consulting Services (BCS)**
207 Dickinson Ave.
Swarthmore, PA 19081-1630
Ph: (610)328-9806
Contact: Thomas K. Casey, President
Scope: Management consulting organization dedicated to providing high quality, professional services to the business, government and non-profit communities. Specializes in the two key areas of business performance improvement and information technology consulting. Specifically for small business owners. **Founded:** 1991. **Publications:** "If You Fail To Plan"; "The True Cost Of Technology"; "Why Projects Fail"; "Planning For A Business Disruption". **Seminars:** How To Select, Manage and Contract Consultants, and Other Resources; How To Market Professional Services; Introduction To Management Consulting.

2827 ■ **Business Improvement Architects (BIA)**
33 Riderwood Dr.
Toronto, ON, Canada M2L 2X4
Ph: (416)444-8225
Free: 866-346-3242
Fax: (416)444-6743
Co. E-mail: info@bia.ca
URL: http://www.bia.ca
Contact: Michael Stanleigh, Chief Executive Officer
E-mail: mstanleigh@bia.ca
Scope: Provider of the following services: strategic planning, leadership development, innovation and project and quality management. Specialize in strategic planning, change management, leadership assessment, and development of skills. **Founded:** 1989. **Publications:** "Avoiding Pit falls to Innovation"; "Create a New Dimension of Performance with Innovation"; "The Power of Appreciation in Leadership"; "Why It Makes Sense To Have a Strategic Enterprise Office"; "Burning Rubber at the Start of Your Project"; "Accounting for Quality"; "How Pareto Charts Can Help You Improve the Quality of Business Processes"; "Managing Resistance to Change". **Seminars:** The Innovation Process. . .From Vision to Reality, San Diego, Oct, 2007; Critical Thinking, Kuala Lump or, Sep, 2007; Critical Thinking, Brunei, Sep, 2007; Delivering Project Assurance, Auckland, Jun, 2007; From Crisis to Control: A New Era in Strategic Project Management, Prague, May, 2007; What Project Leaders Need to Know to Help Them Sleep Better At Night, London, May, 2007; Innovation Process. . .From Vision To Reality, Orlando, Apr, 2007. **Special Services:** Project Planning Tool™.

2828 ■ **ByrneMRG Corp.**
22 Isle of Pines Dr.
Hilton Head Island, SC 29928
Ph: (215)630-7411
Free: 888-816-8080
Co. E-mail: info@byrnemrg.com
URL: http://www.byrnemrg.com
Contact: Patrick J. Boyle, President
E-mail: pjboyle@byrnemrg.com
Scope: Specializes in management consulting, including department management, equipment evaluation and selection, project management, research

and development planning; and database design and management. **Founded:** 1972. **Publications:** "Implementing Solutions to Everyday Issues". **Telecommunication Services:** pjboyle@byrnemrg.com.

2829 ■ Canadian Business Resource Centre (CBRC)
145 Front St. E, Ste. 101
Toronto, ON, Canada M5A 1E3
Ph: (416)415-2370
Fax: (416)415-2371
Co. E-mail: info@cbrc.com
Contact: Gabriella Zoltan-Johan, Principal
Scope: Management consulting and training services to the small and medium enterprise sector, to design and deliver entrepreneurship and small business training and provide consulting advice and information to individuals, organizations and municipalities interested in developing businesses and/or community economic development projects. **Founded:** 1989.

2830 ■ Capell & Associates—Capell's Circulation Report
601 Central Ave.
Barnegat Light, NJ 08006
Ph: (202)572-8774
Fax: (609)494-7369
Co. E-mail: contact@capellandassociates.com
URL: http://www.capellandassociates.com
Contact: E. Daniel Capell, President
E-mail: dan_capell@att.net
Scope: Specialized consulting firm focused on direct marketing, magazine publishing and circulation. Consulting services include due diligence, circulation audits, benchmarking and list rental analysis. **Founded:** 1982. **Seminars:** Circulation for the Non-Circulator.

2831 ■ Casino, Hotel & Resort Consultants L.L.C.
4825 Quality Ct., Ste. B
Las Vegas, NV 89103
Ph: (702)528-9537
Co. E-mail: info@hraba.com
URL: http://www.hraba.com
Contact: John S. Hraba, President
E-mail: jshraba@aol.com
Scope: Casino and hospitality industry consultants. Firm specializes in developing and implementing customized forecast and labor management control systems that deliver immediate, positive impact to the company's bottom line. Involved in production planning, employ surveys and communication, inventory management, business process reviews, audits, development and implementation of key management reports. **Founded:** 1989. **Seminars:** Payroll Cost Control; Effective Staff Scheduling. **Telecommunication Services:** john.hraba@hraba.com.

2832 ■ Jim Castello Marketing Communications Consultants
711 Red Wing Dr.
Lake Mary, FL 32746
Ph: (407)321-6322
Fax: (407)321-8460
Contact: James E. Castello, Jr., President
Scope: Consultant develops creative ideas and marketing strategies, including collateral programs, public relations, advertising, and brochures. Industries served: All golf related industry/business, golf manufacturers, golf resorts, golf residential developments, golf professionals, golf clothing, golf accessories, golf associations, and golf travel. **Founded:** 1989. **Seminars:** How To Seminar for Family Fun Center Entrepreneurs; How To Seminar for Creativity in Golf Marketing; The Golf Business on the Internet.

2833 ■ CBIZ Inc.
6050 Oak Tree Blvd. S, Ste. 500
Cleveland, OH 44131-6951
Ph: (216)447-9000
Fax: (216)447-9007
URL: http://www.cbizinc.com
Contact: Jerome P. Grisko, President
URL(s): www.cbiz.com. **Scope:** A business consulting and tax services firm providing financial, consulting, tax and business services through seven groups: Financial management, tax advisory, construction

and real estate, health-care, litigation support, capital resource and CEO outsource. **Founded:** 1996. **Publications:** "FAS 154: Changes in the Way We Report Changes," 2006; "Equity-Based Compensation: How Much Does it Really Cost Your Business," 2006; "Preventing Fraud - Tips for Nonprofit Organizations"; "Today's Workforce and Nonprofit Organizations: Meeting a Critical Need"; "IRS Highlights Top Seven Form 990 Errors". **Seminars:** Health Care - What the Future Holds; Consumer Driven Health Plans; Executive Plans; Health Savings Accounts; Healthy Wealthy and Wise; Legislative Update; Medicare Part D; Retirement Plans.

2834 ■ Center for Lifestyle Enhancement - Columbia Medical Center of Plano
3901 W 15th St.
Plano, TX 75075
Ph: (972)596-6800
Fax: (972)519-1299
Co. E-mail: mcp.cle@hcahealthcare.com
URL: http://www.medicalcenterofplano.com
Contact: Harvey Fishero, President
Scope: Provides professional health counseling in the areas of general nutrition for weight management, eating disorders, diabetic education, cholesterol reduction and adolescent weight management. Offers work site health promotion and preventive services. Also coordinates speaker's bureau, cooking classes and physician referrals. Industries served: education, insurance, healthcare, retail or wholesale, data processing and manufacturing throughout Texas. **Founded:** 1975. **Seminars:** Rx Diet and Exercise; Smoking Cessation; Stress Management; Health Fairs; Fitness Screenings; Body Composition; Nutrition Analysis; Exercise Classes; Prenatal Nutrition; SHAPEDOWN; Successfully Managing Diabetes; Gourmet Foods for Your Heart; The Aging Heart; Heart Smart Saturday featuring Day of Dance; Weight-Loss Management Seminars; The Right Stroke for Men; Peripheral Artery Disease Screening; Menstruation: The Cycle Begins; Boot Camp for New Dads; Grand parenting 101: Caring for Kids Today; Teddy Bear Camp; New Baby Day Camp; Safe Sitter Baby-Sitting Class.

2835 ■ The Center for Organizational Excellence Inc.
15204 Omega Dr., Ste. 300
Rockville, MD 20850
Ph: (301)948-1922
Free: 877-674-3923
Fax: (301)948-2158
Co. E-mail: results@center4oe.com
URL: http://www.center4oe.com
Contact: Stephen Goodrich, President
E-mail: sgoodrich@center4oe.com
Scope: An organizational effectiveness consulting firm specializing in helping organizations achieve results through people, process, and performance. Service areas include organizational performance systems, leadership systems, customer systems, and learning systems. **Founded:** 1984.

2836 ■ Center for Personal Empowerment
102 N Main St., Ste. 1
Columbia, IL 62236-1702
Ph: (618)281-3565
Free: 888-657-1530
Fax: (618)476-7083
Co. E-mail: personalempowerment@wholenet.net
Contact: Cherri Hendrix, Owner
Scope: Private consultations and trainings to educate on how to determine which emotions, events, beliefs from the past prevent you from achieving success. Methods used include time line therapy, news linguistic programming and hypnosis. Behavior modification through NLP trainings. **Founded:** 1996. **Seminars:** NLP Practitioner Training; Hypnosis Certification Training; Lifemap Seminars.

2837 ■ CEO Advisors
848 Brickell Ave., Ste. 603
Miami, FL 33131
Ph: (305)371-8560

Fax: (305)371-8563
Co. E-mail: ciaizpurua@ceoadvisors.us
URL: http://www.ceoadvisors.us
Contact: Roberto J. Arguello, President
E-mail: rjarguello@ceoadvisors.us
Scope: Business consulting firm offering clients services in strategy, mergers and acquisitions, corporate finance, corporate advisory, supply chain management, government relations and public affairs. Specializes in strategic planning, profit enhancement, start-up businesses, venture capital, appraisals and valuations. **Founded:** 1989.

2838 ■ Chamberlain & Cansler Inc.
2251 Perimeter Park Dr.
Atlanta, GA 30341
Ph: (770)457-5699
Contact: Charles L. Cansler, Owner
Scope: Firm specializes in strategic planning; profit enhancement; small business management; interim management; crisis management; turnarounds. **Founded:** 1986.

2839 ■ Charismedia
610 W End Ave., Ste. B1
New York, NY 10001
Ph: (212)362-6808
Fax: (212)362-6809
Co. E-mail: charismedia@earthlink.net
URL: http://www.charismedia.net
Contact: Dr. Doe Lang, President
E-mail: charismedia@earthlink.net
Scope: Offers speech and image training as well as speech writing services for effective presentation skills. Conducts workshops like anti-stage fright breathing, psychophysical exercises, transformational success imagery, face reading and body language, EMDR (Eye Movement Desensitization Re-Processing) for Permanent Trauma and Fear Removal, Bach Flower remedies, thought field therapy, cross-cultural communication, speech, voice and diction; regional and foreign accent elimination and acquisition, Positive Perception Management (P.P.M.), Ad-libbing, humor and spontaneity training, fast creative speech preparation, Neuro-Linguistic Programming and Hypnosis. **Founded:** 1974. **Publications:** "Flaunt It"; "Improve Your Sex Life"; "Phone Power"; "Train Your Voice"; "Turning Tinny, Tiny Tones To Gold"; "The New Secrets of Charisma: How to Discover and Unleash your Hidden Powers," McGraw-Hill, Jul, 1999. **Seminars:** Services for Comfortable Effective Speaking.

2840 ■ Chartered Management Co.
10 S Riverside Plz., Ste. 1800
Chicago, IL 60606
Ph: (312)214-2575
Contact: William B. Avellone, President
Scope: Operations improvement consultants. Specializes in strategic planning; feasibility studies; management audits and reports; profit enhancement; start-up businesses; mergers and acquisitions; joint ventures; divestitures; interim management; crisis management; turnarounds; business process reengineering; venture capital; and due diligence. **Founded:** 1985.

2841 ■ The Children's Psychological Trauma Center
2105 Divisadero St.
San Francisco, CA 94115
Ph: (415)292-7119
Fax: (415)749-2802
Co. E-mail: gil.kliman@cphc-sf.org
URL: http://www.cphc-sf.org
Contact: Gilbert Kliman, Director
Scope: Treats those with psychological trauma claimed from stressors including institutional negligence, vehicular and aviation accidents, wrongful death in the family, rape, molestation, fire, explosion, flood, earthquake, loss of parents, terrorism, kidnapping, disfiguring events, emotional damage from social work, medical malpractice or defective products. Provides evaluation and reports to referring professionals. Experienced in forensic consultation and testimony. **Founded:** 1992. **Publications:** "My Personal Story About Tropical Storm Stan," Feb, 2006; "My Personal Story About Hurricanes Katrina and Rita: A guided activity workbook to help coping,

learning and Healthy expression," Sep, 2005; "Helping Patients and their Families Cope in a National Disaster," Jan, 2002; "The practice of behavioral treatment in the acute rehabilitation setting".

2842 ■ Claremont Consulting Group

4525 Castle Ln.
La Canada, CA 91011-1436
Ph: (818)249-0584
Fax: (818)249-5811
Contact: Donald S. Remer, Partner
Scope: Consulting, coaching, training, and litigation support in project management, engineering management, system engineering and cost estimating. **Founded:** 1979. **Publications:** "What Every Engineer Should Know About Project Management"; "100% product-oriented work breakdown structures and their importance to system engineering". **Seminars:** Project Management, System Engineering and Cost Estimating.

2843 ■ Clayton/Curtis/Cottrell

1722 Madison Ct.
Louisville, CO 80027-1121
Ph: (303)665-2005
Contact: Robert Cottrell, President
Scope: Market research firm specializes in providing consultations for packaged goods, telecommunications, direct marketing and printing, and packaging industries. Services include strategic planning; profit enhancement; startup businesses; mergers and acquisitions; joint ventures; divestitures; interim management; crisis management; turnarounds; market size, segmentation and rates of growth; competitor intelligence; image and reputation, and competitive analysis. **Founded:** 1981. **Publications:** "Turn an attitude into a purchase," Jul, 1995; "Mixed results for private label; price assaults by the national brands are getting heavy, but there's still a place for private label," Jun, 1995; "In-store promotion goes high-tech: is the conventional coupon destined for obsolescence?," Jun, 1995.

2844 ■ Colmen Menard Company Inc. (CMCI)

The Woods, 994 Old Eagle School Rd., Ste. 1000
Wayne, PA 19087
Ph: (484)367-0300
Fax: (484)367-0305
Co. E-mail: cmci@colmenmenard.com
URL: http://www.colmenmenard.com
Contact: David W. Menard, President
E-mail: dmenard@colmenmenard.com
Scope: Merger and acquisition corporate finance and business advisory services for public and private companies located in North America. **Founded:** 1982. **Publications:** "Success in Selling a Troubled Company," Nov, 2002; "Savvy Dealmakers," May, 2001; "Success in Selling a Troubled Company feature article from The Technology Times bimonthly newspaper," Apr, 2002; "Truisms," M&A Today, Nov, 2000.

2845 ■ Columbia Consultants Ltd.—Columbia Consultants.Net L.L.C.

8950 State Route 108, Ste. 226
Columbia, MD 21045
Ph: (410)992-4700
Free: 800-783-7574
Fax: (410)992-4518
Contact: Carol Price, President
Scope: A complete personnel service offering placement of both permanent and temporary employees. Provides professional services and integrated solutions. **Founded:** 1969.

2846 ■ Comer & Associates L.L.C.—Energy Alliance Group

5255 Holmes Pl.
Boulder, CO 80303
Ph: (303)786-7986
Free: 888-950-3190
Fax: (303)895-2347
Co. E-mail: jerry@comerassociates.com
URL: http://www.comerassociates.com
Contact: Jerry C. Comer, President
E-mail: jerry@comerassociates.com
URL(s): www.energyalliance.biz. **Scope:** Specialize in developing markets and businesses. Marketing support includes: Developing and writing strategic

and tactical business plans; developing and writing focused, effective market plans; researching market potential and competition; implementing targeted marketing tactics to achieve company objectives; conducting customer surveys to determine satisfaction and attitudes toward client. Organization development support includes: Executive management training programs; executive coaching; team building; developing effective organization structures; and management of change in dynamic and competitive environments; individual coaching for management and leadership effectiveness. **Founded:** 1993. **Seminars:** Developing a Strategic Market Plan; Market Research: Defining Your Opportunity; Management and Leadership Effectiveness; Team Building; Developing a Business Plan; How to Close; Using Questions to Sell; Sales System Elements and Checklist; Working With Independent Reps; Features vs. Benefits; Overcoming Objections; Sales Force Automation.

2847 ■ Consultants National Resource Center (CNRC)—National Association of Business Coaches

27-A Big Spring Rd.
Clear Spring, MD 21722
Ph: (301)791-9332
Free: 800-290-3196
Fax: (301)582-3639
Co. E-mail: cnrc@erols.com
Contact: Lewis Williams, Director
Scope: Provider of marketing and strategic planning services for consultants. Also serves as membership center for the professional management institute. Industries served: all consulting disciplines. **Founded:** 1981. **Publications:** "Consulting Opportunities Journal"; "How to Master Continuous Learning". **Seminars:** How to Series on Starting and Building a Consulting Practice; Introduction to the Professional Management Institute; Consulting Boot camp; Planagement®.

2848 ■ Consulting & Conciliation Service (CCS)

2219 H St., Ste. 1
Sacramento, CA 95816
Ph: (916)396-0480
Free: 888-898-9780
Fax: (916)441-2828
Co. E-mail: service@azurewings.net
Contact: Jane A. McCluskey, Principal
E-mail: service@azurewings.net
Scope: Offers consulting and conciliation services. Provides pre-mediation counseling, training and research on preparing for a peaceful society, mediation and facilitation, and preparation for shifts in structure, policy and personnel. Offers sliding scale business rates and free individual consultation. **Publications:** "Native America and Tracking Shifts in US Policy"; "Biogenesis: A Discussion of Basic Social Needs and the Significance of Hope". **Seminars:** Positive Approaches to Violence Prevention: Peace building in Schools and Communities.

2849 ■ The Consulting Exchange

1770 Mass Ave., Ste. 288
Cambridge, MA 02140
Ph: (617)576-2100
Free: 800-824-4828
Co. E-mail: gday@consultingexchange.com
Contact: Geoffrey Day, President
E-mail: gday@consultingexchange.com
Scope: A consultant referral service for management and technical consultants. Serves a local, regional and international client base. **Founded:** 1982. **Publications:** "Looking for a Consultant? Success Points for Finding the Right One," Boston Business Journal, Jun, 2001; "Getting Full Value From Consulting is in Your Hands," Mass High Tech, May, 1998; "Developing Knowledge-Based Client Relationships, The Future of Professional Services"; "The Consultant's Legal Guide"; "The Business of Consulting: The Basics and Beyond".

2850 ■ The Corlund Group L.L.C. (CG)

101 Federal St., Ste. 310
Boston, MA 02110
Ph: (617)423-9364

Fax: (617)423-9371
Co. E-mail: info@corlundgroup.com
URL: http://www.corlundgroup.com
Contact: Wilmot J. Gravenslund, Director
E-mail: wgravenslund@corlundgroup.com
Scope: Boutique firm offering services in the areas of leadership, governance, and change with a particular focus on CEO and senior executive succession planning, including assessment, development, and orchestrating succession processes with management and Boards of Directors. Also Board governance effectiveness. **Founded:** 1996. **Publications:** "Are You Rolling the Dice on CEO Succession?" Center for Healthcare Governance, 2006; "Leadership Due Diligence: The Neglected Governance Frontier," Directorship, Sep, 2001; "Leadership Due Diligence: Managing the Risks," The Corporate Board, Aug, 2001; "Succession: The need for detailed insight," Directors and Boards, 2001; "CEO Succession: Who's Doing Due Diligence?," 2001. **Telecommunication Services:** corlund@corlundgroup.com.

2851 ■ Corporate Consulting Inc.

3333 Belcaro Dr.
Denver, CO 80209-4912
Ph: (303)698-9292
Fax: (303)698-9292
Co. E-mail: corpcons@compuserve.com
Contact: Devereux C. Josephs, President
Scope: Specializes in feasibility studies, organizational development, small business management, mergers and acquisitions, joint ventures, divestitures, interim management, crisis management, turnarounds, financing, appraisals valuations and due diligence studies. **Founded:** 1983.

2852 ■ Coyne Associates

4010 E Lake St.
Minneapolis, MN 55406-2201
Ph: (612)724-1188
Fax: (612)722-1379
Contact: John T. Coyne, Chief Executive Officer
Scope: A marketing and public relations consulting firm that specializes in assisting architectural, engineering, and contractor/developer firms. Services include: marketing plains and audits, strategic planning, corporate identity, turnarounds, and sales training. **Founded:** 2008.

2853 ■ Creative Computer Resources Inc.

5001 Horizons Dr., Ste. 200
Columbus, OH 43220-5291
Ph: (614)384-7557
Free: 866-720-0209
Fax: (614)573-6331
Co. E-mail: team@planet-ccr.com
URL: http://www.planet-ccr.com
Contact: M. Erik Mueller, President
E-mail: merikm@planet-ccr.com
Scope: Offers information systems support, custom software development, website design, development and implementation. Provides information technology support and management services to small and mid-size businesses. **Founded:** 1996.

2854 ■ Crystal Clear Communications Inc.

1633 W Winslow Dr., Ste. 210
Mequon, WI 53092
Ph: (262)240-0072
Fax: (262)240-0073
Co. E-mail: contact@crystalclear1.com
URL: http://www.crystalclear1.com
Contact: Barry J. Moze, Partner
E-mail: barrymoze@crystalclearl.com
Scope: Specialize in helping executives identify impediments to success, and then develop strategies to surmount them. Serves to identify core problems, suggest appropriate business changes, work with the organization to support these changes, and help executives articulate the behavior that will uphold these changes. Specializes in strategic planning; organizational development; small business management; executive coaching. **Founded:** 1986. **Publications:** "Weakest Link"; "Aware Leadership"; "Integrity"; "When Your Plate is Full"; "Problem Solving"; "Strategic Thinking".

2855 ■ CUFFE & Associates Inc.
27435 Everett St.
Southfield, MI 48076-5130
Ph: (248)557-8541
Fax: (248)557-5144
Co. E-mail: caimmts@aol.com
Contact: Stafford S. Cuffe, President
E-mail: caimmts@aol.com
Scope: Specializes in the following areas: E-commerce, analysis, assessment, mapping and research and planning, risk mitigation and crisis management, glass technology, business process re-engineering, productivity improvements, quality tools. Performed assessments in manufacturing, management, financial, operations, and IT. **Founded:** 1997.

2856 ■ De Bellas & Co.
7700 Irvine Center Dr., Ste. 800
Irvine, CA 92618
Ph: (949)859-3332
Fax: (949)859-9333
Co. E-mail: info@debellas.com
URL: http://www.debellas.com
Contact: Alfred F. de, Jr., President
E-mail: adebellas@debellas.com
Scope: Provides merger, acquisition and financial advisory services to staffing and information technology services businesses and professional employer service organizations. **Founded:** 1983. **Publications:** "Tools to Take Advantage of the Current IT Staffing M and A Market," 2005; "Healthcare Staffing: Buy, Sell or Build," 2005.

2857 ■ The Devine Group Inc.
7755 Montgomery Rd., Ste. 180
Cincinnati, OH 45236
Ph: (513)792-7500
Free: 866-792-7500
Fax: (513)793-8535
Co. E-mail: sales@devinegroup.com
URL: http://www.devinegroup.com
Contact: David C. Devine, Chief Executive Officer
E-mail: david@devinegroup.com
Scope: A human resource consulting company devoted to providing reliable and responsive information focusing on performance issues and answers. Dedicated to analyzing and enhancing job performance. Custom design and implement programs and workshops that will result in demonstrable behavior change on the job. Assist clients enhance their productivity via behavior analysis. **Founded:** 1970. **Publications:** "Leveraging Assessments for Enterprise Improvement," Oct, 2006; "Evaluation of Assessment Tools: The Five Criteria," Oct, 2006; "People Improvement Using Behavior Assessment," Aug, 2005; "Measuring Personality: The Good, the Bad and the Ugly". **Special Services:** The Devine Inventory®.

2858 ■ Dimond Hospitality Consulting Group Inc.
5710 Stoneway Trl.
Nashville, TN 37209
Ph: (615)353-0033
Fax: (615)352-5290
Co. E-mail: drew@dimondhotelconsulting.com
URL: http://www.dimondhotelconsulting.com
Contact: Drew W. Dimond, President
E-mail: drew@dimondhotelconsulting.com
Scope: Specializes in strategic planning; start-up businesses; business process re-engineering; team building; competitive analysis; venture capital; competitive intelligence; and due diligence. Offers litigation support. Comprehensive hospitality consulting firm that serves as an adviser to leading hotel companies, independent hotels, lending institutions, trustees, law firms, investment companies and municipalities in the areas of: Asset management, Acquisition due diligence, Arbitration, Disposition advisory services, Exit strategies, Financial review and analysis, Impact studies, Mediation. **Founded:** 1985. **Publications:** "The distressed debt conundrum," Jul, 2009; "How to buy distressed assets," Apr, 2009; "Cmbs Loans: A History and the Future," Apr, 2009; "Opportunity Knocks," Apr, 2009; "Another Reality Check," Mar, 2009; "An Inkling of Hope," Mar, 2009; "Strong World Tourism Growth in 2007," 2007; "Les U.S. Construction Pipeline Sets Another Record

at 5011 Hotels with 654503 Rooms"; "Hotel Capitalization Rates Hold for Now"; "Winning Cornell Hotel and Restaurant Administration Quarterly Article Provides Hotel Brand Analysis"; "Breaking News for Lifestyle Hotels. Ian Schrager and Bill Marriott Announce Their Marriage Will the Schrager-Marriott Marriage Lead to Eternal Bliss Or End in Divorce What Will the M Hotels Children Be Named"; "Brands Vs Independents"; "Nyu Conf Takes Industry Temp"; "Economy Hotel Performance Indication of Travel Trends"; "Hotel Sales Continue at Brisk Pace"; "Fundamentals Strong, Weakening Undercurrent"; "Hotel Investments: Where Do We Go From Here"; "On the Road: Aahoa Panel Commits to Change"; "Cuba Not Ready, But Expecting U.S. Tourists".

2859 ■ Diversified Health Resources Inc.
875 N Michigan Ave., Ste. 3250
Chicago, IL 60611-1901
Ph: (312)266-0466
Fax: (312)266-0715
Contact: Andrea R. Rozran, President
Scope: Offers health care consulting for hospitals, nursing homes including homes for the aged, and other health related facilities and companies. Specializes in planning and marketing. Also conducts executive searches for top level health care administrative positions. Serves private industries as well as government agencies. **Founded:** 1979. **Publications:** "City Finance".

2860 ■ Dubuc Lucke & Company Inc.—Adventa Global Intermediaries
120 W 5th St.
Cincinnati, OH 45202-2713
Ph: (513)579-8330
Fax: (513)241-6669
Contact: Kenneth E. Dubuc, President
Scope: Provides consulting services in the areas of profit enhancement; small business management; mergers and acquisitions; joint ventures; divestitures; interim management; crisis management; turnarounds; appraisals; valuations; due diligence; and international trade. **Founded:** 1999.

2861 ■ The DuMond Group
5282 Princeton Ave.
Westminster, CA 92683-2753
Ph: (714)373-0610
Contact: Adrianne H. Geiger-Dumond, President
Scope: Human resources and executive search consulting firm that specializes in organizational development; small business management; employee surveys and communication; performance appraisals; and team building. **Founded:** 1992.

2862 ■ Dunelm International
437 Colebrook Ln.
Bryn Mawr, PA 19010-3216
Ph: (610)989-0144
Fax: (610)964-9524
Co. E-mail: jecdunelm@worldnet.att.net
Contact: John E. Crowther, President
E-mail: Jecdunelm@dunelm.org.uk
Scope: Firm specializes in feasibility studies; start-up businesses; interim management; crisis management; turnarounds; business process re-engineering; sales forecasting; supply chain solution and project management. **Founded:** 1988.

2863 ■ Eastern Point Consulting Group Inc.
36 Glen Ave.
Newton, MA 02464
Ph: (617)965-4141
Fax: (617)965-4172
Co. E-mail: info@eastpt.com
URL: http://www.eastpt.com
Contact: Katherine A. Herzog, President
E-mail: kherzog@eastpt.com
Scope: Specializes in bringing practical solutions to complex challenges. Provides consulting and training in managing diversity; comprehensive sexual-harassment policies and programs; organizational development; benchmarks 360 skills assessment; executive coaching; strategic human resource planning; team building; leadership development for women; mentoring programs; and gender issues in the workplace. **Founded:** 1995. **Seminars:** Leadership Development for Women.

2864 ■ Education Development Center Inc. (EDC)
43 Foundry Ave.
Waltham, MA 02453-8313
Ph: (617)969-7100
Free: 800-225-4276
Fax: (617)969-5979
Co. E-mail: comment@edc.org
URL: http://www.edc.org
Contact: Luther Luedtke, President
Description: Seeks to build bridges among research, policy and practice; programs and products, developed in collaboration with partners worldwide, consistently advance learning and health development for individuals of all ages; manages 335 projects in 50 countries; works to strengthen nearly every facet of society, including early child development, K-12 education, health promotion, workforce preparation, community development, learning technologies, basic and adult education, institutional reform, and social justice. **Scope:** Services include research, training, educational materials and strategy, with activities ranging from seed projects to large-scale national and international initiatives. Specialize in program and fiscal management. Serves to design, deliver and evaluate innovative programs to address some of the world's most urgent challenges in education, health, and economic opportunity. Renders services to U.S. and foreign government agencies, private foundations, healthcare sectors, educational institutions, nonprofit organizations, universities, and corporations. **Founded:** 1958. **Publications:** "A Call to Action: HIV/AIDS, Health, Safety, and the Youth Employment Summit"; "A Case Against "Binge" as the Term of Choice: How to Get College Students to Personalize Messages about Dangerous Drinking"; "A Description of Foundation Skills Interventions for Struggling Middle-Grade Readers in Four Urban Northeast and Islands Region School Districts"; "A Guide to Facilitating Cases in Education"; "A Look at Social, Emotional, and Behavioral Screening Tools for Head Start and Early Head Start"; "A Multifaceted Social Norms Approach to Reduce High-Risk Drinking: Lessons from Hobart and William Smith Colleges"; "The New Media Literacy Handbook"; "Helping Children Outgrow War"; "Worms, Shadows, and Whirlpools: Science in the Early Childhood Classroom"; "Teacher Leadership in Mathematics and Science Casebook and Facilitator's Guide"; "Teachers' Professional Development and the Elementary Mathematics Classroom: Bringing Understandings to Light". **Seminars:** Designed to Introduce the Materials; To Guide Schools Through the Issues. **Telecommunication Services:** contact@edc.org; lluedtke@edc.org.

2865 ■ Effective Compensation Inc. (ECI)
30792 Southview Dr., Ste. 101
Evergreen, CO 80439
Ph: (303)854-1000
Free: 877-746-4324
Fax: (303)854-1030
Co. E-mail: eci@effectivecompensation.com
URL: http://www.effectivecompensation.com
Contact: Terry L. Isselhardt, Chief Executive Officer
E-mail: tisselhardt@effectivecompensation.com
Scope: Independent compensation consulting firm specializing in working with clients on a collaborative basis to improve their organization's efficiency through competitive, focused total compensation processes. Helps organizations determine how to competitively pay their employees. Provides quality, culture sensitive, compensation consulting assistance to all types of employers. Specializes in surveys like drilling industry compensation surveys, environmental industry compensation surveys, liquid pipeline round table compensation surveys; and oil and gas E and P industry compensation surveys. **Founded:** 1991. **Publications:** "Alternative Job Evaluation Approaches"; "Broad Banding: A Management Overview"; "Job Evaluation: Understanding the Issues"; "Industry Compensation Surveys"; "Skill Based Pay"; "Four Levels of Team Membership"; "Factors in Designing an Incentive Plan"; "Key Stock Allocation Issues"; "Stock Plans Primer". **Seminars:** Alternative Job Evaluation Approaches; Broad Banding: A Management Overview; Skill Based Pay; Job Evalua-

tion: Understanding the Issues; Designing Compensation Programs that Motivate Employees; Master the Compensation Maze; Base Salary Administration Manual.

2866 ■ Effectiveness Resource Group Inc.
2529 170th Pl. SE
Bellevue, WA 98008-5520
Ph: (206)949-4171
Fax: (425)957-9186
Co. E-mail: don@consultdon.com
Contact: Donald H. Swartz, President
E-mail: dhsergsri@aol.com
Scope: Provider of problem solving help to client organizations in public and private sectors so they can release and mobilize the full potential of their personnel to achieve productive and satisfying results. Emphasis is on technical or human productivity improvement projects and systems, total human resource systems design and implementation, and a whole systems approach to organizational change design and implementation. Serves private industries as well as government agencies. Consults with both internal and external consultants via e-mail and phone. Also offers executive coaching. **Founded:** 1973. **Seminars:** Life/Work Goals Exploration; Influencing Change Thru Consultation; Designing and Leading Participative Meetings; Designing, Leading and Managing Change; Project Management and Leadership; Performance Management; Productive Management of Differences; Performance Correction.

2867 ■ Environmental Business International Inc. (EBI)—Environmental Business Journal
4452 Park Blvd., Ste. 306
San Diego, CA 92116
Ph: (619)295-7685
Fax: (619)295-5743
Co. E-mail: ebi@ebiusa.com
URL: http://www.ebiusa.com
Contact: Grant Ferrier, President
URL(s): www.ebiresearch.com. **Scope:** Offers a variety of research and professional services to deliver the market information and business intelligence required for growth and profit in today's rapidly changing business climate. **Founded:** 1988. **Publications:** "Water view Report: Water & Wastewater Markets," Dec, 2006; "Report 2020 the U.S. Environmental Industry & Global Markets"; "Mergers & Acquisitions in the Environmental Industry". **Telecommunication Services:** info@ebiresearch.com.

2868 ■ Environmental Health Science Inc.
418 Wall St.
Princeton, NJ 08540
Ph: (609)924-7616
Free: 800-841-8923
Fax: (609)924-0793
Co. E-mail: healthscience@comcast.net
URL: http://www.speechgeneratingdevices.com
Contact: David Goldberg, President
E-mail: davidg@patmedia.net
Scope: Specialists in rehabilitation technology for speech disorder and physically disabled persons. Offers demonstrations, evaluations and sales of the following types of equipment: augmentative speech communication systems, adaptive switches and specialty controls, and computer access devices. Industries served: hospitals and rehabilitation centers, schools, and special service organizations such as United Cerebral Palsy Association, Department of Human Services, etc. **Founded:** 1984. **Publications:** "Play & Learn"; "Bookworm Literacy Tool"; "Meville to Weville". **Seminars:** Augmentative Communication and Assistive Devices. **Special Services:** Boardmaker®; Dynamically Pro®.

2869 ■ Everest Marketing
957 Ashland Ave.
Saint Paul, MN 55104-7019
Ph: (612)581-1333
Fax: (651)221-1978
Contact: Rebecca Aistrup, President
Scope: Provides business-to-business marketing services including marketing plan development, marketing communications, market research and business intelligence. **Founded:** 1993. **Publications:** "Finding and Using Local Market Research To

Improve Your Sales"; "Marketing to the Right People at the Right Time"; "Marketing in a Sales-Driven Environment"; "Money Well Spent! (Eight Steps to a successful consulting project)"; "Does this sound like you?"; "Marketing Quickies". **Seminars:** Market Research Basics for Managers; Profiting from Your Customer Database; Developing Your Strategic Marketing Plan from the Ground Up; A Team Process for Developing Your Marketing Plan; Developing a Commercialization Plan for Your SBIR (Small Business Innovation Research)Proposal; Using Marketing Strategies to Jump-Start Your Sales; Marketing in a Sales-Driven Environment and Marketing in a Technology-Driven Environment.

2870 ■ Everett & Co.
3126 S Franklin St.
Englewood, CO 80113
Ph: (303)761-7999
Fax: (303)781-8296
Contact: Robert W. Everett, Manager
Scope: Provides strategic real estate solutions and project management. **Founded:** 1993.

2871 ■ Facility Directions Inc.
PO Box 761
Manchester, MO 63011
Ph: (636)256-4400
Free: 800-536-0044
Fax: (636)227-2868
Co. E-mail: walty@facilitydirections.com
URL: http://www.facilitydirections.com
Contact: Walter E. Yesberg, President
E-mail: walty@facilitydirections.com
Scope: Specializes in service to financial institutions; strategic planning; feasibility studies; facility and space planning; attitude surveys; site selection. **Founded:** 1990.

2872 ■ Family Business Institute Inc.—Family Business Experts
904 Steffi Ct.
Lawrenceville, GA 30044-6933
Ph: (770)952-4085
Fax: (770)432-6660
Co. E-mail: asktheexpert@family-business-experts. com
URL: http://www.family-business-experts.com
Contact: Wayne Rivers, President
Scope: Assists families in business to achieve personal, family, and organizational goals by meeting challenges that are unique to family-owned businesses. Provides coordinated and integrated assessments and solutions for family issues and needs; for company finance and for human resource and operational requirements. **Founded:** 1985. **Publications:** "Professional Intervention in the Family Owned Business"; "Building Consensus in a Family Business"; "Professionalizing Family Business Management"; "Recognizing generations - know them by their weekends"; "Succession planning tactics"; "Succession Planning Obstacles in Family Business"; "Succession: three ways to ease the transition"; "Pruning the family business tree"; "Responsibility diffusion - the most critical impediment to successfully growing any kind of business"; "Breaking Up is Hard to Do: Divorce in the Family Business".

2873 ■ Family Resource Center on Disabilities (FRCD)
20 E Jackson Blvd., Ste. 300
Chicago, IL 60604-2265
Ph: (312)939-3519
Free: 800-952-4199
Fax: (312)939-7297
Co. E-mail: contact@frcd.org
URL: http://www.frcd.org
Contact: Michelle Phillips, Executive Director
Description: Parents, professionals, and volunteers seeking to improve services for all children with disabilities. Originally organized as a result of the 1969 Illinois law mandating the education of all children with disabilities and operates as a coalition to inform and activate parents. Provides information and referral services, individualized support services for low-income Chicago families, transition services, and special education rights training. **Scope:** Provider of consulting services to advocacy groups and individuals seeking support for children with disabilities.

Founded: 1969. **Publications:** "How to Get Services By Being Assertive"; "How to Organize an Effective Parent/Advocacy Group and Move Bureaucracies"; "Main roads Travel to Tomorrow - a Road Map for the Future"; "Does Your Child Have Special Education Needs"; "How to Prepare for a Successful Due Process Hearing"; "How to Participate Effectively in Your Child's IEP Meeting"; "Tax Guide for Parents". **Seminars:** How to Support Parents as Effective Advocates; How to Get Services by Being Assertive; How to Develop an Awareness Program for Nondisabled Children; How to Organize a Parent Support Group; How to Move Bureaucratic Mountains; How to Raise Money Painlessly through Publishing; How to Use Humor in Public Presentations. **Telecommunication Services:** frcdptiil@ameritech.net; info@frcd. org.

2874 ■ FCP Consulting
500 Sutter St., Ste. 507
San Francisco, CA 94102-1114
Ph: (415)956-5558
Fax: (415)956-5722
Contact: Cox Ferrall, President
Scope: Management consulting in Business-To-Business sales. **Founded:** 1986.

2875 ■ Flett Research Ltd.
440 DeSalaberry Ave.
Winnipeg, MB, Canada R2L 0Y7
Ph: (204)667-2505
Fax: (204)667-2505
Co. E-mail: flett@flettresearch.ca
URL: http://www.flettresearch.ca
Contact: Dr. Robert Flett, President
E-mail: flett@flettresearch.ca
Scope: Provider of environmental audits and assessments. Offers contract research and consultation on environmental topics, specializing in limnology, with emphasis in microbiology, bio-geochemistry and radio-chemistry. Performs dating of sediments via Pb-210 and CS-137 methods, to determine sediment accumulation rates in lakes. One of a handful of labs in the world able to carry out total mercury and methyl mercury analyses at the sub-nanogram and L concentration in water. **Founded:** 1978. **Seminars:** Comparison of Two Methods for the Measurement of Methyl Mercury Concentrations in Penobscot River Sediments.

2876 ■ Fowler, Anthony & Co.
20 Walnut St.
Wellesley, MA 02481
Ph: (781)237-4201
Fax: (781)237-7718
Contact: John A. Quagliaroli, President
E-mail: jquagliaroli@mediaone.net
Scope: Offers consulting services and direct investment into small businesses in mergers and acquisitions, capital financing and venture capital. Active with the following industries: Communications, computer related, consumer, distribution, electronic components and instrumentation, multimedia, on-line database/publishing, industrial products and equipment, food processing, multimedia, health care services, medical/health related and publishing. **Founded:** 1976.

2877 ■ The Franchise Consulting Group
1801 Century Pk. E, Ste. 2400
Los Angeles, CA 90067-2302
Ph: (310)552-2901
Fax: (310)440-2604
Co. E-mail: info@franchiseconsulting.com
URL: http://www.franchiseconsulting.com
Contact: Edward Kushell, President
E-mail: ekushell@franchiseconsulting.com
Scope: Offers consulting services specializing in new business start up and company expansion programs. Performs analysis, research, planning and development of product service distribution systems, national and international. Serves as consultants to new and established franchisers and as expert witness in franchise litigation. Also provides services: expansion of an existing business; development of a new business concept; capital formation consulting; sales and marketing for international markets; litigation consulting, or other specific franchise development and marketing needs. **Founded:** 1978.

2878 ■ Freese & Associates Inc.
PO Box 814
Chagrin Falls, OH 44022-0814
Ph: (440)564-9183
Fax: (440)564-7339
Co. E-mail: tfreese@freeseinc.com
URL: http://www.freeseinc.com
Contact: Duane L. Hile, Manager
Scope: A management consulting firm offering advice in all forms of business logistics. Consulting services are in the areas of strategic planning; network analysis, site selection, facility layout and design, outsourcing, warehousing, transportation and customer service. Typical projects include 3PL marketing surveys; third party outsourcing selection; operational audits; competitive analysis; inventory management; due diligence; and implementation project management. **Founded:** 1987. **Publications:** "Building Relationships is Key to Motivation," Distribution Center Management, Apr, 2006; "Getting Maximum Results from Performance Reviews," WERC Sheet, Oct, 2003; "SCM: Making the Vision a Reality," Supply Chain Management Review, Oct, 2003; "Contents Under Pressure," DC Velocity, Aug, 2003; "When Considering Outsourcing, It's Really a Financial Decision," Inventory Management Report, Mar, 2003. **Seminars:** WERC/CAWS Warehousing in China Conference, Sep, 2008; CSCMP Annual Conference, Denver, Oct, 2008; Keys to Retaining and Motivating Your Associates, Dallas, Mar, 2006; The Value and Challenges of Supply Chain Management, Dubai, Feb, 2006; Best Practices in Logistics in China, Jun, 2005; Keys to Motivating Associates, Dallas, May, 2005; The Goal and the Way of International Cooperation in Logistics, Jenobuk, Apr, 2005.

2879 ■ Full Voice
3217 Broadway Ave., Ste. 300
Kansas City, MO 64111
Ph: (816)941-0011
Free: 800-684-8764
Fax: (816)931-8887
Co. E-mail: info@infullvoice.com
URL: http://www.fullvoice.us
Contact: Michienne Dixon, Principal
Scope: Vocal performance training firm offering consulting services and personal training sessions in the implementation of effective vocal communication techniques for the development of business relationships and career enhancement. Formalizes a program of proven techniques into a practical method of helping individuals improve their ability to better present themselves when speaking in a professional situation. Industries served: All. **Founded:** 1992. **Publications:** "You Can Sound Like You Know What You're Saying". **Seminars:** You Can Sound Like You Know What You're Saying; The Psychology of Vocal Performance; Security. . .the Ability to Accept Change; Knowing. . .the Key to Relaxed Public Communication; The Effective Voice for Customer Service Enhancement; You Can Speak With Conviction; How To Make Yours a Championship Team; Functional English For Foreign Trade. **Special Services:** FULL VOICE™.

2880 ■ GEC Consultants Inc.
4604 Birchwood Ave.
Skokie, IL 60076-3835
Ph: (847)674-6310
Fax: (847)674-3946
Co. E-mail: experts@gecconsultants.com
URL: http://www.gecconsultants.com
Contact: Lloyd M. Gordon, President
E-mail: legal@gecconsultants.com
Scope: Consulting in all areas of bar and restaurant operations. Restaurant manager development appraises existing locations or sites. Studies the feasibility of projects. Develop new concepts. Assist in expanding, existing food operations, marketing, expert witness (legal) for hospitality/restaurant industry. **Founded:** 1963. **Publications:** "How You Can Fight Back to Minimize This Recession!"; "New Thoughts On Leases"; "The Use of Job Analysis to Actually Reduce Payroll Costs"; "Do You Need a Feasibility Study?"; "Combat Negative Hospitality"; "How To Run A Successful Night club"; "Are Capitalists In Your Cabinet?"; "Marketing For The 21st Century"; "Profitability In The Banquet Industry";

"Starting a Restaurant, Bar or Catering Business"; "How To Find And Retain Suitable Employees"; "26 Things To Do To Plan A Restaurant"; "Wall Fabric or Paint: Decor Magic It's Your Call"; "The Art of Cafe Ambiance"; "Why You Need A Consultant". **Telecommunication Services:** legal@gecconsultants.com.

2881 ■ Gerson Goodson Inc. (GGI)
2451 McMullen Booth Rd., Ste. 201
Clearwater, FL 33759
Ph: (727)726-7619
Free: 888-237-7424
Fax: (727)726-2406
Co. E-mail: getrich@richgerson.com
URL: http://www.richgerson.com
Contact: Dr. Richard F. Gerson, President
E-mail: richard.gerson@richgerson.com
Scope: Independent consulting firm provides performance management solutions to improve performance and maximize productivity in organizations. Provides assistance to organizations in talent and performance management, leadership development, selection and hiring practices, employee and customer retention, and customer service. Conducts a systematic needs analysis of the entire marketing, sales and customer service operations of the company. Identifies hidden, neglected and underutilized marketing, sales and customer service assets. **Founded:** 1979. **Publications:** "Winning The Inner Game Of Selling," 1999; "Marketing Strategies for Small Businesses," 1994; "Measuring Customer Satisfaction," 1993; "Beyond Customer Service," 1992; "Achieving High Performance"; "Guaranteeing Performance Improvement"; "The Executive Athlete"; "Positive Performance Improvement". **Seminars:** Marketing Real Estate Services Management Development, Oct, 2007; Presentation Skills, Oct, 2007; From Member Service to Sales, Sep, 2007; Leadership Development, Sep, 2007; The Marketing Difference That Makes The Difference: How To Position Your Company For Rapid Growth Regardless Of The Economy Or The Competition; Growing Your Business With What You Already Have: How To Identify And Profit From The Hidden Marketing Assets That Are Currently Costing You Money; The R Factor In Customer Service: 5Ways To Grow Your Business For Little Or No Cost.

2882 ■ Global Business Consultants (GBC)
200 Lake Hills Rd.
Pinehurst, NC 28374-0776
Ph: (910)295-5991
Fax: (910)295-5991
Co. E-mail: gbc@pinehurst.net
Contact: Nan S. Leaptrott, President
E-mail: nan@yourculturecoach.com
Scope: Firm specializes in human resources management; project management; software development; and international trade. Offers litigation support. **Founded:** 1987. **Publications:** "Culture to Culture: Mission Trip Do's and Don'ts," Jul, 2005; "Rules of the Game: Global Business Protocol". **Seminars:** Cross-Cultural Training.

2883 ■ Global Technology Transfer L.L.C.
1500 Dixie Hwy.
Park Hills, KY 41011-2819
Ph: (859)431-1262
Fax: (859)431-5148
Contact: Anthony Zembrodt, President
Scope: Firm specializes in product development; quality assurance; new product development; and total quality management focusing on household chemical specialties, especially air fresheners. Utilizes latest technology from global resources. Specializes in enhancement products for home and automobile. **Founded:** 1992.

2884 ■ Goldore Consulting Inc.
120-5 St. NW, Ste. 1
Linden, AB, Canada T0M 1J0
Ph: (403)546-4208
Fax: (403)546-4208
Co. E-mail: goldore@leadershipessentials.com
Contact: Robert A. Orr, President
E-mail: orr@leadershipessentials.com
Description: Description: Publishes materials on leadership and management skills for churches and charitable organizations that provide services to

developing countries. Also publishes in Spanish and Portuguese. Does not accept unsolicited manuscripts. Reaches market through direct mail and wholesalers and distributors, including Leadership Training Ministry Foundation, Inc. **Scope:** Provides consulting service in leadership and management skills. Industries served: primarily charities, non-profits; some businesses. **Founded:** 1990. **Seminars:** The Challenge Of Leadership.

2885 ■ Great Lakes Consulting Group Inc.
54722 Little Flower Trl.
Mishawaka, IN 46545
Ph: (574)287-4500
Fax: (574)233-2688
Contact: James E. Schrager, President
Scope: Provides consulting services in the areas of strategic planning; feasibility studies; start-up businesses; small business management; mergers and acquisitions; joint ventures; divestitures; interim management; crisis management; turnarounds; business process re-engineering; venture capital; and international trade. **Founded:** 1989.

2886 ■ Joel Greenstein & Associates (JGA)
6212 Nethercombe Ct.
McLean, VA 22101
Ph: (703)893-1888
Co. E-mail: jgreenstein@contractmasters.com
Contact: Joel Greenstein, Principal
E-mail: jgreenstein@contractmasters.com
Scope: Provides services to minority and women-owned businesses and government agencies. Specializes in interpreting federal, agency-specific acquisition regulations and contract terms and conditions. Offers assistance with preparing technical, cost proposals and sealed bids.

2887 ■ Grief Counseling & Support Services
8600 W Chester Pke., Ste. 304
Upper Darby, PA 19082
Ph: (610)789-7707
Fax: (610)469-9499
Contact: Jeffrey Kauffman, President
E-mail: jkharry@voicenet.com
Scope: Specializing in consulting and training services for organizations dealing with loss, trauma and grief issues. These services may include management consultations, crisis intervention, educational programming, policy development, program design, group process work, individual counseling or other support services. Training and support services also provided for loss issues for mental retardation service providers. Serves private industries as well as government agencies. **Founded:** 1984.

2888 ■ Grimmick Consulting Services (GCS)
455 Donner Way
San Ramon, CA 94582
Ph: (925)735-1036
Fax: (925)735-1100
Co. E-mail: hank@grimmickconsulting.com
URL: http://www.grimmickconsulting.com
Contact: Henry Grimmick, President
E-mail: hank@grimmickconsulting.com
Scope: Provider of consulting services in the areas of strategic planning; organizational assessment; organizational development; leadership and management development Baldrige criteria, process improvement and balanced scorecards and team dynamics. **Founded:** 1993.

2889 ■ Hardy Stevenson and Associates Ltd.
364 Davenport Rd.
Toronto, ON, Canada M5R 1K6
Ph: (416)944-8444
Free: 877-267-7794
Fax: (416)944-0900
Co. E-mail: hsa@hardystevenson.com
URL: http://www.hardystevenson.com
Contact: Glynn Gomes, Principal
Scope: Firm specialize in land use and environmental planning social economic impact assessment facilitation, conflict resolution community relations, public consultation strategic planning policy and project management consulting. **Founded:** 1990.

2890 ■ Health Strategy Group Inc.
46 River Rd.
Chatham, NY 12037
Ph: (518)392-6770
Contact: Cameron Battley, President
Scope: Provides consulting services in the areas of strategic planning, feasibility studies, start-up businesses, organizational development, market research, customer service audits, new product development, marketing, public relations. **Founded:** 1981. **Publications:** "Online Consumer Surveys as a Methodology for Assessing the Quality of the United States Health Care System," 2004.

2891 ■ Edward M. Hepner & Associates
4667 Macarthur Blvd., Ste. 405
Newport Beach, CA 92660
Ph: (714)250-0818
Fax: (714)553-8437
Contact: Edward M. Hepner, President
Scope: An immigration consultant and labor certification specialist. Assists in obtaining visa for work, immigration and business development within the United States and Canada.

2892 ■ Hewitt Development Enterprises (HDE)
1717 N Bayshore Dr., Ste. 2154
Miami, FL 33132
Ph: (305)372-0941
Fax: (305)372-0941
Co. E-mail: info@hewittdevelopment.com
URL: http://www.hewittdevelopment.com
Contact: Robert G. Hewitt, Principal
E-mail: bob@hewittdevelopment.com
Scope: Specializes in strategic planning; profit enhancement; start-up businesses; interim management; crisis management; turnarounds; production planning; just-in-time inventory management; and project management. Serves senior management (CEOs, CFOs, division presidents, etc.) and acquirers of distressed businesses. **Founded:** 1985.

2893 ■ Hickey & Hill Inc.
1009 Oak Hill Rd., Ste. 201
Lafayette, CA 94549-3812
Ph: (925)906-5331
Contact: Edwin L. Hill, Chief Executive Officer
Scope: Firm provides management consulting services to companies in financial distress. Expertise area: Corporate restructuring and turnaround. **Founded:** 1984.

2894 ■ hightechbiz.com—Leahy & Associates Inc.
4209 Santa Monica Blvd., Ste. 201
Los Angeles, CA 90029-3027
Ph: (323)913-3355
Free: 877-648-4753
Fax: (323)913-3355
URL: http://www.hightechbiz.com
Contact: Steven L. Hayes, Principal
Scope: A full service marketing agency specializing in integrated marketing solutions. Services include: marketing surveys; positioning surveys; strategic and tactical plans; implementation plans; management consulting; product brochures; product catalogs; product packaging; product data sheets; direct mail programs; media research; competitive research; complete creative; production and film; media placement; corporate identity; in-house creative; public relations. **Founded:** 1980.

2895 ■ Hills Consulting Group Inc.
6 Partridge Ct.
Novato, CA 94945-1315
Ph: (415)898-3944
Contact: Michael R. Hills, President
Scope: Specializes in strategic planning; marketing surveys; market research; customer service audits; new product development; competitive analysis; and sales forecasting. **Founded:** 1985.

2896 ■ Holt Capital
1916 Pike Pl., Ste. 12-344
Seattle, WA 98101
Ph: (206)484-0403
Fax: (206)789-8034
Co. E-mail: info@holtcapital.com
URL: http://www.holtcapital.com
Contact: Marilyn J. Holt, Chief Executive Officer
E-mail: mjholt@holtcapital.com
Scope: Registered investment advisory firm. Services include: Debt planning, private equity, mergers, divestitures and acquisitions, transaction support services. Connects companies with capital. **Founded:** 1980. **Publications:** "Early Sales Key to Early-Stage Funding"; "Financial Transactions: Who Should Be At Your Table"; "Get the Deal Done: The Four Keys to Successful Mergers and Acquisitions"; "Is Your First Paragraph a Turn-off"; "Bubble Rubble: Bridging the Price Gap for an Early-Stage Business"; "Are You Ready For The new Economy"; "Could I Get Money or Jail Time With That The Sarbanes-Oxley Act Of 2002 gives early-stage companies More Risks". **Seminars:** Attracting Private Investors; Five Proven Ways to Finance Your Company; How to Get VC Financing; Venture Packaging; How to Finance Company Expansion.

2897 ■ Hornberger & Associates (H&A)
1966 Lombard St.
San Francisco, CA 94123
Ph: (415)346-2106
Fax: (415)346-9993
Co. E-mail: info@hornbergerassociates.com
URL: http://www.hornbergerassociates.com
Contact: Deborah Hornberger, President
E-mail: deborah@hornbergerassociates.com
Scope: Specialized services include wealth management, retirement programs, small business banking, personal trust, investment management, brokerage services, mutual funds, relationship management, private banking and employee banking. Help clients by offering strategic marketing plans, market segmentation/niche marketing, website strategies and development; product development and introduction; client communications; product, sales and referral training; client retention programs and project management. **Founded:** 1992. **Publications:** "Establishing a Mini-trust Product," Bank Marketing, Oct, 1997. **Seminars:** Building a Marketing Plan Directed at Emerging Wealth Baby Boomers, Strategy Institute conference, Jun, 1999.

2898 ■ I.H.R. Solutions
3333 E Bayaud Ave., Ste. 219
Denver, CO 80209
Ph: (303)588-4243
Fax: (303)978-0473
Co. E-mail: dhollands@ihrsolutions.com
Contact: Deborah Hollands, Owner
E-mail: dhollands@ihrsolutions.com
Scope: Provides joint-venture and start-up human resource consulting services as well as advice on organization development for international human capital. Industries served: high-tech and telecommunications. **Founded:** 1997.

2899 ■ IMC Consulting & Training
901 McHenry Ave., Ste. A
Modesto, CA 95350
Ph: (209)572-2271
Fax: (209)572-2862
Co. E-mail: info@imc-1.net
URL: http://www.imc-1.net
Contact: Michael J. Loschke, President
E-mail: michael@imc-1.net
Scope: Helps businesses and professionals identify, develop and market their selling proposition to increase profits. Services include B-to-B surveys, direct marketing, media relations, planning and strategy, sales management, training and leadership coaching. **Founded:** 1994. **Publications:** "Consultant Earns Advanced Certificate," Hccsc Business Review, Dec, 2004; "Adapting to Change - the New Competitive Advantage," Business Journal, Jul, 2004; "Loyalty Marketing Can Divide New Business," Jun, 2004; "Eleven Major Marketing Mistakes," Jul, 2003; "Planning to Win or Racing to Fail," Jun, 2003. **Seminars:** Negotiating High Profit Sales; How to Write Winning Proposals, Modesto Chamber of Commerce, Oct, 2007; Winning the 2nd Half: A 6-month Plan to Score New Customers and Profits. **Telecommunication Services:** imcinfo@imc-1.net.

2900 ■ In Plain English—R.H. Wohl & Associates Inc.
14501 Antigone Dr.
Gaithersburg, MD 20885-3300
Ph: (301)340-2821
Free: 800-274-9645
Fax: (301)279-0115
Co. E-mail: rwohl@inplainenglish.com
URL: http://www.inplainenglish.com
Contact: Ronald H. Wohl, President
E-mail: rwohl@inplainenglish.com
Scope: Management consultants helping government and businesses research, design, write and produce user oriented management information for human resources, employee benefits, business process, corporate and marketing needs. Services include: GSA mob is schedule for consulting to the government; employee benefit communications, plain English business writing workshops for print and electronic media; communicating strategy and tactics; marketing research, business planning and communications; readability testing; usability testing and monitoring strategy. **Founded:** 1977. **Publications:** "The Benefits Communication"; "The Employee Benefits Communication ToolKit," Commerce Clearinghouse; "Benefits Communication," Business and Legal Reports. **Seminars:** Plain English Writing Training; Summary Plan Description Compliance workshops; Re-Humanizing the Corporation, Human Resources and Employee Benefits Communication Workshop; 21 Writing Tips for the 21st Century; Make the Write Impression; Writing to Inform and Instruct; The Dreaded Nuts and Bolts; Writing to Persuade; Writing Policy and Procedure Manuals In Plain English; Writing for Accountants and Auditors In Plain English. **Special Services:** In Plain English®.

2901 ■ Innovative Scientific Analysis & Computing (ISAac)
6168 Flagstaff Rd.
Boulder, CO 80302
Ph: (303)440-7673
Fax: (303)545-6674
Co. E-mail: ros5e@isaac.com
URL: http://www.ros5e.com
Contact: Charlie E. Rose, President
E-mail: ros5e@isaac.com
Scope: Engineering services includes mathematical analysis specializing in optimal estimation, scientific programming, and database design and development, data encryption and security. **Founded:** 1993.

2902 ■ The Institute for Management Excellence
PO Box 5459
Lacey, WA 98509-5459
Ph: (360)412-0404
Co. E-mail: pwoc@itstime.com
URL: http://www.itstime.com
Contact: Michael Anthony, Director
Scope: Management consulting and training focuses on improving productivity, using practices and creative techniques. Practices based on the company's theme: It's time for new ways of doing business. Industries served: public sector, law enforcement, finance or banking, non profit, computers or high technology, education, human resources, utilities. **Founded:** 1995. **Publications:** "Income Without a Job," 2008; "The Other Side of Midnight, 2000: An Executive Guide to the Year 2000 Problem"; "Concordance to the Michael Teachings"; "Handbook of Small Business Advertising"; "The Personality Game"; "How to Market Yourself for Success". **Seminars:** The Personality Game; Power Path Seminars; Productivity Plus; Sexual Harassment and Discrimination Prevention; Worker's Comp Cost Reduction; Americans with Disabilities Act; In Search of Identify: Clarifying Corporate Culture.

2903 ■ Institute of Public Administration (IPA)
295 Lafayette St., Fl. 2
New York, NY 10003
Ph: (212)992-9898
Free: 800-258-1102

Fax: (212)995-4876
Co. E-mail: p553@nyu.edu
URL: http://www.theipa.org
Contact: David Mammen, President
Scope: Provider of consulting and research services. It serves local, state and federal governments, international aid agencies, and foreign governments. **Founded:** 1906. **Publications:** "Local Governance Approach to Social Reintegration and Economic Recovery in Post Conflict Countries: The Political Context for Programs of UNDP/UNCDF Assistance"; "Local Governance Approach to Social Reintegration and Economic Recovery in Post Conflict Countries: Programming Options for UNDP/UNCDF Assistance"; "Local Governance Approach to Social Reintegration and Economic Recovery in Post Conflict Countries: The View from Mozambique"; "Local Governance Approach to Social Reintegration and Economic Recovery in Post Conflict Countries: Towards a Definition and a Rationale"; "Local Governance Approach to Post Conflict Recovery: Perspective from Cambodia"; "The Sustainable Human Development Strategy: A Proposal for Post Conflict Recovery Societies"; "Local Governance Approach to Post Conflict Recovery: Proceedings Report on the Workshop Organized by the Institute of Public Administration". **Seminars:** A Local Governance Approach to Post Conflict Recovery.

2904 ■ Interminds & Federer Resources Inc.
106 E 6th St., Ste. 310
Austin, TX 78701-3659
Ph: (512)476-8800
Fax: (512)476-8811
Co. E-mail: yesyoucan@interminds.com
URL: http://www.interminds.com
Contact: Frank Federer, President
E-mail: ffederer@integra100.com
Scope: Specializes in feasibility studies; startup businesses; small business management; mergers and acquisitions; joint ventures; divestitures; interim management; crisis management; turnarounds; production planning; team building; appraisals and valuations. **Founded:** 1985. **Publications:** "Yes You Can: How To Be A Success No Matter Who You Are Or Where You're From".

2905 ■ Interpersonal Coaching & Consulting (ICC)
1516 W Lake St., Ste. 2000S
Minneapolis, MN 55408
Ph: (612)381-2494
Fax: (612)381-2494
Co. E-mail: mail@interpersonal-coaching.com
URL: http://www.interpersonal-coaching.com
Contact: Mary Belfry, Partner
Scope: Provider of coaching and consulting to businesses and organizations. Assesses the interpersonal workplace through interviews, assessment instruments and individual group settings. Experienced as a therapist for over a decade. **Publications:** "Sexual Harassment In The Workplace For Newspapers". **Seminars:** More On Relationships; Sexual harassment and discrimination issues.

2906 ■ Jest for the Health of It Services
PO Box 8484
Santa Cruz, CA 95061-8484
Ph: (831)425-8436
Fax: (831)425-8437
Co. E-mail: pwooten@jesthealth.com
URL: http://www.jesthealth.com
Contact: Shirley Trout, Manager
E-mail: strout@nurseswhostay.com
Scope: Develops and presents seminars, keynotes and skill shops about the power of humor. Provides consulting services for development of humor rooms and comedy carts in hospitals. Conducts training for clowns to make visits in hospitals and nursing homes. Industries served: health professionals and businesses wishing to educate staff about healthy lifestyle choices. **Founded:** 1982. **Publications:** "Heart Humor and Healing"; "Compassionate Laughter: Jest for Your Health"; "The Hospital Clown: A Closer Look"; "Humor: An Antidote for Stress"; "Humor, Laughter and Play: Maintaining Balance in a Serious World"; "You've Got to Be Kidding: Humor Skills for Surviving

Managed Care"; "Laughter as Therapy for Patient and Caregiver"; "Patty Wooten: Nurse Healer"; "Humor: An antidote for stress".

2907 ■ Johnston Co.
78 Bedford St.
Lexington, MA 02420
Ph: (781)862-7595
Fax: (781)862-9066
Co. E-mail: info@johnstoncompany.com
URL: http://www.johnstoncompany.com
Contact: Claire Sehringer, Manager
Scope: Specializes in management audits and reports; start-up businesses; small business management; mergers and acquisitions; joint ventures; divestitures; interim management; crisis management; turnarounds; cost controls; financing; venture capital; controller services; financial management, strategic and advisory services. **Founded:** 1987. **Publications:** "Why are board meetings such a waste of time," Boston Business Journal, Apr, 2004.

2908 ■ Kaufman Global L.L.C.
5975 Castle Creek Pky., Dr.North., Ste. 440
Indianapolis, IN 46250
Ph: (317)818-2430
Fax: (317)818-2434
Co. E-mail: info@kaufmanglobal.com
URL: http://www.kaufmanglobal.com
Contact: Jerry Timpson, President
Scope: Consulting firm addresses cultural, emotional and political elements of change throughout the workplace. **Founded:** 1995. **Publications:** "What You Do Not Know Can Hurt You," Aug, 2012; "The Small Stuff is the Big Stuff," May, 2012; "Understanding the Value of Information as a Corporate Asset," Jul, 2012; "Do Not Waste Your Time with Marketing," Jun, 2012; "ArvinMeritor: A Lean Culture"; "The Struggle to Get Lean"; "The Missing Link of Lean Success"; "Using a Full-Court Press to Transform a Business"; "Managing Growth - BD Finds Success Integrating Lean and Six Sigma". **Seminars:** Conducting Office Rapid Improvement Events; Developing Lasting Capability Inside the Organization; Building Sustainable Solutions; A Structured and Proven Process for Engaging the Organization and Delivering Results. **Special Services:** Lean Leadership®; SLIM-IT®; Lean Daily Management System LDMS®; 20 Keys®; WIn-Lean®; Lean Six Sigma.

2909 ■ Keiei Senryaku Corp.
19191 S Vermont Ave., Ste. 530
Torrance, CA 90502-1049
Ph: (310)366-3331
Free: 800-951-8780
Fax: (310)366-3330
Co. E-mail: takenakaes@earthlink.net
Contact: Kurt Miyamoto, President
Scope: Offers consulting services in the areas of strategic planning; feasibility studies; profit enhancement; organizational development; start-up businesses; mergers and acquisitions; joint ventures; divestitures; executive searches; sales management; and competitive analysis. **Founded:** 1989.

2910 ■ Koch Group Inc.
129 Fairfield Way, Ste. 219
Bloomingdale, IL 60108
Ph: (630)941-1100
Free: 800-470-7845
Fax: (630)941-3865
Co. E-mail: info@kochgroup.com
URL: http://www.kochgroup.com
Contact: Peter Koch, Manager
Scope: Provider of industrial marketing consulting services to small to mid-sized manufacturers. Primary assistance includes industrial market research and analysis, identification of potential markets, strategic planning and plan implementation, market planning, sales analysis, competitor analysis. Specializes in assisting manufacturers identify, recruit, and manage agents and reps and developing website for business promotion. **Founded:** 1967. **Seminars:** Niche Marketing; Regional Industrial Association Recruiting; Strategic Marketing for Manufacturers; Strategic Marketing; How To Identify, Screen, Interview and Select High Quality Agents; Basics of Industrial Market Research; Elements of Industrial Marketing; Trade Adjustment Assistance For Firms; Developing

New Business; Selecting An Industrial Web Site Developer; Strategic Selling; Pick Your Customer; Strategic and Tactical Marketing.

2911 ■ Kostka & Company Inc.
9 Wild Rose Ct.
Cromwell, CT 06416
Ph: (860)257-1045
Contact: Peter Kostka, Managing Partner
E-mail: peterpk@gmail.com
Scope: Areas of expertise: management consulting, global technology sourcing, complex project management, SKU management and new product introduction, application development, medical point-of-sale, multi-touch user interface, made-to-order management systems and Smartphone ERP connectivity. Clients include global fortune 500 companies as well as small and medium-sized businesses and startups. **Founded:** 1994.

2912 ■ Kubba Consultants Inc.
1255 Montgomery Dr.
Deerfield, IL 60015
Ph: (847)867-0874
URL: http://www.kubbainc.com
Contact: Ed Kubba, President
E-mail: edkubba@aol.com
Scope: Industrial and business-to-business marketing research and consulting. Services include new product research, new market evaluation, competitor analysis and customer value analysis. **Founded:** 1987.

2913 ■ William E. Kuhn & Associates
234 Cook St.
Denver, CO 80206-5305
Ph: (303)322-8233
Fax: (303)331-9032
Co. E-mail: billkuhn1@cs.com
Contact: William E. Kuhn, Owner
E-mail: billkuhn1@cs.com
Scope: Firm specializes in strategic planning; profit enhancement; small business management; mergers and acquisitions; joint ventures; divestitures; human resources management; performance appraisals; team building; sales management; appraisals and valuations. **Founded:** 1980. **Publications:** "Creating a High-Performance Dealership," Office SOLUTIONS & Office DEALER, Jul-Aug, 2006.

2914 ■ L G Anthony Associates
40 Wellington Blvd.
Reading, PA 19610
Ph: (610)670-0477
Contact: Louis G. Anthony, Owner
Scope: Provides food service facility planning, layout and design, including equipment selection and specification. Also offers management systems and operations analysis, such as the development of operating policies and procedures. Firm can design menu planning and recipe development, food selection and specification, work simplification, service, and quality control around current concepts in the field. Industries served: hospital, nursing home, restaurant, group homes; commercial and institutional food service industries. **Founded:** 1986. **Seminars:** Food Service Sanitation; Menu Planning; Work Simplification; Quality Control in Food Service.

2915 ■ Liberty Business Strategies Ltd.
The Times Bldg., Ste. 400, Suburban Sq.
Ardmore, PA 19003
Ph: (610)649-3800
Fax: (610)649-0408
Co. E-mail: info@libertystrategies.com
URL: http://www.libertystrategies.com
Contact: Emmy S. Miller, President
E-mail: emmym@libertystrategies.com
Scope: Management consulting firm working with clients to gain speed and agility in driving their business strategy. The consulting model builds the alignment of strategy, organization commitment, and technology. Provides senior leader coaching and team development coaching. **Founded:** 1980. **Seminars:** Winning with Talent, Morison Annual Conference, Jul, 2009.

2916 ■ Linda Lipsky Restaurant Consultants Inc.
216 Foxcroft Rd.
Broomall, PA 19008-2039
Ph: (610)325-3663
Free: 877-425-3663
Fax: (610)325-3329
Co. E-mail: lipsky@restaurantconsult.com
URL: http://www.restaurantconsult.com
Contact: Linda J. Lipsky, President
E-mail: lipsky@restaurantconsult.com
Scope: Provider of marketing and survey solutions. It offers management training and evaluation programs, recipe documentation, cost analysis, and bridge management services. **Founded:** 1988. **Seminars:** Designing Menus for Maximum Sales and Profits; How to Maximize Your Check Average; Going Beyond Your Customer's Expectations; Seeing Your Restaurant Through a Customer's Eyes; Making the Best First and Last Impression; Basic Training in Kitchen Management Techniques; Basic Training in Bar Management Techniques; Make Every Labor Dollar Count; Back to Basics/More Than Shift Management; Conducting Your Own In-House Inspection; Basics of Sanitation Training for Kitchen Employees; Basics of Sanitation Training for Dining Room Employees.

2917 ■ May Toy Lukens
3226 NE 26th Ct.
Renton, WA 98056
Ph: (425)891-3226
Contact: May T. Lukens, Principal
Scope: Provides training to teach people to think of ways to improve their operations continuously by changing the way they think. Industries served: All, particularly financial. Operational analysis and training. **Founded:** 1996. **Seminars:** Seminars and workshops in maximizing resource utilization and staff potential.

2918 ■ Lupfer & Associates (L&A)
92 Glen St.
Natick, MA 01760-5646
Ph: (508)655-3950
Fax: (508)655-7826
Co. E-mail: donlupfer@aol.com
Contact: Donald Lupfer, Owner
E-mail: don.lupfer@lupferassociates.com
Scope: Assists off shore hi-tech companies in entering United States markets and specializes in channel development for all sorts of products. Perform MARCOM support for hi-tech United States clients. **Founded:** 1988. **Publications:** "What's Next For Distribution-Feast or Famine"; "The Changing Global Marketplace"; "Making Global Distribution Work". **Seminars:** How to do Business in the United States.

2919 ■ Management Network Group Inc.—TMNG GlobalCambridge Strategic Management Group Inc.;
7300 College Blvd., Ste. 302
Overland Park, KS 66210-1879
Ph: (913)345-9315
Fax: (913)451-1845
URL: http://www.tmng.com
Contact: Micky K. Woo, President
E-mail: micky.woo@tmng.com
Scope: A provider of strategy, management, marketing, operational and technology consulting services to the global telecommunications industry. **Founded:** 1990. **Special Services:** Lexicon™; QBC™; QSA™.

2920 ■ Management Resource Partners
181 2nd Ave., Ste. 542
San Mateo, CA 94401
Ph: (650)401-5850
Fax: (650)401-5850
Contact: John C. Roberts, Owner
Scope: Firm specializes in strategic planning; small business management; mergers and acquisitions; joint ventures; divestitures; interim management; crisis management; turn around; venture capital; appraisals and valuations. **Founded:** 1981.

2921 ■ Management Strategies
1000 S Old Woodward Ave., Ste. 105
Birmingham, MI 48009
Ph: (248)258-2756

Fax: (248)258-3407
Co. E-mail: bob@hois.com
Contact: Robert E. Hoisington, President
E-mail: bob@hois.com
Scope: Firm specializes in strategic planning; feasibility studies; profit enhancement; organizational studies; start up businesses; turnarounds; business process re engineering; industrial engineering; marketing; ecommerce. **Founded:** 1985.

2922 ■ Marketing Leverage Inc.
2022 Laurel Oak Ln.
Palm City, FL 34990
Ph: (772)878-6495
Free: 800-633-1422
Fax: (772)659-8664
Co. E-mail: lkelly@marketingleverage.com
Contact: Lynn C. Kelly, President
E-mail: lkelly@marketingleverage.com
Scope: Consulting and research firm focusing on the targeting, retention and satisfaction of customers. Consulting is offered for due diligence; marketing and customer retention strategy; program design and implementation. Research services offered help clients determine service improvements that increase customer loyalty; boosting sales through better understanding buyer motivations; increasing the odds of product acceptance through new product concept testing; and improving the effectiveness of advertising, collateral, publications through audience evaluation. Clients include top financial services, insurance, health care, technology and management services organizations. **Founded:** 1987. **Publications:** "Creating Strategic Leverage"; "Exploring Corporate Strategy"; "Competitive Advantage"; "Breakpoint and Beyond "; "Competitive Strategy ". **Seminars:** Best Practices in Brainstorming; Getting Results in the Real World; Finding the Leverage in Your Customer Strategy; The Role of Communications in Building Customer Loyalty; Building a Customer Centered Relationship and Making it Pay. **Special Services:** The Marketing Leverage Win/Loss Tracking System™.

2923 ■ McCreight & Company Inc.
36 Grove St.
New Canaan, CT 06840
Ph: (203)801-5000
Fax: (866)646-8339
Co. E-mail: roc@implementstrategy.com
URL: http://www.implementstrategy.com
Contact: John A. McCreight, President
E-mail: jmc@implementstrategy.com
Scope: Assist the global clients with strategy implementation involving large scale change, including mergers, divestitures, alliances and new business launches. **Founded:** 1983. **Publications:** "The Board's Role in Strengthening M and A Success," Boardroom Briefing, 2008; "Creating the Future," Ask Magazine, 2007; "Strategy Implementation Insights," Mccreight and Company Inc, Oct, 2007; "Sustaining Growth," Deloitte and Ct Technology Council, Jul, 2006; "A Four Phase Approach to Succession Planning," Southern Connecticut Newspapers Inc, 2005. **Seminars:** Successful Mergers and Acquisitions-An Implementation Guide; Global 100One-Face-to-the-Customer; Implementation of Strategic Change.

2924 ■ McDonald Consulting Group Inc.
1900 W Park Dr., Ste. 280
Westborough, MA 01581
Co. E-mail: info@mcdonaldconsultinggroup.com
URL: http://www.mcdonaldconsultinggroup.com
Contact: Ron A. McDonald, President
E-mail: rmcdonald@mcdonaldconsultinggroup.com
Scope: A management consulting firm specializing in assisting insurance companies improve operations. Provides services in the areas of strategic planning; profit enhancement; organizational development; interim management; crisis management; turnarounds; business process re-engineering; benefits and compensation planning and total quality management. **Founded:** 1993. **Publications:** "Improving Customer Focus through Organizational Structure," AASCIF News; "Changing Strategies in Hard Markets," The National Underwriter; "Moving Beyond Management 101: Postgraduate Time Management for Executives," The National Underwriter; "A New Attitude: 3 Clients Improved Results Through Our

Fundamental Change Process," Bests Review; "How to Organize Your Company Around Your Customers," Bests Review. **Seminars:** How to establish "expense allowable"; How to design an incentive compensation plan around a units core success measures.

2925 ■ McMann & Ransford
1 Sugar Creek Center Blvd., Ste. 300
Sugar Land, TX 77478
Free: 866-267-0299
Co. E-mail: contact@mcmannransford.com
URL: http://www.mcmannransford.com
Contact: Dean E. McMann, Chief Executive Officer
E-mail: dmcmann@mcmannransford.com
Scope: Provides of management consulting, training, executive recruiting and market research services specializing in the professional services industry. **Founded:** 1990.

2926 ■ McShane Group Inc.
2345 York Rd., Ste. 102
Timonium, MD 21093
Ph: (410)560-0077
Fax: (410)560-2718
Co. E-mail: tmcshane@mcshanegroup.com
URL: http://www.mcshanegroup.com
Contact: Thomas P. McShane, President
E-mail: tmcshane@mcshanegroup.com
Scope: Turnaround consulting and crisis management firm. Specializes in due diligence services, interim management, strategic business realignments, business sale and asset depositions and debt restructuring. Industries served: technology, financial, retail, distribution, medical, educational, manufacturing, contracting, environmental and health care. **Founded:** 1987.

2927 ■ MeasureNet
137 Pioneer Dr.
West Hartford, CT 06117
Ph: (860)913-3767
Co. E-mail: greilly@business.uconn.edu
URL: http://www.measure.net
Contact: Greg Reilly, President
E-mail: greilly@sbcglobal.net
Scope: Firm seeks to improve corporate performance measurement systems through measurement audit and improvement services. **Founded:** 1997. **Publications:** "Value-linked Measurement at Dell," Journal of Cost Management, Jul, 2002; "Performance Measurement for Improved Working Capital Management," Journal of Cost Management, May, 2002; "Improving the Quality of Performance Information," Journal of Cost Management, Mar, 2002; "Developing Managers Through Performance Measurement," Journal of Cost Management, Nov, 2001; "Improving Corporate Performance Measurement," Journal of Cost Management, Jul, 2001; "Value Measurement: Using a Measure Network to Understand and Deliver Value," Journal of Cost Management, Nov, 2000. **Special Services:** Measure Network™.

2928 ■ Medical Imaging Consultants Inc. (MIC)
1037 US Highway 46, Ste. G-2
Clifton, NJ 07013-2445
Ph: (973)574-8000
Free: 800-589-5685
Fax: (973)574-8001
Co. E-mail: info@micinfo.com
URL: http://www.micinfo.com
Contact: Dr. Philip A. Fernano, President
E-mail: phil@micinfo.com
Scope: Provider of professional support services for radiology management and comprehensive continuing education programs for radiologic technologists. Management services include resource-critical database logistics; customer registration in educational programs; educational program development and Category A accreditation; national agency notification (e.g., ASRT, SNM-TS) of CE credits earned; meeting planning; manpower assessment; market research; expert witness; think-tank probes and executive summaries of industry issues. **Founded:** 1991. **Seminars:** Sectional Anatomy and Imaging Strategies; CT Cross-Trainer; CT Registry

Review Program; MR Cross Trainer; MRI Registry Review Program; Digital Mammography Essentials for Technologists; Radiology Trends for Technologists.

2929 ■ Medical Outcomes Management Inc.

132 Central St., Ste. 215
Foxborough, MA 02035-2422
Ph: (508)543-0050
Fax: (508)543-1919
Co. E-mail: info@mom-inc.com
Contact: Alan F. Kaul, President
E-mail: alan@mom-inc.com

Scope: Management and technology consulting firm providing a specially focused group of services such as disease management programs and pharmaco-economic studies. Services include clinical and educational projects, medical writing and editing, marketing and sales projects, disease registries, educational seminars, strategic planning projects, managed care organizations; and pharmaceutical and biotechnology companies. **Founded:** 1991. **Publications:** "Treatment of acute exacerbation's of chronic bronchitis in patients with chronic obstructive pulmonary disease: A retrospective cohort analysis logarithmically extended release vs. Azithromycin," 2003; "A retrospective analysis of cyclooxygenase-II inhibitor response patterns," 2002; "DUE criteria for use of regional urokinase infusion for deep vein thrombosis,"2002; "The formulary management system and decision-making process at Horizon Blue Cross Blue Shield of New Jersey," Pharmaco therapy, 2001. **Seminars:** Economic Modeling as a Disease Management Tool, Academy of Managed Care Pharmacy, Apr, 2005; Integrating Disease State Management and Economics, Academy of Managed Care Pharmacy, Oct, 2004; Clinical and economic outcomes in the treatment of peripheral occlusive diseases, Mar, 2003.

2930 ■ Mefford, Knutson & Associates Inc. (MK)

6437 Lyndale Ave. S, Ste. 103
Richfield, MN 55423-1465
Ph: (612)869-8011
Free: 800-831-0228
Fax: (612)869-8004
Co. E-mail: info@mkaonline.net
URL: http://www.mkaonline.net
Contact: Jeanette Mefford, Director
E-mail: jmefford@mkaonline.com

Scope: A consulting and licensed business brokerage firm specializing in start-up businesses; strategic planning; mergers and acquisitions; joint ventures; divestitures; business process re-engineering; personnel policies and procedures; market research; new product development and cost controls. **Founded:** 1990.

2931 ■ Harvey A. Meier Co. (HAM)

410 W Nevada St.
Ashland, OR 97520-1043
Ph: (509)458-3210
Fax: (541)488-7905
Co. E-mail: harvey@harveymeier.com
URL: http://www.harveymeier.com
Contact: Dr. Harvey A. Meier, President
E-mail: harvey@harveymeier.com

Scope: Provider of service to chief executive officers and board of directors. Specializes in interim management, strategic planning, financial planning and organization governance. **Publications:** "The D'Artagnan Way".

2932 ■ Midwest Computer Group L.L.C. (MCG)

6060 Franks Rd.
House Springs, MO 63051
Ph: (314)954-1222
Co. E-mail: sales@mcgcomputer.com
URL: http://www.mcgcomputer.com
Contact: Leon Sanford, Jr., President
E-mail: leonjr@mcgcomputer.com

Scope: Specializes in helping businesses create accounting, marketing and business information systems; software development and database design and management. **Founded:** 1980.

2933 ■ Midwest Research Institute (MRI)

425 Volker Blvd.
Kansas City, MO 64110-2241
Ph: (816)753-7600
Fax: (816)753-8420
Co. E-mail: info@mriresearch.org
URL: http://www.mriresearch.org
Contact: James L. Spigarelli, President

Scope: Independent not-for-profit research institute offering scientific services in the areas of national defense, health sciences, agriculture and food safety, engineering, energy, and infrastructure. Services include biomedical electronics, remote sensing, automation and control electromagnetic radiation, environmental sampling and analysis programs for industry and government, program management, engineering studies, exposure and risk assessment, waste management strategies, contaminant identification, pollution prevention, and waste minimization. Expertise in highway safety/accident analysis, chemometrics/pattern recognition/neural networks, statistical support, process and product engineering. **Founded:** 1943. **Telecommunication Services:** bduncan@mriresearch.org

2934 ■ Miller, Hellwig Associates

150 W End Ave.
New York, NY 10023-5713
Ph: (212)799-0471
Fax: (212)877-0186
Co. E-mail: millerhelwig@earthlink.net
Contact: Ernest C. Miller, President

Scope: Consulting services in the areas of start-up businesses; small business management; employee surveys and communication; performance appraisals; executive searches; team building; personnel policies and procedures; market research. Also involved in improving cross-cultural and multi-cultural relationships, particularly with Japanese clients. **Founded:** 1984. **Seminars:** Objectives and standards/recruiting for boards of directors.

2935 ■ R.E. Moulton Inc.

50 Doaks Ln.
Marblehead, MA 01945
Ph: (781)631-1325
Fax: (781)631-2165
Co. E-mail: mike_lee@remoultoninc.com
URL: http://www.oneamerica.com/wps/wcm/connect/REMoulton
Contact: Willard A. Knarr, Jr., President

Scope: Offers underwriting services, marketing solutions, claims administration and adjudication; policy and commission administration; and risk management solutions to clients. Supplementary service s include risk management and employee assistance. Clients include individuals, business men, employers and finance professionals. **Founded:** 1976.

2936 ■ Murray Dropkin & Associates—Dropkin Consulting

390 George St.
New Brunswick, NJ 08901
Ph: (732)828-3211
Fax: (732)828-4118
Co. E-mail: murray@dropkin.com
URL: http://www.dropkin.com
Contact: Murray Dropkin, President
E-mail: murray@dropkin.com

Scope: Specializes in feasibility studies; business management; business process re-engineering; and team building, health care and housing. **Founded:** 1969. **Publications:** "Bookkeeping for Nonprofits," Jossey Bass, 2005; "Guide to Audits of Nonprofit Organizations," PPC; "The Nonprofit Report," Warren, Gorham & Lamont; "The Budget Building Book for Nonprofits," Jossey-Bass; "The Cash Flow Management Book for Nonprofits," Jossey-Bass.

2937 ■ National Center for Public Policy Research (NCPPR)

501 Capitol Ct. NE
Washington, DC 20002
Ph: (202)543-4110

Fax: (202)543-5975
Co. E-mail: info@nationalcenter.org
URL: http://www.nationalcenter.org
Contact: Amy Moritz Ridenour, President
E-mail: aridenour@nationalcenter.org

Description: Educates the public about public policy issues. Conducts research; distributes national policy analysis papers, memorandums, brochures, newsletters, article reprints, and other materials to the public, libraries, and the media. **Scope:** A communications and research nonprofit organization offering advice and information on international affairs and United States domestic affairs. Sponsors Project 21. Gives special emphasis an environmental and regulatory issues and civil rights issues. **Founded:** 1982. **Publications:** "National Policy Analysis"; "Legal Briefs"; "White Paper: National Policy Analysis 523"; "Shattered Dreams: One Hundred Stories of Government Abuse"; "Shattered Lives: 100 Victims of Government Health Care".

2938 ■ National Insurance Professionals Corp. (NIPC)

1040 NE Hostmark St., Ste. 200
Poulsbo, WA 98370-7454
Ph: (360)697-3611
Free: 800-275-6472
Fax: (360)697-3688
Co. E-mail: kathy_schufreider@rpsvcs.com
URL: http://www.nipc.com
Contact: Bill Reese, President

Scope: Program administrators for alternative specialty markets. Includes social service agencies and bicycle tour operators. Provides retail and wholesale insurance brokers access to specialty insurance carriers. **Founded:** 1976.

2939 ■ Navarro, Kim & Associates

529 N Charles St., Ste. 202
Baltimore, MD 21201-5043
Ph: (410)837-6317
Fax: (410)837-6294
Co. E-mail: bnavarro@sprynet.com
Contact: Beltran Navarro, Director
E-mail: bnavarro@sprynet.com

Scope: Specializes in bridging the gap between firms and non-traditional ethnic communities, especially in community development and institutional building. **Founded:** 1984.

2940 ■ New Commons

545 Pawtucket Ave., Studio 106A
Pawtucket, RI 02860
Ph: (401)351-7110
Fax: (401)351-7158
Co. E-mail: info@newcommons.com
URL: http://www.newcommons.com
Contact: Robert Leaver, Chief Executive Officer
E-mail: rleaver@newcommons.com

Scope: Builder of agile human networks to champion innovation and mobilize change; to pursue business opportunities; to custom design agile organizations and communities, to foster civic engagement. Clients include organizations on-profits, corporations, government agencies, educational institutions; networks-Trade/professional groups, IT services collaborations; service-sharing collectives; and communities- municipalities, states and statewide agencies, regional collaborations. **Founded:** 1982. **Publications:** "Plexus Imperative," Sep, 2005; "Creating 21st Century Capable Innovation Systems," Aug, 2004; "Call to Action: Building Providences Creative and Innovative Economy"; "Getting Results from Meetings"; "The Entrepreneur as Artist," Commonwealth Publications; "Leader and Agent of Change," Commonwealth Publications; "Achieving our Providence: Lessons of City-Building," Commonwealth Publications. **Seminars:** Introduction to Social Computing (Web 2.0), Jan, 2009; Every Company Counts, Jun, 2009; Facilitating for Results; Story-Making and Story-Telling. **Telecommunication Services:** inquiries@newcommons.com.

2941 ■ The New Marketing Network Inc.

300 Park Ave., 17th Fl.
New York, NY 10022

Ph: (212)572-6392
Co. E-mail: info@newmarketingnetwork.com
URL: http://www.newmarketingnetwork.com
Contact: Pamela S. Boynton, Director
Scope: Full service firm assisting companies in marketing, creative, research, branding and communications specialties. The firm assists companies achieve their growth initiatives, increase profits and establish a sustainable competitive advantage through successful new products, accurate trend identification; application; business and brand franchise expansion. Additional services include strategic planning and positioning; qualitative and quantitative research. **Founded:** 1989.

2942 ■ **Nightingale Associates**
7445 Setting Sun Way
Columbia, MD 21046
Ph: (410)381-4280
Fax: (410)381-4280
Co. E-mail: fredericknightingale@nightingaleassociates.net
URL: http://www.nightingaleassociates.net
Contact: Frederick C. Nightingale, Managing Director
E-mail: fredericknightingale@nightingaleAssociates.net
Scope: Management training and consulting firm offering the following skills: productivity and accomplishment; leadership skills for the experienced manager; management skills for the new manager; leadership and teambuilding; supervisory development; creative problem solving; real strategic planning; providing superior customer service; international purchasing and supply chain management; negotiation skills development and fundamentals of purchasing. **Founded:** 1984. **Seminars:** Productivity and Accomplishment Management Skills for the New Manager; Leadership and Team building; Advanced Management; Business Process Re engineering; Strategic Thinking; Creative Problem Solving; Customer Service; International Purchasing and Materials Management; Fundamentals of Purchasing; Negotiation Skills Development; Providing superior customer service; Leadership skills for the experienced manager.

2943 ■ **North Carolina Fair Share (NCFS)**
3824 Barrett Dr., Ste. 312
Raleigh, NC 27609
Ph: (919)786-7474
Fax: (919)786-7475
Co. E-mail: ncfslrw@aol.com
URL: http://www.ncfairshare.org
Scope: Social services firm consults on community organizing and lobbying for health issues. **Founded:** 1987.

2944 ■ **Occupational & Environmental Health Consulting Services Inc.**
635 Harding Rd.
Hinsdale, IL 60521-4814
Ph: (630)325-2083
Fax: (630)325-2098
Co. E-mail: bobb@safety-epa.com
URL: http://www.oehcs.com
Contact: Robert C. Brandys, President
E-mail: bobb@safety-epa.com
Scope: Provider of consulting to industry on safety program development and implementation, industrial hygiene monitoring programs, occupational health nursing, wellness programs, medical monitoring, accident trending and statistics, emergency response planning, multilingual training, right-to-know compliance and training, hazardous waste management, random monitoring and mitigation, asbestos school inspection, and project management. Also offers indoor air quality, expert witnessing service. **Founded:** 1984. **Publications:** "Worldwide Exposure Standards for Mold and Bacteria"; "Global Occupational Exposure Limits for Over 5000 Specific Chemicals"; "Post-Remediation Verification and Clearance Testing for Mold and Bacteria Risk Based Levels of Cleanliness". **Seminars:** Right-To-Know Compliance; Setting Internal Exposure Standards; Hospital Right-to-Know and Contingency Response; Ethylene Oxide Control; Industrial Hygiene Training; Asbestos Worker Training; Biosafety; Asbestos Operations and Maintenance. **Special Services:** Safety Software Program, Audiogram Analysis, First

Report of Injury Form, Human Resources Database; Material Safety Data Sheet (MSDS); NPDES Monthly Reports; Lockout/Tagout (LOTO) Procedure Software; VOC Usage Tracking and Reporting Software, Medical Department Patient Records Database, Pictorial Labels for Chemical Containers, TIER II Hazardous Material Inventory Form & Database.

2945 ■ **Optial Corp.**
12600 Deerfield Pkwy., Ste. 100
Alpharetta, GA 30004
Ph: (770)753-0128
Fax: (770)216-1841
Co. E-mail: info@optial.com
URL: http://www.optial.com
Contact: Chris O'Brien, Chief Executive Officer
E-mail: chris.obrien@optial.com
Scope: Consultants in the following areas to develop integrated compliance and risk management solutions: Financial operational risk management, healthcare administration, business and property insurance, occupational safety and health, environmental. **Founded:** 1993. **Publications:** "Optial OpRisk on Demand," May, 2010; "Operational Risk," May, 2010; "Making Room for Treasury," May, 2010; "Tackling Operational Risk in a Sub-prime World," May, 2010; "Operational risk concerns concentrate on due diligence," May, 2010; "Cultural aspects of Operational risk," May, 2010. **Special Services:** Optial™.

2946 ■ **Organizational Improvement Associates L.L.C. (OIA)—OIAUS L.L.C.**
40 Gilbert St.
Ridgefield, CT 06877
Ph: (203)417-4957
Fax: (203)244-5737
Co. E-mail: daveknibbe@oiaus.com
URL: http://www.oiaus.com
Contact: Dr. David S. Knibbe, President
E-mail: daveknibbe@oiaus.com
Scope: Specializes in high-performance team development, executive coaching, employee development programs, performance management and reward systems and dispute mediation. Industries served: Consumer products, telecommunications, finance, health-care, amusement/leisure, hospitality/lodging, retail and pharmaceuticals. **Founded:** 1991.

2947 ■ **P2C2 Group Inc.**
4101 Denfeld Ave.
Kensington, MD 20895-1514
Ph: (301)942-7985
Fax: (301)942-7986
Co. E-mail: info@p2c2group.com
URL: http://www.p2c2group.com
Contact: James E. Kendrick, President
E-mail: kendrick@p2c2group.com
Scope: Works with clients on the business side of federal program and project management. Services include program/project planning and optimization; acquisition strategy and work statements; IT Capital Planning and Investment Control (CPIC); business cases - new, revisions, critiques; budget analysis - cost benefits- alternatives; CPIC, SELC, and security documentation; research, metrics, analysis, and case studies. Consulting support helping to: Define or redefine programs; strengthen portfolio management; identify alternatives for lean budgets; improve capital planning and investment; develop better plans and documentation, and evaluate performance of existing program investments. **Founded:** 1994. **Publications:** "OMB 300s Go Online," Federal Sector Report, Mar, 2007; "Using Risk-Adjusted Costs for Projects," Federal Sector Report, Feb, 2007; "Make Better Decisions Using Case Studies," Federal Sector Report, Jan, 2007; "PMO Performance Measurement & Metrics"; "Executive Sponsors for Projects"; "ABCs of the Presidential Transition"; "Financial Systems and Enterprise Portfolio Management"; "The Future of CPIC"; "Critical Factors for Program and Project Success"; "Using Risk-Adjusted Costs for Projects"; "Tactics for a Successful Year of CPIC"; "Operational Analysis Reviews"; "Successful IT Strategic Planning"; "Information Technology Investment Management". **Seminars:** Requests For Information; Pre Solicitation Marketing; Qualifications Statement Support For The Capital Planning And Investment Control (cpic) Process; How To Hire A Management Consultant And Get The Results You Expect.

2948 ■ **Papa and Associates Inc.**
200 Consumers Rd., Ste. 305
Toronto, ON, Canada M2J 4R4
Ph: (416)512-7272
Fax: (416)512-2016
Co. E-mail: ppapa@papa-associates.com
URL: http://www.papa-associates.com
Contact: Peter Papakostantinu, President
E-mail: ppapa@papa-associates.com
Scope: Provider of broad based management consulting services in the areas of quality assurance, environmental, health and safety and integrated management systems. **Founded:** 1989.

2949 ■ **Parker Consultants Inc.**
230 Mason St.
Greenwich, CT 06830-6633
Ph: (203)861-6698
Contact: Donald L. Parker, President
Scope: Firm specializes in strategic planning; organizational development; small business management; performance appraisals; executive searches; team building; and customer service audits. **Founded:** 1988.

2950 ■ **Partners for Market Leadership L.L.C.**
400 Galleria Pky., Ste. 1500
Atlanta, GA 30339
Ph: (770)850-1409
Free: 800-984-1110
Co. E-mail: dcarpenter@market-leadership.com
URL: http://www.market-leadership.com
Contact: Nancy Surdyka, Manager
E-mail: nsurdyka@market-leadership.com
Scope: Boutique consulting firm focused on assisting clients to develop sustainable market leadership in geographic, practice area and/or industry markets. Provides consulting on market leadership, revenue enhancement, strategic development and change facilitation. Additional services are offered to legal, accounting, valuation and financial firms. **Founded:** 1995.

2951 ■ **Pathways To Wellness**
617 Everhart Rd.
Corpus Christi, TX 78411
Ph: (361)985-9642
Fax: (361)949-4627
Co. E-mail: path2wellness@earthlink.net
URL: http://www.path2wellness.com
Contact: Evy Coppola, Owner
Scope: Offer natural holistic health counseling, yoga and hatha yoga classes, teachers training and cookery classes for individuals and companies. Health counseling includes nutritional guidance, kinesiology, iridology, reflexology, energy healing, massage therapy, herbal and vitamin therapy, creative visualization and meditation. Provides supplements which bring about the same effects as that of natural sunshine. **Founded:** 1988. **Seminars:** Is It You Holding You Back?; The Balancing Act. . .Career. . . Family. . .and Self; Learning the Art of Friendly Persuasion; Stop Accepting What You Are Getting and Start Asking for What You Want!; Introduction to Natural Health and Healthy Living; Learn Why One Size Approaches to the Answers on Health Do Not Work; Introduction to Yoga. What is it? Who can do it? What can it do for you.

2952 ■ **Performance Consulting Associates Inc. (PCA)**
3700 Crestwood Pky., Ste. 100
Duluth, GA 30096
Ph: (770)717-2737
Fax: (770)717-7014
Co. E-mail: info@pcaconsulting.com
URL: http://www.pcaconsulting.com
Contact: Richard A. Defazio, President
E-mail: defazio@pcaconsulting.com
Scope: Maintenance consulting and engineering firm specializing in production planning, project management, team building, and re-engineering maintenance. **Founded:** 1976. **Publications:** "Does Planning Pay," Plant Services, Nov, 2000; "Asset Reliability Coordinator," Maintenance Technology, Oct, 2000; "Know What it is You Have to Maintain," Maintenance Technology, May, 2000; "Does Mainte-

nance Planning Pay," Maintenance Technology, Nov, 2000.; "What is Asset Management?"; "Implementing Best Business Practices".

2953 ■ Performance Consulting Group Inc.
8031 SW 35th Terr.
Miami, FL 33155-3443
Ph: (305)264-5577
Fax: (305)264-9079
Contact: Patrick J. O'Brien, President
Scope: Firm provides consulting services in the areas of strategic planning; profit enhancement; product development; and production planning. **Founded:** 1980.

2954 ■ Performance Dynamics Group L.L.C.
1 Ridge Rd.
Green Brook, NJ 08812
Free: 888-720-7337
Co. E-mail: info@performance-dynamics.net
URL: http://www.performance-dynamics.net
Contact: Mark E. Green, President
E-mail: mark.green@performance-dynamics.net
Scope: An organizational consulting group whose approach to learning and employee empowerment is designed to be both effective and efficient in achieving the specific knowledge and skill goals of a given program, in developing changes in thinking and behavior and also to foster and develop initiative, self confidence, creative problem-solving ability and interpersonal effectiveness of all participants. Brings improvement in areas of revenue growth, profitability, sales, marketing effectiveness, and employee and customer loyalty. **Founded:** 2003. **Seminars:** Accelerated Approach to Change; Commitment to Quality; Managing Cultural Diversity; The Corporate Energizer; The Power Pole Experience; Team Assessment; Self-Directed Work Teams.

2955 ■ Practice Development Counsel
60 Sutton Pl. S
New York, NY 10022
Ph: (212)593-1549
Fax: (212)980-7940
Co. E-mail: pwhaserot@pdcounsel.com
URL: http://www.pdcounsel.com
Contact: Phyllis Weiss Haserot, President
E-mail: pwhaserot@pdcounsel.com
Scope: Specializes in business and organizaationdal development, and conflict resolution for professional firms. It serves the law, accounting, real estate, and management consulting organizations. **Founded:** 1982. **Publications:** "The Rainmaking Machine: Marketing Planning, Strategy and Management For Law Firms"; "The Marketer's Handbook of Tips & Checklists"; "Venturesome Questions: The Law Firms Guide to Developing a New Business Venture"; "Navigating the Whitewater of Internal Politics"; "Changing Attitudes on Firm Flexibility"; "Transition Planning: A Looming Challenge"; "Don't You Think the Solution Is to Bring In a Good Rainmaker?"; "Aligning Firm Culture with the Needs of the Times"; "What New Partners Need to Know"; "Dangers of Lack of Diversity"; "Learn to Respect Emotion in Business"; "What New Partners Need to Know"; "Taking Responsibility: Implementing Personal Marketing Plans"; "How to Change Unwritten Rules"; "Mentoring and Networking Converge"; "Integrating a New Practice into the Firm"; "Using Conflict Resolution Skills for Marketing Success"; "Sports Team Models for Law Firm Management". **Seminars:** Managing Work Expectations; Effective Coaching Skills; Service Quality; End-Running the Resistance Professionals Have to Getting Client Input; Ancillary Business Activities; Marketing for Professional Firms; Marketing Ethics; Business Development Training; Trends in Professional Services Marketing; Client Relationship Management; Collaborative Culture; Reaching Consensus; Conflict Resolution; Work life Balance; Generaltional Issues; Preparing New Partners; Becoming the Employer of Choice; A Marketing Approach to Recruiting; Implementing Workplace Flexibility; The Business Case for Flexible Work Arrangements.

2956 ■ Praxis Media Inc.
9 Twilight Pl.
Norwalk, CT 06854
Ph: (203)866-6666
Co. E-mail: aldo@praxismediainc.com
Contact: Christopher Campbell, President
Scope: Media needs analysis and project planning specialists provide services in product introductions, communications planning, technology application, promotion and marketing communications. Also assists with focus groups, research, concept development, creative development, scripting and executive speech coaching/training. Industries served: Financial services, high-tech, travel and leisure, health and pharmaceutical and telecommunications. **Founded:** 1979.

2957 ■ Professional Counseling Centers Inc.
543 Coventry Way
Noblesville, IN 46062-9024
Ph: (317)877-3111
Contact: Jack W. Schinderle, President
Scope: Business counselors offering services in the following areas: employee assistance, managed care, alcohol and drug treatment, labor and union consultation, and industrial mental health.

2958 ■ Public Policy Communications
4163 Dingman Dr.
Sanibel, FL 33957
Ph: (941)395-6773
Fax: (941)395-6779
Contact: Robert Schaeffer, President
E-mail: bobschaeffer@earthlink.net
Scope: Provides strategic communications for progressive causes, candidates and socially-responsible businesses. These include public relations strategies, political campaign planning, organizational development and training. Substantial work in report writing, editing and design as well as production of a full range of media materials. Industries served: nonprofit, social change organizations, foundations, political campaigns, environmentally and consumer-oriented businesses, government agencies. **Founded:** 1985. **Publications:** "Winning Local and State Elections," Free Press MacMillan; "Giving the Media Your Message, and The News Media and the Big Lie". **Seminars:** Giving the Media Your Message; Effective Public Relations Practices; Winning Your Election; Understanding the Government Budget Process; How to Be an Effective Advocate; Strategic Planning for Non-Profits; How to Run a News Conference: Ten Key Steps, 1998.

2959 ■ Public Sector Consultants Inc. (PSC)
600 W St. Joseph St., Ste. 10
Lansing, MI 48933-2267
Ph: (517)484-4954
Fax: (517)484-6549
Co. E-mail: psc@pscinc.com
URL: http://www.pscinc.com
Contact: William R. Rustem, President
E-mail: wrustem@pscinc.com
Scope: Offers policy research expertise, specializing in opinion polling, public relations, conference planning, and legislative and economic analysis. Industries served: Associations, education, environment, health-care, and public finance. **Founded:** 1980. **Publications:** "The New Landscape of Civic Business: How Business Leadership Is Influencing Civic Progress in Our Metropolitan Regions Today," Feb, 2012; "Saginaw Bay Watershed and Area of Concern," Mar, 2012; "Michigan Public School Employees Retirement System: Major Changes in Recent Years and More Changes to Come," May, 2012; "Saginaw River/Bay Area of Concern: Restoration Plan for the Habitat and Populations BUIs," Sep, 2012; "Proposal 3: Key Questions and Answers," Sep, 2012; "Final Report of the Michigan State Park and Recreation Blue Ribbon Panel," Oct, 2012; "The Impact of Reducing PIP Coverage in Michigan," Sep, 2011; "Michigan Sales Tax Collection and the Internet: A Need for Fairness," Sep, 2011; "Ingham Community Voices Final Evaluation Report," Nov, 2008; "First Class Schools Analysis," Aug, 2008; "Opportunities for Achieving Efficiency in the Aging, Community Mental Health, Local Public Health, and Substance Abuse Coordinating Agency Networks," Aug, 2008; "Saginaw River Bay Area of Concern," Jun, 2008; "Portage Lake Water shed Forever Plan," May, 2008; "Smoke Free Workplaces," Apr, 2008; "Protecting and Restoring the Upper Looking Glass River," Feb, 2008;

"Market Structures and the 21st Century Energy Plan," Sep, 2007; "The Growing Crisis of Aging Dams," Apr, 2007; "Financing Community Health Workers Why and How," Jan, 2007; "Hastings Area: Inter local Approaches to Growth Management," Jan, 2007; "Michigan's Part 201 Environmental Remediation Program Review," Jan, 2007.

2960 ■ The Purchasing Department (TPD)
34 Claremont Ave.
Maplewood, NJ 07040-2118
Fax: (973)275-0749
Co. E-mail: eostpd@aol.com
Contact: James T. Milway, Principal
E-mail: jtmtpd@aol.com
Scope: Provides state of the art procurement arrangements, process re-engineering and outsourcing assistance to any business wishing to achieve purchasing savings and efficiencies to improve bottom line results. Available to provide contract services to businesses requiring specialized supplemental assistance to back up own personnel on special projects. **Founded:** 1992. **Seminars:** Green Purchasing: Buying Recycled Products; Ethics; Measuring Purchasing Performance; Supplier Teaming and Quality; Preparing for ISO 9000 in the Purchasing Department.

2961 ■ Queens Business Consulting (QBC)
Queens School of Business, Goodes Hall, 143 Union St.
Kingston, ON, Canada K7L 3N6
Ph: (613)533-2309
Fax: (613)533-2370
Co. E-mail: qbc@business.queensu.ca
URL: http://www.qsbc.com
Contact: Michelle Miatello, Director
E-mail: mmiatello@business.queensu.ca
Scope: Provides business plans, feasibility studies, financial planning, competitor analysis, market research, marketing strategies, production planning and systems implementation. **Founded:** 1973. **Publications:** "Information technology, network structure and competitive action. Information Systems Research," 2010; "The role of dominance in the appeal of violent media depictions. Journal of Advertising," 2010; "Great expectations and broken promises: Misleading claims, product failure, expectancy disconfirmation and consumer distrust. Journal of the Academy of Marketing Science," 2010; "Development and psychometric properties of the Transformational Teaching Questionnaire. Journal of Health Psychology," 2010; ". Predicting workplace aggression: myths, realities, and remaining questions," 2009; "The Inconvenient Truth about Improving Vehicle Fuel Efficiency: An MultiAttribute Analysis of the Efficient Frontier of the U.S. Automobile Industry, Transportation Research-Part," 2009; "Fraud in Canadian Nonprofit Organizations as Seen through the Eyes of Canadian Newspapers," 2009; "Disentangling the Indirect Links between SES and Health: The Dynamic Roles of Work Stressors and Personal Contro," 2009; "The strong situation hypothesis. Personality and Social Psychology Review," 2009; " Planning Your Next Crisis Decisively and Effectively. Ivey Business Journal," 2009. **Seminars:** Enabling Innovation Discussion Highlights, 2011; Intellectual Capital, 2010; On the diffusion of knowledge inside the organization, 2010; A model of the tacit knowledge lifecycle for decision-making: From creation to utilization, 2010; Individual, group, and organizational learning; A knowledge management perspective, 2009; Political economies of knowledge, with an example, 2009; The alignment of business and knowledge strategies and structures, 2009; Using IT To Support the Discovery of Novel Knowledge in Organizations, 2008; Leadership: Knowledge Management by a New Name?, 2007; Every User Tells a Story, 2007.

2962 ■ Rental Relocation Inc. (RRI)
281 S Atlanta St.
Roswell, GA 30075
Ph: (770)641-8393
Free: 800-641-7368
Fax: (770)641-8607
Co. E-mail: ahlsinfo@rentalrelocation.com
URL: http://www.rentalrelocation.com
Contact: Christopher Bliss, President
E-mail: cbliss@rentalrelocation.com
Scope: Relocation firm offering services in corporate housing, rentals, free metro Atlanta apartment locat-

ing service, property management, house and condo rental relocation tours. **Founded:** 1989.

2963 ■ Rose & Crangle Ltd.
117 N 4th St.
Lincoln, KS 67455
Ph: (785)524-5050
Fax: (785)524-3130
Co. E-mail: rcltd@nckcn.com
URL: http://www.roseandcrangle.com
Contact: Robert D. Crangle, President
E-mail: rcltd@nckcn.com
Scope: Provider of evaluation, planning and policy analyzes for universities, associations, foundations, governmental agencies and private companies engaged in scientific, technological or educational activities. Special expertise in the development of new institutions. Special skills in providing planning and related group facilitation workshops. **Founded:** 1984. **Publications:** "Preface to Bulgarian Integration Into Europe and NATO: Issues of Science Policy And research Evaluation Practice," Ios Press, 2006; "Allocating Limited National Resources for Fundamental Research," 2005.

2964 ■ Rothschild Strategies Unlimited L.L.C.
19 Thistle Rd.
Norwalk, CT 06851-1909
Ph: (203)846-6898
Fax: (203)847-1426
Co. E-mail: bill@strategyleader.com
URL: http://www.strategyleader.com
Contact: Stephen M. Rothschild, President
Scope: Consults with senior management and business level strategy teams to develop overall strategic direction, set priorities and creates sustainable competitive advantages and differentiators. Enables organizations to enhance their own strategic thinking and leadership skills so that they can continue to develop and implement profitable growth strategies. **Founded:** 1983. **Publications:** "Putting It All Together-a guide to strategic thinking"; "Competitive Advantage"; "Ristaker, Caretaker, Surgeon & Undertaker four faces of strategic leadership"; "The Secret to GE's Success"; "Having the Right Strategic Leader and Team".

2965 ■ Sanford Consulting
52 Perry Corners Rd., RR 1
Amenia, NY 12501
Ph: (845)373-8960
Fax: (845)373-8961
Co. E-mail: sanford@mohawk.com
Contact: Anne Sanford, President
E-mail: sanford@mohawk.com
Scope: Helps businesses find, sell, to, and keep customers. Provides management and marketing services, including problem analysis and solution design for new business development, market analysis and segmentation, departmental organization and administrative policies and procedures. Industries served: small business, telecommunications, professional services, health care and nonprofits in the continental United States. **Founded:** 1986. **Seminars:** Trade show success; Finding customers; Business attitudes at not for profit and others.

2966 ■ SBR International—SBR Global
30 Adelaide St. E, Ste. 600
The Graeme Bldg.
Toronto, ON, Canada M5C 3G8
Ph: (416)962-7500
Fax: (416)962-7505
Co. E-mail: bizdev@sbr-global.com
URL: http://www.sbr-global.com
Contact: Kevin Gauci, Managing Director
Scope: Specializes in the leasing of multi-disciplinary, high-performance work teams at customer in-house cost, under a mixed military/general contracting model. Engagements include BPR, IE, SA, market and competitor intelligence, logistics, strategy, audit, workouts/turnarounds, M and A support/targeting, statistics and micro-economic modeling, PMO support. **Founded:** 1979. **Seminars:** Electronic counter measures; Strategic planning; Project management. **Telecommunication Services:** info@optimussbr. com.

2967 ■ Schneider Consulting Group Inc.
50 S Steele St., Ste. 390
Denver, CO 80209-2834
Ph: (303)320-4413
Fax: (303)320-5795
Contact: Kim Schneider Malek, Vice President
E-mail: kim@scgfambus.com
Scope: Assists family-owned and privately-held business transition to the next generation and/or to a more professionally managed company, turn around consulting for small and medium size companies. **Founded:** 1987.

2968 ■ Scott Ashby Teleselling Inc.
1102 Ben Franklin Dr., Ste. 309
Sarasota, FL 34236
Ph: (941)388-4283
Fax: (941)388-5240
URL: http://www.scottashbyteleselling.com
Contact: R. Scott Ashby, President
E-mail: rscottashby@netscape.net
Scope: Provider of consulting services and customized training programs that emphasize consultative telephone selling techniques. **Founded:** 1979. **Publications:** "How Will the Internet Affect Teleselling Programs?"; "When is Telemarketing Really Not Telemarketing?"; "The Future of Account Management Telesales". **Seminars:** Start-Up Educational, Planning and Strategy Development; Existing Program Audit, Evaluation, State-of-the-Art Best Practices Comparison, Tracking and Measurement Review, Systems and Procedures Analysis, and Optional Selling Skills; Develop New or Revised Consultative Telephone Selling; Helping Clients Build Relationship and Grow Their Business by Phone.

2969 ■ Sklar and Associates Inc.
242 Laurel Bay Dr.
Murrells Inlet, SC 29576
Ph: (843)798-0412
Fax: (843)651-3090
Co. E-mail: sklarincdc@aol.com
URL: http://www.sklarinc.com
Contact: Tim Sklar, President
Scope: Provider of consulting services for business acquisitions, business development and project finance. Provides audit oversight services to listed corporations on Sarbanes-Oxley compliance. Services include: Due diligence analyses and corporate governance. Industries served: transportation sectors, energy sector and commercial real estate industries. **Seminars:** Financial Analysis in MBA; Emerging Company Finance; Due Diligence in Business Acquisition; Business Valuation.

2970 ■ S.B. Smith Consulting Group Inc. (SBS)—SBS Consulting Group Inc.
837 Millwood Rd.
Toronto, ON, Canada M4G 1W5
Ph: (416)467-0011
Fax: (416)467-0071
Co. E-mail: susan@sbsconsulting.ca
URL: http://www.sbsconsulting.ca
Contact: Susan Smith, President
E-mail: susan@sbsconsulting.ca
Scope: Seeks to help overworked and overstressed entrepreneurs regain effective control and release ineffective control. **Founded:** 2000. **Publications:** "What You Can Measure, You Can Manage"; "Leadership By Design"; "How To Find Success in Succession When It's All About The Owner"; "Financial Management - The Right Kind of Numbers"; "Managing The Details - A Professional Service Firm"; "Think and Plan Strategically". **Seminars:** Advisory Boards - Accelerating Success; Alternative Growth Strategies Beyond Succession; Leadership - Understanding Styles and Developing new Leaders; Facing Change Head On - Avoiding Frustrations and Mistrust; Hiring Right and Retaining the Best; Keeping Your Balance - Walking the Cash Flow Tightrope; Strategic Planning - Begin with the End in Mind; What You Can Measure You Can Measure - Developing Polices and Procedures; Understanding your Financial Statements; Financial Management - Beyond the Basics.

2971 ■ Straightline Services Inc.
11 Centre St., Ste. 10
Salem, CT 06420-3845
Ph: (860)889-7929

Fax: (860)885-1894
Co. E-mail: straitln@aol.com
Contact: Wayne J. S. France, President
Scope: Design and implementation of organizational infrastructure, business plans and troubleshooting. Emphasizes on operations with a central and field or satellite offices. Industries served: Construction, resorts, Indian tribes, academies, small-medium sized business, mostly privately held. **Founded:** 1994.

2972 ■ Technology Management Group Co.—Ratafia Ventures
PO Box 3260
New Haven, CT
Ph: (203)387-1430
Fax: (203)387-1470
Co. E-mail: info@commtechsoftware.com
URL: http://www.ratafia.net
Contact: Manny Ratafia, President
E-mail: manny@commtechsoftware.com
Scope: Consulting services include analysis of market opportunities; product introductions; new ventures; acquisitions analysis; licensing, joint ventures, and OEM arrangements. Emphasis on polymers, medical devices, biotechnology, pharmaceuticals, and chemicals. **Founded:** 1981. **Telecommunication Services:** manny@ratafia.net. **Special Services:** CommTechPowerSearch®.

2973 ■ TQM Consulting
1821 Lodgepole Dr.
Kamloops, BC, Canada V1S 1X7
Ph: (250)828-0420
Fax: (250)828-6859
Co. E-mail: info@tqmconsulting.ca
URL: http://www.tqmconsulting.ca
Contact: Don Anderson, President
Scope: Provides individuals and organizations with a competitive edge through our training and consulting services. **Founded:** 1993. **Seminars:** Pre-Entrepreneurial Program for Human Resources Development.

2974 ■ Trendzitions Inc.
25691 Atlantic Ocean, Ste. B13
Lake Forest, CA 92630-8842
Ph: (949)727-9100
Free: 800-266-2767
Fax: (949)727-3444
Co. E-mail: ctooker@trendzitions.com
URL: http://www.trendzitions.com
Contact: Christian Tooker, President
E-mail: ctooker@trendzitions.com
Scope: Provider of services in the areas of communications consulting, project management, construction management, and furniture procurement. Offers information on spatial uses, building codes, ADA compliance and city ordinances. Also offers budget projections. **Founded:** 1986.

2975 ■ Turnaround Inc.
3415 A St. NW
Gig Harbor, WA 98335
Ph: (253)857-6730
Fax: (253)857-6344
Co. E-mail: info@turnround-inc.com
URL: http://www.turnaround-inc.com
Contact: Miles Stover, President
E-mail: mstover@turnaround-inc.com
Scope: Provider of interim executive management assistance and management advisory to small, medium and family-owned businesses that are not meeting their goals. Services include acting as an interim executive or on-site manager. Extensive practices in arena of bankruptcy management. **Founded:** 1997. **Publications:** "How to Identify Problem and Promising Management"; "How to Tell if Your Company is a Bankruptcy Candidate"; "Signs that Your Company is in Trouble"; "The Turnaround Specialist: How to File a Petition Under 11 USC 11". **Seminars:** Competitive Intelligence Gathering.

2976 ■ ValueNomics Value Specialists
50 W San Fernando St., Ste. 600
San Jose, CA 95113

Fax: (408)200-6401
Co. E-mail: info@amllp.com
Contact: Gary E. Jones, Chief Executive Officer
Scope: Consulting is offered in the areas of financial management, process re-engineering, growth business services; governance, risk/compliance, SOX readiness and compliance, SAS 70, enterprise risk management, system security, operational and internal audit; business advisory services; valuation services; CORE assessment; contract assurance; transaction advisory services, IT solutions and litigation support services. **Founded:** 1993. **Publications:** "Dueling Appraisers: How Differences in Input and Assumptions May Control the Value," Apr, 2005; "The Business of Business Valuation and the CPA as an expert witness"; "The Business of Business Valuation," McGraw-Hill Professional Publishers Inc.

2977 ■ Via Nova Consulting
1228 Winburn Dr.
Atlanta, GA 30344
Ph: (404)761-7484
Fax: (404)762-7123
Scope: Consulting services in the areas of strategic planning; privatization; executive searches; market research; customer service audits; new product development; competitive intelligence; and Total Quality Management (TQM). **Founded:** 1994.

2978 ■ Vision Management
149 Meadows Rd.
Lafayette, NJ 07848-3120
Ph: (973)702-1116
Fax: (973)702-8311
Contact: Norman L. Naidish, President
Scope: Firm specializes in profit enhancement; strategic planning; business process reengineering; industrial engineering; facilities planning; team building; inventory management; and total quality management (TQM). **Founded:** 1984. **Publications:** "To increase profits, improve quality," Manufacturing Engineering, May, 2000.

2979 ■ The Visioneering Institute
2780 rue de Lanoraie St.
Quebec, QC, Canada G1W 1M4
Ph: (418)948-1553
Free: 888-788-8844
Co. E-mail: info@visioneering-institute.com
URL: http://www.visioneering-institute.com
Contact: Davender Gupta, President
E-mail: davender@davender.com
Scope: Supports entrepreneurs to create high-performance organizations that unlock the potential of every member of the team, through coaching, consulting, training and leadership. Areas include leadership training, corporate retreat facilitation, mission and vision statement building and corporate culture assessment. **Founded:** 1998. **Seminars:** High Performance Success Coaching; "From Passion to Profit" Success Experience; The "Power Circle" Productivity Experience.

2980 ■ The Walk The Talk Co.—Performance Systems Corp.
1100 Parker Sq., Ste. 250
Flower Mound, TX 75028-7458
Ph: (972)899-8300
Free: 800-888-2811
Fax: (972)899-9291
Co. E-mail: info@walkthetalk.com
URL: http://www.walkthetalk.com
Contact: Eric L. Harvey, President
E-mail: ericharvey@walkthetalk.com
Scope: Assists a wide variety of organizations in implementing proprietary performance management system developed by the firm which concentrates on individual responsibility and decision making instead of disciplinary penalties. Helps organizations develop and implement peer review, a proven system that helps solve employee problems in a remarkable way-through employees and an evaluation process software is used whereby feedback is compiled from a full-range of sources, including a self-evaluation, leadership development workshops and keynote presentations and publications. **Founded:** 1977. **Publications:** "Positive Discipline"; "Leadership Secrets of Santa Claus"; "Leadership Secrets of Santa Claus"; "Start Right-Stay Right"; "Walk Awhile in My Shoes"; "Listen Up, Leader!"; "Five Star Teamwork"; "Ethics4Everyone"; "Leadership Courage"; "The Manager's Communication Handbook"; "180 Ways to Walk the Recognition Talk"; "The Manager's Coaching Handbook"; "The Best Leadership Advice I Ever Got"; "Power Exchange". **Seminars:** Walk the Talk; Coaching for Continuous Improvement; Managing Employee Performance; Customized Management Development Forums; Keynote presentations; Leadership Development Workshops; Consulting Services and Publications; Customer service training; Ethics and Values training.

2981 ■ Weich & Bilotti Inc.
600 Worcester Rd., 4th Fl.
Framingham, MA 01702
Ph: (508)663-1600
Fax: (508)663-1682
Co. E-mail: info@weich-bilotti.com
Contact: Mervyn D. Weich, Director
E-mail: mweich@weich-bilotti.com
Scope: Specializes in business plans, venture capital, computer information systems, turnaround/interim management, retail consulting, start-up process, college recruiting and IS and IT personnel. **Founded:** 1995.

2982 ■ Western Business Services Ltd.
1269 Lindsay St.
Regina, SK, Canada S4N 3B4
Ph: (306)522-1493
Fax: (306)522-9076
Contact: O'Neil Zuck, President
Scope: Provides marketing, financial and accounting services to individuals, on-profit organizations and commercial companies. **Founded:** 1992.

2983 ■ Wheeler and Young Inc.
33 Peter St.
Markham, ON, Canada L3P 2A5
Ph: (905)471-5709
Fax: (905)471-9989
Co. E-mail: wheeler@ericwheeler.ca
URL: http://www.ericwheeler.ca
Contact: Eric S. Wheeler, Managing Partner
E-mail: ewheeler@yorku.ca
Scope: Provider of consulting services to high-tech companies on the implementation of software development processes; quality management systems (including ISO 9000 compliance) and business management systems. Offers business management and knowledge-management services to organizations. Industries served: Knowledge-based industries, including software and hardware development, medical and legal professionals, information service providers. **Founded:** 1994.

2984 ■ Zolfo Cooper L.L.C.
Grace Bldg., 1114 Ave. of the Americas, 41st Fl.
New York, NY 10036
Ph: (212)561-4000
Fax: (212)213-1749
Co. E-mail: rrandall@zolfocooper.com
URL: http://www.zolfocooper.com
Contact: Mark Cervi, Director
Scope: Provider of accounting consulting services to businesses. Specializes in restructuring and turnaround consulting; interim and crisis management; performance improvement; creditor advisory; cross-border restructuring and corporate finance. **Founded:** 1985.

2985 ■ ZS Engineering P.C. (ZSE)
99 Tulip Ave.
Floral Park, NY 11001
Ph: (516)328-3200
Fax: (516)328-6195
Co. E-mail: office@zsengineering.com
URL: http://www.zsengineering.com
Contact: Zygmunt Staszewski, President
E-mail: staszewski@zsengineering.com
Scope: Offers engineering consulting services to building owners, building managers and contractors. Specializes in design and inspections of fire alarm systems, sprinkler systems, smoke control systems, building evaluations for fire code compliance, violations removal. **Founded:** 1989. **Seminars:** Fire protection courses for contractors and building management.

FRANCHISES AND BUSINESS OPPORTUNITIES

2986 ■ ABX-Associates Business Xchange
7604 Oak St.
Frisco, TX 75034
Ph: (214)850-6131
Fax: (866)462-7229
Description: Nationwide franchise brokers network. **Founded:** 1971..

2987 ■ ActionCoach
5781 S Fort Apache
Las Vegas, NV 89118
Ph: (702)795-3188
Fax: (702)795-3183
Description: Business consulting and coaching service. **No. of Franchise Units:** 262. **No. of Company-Owned Units:** 23. **No. of Operating Units:** 315. **Founded:** 1993.. **Franchised:** 1997. **Equity Capital Needed:** $68,750-$473,530. **Franchise Fee:** $35,000-$275,000. **Royalty Fee:** $1,500-$1,800/month. **Financial Assistance:** Limited third party financing available. **Training:** Offers 10 days at headquarters, 10 days at various locations with ongoing support.

2988 ■ Alliance Cost Containment LLC
222 S First St., Ste. 301
Louisville, KY 40202
Ph: (502)635-3208
Fax: (502)238-1830
Description: Expense-reduction consulting services. **No. of Franchise Units:** 28. **No. of Company-Owned Units:** 1. **Founded:** 1992.. **Franchised:** 2004. **Equity Capital Needed:** $47,600-$64,600. **Franchise Fee:** $34,500. **Royalty Fee:** 9%. **Training:** Training includes 3-4 days at headquarters, 3 days at annual conference and ongoing support.

2989 ■ Alpha Legal Forms & More, Inc.
Alpha Publications of America, Inc.
PO Box 12488
Tucson, AZ 85732
Ph: (520)795-7100
Free: 800-770-4329
Description: Legal forms. **Founded:** 1976..

2990 ■ The Alternative Board (TAB)
Tab Boards International, Inc.
11031 Sheridan Blvd.
Westminster, CO 80020
Ph: (303)839-4744
Free: 800-727-0126
Fax: (303)839-0012
Description: Coordination of advisory business groups. **No. of Franchise Units:** 143. **No. of Company-Owned Units:** 1. **Founded:** 1990.. **Franchised:** 1996. **Equity Capital Needed:** $85,121-$96,021. **Franchise Fee:** $44,000. **Training:** Training available at headquarters for 6 days and 4 weeks onsite with monthly/quarterly conference calls.

2991 ■ American Association of Franchisees & Dealers (AAFD)
3500 5th Ave.
San Diego, CA 92103
Ph: (619)209-3775
Free: 800-733-9858
Fax: (619)209-3777
Co. E-mail: benefits@aafd.org
URL: http://www.aafd.org
Contact: Peter Hanson, President
Description: Franchisees and business services. **Scope:** A nonprofit organization providing referrals and other member benefits and services for franchisees. **Founded:** 1992. **Publications:** "Nsights the Art of Positive Emotions," Sep-Oct, 2003; "Nsights Understanding Basic Human Behaviors at Work," Aug, 2003; "Nsights Pinkerton," Aug, 2002. **Educational Activities:** Total Quality Franchising (Annual). **Awards:** Fair Franchising Seal (Periodic). **Seminars:** Driving Your Association to the Next Level; Keeping your Association on the Fairway: Re-Model and Re-Imaging in Today's Economy; Avoid being an Association duffer: Recruiting and Retaining Membership Dos and Don'ts!; Clubhouse Chatter: The Most Cost Effective Ways to Communicate.

2992 ■ American Franchise Consultants

520 W Gleneagles Dr.
Phoenix, AZ 85023
Free: 800-424-0749
Description: Business consultants. **Founded:** 1995..

2993 ■ Crestcom International, Ltd.

6900 E Belleview Ave., 3rd Fl.
Greenwood Village, CO 80111
Ph: (303)267-8200
Fax: (303)267-8207
Co. E-mail: franchiseinfo@crestcom.com
URL: http://www.crestcom.com
Description: Business centers around marketing and conducting video-based management and sales training. Training is a combination of video instruction, featuring renowned business and management personalities, and hands-on monthly seminars. Training is currently used by many leading organizations throughout the world. **No. of Franchise Units:** 200. **Founded:** 1987.. **Franchised:** 1992. **Equity Capital Needed:** $12,500-$62,500. **Franchise Fee:** $12,500-$62,500. **Financial Assistance:** Yes. **Training:** Initial classroom and field training, ongoing training, a lead assistance program.

2994 ■ Criterium Engineers

22 Monument Sq., Ste. 600
Portland, ME 04101
Ph: (207)828-1969
Fax: (207)775-4405
Description: Nationwide network of registered professional engineers, specializing in buildings and related consulting services. Services include residential and commercial inspections, insurance investigations, environmental assessments, capital reserve studies, design and related services. Clients include buyers, building owners and managers, lenders, attorneys, insurance companies and government agencies. Customized software and unlimited toll-free support. **No. of Franchise Units:** 71. **Founded:** 1957.. **Franchised:** 1958. **Equity Capital Needed:** $41,000-$64,000. **Franchise Fee:** $26,500. **Financial Assistance:** Yes. **Training:** Yes.

2995 ■ Days Inns-Canada

Realstar Hotel Services Corp.
77 Bloor St. W, Ste. 2000
Toronto, ON, Canada M5S 1M2
Ph: (416)966-8387
Free: 800-840-8162
Fax: (416)923-5424
Co. E-mail: irwin.prince@daysinn.ca
URL: http://www.daysinn.ca
Description: Has established franchised properties in all major cities across the country in the moderate-priced segment of the market. **No. of Franchise Units:** 96. **Founded:** 1992.. **Franchised:** 1992. **Equity Capital Needed:** $5,000,000. **Franchise Fee:** $350/room, minimum $35,000 and $10,000. **Royalty Fee:** Marketing fee included in Royalty Fee 6.5%, reservation fee 2.3% of gross. **Training:** Training provided at opening and ongoing. Site selection and advisory council are provided.

2996 ■ DirectBuild

DirectBuild Franchising, LLC
19201 E Mainstreet, Ste. 103
Parker, CO 80134
Ph: (303)805-9294
Fax: (720)851-7160
Description: Home building & remodeling consulting. **No. of Franchise Units:** 1. **No. of Company-Owned Units:** 2. **Founded:** 1995.. **Franchised:** 2006. **Equity Capital Needed:** $176,000. **Franchise Fee:** $29,900. **Royalty Fee:** 7%. **Training:** Available 2 weeks at headquarters, 3 days at franchisee's location and ongoing support.

2997 ■ ESAPP Financial, LLC

6520 E 82nd St., Ste.200
Indianapolis, IN 46250
Ph: (317)577-4995
Fax: (317)577-4996
Description: Financial services company. **Founded:** 1996..

2998 ■ Expense Reduction Analysts

5050 Avenida Encinas, Ste. 200
Carlsbad, CA 92008
Ph: (760)712-3600
Fax: (760)712-3700
Description: Cost management consultancy. **No. of Franchise Units:** 246. **No. of Company-Owned Units:** 5. **Founded:** 1992.. **Franchised:** 2003. **Equity Capital Needed:** $65,000-$300,000. **Franchise Fee:** $59,900-$250,000. **Training:** Yes.

2999 ■ FD & MG Franchise Company Inc.

949 E Pioneer Rd., Ste. B-2
Draper, UT 84020
Ph: (801)352-1400
Fax: (801)619-4038
Description: Franchise consulting. **No. of Franchise Units:** 2. **No. of Company-Owned Units:** 1. **Founded:** 2003.. **Franchised:** 2007. **Equity Capital Needed:** $120,500-$152,100. **Franchise Fee:** $75,000. **Royalty Fee:** 6%. **Financial Assistance:** Third party financing and limited in-house financing available. **Training:** Includes 2 weeks training at headquarters and ongoing support.

3000 ■ Focal Point Business Coaching

5740 S Eastern Ave., Ste. 100
Las Vegas, NV
Ph: (702)932-3870
Free: 877-433-6225
Fax: (702)932-3871
URL: http://www.focalpointcoaching.com
Description: Business coaching and consulting. **No. of Franchise Units:** 72. **Founded:** 1999.. **Franchised:** 2005. **Equity Capital Needed:** $49,950-$115,450. **Franchise Fee:** $40,000. **Royalty Fee:** $1,800/month. **Training:** Provides 1 week at headquarters, 2 months at franchisee's location, virtual training and ongoing support.

3001 ■ Franchise Compliance, Inc.

PO Box 982662
Park City, UT 84098
Ph: (435)757-5071
Fax: (435)563-0163
Description: Provides franchise services and mystery shopping.

3002 ■ Franchise Consultants, Inc.

558 S Osprey Ave.
Sarasota, FL 34236
Ph: (866)372-6484
Fax: (941)954-8462
Description: UFOC preparation, registration and franchise sales. **Founded:** 1986..

3003 ■ Franchise Development International, LLC

370 SE 15 Ave.
Pompano Beach, FL 33060
Ph: (954)942-9424
Fax: (954)783-5177
Description: Franchise development and marketing. **Founded:** 1991..

3004 ■ Franchise Development & Marketing Group

Franchise Development & Marketing Group, Inc.
949 E Pioneer Rd., Ste. 2B
Draper, UT 84020
Ph: (801)352-1400
Fax: (801)619-4038
Description: Assist businesses in all franchise phase. **Founded:** 2003..

3005 ■ Franchise Developments Inc. (FDI)

5001 Baum Blvd., Ste. 660
Pittsburgh, PA 15213
Ph: (412)687-8484
Free: 800-576-5115
Fax: (412)687-0541
Co. E-mail: franchise-dev@earthlink.net
URL: http://www.franchise-dev.com
Contact: Kenneth Franklin, President
Description: Develop, implement and launch franchise programs. **Scope:** Offers clients full development services for the purpose of designing and implementing a total franchise program. **Founded:** 1970. **Publications:** "Franchising Your Business,"

May/Jun, 2003; "Female Entrepreneur," May/Jun, 2003; "Franchising World," May/Jun, 2003; "Canadian Business Franchise," Jul/Aug, 2000. **Seminars:** Has presented franchising seminars under auspices of American Management Association, Management Center Europe and International Franchise Association. Recent programs include Expanding Your Business by Franchising; Writing Effective Franchise Operations Manuals. Also has franchise seminar on Prodigy.

3006 ■ Franchise Foundations

4157 23rd St.
San Francisco, CA 94114
Free: 800-942-4402
Description: Franchise consulting. **Founded:** 1980..

3007 ■ Franchise Recruiters Ltd.

Saddlebrooke Country Club
63284 E Flower Ridge Dr.
Tucson, AZ 85739
Ph: (520)825-9588
Description: Placement of franchise management professionals. **Founded:** 1977..

3008 ■ Franchise Sales

1315 S Villa Ave.
Villa Park, IL 60181
Ph: (630)819-2418
Description: Self franchisees in business now. **Founded:** 1991..

3009 ■ Franchise Search, Inc.

Kushell Associates Inc.
48 Burd St., Ste. 101
Nyack, NY 10960
Ph: (845)727-4103
Description: International executive search firm for franchisors. **Founded:** 1982..

3010 ■ Franchise Selection Specialists Inc.

14408 E Carroll Blvd.
Cleveland, OH 44118
Ph: (216)831-2610
Fax: (216)765-7118
Description: Franchise related advice and consulting. **Founded:** 1990..

3011 ■ Franchise Specialists, Inc.

1234 Maple St. Ext.
Moon Twp., PA 15108
Ph: (412)262-5055
Description: Professional franchise development and sales. **Founded:** 1978..

3012 ■ Franchise Strategies Group, Inc.

6594 Andromeda Way
Spring Hill, FL 34606
Ph: (352)556-2430
Description: Franchise consultants. **Founded:** 1984..

3013 ■ FranchiseInc!

2148 Pelham Pky., Bldg. 300
Pelham, AL 35124
Free: 800-961-0420
Fax: (205)682-2939
Description: Franchise consulting service. **No. of Franchise Units:** 24. **No. of Company-Owned Units:** 1. **Founded:** 1995.. **Franchised:** 2006. **Equity Capital Needed:** $36,600-$48,500. **Franchise Fee:** $29,500. **Training:** Includes 5 days training at headquarters, 52 weeks mentoring via teleconference and ongoing support.

3014 ■ FranchiseKnowHow L.L.C.

PO Box 714
Stony Brook, NY 11790
Ph: (631)246-5782
Fax: (631)689-6905
Co. E-mail: ed@franchiseknowhow.com
URL: http://www.franchiseknowhow.com
Contact: Ed Teixeira, President
E-mail: edteixeira@netzero.com
Description: Franchise consulting service. **Scope:** Firm provides a full range of services to companies who desire to begin a franchise operation. Other areas of expertise include international franchising. **Founded:** 2003. **Publications:** "Flame"; "Franchising From the Inside Out"; "The Benefits of Acquiring an

Existing Franchise Business"; "Meeting the Franchisor"; "Negotiating the Franchise Agreement," Franchise Trade; "Franchising Your Company," Franchise Trade; "How Franchisees Can Promote Positive Franchise Relations," Franchise Trade; "Meeting the Franchisor," Fracnhisehandbook.Com; "Franchising an Independent Business," Franchise Trade; "Key Factors in Evaluating and Operating a Franchise"; "Understanding the Chinese Market"; "Utilizing Your Franchise Attorney to Maintain and Promote Positive"; "Going International"; "Establishing a Franchise Program". **Seminars:** Meeting the Franchisor. **Telecommunication Services:** franchiseknowhow@gmail.com. **Special Services:** FLAME®.

3015 ■ FranchiseMart / Biz1Brokers
2121 Vista Pky.
West Palm Beach, FL 33411
Ph: (877)757-6550
Fax: (561)478-4340
Co. E-mail: franchise@franchisemart.com
URL: http://www.franchisemart.com
Description: Franchise consulting services. **No. of Franchise Units:** 5. **Founded:** 2006.. **Franchised:** 2007. **Equity Capital Needed:** $30,000-$35,000 initial, total investment $110,000-$115,000. **Franchise Fee:** $29,500. **Financial Assistance:** Yes. **Training:** Yes.

3016 ■ Franchises Unlimited Network LLC
36601 Samoa Dr.
Sterling Heights, MI 48312
Free: 866-583-5311
Description: Franchise consulting service.

3017 ■ Francorp Inc.
20200 Governors Dr.
Olympia Fields, IL 60461
Ph: (708)481-2900
Free: 800-372-6244
Fax: (708)481-5885
Co. E-mail: info@francorp.com
URL: http://www.francorp.com
Contact: Ramon Vinay, President
Description: Offers consultancy on franchising business. Consultants have provided full development programs, including feasibility studies, business plans, legal documents, operations manuals, and marketing materials for clients since 1976. **Scope:** A management consulting firm specializing in franchise development. Provides full development programs, including feasibility studies, business plans, legal documents, operations manuals and marketing materials. Also provides post-development services for established franchisers including lead generation programs, franchise brochures, videotapes, international brokerage, public relations and expert witness services. **Founded:** 1976. **Training:** Provides post-development services for establishing franchisors, including lead generation programs, brochures, videotapes, international brokerage, PR, and expert witness service. **Seminars:** Franchise Your Business, Sep, 2006; A review of both Federal and State laws which govern franchising; An overview of different franchise strategies available for expansion, as well as guidance in choosing the right one for your business; A comparison of the cost of various growth strategies; An overview of revenue streams through franchising; The estimated costs of franchising your business; Calculating returns on franchise development and support costs.

3018 ■ Frandocs, Experts in Franchising
Franchise 123, Inc.
PO Box 149
Islamorada, FL 33036
Free: 800-655-0343
Co. E-mail: frandocs@aol.com
URL: http://www.frandocs.com
Description: Frandocs has developed franchise software and the Franchisor fills in the blanks to complete the documents. **Founded:** 1980..

3019 ■ Global Recruiters Network - GRN
2001 Butterfield Rd., Ste. 102
Downers Grove, IL 60515
Ph: (866)476-8200
Description: Employee search and placement services. **No. of Franchise Units:** 150. **Founded:** 2003.. **Franchised:** 2003. **Franchise Fee:** $89,000. **Financial Assistance:** Yes. **Training:** Yes.

3020 ■ The Growth Coach, Inc.
10700 Montgomery Rd., Ste. 300
Cincinnati, OH 45242
Ph: (866)708-9188
Fax: (513)563-2691
Co. E-mail: inquiry@TheGrowthCoach.com
URL: http://www.TheGrowthCoach.com
Description: Small business and self-employed coaching. Since you will be taught how to facilitate a proven-strategic process, you only need minimal business experience. You'll be able to leverage your time and enjoy a huge income potential while serving groups of small business owners and managers on a regular and ongoing basis. **No. of Franchise Units:** 144. **Founded:** 2002. **Franchised:** 2002. **Equity Capital Needed:** $47,200-$76,400 total investment. **Franchise Fee:** $39,900. **Financial Assistance:** Yes. **Training:** Yes.

3021 ■ iFranchise Group
905 W 175th St., 2nd Fl.
Homewood, IL 60430
Ph: (708)957-2300
Fax: (708)957-2395
Co. E-mail: info@ifranchise.net
URL: http://www.ifranchise.com
Description: Offers services on strategic planning, franchise law, operations documentation, marketing and sales, and executive recruiting for franchisors.

3022 ■ Inner Circle
Inner Circle International, LTD
3208 W Lake St., Unit 3
Minneapolis, MN 55416
Ph: (952)933-6249
Fax: (952)935-5269
Description: Peer groups for business owners. **No. of Franchise Units:** 5. **No. of Company-Owned Units:** 1. **Founded:** 1989.. **Franchised:** 1996. **Equity Capital Needed:** $67,000-$84,000. **Franchise Fee:** $56,000. **Training:** Yes.

3023 ■ International Business Opportunities
Worldwide Canadian Management Consultants, Inc.
PO Box 639
Pickering, ON, Canada L1V 3T3
Ph: (905)686-0469
Fax: (905)686-0469
Description: Worldwide virtual and home office. **No. of Franchise Units:** 37. **No. of Company-Owned Units:** 2. **Founded:** 1976.. **Franchised:** 1981. **Equity Capital Needed:** Canadian and U.S. $6,599; other countries $15,000 U.S.; home offices $15,000 U.S. **Franchise Fee:** $6,599 U.S. **Financial Assistance:** Yes. **Training:** Yes.

3024 ■ International Management Tech. Co., LLC (IMTEC)
78 Fox Hill Rd.
Stamford, CT 06903
Ph: (203)322-6175
Fax: (203)322-6274
Description: Full services to achieve international expansion. **Founded:** 1982..

3025 ■ International Mergers and Acquisitions
International Mergers and Acquisitions, Inc.
4300 N Miller Rd., Ste. 230
Scottsdale, AZ 85251
Ph: (480)990-3899
Fax: (480)990-7480
Description: Members are engaged in the profession of serving merger and acquisition-minded companies in the areas of consulting, financing, divestitures, mergers and acquisitions. Creative work sessions throughout the year. **No. of Franchise Units:** 30. **Founded:** 1969.. **Franchised:** 1979. **Equity Capital Needed:** Suggested $40,000-$50,000. **Franchise Fee:** $15,000. **Training:** Yes.

3026 ■ The Lease Coach
9697 45 Ave.
Edmonton, AB, Canada T6E 5Z8
Ph: (780)448-2645
Free: 800-738-9202
Fax: (780)448-2670
Co. E-mail: DaleWillerton@theleasecoach.com
URL: http://www.TheLeaseCoach.com
Description: Commercial lease consultants representing tenants. **No. of Franchise Units:** 1. **No. of Company-Owned Units:** 2. **Founded:** 1993.. **Franchised:** 2006. **Equity Capital Needed:** $25,000-$35,000. **Franchise Fee:** $11,800. **Training:** Provides 1 week training and ongoing support.

3027 ■ The Lease Coach
Terrace Plaza
4445 Calgary Trl., Unit 820
Edmonton, AB, Canada T6H 5R7
Free: 800-738-9202
Fax: (780)448-2670
Description: Commercial lease consulting services. **No. of Franchise Units:** 2. **No. of Company-Owned Units:** 1. **Founded:** 1999.. **Franchised:** 2001. **Equity Capital Needed:** $25,000-$45,000. **Franchise Fee:** $11,800. **Royalty Fee:** $2,200-$3,200/month. **Training:** Includes 1 week training at headquarters and ongoing training via teleconference/webconference.

3028 ■ Leon Gottlieb USA/Int'l Franchise/ Restaurant Consultants
Leon Gottlieb & Associates
4601 Sendero Pl.
Tarzana, CA 91356-4821
Ph: (818)757-1131
Fax: (818)757-1816
Description: Consultant, expert witness, arbitrator. **Founded:** 1960..

3029 ■ Manufacturing Management Associates
700 Commerce Dr., Ste. 500
Oak Brook, IL 60523
Ph: (630)575-8700
Description: Has built its reputation providing small to mid-sized manufacturing and distribution companies with the technical and advisory services they need to achieve their individual business goals. Areas of expertise include manufacturing systems and network technology, process flow (JIT), quality (TQC), cost management, human resource change management, ISO 9000 certification preparation and work cell design/factory layout. days of training in Chicago, IL. Will also assist the franchisee in sales and marketing efforts to promote the success of the franchise. Other notable benefits include potential client leads, alliances with industry experts, project management methodologies, proprietary computer software systems, reference proposals and R & D. **No. of Franchise Units:** 8. **No. of Company-Owned Units:** 1. **Founded:** 1982.. **Franchised:** 1993. **Equity Capital Needed:** $14,900-$49,450. **Franchise Fee:** $10,000. **Training:** An intensive 8 day seminar in Chicago, IL, where the franchisee will be exposed to a working office and receive extensive training in the policies of running a successful franchise. The franchisee will receive a thorough explanation of proven methodologies, as well as training in proprietary software and business systems.

3030 ■ Marketing Resources Group
83-26 Lefferts Blvd.
Kew Gardens, NY 11415
Ph: (718)261-8882
Description: Franchise development, marketing, and sales.

3031 ■ McGrow Consulting
30 North St.
Hingham, MA 02043
Ph: (800)358-8011
Description: Franchise consulting firm. **Founded:** 1980..

3032 ■ MFV Expositions
210 E Rte. 4, Ste. 403
Paramus, NJ 07652
Ph: (201)226-1130

Fax: (201)226-1131

Description: Producer of franchise expos.

3033 ■ Moresales.ca

231 Shearson Crescent, Ste. 207B
Cambridge, ON, Canada N1T 1J5
Ph: (519)620-8127
Co. E-mail: mike@moresales.ca
URL: http://www.moresales.ca

Description: MoreSALES.ca is a unique franchise opportunity. If you are a Sales or Marketing Professional looking to own your own business, we offer low start-up costs, a fixed franchise fee, a proven training program & a short ramp-up time. We make owning your own business a reality! Structured as a network of business growth professionals, MoreSALES.ca franchisees offer cost effective sales & marketing expertise to help companies reach more customers, communicate more effectively & close more sales. **No. of Franchise Units:** 3. **No. of Company-Owned Units:** 1. **Founded:** 2005.. **Franchised:** 2007. **Equity Capital Needed:** $50,000. **Franchise Fee:** $25,000. **Training:** 5-part training program included in franchise fee.

3034 ■ National Franchise Associates Inc.

240 Lake View Ct.
Lavonia, GA 30553
Ph: (770)945-0660
Fax: (770)356-5180
Co. E-mail: nfa@nationalfranchise.com
URL: http://www.nationalfranchise.com
Contact: Stephen S. Raines, President

Description: Full service consulting and developmental firm with expertise in feasibility studies, Franchise agreements and UFOC's, advertising and public relations campaigns, operations and training manuals, franchise sales programs, and ongoing franchise consulting. **Scope:** An international franchise consulting firm providing full-service program to franchise companies. Services include: Feasibility studies, franchise plans, venture capital, franchise agreement, FTC disclosure document, state registration applications, operations manuals, training materials, advertising and public relations, computer software programs and sales and marketing of franchises. **Founded:** 1981. **Publications:** "Keys To Successful Franchising: Franchise Marketing Reflections Of A Franchise Consultant"; "Keys To A Successful Franchise Training"; "Keys To Successful Franchise Development: Will The Franchise Generate Sufficient Money? Reflections Of A Franchise Consultant"; "Focus on Operations Manuals & Marketing"; "Keys To Successful Franchising: Will Your Franchise Program Make Enough Money?"; "Keys To Successful Franchise Planning: Selecting The Right Franchisees"; "DePalma's expanding into Asia"; "Spirit Of Ingenuity"; "Why a Franchise Consultant Can Be Helpful". **Seminars:** Franchise Training Program.

3035 ■ Nationwide Franchise Marketing Services

18715 Gibbons Dr.
Dallas, TX 75287-4045
Ph: (972)733-9942
Free: 866-740-5815
Fax: (972)733-9942
Co. E-mail: fmmigdol@tx.rr.com
Contact: Marvin J. Migdol, President
E-mail: marvmigdol@aol.com

Description: Full service franchise development evaluations. **Scope:** Helps franchisors in areas such as food services, automotive products and services, apparel, education, personnel, health and beauty aids, maintenance, entertainment and service businesses. **Founded:** 1971. **Publications:** "Starting a Business"; "Winning in the 90S"; "How to Get Organized in 30Days"; "25 Tips for Producing an Effective Direct Mail Brochure"; "How to Land That Job"; "How to Keep a Job"; "How to Buy the Right Franchise"; "Fund-Raising for Business"; "Fund-Raising for Non-Profit Organizations, Public Relations: A Growing Management Function for Today"; "How to Prevent Legal Problems in Hiring"; "Comics As a Public Relations Tool in Communications and Greater Virility".

3036 ■ OneCoach Int'l. LLC

5963 La Place Ct., Ste. 105
Carlsbad, CA 92008
Ph: (760)904-5287
Fax: (858)792-1270

Description: Small business coaching services. **No. of Franchise Units:** 17. **No. of Company-Owned Units:** 1. **Founded:** 2005.. **Franchised:** 2007. **Equity Capital Needed:** $40,100-$318,800. **Franchise Fee:** $23,500-$265,000. **Royalty Fee:** $750/month. **Training:** Provides 8-10 days training at headquarters, 6-9 days virtual training and ongoing training and boot camps.

3037 ■ Osler, Hoskin & Harcourt LLP

1 First Canadian Pl.
Toronto, ON, Canada M5X 1B8
Ph: (416)362-2111
Fax: (416)862-6666

Description: Canadian and international franchise law. **Founded:** 1862..

3038 ■ "Partner" On-Call Network

"Partner" On-Call Network LLC
730 Sandy Point Ln.
N Palm Beach, FL 33410
Ph: (561)776-2515
Fax: (561)868-6892
Co. E-mail: partneroncall@comcast.net
URL: http://www.PartnerOnCall.com

Description: Consulting business. **No. of Franchise Units:** 23. **Founded:** 2005.. **Franchised:** 2006. **Equity Capital Needed:** $56,000-$76,000. **Franchise Fee:** $25,000. **Financial Assistance:** Yes. **Training:** 10 day home study, plus 5 days at headquarters and 3 days on-call via telephone and fax, conferences and proactive training & mentoring from a consultant seasoned in our business.

3039 ■ Performance Group, Ltd.

PO Box 437
Barrington, IL 60011
Ph: (847)526-9298

Description: Franchise program development and enhancement. **Founded:** 1979..

3040 ■ PRO, President's Resource Organization

100 E Bellevue, Ste. 4E
Chicago, IL 60611
Ph: (312)337-3658

Description: Facilitate peer advisory boards. **No. of Franchise Units:** 3. **No. of Company-Owned Units:** 2. **Founded:** 1993.. **Franchised:** 1999. **Equity Capital Needed:** $12,000-$40,000. **Franchise Fee:** $8,500-$36,000. **Financial Assistance:** Yes. **Training:** Yes.

3041 ■ Red Wheel Fundraising

RWFR, Inc.
16 S 15th St.
Council Bluffs, IA 51501
Ph: (816)221-2699
Free: 800-269-0667
Co. E-mail: redwheel@mitec.net
URL: http://www.redwheelfundraising.com

Description: The franchise offers general business. **No. of Franchise Units:** 18. **Founded:** 1984.. **Franchised:** 1988. **Equity Capital Needed:** $10,000-$12,000. **Franchise Fee:** $10,000. **Training:** Yes.

3042 ■ Renaissance Executive Forums, Inc.

7855 Ivanhoe Ave., Ste. 300
La Jolla, CA 92037
Ph: (858)551-6600
Fax: (858)551-8777

Description: Interactive peer review forums for business professionals. **No. of Franchise Units:** 45. **Founded:** 1994.. **Franchised:** 1994. **Equity Capital Needed:** $76,000 liquid capital; $500,000 net worth. **Franchise Fee:** $24,500. **Training:** Yes.

3043 ■ Seller Direct, Inc.

1954 First St., Ste. 161
Highland Park, IL 60035
Ph: (847)266-0082

Description: Brokerage support of franchise resales. **Founded:** 1995..

3044 ■ Sunbelt Business Brokers

Sunbelt Business Advisors Network
3212 Rice St.
St. Paul, MN 55126
Ph: (651)484-2677
Fax: (651)484-9658
Co. E-mail: hschilling@sunbeltnetwork.com
URL: http://www.sunbeltnetwork.com

Description: Offer franchise consulting & re-sales programs for prospective franchisors and franchisees. Provides consumers a no-cost personal consultation to determine the best available business to meet your personal and financial needs. **Founded:** 1979..

3045 ■ Turbo Leadership Systems Ltd.

36280 NE Wilsonville Rd.
Newberg, OR 97132
Ph: (503)625-1867
Fax: (503)625-2699

Description: Management training and team building training. **No. of Company-Owned Units:** 1. **Founded:** 1985.. **Franchised:** 1995. **Equity Capital Needed:** $49,000. **Franchise Fee:** $39,000. **Training:** Yes.

3046 ■ Upside Group Franchise Consulting Corp.

11445 E Via Linda, Ste. 2-495
Scottsdale, AZ 85259
Ph: (888)445-2882
Fax: (480)664-1627

Description: Full franchise consulting/sales development. **Founded:** 2000.. **Training:** Yes.

3047 ■ Venture Marketing Associates

800 Palisade Ave., Ste. 907
Fort Lee, NJ 07024
Ph: (201)924-7435

Description: Business development/franchise consultants. **Founded:** 1976..

3048 ■ West Coast Commercial Credit

PO Box 19241
San Diego, CA 92159
Ph: (800)804-7901
Fax: (619)280-2575

Description: Nationwide commercial financing. **Founded:** 1987..

COMPUTERIZED DATABASES

3049 ■ ABI/INFORM®

789 E Eisenhower Pkwy.
Ann Arbor, MI 48106-1346
Ph: (734)761-4700
Free: 800-521-0600
Co. E-mail: info@il.proquest.com
URL: http://www.il.proquest.com
Contact: Matt Dunie, President

Availability: Online: ProQuest Co.; ProQuest LLC-Dialog; ProQuest LLC - Dialog; LexisNexis Group; STN International; Wolters Kluwer Health - Ovid. **Type:** Full-text; Bibliographic; Image.

3050 ■ NewsEdge™

3 Becker Farm Rd., Ste. 401
Roseland, NJ 07068
Ph: (973)422-0800
Co. E-mail: info@acquiremedia.com
URL: http://www.acquiremedia.com

Availability: Online: Acquire Media. **Type:** Full-text; Numeric; Statistical.

3051 ■ PROMT® - Predicast's Overview of Markets and Technology

10650 Toebben Dr.
Independence, KY 41051
Free: 800-354-9706
Fax: (800)487-8488
Co. E-mail: investors@cengage.com
URL: http://www.gale.cengage.com
Contact: Ronald Dunn, President

Availability: Online: ProQuest LLC-Dialog; ProQuest LLC - Dialog; Cengage Learning Inc. **Type:** Bibliographic; Full-text.

LIBRARIES

3052 ■ Alameda County Library - Business Library
2400 Stevenson Blvd.
Fremont, CA 94538
Ph: (510)505-7001
URL: http://www.aclibrary.org
Contact: Janet Cronbach
Scope: Starting and managing a business, small business, investments, real estate, International business, management and personnel, career planning, San Francisco Bay area business. **Services:** Interlibrary loan; copying; library open to the public. **Founded:** 1968. **Holdings:** 18,000 books; 300 audiocassettes; 100 videocassettes. **Subscriptions:** 400 journals and other serials; 20 newspapers.

3053 ■ American Society for Training and Development - Information Center
1640 King St.
Alexandria, VA 22313-2043
Ph: (703)683-8100
Free: 800-628-2783
Fax: (703)683-1523
Co. E-mail: customercare@astd.org
URL: http://www.astd.org
Scope: Human resource development - general, management, training, career development, Organization development, consulting skills. **Services:** Library open to national members of the Society. **Founded:** 1984. **Holdings:** 3000 bound volumes. **Subscriptions:** 60 journals and other serials.

3054 ■ Franchise Consultants International Association Library
5147 S. Angela Rd.
Memphis, TN 38117
Ph: (901)368-3361
Fax: (901)368-1144
Co. E-mail: franmark@msn.com
URL: http://www.FranchiseStores.com
Contact: R. Richey
URL(s): www.FranchiseStores.Net, consultant-samerica.net. **Scope:** Franchise law, demographics, statistics, logistics, suppliers, technology, advertising, management, legal consulting. **Services:** Members only participants for reference use. **Founded:** 1976. **Holdings:** 2800 books, periodicals, clippings, audio/visuals, and audio recordings; reports; manuscripts; archives; patents. **Subscriptions:** 143 magazines.

RESEARCH CENTERS

3055 ■ Auburn University at Montgomery - Center for Business (CBED)
600 S Ct. St.
Montgomery, AL 36104
Ph: (334)244-3700
Free: 888-94CENTER
Fax: (334)244-3718
Co. E-mail: cforehand@cbed.aum.edu
URL: http://cbed.aum.edu
Contact: Cynthia W. Forehand, Director
Services: Human resources consulting. **Founded:** 1973. **Publications:** *CBED Research reports* (Periodic). **Telecommunication Services:** info@cbed.aum.edu.

START-UP INFORMATION

3056 ■ *"Visual Appeal" in Small Business Opportunities (Fall 2007)*
Pub: Harris Publications Inc.
Ed: Michael L. Corne. **Description:** Profile of Jim Huffman, who launched his new Video Business Card Distributorship. The business cards allow companies and individuals to put personal video messages on their cards explaining the benefits of doing business with them. The cards take prospective customers to Websites and even provide a printable document for brochures or special offers.

ASSOCIATIONS AND OTHER ORGANIZATIONS

3057 ■ **National Association for Business Organizations (NAFBO)**
5432 Price Ave.
Baltimore, MD 21215
Ph: (410)367-5309
Co. E-mail: nahbb@msn.com
URL: http://www.ameribizs.com/global
Contact: Rudolph Lewis, President
Description: Business organizations that develop and support small businesses that have the capability to provide their products or services on a national level. Promotes small business in a free market system; represents the interests of small businesses to government and community organizations on small business affairs; monitors and reviews laws that affect small businesses; promotes a business code of ethics. Supplies members with marketing and management assistance; encourages joint marketing services between members. Operates a Home Based Business Television Network that provides an affordable audio/visual media for small and home based businesses. **Founded:** 1986. **Awards:** Entrepreneur Certificate.

REFERENCE WORKS

3058 ■ *"Windstream Expands Business Service Into Monroe" in Marketing Weekly News (January 23, 2010, pp. 77)*
Pub: Investment Weekly News
Description: Windstream Corp. announces the expansion of its data and voice services into Monroe, N.C., which will give local businesses a new choice for advanced communication services and network security.

TRADE PERIODICALS

3059 ■ *Worldgram Newsletter*
Pub: Worldprofit Inc.
Ed: Dr. Jeffrey Lant, Editor, drjlant@worldprofit.com. **Released:** Bimonthly. **Price:** Free. **Description:** Internet newsletter with a marketing focus for businesses. Also offers tips on how to profit from the World Wide Web.

CONSULTANTS

3060 ■ **BioSciCon Inc.**
14905 Forest Landing Cir.
Rockville, MD 20850
Ph: (301)610-9130
Fax: (301)610-7662
Co. E-mail: info@bioscicon.com
URL: http://www.bioscicon.com
Contact: Nenad Markovic, President
Scope: Sponsoring development of the technology of the Pap test accuracy via introduction of a new bio-marker that enhances visibility of abnormal cells on Pap smears or mono-layers of cervical cells obtained in solution. Conducts clinical trials for assessment of the test efficacy and safety, manufactures research tools for conduct of trials, and markets IP to license manufacturing, marketing, sales and distribution rights of the new technology line of products. **Founded:** 1996. **Publications:** "Cervical Acid Phosphates: A Biomarker of Cervical Dysplasia and Potential Surrogate Endpoint for Colposcopy," 2004; "Enhancing Pap test with a new biological marker of cervical dysplasia," 2004; "A cytoplasmic biomarker for liquid-based Pap," The FACEB Journal Experimental Biology, 2004; "Pap test and new biomarker-based technology for enhancing visibility of abnormal cells," 2004. **Special Services:** Mark-Pap®; PreservCyt®.

3061 ■ **BPT Consulting Associates Ltd.**
12 Parmenter Rd., Ste. B-6
Londonderry, NH 03053
Ph: (603)437-8484
Free: 888-278-0030
Fax: (603)434-5388
Contact: John Kuczynski, Managing Director
Scope: Provides management consulting expertise and resources to cross-industry clients with services for: Business Management consulting, People/Human Resources Transition and Training programs, and a full cadre of multi-disciplined Technology Computer experts. Virtual consultants with expertise in e-commerce, supply chain management, organizational development, and business application development consulting. **Founded:** 1991.

3062 ■ **Carelli & Associates**
17 Reid Pl.
Delmar, NY 12054
Ph: (518)439-0233
Fax: (518)439-3006
Co. E-mail: truthaboutsupervision@yahoo.com
URL: http://www.carelli.com
Contact: Anne O Brien Carelli, Owner
E-mail: anneobriencarelli@yahoo.com
Scope: Provider of writing and editing services to industry and businesses, health care and educational institutions, and government agencies. Also provides program management in creating and disseminating publications and in implementing related training. Assists organizations in designing and implementing team-based management. Offers supervisory skills training and problem-solving work sessions for managers. Individual Consultation are provided for

managers, CEOs, potential supervisors including 360 degree assessments. **Founded:** 1988. **Publications:** "The Truth About Supervision: Coaching, Teamwork, Interviewing, Appraisals, 360 degree Assessments, and Recognition". **Seminars:** Supervisory Skills Training Series; Problem-Solving Work Sessions for Managers; Effective Leadership.

3063 ■ **Charismedia**
610 W End Ave., Ste. B1
New York, NY 10001
Ph: (212)362-6808
Fax: (212)362-6809
Co. E-mail: charismedia@earthlink.net
URL: http://www.charismedia.net
Contact: Dr. Doe Lang, President
E-mail: charismedia@earthlink.net
Scope: Offers speech and image training as well as speech writing services for effective presentation skills. Conducts workshops like anti-stage fright breathing, psychophysical exercises, transformational success imagery, face reading and body language, EMDR (Eye Movement Desensitization Re-Processing) for Permanent Trauma and Fear Removal, Bach Flower remedies, thought field therapy, cross-cultural communication, speech, voice and diction; regional and foreign accent elimination and acquisition, Positive Perception Management (P.P.M.), Ad-libbing, humor and spontaneity training, fast creative speech preparation, Neuro-Linguistic Programming and Hypnosis. **Founded:** 1974. **Publications:** "Flaunt It"; "Improve Your Sex Life"; "Phone Power"; "Train Your Voice"; "Turning Tinny, Tiny Tones To Gold"; "The New Secrets of Charisma: How to Discover and Unleash your Hidden Powers," McGraw-Hill, Jul, 1999. **Seminars:** Services for Comfortable Effective Speaking.

3064 ■ **The Consulting Exchange**
1770 Mass Ave., Ste. 288
Cambridge, MA 02140
Ph: (617)576-2100
Free: 800-824-4828
Co. E-mail: gday@consultingexchange.com
Contact: Geoffrey Day, President
E-mail: gday@consultingexchange.com
Scope: A consultant referral service for management and technical consultants. Serves a local, regional and international client base. **Founded:** 1982. **Publications:** "Looking for a Consultant? Success Points for Finding the Right One," Boston Business Journal, Jun, 2001; "Getting Full Value From Consulting is in Your Hands," Mass High Tech, May, 1998; "Developing Knowledge-Based Client Relationships, The Future of Professional Services"; "The Consultant's Legal Guide"; "The Business of Consulting: The Basics and Beyond".

3065 ■ **Development Resource Consultants (DRC)**
PO Box 118
Rancho Cucamonga, CA 91729
Ph: (909)902-7655

Fax: (909)476-6942
Co. E-mail: drc@gotodrc.com
URL: http://www.gotodrc.com
Contact: Jerry R. Frey, Business Manager
E-mail: jfrey@gotodrc.com
Scope: Specializes in office re-organization, employee training in office organization, communication skills, sales training and career counseling. **Founded:** 1985. **Publications:** "Institute of Management Consultants Southern California Chapter," Jan, 2006.

3066 ■ DRI Consulting (DRIC)
2 Otter Ln.
Saint Paul, MN 55127-6436
Ph: (651)415-1400
Free: 866-276-4600
Fax: (651)415-9968
Co. E-mail: dric@dric.com
URL: http://www.dric.com
Contact: Megan Brogger, Principal
E-mail: meganbrogger@dric.com
Scope: Provides high-quality, research-based services and training in leadership, team processes, supervision, and management, and organizational development, clients with direct and substantial impact on individual and team performance and on organizational success through proven processes for selecting, developing and deploying leaders. **Founded:** 1991.

3067 ■ Family Business Institute Inc.—Family Business Experts
904 Steffi Ct.
Lawrenceville, GA 30044-6933
Ph: (770)952-4085
Fax: (770)432-6660
Co. E-mail: asktheexpert@family-business-experts.com
URL: http://www.family-business-experts.com
Contact: Wayne Rivers, President
Scope: Assists families in business to achieve personal, family, and organizational goals by meeting challenges that are unique to family-owned businesses. Provides coordinated and integrated assessments and solutions for family issues and needs; for company finance and for human resource and operational requirements. **Founded:** 1985. **Publications:** "Professional Intervention in the Family Owned Business"; "Building Consensus in a Family Business"; "Professionalizing Family Business Management"; "Recognizing generations - know them by their weekends"; "Succession planning tactics"; "Succession Planning Obstacles in Family Business"; "Succession: three ways to ease the transition"; "Pruning the family business tree"; "Responsibility diffusion - the most critical impediment to successfully growing any kind of business"; "Breaking Up is Hard to Do: Divorce in the Family Business".

3068 ■ First Strike Management Consulting Inc.—FSMC Inc.
4001 Loblolly Ave.
Little River, SC 29566-1188
Ph: (843)385-6338
Fax: (843)390-1004
Co. E-mail: info@fsmc.com
URL: http://www.fsmc.com
Contact: J. D. Lewis, Chief Executive Officer
E-mail: jd.lewis@fsmc.com
Scope: Offers proposal management and program management services. Specializes in enterprise systems, management systems, and staff augmentation. Serves the following industries: Nuclear/Fossil Power, Petro-Chemical, Aerospace and Defense, Telecommunications, Engineering and Construction, Information Technology, Golf Course Construction/Management, Utility Engineering/Construction, Civil Works, and Housing Development. **Founded:** 1991. **Publications:** "Project Management for Executives"; "Project Risk Management"; "Project Communications Management"; "Winning Proposals, Four Computer Based Training (CBT) courses"; "Principles of Program Management". **Seminars:** Preparing Winning Proposals in Response to Government RFPs.

3069 ■ Full Voice
3217 Broadway Ave., Ste. 300
Kansas City, MO 64111
Ph: (816)941-0011

Free: 800-684-8764
Fax: (816)931-8887
Co. E-mail: info@infullvoice.com
URL: http://www.fullvoice.us
Contact: Michienne Dixon, Principal
Scope: Vocal performance training firm offering consulting services and personal training sessions in the implementation of effective vocal communication techniques for the development of business relationships and career enhancement. Formalizes a program of proven techniques into a practical method of helping individuals improve their ability to better present themselves when speaking in a professional situation. Industries served: All. **Founded:** 1992. **Publications:** "You Can Sound Like You Know What You're Saying". **Seminars:** You Can Sound Like You Know What You're Saying; The Psychology of Vocal Performance; Security. . .the Ability to Accept Change; Knowing. . .the Key to Relaxed Public Communication; The Effective Voice for Customer Service Enhancement; You Can Speak With Conviction; How To Make Yours a Championship Team; Functional English For Foreign Trade. **Special Services:** FULL VOICE™.

3070 ■ Great Western Association Management Inc.
7995 E Prentice Ave., Ste. 100
Greenwood Village, CO 80111
Ph: (303)770-2220
Fax: (303)770-1614
Co. E-mail: info83@gwami.com
URL: http://www.gwami.com
Contact: Karen M. Wojdyla, President
E-mail: kwojdyla@gwami.com
Scope: Provider of clients with products and services to effectively manage existing and startup, for- and not-for-profit organizations. Clients select from a menu of services including association development and public relations, conferences and seminars, financial management, membership communications, and governance. Expertise also includes association strategic planning, compliance, lobbying, meeting planning, fundraising, marketing and communications. Serves national, regional and state organizations. **Founded:** 1983. **Seminars:** Site selection; Creative program development; Contract negotiations; On-site conference management; Trade show management; Travel and logistics.

3071 ■ Joel Greenstein & Associates (JGA)
6212 Nethercombe Ct.
McLean, VA 22101
Ph: (703)893-1888
Co. E-mail: jgreenstein@contractmasters.com
Contact: Joel Greenstein, Principal
E-mail: jgreenstein@contractmasters.com
Scope: Provides services to minority and women-owned businesses and government agencies. Specializes in interpreting federal, agency-specific acquisition regulations and contract terms and conditions. Offers assistance with preparing technical, cost proposals and sealed bids.

3072 ■ Edward M. Hepner & Associates
4667 Macarthur Blvd., Ste. 405
Newport Beach, CA 92660
Ph: (714)250-0818
Fax: (714)553-8437
Contact: Edward M. Hepner, President
Scope: An immigration consultant and labor certification specialist. Assists in obtaining visa for work, immigration and business development within the United States and Canada.

3073 ■ I.H.R. Solutions
3333 E Bayaud Ave., Ste. 219
Denver, CO 80209
Ph: (303)588-4243
Fax: (303)978-0473
Co. E-mail: dhollands@ihrsolutions.com
Contact: Deborah Hollands, Owner
E-mail: dhollands@ihrsolutions.com
Scope: Provides joint-venture and start-up human resource consulting services as well as advice on organization development for international human capital. Industries served: high-tech and telecommunications. **Founded:** 1997.

3074 ■ IMC Consulting & Training
901 McHenry Ave., Ste. A
Modesto, CA 95350
Ph: (209)572-2271
Fax: (209)572-2862
Co. E-mail: info@imc-1.net
URL: http://www.imc-1.net
Contact: Michael J. Loschke, President
E-mail: michael@imc-1.net
Scope: Helps businesses and professionals identify, develop and market their selling proposition to increase profits. Services include B-to-B surveys, direct marketing, media relations, planning and strategy, sales management, training and leadership coaching. **Founded:** 1994. **Publications:** "Consultant Earns Advanced Certificate," Hccsc Business Review, Dec, 2004; "Adapting to Change - the New Competitive Advantage," Business Journal, Jul, 2004; "Loyalty Marketing Can Divide New Business," Jun, 2004; "Eleven Major Marketing Mistakes," Jul, 2003; "Planning to Win or Racing to Fail," Jun, 2003. **Seminars:** Negotiating High Profit Sales; How to Write Winning Proposals, Modesto Chamber of Commerce, Oct, 2007; Winning the 2nd Half: A 6-month Plan to Score New Customers and Profits. **Telecommunication Services:** imcinfo@imc-1.net.

3075 ■ The Institute for Management Excellence
PO Box 5459
Lacey, WA 98509-5459
Ph: (360)412-0404
Co. E-mail: pwoc@itstime.com
URL: http://www.itstime.com
Contact: Michael Anthony, Director
Scope: Management consulting and training focuses on improving productivity, using practices and creative techniques. Practices based on the company's theme: It's time for new ways of doing business. Industries served: public sector, law enforcement, finance or banking, non profit, computers or high technology, education, human resources, utilities. **Founded:** 1995. **Publications:** "Income Without a Job," 2008; "The Other Side of Midnight, 2000: An Executive Guide to the Year 2000 Problem"; "Concordance to the Michael Teachings"; "Handbook of Small Business Advertising"; "The Personality Game"; "How to Market Yourself for Success". **Seminars:** The Personality Game; Power Path Seminars; Productivity Plus; Sexual Harassment and Discrimination Prevention; Worker's Comp Cost Reduction; Americans with Disabilities Act; In Search of Identify: Clarifying Corporate Culture.

3076 ■ Interpersonal Coaching & Consulting (ICC)
1516 W Lake St., Ste. 2000S
Minneapolis, MN 55408
Ph: (612)381-2494
Fax: (612)381-2494
Co. E-mail: mail@interpersonal-coaching.com
URL: http://www.interpersonal-coaching.com
Contact: Mary Belfry, Partner
Scope: Provider of coaching and consulting to businesses and organizations. Assesses the interpersonal workplace through interviews, assessment instruments and individual group settings. Experienced as a therapist for over a decade. **Publications:** "Sexual Harassment In The Workplace For Newspapers". **Seminars:** More On Relationships; Sexual harassment and discrimination issues.

3077 ■ Invent Resources Inc. (IRI)
PO Box 548
Lexington, MA 02420-0005
Ph: (781)862-0200
Fax: (781)721-2300
Co. E-mail: pavelle@comcast.net
URL: http://www.weinvent.com
Contact: Dr. Richard Pavelle, President
E-mail: pavelle@comcast.net
Scope: Provider of consultancy services to provide support in developing and prototyping new, proprietary products. Offer inventory services on demand. Assist clients who need innovations in product lines, have hit technical bottlenecks, or need improvements in manufacturing processes. Provide assistance to

individuals and clients in obtaining, reviewing, and strengthening patents. **Founded:** 1991. **Telecommunication Services:** rp@theworld.com.

3078 ■ May Toy Lukens
3226 NE 26th Ct.
Renton, WA 98056
Ph: (425)891-3226
Contact: May T. Lukens, Principal
Scope: Provides training to teach people to think of ways to improve their operations continuously by changing the way they think. Industries served: All, particularly financial. Operational analysis and training. **Founded:** 1996. **Seminars:** Seminars and workshops in maximizing resource utilization and staff potential.

3079 ■ Navarro, Kim & Associates
529 N Charles St., Ste. 202
Baltimore, MD 21201-5043
Ph: (410)837-6317
Fax: (410)837-6294
Co. E-mail: bnavarro@sprynet.com
Contact: Beltran Navarro, Director
E-mail: bnavarro@sprynet.com
Scope: Specializes in bridging the gap between firms and non-traditional ethnic communities, especially in community development and institutional building. **Founded:** 1984.

3080 ■ On-Q Software Inc.
13764 SW 11 St.
Miami, FL 33184
Ph: (305)553-2400
Free: 800-553-2862
Fax: (305)220-2666
Co. E-mail: info@on-qsoftware.com
URL: http://www.on-qsoftware.com
Contact: Hermenegildo Cajigas, Treasurer
E-mail: hcajigas@on-qsoftware.com
Scope: Provider of the small business community with simple to use, feature rich software. Provides software solutions including time and fixed fee billing, due date tracking and practice manager. **Founded:** 1987.

3081 ■ Pathways To Wellness
617 Everhart Rd.
Corpus Christi, TX 78411
Ph: (361)985-9642
Fax: (361)949-4627
Co. E-mail: path2wellness@earthlink.net
URL: http://www.path2wellness.com
Contact: Evy Coppola, Owner
Scope: Offer natural holistic health counseling, yoga and hatha yoga classes, teachers training and cookery classes for individuals and companies. Health counseling includes nutritional guidance, kinesiology, iridology, reflexology, energy healing, massage therapy, herbal and vitamin therapy, creative visualization and meditation. Provides supplements which bring about the same effects as that of natural sunshine. **Founded:** 1988. **Seminars:** Is It You Holding You Back?; The Balancing Act. . .Career. . . Family. . .and Self; Learning the Art of Friendly Persuasion; Stop Accepting What You Are Getting and Start Asking for What You Want!; Introduction to Natural Health and Healthy Living; Learn Why One Size Approaches to the Answers on Health Do Not Work; Introduction to Yoga. What is it? Who can do it? What can it do for you.

3082 ■ ProActive English
4355 SE 29th Ave.
Portland, OR 97202
Ph: (503)231-2906
Co. E-mail: infopae@proactive-english.com
URL: http://www.proactive-english.com
Contact: Margaret Lyman, Manager
E-mail: mlyman@proactive-english.com
Scope: Offers on-site individual and small group language and communication training. Sets up learning plans tailored to the needs and schedules of managers and executives who are non-native English speakers. Serves all industries. **Founded:** 1997. **Seminars:** Communicating in Business Situations; Presentations and Pronunciation; Tailored Curriculum; One-on-One Programs.

3083 ■ Rose & Crangle Ltd.
117 N 4th St.
Lincoln, KS 67455
Ph: (785)524-5050
Fax: (785)524-3130
Co. E-mail: rcltd@nckcn.com
URL: http://www.roseandcrangle.com
Contact: Robert D. Crangle, President
E-mail: rcltd@nckcn.com
Scope: Provider of evaluation, planning and policy analyzes for universities, associations, foundations, governmental agencies and private companies engaged in scientific, technological or educational activities. Special expertise in the development of new institutions. Special skills in providing planning and related group facilitation workshops. **Founded:** 1984. **Publications:** "Preface to Bulgarian Integration Into Europe and NATO: Issues of Science Policy And research Evaluation Practice," los Press, 2006; "Allocating Limited National Resources for Fundamental Research," 2005.

3084 ■ Rothschild Strategies Unlimited L.L.C.
19 Thistle Rd.
Norwalk, CT 06851-1909
Ph: (203)846-6898
Fax: (203)847-1426
Co. E-mail: bill@strategyleader.com
URL: http://www.strategyleader.com
Contact: Stephen M. Rothschild, President
Scope: Consults with senior management and business level strategy teams to develop overall strategic direction, set priorities and creates sustainable competitive advantages and differentiators. Enables organizations to enhance their own strategic thinking and leadership skills so that they can continue to develop and implement profitable growth strategies. **Founded:** 1983. **Publications:** "Putting It All Together-a guide to strategic thinking"; "Competitive Advantage"; "Ristaker, Caretaker, Surgeon & Undertaker four faces of strategic leadership"; "The Secret to GE's Success"; "Having the Right Strategic Leader and Team".

3085 ■ David G. Schantz
29 Wood Run Cir.
Rochester, NY 14612-2271
Ph: (716)723-0760
Fax: (716)723-8724
Co. E-mail: daveschantz@yahoo.com
URL: http://www.daveschantz.freeservers.com
Contact: David G. Schantz, Manager
Scope: Provider of industrial engineering services for photofinishing labs, including amateur-wholesale, professional, commercial, school, and package. **Founded:** 1992.

3086 ■ Schneider Consulting Group Inc.
50 S Steele St., Ste. 390
Denver, CO 80209-2834
Ph: (303)320-4413
Fax: (303)320-5795
Contact: Kim Schneider Malek, Vice President
E-mail: kim@scgfambus.com
Scope: Assists family-owned and privately-held business transition to the next generation and/or to a more professionally managed company, turn around consulting for small and medium size companies. **Founded:** 1987.

3087 ■ Sklar and Associates Inc.
242 Laurel Bay Dr.
Murrells Inlet, SC 29576
Ph: (843)798-0412
Fax: (843)651-3090
Co. E-mail: sklarincdc@aol.com
URL: http://www.sklarinc.com
Contact: Tim Sklar, President
Scope: Provider of consulting services for business acquisitions, business development and project finance. Provides audit oversight services to listed corporations on Sarbanes-Oxley compliance. Services include: Due diligence analyses and corporate governance. Industries served: transportation sectors, energy sector and commercial real estate industries. **Seminars:** Financial Analysis in MBA; Emerging Company Finance; Due Diligence in Business Acquisition; Business Valuation.

3088 ■ Trendzitions Inc.
25691 Atlantic Ocean, Ste. B13
Lake Forest, CA 92630-8842
Ph: (949)727-9100
Free: 800-266-2767
Fax: (949)727-3444
Co. E-mail: ctooker@trendzitions.com
URL: http://www.trendzitions.com
Contact: Christian Tooker, President
E-mail: ctooker@trendzitions.com
Scope: Provider of services in the areas of communications consulting, project management, construction management, and furniture procurement. Offers information on spatial uses, building codes, ADA compliance and city ordinances. Also offers budget projections. **Founded:** 1986.

3089 ■ Turnaround Inc.
3415 A St. NW
Gig Harbor, WA 98335
Ph: (253)857-6730
Fax: (253)857-6344
Co. E-mail: info@turnround-inc.com
URL: http://www.turnaround-inc.com
Contact: Miles Stover, President
E-mail: mstover@turnround-inc.com
Scope: Provider of interim executive management assistance and management advisory to small, medium and family-owned businesses that are not meeting their goals. Services include acting as an interim executive or on-site manager. Extensive practices in arena of bankruptcy management. **Founded:** 1997. **Publications:** "How to Identify Problem and Promising Management"; "How to Tell if Your Company is a Bankruptcy Candidate"; "Signs that Your Company is in Trouble"; "The Turnaround Specialist: How to File a Petition Under 11 USC 11". **Seminars:** Competitive Intelligence Gathering.

3090 ■ Weich & Bilotti Inc.
600 Worcester Rd., 4th Fl.
Framingham, MA 01702
Ph: (508)663-1600
Fax: (508)663-1682
Co. E-mail: info@weich-bilotti.com
Contact: Mervyn D. Weich, Director
E-mail: mweich@weich-bilotti.com
Scope: Specializes in business plans, venture capital, computer information systems, turnaround/interim management, retail consulting, start-up process, college recruiting and IS and IT personnel. **Founded:** 1995.

3091 ■ William J. Yang & Associates
847 N Hollywood Way, Ste. 100
Burbank, CA 91505-2848
Ph: (818)841-1311
Fax: (818)841-7900
Contact: William J. Yang, President
Scope: A mechanical engineering firm that serves commercial businesses. **Founded:** 1966.

3092 ■ Zogby International
901 Broad St.
Utica, NY 13501
Ph: (315)624-0200
Free: 877-462-7655
Fax: (315)624-0210
Co. E-mail: marketing@zogby.com
URL: http://www.zogby.com
Contact: John Zogby, President
E-mail: john@zogby.com
Scope: Specializes in providing market research and analysis services. **Founded:** 1984. **Publications:** "Just who are you calling anyway"; "All of this leads to a very basic question". **Seminars:** The Research Authority, Oct, 2006; Christian Science Monitor Break fast, Oct, 2006.

3093 ■ Zolfo Cooper L.L.C.
Grace Bldg., 1114 Ave. of the Americas, 41st Fl.
New York, NY 10036
Ph: (212)561-4000

Fax: (212)213-1749
Co. E-mail: rrandall@zolfocooper.com
URL: http://www.zolfocooper.com
Contact: Mark Cervi, Director
Scope: Provider of accounting consulting services to businesses. Specializes in restructuring and turnaround consulting; interim and crisis management; performance improvement; creditor advisory; cross-border restructuring and corporate finance. **Founded:** 1985.

FRANCHISES AND BUSINESS OPPORTUNITIES

3094 ▪ Alpha Legal Forms & More, Inc.
Alpha Publications of America, Inc.
PO Box 12488
Tucson, AZ 85732
Ph: (520)795-7100
Free: 800-770-4329
Description: Legal forms. **Founded:** 1976..

3095 ▪ American Association of Franchisees & Dealers (AAFD)
3500 5th Ave.
San Diego, CA 92103
Ph: (619)209-3775
Free: 800-733-9858
Fax: (619)209-3777
Co. E-mail: benefits@aafd.org
URL: http://www.aafd.org
Contact: Peter Hanson, President
Description: Franchisees and business services.
Scope: A nonprofit organization providing referrals and other member benefits and services for franchisees. **Founded:** 1992. **Publications:** "Nsights the Art of Positive Emotions," Sep-Oct, 2003; "Nsights Understanding Basic Human Behaviors at Work," Aug, 2003; "Nsights Pinkerton," Aug, 2002. **Educational Activities:** Total Quality Franchising (Annual). **Awards:** Fair Franchising Seal (Periodic). **Seminars:** Driving Your Association to the Next Level; Keeping your Association on the Fairway: Re-Model and Re-Imaging in Today's Economy; Avoid being an Association duffer: Recruiting and Retaining Membership Dos and Don'ts!; Clubhouse Chatter: The Most Cost Effective Ways to Communicate.

3096 ▪ AmSpirit Business Connections
AmSpirit Franchise Corp.
158 W Johnstown Rd.
Columbus, OH 43230-0724
Ph: (614)476-5540
Free: 888-267-7474
Fax: (614)476-6699
Description: Establish and support networking groups. **No. of Franchise Units:** 2. **No. of Company-Owned Units:** 7. **Founded:** 1997.. **Equity Capital Needed:** $10,000. **Franchise Fee:** $10,000. **Training:** Yes.

3097 ▪ Business Cards Tomorrow
Business Cards Tomorrow, Inc.
3000 NE 30th Pl., 5th Fl.
Ft. Lauderdale, FL 33306
Ph: (954)563-1224
Free: 800-627-9998
Fax: (954)565-0742
Description: Professional, niche wholesale service business. **No. of Franchise Units:** 64. **No. of Company-Owned Units:** 5. **Founded:** 1975.. **Franchised:** 1977. **Equity Capital Needed:** $991,700-$1,100,000. **Franchise Fee:** $35,000. **Royalty Fee:** 6%. **Financial Assistance:** Third party financing available. **Training:** Provides 2 weeks at headquarters, 4 weeks onsite and ongoing support.

3098 ▪ The Canadian Badge Maker Ltd.
2806 W King Edward Ave.
Vancouver, BC, Canada V6L 1T9
Ph: (604)733-4323
Fax: (604)736-8419
Co. E-mail: wunday@shae.ca
URL: http://www.recognitionexpress.ca
Description: Focus on corporate employee identification through name tags with full corporate logos, colours, etc. **No. of Franchise Units:** 8. **Founded:** 1978.. **Franchised:** 1978. **Franchise Fee:** $39,500. **Training:** Offers 1 week training.

3099 ▪ Cybertary
1217 Pleasant Grove Blvd., Ste. 100
Roseville, CA 95678
Ph: (916)781-7799
Free: 888-292-8279
Fax: (877)292-8279
Co. E-mail: Franchise@Cybertary.com
URL: http://www.CybertaryFranchise.com
Description: Virtual assistant (VA) industry providing on-demand administrative support to businesses, entrepreneurs, and busy people through a nationwide team network to meet the needs of any business. This home-based B2B service offers low overhead and a flexible schedule. **No. of Franchise Units:** 23. **Founded:** 2005.. **Franchised:** 2006. **Equity Capital Needed:** $39,500-$78,500. **Franchise Fee:** $37,500-$56,250. **Royalty Fee:** 5%. **Training:** Receive 4 days of intensive training.

3100 ▪ A Day to Cherish Wedding Videos
10174 S Memorial Dr.
South Jordan, UT 84095
Ph: (801)253-2450
Description: Wedding and special occasion videos. **No. of Franchise Units:** 2. **No. of Company-Owned Units:** 1. **Founded:** 2004.. **Franchised:** 2004. **Equity Capital Needed:** $33,400-$39,400 total investment. **Franchise Fee:** $17,500. **Royalty Fee:** 6%. **Training:** Provides 6 days at headquarters and 2 days at franchisee's location with ongoing support.

3101 ▪ Decorating Elves
Decorative Lighting, Inc.
10460 Roosevelt Blvd., Ste. 292
St. Petersburg, FL 33716
Ph: (813)935-5087
Free: 800-695-4837
Fax: (813)425-5799
Description: Holiday lighting. **No. of Franchise Units:** 3. **No. of Company-Owned Units:** 2. **Founded:** 2006.. **Franchised:** 2007. **Equity Capital Needed:** $15,500-$62,500. **Franchise Fee:** $8,500+. **Financial Assistance:** Yes. **Training:** Yes.

3102 ▪ Discount Imaging Franchise Corporation
206 Texas Ave.
Monroe, LA 71201
Ph: (318)324-8977
Co. E-mail: tim@discountimaging.com
URL: http://www.difcorp.com
Description: Business to business model providing solutions for the full range of printer, fax and copier supplies and service. **No. of Franchise Units:** 11. **No. of Company-Owned Units:** 1. **Founded:** 1995.. **Franchised:** 1998. **Equity Capital Needed:** $75,000. **Franchise Fee:** $25,000. **Training:** Provides 2 week training at home office.

3103 ▪ ESAPP Financial, LLC
6520 E 82nd St., Ste.200
Indianapolis, IN 46250
Ph: (317)577-4995
Fax: (317)577-4996
Description: Financial services company. **Founded:** 1996..

3104 ▪ Franchise Recruiters Ltd.
Saddlebrooke Country Club
63284 E Flower Ridge Dr.
Tucson, AZ 85739
Ph: (520)825-9588
Description: Placement of franchise management professionals. **Founded:** 1977..

3105 ▪ Franchise Sales
1315 S Villa Ave.
Villa Park, IL 60181
Ph: (630)819-2418
Description: Self franchisees in business now. **Founded:** 1991..

3106 ▪ Franchise Search, Inc.
Kushell Associates Inc.
48 Burd St., Ste. 101
Nyack, NY 10960
Ph: (845)727-4103
Description: International executive search firm for franchisors. **Founded:** 1982..

3107 ▪ Goin' Postal
4941 4th St.
Zephyrhills, FL 33542
Ph: (813)782-1500
Description: Retail shipping & business services. **No. of Franchise Units:** 233. **No. of Company-Owned Units:** 1. **Founded:** 2002. **Franchised:** 2004. **Equity Capital Needed:** $46,865-$139,500. **Franchise Fee:** $15,000. **Royalty Fee:** $360/month. **Financial Assistance:** Limited third party financing available. **Training:** 1 week training at headquarters, 1 week at franchisee's location, refresher training at corporate location throughout term of the franchise and ongoing support.

3108 ▪ Handyman-Network Franchise Systems LLC
Handyman Franchise Systems, Inc.
2760 E Spring St., Ste. 212
Long Beach, CA 90806
Ph: (562)216-9292
Free: 877-942-6396
Fax: (562)216-9296
Co. E-mail: franchise@handyman-network.com
URL: http://www.handyman-network.com
Description: Provides homeowners with service, people, systems, and technology. **No. of Franchise Units:** 5. **Founded:** 2000.. **Franchised:** 2002. **Equity Capital Needed:** $67,388-$107,044 total start-up, including franchise fee. **Franchise Fee:** $30,000. **Royalty Fee:** 6%. **Training:** Start-up program is an extensive 3 module training program. Includes 2 weeks of on the job training at headquarters, and 4 days of onsite training. Each module is supported with manuals with ongoing support.

3109 ▪ Ink Solution & Postal
9524 Hebron Commerce Dr.
Charlotte, NC 28273
Free: 866-482-4657
Fax: (704)523-8720
Description: Inkjet & toner cartridge recycling/postal services. **No. of Franchise Units:** 19. **Founded:** 2001. **Franchised:** 2007. **Equity Capital Needed:** $118,000. **Franchise Fee:** $29,000. **Royalty Fee:** 4%. **Training:** Provides 1 week training at headquarters, 1 week at franchisee's location, 1 week at corporate store and ongoing support.

3110 ▪ InkTone
26722 Plaza Dr.
Mission Viejo, CA 92691
Free: 888-465-9481
Fax: (888)465-9452
Description: Inkjet & toner replacements. **Founded:** 2006. **Franchised:** 2006. **Equity Capital Needed:** $130,000-$170,000. **Franchise Fee:** $25,000. **Royalty Fee:** 6%. **Training:** Offers 2 weeks training at headquarters, 1 week at franchisee's location and ongoing support.

3111 ▪ Liberty Tax Service
110 Riviera Dr., Ste. 16
Markham, ON, Canada L3R 5M1
Ph: (905)943-2640
Free: 800-790-3863
Fax: (866)902-1245
Co. E-mail: sales@libtax.com
URL: http://www.libertytaxcanada.ca
Description: Tax preparation service. **No. of Franchise Units:** 252. **No. of Company-Owned Units:** 31. **Founded:** 1972.. **Franchised:** 1997. **Equity Capital Needed:** $33,350-$54,900. **Franchise Fee:** $25,000. **Training:** Provides 5 days training.

3112 ▪ Lord & Partners Ltd.
9-741 Muskoka Rd., Ste. 3 N
Huntsville, ON, Canada P1H 2L3
Ph: (705)788-1966
Free: 877-490-6660
Fax: (705)788-1969
Co. E-mail: info@lordandpartners.com
URL: http://www.lordandpartners.com
Description: Unique business to business franchise network serving a growing $30 billion market in representing Canadian manufactured environmentally responsible solutions that replace hazardous traditional chemicals in the workplace and reduce environmental aspects and impacts on the community. **No.**

of Franchise Units: 4. **No. of Company-Owned Units:** 2. **Founded:** 1990.. **Franchised:** 2005. **Equity Capital Needed:** $200,000. **Franchise Fee:** $50,000. **Training:** Provides 29 days training on the proven proprietary business, marketing systems, a demo 'showroom on wheels,' with ongoing support for a protected territory.

3113 ■ Luxury Bath Systems

1958 Brandon Ct.
Glendale Heights, IL 60139
Ph: (630)295-9084
Free: 800-354-2284
Fax: (630)295-9418
URL: http://www.luxurybath.com

Description: Acrylic and solid surface bathroom remodeling using the latest technology. **No. of Franchise Units:** 100. **Founded:** 1994. **Equity Capital Needed:** $20,000-$40,000. **Franchise Fee:** $16,000. **Training:** 5 days covering marketing, installation and support and 3 days at franchisee's location with ongoing support.

3114 ■ Mail Boxes Etc. - MBEC Communications, Inc.

MBEC Communications, Inc.
1115 North Service Rd. W, Unit 1
Oakville, ON, Canada L6M 2V9
Ph: (905)338-9754
Free: 800-661-6232
Fax: (905)338-7491
Co. E-mail: customerservice@theupsstore.ca
URL: http://www.mbe.ca

Description: With over 4,000 locations worldwide and over 260 centers operating in Canada, MBE is one of the largest and fastest growing business and communications service franchise. Services include expert packing services, shipping, worldwide courier services, black and white and color photocopies, electronic document services, digital color printing, fax sending and receiving, computer rental, word processing, Internet/email access and mail receiving services. **No. of Franchise Units:** 351. **Founded:** 1990.. **Franchised:** 1991. **Equity Capital Needed:** $146,150-$179,550 plus working capital. **Franchise Fee:** $35,900. **Royalty Fee:** 6% of gross. **Training:** Complete pre-opening support provided, including site selection, lease negotiation, design and construction, training, marketing, as well as ongoing operational and marketing field support.

3115 ■ Padgett Business Services

400 Blue Hill Dr., Ste. 201
Westwood, MA 02090
Free: 877-729-8725 x225
Co. E-mail: padgett@smallbizpros.com
URL: http://www.smallbizpros.com

Description: Padgett provides an array of services to small businesses, such as consulting, financial reporting, government compliance, payroll and tax preparation services. Padgett also offers credit card processing, pension and 125 plan administration, equipment financing and workers' compensation payment service. **No. of Franchise Units:** 435. **Founded:** 1966. **Franchised:** 1975. **Equity Capital Needed:** Total investment and net worth $105,955; liquid or cash $78,750. **Franchise Fee:** $56,000. **Financial Assistance:** Third party financing up to $75,000. Also enrolled in the SBA registry. **Training:** Initial training 12 days field visits, covering marketing, operations, and software. Ongoing training and support is provided through regular seminars in marketing, operations, tax, etc. Support is delivered through toll-free telephone and a wide range of information and material is provided via the company's web site.

3116 ■ Padgett Business Services (Oakville, Canada)

3100 boul le Carrefour, Ste. 554
Laval, QC, Canada H7T 2K7
Ph: (888)723-4388
Fax: (877)231-4911
URL: http://www.padgetfranchises.ca

Description: Supplier of small business services including accounting, tax preparation and consultation, payroll services and business advice. **No. of Franchise Units:** 120. **Founded:** 1966.. **Franchised:** 1975. **Equity Capital Needed:** $40,000-$48,000

investment required; $30,000-$50,000 start-up capital required. **Franchise Fee:** $25,000. **Training:** Complete program of training and support.

3117 ■ Profit-Tell International, Inc.

201 Ogden Ave.
Hinsdale, IL 60521
Ph: (630)655-3700
Fax: (630)655-4100
URL: http://www.Profit-Tell.com

Description: Cutting edge marketing systems. **No. of Franchise Units:** 31. **No. of Company-Owned Units:** 1. **Founded:** 1993.. **Franchised:** 2002. **Equity Capital Needed:** $42,000-$60,000. **Franchise Fee:** $42,000 turnkey. **Financial Assistance:** Yes. **Training:** Yes.

3118 ■ ProFleet Care Franchising

51 Sundial Dr.
Dundas, ON, Canada L9M 7R6
Ph: (905)667-8595
Free: 866-787-8645
Co. E-mail: info@profleetcare.com
URL: http://www.profleetcare.com

Description: Pro Fleet Care is a unique and comparatively low start-up cost franchise in the highly profitable rust protection industry. Being the only mobile concept in the industry, Pro Fleet Care prides itself in offering its customers the ability to save money, protect and extend the life of expensive equipment. We are providers of Exceptional Rust Control Service, On site, On time and as Promised. The franchise package includes everything you need to get started in this highly profitable industry. **No. of Franchise Units:** 15. **No. of Company-Owned Units:** 1. **Founded:** 1981.. **Franchised:** 2007. **Equity Capital Needed:** $33,000-$70,000, varies if purchase truck outright. **Franchise Fee:** $20,000. **Training:** Provides 2 weeks training, including technical and operational and ongoing.

3119 ■ Resource Associates Corp.

One Meridian Blvd., Ste. 1C02
Wyomissing, PA 19601
Ph: (800)762-6277
Fax: (610)775-9686
URL: http://www.rac-tqi.com

Description: Network of consultants focusing on people development, strategy, and processes. **No. of Franchise Units:** 600. **Founded:** 1978.. **Equity Capital Needed:** $29,000. **Franchise Fee:** None. **Financial Assistance:** Yes. **Training:** Yes.

3120 ■ Services Select Franchise Company, LLC

1206 Pointe Centre Dr., Ste. 120
Chattanooga, TN 37421
Ph: (423)413-6258
Fax: (423)892-1803

Description: Award system for businesses. **No. of Franchise Units:** 4. **Founded:** 2004.. **Franchised:** 2007. **Equity Capital Needed:** $51,850-$57,350. **Franchise Fee:** $50,000. **Training:** Yes.

3121 ■ The UPS Store / Mail Boxes Etc.

6060 Cornerstone Ct., W
San Diego, CA 92121-3795
Ph: (858)597-8513
Free: 877-623-7253
Fax: (858)546-7492
Co. E-mail: usafranchise@mbe.com
URL: http://www.theupsstore.com

Description: Retail shipping, postal and business services. **No. of Franchise Units:** 4,342. **Founded:** 1980.. **Franchised:** 1980. **Equity Capital Needed:** $176,066-$331,353. **Franchise Fee:** $29,950. **Royalty Fee:** 5%. **Financial Assistance:** Third party and limited in-house financing available. **Training:** Offers 2 weeks at headquarters, 2 weeks at franchisee's location and ongoing support.

3122 ■ We the People USA Inc.

Dollar Financial Group
1436 Lancaster Ave., Ste. 340
Berwyn, PA 19312
Free: 866-429-2785

Fax: (866)480-6970
Co. E-mail: info@wethepeopleusa.com
URL: http://www.wethepeopleusa.com

Description: Legal document preparation. **No. of Franchise Units:** 151. **No. of Company-Owned Units:** 26. **Founded:** 1985. **Franchised:** 1996. **Equity Capital Needed:** $123,200-$169,500. **Franchise Fee:** $89,500. **Training:** Offers 1 week at headquarters, 1 week at franchisee's location and ongoing support.

COMPUTERIZED DATABASES

3123 ■ *Business & Management Practices™*

10650 Toebben Dr.
Independence, KY 41051
Free: 800-354-9706
Fax: (800)487-8488
Co. E-mail: investors@cengage.com
URL: http://www.gale.cengage.com
Contact: Ronald Dunn, President

Availability: Online: ProQuest LLC - Dialog; Cengage Learning Inc. **Type:** Full-text; Bibliographic.

3124 ■ *Florida Trend*

490 First Ave. S, 8th Fl.
Saint Petersburg, FL 33701
Ph: (727)821-5800
Fax: (727)822-5083
Co. E-mail: custrelations@floridatrend.com
URL: http://www.floridatrend.com

Availability: Online: Trend Magazines Inc. **Type:** Full-text.

LIBRARIES

3125 ■ Alabama A & M University - J.F. Drake Memorial Learning Resources Center—Alabama Agricultural and Mechanical University.

4900 Meridian St.
Normal, AL 35762
Ph: (256)372-4747
Fax: (256)372-5764
URL: http://www.aamu.edu/administrativeoffices/library/pages/about-the-library.aspx

Contact: Sadie Davis, Specialist, Circulation

Scope: Education, business and economics, agriculture, the sciences, computer science, literature. **Services:** Interlibrary loan; copying; media services; Center open to the public (courtesy card must be purchased for check out of materials by persons not enrolled at the university or at one of the cooperating institutions). **Founded:** 1904. **Holdings:** 236,147 books; 25,517 bound periodical volumes; 5044 AV programs; 20,869 periodicals on microfilm; 1053 college catalogs; various telephone directories; 16,166 ERIC microfiche; 141,376 government documents; Wall Street Journal on microfiche (11,643). **Subscriptions:** 1657 journals and other serials; 93 newspapers; 359 microfilm subscriptions.

3126 ■ Alameda County Library - Business Library

2400 Stevenson Blvd.
Fremont, CA 94538
Ph: (510)505-7001
URL: http://www.aclibrary.org
Contact: Janet Cronbach

Scope: Starting and managing a business, small business, investments, real estate, International business, management and personnel, career planning, San Francisco Bay area business. **Services:** Interlibrary loan; copying; library open to the public. **Founded:** 1968. **Holdings:** 18,000 books; 300 audiocassettes; 100 videocassettes. **Subscriptions:** 400 journals and other serials; 20 newspapers.

3127 ■ Balch & Bingham LLP - Library

1901 6th Ave. N., Ste. 1500
Birmingham, AL 35203
Ph: (205)251-8100

Fax: (205)226-8798
Co. E-mail: amorrisonlow@balch.com
URL: http://www.balch.com
Contact: Anne Morrison-Low, Director, Library Services
Scope: Law, business. **Services:** Interlibrary loan; Library not open to the public. **Founded:** 1920. **Holdings:** 35,000 volumes; legislative and government documents. **Subscriptions:** 266 journals and other serials.

3128 ■ Boston Consulting Group - Chicago Information and Research Group
300 N. La Salle
Chicago, IL 60654
Ph: (312)993-3300
Fax: (312)876-0771
Co. E-mail: bcgchicago@bcg.com
URL: http://www.bcg.com
URL(s): chicago.bcg.com/. **Scope:** Statistics, finance, industry. **Services:** Interlibrary loan; Library not open to the public. **Founded:** 1979. **Holdings:** 4500 books; 3000 Annual reports; 21 lin.ft. of microfiche; 84 reels of microfilm. **Subscriptions:** 100 journals and other serials; 5 newspapers.

3129 ■ Business Trend Analysts Library
2171 Jericho Tpke., Ste. 200
Commack, NY 11725
Ph: (631)462-5454
Free: 800-866-4648
Fax: (631)462-1842
Co. E-mail: sales@bta-ler.com
URL: http://www.businesstrendanalysts.com
Contact: J. Marquardt, Librarian
Scope: Marketing, business, economics. **Services:** Library not open to the public. **Founded:** 1979. **Holdings:** 200 reports. **Subscriptions:** 400 journals and other serials; 8 newspapers.

3130 ■ California Polytechnic State University - Robert F. Kennedy Library - Government Documents and Map Department - Diablo Canyon Power Plant Depository Library
Bldg. 35
University Dr. cor. N. Perimeter Rd.
San Luis Obispo, CA 93407
Ph: (805)756-2345
Fax: (805)756-2346
Co. E-mail: akgold@calpoly.edu
URL: http://lib.calpoly.edu
Contact: Michael D. Miller, Dean, Library Services
Scope: Nuclear power plants. **Services:** Interlibrary loan; copying; Wi-Fi access; library open to the public. **Holdings:** Figures not available.

3131 ■ Canada Public Works & Government Services - Consulting and Audit Canada Information Centre
112 Kent St., Tower B
Ottawa, ON, Canada K1A 0S5
Ph: (613)943-8387
Fax: (613)947-8159
Co. E-mail: svcinfo-ascinfo@tpsgc-pwgsc.gc.ca
URL: http://www.tpsgc-pwgsc.gc.ca/comm/index-eng.html
Contact: Janet Campbell, Director
Scope: Business, finance, public administration, management consulting. **Services:** Library not open to the public. **Holdings:** Figures not available. **Telecommunication Services:** questions@tpsgc-pwgsc.gc.ca.

3132 ■ Golden Gate University - University Library
536 Mission St.
San Francisco, CA 94105-2968
Ph: (415)442-7244
Free: 877-448-8543
Fax: (415)543-6779
Co. E-mail: jcarter@ggu.edu
URL: http://www.ggu.edu/libraries/university-library
Contact: Aira Lipson, Librarian, Reference
Scope: Business, public administration, information systems, telecommunications. **Services:** Interlibrary loan; libraries open to the public on Annual fee basis. **Founded:** 1901. **Holdings:** 90,000 volumes; 264 microfiche; 435 microfilms. **Subscriptions:** 3000 journals and other serials. **Telecommunication Services:** askalibrarian@ggu.edu.

3133 ■ A.T. Kearney, Inc. - Information Research Center
222 W. Adams St.
Chicago, IL 60606
Ph: (312)648-0111
Fax: (312)223-7242
URL: http://www.atkearney.com
Contact: Noreen Curran, Manager
Scope: Management consulting, automotive industries, benchmarking, business processes, consumer industries, economics, information technology, knowledge management, manufacturing, retail, strategic innovation, strategic sourcing, supply chain integration, transportation. **Services:** Interlibrary loan; Center not open to the public. **Founded:** 1975. **Holdings:** 4300 books; 3 CD-ROMs. **Subscriptions:** 150 journals and other serials.

3134 ■ McKinsey & Company, Inc. - Resource Library
110 Charles St., W.
Toronto, ON, Canada M5S 1K9
Ph: (416)313-3700
Fax: (416)313-2999
URL: http://www.mckinsey.com
Scope: Strategic planning, organization and operations effectiveness, management consulting. **Services:** Interlibrary loan; SDI; center open to clients. **Founded:** 1969. **Holdings:** 3000 books; full depository collection of Statistics Canada documentation. **Subscriptions:** 350 journals and other serials; 12 newspapers.

3135 ■ Towers Watson Information Center
1800 McGill College Ave., 22nd Fl.
Montreal, QC, Canada H3A 3J6
Ph: (514)982-9411
Fax: (514)982-9269
URL: http://www.towerswatson.com/
Scope: Employee benefits, compensation, actuarial science, taxation, labor, social security, employee communications, insurance, human resource management. **Services:** Center not open to the public. **Founded:** 1976. **Holdings:** 2000 books; 100 internal reports; 40 VF drawers of pamphlets and clippings; 1000 microfiche; AV materials. **Subscriptions:** 100 journals and other serials; 6 newspapers.

ASSOCIATIONS AND OTHER ORGANIZATIONS

3136 ■ American Association of Meat Processors (AAMP)
PO Box 269
Elizabethtown, PA 17022
Ph: (717)367-1168
Free: 877-877-0168
Fax: (717)367-9096
Co. E-mail: aamp@aamp.com
URL: http://www.aamp.com
Contact: Jon Frohling, President
Description: Represents small and mid-sized packers, processors, wholesalers, home food service businesses, meat retailers, deli, mail order businesses and catering operators and their suppliers. Represents its members at the federal level of government. Provides education, insurance options and business management assistance to the independent segment of the meat industry. **Scope:** processing, marketing, training, equipment. **Founded:** 1939. **Subscriptions:** 600. **Publications:** *AAMPlifier* (Semimonthly); *Capitol Line-Up* (Semimonthly); *The Membership Directory and Buyers' Guide of the American Association of Meat Processors* (Biennial). **Educational Activities:** American Association of Meat Processors Convention (Annual). **Awards:** Accomplishment Award (Annual); Achievement Award (Annual); American Cured Meat Championship Award (Annual); Best Booth Awards (Annual); Cured Meat Hall of Fame Award (Annual); F.W. Witt Supplier Award (Annual); Golden Cleaver Trophy (Annual); Outstanding Service Award (Annual); Package Wrapping Award (Annual); Sharpest Knife in North America (Annual); Stephen Krut Scholarship Award (Annual); Achievement Award; Cured Meats Hall of Fame; Accomplishment Award; Golden Cleaver Trophy; Best Booth Award; Outstanding Service Award; American Cured Meat Championship Awards; Clarence Knebel Best of Show Memorial Award (Annual); F. W. Witt Supplier of the Year Award; Clarence Knebel Best of Show Memorial Award; Sharpest Knife in North America Award.

3137 ■ American Meat Institute (AMI)
1150 Connecticut Ave. NW, 12th Fl.
Washington, DC 20036
Ph: (202)587-4200
Fax: (202)587-4300
Co. E-mail: webmaster@meatami.com
URL: http://www.meatami.com/
Contact: J. Patrick Boyle, President
Description: Represents the interests of packers and processors of beef, pork, lamb, veal, and turkey products and their suppliers throughout North America. Provides legislative, regulatory, and public relations services. Conducts scientific research. Offers marketing and technical assistance. Sponsors educational programs. **Founded:** 1919. **Educational Activities:** Worldwide Food Expo (Annual); AMI - International Meat Industry Convention and Exposition; International Meat, Poultry, and Seafood Convention and Exposition (Annual). **Awards:** Edward C. Jones Community Service Award; Industry Advancement Award; Supplier of the Year Award.

3138 ■ Canadian Meat Council (CMC)—Conseil des Viandes du Canada (CVC)
1545 Carling Ave., Ste. 407
Ottawa, ON, Canada K1Z 8P9
Ph: (613)729-3911
Fax: (613)729-4997
Co. E-mail: info@cmc-cvc.com
URL: http://www.cmc-cvc.com
Contact: James M. Laws, Executive Director
Description: Meat packers and distributors. Promotes growth and development of the meat industries. Represents members' interests; sponsors promotional campaigns. **Founded:** 1919. **Publications:** *Food Service Meat Manual*.

3139 ■ *Food Service Meat Manual*
1545 Carling Ave., Ste. 407
Ottawa, ON, Canada K1Z 8P9
Ph: (613)729-3911
Fax: (613)729-4997
Co. E-mail: info@cmc-cvc.com
URL: http://www.cmc-cvc.com
Contact: James M. Laws, Executive Director
Price: C$30, 1-9 copies; C$25, 10 copies and above.

3140 ■ National Cattlemen's Beef Association (NCBA)
9110 E Nichols Ave., Ste. 300
Centennial, CO 80112
Ph: (303)694-0305
Free: 866-233-3872
Fax: (303)694-2851
Co. E-mail: membership@beef.org
URL: http://www.beefusa.org
Contact: Jan Lyons, President
URL(s): www.beef.org. **Description:** Represents 149 organizations of livestock marketers, growers, meat packers, food retailers, and food service firms. Conducts extensive program of promotion, education and information about beef, veal, and associated meat products. Conducts projects such as recipe testing and development, food demonstrations, food photography, educational service to colleges, experimental meat cutting methods, merchandising programs, and preparation of materials for newspapers, magazines, radio, and television. **Founded:** 1922. **Publications:** *National Cattlemen Magazine* (Monthly). **Educational Activities:** Cattle Industry Convention & Trade Show (Annual); National Cattlemen's Beef Association Annual Convention and Trade Show (Annual). **Awards:** Distinguished Service Award (Annual). **Telecommunication Services:** nationalcattleman@beef.org.

REFERENCE WORKS

3141 ■ *"Dick Haskayne" in Canadian Business (Vol. 81, March 31, 2008, No. 5, pp. 72)*
Pub: Rogers Media
Ed: Andy Holloway. **Description:** Dick Haskayne says that he learned a lot about business from his dad who ran a butcher shop where they had to make a decision on buying cattle and getting credit.

Haskayne says that family, friends, finances, career, health, and infrastructure are benchmarks that have to be balanced.

3142 ■ *Urner Barry's Meat and Poultry Directory*
Pub: Urner Barry Publications Inc.
URL(s): www.urnerbarry.com/frameset/products_frameset.htmshop.urnerbarry.com. **Ed:** Joseph Soja. **Released:** Biennial; latest edition 2010-2011. **Price:** $199, Individuals. **Covers:** More than 10,000 slaughterers, wholesalers, importers and exporters, brokers, and other processors and handlers of meat and poultry. **Entries include:** Company name, address, phone, fax, names and titles of key personnel, branch offices, brand names, type or nature of business, products handled, and other information, e-mail address. **Arrangement:** Geographical. **Indexes:** Type of business, product, brand name, key personnel, fax.

STATISTICAL SOURCES

3143 ■ *Poultry - U.S.*
MarketResearch.com
Released: 2008. **Price:** $3995.00.

TRADE PERIODICALS

3144 ■ *AAMPlifier*
Pub: American Association of Meat Processors
Ed: Steve Krut, Editor, steve@aamp.com. **Released:** Bimonthly, 2/month. **Description:** Covers association meetings, news of members, industry trends and guidelines, the activities of related organizations.

3145 ■ *Capitol Line-Up*
Pub: American Association of Meat Processors
Ed: Bernard F. Shire, Editor, ber@aamp.com. **Released:** Bimonthly, 26/year. **Price:** $50, nonmembers. **Description:** Features news and information on meat products, issues brought up by the United States Department of Agriculture (USDA) and its Food Safety and Inspection Service (FSIS), other government agencies, and current market conditions. Recurring features include news of research, a calendar of events, reports of meetings, and legislative and regulatory news.

3146 ■ *Iowa Grocer*
Pub: Iowa Grocery Industry Association
Contact: Michelle Hurd, Director
URL(s): www.iowagrocers.com/igia-magazine.cfm. **Released:** Bimonthly

3147 ■ *Lean Trimmings*
Pub: National Meat Association
Ed: Kiran Kernellu, Editor, kiran@nmaonline.org. **Released:** Weekly. **Price:** Included in membership. **Description:** Deals with the latest regulatory and business news on the meat industry. Recurring features include news of research, a calendar of events, reports of meetings, job listings, and sections on members, labor relations, and marketing trends. Remarks: Also available via e-mail.

3148 ■ *Meat & Poultry: The Business Journal of the Meat & Poultry Industry*
Pub: Sosland Publishing Co.
URL(s): www.meatpoultry.com. Ed: Dr. Temple Grandin, Steve Kay, Joel Crews. Released: Monthly Price: $85, Other countries print; $165, Other countries print, airmail delivery.

VIDEOCASSETTES/ AUDIOCASSETTES

3149 ■ *Practice Beef Quality Grading II*
CEV Multimedia
1020 SE Loop 289
Lubbock, TX 79404
Ph: (806)745-8820
Free: 877-610-5017
Fax: (800)243-6398
Co. E-mail: cev@cevmultimedia.com
URL: http://www.cevmultimedia.com
Contact: Jeff Lansdell, President
Released: 19??. Price: $49.95. Description: Centers on the practice of beef quality grading by presenting a wide variety of 50 carcasses for practice grading. Availability: VHS.

3150 ■ *Practice Retail Cut Identification II*
CEV Multimedia
1020 SE Loop 289
Lubbock, TX 79404
Ph: (806)745-8820
Free: 877-610-5017
Fax: (800)243-6398
Co. E-mail: cev@cevmultimedia.com
URL: http://www.cevmultimedia.com
Contact: Jeff Lansdell, President
Released: 19??. Price: $49.95. Description: Furnishes 25 second views of 75 retail cuts from five different meat classes allowing the viewer a chance to practice their retail cut identification skills. Also provides a scoring key. Cuts were selected from the National FFA Meats Evaluation and Management ontest list of 126 approved cuts. Availability: VHS.

3151 ■ *Practice Retail Cut Identification III*
CEV Multimedia
1020 SE Loop 289
Lubbock, TX 79404
Ph: (806)745-8820
Free: 877-610-5017
Fax: (800)243-6398
Co. E-mail: cev@cevmultimedia.com
URL: http://www.cevmultimedia.com
Contact: Jeff Lansdell, President
Released: 19??. Price: $59.95. Description: Practice retail cut identification program which offers 25-second views of 75 different cuts of meat from five different classes. Provides a scoring key. The cuts were selected from the National FFA Meat Evaluation and Management Contest approved list of more than 100 cuts. Availability: VHS.

3152 ■ *Practice Retail Cut Identification IV*
CEV Multimedia
1020 SE Loop 289
Lubbock, TX 79404
Ph: (806)745-8820
Free: 877-610-5017
Fax: (800)243-6398
Co. E-mail: cev@cevmultimedia.com
URL: http://www.cevmultimedia.com
Contact: Jeff Lansdell, President
Released: 19??. Price: $59.95. Description: Presents 25-second views of 75 retail cuts from five different classes allowing the viewer to practice their retail cut identification skills. Provides a scoring key. Cuts were selected from the National FFA Meat Evaluation and Management Contest approved list of 126 cuts. Availability: VHS.

TRADE SHOWS AND CONVENTIONS

3153 ■ American Convention of Meat Processors
American Association of Meat Processors
One Meating Pl.
Elizabethtown, PA 17022
Ph: (717)367-1168
Free: 877-877-0168
Fax: (717)367-9096
Co. E-mail: aamp@aamp.com
URL: http://www.aamp.com
Contact: Daniel Glier, President
URL(s): www.aamp.com. Frequency: Annual. Audience: Slaughtering; packing; meat, poultry and seafood processors; wholesalers, retailers, and supermarkets; catalog businesses; catering and deli operators/owners. Principal Exhibits: Processing equipment; packaging supplies and equipment; technical and computer services; deli, mail order, and catering supplies; marketing aids; transportation; chilling and building information; laboratory services and testing equipment; consultants in various food processing areas. Telecommunication Services: aamp@aamp.com.

FRANCHISES AND BUSINESS OPPORTUNITIES

3154 ■ Logan Farms Honey Glazed Hams
10560 Westheimer Rd.
Houston, TX 77042
Ph: (713)781-4335
Free: 800-833-HAMS
Description: Gourmet meat stores, specializing in the sale of honey-glazed, spiral-sliced hams. Also sells gourmet rib eye roast, pork loins, chicken breast, smoked turkeys, spiral-sliced boneless hams, spiral-sliced honey-glazed turkey breast, smoked sausage, bacon, cheesecakes and a variety of honey mustard and preserves. Stores also have a deli department making a variety of sub sandwiches and poor-boys. conduct of the franchisees business. No. of Franchise Units: 12. No. of Company-Owned Units: 1. Founded: 1984.. Equity Capital Needed: $100,000 cash. Franchise Fee: $30,000. Training: 2 weeks on procedures and techniques in manufacturing and marketing the products, manuals for advertising and market programs, record-keeping and inventory control.

3155 ■ M & M Meat Shops, Ltd.
640 Trillium Dr.
Kitchener, ON, Canada N2H 6M3
Ph: (519)895-1075
Fax: (519)895-0762
Description: Sells specialty flash-frozen foods, including beef, pork, poultry, seafood, party foods, vegetables, desserts, etc. Primarily heat-and-serve convenience foods. Most portions are controlled. No. of Company-Owned Units: 4. Founded: 1980.. Franchised: 1981. Equity Capital Needed: $320,000. Franchise Fee: $30,000. Royalty Fee: 3%. Training: Provides 2 weeks at headquarters, 2 days at franchisees location with ongoing support.

LIBRARIES

3156 ■ National Cattlemen's Beef Association Library
9110 E. Nichols Ave., Ste. 300
Centennial, CO 80112-3425
Ph: (303)694-0305
Fax: (303)694-2851
Co. E-mail: nationalcattlemen@beef.org
URL: http://www.beefusa.org/
Contact: Forrest Roberts, Chief Executive Officer
Scope: Meat, nutrition, food economics, cookery. Services: Interlibrary loan; copying; center open to industry members by appointment. Founded: 1976. Holdings: 5000 books; 600 reports; 28 VF drawers of reprints, clippings, government documents. Subscriptions: 400 journals and other serials; 8 newspapers. Telecommunication Services: information@ beef.org.

ASSOCIATIONS AND OTHER ORGANIZATIONS

3157 ■ CTAM - Cable and Telecommunications Association for Marketing
120 Waterfront St., Ste. 200
Oxon Hill, MD 20745
Ph: (301)485-8900
Fax: (301)560-4964
Co. E-mail: info@ctam.com
URL: http://www.ctam.com
Contact: Char Beales, President
Description: Network of cable and telecommunications professionals dedicated to the pursuit of marketing excellence. Provides its members with competitive marketing resources including education, research, networking and leadership opportunities. **Scope:** cable and telecommunications marketing. **Founded:** 1975. **Subscriptions:** 300. **Publications:** *CTAM Quarterly Journal* (Quarterly). **Awards:** Chairman's Award (Periodic); CTAM Hall of Fame (Annual); Grand TAM Award (Annual); Mark Awards (Annual); Rainmaker Award (Annual); TAMI Awards (Annual); One of a Kind Award (Periodic).

3158 ■ Jones NCTI
9697 E Mineral Ave.
Centennial, CO 80112
Ph: (303)797-9393
Free: 866-575-7206
Fax: (303)797-9394
Co. E-mail: customerservice@ncti.com
URL: http://www.ncti.com
Contact: Timothy J. Burke, President
URL(s): www.jonesncti.com. **Description:** Provides comprehensive broadband training for the cable television industry. Offers career training resources and courses in areas ranging from customer service procedures to optical fiber system design, installation, and maintenance. **Founded:** 1968. **Publications:** *Spanish/English CATV Dictionary.* **Telecommunication Services:** infouse@ncti.com; info@jonesncti.com; customercare@jonesncti.com.

3159 ■ National Cable and Telecommunications Association (NCTA)
25 Massachusetts Ave. NW, Ste. 100
Washington, DC 20001-1413
Ph: (202)222-2300
Fax: (202)222-2514
Co. E-mail: webmaster@ncta.com
URL: http://www.ncta.com
Contact: Michael K. Powell, President
Description: Franchised cable operators, programmers, and cable networks; associate members are cable hardware suppliers and distributors; affiliate members are brokerage and law firms and financial institutions; state and regional cable television associations cooperate, but are not affiliated, with the organization. Serves as national medium for exchange of experiences and opinions through research, study, discussion, and publications. Represents the cable industry before Congress, the Federal Communications Commission and various courts on issues of primary importance. Conducts research program in conjunction with National Academy of Cable Programming. Sponsors, in conjunction with Motion Picture Association of America, the Coalition Opposing Signal Theft, an organization designed to deter cable signal theft and to develop anti-piracy materials. Provides promotional aids and information on legal, legislative and regulatory matters. Compiles statistics. **Founded:** 1952. **Publications:** *Cable Industry Overview* (Semiannual). **Educational Activities:** National Cable Show (Annual). **Awards:** Distinguished Vanguard Awards for Leadership; Vanguard Award for Cable Operations Management.

3160 ■ Society of Cable Telecommunications Engineers (SCTE)
140 Philips Rd.
Exton, PA 19341-1318
Ph: (610)363-6888
Free: 800-542-5040
Fax: (610)363-5898
Co. E-mail: scte@scte.org
URL: http://www.scte.org
Contact: Mark Dzuban, President
E-mail: mdzuban@scte.org
Description: Persons engaged in engineering, construction, installation, technical direction, management, or administration of cable telecommunications and broadband communications technologies. Also eligible are students in communications, educators, government and regulatory agency employees, and affiliated trade associations. Dedicated to the technical training and further education of members. Provides technical training and certification and is an American National Standards Institute (ANSI) approved Standards Development Organization for the cable communications industry. **Founded:** 1969. **Publications:** *Communications Technology* (Monthly); *Interval* (Monthly); *Society of Cable Telecommunications Engineers--Membership Directory and Yearbook* (Annual). **Educational Activities:** Cable-Tec Expo (Annual); Mid-America Cable Telecommunications Association Meeting & Show (Annual). **Awards:** Member of the Year; Chairman's Award. **Telecommunication Services:** membership@scte.org; information@scte.org.

3161 ■ Women in Cable Telecommunications (WICT)
14555 Avion Pkwy., Ste. 250
Chantilly, VA 20151
Ph: (703)234-9810
Fax: (703)817-1595
Co. E-mail: mbrennan@wict.org
URL: http://www.wict.org
Contact: Kathy Payne, Chairwoman
Description: Empowers and educates women to achieve their professional goals by providing opportunities for leadership, networking and advocacy. **Founded:** 1979. **Publications:** *The Catalyst* (Monthly); *Insights* (Quarterly); *WICT Wire.* **Educational Activities:** Women's Leadership Summit (Annual). **Awards:** Woman of the Year Award; Forerunner Accolades (Annual); Woman of the Year (Annual); Woman to Watch (Annual).

REFERENCE WORKS

3162 ■ *"10 Trends That Are Shaping Global Media Consumption"* in Advertising Age (Vol. 81, December 6, 2010, No. 43, pp. 3)
Pub: Crain Communications, Inc.
Ed: Ann Marie Kerwin. **Description:** Ad Age offers the statistics from the TV penetration rate in Kenya to the number of World Cup watchers and more.

3163 ■ *"Advertising May Take a Big Hit in Southwest/AirTran Merger"* in Baltimore Business Journal (Vol. 28, October 1, 2010, No. 21, pp. 1)
Pub: Baltimore Business Journal
Ed: Gary Haber. **Description:** Advertising on television stations and the publishing industry in Baltimore could drop as a result of the merger between rival discount airlines Southwest Airlines and AirTran Airways. Southwest is among the top advertisers in the U.S., spending $126 million in 2009. No local jobs are expected to be affected because neither airline uses a local advertising firm.

3164 ■ *"At 5-Year Mark, News 9 Makes Presence Felt in Competition for Ad Dollars"* in Business Review, Albany New York (October 5, 2007)
Pub: American City Business Journals, Inc.
Ed: Barbara Pinckney. **Description:** The 24-hour news channel Capital News 9 can be watched live by viewers on their cell phones beginning late 2007 or early 2008 as part of a deal between Time Warner Cable and Sprint Nextel Corporation to bring Sprint's Pivot technology. News 9 marked its fifth year and plans to continue expanding coverage and provide better services to viewers.

3165 ■ *"Baxter Baker Wins in Hot Finale of 'Cupcake Wars"* in Fort Mill Times (September 13, 2011)
Pub: McClatchy Company
Ed: Jenny Overmann. **Description:** Heather McDonnell, owner of Cupcrazed Cakery, and her assistant Debbie McDonnell, vied for a chance to win $10,000 on the cable network show called 'Cupcake Wars', and to serve cupcakes at the album release party for country singer Jennette McCurdy. At the end of the show, the sisters-in-law won the top prize.

3166 ■ *"Black Network Shifts Gears: Struggling Channel To Focus On Broadband TV"* in Black Enterprise (Vol. 38, November 2007, No. 4, pp. 34)
Pub: Earl G. Graves Publishing Co. Inc.
Ed: Wendy Isom. **Description:** Rick Newberger, president and CEO of Black Family Channel's television platform discusses its plans to switch to broadband format programming offering various channels simultaneously with fewer costs.

3167 ■ *Bowdens International Directory*
Pub: Cision Canada Inc.
Contact: Terry G. Foster, President
URL(s): ca.cision.com/. **Released:** 3 times a year. **Price:** $275, Individuals per year (book). **Covers:** Daily and community newspapers, periodicals, radio

and television broadcasting stations, and cable television systems; network television personnel, wire service offices, and other media in Canada. **Entries include:** For newspapers and periodicals--Name, address, phone, fax, telex, circulation, ownership, news service, publisher and editors. For radio and television stations--Call letters, address, phone, fax, telex, type of programming, names and titles of key personnel, watts, air personalities, local programs aired including times and names of contacts. For cable television systems--Firm name, address, fax, names and titles of key personnel, ownership, programming hours. **Arrangement:** Geographical.

3168 ■ *Burrelle's New Jersey Media Directory*
Pub: BurrellesLuce
Contact: Robert Waggoner, Chief Executive Officer
URL(s): www.burrellesluce.com. **Released:** Annual **Price:** $60, plus $4.00 shipping. **Covers:** Over 1,200 New Jersey periodicals, newspapers, college publications, radio and television stations, and cable television systems. Also includes New York City and Philadelphia daily newspapers. **Entries include:** For publications--Title, publisher name, address, phone, names and titles of key personnel, frequency, circulation, geographical area covered, advertising and editorial deadlines. For others--Call letters and/or company name and address, names and titles of key personnel, markets covered. **Arrangement:** Classified by type of media, then town. **Indexes:** Alphabetical, geographical (county).

3169 ■ *Cable TV Facts*
Pub: Cabletelevision Advertising Bureau
URL(s): www.thecab.tv. **Released:** Annual; Latest edition 2012. **Price:** $10.99, Members 1-49 each; $24, Nonmembers; $10.25, Members 50-99 each; $9.25, Members 100-249 each; $8.25, Members 250 plus, each. **Publication includes:** List of ad-supported cable networks. Principal content of publication is discussion of the growth of the cable television industry, changes in viewership, marketing, and research trends. Covers demographic information, audience ratings, cable penetration, regional sports and news networks, major market inter-connects.

3170 ■ *Call Me Ted*
Pub: Grand Central Publishing
Ed: Ted Turner. **Released:** 2008. **Price:** $30.00. **Description:** Media mogul, Ted Turner's biography is full of personal and business details from his careers in advertising and broadcasting.

3171 ■ *"Comcast Launches New Home Security Service, Developed in Portland" in The Oregonian (June 7, 2011)*
Pub: McClatchy-Tribune Regional News
Ed: Mike Rogoway. **Description:** Comcast introduced its new high-end home security system that provides 24-hour monitoring and control of homes and utilities, along with Web and mobile access.

3172 ■ *"Commercials Make Us Like TV More" in Harvard Business Review (Vol. 88, October 2010, No. 10, pp. 36)*
Pub: Harvard Business School Publishing
Ed: Leif Nelson. **Description:** Research indicates that people prefer commercial interruption over uninterrupted shows due to the break creating a reactivation of the initial pleasure when beginning a desirable activity.

3173 ■ *"'Cupcake Wars' TV Show Returns to Hampton Roads" in Virginian-Pilot (September 11, 2011)*
Pub: McClatchy Company
Ed: Carolyn Shapiro. **Description:** Virginia Beach, Virginia sweet shop called Just Cupcakes and Carolina Cupcakery will compete for prizes on cable TV's Food Network Channel. Carla Hesseltine, owner of Just Cupcakes made it to the final rounds.

3174 ■ *"Detroit Pawn Shop to be Reality TV Venue" in UPI NewsTrack (July 10, 2010)*
Pub: United Press International-USA
Description: TruTV will present a new series called 'Hardcore Pawn' to compete with the History Channel's successful show 'Pawn Stars'. The show will

feature American Jewelry and Loan in Detroit, Michigan and its owner Les Gold, who runs the store with his wife and children.

3175 ■ *"Don't' Hate the Cable Guy" in Saint Louis Business Journal (Vol. 31, August 5, 2011, No. 50, pp. 1)*
Pub: Saint Louis Business Journal
Ed: Angela Mueller. **Description:** Charter Communications named John Birrer as senior vice president of customer experience. The company experienced problems with its customer services.

3176 ■ *"Exiting Stage Left" in Baltimore Business Journal (Vol. 28, June 18, 2010, No. 6, pp. 1)*
Pub: Baltimore Business Journal
Ed: Scott Dance. **Description:** Film professionals including crew members and actors have been leaving Maryland to find work in other states such as Michigan, Louisiana, and Georgia where bigger budgets and film production incentives are given. Other consequences of this trend in local TV and film production are discussed.

3177 ■ *"For Apple, It's Showtime Again" in Barron's (Vol. 90, August 30, 2010, No. 35, pp. 29)*
Pub: Barron's Editorial & Corporate Headquarters
Ed: Eric J. Savitz. **Description:** Speculations on what Apple Inc. will unveil at its product launch event are presented. These products include a possible new iPhone Nano, a new update to its Apple TV, and possibly a deal with the Beatles to distribute their songs over iTunes.

3178 ■ *Freelancing for Journalists*
Pub: Routledge
Ed: Diana Harris. **Released:** January 1, 2010. **Price:** $110.00. **Description:** Comprehensive guide showing the specific skills required for those wishing to freelance in newspapers, magazines, radio, television, and as online journalists.

3179 ■ *"iControl Networks Powers Comcast's XFINITY (Reg) Home Security Service" in Benzinga.com (June 9, 2011)*
Pub: Benzinga.com
Ed: Benzinga Staff. **Description:** Comcast's XFINITY Home Security Service is powered by iControl Networks' OpenHome (TM) software platform. The service provides intrusion and fire protection along with interactive features such as home monitoring, home management, and energy management services with Web and mobile access.

3180 ■ *International Television and Video Almanac*
Pub: Quigley Publishing Co.
Contact: William J. Quigley, President
URL(s): quigleypublishing.com/. **Ed:** Eileen Quigley. **Released:** Annual; January; latest edition 2013. **Price:** $235, Individuals. **Covers:** "Who's Who in Motion Pictures and Television and Home Video," television networks, major program producers, major group station owners, cable television companies, distributors, firms serving the television and home video industry, equipment manufacturers, casting agencies, literary agencies, advertising and publicity representatives, television stations, associations, list of feature films produced for television; statistics, industry's year in review, award winners, satellite and wireless cable provider, primetime programming, video producers, distributors, wholesalers. **Entries include:** Generally, company name, address, phone; manufacturer and service listings may include description of products and services and name of contact; producing, distributing, and station listings include additional detail, and contacts for cable and broadcast networks. **Arrangement:** Classified by service or activity. **Indexes:** Full.

3181 ■ *"Johnson Publishing Expands: Moving Into Television and Internet To Extend Brand" in Black Enterprise (October 2007)*
Pub: Earl G. Graves Publishing Co. Inc.
Ed: Tamara E. Holmes. **Description:** Johnson Publishing Company has followed the lives of black families in both Ebony and Jet magazines. The media

firm has expanded its coverage by developing entertainment content for television, the Internet and other digital arenas.

3182 ■ *"KXAN Seeks Larger Studio, Office Space" in Austin Business Journal (Vol. 31, May 27, 2011, No. 12, pp. A1)*
Pub: American City Business Journals Inc.
Ed: Cody Lyon. **Description:** Austin NBC affiliate KXAN Television is opting to sell its property north of downtown and relocate to another site. The station is now inspecting possible sites to house its broadcasting facility and employees totaling as many as 200 people. Estimated cost of the construction of the studios and offices is $13 million plus another million in moving the equipment.

3183 ■ *"Local TV Hits Media Radar Screen" in Business Courier (Vol. 27, July 2, 2010, No. 9, pp. 1)*
Pub: Business Courier
Ed: Dan Monk. **Description:** Fort Wright, Kentucky-based broadcasting company Local TV LLC has acquired 18 television stations since its founding in 2007, potentially boosting its chances of becoming a media empire. In the last twelve months that ended in March 2010, Local TV LLC has posted total revenues of $415 million. How Local TV LLC has entered into cost-sharing deals with other stations is also discussed.

3184 ■ *Matthews CATV Directory*
Pub: Marketwire
URL(s): www.cdn-news.com. **Released:** Annual; Published in May and November. **Price:** $280, Single issue blue and green; $415, Individuals blue and green (one year); $740, Two years blue and green; $350, Single issue red plus green or blue; $510, Individuals red plus green or blue (one year); $910, Two years red plus green or blue; $150, Single issue green or blue only; $225, Individuals green or blue only (one year); $400, Two years green or blue only. **Covers:** Cable television systems and pay television specialty channels, microwave, and satellite services in Canada.

3185 ■ *Media, Organizations and Identity*
Pub: Palgrave Macmillan
Ed: Lilie Chouliaraki, Mette Morsing. **Released:** January 19, 2010. **Price:** $90.00. **Description:** The mass media, press and television are a essential in the formation of corporate identity and the promotion of business image and reputation. This book offers a new perspective into the interrelationships between media and organizations over three dimensions: media as business, media in business and business in the media.

3186 ■ *"Political Ads Big Boost to Local Media" in Baltimore Business Journal (Vol. 28, October 22, 2010, No. 24, pp. 1)*
Pub: Baltimore Business Journal
Ed: Scott Dance. **Description:** Information about the intense demand for advertising time from political campaigns in Baltimore, Maryland is provided. The surge in political advertisement spending would mean big money for local broadcasters, because they see a surging demand for local advertising time for virtually any time of day.

3187 ■ *"Prime-Time Exposure" in Inc. (March 2008, pp. 66, 68)*
Pub: Gruner & Jahr USA Publishing
Ed: Adam Bluestein. **Description:** Product placement in television shows has increase sales for many companies. Tips for placing products or services into TV shows are explained: consider hiring an agency, target efforts, dream up a plot point, be ready to go on short notice, and work the niches.

3188 ■ *"Ready, Aim, (Cool) Fire" in Saint Louis Business Journal (Vol. 32, September 2, 2011, No. 1, pp. 1)*
Pub: Saint Louis Business Journal
Ed: E.B. Solomont. **Description:** Coolfire Originals' CEO Jeff Keane is co-producing 'Welcome Sweetie Pie's' with Los Angeles, California-based Pilgrims Films and Television Films for the Oprah Winfrey

Network. The reality show focuses on restaurant owner Robbie Montgomery of Sweetie Pie's in St. Louis, Missouri.

3189 ■ "Recovery on Tap for 2010?" in Orlando Business Journal (Vol. 26, January 1, 2010, No. 31, pp. 1)
Pub: American City Business Journals

Ed: Melanie Stawicki Azam, Richard Bilbao, Christopher Boyd, Anjali Fluker. **Description:** Economic forecasts for Central Florida's leading business sectors in 2010 are presented. These sectors include housing, film and TV, sports business, law, restaurants, aviation, tourism and hospitality, banking and finance, commercial real estate, retail, health care, insurance, higher education, and manufacturing. According to some local executives, Central Florida's economy will slowly recover in 2010.

3190 ■ "Reds Hit Ratings Homer" in Business Courier (Vol. 27, July 30, 2010, No. 13, pp. 1)
Pub: Business Courier

Ed: Steve Watkins, James Ourand. **Description:** Cincinnati Reds fans have tuned in to their TVs and radios as their team made a hottest start to a season. The Reds TV ratings have increased 49 percent during the first six months of 2010 and continued to rise while the Reds' games broadcast on WLW-AM reported the highest average audience share per game of any Major League Baseball team.

3191 ■ "Storytelling Star of Show for Scripps" in Business Courier (Vol. 26, November 13, 2009, No. 29, pp. 1)
Pub: American City Business Journals, Inc.

Ed: Dan Monk. **Description:** Rich Boehne, CEO Of the EW Scripps Company in Cincinnati has authorized a new training program in storytelling for employees at Scripps' 10 television stations. He believes that the training will improve the quality of broadcasting content. His plans to improve quality of newspaper content are also discussed.

3192 ■ "Summit, Lions Gate are in Talks to Merge Studios" in Wall Street Journal Eastern Edition (November 29, 2011, pp. B2)
Pub: Dow Jones & Company Inc. Enterprise Media Group

Contact: Clare Hart, President

Ed: Erica Orden, Michelle Kung. **Description:** Movie studio Summit Entertainment LLC is in talks with television producer Lions Gate Entertainment Corporation about a possible merger. Previous talks have taken place, but no deal was ever reached. Such a deal would create a large, independent studio able to compete in the market with the big Hollywood giants.

3193 ■ "Television Broadcasting" in MarketingMagazine (Vol. 115, September 27, 2010, No. 13, pp. 16)
Pub: Rogers Publishing Ltd.

Description: Market statistics covering the Canadian television broadcasting industry are covered.

3194 ■ "Two Local Bakers Winners of TV's 'Cupcake Wars" in Toledo Blade (July 6, 2011)
Pub: Toledo Times

Description: Winners of cable network Food Channel's Cupcake Wars, Lori Jacobs and Dana Iliev own Cake in a Cup in Toledo, Ohio. The partners shop features creative cupcakes with names such as Monkey Business, Pretty in Pink, and Tropical Getaway.

3195 ■ "Waco Pawn Shop Owners Say Reality Isn't Much Like 'Pawn Stars' TV Show" in Waco Tribune-Herald (August 15, 2010)
Pub: Waco Tribune-Herald

Ed: Mike Copeland. **Description:** Area pawn shop owners report that the television show on cable TV does not represent the true life operations of a pawn shop. The Las Vegas shop represented on TV boasts 30 employees and 21 on-call experts, which is not the case in reality.

3196 ■ The Weather Channel
Pub: Harvard Business School Press

Ed: Frank Batten with Jeffrey L. Cruikshank. **Released:** 2002. **Price:** $29.95. **Description:** Frank Batten illustrates the power of a resourceful growth strategy along with details the journey he successfully took his small, private newspaper into the cable industry.

3197 ■ "A Whiff of TV Reality" in Houston Business Journal (Vol. 40, January 22, 2010, No. 37, pp. A1)
Pub: American City Business Journals

Ed: Christine Hall. **Description:** Houston, Texas-based Waste Management Inc.'s president and chief operation officer, Larry O'Donnell shares some of his experience as CBS Television Network reality show 'Undercover Boss' participant. O'Donnell believes the show was a great way to show the customers how tough their jobs are and reveals that the most difficult job was being a sorter at the recycling center.

SOURCES OF SUPPLY

3198 ■ FINDERBINDER--Arizona: Arizona's Updated Media Directory
Rita Sanders Advertising Public Relations
Contact: Rita Sanders, Owner
E-mail: rita@ritasanders.com

URL(s): www.finderbinderaz.com. **Released:** Annual **Description:** "FINDERBINDER" directories are loose-leaf directories of broadcast and print media covering states or smaller areas published by companies, licensed to use the name and format by Finderbinder (see entry for "FINDERBINDER--San Diego"). Types of media covered include daily and weekly local and outstate newspapers; religious, ethnic, and labor papers; business, trade, sports, recreation, and general interest publications; college papers; and radio and television stations in Arizona. **Entries include:** Publication or station name, names of management, editorial, and advertising personnel, deadlines, frequency or circulation as appropriate, and other data; cable TV listings. **Arrangement:** Classified by type of medium. **Indexes:** Publication or station name.

3199 ■ FINDERBINDER--Greater Detroit
C & E Communications Inc.
Contact: Sharon Castle, President

URL(s): www.michiganfinderbinder.com. **Released:** Annual; September; bimonthly updates. **Price:** $250, Individuals set including outside Michigan. **Description:** "FINDERBINDER" directories are loose-leaf directories of broadcast and print media covering states or smaller areas published by companies, usually advertising and public relations firms, licensed to use the name and format by Finderbinder (see separate entry for "FINDERBINDER--San Diego"). Detroit's FINDERBINDER covers more than 440 media, including daily and weekly newspapers; religious, ethnic, and labor papers; business, trade, sports, recreation, and general interest publications; college papers; and radio and television stations in the seven-county Detroit metro area. **Entries include:** Publication or station name, names of management, editorial, and advertising personnel, deadlines, frequency or circulation as appropriate, and other data; radio, TV, and cable TV listings give name of public service announcement (PSA) director, interview format programs. **Arrangement:** Classified by type of medium. **Indexes:** Publication or station name, geographical, cable by community.

3200 ■ FINDERBINDER--Oklahoma
FINDERBINDER of Oklahoma

URL(s): www.finderbinderok.com. **Released:** Annual **Description:** 'FINDERBINDER' directories are loose-leaf directories of broadcast and print media covering states or smaller areas published by companies, usually advertising and public relations firms, licensed to use the name and format by Finderbinder (see entry for 'FINDERBINDER--San Diego'). Types of media covered include daily and weekly local and outstate newspapers; religious, ethnic, and labor papers; business, trade, sports, recreation, and general interest publications; college papers; and radio and television stations in Oklahoma. **Entries include:** Publication

or station name, names of management, editorial, and advertising personnel, deadlines, frequency or circulation as appropriate, and other data; cable TV listings show homes served. **Arrangement:** Classified by type of medium. **Indexes:** Publication or station name.

TRADE PERIODICALS

3201 ■ Cable Yellow Pages
Pub: Teton Media Inc.

URL(s): www.cableyellowpages.com. **Released:** Annual **Price:** $42.95, Individuals.

3202 ■ Movie Entertainment
Pub: Feature Publishing Ltd.

URL(s): www.movieentertainment.ca/. **Released:** Monthly **Price:** $17, Individuals.

3203 ■ Russian Telecom Newsletter
Pub: Information Gatekeepers Inc.
Contact: Jeremy Awori, Publisher

Ed: Prof. Sergei L. Galkin, Editor. **Released:** Monthly. **Price:** $695, U.S. and Canada; $745, elsewhere; $695 PDF email version. **Description:** Covers the telecommunications industry in Russia, including competition, government regulations, international business and ventures, cellular, satellites, and market intelligence. Also features new products and conference reports.

3204 ■ TelevisionWeek
Pub: Crain Communications Inc.

URL(s): www.tvweek.com/. **Released:** Weekly **Price:** $119, Individuals; $171, Canada incl. GST; $309, Other countries airmail.

3205 ■ TV International Daily
Pub: Informa Publishing Group

Released: Daily. **Price:** $1,995, U.S. via fax; $1,995, U.S. via e-mail; $2,495, U.S. via fax and. **Description:** Provides news on international television, cable, satellite, digital, and pay and pay-per-view. Remarks: Available via fax or e-mail.

3206 ■ Utilities Telecommunications News
Pub: Information Gatekeepers Inc.
Contact: Paul Polishuk, Managing Editor

Released: Monthly. **Price:** $695, U.S. and Canada; $745, elsewhere; $695 PDF email version. **Description:** Focuses on the role of utilities in telecommunications. Topics include government and regulations, business, and the Internet. Also features new products and conferences.

TRADE SHOWS AND CONVENTIONS

3207 ■ Broadcast Cable Financial Management Association Conference
Broadcast Cable Financial Management Association
550 Frontage Rd., Ste. 3600
Northfield, IL 60093
Ph: (847)716-7000
Fax: (847)716-7004
Co. E-mail: info@bcfm.com
URL: http://www.bcfm.com
Contact: Joe Barlek, Chairman of the Board
E-mail: jbarlek@suscom.com

URL(s): www.bcfm.com. **Price:** $895, Pre-registered, members; $795, Pre-registered, members corporate member advance registration; $695, Members past MFM/BCCA Chairpersons; $1095, Non-members. **Frequency:** Annual. **Audience:** Business managers, CFOs. **Principal Exhibits:** Exhibits relating to the financial management of radio, television, and cable television operations, including issues such as industry - specific software, collection agencies, insurance, investments, banking, accounting firms and music licensing.

3208 ■ Cabletelevision Advertising Bureau - Cable Advertising Conference
Cabletelevision Advertising Bureau
830 3rd Ave., 2nd Fl.
New York, NY 10022
Ph: (212)508-1200

Fax: (212)832-3268
URL: http://www.thecab.tv/
URL(s): www.thecab.tv/. **Price:** $800, Members. **Frequency:** Annual. **Audience:** Cable television and advertising trade. **Principal Exhibits:** Cable television and advertising equipment, supplies, and services.

FRANCHISES AND BUSINESS OPPORTUNITIES

3209 ■ The Utility Company Ltd.
One Hines Rd., Ste. 301
Kanata, ON, Canada K2K 3C7
Ph: (613)591-9800
Fax: (613)591-3966
URL: http://www.theutilitycompany.com
Description: Supplier of information technology delivered as a utility service to small and medium businesses, providing the required hardware, software and service for a monthly fee per user. Our Connected Office service suite empowers people to operate, communicate and manage their business more effectively. **No. of Franchise Units:** 52. **No. of Company-Owned Units:** 2. **Founded:** 2006.. **Franchised:** 2006. **Equity Capital Needed:** $45,119-$70,357 investment required; $45,119 start-up capital required. **Franchise Fee:** $39,000. **Training:** Yes.

LIBRARIES

3210 ■ Alliance for Community Media Library
1760 Old Meadow Rd., Ste. 500
McLean, VA 22102-4306

Ph: (703)506-2889
Co. E-mail: info@allcommunitymedia.org
URL: http://www.allcommunitymedia.org/
Contact: Sylvia Strobel, Executive Director
Scope: Cable television - community access, local origination, legislation, industry, franchising; public television; educational television; governmental access television. **Services:** Library not open to the public. **Founded:** 1976. **Holdings:** 6 books; 1 bound periodical volume. **Subscriptions:** 1 journal.

3211 ■ American Film Institute - Louis B. Mayer Library
2021 N. Western Ave.
Box 27999
Los Angeles, CA 90027-1657
Ph: (323)856-7654
Fax: (323)856-7803
Co. E-mail: library@afi.com
URL: http://www.afi.com/about/library.aspx
Contact: Caroline Sisneros, Librarian
Scope: Moving pictures, television, video, cable, satellite. **Services:** Copying; indexing (microfiche); library open to the public. **Founded:** 1969. **Holdings:** 14,000 books; 900 bound periodical volumes; 6000 motion picture and television scripts; 44 oral history transcripts; 535 seminar transcripts; 600 seminar audiotapes; 75 reels of microfilm. **Subscriptions:** 100 journals and other serials (approximately); 5 newspapers.

3212 ■ CBS Television Law Library
51 W. 52nd St., 36th Fl.
New York, NY 10019
Ph: (212)975-4260

Fax: (212)975-7292
URL: http://www.cbs.com
Contact: Marilee N. Martel, Manager, Information Services
Scope: Communications, copyright, cable television, entertainment law, broadcasting, intellectual property. **Services:** Copying; Library open to the public by appointment (LLAGNY and SLA members only). **Holdings:** 4800 books. **Subscriptions:** 30 journals and other serials; 5 newspapers.

3213 ■ National Cable Television Institute Resource Center—NCTI - Resource Center.
9697 E. Mineral Ave.
Centennial, CO 80112-3408
Ph: (303)797-9393
Free: 866-575-7206
URL: http://www.jonesncti.com
Contact: Glen R. Jones, Chief Executive Officer
Scope: Technical careers in broadband communications. **Services:** Library not open to the public. **Founded:** 1968. **Holdings:** 20,000 training manuals.

3214 ■ Quebec Province Communications et Societe - Centre de Documentation
1340 Boulevard St. Joseph, E.
Montreal, QC, Canada H2J 1M3
Ph: (514)524-8223
Fax: (514)524-8522
Co. E-mail: ocs@officecom.qc.ca
URL: http://www.officecom.qc.ca
Contact: Martin Girard, Director
Scope: Cinema, radio, television, cablevision, videotext, the press. **Services:** Copying; library open to the media, with restrictions. **Founded:** 1957. **Holdings:** 6000 books; 400 bound periodical volumes; microfilm; unbound documents. **Subscriptions:** 60 journals and other serials; 10 newspapers. **Telecommunication Services:** dg@office.com.qc.ca.

Calligraphy Service

ASSOCIATIONS AND OTHER ORGANIZATIONS

3215 ■ Association for the Calligraphic Arts (ACA)
26 Main St.
East Greenwich, RI 02818
Co. E-mail: aca@calligraphicarts.org
URL: http://www.calligraphicarts.org
Contact: Joan Merrell, President
Scope: calligraphy. **Purpose:** Promotes the art of calligraphy. **Founded:** 1997. **Subscriptions:** artwork books. **Publications:** *The Newsletter* (Quarterly).

3216 ■ Society of Scribes (SOS)
PO Box 933
New York, NY 10150
Ph: (212)452-0139
Co. E-mail: info@societyofscribes.org
URL: http://www.societyofscribes.org
Contact: Chi Nguyen, President
Description: Calligraphers, bookbinders, lettering artists, and individuals with an interest in book arts. Promotes calligraphy and related lettering arts. Collects and disseminates information. Conducts exhibitions, workshops, lecturers, programs, and publications. **Scope:** calligraphy and lettering arts. **Founded:** 1974. **Subscriptions:** business records periodicals. **Publications:** *Classes and Workshops* (Semiannual); *Letters from New York* (Semiannual); *NewSOS* (Semiannual). **Educational Activities:** Holiday Fair (Annual).

3217 ■ Washington Calligraphers Guild (WCG)
PO Box 3688
Merrifield, VA 22116-3688
Co. E-mail: swerdloff@gmail.com
URL: http://www.calligraphersguild.org
Contact: Pamela Klinedinst, President
Description: Calligraphers and individuals interested in calligraphy. Promotes the appreciation of calligraphy and its applications and history. Seeks to foster a greater understanding of calligraphy as an art. Conducts studies on calligraphy; sponsors charitable and educational programs. **Scope:** lettering and book arts. **Founded:** 1976. **Subscriptions:** 300 books periodicals. **Publications:** *Scripsit* (Semiannual). **Educational Activities:** Art Exhibit (Annual); Letterforum (Periodic). **Awards:** Hermann Zapf Educational Fund Scholarship (Biennial).

REFERENCE WORKS

3218 ■ *Guild of Book Workers--Supplies and Services Directory*
Pub: Guild of Book Workers Inc.
Contact: Andrew Huot, President
E-mail: vicepresident@guildofbookworkers.allmail.net
URL(s): www.guildofbookworkers.org/resources/supply/search.php. **Ed:** Bernadette G. Callery, Susan B. Martin. **Released:** Irregular; Latest edition November 2008. **Price:** $15, Individuals 2001 issue. **Covers:** More than 250 manufacturers and suppliers of products used in bookbinding, calligraphy, and repair and conservation of documents and books; coverage includes Canada. **Entries include:** Name of firm, address, phone, products or services, minimum order requirements, shipping restrictions, whether catalog or samples are available. **Arrangement:** Geographical, then by product or service. **Indexes:** Alphabetical.

3219 ■ *Society for Calligraphy--Membership Directory*
Pub: Society for Calligraphy
Contact: Carrie Imai, President
URL(s): www.societyforcalligraphy.com/members.asp. **Released:** Annual; September. **Covers:** About 1,200 members and societies interested in calligraphy, including calligraphers, illustrators, graphic artists, and curators; international coverage. **Entries include:** For individual members--Name, address, phone, title. For societies--Contact name, address, phone; committee members. **Arrangement:** Alphabetical. **Indexes:** Personal name.

TRADE PERIODICALS

3220 ■ *Amphora*
Pub: Alcuin Society
Contact: Howard Greaves, Chairperson
E-mail: hgreaves@axion.net
Released: Quarterly. **Price:** Included in membership. **Description:** Carries articles about all aspects of the book and reading, including the book arts, private presses, book selling, book collecting, and notable library collections.

3221 ■ *Colorado Calligraphers' Guild Newsletter*
Pub: Colorado Calligraphers' Guild
Ed: Margaret Stookesberry, Editor. **Released:** Quarterly. **Price:** Included in membership. **Description:** Reports the business of the Guild. Supplies tips on techniques and materials used by calligraphers, and news of other calligraphic organizations. Recurring features include book reviews, workshop reprints, and listings of educational opportunities.

3222 ■ *Guild of Book Workers Newsletter*
Pub: Guild of Book Workers Inc.
Contact: Andrew Huot, President
E-mail: vicepresident@guildofbookworkers.allmail.net
Ed: Margaret Johnson, Editor. **Released:** Bimonthly, Every 2 months. **Price:** Included in membership. **Description:** Covers issues in book arts, binding, book conservation, calligraphy, and printing. Recurring features include letters to the editor, interviews, news of research, a calendar of events, reports of meetings, news of educational opportunities, job listings, book reviews, and notices of publications available.

3223 ■ *Ink, Inc.*
Pub: New Orleans Lettering Arts Association Inc.
Ed: Theresa P. Williams, Editor. **Released:** 3/year. **Price:** Included in membership. **Description:** Dedicated to promoting calligraphy and the fine art of lettering. Contains articles on such topics as copperplate calligraphy, paper for calligraphers, and Chinese ink lettering. Alerts calligraphers to new supplies and where to obtain them. Recurring features include profiles of successful calligraphers and typographers, news of the Association and its activities, announcements of calligraphy classes and exhibitions, and book reviews.

3224 ■ *Valley Calligraphy Guild Newsletter*
Pub: Valley Calligraphy Guild
Contact: Barbara Snow, Officer, Membership
Released: 3/year. **Price:** Included in membership. **Description:** Dedicated to preserving the art of calligraphy. Contains tips and techniques on lettering, italic handwriting, design, color use, and such crafts as papermaking, bookmaking, and bookbinding. Offers articles on workshop reviews, supplies, projects, artists, and activities of the Guild. Recurring features include schedules of classes, meetings, workshops, shows, and news of the activities of other societies of interest. **Remarks:** Newsletter text is primarily handwritten in calligraphy.

VIDEOCASSETTES/ AUDIOCASSETTES

3225 ■ *Learn & Earn with Calligraphy*
Instructional Video
2219 C St.
Lincoln, NE 68502
Ph: (402)475-6570
Free: 800-228-0164
Fax: (402)475-6500
Co. E-mail: feedback@insvideo.com
URL: http://www.insvideo.com
Released: 19??. **Price:** $39.95. **Description:** Demonstrates eight different techniques that can be used to learn and develop calligraphy skills to produce items such as invitations, certificates, awards, advertising, T-shirts, wine labels, and framed quotations. **Availability:** VHS.

LIBRARIES

3226 ■ Long Beach Public Library - Performing Arts Department
101 Pacific Ave.
Long Beach, CA 90822
Ph: (562)570-7500
Fax: (562)570-7408
Co. E-mail: elizabeth.rogers@lbpl.org
URL: http://www.lbpl.org
Contact: Elizabeth Rogers, Librarian
Scope: Art history and techniques, music history and scores, dance, flower arranging, antiques, theater, moving pictures, sports. **Services:** Interlibrary loan; department open to the public with restrictions. **Founded:** 1926. **Holdings:** 34,103 books; 8624 bound scores; 7099 pieces of sheet music; 91,043 mounted pictures; 9000 videocassettes; 10,000 phonograph records; 5000 cassettes; 5500 CDs.

3227 ■ Rochester Institute of Technology - Melbert B. Cary, Jr. Graphic Arts Collection
Wallace Memorial Library
90 Lomb Memorial Dr.
Rochester, NY 14623-5604

Ph: (585)475-2408
Fax: (585)475-6900
Co. E-mail: ahfwml@rit.edu
URL: http://library.rit.edu/cary
Contact: Steven K. Galbraith, Curator
Scope: Printing history, type specimens, typography, book arts, press books, calligraphy, papermaking, graphic arts, bookbinding. **Services:** Copying (limited); collection open to the public. **Founded:** 1969. **Holdings:** 50,000 books; 20 VF drawers of clippings; ephemera; pamphlets; 50 boxes of posters, broadsides, drawings; 400 boxes of correspondence and manuscript material. **Subscriptions:** 20 journals and other serials. **Telecommunication Services:** skgtwc@rit.edu; circwml@rit.edu.

3228 ■ Society for Calligraphy Library
PO Box 64174
Los Angeles, CA 90064
Co. E-mail: resources@societyforcalligraphy.org
URL: http://www.societyforcalligraphy.com
Contact: Kathleen Dunning-Torbett, Librarian
Scope: Calligraphy, lettering, bookbinding, paper arts, and related fields. **Services:** Library not open to the public. **Founded:** 1974. **Holdings:** 450 volumes; slides; movies; videos.

3229 ■ Yale University - Arts Library - Special Collections
Robert B. Haas Family Arts Library, Lower Level
180 York St.
New Haven, CT 06520-8318

Ph: (203)432-4439
Fax: (203)432-0549
Co. E-mail: jae.rossman@yale.edu
URL: http://www.library.yale.edu/arts/specialcollections
Contact: Jae Jennifer Rossman, Assistant Director
Scope: Typography, book illustration and design, bookbinding, papermaking, bookplates, private presses, artists' books, conceptual books, and fine printing. **Services:** Collection open to the public. **Founded:** 1967. **Holdings:** 20,000 books; prints and broadsides; type specimens; archive of student printing, including masters' theses from School of Graphic Design and School of Photography at Yale; 1 million bookplates; Japanese prints; stage and costume designs. **Subscriptions:** 20 journals and other serials.

ASSOCIATIONS AND OTHER ORGANIZATIONS

3230 ■ Photoimaging Manufacturers and Distributors Association (PMDA)
7600 Jericho Tpke., Ste. 301
Woodbury, NY 11797
Ph: (516)802-0895
Fax: (516)364-0140
Co. E-mail: jerry@pmda.com
URL: http://www.pmda.com
Contact: Joellyn Gray, President

Description: Represents manufacturers, wholesalers, distributors, and importers of photographic equipment. Holds lecture meetings presenting programs on topics facing the photographic industry. Helps to further the consumer's interest in photography through its website and a traveling information booth. **Founded:** 1939. **Awards:** Person of the Year Award (Annual); Professional Photographer Award (Annual); Technical Achievement Award (Annual).

3231 ■ Professional School Photographers of America
3000 Picture Pl.
Jackson, MI 49201
Ph: (517)788-8100
Free: 800-762-9287
Fax: (517)788-8371
Co. E-mail: pma_trade_exhibits@pmai.org
URL: http://www.pmai.org
Contact: Allen Showalter, President

Description: Retailers of photo and video equipment, film, and supplies; firms developing and printing film. Maintains hall of fame. Compiles statistics; conducts research and educational programs. **Scope:** photo finishing, retailing. **Founded:** 1924. **Subscriptions:** 200 periodicals. **Publications:** *Photo Marketing*; *PMA Magazine: Connecting the Imaging Communities* (Monthly); *Cost of Doing Business Survey*; *NAPET News* (Bimonthly); *Photo Marketing Association International--Newsline* (Semimonthly); *Photo Marketing Magazine* (Monthly); *Sales Counter* (Monthly); *Specialty Lab Update* (Monthly); *Who's Who in Photographic Management* (Annual); *Who's Who in Photographic Management* (Annual); *School Photographer*. **Educational Activities:** PMA Europe (Biennial); PMAI Imaging Conference & Mini-Trade Show (Annual); Photo Marketing Association International Annual Convention and Trade Show (PMA) (Annual).

REFERENCE WORKS

3232 ■ "Five Things..For Photo Fun" in Hawaii Business (Vol. 53, October 2007, No. 4, pp. 20)
Pub: Hawaii Business Publishing

Ed: Cathy S. Cruz-George. **Description:** Featured is a buyers guide of products used for capturing or displaying digital photos; products featured include the Digital Photo Wallet and Light Affection.

3233 ■ "Get the Picture: Here's How to Choose the Best Digital Camera For Your Needs" in Black Enterprise (November 2007)
Pub: Earl G. Graves Publishing Co. Inc.

Ed: Laura Turley. **Description:** Information for finding the best digital camera for your needs is provided. A professional photographer and digital media/photography teacher at the International Center of Photography recommends several cameras from each category.

3234 ■ "Olympus is Urged to Revise Board" in Wall Street Journal Eastern Edition (November 28, 2011, pp. B3)
Pub: Dow Jones & Company Inc. Enterprise Media Group
Contact: Clare Hart, President

Ed: Phred Dvorak. **Description:** Koji Miyata, once a director on the board of troubled Japanese photographic equipment company, is urging the company to reorganize its board, saying the present group should resign their board seats but keep their management positions. The company has come under scrutiny for its accounting practices and costly acquisitions.

3235 ■ "Our Gadget of the Week: Easy as a Snap" in Barron's (Vol. 90, September 13, 2010, No. 37, pp. 35)
Pub: Barron's Editorial & Corporate Headquarters

Ed: Jay Palmer. **Description:** SanMyPhotos.com offers a service whereby people can receive an empty box they can fill with photos then send back to the company to be stored digitally. The photos are returned to the customer with a disc containing the digital photographs. The service costs $150 for one box and $300 for three boxes.

3236 ■ "Play By Play: These Video Products Can Add New Life to a Stagnant Website" in Black Enterprise (Vol. 41, December 2010, No. 5)
Pub: Earl G. Graves Publishing Co. Inc.

Ed: Marcia Wade Talbert. **Description:** Web Visible, provider of online marketing products and services, cites video capability as the fastest-growing Website feature for small business advertisers. Profiles of various devices for adding video to a Website are included.

3237 ■ "Red One and The Rain Chronicles" in Michigan Vue (Vol. 13, July-August 2008, No. 4, pp. 30)
Pub: Entrepreneur Media Inc.

Ed: Evan Cornish. **Description:** Troy-based film school the Motion Picture Institute (MPI) implemented the latest technology by shooting the second of their trilogy, 'The Rain Chronicles', on the Red One camera. This is the first feature film in Michigan to utilize this exciting new camera, which includes proprietary software for rendering and color correction. Brian K. Johnson heads up the visual effects team as visual effects supervisor and lead CG artist. His company, Dream Conduit Studios, had to tackle the task of employing the new work flow through a post-production pipeline that would allow him to at-

tack complex visual effects shots, many of which were shot with a moving camera, a technique rarely seen in films at this budgetary level where the camera is traditionally locked off.

STATISTICAL SOURCES

3238 ■ RMA Annual Statement Studies
Pub: Risk Management Association
Contact: Kevin M. Blakey, President

Released: Annual. **Price:** $175.00 2006-07 edition, $105.00. **Description:** Contains composite balance sheets and income statements for more than 360 industries, including the accounting, auditing, and bookkeeping industries. Also contains five years of comparative historical data for discerning trends. Includes 16 commonly used ratios, computed for most of the size groupings for nearly every industry.

TRADE PERIODICALS

3239 ■ Light and Shade
Pub: Pictorial Photographers of America

Ed: Sylvia Mavis, Editor. **Released:** Monthly. **Price:** Included in membership. **Description:** Designed to help amateur and professional photographers perfect their photographic techniques. Carries how-to articles and information on photography equipment. Recurring features include organizational news, announcements of educational opportunities, and book reviews.

3240 ■ Professional Photographer: the official magazine of Professional Photographers of America
Pub: Professional Photographers of America
Contact: Tim Walden, President

URL(s): www.ppa.com/ppmag/. **Released:** Monthly **Price:** $19.95, Individuals print (U.S.); $35.95, Individuals print (Canada).

VIDEOCASSETTES/AUDIOCASSETTES

3241 ■ Home Video Hits: Great Ideas for Creating Better Home Videos
Leslie T. McClure
PO Box 1223
Pebble Beach, CA 93953
Ph: (831)656-0553
Fax: (831)656-0555
Co. E-mail: leslie@411videoinfo.com
URL: http://www.411videoinfo.com

Released: 1997. **Price:** $19.95. **Description:** Demonstrates a variety of camera angles, focus options, camera movements and in-camera editing techniques. **Availability:** VHS.

TRADE SHOWS AND CONVENTIONS

3242 ■ Photo Marketing Association International Annual Convention and Trade

Show (PMA)
Professional School Photographers of America
3000 Picture Pl.
Jackson, MI 49201
Ph: (517)788-8100
Free: 800-762-9287
Fax: (517)788-8371
Co. E-mail: pma_trade_exhibits@pmai.org
URL: http://www.pmai.org
Contact: Allen Showalter, President

URL(s): www.pmai.org. **Frequency:** Annual. **Audience:** Trade professionals from the following groups: photo/video/optics/imaging products retailers; photo processing equipment and related service groups. **Principal Exhibits:** Profile of exhibitors: film, cameras and photo accessory manufacturers and distribu tors; photo processing equipment and materials suppliers; digital imaging hardware and software marketers; studio imaging equipment distributors; and original equipment manufacturers (OEMs). **Telecommunication Services:** PMA_Information_Central@pmai.org.

ASSOCIATIONS AND OTHER ORGANIZATIONS

3243 ■ American Camping Association
5000 State Rd., 67 N
Martinsville, IN 46151-7902
Ph: (765)342-8456
Free: 800-428-2267
Fax: (765)342-2065
Co. E-mail: exhibitors@acacamps.org
URL: http://www.acacamps.org
Contact: Marla Coleman, President
E-mail: marla@colemanfamilycamps.com

Description: Camp owners, directors, program directors, businesses, and students interested in resident and day camp programming for youth and adults. Conducts camp standards. Offers educational programs in areas of administration, staffing, child development, promotion, and programming. **Publications:** *Camping Magazine* (Bimonthly); *Camping Magazine; Guide to Accredited Camps* (Annual); *Accreditation Process Guide; Guide to ACA-Accredited Camps* (Annual); *Camping Magazine--Buyer's Guide Issue* (Annual). **Educational Activities:** American Camping Association Conference & Exhibits (Annual). **Awards:** Distinguished Service Award (Annual); Hedley S. Dimock Award (Annual); Honor Award (Annual); Special Recognition Award (Annual); Hedley S. Dimock Award; Distinguished Service Award; National Honor Award; Special Recognition Award; Eleanor P. Eells Award for Program Excellence.

3244 ■ Best Holiday Trav-L-Park Association (BHTPA)
4809 E Marshall Dr.
Vestal, NY 13850
Ph: (607)241-7531
Co. E-mail: info@bestholiday.org
URL: http://www.bestholiday.org
Description: Independently owned campgrounds. Seeks to increase business of members through networking and the establishment of a common logo. **Founded:** 1981. **Publications:** *Best Holiday Directory* (Annual).

3245 ■ Canadian Camping Association (CCA)—Association des Camps du Canada
c/o Yves Dubois, Exec. Dir.
4545 Pierre de Coubertin
CP 1000 Succursale M
Montreal, QC, Canada H1V 3R2
Ph: (514)252-3113
Free: 800-361-3586
Fax: (514)252-1650
Co. E-mail: info@camps.qc.ca
URL: http://www.ccamping.org
Contact: Jeff Bradshaw, President
Description: Commercial camps and nonprofit organizations and individuals with an interest in camping. Promotes the "growth and development of organized camping for all populations in Canada." Furthers the interests and welfare of children, youth and adults through camping. Functions as a coordinating body for organized camping nationwide.

Develops and enforces standards of practice and facilities among commercial camps; provides guidance, advocacy, and resources for camping leaders. Offers services to members including discount insurance, credit card, and online programs. Compiles industry statistics; operates bookstore. **Founded:** 1936. **Awards:** Certificate of Appreciation; Volunteer Award; Achievement of Excellence; Award of Honour; Achievement of Excellence (Annual); Certificate of Appreciation (Periodic); Jack Pearse Award of Honour (Annual); Letter from the CCA/ACC President (Periodic); Volunteer Award (Annual).

3246 ■ Canadian Family Camping Federation (CFCF)
c/o Deb Daub, Treas.
175 Elizabeth Ave.
Ingersoll, ON, Canada N5C 3Y1
Ph: (905)338-9638
Co. E-mail: junniebear@hotmail.com
URL: http://www.canadianfamilycampers.com
Contact: June Beaudry, Chairman
Description: Families with an interest in camping. Promotes camping as a recreational pastime. Serves as a clearinghouse on family camping opportunities; conducts social and educational programs.

3247 ■ Christian Camping International/USA
405 W Rockrimmon Blvd.
Colorado Springs, CO 80919
Ph: (719)260-9400
Fax: (719)260-6398
Co. E-mail: ghunter@ccca.org
URL: http://www.cciworldwide.org/regions/north-america/usa
Contact: Gregg Hunter, President
Description: Exists to proclaim the power of the Christian camp and conference experience and to interpret its benefits to the Church and the public at large; and to provide leaders at member organizations with ongoing encouragement, professional training, and timely resources. **Publications:** *Executive Briefing* (Monthly); *InSite* (Bimonthly); *CCI/USA Membership Directory* (Annual). **Educational Activities:** Christian Camping Convention & Exposition.

3248 ■ Family Campers and RVers (FCRV)
4804 Transit Rd., Bldg. 2
Depew, NY 14043
Ph: (716)668-6242
Free: 800-245-9755
Co. E-mail: fcrvnat@verizon.net
URL: http://www.fcrv.org
Contact: Jack Smye, President
Description: Family campers and hikers; others interested in outdoor activities. Promotes and enhances the experience of "family" style camping/RV-ing. **Founded:** 1949. **Publications:** *Camping Today* (Monthly). **Educational Activities:** Campvention (Annual).

3249 ■ KampGround Owners Association (KOA)
3416 Primm Ln.
Birmingham, AL 35216
Ph: (205)824-0022

Free: 800-678-9976
Co. E-mail: info@koaowners.org
URL: http://www.koaowners.org
Contact: William Ranieri, Executive Director
Description: Represents KOA franchisees. Offers seminars and workshops. Compiles statistics; maintains speakers' bureau, charitable program, and several committees. **Founded:** 1964.

3250 ■ National Association of RV Parks and Campgrounds (National ARVC)
9085 E Mineral Cir., Ste. 200
Centennial, CO 80112
Ph: (303)681-0401
Free: 800-395-2267
Fax: (303)681-0426
Co. E-mail: lprofaizer@arvc.org
URL: http://www.arvc.org
Contact: Rob Schutter, Chairman
Description: Regular members are commercial campground owners and operators; associate members are manufacturers and suppliers of campground products and services. Promotes and protects the interests of the commercial campground industry, with government officials and agencies, campers, the press and the general public. Represents the campground industry in contact with RV manufacturers, RV dealers and other branches of the camping business. Offers specialized education. Works to develop better, more efficient, more profitable campground management and business methods. Compiles statistics. Operates National RV Park and Campground Industry Education Foundation and a Certified Park Operators program. **Founded:** 1966. **Publications:** *Direct Line* (Monthly); *ARVC Report* (Monthly); *Membership Directory and Buyer's Guide* (Annual). **Awards:** Park of the Year (Annual); Stan Martin Memorial Award (Annual); RV Park Operator of the Year (Annual); Park of the Year; State Executive of the Year; Stan Martin Memorial Award.

3251 ■ National Forest Recreation Association (NFRA)
PO Box 488
Woodlake, CA 93286
Ph: (559)564-2365
Fax: (559)564-2048
Co. E-mail: info@nfra.org
URL: http://www.nfra.org
Contact: Marily Reese, Executive Director
Description: Owners and operators of resorts, winter sports areas, marinas, campgrounds, stores, river trip outfitters, packer-outfitters, restaurants, and motels located on or adjacent to federal land. Participates in trade and public relations matters that is of interest to members, including legislation and relationships with U.S. agencies; state and local officials in matters of taxation, insurance, finance, health, and building requirements; and employment. **Founded:** 1948. **Awards:** Ranger of the Year Award (Annual).

3252 ■ North American Family Campers Association (NAFCA)
PO Box 345
Billerica, MA 01821

Ph: (781)396-9398
Co. E-mail: ejdj38@aol.com
URL: http://www.nafca.org
Contact: Everett Mitchell, President
Description: Families interested in camping; sustaining members are manufacturers and dealers of camping equipment, campgrounds, and other services related to family campers. Works to improve camping conditions, inform members about camping areas, equipment, and techniques, promote good camping manners, and foster fellowship among family campers. Encourages and guides development of campgrounds; cooperates with conservation and legislative agencies for the good of camping. Conducts conservation and antilitter programs. **Founded:** 1957. **Publications:** *Campfire Chatter* (Monthly). **Awards:** Leadership Conference Scholarship (Annual).

REFERENCE WORKS

3253 ■ *Camping Magazine--Buyer's Guide Issue*
Pub: American Camping Association
Contact: Marla Coleman, President
E-mail: marla@colemanfamilycamps.com
URL(s): www.acacamps.org/campmag. **Released:** Annual; November/December Issue; Latest edition 2012. **Price:** $29.95, Individuals. **Publication includes:** List of over 200 firms providing sporting equipment, food, infirmary supplies, etc. For children's and other organized camps. **Entries include:** Company name, address, product or service provided. **Arrangement:** Alphabetical. **Indexes:** Product.

3254 ■ *Frontier West/Great Plains & Mountain Region Campground Guide*
Pub: Woodall Publications Corp.
Contact: Mellissa Robinson, Manager
E-mail: mrobinson@affinityroup.com
URL(s): www.woodalls.com. **Released:** Annual; latest edition 2012. **Price:** $4.95, Individuals discounted price. **Covers:** Campground site listings for Colorado, Montana, Nebraska, North Dakota, South Dakota, Utah, and Wyoming. **Entries include:** Site name, address, phone, facility description, driving directions, camping fees, attractions and seasonal events. It also includes, new for 2004, "Discover Outdoor RV Adventures" and Woodall's Guide to Seasonal Sites.

3255 ■ *Good Sam RV Travel Guide and Camping Directory*
Pub: Woodall Publications Corp.
Contact: Mellissa Robinson, Manager
E-mail: mrobinson@affinityroup.com
URL(s): www.woodalls.com. **Released:** Annual; Latest edition 2013. **Price:** $14.95, Individuals North American edition; $25.95, Individuals retail price. **Covers:** Private and public campgrounds in the United States, Canada, and Mexico. Separate listing of over 15,000 service locations for recreational vehicles. Three major editions: North America; eastern United States and Canada; and western United States, Canada, and Mexico. Also editions for New York, New England, Mid-Atlantic, Great Lakes, Great Plains and Mountain States, Far West, Frontier West, South, Canada. These eight regional editions cover all of the United States and Canada. **Entries include:** Name of campground, location, directions from major highways, camping rates per night, ratings of facilities and of recreation. **Database includes:** Sightseeing information and special events. **Arrangement:** Geographical.

3256 ■ *Guide to ACA-Accredited Camps*
Pub: American Camping Association
Contact: Marla Coleman, President
E-mail: marla@colemanfamilycamps.com
URL(s): bookstore.acacamps.org/. **Released:** Annual; January; Latest edition 2004. **Covers:** Over 2,400 summer camps. **Entries include:** Name of camp, address, phone, fax, email addresses, age and sex of children accepted, rates, season, capacity, facilities, programs, activities offered and camp philosophy. **Arrangement:** Geographical, then by day or resident camp. **Indexes:** Activity, special clientele, camp name, specific disabilities.

3257 ■ *Guide to Summer Camps and Summer Schools*
Pub: Porter Sargent Publishers Inc.
Contact: Leslie A. Weston, Manager, Production
URL(s): www.portersargent.com/gsc.php. **Released:** Biennial; Latest edition 33rd, 2012-2013. **Price:** $45, Individuals cloth, plus shipping; $27, Individuals paper, plus shipping. **Covers:** 1,700 residential summer camping, recreational, pioneering, and academic programs in the United States and Canada, as well as travel programs worldwide. Includes special programs for the handicapped, maladjusted, and those with learning disabilities. **Entries include:** Program name, address, phone, fax, enrollment, director's name, title and winter address, fees, length of camping period, type of housing, whether camp has counselor-in-training program, year established, description of programs, sex and age range, amenities, URL, e-mail, term length, descriptive paragraph. **Arrangement:** Classified by type of camp, or school then geographical, cross indexed by enrollment, age ranges, sexes accepted. **Indexes:** Alphabetical by school name, features, religion, military programs.

3258 ■ *New York/New England & Eastern Canada Campground Guide*
Pub: Woodall Publications Corp.
Contact: Mellissa Robinson, Manager
E-mail: mrobinson@affinityroup.com
URL(s): www.woodalls.com. **Released:** Annual; Latest edition 2012. **Price:** $10.95, retail price; $4.95, discounted price. **Covers:** Campground site listings for New England states, including Maine, Connecticut, Massachusetts, New Hampshire, New York, Rhode Island, Vermont, and Ontario. **Entries include:** Site name, address, phone, facility description, driving directions, camping fees, attractions and seasonal events.

3259 ■ *Who's Who in Grounds Management*
Pub: Professional Grounds Management Society
Contact: Mike Mongon, President
URL(s): www.pgms.org/. **Released:** Annual; October. **Covers:** About 1400 managers of large institutional grounds, grounds maintenance firms, parks, recreation areas, golf courses, cemeteries, botanical gardens, arboretums, and other private and public grounds; educators; certified grounds managers; researchers and horticulturists; and government and university officials engaged in extension services; coverage includes Canada. **Entries include:** Name, home address, office address, title or affiliation. **Arrangement:** Alphabetical. **Indexes:** Geographical.

3260 ■ *Woodall's Canada Campground Guide*
Pub: Woodall Publications Corp.
Contact: Mellissa Robinson, Manager
E-mail: mrobinson@affinityroup.com
URL(s): www.woodalls.com. **Released:** Latest edition 2010. **Price:** $8.96, Individuals discounted; $9.95, Individuals retail price. **Covers:** Campground site listings for all Canadian provinces. **Entries include:** Site name, address, phone, facility description, driving directions, camping fees, attractions and seasonal events.

3261 ■ *Woodall's Far West Campground Guide*
Pub: Woodall Publications Corp.
Contact: Mellissa Robinson, Manager
E-mail: mrobinson@affinityroup.com
URL(s): www.woodalls.com. **Released:** Annual; Latest edition 2012. **Price:** $4.95, Individuals; $10.95, retail price. **Covers:** Campground site listings for the Far West U.S., including Alaska, Arizona, California, Idaho, Nevada, Oregon, Washington, and British Columbia, Mexico, and the Yukon. **Entries include:** Site name, address, phone, facility description, driving directions, camping fees, attractions and seasonal events.

3262 ■ *Woodall's Frontier West/Great Plains & Mountain Region Campground Guide*
Pub: Woodall Publications Corp.
Contact: Mellissa Robinson, Manager
E-mail: mrobinson@affinityroup.com
URL(s): www.woodalls.com/. **Released:** Latest edition 2010. **Price:** $4.95, Individuals; $9.95, Individuals retail price. **Covers:** Campground site listings for

Arkansas, Kansas, Missouri, New Mexico, Oklahoma, Texas, and Mexico. **Entries include:** Site name, address, phone, facility description, driving directions, camping fees, attractions and seasonal events.

3263 ■ *Woodall's Great Lakes Campground Guide*
Pub: Woodall Publications Corp.
Contact: Mellissa Robinson, Manager
E-mail: mrobinson@affinityroup.com
URL(s): www.woodalls.com/. **Released:** Annual; Latest edition 2012. **Price:** $4.95, Individuals; $10.95, Individuals retail price. **Covers:** Campground site listings for Great Lakes states, including Illinois, Indiana, Iowa, Michigan, Minnesota, Ohio, and Wisconsin. **Entries include:** Site name, address, phone, facility description, driving directions, camping fees, attractions and seasonal events.

3264 ■ *Woodall's Mid-Atlantic Campground Guide*
Pub: Woodall Publications Corp.
Contact: Mellissa Robinson, Manager
E-mail: mrobinson@affinityroup.com
URL(s): www.woodalls.com. **Released:** Annual; latest edition 2012. **Price:** $4.95, Individuals; $10.95, retail price. **Covers:** Campground site listings for Mid-Atlantic states, including Delaware, District of Columbia, Maryland, New Jersey, Pennsylvania, Virginia, and West Virginia. **Entries include:** Site name, address, phone, facility description, driving directions, camping fees, attractions and seasonal events.

3265 ■ *Woodall's South Campground Guide*
Pub: Woodall Publications Corp.
Contact: Mellissa Robinson, Manager
E-mail: mrobinson@affinityroup.com
URL(s): www.woodalls.com. **Released:** Annual; Latest edition 2012. **Price:** $10.95, Individuals Retail price; $4.95, Individuals Discounted. **Covers:** Campground site listings for the 9 Southern U.S. states, including Alabama, Florida, Georgia, Kentucky, Louisiana, Mississippi, North Carolina, South Carolina, and Tennessee. **Entries include:** Site name, address, phone, facility description, driving directions, camping fees, attractions and seasonal events.

3266 ■ *YMCA Resident Camp Directory*
Pub: Camping Programs YMCA of the USA
Contact: Wanda Denson-Low, Director
URL(s): www.ymca.net/find_ymca_camps/. **Ed:** Robert Telleen. **Released:** updated weekly. **Entries include:** Association name, camp name, address and phone of winter office, camp location and summer address and phone, name of director, seasons of operation, capacity; whether coed or restricted to boys or girls, or available for family and adult camping; special programs offered. **Database covers:** Over 235 resident camps and conference and retreat centers operated by local YMCA associations in the United States. **Arrangement:** Classified by type of camp (resident, family, conference centers).

TRADE PERIODICALS

3267 ■ *Campgroundata*
Pub: Campground Data Resource
Ed: Dale S. Bourdette, Editor, dale_bourdette@worldnet.att.net. **Released:** Bimonthly. **Description:** Provides information for campground buyers and sellers to help them make informed buy or sell decisions.

3268 ■ *Camping Magazine*
Pub: American Camping Association
Contact: Marla Coleman, President
E-mail: marla@colemanfamilycamps.com
URL(s): www.acacamps.org/campmag/. **Released:** Bimonthly **Price:** $29.95, Individuals U.S. mainland; $56, Two years U.S. mainland; $48, Individuals Alaska, Hawaii, Puerto Rico; Canada & Mexico; $92, Two years Alaska, Hawaii, Puerto Rico; Canada & Mexico; $54, Other countries; $104, Other countries 2 years.

3269 ■ *InSite*
Pub: Christian Camping International/USA
Contact: Gregg Hunter, President
URL(s): www.ccca.org/public/publications/insite.asp. **Ed:** Martha Krienke. **Released:** Bimonthly **Price:** $29.95, Nonmembers; $39.95, Out of country nonmembers; $4.99, Single issue.

3270 ■ *Trailer Life: America's No. 1 RV Magazine*

Pub: TL Enterprises Inc. Affinity Group Inc.

Contact: Rebecca Zuniga, Manager

E-mail: rzuniga@affinitygroup.com

URL(s): www.trailerlife.com. **Released:** Monthly **Price:** $15.97, Individuals print; $27.97, Two years print; $27.97, Canada print; $51.97, Canada print; 2 years.

3271 ■ *Woodall's Northeast Outdoors*

Pub: Woodall Publications Corp.

Contact: Mellissa Robinson, Manager

E-mail: mrobinson@affinityroup.com

URL(s): www.woodalls.biz/output.cfm?id=1017811. **Released:** Bimonthly **Price:** $20, Individuals.

TRADE SHOWS AND CONVENTIONS

3272 ■ American Camping Association Conference & Exhibits

American Camping Association

5000 State Rd., 67 N

Martinsville, IN 46151-7902

Ph: (765)342-8456

Free: 800-428-2267

Fax: (765)342-2065

Co. E-mail: exhibitors@acacamps.org

URL: http://www.acacamps.org

Contact: Marla Coleman, President

E-mail: marla@colemanfamilycamps.com

URL(s): www.acacamps.org. **Frequency:** Annual. **Audience:** Camp directors, counselors, and exhibitors. **Principal Exhibits:** Arts and crafts, computer software, sporting goods, waterfront equipment, insurance imprinted wear, bedding, and food. **Telecommunication Services:** conference@acacamps.org.

FRANCHISES AND BUSINESS OPPORTUNITIES

3273 ■ Kampgrounds of America, Inc

550 N 31st St.

Billings, MT 59114

Ph: (406)248-7444

Fax: (406)254-7440

Description: Franchisor of campgrounds. **No. of Franchise Units:** 482. **No. of Company-Owned Units:** 27. **Founded:** 1961.. **Franchised:** 1962. **Equity Capital Needed:** $200,000+. **Franchise Fee:** $7,750-$22,500. **Training:** Yes.

3274 ■ Yogi Bear's Jellystone Park Camp-Resorts

Leisure Systems, Inc.

50 W TechneCenter Dr., Ste. G

Milford, OH 45150

Ph: (513)831-2100

Free: 800-626-3720

Fax: (513)576-8670

URL: http://www.jellystonefranchise.com

Description: Leisure Systems, Inc. holds an exclusive license to franchise Yogi Bear's Jellystone Park Camp/Resorts in the US and Canada. Presently, there are 70 units in the U.S. and 3 in Canada. **No. of Franchise Units:** 71. **Founded:** 1969.. **Franchised:** 1970. **Equity Capital Needed:** $25,000+. **Franchise Fee:** $20,000. **Financial Assistance:** Yes. **Training:** Franchisee's are required to attend a 5 day training program held at the home office in Cincinnati, OH. Additional onsite training is also conducted for a period of 2-3 days.

LIBRARIES

3275 ■ American Camp Association Library

5000 State Rd., 67 N.

Martinsville, IN 46151-7902

Ph: (765)349-3313

Free: 800-428-2267

Fax: (765)342-2065

Co. E-mail: psmith@acacamps.org

URL: http://www.acacamps.org

Contact: Peg Smith, Chief Executive Officer

Scope: Camping, ecosystems. **Services:** Library open to members and staff only. **Holdings:** Figures not available.

ASSOCIATIONS AND OTHER ORGANIZATIONS

3276 ■ American Association of Candy Technologists (AACT)
PO Box 266
Princeton, WI 54968
Ph: (920)295-6969
Fax: (920)295-6843
Co. E-mail: aactinfo@gomc.com
URL: http://www.aactcandy.org
Contact: Randy Hofberger, President
Description: Candy technologists who seek to further the education of the technical community of the confectionery industry. **Founded:** 1948. **Awards:** Stoud Jordan Award (Annual).

3277 ■ American Wholesale Marketers Association (AWMA)
2750 Prosperity Ave., Ste. 530
Fairfax, VA 22031
Ph: (703)208-3358
Free: 800-482-2962
Fax: (703)573-5738
Co. E-mail: info@awmanet.org
URL: http://www.awmanet.org
Contact: Scott Ramminger, President
E-mail: scottr@awmanet.org
Description: Represents the interests of distributors of convenience-related products. Its members include wholesalers, retailers, manufacturers, brokers and allied organizations from across the U.S. and abroad. Programs include strong legislative representation in Washington and a broad spectrum of targeted education, business and information services. Sponsors the country's largest show for candy and convenience related products in conjunction with its semi-annual convention. **Founded:** 1991. **Publications:** *Buying Guide and Membership Directory* (Annual); *Convenience Distribution: AWMA's Magazine for Candy, Tobacco, Grocery, Foodservice and General Merchandiser Marketers*; *Quick Topics Newsletter*; *Convenience Distribution*; *Distribution Channels Buying Guide & AWMA Membership Directory* (Monthly). **Educational Activities:** Summit and Business Exchange (Annual); The Convenience Distributor Conference & Expo (Annual); Real Deal Expo (Annual); The AWMA Show - The Convenience Distributor Conference and Expo (Annual). **Awards:** Hall of Fame, Deans (Annual).

3278 ■ National Confectioners Association of the U.S. (NCA)
1101 30th St. NW, Ste. 200
Washington, DC 20007
Ph: (202)534-1440
Fax: (202)337-0637
Co. E-mail: info@candyusa.com
URL: http://www.candyusa.com
Contact: Mr. Mitchell T. Goetze, Chairman of the Board
Description: Represents manufacturers of confectionery products; suppliers to the industry. Conducts research and technical and governmental services;

provides information to the public; conducts annual confectionery technology course at the University of Wisconsin, Madison; gathers statistics on the industry. **Founded:** 1884. **Publications:** *A Year of Confectionery* (Annual). **Educational Activities:** All Candy Expo (Annual).

3279 ■ National Confectionery Sales Association (NCSA)
Spitfire House
3135 Berea Rd.
Cleveland, OH 44111
Ph: (216)631-8200
Fax: (216)631-8210
Co. E-mail: info@candyhalloffame.org
URL: http://www.candyhalloffame.org
Contact: Alastair Northway, President
Description: Salespersons, brokers, sales managers, wholesalers, and manufacturers in the candy industry. Maintains Candy Hall of Fame. **Founded:** 1899. **Publications:** *National Confectionery Sales Association of America-Journal* (Annual). **Educational Activities:** National Confectionery Sales Association Meeting (Annual). **Awards:** Candy Hall of Fame Award (Annual).

3280 ■ PMCA: An International Association of Confectioners
2980 Linden St., Ste. E3
Bethlehem, PA 18017
Ph: (610)625-4655
Fax: (610)625-4657
Co. E-mail: info@pmca.com
URL: http://www.pmca.com
Contact: Steve Marcanello, President
Description: Manufacturers and suppliers of confectionery and chocolate products. Conducts research and educational programs. **Scope:** research and production, confectionery technology. **Founded:** 1907. **Subscriptions:** 1000 books. **Publications:** *Annual Production Conference Proceedings* (Annual); *PMCA News Update* (Quarterly); *Proceedings of Annual Production Conference* (Annual); *Proceedings of Annual Production Conference* (Annual). **Educational Activities:** Production Conference (Annual); Production (Annual); PMCA: An International Association of Confectioners Production Conference (Annual). **Awards:** AACT Undergraduate Scholarships; PMCA Graduate Fellowships for Confectionery Research at Pennsylvania State University; Graduate Confectionery Fellowship at Penn State (Biennial); The Graduate Confectionery Fellowship - Penn State University (Biennial).

3281 ■ Retail Confectioners International (RCI)
2053 S Waverly, Ste. C
Springfield, MO 65804
Ph: (417)883-2775
Free: 800-545-5381
Fax: (417)883-1108
Co. E-mail: @retailconfectioners.org
URL: http://www.retailconfectioners.org
Contact: Terry Hicklin, President
Description: Manufacturing retail confectioners who make and sell their own candies through directly-owned retail candy shops; associates are suppliers

to the industry. Provides education, promotion and legislative and information service. Monitors legislative activities that affect the industry at state and national levels. Holds comprehensive two-week course and one-week specialized course on retail candy making biennially. **Founded:** 1917.

REFERENCE WORKS

3282 ■ *Candy Buyers' Directory*
Pub: Manufacturing Confectioner Publishing Corp.
Contact: Coralene Kate Allured, Editor
URL(s): www.gomc.com. **Released:** Annual; latest edition 2012. **Price:** $80, Individuals. **Covers:** Wholesale confectionery manufacturers and candy importers. **Entries include:** Company name, address, phone, name of sales manager (for manufacturers and importers), and products and brand names manufactured or distributed. Broker and importer listings also show territory covered and countries from which imported. **Arrangement:** Alphabetical; brokers are listed geographically. **Indexes:** Brand, product, brokers, manufacturer.

3283 ■ *Candy Industry Buyer's Guide*
Pub: BNP Media
Contact: Al Reser, President
URL(s): www.candyindustry.com/guide. **Released:** Annual; Latest edition 2010. **Publication includes:** List of approximately 682 suppliers of ingredients, equipment, and services to the candy industry. **Entries include:** Company name, address, phone. **Arrangement:** Alphabetical. **Indexes:** Product.

3284 ■ *"Cold Stone in Licensing Agreement with Turin Chocolates" in Ice Cream Reporter* (Vol. 22, December 20, 2008, No. 1, pp. 2)
Pub: Ice Cream Reporter
Description: Cold Stone Creamery and Turin Chocolatier are teaming up to offer a new line of chocolate truffles under the Cold Stone label. The treats will feature four the most popular Cold Stone flavors: Coffee Lovers Only, Chocolate Devotion, Our Strawberry Blonde, and Peanut Butter Cup Perfection.

3285 ■ *Distribution Channels Buying Guide & AWMA Membership Directory*
Pub: American Wholesale Marketers Association
Contact: Scott Ramminger, President
E-mail: scottr@awmanet.org
URL(s): www.awmanet.org. **Released:** Monthly; except January/February and August/September, 10/yr; Latest edition 2010. **Price:** $36, Individuals domestic (within the U.S. and territories); $66, Individuals Canada/international. **Publication includes:** List of 3,000 manufacturers, suppliers, brokers, and wholesalers of confectionery, tobacco, and snack products; state associations of the candy and tobacco industry; industry events calendar. **Entries include:** Firm name, address, phone, fax, product line carried, description of products. **Database includes:** Photographs, industry information about meetings and member services. **Arrangement:** Separate alphabetical sections for members, associations, and suppliers. **Indexes:** Distribution Channels magazine 2001 editorial index.

3286 ■ *"Hyde Park Hungry for Expansion at Cap"* in Business First-Columbus (October 12, 2007, pp. A1)
Pub: American City Business Journals, Inc.
Ed: Dan Eaton. Description: The Cap, an area developed for the retail and restaurant industry, is experiencing major changes such as Hyde Park Restaurant System's planned expansion, and the expected departure of other tenants. The expansion of Hyde Park will lead to the relocation of Schakolad Chocolate Factory.

3287 ■ *"Juicy Feud; Deal Caps Years of Rancor in Wrigley Gum Dynasty"* in Crain's Chicago Business (Vol. 31, May 5, 2008, No. 18, pp. 1)
Pub: Crain Communications, Inc.
Ed: David Sterrett. Description: Discusses the sale of Wm. Wrigley Jr. Co. to Mars Inc. and Warren Buffett for $23 billion as well as the intra-family feuding which has existed for nearly a decade since William Wrigley Jr. took over as CEO of the company following his father's death.

3288 ■ *"Kaminsky Back in the Business of Selling Her Chocolate Treats"* in Business First Buffalo (October 5, 2007, pp. 4)
Pub: American City Business Journals, Inc.
Ed: Tracey Drury. Description: Loretta Kaminsky, the original owner of Lou-Retta's Custom Chocolates brand, has decided to bring her products back into the market after winning a breach of contract lawsuit against Art Coco. Kaminsky sold her business to Art Coco in 2003, agreeing to the deal that Kaminsky will promote the products for two years in exchange for royalties and Art Coco's maintaining of product quality. Details of the distribution agreement with Wegmans, which will reintroduce Kaminsky's products are presented.

3289 ■ *Manufacturing Confectioner--Directory of Ingredients, Equipment and Packaging*
Pub: Manufacturing Confectioner Publishing Corp.
Contact: Coralene Kate Allured, Editor
URL(s): www.gomc.com/display.asp?pageId=dir. Ed: Kate Allured. Released: Annual; July. Price: $50, Individuals. Publication includes: Suppliers of machinery, equipment, raw materials, and supplies to the confectionery industry; laboratory instrumentation and services. Entries include: Company name, address, phone, telex, fax. Arrangement: Separate alphabetical sections for raw materials, equipment, agents, packaging, laboratory instrumentation, and services. Indexes: Product, trade name.

3290 ■ *"The Oracle's Endgame; Wrigley Investment Isn't What Many Call a Classic Buffett Play"* in Crain's Chicago Business (May 5, 2008)
Pub: Crain Communications, Inc.
Ed: Ann Saphir. Description: Discusses Warren Buffett's deal with Mars Inc. to buy Wm. Wrigley Jr. Co., a move which would make Mr. Buffett a minority shareholder in a privately held company, a departure from his typical investment strategy. Mr. Buffett's Berkshire Hathaway Inc. agreed to provide $4.4 billion to help finance the $23 billion deal to pay another $2.1 billion for an equity stake in the company once it became a subsidiary of Mars.

3291 ■ *Progressive Grocer's Marketing Guidebook: The Comprehensive Source for Grocery, Drug and Mass Merchant Insights*
Pub: Trade Dimensions
Contact: Lynda Gutierrez, Director
URL(s): www.tradedimensions.com. Released: Annual; Latest edition 2011. Covers: Over 1,000 U.S. and Canadian supermarket chains, large independents and wholesalers; also includes 350 specialty distributors include smaller food wholesalers, food brokers, non-food distributors, and candy/tobacco/media distributors and over 15,000 key executives and buyers. Entries include: For retailers and wholesalers--Company name, address, phone, email and websites, number of stores operated or served, areas of operation, major grocery supplier, three-year financial summary, buying policies, private label information, lists of executives, buyers, and merchan-

disers. For specialty distributors--Name, address, phone, list of key personnel including buyers' categories, list of items handled, URL. Arrangement: Alphabetical by hierarchy, geographical by eight regions and 50 market areas. Indexes: Grocery related organizations, chain and wholesalers, state index, store operating name/parent company reference.

3292 ■ *"Shari's Berries Founder Shuts Last of Her Stores"* in Sacramento Business Journal (Vol. 28, September 2, 2011, No. 27, pp. 1)
Pub: Sacramento Business Journal
Ed: Kelly Johnson. Description: Sacramento, California-based Shari's Berries owner Shari Fitzpatrick closed the company's last three stores called The Berry Factory. Fitzpatrick also filed for business bankruptcy protection. The weak economy is blamed for the company's failure.

3293 ■ *"The Sky's the Limit"* in Retail Merchandiser (Vol. 51, July-August 2011, No. 4, pp. 64)
Pub: Phoenix Media Corporation
Ed: John Capizzi. Description: Mars Retail Group (MRG) is the licensing division handling M&M's Brand Candies. Since taking over the brand they have expanded from 12 licensees to 50 licensees with new offerings.

3294 ■ *"Wrigley's a Rich Meal for Mars"* in Crain's Chicago Business (Vol. 31, May 5, 2008, No. 18, pp. 2)
Pub: Crain Communications, Inc.
Ed: Steven R. Strahler. Description: Mars Inc. will have to manage wisely in order to make their acquisition of Wm. Wrigley Jr. Co. profitable due to the high selling price of Wrigley which far exceeds the industry norm. Statistical data included.

TRADE PERIODICALS

3295 ■ *Candy Industry: The Global Magazine of Chocolate Confectionery*
Pub: BNP Media
Contact: Al Reser, President
URL(s): www.candyindustry.com. Released: Monthly

3296 ■ *Convenience Distribution: AWMA's Magazine for Candy, Tobacco, Grocery, Foodservice and General Merchandiser Marketers*
Pub: American Wholesale Marketers Association
Contact: Scott Ramminger, President
E-mail: scottr@awmanet.org
URL(s): www.awmanet.org/dc_latest. Ed: Joan Fay. Released: 10/yr. Price: $36, Individuals domestic; $66, Other countries.

3297 ■ *Fancy Food & Culinary Products*
Pub: Talcott Communication Corp.
URL(s): www.fancyfoodmagazine.comwww.talcott.com/contact.htm. Ed: Erika Flynn. Released: Monthly Price: $26, Individuals; $37, Two years; $47, Canada 3 years; $32, Canada; $60, Other countries.

3298 ■ *Quick Topics Newsletter*
Pub: American Wholesale Marketers Association
Contact: Scott Ramminger, President
E-mail: scottr@awmanet.org
Ed: Barbara Valakos, Editor, barbarav@awmanet.org. Released: 12/year. Price: Included in membership. Description: Provides wholesalers of candy and tobacco products, brokers, salespersons, and manufacturers with industry news. Recurring features include news of members and notices of Association activities, events, awards, and research and educational programs.

TRADE SHOWS AND CONVENTIONS

3299 ■ International Fancy Food and Confection Show/Winter
National Association for the Specialty Food Trade Inc.
8 W 40th St., 4th Fl.
New York, NY 10018-3901

Ph: (212)921-1690
Fax: (212)921-1898
URL(s): www.specialtyfood.com. Frequency: Annual. Audience: Retailers, brokers, importers, buyers, chefs, caterers and related personnel. Principal Exhibits: Pates, cheeses, specialty meats and seafood, condiments, sauces, mustards, vinegars, chocolates, fine candies, biscuits, cookies, cakes, jams, jellies, preserves, coffees, teas, fruits, nuts, special beverages, beer, wine, ice creams, desserts, and cooking accessories. Dates and Locations: , Moscone Convention Center.

FRANCHISES AND BUSINESS OPPORTUNITIES

3300 ■ AmeriCandy Retail Interactive Kiosk (AIRK)
AmeriCandy Co., Inc.
3618 St. Germaine Ct.
Louisville, KY 40207
Ph: (502)583-1776
Fax: (502)583-1776
Description: Markets confections and chocolates representing 50 states in red and gold AmeriCandy presentation boxes. Distributes its products through retail stores, specialty shops and catalogs. No. of Company-Owned Units: 2. Founded: 2006. Franchised: 1992. Equity Capital Needed: $60,000. Franchise Fee: $10,000. Financial Assistance: Yes. Training: Yes.

3301 ■ Candy Bouquet International
510 McLean
Little Rock, AR 72201
Ph: (501)375-9990
Fax: (501)375-9998
URL: http://www.candybouquet.com
Description: Hand-crafted candy bouquet gift arrangements. No. of Franchise Units: 333. Founded: 1989.. Franchised: 1993. Equity Capital Needed: $8,500. Franchise Fee: $5,000-$33,500. Training: Yes.

3302 ■ Kilwin's Chocolates and Ice Cream
1050 Bay View Rd.
Petoskey, MI 49770
Ph: (866)596-7273
Fax: (231)439-6829
Description: Full-line confectionery shops, featuring Kilwin's handmade chocolates, fudge and original-recipe ice cream. No. of Franchise Units: 82. No. of Company-Owned Units: 2. Founded: 1947. Franchised: 1981. Equity Capital Needed: $125 cash injection; $500,000 net worth. Franchise Fee: $40,000. Training: Yes.

3303 ■ Powell's Sweet Shoppe
Powell's Sweet Shoppe USA, LLC
PO Box 1079
Windsor, CA 95492
Ph: (707)838-4898
Fax: (707)838-8318
Co. E-mail: Michael.powell@powellsss.com
URL: http://www.powellsss.com
Description: Candy, gelato, and nostalgic toys. No. of Franchise Units: 8. No. of Company-Owned Units: 1. Founded: 2003.. Franchised: 2005. Equity Capital Needed: $370,000-$440,000. Franchise Fee: $30,000. Royalty Fee: 6%.

3304 ■ Ricky's Candy, Cones And Chaos
Ricky's Franchise Group, LLC
2865 S Eagle Rd.
Newtown, PA 18940
Ph: (267)987-2287
Fax: (215)579-2748
Description: Nostalgic and bulky candy, ice cream. No. of Franchise Units: 43. No. of Company-Owned Units: 1. Founded: 2004.. Franchised: 2004. Equity Capital Needed: $100,000 initial investment. Franchise Fee: $30,000. Training: Yes.

3305 ■ Rocky Mountain Chocolate Factory, Inc.
265 Turner Dr.
Durango, CO 81301
Ph: (970)259-0554

Fax: (970)259-5895
Co. E-mail: franchise@rmcf.net
URL: http://www.sweetfranchise.com
Description: Retail and wholesale of packaged and bulk chocolates, brittles, truffles, sauces, cocoas, coffees and related chocolate and non-chocolate items. In-store preparation of fudges, caramel apples and dipped fruits via interactive cooking demonstrations. Complete line of gift and holiday items. Supplemental retail sale of soft drinks, ice cream, cookies and brewed coffee. **No. of Franchise Units:** 355. **No. of Company-Owned Units:** 12. **Founded:** 1981.. **Franchised:** 1982. **Equity Capital Needed:** $50,000 cash; ability to finance an additional $199,771-$599,336. **Franchise Fee:** $24,500. **Training:** Training provided in customer service, record keeping, merchandising, inventory control and marketing during 10 day program at corporate headquarters, in addition to several days onsite for store opening.

3306 ■ Schakolad Chocolate Factory
5966 Lakehurst Dr.
Orlando, FL 32819
Ph: (407)248-6400
Fax: (407)248-1466
Description: Handmade fine chocolate. **No. of Franchise Units:** 22. **Founded:** 1995.. **Franchised:** 1999. **Equity Capital Needed:** $111,600-$144,000.

Franchise Fee: $30,000. **Royalty Fee:** $600/month. **Financial Assistance:** Limited third party financing available. **Training:** Offers 1-2 weeks at headquarters and 1-2 weeks at franchisee's location and ongoing support.

3307 ■ The South Bend Chocolate Company Inc.
3300 W Sample St.
South Bend, IN 46619
Ph: (574)233-2577
Free: 800-301-4961
Fax: (574)233-3150
Co. E-mail: info@sbchocolate.com
URL: http://www.sbchocolate.com
Contact: Mark Tarner, President
Description: Gourmet chocolate and confectionery manufacturer. **No. of Franchise Units:** 13. **No. of Company-Owned Units:** 10. **Founded:** 1991. **Franchised:** 1997. **Equity Capital Needed:** $74,950-$295,500. **Franchise Fee:** $35,000. **Royalty Fee:** 4%. **Training:** Offers 10 days at headquarters, 80 hours at franchisees location with ongoing support.

LIBRARIES

3308 ■ M&M/Mars Research Library
800 High St.
Hackettstown, NJ 07840-1500

Ph: (908)852-1000
URL: http://www.mars.com
Contact: Richard Warre
Scope: Confectionery, business. **Services:** Interlibrary loan (responds to fax requests); Library not open to the public. **Founded:** 1983. **Holdings:** 500 books; 75 reels of microfilm; 160 videocassettes; 8 journals. **Subscriptions:** 50 journals and other serials; 3 newspapers.

3309 ■ PMCA, an International Association of Confectioners - Bibliography of Technical Papers Collection—Pennsylvania Manufacturing Confectioners' Association - Bibliography of Technical Papers Collection.
2980 Linden St., Ste. E3
Bethlehem, PA 18017
Ph: (610)625-4655
Fax: (610)625-4657
Co. E-mail: info@pmca.com
URL: http://www.pmca.com
Contact: Yvette Thomas, Director, Administration
URL(s): www.pmca.com/library.asp. **Scope:** Chocolate technology; confectionery products production. **Services:** Copying (fee); library not open to the public. **Founded:** 1907. **Holdings:** Annual Production Proceedings (1947 to present).

ASSOCIATIONS AND OTHER ORGANIZATIONS

3310 ■ International Auto Sound Challenge Association (IASCA)
2200 S Ridgewood Ave.
South Daytona, FL 32119
Ph: (386)322-1551
Fax: (386)761-2120
Co. E-mail: paul@iasca.com
URL: http://www.iasca.com
Contact: Paul Papadeas, President

Description: Manufacturers, retailers, and representatives/distributors of auto stereos; other interested individuals. Promotes the automotive stereo industry; holds sound quality and security contests; conducts consumer education. **Founded:** 1987. **Educational Activities:** Consumer Electronics (Semiannual); International Electronics Expo (Annual).

REFERENCE WORKS

3311 ■ *Surviving in the Security Alarm Business*
Pub: Butterworth-Heinemann
Ed: Lou Sepulveda. **Released:** 1998. **Price:** $19.95.

TRADE PERIODICALS

3312 ■ *Consumer Electronics Vision*
Pub: Consumer Electronics Association
Contact: Gary Shapiro, President
E-mail: gshapiro@ce.org
Ed: Robert MacMillan, Editor, cstevens@ce.org. **Released:** Quarterly, 6/year. **Price:** Free. **Description:** Provides news and information concerning mobile electronics, audio, radar, security, and cellular communications. Examines the manufacture, market trends, and installation of mobile electronics. Covers legislative and regulatory issues at the state and federal levels with particular emphasis on business, manufacturing, and insurance issues. Recurring features include a monthly series of retail management information and news of the Association.

3313 ■ *Security Sales & Integration*
Pub: Bobit Business Media
Contact: Ty Bobit, President
URL(s): www.securitysales.com. **Released:** Monthly **Price:** Free. **Telecommunication Services:** Email: info@securitysales.com .

FRANCHISES AND BUSINESS OPPORTUNITIES

3314 ■ Alta Mere Toys for Your Car
Moran Industries, Inc.
4444 W 147th St.
St. Midlothian, IL 60445

Ph: (708)389-5922
Free: 800-581-8468
Fax: (708)389-9882

Description: Auto tinting and alarm installation facilities. **No. of Franchise Units:** 14. **Founded:** 1986. **Franchised:** 1993. **Equity Capital Needed:** $60,000. **Franchise Fee:** $30,000. **Financial Assistance:** Yes. **Training:** Provides 1 week training at headquarters, 3 weeks at franchisee's location with ongoing support.

3315 ■ Ziebart
Ziebart International Corp.
1290 E Maple Rd.
Troy 48083-2817
Ph: (248)588-4100
Fax: (248)588-2513
Co. E-mail: info@ziebart.com
URL: http://www.ziebart.com

Description: Automotive application of detailing-accessories and protection services. **No. of Franchise Units:** 400. **No. of Company-Owned Units:** 14. **Founded:** 1954.. **Franchised:** 1962. **Equity Capital Needed:** $100,000-$250,000. **Franchise Fee:** $25,000. **Financial Assistance:** Yes. **Training:** Yes.

REFERENCE WORKS

3316 ■ *"How Not to Build a Website"* in *Women Entrepreneur (December 24, 2008)*
Pub: Entrepreneur Media Inc.
Ed: Erica Ruback; Joanie Reisen. **Description:** Tips for producing a unique and functional Website are given as well as a number of lessons a pair of entrepreneurs learned while trying to launch their networking website, MomSpace.com.

CONSULTANTS

3317 ■ **Dynamotive Engineering Inc.**
101 Foxfell Dr.
Kennett Square, PA 19348
Ph: (610)444-3636
Fax: (610)444-3636
Co. E-mail: dynamotive@kennett.net
Contact: William G. Mears, President
Scope: Specialist in the design, application and use of chassis roll dynamometers for testing automobiles and trucks. This includes facilities, such as environmental chambers, in which chassis roll dynamometers are operated and accessory equipment such as vehicle restraints and automatic drivers used in conjunction with chassis roll operation. Industries served: Automotive, petroleum, automotive accessories, dynamometer fabrication and control, automotive emissions testing, automotive diagnostic systems and inspection-maintenance programs. **Founded:** 1990. **Seminars:** Available for seminars on chassis roll dynamometer simulation accuracy and estimation of vehicle road load settings on chassis roll dynameters.

FRANCHISES AND BUSINESS OPPORTUNITIES

3318 ■ **Snap-On Tools Of Canada Ltd.**
6500 Millcreek Dr.
Mississauga, ON, Canada L5N 2W6
Free: 800-665-8665
Fax: (877)234-0180
URL: http://www.snaponfranchise.com
Description: Distributes quality automotive and industrial tools and diagnostic equipments. **No. of Franchise Units:** 350. **No. of Company-Owned Units:** 12. **No. of Operating Units:** 4,996. **Founded:** 1931.. **Franchised:** 1994. **Equity Capital Needed:** $198,243-$292,433 investment required; $50,083-$69,273 start-up capital required. **Franchise Fee:** $7,500-$15,000. **Training:** Initial training and ongoing.

ASSOCIATIONS AND OTHER ORGANIZATIONS

3319 ■ Towing and Recovery Association of America (TRAA)
2121 Eisenhower Ave., Ste. 200
Alexandria, VA 22314
Ph: (703)684-7713
Free: 800-728-0136
Fax: (703)684-6720
Co. E-mail: towserver@aol.com
URL: http://www.towserver.net
Contact: Alan Gregg, President

Description: Tow truck owners or operators; associate members are wrecker and accessory manufacturers and vendors. Aims to upgrade and promote the industry. Promotes uniform legislation; offers specialized education and National Driver Certification Program. **Founded:** 1979. **Publications:** *TRAA Membership Directory* (Annual).

REFERENCE WORKS

3320 ■ *Tow Times' Annual Sourcebook*
Pub: T.T. Publications Inc.
Contact: Dave Jones, President

URL(s): www.towtimes.com. **Released:** Annual; Latest edition 2011-2012. **Publication includes:** Lists of approximately 100 suppliers in the U.S. serving towing and recovery operators. **Entries include:** Company name, address, phone, fax, name and title of contact, cross reference code to products and services. Principal content of publication is articles of interest to towing and recovery professionals. **Database includes:** List of state towing and recovery associations, with contact information. **Arrangement:** Classified by line of business. **Indexes:** Product/service.

SOURCES OF SUPPLY

3321 ■ *Truck Frame & Axle Repair Association--Membership Directory*
Truck-frame & Axle Repair Association
Contact: Paul Jones, President
E-mail: pjonesafa@aol.com

URL(s): www.taraassociation.com. **Released:** Biennial; August of odd years. **Price:** Free. **Covers:** About

150 regular and associate members that repair heavy-duty truck equipment or supply the industry. **Entries include:** Firm name, address, phone, key personnel, coding to indicate specialties. **Database includes:** Map showing locations of members. **Arrangement:** Geographical.

TRADE PERIODICALS

3322 ■ *National Towing News*
Pub: Towing and Recovery Association of America

Released: Monthly. **Price:** Included in membership. **Description:** Gives news of the Association. Recurring features include a column titled From the State Line.

3323 ■ *Towing and Recovery Footnotes: The Community Newspaper and Marketplace for the Nation's Towers*
Pub: Dominion Enterprises
Contact: Jack Ross, President

URL(s): www.trfootnotes.com. **Released:** Monthly **Price:** $30, Individuals; $55, Two years.

START-UP INFORMATION

3324 ■ *"Cleaning Up" in Small Business Opportunities (Get Rich At Home 2010)*
Pub: Harris Publications Inc.
Description: Break into the $23 billion pro car wash business with no experience needed. Profile of Team Blue, founded by father and son team, Jeff and Jason Haas along with franchise opportunities is included.

ASSOCIATIONS AND OTHER ORGANIZATIONS

3325 ■ **Canadian Carwash Association (CCA)**
4195 Dundas St. W, Ste. 346
Toronto, ON, Canada M8X 1Y4
Ph: (416)239-0339
Fax: (416)239-1076
Co. E-mail: office@canadiancarwash.ca
URL: http://www.canadiancarwash.ca
Contact: Scott Murray, President
Description: Owners of car wash facilities. Promotes growth and development of the industry. Facilitates exchange of information among members; monitors legislation of interest to members and conducts lobbying activities; makes available continuing professional education programs; conducts public relations campaigns. Provides benefits to members including discount insurance programs and customer handouts. **Publications:** *Wash-Word* (Quarterly). **Awards:** Ted Snyders Memorial Award (Annual).

3326 ■ **International Carwash Association (ICA)**
401 N Michigan Ave., Ste. 2200
Chicago, IL 60611
Ph: (312)321-5199
Free: 888-422-8422
Fax: (312)527-6774
Co. E-mail: info@carwash.org
URL: http://www.carwash.org
Contact: Jerry Miller, President
Description: Membership consists of car wash and detail operators, manufacturers, and supplier's distributors. Promotes the car wash industry by providing educational opportunities to members and gathering information on the industry and its customer. **Scope:** car wash industry. **Founded:** 1955. **Subscriptions:** books periodicals. **Publications:** *International Carwash Association--Member Directory and Buyers Guide* (Annual); *ICA News* (Monthly); *ICA Directory and Buyer's Guide* (Annual). **Educational Activities:** Car Care World Expo (Annual); Car Care World Expo presented by the International Carwash Association (Annual); International Carwash Association Annual Convention and Exhibition (Annual). **Awards:** Brian Campbell Leadership in Innovation Award (Annual); Car Wash Hall of Fame Award (Annual); Environmental Leadership Award (Annual). **Telecommunication Services:** ica@sba.com.

3327 ■ *Wash-Word*
4195 Dundas St. W, Ste. 346
Toronto, ON, Canada M8X 1Y4
Ph: (416)239-0339
Fax: (416)239-1076
Co. E-mail: office@canadiancarwash.ca
URL: http://www.canadiancarwash.ca
Contact: Scott Murray, President
Released: Quarterly

REFERENCE WORKS

3328 ■ *"Casey's Buys Second Marion Convenience Store" in Gazette (December 14, 2010)*
Pub: Gazette
Ed: Dave DeWitte. **Description:** Casey's General Stores Inc. has acquired a Short Stop convenience store on Marion's west side in Iowa. The new store includes a car and truck wash.

3329 ■ *"Dry Idea" in Entrepreneur (Vol. 36, April 2008, No. 4, pp. 20)*
Pub: Entrepreneur Media, Inc.
Ed: Tiffany Meyers. **Description:** Lucky Earth LLC is an Inglewood, California-based company that markets 'Waterless' Carwash, an organic product that is sprayed on to the car and wiped down without using water. Businesses related to water conservation are being created, as water shortage is anticipated in 36 states in the U.S. by 2013.

STATISTICAL SOURCES

3330 ■ *RMA Annual Statement Studies*
Pub: Risk Management Association
Contact: Kevin M. Blakey, President
Released: Annual. **Price:** $175.00 2006-07 edition, $105.00. **Description:** Contains composite balance sheets and income statements for more than 360 industries, including the accounting, auditing, and bookkeeping industries. Also contains five years of comparative historical data for discerning trends. Includes 16 commonly used ratios, computed for most of the size groupings for nearly every industry.

TRADE PERIODICALS

3331 ■ *Auto Laundry News: The Voice of the Car Care Industry Since 1953*
Pub: E.W. Williams Publications Co.
Contact: Andrew Williams, President
E-mail: awilliams@ewwpi.com
URL(s): www.carwashmag.com. **Released:** Monthly **Price:** $72, Individuals; $83, Canada; $125, Elsewhere airmail; $108, Two years; $106, Canada 2 years; $200, Elsewhere 2 years, airmail; $125, Individuals 3 years; $15, Individuals annual directory; $20, Canada annual directory; $7, Single issue.

3332 ■ *Professional Carwashing & Detailing*
Pub: National Trade Publications Inc.
Contact: Mike Perkins, Director
E-mail: mperkins@ntpinc.com
URL(s): www.carwash.com/. **Ed:** Deb Gorgos. **Released:** Monthly

TRADE SHOWS AND CONVENTIONS

3333 ■ **International Carwash Association Annual Convention and Exhibition**
International Carwash Association (ICA)
401 N Michigan Ave., Ste. 2200
Chicago, IL 60611
Ph: (312)321-5199
Free: 888-422-8422
Fax: (312)527-6774
Co. E-mail: info@carwash.org
URL: http://www.carwash.org
Contact: Jerry Miller, President
URL(s): www.carwash.com. **Frequency:** Annual. **Audience:** Carwash and detail shop operators. **Principal Exhibits:** Carwash and detailing equipment, supplies and services.

FRANCHISES AND BUSINESS OPPORTUNITIES

3334 ■ **Cactus Car Wash**
2980-A Piedmont Rd.
Atlanta, GA 30080
Ph: (770)436-0985
Fax: (770)818-5885
Description: Full-service car wash. **No. of Company-Owned Units:** 4. **Founded:** 1996.. **Franchised:** 2005. **Equity Capital Needed:** $1,200,000-$1,600,000. **Franchise Fee:** $30,000. **Royalty Fee:** 5.5%. **Training:** Offers 2 weeks at headquarters, 2 weeks onsite and ongoing support.

3335 ■ **Fine Details Inc.**
481 N Service Rd. W, Unit A13
Oakville, ON, Canada L6M 2V6
Ph: (905)825-4200
Free: 888-843-9274
Fax: (905)825-4035
URL: http://www.finedetails.ca
Description: Offers interior/exterior hand car cleaning. There are 13 different types of services to satisfy the needs of the vehicle as well as the client's budget. **No. of Franchise Units:** 20. **Founded:** 1995. **Franchised:** 1998. **Equity Capital Needed:** $120,000. **Franchise Fee:** $30,000. **Training:** 2 weeks training with ongoing operational and marketing support.

3336 ■ **The Shine Factory**
Shine Factory Systems Inc.
75 Akerley Blvd.
Dartmouth, NS, Canada B3B 1R7
Ph: (902)405-3171
Fax: (902)405-3484
Co. E-mail: info@shinefactory.com
URL: http://www.shinefactory.com
Description: Canada's automotive and polishing franchise. **No. of Franchise Units:** 16. **Founded:** 1981. **Franchised:** 1981. **Equity Capital Needed:** $100,000+. **Franchise Fee:** $25,000 depending upon market area study. **Training:** Training conducted in Halifax, NS.

3337 ■ Super Wash
707 W Lincolnway
Morrison, IL 61270
Ph: (815)772-2111
Free: 800-633-7625 x114

Fax: (815)772-7160
URL: http://www.superwash.com
Description: Franchisor of car washes. **No. of Franchise Units:** 288. **No. of Company-Owned Units:** 65. **Founded:** 1982.. **Franchised:** 2001. Eq-

uity **Capital Needed:** $468,000-$1,100,100. **Franchise Fee:** $9,000. **Royalty Fee:** Varies. **Financial Assistance:** Third party financing available. **Training:** Training available at headquarters, onsite and ongoing support provided.

ASSOCIATIONS AND OTHER ORGANIZATIONS

3338 ■ American Counseling Association (ACA)
5999 Stevenson Ave.
Alexandria, VA 22304
Ph: (703)823-6862
Free: 800-347-6647
Fax: (703)823-0252
Co. E-mail: ryep@counseling.org
URL: http://www.counseling.org
Contact: Brian S. Canfield, President
E-mail: bcanfield@counseling.org
Description: Counseling professionals in elementary and secondary schools, higher education, community agencies and organizations, rehabilitation programs, government, industry, business, private practice, career counseling, and mental health counseling. Conducts professional development institutes and provides liability insurance. Maintains Counseling and Human Development Foundation to fund counseling projects. **Scope:** Continuing education specialists in the areas of counseling, guidance and human resource development. The organization is committed to the principle that continuing education is a paramount service obligation. Target audience: practicing counselors and guidance supervisors in the fields of education, mental health, rehabilitation, employment, private practice and business/industrial sectors. **Founded:** 1952. **Publications:** "Compelling Counseling Interventions, VISTAS 2009"; "The Professional Counselor, Fourth Edition"; "The ACA Encyclopedia of Counseling"; "The Counselor and the Law"; "The Life and Work of Carl Rogers"; "Active Interventions for Kids and Teens"; "Youth at Risk: A Prevention Resource, 5th Edition"; "Girl's and Women's Wellness"; "Counseling Multiple Heritage Individuals, Couples and Families"; "Ethics Desk Reference for Counselors"; Clinical Supervision in the Helping Professions"; "Developing Clinical Skills in Substance Abuse Counseling"; Creating Your Professional Path"; "ACA Advocacy Competencies: A Social Justice Framework"; "Terrorism, Trauma and Tragedies". **Educational Activities:** American Counseling Association Conference and Exposition (Annual). **Awards:** Ross Trust Graduate Student Scholarships; Extended Research Award; Federal Legislative Service Award; Professional Development Award; Research Award; Ralph F. Berdie Memorial Research Award (Annual); Carl D. Perkins Government Relations Award; David K. Brooks Distinguished Mentor Award; Don Dinkmeyer Social Interest Award; Best Practices Award; Robert Rencken Emerging Professional Leader Award; Counselor Educator Advocacy Award; ACA Extended Research Award (Annual); ACA Legislative Service Award; ACA Professional Development Award (Annual); ACA Research Award; Arthur A. Hitchcock Award (Annual); Kitty Cole Human Rights Award; National Graduate Student Glen E. Hubele Award; Arthur A. Hitchcock Distinguished Professional Service Award; Glen E. Hubele National Graduate Student Award; Gilbert and Kathleen Wrenn Award for a Humanitarian and Caring Person; Courtland C. Lee Multicultural Excellence Scholarship Award; Gilbert and Kathleen Wrenn Award for a Humanitarian and Caring Person (Annual). **Seminars:** Aging in America; Anger Management: Strategies Toward Resolutions; Brief Counseling: Strategies and Technique; Treating the Blues: Strategies and Techniques for Clinical Depression; DSM-IV: Diagnosis and Treatment Planning; Ethics in Counseling; Group Counseling Skills; Jest for Health: Humor in Counseling; Legal Aspects of Counseling; Multicultural Counseling Competencies; Treating Clients on Medication: What Helping Professionals Need to Know About Psychopharmacology; School-To-Work; Treating Personality Disorders; Treatment Planning; Treating Violence and Conflicting Families. **Telecommunication Services:** aca@counseling.org; membership@counseling.org; cwelch@counseling.org.

3339 ■ Association of Canadian Search, Employment and Staffing Services (ACSESS)—Association Nationale des Enterprises en Recrutement et Placement de Personnel
2233 Argentia Rd., Ste. 100
Mississauga, ON, Canada L5N 2X7
Ph: (905)826-6869
Free: 888-232-4962
Fax: (905)826-4873
Co. E-mail: acsess@acsess.org
URL: http://www.acsess.org
Contact: Amanda Curtis, Executive Director
Description: Promotes employment, recruitment, and staffing services industry in Canada, including direct-hire and executive search services, temporary and contract staffing services. Promotes advancement and growth, advocates for professional ethics and standards in the industry; coordinates government relations, educational and promotional and communications initiatives; provides support services on relevant legislative, regulatory and procurement issues. Promotes best industry practices and adherence to employment legislation and regulations. Monitors industry standards. Provides professional certification and training, including Certified Personnel Consultant Designation Program. Coordinates educational programs and conferences. Promotes public awareness of the industry and keeps members informed of issues affecting the industry. Collects and provides industry statistics. **Founded:** 1998. **Publications:** *Dialogue* (3/year). **Telecommunication Services:** acurtis@bbandc.com.

3340 ■ Career Planning and Adult Development Network (CPADN)
543 Vista Mar Ave.
Pacifica, CA 94044
Ph: (650)773-0982
Fax: (650)359-3089
Co. E-mail: admin@careernetwork.org
URL: http://www.careernetwork.org
Description: Counselors, trainers, consultants, therapists, educators, personnel specialists, and graduate students who work in business, educational, religious, and governmental organizations, and focus on career planning and adult development issues. Seeks to: establish a link between professionals working with adults in a variety of settings; identify and exchange effective adult development methods and techniques; develop a clearer understanding of the directions and objectives of the career planning and the adult development movement. Keeps members informed of developments in career decision-making, career values clarification, preretirement counseling, dual-career families, job search techniques, and mid-life transitions. Cosponsors professional seminars; maintains biographical archives. **Founded:** 1979. **Publications:** *Career Planning & Adult Development Network Newsletter*; *Career Planning & Adult Development Network Newsletter*. **Educational Activities:** International Career Development Conference (Annual); International Career Development Conference (Annual). **Awards:** Professional Resource Award (Annual).

3341 ■ *Dialogue*
2233 Argentia Rd., Ste. 100
Mississauga, ON, Canada L5N 2X7
Ph: (905)826-6869
Free: 888-232-4962
Fax: (905)826-4873
Co. E-mail: acsess@acsess.org
URL: http://www.acsess.org
Contact: Amanda Curtis, Executive Director
Released: 3/year

3342 ■ International Association of Counseling Services (IACS)
101 S Whiting St., Ste. 211
Alexandria, VA 22304-3416
Ph: (703)823-9840
Fax: (703)823-9843
Co. E-mail: iacsinc@earthlink.net
URL: http://www.iacsinc.org/
Contact: Mary Chandler Bolin, President
Description: Represents accredited university and four-year college counseling services in the U.S., Canada, and Australia. Fosters communications and cooperation among counseling services. **Founded:** 1972. **Publications:** *Directory of Accredited Counseling Services* (Annual); *National Survey of Counseling Center Directors* (Annual); *Counseling Services: IACS Newsletter*.

3343 ■ National Board for Certified Counselors and Affiliates (NBCC)
3 Terrace Way
Greensboro, NC 27403-3660
Ph: (336)547-0607
Fax: (336)547-0017
Co. E-mail: nbcc@nbcc.org
URL: http://www.nbcc.org
Contact: Sherry Allen, Executive Director
URL(s): www.nbcc.org/newsletter. **Description:** Establishes and monitors professional credentialing standards for counselors. Identifies individuals who have obtained voluntary certification as a National Certified Counselor, one who assists persons with aging, vocational development, adolescence, family, and marital concerns, or a National Certified School Counselor, one who specializes in counseling within the school setting, or a Certified Clinical Mental Health Counselor, one who specializes in working in clinical settings, or a Master Addictions Counselor,

one who specializes in addictions counseling. Maintains a database of nearly 37,000 certified counselors. **Founded:** 1982. **Publications:** *The National Certified Counselor* (3/year); *NCC*; *Preparation Guide for the National Counselor Examination for Licensure and Certification.*

3344 ■ National Career Development Association (NCDA)
305 N Beech Cir.
Broken Arrow, OK 74012
Ph: (918)663-7060
Free: 866-367-6232
Fax: (918)663-7058
Co. E-mail: dosborn@fsu.edu
URL: http://associationdatabase.com/aws/NCDA/pt/
sp/Home_Page
Contact: Deb Osborn, President
URL(s): www.ncda.org. **Description:** Represents professionals and others interested in career development or counseling in various work environments. Supports counselors, education and training personnel, and allied professionals working in schools, colleges, business/industry, community and government agencies, and in private practice. Provides publications, support for state and local activities, human equity programs, and continuing education and training for these professionals. Provides networking opportunities for career professionals in business, education, and government. **Founded:** 1913. **Publications:** *Career Development Quarterly* (Quarterly). **Telecommunication Services:** dpenn@ncda.org.

3345 ■ National Employment Counseling Association (NECA)
c/o Michael C. Lazarchick, PhD, Pres.
7414 Dritwood Ln.
Weymouth, NJ 08330
Ph: (609)625-7493
Co. E-mail: employmentcounseling@yahoo.com
URL: http://www.employmentcounseling.org
Contact: Michael C. Lazarchick, President
Description: Serves as a division of the American Counseling Association. Represents individuals who are engaged in employment counseling, counselor education, research, administration or supervision in business and industry, colleges and universities, and federal and state governments; students. Offers professional leadership and development services; provides opportunities for professional growth through workshops and special projects. **Founded:** 1964. **Publications:** *Journal of Employment Counseling* (Quarterly).

DIRECTORIES OF EDUCATIONAL PROGRAMS

3346 ■ *The Directory of Canadian Recruiters*
Pub: Continental Records Company Ltd.
Contact: Neil Patte, President
URL(s): www.gocontinental.comwww.directoryofrecruiters.com/canadabook.html. **Released:** Annual; Latest edition 2011-12. **Price:** $79.95, Individuals GST plus shipping cost; $99.95, Individuals Professional CD ed. plus shipping cost plus tax. **Covers:** 2,655 recruiting firms and more than 5,600 executive recruiting firms in Canada. **Entries include:** Firm name, address, phone, fax, e-mail, URL, industries, positions, salary levels, name and title of contact. **Indexes:** Industry, position filled, salary level.

3347 ■ *Who's Hiring: 5,000 Canadian Employers Indexed by Occupation*
Pub: Mediacorp Canada Inc.
URL(s): www.mediacorp.ca/2005/2.html. **Ed:** Anthony W. Meehan. **Released:** Annual; 2005. **Price:** $42.95, Individuals book and CD-ROM. **Covers:** Ranks Canada's 5,000 fastest-growing employers in 61 major occupational categories. **Entries include:** Company name, address, phone, fax, e-mail, and URL addresses, human resources contacts, positions recently advertised, description of employer's business. **Indexes:** Geographical; occupational.

REFERENCE WORKS

3348 ■ *"Design program in Athletic Footwear"* in Occupational Outlook Quarterly (Vol. 55,

Fall 2011, No. 3, pp. 21)
Pub: U.S. Bureau of Labor Statistics
Description: The Fashion Institute of Technology offers the only certificate program in performance athletic footwear design in the U.S. The program focuses on conceptualizing and sketching shoe designs and covers ergonomic, anatomical, and material considerations for athletic footwear design.

3349 ■ *"Encouraging Study in Critical Languages"* in Occupational Outlook Quarterly (Vol. 55, Summer 2011, No. 2, pp. 23)
Pub: U.S. Bureau of Labor Statistics
Description: Proficiency in particular foreign languages is vital to the defense, diplomacy, and security of the United States. Several federal programs provide scholarships and other funding to encourage high school and college students to learn languages of the Middle East, China, and Russia.

3350 ■ *"Finishing High School Leads to Better Employment Prospects"* in Occupational Outlook Quarterly (Vol. 55, Summer 2011, No. 2, pp. 36)
Pub: U.S. Bureau of Labor Statistics
Description: Students who drop out of high school are more likely to face unemployment than those who finish. Statistical data included.

3351 ■ *"Genetic Counselor"* in Occupational Outlook Quarterly (Vol. 55, Summer 2011, No. 2, pp. 34)
Pub: U.S. Bureau of Labor Statistics
Ed: John Mullins. **Description:** Genetic counseling involves the practice of informing clients about genetic disorders and to help them understand and manage a disorder. There are approximately 2,400 certified genetic counselors in the U.S. and earn a median annual salary of about $63,000, according to the American Board of Genetic Counseling. The US Bureau of Labor Statistics does not have data on employment or wages for genetic counselors.

3352 ■ *"Online Tools for Jobseekers"* in Occupational Outlook Quarterly (Vol. 55, Fall 2011, No. 3, pp. 20)
Pub: U.S. Bureau of Labor Statistics
Description: U.S. Department of Labor's CareerOneStop provides a collection of Web-based tools serving students, jobseekers, employers, and the workforce. The top six categories for job listings nationwide include general job boards, niche job boards, career planning tools, career explorations sites, social media job search sites, and other tools which include interview preparation tools and training grants.

3353 ■ *"Paid to Persuade: Careers in Sales"* in Occupational Outlook Quarterly (Vol. 55, Summer 2011, No. 2, pp. 24)
Pub: U.S. Bureau of Labor Statistics
Ed: Ilka Maria Torpey. **Description:** Sales workers are paid to persuade others to buy goods and services. There were over 13 million wage and salary sales workers in the US in 2010. Wages in sales careers can vary and some become lucrative, lifelong career positions. Seven sales occupations with annual wages higher than $33,000 are profiled.

3354 ■ *"Physics for Females"* in Occupational Outlook Quarterly (Vol. 55, Summer 2011, No. 2, pp. 22)
Pub: U.S. Bureau of Labor Statistics
Description: Free resources to help females investigate careers in medical physics and health physics are available from the American Physical Society. The booklet is designed for girls in middle and high school and describes the work of 15 women who use physics to solve medical mysteries, discover planets, research new materials, and more.

3355 ■ *"Plan Your Future with My Next Move"* in Occupational Outlook Quarterly (Vol. 55, Summer 2011, No. 2, pp. 22)
Pub: U.S. Bureau of Labor Statistics
Description: My Next Move, an online tool offering a variety of user-friendly ways to browse more than 900 occupations was created by the National Center for O NET Development for the US Department of

Labor's Employment and Training Administration. Clicking on an occupation presents a one-page profile summarizing key information for specific careers.

3356 ■ *"Work for Play: Careers in Video Game Development"* in Occupational Outlook Quarterly (Vol. 55, Fall 2011, No. 3, pp. 2)
Pub: U.S. Bureau of Labor Statistics
Ed: Drew Liming, Dennis Vilorio. **Description:** Game developers make a living creating the games the public enjoys playing. The video gaming industry reported sales over $10 billion in 2009 and employed 32,000 people in 34 states. Career options in video game development are featured.

TRADE PERIODICALS

3357 ■ *AACE Bonus Briefs*
Pub: American Association for Career Education
Ed: Pat Nellor Wickwire, Editor. **Released:** Quarterly. **Price:** Included in membership. **Description:** Contains brief papers by American Association for Career Education members on current issues in careers, education, and employment.

3358 ■ *AACE Distinguished Member Series*
Pub: American Association for Career Education
Ed: Pat Nellor Wickwire, Editor. **Released:** Periodic. **Price:** Included in membership. **Description:** Publication of the American Association for Career Education. Provides information on careers, education, and employment.

3359 ■ *Career Development Quarterly*
Pub: National Career Development Association
Contact: Deb Osborn, President
URL(s): associationdatabase.com/aws/NCDA/pt/sp/cdquarterly. **Ed:** Dr. Jerry Trusty. **Released:** Quarterly **Price:** $68, Individuals; $105, Institutions.

3360 ■ *Career Planning & Adult Development Network Newsletter*
Pub: Career Planning and Adult Development Network
Released: BIM. **Price:** $59, Free payment must accompany order; $74, other countries payment must. **Description:** Contains features and news items on career development and human resources: theory, methodology, research, practices, and techniques. Deals with manpower, organizational planning, counseling, training, equal opportunity, career transition, marketing skills, and adult learning. Recurring features include notices of resources, materials, publications of interest, conferences, workshops, seminars, employment opportunities, book reviews, network news, and a column on publishers of career development books.

3361 ■ *Career World*
Pub: Weekly Reader Corp.
URL(s): www.weeklyreader.com/pubstore/pc-10-3-career-worldreg.aspx. **Released:** Bimonthly; during academic year. **Price:** $10.25, Individuals.

3362 ■ *Careers & Colleges*
Pub: 360 Youth L.L.C.
URL(s): www.alloyeducation.com/careersColleges.htm. **Released:** Bimonthly; (during the school year).

3363 ■ *Changing Course*
Pub: Making Waves, Publishers
Ed: Valerie Young, Editor, vyoung@changingcourse.com. **Released:** Bimonthly. **Price:** $29, U.S.; $49, two years USA; $35, Canada; $57, two years Canada. **Description:** Contains inspiration and information on creating more satisfying work lives outside the 9-to-5 job world. Recurring features include letters to the editor, interviews, book reviews, and columns titled Opportunities Knock: Creative Alternatives to Working 9-5, Resources for a Change, and Dollar/Sense.

3364 ■ *Counseling Today*
Pub: American Counseling Association
Contact: Brian S. Canfield, President
E-mail: bcanfield@counseling.org
URL(s): ct.counseling.org. **Ed:** Jonathan Rollins. **Released:** Monthly

3365 ■ Enrich!
Pub: National Chamber of Commerce for Women
Contact: Jay Orson, Manager, Advertising
Ed: R. Wright, Editor. **Released:** Bimonthly. **Price:** $96. **Description:** Strives to assist readers on business-plan, career-path, and pay-comparison goals.

3366 ■ Journal of Employment Counseling
Pub: American Counseling Association
Contact: Brian S. Canfield, President
E-mail: bcanfield@counseling.org
URL(s): www.counseling.org/Publications/Journals.aspx. **Ed:** Dr. Roberta A. Neault. **Released:** Quarterly **Price:** $150, Institutions non-member; $173, Institutions.

VIDEOCASSETTES/ AUDIOCASSETTES

3367 ■ The American Professionals Series
RMI Media
1365 N. Winchester St.
Olathe, KS 66061-5880
Ph: (913)768-1696
Free: 800-745-5480
Fax: (800)755-6910
Co. E-mail: actmedia@act.org
URL: http://www.actmedia.com
Released: 1984. **Description:** In this series of 21 half hour programs, various occupations are examined in depth, including a day in the life of each worker. **Availability:** VHS; 3/4 U.

3368 ■ Career Assessment Video
Cambridge Educational
c/o Films Media Group
132 West 31st Street, 17th Floor
Ste. 124
New York, NY 10001
Free: 800-257-5126
Fax: (609)671-0266
Co. E-mail: custserve@films.com
URL: http://www.cambridgeol.com
Released: 1991. **Price:** $395.00. **Description:** Contains information on the requirements and typical settings of different careers, including interests, abilities, work areas, work activities, school subjects, aptitudes, work situations, math and language, work load, physical skills, indoor-outdoor, work environment, and education level. Includes guidebook, test booklet, worksheet, and two diskettes. **Availability:** VHS; Special order formats.

3369 ■ The Career Encounters Series
Cambridge Educational
c/o Films Media Group
132 West 31st Street, 17th Floor
Ste. 124
New York, NY 10001
Free: 800-257-5126
Fax: (609)671-0266
Co. E-mail: custserve@films.com
URL: http://www.cambridgeol.com
Released: 199?. **Price:** $599.00. **Description:** Nine-part career information series that provides information on matching individual characteristics to appropriate careers. Covers academic routes to take to prepare for a certain career, opportunities and challenges in each career field, and other career-related information. **Availability:** VHS.

3370 ■ Career Moves: A Winning Strategy
University of Wisconsin-Madison Center on Education & Work
1025 W. Johnson St., Rm. 964
Madison, WI 53706-1796
Ph: (608)265-6700
Free: 800-862-1071
Co. E-mail: cewmail@education.wisc.edu
URL: http://www.cew.wisc.edu
Released: 19??. **Price:** $48.00. **Description:** Discusses various career issues, including the state of job opportunities, employment and training options, and balancing family and work. **Availability:** VHS.

3371 ■ Career Planning Steps
Cambridge Educational
c/o Films Media Group
132 West 31st Street, 17th Floor
Ste. 124
New York, NY 10001
Free: 800-257-5126
Fax: (609)671-0266
Co. E-mail: custserve@films.com
URL: http://www.cambridgeol.com
Released: 19??. **Price:** $98.00. **Description:** Uses real-life examples and realistic scenarios to outline the career development process, including self-examination, career exploration methods, interviewing for information, training and educational options available, and job searching. Includes study manual. **Availability:** VHS.

3372 ■ Career Strategies
Educational Video Network
1401 19th St.
Huntsville, TX 77340
Ph: (936)295-5767
Free: 800-762-0060
Fax: (936)294-0233
URL: http://www.evndirect.com
Released: 19??. **Price:** $59.95. **Description:** Offers methods for career planners to use to succeed in their quest. **Availability:** VHS.

3373 ■ Choosing Careers
Cambridge Educational
c/o Films Media Group
132 West 31st Street, 17th Floor
Ste. 124
New York, NY 10001
Free: 800-257-5126
Fax: (609)671-0266
Co. E-mail: custserve@films.com
URL: http://www.cambridgeol.com
Released: 1986. **Description:** A series of tapes, available separately, aimed toward the high school student choosing his or her life's path. **Availability:** VHS.

3374 ■ Choosing a Job
Encyclopedia Britannica
331 N. LaSalle St.
Chicago, IL 60654
Ph: (312)347-7159
Free: 800-323-1229
Fax: (312)294-2104
URL: http://www.britannica.com
Released: 1971. **Description:** How career education programs may save young students from frustrating job-hopping after finishing school. From the "Careers in the Office" series. **Availability:** VHS; 3/4 U.

3375 ■ Effective Resumes & Job Applications
Cambridge Educational
c/o Films Media Group
132 West 31st Street, 17th Floor
Ste. 124
New York, NY 10001
Free: 800-257-5126
Fax: (609)671-0266
Co. E-mail: custserve@films.com
URL: http://www.cambridgeol.com
Released: 1992. **Price:** $99.00. **Description:** Provides tips on writing effective job resumes and cover letters and filling out applications. Includes user guide. **Availability:** VHS.

3376 ■ How to Get a Job
Home Vision Cinema
c/o Image Entertainment
20525 Nordhoff St., Ste. 200
Chatsworth, CA 91311
Co. E-mail: inquiries@image-entertainment.com
URL: http://www.homevision.com
Released: 1979. **Description:** The Self-Directed Placement Corporation helps unemployed people recognize their self-worth, providing direction and hope in their search for jobs. **Availability:** VHS; 3/4 U.

3377 ■ In the Prime: Changing Careers with Carole Hyatt
Leslie T. McClure
PO Box 1223
Pebble Beach, CA 93953
Ph: (831)656-0553
Fax: (831)656-0555
Co. E-mail: leslie@411videoinfo.com
URL: http://www.411videoinfo.com
Released: 1997. **Price:** $19.95. **Description:** Presents simple exercises to discover what your next career move should be. **Availability:** VHS.

3378 ■ Lifelines: A Career Profile Study
The Cinema Guild
115 W 30th St., Ste. 800
New York, NY 10001
Ph: (212)685-6242
Free: 800-723-5522
Fax: (212)685-4717
Co. E-mail: info@cinemaguild.com
URL: http://www.cinemaguild.com
Released: 1977. **Description:** Dr. Edgar Schein of the Sloan School of Management at the Massachusetts Institute of Technology discusses some the results of his research studies in career formation. Dr. Schein explains that each of us has a "career lifeline"-a path that directs our choice of work. With illustrations from three actual cases, Dr. Schein's concept of "career anchors"-patterns by which people discover what they are good at and what they would like to do for the rest of their lives is examined. **Availability:** 3/4 U; Special order formats.

3379 ■ People in Management
Phoenix Learning Group
2349 Chaffee Dr.
Saint Louis, MO 63146-3306
Ph: (314)569-0211
Free: 800-221-1274
Fax: (314)569-2834
URL: http://www.phoenixlearninggroup.com
Released: 1976. **Description:** This documentary film follows the daily activities of several men and women at all stages of management, from trainee to company president of a large corporation. **Availability:** VHS; 3/4 U.

3380 ■ People Who Help: Health Careers
Phoenix Learning Group
2349 Chaffee Dr.
Saint Louis, MO 63146-3306
Ph: (314)569-0211
Free: 800-221-1274
Fax: (314)569-2834
URL: http://www.phoenixlearninggroup.com
Released: 1975. **Description:** Few of us realize how many different professions and jobs it takes to run a modern hospital. This film creates, through documentary footage, the atmosphere of such a hospital. **Availability:** VHS; 3/4 U.

3381 ■ People Who Sell Things
Phoenix Learning Group
2349 Chaffee Dr.
Saint Louis, MO 63146-3306
Ph: (314)569-0211
Free: 800-221-1274
Fax: (314)569-2834
URL: http://www.phoenixlearninggroup.com
Released: 1975. **Description:** What kind of people are best suited to work in sales? This documentary film follows the lively daily activities of four successful salespersons. **Availability:** VHS; 3/4 U.

3382 ■ People Who Work in Manufacturing
Phoenix Learning Group
2349 Chaffee Dr.
Saint Louis, MO 63146-3306
Ph: (314)569-0211
Free: 800-221-1274
Fax: (314)569-2834
URL: http://www.phoenixlearninggroup.com
Released: 1975. **Description:** Creates, through exciting documentary footage, the atmosphere of a sophisticated electronics factory. **Availability:** VHS; 3/4 U.

3383 ■ *Power Interviewing: A Headhunter's Guide to Getting Hired in the '90s*
Waterford Executive Group Ltd.
1 N. 141 County Farm Rd.
Winfield, IL 60190-2023
Ph: (630)690-0055
Fax: (630)690-5533
Co. E-mail: info@waterfordgroup.com
URL: http://waterfordgroup.com
Released: 1991. **Price:** $59.95. **Description:** A detailed examination of how to interview successfully, including proper wardrobe, resumes, acquiring interviews and more. **Availability:** VHS.

3384 ■ *Resume Preparation*
University of Arizona
University Teaching Center
1600 E. 1st St.
Tucson, AZ 85721-0129
Ph: (520)621-7788
Fax: (520)626-7314
URL: http://www.utc.arizona.edu
Released: 197?. **Description:** This program is designed to aid the prospective job-hunter or job-changer in presenting the necessary information to an employer through a resume. **Availability:** VHS; EJ; 3/4 U.

3385 ■ *Strategic Job Search*
American Media, Inc.
4621 121st St.
Urbandale, IA 50323-2311
Ph: (515)224-0919
Free: 888-776-8268
Fax: (515)327-2555
Co. E-mail: custsvc@ammedia.com
URL: http://www.ammedia.com
Released: 1989. **Price:** $425.00. **Description:** A course is plotted for people who are looking for a new job. **Availability:** VHS; 3/4 U.

3386 ■ *The Video Career Library*
RMI Media
1365 N. Winchester St.
Olathe, KS 66061-5880
Ph: (913)768-1696
Free: 800-745-5480
Fax: (800)755-6910
Co. E-mail: actmedia@act.org
URL: http://www.actmedia.com
Released: 1987. **Description:** Information on 165 occupations is provided, including job duties, working conditions, wages and salaries, job outlook, and required education and training. Also describes current labor market status and offers a list of addresses where one can write for more information about each job. **Availability:** VHS; 3/4 U.

3387 ■ *Vocational Visions Career Series*
Cambridge Educational
c/o Films Media Group
132 West 31st Street, 17th Floor
Ste. 124
New York, NY 10001
Free: 800-257-5126
Fax: (609)671-0266
Co. E-mail: custserve@films.com
URL: http://www.cambridgeol.com
Released: 1989. **Price:** $39.95. **Description:** A series of tapes providing insight into various careers through interviews with people working in those jobs. The ten tapes can be purchased individually or as a set. **Availability:** VHS.

TRADE SHOWS AND CONVENTIONS

3388 ■ *International Career Development Conference*
Career Planning and Adult Development Network (CPADN)
543 Vista Mar Ave.
Pacifica, CA 94044
Ph: (650)773-0982

Fax: (650)359-3089
Co. E-mail: admin@careernetwork.org
URL: http://www.careernetwork.org
URL(s): www.careernetwork.com. **Frequency:** Annual. **Audience:** Career counselors from schools, universities, business, and other industries. **Principal Exhibits:** Career education and guidance information, including books, tests, and computer software. **Telecommunication Services:** icdc-registration@careerccc.com.

CONSULTANTS

3389 ■ *Lou Antonelli—Lou Antonelli Rehabilitation Consultant*
175 Cooper St.
Sonoma, CA 95476-6709
Ph: (707)996-0629
Fax: (707)996-2316
Contact: Lou Antonelli, Owner
Scope: Rehabilitation consultant who provides vocational consulting services to industrial insurance carriers and injured workers. Services include dissolution evaluations and career workshops. Recent experience with compliance of new Americans with Disabilities Act. Provides forensic expert witness services also. **Founded:** 1979.

3390 ■ *Career Dimensions Inc.*
6535 Southpoint Dr.
Dallas, TX 75248
Ph: (972)931-6853
Co. E-mail: tauneeb@careerdimensions-dfw.com
URL: http://www.careerdimensions-dfw.com
Contact: Taunee Besson, President
E-mail: tauneeb@careerdimensions-dfw.com
Scope: Provider of seminars and consulting in the following areas: career planning, spouse employment relocation, outplacement, employee career development, and small business strategies; life planning time and stress management, pre retirement planning, balancing personal and professional responsibilities; and professional development team building, goal setting and action planning, effective communication, negotiating, networking within the organization and community, employee recruiting and selection, management development, and women and their careers, recruiting strategies for women and minorities. **Founded:** 1979. **Publications:** "What Do I Say When I Don't Know What Career to Pursue?"; "How Do I Choose a College Major?"; "The National Business Employment Weekly's Premier Guide to Resumes"; "The National Business Employment Weekly's Premier Guide to Cover Letters"; "Ten Common Interview Mistakes and How to Avoid Them"; "Eating Your Way Through an Interview"; "How to Respond to 'Tell Me About Yourself'"; "Interview to Stand Out From the Crowd". **Seminars:** What Do I Do When I am Bored With My Job?.

3391 ■ *Career Evaluation Systems Inc.*
1022 N Oakley Blvd.
Chicago, IL 60622
Ph: (312)645-1363
Co. E-mail: dougfaller@aol.com
Contact: Doug Faller, Principal
E-mail: dougfaller@aol.com
Scope: Provider of vocational testing instruments to evaluation and counseling facilities, and serves those facilities with computerized test scoring and counseling advice. Facilities may be career counselors, businesses, schools, psychologists, hospitals, rehabilitation centers, and prisons. Used for assessing occupational potential, pre-training screening, worker's compensation and SSD depositions. **Founded:** 1982.

3392 ■ *Centennial Rehabilitation Associates*
14364 E Evans Ave.
Aurora, CO 80014
Ph: (303)368-4500
Fax: (303)368-1333
Co. E-mail: centen@centen.net
URL: http://www.centen.net
Contact: Fran Tafuro, Director
E-mail: ftafuro@centen.net
Scope: Offers vocational rehabilitation and medical case management services in Colorado and Nebraska. **Founded:** 1979.

3393 ■ *Constructive Leisure*
511 N La Cienega Blvd.
Los Angeles, CA 90048
Ph: (310)652-7389
Fax: (213)874-0663
Contact: Patsy B. Edwards, President
Scope: A life planning, career, and leisure consulting firm serving adults and youth. Develops and markets original books, surveys, audio tapes, software, and materials for career or leisure counseling and assessment. Materials are designed mainly to assist adults and youth with career or leisure guidance in terms of life planning, self-knowledge, career changing, educational selection, pre retirement or retirement, and preventive health services through life satisfaction. **Founded:** 1968. **Publications:** "Adapting to Change: The NVAB Program" Jul, 2000. **Special Services:** Leisure PREF and The NVAB Program.

3394 ■ *Jobs In Horticulture Inc.*
57 Rosedown Blvd.
Debary, FL 32713
Ph: (386)753-0996
Free: 800-428-2474
Fax: (386)753-0997
Co. E-mail: info@hortjobs.com
URL: http://www.hortjobs.com
Contact: David Shaw, Director
Scope: Career consulting and career services with emphasis on horticulture. **Founded:** 1993.

FRANCHISES AND BUSINESS OPPORTUNITIES

3395 ■ *AAA Franchise Legal Help Hotline*
Franchise Foundations
4157 23rd St.
San Francisco, CA 94114
Free: 800-942-4402
Description: Advice on franchise legal issues. **Founded:** 1980..

3396 ■ *Carter & Tani*
402 E Roosevelt Rd., Ste. 206
Wheaton, IL 60187
Ph: (630)668-2135
Description: Assist start-up franchisees and franchisors. **Founded:** 1977..

COMPUTERIZED DATABASES

3397 ■ *Annual Employment by Industry*
60 E 42nd St.
New York, NY 10165
Ph: (212)986-9300
Fax: (212)986-5857
Co. E-mail: data@haver.com
URL: http://www.haver.com
Availability: Online: Haver Analytics - HaverSelect. **Type:** Time Series.

3398 ■ *Oregon Career Information System (CIS)*
328 E Broadway
Eugene, OR 97401
Ph: (541)346-3872
Free: 800-495-1266
Fax: (541)346-3823
Co. E-mail: cherylb@orcis.uoregon.edu
URL: http://oregoncis.uoregon.edu
Availability: Online: Oregon Career Information System. **Type:** Directory.

LIBRARIES

3399 ■ *Chicago Public Library Central Library - Business/Science/Technology Division*
Harold Washington Library Center
400 S. State St., 4th Fl.
Chicago, IL 60605
Ph: (312)747-4450

Fax: (312)747-4975
URL: http://www.chipublib.org/branch/details/library/
harold-washington/p/Bst
Scope: Small business, marketing, technology, corporate reports, investments, management, personnel, patents, physical and biological sciences, medicine, health, computer science, careers, environmental information, gardening, cookbooks. **Services:** Interlibrary loan; copying; division open to the public. **Founded:** 1977. **Holdings:** 415,000 books; 52,100 bound periodical volumes; 33,000 reels of microfilm; Securities and Exchange Commission (SEC) reports; federal specifications and standards; American National Standards Institute standards; corporate Annual reports. **Subscriptions:** 4000 journals and other serials; 8 newspapers.

3400 ■ Eureka, The California Career Information System Library
PO Box 647
Richmond, CA 94808-0647
Ph: (510)669-0996
Free: 888-463-2247
Fax: (510)669-0992
Co. E-mail: msb@eurekanet.org
URL: http://www.eurekanet.org
Contact: M. Sumyyah Bilal, Director
URL(s): www.eureka.org. **Scope:** Career exploration, California and National occupational and school information, International occupational information, job search and financial aid, programs of study and training, skills assessment. **Services:** Copying. **Founded:** 1976. **Holdings:** Figures not available. **Telecommunication Services:** techserv@eurekanet.org.

3401 ■ Florida State University - Career Center Library
100 S. Woodward Ave.
Tallahassee, FL 32306-4162
Ph: (850)644-6431
Fax: (850)644-3273
Co. E-mail: mhoover@fsu.edu
URL: http://www.career.fsu.edu/library
Contact: Jim Jean, Director
Scope: Career planning, occupational information, education and training, work experience, job hunting, employer information. **Services:** Library open to the public. **Founded:** 1975. **Holdings:** 1000 books; 600 occupational files; 44 VF drawers; 100 videotapes; 66 CD-ROMs. **Subscriptions:** 35 journals and other serials.

3402 ■ Howard High School of Technology - Media Center
401 E. 12th St.
Wilmington, DE 19801
Ph: (302)571-5437
Fax: (302)571-5849
Co. E-mail: jlaugin@nccvt.k12.de.us
URL: http://www.nccvthighschools.com/HOWARD
Contact: Jane M. Lauginiger, Librarian
Scope: Vocational and technical careers. **Services:** Interlibrary loan; Library not open to the public. **Holdings:** 6000 books. **Subscriptions:** 50 journals and other serials; 3 newspapers.

3403 ■ Indian River Area Library
PO Box 160
Indian River, MI 49749
Ph: (231)238-8581
Fax: (231)238-9494
Co. E-mail: indrivl@northland.lib.mi.us
URL: http://www.libnet.org/iriver/
Contact: Cindy Lou Poquette, Director
Scope: Small business, careers, fine arts, music, dance. **Services:** Interlibrary loan; copying; library open to the public (fee for non-residents to check out materials). **Founded:** 1976. **Holdings:** 52,000 books; 32,000 videocassettes and DVDs; 2000 microfiche;

sound cassettes; DVDs; CDs; periodicals; large print books. **Subscriptions:** 80 journals and other serials; 3 newspapers.

3404 ■ Kershaw County Applied Technology Education Campus - Vocational-Technical Library
874 Vocational Ln.
Camden, SC 29020
Ph: (803)425-8980
Fax: (803)425-8983
URL: http://atec.kcsdschools.com/home.aspx?
Contact: Cynthia Sparks, Librarian
Scope: Vocational education. **Services:** Library open to the public. **Founded:** 1970. **Holdings:** 5000 books. **Subscriptions:** 80 journals and other serials; 2 newspapers.

3405 ■ National Association of Colleges & Employers Information Center—NACE - Information Center.
62 Highland Ave.
Bethlehem, PA 18017
Ph: (610)868-1421
Free: 800-544-5272
Fax: (610)868-0208
Co. E-mail: cnader@naceweb.org
URL: http://www.naceweb.org/
Contact: Cecelia M. Nader, Administrator
Scope: Career planning and development, employer relations and recruitment, education statistics. **Services:** Center available to NACE members only. **Holdings:** Figures not available. **Telecommunication Services:** customer_service@naceweb.org.

3406 ■ Ohio State University - Career Connection
Younkin Success Ctr., 2nd Fl.
1640 Neil Ave.
Columbus, OH 43201
Ph: (614)688-3898
Fax: (614)688-3440
Co. E-mail: careerconnection@studentlife.osu.edu
URL: http://careerconnection.osu.edu
Contact: Christina A. Rideout, PhD, Director
Scope: Personal and career self-assessment, career exploration, training opportunities, job search resources. **Services:** Copying; Center open to the public for reference use only. **Holdings:** 400 books. **Subscriptions:** 15 journals and other serials. **Telecommunication Services:** rideout.1@osu.edu.

3407 ■ Social Development Canada and Human Resources and Skills Development Canada - Departmental Library - Career Library—Developpement Social Canada et Ressources Humaines et Developpement des Competences Canada - Bibliotheque Ministerielle.
235 Lansdowne St.
Kamloops, BC, Canada V2C 1X8
Ph: (819)953-9134
Fax: (250)372-0761
Co. E-mail: matt.treger@hrdc-drhc.gc.ca
URL: http://www.hrdc-drhc.gc.ca/redirect_hr.html
Contact: Helen Apouchtine, Librarian
Scope: Human resources. **Services:** Library open to the public for reference use only. **Holdings:** 50 reports.

3408 ■ University of Oregon - Career Center Library
1408 University St.
220 Hendricks Hall
Eugene, OR 97403-0257
Ph: (541)346-6006

Fax: (541)346-6038
Co. E-mail: thaynes@uoregon.edu
URL: http://career.uoregon.edu
Contact: Tina Haynes, Librarian
Scope: Career direction, career information, job search, employment preparation tools, employer directories, International resources, majors and careers resources, internships, graduate school resources, computer lab. **Services:** Career Library services provided to current students and UO alumni; Career Library open to the public with limited services. **Founded:** 1972. **Holdings:** 800-850 books and binders. **Subscriptions:** 5 journals and other periodicals; 4 newspapers. **Telecommunication Services:** career@uoregon.edu.

3409 ■ University of South Carolina - Career Center Library
H. William Close Bldg., 6th Fl.
Columbia, SC 29208
Ph: (803)777-7280
Fax: (803)777-7556
Co. E-mail: career@sc.edu
URL: http://www.sc.edu/career
Contact: Julie Hutt, Assistant Director
Scope: Career development, self-assessment, career planning, job searching. **Holdings:** Figures not available. **Telecommunication Services:** aorange@mailbox.sc.edu; info@sc.edu.

3410 ■ West Virginia Junior College Library
1000 Virginia St. E.
Charleston, WV 25301
Ph: (304)345-2820
Fax: (304)345-1425
Co. E-mail: wvjc_chas@hotmail.com
URL: http://www.wvjc.edu
Contact: Belinda L. Yerkey-Hammack
Scope: Business, medical assisting, legal office assisting, computer technology. **Services:** Copying; library not open to the public. **Founded:** 1892. **Holdings:** 6000 books; 50 CD-ROMs. **Subscriptions:** 25 journals and other serials; 2 newspapers. **Telecommunication Services:** admissions@wvjc.edu.

3411 ■ York University - Glendon Campus Counselling & Career Centre
Glendon Hall, E103
2275 Bayview Ave.
Toronto, ON, Canada M4N 3M6
Ph: (416)487-6709
Fax: (416)440-9237
Co. E-mail: starshis@glendon.yorku.ca
URL: http://www.glendon.yorku.ca/counselling/career.html
Contact: Sharon Tarshis, Counselor
Scope: Careers for liberal arts graduates. **Services:** Library not open to the public. **Founded:** 1982. **Holdings:** Figures not available. **Telecommunication Services:** counselling@glendon.yorku.ca.

3412 ■ YWCA Resource Center Library
2222 14th St.
Boulder, CO 80302
Ph: (303)443-0419
Fax: (303)443-5098
Co. E-mail: frontdesk@ywcaboulder.org
URL: http://www.ywcaboulder.org
Contact: Janet L. Beardsley, Executive Director
Scope: Careers, job searching, educational resources, parenting, divorce, women's literature. **Services:** Copying; library open to the public. **Founded:** 1988. **Holdings:** 550 books. **Subscriptions:** 6 journals and other serials; 2 newspapers.

ASSOCIATIONS AND OTHER ORGANIZATIONS

3413 ■ **Architectural Woodwork Institute (AWI)**
46179 Westlake Dr., Ste. 120
Potomac Falls, VA 20165
Ph: (571)323-3636
Fax: (571)323-3630
Co. E-mail: info@awinet.org
URL: http://www.awinet.org
Contact: Matthew Lundahl, President
Description: Manufacturers of architectural woodwork products (casework, fixtures, and paneling) and associated suppliers of equipment and materials. Works to: raise industry standards; research new and improved materials and methods; publish technical data helpful in the design and use of architectural woodwork. Conducts seminars and training course. **Founded:** 1953. **Publications:** *Architectural Woodwork Institute--Source Book*; *Quality Standards Illustrated* (Periodic). **Educational Activities:** Architectural Woodwork Institute Annual Convention (Annual). **Awards:** Standard of Excellence Award (Annual).

3414 ■ **Moulding and Millwork Producers Association (MMPA)**
507 1st St.
Woodland, CA 95695
Ph: (530)661-9591
Free: 800-550-7889
Fax: (530)661-9586
Co. E-mail: info@wmmpa.com
URL: http://www.wmmpa.com
Contact: John Morrison, President
Description: Represents manufacturers of wood mouldings and millwork. Provides promotion, standardization and marketing information services. **Scope:** industry standards. **Founded:** 1963. **Publications:** *Wood Moulding and Millwork Producers Association--Directory* (Annual); *Case 'n Base News* (Monthly); *Wood Moulding and Millwork Producers Association--Products and Services Membership Directory* (Annual). **Awards:** Warren C. Jimerson Award (Annual).

3415 ■ **National Sash and Door Jobbers Association**
10047 Robert Trent Jones Parkway
New Port Richey, FL 34655-4649
Ph: (727)372-3665
Free: 800-786-5174
Fax: (727)372-2879
Co. E-mail: mail@nsdja.com
URL: http://www.nsdja.com
Contact: Daniel Warren, President
Description: Wholesale distributors of windows, door, millwork and related products. Conducts research and statistical studies. Offers millwork home study course and audiovisual program dealing with product knowledge; furnishes group insurance. Compiles statistics. **Publications:** *AMD News* (Monthly); *Membership Directory and Products' Guide* (Annual); *National Sash & Door Jobbers Association--Membership Directory* (Annual); *Furniture Manufacturing Management* (Monthly). **Educational Activities:** National Sash and Door Jobbers Association Convention (Annual). **Awards:** Ron Taylor Award. **Telecommunication Services:** info@nsdja.com.

3416 ■ **Window and Door Manufacturers Association (WDMA)**
401 N Michigan Ave., Ste. 2200
Chicago, IL 60611
Ph: (312)321-6802
Free: 800-223-2301
Fax: (312)673-6922
Co. E-mail: wdma@wdma.com
URL: http://www.wdma.com
Contact: Michael O'Brien, President
E-mail: mobrien@wdma.com
Description: Manufacturers of doors, windows, frames, and related products. Fosters, promotes, and protects members' interests; encourages product use. Establishes quality and performance standards; conducts research in all areas of door and window manufacture. Issues seals of approval for wood preservative treatment, hardwood doors, and window unit manufacture. **Founded:** 1927. **Publications:** *Millwork Sources of Supply* (Annual); *WDMA Newsletter* (Monthly); *Window and Door Manufacturers Association--Membership and Product Directory* (Annual); *Window and Door Manufacturers Association--Member & Product Directory* (Annual).

DIRECTORIES OF EDUCATIONAL PROGRAMS

3417 ■ *Directory of Private Accredited Career Schools and Colleges of Technology*
Pub: Accrediting Commission of Career Schools and Colleges of Technology
Contact: Michale S. McComis, Executive Director
Released: On web page. **Price:** Free. **Description:** Covers 3900 accredited post-secondary programs that provide training programs in business, trade, and technical fields, including various small business endeavors. Entries offer school name, address, phone, description of courses, job placement assistance, and requirements for admission. Arrangement is alphabetical.

REFERENCE WORKS

3418 ■ *"Hard Rock on Pike"* in Puget Sound Business Journal (Vol. 29, September 5, 2008, No. 20, pp. 1)
Pub: American City Business Journals
Ed: Jeanne Lang Jones. **Description:** A branch of the Hard Rock Cafe is opening in 2009 in the Liberty Building on Pike Street in downtown Seattle, Washington. The location is being renovated as a green building; the restaurant and concert venue will seat 300 patrons and has a rooftop deck and memorabilia shop.

3419 ■ *"Ronald Taketa"* in Hawaii Business (Vol. 54, September 2008, No. 3, pp. 28)
Pub: Hawaii Business Publishing
Ed: Shara Enay. **Description:** Interview with Ronald Taketa of the Hawaii Carpenters Union who states that the economic downturn has affected the construction industry as 20 percent of the union's 7,800 members are unemployed. He shares his thoughts about the industry's economic situation, the union's advertisements, and his role as a leader of the union.

3420 ■ *"Troubled Project In Court"* in The Business Journal-Portland (Vol. 25, July 25, 2008, No. 20, pp. 1)
Pub: American City Business Journals, Inc.
Ed: Wendy Culverwell. **Description:** Views and information on Salpare Bay's Hayden Island project, as well as on financing problems and cases associated with the project, are presented. Construction of luxurious waterside condominiums stopped last fall, after the discovery of financing problems and subcontractors and other parties started filing claims and counterclaims.

STATISTICAL SOURCES

3421 ■ *RMA Annual Statement Studies*
Pub: Risk Management Association
Contact: Kevin M. Blakey, President
Released: Annual. **Price:** $175.00 2006-07 edition, $105.00. **Description:** Contains composite balance sheets and income statements for more than 360 industries, including the accounting, auditing, and bookkeeping industries. Also contains five years of comparative historical data for discerning trends. Includes 16 commonly used ratios, computed for most of the size groupings for nearly every industry.

TRADE PERIODICALS

3422 ■ *AMD Newsletter*
Pub: Association of Millwork Distributors
Released: Monthly. **Price:** $40. **Description:** Provides information on the activities of the National Sash and Door Jobbers Association. Promotes wholesale distribution of windows, door, millwork, and related products.

3423 ■ *Architectural Designs*
Pub: Architectural Designs Inc.
Contact: Joel Davis, President
URL(s): www.architecturaldesigns.com/. **Released:** Quarterly

3424 ■ *The Carpenter*
Pub: United Brotherhood of Carpenters and Joiners of America, AFL-CIO
URL(s): www.carpenters.org/. **Ed:** Andris Silins. **Released:** Bimonthly **Price:** $10, Individuals; $2, Single issue.

3425 ■ *CWB Custom Woodworking Business: Environmental Studies*
Contact: Bill Esler, Associate Publisher
E-mail: besler@vancepublishing.com
URL(s): www.vancepublishing.com/. **Ed:** Karen Koenig. **Released:** Monthly

3426 ■ Fine Woodworking
Pub: Taunton Press Inc.
Contact: John Lively, Chief Executive Officer
URL(s): www.finewoodworking.com. Ed: Timothy D. Schreiner. Released: 7/yr. Price: $34.95, U.S. and Canada; $59.95, U.S. and Canada two years; $83.95, U.S. and Canada three years.

3427 ■ Modern Woodworking
Pub: BNP Media
Contact: Al Reser, President
URL(s): www.modernwoodworking.com.

3428 ■ Wood Digest: Productivity Solutions for Manufacturers of Furniture, Cabinets, Millworks and Speciality Wood Products
Pub: NueMedia LLC
URL(s): woodiq.com. Released: Monthly

3429 ■ Wood & Wood Products
Contact: Rich Christianson, Associate Publisher
E-mail: rchristianson@vancepublishing.com
URL(s): www.vancepublishing.comwoodworkingnetwork.com/IssueArchives.aspx?fid=WWN-WWP-ARCHIVES. Ed: Rich Christianson. Released: Monthly

3430 ■ Woodshop News: The News Magazine for Professional Woodworkers
Pub: Dominion Enterprises
Contact: Jack Ross, President
URL(s): www.woodshopnews.com. Ed: Tod Riggio. Released: Monthly Price: $21.95, Individuals; $33.95, Canada; $35.95, Other countries; $35.95, Two years; $59.95, Canada 2 years; $63.95, Other countries 2 years.

3431 ■ Words From Woody
Pub: David W. Wood
Ed: David W. Wood, Editor. Released: Quarterly. Price: $24.95; $39.95, two years. Description: Contains information of interest to construction-related firms. Also includes business and marketing tips.

VIDEOCASSETTES/ AUDIOCASSETTES

3432 ■ Building Dreams
CA Working Group/We Do the Work
1611 Telegraph Ave Suite 1550
Oakland, CA 94612
Ph: (510)268-9675
Fax: (510)268-3606
Co. E-mail: infotheatreworkinggroup.org
URL: http://www.pbs.org/livelyhood
Released: 19??. Price: $59.00. Description: Examination of Los Angeles carpenters at work on various projects. Offers insight from the carpenters on passing on their skills and knowledge to the young men and women of South Central L.A. Availability: VHS.

3433 ■ Small Shop Tips and Techniques
Taunton Press Inc.
63 S Main St.
Newtown, CT 06470
Ph: (203)426-8171
Free: 800-477-8727
Fax: (203)426-3434
Co. E-mail: booksales@taunton.com
URL: http://www.taunton.com
Contact: John Lively, Chief Executive Officer
Released: 1989. Price: $29.95. Description: The former editor of "Fine Woodworking" magazine shows off a few carpentry tips. Availability: VHS.

3434 ■ Woodworking
RMI Media
1365 N. Winchester St.
Olathe, KS 66061-5880
Ph: (913)768-1696
Free: 800-745-5480
Fax: (800)755-6910
Co. E-mail: actmedia@act.org
URL: http://www.actmedia.com
Released: 1987. Price: $39.95. Description: Offers step-by-step instructions for special woodworking projects. Availability: VHS; 3/4 U.

FRANCHISES AND BUSINESS OPPORTUNITIES

3435 ■ Archadeck
U.S. Structures Inc.
2924 Emerywood Pky., Ste. 101
Richmond, VA 23294
Ph: (804)353-6999
Free: 800-789-3325
Fax: (804)358-1878
Co. E-mail: Franchising@ussi.net
URL: http://www.archadeck.com
Description: Custom design deck franchise. When a deck design is chosen, franchisees send preliminary sketches to the company's drafting division which will supply full construction plans with complete material layouts and specifications. Subcontracted Archadeck-trained carpenters will usually build the deck in 2-3 days. No. of Franchise Units: 75. Founded: 1980. Franchised: 1984. Equity Capital Needed: $69,000-$102,900. Franchise Fee: $49,500. Financial Assistance: Yes. Training: Yes.

3436 ■ Dollar Castle Inc.
7031 Orchard Lake Rd., Ste. 201
West Bloomfield, MI 48322
Ph: (248)539-3100
Fax: (248)539-1778
Description: Retail dollar store. No. of Franchise Units: 25. No. of Company-Owned Units: 7. Founded: 1992.. Franchised: 1992. Equity Capital Needed: $200,000. Franchise Fee: $30,000. Training: Yes.

3437 ■ DreamMaker Bath and Kitchen
PO Box 148
Waco, TX 76703
Ph: (800)253-9153
Fax: (800)396-6154
Co. E-mail: franchising@dwyergroup.com
URL: http://www.dreammaker-remodel.com
Description: Specializes in bath and kitchen remodeling options. No. of Franchise Units: 46. Founded: 1970.. Franchised: 1971. Equity Capital Needed: $88,150-$315,000 cash; $112,750-$237,000 total investment. Franchise Fee: $37,000. Financial Assistance: Yes. Training: Extensive business, marketing and management training provided including team training conferences, an annual convention (Reunion) offers networking opportunities with other Dream-Maker Bath & Kitchen franchisees, and continuous training.

3438 ■ DRY-B-LO International, Inc.
5287 Camp Wahsega Rd.
Dahlonega, GA 30533
Ph: (706)864-0049
Co. E-mail: corporate@dry-b-lo.com
URL: http://www.dry-b-lo.com
Description: Professionally installed deck drain system company in the United States. Multi-patented system that provides homeowners with a new approach to outdoor entertainment areas. No. of Franchise Units: 39. Founded: 1993. Franchised: 1997. Equity Capital Needed: $44,700-$150,300. Franchise Fee: $25,000. Royalty Fee: 7.5%. Training: Offers 1 week at headquarters, 3 days at franchisee's location, 1 week in Denver, CO and ongoing support.

3439 ■ Exovations
1550-A Oak Industrial Ln.
Cumming, GA 30041
Ph: (770)205-2995
URL: http://www.exovations.com
Description: Exterior home remodeling. No. of Franchise Units: 1. No. of Company-Owned Units: 2. Founded: 1996.. Franchised: 2006. Equity Capital Needed: $86,050-$198,750. Franchise Fee: $28,000-$75,000. Royalty Fee: 5%. Financial Assistance: Third party assistance with payroll. Training: Offers 2 weeks at headquarters, 2 weeks at franchisee's location and ongoing support.

3440 ■ Garagetek
5 Aerial Way, Ste. 200
Syosset, NY 11791
Ph: (516)621-4300

Fax: (516)992-8600
Co. E-mail: SBarrett@GarageTek.com
URL: http://www.GarageTek.com
Description: Franchise of construction, remodeling, bath and closet services. No. of Franchise Units: 55. No. of Company-Owned Units: 2. Founded: 2000.. Franchised: 2001. Equity Capital Needed: $250,000. Franchise Fee: $50,000. Training: Provides 2 weeks at corporate and ongoing field support.

3441 ■ Granite Transformations
RockSolid Granit USA Inc.
10360 USA Today Way
Miramar, FL 33025
Ph: (954)435-5538
Free: 866-685-5300
Fax: (954)435-5579
Co. E-mail: info@granittransformations.com
URL: http://www.granitetransformations.com
Description: Construction, remodeling, and bath and closets services. No. of Franchise Units: 79. No. of Company-Owned Units: 1. Founded: 2001.. Franchised: 2001. Equity Capital Needed: $127,000-$350,000. Franchise Fee: $25,000-$75,000. Training: Training program consists of operations, installations, and sales training. Each training module is supported with training material. Training facility is an actual working location allowing trainees to evaluate, test, and see results. Grand opening supported by sales manager onsite and ongoing support.

3442 ■ House Doctors Handyman Service
575 Chamber Dr.
Milford, OH 45150
Ph: (800)319-3359
Co. E-mail: info@housedoctors.com
URL: http://www.housedoctors.com
Description: Minor home repairs. No. of Franchise Units: 90. Founded: 1994.. Equity Capital Needed: $70,000-$120,000. Franchise Fee: $9,800. Financial Assistance: Yes. Training: 5 days of training includes marketing, technical knowledge, and business procedures.

3443 ■ Interior Door Replacement Co.
IDRC Franchising Corp.
300 Pioneer Way, Ste. B
Mountain View, CA 94041
Ph: (650)965-IDRC
Free: 866-315-IDRC
Fax: (650)938-6879
Description: Franchise of construction, remodeling and carpentry services. No. of Company-Owned Units: 1. Founded: 1997.. Franchised: 2001. Equity Capital Needed: $126,500-$178,000. Franchise Fee: $10,000. Training: Yes.

3444 ■ Kitchen Solvers
301 4th St. S
La Crosse, WI 54601
Ph: (800)845-6779
Fax: (608)784-2917
Description: Kitchen cabinet refacing, replacing doors and drawer fronts with new solid wood doors and covering framework with 1/8 wood panel. No. of Franchise Units: 78. Founded: 1982.. Franchised: 1984. Equity Capital Needed: $38,400-$96,650. Franchise Fee: $15,000, including terr. fee. Financial Assistance: Yes. Training: Yes.

3445 ■ Kitchen Tune-Up & Kitchen Tune-Up Express
KTU Worldwide Inc.
813 Circle Dr.
Aberdeen, SD 57401
Ph: (8)333-6385
Fax: (605)225-1371
Co. E-mail: ktu@kitchentuneup.com
URL: http://www.kitchentuneup.com
Description: Provides inexpensive wood care services to both the residential homeowner and the commercial property owner. Also offers door replacement materials. This is a home-based, no-inventory, high-profit margin business. Offers potential franchise owners the unique opportunity to attend training and evaluate the franchise before signing the franchise agreement. No. of Franchise Units: 204. Founded: 1975.. Franchised: 1988. Equity Capital Needed:

$58,000- $66,000 or $22,000-$25,000 for Express. **Franchise Fee:** $25,000 or $10,000 for Kitchen Tune-Up Express. **Financial Assistance:** Yes. **Training:** Initial training and ongoing support.

3446 ■ Millicare Commercial Carpet Care
201 Lukken Industrial Dr., W
LaGrange, GA 30240
Free: 877-812-8803
Fax: (706)880-3279
Description: Offers maintenance and cleaning services. **No. of Franchise Units:** 79. **Founded:** 1979.. **Franchised:** 1996. **Equity Capital Needed:** $50,000 liquid; $150,000 net worth. **Franchise Fee:** $20,000. **Training:** Yes.

3447 ■ Ready Decks Franchise Systems Inc.
1250 New Natchitoches Rd.
West Monroe, LA 71292
Ph: (318)362-9990
Free: 866-323-3257

Fax: (713)621-8200
URL: http://www.readydecks.com
Description: Decking services. **No. of Franchise Units:** 2. **No. of Company-Owned Units:** 2. **Founded:** 2001.. **Franchised:** 2005. **Equity Capital Needed:** $84,000-$168,000. **Franchise Fee:** $29,000. **Royalty Fee:** 5%. **Financial Assistance:** Limited third party financing and assistance with franchise fee. **Training:** Offers 2 weeks at headquarters, 1 week onsite and ongoing support.

3448 ■ RENOCanada-Bathroom & Kitchen Makeover Specialists
1534 Midland Ave.
Scarborough, ON, Canada M1P 3C2
Ph: (416)285-6798
Fax: (416)285-1825
Co. E-mail: info@renosystems.com
URL: http://www.renosystems.com
Description: New concept in home renovation where home improvement is not about the house, it's about

self-improvement (lifestyle) and that bathrooms and kitchens are personal. **No. of Franchise Units:** 3. **No. of Company-Owned Units:** 3. **Founded:** 2006. **Franchise Fee:** $25,000. **Training:** Intensive franchisee training at Head Office, in-store, pre-opening and grand opening assistance with ongoing support.

3449 ■ United States Seamless
United States Seamless, Inc.
474 45th St. S
Fargo, ND 58108
Ph: (701)241-8888
Fax: (701)241-9999

Description: Seamless steel siding. **No. of Franchise Units:** 48. **Founded:** 1992.. **Franchised:** 1992. **Equity Capital Needed:** $52,250-$102,650. **Franchise Fee:** $2,450. **Financial Assistance:** Limited in-house and third party financing available. **Training:** Available unlimited at headquarters, annual training, and ongoing support.

START-UP INFORMATION

3450 ■ *55 Surefire Food-Related Businesses: You Can Start for Under $5000*
Pub: Entrepreneur Press
Contact: Perlman Neil, President
Ed: Cheryl Kimball. **Released:** March 1, 2009. **Price:** $17.95. **Description:** Advice is given to start 55 various food-related companies and goes beyond restaurant or catering services. Home-based, retail and mail order ventures are covered, as well as food safety and standards.

3451 ■ *Culinary Careers: How to Get Your Dream Job in Food with Advice from Top Culinary Professionals*
Pub: Crown Business Books
Ed: Rick Smilow, Anne E. McBride. **Released:** May 4, 2010. **Price:** $16.99. **Description:** Top culinary experts offer advice for working in or owning a food service firm.

3452 ■ *How to Start a Home-Based Catering Business*
Pub: Globe Pequot Press, The
Ed: Denise Vivaldo. **Released:** 2002, 4th edition. **Price:** $17.95.

3453 ■ *How to Start a Home-Based Personal Chef Business*
Pub: Globe Pequot Press
Ed: Denise Vivaldo. **Released:** December 2006. **Price:** $18.95. **Description:** Everything needed to know to start a personal chef business is featured.

3454 ■ *"It Sure Beats Pizza: San Francisco Company Delivers Gourmet Lunches to Businesses" in Inc. (Vol. 33, November 2011, No. 9, pp. 30)*
Pub: Inc. Magazine
Ed: Bobbie Gossage. **Description:** Gastronaut caters daily meals to local companies. The firm was started by two former chefs at Google and employs 24 people to deliver buffet-style meals to eight businesses, with lunches costing $16 to $18 per serving.

3455 ■ *The Professional Chef: The Business of Doing Business As a Personal Chef*
Pub: John Wiley and Sons Inc.
Ed: Candy Wallace; Greg Forte. **Released:** February 2007. **Price:** $50.00. **Description:** Resources for starting a personal chef business are covered; CD-ROM included.

3456 ■ *Start and Run a Home-Based Food Business*
Pub: Self-Counsel Press, Inc.
Ed: Mimi Shotland Fix. **Released:** January 10, 2010. **Price:** $21.95. **Description:** Information is shared to help start and run a home-based food business, selling your own homemade foods.

ASSOCIATIONS AND OTHER ORGANIZATIONS

3457 ■ *Canadian Foodservice Industry Operations Report*
316 Bloor St. W
Toronto, ON, Canada M5S 1W5
Ph: (416)923-8416
Free: 800-387-5649
Fax: (416)923-1450
Co. E-mail: info@crfa.ca
URL: http://www.crfa.ca
Contact: Garth Whyte, President
Released: Biennial

3458 ■ Canadian Restaurant and Foodservices Association (CRFA)—Association Canadienne des Restaurateurs et des Services Alimentaires
316 Bloor St. W
Toronto, ON, Canada M5S 1W5
Ph: (416)923-8416
Free: 800-387-5649
Fax: (416)923-1450
Co. E-mail: info@crfa.ca
URL: http://www.crfa.ca
Contact: Garth Whyte, President
Description: Restaurant and food service corporations, hotels, caterers, and food service suppliers and educators. Seeks to create a favorable business environment for members. Represents members' interests before government; conducts trade research. Makes available group buying programs and other services to members; owns and operates three industry trade shows. **Scope:** hospitality industries. **Founded:** 1944. **Subscriptions:** books periodicals. **Publications:** *Foodservice Facts* (Annual); *Legislation Guide* (Quarterly); *Canadian Foodservice Industry Operations Report* (Biennial); *CRFA National Hospitality News.* **Educational Activities:** Canadian Food and Beverage Show (Annual); ApEx; Canadian International Food and Beverage Show (Annual).

3459 ■ Convenience Caterers and Food Manufacturers Association (CCFMA)
1205 Spartan Dr.
Madison Heights, MI 48071
Ph: (248)982-5379
Co. E-mail: ccfma@ymail.com
URL: http://www.mobilecaterers.com
Description: Firms and corporations engaged in the mobile catering business and in any other business catering to industrial feeding by mobile equipment; associate members are suppliers and manufacturers. Deals with common intra-industry problems through exchange of ideas, advice on legal problems, and safety standards and licensing regulations. **Founded:** 1965. **Publications:** *alaCARTE* (Monthly). **Educational Activities:** Convenience Caterers and Food Manufacturers Association Competition (Annual).

3460 ■ *Foodservice Facts*
316 Bloor St. W
Toronto, ON, Canada M5S 1W5
Ph: (416)923-8416
Free: 800-387-5649
Fax: (416)923-1450
Co. E-mail: info@crfa.ca
URL: http://www.crfa.ca
Contact: Garth Whyte, President
Released: Annual

3461 ■ *Legislation Guide*
316 Bloor St. W
Toronto, ON, Canada M5S 1W5
Ph: (416)923-8416
Free: 800-387-5649
Fax: (416)923-1450
Co. E-mail: info@crfa.ca
URL: http://www.crfa.ca
Contact: Garth Whyte, President
Released: Quarterly

3462 ■ National Association of Catering Executives (NACE)
9891 Broken Land Pkwy., Ste. 301
Columbia, MD 21046
Ph: (410)290-5410
Fax: (410)290-5460
Co. E-mail: aschultz@200peachtree.com
URL: http://www.nace.net
Contact: Allison Schultz, Chairwoman
Description: Professional caterers, affiliate members, the local and national suppliers and vendors in the many disciplines that impact and influence the catering business. Addresses banquet facilities, off-premise, country club, military and resort catering. Provides continuing education, certification, networking and career support. **Founded:** 1958. **Publications:** *NACE News Network* (Monthly); *Professional Caterer* (Quarterly). **Educational Activities:** Education Conference (Annual). **Awards:** Chapter of the Year Award (Annual); George Zell Spirit of NACE Award (Annual).

3463 ■ National Barbecue Association (NBBQA)
455 S Fourth St., Ste. 650
Louisville, KY 40202
Free: 888-909-2121
Fax: (502)589-3602
Co. E-mail: nbbqa@hqtrs.com
URL: http://www.nbbqa.org
Contact: Kell Phelps, President
Description: Industry professionals and barbecue enthusiasts including restaurants, caterers, specialty equipment retailers, grill manufacturers and distributors, smoker manufacturers and distributors, food product suppliers and distributors, sauces and spice distributors, backyard hobbyists. **Founded:** 1991. **Publications:** *National Barbecue News* (Monthly); *NBBQA Barbecue Buyers' Guide* (Annual). **Awards:** Award of Excellence and People's Choice (Annual).

DIRECTORIES OF EDUCATIONAL PROGRAMS

3464 ■ *Major Food & Drink Companies of the World*
Pub: Graham & Whiteside
URL(s): www.gale.cengage.com. **Ed:** Heather Brewin, Sandra James, Helen Porter, Chris Tapster. **Released:** Annual; Latest edition 16th; Published May, 2012. **Price:** $1460, Individuals. **Covers:** Over 9,200 worldwide companies involved in the food and

3465 ■ Catering Service

SMALL BUSINESS PROFILES

drink industry. **Entries include:** Company name, address, phone and names and titles of key personnel. **Availability:** Online: Cengage Learning Inc. **Type:** Directory.

REFERENCE WORKS

3465 ■ *"The Caterer and Hotelkeeper Interview Patrick Harbour and Nathan Jones"* in *Caterer & Hotelkeeper (October 28, 2011, No. 288)*

Pub: Reed Reference Publishing

Description: Profiles of Patrick Harbour and Nathan Jones who quit their jobs to start their own catering business. The partners discuss their business strategy when launching their boutique catering firm and ways they are adapting to the slow economy in order to remain successful.

3466 ■ *Directory of Foodservice Distributors*
Pub: Chain Store Guide
Contact: Lisa Patterson, President

URL(s): www.chainstoreguide.com. **Released:** Annual; Latest edition 2012. **Price:** $425, Individuals Directory; $495, Individuals online lite; $1175, Individuals online pro; $1475, Individuals online pro plus. **Covers:** About 4,700 companies in the United States and Canada with at least $500,000 in sales to foodservice companies. Included companies must distribute more than one product line and obtain no more than 95% of its total sales volume from self-manufactured merchandise. **Entries include:** Company name, address, phone and fax numbers, e-mail and web addresses; Internet order processing indicator and sales percentage; total sales; foodservice and wholesale sales; product lines; total units served; foodservice accounts served; trading areas; distribution center locations; markets served; buying/marketing group name and location; subsidiaries names and locations; divisional, regional and branch office locations; year founded; public company indicator; key personnel with titles; 21,700 foodservice distribution contacts; 9,642 Name, address, phone, fax. **Arrangement:** Geographical. **Indexes:** Product lines, alphabetical, exclusions.

3467 ■ *"Edible Endeavors"* in *Black Enterprise (March 2008)*
Pub: Earl G. Graves Publishing Co. Inc.

Ed: Carolyn M. Brown. **Description:** Profile of Jacqueline Frazer, woman entrepreneur who turned her love for cooking into a catering business. She is chef and owner of Command Performance in New York City. The firm works with more than 50 clients annually and generates annual revenues of about $350,000.

3468 ■ *Foodservice Consultants Society International--Membership Directory*
Pub: Foodservice Consultants Society International

URL(s): www.fcsi.org. **Released:** Annual; 2002-2003. **Price:** $450. **Covers:** About 1,400 members who design and advise on management and other aspects of food service operations. **Entries include:** Name, company name, address, business phone, home phone (if available), fax, e-mail, areas of specialty. **Arrangement:** Classified by membership type. **Indexes:** Geographical, company name.

3469 ■ *"Prepping for the Unpredictable"* in *Crain's Cleveland Business (Vol. 30, June 15, 2009, No. 23, pp. 16)*
Pub: Crain Communications, Inc.

Ed: Joel Hammond. **Description:** Michael Ferrara, event planner and designer for Executive Caterers discusses the many events he has planned.

3470 ■ *"Professional Help: Cross That Off Your To-Do List"* in *Inc. (November 2007, pp. 89-90, 92)*
Pub: Gruner & Jahr USA Publishing

Ed: Alison Stein Wellner. **Description:** Small business owners are finding that it pays to hire someone to takeover the personal tasks of daily living, including hiring a personal assistant, chauffeur, chef, stylist, pet caregiver, or concierge service.

3471 ■ *"Revelations Derek Johnstone, Head Chef, Greywalls Hotel and Chez Roux"* in *Caterer & Hotelkeeper (October 28, 2011, No. 288)*
Pub: Reed Reference Publishing

Description: Profile of Derek Johnstone, head chef at Greywalls Hotel and Chez Roux and his love for catering.

3472 ■ *"Savvy Solutions"* in *Black Enterprise (Vol. 41, October 2010, No. 3, pp. 52)*
Pub: Earl G. Graves Publishing Co. Inc.

Ed: Tennille M. Robinson. **Description:** Husband and wife team seek advice for expanding their catering business. They are also seeking funding resources.

TRADE PERIODICALS

3473 ■ *Cooking for Profit*
Pub: CP Publishing Inc.
Contact: Craig Culver, President

URL(s): www.cookingforprofit.com/home.html. **Released:** Monthly **Price:** $30, Individuals; $55, Two years; $52, Canada; $98, Canada 2 years; $85, Other countries; $160, Other countries 2 years.

3474 ■ *The National Culinary Review: Official Magazine of the American Culinary Federation*
Contact: Kay Orde, Editor
E-mail: korde@acfchefs.net

URL(s): www.acfchefs.org/Content/NavigationMenu2/About/Media/Publications/de fault.htm. **Ed:** Kay Orde. **Released:** Monthly **Price:** $60, Individuals; $200, Other countries.

VIDEOCASSETTES/ AUDIOCASSETTES

3475 ■ *Food Services*
RMI Media
1365 N. Winchester St.
Olathe, KS 66061-5880
Ph: (913)768-1696
Free: 800-745-5480
Fax: (800)755-6910
Co. E-mail: actmedia@act.org
URL: http://www.actmedia.com

Released: 1987. **Description:** Methods of food preparation and equipment maintenance used in the food industry are discussed. **Availability:** VHS; 3/4 U.

TRADE SHOWS AND CONVENTIONS

3476 ■ *ApEx*
Canadian Restaurant and Foodservices Association (CRFA)
316 Bloor St. W
Toronto, ON, Canada M5S 1W5
Ph: (416)923-8416
Free: 800-387-5649
Fax: (416)923-1450
Co. E-mail: info@crfa.ca
URL: http://www.crfa.ca
Contact: Garth Whyte, President

URL(s): www.crfa.ca/tradeshows/apex. **Audience:** Trade. **Principal Exhibits:** Products and services for the restaurant and hospitality industry, as well as institutions, convenience stores, delis and bakeries. **Telecommunication Services:** escanlan@crfa.ca.

3477 ■ *HSMAI - Affordable Meetings West*
Hospitality Sales and Marketing Association International (HSMAI)
1760 Old Meadow Rd., Ste. 500
McLean, VA 22102
Ph: (703)506-3280
Free: 877-643-3511
Fax: (703)506-3266
Co. E-mail: info@hsmai.org
URL: http://www.hsmai.org
Contact: Robert A. Gilbert, President
E-mail: bgilbert@hsmai.org

URL(s): events.jspargo.com/AMW09/public/enter. aspx. **Frequency:** Annual. **Audience:** Trade professionals. **Principal Exhibits:** Equipment, supplies, and services for the hospitality and marketing industry. **Telecommunication Services:** affordable-meetings@jspargo.com.

3478 ■ *International Restaurant & Foodservice Show of New York*
Reed Exhibitions North American Headquarters
383 Main Ave.
Norwalk, CT 06851
Ph: (203)840-4800
Fax: (203)840-5805
Co. E-mail: inquiry@reedexpo.com
URL: http://www.reedexpo.com

URL(s): www.internationalrestaurantny.com/. **Frequency:** Annual. **Principal Exhibits:** Equipment, supplies, and services for the food products, foodservice, restaurant, and institutional food service industries. **Dates and Locations:** , Jacob K. Javits Convention Center.

3479 ■ *Ottawa Wine and Food Show*
Player Expositions International
255 Clemow Ave.
Ottawa, ON, Canada K1S 2B5
Ph: (613)567-6408
Fax: (613)567-2718
URL: http://www.playerexpo.com

URL(s): www.playerexpo.com. **Frequency:** Annual. **Audience:** Restaurant, hotels, clubs, catering-fine food stores, specialty food stores, wine clubs, and the general public. **Principal Exhibits:** Fine wines and foods, and beer from around the world. **Dates and Locations:** Congress Centre. **Telecommunication Services:** wineshow@playerexpo.com.

CONSULTANTS

3480 ■ *Cini-Little International Inc.*
20251 Century Blvd., Ste. 375
Germantown, MD 20874
Ph: (301)528-9700
Fax: (301)528-9711
Co. E-mail: info@cinilittle.com
URL: http://www.cinilittle.com
Contact: James H. Little, Chief Executive Officer
E-mail: jlittle@cinilittle.com

Scope: Offers a full range of independent management and design consulting services in all aspects of food service to industries such as hospitality, business, and health care. Services include feasibility studies and or operations analyses, food service programs and concepts, operational training programs and manuals, food service contractor selection, contract documents, review of contractor submittal and site inspections. Offers consulting in materials management, materials handling, vertical horizontal transport elevator escalator moving sidewalks to all segments of the construction, hospitality, health-care and related industries. **Founded:** 1968.

FRANCHISES AND BUSINESS OPPORTUNITIES

3481 ■ *City Kitchen*
950 S Flower St., Ste. 105
Los Angeles, CA 90015
Free: 800-704-2070
Fax: (213)236-0951

Description: Fine food catering. **No. of Company-Owned Units:** 1. **Founded:** 2001.. **Franchised:** 2004. **Equity Capital Needed:** $150,000-$500,000. **Franchise Fee:** $30,000. **Royalty Fee:** 6%.

3482 ■ *Corporate Caterers Franchise*
Corporate Caterers Inc.
Description: Catering for professional offices and business events. **No. of Franchise Units:** 10. **No. of Company-Owned Units:** 3. **Founded:** 1997.. **Franchised:** 2008. **Equity Capital Needed:** $79,000-$143,500. **Franchise Fee:** $30,000. **Training:** Yes.

250

Small Business Sourcebook • 30th Edition

3483 ■ Steak-Out Charbroiled Delivery

Steak-Out Franchising, Inc.
3091 Governors Lake Dr., Ste. 500
Norcross, GA 30071
Ph: (678)533-6000
Free: 877-878-3257
Fax: (678)291-0222
Co. E-mail: jmccord@steakout.com
URL: http://www.steakout.com

Description: Full meal delivery chain featuring charbroiled steaks, chicken, seafood, burgers, chef salads & deserts. Steak-Out serves the busy office worker that doesn't have time to go for lunch & the on-the-go family that needs a wholesome meal when there is no time to cook. Steak-Out features delivery, carry-out & catering. **No. of Franchise Units:** 42. **No. of Company-Owned Units:** 2. **Founded:** 1986.. **Franchised:** 1987. **Equity Capital Needed:** $100,000 liquid; $400,000 net worth. **Franchise Fee:** $30,000. **Financial Assistance:** Yes. **Training:** Training is 4 weeks in the store and at headquarters for 3 to 4 management employees. Complete support in site finding, store opening, marketing and ongoing.

LIBRARIES

3484 ■ American Institute of Food Distribution, Inc. - Information and Research Center—The Food Institute.

1 Broadway Plaza, 2nd Fl.
Elmwood Park, NJ 07407
Ph: (201)791-5570
Fax: (201)791-5222
Co. E-mail: jkastrinsky@foodinstitute.com
URL: http://www.foodinstitute.com/
Contact: Brian Todd, President
Scope: Food industry. **Services:** Center open to the public on fee basis. **Founded:** 1928. **Subscriptions:** 400 journals and other serials. **Publications:** *Food Business Mergers and Acquisitions.* **Telecommunication Services:** food1@foodinstitute.com.

3485 ■ City College of San Francisco - Department - Culinary Arts and Hospitality Studies Alice Statler Library

50 Phelan Ave.
Statler Wing, Rm. 10
San Francisco, CA 94112
Ph: (415)239-3460
Co. E-mail: aniosi@ccsf.edu
URL: http://www.ccsf.edu/NEW/en/library/about-library/library-locations/statler.html
Contact: Andrea Niosi, Librarian
Scope: Public hospitality industries - hotels, motels, restaurants, catering services, cookery and nutrition; tourism; beverages. **Services:** Copying; Wi-Fi; library open to the public for reference use only. **Founded:** 1964. **Holdings:** 10,000 books; 3500 pamphlets; 900 menus; videotapes; archives. **Subscriptions:** 80 journals and other serials. **Telecommunication Services:** astatler@ccsf.edu.

3486 ■ Culinary Institute of America - Conrad N. Hilton Library

1946 Campus Dr.
Hyde Park, NY 12538-1499
Ph: (845)452-9600
URL: http://www.ciachef.edu/newyork/library/
URL(s): library.culinary.edu/. **Scope:** Cookery, food service, restaurant management, hospitality. **Services:** Interlibrary loan; copying; Library open to the public by appointment. **Founded:** 1972. **Holdings:** 86,000 volumes; 30,000 menus; 4500 DVDs and videos. **Subscriptions:** 280 journals and other serials.

3487 ■ Johnson & Wales University - Harborside Culinary Library

321 Harborside Blvd.
Providence, RI 02905
Ph: (401)598-1282
Co. E-mail: bjanson@jwu.edu
URL: http://www.jwu.edu
Contact: Barbara Janson, Librarian
Scope: Cookbooks, food service, menu planning, nutrition, professional management, catering and banquets, household manuals, canning, preserving and freezing, hotel and motel management. **Services:** Copying; Library open to the public. **Founded:** 1979. **Holdings:** 10,000 books; 700 menus. **Subscriptions:** 100 journals and other serials.

3488 ■ Noble and Associates Library

2155 W. Chesterfield Blvd.
Springfield, MO 65807
Ph: (417)875-5000
Co. E-mail: julie.tumy@noble.net
URL: http://www.noble.net
Contact: Julie Tumy, President
Scope: Food, food service, advertising, construction, agriculture. **Services:** Interlibrary loan; copying; SDI; Library not open to the public. **Holdings:** 500 books; 1000 reports. **Subscriptions:** 300 journals and other serials; 5 newspapers.

CD-ROM Developer/Producer

START-UP INFORMATION

3489 ■ *The 100 Best Businesses to Start When You Don't Want To Work Hard Anymore*

Pub: Career Press Inc.

Ed: Lisa Rogak. **Price:** $16.99. **Description:** Author helps burned-out workers envision a new future as a small business owner. Systems analysis, adventure travel outfitting, bookkeeping, food delivery, furniture making, and software development are among the industries examined.

3490 ■ *"Local Startup Hits Big Leagues" in Austin Business JournalInc. (Vol. 28, December 19, 2008, No. 40, pp. 1)*

Pub: American City Business Journals

Ed: Christopher Calnan. **Description:** Qcue LLC, an Austin, Texas-based company founded in 2007 is developing a software system that can be used by Major League Baseball teams to change the prices of their single-game tickets based on variables affecting demand. The company recently completed a trial with the San Francisco Giants in 2008.

3491 ■ *"OtherInbox Ready for Revenue: Software Startup Expects Profits in '09" in Austin Business JournalInc. (Vol. 28, January 2, 2009)*

Pub: American City Business Journals

Ed: Christopher Calnan. **Description:** Founder of Austin, Texas-based OtherBox Inc. expects the company to generate revenue through subscriptions and advertising and also reach profitability in 2009. The company's email management tool sends secondary mail to an alternate location thereby freeing up the work inbox for more urgent messages.

REFERENCE WORKS

3492 ■ *"Abacast, Citadel Strike Radio Ad Deal" in Business Journal Portland (Vol. 27, December 31, 2010, No. 44, pp. 3)*

Pub: Portland Business Journal

Ed: Erik Siemers. **Description:** Software firm Abacast Inc. has partnered with Citadel Media to aid the latter's advertising sales. Citadel provides radio networks and syndicated programs to 4,200 affiliate stations.

3493 ■ *"ACC Game Development Program Opens" in Austin Business JournalInc. (Vol. 28, October 31, 2008, No. 33, pp. 1)*

Pub: American City Business Journals

Ed: Sandra Zaragoza. **Description:** Austin, Texas-based Austin Community College has launched its Game Development Institute. The institute was created to meet the gaming industry's demand for skilled workers. One hundred students have enrolled with the institute.

3494 ■ *"All Those Applications, and Phone Users Just Want to Talk" in Advertising Age*

(Vol. 79, August 11, 2008, No. 31, pp. 18)

Pub: Crain Communications, Inc.

Ed: Mike Vorhaus. **Description:** Although consumers are slowly coming to text messaging and other data applications, a majority of those Americans surveyed stated that they simply want to use their cell phones to talk and do not care about other activities. Statistical data included.

3495 ■ *"AMT's Partner Program Enables New Security Business Models" in Internet Wire (August 12, 2010)*

Pub: Comtex

Description: AMT, technical provider of physical access control Software as a Service (Saas) solutions, has developed a new Partner Program that allows partners to outsource any technical abilities lacking to AMT with no upfront fees.

3496 ■ *"Angel Investments Tripled in 2009" in Austin Business JournalInc. (Vol. 29, January 8, 2010, No. 44, pp. 1)*

Pub: American City Business Journals

Ed: Christopher Calnan. **Description:** Central Texas Angel Network (CTAN) has invested $3.5 million in 12 ventures, which include 10 in Austin, Texas in 2009 to triple the amount it invested during 2008. The largest recipient of CTAN's investments is life sciences, which attracted 20 percent of the capital, while software investments fell to 18 percent. The new screening process that helps startups secure CTAN capital is explored.

3497 ■ *"Apps For Anybody With an Idea" in Advertising Age (Vol. 79, October 20, 2008, No. 39, pp. 29)*

Pub: Crain Communications, Inc.

Ed: Beth Snyder Bulik. **Description:** Apple's new online App Store is open to anyone with an idea and the ability to write code and many of these developers are not only finding a sense of community through this venue but are also making money since the sales are split with Apple, 30/70 in the developer's favor.

3498 ■ *"Arctic IT Honored" in Alaska Business Monthly (Vol. 27, October 2011, No. 10, pp. 10)*

Pub: Alaska Business Publishing Company

Ed: Nancy Pounds. **Description:** Arctic Information Technology Inc. was named to Everything Channel's 2011 Computer Reseller News (CRN) Next-Generation 250 list. The firm provides business software and network infrastructure solutions.

3499 ■ *"Arizona Firms In Chicago Go For Gold With '08 Games" in The Business Journal - Serving Phoenix and the Valley of the Sun (Vol. 28, August 8, 2008, No. 49, pp. 1)*

Pub: American City Business Journals, Inc.

Ed: Patrick O'Grady. **Description:** More than 20 U.S. athletes will wear Arizona-based eSoles LLC's custom-made insoles to increase their performance at the 2008 Beijing Olympics making eSoles one of the beneficiaries of the commercialization of the

games. Translation software maker Auralog Inc saw a 60 percent jump in sales from its Mandarin Chinese language applications.

3500 ■ *"Attivio Brings Order to Data" in Information Today (Vol. 26, February 2009, No. 2, pp. 14)*

Pub: Information Today, Inc.

Ed: Marji McClure. **Description:** Profile of Attivio, the high tech firm offering next-generation software that helps businesses to consolidate data and eliminate enterprise silos.

3501 ■ *"AVG Introduces Security Software Suite for SMBs 551179" in eWeek (October 12, 2010)*

Pub: Ziff Davis Enterprise

Description: AVG Technologies is offering its AVG Internet Security 2011 Business Edition and AVG Anti-Virus Business Edition designed to give Internet-active SMB owners protection. The system protects online transactions and email communications as well as sensitive customer data and AVG Anti-Virus 2011 Business edition offers real-time protection against the latest online threats.

3502 ■ *"BancVue to Expand" in Austin Business JournalInc. (Vol. 29, November 27, 2009, No. 38, pp. 1)*

Pub: American City Business Journals

Ed: Kate Harrington. **Description:** Significant growth of BancVue in the past six years has prompted the company to look for a site that could increase its office space from 25,000 square feet to 65,000 square feet. BancVue offers bank and credit union software solutions and is planning to lease or buy a property in Austin, Texas.

3503 ■ *"Bar Hopping: Your Numbers At a Glance" in Inc. (January 2008, pp. 44-45)*

Pub: Gruner & Jahr USA Publishing

Ed: Michael Fitzgerald. **Description:** Software that helps any company analyze data include Crystal Xcelsius, a program that takes data from Excel documents and turns them into animated gauges, charts and graphs; CashView, a Web-based application that tracks receivables and payables; iDashboards, a Web-based programs that produces animated gauges, maps, pie charts and graphs; Corda Human Capital Management, that transforms stats like head count, productivity, and attrition into graphs and dials; NetSuite, a Web-based application that tracks key indicators; and Cognos Now, that gauges, dials, and graphs data.

3504 ■ *"BayTSP, NTT Data Corp. Enter Into Reseller Pact to Market Online IP Monitoring" in Professional Services Close-Up (Sept. 11, 2009)*

Pub: Close-Up Media

Description: Due to incredible interest from distributors and content owners across Asia, NTT Data Corp. will resell BayTSP's online intellectual property monitoring, enforcement, business intelligence and monetization services in Japan.

3505 ■ *"Behind the Scenes: Companies At the Heart of Everyday Life"* in *Inc. (February 2008, pp. 26-27)*
Pub: Gruner & Jahr USA Publishing

Ed: Athena Schindelheim. **Description:** Profiles of companies providing services to airports, making the environment safer and more efficient, as well as more comfortable for passengers and workers. Centerpoint Manufacturing provides garbage bins that can safely contain explosions producing thousands of pounds of pressure; Infax, whose software displays arrival and departure information on 19-foot-wide screens; Lavi Industries, whose products include security barricades, hostess stands, and salad-bar sneeze guards; and SATech maker of rubber flooring that helps ease discomfort for workers having to stand for long periods of time.

3506 ■ *"Being all a-Twitter"* in *Canadian Business (Vol. 81, December 8, 2008, No. 21, pp. 22)*
Pub: Rogers Media Ltd.

Ed: Andrew Wahl. **Description:** Marketing experts suggest that advertising strategies have to change along with new online social media. Companies are advised to find ways to incorporate social software because workers and customers are expected to continue its use.

3507 ■ *"Best Managed Companies (Canada)"* in *Canadian Business (Vol. 82, Summer 2009, No. 8, pp. 38)*
Pub: Rogers Media

Ed: Calvin Leung. **Description:** Agrium Inc. and Barrick Gold Corporation are among those that are found to be the best managed companies in Canada. Best managed companies also include software firm Open Text Corporation, which has grown annual sales by 75 percent and annual profits by 160 percent since 1995. Open Text markets software that allow firms to manage word-based data, and has 46,000 customers in 114 countries.

3508 ■ *"Beyond Microsoft and Yahoo!: Some M&A Prospects"* in *Barron's (Vol. 88, March 17, 2008, No. 11, pp. 39)*
Pub: Dow Jones & Company, Inc.

Ed: Eric J. Savitz. **Description:** Weak quarterly earnings report for Yahoo! could pressure the company's board to cut a deal with Microsoft. Electronic Arts is expected to win its hostile $26-a-share bid for Take-Two Interactive Software. Potential targets and buyers for mergers and acquisitions are mentioned.

3509 ■ *"Beyond YouTube: New Uses for Video, Online and Off"* in *Inc. (October 2007, pp. 53-54)*
Pub: Gruner & Jahr USA Publishing

Ed: Leah Hoffmann. **Description:** Small companies are using video technology for embedding messages into email, broadcasting live interactive sales and training seminars, as well as marketing campaigns. Experts offer insight into producing and broadcasting business videos.

3510 ■ *The Big Switch*
Pub: W. W. Norton & Company, Inc.

Ed: Nicholas Carr. **Released:** January 19, 2009. **Price:** $16.95 paperback. **Description:** Today companies are dismantling private computer systems and tapping into services provided via the Internet. This shift is remaking the computer industry, bringing competitors such as Google to the forefront and threatening traditional companies like Microsoft and Dell. The book weaves together history, economics, and technology to explain why computing is changing and what it means for the future.

3511 ■ *"Blog Buzz Heralds Arrival of IPhone 2.0"* in *Advertising Age (Vol. 79, June 9, 2008, No. 40, pp. 8)*
Pub: Crain Communications, Inc.

Ed: Abbey Klaasen. **Description:** Predictions concerning the next version of the iPhone include a global-positioning-system technology as well as a configuration to run on a faster, 3G network.

3512 ■ *Business Feasibility Analysis Pro*
Pub: Prentice Hall PTR

Ed: Palo Alto Software. **Released:** August 2006. **Price:** $28.40. **Description:** Profile of software developed to support small business management and/or entrepreneurship text. Step-by-step instructions are provided.

3513 ■ *"BusinessOnLine Launches a New Web-Based Search Engine Optimization Tool"* in *Internet Wire (October 19, 2009)*
Pub: Comtex News Network, Inc.

Description: First Link Checker, a complimentary new search engine optimization tool that helps site owners optimize their on-page links by understanding which of those links are actually being counted in Google's relevancy algorithm, was developed by BusinessOnLine, a rapidly growing Internet marketing agency. This tool will make it easy for the average web master to ensure that their internal link structure is optimized.

3514 ■ *"A Case Study: Real-Life Business Planning"* in *Entrepreneur (February 3, 2009)*
Pub: Entrepreneur Media Inc.

Ed: Tim Berry. **Description:** Provides a case study of a two-day planning meeting for Palo Alto Software in which the executives of the company met for their annual planning cycle and discussed ways in which the company needed to change in order to stay viable in today's tough economic climate.

3515 ■ *"Cerner Works the Business Circuit"* in *Business Journal-Serving Metropolitan Kansas City (Vol. 26, October 5, 2007, No. 4, pp. 1)*
Pub: American City Business Journals, Inc.

Ed: Rob Roberts. **Description:** Cerner Corporation is embracing the coming of the electronic medical record exchange by creating a regional health information organization (RHIO) called the CareEntrust. The RHIO convinced health insurers to share claims data with patients and clinicians. At the Center Health Conference, held October 7 to 10, Cerner will demonstrate the software it developed for CareEntrust to the 40,000 healthcare and information technology professionals.

3516 ■ *"ChemSW Software Development Services Available for Outsourcing"* in *Information Today (Vol. 26, February 2009, No. 2, pp. 30)*
Pub: Information Today, Inc.

Description: ChemSW software development services include requirements analysis, specification development, design, development, testing, and system documentation as an IT outsourcing solution. The company can also develop software tracking systems for satellite stockrooms, provide asset management integration solutions and more.

3517 ■ *"ClickFuel Launches New Products to Help Small and Mid-Sized Businesses Bolster Their Brand Online"* in *Internet Wire (Dec. 3, 2009)*
Pub: Comtex News Network, Inc.

Description: Boostability, a provider of Enterprise Search Engine Optimization (SEO) software technology, has partnered with ClickFuel, a firm that designs, tracks and manages Internet marketing campaigns in order to leverage Boostability's technology in order to deliver comprehensive SEO solutions to small and mid-size businesses; three new products will also become available for these business clients to help them manage all facets of their online presence.

3518 ■ *"ClickFuel Launches New Products to Help Small and Mid-Sized Businesses Bolster Their Brand Online"* in *Internet Wire (Dec. 3, 2009)*
Pub: Comtex News Network, Inc.

Description: Boostability, a provider of Enterprise Search Engine Optimization (SEO) software technology, has partnered with ClickFuel, a firm that designs, tracks and manages Internet marketing campaigns in order to leverage Boostability's technology in order to deliver comprehensive SEO solutions to small and mid-size businesses; three new products will also become available for these business clients to help them manage all facets of their online presence.

3519 ■ *"ClickFuel Unveils Internet Marketing Tools for Small Businesses"* in *Internet Wire (October 19, 2009)*
Pub: Comtex News Network, Inc.

Description: ClickFuel, a firm that manages, designs and tracks marketing campaigns has unveiled a full software suite of affordable services and technology solutions designed to empower small business owners and help them promote and grow their businesses through targeted Internet marketing campaigns.

3520 ■ *"Clouds in the Forecast"* in *Information Today (Vol. 28, September 2011, No. 8, pp. 10)*
Pub: Information Today, Inc.

Ed: Paula J. Hane. **Description:** Cloud computing is software, applications, and data stored remotely and accessed via the Internet with output displayed on a client device. Recent developments in cloud computing are explored.

3521 ■ *Computer Accounting Essentials with Microsoft Office Accounting 2010*
Pub: McGraw-Hill Higher Education

Ed: Carol Yacht, Susan Crosson. **Released:** March 10, 2010. **Description:** Step-by-step guide to using Microsoft's Office Professional 2007 Accounting program.

3522 ■ *"Cut Energy Waste"* in *Inc. (Vol. 31, January-February 2009, No. 1, pp. 42)*
Pub: Mansueto Ventures LLC

Description: Carbon Control, Edison, and Saver software programs help companies cut carbon emissions by reducing the amount of energy consumed by computers while they are idle.

3523 ■ *"Dear Customer: Managing E-Mail Campaigns"* in *Inc. (March 2008, pp. 58-59)*
Pub: Gruner & Jahr USA Publishing

Ed: Ryan Underwood. **Description:** Internet services that help firms manage their online business including email marketing, to manage subscriber lists, comply with spam regulations, monitor bouncebacks, and track potential customers are profiled. Constant Contact, MobileStorm Stun, Campaign Monitor, Pop Commerce, Emma, and StrongMail E-mail Server are among software and services highlighted.

3524 ■ *"Design Programs for HVAC Sizing Solutions"* in *Contractor (Vol. 57, January 2010, No. 1, pp. 44)*
Pub: Penton Media, Inc.

Ed: William Feldman; Patti Feldman. **Description:** Rhvac 8 is an HVAC design program that lets users calculate peak heating and cooling load requirements for rooms, zones, systems, and entire buildings. The HVAC Pipe Sizer software for the iPhone enables quick sizing of a simple piping system.

3525 ■ *"A Dog-Day Pooch"* in *Canadian Business (Vol. 79, September 11, 2006, No. 18, pp. 19)*
Pub: Rogers Media

Ed: Andrew Wahl. **Description:** Acquisition deal of Hummingbird Ltd by Canadian software maker Open Text Corp., is discussed.

3526 ■ *"Don't Touch My Laptop, If You Please Mr. Customs Man"* in *Canadian Electronics (Vol. 23, June-July 2008, No. 4, pp. 6)*
Pub: Action Communication Inc.

Ed: Mark Borkowski. **Description:** Canadian businessmen bringing electronic devices to the US can protect the contents of their laptops by hiding their data from US border agents. They can also choose to clean up the contents of their laptop using file erasure programs.

3527 ■ *"DST Turns to Banks for Credit"* in *The Business Journal-Serving Metropolitan Kansas City (Vol. 27, October 3, 2008, No. 3, pp. 1)*
Pub: American City Business Journals, Inc.

Ed: Rob Roberts. **Description:** Kansas City, Missouri-based DST Systems Inc., a company that provides sophisticated information processing, computer software services and business solutions, has secured a new five-year, $120 million credit facility from Enterprise Bank and Bank of the West. The deal is seen to reflect that the region and community-banking model remain stable. Comments from executives are also provided.

3528 ■ "Eagles Measure Suite Success" in Philadelphia Business Journal (Vol. 30, September 9, 2011, No. 30, pp. 1)
Pub: American City Business Journals Inc.

Ed: John George. **Description:** Philadelphia Eagles have a new software program that helps suite holders keep track of how their suite is being used and whether they are getting a return on their investment. The software allows suite holders to better utilize and distribute their tickets.

3529 ■ "EBSCO Adds New Features to EBSCOhost Content Viewer" in Information Today (Vol. 26, February 2009, No. 2, pp. 31)
Pub: Information Today, Inc.

Description: EBSCOhost Content Viewer historical digital archive collection provides a visual overview of a displayed document, highlighting search keywords on the page as well as providing a document map that shows the number of times a given keyword is mentioned in a periodical, monograph, article, or other document. For periodical content, the viewer lets users browse multiple issues in a volume without leaving the interface; features include zoom and pan technology similar to online maps.

3530 ■ "Elastic Path Software Joins Canada in G20 Young Entrepreneur Summit" in Internet Wire (June 14, 2010)
Pub: Comtex

Description: The Canadian Youth Business Foundation hosted the G20 Young Entrepreneur Summit and announced that Harry Chemko of British Columbia's Elastic Path Software will be a member of the Canadian delegation at the G20 Young Entrepreneur Summit. Details are included.

3531 ■ "The Emergence of Governance In an Open Source Community" in Academy of Management Journal (Vol. 50, No. 5, October 2007, pp. 1079)
Pub: Academy of Management

Contact: Ming-Jer Chen, President

Ed: Siiobhan O'Mahony, Fabrizio Ferraro. **Description:** Study examined the method of self-governance among small communities producing collective goods, focusing on an open source software community. Results revealed that a combination of bureaucratic and democratic practices helped its governance system.

3532 ■ "Empire of Pixels" in Entrepreneur (Vol. 37, September 2009, No. 9, pp. 50)
Pub: Entrepreneur Media, Inc.

Ed: Jason Daley. **Description:** Entrepreneur Jack Levin has successfully grown Imageshack, an image-hosting Web service. The Website currently gets 50 million unique visitors a month. Levin has launched Y-Frog, an application that uses Imageshack to allow Twitter users to add images to their posts.

3533 ■ The Entrepreneurial Culture Network Advantage Within Chinese and Irish Software Firms
Pub: Edward Elgar Publishing, Incorporated

Ed: Tsang. **Released:** October 2006. **Price:** $95.00. **Description:** Ways national cultural heritage influences entrepreneurial ventures are discussed.

3534 ■ "Ex Libris Rosetta Hits the Market" in Information Today (Vol. 26, February 2009, No. 2, pp. 30)
Pub: Information Today, Inc.

Description: Ex Libris Rosetta, the latest version of the Ex Libris Group's Digital Preservation System supports the acquisition, validation, ingest, storage, management, preservation, and dissemination of digital objects, allowing libraries the infrastructure and technology to preserve and facilitate access to digital collections. The firm's Ex Libris Rosseta

Charter Program helps users develop strategic collaboration between Ex Libris and its customers to improve the product.

3535 ■ "Fly Phishing" in Canadian Business (Vol. 80, October 22, 2007, No. 21, pp. 42)
Pub: Rogers Media

Ed: Andy Holloway. **Description:** Symantec Corporation's report shows consumers and companies have effectively installed network defenses that prevent unwanted access. Phishing packages are readily available and are widely used. Other details of the Internet Security Threat Report are presented.

3536 ■ "The Folly of Google's Latest Gambit" in Barron's (Vol. 89, July 13, 2009, No. 28, pp. 23)
Pub: Dow Jones & Co., Inc.

Ed: Eric J. Savitz. **Description:** Google will enter the operating systems business with the introduction of the Google Chrome OS but its success is dubious because the project is still a year or so away while Microsoft will release an updated version of Windows by then; another problem is that Google already has another OS called Android which will overlap with the Chrome OS's market.

3537 ■ "Game On! African Americans Get a Shot at $17.9 Billion Video Game Industry" in Black Enterprise (Vol. 38, July 2008, No. 12, pp. 56)
Pub: Earl G. Graves Publishing Co. Inc.

Ed: Carolyn M. Brown. **Description:** Despite the economic crisis, consumers are still purchasing the hottest video games and hardware. Tips for African American developers who want to become a part of this industry that lacks content targeting this demographic are offered.

3538 ■ "Game Plan" in Canadian Business (Vol. 79, September 11, 2006, No. 18, pp. 50)
Pub: Rogers Media

Ed: Joe Castaldo. **Description:** Strategies adopted by gaming companies to revitalize their business and give a stimulus to their falling resources are presented.

3539 ■ "German Win Through Sharing" in Canadian Business (Vol. 83, September 14, 2010, No. 15, pp. 16)
Pub: Rogers Media Ltd.

Ed: Jordan Timm. **Description:** German economic historian Eckhard Hoffner has a two-volume work showing how German's relaxed attitude toward copyright and intellectual property helped it catch up to industrialized United Kingdom. Hoffner's research was in response to his interest in the usefulness of software patents. Information on the debate regarding Canada's copyright laws is given.

3540 ■ "Getting Rid of Global Glitches: Choosing Software For Trade Compliance" in Black Enterprise (Vol. 41, September 2010, No. 2, pp. 48)
Pub: Earl G. Graves Publishing Co. Inc.

Ed: Marcia Wade Talbert. **Description:** Compliance software for trading with foreign companies must be compatible with the U.S. Census Bureau's Automated Export System (www.aesdirect.gov). It has to be current with regulatory requirements for any country in the world. Whether owners handle their own compliance or hire a logistics company, they need to be familiar with this software in order to access reports and improve transparency and efficiency of theft supply chain.

3541 ■ "Global: Put It on Autopilot" in Entrepreneur (Vol. 35, October 2007, No. 10, pp. 110)
Pub: Entrepreneur Media Inc.

Ed: Laurel Delaney. **Description:** A business that aims to enter the global market must first streamline its global supply chain (GSC). A streamlined GSC can be achieved by laying out the company's processes and by automating it with supply chain management software. Advantages of GSC automation such as credibility are provided.

3542 ■ "Google Places a Call to Bargain Hunters" in Advertising Age (Vol. 79, September 29, 2008, No. 36, pp. 13)
Pub: Crain Communications, Inc.

Ed: Abbey Klaassen. **Description:** Google highlighted application developers who have created tools for its Android mobile phone in the device's unveiling; applications such as ShopSavvy and CompareEverywhere help shoppers to find bargains by allowing them to compare prices in their local areas and across the web.

3543 ■ "A Hacker in India Hijacked His Website Design and Was Making Good Money Selling It" in Inc. (December 2007, pp. 77-78, 80)
Pub: Gruner & Jahr USA Publishing

Ed: Darren Dahl. **Description:** John Anton, owner of an online custom T-shirt business and how a company in India was selling software Website templates identical to his firm's Website.

3544 ■ "His Banking Industry Software Never Caught On, so Bill Randle is Now Targeting the Health Care Market" in Inc. (March 2008)
Pub: Gruner & Jahr USA Publishing

Ed: Alex Salkever. **Description:** Profile of Bill Randle, bank executive turned entrepreneur; Randle tells how he changed his focus for his company from banking software to healthcare software. The firm employs ten people who secure online billing and recordkeeping systems for hospitals and insurers. Randle discusses critical decisions that will impact his firm in the coming year. Three experts offer advice.

3545 ■ "Holiday Sales Look Uncertain for Microsoft and PC Sellers" in Puget Sound Business Journal (Vol. 29, November 28, 2008, No. 32)
Pub: American City Business Journals

Ed: Todd Bishop. **Description:** Personal computer makers face uncertain holiday sales for 2008 as a result of the weak U.S. economy and a shift toward low-cost computers. Personal computer shipments for the fourth quarter 2008 are forecast to drop 1 percent compared to the same quarter 2007.

3546 ■ "How Hard Could It Be? Adventures In Software Demo'l'ing" in Inc. (December 2007, pp. 99-100)
Pub: Gruner & Jahr USA Publishing

Ed: Joel Spolsky. **Description:** Founder and CEO of Fog Creek Software, a New York City software developer shares insight into his software demo tour used to promote his firm's products.

3547 ■ "HR Tech on the Go" in Workforce Management (Vol. 88, November 16, 2009, No. 12, pp. 1)
Pub: Crain Communications Inc.

Ed: Ed Frauenheim. **Description:** Examination of the necessity of mobile access of human resources software applications that allow managers to recruit, schedule and train employees via their mobile devices; some industry leaders believe that mobile HR applications are vital while others see this new technology as hype.

3548 ■ "iControl Networks Powers Comcast's XFINITY (Reg) Home Security Service" in Benzinga.com (June 9, 2011)
Pub: Benzinga.com

Ed: Benzinga Staff. **Description:** Comcast's XFINITY Home Security Service is powered by iControl Networks' OpenHome (TM) software platform. The service provides intrusion and fire protection along with interactive features such as home monitoring, home management, and energy management services with Web and mobile access.

3549 ■ "Image Conscious" in Canadian Business (Vol. 81, March 17, 2008, No. 4, pp. 36)
Pub: Rogers Media

Ed: Andrew Wahl. **Description:** Idee Inc. is testing an Internet search engine for images that does not rely on tags but compares its visual data to a database of other images. The company was founded and managed by Leila Boujnane as an off-shoot of their risk-management software firm. Their software has already been used by image companies to track copyrighted images and to find images within their own archives.

3550 ■ *"Inside Intel's Effectiveness System for Web Marketing"* in *Advertising Age* (Vol. 81, January 25, 2010, No. 4, pp. 4)
Pub: Crain's Communications
Ed: Beth Snyder Bulik. **Description:** Overview of Intel's internally developed program called Value Point System in which the company is using in order to evaluate and measure online marketing effectiveness.

3551 ■ *"Intel to Buy McAfee Security Business for 768B"* in *eWeek* (August 19, 2010)
Pub: Ziff Davis Enterprise
Description: Intel will acquire security giant McAfee for approximately $7.68 billion, whereby McAfee would become a wholly owned subsidiary of Intel and would report to Intel's Software and Services Group.

3552 ■ *"iPhone Apps Big Business"* in *Austin Business JournalInc.* (Vol. 28, November 14, 2008, No. 35, pp. 1)
Pub: American City Business Journals
Ed: Christopher Calnan. **Description:** Members of the computer software industry in Austin, Texas have benefited from developing applications for Apple Inc.'s iPhone. Pangea Software Inc.'s revenues have grown by developing iPhone applications. Lexcycle LLC, on the other hand, has created an application that enables users to read books on the iPhone.

3553 ■ *"iPhone Apps In a Flash"* in *Entrepreneur* (Vol. 37, October 2009, No. 10, pp. 38)
Pub: Entrepreneur Media, Inc.
Description: Ansca is developing Corona, a software development kit for the Apple iPhone. The kit reduces development time and allows individuals with knowledge of software to develop iPhone applications.

3554 ■ *"Is It Time to Ban Swearing at Work?"* in *HR Specialist* (Vol. 8, September 2010, No. 9, pp. 2)
Pub: Capitol Information Group Inc.
Description: Screening software has been developed to identify profanity used in business correspondence.

3555 ■ *"iSymmetry's Technological Makeover Or, How a Tech Company Finally Grew Up and Discovered the World Wide Web"* in *Inc.* (October 2007)
Pub: Gruner & Jahr USA Publishing
Description: Profile of iSymmetry, an Atlanta, Georgia-based IT recruiting firm, covering the issues the company faces keeping its technology equipment up-to-date. The firm has devised a program that will replace its old server-based software systems with on-demand software delivered via the Internet, known as software-as-a-service. Statistical information included.

3556 ■ *"Johnny Royal of Luthier Society Unveils Archimedes 1.0 Trailer"* in *Internet Wire* (October 22, 2009)
Pub: Comtex News Network, Inc.
Description: Luthier Society, a social media and viral branding agency, has released the first viral video for the company's ROI weighted-value software platform named Archimedes 1.0; users of the software will be able to determine the depth of their outreach efforts, saturation rate, value of their Internet presence and the geo-spatial location of their audience; this will give a true, monetized value for ROI (Return on Investment) in social media marketing.

3557 ■ *"Keeping Up With the Joneses: Outfitting Your Company With Up-To-Date Technology is Vital"* in *Black Enterprise* (November 2007)
Pub: Earl G. Graves Publishing Co. Inc.
Ed: Sonya A. Donaldson. **Description:** Small businesses, whether home-based or not, need to keep up with new technological developments including hardware, software, and the Internet.

3558 ■ *"Lights, Camera, Action: Tools for Creating Video Blogs"* in *Inc.* (Volume 32, December 2010, No. 10, pp. 57)
Pub: Inc. Magazine
Ed: John Brandon. **Description:** A video blog is a good way to spread company news, talk about products, and stand out among traditional company blogs. New editing software can create two- to four-minute blogs using a webcam and either Windows Live Essentials, Apple iLife 2011, Powerdirector 9 Ultra, or Adobe Visual Communicator 3.

3559 ■ *"Make Relationships Count: CRM Software That Works"* in *Black Enterprise* (Vol. 38, February 2008, No. 7, pp. 60)
Pub: Earl G. Graves Publishing Co. Inc.
Ed: Fiona Haley. **Description:** Customer relationship management (CRM) software can help any small business keep track of clients. Descriptions of the latest CRM software offered are profiled, including Salesforce.com, Microsoft Dynamics, and Saga Software.

3560 ■ *"Media Software and Data Services"* in *MarketingMagazine* (Vol. 115, September 27, 2010, No. 13, pp. 78)
Pub: Rogers Publishing Ltd.
Description: Media software and data services information in Canada is presented.

3561 ■ *"Meetings Go Virtual"* in *HRMagazine* (Vol. 54, January 2009, No. 1, pp. 74)
Pub: Society for Human Resource Management
Contact: Henry G. Jackson, President
E-mail: hjackson@shrm.org
Ed: Elizabeth Agnvall. **Description:** Microsoft Office Live Meeting conferencing software allows companies to schedule meetings from various company locations, thus saving travel costs.

3562 ■ *"Microsoft Clicks Into High Speed"* in *Hispanic Business* (Vol. 30, July-August 2008, No. 7-8, pp. 54)
Pub: Hispanic Business, Inc.
Ed: Derek Reveron. **Description:** Microsoft's diversity hiring and vendor diversity program to capture more Hispanic consumer and business-to-business market is described. One of the main goals of these programs is to hire more Hispanic executives and managers who will help the company develop and market products and services that will appeal and benefit Hispanic consumers.

3563 ■ *"Microsoft Goes Macrosoft"* in *Barron's* (Vol. 89, July 27, 2009, No. 30, pp. 25)
Pub: Dow Jones & Co., Inc.
Ed: Mark Veverka. **Description:** Microsoft reported a weak quarter on the heels of a tech rally which suggests the economy has not turned around. Marc Andreesen describes his new venture-capital fund as focused on 'classic tech' and that historical reference places him in the annals of the last millennium.

3564 ■ *"Microsoft Releases Office Security Updates"* in *Mac World* (Vol. 27, November 2010, No. 11, pp. 66)
Pub: Mac Publishing
Ed: David Dahlquist. **Description:** Office for Mac and Mac Business Unit are Microsoft's pair of security- and stability-enhancing updates for Office 2008 and Office 2004. The software will improve the stability and compatibility and fixes vulnerabilities that would allow attackers to overwrite Mac's memory with malicious code.

3565 ■ *"Mimosa Systems Gains 150,000 New NearPoint Users"* in *Information Today* (Vol. 26, February 2009, No. 2, pp. 31)
Pub: Information Today, Inc.
Description: Mimosa System's NearPoint archive solution features email and file archiving, e-discovery, archive virtualization, and disaster recovery capabilities.

3566 ■ *"More Leading Retailers Using Omniture Conversion Solutions to Boost Sales and Ecommerce Performance"* in *Internet Wire* (Sept. 22,2009)
Pub: Comtex News Network, Inc.
Description: Many retailers are utilizing Omniture conversion solutions to improve the performance of their ecommerce businesses; recent enhancements to Omniture Merchandising and Omniture Recommendations help clients drive increased conversion to their Internet ventures.

3567 ■ *"More Leading Retailers Using Omniture Conversion Solutions to Boost Sales and Ecommerce Performance"* in *Internet Wire* (Sept. 22,2009)
Pub: Comtex News Network, Inc.
Description: Many retailers are utilizing Omniture conversion solutions to improve the performance of their ecommerce businesses; recent enhancements to Omniture Merchandising and Omniture Recommendations help clients drive increased conversion to their Internet ventures.

3568 ■ *"My Favorite Tool for Organizing Data"* in *Inc.* (Vol. 33, November 2011, No. 9, pp. 46)
Pub: Inc. Magazine
Ed: Abram Brown. **Description:** Intelligence software firm uses Roambi, a Web-based service that turns spreadsheet data into interactive files for iPhones and iPads.

3569 ■ *"New Database Brings Doctors Out of the Dark"* in *Business Courier* (Vol. 26, October 23, 2009, No. 26, pp. 1)
Pub: American City Business Journals, Inc.
Ed: James Ritchie. **Description:** A database created by managed care consulting firm Praesentia allows doctors in Cincinnati to compare average reimbursements from health insurance companies to doctors in different areas. Specialist doctors in the city are paid an average of $172.25 for every office consultation.

3570 ■ *"New IPhone Also Brings New Way of Mobile Marketing"* in *Advertising Age* (Vol. 79, June 16, 2008, No. 24, pp. 23)
Pub: Crain Communications, Inc.
Ed: Abbey Klaasen. **Description:** Currently there are two kinds of applications for the iPhone and other mobile devices: native applications that allow for richer experiences and take advantage of features that are built into a phone and web applications, those that allow access to the web through specific platforms. Marketers are interested in creating useful experiences for customers and opening up the platforms which will allow them to do this.

3571 ■ *"New Sprint Phone Whets Appetite for Applications"* in *The Business Journal-Serving Metropolitan Kansas City* (Vol. 26, July 25, 2008)
Pub: American City Business Journals, Inc.
Ed: Suzanna Stagemeyer. **Description:** Firms supporting the applications of the new Samsung Instinct, which was introduced by Sprint Nextel Corp. in June 2008, have reported usage rates increase for their products. Handmark, whose mobile services Pocket Express comes loaded with Instinct, has redirected employees to meet the rising demand for the services. Other views and information on Instinct, are presented.

3572 ■ *"New Wave of Business Security Products Ushers in the Kaspersky Anti-Malware Protection System"* in *Internet Wire* (October 26, 2010)
Pub: Comtex
Description: Kaspersky Anti-Malware System provides anti-malware protection that requires minimal in-house resources for small businesses. The system offers a full range of tightly integrated end-to-end protection solutions, ensuring unified protection across an entire network, from endpoint and mobile device protection to file server, mail server, network storage and gateway protection. It provides flexible centralized management, immediate threat visibility and a level of responsiveness not seen in other anti-malware approaches.

3573 ■ *"Nonprofit NAIC Acquires Software Developer as For-Profit Arm"* in Crain's Detroit Business (Vol. 25, June 22, 2009, No. 25, pp. 10)
Pub: Crain Communications Inc. - Detroit
Ed: Sherri Begin Welch. **Description:** Details of National Association of Investors Corporation's acquisition of a Massachusetts investment software developer in order to offer more products to investment clubs and individual investors nationwide.

3574 ■ *"Not Your Father's Whiteboard"* in Inc. (Vol. 33, November 2011, No. 9, pp. 50)
Pub: Inc. Magazine
Ed: Adam Baer. **Description:** Sharp's new interactive whiteboard is really a 70-inch touch screen monitor with software for importing presentations from any Windows 7 computer.

3575 ■ *"Nothing Like a Weak Team Or An Unrealistic Schedule To Start a Project Off Right"* in Inc. (November 2007, pp. 85-87)
Pub: Gruner & Jahr USA Publishing
Ed: Joel Spolsky. **Description:** Five easy ways to fail meeting a project deadline are discussed by the owner of a software development company: start with second-rate team of developers, set weekly milestones, negotiate a deadline, divide tasks equitably, and work until midnight.

3576 ■ *"OCE Boosts JetStream Productivity"* in American Printer (Vol. 128, August 1, 2011, No. 8)
Pub: Penton Media Inc.
Description: New Oce JetStream 1400 and 3000 digital full-color inkjet presses are profiled. The new models promise higher speed to grow print volume.

3577 ■ *"Oce Business Services: Discovery Made Easy"* in Information Today (Vol. 26, February 2009, No. 2, pp. 31)
Pub: Information Today, Inc.
Ed: Barbara Brynko. **Description:** Oce Business Services provides document process management and electronic discovery through its CaseData repertoire of legal management solutions.

3578 ■ *"Omniture's Next Version of SearchCenter Delivers Landing Page Optimization"* in Internet Wire (September 24, 2009)
Pub: Comtex News Network, Inc.
Description: Omniture, Inc., a leading provider of online business optimization software, has announced a new release of Omniture SearchCenter; this latest version will allow search engine marketers to test landing pages across campaigns and ad groups.

3579 ■ *"On Beyond Powerpoint: Presentations Get a Wake-Up Call"* in Inc. (November 2007, pp. 58-59)
Pub: Gruner & Jahr USA Publishing
Ed: Michael Fitzgerald. **Description:** New software that allows business presentations to be shared online are profiled, including ProfCast, audio podcasts for sales, marketing, and training; SmartDraw2008, software that creates professional graphics; Dimdim, an open-Web conferencing tool; Empressr, a hosted Web service for creating, managing, and sharing multimedia presentations; Zentation, a free tool that allows users to watch slides and a videos of presenter; Spresent, a Web-based presentation tool for remote offices or conference calls.

3580 ■ *"Open Source Solutions for Small Business Problems"*
Pub: Charles River Media
Ed: John Locke. **Released:** May 2004. **Price:** $35.95. **Description:** Open source software provides solutions to many small business problems such as tracking electronic documents, scheduling, accounting functions, managing contact lists, and reducing spam.

3581 ■ *"Oracle and Tauri Group Honored by Homeland Security and Defense Business Council"* in Wireless News (December 15, 2009)
Pub: Close-Up Media
Description: Selected as members of the year by the Homeland Security and Defense Business Council were Oracle, a software company that has provided thought leadership and strategic insights as well as The Tauri Group, an analytical consultancy, that has demonstrated a unique understanding of the role of small business and its vital contribution to the success of the country's security.

3582 ■ *"Our Gadget of the Week"* in Barron's (Vol. 88, March 24, 2008, No. 12, pp. 47)
Pub: Dow Jones & Company, Inc.
Ed: Tiernan Ray. **Description:** Review of the $299 Apple Time Capsule, which is a 500-megabyte hard disk drive and a Wi-Fi router, rolled into one device. The device allows users to create backup files without the need for sophisticated file management software.

3583 ■ *"Owner of IT Firm MK2 Tying Future to Software"* in Crain's Cleveland Business (Vol. 30, June 15, 2009, No. 23, pp. 3)
Pub: Crain Communications, Inc.
Ed: Chuck Soder. **Description:** Donald Kasper, owner of MK2 Technologies LLC of Cleveland, Ohio discusses his recent acquisition of a portion of ProSource Solution. The move will help expand the two companies' custom software development plans.

3584 ■ *"Paging Dr. Phil"* in Canadian Business (Vol. 79, September 25, 2006, No. 19, pp. 21)
Pub: Rogers Media
Ed: John Gray. **Description:** Increasing corporate crimes in software industry is discussed by focusing on recent case of Hewlett and Packard.

3585 ■ *"Panda Security for Business 4.05"* in SC Magazine (Vol. 21, July 2010, No. 7, pp. 50)
Pub: Haymarket Media Inc.
Description: Profile of Panda Security for Business, software offering endpoint security protection for computer desktops and servers is presented.

3586 ■ *"The Paper Shredder"* in Business Courier (Vol. 26, September 11, 2009, No. 20, pp. 1)
Pub: American City Business Journals, Inc.
Ed: Dan Monk. **Description:** DotLoop Company, owned by entrepreneur Austin Allison, is developing the DotLoop software, which eliminates paperwork in the processing of real estate contracts. The software allows realtors to take control of the negotiation process and is adaptable to the rules of different US states.

3587 ■ *"Paperless Bookkeeping Program"* in Fleet Owner Online (February 15, 2011)
Pub: Penton Business Media Inc.
Description: TruckTax launched its new paperless bookkeeping system to help manage bookkeeping tasks, accounting and business tax information and filings for truckers.

3588 ■ *"PC Connection Acquires Cloud Software Provider"* in New Hampshire Business Review (Vol. 33, March 25, 2011, No. 6, pp. 8)
Pub: Business Publications Inc.
Description: Merrimack-based PC Connection Inc. acquired ValCom Technology, a provider of cloud-based IT service management software. Details of the deal are included.

3589 ■ *"PC Running Slowly? How to Rev Up Your Machine"* in Inc. (Vol. 33, November 2011, No. 9, pp. 46)
Pub: Inc. Magazine
Ed: John Brandon. **Description:** Software that keeps PCs tuned up and running smoothing are profiled: AUSLO6ICS BOOSTSPEED 5, $50; Tuneup Utilities 2011, $40; Slimware Slimcleaner 1.9, free; and IOBIT Advanced Systemcare Pro 4, $20 a year.

3590 ■ *"PopCap Games Achieves Significant Increase in Return on Ad Spend With Omniture SearchCenter"* in Internet Wire (September 15, 2009)
Pub: Comtex News Network, Inc.
Description: PopCap Games, a leading computer games provider, is using Omniture SearchCenter together with Omniture SiteCatalyst to increase revenue from its search engine marketing campaign. Omniture, Inc. is a leading provider of Internet business optimization software.

3591 ■ *"The Power of Negative Thinking"* in Inc. (Volume 32, December 2010, No. 10, pp. 43)
Pub: Inc. Magazine
Ed: Jason Fried. **Description:** A Website is software and most businesses need and have a good Website to generate business. Understanding for building a powerful Website is presented.

3592 ■ *"Power Ranger"* in Inc. (November 2007, pp. 131)
Pub: Gruner & Jahr USA Publishing
Ed: Nitasha Tiku. **Description:** Surveyor software is designed to power down computers when not in use, in order to save energy.

3593 ■ *"Practical Tech for Your Business"*
Pub: Kiplinger Books and Tapes
Ed: Michael J. Martinez. **Released:** 2002. **Description:** Advice is offered to help small business owners choose the right technology for their company. The guide tells how to get started, network via the Internet, create an office network, use database software, and conduct business using mobile technology.

3594 ■ *"Precision Crop Control with Valley Irrigation/CropMetrics Partnership"* in Farm Industry News (January 6, 2011)
Pub: Penton Business Media Inc.
Description: Irrigation systems have become a precision farming tool since partnering with agronomic software systems to apply products across the field by prescription. Valley Irrigation and CropMetrics have partnered in order to variably control water, fertilizer and other crop management products through a center pivot irrigation system.

3595 ■ *"Press Release: Trimble Introduces CFX-750 Display"* in Farm Industry News (January 4, 2011)
Pub: Penton Business Media Inc.
Description: Trimble is offering a touch screen display called the CFX-750. The new 8-inch full-color display allows farmers to choose the specific guidance, steering and precision agriculture capabilities that best fit their farm's particular needs. The display can be upgraded as business needs change, including the addition of GLONASS capabilities, or the addition of section and rate control for crop inputs such as seed, chemicals and fertilizer.

3596 ■ *"Programs Provide Education and Training"* in Contractor (Vol. 56, September 2009, No. 9, pp. 56)
Pub: Penton Media, Inc.
Ed: William Feldman; Patti Feldman. **Description:** Opportunity Interactive's Showroom v2 software provides uses computer graphics to provide education and training on HVAC equipment and systems. It can draw heat pump balance points for a specific home. Meanwhile, Simutech's HVAC Training Simulators provide trainees with 'hands-on' HVACR training.

3597 ■ *"Protection One Introduces Home and Business Security iPhone App"* in Wireless News (November 13, 2009)
Pub: Close-Up Media
Description: Protection One, Inc., a provider of security systems to business and residential customers, has developed an application that allows users to access their security panels and receive real-time updates from their iPhone or iPod touch devices.

3598 ■ *"Providers Ride First Wave of eHealth Dollars"* in Boston Business Journal (Vol. 31, June 10, 2011, No. 20, pp. 1)
Pub: Boston Business Journal
Ed: Julie M. Donnelly. **Description:** Health care providers in Massachusetts implementing electronic medical records technology started receiving federal stimulus funds. Beth Israel Deaconess Medical Center was the first hospital to qualify for the funds.

3599 ■ *"Publishing Technology Introduces IngentaConnect Mobile" in Information Today (Vol. 26, February 2009, No. 2, pp. 33)*
Pub: Information Today, Inc.
Description: College undergraduates will find Publishing Technology's newest publisher product, IngentaConnect Mobile helpful. The product allows users to read articles and abstracts on mobile devices. According to a recent study, 73 percent of young adults with wireless hand-held devices use them to access non-voice data on any given day.

3600 ■ *"Putting the App in Apple" in Inc. (Vol. 30, November 2008, No. 11, pp.)*
Pub: Mansueto Ventures LLC
Ed: Nitasha Tiku. **Description:** Aftermarket companies are scrambling to develop games and widgets for Apple's iPhone. Apple launched a kit for developers interested in creating iPhone-specific software along with the App Store, and an iTunes spinoff. Profiles of various software programs that may be used on the iPhone are given.

3601 ■ *QuickBooks All-in-One Desk Reference for Dummies*
Pub: John Wiley & Sons, Incorporated
Ed: Stephen L. Nelson. **Released:** January 2007. **Price:** $29.99 (US), $42.99 (Canadian). **Description:** Compilation of nine self-contained minibooks to get the most from QuickBooks accounting software. Companion Web site with sample business plan workbook and downloadable profit-volume cost analysis workbook included.

3602 ■ *QuickBooks Simple Start for Dummies*
Pub: John Wiley and Sons, Inc.
Ed: Stephen L. Nelson. **Released:** October 2004. **Price:** $21.99. **Description:** Profile of Intuits new accounting software geared to micro businesses. Advice is offered on daily, monthly, and yearly accounting activities covering records, sales tax, and reports.

3603 ■ *QuickBooks X on Demand*
Pub: Que
Ed: Gail Perry. **Released:** December 2006. **Price:** $34.99. **Description:** Step-by-step training for using various small business financial software programs; includes illustrated, full color explanations.

3604 ■ *QuickBooks X for Dummies*
Pub: John Wiley & Sons, Incorporated
Ed: Stephen L. Nelson. **Released:** November 2006. **Price:** $21.99. **Description:** Key features of QuickBooks software for small business are introduced. Invoicing and credit memos, recoding sales receipts, accounting, budgeting, taxes, payroll, financial reports, job estimating, billing, tracking, data backup, are among the features.

3605 ■ *"Quickoffice's MobileFiles Pro App Enables Excel Editing On-the-Go" in Information Today (Vol. 26, February 2009, No. 2, pp. 31)*
Pub: Information Today, Inc.
Description: Quickoffice Inc. introduced MobileFiles Pro, which features editable Microsoft Office functionality for the iPone and iPod touch. The application allows users to edit and save Microsoft Excel files in .xls format, transfer files to and from PC and Mac desktops via Wi-Fi, and access and synchronize with Apple MobileMe accounts.

3606 ■ *"Remote Control: Working From Wherever" in Inc. (February 2008, pp. 46-47)*
Pub: Gruner & Jahr USA Publishing
Ed: Ryan Underwood. **Description:** New technology allows workers to perform tasks from anywhere via the Internet. Profiles of products to help connect to your office from afar include, LogMein Pro, a Web-based service that allowsaccess to a computer from anywhere; Xdrive, an online service that allows users to store and swap files; Basecamp, a Web-based tools that works like a secure version of MySpace; MojoPac Freedom, is software that allows users to copy their computer's desktop to a removable hard drive and plug into any PC; WatchGuard Firebox X Core e-Series UTM Bundle, hardware that blocks

hackers and viruses while allowing employees to work remotely; TightVNC, a free open-source software that lets you control another computer via the Internet.

3607 ■ *"RES Stakes Its Claim in Area" in Philadelphia Business Journal (Vol. 28, January 29, 2010, No. 50, pp. 1)*
Pub: American City Business Journals
Ed: Peter Key. **Description:** RES Software Company Inc. of Amsterdam, Netherlands appointed Jim Kirby as president for the Americas and Klaus Besier as chairman in an effort to boost the firm's presence in the US. Brief career profiles of Kirby and Besier are included. RES develops software that allows management of information flow between an organization and its employees regardless of location.

3608 ■ *"Route Optimization Impacts the Bottom Line" in Contractor (Vol. 56, November 2009, No. 11, pp. 48)*
Pub: Penton Media, Inc.
Ed: Dave Beaudry. **Description:** Plumbing and HVAC businesses can save a significant amount of money from route optimization. The process begins with gathering information on a fleet and a routing software tool can determine the effectiveness of current route configurations and identify preferable route plans.

3609 ■ *Salesforce.com Secrets of Success: Best Practices for Growth and Profitability*
Pub: Prentice Hall Business Publishing
Contact: Jerome Grant, President
Ed: David Taber. **Released:** May 15, 2009. **Price:** $34.99. **Description:** Guide for using Salesforce. com; it provides insight into navigating through user groups, management, sales, marketing and IT departments in order to achieve the best results.

3610 ■ *"Save the Date" in Barron's (Vol. 90, September 13, 2010, No. 37, pp. 35)*
Pub: Barron's Editorial & Corporate Headquarters
Ed: Mark Veverka. **Description:** Mark Hurd is the new Co-President of Oracle after being forced out at Hewlett-Packard where he faced a harassment complaint. HP fired Hurd due to expense account malfeasance. Hurd is also set to speak at an Oracle trade show in San Francisco on September 20, 2010.

3611 ■ *"Scitable Puts Nature Education on the Map" in Information Today (Vol. 26, February 2009, No. 2, pp. 29)*
Pub: Information Today, Inc.
Description: Nature Education, a division of the Nature Publishing Group, released its first product, Scitable, a free online resource for undergraduate biology students and educators. The service includes over 180 overviews of key genetics concepts as well as social networking features, including groups and functionality, that lets students work with classmates and others. Teachers can use the service to set up public or private groups for students.

3612 ■ *"Second Cup?" in Canadian Business (Vol. 81, July 21, 2008, No. 11, pp. 50)*
Pub: Rogers Media Ltd.
Ed: Calvin Leung. **Description:** Profile of James Gosling who is credited as the inventor of the Java programming language; however, the 53-year-old software developer feels ambivalent for being credited as inventor since many people contributed to the language. Netscape and Sun Microsystems incorporation of the programming language into Java is presented.

3613 ■ *"Sense of Discovery" in Business Journal Portland (Vol. 27, November 19, 2010, No. 38, pp. 1)*
Pub: Portland Business Journal
Ed: Erik Siemers. **Description:** Tigard, Oregon-based Exterro Inc. CEO Bobby Balachandran announced plans to go public without the help of an institutional investor. Balachandran believes Exterro could grow to a $100 million legal compliance software company in the span of three years. Insights on Exterro's growth as market leader in the $1 billion legal governance software market are also given.

3614 ■ *"Serials Solutions Launches 360 Resource Manager Consortium Edition" in Information Today (Vol. 26, February 2009, No. 2, pp. 32)*
Pub: Information Today, Inc.
Description: Serials Solutions new Serials Solutions 360 Resource Manager Consortium Edition helps consortia, groups and member libraries with their e-resource management services. The products allows users to consolidate e-resource metadata and acquisition information into one place, which enables groups to manage holdings, subscriptions, licensing, contacts, and cost information and to streamline delivery of information to members.

3615 ■ *"A Side Project Threatens To Get Totally Out of Control and I Think, 'How Fun'" in Inc. (October 2007, pp. 81-82)*
Pub: Gruner & Jahr USA Publishing
Ed: Joel Spolsky. **Description:** Profile of Fog Creek Software, makers of project-management software for other software developers. Fog Creek's owner discusses his idea to create a new product for his firm.

3616 ■ *"Skype on Steroids" in Inc. (Vol. 31, January-February 2009, No. 1, pp. 46)*
Pub: Mansueto Ventures LLC
Ed: Nitasha Tiku. **Description:** Free software called VoxOx allows users to make calls over the Internet and connects all email and IM accounts.

3617 ■ *"Small is Bountiful for Intuit" in Barron's (Vol. 90, September 13, 2010, No. 37, pp. 22)*
Pub: Barron's Editorial & Corporate Headquarters
Ed: Mark Veverka. **Description:** Finance software maker Intuit wants to tap the underserved small business market. One analyst sees Intuit's shares rising 25 percent to 55 percent in the next 12 months from September 2010.

3618 ■ *"A Software Company's Whimsical Widgets Were an Instant Hit. But Its Core Product Was Getting Overshadowed" in Inc. (Jan. 2008)*
Pub: Gruner & Jahr USA Publishing
Ed: Alex Salkever. **Description:** A widget designed as a marketing tool tuned into a hit on Facebook. Should ChipIn shift its focus?.

3619 ■ *"Software Solutions Increase Productivity" in Contractor (Vol. 57, February 2010, No. 2, pp. 26)*
Pub: Penton Media, Inc.
Ed: William Feldman; Patti Feldman. **Description:** Singletouch is a real-time data capture solution for mechanical and other contractors that work in jobs that require materials and workload tracking. Contractors get information on extreme weather and sudden changes in the cost of materials. The OptimumHVAC optimization software by Optimum Energy is designed to optimize energy savings in commercial buildings.

3620 ■ *"Software Solutions from Trane and Carrier" in Contractor (Vol. 56, July 2009, No. 7, pp. 38)*
Pub: Penton Media, Inc.
Ed: William Feldman; Patti Feldman. **Description:** Trane Trace 700 software helps HVAC contractors optimize the design of a building's HVAC system and aids in the evaluation of various key energy-saving concepts, including daylighting, high-performance glazing, and other optimization strategies. Carrier's E20-II family of software programs lets contractors increase the accuracy of an HVAC system estimate.

3621 ■ *"Software's Last Hurrah" in Canadian Business (Vol. 81, December 24, 2007, No. 1, pp. 27)*
Pub: Rogers Media
Ed: Andrew Wahl. **Description:** Canada's software industry could be facing a challenge with IBM's acquisition of Cognos, which was the country's last major independent business intelligence company and was also IBM's largest acquisition ever. Next in line to Cognos in terms of prominence is Open Text Corporation, which could also be a possible candidate for acquisition, as analysts predict.

3622 ■ "Startup on Cusp of Trend" in Austin Business JournalInc. (Vol. 29, January 8, 2010, No. 44, pp. 1)
Pub: American City Business Journals

Ed: Christopher Calnan. **Description:** Austin-based Socialware Inc. introduced a new business called social middleware, which is a software that is layered between the company network and social networking Website used by workers. The software was designed to give employers a measure of control over content while allowing workers to continue using online social networks.

3623 ■ "The State of the Art in End-User Software Engineering" in ACM Computing Surveys (Vol. 43, Fall 2011, No. 3, pp. 21)
Pub: Association for Computing Machinery

Description: Most programs today are not written by professional software developers but by people with expertise in other domains working towards goals for which they need computational support. A discussion of empirical research about end-user software engineering activities and the technologies designed to support them is presented. Several crosscutting issues in the design of EUSE tools, including the roles of risk, reward, and domain complexity, and self-efficacy in the design of EUSE tools and the potential of educating users about software engineering principles are also examined.

3624 ■ "The Story Of Diane Greene" in Barron's (Vol. 88, July 14, 2008, No. 28, pp. 31)
Pub: Dow Jones & Co., Inc.

Ed: Mark Veverka. **Description:** Discusses the ousting of Diane Greene as a chief executive of VMWare, a developer of virtualization software, after the firm went public; in this case Greene, a brilliant engineer, should not be negatively impacted by the decision because it is common for companies to bring in new executive leadership that is more operations oriented after the company goes public.

3625 ■ "A Survey of Combinatorial Testing" in ACM Computing Surveys (Vol. 43, Summer 2011, No. 2, pp. 11)
Pub: Association for Computing Machinery

Ed: Changhai Nie, Hareton Leung. **Description:** Combinatorial Testing (CT) can detect failures triggered by interactions of parameters in the Software Under Test (SUT) with a covering array test suite generated by some sampling mechanisms. Basic concepts and notations of CT are covered.

3626 ■ "A Survey of Comparison-Based System-Level Diagnosis" in ACM Computing Surveys (Vol. 43, Fall 2011, No. 3, pp. 22)
Pub: Association for Computing Machinery

Ed: Elias P. Duarte Jr., Roverli P. Ziwich, Luiz C.P. Albini. **Description:** The growing complexity and dependability requirements of hardware, software, and networks demand efficient techniques for discovering disruptive behavior in those systems. Comparison-based diagnosis is a realistic approach to detect faulty units based on the outputs of tasks executed by system units. This survey integrates the vast amount of research efforts that have been produced in this field.

3627 ■ "Taking the Steps Into the Clouds" in New Hampshire Business Review (Vol. 33, March 25, 2011, No. 6, pp. 19)
Pub: Business Publications Inc.

Ed: Tim Wessels. **Description:** Cloud services include Internet and Web security, spam filtering, message archiving, work group collaboration, IT asset management, help desk and disaster recovery backup.

3628 ■ "Tech Deal Couples Homegrown Firms" in The Business Journal-Serving Greater Tampa Bay (Vol. 28, July 4, 2008, No. 28, pp. 1)
Pub: American City Business Journals, Inc.

Ed: Michael Hinman. **Description:** Tampa Bay, Florida-based Administrative Partners Inc. was acquired by Tribridge Inc. resulting in the strengthen-

ing of the delivery of Microsoft products to clients. Other details of the merger of the management consulting services companies are presented.

3629 ■ "Technology to the Rescue" in Contractor (Vol. 56, July 2009, No. 7, pp. 22)
Pub: Penton Media, Inc.

Ed: Candace Ruolo. **Description:** Features of several products that will make the job of a mechanical contractor easier are discussed. These include Ridgid's line of drain and sewer inspection cameras and monitors, Motion Computing's Motion F5 tablet rugged tablet PC, the JobClock from Exaktime, and the TeleNav Track tool for mobile workforce management.

3630 ■ "Technology: What Seems To Be the Problem? Self Service Gets a Tune-Up" in Inc. (February 2008, pp. 43-44)
Pub: Gruner & Jahr USA Publishing

Ed: Darren Dahl. **Description:** Self-service software can save companies money when responding to customer service phone calls, text or email messages. More companies are relying on alternatives such as automated Web-based self-service systems.

3631 ■ "Ted Stahl: Executive Chairman" in Inside Business (Vol. 13, September-October 2011, No. 5, pp. NC6)
Pub: Great Lakes Publishing Co.

Ed: Miranda S. Miller. **Description:** Profile of Ted Stahl, who started working in his family's business when he was ten years old is presented. The firm makes dies for numbers and letters used on team uniforms. Another of the family firms manufactures stock and custom heat-printing products, equipment and supplies. It also educates customers on ways to decorate garments with heat printing products and offers graphics and software for customers to create their own artwork.

3632 ■ "Thinking Strategically About Technology" in Franchising World (Vol. 42, August 2010, No. 8, pp. 9)
Pub: International Franchise Association

Ed: Bruce Franson. **Description:** Nearly 25 percent of companies waste money from their technology budget. Most of the budget is spent on non-strategic software. Ways to spend money on technology for any franchise are examined.

3633 ■ "A Timely Boon for Small Investors" in Barron's (Vol. 88, March 24, 2008, No. 12, pp. 48)
Pub: Dow Jones & Company, Inc.

Ed: Theresa W. Carey. **Description:** Nasdaq Data Store's new program called Market Replay allows investors to accurately track stock price movements. The replay can be as long as a day of market time and allows investors to determine whether they executed stock trades at the best possible price.

3634 ■ "Touching the Future" in Canadian Business (Vol. 81, July 21, 2008, No. 11, pp. 41)
Pub: Rogers Media Ltd.

Ed: Matt McClearn. **Description:** Microsoft Corp. has launched a multi-touch product which is both a software and hardware technology called Microsoft Surface. The innovative product allows people to use it at the same time, however touch-based computers are reported to be around $100,000. Other features and benefits of the product are presented.

3635 ■ "Trust But Verify: FMLA Software Isn't Foolproof, So Apply a Human Touch" in HR Specialist (Vol. 8, September 2010, No. 9, pp. 3)
Pub: Capitol Information Group Inc.

Description: Employers are using software to track FMLA information, however, it is important for employers to review reasons for eligibility requirements, particularly when an employee is reportedly overstepping the bounds within leave regulations due to software error.

3636 ■ "Two Field Service Management Solutions" in Contractor (Vol. 56, November

2009, No. 11, pp. 37)
Pub: Penton Media, Inc.

Ed: William Feldman; Patti Feldman. **Description:** Bella Solutions Field Service Software v. 4.2 is a web based solution for HVAC service contractors that enables scheduling of emergency, one-time, multi-visit or periodically recurring jobs with drag and drop appointments. VaZing is another web based solution that costs $99 per month for contractors. It can handle line-item discounting and invoices aside from scheduling.

3637 ■ "Two Ways to Find New Customers" in Inc. (Vol. 31, January-February 2009, No. 1, pp. 41)
Pub: Mansueto Ventures LLC

Description: Latest software programs that help sales staff connect to new leads are profiled. Salesconx provides online leads while Demandbase reports users on a particular Website.

3638 ■ "Unbound ID Raises $2 Million" in Austin Business JournalInc. (Vol. 28, December 12, 2008, No. 39, pp. 1)
Pub: American City Business Journals

Ed: Christopher Calnan. **Description:** Austin, Texas-based Unbound ID Corporation has secured $2 million in funding from venture capital firm Silverton Partners. The company has developed identity management software for network directories. The market for identity management technology is expected to grow to more than $12.3 billion by 2014.

3639 ■ "uTest Discusses the Evolution of Crowdsourcing Models at CrowdConf 2010" in Internet Wire (October 1, 2010)
Pub: Comtex

Description: World's largest software testing marketplace, uTest, announces its first conference dedicated to the emerging field of crowdsourcing along with the future of distributed work. A panel of experts will discuss common misconceptions about crowdsourcing using real-world examples.

3640 ■ "Video Surveillance Enters Digital Era, Makes Giant Strides" in Arkansas Business (Vol. 26, September 28, 2009, No. 39, pp. 1)
Pub: Journal Publishing Inc.

Ed: Jamie Walden. **Description:** Arkansas business owners are finding that the newest technology in video surveillance is leading to swift apprehension of thieves due to the high-quality digital imagery now being captured on surveillance equipment. Motion detection software for these systems is enhancing the capabilities of these systems and providing opportunities for businesses that would normally have problems integrating these systems.

3641 ■ "A Virtual Jog Mode for CAM" in Modern Machine Shop (Vol. 84, November 2011, No. 6, pp. 22)
Pub: Gardner Business Media, Inc.
Contact: Richard G. Kline, President
E-mail: rkline@gardnerweb.com

Ed: Edwin Gasparraj. **Description:** In many cases, CAM programming required a specific, user-defined path. Siemens PLMs Generic Motion Controller is an alternative that defines the tool path within CAM. The program is a virtual 'teach' mode that enables the user to capture cutter locations by jogging machines axes within CAM.

3642 ■ "What Has Sergey Wrought?" in Barron's (Vol. 89, July 13, 2009, No. 28, pp. 8)
Pub: Dow Jones & Co., Inc.

Ed: Alan Abelson. **Description:** Sergey Aleynikov is a computer expert that once worked for Goldman Sachs but he was arrested after he left the company and charged with theft for bringing with him the code for the company's proprietary software for high-frequency trade. The stock market has been down for four straight weeks as of July 13, 2009 which reflects the reality of how the economy is still struggling.

3643 ■ "Will the Force Be With Salesforce?" in Barron's (Vol. 88, March 24, 2008, No. 12, pp. 20)
Pub: Dow Jones & Company, Inc.

Ed: Mark Veverka. **Description:** Shares of Salesforce.com are likely to drop from the $44.83-a-share level in the face of a deteriorating economy and financial sector and thus lower demand for business software. The company is unlikely to deliver on its ambitious earnings forecasts for 2008 especially with strengthening competition from Oracle.

3644 ■ *"Women Losing IT Ground" in Marketing to Women (Vol. 21, February 2008, No. 2, pp. 6)*
Pub: EPM Communications Inc.
Contact: Ira Mayer, President
E-mail: imayer@epmcom.com
Description: According to a study conducted by The National Center for Women & Information Technology, women in technology are losing ground. Statistical data included.

3645 ■ *"Yammer Gets Serious" in Inc. (Volume 32, December 2010, No. 10, pp. 58)*
Pub: Inc. Magazine
Ed: Eric Markowitz. **Description:** Yammer, an internal social network for companies, allows coworkers to share ideas and documents in real-time. Details of this service are included.

3646 ■ *"Yes, No, and Somewhat Likely: Survey the World with Web Polls" in Inc. (October 2007, pp. 58-59)*
Pub: Gruner & Jahr USA Publishing
Ed: Don Steinberg. **Description:** Online tools for surveying customers, employees and the general public include Zoomergan zPro and Zoomerang Sample, software designed to send surveys and allows viewing results; SurveyMonkey software creates, administers and allows viewing online surveys and results; Vizu software places a one-question poll on a particular Website; and Vovici EFM Feedback, a subscription service providing ongoing surveys to customers or employees.

3647 ■ *"Zeon Solutions Teams with Endeca for SaaS Version of Endeca InFront" in Entertainment Close-Up (October 25, 2011)*
Pub: Close-Up Media
Description: Zeon Solutions, an enterprise e-commerce and Website development firm announced a special licensing partnership with Endecca Technologies. Endeca is an information management software company that provides small and mid-size retailers with high-performance Customer Experience Management technology.

TRADE PERIODICALS

3648 ■ *CD Computing News*
Pub: Worldwide Videotex
Ed: Mark Wright, Editor, markedit@juno.com. **Released:** Monthly. **Price:** $165, U.S. and Canada; $180, elsewhere. **Description:** Provides coverage of the projects, products, and developments of the commercial applications of CD-ROM, CD-I, and all the other optical storage devices used in computing. Concentrates on information relating to successful marketing strategies.

3649 ■ *DCLNews*
Pub: Data Conversion Laboratory
Contact: Mark Gross, President
Released: Monthly. **Price:** Included in membership;. **Description:** E-journal providing you insider information on XML and SGML, along with the latest technology and e-publishing news.

3650 ■ *Electric Pages*
Pub: International Informatics Institute
Released: Enewsletter. **Price:** Free. **Description:** Covers new publishing and media technologies from a publisher's perspective. Discusses such topics as digital printing, fax publishing, CD-ROM audiotex, videotex, electronic advertising, telecommunications, multimedia, and other interactive publishing tools. Recurring features include letters to the editor, interviews, news of research, book reviews, notices of publications available, and technology reviews. Publishes solely on the Internet.

3651 ■ *EMediaLive: Practical Solutions Using Optical Disc Technologies, Tools, and Services*
Pub: Online, A Division of Information Today Inc.
URL(s): www.emedialive.com/. **Ed:** Stephen Nathans. **Released:** Monthly **Price:** Free.

3652 ■ *Media Computing*
Pub: Dreamscape Productions
Ed: Sheridan Tatsuno, Editor, statsuno@aol.com.
Released: Monthly. **Price:** $495, institutions in the U.S. and Canada; $550, institutions elsewhere. **Description:** Supplies analysis of multimedia, internet, intranet, and web computing issues. Recurring features include interviews and reports of meetings.

TRADE SHOWS AND CONVENTIONS

3653 ■ ARMA International Annual Conference and Expo
ARMA International
11880 College Blvd., Ste. 450
Overland Park, KS 66210
Ph: (913)341-3808
Free: 800-422-2762
Fax: (913)341-3742
Co. E-mail: hq@arma.org
URL: http://www.arma.org
Contact: Galina Datskovsky, President
URL(s): www.arma.org/conference/2012/Chicago. aspx. **Price:** $899, Members early registration; $1149, Non-members early registration; $999, Onsite registered, members regular, after September 1; $1249, Onsite registered, non-members regular, after September 1. **Frequency:** Annual. **Audience:** Record managers. **Principal Exhibits:** Optical disk, CD-ROM, and optical storage technology; automated document storage and retrieval, micrographics, and reprographics; information management software; WORM; copying/duplicating equipment; image management systems; and record management systems. **Telecommunication Services:** mtoohey@arma.org.

CONSULTANTS

3654 ■ Century Small Business Solutions
152 N El Camino Real
Encinitas, CA 92024-2849
Ph: (760)633-4725
Contact: John R. Todd, Principal
Scope: Focuses on improving the profitability of growth-oriented small businesses through business planning, controlling expenses, marketing to find new customers and tax planning to minimize taxes. **Founded:** 1993. **Seminars:** QuickBooks training and Budgeting for your Small Business.

3655 ■ CheckMark Software Inc.
724 Whalers Way, Bldg. H, Ste. 101
Fort Collins, CO 80525-7578
Ph: (970)225-0522
Free: 800-444-9922
Fax: (970)225-0611
Co. E-mail: info@checkmark.com
URL: http://www.checkmark.com
Contact: Jim Mathre, President
Scope: Developer of accounting software tools for small businesses and provides fast, easy to use, affordable accounting and payroll solutions to small and medium sized businesses. Provides payroll software and multiledger integrated accounting software. **Founded:** 1984. **Publications:** *Multi-Ledger*; *CheckMark Payroll for Macintosh*; *Check-Mark Payroll for Windows*. **Special Services:** Multi-Ledger™; Payroll.

3656 ■ Cognetics Corp.
52 Mill Rd.
Princeton Junction, NJ 08550-1706
Ph: (609)799-5005
Fax: (609)799-8555
URL: http://www.cognetics.com
Contact: Anne Pauker Kreitzberg, President
E-mail: anne@cognetics.com
Scope: Offers services including technical, programming, human factors, content, graphics, and writing. Designs interactive products such as website, web applications and web communities. **Founded:** 1982. **Publications:** "10 Steps to Creating the Perfect Web Site"; "The Beginning of the End or the End of the Beginning"; "Is Your Project at Risk"; "Selling Us-

ability: Scope and Schedule Estimates," Society for Technical Communication, Dec, 2003. **Special Services:** LUCID™.

3657 ■ DacEasy Inc.—Sage Software Inc.
1715 N Brown Rd.
Lawrenceville, GA 30043
Free: 800-222-0505
Co. E-mail: sales@daceasy.com
URL: http://www.daceasy.com
Contact: Greg Hammermaster, President
URL(s): www.sagedaceasy.com. **Scope:** Develops an accounting system for small businesses that integrates accounting, invoicing, payroll, communications, and management software into a single package. **Founded:** 1981. **Seminars:** Tech Tuesday - Sage DacAccess Query and Publisher: Creating Basic Queries and Formatting, May, 2012; Tech Tuesday - Graphics Form Designer, Mar, 2012; Tech Tuesday - Year End Processes with Sage DacEasy; DacEasy Training.

3658 ■ Data Conversion Laboratory
61-18 190th St., 2nd Fl.
Fresh Meadows, NY 11365-2723
Ph: (718)357-8700
Free: 800-321-2816
Fax: (718)357-8776
Co. E-mail: info@dclab.com
URL: http://www.dclab.com
Contact: Mark Gross, President
Scope: Provides electronic document conversion services. Services help to refine document conversion strategies, identify content redundancy, extract metadata, and transform legacy and future documents. Specialize in projects comprised of complex technical documentation typically characterized by elaborate tables, equations, cross-referencing, special characters, footnotes, and specialized imaging requirements. Our proprietary software can be adapted and modified to manage any data set producing any uncompromisingly consistent end-product. Expertise in Document Conversion, Content Reuse Analysis, Digital Publishing Services, eBook Production Services, Structured Product Labeling, PubMed XML Conversion, Consulting & Management. **Founded:** 1981. **Publications:** *DCLNews*. **Seminars:** Data Conversion Panel, May, 2010. **Telecommunication Services:** convert@delab.com. **Special Services:** Harmonizer?.

3659 ■ Earth View Inc.
6523 California Ave. SW, Ste. 322
Seattle, WA 98136
Ph: (206)527-3168
Co. E-mail: info@self-guided.com
URL: http://www.earthview.com
Contact: Bryan Brewer, President
Scope: Offers market analysis, application design, and development of CD-ROM and Internet publishing for business and consumer markets. Also works with government agencies. Provides Internet consulting services. **Founded:** 1978. **Publications:** "Eclipse," 1978; "The Compact Disc Book".

3660 ■ Future Communications Corp.
104 W 40th St.
New York, NY 10018
Ph: (212)400-6000
Fax: (212)937-3892
Co. E-mail: info@futurecomusa.com
URL: http://www.futurecomusa.com
Contact: Colin Foster, President
E-mail: cmorettin@futurecomusa.com
Scope: Provider of video conferencing solutions including custom room solution for conference rooms, board rooms, distance education and command centers; room rental and equipment rental solutions; video consulting solutions such as managing video conferencing room and equipment, implementing video in an IP and ISDN environment; virtual private network design solutions and PC/Network solutions. **Founded:** 1989.

3661 ■ SiteShapers
4070 Goldfinch St., Ste. D
San Diego, CA 92103
Ph: (619)231-6907

Fax: (619)231-7061
Co. E-mail: inquiry@siteshapers.com
URL: http://www.siteshapers.com
Contact: Irene Jernigan, Manager
Scope: Conducts needs assessment and marketing productivity workshops for high-technology manufacturers and service firms. Specializes in web site strategies and design, marketing strategies, planning, research and promotion. Serves electronics and software, instruments and health care industries. **Founded:** 1985.

3662 ■ S.V. Writing Services
4471 Park Bristol Pl.
San Jose, CA 95136-2510
Ph: (408)972-2476
Fax: (408)224-8496
Contact: Tarlochan S. Nahal, President
Scope: Firm specializes in computer hardware and software documentation; online documentation; wafer processing equipment manuals; desktop publishing and illustration. Uses in-house Macintosh Quadra and Pentium-based computers running Inter leaf, Frame Maker, Word Perfect, Microsoft Word, and Ventura. Serves the semiconductor, electronics, and computer hardware or software industries. **Founded:** 1985.

LIBRARIES

3663 ■ Automated Sciences Group, Inc. - Library
1100 N. Glebe Rd.
Arlington, VA 22201-4798
Ph: (703)587-8750
Fax: (703)565-9412
Contact: Marvin L. Doxie

Scope: Telecommunications, systems and software engineering, system integration, hardware, software, peripherals. **Services:** Library not open to the public. **Founded:** 1974. **Holdings:** 400 books; 200 reports; hardware and software specifications; government directories; ADP forecast/industry profiles. **Subscriptions:** 75 journals and other serials.

3664 ■ University of Guam - Robert F. Kennedy Memorial Library - Instructional Media Division
Tan Siu Lin Bldg.
UOG Station
Mangilao, GU 96923
Ph: (671)735-2326

Fax: (671)734-6882
Co. E-mail: millhoff@uog9.uog.edu
URL: http://www.uog.edu
Contact: Brian L. Millhoff, Coordinator, Media Services
Scope: Multimedia; graphics. **Services:** Interlibrary loan. **Holdings:** 2388 videotapes; 110 CD-ROMs; 28 laser discs; 139 audio programs tape/CD; 200 pieces of media equipment. **Telecommunication Services:** angelp@uog9.uog.edu.

RESEARCH CENTERS

3665 ■ Santa Clara University - Institute for Information Storage Technology (IIST)
IIST Engineering Bldg.
Santa Clara, CA 95053
Ph: (408)554-4032
Fax: (408)554-7841
Co. E-mail: ahoagland@scu.edu
URL: http://www.iist.scu.edu/iist/hoagland/about.html
Contact: Dr. Albert S. Hoagland, Director
Services: Cooperative research projects with corporate sponsors, and technical support. **Founded:** 1984. **Educational Activities:** Undergraduate and graduate courses and short courses to the professional community; IIST Workshops. **Awards:** IIST Fellowships. **Telecommunication Services:** iist@iist.scu.edu.

START-UP INFORMATION

3666 ■ *"Head West, Young Startup?" in Boston Business Journal (Vol. 30, October 22, 2010, No. 39, pp. 1)*
Pub: Boston Business Journal
Ed: Galen Moore. **Description:** Startup companies Lark Technologies, Baydin and E la Cart Inc. are planning to leave Boston, Massachusetts for Silicon Valley. Lark has developed a vibrating wrist strap that syncs with a mobile phone's alarm clock.

3667 ■ *Starting an iPhone Application Business for Dummies*
Pub: Wiley Publishing Inc.
Contact: William J. Pesce, President
Ed: Aaron Nicholson, Joel Elad, Damien Stolarz. **Released:** October 26, 2009. **Price:** $24.99. **Description:** Ways to create a profitable, sustainable business developing and marketing iPhone applications are profiled.

ASSOCIATIONS AND OTHER ORGANIZATIONS

3668 ■ **Canadian Wireless Telecommunications Association (CWTA)—Association Canadienne des Telecommunications Sans Fil (ACTS)**
130 Albert St., Ste. 1110
Ottawa, ON, Canada K1P 5G4
Ph: (613)233-4888
Fax: (613)233-2032
Co. E-mail: info@cwta.ca
URL: http://www.cwta.ca
Contact: Bernard Law, President
Description: Promotes the wireless communications industry in Canada in order to create and maintain a positive economic environment; encourages further investment by the industry to improve the delivery of existing services and create further innovation. **Founded:** 1969. **Publications:** *Wireless Telecom: The Magazine of the Canadian Wireless Telecommunications Association; Wireless Telecom* (3/year); *CWTA Membership - Products and Services Directory.* **Educational Activities:** EXPO COMM Canada Communications.

3669 ■ **Communications Marketing Association (CMA)**
PO Box 5680
Lago Vista, TX 78645-0025
Ph: (512)267-7747
Fax: (512)267-7760
Co. E-mail: cmaexecdirector@aol.com
URL: http://www.cma-cmc.org
Contact: Elaine Baugh Walsh, President
Description: Manufacturers, independent manufacturers' representatives, and distributors who deal in two-way radio and wireless communication equipment and associated products. Promotes effective marketing and ensures professional industry standards. **Founded:** 1974. **Publications:** *CMA Newsletter* (Quarterly). **Educational Activities:** Communications Marketing Conference (Annual). **Awards:** Foundation Award (Annual).

3670 ■ **CTIA - The Wireless Association**
1400 16th St. NW, Ste. 600
Washington, DC 20036
Ph: (202)736-3200
Fax: (202)785-0721
Co. E-mail: memberservices@ctia.org
URL: http://www.ctia.org
Contact: Steve Largent, President
Description: Individuals and organizations actively engaged in cellular radiotelephone communications, including: telephone companies and corporations providing radio communications; lay firms; engineering firms; consultants and manufacturers. (A cellular radiotelephone is a mobile communications device. An area is geographically divided into low frequency cells monitored by a computer that switches callers from one frequency to another as they move from cell to cell.) Objectives are to: promote, educate, and facilitate the professional interests, needs, and concerns of members with respect to the development and commercial applications of cellular technology; provide an opportunity for exchanging experience and concerns; broaden the understanding and importance of cellular communication technology. Conducts discussions, studies, and courses. **Founded:** 1984. **Publications:** *Cellular Technology Report* (Monthly); *Industry Data Survey* (Semiannual). **Educational Activities:** CTIA Wireless (Annual). **Awards:** VITA Award (Annual). **Telecommunication Services:** bdempsey@ctia.org.

3671 ■ *CWTA Membership - Products and Services Directory*
130 Albert St., Ste. 1110
Ottawa, ON, Canada K1P 5G4
Ph: (613)233-4888
Fax: (613)233-2032
Co. E-mail: info@cwta.ca
URL: http://www.cwta.ca
Contact: Bernard Law, President

3672 ■ **Organization for the Promotion and Advancement of Small Telecommunications Companies (OPASTCO)**
2020 K St. NW, 7th Fl.
Washington, DC 20006
Ph: (202)659-5990
Fax: (202)659-4619
Co. E-mail: mks@opastco.org
URL: http://www.opastco.org
Contact: Mark Gailey, Board Member
Description: Small, independent telephone companies and cooperatives serving rural areas; associate members are telephone equipment and service suppliers. Seeks to promote and advance small, independent telephone companies and provide a forum for the exchange of ideas and discussion of mutual problems. Represents rural companies' interests before Congress and regulatory bodies. Provides clearinghouse for the compilation, publication, and distribution of information of interest to members. Offers guidance to members on matters of industry-wide importance. Encourages recognition of the contribution made to the telephone industry by members. **Founded:** 1963. **Publications:** *OPASTCO 411* (Biweekly); *OPASTCO Online Membership Directory* (Annual); *OPASTCO Roundtable: The Magazine of Ideas for Small Telephone Companies* (Quarterly). **Educational Activities:** Organization for the Protection and Advancement of Small Telephone Companies Conference (Annual). **Awards:** Associate Member Distinguished Service Award (Annual); Chairman's Award (Annual); Grassroots Advocacy Excellence Award (Annual); Lifetime Achievement Award (Annual). **Telecommunication Services:** lam@opastco.org; tnb@opastco.org.

3673 ■ **PCIA - The Wireless Infrastucture Association (PCIA)**
901 N Washington St., Ste. 600
Alexandria, VA 22314
Ph: (703)535-7518
Free: 800-759-0300
Fax: (703)836-1608
Co. E-mail: membership@pcia.com
URL: http://www.pcia.com
Contact: Dave Mayo, Director
Description: Promotes the wireless infrastructure, tower and siting industry through advocacy, education, programs, a trade show and other marketplace initiatives. **Scope:** personal communications services. **Founded:** 1949. **Subscriptions:** books papers periodicals reports. **Publications:** *The Bulletin* (Bimonthly); *PICA Bulletin: News and Analysis for the Personal Communication Industry; PCIA Zoning Field Guide: Information and Resources for Tower Siting.* **Educational Activities:** PCIA GlobalXChange (Annual); PCIA Wireless Infrastructure Show (Annual); PCIA Wireless Infrastructure Conference and Expo (Annual). **Awards:** PCIA Industry Awards (Annual); PCIA Marketing Awards (Annual); Eugene C. Bowler Award (Annual); Eugene C. Bowler Scholarship (Annual). **Telecommunication Services:** nancy.touhill@pcia.com; consumerinfo@pica.com; ebrahiml@pcia.com.

3674 ■ **Telecommunications Industry Association (TIA)**
2500 Wilson Blvd., Ste. 300
Arlington, VA 22201
Ph: (703)907-7700
Free: 703-907-7776
Fax: (703)907-7727
Co. E-mail: tia@tiaonline.org
URL: http://www.tiaonline.org
Contact: Grant Seiffert, President
Description: Serves the communications and IT industry, with proven strengths in standards development, domestic and international public policy, and trade shows. Facilitates business development and opportunities and a competitive market environment; provides a forum for member companies, the manufacturers and suppliers of products and services used in global communications. Represents the communications sector of the Electronic Industries Alliance. **Founded:** 1988. **Publications:** *Industry Pulse; Channel Intelligence Report; Industry Beat* (Weekly); *PulseOnline* (Monthly); *TIA Network* (Weekly); *TIA*

Directory and Desk Reference. **Educational Activities:** NXTcomm (Annual). **Telecommunication Services:** gseiffert@tiaonline.org; tia@tia.eia.org.

3675 ■ Wireless Telecom
130 Albert St., Ste. 1110
Ottawa, ON, Canada K1P 5G4
Ph: (613)233-4888
Fax: (613)233-2032
Co. E-mail: info@cwta.ca
URL: http://www.cwta.ca
Contact: Bernard Law, President
Released: 3/year

REFERENCE WORKS

3676 ■ "Actiontec and Verizon Team Up for a Smarter Home" in Ecology,Environment & Conservation Business (November 5, 2011, pp. 3)
Pub: HighBeam Research
Description: Verizon is implementing Actiontec Electronics' SG200 Service Gateway as a basic component of its Home Monitoring and Control service. This new smart home service allows customers to remotely check their homes, control locks and appliances, view home-energy use and more using a smartphone, PC, or FiOS TV.

3677 ■ "After Price Cuts, Competition GPS Makers Lose Direction" in Brandweek (Vol. 49, April 21, 2008, No. 16, pp. 16)
Pub: VNU Business Media, Inc.
Ed: Steve Miller. **Description:** Garmin and TomTom, two of the leaders in portable navigation devices, have seen lowering revenues due to dramatic price cuts and unexpected competition from the broadening availability of personal navigation on mobile phones. TomTom has trimmed its sales outlook for its first quarter while Garmin's stock dropped 40 percent since February.

3678 ■ "Agricharts Launches New Mobile App for Ag Market" in Farm Industry News (December 1, 2011)
Pub: Penton Business Media Inc.
Description: AgriCharts provides market data, agribusiness Website hosting and technology solutions for the agricultural industry. AgriCharts is a division of Barchart.com Inc. and announced the release of a new mobile applications that offers real-time or delayed platform for viewing quotes, charts and analysis of grains, livestock and other commodity markets.

3679 ■ "Aiming at a Moving Web Target" in Entrepreneur (Vol. 37, August 2009, No. 8, pp. 30)
Pub: Entrepreneur Media, Inc.
Ed: Dan O'Shea. **Description:** Rapidly increasing numbers of businesspeople are web surfing on mobile phones. To make a website that is accessible to people on the move, the main page should be light on images and graphics and the most important information should be put near the top. A more intensive route is to create a separate mobile-specific website.

3680 ■ "All Those Applications, and Phone Users Just Want to Talk" in Advertising Age (Vol. 79, August 11, 2008, No. 31, pp. 18)
Pub: Crain Communications, Inc.
Ed: Mike Vorhaus. **Description:** Although consumers are slowly coming to text messaging and other data applications, a majority of those Americans surveyed stated that they simply want to use their cell phones to talk and do not care about other activities. Statistical data included.

3681 ■ "App Time: Smartphone Applications Aren't Just for Fun and Games Anymore" in Inc. (Volume 32, December 2010, No. 10, pp. 116)
Pub: Inc. Magazine
Ed: Jason Del Rey. **Description:** Smart phone technology can help any small business market their products and services.

3682 ■ "Apps For Anybody With an Idea" in Advertising Age (Vol. 79, October 20, 2008, No. 39, pp. 29)
Pub: Crain Communications, Inc.
Ed: Beth Snyder Bulik. **Description:** Apple's new online App Store is open to anyone with an idea and the ability to write code and many of these developers are not only finding a sense of community through this venue but are also making money since the sales are split with Apple, 30/70 in the developer's favor.

3683 ■ "Aptitudes for Apps" in Boston Business Journal (Vol. 31, July 1, 2011, No. 23, pp. 3)
Pub: Boston Business Journal
Ed: Kyle Alspach. **Description:** Startups Apperian Inc. and Kinvey Inc. are aiming to accelerate the development and deployment of mobile applications and have received fund pledges from Boston-area venture capital firms.

3684 ■ "At 5-Year Mark, News 9 Makes Presence Felt in Competition for Ad Dollars" in Business Review, Albany New York (October 5, 2007)
Pub: American City Business Journals, Inc.
Ed: Barbara Pinckney. **Description:** The 24-hour news channel Capital News 9 can be watched live by viewers on their cell phones beginning late 2007 or early 2008 as part of a deal between Time Warner Cable and Sprint Nextel Corporation to bring Sprint's Pivot technology. News 9 marked its fifth year and plans to continue expanding coverage and provide better services to viewers.

3685 ■ "AT&T To Acquire Black Telecom Firm" in Black Enterprise (Vol. 38, January 2008, No. 6, pp. 24)
Pub: Earl G. Graves Publishing Co. Inc.
Ed: Alan Hughes. **Description:** Details of AT&T's acquisition of ChaseCom LP, a telecommunications company based in Houston, Texas, are covered.

3686 ■ "Awaiting a Call from Deutsche Telekom" in Barron's (Vol. 90, September 6, 2010, No. 36, pp. M5)
Pub: Barron's Editorial & Corporate Headquarters
Ed: Vito J. Racanelli. **Description:** Deutsche Telekom's (DT) T-Mobile USA Unit has settled in the number four position in the market and the parent company will need to decide if it will hold onto the company in the next 12-18 months from September 2010. T-Mobile's rivals will make critical improvements during this time and DT has the option to upgrade T-Mobile at the cost of improvements to its other units.

3687 ■ "BCE Wireless Growth Flags in Fourth Quarter" in Globe & Mail (February 8, 2007, pp. B5)
Pub: CTVglobemedia Publishing Inc.
Ed: Catherine McLean. **Description:** BCE Inc., the largest telecommunications provider in Canada, reported $699 million profit in the final quarter of 2006. The company signed up 169,000 wireless customers in the important holiday season.

3688 ■ "Bet on China" in Canadian Business (Vol. 80, November 5, 2007, No. 22, pp. 30)
Pub: Rogers Media
Ed: Thomas Watson. **Description:** Former U.S. Federal Reserve Board head, Alan Greenspan, warns that contraction will happen in the Chinese market. However, the economic success of China does not seem to be at the point of ending, as the country remains the largest market for mobile telecommunications. Forecasts for Chinese trading and investments are provided.

3689 ■ "Beyond the RAZR's Edge" in Canadian Business (Vol. 79, November 6, 2006, No. 22, pp. 15)
Pub: Rogers Media
Ed: Andrew Wahl. **Description:** Features of Motorola RAZR, such as low weight and camera accessibility, are presented.

3690 ■ "Big Trouble at Sony Ericsson" in Barron's (Vol. 88, March 24, 2008, No. 12, pp. M9)
Pub: Dow Jones & Company, Inc.
Ed: Angelo Franchini. **Description:** Sony Ericsson is facing trouble as it warned that its sales and net income before taxes will fall by nearly half for the first quarter of 2008. The joint venture of Sony and Ericsson has a global mobile phone market share of nine percent as of 2007, fourth largest in the world.

3691 ■ "Blog Buzz Heralds Arrival of IPhone 2.0" in Advertising Age (Vol. 79, June 9, 2008, No. 40, pp. 8)
Pub: Crain Communications, Inc.
Ed: Abbey Klaasen. **Description:** Predictions concerning the next version of the iPhone include a global-positioning-system technology as well as a configuration to run on a faster, 3G network.

3692 ■ "Bon Voyager" in Entrepreneur (Vol. 36, April 2008, No. 4, pp. 58)
Pub: Entrepreneur Media, Inc.
Ed: Heather Clancy. **Description:** LG Voyager, especially made for Verizon Wireless, is a smart phone that is being compared to Apple iPhone. The Voyager has a 2.8-inch external touchscreen and has a clamshell design, which features an internal keyboard. It does not have Wi-Fi support like iPhone, but it has 3G support. Other differences between the two phones are discussed.

3693 ■ "Boosting Your Merchant Management Services With Wireless Technology" in Franchising World (Vol. 42, August 2010, No. 8, pp. 27)
Pub: International Franchise Association
Ed: Michael S. Slominski. **Description:** Franchises should have the capability to accept credit cards away from their businesses. This technology will increase sales.

3694 ■ "Boots Treat Street Rolls Out Trolley Dash App on Androis and iPhone OS" in Entertainment Close-Up (October 24, 2011)
Pub: Close-Up Media
Description: Shoppers using Boots Treat Street can now download the Trolley Dash app game, available from the Apple Store and the Android Market, and enjoy the pastel colored street featuring favorite retailers such as eBay, New Look and Play.com collecting prizes while avoiding hazards.

3695 ■ "Break Up the Gang?" in Canadian Business (Vol. 81, November 10, 2008, No. 19, pp. 24)
Pub: Rogers Media Ltd.
Ed: Andrew Wahl. **Description:** Nortel Networks Corporation announced they will their Metro Ethernet Network division, suggesting desperation on the part of the company. Some analysts suggest the division is promising, if still unprofitable.

3696 ■ "Broadband Reaches Access Limits in Europe" in Information Today (Vol. 26, February 2009, No. 2, pp. 22)
Pub: Information Today, Inc.
Ed: Jim Ashling. **Description:** Eurostat (the Statistical Office of the European communities) reports results from is survey regarding Internet use by businesses throughout its 27-member states. Iceland, Finland and the Netherlands provide the most access at broadband speeds, followed by Belgium, Spain and France.

3697 ■ "The Business Case for Mobile Content Acceleration" in Streaming Media (November 2011, pp. 78)
Pub: Information Today Inc.
Ed: Dan Rayburn. **Description:** Last holiday season, eBay became a mobile commerce (m-commerce) giant when sales rose by 134 percent, as most online retailers offered customers the ability to purchase items using their mobile devices.

3698 ■ Buyology: Truth and Lies About Why We Buy
Pub: Doubleday, a Division of Random House
Ed: Martin Lindstrom. **Released:** 2009. **Price:** $24.95. **Description:** Marketers study brain scans to determine how consumers rate Nokia, Coke, and Ford products.

3699 ■ *"Call of Prepaid Heard by More" in Chicago Tribune (November 26, 2008)*
Pub: McClatchy-Tribune Information Services

Ed: Wailin Wong. **Description:** Due to the economic downturn, more consumers are switching to no-contract, prepaid cell phone service. Customers find that the cost savings, flexibility and lack of contract are appealing in such uncertain times.

3700 ■ *"Call Them Gorgeous" in Entrepreneur (Vol. 35, October 2007, No. 10, pp. 54)*
Pub: Entrepreneur Media Inc.

Ed: Amanda C. Kooser. **Description:** Smart phones are known for their high technology features, unique names and extraordinary design. Features of the Apple iPhone, Helio Ocean, Blackberry Curve, T-Mobile Wing and Motorola Razr2 V9 are described.

3701 ■ *"Can You Hear Them Now?" in Hawaii Business (Vol. 54, August 2008, No. 2, pp. 48)*
Pub: Hawaii Business Publishing

Ed: Jason Ubay. **Description:** Coral Wireless LLC (dba Mobi PCS) is ranked 237 in Hawaii Business' list of the state's top 250 companies for 2008. The company is a local wireless phone provider, which has expanded its market to Oahu, Maui and the Big Island since opening in 2006, offering 13 phones and unlimited texts and calls. Details on the company's sales are provided.

3702 ■ *"Cell Phone the Ticket on American Airlines" in Chicago Tribune (November 14, 2008)*
Pub: McClatchy-Tribune Information Services

Ed: Julie Johnsson. **Description:** American Airlines is testing a new mobile boarding pass at O'Hare International Airport. Travelers on American can board flights and get through security checkpoints by flashing a bar code on their phones. Passengers must have an Internet-enabled mobile device and an active e-mail address in order to utilize this service.

3703 ■ *Cisco Network Design Solutions for Small-Medium Businesses*
Pub: Cisco Press

Ed: Peter Rybaczyk. **Released:** August 2004. **Price:** $55.00. **Description:** Solutions for computer networking professionals using computer networks within a small to medium-sized business. Topics cover not only core networking issues and solutions, but security, IP telephony, unified communications, customer relations management, wireless LANs, and more.

3704 ■ *"Citizens Unveils Mobile App for Business Customers" in New Hampshire Business Review (Vol. 33, March 25, 2011, No. 6, pp. 27)*
Pub: Business Publications Inc.

Description: Citizens Financial Group offers a new mobile banking application that allows business customers to manage cash and payments from a mobile device.

3705 ■ *"Comcast Launches New Home Security Service, Developed in Portland" in The Oregonian (June 7, 2011)*
Pub: McClatchy-Tribune Regional News

Ed: Mike Rogoway. **Description:** Comcast introduced its new high-end home security system that provides 24-hour monitoring and control of homes and utilities, along with Web and mobile access.

3706 ■ *"Connections: United We Gab" in Entrepreneur (Vol. 35, October 2007, No. 10, pp. 60)*
Pub: Entrepreneur Media Inc.

Ed: Mike Hogan. **Description:** T-Mobile and AT&T introduced dual-mode service to consumers, helping them to switch between cellular and Wi-Fi networks easily. These services, such as Hotspot@Home, reduces the cost of long distance calls by routing them over the Internet with the use of WiFi. Benefits of dual mode service, such as lower hardware price and better call coverage are given.

3707 ■ *"Consumer Electronics: Brick and Mortar Vs. Online" in Retail Merchandiser (Vol. 51, September-October 2011, No. 5, pp. 15)*
Pub: Phoenix Media Corporation

Description: Brick and mortar retailers with Websites are discovering that the Internet is used more for research than purchasing when it comes to electronics products. According to a recent study conducted by The NPD Group shows that 56 percent of consumers research televisions online before purchasing, but only 19 percent actually buy them online.

3708 ■ *"Corporate Elite Face Steep Challenges" in Hispanic Business (January-February 2008, pp. 20, 22, 24, 26, 28, 30, 32)*
Pub: Hispanic Business

Ed: Jonathan Higuera. **Description:** Hispanic men and women are moving up corporate ranks at leading companies in the U.S., including Ralph de la Vega, president and CEO of AT&T Mobility. Profiles of Vega and other Hispanic business leaders are included.

3709 ■ *"Cox Opens Norfolk Mall Kiosk; Wireless Service Not Ready" in Virginian-Pilot (September 20, 2010)*
Pub: Virginian-Pilot

Ed: Carolyn Shapiro. **Description:** Cox Communications opened a kiosk at MacArthur Center that will sell wireless telephone devices and plans.

3710 ■ *"Cyberwise" in Black Enterprise (Vol. 41, December 2010, No. 5, pp. 50)*
Pub: Earl G. Graves Publishing Co. Inc.

Ed: Marica Wade Talbert. **Description:** Information is given regarding single platforms that can be used to develop applications for iPhone, Android, Blackberry, and Nokia.

3711 ■ *"The Data Drivers" in Canadian Business (Vol. 81, September 15, 2008, No. 14-15, pp. 1)*
Pub: Rogers Media Ltd.

Ed: Andrew Wahl. **Description:** Canadian regulators hope that an auction of telecommunications companies will inject more competition into the industry; however, newcomers may not be able to rely on lower prices in order to gain market share from the three major telecommunications companies that already have a stronghold on the market. Analysts feel that providing additional data service is the key to surviving market disruptions.

3712 ■ *"Death of the PC" in Canadian Business (Vol. 83, October 12, 2010, No. 17, pp. 44)*
Pub: Rogers Media Ltd.

Ed: Joe Castaldo. **Description:** The future of the personal computer (PC) is looking bleak as consumers are relying more on new mobile devices instead of their PC. A 'Wall Street Journal' article published in September 2010 reported that the iPad had cannibalized sales of laptops by as much as 50 percent. The emergence of tablet computers running alternative operating systems is also explained.

3713 ■ *"The Digital Revolution is Over. Long Live the Digital Revolution!" in Business Strategy Review (Vol. 21, Spring 2010, No. 1, pp. 74)*
Pub: Wiley-Blackwell

Ed: Gianvito Lanzolla, Jamie Anderson. **Description:** Many businesses are now involved in the digital marketplace. The authors argue that the new reality of numerous companies offering overlapping products means that it is critical for managers to understand digital convergence and to observe the imperatives for remaining competitive.

3714 ■ *"A Direct Approach" in Business Journal-Portland (Vol. 24, November 9, 2007, No. 36, pp. 1)*
Pub: American City Business Journals, Inc.

Ed: Matthew Kish. **Description:** Respond 2 LLC's annual revenue has increased from $14.2 million in 2004 to almost $50 million in 2007. The growth is at-

tributed to a $100 million contract with Vonage. The role of the popularity of infomercials on the success of the Portland-based marketing company is evaluated.

3715 ■ *"Diversity Elite Scorecard" in Hispanic Business (September 2007, pp. 72-74, 76, 78, 80, 82, 84)*
Pub: Hispanic Business

Description: Special report on companies committed to diversity in 2007 is presented along with a brief profile of each company. Southern California Edison and AT&T Inc. topped the list.

3716 ■ *"Don't Hang Up On FairPoint" in Barron's (Vol. 88, July 7, 2008, No. 27, pp. M5)*
Pub: Dow Jones & Co., Inc.

Ed: Fleming Meeks. **Description:** Shares of Fair-Point Communications, priced at $6.63 each, are undervalued and should be worth over $12 each. The company increased its size by more than five times by acquiring Verizon's local telephone operations in Vermont, New Hampshire, and Maine, but must switch customers in those areas into their system by the end of September 2007.

3717 ■ *"Don't' Hate the Cable Guy" in Saint Louis Business Journal (Vol. 31, August 5, 2011, No. 50, pp. 1)*
Pub: Saint Louis Business Journal

Ed: Angela Mueller. **Description:** Charter Communications named John Birrer as senior vice president of customer experience. The company experienced problems with its customer services.

3718 ■ *"Double Duty" in Black Enterprise (Vol. 38, February 2008, No. 7, pp. 56)*
Pub: Earl G. Graves Publishing Co. Inc.

Description: Pantech Wireless is offering its new Duo cellular phone that combines multiple features of a phone with the high speed data functions of a Blackberry-style smartphone.

3719 ■ *"Dow Jones Gives Apple-Loving Sales Professionals a Boost" in Information Today (Vol. 26, February 2009, No. 2, pp. 30)*
Pub: Information Today, Inc.

Description: Dow Jones Sales Triggers for iPhone and iPod program helps sales professionals stay current to prospects and customers in their fields by providing real-time news on business changes, including management moves, mergers, and new investments. The application presents events that trigger best opportunities and allows users to look up companies and executives to retrieve information.

3720 ■ *"Dropped Calls" in Canadian Business (Vol. 80, November 5, 2007, No. 22, pp. 34)*
Pub: Rogers Media

Ed: Andrew Wahl. **Description:** Control over Canada's telecommunications market by Telus, Rogers and Bell Canada has resulted in a small number of innovations. The pricing regimes of these carriers have also stifled innovations in the telecommunications industry. The status of Canada's telecommunications industry is further analyzed.

3721 ■ *"eBay Inc. Completes Acquisition of Zong" in Benzinga.com (October 29, 2011)*
Pub: Benzinga.com

Ed: Benzinga Staff. **Description:** eBay Inc. acquired Zong, a provider of payments through mobile carrier billing. Terms of the agreement are outlined.

3722 ■ *Electronic Commerce*
Pub: Course Technology

Ed: Gary Schneider, Bryant Chrzan, Charles McCormick. **Released:** May 1, 2010. **Price:** $117.95. **Description:** E-commerce can open the door to more opportunities than ever before for small business. Packed with real-world examples and cases, the book delivers comprehensive coverage of emerging online technologies and trends and their influence on the electronic marketplace. It details how the landscape of online commerce is evolving, reflecting changes in the economy and how business and society are responding to those changes. Balancing technological issues with the strategic business aspects of successful e-commerce, the new edition includes expanded coverage of international issues, social networking, mobile commerce, Web 2.0 technologies, and updates on spam, phishing, and identity theft.

3723 ■ *"Etextbook Space Heats Up"* in *Information Today (Vol. 28, November 2011, No. 10, pp. 10)*
Pub: Information Today, Inc.
Ed: Paula J. Hane. **Description:** The use of etextbooks is expected to grow with the use of mobile devices and tablets. A new group of activists is asking students, faculty members and others to sign a petition urging higher education leaders to prioritize affordable textbooks or free ebooks over the traditional, expensive new books required for classes.

3724 ■ *"Executive Decision: To Make Inroads Against RIM, Palm Steals Its Strategy"* in *Globe & Mail (March 25, 2006, pp. B3)*
Pub: CTVglobemedia Publishing Inc.
Ed: Simon Avery. **Description:** The Palm Inc., global leader in portable device manufacturing, is looking forward to improve its sales of Palm Treos, a wireless portable device that connects to internet and email. Palm is also planning to build partnerships, under the efficient management of Michael Moskowitz, general manager and vice-president of Palm Inc., with the other companies to increase the sales of its wireless devices.

3725 ■ *Extraordinary Circumstances: The Journey of a Corporate Whistleblower*
Pub: John Wiley & Sons, Inc.
Ed: Cynthia Cooper. **Released:** 2009. **Price:** $27.95.
Description: Cynthia Cooper offers details of the events that led to the implosion of telecom giant WorldCom.

3726 ■ *"Faster and Shorter"* in *Canadian Business (Vol. 81, October 13, 2008, No. 17, pp. 25)*
Pub: Rogers Media Ltd.
Ed: Terri Goveia. **Description:** Study revealed that instant messaging (IM) technologies are slowly becoming legitimate in the corporate world. IM is traditionally considered as a distraction, but it was found to let workers make targeted inquiries that gives them what they need in an instant. Other views and information about IMs are included.

3727 ■ *"Firm Restricts Cellphone Use While Driving"* in *Globe & Mail (January 30, 2006, pp. B3)*
Pub: CTVglobemedia Publishing Inc.
Ed: Catherine McLean. **Description:** The details on AMEC Plc, which adopted cellphone-free driving policy, are presented.

3728 ■ *"For Apple, It's Showtime Again"* in *Barron's (Vol. 90, August 30, 2010, No. 35, pp. 29)*
Pub: Barron's Editorial & Corporate Headquarters
Ed: Eric J. Savitz. **Description:** Speculations on what Apple Inc. will unveil at its product launch event are presented. These products include a possible new iPhone Nano, a new update to its Apple TV, and possibly a deal with the Beatles to distribute their songs over iTunes.

3729 ■ *"gdgt: The New Online Home for Gadget Fans"* in *Hispanic Business (July-August 2009, pp. 15)*
Pub: Hispanic Business
Ed: Jeremy Nisen. **Description:** Profile of the new online Website for gadget lovers. The site combines a leek interface, gadget database, and social networking-type features which highlights devices for the consumer.

3730 ■ *"Generation Y Chooses the Mobile Web"* in *PR Newswire (November 24, 2010)*
Pub: PR Newswire Association LLC
Description: Generation Y individuals between the ages of 18 - 27 use their mobile phones to browse the Internet more often than a desktop or laptop computer, according to a survey conducted by Opera, a Web browser company.

3731 ■ *"Get Paid and Get Moving"* in *Entrepreneur (Vol. 37, October 2009, No. 10, pp. 38)*
Pub: Entrepreneur Media, Inc.
Description: GoPayments application from Intuit allows mobile telephones to process payments like credit card terminals. The application costs $19.95 a month and can be used on the Internet browsers of mobile telephones.

3732 ■ *"Google Places a Call to Bargain Hunters"* in *Advertising Age (Vol. 79, September 29, 2008, No. 36, pp. 13)*
Pub: Crain Communications, Inc.
Ed: Abbey Klaassen. **Description:** Google highlighted application developers who have created tools for its Android mobile phone in the device's unveiling; applications such as ShopSavvy and CompareEverywhere help shoppers to find bargains by allowing them to compare prices in their local areas and across the web.

3733 ■ *"Growing at the Margins"* in *Business Journal Serving Greater Tampa Bay (Vol. 30, November 5, 2010, No. 46, pp. 1)*
Pub: Tampa Bay Business Journal
Ed: Margie Manning. **Description:** Jabil Circuit Inc. has reported an increase in revenues from its smart phones and medical devices. The company has been focusing on its core services such as making smart phone parts and medical devices.

3734 ■ *"Hewlett-Packard Mini: Ultra-Portable, and Affordable"* in *Hispanic Business (July-August 2009, pp. 36)*
Pub: Hispanic Business
Ed: Jeremy Nisen. **Description:** Hewlett-Packard's 1151 NR computers works a lot like a smartphone online, it can dial up fast speeds on Verizon's 3G network almost anywhere.

3735 ■ *"Hold the IPhone"* in *Canadian Business (Vol. 80, January 15, 2007, No. 2, pp. 22)*
Pub: Rogers Media
Ed: Andrew Wahl. **Description:** The rise in the price of shares of Apple Inc. after the introduction of its new product, the iPhone, is discussed.

3736 ■ *"Hoover's Mobile, MobileSP Now Available"* in *Information Today (Vol. 26, February 2009, No. 2, pp. 29)*
Pub: Information Today, Inc.
Description: Hoover's Inc. introduced its Hoover's Mobile for iPhone, BlackBerry and Windows Mobile smartphones along with Hoover's MobileSP for BlackBerry and Windows Mobile. Both products allow users to access customer, prospect, and partner information; analyze competitors; prepare for meetings; and find new opportunities. In addition, MobileSP adds one-click calling to executives, GPS-enabled location searches, advanced search and list building, and a custom call queue and a 'save to contacts' capabilities.

3737 ■ *"How Dell Will Dial for Dollars"* in *Austin Business JournalInc. (Vol. 29, December 4, 2009, No. 39, pp. 1)*
Pub: American City Business Journals
Ed: Christopher Calnan. **Description:** Dell Inc. revealed plans to launch a Mini3i smartphone in China which could enable revenue sharing by bundling with wireless service subscription. Dell's smartphone plan is similar to the netbook business, which Dell sold with service provided by AT&T Inc.

3738 ■ *"How to Play the Tech Mergers"* in *Barron's (Vol. 90, August 30, 2010, No. 35, pp. 18)*
Pub: Barron's Editorial & Corporate Headquarters
Ed: Tiernan Ray. **Description:** The intense bidding by Hewlett-Packard and Dell for 3Par was foreseen in a previous Barron's cover story and 3Par's stock has nearly tripled since reported. Other possible acquisition targets in the tech industry include Brocade Communication Systems, NetApp, Xyratex, and Isilon Systems.

3739 ■ *"HR Tech on the Go"* in *Workforce Management (Vol. 88, November 16, 2009, No. 12, pp. 1)*
Pub: Crain Communications Inc.
Ed: Ed Frauenheim. **Description:** Examination of the necessity of mobile access of human resources software applications that allow managers to recruit, schedule and train employees via their mobile devices; some industry leaders believe that mobile HR applications are vital while others see this new technology as hype.

3740 ■ *"iControl Networks Powers Comcast's XFINITY (Reg) Home Security Service"* in *Benzinga.com (June 9, 2011)*
Pub: Benzinga.com
Ed: Benzinga Staff. **Description:** Comcast's XFINITY Home Security Service is powered by iControl Networks' OpenHome (TM) software platform. The service provides intrusion and fire protection along with interactive features such as home monitoring, home management, and energy management services with Web and mobile access.

3741 ■ *"Ideas at Work: Total Communicator"* in *Business Strategy Review (Vol. 21, Autumn 2010, No. 3, pp. 10)*
Pub: Wiley-Blackwell
Ed: Stuart Crainer. **Description:** Vittorio Colao has been chief executive of Vodafone Group for two years. He brings to the company some special experience: from 2004-2006 he was CEO of RCS Media-Group in Milan, which publishes newspapers, magazines and books in Italy, Spain and France. Colao shares his views on business, the global economy and leading Vodafone.

3742 ■ *"Impressive Numbers: Companies Experience Substantial Increases in Dollars, Employment"* in *Hispanic Business (July-August 2007)*
Pub: Hispanic Business
Ed: Derek Reveron. **Description:** Profiles of five fastest growing Hispanic companies reporting increases in revenue and employment include Brightstar, distributor of wireless products; Greenway Ford Inc., a car dealership; Fred Loya Insurance, auto insurance carrier; and Group O, packaging company; and Diverse Staffing, Inc., an employment and staffing firm.

3743 ■ *"Internet and Mobile Media"* in *MarketingMagazine (Vol. 115, September 27, 2010, No. 13, pp. 60)*
Pub: Rogers Publishing Ltd.
Description: Market data covering the Internet and mobile media in Canada is given.

3744 ■ *"Into the Groove: Fine-Tune Your Biz By Getting Into the Good Habit Groove"* in *Small Business Opportunities (Spring 2008)*
Pub: Harris Publications Inc.
Description: Profile of Ty Freyvogel and his consulting firm Freyvogel Communications. Freyvogel serves the telecommunications need of Fortune 500 and mid-sized businesses.

3745 ■ *"IPhone 3G"* in *Advertising Age (Vol. 79, November 17, 2008, No. 43, pp. 15)*
Pub: Crain Communications, Inc.
Ed: Beth Snyder Bulik. **Description:** Review of Apple's new iPhone 3G which includes the addition of smart-phone applications as well as a price drop; the new functionalities as well as the lower price seems to be paying off for Apple who reported sales of 6.9 million iPhones in its most recent quarter, in which the 3G hit store shelves.

3746 ■ *"iPhone Apps Big Business"* in *Austin Business JournalInc. (Vol. 28, November 14, 2008, No. 35, pp. 1)*
Pub: American City Business Journals
Ed: Christopher Calnan. **Description:** Members of the computer software industry in Austin, Texas have benefited from developing applications for Apple Inc.'s iPhone. Pangea Software Inc.'s revenues have grown by developing iPhone applications. Lexcycle LLC, on the other hand, has created an application that enables users to read books on the iPhone.

3747 ■ *"The iPhone Gets Some Competition"* in Inc. (Vol. 31, January-February 2009, No. 1, pp. 42)
Pub: Mansueto Ventures LLC
Ed: Mark Spoonauer. **Description:** RIM's BlackBerry Storm and T-Mobile's G1 are competing with the iPhone 3G technology; the three systems are profiled.

3748 ■ *"Israeli Spam Law May Have Global Impact"* in Information Today (Vol. 26, February 2009, No. 2, pp. 28)
Pub: Information Today, Inc.
Ed: David Mirchin. **Description:** Israels new law, called Amendment 40 of the Communications Law, will regulate commercial solicitations including those sent without permission via email, fax, automatic phone dialing systems, or short messaging technologies.

3749 ■ *"It Was a Very Good Year..To Be Ted Rogers"* in Canadian Business (Vol. 80, Winter 2007, No. 24, pp. 121)
Pub: Rogers Media
Ed: Andrew Wahl. **Description:** Ted Rogers had a banner year in 2007 as Rogers Communications Inc. (RCI) took in huge profits from its phone and wireless business and his personal wealth grew sixty-seven percent to $7.6 billion. Rogers has record of betting on technologies that get the best returns relative to the investment in the marketplace such as its use of the GSM network and its cable hybrid fiber coaxial network.

3750 ■ *"It's Not About the G1; Google Just Wants You to Use the Mobile Web"* in Advertising Age (Vol. 79, September 29, 2008, No. 36, pp. 32)
Pub: Crain Communications, Inc.
Ed: Abbey Klaassen. **Description:** Google's Android is the first serious competitor to Apple's iPhone; the company says that its goal is to simplify the mobile market and get wireless subscribers to use the mobile Internet and purchase smartphones.

3751 ■ *"Jump Ship On Your Wireless Contract"* in Black Enterprise (Vol. 38, January 2008, No. 6, pp. 87)
Pub: Earl G. Graves Publishing Co. Inc.
Ed: Nicole Norfleet. **Description:** Better Business Bureau reported it received more than 28,000 complaints in 2007. Four situations that allow consumers to be released from a long-term service contract with a carrier without paying penalty fees are addressed.

3752 ■ *"Kenyans Embrace Moving Money By Text Message"* in Chicago Tribune (October 7, 2008)
Pub: McClatchy-Tribune Information Services
Ed: Laurie Goering. **Description:** Cell phone banking services are becoming more common, especially for foreign residents; customers are able to establish a virtual cell phone bank account through companies such as M-Pesa which allows their customers to pay bills, withdraw cash, pay merchants or text money to relatives.

3753 ■ *"Like All Great Visionaries, Steve Jobs has a Dark Side"* in Canadian Business (Vol. 83, July 20, 2010, No. 11-12, pp. 11)
Pub: Rogers Media Ltd.
Ed: Steve Maich. **Description:** All the adoration piled onto Apple can go to a man's head, especially its CEO Steve Jobs. Jobs is a true visionary but his leadership comes with an autocratic side that is worth watching out for; this is shown by his condescending response to the reported reception problems of the iPhone 4.

3754 ■ *"Look, No Hands!"* in Inc. (Vol. 33, September 2011, No. 7, pp. 52)
Pub: Inc. Magazine
Ed: John Brandon. **Description:** The Jabra Freeway, a small Bluetooth speakerphone clips to a car visor and allows the user to place, answer and ignore calls by speaking commands.

3755 ■ *"Looking Out for the Little Guys"* in Black Enterprise (Vol. 38, October 2007, No. 3, pp. 58)
Pub: Earl G. Graves Publishing Co. Inc.
Ed: Kaylyn Kendall Dines. **Description:** Biz Tech-Connect is a Web portal that offers free online and social networking, along with four modules that help small businesses with marketing and advertising, communications and mobility, financial management, and customer relationship management.

3756 ■ *"Making Visitors Out Of Listeners"* in Hawaii Business (Vol. 54, July 2008, No. 1, pp. 18)
Pub: Hawaii Business Publishing
Ed: Casey Chin. **Description:** Japanese workers are subscribing to the Official Hawaii Podcast in iTunes, which offers a free 20-minute, Japanese-language audio content on different topics, such as dining reviews and music from local artists. The concept is a way to attract Japanese travelers to come to Hawaii.

3757 ■ *"Marketers Push for Mobile Tuesday as the New Black Friday"* in Advertising Age (Vol. 79, December 1, 2008, No. 44, pp. 21)
Pub: Crain Communications, Inc.
Ed: Natalie Zmuda. **Description:** Marketers are using an innovative approach in an attempt to stimulate business on the Tuesday following Thanksgiving by utilizing consumer's cell phones to alert them of sales or present them with coupons for this typically slow retail business day; with this campaign both advertisers and retailers are hoping to start Mobile Tuesday, another profitable shopping day in line with Black Friday and Cyber Monday.

3758 ■ *"Mobile: Juanes Fans Sing for Sprint"* in Advertising Age (Vol. 79, November 3, 2008, No. 41, pp. 22)
Pub: Crain Communications, Inc.
Ed: Laurel Wentz. **Description:** Marketers are appealing to the Hispanic market since they are more prone to use their cell phones to respond to contests, download videos, ringtones, or other data activity. Sprint recently sponsored a contest inviting people to sing like Colombian megastar Juanes; the participants filmed and sent their videos using their cell phones rather than laptops or camcorders illustrating the Hispanic overindex on mobile-phone technology. The contest generated hundreds of thousands of dollars in additional fee revenue, as monthly downloads increased 63 percent.

3759 ■ *"Mobile Marketing Grows With Size of Cell Phone Screens"* in Crain's Detroit Business (Vol. 24, January 14, 2008, No. 2, pp. 13)
Pub: Crain Communications Inc. - Detroit
Ed: Bill Shea. **Description:** Experts are predicting increased marketing for cell phones with the inception of larger screens and improved technology.

3760 ■ *Mobile Office: The Essential Small Business Guide to Office Technology*
Pub: Double Storey Books
Ed: Arthur Goldstruck, Steven Ambrose. **Released:** September 1, 2009. **Price:** $6.95. **Description:** Essential pocket guide for startup businesses and entrepreneurs which provides information to create a mobile office in order to maximize business potential while using current technologies.

3761 ■ *"Mobile Presence, in a Flash: DIY Tools for Creating Smartphone-Friendly Websites"* in Inc. (Vol. 33, November 2011, No. 9, pp. 50)
Pub: Inc. Magazine
Ed: John Brandon. **Description:** DudaMobile and FiddleFly convert regular Websites into mobile sites that work on most smartphones. Profiles of both apps services are included.

3762 ■ *"Mobile Security for Business V5"* in SC Magazine (Vol. 20, August 2009, No. 8, pp. 55)
Pub: Haymarket Media, Inc.
Description: Review of F-Secure's Mobile Security for Business v5 which offers protection for business smartphones that can be centralized for protection monitoring by IT administrators.

3763 ■ *"Mobility: So Happy Together"* in Entrepreneur (Vol. 35, October 2007, No. 10, pp. 64)
Pub: Entrepreneur Media Inc.
Ed: Heather Clancy. **Description:** Joshua Burnett, CEO and founder of 9ci, uses index cards to keep track of what he needs to do despite the fact that he has a notebook computer, cell phone and PDA. Kim Hahn, a media entrepreneur, prefers jotting her ideas down in a spiral notebook, has a team that would organize her records for her, and a personal assistant that would keep track of changes to her schedule. Reasons why these entrepreneurs use old-fashioned methods along with new technology are given.

3764 ■ *"Moosylvania Releases Latest XL Marketing Trends Report"* in Wireless News (October 6, 2009)
Pub: Close-Up Media
Description: Moosylvania, a digital promotion and branding agency that also has an on-site research facility, has released its 2nd XL Marketing Trends Report which focuses on digital video; the study defines the top digital video trends marketers must focus on now and well into the future and notes that in 2010, Mobile Web Devices, such as smart phones will outnumber computers in this country. Statistical data included.

3765 ■ *"More Callers Are Cutting Their Landlines"* in Chicago Tribune (December 30, 2008)
Pub: McClatchy-Tribune Information Services
Ed: Eric Benderoff. **Description:** Despite sporadic outages for cell phone users, the trend for consumers to cut out the expense of a landline does not appear to be slowing; experts believe that the recession will further increase the number of consumers who decide to go completely wireless.

3766 ■ *"A Motorola Spinoff Is No Panacea"* in Barron's (Vol. 88, March 31, 2008, No. 13, pp. 19)
Pub: Dow Jones & Company, Inc.
Ed: Mark Veverka. **Description:** Motorola's plan to try and spinoff their handset division is bereft of details as to how or specifically when in 2009 the spinoff would occur. There's no reason to buy the shares since there's a lot of execution risk to the plan. Motorola needs to hire a proven cellphone executive and develop a compelling new cellphone platform.

3767 ■ *"Motorola's New Cell Phone Lineup Includes Green Effort"* in Chicago Tribune (January 14, 2009)
Pub: McClatchy-Tribune Information Services
Ed: Eric Benderoff. **Description:** Motorola Inc. introduced a new line of mobile phones at the Consumer Electronics Show in Las Vegas; the phones are made using recycled water bottles for the plastic housing.

3768 ■ *"My Favorite Tool for Managing Expenses"* in Inc. (Volume 32, December 2010, No. 10, pp. 60)
Pub: Inc. Magazine
Ed: J.J. McCorvey. **Description:** Web-based service called Expensify is outlined. The service allows companies to log expenses while away from the office using the service's iPhone application.

3769 ■ *"My Favorite Tool for Organizing Data"* in Inc. (Vol. 33, November 2011, No. 9, pp. 46)
Pub: Inc. Magazine
Ed: Abram Brown. **Description:** Intelligence software firm uses Roambi, a Web-based service that turns spreadsheet data into interactive files for iPhones and iPads.

3770 ■ *"Naked Ambitions Put Telus on the Spot"* in Globe & Mail (February 6, 2007, pp. B3)
Pub: CTVglobemedia Publishing Inc.
Ed: Catherine McLean. **Description:** The offering of pornographic content on mobile phones by the telecommunications company Telus Corp., is discussed.

3771 ■ *"The New Basics of Marketing" in Inc. (February 2008, pp. 75-81)*
Pub: Gruner & Jahr USA Publishing
Ed: Leigh Buchanan. **Description:** New tools for marketing a business or service include updating or upgrading a Website, using email or texting, or advertising on a social Internet network.

3772 ■ *"The New Guard" in Entrepreneur (Vol. 36, February 2008, No. 2, pp. 46)*
Pub: Entrepreneur Media Inc.
Ed: Amanda C. Kooser. **Description:** A natural language search engine is being developed by Powerset for better online searching. Zannel Inc. offers Instant Media Messaging platform, which allows for social networking using phones. Ning is an online platform that allows users to customize and control their social networks.

3773 ■ *"New IPhone Also Brings New Way of Mobile Marketing" in Advertising Age (Vol. 79, June 16, 2008, No. 24, pp. 23)*
Pub: Crain Communications, Inc.
Ed: Abbey Klaasen. **Description:** Currently there are two kinds of applications for the iPhone and other mobile devices: native applications that allow for richer experiences and take advantage of features that are built into a phone and web applications, those that allow access to the web through specific platforms. Marketers are interested in creating useful experiences for customers and opening up the platforms which will allow them to do this.

3774 ■ *"New Sprint Phone Whets Appetite for Applications" in The Business Journal-Serving Metropolitan Kansas City (Vol. 26, July 25, 2008)*
Pub: American City Business Journals, Inc.
Ed: Suzanna Stagemeyer. **Description:** Firms supporting the applications of the new Samsung Instinct, which was introduced by Sprint Nextel Corp. in June 2008, have reported usage rates increase for their products. Handmark, whose mobile services Pocket Express comes loaded with Instinct, has redirected employees to meet the rising demand for the services. Other views and information on Instinct, are presented.

3775 ■ *"New Ways To Think About Data Loss: Data Loss Is Costly and Painful" in Franchising World (Vol. 42, August 2010, No. 8, pp. 21)*
Pub: International Franchise Association
Ed: Ken Colburn. **Description:** Information for maintaining data securely for franchised organizations, including smart phones, tablets, copiers, computers and more is given.

3776 ■ *"New Year's Resolutions: How Three Companies Came Up With Their 2008 Growth Strategies" in Inc. (January 2008, pp. 47-49)*
Pub: Gruner & Jahr USA Publishing
Ed: Martha C. White. **Description:** Three companies share 2008 growth strategies; companies include a candle company, a voice mail and text messaging marketer, and hotel supplier of soap and shampoo.

3777 ■ *"The Next Generation of Bluetooth Headsets" in Inc. (Vol. 31, January-February 2009, No. 1, pp. 41)*
Pub: Mansueto Ventures LLC
Ed: Mark Spoonauer. **Description:** Information on the latest Bluetooth headsets that allow users to talk hands-free and the new technology that blocks ambient sounds is given. Aliph Jawbone, Plantronics Voyager Jabra BT530, and Motorola Motopure H15 are profiled.

3778 ■ *"Nine Sectors to Watch: Telecom" in Canadian Business (Vol. 81, December 24, 2007, No. 1, pp. 44)*
Pub: Rogers Media
Ed: Andrew Wahl. **Description:** Forecasts on the Canadian telecommunications industry for 2008 are presented. Details on consumer spending growth, the popularity of broadband, and activities in the wireless sector are also discussed.

3779 ■ *The Nokia Revolution: The Story of an Extraordinary Company That Transformed an Industry*
Pub: AMACOM
Ed: Dan Steinbock. **Released:** May 31, 2001. **Description:** Profile of Nokia, the world's largest wireless communications company. Nokia started in 1865 in rural Finland and merged its rubber company and a cabling firm to form the corporation around 1965. The firm's corporate strategy in the mobile communications industry is highlighted.

3780 ■ *"Note-Taking App, Supercharged" in Inc. (Vol. 33, October 2011, No. 8, pp. 48)*
Pub: Inc. Magazine
Ed: Adam Baer. **Description:** Note Taker HD is an iPad app that lets the user text by typing with finger or stylus with various colors, fonts and sizes; Extensive Notes creates notes, records audio memos, and takes photos and videos; Evernote allows users to create notes, take snapshots, and record voice memos.

3781 ■ *"One Charger, Many Devices: the Skinny on Wireless Power Pads" in Inc. (Volume 32, December 2010, No. 10, pp. 58)*
Pub: Inc. Magazine
Ed: John Brandon. **Description:** Wireless charging pads eliminate the need for multiple cords and wall outlets. Powermat 2X, Energizer Q1, Pure Energy Solutions Wildcharge Pad, and Curacell mygrid are profiled.

3782 ■ *"Online Translation Service Aids Battlefield Troops" in Product News Network (August 30, 2011)*
Pub: Thomas Publishing Company
Description: Linquist online service, LinGo Link provides real-time interpreter support to military troops overseas. Interpreters skilled in multiple languages and dialects are used in various areas and in multiple instances without requiring physical presence. The service is available through commercial cellular or WiFi services or tactical communications network. The system accommodates exchange of audio, video, photos, and text during conversations via smartphones and mobile peripheral devices.

3783 ■ *"Our Gadget of the Week: Mostly, I Liked It" in Barron's (Vol. 88, July 14, 2008, No. 28, pp. 31)*
Pub: Dow Jones & Co., Inc.
Ed: Jay Palmer. **Description:** Review of the Apple iPhone 3G, which costs $199, has better audio and is slightly thicker than its predecessor; using the 3G wireless connection makes going online faster but drains the battery faster too.

3784 ■ *"Our Hoarder Mentality: Blame the Hard Disk" in PC Magazine (Vol. 30, November 2011, No. 11, pp. 46)*
Pub: Ziff-Davis Inc.
Contact: Vivek Shah, Chief Executive Officer
Ed: John C. Dvorak. **Description:** Computer programmers, once referred to as computer users, are slowly being replaced by passive consumers of products and content of tablets and handheld mobile phones and devices of the future. Understanding is garnered as this article examines this industry trend.

3785 ■ *"Play By Play: These Video Products Can Add New Life to a Stagnant Website" in Black Enterprise (Vol. 41, December 2010, No. 5)*
Pub: Earl G. Graves Publishing Co. Inc.
Ed: Marcia Wade Talbert. **Description:** Web Visible, provider of online marketing products and services, cites video capability as the fastest-growing Website feature for small business advertisers. Profiles of various devices for adding video to a Website are included.

3786 ■ *Power Up Your Small-Medium Business: A Guide to Enabling Network Technologies*
Pub: Cisco Press
Ed: Robyn Aber. **Released:** March 2004. **Price:** $39.95 (US), $57.95 (Canadian). **Description:** Network technologies geared to small and medium-

size business, focusing on access, IP telephony, wireless technologies, security, and computer network management.

3787 ■ *Practical Tech for Your Business*
Pub: Kiplinger Books and Tapes
Ed: Michael J. Martinez. **Released:** 2002. **Description:** Advice is offered to help small business owners choose the right technology for their company. The guide tells how to get started, network via the Internet, create an office network, use database software, and conduct business using mobile technology.

3788 ■ *"Prepaid Phones Surge in Bad Economy" in Advertising Age (Vol. 79, November 17, 2008, No. 43, pp. 6)*
Pub: Crain Communications, Inc.
Ed: Rita Chang. **Description:** Prepay cell phone offerings are becoming increasingly competitive amid a greater choice of plans and handsets. In an economic environment in which many consumers are unable to pass the credit checks required for traditional cell phone plans, the prepay market is surging.

3789 ■ *"Presidential Address: Innovation in Retrospect and Prospect" in Canadian Journal of Electronics (Vol. 43, November 2010, No. 4)*
Pub: Journal of the Canadian Economics Association
Ed: James A. Brander. **Description:** Has innovation slowed in recent decades? While there has been progress in information and communications technology, the recent record of innovation in agriculture, energy, transportation and healthcare sectors is cause for concern.

3790 ■ *"Providing Expertise Required to Develop Microsystems" in Canadian Electronics (Vol. 23, February 2008, No. 1, pp. 6)*
Pub: CLB Media Inc.
Ed: Ian McWalter. **Description:** CMC Microsystems, formerly Canadian Microelectronics Corporation, is focused on empowering microelectronics and Microsystems research in Canada. Microsystems offers the basis for innovations in the fields of science, environment, technology, automotives, energy, aerospace and communications technology. CMC's strategy in developing Microsystems in Canada is described.

3791 ■ *"Publishing Technology Introduces IngentaConnect Mobile" in Information Today (Vol. 26, February 2009, No. 2, pp. 33)*
Pub: Information Today, Inc.
Description: College undergraduates will find Publishing Technology's newest publisher product, IngentaConnect Mobile helpful. The product allows users to read articles and abstracts on mobile devices. According to a recent study, 73 percent of young adults with wireless hand-held devices use them to access non-voice data on any given day.

3792 ■ *"Put a Projector in Your Pocket" in Inc. (Vol. 31, January-February 2009, No. 1, pp. 42)*
Pub: Mansueto Ventures LLC
Description: PowerPoint presentations can be given using the Optoma Pico Pocket Projector. The device can be connected to laptops, cell phones, digital cameras, and iPods.

3793 ■ *"Putting the App in Apple" in Inc. (Vol. 30, November 2008, No. 11, pp.)*
Pub: Mansueto Ventures LLC
Ed: Nitasha Tiku. **Description:** Aftermarket companies are scrambling to develop games and widgets for Apple's iPhone. Apple launched a kit for developers interested in creating iPhone-specific software along with the App Store, and an iTunes spinoff. Profiles of various software programs that may be used on the iPhone are given.

3794 ■ *"Q&A Patrick Pichette" in Canadian Business (Vol. 81, October 13, 2008, No. 17, pp. 6)*
Pub: Rogers Media Ltd.
Ed: Andrew Wahl. **Description:** Patrick Pichette finds challenge in taking over the finances of an Internet company that has a market cap of about $140 billion.

He feels, however, that serving as Google's chief financial officer is nothing compared to running Bell Canada Enterprises (BCE). Pichette's other views on Google and BCE are presented.

3795 ■ *"Qualcomm Could Win Big as the IPhone 3G Calls" in Barron's (Vol. 88, July 4, 2008, No. 28, pp. 30)*
Pub: Dow Jones & Co., Inc.

Ed: Eric J. Savitz. **Description:** Apple iPhone 3G's introduction could widen the smartphone market thereby benefiting handset chipmaker Qualcomm in the process. Qualcomm Senior V.P., Bill Davidson sees huge potential for his company's future beyond phones with their Snapdragon processor. The prospects of Sun Microsystems' shares are also discussed.

3796 ■ *"Quickoffice's MobileFiles Pro App Enables Excel Editing On-the-Go" in Information Today (Vol. 26, February 2009, No. 2, pp. 31)*
Pub: Information Today, Inc.

Description: Quickoffice Inc. introduced MobileFiles Pro, which features editable Microsoft Office functionality for the iPone and iPod touch. The application allows users to edit and save Microsoft Excel files in .xls format, transfer files to and from PC and Mac desktops via Wi-Fi, and access and synchronize with Apple MobileMe accounts.

3797 ■ *"Remote Control: Working From Wherever" in Inc. (February 2008, pp. 46-47)*
Pub: Gruner & Jahr USA Publishing

Ed: Ryan Underwood. **Description:** New technology allows workers to perform tasks from anywhere via the Internet. Profiles of products to help connect to your office from afar include, LogMein Pro, a Web-based service that allowsaccess to a computer from anywhere; Xdrive, an online service that allows users to store and swap files; Basecamp, a Web-based tools that works like a secure version of MySpace; MojoPac Freedom, is software that allows users to copy their computer's desktop to a removable hard drive and plug into any PC; WatchGuard Firebox X Core e-Series UTM Bundle, hardware that blocks hackers and viruses while allowing employees to work remotely; TightVNC, a free open-source software that lets you control another computer via the Internet.

3798 ■ *"Research and Markets Adds Report: The U.S. Mobile Web Market" in Entertainment Close-Up (December 10, 2009)*
Pub: Close-Up Media

Description: Highlights of the new Research and Markets report 'The U.S. Mobile Web Market: Taking Advantage of the iPhone Phenomenon' include: mobile Internet marketing strategies; the growth of mobile web usage; the growth of revenue in the mobile web market; and a look at Internet business communications, social media and networking.

3799 ■ *"RIM Opts to Be Little Less Open" in Canadian Business (Vol. 83, October 12, 2010, No. 17, pp. 13)*
Pub: Rogers Media Ltd.

Ed: Joe Castaldo. **Description:** RIM is planning to stop releasing quarterly subscriber updates. However, some analysts are skeptical about the change due to the previous drop in company subscribers. The company also decided to stop reporting the average selling price of the BlackBerry, which analysts have also scrutinized.

3800 ■ *"Rough and Ready: Putting Rugged Phones to the Test" in Inc. (Vol. 33, November 2011, No. 9, pp. 45)*
Pub: Inc. Magazine

Ed: John Brandon. **Description:** Smartphones were roughed up in order to discover their durability. Tests involved the Casio G'Zone Commando, the Sonim XP3300 Force, Motorola Titaniu, and the Samsung Convoy 2.

3801 ■ *"Sales Communications in a Mobile World" in Business Communication Quarterly (December 2007, pp. 492)*
Pub: SAGE Publications USA

Contact: Blaise R. Simqu, President

Ed: Daniel T. Norris. **Description:** Salespeople can take advantage of the latest mobile technologies while maintaining a personal touch with clients and customers through innovation, formality in interactions, client interactions, and protection and security of mobile data.

3802 ■ *"Samsung's Metamorphosis" in Austin Business Journal (Vol. 31, May 20, 2011, No. 11, pp. 1)*
Pub: American City Business Journals Inc.

Ed: Christopher Calnan. **Description:** Samsung Austin Semiconductor LP, a developer of semiconductors for smartphones and tablet computers, plans to diversify its offerings to include niche products: flash memory devices and microprocessing devices. In light of this strategy, Samsung Austin will be hiring 300 engineers as part of a $3.6 billion expansion of its plant.

3803 ■ *"Show and Tell" in Entrepreneur (Vol. 36, May 2008, No. 5, pp. 54)*
Pub: Entrepreneur Media, Inc.

Ed: Heather Clancy. **Description:** FreshStart Telephone uses recorded video testimonials of customers, by using Pure Digital Flip Video that downloads content directly to the computer, and uploads it in the company's website to promote their wireless phone service.

3804 ■ *"Skype Ltd. Acquired GroupMe" in Information Today (Vol. 28, October 2011, No. 9, pp. 12)*
Pub: Information Today, Inc.

Description: Skype Ltd. acquired GroupMe, a group messaging company that allows users to form impromptu groups where they can text message, share data, and make conference calls for free and is supported on Android, iPhone, BlackBerry, and Windows phones.

3805 ■ *"Skype on Steroids" in Inc. (Vol. 31, January-February 2009, No. 1, pp. 46)*
Pub: Mansueto Ventures LLC

Ed: Nitasha Tiku. **Description:** Free software called VoxOx allows users to make calls over the Internet and connects all email and IM accounts.

3806 ■ *"A Socko Payout Menu: Rural Phone Carrier Plots to Supercharge Its Shares" in Barron's (Vol. 88, June 30, 2008, No. 26, pp. M5)*
Pub: Dow Jones & Co., Inc.

Ed: Shirley A. Lazo. **Description:** CenturyTel boosted its quarterly common payout to 70 cents from 6.75 cents per share die to its strong cash flows and solid balance sheet. Eastman Kodak's plan for a buyback will be partially funded by its $581 million tax refund. CME Group will buyback stocks through 2009 worth $1.1 billion.

3807 ■ *"Sprint Tries to Wring Out Positives" in The Business Journal-Serving Metropolitan Kansas City (Vol. 26, August 8, 2008, No. 48)*
Pub: American City Business Journals, Inc.

Ed: Suzanna Stagemeyer. **Description:** Sprint Nextel Corp. reported that 901,000 subscribers left the company in the quarter ending June 30, 2008; fewer than the nearly 1.1 million it lost in the previous quarter. Customer turnover also dropped to just less than 2 percent, compared to 2.45 percent in the first quarter of 2008.

3808 ■ *"Startup to Serve Bar Scene" in Austin Business JournalInc. (Vol. 29, December 18, 2009, No. 41, pp. 1)*
Pub: American City Business Journals

Ed: Christopher Calnan. **Description:** Startup ATX Innovation Inc. of Austin, Texas has developed a test version of TabbedOut, a Web-based tool that would facilitate mobile phone-based restaurant and bar bill payment. TabbedOut has been tested by six businesses in Austin and will be available to restaurant and bar owners for free. Income would be generated by ATX through a 99-cent convenience charge per transaction.

3809 ■ *"State Efforts to Boost Contract Efficiency Hurt Smaller Firms" in Boston Business Journal (Vol. 27, November 9, 2007, No. 41, pp. 1)*
Pub: American City Business Journals Inc.

Ed: Lisa van der Pool. **Description:** Massachusetts Operational Services Division, which provides statewide telecommunications and data infrastructure contracts, announced that it is cutting the list of companies on the new contract from twelve to six. The cost-cutting efforts began in 2005, after a review by an independent consultant advised the state to adopt strategies that would save millions of dollars.

3810 ■ *"Stay in Touch, Wherever You Roam: Smartphones for Overseas Travel" in Inc. (Volume 32, December 2010, No. 10, pp. 60)*
Pub: Inc. Magazine

Description: International cell phones services are profiled, including HTC Aria, Nokia E73 Mode, Samsung Captivate, and Blackberry Bold 9650.

3811 ■ *"Strictly Business" in Black Enterprise (Vol. 38, October 2007, No. 3, pp. 62)*
Pub: Earl G. Graves Publishing Co. Inc.

Description: Profile of the HP iPAQ hw6925 smartphone suited to small business use. The phone offers mobile word processing and messaging features great for the tech-savvy business traveler.

3812 ■ *"Study: Instant Messaging Can Benefit Workplaces" in HRMagazine (Vol. 53, August 2008, No. 8, pp. 20)*
Pub: Society for Human Resource Management

Contact: Henry G. Jackson, President

E-mail: hjackson@shrm.org

Description: Using text messaging at work is less, not more disruptive, even as it promotes more frequent communication, according to a study published in the Journal of Compute-Mediated Communication.

3813 ■ *"Tale of the Tape: IPhone Vs. G1" in Advertising Age (Vol. 79, October 27, 2008, No. 40, pp. 6)*
Pub: Crain Communications, Inc.

Ed: Rita Chang. **Description:** T-Mobile's G1 has been positioned as the first serious competitor to Apple's iPhone. G1 is the first mobile phone to run on the Google-backed, open-source platform Android.

3814 ■ *"Tap the iPad and Mobile Internet Device Market" in Franchising World (Vol. 42, September 2010, No. 9, pp. 43)*
Pub: International Franchise Association

Ed: John Thomson. **Description:** The iPad and other mobile Internet devices will help franchise owners interact with customers. It will be a good marketing tool for these businesses.

3815 ■ *"Technology Drivers to Boost Your Bottom Line" in Franchising World (Vol. 42, August 2010, No. 8, pp. 15)*
Pub: International Franchise Association

Ed: Dan Dugal. **Description:** Technological capabilities are expanding quickly and smart franchises should stay updated on all the new developments, including smart phones, global positioning systems, and social media networks.

3816 ■ *Telecommunications Directory*
Pub: Cengage Learning Inc.

Contact: Ronald Dunn, President

URL(s): www.gale.cengage.comhttp://www.gale.cengage.com/servlet/BrowseSeriesServlet?region=9&imprint=000&cf=es&titleCode=CSSG&edition=. **Released:** Annual; Latest edition 23rd; April, 2012. **Price:** $993, Individuals. **Covers:** Two volumes-North America and International, Cover approximately 6,000 national and international voice and data communications networks, electronic mail services, teleconferencing facilities and services, facsimile services, Internet access providers, videotex and teletext operations, transactional services, local area networks, audiotex services, microwave systems/networkers, satellite facilities, and others involved in telecommunications, including related consultants, advertisers/marketers; associations, regulatory bodies, and publishers. **Entries include:** Company or organization name, address, phone, fax, year established, name and title of contact, executive officers and board of directors, function or type of service; geographical area served; NAICS and SIC codes; number of employees; general description, including telecommunications-related activities; product/ service; specific applications; means of access and equipment required; publications; intended market and availability; pricing; stock exchanges traded and ticker symbols; financial figures. **Database includes:** Extensive glossary of terms, acronyms, and concepts. **Arrangement:** Alphabetical by company name; within geographic region. **Indexes:** Name of firm/acronym, personal name, geographical (with name, address, phone, and director), and function/type of service (with name, address, phone). Indexes are cumulative. **Availability:** Online: Cengage Learning Inc. **Type:** Directory.

3817 ■ *"TELUS Drawing More Power From Its Wireless Operations" in Globe & Mail (February 17, 2007, pp. B3)*
Pub: CTVglobemedia Publishing Inc.

Ed: Catherine McLean. **Description:** TELUS Corp., the fast-growing wireless business company, posted tripled profits in the fourth quarter of 2006. The revenues of the company increased 8 percent in the same period.

3818 ■ *"Titan to Become New York's Largest Provider of Phone Kiosk Advertising" in Marketing Weekly News (September 11, 2010, pp. 150)*
Pub: VerticalNews

Description: Titan will acquire from Verizon 1,900 payphones at 1,300 phone kiosk locations in New York City, New York. This transaction will triple the firm's inventory of New York Phone Kiosk media to over 5,000 advertising faces. Details are included.

3819 ■ *"Top IPhone Apps" in Advertising Age (Vol. 79, December 15, 2008, No. 46, pp. 17)*
Pub: Crain Communications, Inc.

Ed: Marissa Miley. **Description:** Free and low cost applications for the iPhone are described including Evernote, an application that allows users to outsource their memory to keep track of events, notes, ides and more; Handshake, a way for users to exchange business cards and pictures across Wi-Fi and 3G; CityTransit, an interactive map of the New York subway system that uses GPS technology to find nearby stations and also tells the user if a train is out of commission that day; and Stage Hand which allows users to deliver a presentation, control timing and slide order on the spot.

3820 ■ *"A Torch in the Darkness" in Canadian Business (Vol. 83, August 17, 2010, No. 13-14, pp. 66)*
Pub: Rogers Media Ltd.

Ed: Joe Castaldo. **Description:** Research In Motion (RIM) unveiled the BlackBerry Touch, featuring a touch screen as well as a physical keyboard, in an attempt to repel competitors and expand share in the consumer smart phone market. RIM shares have fallen 43 percent from its peak in 2009.

3821 ■ *"Touch and Go" in Black Enterprise (Vol. 38, January 2008, No. 6, pp. 46)*
Pub: Earl G. Graves Publishing Co. Inc.

Ed: Anthony Calypso. **Description:** Profile of HTC Touch Smartphone, which operates on the Windows Mobile 6 Pro platform. The phone is about the size of a credit card and weighs less than four ounces and can connect to Bluetooth, GSM/GPRS/EDGE/Wi-Fi.

3822 ■ *"Turnaround Plays: The Return of Wi-LAN" in Canadian Business (Vol. 80, January 29, 2007, No. 3, pp. 68)*
Pub: Rogers Media

Ed: Joe Castaldo. **Description:** The recovery of the wireless equipment manufacturing firm Wi-LAN from near-bankruptcy, under the leadership of Jim Skippen, is described.

3823 ■ *"U.S. Enters BlackBerry Dispute Compromise Sought Over Security Issues" in*

Houston Chronicle (August 6, 2010)
Pub: Houston Chronicle

Ed: Matthew Lee. **Description:** U.S. State Department is working for a compromise with Research in Motion, manufacturer of the BlackBerry, over security issues. The Canadian company makes the smartphones and foreign governments believe they pose a security risk.

3824 ■ *"Uniting Spring in OP Could Reduce Static" in Business Journal-Serving Metropolitan Kansas City (October 19, 2007)*
Pub: American City Business Journals, Inc.

Ed: Jim Davis, Steve Vockrodt. **Description:** Sprint Nextel, the result of Sprint Corporation and Nextel Communications Inc. has been using Nextel's Reston office as corporate headquarters. The consolidation of Sprint Nextel's headquarters is expected to result in saving on cost of living and leases. The benefits of choosing Kansas City as the headquarters are evaluated.

3825 ■ *"VeriFone Announces Global Security Solutions Business" in Marketing Weekly News (October 3, 2009)*
Pub: Investment Weekly News

Description: Focused on delivering innovative security solutions, VeriFone Holdings, Inc. announced the formation of its Global Security Solutions Business Unit, including VeriShield Protect, an end-to-end encryption to protect cardholder data throughout the merchant and processor systems. The business will focus on consulting, sales and implementation of these new products in order to help retailers and processors protect customer data.

3826 ■ *"Verizon Comes Calling With 500 Jobs" in Business First Columbus (Vol. 25, September 15, 2008, No. 4, pp. 1)*
Pub: American City Business Journals

Ed: Brian R. Ball. **Description:** Hilliard, Ohio offered Verizon Wireless a 15-year incentive package worth $3.4 million for the company to move 300 customer financial services jobs to the city in addition to the 200 jobs from their facility in Dublin, Ohio. The incentives include a return of 15 percent of the income tax generated by the jobs.

3827 ■ *"Verizon Small Business Awards Give Companies a Technology Edge" in Hispanic Business (July-August 2009, pp. 32)*
Pub: Hispanic Business

Ed: Patricia Marroquin. **Description:** Verizon Wireless awards grants to twenty-four companies in California. The winning businesses ranged from barbershop to coffee shop, tattoo parlor to florist.

3828 ■ *"Verizon, Union Dispute is a Vestige of the Past" in Philadelphia Business Journal (Vol. 30, August 26, 2011, No. 28, pp. 1)*
Pub: American City Business Journals Inc.

Ed: Peter Key. **Description:** Verizon is arguing that some of the provisions of its unionized workers' contracts date back to the days before AT&T were forced to spin off its local phone-service providers in 1984. The evolution of Verizon through the years and its relations with its unions are discussed.

3829 ■ *"Vonage V-Phone: Use Your Laptop to Make Calls Via the Internet" in Black Enterprise (Vol. 37, January 2007, No. 6, pp. 52)*
Pub: Earl G. Graves Publishing Co. Inc.

Ed: James C. Johnson. **Description:** Overview of the Vonage V-Phone, which is small flash drive device that lets you make phone calls through a high-speed Internet connection and plugs into any computer's USB port. Business travels may find this product to be a wonderful solution as it includes 250MB of memory and can store files, digital photos, MP3s, and more.

3830 ■ *"Wattles Plugs Back Into State" in Business Journal Portland (Vol. 27, November 19, 2010, No. 38, pp. 1)*
Pub: Portland Business Journal

Ed: Wendy Culverwell. **Description:** Denver, Colorado-based Ultimate Electronics Inc.'s first store in Oregon was opened in Portland and the 46th store

in the chain of electronic superstores is expected to employ 70-80 workers. The venture is the latest for Mark Wattles, one of Oregon's most successful entrepreneurs, who acquired Ultimate from bankruptcy.

3831 ■ *"Weathering the BlackBerry Storm" in Hispanic Business (January-February 2009, pp. 52)*
Pub: Hispanic Business

Ed: Jeremy Nisen. **Description:** Profile of BlackBerry Storm, the smartphone from Research in Motion.

3832 ■ *"Why-Max?" in Canadian Business (Vol. 81, July 22, 2008, No. 12-13, pp. 19)*
Pub: Rogers Media Ltd.

Ed: Andrew Wahl. **Description:** Nascent technology known as LTE (Long Term Evolution) is expected to challenge Intel's WiMax wireless technology as the wireless broadband standard. LTE , which is believed to be at least two years behind WiMax in development, is likely to be supported by wireless and mobile-phone carriers. Views and information on WiMax and LTE are presented.

3833 ■ *"Will mCommerce Make Black Friday Green?" in Retail Merchandiser (Vol. 51, September-October 2011, No. 5, pp. 8)*
Pub: Phoenix Media Corporation

Ed: Scott Miller. **Description:** Retailers speculate the possibilities of mobile commerce and are implementing strategies at their stores. Consumers using mobile devices accounted for only 0.1 percent of visits to retail Websites on Black Friday 2009 and rose to 5.6 percent in 2010; numbers are expected to rise for 2011.

3834 ■ *"Wireless: Full Service" in Entrepreneur (Vol. 35, October 2007, No. 10, pp. 60)*
Pub: Entrepreneur Media Inc.

Ed: Amanda C. Kooser. **Description:** Palm Foleo, the $599 smart phone enables users to access and compose email, browse the Internet, view documents and play Powerpoint files. It weighs 2.5 pounds and has a 10-inch screen. Other features, such as built-in WiFi are described.

3835 ■ *"A Wireless Makes 8 Store-In-Store Kiosk Acquisitions" in Wireless News (October 16, 2010)*
Pub: Close-Up Media Inc.

Description: A Wireless, a retailer for Verizon Wireless has acquired eight of Verizon's retail kiosks that are positioned in home appliance and electronics stores.

3836 ■ *"Wireless Provider's Star Grows $283 Million Brighter" in Hispanic Business (July-August 2007, pp. 60)*
Pub: Hispanic Business

Description: Profile of Brightstar Corporation, the world's largest wireless phone distribution and supply chain reported record growth in 2007.

3837 ■ *"Words at Work" in Information Today (Vol. 26, February 2009, No. 2, pp. 25)*
Pub: Information Today, Inc.

Description: Current new buzzwords include the following: digital amnesia, or overload by availability, speed and volume of digital information; maternal profiling, a form a discrimination against women; recipe malpractice, a reminder that just because you can turn on a stove it doesn't make you a chef; ringxiety, the act when everyone reaches for their cell phone when one rings; verbing, the practice of turning good nouns into verbs.

STATISTICAL SOURCES

3838 ■ *RMA Annual Statement Studies*
Pub: Risk Management Association
Contact: Kevin M. Blakey, President

Released: Annual. **Price:** $175.00 2006-07 edition, $105.00. **Description:** Contains composite balance sheets and income statements for more than 360 industries, including the accounting, auditing, and bookkeeping industries. Also contains five years of comparative historical data for discerning trends. Includes 16 commonly used ratios, computed for most of the size groupings for nearly every industry.

3839 ■ *Standard & Poor's Industry Surveys*

Pub: Standard & Poor's Corp.

Released: Annual. **Price:** $3633.00. **Description:** Two-volume book that examines the prospects for specific industries, including trucking. Also provides analyses of trends and problems, statistical tables and charts, and comparative company analyses.

3840 ■ *Wireless Communications*

Pub: Business Communications Co., Inc.

Released: 1993. **Price:** $2250.00. **Description:** Report analyzing and forecasting the market for wireless frequencies transmitting voice and data to 1997. Covers wireless LANS, cellular data/voice, wireless WANS/MANS, pagers, and wireless PBX/Centrex.

TRADE PERIODICALS

3841 ■ *1394 Newsletter*

Pub: Information Gatekeepers Inc.

Ed: Paul Polishuk, Editor. **Released:** Monthly. **Price:** $695, U.S. and Canada; $745, elsewhere. **Description:** Covers developments in the computer and consumer electronic markets, including new technology and related fields.

3842 ■ *Communications Daily*

Pub: Warren Communications News Inc.

Contact: Daniel Warren, President

E-mail: dwarren@warren-news.com

Released: Daily, 5/wk. **Price:** $3,695. **Description:** Covers telephone and data communications, broadcasting, cable TV, teleconferencing, satellite communications, electronic publishing, and emerging technologies. Recurring features include personnel updates, obituaries, statistics, trade show news, and news of research.

3843 ■ *Connected Planet: Intelligence for the Broadband Economy*

Pub: Penton

Contact: Raymond E. Maloney, President

URL(s): connectedplanetonline.com/. **Released:** Monthly

3844 ■ *Industry Pulse*

Pub: Telecommunications Industry Association

Contact: Grant Seiffert, President

Ed: Ian Martinez, Editor. **Released:** 4/year. **Price:** Included in membership. **Description:** Publishes news of the Association, its members, and its activities.

3845 ■ *Internet Telephone / Green Data Centers*

Pub: Information Gatekeepers Inc.

Contact: Paul Polishuk, President

E-mail: ppolishuk@igigroup.com

Ed: Tony Carmona, Editor. **Released:** Monthly. **Price:** $695, U.S. and Canada; $745, elsewhere. **Description:** Provides marketing and technology information on new developments in the internet telephone industry on a worldwide basis.

3846 ■ *Russian Telecom Newsletter*

Pub: Information Gatekeepers Inc.

Contact: Jeremy Awori, Publisher

Ed: Prof. Sergei L. Galkin, Editor. **Released:** Monthly. **Price:** $695, U.S. and Canada; $745, elsewhere; $695 PDF email version. **Description:** Covers the telecommunications industry in Russia, including competition, government regulations, international business and ventures, cellular, satellites, and market intelligence. Also features new products and conference reports.

3847 ■ *Sound & Communications Magazine*

Pub: Testa Communications

Contact: Vincent P. Testa, President

URL(s): www.soundandcommunications.com. **Ed:** David Silverman. **Released:** Monthly

3848 ■ *Urgent Communications: Technical Information for Paging, Trunking and Private Wireless Networks*

Pub: Penton

Contact: Raymond E. Maloney, President

URL(s): urgentcomm.com/. **Ed:** Donny Jackson. **Released:** Monthly

3849 ■ *Utilities Telecommunications News*

Pub: Information Gatekeepers Inc.

Contact: Paul Polishuk, Managing Editor

Released: Monthly. **Price:** $695, U.S. and Canada; $745, elsewhere; $695 PDF email version. **Description:** Focuses on the role of utilities in telecommunications. Topics include government and regulations, business, and the Internet. Also features new products and conferences.

3850 ■ *Wireless Business & Technology*

Pub: SYS-CON Media

URL(s): wireless.sys-con.com/. **Released:** Bimonthly **Price:** $4, Single issue; $129, Two years digital edition; $99, Individuals digital edition.

3851 ■ *Wireless Cellular / WMAX*

Pub: Information Gatekeepers Inc.

Ed: Paul Polishuk, Editor. **Released:** Monthly. **Price:** $695, U.S. and Canada; $745, elsewhere. **Description:** Covers international developments in the wireless cellular industry, including new products, market opportunities and forecasts, regulations and standards, procurements, mergers and acquisitions, and applications.

TRADE SHOWS AND CONVENTIONS

3852 ■ Wireless

Cellular Telecommunications Industry Association
1400 16th St. NW, Ste. 600
Washington, DC 20036
Ph: (202)736-3200
Fax: (202)785-0721
Co. E-mail: research@ctia.org
URL: http://www.ctia.org
Contact: Steven Largent, Chief Executive Officer

URL(s): www.ctia.org/conventions_events/wireless/. **Frequency:** Annual. **Audience:** Managerial level members of the cellular and wireless communications industry. **Principal Exhibits:** Cellular and wireless equipment and support services.

CONSULTANTS

3853 ■ CTA Communications Inc.

20715 Timberlake Rd., Ste. 106
Lynchburg, VA 24502
Ph: (434)239-9200
Fax: (434)239-9221
Co. E-mail: home@ctacommunications.com
URL: http://www.ctacommunications.com
Contact: Cheryl Giggetts, President

Scope: An engineering and consulting firm, providing service in the area of specification, design, installation and implementation of communication systems including mobile, cellular, fiber optics, data and telecommunications systems. Work involves system planning, system design, system implementation, requirement analysis, specification development, site management, traffic studies, proposal development, training, analog design, digital design, path loss analysis, and data communication design. Industries served: public safety, local government, utilities, and general industry. **Founded:** 1947. **Publications:** "Alternative Centers: Where's My Backup," Sep, 2006; "Are you ready for Narrowband," May, 2006; "Rebanding the 800 MHz Frequencies: Just retuning? Think again," Aug, 2005; "Wireless 9-1-1: Help, or Needs Help," Feb, 2004. **Seminars:** Wide Area Trunking Considerations-Applications in Systems Large and Small; Coverage Proof of Performance-Hocus Pocus or Real World; Digital Radio Concepts for Public Safety Applications; The Digital Journey; Daddy Aren't We There Yet?. **Telecommunication Services:** home@ctacommunications.com.

3854 ■ Trott Communications Group Inc.

4320 N Beltline Rd., Ste. A100
Irving, TX 75038
Ph: (972)252-9280
Free: 800-536-1806
Fax: (972)258-8172
Co. E-mail: info@trottgroup.com
URL: http://www.trottgroup.com
Contact: Walter Jon Stewart, President

Scope: Provides engineering consulting services to the land mobile and telecommunications industries. Services include: RF system design, microwave path engineering, propagation analyzes, interference studies, site management services, specification preparation, and equipments election and RF radiation studies. **Founded:** 1978.

3855 ■ W & J Partnership

PO Box 2499
Castro Valley, CA 94546-0499
Ph: (510)583-7751
Fax: (510)583-7645
Co. E-mail: jemorgan@wjpartnership.com
URL: http://www.wjpartnership.com
Contact: Judith E. Morgan, Partner
E-mail: jemorgan@wjpartnership.com

Scope: Management and technical consulting in complex network design, operations, administration, maintenance and products for large enterprises, carriers and service providers (wire-line and wireless) and governments, especially VoIP, security; R and D for vendors. Review product plans and investment opportunities. Software and hardware: Architectures, design, development and testing for manufacturers. No work for vendors and business at the same time. **Founded:** 1982. **Telecommunication Services:** wamorgan@wjpartnership.com.

FRANCHISES AND BUSINESS OPPORTUNITIES

3856 ■ Worldwide Wireless

Worldwide Wireless Franchise Services LLC
1000 Eagle Ridge Dr.
Schererville, IN 46375
Ph: (219)864-9991
Free: 877-346-3999
Fax: (219)864-9992
URL: http://www.worldwidewirelessinc.com

Description: Exclusive Sprint dealership. **Founded:** 1999.. **Franchised:** 2006. **Equity Capital Needed:** $75,000-$150,000. **Franchise Fee:** $30,000. **Financial Assistance:** Yes. **Training:** Yes.

3857 ■ Yakety Yak Wireless

3400 Irvine Ave., Ste. 118
Newport Beach, CA 92660
Ph: (949)851-1900
Free: 888-925-4887
Fax: (949)486-6001

Description: Wireless services & related products. **No. of Franchise Units:** 30. **Founded:** 1999.. **Franchised:** 2005. **Equity Capital Needed:** $79,000-$301,500. **Franchise Fee:** $29,000. **Royalty Fee:** $300-$1,000/month. **Training:** Offers 2 weeks at headquarters, daily conference calls and ongoing support.

COMPUTERIZED DATABASES

3858 ■ *The Telecom Manager's Voice Report*

2 Washingtonian Ctr., Ste. 100
9737 Washingtonian Blvd.
Gaithersburg, MD 20878
Ph: (301)287-2700
Free: 888-275-2264
Fax: (301)287-2170
Co. E-mail: support@ccmi.com
URL: http://www.ccmi.com

Availability: Online: ProQuest Co.; United Communications Group - Center for Communications Management Information. **Type:** Full-text.

LIBRARIES

3859 ■ Manitoba Telecom Services Corporate Library
333 Main St.
Winnipeg, MB, Canada R3C 3V6
Ph: (204)941-6344
Fax: (204)944-0830
URL: http://www.mts.ca
Contact: Tanya L. Evancio, Librarian

Scope: Telecommunications industry. **Services:** Library not open to the public. **Founded:** 1977. **Holdings:** 2000 books. **Subscriptions:** 100 journals and other serials.

3860 ■ Museum of Independent Telephony - Archives Collection
412 S. Campbell
Abilene, KS 67410
Ph: (785)263-2681
Co. E-mail: heritagecenterdk@sbcglobal.net
URL: http://www.heritagecenterdk.com/museum_of_independent_telephony.html
Contact: Jeff Sheets

Scope: Telephone history and technology. **Services:** Copying; collection open to the public. **Founded:** 1973. **Holdings:** 1000 books; 1000 bound periodical volumes; 1000 other cataloged items; 500 manuscripts; 120 boxes of loose periodicals; 150 tapes. **Subscriptions:** 10 journals and other serials.

3861 ■ Ohio Bell - Corporate Information Resource Center
45 Erieview Plaza, Rm. 820
Cleveland, OH 44114-1813
Ph: (216)822-2740
Contact: John Jakovcic, Assistant Manager

Scope: Business, management, telecommunications, personnel, computers, marketing, Ohio Bell and Bell System history. **Services:** Interlibrary loan; copying; Library open to the public at librarian's discretion. **Founded:** 1951. **Holdings:** 5000 books. **Subscriptions:** 150 journals and other serials; 10 newspapers.

3862 ■ U.S. Federal Communications Commission Library
445 12th St. SW, Rm. TW-8505
Washington, DC 20554
Ph: (202)418-0450
Free: 888-225-5322
Fax: (202)418-2805
Co. E-mail: ecclibrary@fcc.gov
URL: http://www.fcc.gov
Contact: Ms. Gloria Thomas, Librarian, Reference Senior Librarian

Scope: Telecommunications, electrical engineering, law, economics, public utility regulation, public administration, management, statistics. **Services:** SDI; Library not open to the public. **Founded:** 1934. **Holdings:** 45,000 books; 123 bound periodical volumes; 6200 VF materials; 3000 reels of microfilm. **Subscriptions:** 305 journals and other serials. **Telecommunication Services:** fccinfo@fcc.gov.

ASSOCIATIONS AND OTHER ORGANIZATIONS

3863 ■ Boat Owners Association of the United States (BOAT US)—BoatUS
880 S Pickett St.
Alexandria, VA 22304-4695
Ph: (703)461-4666
Free: 800-395-2628
Fax: (703)461-2847
Co. E-mail: membership@boatus.com
URL: http://www.boatus.com
Contact: Nancy Michelman, President
E-mail: NMichelman@boatus.com
Description: Represents owners or prospective owners of recreational boats. Independent, consumer service organization offering representation, benefits, and programs for boat owners. Services include: legislative and regulatory representation on issues affecting boaters' interests; marine insurance; magazines; trailering club; marina discounts; long-term boat financing; boating regulations and forms service; charter and group travel services; sale and chartering exchange; marine surveyor and admiralty lawyer reference service; assistance with individual boating problems and towing reimbursement; association flag. Maintains Consumer Protection Bureau, which utilizes comprehensive consumer experience files to pursue individual complaints. **Founded:** 1966. **Publications:** *BOAT U.S. Magazine* (Bimonthly); *Equipment Catalog* (Annual); *Seaworthy* (Quarterly); *Boater's Source Directory* (Semiannual); *Seaworthy*; *Boat U.S. Trailering Magazine* (Bimonthly). **Telecommunication Services:** mail@boatus.com.

3864 ■ National Women's Sailing Association (NWSA)
1 Esquire Dr.
Peabody, MA 01960
Ph: (401)682-2064
Co. E-mail: wsf@womensailing.org
URL: http://www.womensailing.org
Contact: Joan Thayer, President
Description: Works to enhance the lives of women and girls through education and access to the sport of sailing. **Founded:** 1993. **Publications:** *Women's Sailing Resource* (Biennial). **Educational Activities:** Pacific Sail Expo (Annual); Sail Boat Show (Annual); Sail Expo (Annual).

3865 ■ Passenger Vessel Association (PVA)
103 Oronoco St., Ste. 200
Alexandria, VA 22314
Ph: (703)518-5005
Free: 800-807-8360
Fax: (703)518-5151
Co. E-mail: pvainfo@passengervessel.com
URL: http://www.passengervessel.com
Contact: Paul Belforti, President
Description: Owners, operators and suppliers of U.S. and Canadian flagged passenger vessels, including dinner vessels, private charter, tour and excursion boats, casino gambling boats, overnight cruise vessels and whale watching and eco-tourism operators. Monitors and disseminates information on current and proposed federal regulation and legislation affecting passenger ship owners; represents the industry's views to legislative and regulatory bodies. **Founded:** 1971. **Publications:** *Foghorn* (Monthly). **Awards:** Roger Murphy National Marine Safety Award (Annual).

3866 ■ States Organization for Boating Access (SOBA)
231 S LaSalle St., Ste. 2050
Chicago, IL 60604
Ph: (312)946-6283
Fax: (312)946-0388
Co. E-mail: info@sobaus.org
URL: http://www.sobaus.org
Contact: Steven W. Miller, President
Description: Individuals interested in recreational boating facilities. Provides information regarding the construction, maintenance, financing and administration of recreational boating facilities to state program administrators charged with their management. **Founded:** 1986. **Publications:** *Design Handbook and Operations and Maintenance Guidelines.* **Educational Activities:** States Organization for Boating Access Annual Conference (Annual). **Awards:** Outstanding Project Awards; Outstanding Service Award; Professional Service Award; Special Recognition Award; William H. Ivers Award; Meritorious Service Award (Annual); Outgoing President Award; Outstanding Project Awards (Annual); Outstanding Service Award (Annual); Professional Service Award (Annual); Special Recognition Award (Annual); State Boating Access Program Excellence Award (Annual); State CVA Program Excellence Award (Annual); William H. Ivers Award (Annual); State Boating Access Program Excellence Award; State Clean Vessel Act Program Excellence Award.

REFERENCE WORKS

3867 ■ *Atlantic Boating Almanac*
Pub: Atlantic Boating Almanac
Contact: Peter L. Griffes, Publisher
URL(s): www.prostarpublications.com. **Released:** Annual; Latest edition 2006. **Price:** $26.95, Individuals. **Covers:** Listings on coast piloting, electronics, GPS by Gordon West, first aid, weather, facilities and fuel docks. There are four separate regional editions: Florida & Bahamas; North & South Carolina and Georgia; Massachusetts, Rhode Island, Connecticut and Long Island; and Maine, New Hampshire & Massachusetts. **Database includes:** Tide and current tables; maps and fishing charts; navigation and star charts; first aid; US coast pilot. **Arrangement:** Geographical.

TRADE PERIODICALS

3868 ■ *Current*
Pub: National Marine Manufacturers Association
Released: Semiannual. **Price:** Included in membership. **Description:** Reviews boat shows. Reports industry trends. Offers trade and consumer show advice. Recurring features include interviews, a calendar of events, and reports of meetings.

3869 ■ *Marine Business Journal: The Voice of the Marine Industries*
Pub: Marine Business Journal Inc.
Contact: Mike Myers, President
URL(s): www.marinebusinessjournal.com/. **Released:** Bimonthly **Price:** $30, Other countries.

3870 ■ *Seaworthy*
Pub: Boat Owners Association of the United States
Contact: Nancy Michelman, President
E-mail: NMichelman@boatus.com
Ed: Robert Adriance, Jr., Editor, badriance@boatus.com. **Released:** Quarterly. **Price:** $10 for noninsured; Free. **Description:** Seeks to help boaters avoid accidents or problems by listing actual insurance claims. Includes case stuides that provide insight in to how to avoid accidents, breakdowns, injuries, and other 'unexpected' circumstances that can jeopardize the safety of their boat, themselves, and guests.

TRADE SHOWS AND CONVENTIONS

3871 ■ Cleveland Sport, Travel & Outdoor Show
Expositions Inc.
PO Box 550, Edgewater Br.
Cleveland, OH 44107-0550
Ph: (216)529-1300
Fax: (216)529-0311
Co. E-mail: showinfo@expoinc.com
URL: http://www.expoinc.com
URL(s): www.sportandtravel.com/cleveland/. **Frequency:** Annual. **Principal Exhibits:** Sport fishing. **Telecommunication Services:** cmfassnacht@gmail.com.

3872 ■ Eastern Fishing and Outdoor Exposition
Eastern Fishing and Outdoor Exposition Inc.
750 Central Ave., Ste. R
Dover, NH 03820
Ph: (603)431-4315
Fax: (603)431-1971
Co. E-mail: info@sportshows.com
URL: http://www.sportshows.com
URL(s): www.sportshows.com/. **Price:** $9. **Frequency:** Annual. **Audience:** Metro Boston/Worcester Market. **Principal Exhibits:** Fishing and outdoor sports. **Telecommunication Services:** info@sportshows.com.

3873 ■ Louisville Boat, RV & Sportshow
Douglas Expositions Inc.
10000 Shelbyville Rd., No. 111
Anchorage, KY 40223-2950
Ph: (502)244-5660
URL(s): www.louisvilleboatshow.com. **Frequency:** Annual. **Principal Exhibits:** Sports, boating and vacations, hunting and fishing, recreational vehicles. **Telecommunication Services:** kmuncy@nmma.org.

3874 ■ Quad City Boat and Vacation Show
International Sport Show Producers Association (IS-SPA)
PO Box 480084
Denver, CO 80248-0084
Ph: (303)892-6800
Free: 800-457-2434
Fax: (303)892-6322
Co. E-mail: dseymour@iei-expos.com
URL: http://www.sportshow.org
Contact: Jeff Haughton, President
URL(s): www.iowashows.com. **Price:** $6; kids ages 12 and under. **Frequency:** Annual. **Principal Exhib-** its: Boats, fishing tackle, resorts, tourism associations, motorhomes. **Dates and Locations:** River Center.

FRANCHISES AND BUSINESS OPPORTUNITIES

3875 ■ The Cruising Club Fractional Boat Ownership
20 Calabria Ave., Ste. 505
Coral Gables, FL 33134
Ph: (954)397-1185
Co. E-mail: carlton@thecruisingclub.com
URL: http://www.thecruisingclub.com

Description: Fractional boat ownership. **No. of Franchise Units:** 6. **No. of Company-Owned Units:** 5. **Founded:** 1998.. **Franchised:** 2004. **Equity Capital Needed:** Varies, $35,000-$500,000. **Franchise Fee:** $25,000-$100,000. **Training:** Yes.

REFERENCE WORKS

3876 ■ *"Kenyans Embrace Moving Money By Text Message" in Chicago Tribune (October 7, 2008)*
Pub: McClatchy-Tribune Information Services
Ed: Laurie Goering. **Description:** Cell phone banking services are becoming more common, especially for foreign residents; customers are able to establish a virtual cell phone bank account through companies such as M-Pesa which allows their customers to pay bills, withdraw cash, pay merchants or text money to relatives.

FRANCHISES AND BUSINESS OPPORTUNITIES

3877 ■ **ACE America's Cash Express**
ACE Cash Express Inc.
1231 Greenway Dr., Ste. 600
Irving, TX 75038
Ph: (972)550-5000
Free: 800-713-3338
Fax: (972)582-1409
Co. E-mail: franchisedevelopment@acecashexpress. com
URL: http://www.acecashexpress.com
Description: Check cashing, loans, money orders, wire transfers, bill payments, cash advances, prepaid telecommunication products. **No. of Franchise Units:** 220. **No. of Company-Owned Units:** 1,353. **Founded:** 1968.. **Franchised:** 1996. **Equity Capital Needed:** $141,632-$227,950/$240,132-$282,950. **Franchise Fee:** $15,000-$30,000. **Training:** Site selection, store design, complete classroom and on-site training, manuals, advertising, annual conference and ongoing operation evaluations.

3878 ■ **Advantage Cash Advance**
Advantage Cash Corp.
4744 Keithdale Ln.
Bloomfield Hills, MI 48302
Ph: (810)423-1375
Fax: (248)399-4771
Description: Payday advance business. **No. of Franchise Units:** 7. **Founded:** 2005.. **Franchised:** 2005. **Equity Capital Needed:** $90,000-$135,000. **Training:** Yes.

3879 ■ **Cash Plus**
Cash Plus, Inc.
3002 Dow Ave., Ste, 120
Tustin, CA 92780
Ph: (714)731-2274
Free: 888-707-2274
Fax: (714)731-2099
Description: Check cashing service and related services, including money orders, wire transfers, cash advances, mailboxes, notary, UPS, fax, snacks, tax filing and other items. **No. of Franchise Units:** 91. **No. of Company-Owned Units:** 2. **Founded:** 1984.. **Franchised:** 1988. **Equity Capital Needed:** $190,200-$269,700. **Franchise Fee:** $35,000. **Financial Assistance:** Yes. **Training:** Provides training including easy-to-run computerized operating system, promotions and check verification and payday advance process.

3880 ■ **Commission Express**
Commission Express National
8306 Professional Hill Dr.
Fairfax, VA 22031
Ph: (703)560-5500
Fax: (703)560-5502
Co. E-mail: manager@commissionexpress.com
URL: http://www.commissionexpress.com
Description: Buy real estate agent commissions. **No. of Franchise Units:** 74. **No. of Company-Owned Units:** 1. **Founded:** 1992.. **Franchised:** 1996. **Equity Capital Needed:** $94,300-$213,500. **Franchise Fee:** $20,000-$80,000. **Training:** Provides 1 week at Fairfax, VA and annual conference.

3881 ■ **Family Financial Centers**
99 Lantern Drive, Ste. 101
Doylestown, PA 18901
Free: 877-236-5508
Fax: (215)230-5538
Co. E-mail: contactus@familyfinancialcenters.com
URL: http://www.familyfinancialcenters.com
Description: Check cashing & other financial services. **No. of Franchise Units:** 29. **Founded:** 2004.. **Franchised:** 2004. **Equity Capital Needed:** $147,000-$149,000. **Franchise Fee:** $34,500. **Royalty Fee:** 0.2%. **Training:** Offers 1 week training at headquarters, 1 week field training and ongoing support.

3882 ■ **FastBucks**
FastBucks Franchise Corp.
7920 Beltline Rd., Ste. 600
Dallas, TX 75254
Ph: (972)490-3330
Fax: (972)490-8297
Description: Payday loans. **No. of Franchise Units:** 6. **No. of Company-Owned Units:** 52. **Founded:** 1998. **Franchised:** 2003. **Equity Capital Needed:** $125,000-$150,000. **Franchise Fee:** $27,500. **Royalty Fee:** 7%. **Training:** Offers 2 weeks at headquarters, 1 week at franchisee's location with ongoing support.

3883 ■ **Mr. Payroll Check Cashing**
Cash America Intl.
1600 W 7th St.
Fort Worth, TX 76102
Ph: (800)322-3250
Fax: (817)333-1934
URL: http://www.cashamerica.com
Description: Operates as a financial services kiosk inside a busy retail business, such as a grocery and convenience stores. Our pre-fabricated 48 square foot kiosk is space efficient and helps retailers increase sales from check cashing customers. Franchisees may be owners of such retail businesses or can operate as subtenants. Services include check cashing, money orders, wire transfers, bill payments, pre-paid phones and ancillary services. **No. of Franchise Units:** 113. **No. of Company-Owned Units:** 6. **Founded:** 1988.. **Franchised:** 1990. **Equity Capital Needed:** $75,300-$326,500. **Franchise Fee:** $10,000. **Royalty Fee:** 10%. **Training:** Offers 3 days at headquarters with ongoing support.

3884 ■ **United Check Cashing**
United Financial Services Group, Inc.
325 Chestnut St., Ste. 3000
Philadelphia, PA 19106
Ph: (215)238-0300
Free: 800-626-0787
Fax: (215)238-9056
Co. E-mail: info@unitedfsg.com
URL: http://www.unitedfsg.com
Description: Check cashing, money orders, wire transfers, authorized bill payments, fax, copies, notary, consumer loans, ATM's, lottery, credit card advances, tax service, photo ID systems and beeper sales. **No. of Franchise Units:** 132. **Founded:** 1977.. **Franchised:** 1992. **Equity Capital Needed:** $103,500 (kiosk)-$297,000 which allows for $50,000 (kiosk)-$120,000 in operating cash. **Franchise Fee:** $30,000. **Financial Assistance:** Yes. **Training:** Receive training in customer servicing, sales, human resources, loss prevention and risk management.

START-UP INFORMATION

3885 ■ *In Fashion: From Runway to Retail, Everything You Need to Know to Break Into the Fashion Industry*
Pub: Crown Business Books
Ed: Annemarie Iverson. **Released:** August 10, 2010. **Price:** $16.99. **Description:** Whether your dream is to photograph models, outfit celebrities, design fashions, this book provides details into every aspect for working in the fashion industry.

3886 ■ *"Mount Laurel Woman Launches Venture Into Children's Used Clothing" in Philadelphia Inquirer (September 17, 2010)*
Pub: Philadelphia Media Network
Ed: Maria Panaritis. **Description:** Profile of Jennifer Frisch, stay-at-home mom turned entrepreneur. Frisch started a used-clothing store Once Upon a Child after opening her franchised Plato's Closet, selling unwanted and used baby clothing and accessories at her new shop, while offering used merchandise to teens at Plato's Closet.

ASSOCIATIONS AND OTHER ORGANIZATIONS

3887 ■ **American Apparel and Footwear Association (AAFA)**
1601 N Kent St., 12 th Fl., Ste. 1200
Arlington, VA 22209
Ph: (703)524-1864
Free: 800-520-2262
Fax: (703)522-6741
Co. E-mail: info@apparelandfootwear.org
URL: http://www.apparelandfootwear.org
Contact: Kevin M. Burke, President
Description: Manufacturers of infants', children's, boys', girls', juniors', men's, and women's wearing apparel; associate members are suppliers of fabrics, equipment, accessories, and services to the apparel industry. Operates the Apparel Foundation; offers placement service through newsletter. Compiles statistics. **Founded:** 2000. **Publications:** *SoleSource: The footwear industry reservice directory* (Annual); *Technical Advisory Committee Bulletin* (Periodic); *SoleSource: The Footwear Industry Directory* (Annual); *AAFA Directory of Members and Associate Members* (Annual). **Educational Activities:** Bobbin Show (Annual); Global Leather (Annual). **Telecommunication Services:** pcarty@apparelandfootwear.org; mrust@apparelandfootwear.org; rmond@apparelandfootwear.org.

REFERENCE WORKS

3888 ■ *"Consignment Shop Offers Children's Clothes, Products" in Frederick News-Post (August 19, 2010)*
Pub: Federick News-Post
Ed: Ed Waters Jr. **Description:** Sweet Pea Consignments for Children offers used items for newborns to pre-teens. The shop carries name brand clothing as well as toys, books and baby products.

3889 ■ *Directory of Apparel Specialty Stores*
Pub: Chain Store Guide
Contact: Lisa Patterson, President
URL(s): www.chainstoreguide.com. **Released:** Annual; Latest edition 2012. **Price:** $395, Individuals Directory; $445, Individuals online lite; $1075, Individuals online pro; $1375, Individuals online pro plus. **Covers:** 5,040 apparel and sporting goods specialty retailers in the United States and Canada, operating more than 70,700 stores. Apparel retailers must have annual retail sales of at least $500,000; sporting goods specialty retailers must also have $500,000 in annual sales, with the condition that at least 20% of product sales are from sporting goods equipment. **Entries include:** Company name, phone, and fax numbers; physical and mailing addresses; company e-mail and web addresses; Internet order processing indicator; percentage of Internet sales; type of business; listing type; product lines; total, industry, and product group sales; total selling square footage; store prototype sizes; total stores; trading areas; projected openings and remodeling; units by trade name; distribution center locations; resident buyer's name and location; mail order indicator; percentage of mail order sales; catalog names; private label indicator; private label credit card indicator; apparel price lines; average number of checkouts; year founded; public company indicator; parent company name and location; and key personnel with titles; 7,200 personnel email addresses . **Arrangement:** Geographical. **Indexes:** Alphabetical, product lines, exclusions.

3890 ■ *"Green It Like You Mean It" in Special Events Magazine (Vol. 28, February 1, 2009, No. 2)*
Pub: Special Events Magazine
Ed: Christine Landry. **Description:** Eco-friendly party planners offer advice for planning and hosting green parties or events. Tips include information for using recycled paper products, organic food and drinks. The Eco Nouveau Fashion Show held by Serene Star Productions reused old garments to create new fashions as well as art pieces from discarded doors and window frames for the show; eco-friendly treats and gift bags were highlighted at the event.

3891 ■ *"Intrepid Souls: Meet a Few Who've Made the Big Leap" in Crain's Chicago Business (Vol. 31, November 10, 2008, No. 45, pp. 26)*
Pub: Crain Communications, Inc.
Ed: Meredith Landry. **Description:** Advice is given from entrepreneurs who have launched businesses in the last year despite the economic crisis. Among the types of businesses featured are a cooking school, a child day-care center, a children's clothing store and an Internet-based company.

3892 ■ *"Let It Shine: Organization Helps Disadvantaged Girls See Their Worth" in Black Enterprise (Vol. 38, February 2008, No. 7, pp. 142)*
Pub: Earl G. Graves Publishing Co. Inc.
Ed: George Alexander. **Description:** Wilson Mourning, founder of the clothing label Honey Child, attributes her success to her mother and other positive

women who helped her through her adolescence. Mourning created a mentoring organization that helps young girls in the Miami, Florida area to develop life skills.

3893 ■ *Men's & Boys' Wear Buyers*
Pub: Briefings Media Group
Contact: Alan M. Douglas, President
E-mail: adouglas@douglaspublications.com
URL(s): www.thesalesmansguide.comwww.douglaspublications.com. **Released:** Annual; latest edition 2011-2012. **Price:** $329, Individuals directory price; $699, Individuals directory/CD combo price. **Covers:** 9,000 buyers and 5,100 stores in the men's and boys' retail industry. **Entries include:** Store name, address, phone, fax; names and titles of key personnel; e-mail; URL; financial data; branch/subsidiary name and address; products/services provided; price points and sales volume; parent company; type and number of stores for companies; corporate buying office. **Arrangement:** Geographical. **Indexes:** Store name, new listings, mail order, buying office, online retailer.

3894 ■ *"Research and Market Adds: 2010 US Women's and Children's Clothing Wholesale Report" in Wireless News (November 8, 2009)*
Pub: Close-Up Media
Description: Highlights of the annual Research and Markets '2010 U.S. Women's and Children's Clothing Wholesale Report' include industry statistics, demographics and forecasts.

3895 ■ *"Research and Markets Adds: 2011 U.S. Women's & Children's Clothing Wholesale Report" in Health & Beauty Close-Up (October 16, 2010)*
Pub: Close-Up Media Inc.
Description: The Women's & Children's Clothing Wholesale Report is an annual report containing timely and accurate industry statistics, forecasts and demographics.

3896 ■ *"Retail News: Children's Boutique Relocates to Conway" in Sun News (June 4, 2010)*
Pub: The Sun News
Description: Little Angel's Children's Boutique and Big Oak Frame Shop have moved to downtown locations in Conway, South Carolina. Little Angel's will sell children's clothing and accessories, shoes and gifts, while the frame shop will offer custom framing along with the sale of stationary, invitations and local prints.

3897 ■ *"Weaving a Stronger Fabric: Organizing a Global Sweat-Free Apparel Production Agreement" in WorkingUSA (Vol. 11, June 2008, No. 2)*
Pub: Blackwell Publishers Ltd.
Ed: Eric Dirnbach. **Description:** Tens of millions of workers working under terrible sweatshop conditions in the global apparel industry. Workers are employed at apparel contractors and have been largely unsuccessful in organizing and improving their working conditions. The major apparel manufacturers and retailers have the most power in this industry, and

they have adopted corporate social responsibility programs as a false solution to the sweatshop problem. The major North American apparel unions dealt with similar sweatshop conditions a century ago by organizing the contractors and brands into joint association contracts that significantly raised standards. Taking inspiration from their example, workers and their anti-sweatshop allies need to work together to coordinate a global organizing effort that builds worker power and establishes a global production agreement that negotiates with both contractors and the brands for improved wages, benefits, and working conditions.

3898 ■ Women's & Children's Wear Buyers
Pub: Briefings Media Group
Contact: Alan M. Douglas, President
E-mail: adouglas@douglaspublications.com
URL(s): www.thesalesmansguide.comwww.douglaspublications.com. **Released:** Annual; latest edition 2011-2012. **Price:** $329, directory price; $699, directory/CD combo price. **Covers:** Over 9,000 retailers and 17,000 buyers in women's and children's wear industry. **Entries include:** Company name, address, phone, fax; e-mail; URL; names and titles of key personnel; financial data; branch or subsidiary name and address; products and/or services provided; names and titles of buyers; price points and sales volume; type and number of stores for companies; parent companies, and corporate buying offices. **Arrangement:** Geographical. **Indexes:** Store name, new listings, mail order, buying office, online retailer.

3899 ■ "Zakkamono Taps Growing Market for Collectibles" in Hawaii Business (Vol. 54, September 2008, No. 3, pp. 68)
Pub: Hawaii Business Publishing
Ed: Casey Chin. **Description:** Profile of Zakkamono, a business that designs and sells designer toys, shirts and other collectibles; the first toys being Mousubi and Miao figurines. Owners Zakka and Rae Huo say that one of the business' challenges is finding manufacturing resources. Other details about Zakkamono are discussed.

SOURCES OF SUPPLY

3900 ■ Denver Merchandise Mart Directory
Denver Merchandise Mart
Contact: Darrell Hare, President
URL(s): www.denvermart.com/martset.html. **Released:** Annual; December/January. **Covers:** About 4,000 manufacturers, importers, and wholesale distributors of men's, women's, and children's clothing, western apparel, shoes, gifts, gourmet items, bath accessories, jewelry, resort merchandise, and home furnishings who are represented in the Denver Merchandise Mart. **Entries include:** Firm name, mart address; alphabetical listings include phone. **Arrangement:** Alphabetical by product classification.

TRADE PERIODICALS

3901 ■ Apparel News South
Pub: Apparel News Group
Contact: John Irwin, Manager
URL(s): www.apparelnews.net. **Released:** 5/yr. **Price:** $89, Individuals.

3902 ■ California Apparel News
Pub: Apparel News Group
Contact: John Irwin, Manager
URL(s): www.apparelnews.net. **Released:** Weekly (Fri.) **Price:** $89, Individuals print; $99, Individuals online.

3903 ■ Chicago Apparel News
Pub: Apparel News Group
Contact: John Irwin, Manager
URL(s): www.apparelnews.net. **Released:** Weekly **Price:** $83, Individuals; $140, Two years.

3904 ■ Dallas Apparel News
Pub: Apparel News Group
Contact: John Irwin, Manager
URL(s): www.apparelnews.net. **Ed:** N. Jayne Seward. **Released:** 5/yr.

3905 ■ DNR: Defining Men's Fashion
Pub: Fairchild Publications
URL(s): www.dnrnews.com/. **Released:** Daily (morn.) **Price:** $129, Individuals; $99, Individuals online; $169, Individuals online + print; $895, Individuals online archive.

3906 ■ Kids Creations
Pub: Children's Apparel Manufacturers' Association
URL(s): www.cama-apparel.org/. **Released:** Quarterly **Price:** $37, Canada; $50, Individuals U.S.; $110, Other countries; $64, Two years Canada; $90, Two years U.S.; $210, Two years other countries.

3907 ■ New York Apparel News
Pub: Apparel News Group
Contact: John Irwin, Manager
URL(s): www.apparelnews.net/fashion/NY-Fashion-Week-Spring-2011. **Ed:** Connie Cho. **Released:** 5/yr. **Price:** $20, Individuals; $4, Single issue.

TRADE SHOWS AND CONVENTIONS

3908 ■ Dallas Men's and Boys' Apparel Market
Dallas Market Center Co.
2100 Stemmons Fwy.
Dallas, TX 75207
Ph: (214)655-6100
Free: 800-DAL-MKTS
Co. E-mail: lvillarreal@dmcmail.com
URL: http://www.dallasmarketcenter.com/
URL(s): www.dallasmarketcenter.com. **Frequency:** Quarterly. **Principal Exhibits:** Men's clothing and accessories. **Dates and Locations:** Market Hall. **Telecommunication Services:** info@dmcmail.com.

3909 ■ Denver Apparel and Accessory Market
Denver Merchandise Mart
451 E. 58th Ave., Ste. 4270
Denver, CO 80216-8470
Ph: (303)292-6278
Free: 800-289-6278
Fax: (303)297-8473
Co. E-mail: info@denvermart.com
URL: http://www.denvermart.com
URL(s): www.denvermart.com. **Frequency:** 5/year. **Audience:** Retailers of women's, children's, and men's apparel and accessories. **Principal Exhibits:** Women's, men's, and children's apparel and accessories. **Dates and Locations:** Merchandise Mart. **Telecommunication Services:** info@denvermart.com.

3910 ■ Florida Fashion Focus Show
Southern Apparel Exhibitors, Inc.
1856 Sheridan St.
Evanston, IL 60201
Ph: (847)475-1856
Free: 888-249-1377
Co. E-mail: info@saemiami.com.
URL: http://www.saemiami.com
Contact: John Harper, President
E-mail: harper@saemiami.com
URL(s): www.floridafashionfocus.com/. **Frequency:** 5/year. **Audience:** Trade buyers. **Principal Exhibits:** Ladies ready-to-wear clothing; handbags, jewelry, and accessories. Order-writing for future delivery. **Dates and Locations:** Merchandise Mart. **Telecommunication Services:** Info@FocusTradeshow.com.

3911 ■ Just Kidstuff - A Division of the New York International Gift Fair
George Little Management, LLC
1133 Westchester Ave., Ste. N136
White Plains, NY 10606
Ph: (914)421-3200
Free: 800-272-SHOW
Co. E-mail: cathy_steel@glmshows.com
URL: http://www.glmshows.com
URL(s): www.nyigf.com. **Frequency:** Semiannual. **Audience:** Buyers from specialty and department stores, giftshops, jewelry stores, interior designers, importers and distributors of home products, mail order catalogs. **Principal Exhibits:** Presents a wide variety of upscale products for children of all ages, including bedding, furniture, dolls, toys and games, gifts, clothes, books and educational products and accessories. **Telecommunication Services:** deborah_hilfman@glmshows.com.

3912 ■ Just Kidstuff - A Division of the San Francisco International Gift Fair
George Little Management, LLC
1133 Westchester Ave., Ste. N136
White Plains, NY 10606
Ph: (914)421-3200
Free: 800-272-SHOW
Co. E-mail: cathy_steel@glmshows.com
URL: http://www.glmshows.com
URL(s): www.sfigf.com. **Frequency:** February and August. **Audience:** Specialty and department stores, gift shops, jewelry stores, interior designers, importers and distributors of home products, mail order catalogs, museums, etc. **Principal Exhibits:** Upscale products for children of all ages, including bedding, furniture, dolls, toys and games, gifts, clothes, books, and educational products and accessories. **Dates and Locations:** Moscone Convention Center. **Telecommunication Services:** sfigf@glmshows.com.

3913 ■ Women's and Children's Apparel and Accessories Mart
Dallas Market Center Co.
2100 Stemmons Fwy.
Dallas, TX 75207
Ph: (214)655-6100
Free: 800-DAL-MKTS
Co. E-mail: lvillarreal@dmcmail.com
URL: http://www.dallasmarketcenter.com/
Audience: Apparel and accessories and home furnishings retailers. **Principal Exhibits:** Regional Merchandising Mart servicing department and specialty store buyers nationwide.

FRANCHISES AND BUSINESS OPPORTUNITIES

3914 ■ Baby News Children's Stores
6909 Las Positas Rd., Ste. A
Livermore, CA 94551
Ph: (925)245-1370
Fax: (952)245-1376
Description: Children's store. **No. of Franchise Units:** 50. **No. of Company-Owned Units:** 1. **Founded:** 1949.. **Equity Capital Needed:** $200,000. **Franchise Fee:** $15,000. **Training:** Yes.

3915 ■ Children's Orchard
Children's Orchard, Inc.
900 Victors Way, Ste. 200
Ann Arbor, MI 48108
Ph: (734)994-9199
Free: 800-999-5437
Fax: (734)994-9323
Description: Children's upscale/resale retail store. **No. of Franchise Units:** 93. **No. of Company-Owned Units:** 1. **Founded:** 1980. **Franchised:** 1985. **Equity Capital Needed:** $115,600-$197,000. **Franchise Fee:** $25,000. **Royalty Fee:** 5%. **Training:** Provides 12 days training at headquarters, 3 days onsite and ongoing support.

3916 ■ Educational Outfitters L.P.
8002 E Brainerd Rd.
Chattanooga, TN 37421-3205
Ph: (877)814-1222
Co. E-mail: info@educationaloutfitters.com
URL: http://www.educationaloutfitters.com
Contact: Jamey Elrod, President
URL(s): www.eschoolclothes.com. **Description:** Franchise of school uniforms and dress-code apparel for schools. **No. of Franchise Units:** 22. **No. of Company-Owned Units:** 1. **Founded:** 1999. **Franchised:** 2001. **Equity Capital Needed:** $80,000-$198,000. **Franchise Fee:** $29,500. **Training:** initial training at store, additional training at the franchisees location along with on-going support.

RESEARCH CENTERS

3917 ■ Texas A&M University - Center for Retailing Studies
Wehner Bldg., Ste. 201
Mays Business School
4112 TAMU
College Station, TX 77843-4112

Ph: (979)845-0325
Co. E-mail: c-bridges@mays.tamu.edu
URL: http://www.crstamu.org
Contact: Cheryl Holland Bridges, Director
Founded: 1983. **Publications:** *Faculty retailing research Papers*; *Retailing Issues Letter* (Quarterly). **Educational Activities:** Retailing Summit, held in September for retailing executives and academics;

Thought Leadership Conference (Annual), brings together academic scholars and industry professionals from around the globe to develop position papers on retailing research issues. **Awards:** M.B. Zale Visionary Merchant Award and Lecture (Annual), held in spring to honor outstanding performance by a leading retailer.

START-UP INFORMATION

3918 ■ *"Franchises with an Eye on Chicago" in Crain's Chicago Business (Vol. 34, March 14, 2011, No. 11, pp. 20)*
Pub: Crain Communications Inc.
Description: Profiles of franchise companies seeking franchisees for the Chicago area include: Extreme Pita, a sandwich shop; Hand and Stone, offering massage, facial and waxing services; Molly Maid, home-cleaning service; Primrose Schools, private accredited schools for children 6 months to 6 hears and after-school programs; Protect Painters, residential and light-commercial painting contractor; and Wingstop, a restaurant offering chicken wings in nine flavors, fries and side dishes.

3919 ■ *"Fun And Easy Gold Mines" in Small Business Opportunities (Fall 2008)*
Pub: Entrepreneur Media Inc.
Description: Twenty-five businesses that cater to the booming children's market are profiled; day care services, party planning, special events videomaking, tutoring, personalized children's toys and products and other services geared toward the kids market are included.

3920 ■ *"Making Money? Child's Play!" in Small Business Opportunities (March 2008)*
Pub: Harris Publications Inc.
Description: Proven system helps launch a successful child care business.

ASSOCIATIONS AND OTHER ORGANIZATIONS

3921 ■ **American Montessori Society (AMS)**
116 E 16th St.
New York, NY 10003-2163
Ph: (212)358-1250
Fax: (212)358-1256
Co. E-mail: ams@amshq.org
URL: http://www.amshq.org
Contact: Richard A. Ungerer, Executive Director
Description: School affiliates and teacher training affiliates; heads of schools, teachers, parents, non-Montessori educators, and other interested individuals dedicated to stimulating the use of the Montessori teaching approach and promoting better education for all children. Seeks to meet demands of growing interest in the Montessori approach to early learning. Assists in establishing schools; supplies information and limited services to member schools in other countries. Maintains school consultation and accreditation service; provides information service; assists research and gathers statistical data; offers placement service. Maintains Montessori and related materials exhibit. **Scope:** education. **Founded:** 1960. **Subscriptions:** archival material books. **Publications:** *School Directory* (Annual); *American Montessori Society School Directory; Montessori Life* (Quarterly). **Awards:** AMS Teacher Education Scholarships; Teacher Education Scholarships (Annual); Thesis and Dissertation Awards (Annual).

3922 ■ **Association for Childhood Education International (ACEI)**
17904 Georgia Ave., Ste. 215
Olney, MD 20832
Ph: (301)570-2111
Free: 800-423-3563
Fax: (301)570-2212
Co. E-mail: headquarters@acei.org
URL: http://www.acei.org
Contact: Debora Wisneski, President
E-mail: deboraw@uwm.edu
Description: Promotes and supports in the global community, optimal education and development of children, from birth through early adolescence. Influences the professional growth of educators and the efforts of others who are committed to the needs of children in a changing society. Strives to dedicate to a flexible, child-centered approach to education. Conducts advocacy through a variety of public forums and major coalitions for children and education. **Scope:** birth, kindergarten/early childhood education, middle childhood/early adolescence education, special needs. **Founded:** 1892. **Subscriptions:** 100 archival material articles. **Publications:** *Childhood Education* (Bimonthly); *Focus on Elementary* (Quarterly); *Journal of Research in Childhood Education* (Quarterly); *Childhood Education: Infancy Through Early Adolescence* (Bimonthly); *ACEI Exchange; Journal of Research in Childhood Education* (Quarterly). **Educational Activities:** Association for Childhood Education International Annual International Conference & Exhibition (Annual). **Awards:** Friends of Children Award (Annual); Mini-Grant (Annual); Outstanding Service Awards (Annual); Patty Smith Hill (Annual); Student Leadership Award (Annual); Friends of Children Award; Student Leadership Award; Mini-Grants for Special Projects; Outstanding Member Service Award; Patty Smith Hill Award for Professional Achievement.

3923 ■ **Child Welfare League of America (CWLA)**
1726 M St. NW, Ste. 500
Washington, DC 20036-4522
Ph: (202)688-4200
Fax: (202)833-1689
Co. E-mail: register@cwla.org
URL: http://www.cwla.org
Contact: Terri Braxton, Vice President, Business Development
Description: Works to improve care and services for abused, dependent, or neglected children, youth, and their families. Provides training and consultation; conducts research; maintains information service and develops standards for child welfare practice. **Founded:** 1920. **Educational Activities:** National Child Welfare Data and Technology Conference (Biennial). **Awards:** Anna Quindlen Award for Journalism (Annual); Kids to Kids National Service Awards (Annual); National Corporate Advocate of the Year (Annual); National Corporate Friend of Children Awards (Annual).

3924 ■ **Children's Defense Fund (CDF)**
25 E St. NW
Washington, DC 20001

Ph: (202)628-8787
Free: 800-233-1200
Fax: (202)662-3510
Co. E-mail: cdfinfo@childrensdefense.org
URL: http://www.childrensdefense.org
Contact: Geoffrey Canada, Chairman
Description: Provides systematic, long-range advocacy on behalf of the nation's children and teenagers. Engages in research, public education, monitoring of federal agencies, litigation, legislative drafting and testimony, assistance to state and local groups, and community organizing in areas of child welfare, child health, adolescent pregnancy prevention, child care and development, family income, family services, prevention of violence against and by children and child mental health. Works with individuals and groups to change policies and practices resulting in neglect or maltreatment of millions of children. Advocates: access to existing programs and services; creation of new programs and services where necessary; consistent emphasis on prevention; enforcement of civil rights laws; program accountability; strong parent and community role in decision-making; adequate funding for essential programs for children. Compiles statistics. **Founded:** 1973. **Publications:** *America's Cradle to Prison Pipeline.* **Awards:** Beat the Odds Award (Annual).

3925 ■ **National Association of Child Care Professionals (NACCP)**
PO Box 90723
Austin, TX 78709
Ph: (512)301-5557
Fax: (512)301-5080
Co. E-mail: admin@naccp.org
URL: http://www.naccp.org
Contact: Bobette Thompson, President
Description: Child care supervisors and individuals involved in decision-making at a child care facility. Offers networking opportunities and support services to child care professionals. Dedicated to the professional development of child care directors. Conducts educational programs. **Founded:** 1984. **Publications:** *Caring for Your Children* (Quarterly); *Professional Connections* (Quarterly); *Team Work* (Quarterly); *Immunizing Children Against Disease: A Guide For Child Care Providers.* **Educational Activities:** Training Seminars; How Successful Directors Manage National Conference (Annual); How Successful Directors Manage State Conference (Annual). **Awards:** National Child Care Director of the Year Award (Annual).

3926 ■ **National Association for the Education of Young Children (NAEYC)**
1313 L St. NW, Ste. 500
Washington, DC 20005
Ph: (202)232-8777
Free: 800-424-2460
Fax: (202)328-1846
Co. E-mail: naeyc@naeyc.org
URL: http://www.naeyc.org
Contact: Stephanie Fanjul, President
Description: Teachers and directors of preschool and primary schools, kindergartens, child care centers, and early other learning programs for young

childhood; early childhood education and child development educators, trainers, and researchers and other professionals dedicated to young children's healthy development. **Founded:** 1926. **Publications:** *Young Children* (Bimonthly); *GOAL ONE Resource Directory* (Irregular); *Young Children: The Journal of the National Association for the Education of Young Children*. **Educational Activities:** National Association for the Education of Young Children Annual Conference (Annual). **Telecommunication Services:** webmaster@naeyc.org

3927 ■ National Black Child Development Institute (NBCDI)
1313 L St. NW, Ste. 110
Washington, DC 20005-4110
Ph: (202)833-2220
Free: 800-556-2234
Fax: (202)833-8222
Co. E-mail: moreinfo@nbcdi.org
URL: http://nbcdi.org
Contact: Felicia DeHaney, President
URL(s): www.nbcdi.org. **Description:** Aims to improving the quality of life for African American children and youth. Conducts direct services and advocacy campaigns aimed at both national and local public policies focusing on issues of health, child welfare, education, and child care. Organizes and trains network of members in a volunteer grassroots affiliate system to voice concerns regarding policies that affect black children and their families. Stimulates communication between black community groups, through conferences and seminars, to discuss and make recommendations that will be advantageous to the development of black children. Analyzes selected policy decisions and legislative and administrative regulations to determine their impact on black children and youth. Informs national policymakers of issues critical to black children. **Founded:** 1970. **Publications:** *Child Health Talk* (Quarterly); *School Readiness and Social Emotional Development: Perspectives on Cultural Diversity*.

3928 ■ National Coalition for Campus Children's Centers (NCCCC)
950 Glenn Dr., Ste. 150
Folsom, CA 95630
Free: 877-736-6222
Fax: (916)932-2209
Co. E-mail: info@campuschildren.org
URL: http://www.campuschildren.org
Contact: Tonya Palla, Executive Director
Description: Promotes child care centers on college campuses and provides information on organizing and operating these centers. Believes that campus child care programs should be an integral part of higher education systems and should provide safe and healthy environments for children, developmentally sound educational programs, and services to both parents and campus programs. **Founded:** 1980.

3929 ■ National Head Start Association (NHSA)
1651 Prince St.
Alexandria, VA 22314
Ph: (703)739-0875
Free: 866-677-8724
Fax: (703)739-0878
Co. E-mail: nhsamembership@nhsa.org
URL: http://www.nhsa.org
Contact: Ron Herndon, Chairman
Description: Members of National Head Start Parent Association, National Head Start Directors Association, National Head Start Staff Association, National Head Start Friends Association, and others interested in the Head Start Program. Upgrades the quality and quantity of Head Start Program services. Integrates the activities of the 4 divisions to present cohesive policies, positions, and statements. Conducts seminars and training sessions in early childhood education. Maintains speakers' bureau. **Founded:** 1973. **Publications:** *Children and Families* (Quarterly); *NHSA Newsletter* (Quarterly); *Children and Families: Magazine of the National Head Start Association* (Quarterly). **Educational Activities:** National Head Start Association Conference (Annual); Parent Training (Annual); National Head Start Association Conference (Annual). **Awards:** Edward Zigler Research Award (Annual).

3930 ■ National Resource Center for Health and Safety in Child Care and Early Education (NRC)
c/o University of Colorado College of Nursing
Campus Mail Stop F541
13120 E 19th Ave.
Aurora, CO 80045-0508
Ph: (303)724-0654
Free: 800-598-KIDS
Fax: (303)724-0960
Co. E-mail: info@nrckids.org
URL: http://nrckids.org
Contact: Marilyn J. Krajicek, Director
Description: Seeks to enhance the quality of child care and early education by supporting state and local health departments, child care regulatory agencies, child care providers/teachers, and parents/guardians in their effort to promote health and safety in child care and early education. Provides information services and technical assistance. **Founded:** 1992.

3931 ■ Southern Early Childhood Association (SECA)
1123 S University Ave., Ste. 255
Little Rock, AR 72204
Ph: (501)221-1648
Free: 800-305-7322
Fax: (501)227-5297
Co. E-mail: info@southernearlychildhood.org
URL: http://www.southernearlychildhood.org
Contact: Nancy Jane Cheshire, President
Description: Early childhood educators, day care providers, program administrators, researchers, teacher trainers, and parents from the U.S. and abroad who share a common concern for the well-being of young children. Provides a unified voice on vital local, state, and federal issues affecting young children. Exchanges information and ideas through conferences and workshops. Explores contemporary issues in child development and early education through publications. **Founded:** 1948. **Publications:** *Dimensions of Early Childhood* (3/year); *Dimensions of Early Childhood*. **Awards:** Friend of Children (Annual); Marian B. Hamilton Award (Annual).

3932 ■ U.S.A. Toy Library Association (USA-TLA)
2719 Broadway Ave.
Evanston, IL 60201
Ph: (847)612-6966
Fax: (847)864-8473
Co. E-mail: jqi@comcast.net
URL: http://usatla.org
Contact: Judith Q. Iacuzzi, Executive Director
Description: Child care professionals, parents, and others interested in the role of toys and play in child development. Promotes the importance of play and the development of toy libraries in public and school libraries, hospitals, day care centers, and mobile collections. Seeks to broaden understanding of how toys can educate, increase parent-child interaction, and aid in development and therapy of disabled children. **Founded:** 1984.

3933 ■ World Organization for Early Childhood Education—Organisation Mondiale pour l'Education Prescolaire (OMEP)
4503, Claudette
Laval, QC, Canada H7C 1J1
Co. E-mail: omep-canada@videotron.ca
URL: http://www.omep-canada.org
Contact: Ginette Beausejour, President
Description: Organizations and individuals in 72 countries concerned with the health, education, and welfare of children. Promotes greater understanding of children from birth to age 8. Facilitates international exchange of research experience and knowledge on topics including child psychology, toys and play materials, living conditions of families with young children, preschool education and care, and other issues in education. Members promote research on early childhood education, conduct surveys of nursery schools and teacher training, and encourage parent education. Maintains speakers' bureau; conducts seminars and forums. **Founded:** 1948.

DIRECTORIES OF EDUCATIONAL PROGRAMS

3934 ■ *Directory of Private Accredited Career Schools and Colleges of Technology*
Pub: Accrediting Commission of Career Schools and Colleges of Technology
Contact: Michale S. McComis, Executive Director
Released: On web page. **Price:** Free. **Description:** Covers 3900 accredited post-secondary programs that provide training programs in business, trade, and technical fields, including various small business endeavors. Entries offer school name, address, phone, description of courses, job placement assistance, and requirements for admission. Arrangement is alphabetical.

REFERENCE WORKS

3935 ■ *"The Best Advice I Ever Got" in Harvard Business Review (Vol. 86, September 2008, No. 9, pp. 29)*
Pub: Harvard Business School Press
Ed: Daisy Wademan Dowling. **Description:** Bright Horizons Family Solutions founder and chair Linda Mason illustrates how letting one's life passion direct entrepreneurship and business success. She describes how her humanitarian interests and efforts gave her the drive to launch a childcare service.

3936 ■ *"Child-Care Policy and the Labor Supply of Mothers with Young Children" in University of Chicago Press (Vol. 26, July 2008, No. 3)*
Pub: University of Chicago Press
Contact: Garrett P. Kiely, Director
E-mail: gkiely@press.uchicago.edu
Ed: Pierre Lefebvre, Philip Merrigan. **Description:** In 1997, the provincial government of Quebec, the second most populous province in Canada, initiated a new childcare policy. Licensed childcare service providers began offering day care spaces at the reduced fee of $5 per day per child for children aged four. By 2000, the policy applied to all children not in kindergarten. Using annual data (1993-2002) drawn from Statistics Canada's Survey of Labour and Income Dynamics, the results show that the policy had a large and statistically significant impact on the labor supply of mothers with preschool children.

3937 ■ *"Day Care for Affluent Drawing a Crowd" in Business First Columbus (Vol. 24, August 15, 2008, No. 52, pp. 1)*
Pub: American City Business Journals
Ed: Carrie Ghose. **Description:** Day care centers for affluent families have grown in popularity in Columbus, Ohio. Primrose Schools Franchising Company has opened three such schools in the area. Statistical data included.

3938 ■ *"Day-Care Center Owner to Argue Against Liquor Store Opening Nearby" in Chicago Tribune (March 13, 2008)*
Pub: McClatchy-Tribune Information Services
Ed: Matthew Walberg. **Description:** NDLC's owner feels that Greenwood Liquors should not be granted its liquor license due to the claim that the NDLC is not only a day-care center but also a school that employs state-certified teachers.

3939 ■ *"Daycare Dollars" in Small Business Opportunities (Winter 2009)*
Pub: Entrepreneur Media Inc.
Description: Profile of Maui Playcare, a franchise that provides parents drop-in daycare for their children without having to purchase a membership, make reservations or pay costly dues; the company is expanding beyond its Hawaiian roots onto the mainland and is expected to have between 40 and 50 locations signed by the end of 2010.

3940 ■ *"Intrepid Souls: Meet a Few Who've Made the Big Leap" in Crain's Chicago Business (Vol. 31, November 10, 2008, No. 45, pp. 26)*
Pub: Crain Communications, Inc.
Ed: Meredith Landry. **Description:** Advice is given from entrepreneurs who have launched businesses in the last year despite the economic crisis. Among

the types of businesses featured are a cooking school, a child day-care center, a children's clothing store and an Internet-based company.

3941 ■ "Manulife Posts Billion-Dollar Profit" in Globe & Mail (February 14, 2007, pp. B7)
Pub: CTVglobemedia Publishing Inc.
Ed: Andrew Willis. **Description:** Manulife Financial Corp., Canada's largest insurer, reported $1.1 billion profit in the fourth quarter of 2006. The financial results of Manulife reflected a 39 percent rise in quarterly profit at the nation's wealth management division.

3942 ■ "Susan Leger Ferraro Built a $7.2 Million Day Care Business. Now She Wants To Expand-And Cash Out" in Inc. (January 2008, pp. 50-53)
Pub: Gruner & Jahr USA Publishing
Ed: Dalia Fahmy. **Description:** Profile of Susan Leger Ferraro who wants to expand her chain of day care centers into Florida and California and sell part of her 87 percent stake to reduce financial risk.

STATISTICAL SOURCES

3943 ■ RMA Annual Statement Studies
Pub: Risk Management Association
Contact: Kevin M. Blakey, President
Released: Annual. **Price:** $175.00 2006-07 edition, $105.00. **Description:** Contains composite balance sheets and income statements for more than 360 industries, including the accounting, auditing, and bookkeeping industries. Also contains five years of comparative historical data for discerning trends. Includes 16 commonly used ratios, computed for most of the size groupings for nearly every industry.

3944 ■ U.S. Child Day Care Services: An Industry Analysis 6th Edition
Pub: MarketResearch.com
Released: 2005. **Price:** $2695.00. **Description:** A major source of public information about any industry or market analyzed by Marketdata is the U.S. Government--the most prolific producer of business information in the world.

TRADE PERIODICALS

3945 ■ ACEI Exchange
Pub: Association for Childhood Education International
Contact: Debora Wisneski, President
E-mail: deboraw@uwm.edu
Ed: Deborah Jordan Kravitz, Editor, aceied@aol.com. **Released:** 5/year. **Price:** Included in membership. **Description:** Concerned with the Association's goal of promoting good educational programs and practices for children from infancy through early adolescence. Provides information on resources, publications, and Association activities. Recurring features include calls for papers and presenters, letters to the editor, and a calendar of events.

3946 ■ Change: The Magazine of Higher Learning
Pub: Heldref Publications
URL(s): www.heldref.org/change.php. **Released:** Bimonthly **Price:** €52, Individuals print only; £39, Institutions print only; $64, Individuals print and online; $207, Institutions print and online.

3947 ■ Child Care Bridges
Pub: Manitoba Child Care Association
Contact: Pat Wedge, Executive Director
E-mail: clairefunk@mccahouse.org
Description: advocates for a quality system of child care, to advance early childhood education as a profession , and to provide services to our members.

3948 ■ Child Care Plus
Pub: The University of Montana
Ed: Sandra L. Morris, Editor, slmorris@selway.umt. edu. **Released:** Quarterly. **Price:** $8; $15, two years; $20 three years. **Description:** Aims to support the efforts of care providers who care for children with physical, developmental, or medical disabilities in the child-care setting. Provides practical hints, notes from

parents, community collaboration, answers to common questions, and spotlighted programs and resources.Includes columns titled Spotlight, What Do I Do When, From the Source, Notes from Home, Making it Work, and Resource Review.

3949 ■ Child Welfare: Journal of Policy, Practice, and Program
Pub: Child Welfare League of America Inc.
Contact: Chris James-Brown, President
E-mail: cjamesbrown@cwla.org
URL(s): www.cwla.org/pubs/welcome.htm. **Released:** Bimonthly **Price:** $140, Canada and Mexico; $195, Institutions; $210, Other countries; $265, Institutions, other countries; $255, Individuals 2 years; $395, Other countries 2 years; $340, Institutions 2 years; $480, Institutions, other countries 2 years.

3950 ■ School Age Notes
Pub: Richard T. Scofield
Ed: Richard T. Scofield, Editor. **Released:** Monthly. **Price:** $31.95, U.S.; $31.95, Canada; $33.95, elsewhere. **Description:** Carries ideas for activities and games that are developmentally oriented for school-age children. Offers curricula, advice, news, and think-pieces for improving school-age child care. Recurring features include book reviews, a list of resources, notices of events, and columns titled Director's Corner, Developmental Notes, Activities, Curriculum Corner, and Administrative Notes.

3951 ■ Young Children: The Journal of the National Association for the Education of Young Children
Pub: National Association for the Education of Young Children
Contact: Stephanie Fanjul, President
URL(s): www.naeyc.org/yc/. **Released:** 5/yr. **Price:** $65, Individuals; $100, Institutions; $85, Other countries; $120, Institutions, other countries.

VIDEOCASSETTES/ AUDIOCASSETTES

3952 ■ The Adventures of Elmer and Friends: Freedom Rocks
Leslie T. McClure
PO Box 1223
Pebble Beach, CA 93953
Ph: (831)656-0553
Fax: (831)656-0555
Co. E-mail: leslie@411videoinfo.com
URL: http://www.411videoinfo.com
Released: 1998. **Price:** $14.95. **Description:** Live action musical program for children stars Elmer the tree and a variety of friends. Stresses the importance of nature and equality. **Availability:** VHS.

3953 ■ The Adventures of Elmer and Friends: Pirate Island
Leslie T. McClure
PO Box 1223
Pebble Beach, CA 93953
Ph: (831)656-0553
Fax: (831)656-0555
Co. E-mail: leslie@411videoinfo.com
URL: http://www.411videoinfo.com
Released: 1998. **Price:** $14.95. **Description:** Live action musical program for children stars Elmer the tree and a variety of friends. Stresses the importance of friendship. **Availability:** VHS.

3954 ■ The Adventures of Elmer and Friends: The Magic Map
Leslie T. McClure
PO Box 1223
Pebble Beach, CA 93953
Ph: (831)656-0553
Fax: (831)656-0555
Co. E-mail: leslie@411videoinfo.com
URL: http://www.411videoinfo.com
Released: 1998. **Price:** $14.95. **Description:** Live action musical program for children stars Elmer the tree and a variety of friends. Stresses the importance of reading. **Availability:** VHS.

3955 ■ The Adventures of Elmer and Friends: Treasure Beyond Measure
Leslie T. McClure
PO Box 1223
Pebble Beach, CA 93953
Ph: (831)656-0553
Fax: (831)656-0555
Co. E-mail: leslie@411videoinfo.com
URL: http://www.411videoinfo.com
Released: 1998. **Price:** $14.95. **Description:** Live action musical program for children stars Elmer the tree and a variety of friends. Stresses the importance of self-esteem. **Availability:** VHS.

3956 ■ Ages of Infancy: Caring for Young, Mobile, and Older Infants
California State Department of Education
CDE Press
1430 N St.
Sacramento, CA 95814-5901
Ph: (916)445-1260
Free: 800-995-4099
Fax: (916)323-0823
URL: http://www.cde.ca.gov/
Released: 1990. **Price:** $65.00. **Description:** Identifies the three stages of infant development, as well as each stage's accompanying development issue. Provides guidelines and suggestions for caregiving in each stage. A 10-page video magazine is included. **Availability:** VHS.

3957 ■ The Alphabet Jungle Game
Sony Wonder
550 Madison Ave.
New York, NY 10022-3211
Ph: (212)833-8100
Co. E-mail: Lisa_Davis@sonyusa.com
URL: http://www.sonywondertechlab.com
Released: 1998. **Price:** $12.98. **Description:** Sesame Street characters Elmo, Zoe, and Telly explore the alphabet in this collection of segments from the popular children's show. **Availability:** VHS.

3958 ■ Art Surprises
Tapeworm Video Distributors
25876 The Old Road #141
Stevenson Ranch, CA 91381
Ph: (661)257-4904
Fax: (661)257-4820
Co. E-mail: sales@tapeworm.com
URL: http://www.tapeworm.com
Released: 1998. **Price:** $29.95. **Description:** Donna Erickson presents creative projects for children of all ages, including Fish Prints and Potato Jewelry. **Availability:** VHS.

3959 ■ Baby See, Baby Do
Leslie T. McClure
PO Box 1223
Pebble Beach, CA 93953
Ph: (831)656-0553
Fax: (831)656-0555
Co. E-mail: leslie@411videoinfo.com
URL: http://www.411videoinfo.com
Released: 1998. **Price:** $14.95. **Description:** Contains images and sounds intended to delight infants and their caregivers. **Availability:** VHS.

3960 ■ Backyard Safari
GPN Educational Media
1550 Executive Drive
Elgin, IL 60123
Ph: (402)472-2007
Free: 800-228-4630
Fax: (800)306-2330
Co. E-mail: askgpn@smarterville.com
URL: http://www.shopgpn.com
Released: 1998. **Price:** $467.35. **Description:** Series of 13 30-minute videos designed to teach preschool children through grade six basic science and natural history. **Availability:** VHS.

3961 ■ The Big Comfy Couch: Are You Ready for School?
Tapeworm Video Distributors
25876 The Old Road #141
Stevenson Ranch, CA 91381
Ph: (661)257-4904

Fax: (661)257-4820
Co. E-mail: sales@tapeworm.com
URL: http://www.tapeworm.com
Released: 1998. **Price:** $12.99. **Description:**
Loonette and Molly entertain children and stress
important themes, including sharing and cooperation.
Availability: VHS.

**3962 ■ The Big Comfy Couch: Be Nice,
Snicklefritz!**
Tapeworm Video Distributors
25876 The Old Road #141
Stevenson Ranch, CA 91381
Ph: (661)257-4904
Fax: (661)257-4820
Co. E-mail: sales@tapeworm.com
URL: http://www.tapeworm.com
Released: 1998. **Price:** $12.99. **Description:**
Loonette and Molly entertain children and stress
important themes, including sharing and cooperation.
Availability: VHS.

**3963 ■ The Big Comfy Couch: Dustbunny
Dreams**
Tapeworm Video Distributors
25876 The Old Road #141
Stevenson Ranch, CA 91381
Ph: (661)257-4904
Fax: (661)257-4820
Co. E-mail: sales@tapeworm.com
URL: http://www.tapeworm.com
Released: 1998. **Price:** $12.99. **Description:**
Loonette and Molly entertain children and stress
important themes, including sharing and cooperation.
Availability: VHS.

3964 ■ Blue's Clues: Arts and Crafts
Paramount Home Video
5555 Melrose Ave.
Los Angeles, CA 90038
Ph: (323)956-5000
URL: http://www.paramount.com
Released: 1998. **Price:** $9.95. **Description:** Ani-
mated puppy "Blue" and live action host Steve invite
youngsters to learn through solving clues in "Adven-
tures in Art" and "What Does Blue Want to Make?".
Availability: VHS.

3965 ■ Blue's Clues: Story Time
Paramount Home Video
5555 Melrose Ave.
Los Angeles, CA 90038
Ph: (323)956-5000
URL: http://www.paramount.com
Released: 1998. **Price:** $9.95. **Description:** Ani-
mated puppy "Blue" and live action host Steve invite
youngsters to learn through solving clues in "What's
Blue's Favorite Story?" and "What Story Does Blue
Want to Play?". **Availability:** VHS.

3966 ■ Child Safety
Janson Media
88 Semmens Rd.
Harrington Park, NJ 07640
Ph: (201)784-8488
Free: 800-818-4066
Fax: (201)784-3993
Co. E-mail: betsy@janson.com
URL: http://www.janson.com
Contact: Stephen Janson, President
Released: 1998. **Price:** $19.95. **Description:** Guides
parents and caregivers in keeping children safe from
accidental harm. **Availability:** VHS.

3967 ■ Child's Play: The World of Learning
Educational Productions Inc.
7101 Wisconsin Ave., Ste. 700
Bethesda, MD 20814
Free: 800-637-3652
Fax: (301)634-0826
Co. E-mail: customerrelations@teachingstrategies.
  com
URL: http://www.edpro.com
Released: 1990. **Price:** $295.00. **Description:** This
video for teachers, administrators, parents, students
and aides takes a look at the implications of children's
play, including how they build thinking, language, mo-

tor, social and emotional skills, prepare for academic
learning, set foundations for reading and writing and
much more. **Availability:** VHS; 3/4 U.

3968 ■ Colors and Shapes Circus
Leslie T. McClure
PO Box 1223
Pebble Beach, CA 93953
Ph: (831)656-0553
Fax: (831)656-0555
Co. E-mail: leslie@411videoinfo.com
URL: http://www.411videoinfo.com
Released: 1998. **Price:** $19.95. **Description:**
Teaches young children primary and secondary
colors and basic shapes. **Availability:** VHS.

3969 ■ Connecting—Grades K-8
Crystal Productions
1812 Johns Dr.
Box 2159
Glenview, IL 60025-6519
Ph: (847)657-8144
Free: 800-255-8629
Fax: (847)657-8149
Co. E-mail: custserv@crystalproductions.com
URL: http://www.crystalproductions.com
Released: 19??. **Price:** $239.00. **Description:** Still-
frame teaching aid for art appreciation presents art
work in themes so that relationships, comparisons,
and connections are more easily seen. **Availability:**
VHS.

3970 ■ Day Care Grows Up
Films for the Humanities & Sciences
132 West 31st Street
New York, NY 10001
Ph: (609)671-1000
Free: 800-257-5126
Fax: (609)671-0266
Co. E-mail: custserv@films.com
URL: http://www.films.com
Released: 1991. **Price:** $159.00. **Description:**
Discusses the new attitudes and measures being
taken to increase the quality of childcare in the U.S.
Availability: VHS.

3971 ■ Fingerplays and Footplays
Educational Activities, Inc.
PO Box 87
Baldwin, NY 11510
Free: 800-797-3223
Fax: (516)623-9282
URL: http://www.edact.com
Released: 1997. **Price:** $19.95. **Description:** Pre-
sents activities that encourage dramatic play and help
focus children's attention. **Availability:** VHS.

**3972 ■ First Moves: Welcoming a Child to a
New Caregiving Setting**
California State Department of Education
CDE Press
1430 N St.
Sacramento, CA 95814-5901
Ph: (916)445-1260
Free: 800-995-4099
Fax: (916)323-0823
URL: http://www.cde.ca.gov/
Released: 1988. **Price:** $65.00. **Description:** Child-
care professionals are taught how to make their kids
comfortable right from the start. **Availability:** VHS.

3973 ■ Friends and Strangers
Tapeworm Video Distributors
25876 The Old Road #141
Stevenson Ranch, CA 91381
Ph: (661)257-4904
Fax: (661)257-4820
Co. E-mail: sales@tapeworm.com
URL: http://www.tapeworm.com
Released: 19??. **Price:** $14.95. **Description:** Pro-
vides children with tips to distinguish the differences
between friends and strangers. **Availability:** VHS.

3974 ■ Good Choices . . . Bad Choices
Tapeworm Video Distributors
25876 The Old Road #141
Stevenson Ranch, CA 91381
Ph: (661)257-4904

Fax: (661)257-4820
Co. E-mail: sales@tapeworm.com
URL: http://www.tapeworm.com
Released: 19??. **Price:** $14.95. **Description:** Pro-
vides children with tips to distinguish the differences
between good choices and bad choices. **Availability:**
VHS.

3975 ■ Good Discipline, Good Kids
Sunburst Digital Inc.
1550 Executive Dr.
Elgin, IL 60123-9311
Free: 800-321-7511
Fax: (914)747-4109
Co. E-mail: service@sunburst.com
URL: http://www.sunburst.com
Contact: Dan Figurski, President
Released: 1998. **Price:** $99.95. **Description:** Parent-
ing experts Adele Faber and Elaine Mazlish provide
tips and techniques to develop a consistent approach
to disciplining children. **Availability:** VHS.

3976 ■ The Great Numbers Game
Sony Wonder
550 Madison Ave.
New York, NY 10022-3211
Ph: (212)833-8100
Co. E-mail: Lisa_Davis@sonyusa.com
URL: http://www.sonywondertechlab.com
Released: 1998. **Price:** $12.98. **Description:**
Sesame Street characters Elmo, Gabi, and Telly learn
about numbers in this collection of segments from
the popular children's show. **Availability:** VHS.

3977 ■ Help Your Child Succeed in School
Sunburst Digital Inc.
1550 Executive Dr.
Elgin, IL 60123-9311
Free: 800-321-7511
Fax: (914)747-4109
Co. E-mail: service@sunburst.com
URL: http://www.sunburst.com
Contact: Dan Figurski, President
Released: 1998. **Price:** $99.95. **Description:** Parent-
ing experts Adele Faber and Elaine Mazlish provide
tips and techniques to develop the self-discipline and
self-confidence needed for a child's success in
school. **Availability:** VHS.

3978 ■ Hola Amigos: Spanish for Kids
PBS Home Video
Catalog Fulfillment Center
Charlotte, NC 28275-1089
Ph: (800)531-4727
Free: 800-645-4PBS
Co. E-mail: info@pbs.org
URL: http://www.pbs.org
Released: 1998. **Price:** $54.95. **Description:** Roung
viewers will learn the basics of Spanish, including the
words for colors, letters, numbers, pets and animals,
musical instuments and sports. Uses the adventures
of cartoon dog Paco to ease youngsters into the
Spanish language. Two hours and 30 minutes on
three videocassettes. **Availability:** VHS.

3979 ■ Imagineria
Crystal Productions
1812 Johns Dr.
Box 2159
Glenview, IL 60025-6519
Ph: (847)657-8144
Free: 800-255-8629
Fax: (847)657-8149
Co. E-mail: custserv@crystalproductions.com
URL: http://www.crystalproductions.com
Released: 19??. **Price:** $9.98. **Description:** Com-
puter animated teaching aid for art education de-
signed for children. **Availability:** VHS.

3980 ■ Imaginit
Crystal Productions
1812 Johns Dr.
Box 2159
Glenview, IL 60025-6519
Ph: (847)657-8144
Free: 800-255-8629

Fax: (847)657-8149
Co. E-mail: custserv@crystalproductions.com
URL: http://www.crystalproductions.com
Released: 19??. **Price:** $12.98. **Description:** Computer animated teaching aid for art education that encourages children to imagine. **Availability:** VHS.

3981 ■ Inside Business Today
GPN Educational Media
1550 Executive Drive
Elgin, IL 60123
Ph: (402)472-2007
Free: 800-228-4630
Fax: (800)306-2330
Co. E-mail: askgpn@smarterville.com
URL: http://www.shopgpn.com
Released: 1989. **Description:** Leaders in business and industry tell their success stories in this extensive series. **Availability:** VHS; 3/4 U.

3982 ■ The Just So Stories, Vol. 1
Interama, Inc.
301 W. 53rd St., Ste. 19E
New York, NY 10019
Ph: (212)977-4830
Fax: (212)581-6582
Released: 1998. **Price:** $14.95. **Description:** Animated rendering of Rudyard Kipling's tales of the natural world. Includes "How the Elephant Got His Trunk," "How the Rhinoceros Got His Skin," and "The Beginning of Armadillos.". **Availability:** VHS.

3983 ■ The Just So Stories, Vol. 2
Interama, Inc.
301 W. 53rd St., Ste. 19E
New York, NY 10019
Ph: (212)977-4830
Fax: (212)581-6582
Released: 1998. **Price:** $14.95. **Description:** Animated rendering of Rudyard Kipling's tales of the natural world. Includes "How the Whale Got His Throat," "How the Leopard Got His Spots," and "How the Camel Got His Hump.". **Availability:** VHS.

3984 ■ The Just So Stories, Vol. 3
Interama, Inc.
301 W. 53rd St., Ste. 19E
New York, NY 10019
Ph: (212)977-4830
Fax: (212)581-6582
Released: 1998. **Price:** $14.95. **Description:** Animated rendering of Rudyard Kipling's tales of the natural world. Includes "Why the Cat Is Walking By Himself" and "How the Crab Played with the Sea.". **Availability:** VHS.

3985 ■ Kitchen Capers
Tapeworm Video Distributors
25876 The Old Road #141
Stevenson Ranch, CA 91381
Ph: (661)257-4904
Fax: (661)257-4820
Co. E-mail: sales@tapeworm.com
URL: http://www.tapeworm.com
Released: 1998. **Price:** $9.99. **Description:** Donna Erickson presents creative projects for children of all ages, including Wacky Bubble Brew, Handmade Ice Cream, and Gooey Goop. **Availability:** VHS.

3986 ■ Learning about Honesty
Sunburst Digital Inc.
1550 Executive Dr.
Elgin, IL 60123-9311
Free: 800-321-7511
Fax: (914)747-4109
Co. E-mail: service@sunburst.com
URL: http://www.sunburst.com
Contact: Dan Figurski, President
Released: 1998. **Price:** $59.95. **Description:** Provides children grades K-2 with a basis for understanding honesty through vignettes and an entertaining host, "The Truth Fairy.". **Availability:** VHS.

3987 ■ Let's Create for Halloween
Crystal Productions
1812 Johns Dr.
Box 2159
Glenview, IL 60025-6519
Ph: (847)657-8144

Free: 800-255-8629
Fax: (847)657-8149
Co. E-mail: custserv@crystalproductions.com
URL: http://www.crystalproductions.com
Released: 19??. **Price:** $24.95. **Description:** Guides children through a number of art activities appropriate for Halloween. **Availability:** VHS.

3988 ■ Let's Create for Thanksgiving
Crystal Productions
1812 Johns Dr.
Box 2159
Glenview, IL 60025-6519
Ph: (847)657-8144
Free: 800-255-8629
Fax: (847)657-8149
Co. E-mail: custserv@crystalproductions.com
URL: http://www.crystalproductions.com
Released: 19??. **Price:** $24.95. **Description:** Guides children through a number of art activities appropriate for Thanksgiving. **Availability:** VHS.

3989 ■ Moving Freely: A Creative Dance Class
Tapeworm Video Distributors
25876 The Old Road #141
Stevenson Ranch, CA 91381
Ph: (661)257-4904
Fax: (661)257-4820
Co. E-mail: sales@tapeworm.com
URL: http://www.tapeworm.com
Released: 19??. **Price:** $14.95. **Description:** Presents a movement class for children 3-10 incorporating elements of technique, rhythm, locomotion, composition and sharing. **Availability:** VHS.

3990 ■ The Number Express
Leslie T. McClure
PO Box 1223
Pebble Beach, CA 93953
Ph: (831)656-0553
Fax: (831)656-0555
Co. E-mail: leslie@411videoinfo.com
URL: http://www.411videoinfo.com
Released: 1998. **Price:** $19.95. **Description:** The engineer of a steam engine teaches young children numbers, number relationships, and counting skills. **Availability:** VHS.

3991 ■ 101 Dalmatians: Pongo and Perdita Sing Along Songs
Buena Vista Home Entertainment
500 S Buena Vista St.
Burbank, CA 91521-1120
Ph: (800)723-4763
Fax: (818)845-8728
URL: http://www.bvhe.com
Contact: Bob Chapek, President
Released: 1997. **Price:** $12.99. **Description:** Encourages children to sing, dance and play along with a collection of "dog-themed" tunes. **Availability:** VHS.

3992 ■ Potty Training One, Two, Three
Tapeworm Video Distributors
25876 The Old Road #141
Stevenson Ranch, CA 91381
Ph: (661)257-4904
Fax: (661)257-4820
Co. E-mail: sales@tapeworm.com
URL: http://www.tapeworm.com
Released: 1997. **Price:** $19.95. **Description:** Genie Z. Laborde, Ph.D., provides guidelines for quick and easy potty training. **Availability:** VHS.

3993 ■ Respectfully Yours: Magda Gerber's Approach to Professional Infant/Toddler Care
California State Department of Education
CDE Press
1430 N St.
Sacramento, CA 95814-5901
Ph: (916)445-1260
Free: 800-995-4099
Fax: (916)323-0823
URL: http://www.cde.ca.gov/
Released: 1988. **Price:** $65.00. **Description:** This is an introductory guide for people who want to learn how to care for young children. **Availability:** VHS.

3994 ■ Schedules and Routines: Why Bother?
AAVIM
220 Smithonia Rd.
Winterville, GA 30683-9257
Ph: (706)742-5355
Free: 800-228-4689
Fax: (706)742-7005
Co. E-mail: sales@aavim.com
URL: http://www.aavim.com
Released: 19??. **Price:** $89.95. **Description:** Part of the Child Care Worker Series. Offers advice on planning schedules according to objectives of the child care facility, including times children arrive and leave, amount of time at the facility, number and ages of children and adults, balance of active and quiet activities, and the time of the year and weather. Includes study guide. **Availability:** VHS.

3995 ■ See How They Grow: Farm Animals
Environmental Media
PO Box 99
Beaufort, SC 29901
Ph: (843)474-0147
Free: 800-368-3382
Fax: (843)986-9093
Co. E-mail: bpendergraft@envmedia.com
URL: http://www.envmedia.com
Released: 19??. **Price:** $12.95. **Description:** Part of a ten-volume teaching aid for environmental education that presents the birth and growth of different animal groups in a manner appropriate for young children. Covers chickens, pigs, calves, and lambs. **Availability:** VHS.

3996 ■ See How They Grow: Forest Animals
Environmental Media
PO Box 99
Beaufort, SC 29901
Ph: (843)474-0147
Free: 800-368-3382
Fax: (843)986-9093
Co. E-mail: bpendergraft@envmedia.com
URL: http://www.envmedia.com
Released: 19??. **Price:** $12.95. **Description:** Part of a ten-volume teaching aid for environmental education that presents the birth and growth of different animal groups in a manner appropriate for young children. Covers owls, mice, ants, and chipmunks. **Availability:** VHS.

3997 ■ See How They Grow: Insects and Spiders
Environmental Media
PO Box 99
Beaufort, SC 29901
Ph: (843)474-0147
Free: 800-368-3382
Fax: (843)986-9093
Co. E-mail: bpendergraft@envmedia.com
URL: http://www.envmedia.com
Released: 19??. **Price:** $12.95. **Description:** Part of a ten-volume teaching aid for environmental education that presents the birth and growth of different animal groups in a manner appropriate for young children. Covers ladybugs, spiders, butterflies, and grasshoppers. **Availability:** VHS.

3998 ■ See How They Grow: Pets
Environmental Media
PO Box 99
Beaufort, SC 29901
Ph: (843)474-0147
Free: 800-368-3382
Fax: (843)986-9093
Co. E-mail: bpendergraft@envmedia.com
URL: http://www.envmedia.com
Released: 19??. **Price:** $12.95. **Description:** Part of a ten-volume teaching aid for environmental education that presents the birth and growth of different animal groups in a manner appropriate for young children. Covers puppies, kittens, parakeets, and goldfish. **Availability:** VHS.

3999 ■ See How They Grow: Pond Animals
Environmental Media
PO Box 99
Beaufort, SC 29901

Ph: (843)474-0147
Free: 800-368-3382
Fax: (843)986-9093
Co. E-mail: bpendergraft@envmedia.com
URL: http://www.envmedia.com
Released: 19??. **Price:** $12.95. **Description:** Part of a ten-volume teaching aid for environmental education that presents the birth and growth of different animal groups in a manner appropriate for young children. Covers dragonflies, frogs, ducks, and salamanders. **Availability:** VHS.

4000 ■ See How They Grow: Wild Animals
Environmental Media
PO Box 99
Beaufort, SC 29901
Ph: (843)474-0147
Free: 800-368-3382
Fax: (843)986-9093
Co. E-mail: bpendergraft@envmedia.com
URL: http://www.envmedia.com
Released: 19??. **Price:** $12.95. **Description:** Part of a ten-volume teaching aid for environmental education that presents the birth and growth of different animal groups in a manner appropriate for young children. Covers rabbits, foxes, pheasants, and snakes. **Availability:** VHS.

4001 ■ So Smart
Tapeworm Video Distributors
25876 The Old Road #141
Stevenson Ranch, CA 91381
Ph: (661)257-4904
Fax: (661)257-4820
Co. E-mail: sales@tapeworm.com
URL: http://www.tapeworm.com
Released: 1997. **Price:** $14.95. **Description:** Infant stimulation video designed to enhance intellectual development. **Availability:** VHS.

4002 ■ S.O.S. Kids: Infant/Child Emergency Life Saving Video
Tapeworm Video Distributors
25876 The Old Road #141
Stevenson Ranch, CA 91381
Ph: (661)257-4904
Fax: (661)257-4820
Co. E-mail: sales@tapeworm.com
URL: http://www.tapeworm.com
Released: 1997. **Price:** $19.95. **Description:** EMT Paramedic Richard Hardman describes and demonstrates what to do in various medical emergencies. **Availability:** VHS.

4003 ■ Table Time for Tots
Tapeworm Video Distributors
25876 The Old Road #141
Stevenson Ranch, CA 91381
Ph: (661)257-4904
Fax: (661)257-4820
Co. E-mail: sales@tapeworm.com
URL: http://www.tapeworm.com
Released: 1997. **Price:** $14.95. **Description:** Introduces children to the basic food groups using poem and song. **Availability:** VHS.

4004 ■ Wilbur Sings the Classics
Tapeworm Video Distributors
25876 The Old Road #141
Stevenson Ranch, CA 91381
Ph: (661)257-4904
Fax: (661)257-4820
Co. E-mail: sales@tapeworm.com
URL: http://www.tapeworm.com
Released: 1997. **Price:** $14.95. **Description:** Wilbur the Cow leads children in singing nursery rhyme favorites. **Availability:** VHS.

4005 ■ Wilton Appreciation Series 100—Grades K-4
Crystal Productions
1812 Johns Dr.
Box 2159
Glenview, IL 60025-6519
Ph: (847)657-8144
Free: 800-255-8629

Fax: (847)657-8149
Co. E-mail: custserv@crystalproductions.com
URL: http://www.crystalproductions.com
Released: 19??. **Price:** $199.00. **Description:** Still-frame teaching aid for art appreciation introduces children to the elements of design. **Availability:** VHS.

TRADE SHOWS AND CONVENTIONS

4006 ■ Association for Childhood Education International Annual International Conference & Exhibition
Association for Childhood Education International (ACEI)
17904 Georgia Ave., Ste. 215
Olney, MD 20832
Ph: (301)570-2111
Free: 800-423-3563
Fax: (301)570-2212
Co. E-mail: headquarters@acei.org
URL: http://www.acei.org
Contact: Debora Wisneski, President
E-mail: deboraw@uwm.edu
URL(s): www.acei.org/. **Price:** $143, Pre-registered, members; $227, Pre-registered, non-members; $179, Onsite registered, members; $239, Onsite registered, non-members. **Frequency:** Annual. **Audience:** Teachers, teacher educators, day-care personnel, and related professionals. **Principal Exhibits:** Commercial and educational exhibits of interest to teachers, teacher educators, college students, daycare personnel and other care givers.

4007 ■ National Association for the Education of Young Children Annual Conference
National Association for the Education of Young Children (NAEYC)
1313 L St. NW, Ste. 500
Washington, DC 20005
Ph: (202)232-8777
Free: 800-424-2460
Fax: (202)328-1846
Co. E-mail: naeyc@naeyc.org
URL: http://www.naeyc.org
Contact: Stephanie Fanjul, President
URL(s): www.naeyc.org/conference/. **Price:** $280, Members early-bird; $370, Non-members early-bird. **Frequency:** Annual. **Audience:** Professionals in early childhood education. **Principal Exhibits:** Educational materials and equipment designed for children ages birth through eight years old. **Telecommunication Services:** conference@naeyc.org.

FRANCHISES AND BUSINESS OPPORTUNITIES

4008 ■ Baby Power / Forever Kids
Searles Corp.
PO Box 526
Annandale, NJ 08801
Ph: (908)7136547
Free: 800-365-4847
Fax: (908)713-6547
Description: Developmentally appropriate gymnastic and musical parent/child play and enrichment programs. Carefully designed to build confidence and promote child development, parent communication and bonding. The purpose of the Baby Power program is to stimulate during the most formative growth period 6 months to 3 years. The Forever Kids programs at Baby Power are designed to develop the second phase in a child's development, 3-5 years. **No. of Franchise Units:** 5. **Founded:** 1975. **Franchised:** 1998. **Equity Capital Needed:** $85,000-$105,000, total investment. **Franchise Fee:** $25,000. **Training:** Yes.

4009 ■ Children's Lighthouse Franchise Co.
101 S Jennings Ave., Ste. 209
Fort Worth, TX 76104
Ph: (888)338-4466

Fax: (817)338-2716
Co. E-mail: info@ChildrensLighthouse.com
URL: http://childrenslighthouse.com
Description: Childcare franchise. **No. of Franchise Units:** 24. **No. of Company-Owned Units:** 8. **Founded:** 1997.. **Franchised:** 1999. **Equity Capital Needed:** $501,500-$3,351,000 total investment. **Franchise Fee:** $60,000. **Royalty Fee:** 7%. **Financial Assistance:** Third party financing available. **Training:** Available at headquarters for 4 weeks, 4 weeks at franchisee's location, unlimited training for the first year and unlimited support.

4010 ■ CHIP - The Child ID Program
30961 Agoura Rd., No. 101
Westlake Village, CA 91361
Ph: (805)557-0577
Fax: (805)557-0587
Description: Child ID and school safety program. **No. of Franchise Units:** 152. **No. of Company-Owned Units:** 1. **Founded:** 2001.. **Franchised:** 2002. **Equity Capital Needed:** $10,990-$14,990. **Franchise Fee:** $10,990-$14,990. **Financial Assistance:** Financial ssistance available for franchise fee. **Training:** Yes.

4011 ■ CLIX
COMON Group, Inc.
2496 W Ridge Rd.
Rochester, NY 14626
Ph: (585)262-2549
Free: 888-2GO-CLIX
Fax: (203)413-6311
Co. E-mail: franchise@getyourclix.com
URL: http://www.clixfranchise.com
Description: Dedicated to creating a digital portrait experience like no other. With the latest in technology, a proprietary proven system, and focus on service and our customer's experience. Offering a unique multifaceted business opportunity. **No. of Franchise Units:** 8. **Founded:** 1999. **Franchised:** 2005. **Equity Capital Needed:** $50,184-$398,000. **Franchise Fee:** $21,000 or $29,500. **Training:** Training includes pre-opening, store set-up and onsite training.

4012 ■ College Nannies & Tutors
Franchise Development Group
1415 Wayzata Blvd., E
Wayzata, MN 55391
Ph: (952)476-0262
Free: 888-92N-anny
Fax: (952)476-0264
Description: Childcare and academic support. **No. of Franchise Units:** 42. **Founded:** 2001.. **Franchised:** 2005. **Equity Capital Needed:** $50,000-$125,000. **Franchise Fee:** $25,000-$35,000. **Training:** Yes.

4013 ■ Creative World School Franchising Co., Inc.
Creative World School, Inc.
25110 Bernwood Dr., St. 104
Bonita Springs, FL 34135
Ph: (561)755-3635
Free: 800-362-5940
Fax: (239)437-0507
URL: http://www.creativeworldschool.com
Description: Childcare centers. **No. of Franchise Units:** 9. **No. of Company-Owned Units:** 11. **Founded:** 1970.. **Franchised:** 2000. **Equity Capital Needed:** $200,000 plus. **Franchise Fee:** $50,000. **Training:** Extensive training at our facility and onsite staff training at your location with ongoing support.

4014 ■ DigiKids
DIGIKIDS, INC.
9463 Hwy. 377 S, Ste. 111
Fort Worth, TX 76126
Free: 888-DIGI-KIDS
Fax: (817)886-3655
Description: Onsite child safety ID program. **No. of Franchise Units:** 10. **Founded:** 2003.. **Franchised:** 2004. **Equity Capital Needed:** $32,310-$40,210 total investment. **Franchise Fee:** $29,900. **Training:** Yes.

4015 ■ Goddard School

Goddard Systems
1016 9th Ave.
King of Prussia, PA 19406
Ph: (800)272-4901
Fax: (610)265-6931
Description: High-quality pre-school, offering day care hours. All Goddard teachers hold 4-year degrees in early childhood or elementary education. **No. of Franchise Units:** 290. **Founded:** 1988.. **Franchised:** 1988. **Equity Capital Needed:** $120,000 liquid; $477,260-$524,600 total investment. **Franchise Fee:** $135,000. **Financial Assistance:** Yes. **Training:** Yes.

4016 ■ Guard-A-Kid

Guard-A-Kid Franchising Corp.
3785 NW 82nd Ave., Ste. 106
Miami, FL 33166
Ph: (305)477-3301
Free: 800-679-4256
Fax: (305)489-0311
Description: Digital child identification and safety program. **No. of Franchise Units:** 160. **No. of Company-Owned Units:** 1. **No. of Operating Units:** 164. **Founded:** 2004.. **Franchised:** 2005. **Equity Capital Needed:** $14,900-$19,900. **Franchise Fee:** $14,900-$19,900. **Financial Assistance:** Third party financing available. **Training:** Provides 2 days training at headquarters, including monthly conference calls, bi-weekly workshops, and ongoing support.

4017 ■ Gymboree Play and Music

Gymboree Corp.
500 Howard St.
San Francisco, CA 94105
Ph: (415)278-7925
Fax: (415)278-7452
Co. E-mail: play_franchise@gymboree.com
URL: http://www.gymboree.com
Description: Parent and child participation play & music program. Specialized equipment, songs and games. Classes offered for children - newborn through 5 years of age. **No. of Franchise Units:** 658. **No. of Company-Owned Units:** 8. **Founded:** 1976.. **Franchised:** 1978. **Equity Capital Needed:** $77,000-$270,950. **Franchise Fee:** $45,000/$25,000 metro model. **Training:** Offers initial training and also regional training. Franchises receive continued support in programming, operations, and marketing.

4018 ■ The Honors Learning Center

PO Box 24055
Chattanooga, TN 37422-4055
Ph: (423)892-1803
Fax: (423)892-1803
Description: Supplemental education and academic testing. **No. of Franchise Units:** 1. **Founded:** 1987.. **Franchised:** 1992. **Equity Capital Needed:** $64,500-$68,700. **Franchise Fee:** $25,000. **Training:** Yes.

4019 ■ JumpBunch, Inc.

302 Annapolis St.
Annapolis, MD 21401
Ph: (410)703-2300
Fax: (410)268-0465
Co. E-mail: tbunchman@jumpbunch.com
URL: http://www.jumpbunch.com
Description: Teaching sports and fitness to children. **No. of Franchise Units:** 28. **Founded:** 1997.. **Franchised:** 2002. **Equity Capital Needed:** $75,000. **Franchise Fee:** $25,000-$30,000. **Training:** Yes.

4020 ■ J.W. Tumbles

312 S Cedros, Ste. 329
Solana Beach, CA 92075
Ph: (858)794-0484
Fax: (858)794-0398
Description: Children's gym for fitness & fun. **No. of Franchise Units:** 33. **No. of Company-Owned Units:** 1. **Founded:** 1994.. **Franchised:** 2004. **Equity Capital Needed:** $138,600-$215,600. **Franchise Fee:** $42,850. **Training:** Yes.

4021 ■ Kid to Kid

BaseCamp Franchising, LLC
170 S 1000 E
Salt Lake City, UT 84102
Ph: (801)359-0071
Free: 888-543-2543

Fax: (801)359-3207
Co. E-mail: sterling@kidtokid.com
URL: http://www.kidtokid.com
Description: Resale store for children's clothing and toys. **No. of Franchise Units:** 72. **No. of Company-Owned Units:** 1. **Founded:** 1992. **Franchised:** 1994. **Equity Capital Needed:** $196,028-$272,718. **Franchise Fee:** $25,000. **Royalty Fee:** 5%. **Financial Assistance:** Third party financing available. **Training:** Offers 10 days at headquarters, 3 days at franchisee's location, 5 days at existing location, and ongoing support.

4022 ■ Kiddie Academy Child Care Learning Centers

3415 Box Hill Corporate Ctr. Dr.
Abingdon, MD 21009
Ph: (800)554-3343
Fax: (410)569-2729
Co. E-mail: sales@kiddieacademy.com
URL: http://www.kiddieacademy.com
Description: Offers an advanced, tested, state-of-the-art curriculum incorporating traditional development milestones, with emphasis on reading skills, language development and social skills. Classes in computers and foreign languages. Infant through age 12. **No. of Franchise Units:** 96. **No. of Company-Owned Units:** 2. **Founded:** 1981.. **Franchised:** 1992. **Equity Capital Needed:** $150,000 liquid; $351,700-$62,000 investment required. **Franchise Fee:** $120,000. **Financial Assistance:** Yes. **Training:** Yes.

4023 ■ Kidokinetics

304 Indian Trace, Ste. 121
Weston, FL 33326
Ph: (954)385-8511
Fax: (954)217-5928
Description: Children's mobile sports/fitness. **No. of Franchise Units:** 3. **No. of Company-Owned Units:** 1. **Founded:** 2000.. **Franchised:** 2007. **Equity Capital Needed:** $42,900-$57,000. **Franchise Fee:** $30,000. **Training:** Yes.

4024 ■ Kidspark, Inc.

2858 Stevens Creek Blvd., Ste. 100
San Jose, CA 95128
Ph: (408)213-0973
Fax: (408)260-7366
Description: Hourly childcare. **No. of Franchise Units:** 14. **No. of Company-Owned Units:** 2. **Founded:** 1988.. **Franchised:** 2004. **Equity Capital Needed:** $172,500-$300,000. **Franchise Fee:** $19,500. **Training:** Yes.

4025 ■ Kinderdance International, Inc.

1333 Gateway Dr., Ste. 1003
Melbourne, FL 32901
Ph: (321)984-4448
Fax: (321)984-4490
Co. E-mail: leads@kinderdance.com
URL: http://www.kinderdance.com
Description: If you enjoy children and have high energy, you can qualify to join in the quality pre-school education through dance, gymnastics and creative movement. No studio required. The program has been taught to thousands of children in hundreds of child-care centers since 1979. Enjoy flexible hours, fulfilling work and adorable customers. Rated one of the top 15 franchises for women by Working Woman Magazine. 24-hours a day, an operations manual, newsletters and active franchisee advisory counsel. **No. of Franchise Units:** 131. **No. of Company-Owned Units:** 2. **Founded:** 1979.. **Franchised:** 1985. **Equity Capital Needed:** $14,950-$46,100, including franchise fee. **Franchise Fee:** $12,000-$40,000. **Financial Assistance:** Yes. **Training:** 1 week training class, field support, ongoing support and an annual training conference provides continuing education.

4026 ■ Little City Kids

10127 Northwestern Ave.
Franksville, WI 53126
Ph: (262)884-4226

Fax: (262)884-4230
Co. E-mail: littlecitykids@tds.net
URL: http://www.littlecitykids.com
Description: Educational playcare for your child. The environment is set into action in an interactive world filled with imagination stations, innovative online curriculum and team teaching methods. We offer two models, the Little City Kids model is for children ages 2-13 years and the Itty Bitty Kids model adds infant and toddler care. **No. of Company-Owned Units:** 1. **Founded:** 1998.. **Franchised:** 2004. **Equity Capital Needed:** $118,000-$189,000. **Franchise Fee:** $35,000. **Royalty Fee:** 7%. **Training:** Available at headquarters 30-60 days, 10 days at franchisee's location and onging support.

4027 ■ The Little Gym

7001 N Scottsdale Rd., Ste. 1050
Scottsdale, AZ 85253
Ph: (480)948-2878
Free: 888-228-2878
Fax: (480)948-2765
Co. E-mail: sales@thelittlegym.com
URL: http://www.thelittlegym.com
Description: Children's fitness centers. **No. of Franchise Units:** 202. **Founded:** 1976. **Franchised:** 1992. **Equity Capital Needed:** $147,500-$294,000. **Franchise Fee:** $39,500-$69,500. **Royalty Fee:** 8%. **Financial Assistance:** Third party financing available. **Training:** Yes.

4028 ■ Little Scientists

25 Higgins Dr.
Milford, CT 06460
Ph: (203)783-1114
Description: Hands-on science education for children. **No. of Franchise Units:** 20. **No. of Company-Owned Units:** 2. **Founded:** 1995.. **Franchised:** 1996. **Equity Capital Needed:** $25,000-$50,000. **Franchise Fee:** $25,000. **Training:** Yes.

4029 ■ Oxford Learning Centers Inc.

747 Hyde Park Rd., Ste. 230
London, ON, Canada N6H 3S3
Ph: (519)473-1207
Free: 888-559-2212
Fax: (519)473-6086
Co. E-mail: franchise@oxfordlearning.com
URL: http://www.oxfordlearning.com
Description: Oxford is an educational franchise in Canada, which provides extensive training in all fields. **No. of Franchise Units:** 108. **No. of Company-Owned Units:** 5. **Founded:** 1984.. **Franchised:** 1991. **Equity Capital Needed:** $140,000-$210,000 plus applicable taxes. **Franchise Fee:** $40,000 plus applicable taxes. **Training:** Provides 2 weeks training and ongoing support.

4030 ■ Pee Wee Workout

Cardiac Carr Co.
34976 Aspenwood Ln.
Willoughby, OH 44094
Ph: (440)946-7888
Fax: (440)946-7888
Description: Fitness programs for children. **No. of Franchise Units:** 25. **No. of Company-Owned Units:** 1. **Founded:** 1986.. **Franchised:** 1987. **Equity Capital Needed:** $2,700. **Franchise Fee:** $2,000. **Training:** Yes.

4031 ■ Primrose School Franchising Co.

3660 Cedarcrest Rd.
Acworth, GA 30101
Ph: (770)529-4100
Fax: (770)529-1551
Co. E-mail: kmusso@primroseschools.com
URL: http://www.primroseschools.com
Description: Quality educational childcare, with proven, traditional curriculum for infants through 4/5 kindergarten, after-school explorers club ages 5-12 years, Spanish, computer intergenerational program and strong parental communication. Programs develop positive self-esteem and a joy of learning. ongoing after opening. **No. of Franchise Units:** 200+. **No. of Company-Owned Units:** 1. **Founded:** 1982.. **Franchised:** 1989. **Equity Capital Needed:** $350,000 minimum liquid assets; $500,000 net worth;

$2,800,000-$4,200,000 (includes land/building). **Franchise Fee:** $70,000. **Training:** Initial training and ongoing support.

4032 ■ Pump It Up - The Inflatable Party Zone

PIU Management, LLC
1860 W University Dr., Ste. 108
Tempe, AZ 85281
Free: 866-635-0029
Fax: (480)371-1201
Co. E-mail: info@pumpitupparty.com
URL: http://www.pumpitupparty.com
Description: Offers a unique way to celebrate children's milestones. With interactive inflateables in a clean, private party facility. We take care of organization, child supervision, party setup and clean up. Offers entrepreneurs a unique, differentiated brand backed by an experienced, dedicated franchise development team. **No. of Franchise Units:** 160. **Franchised:** 2002. **Equity Capital Needed:** $304,550-$703,900, includes franchise fee. **Franchise Fee:** $40,000. **Training:** Training both onsite and at our main offices. Training includes logistics, sales, marketing and more. Ongoing phone support is provided.

4033 ■ Reading Friends Franchise Co.

Reading Friends Holdings Co. L.L.C.
5228 Pershing
Fort Worth, TX 76107
Ph: (817)738-9430
Fax: (817)732-2079
Description: Preschool for children. **No. of Franchise Units:** 4. **No. of Company-Owned Units:** 1. **Founded:** 1980.. **Franchised:** 2002. **Equity Capital Needed:** $119,000-$325,000. **Franchise Fee:** $35,000. **Training:** Yes.

4034 ■ Sunbrook Academy

Sunbrook Franchising Inc.
2933 Cherokee St., Ste. 100
Kennesaw, GA 30144
Ph: (770)426-0619
Fax: (770)426-0724
Co. E-mail: info@sunbrookacademy.com
URL: http://www.sunbrookacademy.com
Description: Provider of childcare programs. **No. of Franchise Units:** 8. **No. of Company-Owned Units:** 3. **Founded:** 1984.. **Franchised:** 1999. **Equity Capital Needed:** $250,000-$450,000. **Franchise Fee:** $55,000. **Training:** 21 day training program prior to opening, and 30 days onsite training with ongoing assistance after opening.

LIBRARIES

4035 ■ BOCES Putnam/Northern Westchester - BOCES Professional Library

200 BOCES Dr.
Yorktown Heights, NY 10598-4399

Ph: (914)245-2700
Fax: (914)248-4519
Co. E-mail: mfeldman@pnwboces.org
URL: http://www.pnwboces.org
Contact: Anita Feldman, President
Scope: Education, child psychology. **Services:** Interlibrary loan; copying; Library open to the public with restrictions (reference use only for those not residing or working in the 18 school districts). **Founded:** 1965. **Holdings:** 8000 books; 16,000 bound periodical volumes; 300,000 nonbook items. **Subscriptions:** 119 journals and other serials.

4036 ■ Georgetown University - Maternal and Child Health Library

2115 Wisconsin Ave. NW, Ste. 601
Washington, DC 20057-1272
Ph: (202)784-9770
Free: 877-624-1935
Fax: (202)784-9777
Co. E-mail: mchgroup@georgetown.edu
URL: http://www.mchlibrary.info
Contact: Olivia K. Pickett, Director, Library Services
Scope: Maternal and child health - genetics, prenatal care, adolescent health, chronic illness/disability, developmental disabilities, infant mortality, nutrition, violence and injury prevention, child health, women's health, public health. **Services:** Library open to health professionals; responds to requests from the public. **Founded:** 1982. **Holdings:** 20,000 books; ephemeral literature; reports from state MCH agencies and discretionary grants of the U.S. Maternal and Child Health Bureau; manuscripts; microfiche; microfilm; archives. **Subscriptions:** 100 journals and other serials.

4037 ■ Illinois Early Childhood Intervention Clearinghouse Library

Early Childhood and Parenting Collaborative
University of Illinois at Urbana-Champaign
Children's Research Ctr., Rm. 20
51 Gerty Dr.
Champaign, IL 61820-7469
Ph: (217)333-1386
Free: 877-275-3227
Fax: (217)244-7732
Co. E-mail: illinois-eic@illlnois.edu
URL: http://www.eiclearinghouse.org/library.html
Contact: Logan Moore, Librarian
Scope: Early childhood, at-risk children, developmental disabilities. **Services:** Interlibrary loan; copying; clearinghouse open to Illinois residents. **Founded:** 1986. **Holdings:** 9850 books; 1785 audiovisuals. **Subscriptions:** 20 journals and other serials.

RESEARCH CENTERS

4038 ■ Arizona State University - Child Development Laboratory (CDL)

PO Box 873701
Tempe, AZ 85287-3701

Ph: (480)965-7257
Fax: (480)965-6779
Co. E-mail: mary.zuzich@asu.edu
URL: http://sites.google.com/a/asu.edu/asu-child-development-lab
Contact: Mary Zuzich, Assistant Director
Educational Activities: Parent Education Seminars.

4039 ■ Arizona State University - Child Study Laboratory

Department of Psychology
950 S McAllister
Tempe, AZ 85287-1104
Ph: (480)965-5320
Fax: (480)965-8544
URL: http://psychology.clas.asu.edu/csl
Contact: Beth Wiley, Director
Founded: 1972.

4040 ■ Jewish Board of Family and Children's Services, Inc. - Child Development Center

120 W 57th St., 11 Fl.
New York, NY 10019
Ph: (212)632-4733
Free: 888-523-2769
Fax: (212)632-4534
Co. E-mail: admin@jbfcs.org
URL: http://www.jbfcs.com
Contact: Marian Davidson-Amodeo, Director
Founded: 1946. **Educational Activities:** Early Childhood Workshops, for early childhood educators and related service providers; Institute for Infants, Toddlers, and Parents, a two-year, post-graduate training program.

4041 ■ University of California, Berkeley - Institute of Human Development - Harold E. Jones Child Study Center (CSC)

2425 Atherton St., No. 6070
Berkeley, CA 94720-6070
Ph: (510)642-7031
Fax: (510)643-7350
Co. E-mail: lisabranum@berkeley.edu
URL: http://ihd.berkeley.edu/child.htm
Contact: Christine Hansel, Program Manager
E-mail: hansel@berkeley.edu
Founded: 1928. **Educational Activities:** Conducts two preschool classrooms.; Research in child development (Annual).

4042 ■ University of Georgia - Institute for Behavioral Research - Center for Family Research (CFR)

1095 College Station Rd.
Athens, GA 30602
Ph: (706)425-2992
Free: 888-542-3068
Fax: (706)425-2985
Co. E-mail: gbrody@uga.edu
URL: http://www.cfr.uga.edu
Contact: Gene H. Brody, Director
Founded: 1984. **Educational Activities:** Colloquium (Annual); CFR Seminar Series (Monthly).

ASSOCIATIONS AND OTHER ORGANIZATIONS

4043 ■ National Chimney Sweep Guild (NCSG)
2155 Commercial Dr.
Plainfield, IN 46168

Ph: (317)837-1500
Fax: (317)837-5365
Co. E-mail: mmcsweeney@ncsg.org
URL: http://www.ncsg.org
Contact: Jay Walker, President
Description: Individuals in the chimney service profession. Provides an opportunity for chimney service professionals to learn about technical aspects of trade and new equipment, and to share ideas for building strong businesses and promoting chimney safety. Conducts training and certification seminars. **Scope:** chimney and venting industry. **Founded:** 1977. **Subscriptions:** 1000 archival material books periodicals video recordings. **Publications:** *Sweeping* (Monthly). **Educational Activities:** Innovation (Annual).

STATISTICAL SOURCES

4044 ■ RMA Annual Statement Studies
Pub: Risk Management Association
Contact: Kevin M. Blakey, President
Released: Annual. **Price:** $175.00 2006-07 edition, $105.00. **Description:** Contains composite balance sheets and income statements for more than 360 industries, including the accounting, auditing, and bookkeeping industries. Also contains five years of comparative historical data for discerning trends. Includes 16 commonly used ratios, computed for most of the size groupings for nearly every industry.

TRADE SHOWS AND CONVENTIONS

4045 ■ Annual Dickens Christmas Show and Festivals Week
Leisure Time Unlimited, Inc.
708 Main St.
Myrtle Beach, SC 29577
Ph: (843)448-9483
Free: 800-261-5591
Fax: (843)626-1513
Co. E-mail: ltushows@sc.rr.com
URL: http://www.leisuretimeunlimited.com/
Contact: Brooke P. Baker, Show Manager
E-mail: dickensshow@sc.rr.com
URL(s): www.dickenschristmasshow.com/. **Price:** $8. 50, adult; $4, children, ages 2-12; $13, multi-day ticket. **Frequency:** Annual. **Audience:** General public. **Principal Exhibits:** Crafts, art, paintings, gifts, and Christmas related items. **Dates and Locations:** , Convention Center. **Telecommunication Services:** dickensshow@sc.rr.com.

4046 ■ Christmas Gift and Hobby Show
HSI Show Productions
PO Box 502797
Indianapolis, IN 46250
Ph: (317)576-9933
Free: 800-215-1700
Fax: (317)576-9955
Co. E-mail: info@hsishows.com
URL: http://www.hsishows.com
URL(s): www.christmasgiftandhobbyshow.com. **Price:** $10; $7, senior admission; $6, groups of twenty or more; free for children 12 and under. **Frequency:** Annual. **Audience:** General public. **Principal Exhibits:** Art, crafts, and giftware. **Dates and Locations:** , Indiana State Fairgrounds. **Telecommunication Services:** info@hsishows.com.

4047 ■ Holiday Fair
Textile Hall Corp.
PO Box 5823
Greenville, SC 29606
Ph: (864)233-2562
Fax: (864)233-0619
Co. E-mail: atmei@textilehall.com
Contact: Butler Mullins, Director
E-mail: bmullins@textilehall.com
URL(s): www.holidayfairgreenville.com/index.html. **Price:** $6, adult general admission; $5, group rate (15 or more) general admission; $4, seniors (60 or over) general admission; $3, seniors group rate (15 or more) general admission. **Frequency:** Annual. **Audience:** General public. **Principal Exhibits:** Arts and crafts. **Dates and Locations:** , Palmetto International Exposition Center. **Telecommunication Services:** kwarner@carolinafirstcenter.com.

4048 ■ Southern Christmas Show
Southern Shows, Inc.
PO Box 36859
Charlotte, NC 28236
Ph: (704)376-6594
Free: 800-849-0248
Fax: (704)376-6345
Co. E-mail: sabernethy@southernshows.com
URL: http://www.southernshows.com
Contact: David J. Zimmerman, President
E-mail: dzimmerman@southernshows.com
URL(s): www.southernshows.com. **Price:** $8, Pre-registered; $7, Onsite; $6.50, Pre-registered for groups of 20 or more; $3, for ages 6-12. **Frequency:** Annual. **Audience:** General public. **Principal Exhibits:** Christmas gifts, crafts, arts, foods, and educational materials, Christmas tree lane, and decorating competitions, and Santa Claus. **Dates and Locations:** , The Park Expo and Conference Center. **Telecommunication Services:** ccipriano@southernshows.com.

FRANCHISES AND BUSINESS OPPORTUNITIES

4049 ■ Christmas Decor Inc.
The Decor Group
PO Box 5946
Lubbock, TX 79408-5946
Ph: (806)722-1225
Free: 800-687-9551
Fax: (806)722-9627
Co. E-mail: info@thedecorgroup.com
URL: http://www.christmasdecor.com
Description: Holiday and event decorations. **No. of Franchise Units:** 240. **Founded:** 1984.. **Franchised:** 1996. **Equity Capital Needed:** $13,150-$35,350. **Franchise Fee:** $5,000. **Royalty Fee:** 5%. **Training:** 4 day quick start training at headquarters, 4 days at regional locations and ongoing support.

ASSOCIATIONS AND OTHER ORGANIZATIONS

4050 ■ **National Christmas Tree Association (NCTA)**
16020 Swingley Ridge Rd., Ste. 300
Chesterfield, MO 63017
Ph: (636)449-5070
Fax: (636)449-5051
Co. E-mail: info@realchristmastrees.org
URL: http://www.christmastree.org
URL(s): www.christmastree.org/dnn/default.aspx. **Description:** Exists to promote the use of real Christmas trees and support the industry that provides them. Includes grower-wholesalers, grower-retailers, and all other retailers that sell real Christmas trees and related green products. Sponsors National Christmas Tree Contest. Maintains information and referral service and provides the option of liability insurance for retailers, and choose and cut growers. **Founded:** 1955. **Publications:** *American Christmas Tree Journal* (Quarterly); *American Christmas Tree Journal* (Quarterly). **Educational Activities:** National Christmas Tree Association - Market Builders Conference and Expo (Biennial).

REFERENCE WORKS

4051 ■ *Pacific Northwest Christmas Tree Association Buy-Sell Directory*
Pub: Pacific Northwest Christmas Tree Association
Contact: Mark Arkills, President
URL(s): www.nwtrees.com/lookout.htm. **Released:** Annual; April. **Price:** Free. **Covers:** Christmas tree sellers and buyers in Washington, Oregon, California, Idaho, and southwestern Canada. **Entries include:** For sellers--Farm or company name, address, phone, name and title of contact, number of acres, year established, number of trees for sale by species. For buyers--Company or individual name, address, phone, name and title of contact, number of trees to be purchased by species. **Database includes:** List of trucking companies and nurseries, with name, address, phone, fax, type of truck, number of units, geographical area served, dates available, and required lead time. **Arrangement:** Separate alphabetical seller and buyer sections.

TRADE PERIODICALS

4052 ■ *American Christmas Tree Journal*
Pub: National Christmas Tree Association
URL(s): www.christmastree.org/journal.cfm. **Released:** Quarterly **Price:** $57, U.S., Canada, and Mexico; $92, Other countries; $37, Members.

4053 ■ *Christmas Trees: World's Leading Christmas Tree Magazine*
Pub: Tree Publishers Inc.
URL(s): www.christmastreesmagazine.com. **Ed:** Catherine Wright Howard. **Released:** Quarterly **Price:** $25, Individuals; $48, Two years; $6.25, U.S., Canada, and Mexico single; $25, Canada and

Mexico; $48, Canada and Mexico 2 years; $45, Other countries; $75, Other countries two years; $9.25, Single issue other countries.

4054 ■ *NAA Reporter*
Pub: Tree Care Industry Association
Contact: Mark Garvin, President
E-mail: garvin@tcia.org
Ed: Peter Gerstenberger, Editor. **Released:** Monthly. **Price:** Included in membership. **Description:** Concerned with the profession of arboriculture. Provides information on 'recognized methods of tree care, new products and services, effective business management, and kindred activities of the association.'.

4055 ■ *The Treeworker*
Pub: Tree Care Industry Association
Contact: Mark Garvin, President
E-mail: garvin@tcia.org
Ed: Robert Rouse, Editor, rouse@natlarb.com. **Released:** Monthly. **Price:** $24.95, Included in membership. **Description:** Provides practical information on worker safety, tree care techniques, skills development, general knowledge of trees, and occupational safety and health in tree care operations.

CONSULTANTS

4056 ■ **Joseph Grahame**
PO Box 503
Elkins, WV 26241-3833
Ph: (304)636-6672
Fax: (304)636-9337
Contact: Joseph W. Grahame, Manager
Scope: Provider of services including timber cruises and appraisals, fire damage appraisals, trespass appraisals, timber sales, forest and game management, forest litigation, wild land surveying, logging road design, court house research and mapping of large surface and mineral ownerships. Serves private industries as well as government agencies. **Founded:** 1974.

4057 ■ **Hutchison Forestry Inc.**
1627 Shackett Rd.
Leicester, VT 05733
Ph: (802)247-3117
Free: 800-439-3117
Co. E-mail: info@mountpleasantmaple.com
URL: http://www.mountpleasantmaple.com
Contact: Galen O. Hutchison, President
Scope: Consulting forester offering counsel on timber and woodland management and Christmas tree management. Serves private industries as well as government agencies. **Founded:** 1964.

4058 ■ **Timmerlinn Inc.—Services Forestiers Timmerlinn Inc.**
18 Saint-Henri E
Sainte-Agathe-des-Monts, QC, Canada J8C 1S9
Ph: (819)326-3559
Fax: (819)326-3602
Contact: Daniel M. Boyer, President
Scope: Offers counsel, planning and management of renewable resources to private land owners, municipalities, governments and companies in forestry,

recreation and wildlife. Main activities include forest resource inventories and plans, timber brokerage, silviculture, reforestation, re-vegetation, land reclamation, maple syrup production, Christmas tree production, soil studies, planning of parks, ski areas, and other recreation facilities. The firm has considerable experience in erosion control and forestry work. **Founded:** 1973. **Seminars:** Marketing Forestry Services to Private Land Owners.

FRANCHISES AND BUSINESS OPPORTUNITIES

4059 ■ **Christmas Decor Inc.**
The Decor Group
PO Box 5946
Lubbock, TX 79408-5946
Ph: (806)722-1225
Free: 800-687-9551
Fax: (806)722-9627
Co. E-mail: info@thedecorgroup.com
URL: http://www.christmasdecor.com
Description: Holiday and event decorations. **No. of Franchise Units:** 240. **Founded:** 1984.. **Franchised:** 1996. **Equity Capital Needed:** $13,150-$35,350. **Franchise Fee:** $5,000. **Royalty Fee:** 5%. **Training:** 4 day quick start training at headquarters, 4 days at regional locations and ongoing support.

RESEARCH CENTERS

4060 ■ **Purdue University - Southeast-Purdue Agricultural Center (SEPAC)**
4425 E County Rd. 350 N
Butlerville, IN 47223-0216
Ph: (812)458-6977
Fax: (812)458-6979
Co. E-mail: biehled@purdue.edu
URL: http://www.agriculture.purdue.edu/pac/sepac/index.html
Contact: Donald J. Biehle, Superintendent
Founded: 1977. **Educational Activities:** Field and Research Report Days (Annual).

4061 ■ **Texas A&M University - Texas Forest Service (TFS)**
John B. Connally Bldg., Ste. 364
301 Tarrow, Ste. 364
College Station, TX 77840-7896
Ph: (979)458-6606
Fax: (979)458-6610
Co. E-mail: tboggus@tfs.tamu.edu
URL: http://txforestservice.tamu.edu/main/default.aspx
Contact: Thomas G. Boggus, Director
Telecommunication Services: tx-stateforester@tfs.tamu.edu.

4062 ■ **University of Wisconsin—Madison - Hancock Agricultural Research Station**
N3909 County Rd. V
Hancock, WI 54943
Ph: (715)249-5961

Fax: (715)249-5850
Co. E-mail: lemere@wisc.edu
URL: http://www.ars.wisc.edu/hancock
Contact: Mary LeMere, Superintendent
Founded: 1916. **Telecommunication Services:** hancock@cals.wisc.edu.

START-UP INFORMATION

4063 ■ "Online Fortunes" in Small Business Opportunities (Fall 2008)
Pub: Entrepreneur Media Inc.

Description: Fifty hot, e-commerce enterprises for the aspiring entrepreneur to consider are featured; virtual assistants, marketing services, party planning, travel services, researching, web design and development, importing as well as creating an online store are among the businesses featured.

4064 ■ "Startup Aims to Cut Out Coupon Clipping" in The Business Journal-Serving Metropolitan Kansas City (Vol. 26, August 15, 2008, No. 49)
Pub: American City Business Journals, Inc.

Ed: Suzanna Stagemeyer. **Description:** TDP Inc., who started operations 18 months ago, aims to transform stale coupon promotions using technology by digitizing the entire coupon process. The process is expected to enable consumers to hunt coupons online where they will be automatically linked to loyalty cards. Other views and information on TDP and its services are presented.

REFERENCE WORKS

4065 ■ Gale Directory of Publications and Broadcast Media
Pub: Cengage Learning Inc.
Contact: Ronald Dunn, President

URL(s): www.gale.cengage.com. **Released:** Annual; Latest edition April 2011. **Price:** $1297, Individuals. **Covers:** Approximately 57,000 publications and broadcasting stations, including newspapers, magazines, journals, radio stations, television stations, radio/television/cable networks, syndicates and cable systems in the U.S. and Canada. Newsletters and directories are excluded. **Entries include:** For publications--Title, publishing and editorial addresses, phone, fax, description, names of editor, publisher, and advertising manager, base advertising rate, page specifications, subscription rate, circulation, frequency, ISSN, former names, additional contacts. For broadcast media--Call letters or cable system name, address, phone, fax, format, networks, owner, date founded, former call letters, operating hours, names and titles of key personnel, local programming, wattage, ad rates, additional contacts. **Database includes:** Appendices with maps and statistical tables, city descriptions, state descriptions with statistics, broadcast and cable networks, news and features syndicates. **Arrangement:** Geographical. **Indexes:** Title; radio station format; publisher; geographic market; lists of agricultural, college, foreign language, Jewish, fraternal, black, women's, Hispanic, religious, general circulation, and trade and technical publications (by subject and/or geographical as needed); daily newspaper; daily periodical; free circulation newspaper; and shopping guides (each geographical); list of feature editors at daily newspapers with 50,000 or more circulation.

4066 ■ Gebbie Press All-in-One Media Directory
Pub: Gebbie Press Inc.
Contact: Mark Gebbie, President

URL(s): www.gebbieinc.com/aio.htm. **Ed:** Mark Gebbie. **Released:** Annual; Latest edition 41st edition, 2012. **Price:** $165, Individuals 2012 all-in-one media directory: print version; $155, Individuals daily and weekly newspaper CD-ROM; $155, Individuals radio and television CD-ROM; $155, Individuals trade and consumer magazines CD-ROM; $395, Individuals all three sets above; $565, Individuals 2008 all-in-one media directory: pro CD software. **Covers:** 1,453 daily newspapers, 6,202 weekly newspapers, 10,789 radio stations, 1,445 television stations, 268 general-consumer magazines, 430 professional business publications, 3,100 trade magazines, 320 farm publications, list of the Black press and radio, Hispanic press and radio, and a list of news syndicates. **Entries include:** For periodicals--Name, address, phone, fax, frequency, editor, circulation, readership. For newspapers--Name, address, phone, fax, circulation. For radio and television stations--Call letters, address, phone, format. **Arrangement:** Classified by type of media.

4067 ■ National Directory of Magazines
Pub: Oxbridge Communications Inc.
Contact: Patricia Hagood, President

URL(s): www.oxbridge.com/NDMCluster/theNDM. asp. **Released:** latest edition 2011. **Price:** $995, Individuals print version; $1195, Individuals CD-ROM single user; $1995, Individuals print and CD-ROM. **Covers:** Over 20,000 magazines; coverage includes Canada. **Entries include:** Title, publisher name, address, phone, fax number, names and titles of contact and key personnel, financial data, editorial and advertising information, circulation. **Arrangement:** Classified by subject. **Indexes:** Title, geographical, publisher.

4068 ■ Oxbridge Directory of Newsletters
Pub: Oxbridge Communications Inc.
Contact: Patricia Hagood, President

URL(s): www.oxbridge.com/ODNCluster/theODN. asp. **Released:** Annual; Latest edition 2011. **Price:** $995, Individuals print version; $1195, Individuals CD-ROM single user; $1995, Individuals print and CD-ROM. **Covers:** Approximately 15,000 newsletters in the U.S. and Canada. **Entries include:** Publication name, publisher name, address, phone; names of editor and other key personnel; description of contents and types of material used, year founded, frequency, advertising and subscription rates, print method, page size, number of pages. **Arrangement:** Classified by subject. **Indexes:** Title, geographical, publisher.

4069 ■ SRDS International Media Guides: Newspapers Worldwide
Pub: Standard Rate and Data Service
Contact: Christopher Lehman, Chief Executive Officer

URL(s): www.srds.comwww.srds.com/frontMatter/ips/img/index.html. **Released:** Annual **Price:** $455, Individuals annual unlimited single-user access. **Cov-**ers: approximately 19,000 newspapers and color newspaper magazines/supplements from 200 countries, including the United States. **Entries include:** Publication name; publisher name, address, phone, fax, e-mail, URL, names of editor, advertising manager, and representatives in the United States and worldwide; advertising rates in U.S. dollars and/or local currency, circulation, mechanical data, ad closing, readership description, etc. **Arrangement:** Geographical.

4070 ■ Standard Periodical Directory
Pub: Oxbridge Communications Inc.
Contact: Patricia Hagood, President

URL(s): www.oxbridge.com. **Ed:** Deborah Striplin. **Released:** Annual; Latest edition January 2011. **Price:** $1995, Individuals print version; $1995, Single issue CD-ROM single user; $2995, Individuals print and CD-ROM. **Covers:** 63,000 magazines, journals, newsletters, directories, house organs, association publications, etc. , in the United States and Canada. **Entries include:** Publication current and former title; publisher name, address, phone; names and titles of key personnel; circulation and advertising rates; description of contents; ISSN, year founded, frequency; subscription rates, print method, page size, number of pages. **Arrangement:** Classified by subject. **Indexes:** Subject, title.

4071 ■ Ulrich's Periodicals Directory: International Periodicals Information Since 1932
Pub: R.R. Bowker L.L.C.

URL(s): www.ulrichsweb.com/ulrichsweb/faqs.asp. **Released:** Annual; Latest edition 2010. **Price:** $1260, Individuals Hardcover, 4 volumes. **Covers:** Nearly 200,000 current periodicals and newspapers published worldwide. **Entries include:** In main list--Publication title; Dewey Decimal Classification number, Library of Congress Classification Number (where applicable), CODEN designation (for sci-tech serials), British Library Document Supply Centre shelfmark number, country code, ISSN; subtitle, language(s) of text, year first published, frequency, subscription prices, sponsoring organization, publishing company name, address, phone, fax, e-mail and website addresses, editor and publisher names; regular features (reviews, advertising, abstracts, bibliographies, trade literature, etc.), indexes, circulation, format, brief description of content; availability of microforms and reprints; whether refereed; CD-ROM availability with vendor name; online availability with service name; services that index or abstract the periodical, with years covered; advertising rates and contact; right and permissions contact name and phone; availability through document deliver. **Arrangement:** Main listing is classified by subject; U.S. general daily and weekly newspapers are listed in a separate volume; lists of cessations, online services, and CD-ROM vendors are alphabetical. **Indexes:** Cessations, subjects, title (including variant, former, and ceased titles), ISSN, periodicals available on CD-ROM, online periodical title, refereed serial, and international organization publication title.

TRADE PERIODICALS

4072 ■ *Business Periodicals Index (BPI)*
Pub: The H.W. Wilson Co.

URL(s): www.hwwilson.com/dd/bus_i.htm. **Ed:** Hiyol Yang. **Released:** Monthly; with annual cumulation. **Price:** An annual subscription is $1,495.00. **Covers:** Index of articles in business periodicals. **Entries include:** Publisher name, address, subscription rate, and frequency. Principal content of publication is annotated index of articles from 400 business periodicals, including book reviews.

COMPUTERIZED DATABASES

4073 ■ *Business Periodicals Index Retrospective™: 1913-1982*
10 Estes St.
Ipswich, MA 01938-2106
Ph: (978)356-6500
Free: 800-653-2726
Fax: (978)356-6565
Co. E-mail: information@ebscohost.com
URL: http://www.ebscohost.com
Contact: Tim Collins, President
E-mail: tcollins@ebscohost.com
Availability: Online: EBSCO Publishing. **Type:** Bibliographic.

4074 ■ *Newspaper Abstracts*
789 E Eisenhower Pkwy.
Ann Arbor, MI 48106-1346
Ph: (734)761-4700
Free: 800-521-0600
Co. E-mail: info@il.proquest.com
URL: http://www.il.proquest.com
Contact: Matt Dunie, President

Availability: Online: ProQuest LLC - Dialog; ProQuest Co. **Type:** Bibliographic.

START-UP INFORMATION

4075 ■ *In Fashion: From Runway to Retail, Everything You Need to Know to Break Into the Fashion Industry*
Pub: Crown Business Books
Ed: Annemarie Iverson. **Released:** August 10, 2010.
Price: $16.99. **Description:** Whether your dream is to photograph models, outfit celebrities, design fashions, this book provides details into every aspect for working in the fashion industry.

4076 ■ *"Money Matters: Using Sound Resources, You Can Find Capital For Your Business" in Black Enterprise (Vol. 38, November 2007, No. 4)*
Pub: Earl G. Graves Publishing Co. Inc.
Ed: Carolyn M. Brown. **Description:** Profile of fashion designer Kara Saun who inspired an angel investor from Connecticut to help launch her Fall 2006 clothing line.

4077 ■ *Start Your Own Fashion Accessories Business*
Pub: Entrepreneur Press
Contact: Perlman Neil, President
Released: March 1, 2009. **Price:** $17.95. **Description:** Entrepreneurs wishing to start a fashion accessories business will find important information for setting up a home workshop and office, exploring the market, managing finances, publicizing and advertising the business and more.

ASSOCIATIONS AND OTHER ORGANIZATIONS

4078 ■ **Association of Knitwear Designers (AKD)**
4532 17th St.
San Francisco, CA 94114
Ph: (415)552-8414
Co. E-mail: info@knitwear-designers.org
URL: http://www.knitwear-designers.org
Contact: Jill Wolcott, President
Description: Promotes the art and business of knitting. Provides networking, professional accreditation and helps freelance knitwear designers worldwide. **Scope:** textiles, design, knitwear, color theory. **Founded:** 1989. **Subscriptions:** 100 books video recordings. **Publications:** *Teachers Directory* (Annual).

4079 ■ **Association of Sewing and Design Professionals (ASDP)**
2885 Sanford Ave. SW, No. 19588
Grandville, MI 49418-1342
Free: 877-755-0303
Co. E-mail: admin@sewingprofessionals.org
URL: http://www.paccprofessionals.org
Contact: Ms. Rae Cumbie, President
URL(s): www.sewingprofessionals.org. **Description:** Encourages the interchange of ideas among individuals involved in the sewing and design fields. Promotes

professions in the industry; represents members' interests. Conducts educational and training programs. **Founded:** 1991. **Awards:** Lifetime Achievement Award.

4080 ■ **Council of Fashion Designers of America (CFDA)**
1412 Broadway, Ste. 2006
New York, NY 10018
Co. E-mail: info@cfda.com
URL: http://www.cfda.com
Contact: Steven Kolb, Chief Executive Officer
Description: Persons of "recognized ability, standing, and integrity, who are actively engaged in creative fashion design in the United States, in the fields of wearing apparel, fabrics, accessories, jewelry, or related products." (Membership is individual and does not extend to the firm or associates.) Seeks "to further the position of fashion design as a recognized branch of American art and culture, to advance its artistic and professional standards, to establish and maintain a code of ethics and practices of mutual benefit in professional, public, and trade relations, and to promote and improve public understanding and appreciation of the fashion arts through leadership in quality and taste". **Founded:** 1962. **Educational Activities:** Council of Fashion Designers of America Dinner (Annual). **Awards:** Fashion Awards; Council of Fashion Designers of America Award (Annual).

4081 ■ **Custom Tailors and Designers Association (CTDA)**
42732 Ridgeway Dr.
Broadlands, VA 20148
Free: 888-248-2832
Fax: (866)661-1240
Co. E-mail: info@ctda.com
URL: http://www.ctda.com
Contact: Kristine Trager, President
Description: Designers and makers of men's custom tailored outerwear and clothing. **Scope:** fashion. **Founded:** 1880.

4082 ■ **Men's Clothing Manufacturers Association (MCMA)—Association des manufacturiers de vetements pour hommes**
979, av. Bourgogne, Ste. 570
Montreal, QC, Canada G1W 2L4
Ph: (418)652-7682
Co. E-mail: amiq@macten.net
URL: http://www.asp-habillement.org/fr/partners/patronales.html
Contact: Alain Plourde, Executive Director
Description: Manufacturers of men's clothing and accessories. Promotes international competitiveness among members. Serves as a clearinghouse on the apparel industry; conducts research and educational programs. **Founded:** 1934. **Publications:** *On The Button* (Quarterly).

4083 ■ *On The Button*
979, av. Bourgogne, Ste. 570
Montreal, QC, Canada G1W 2L4

Ph: (418)652-7682
Co. E-mail: amiq@macten.net
URL: http://www.asp-habillement.org/fr/partners/patronales.html
Contact: Alain Plourde, Executive Director
Released: Quarterly

4084 ■ **Organization of Black Designers (OBD)**
300 M St. SW, Ste. N110
Washington, DC 20024
Ph: (202)659-3918
Co. E-mail: info@obd.org
URL: http://www.obd.org
Contact: David H. Rice, Chairman Founder
Description: African American designers holding college degrees who are practicing graphic advertising, industrial, fashion, textile, and interior design. Provides forum for discussion and educational programs, business, career and economic development. Sponsors competitions and speakers' bureau. **Scope:** design issues that impact black design professionals. **Founded:** 1994. **Subscriptions:** archival material articles. **Publications:** *DesigNation* (Biennial); *OBData*. **Educational Activities:** DesigNation (Annual). **Awards:** OBD Design Award (Annual); OBD Scholarship (Annual).

REFERENCE WORKS

4085 ■ *"Apparel" in Retail Merchandiser (Vol. 51, July-August 2011, No. 4, pp. 14)*
Pub: Phoenix Media Corporation
Description: NPD Group Inc. released current sales statistics for the women's apparel market along with men's apparel. It also reported annual shoes sales for 2010. Statistical data included.

4086 ■ *"As Seen On TV" in Canadian Business (Vol. 80, November 5, 2007, No. 22, pp. 93)*
Pub: Rogers Media
Ed: Zena Olijnyk. **Description:** StarBrand Media Inc. is one of the companies providing fans with information on how and where to purchase the items that television characters are using. StarBrand created the style section found on different television shows' Websites, such as that of the Gossip Girl and Smallville. The benefits of using sites like StarBrand are evaluated.

4087 ■ *"The Bottom Line" in Retail Merchandiser (Vol. 51, July-August 2011, No. 4, pp. 60)*
Pub: Phoenix Media Corporation
Description: Hanky Panky believes that comfort and style don't have to be mutually exclusive when designing their line of intimate apparel for women. The lingerie retailer was launched in 1977.

4088 ■ *"Breadwinner Tries on Designer Jeans" in Houston Business Journal (Vol. 40, December 18, 2009, No. 32, pp. 1)*
Pub: American City Business Journals
Ed: Allison Wollam. **Description:** Chuck Cain, the franchisee who introduced Panera Bread to Houston, Texas has partnered with tax accountant Jim Jacob-

sen to introduce custom-make Tattu Jeans. As more Tattu Jeans outlets are being planned, Cain is using entrepreneurial lessons learned from Panera Bread in the new venture. Both Panera Bread and Tattu Jeans were opened by Cain during economic downturns.

4089 ■ "Bringing Charities More Bang for Their Buck" in Crain's Chicago Business (Vol. 34, May 23, 2011, No. 21, pp. 31)
Pub: Crain Communications Inc.
Ed: Lisa Bertagnoli. **Description:** Marcy-Newberry Association connects charities with manufacturers in order to use excess items such as clothing, janitorial and office supplies.

4090 ■ "Buying Chanel (All Of It)" in Conde Nast Portfolio (Vol. 2, June 2008, No. 6, pp. 34)
Pub: Conde Nast Publications
Contact: David Carey, President
Ed: Willow Duttge. **Description:** Overview of the luxury company Chanel and an estimated guess as to what the company is worth.

4091 ■ "A Change Would Do You Good" in Canadian Business (Vol. 80, November 19, 2007, No. 23, pp. 15)
Pub: Rogers Media
Ed: Geoff Kirbyson. **Description:** Western Glove Works will be manufacturing clothing offshore, including Sheryl Crow's jeans collection, in countries such as China and the Philippines. The company decided to operate offshore after 86 years of existence due to the high price of manufacturing jeans in Canada. Western Glove's focus on producing celebrity-endorsed goods is discussed.

4092 ■ Chief Culture Officer: How to Create a Living, Breathing Corporation
Pub: Basic Books
Ed: Grant McCracken. **Price:** $26.95. **Description:** Business consultant argues that corporations need to focus on 'reading' what's happening in the culture around them. Otherwise, companies will suffer the consequences, as Levi Strauss did when it missed out on the rise of hip-hop (and the baggy pants that are part of that lifestyle).

4093 ■ "Common Thread" in Entrepreneur (Vol. 36, March 2008, No. 3, pp. 144)
Pub: Entrepreneur Media Inc.
Ed: Sara Wilson. **Description:** Profile of Stacey Benet and her business, Alice and Olivia, and how she jumpstarted her career in the clothing industry after she wore a self-designed pair of pants that caught the attention of a Barney's New York representative is presented.

4094 ■ "Consignment Shop Closes Without Warning to Customers, Landlord" in Sun Journal (June 30, 2010)
Pub: Freedom Communications Inc.
Ed: Laura Oleniacz. **Description:** Off The Racks consignment shop located on Glenburnie Road in New Bern, North Carolina closed without warning to customers or its landlord. The consignors who donated clothing to the store were left unpaid.

4095 ■ "Consignment Shop Offers Children's Clothes, Products" in Frederick News-Post (August 19, 2010)
Pub: Federick News-Post
Ed: Ed Waters Jr. **Description:** Sweet Pea Consignments for Children offers used items for newborns to pre-teens. The shop carries name brand clothing as well as toys, books and baby products.

4096 ■ "Design program in Athletic Footwear" in Occupational Outlook Quarterly (Vol. 55, Fall 2011, No. 3, pp. 21)
Pub: U.S. Bureau of Labor Statistics
Description: The Fashion Institute of Technology offers the only certificate program in performance athletic footwear design in the U.S. The program focuses on conceptualizing and sketching shoe designs and covers ergonomic, anatomical, and material considerations for athletic footwear design.

4097 ■ "Designer is Walking Ad for TIBI Line" in Charlotte Observer (February 5, 2007)
Pub: Knight-Ridder/Tribune Business News
Ed: Crystal Dempsey. **Description:** Profile of Amy Smilovic, mother of two children, and clothing designer. Smilovic wears what she designs, making her a great marketing tool for her clothing line TIBI.

4098 ■ The Designer's Guide to Marketing and Pricing: How to Win Clients and What to Charge Them
Pub: F and W Publications, Inc.
Ed: Ilise Benun. **Released:** March 2008. **Price:** $19.99. **Description:** Guide to running a creative services business teaches designers how to be more effective, attract new clients, wages, and how to accurately estimate a project.

4099 ■ "Designers' Hats Foretell a Big Comeback Next Fall" in Charlotte Observer (February 8, 2007)
Pub: Knight-Ridder/Tribune Business News
Ed: Crystal Dempsey. **Description:** According to designer experts, hats are making a comeback and will make a big fashion statement, fall 2007.

4100 ■ "Doing Good: Fair Fashion" in Entrepreneur (Vol. 35, October 2007, No. 10, pp. 36)
Pub: Entrepreneur Media Inc.
Ed: J.J. Ramberg. **Description:** Indigenous Designs was launched in 1993, when organic clothing was not yet popular. However, the company has become successful in the industry, with $4 million dollars in revenue, owing to the growing environment awareness of consumers. A history of how the company was formed and an overview of their production process are provided.

4101 ■ "eBay and Jonathan Adler Team to Launch 'The eBay Inspiration Shop" in Entertainment Close-Up (October 25, 2011)
Pub: Close-Up Media
Description: Designer Jonathan Adler partnered with eBay to create a collection of new must-have merchandise for the fall season. Top trendsetters, including actors, designers, bloggers, stylists, editors, photographers, models and musicians helped curate the items being featured in the windows by sharing their shopping wish lists with users.

4102 ■ "Fall Fever" in Canadian Business (Vol. 81, October 13, 2008, No. 17, pp. S12)
Pub: Rogers Media Ltd.
Description: Buyer's guide of men's suits and jackets for fall are presented, including a suit by Boss Hugo Boss recommended for fun in the city after finishing work. Designers Ermenegildo, Michael Kors, and Arnold Brant are also highlighted.

4103 ■ Fashion Calendar
Pub: Ruth Finley
URL(s): www.fashioncalendar.net. **Released:** Semi-monthly; Latest edition 2010. **Covers:** Events of interest to the fashion industry, including private and public fashion openings, and important events in other fields which are scheduled for principal fashion cities; coverage is heavily New York City, but major cities worldwide are also covered. **Entries include:** For openings--Event name, date, address, phone. For other events--Event name, date, time, location, phone. **Arrangement:** Openings are alphabetical; events are chronological.

4104 ■ The Fashion Designer Survival Guide
Pub: Kaplan Publishing
Ed: Mary Gehlhar; Zac Posen. **Released:** September 1, 2005. **Description:** Professional advice from an insider to help start and run a fashion business.

4105 ■ "Fashionistas Weigh in on the Super-Thin" in Charlotte Observer (February 7, 2007)
Pub: Knight-Ridder/Tribune Business News
Ed: Crystal Dempsey. **Description:** Council of Fashion Designers of America held a panel discussion regarding the weight and ages of models used to highlight clothing.

4106 ■ "Fight Ensues Over Irreplaceable Gowns" in Tampa Bay Business Journal (Vol. 30, January 15, 2010, No. 4, pp. 1)
Pub: American City Business Journals
Ed: Janet Leiser. **Description:** People's Princess Charitable Foundation Inc. founder Maureen Rorech Dunkel has sought Chapter 11 bankruptcy protection before a state court decides on the fate of the five of 13 Princess Diana Gowns. Dunkel and the nonprofit were sued by Patricia Sullivan of HRH Venture LLC who claimed they defaulted on $1.5 million in loans.

4107 ■ "Fledgling Brands May Take the Fall With Steve & Barry's" in Advertising Age (Vol. 79, July 7, 2008, No. 26, pp. 6)
Pub: Crain Communications, Inc.
Ed: Natalie Zmuda. **Description:** Steve & Barry's, a retailer that holds licensing deals with a number of designers and celebrities, may have to declare bankruptcy; this leaves the fate of the retailer's hundreds of licensing deals and exclusive celebrity lines in question.

4108 ■ Fugitive Denim: A Moving Story of People and Pants in the Borderless World of Global Trade
Pub: W.W. Norton & Company
Ed: Rachel Snyder. **Released:** April 2009. **Price:** $16.95. **Description:** In-depth study of the global production and processes of how jeans are designed, sewn, and transported as well as how the cotton for denim is grown, regulated, purchased and processed.

4109 ■ "Going Western with a Touch of Style" in Women In Business (Vol. 63, Summer 2011, No. 2, pp. 8)
Pub: American Business Women's Association
Ed: Maureen Sullivan. **Description:** Tips on ways women should dress up in Western style are presented. The wearing of Western-style denims is recommended. Use of accessories such as belt buckles, boots and hats is also encouraged.

4110 ■ "H&M Offers a Dress for Less" in Canadian Business (Vol. 83, September 14, 2010, No. 15, pp. 20)
Pub: Rogers Media Ltd.
Ed: Laura Cameron. **Description:** Swedish clothing company H&M has implemented loss leader strategy by pricing some dresses at extremely low prices. The economy has forced retailers to keep prices down despite the increasing cost of manufacturing, partly due to Chinese labor becoming more expensive. How the trend will affect apparel companies is discussed.

4111 ■ "Haute Flyers" in Canadian Business (Vol. 80, November 19, 2007, No. 23, pp. 68)
Pub: Rogers Media
Ed: Rachel Pulfer. **Description:** Duckie Brown has been nominated by the Council of Fashion Designers of America as best menswear designer in the U.S. for 2007, along with leaders Calvin Klein and Ralph Lauren. The New York-based company was formed the day after September 11, 2001, but the timing did not hamper its growth. The works and plans of owners Steven Cox and Daniel Silver are described.

4112 ■ "How to Keep Your Cool and Your Friends in a Heat Wave" in Canadian Business (Vol. 83, August 17, 2010, No. 13-14, pp. 79)
Pub: Rogers Media Ltd.
Ed: Angelina Chapin. **Description:** A buyer's guide of menswear clothing for businessmen is presented. The products include an antiperspirant and deodorant, men's dress shorts, shoes and bamboo fabric undershirt.

4113 ■ "How This First Lady Moves Markets" in Harvard Business Review (Vol. 88, November 2010, No. 11, pp. 38)
Pub: Harvard Business School Publishing
Description: A chart is presented demonstrating how First Lady Michelle Obama's choice of fashion designer has impacted the clothing industry.

4114 ■ *Hug Your Customers*

Pub: Hyperion Books

Ed: Jack Mitchell. **Price:** $19.95. **Description:** The CEO of Mitchells/Roberts, two very successful clothing stores, professes his belief in showering customers with attention. His secrets for long-term business success include advice about attracting a good staff, lowering marketing costs, and maintaining higher gross margins and revenues.

4115 ■ *If You Have to Cry, Go Outside: And Other Things Your Mother Never Told You*

Pub: HarperOne

Ed: Kelly Cutrone. **Released:** February 2, 2010. **Price:** $22.99. **Description:** Women's mentor advices on how to make it in one of the most competitive industries in the world, fashion. She has kicked people out of fashion shows, forced some of reality television's shiny start to fire their friends, and built her own company which is one of the most powerful public relations firms in the fashion business.

4116 ■ *"Insider" in Canadian Business (Vol. 80, Winter 2007, No. 24, pp.)*

Pub: Rogers Media

Ed: Zena Olijnyk. **Description:** Luluemon Athletica started in 1998 after Dennis Wilson takes a yoga class and notices a demand from women for breathable clothes. The company opened their first outlet in Vancouver in November 2000 then opened their first U.S. store in 2003 until finally going public July 27, 2007 where its stocks doubled in value within days of trading.

4117 ■ *"Integral USA Magazine Sponsors Eco-Fashion in the Park" in Entertainment Close-Up (September 2, 2011)*

Pub: Close-Up Media

Description: Integral Magazine sponsored Eco-Fashion in the Park, a fashion show for the fashion conscious. Eleven independent designers will show their eco-friendly fashions at the event.

4118 ■ *International Textile & Apparel Association--Membership Directory*

Pub: International Textile and Apparel Association

Contact: Kathleen Rees, President

URL(s): www.itaaonline.org. **Released:** Irregular; Latest edition 2007-2008. **Covers:** About 1,000 college professors of clothing and textile studies. **Entries include:** Name, address, phone, academic credentials. **Arrangement:** Alphabetical; geographical by zip code.

4119 ■ *"Island Co.: Isle Style" in Entrepreneur (Vol. 35, October 2007, No. 10, pp. 172)*

Pub: Entrepreneur Media Inc.

Ed: Sara Wilson. **Description:** Island Co., producer of travel clothing and swimsuits was formed by Spencer Antle in 2002. Its office projects the Caribbean atmosphere, a strategy Antle used to promote the company's theme to its clients. Future plans for the company are also indicated.

4120 ■ *"It's So You! Consignment Chop Owner Thrilled to See Vision Come to Fruition" in News-Herald (August 27, 2010)*

Pub: News-Herald

Ed: Brandon C. Baker. **Description:** Profile of Laurel Howes and her It's So You! Boutique. The consignment shop is located in Willoughby's Pine Ride Plaza in Ohio. The shop targets all women, but particularly those who are not that comfortable with shopping consignment.

4121 ■ *"Let It Shine: Organization Helps Disadvantaged Girls See Their Worth" in Black Enterprise (Vol. 38, February 2008, No. 7, pp. 142)*

Pub: Earl G. Graves Publishing Co. Inc.

Ed: George Alexander. **Description:** Wilson Mourning, founder of the clothing label Honey Child, attributes her success to her mother and other positive women who helped her through her adolescence. Mourning created a mentoring organization that helps young girls in the Miami, Florida area to develop life skills.

4122 ■ *"Life's Work: Manolo Blahnik" in Harvard Business Review (Vol. 88, December 2010, No. 12, pp. 144)*

Pub: Harvard Business School Publishing

Ed: Alison Beard. **Description:** Shoe designer Manolo Blahnik recounts his beginnings in the shoe industry and the influence art has had on his work, as well as balancing art and commerce. He also discusses the importance of quality materials and craftsmanship and the benefits of managing an independent, family-owned business.

4123 ■ *"Making It Work" in Retail Merchandiser (Vol. 51, July-August 2011, No. 4, pp. 43)*

Pub: Phoenix Media Corporation

Ed: Anthony DiPaolo. **Description:** Profile of Anthony DiPaolo and his purchase of the Work 'N Gear retail store in 2002. The brick and mortar shop sells work wear and healthcare apparel and DiPaolo believes customer respect is essential to his success.

4124 ■ *"Meet Joe Fresh" in Canadian Business (Vol. 79, November 6, 2006, No. 22, pp. 49)*

Pub: Rogers Media

Ed: Calvin Leung. **Description:** The efforts of Joseph Mimran, a fashion designer, in improving the business of Joe Fresh style products are analyzed.

4125 ■ *"Military Brides Can Get Free Wedding Gowns" in Virginian-Pilot (November 10, 2010)*

Pub: The Virginia-Pilot

Ed: Jamesetta Walker. **Description:** Seventy-five designer wedding gowns will be given to military brides on a first-come, first-served basis at Maya Couture through the Brides Across America's wedding gown giveaway program. Gowns are valued between $500 to $3,000 and are donated by designers Maggie Sottero, Pronovias and Essense of Australia.

4126 ■ *"Not All Contracts a Good Fit for Fashion Reps" in Agency Sales Magazine (Vol. 39, September-October 2009, No. 9, pp. 10)*

Pub: MANA

Ed: Jack Foster. **Description:** Difficult situations regarding the relationship between sales representatives and their principals in the fashion industry are presented and suggestions on how to create contracts that seek to prevent potential problems are provided. Sales reps should make sure that manufacturer has a viable business that is well thought-out and adequately financed.

4127 ■ *"On a Mission: Ginch Gonch Wants You to Get Rid of Your Tighty Whities" in Canadian Business (Vol. 81, September 29, 2008, No. 16)*

Pub: Rogers Media Ltd.

Ed: Michelle Magnan. **Description:** New Equity Capital acquired underwear maker Ginch Gonch in July 2008; founder Jason Sutherland kept his position as creative director of the company and will retain his title as 'director of stitches and inches'. The company is known for its products, which are reminiscent of the days when people wore underwear covered in cowboys and stars as kids. The company also claims that Nelly, Justin Timberlake, and Hilary Duff have worn their products.

4128 ■ *"Options Abound in Winter Wares" in Pet Product News (Vol. 64, November 2010, No. 11, pp. 1)*

Pub: BowTie Inc.

Ed: Maggie M. Shein. **Description:** Pet supply manufacturers emphasize creating top-notch construction and functional design in creating winter clothing for pets. Meanwhile, retailers and pet owners seek human-inspired style, quality, and versatility for pets' winter clothing. How retailers generate successful sales of pets' winter clothing outside of traditional brand marketing is also examined.

4129 ■ *"Peacocks Launches Its First Wedding Dress" in Benzinga.com (July 1, 2011)*

Pub: Benzinga.com

Ed: Benzinga Staff. **Description:** Peacocks, a leading fashion retailer in the United Kingdom launched its first wedding dress available for sale in August 2011.

4130 ■ *"Portland Wooing Under Armour to West Coast Facility" in Baltimore Business Journal (Vol. 27, January 29, 2010, No. 39, pp. 1)*

Pub: American City Business Journals

Ed: Andy Giegerich. **Description:** Baltimore, Maryland sports apparel maker, Under Armour, is planning a west coast expansion with Portland, Oregon among the sites considered to house its apparel and footwear design center. Portland officials counting on the concentration of nearly 10,000 activewear workers in the city will help lure the company to the city.

4131 ■ *"Research and Markets Adds: 2011 U.S. Women's & Children's Clothing Wholesale Report" in Health & Beauty Close-Up (October 16, 2010)*

Pub: Close-Up Media Inc.

Description: The Women's & Children's Clothing Wholesale Report is an annual report containing timely and accurate industry statistics, forecasts and demographics.

4132 ■ *"Retail News: Children's Boutique Relocates to Conway" in Sun News (June 4, 2010)*

Pub: The Sun News

Description: Little Angel's Children's Boutique and Big Oak Frame Shop have moved to downtown locations in Conway, South Carolina. Little Angel's will sell children's clothing and accessories, shoes and gifts, while the frame shop will offer custom framing along with the sale of stationary, invitations and local prints.

4133 ■ *"Rule of the Masses: Reinventing Fashion Via Crowdsourcing" in WWD (Vol. 200, July 26, 2010, No. 17, pp. 1)*

Pub: Conde Nast Publications

Contact: David Carey, President

Ed: Cate T. Corcoran. **Description:** Large apparel brands and retailers are crowdsourcing as a way to increase customer loyalty and to build their businesses.

4134 ■ *"Skinny Jeans Sticking Around for Fall" in Charlotte Observer (February 5, 2007)*

Pub: Knight-Ridder/Tribune Business News

Ed: Crystal Dempsey. **Description:** Clothing designers were showing skinny jeans in the fall/winter fashion shows for 2007.

4135 ■ *"Stylish Successes" in Women In Business (Vol. 61, October-November 2009, No. 5, pp. 12)*

Pub: American Business Women's Association

Ed: Leigh Elmore; Megan L. Reese. **Description:** Amanda Horan Kennedy, Angela Samuels, Barbara Nast Saletan, and Patty Nast Canton are career women who ventured into entrepreneurship. They are deemed to possess networking and teamwork skills that ensured their success in the garment industry.

4136 ■ *They Made America*

Pub: Little Brown Company/Time Warner Book Group

Ed: Harold Evans, Gail Buckland, David Lefer. **Released:** 2006. **Price:** $18.95. **Description:** Coffee table book highlighting entrepreneurship; this book is filled with interesting illustrated portraits of entrepreneurs and innovators like Thomas Edison, George Doriot (a venture capital pioneer), and Ida Rosenthal (inventor of the Maidenform bra).

4137 ■ *"Trousseaus of Memories Trail Behind Wedding Gowns" in Oregonian (September 4, 2010)*

Pub: The Oregonian

Ed: Anne Saker. **Description:** Readers are asked to share stories about their wedding gowns and what that garment meant to them at the time and now.

4138 ■ *"The Ultimate Home Shopping Network" in Austin Business JournalInc. (Vol. 28, October 17, 2008, No. 31, pp. A1)*

Pub: American City Business Journals

Ed: Sandra Zaragoza. **Description:** New York-based Etcetera sells their clothing through more than 850 fashion consultants in the U.S. Central Texas is one of the company's top markets and the company is looking to increase its fashion consultants in the area from five to about 20 since they believe there is plenty of room to expand their customer base in the area.

4139 ■ "Web Sight: Do You See What I See?" in Entrepreneur (Vol. 35, October 2007, No. 10, pp. 58)
Pub: Entrepreneur Media Inc.

Ed: Heather Clancy. **Description:** Owners of Trunkt, a boutique in New York that showcases independent designs, have created a new style of Website called Trunkt.org. The Website allows buyers to select the products they want to see and designers can choose anytime which of their items will be displayed on the site. An explanation of the strategy that helped bring Trunkt closer to its clients is presented.

4140 ■ "Wedding: Style Gowns Ready to Go" in Houston Chronicle (June 3, 2010)
Pub: Houston Chronicle

Ed: Molly Glentzer. **Description:** Wedding gowns with slender silhouettes travel well for destination weddings. Amsale, Oscar del la Renta and Monique Lhuillier dresses are highlighted.

4141 ■ "Well-Heeled Startup" in Business Journal Portland (Vol. 27, November 12, 2010, No. 37, pp. 1)
Pub: Portland Business Journal

Ed: Erik Siemers. **Description:** Oh! Shoes LLC expects to receive about $1.5 million in funding from angel investors, while marketing a new line of high heel shoes that are comfortable, healthy, and attractive. The new line of shoes will use the technology of athletic footwear while having the look of an Italian designer. Oh! Shoes hopes to generate $35 million in sales by 2014.

4142 ■ "What's Next, Pup Tents in Bryant Park?" in Advertising Age (Vol. 78, January 29, 2007, No. 5, pp. 4)
Pub: Crain Communications, Inc.

Ed: Stephanie Thompson. **Description:** Designers such as Ralph Lauren, Juicy Couture, Burberry and Kiehl's have been expanding their businesses with new clothing lines for pets. Packaged Facts, a division of MarketResearch.com, predicts that pet expenditures will continue to grow in the years to come.

4143 ■ "When Dov Cries" in Canadian Business (Vol. 83, June 15, 2010, No. 10, pp. 71)
Pub: Rogers Media Ltd.

Ed: Joe Castaldo. **Description:** American Apparel disclosed that they will have problems meeting one of its debt covenants which could trigger a chain reaction that could lead to bankruptcy. The prospects look bleak, but eccentric company founder Dov Charney, has always defied expectations.

4144 ■ "Work that Skirt!" in Entrepreneur (Vol. 37, October 2009, No. 10, pp. 17)
Pub: Entrepreneur Media Inc.

Ed: Donnell Alexander. **Description:** Steven Villegas, also called Krash, has captured a segment of the men's clothing market with his skirts called Utilikilts. Villegas has sold 100,000 kilts since starting his business in 2000.

SOURCES OF SUPPLY

4145 ■ American Apparel Producers' Network--Directory for Sourcing Apparel
American Apparel Producers' Network
Contact: Carlos Arias, President
E-mail: carlos.arias@denimatrix.com

URL(s): www.aapnetwork.net/aapmembers/. **Released:** Annual; First quarter. **Covers:** Over 300 member contractors, manufacturers, and suppliers in the apparel industry. **Entries include:** Firm name, address, phone, names and titles of key personnel, apparel and services provided. **Arrangement:** Alphabetical. **Indexes:** Company name, type of apparel.

TRADE PERIODICALS

4146 ■ Clothing Manufacturers Association--News Bulletin
Pub: Clothing Manufacturers Association of the U.S.A.

Ed: Robert A. Kaplan, Editor. **Released:** Semimonthly. **Price:** Included in membership; $297 Associate (supplier) members. **Description:** Disseminates information for the Association relating to developments in or affecting the manufacturing of men's and boy's tailored clothing in the U.S. Contains statistics on sales, production, size, and industry earnings. Recurring features include notices of publications available, labor advisories, import and export statistics and advisories, and news of business opportunities.

4147 ■ Dallas Apparel News
Pub: Apparel News Group
Contact: John Irwin, Manager
URL(s): www.apparelnews.net. **Ed:** N. Jayne Seward. **Released:** 5/yr.

4148 ■ DNR: Defining Men's Fashion
Pub: Fairchild Publications
URL(s): www.dnrnews.com/. **Released:** Daily (morn.). **Price:** $129, Individuals; $99, Individuals online; $169, Individuals online + print; $895, Individuals online archive.

4149 ■ New York Apparel News
Pub: Apparel News Group
Contact: John Irwin, Manager
URL(s): www.apparelnews.net/fashion/NY-Fashion-Week-Spring-2011. **Ed:** Connie Cho. **Released:** 5/yr. **Price:** $20, Individuals; $4, Single issue.

4150 ■ Sew News: Creating For You and Your Home
Pub: Primedia Consumer Media and Magazine Group
URL(s): www.sewnews.com/index.html. **Ed:** Ellen March. **Released:** 6/yr. **Price:** $21.98, Individuals; $38.98, Two years; $27.98, Canada; $33.98, Other countries; $50.98, Two years; $62.98, Institutions 2 years.

4151 ■ Threads
Pub: Taunton Press Inc.
Contact: John Lively, Chief Executive Officer
URL(s): www.threadsmagazine.com. **Released:** Bimonthly **Price:** $32.95, Individuals; $54.95, U.S. and Canada two years; $78.95, U.S. and Canada 3/yr.

4152 ■ Visionaire
Pub: Visionaire Publishing
URL(s): www.visionaireworld.com/index.php. **Released:** 3/yr. **Price:** $675, Individuals.

VIDEOCASSETTES/AUDIOCASSETTES

4153 ■ Cloth by the Yard
New Jersey Network (NJN)
25 S Stockton St.
Trenton, NJ 08625-0777
Ph: (609)777-5273
Free: 800-792-8645
Fax: (609)643-4004
Co. E-mail: productioncenter@njn.org
URL: http://www.njn.net
Contact: Janice Selinger, Director
Released: 1983. **Description:** This documentary visits the Klopman Mills cloth factory to show how designs are woven into fabric. **Availability:** VHS; 3/4 U.

4154 ■ Clothes That Fit
American Educational Products, LLC
401 Hickory St.
Fort Collins, CO 80522
Ph: (970)484-7445
Free: 800-289-9299

Fax: (970)484-1198
Co. E-mail: custserv@amep.com
URL: http://www.amep.com
Released: 1981. **Description:** This program in the "Good Life" series emphasizes the importance of proper fit and appropriate length of clothes, for developmentally disabled adolescents and adults. **Availability:** VHS; EJ; 3/4 U.

4155 ■ Clothing Around the World
Phoenix Learning Group
2349 Chaffee Dr.
Saint Louis, MO 63146-3306
Ph: (314)569-0211
Free: 800-221-1274
Fax: (314)569-2834
URL: http://www.phoenixlearninggroup.com
Released: 1981. **Description:** This film demonstrates many styles of clothing around the world. **Availability:** VHS; 3/4 U.

4156 ■ Clothing and Fashion: A History
Benchmark Media
72 N. State Rd., Ste. 415
Briarcliff Manor, NY 10510-1542
Ph: (914)762-3838
Free: 800-438-5564
Fax: (914)762-3895
Co. E-mail: benchmedia@aol.com
URL: http://www.benchmarkmedia.info
Released: 1972. **Description:** From ancient to modern times, the evolution of fashions in clothing are explored. **Availability:** VHS; 3/4 U.

4157 ■ Cotton Production
CEV Multimedia
1020 SE Loop 289
Lubbock, TX 79404
Ph: (806)745-8820
Free: 877-610-5017
Fax: (800)243-6398
Co. E-mail: cev@cevmultimedia.com
URL: http://www.cevmultimedia.com
Contact: Jeff Lansdell, President
Released: 19??. **Price:** $59.95. **Description:** Outlines all areas of the cotton industry from planting to clothing production. **Availability:** VHS.

4158 ■ Not by Jeans Alone
Phoenix Learning Group
2349 Chaffee Dr.
Saint Louis, MO 63146-3306
Ph: (314)569-0211
Free: 800-221-1274
Fax: (314)569-2834
URL: http://www.phoenixlearninggroup.com
Released: 1981. **Description:** A look at how Levi Strauss Company plans to branch out into the clothing industry. Part of the "Enterprise" series. **Availability:** VHS; 3/4 U.

4159 ■ Sins
Olive Films
707 Colomba Ct., Ste. 109
Saint Charles, IL 60774
Ph: (630)444-1757
Fax: (630)444-1759
Co. E-mail: contact@olivefilms.com
URL: http://www.olivefilms.com
Released: 1985. **Price:** $29.95. **Description:** On her way up the ladder of success in the fashion industry, Helene has stepped on a few toes. Those rivals and her ever-increasing acquisition of power and money make this film an exciting drama. **Availability:** VHS; DVD.

TRADE SHOWS AND CONVENTIONS

4160 ■ Beauty Fair
The Finnish Fair Corp.
PO Box 21
FIN-00521 Helsinki, Finland
Ph: 358 40 4503250

Fax: 358 9 142358
Co. E-mail: info@finnexpo.fi
URL: http://web.finnexpo.fi/en/Yritys/finnishfair/Pages/default.aspx
URL(s): www.finnexpo.fi. Frequency: Annual. Audience: General public. Principal Exhibits: Beauty and fashion, cosmetics and services; hair products and services; clothing, showes, bags, accessories, jewelry, education, and publications.

4161 ■ Mitteldeutsche Handwerksmesse: Central German Handicrafts Fair
Leipziger Messe GmbH
Messe-Allee 1
04356 Leipzig, Germany
Ph: 0341 6 78-0
Fax: 0341 6 78-8762
Co. E-mail: info@leipziger-messe.de
URL: http://www.leipziger-messe.de
Contact: Dr. Arend Oetker, Director
URL(s): www.handwerksmesse-leipzig.de. Frequency: Annual. Audience: General public. Principal Exhibits: Building and conversion, home, arts and crafts, health, lifestyle, food crafts, vehicles, rare handicrafts.

4162 ■ National Costumers Association Annual Convention
National Costumers Association
121 N. Bosart Ave.
Indianapolis, IN 46201
Ph: (317)351-1940
Fax: (317)351-1941
Co. E-mail: office@costumers.org
URL: http://www.costumers.org
Contact: Janie Westendorf, President
URL(s): www.costumers.org. Price: $175, Pre-registered, members; $200, Onsite registered, members; $225, Pre-registered, non-members; $250, Onsite registered, non-members. Frequency: Annual. Principal Exhibits: Exhibits for designers, producers and renters of costumes for all occasions including parties and dance. Telecommunication Services: office@costumers.org.

LIBRARIES

4163 ■ Academy of Art University Library
180 New Montgomery St., 6th Fl.
San Francisco, CA 94105
Ph: (415)618-3842
Fax: (415)263-8803
Co. E-mail: library@academyart.edu
URL: http://library.academyart.edu
Contact: Debra Sampson, Director, Library Services
Scope: Commercial arts, photography, fine arts, art history, interior architecture design, fashion, industrial design, film, advertising art, graphic design, computer graphics. Services: Copying; scanning; Internet access; Library open to the public for reference use only. Founded: 1977. Holdings: 50,000 books; 112,000 slides; VF drawers of art-related ephemera; picture file; 253 CD-ROMs; 1400 videocassettes. Subscriptions: 300 journals and other serials. Telecommunication Services: dsampson@academyart.edu.

4164 ■ American Intercontinental University Library
231 N. Martingale Rd., 6th Fl.
Schaumburg, IL 60173
Ph: (847)851-5000
Free: 877-701-3800
Fax: (866)647-9403
URL: http://www.aiuniv.edu
Scope: Fashion, busines, commercial art, costume history, interior design, information technology, criminal justice, media production. Services: Library not open to the public. Founded: 1982. Holdings: 25,000 books; 225 bound periodical volumes; 25,000 microfiche; fashion clipping file. Subscriptions: 200 journals and other serials; 15 newspapers.

4165 ■ Art Institute of Philadelphia Library
1610 Chestnut St.
Philadelphia, PA 19103

Ph: (215)405-6402
Co. E-mail: rschachter@aii.edu
URL: http://www.artinstitutes.edu/philadelphia
Contact: Ruth Schachter, Director
URL(s): www.artinstitutes.edu/philadelphia/student-life/library.aspx. Scope: Visual communications, interior design, industrial design, animation, fashion marketing, fashion design, visual merchandising, photography, website design, multimedia. Services: Interlibrary loan; copying; library not open to the public (circulation services provided for students and faculty). Founded: 1974. Holdings: 31,000 volumes; 2000 videocassettes; audiocassettes. Subscriptions: 180 print subscriptions and other serials.

4166 ■ Art Institute of Portland Library
1122 NW Davis St.
Portland, OR 97209-2911
Ph: (503)382-4759
Free: 888-228-6528
Fax: (503)228-4227
URL: http://www.artinstitute.edu/portland/
Scope: Fashion and costume history, interior decoration, furniture history, world history, textiles, clothing and fashion industry, graphic design, multimedia, digital media production, media arts and animation, game art, advertising. Services: Copying; color copying; A/V viewing; Library open to professionals in the field. Founded: 1963. Holdings: 21,933 books; 900 videocassettes. Subscriptions: 204 journals and other serials; 3 newspapers.

4167 ■ Bauder College Library
384 Northyards Blvd. NW, Ste. 190 and 400
Atlanta, GA 30313
Ph: (404)237-7573
Free: 800-935-1857
Fax: (404)237-1619
URL: http://atlanta.bauder.edu
Scope: Fashion design and merchandising, interior design, information technology, business administration, graphic design, criminal justice. Services: Library not open to the public. Founded: 1967. Holdings: 7800 books; 500 videotapes; 6500 slide sets; 100 filmstrips. Subscriptions: 160 journals and other serials; 6 newspapers.

4168 ■ Brooklyn Museum - Library
200 Eastern Pkwy.
Brooklyn, NY 11238
Ph: (718)501-6307
Fax: (718)501-6136
Co. E-mail: library@brooklynmuseum.org
URL: http://www.brooklynmuseum.org
Contact: Deirdre E. Lawrence, Librarian
Scope: American and European painting and sculpture; decorative arts; art African, Oceanic, Native American; prints and drawings; Asian art; costumes and textiles. Services: Interlibrary loan; copying; library open to the public. Founded: 1823. Holdings: 300,000 volumes; 25,000 bound periodical volumes; 200 VF drawers of ephemeral materials; 2000 lin.ft. museum archival materials. Subscriptions: 400 journals and other serials.

4169 ■ George Brown College of Applied Arts & Technology - Archives
500 Macpherson Ave., Rm. F-103
Toronto, ON, Canada M5T 2T9
Ph: (416)415-5000, x4771
Fax: (416)415-4772
Co. E-mail: rmacaula@georgebrown.ca
URL: http://www.georgebrown.ca
Contact: Robert Macaulay, Archivist
Scope: College history, labor relations, fashion industry, post-secondary education, nursing schools, collegiate sports. Services: Copying; archives open to the public with restrictions and by appointment only. Founded: 1975. Holdings: 190 cubic meters of records and manuscripts; 2700 linear meters publications, clippings, photographs, filsm, audio and video recordings.

4170 ■ Centennial College of Applied Arts & Technology - Warden Woods Campus Learning & Resource Centre
PO Box 631, Sta. A
Scarborough, ON, Canada M1K 5E9

Ph: (416)289-5000
Co. E-mail: centennial@centennialcollege.ca
URL: http://library.centennialcollege.ca
Contact: Gladys Watson, Director
Scope: Nursing, travel, early childhood education, social services. Services: Interlibrary loan; Center open to the public. Founded: 1966. Holdings: 26,995 volumes. Subscriptions: 189 periodicals. Telecommunication Services: gwatson@centennialcollege.ca.

4171 ■ Conde Nast Publications Library and Information Services
4 Times Sq.
New York, NY 10036
Ph: (212)286-2860
Co. E-mail: communications@condenast.com
URL: http://www.condenastdigital.com
Contact: Sarah Chubb, President
Scope: Fashion, houses, gardens, home furnishings, interior design, health, personalities, photographs. Services: Library not open to public. Founded: 1935. Holdings: 7000 volumes. Subscriptions: 200 journals and other serials; 4 newspapers.

4172 ■ Fashion Institute of Design & Merchandising - Cyril Magnin Resource and Research Center
55 Stockton St., 5th Fl.
San Francisco, CA 94108-5829
Ph: (415)675-5200
Free: 800-422-3436
Fax: (415)296-7299
URL: http://fidm.com
Contact: Jim Glenny, Director, Library Services
Scope: Fashion design and merchandising, interior design, apparel manufacturing, advertising, merchandising, marketing. Services: Center not open to the public. Founded: 1977. Holdings: 4000 books; 800 AV programs; 1000 newspaper clipping files; 4000 videos, DVDs, and slides. Subscriptions: 200 journals and other serials.

4173 ■ Fashion Institute of Design & Merchandising - Orange County Library
17590 Gillette Ave.
Irvine, CA 92614-5610
Ph: (949)851-6200
Free: 888-974-3436
Fax: (949)851-6808
URL: http://fidm.com
Scope: Apparel manufacturing management, cosmetics and fragrance merchandising, fashion design, interior design, merchandise marketing, textile design, visual presentation and space design. Services: Copying; library open to the public by appointment. Founded: 1980. Holdings: 3000 books; 130 bound periodical volumes; 40 pamphlet headings; 475 videotapes; 135 slide sets; 300 retail catalogs; 100 Annual reports; 50 CD-ROMs. Subscriptions: 80 journals and other serials; 8 newspapers.

4174 ■ Fashion Institute of Technology - Gladys Marcus Library
7th Ave. at 27th St.
E-Bldg. E502
New York, NY 10001-5992
Ph: (212)217-4340
Fax: (212)217-4371
Co. E-mail: greta_earnest@fitnyc.edu
URL: http://www.fitnyc.edu/library.asp
Contact: Prof. N.J. Wolfe, Director, Library Services
Scope: Costume, fashion, interior design, management engineering technology, fashion buying and merchandising, textiles, toy design, packaging design, advertising. Services: Interlibrary loan; copying; library open to the public for reference use only by appointment. Founded: 1944. Holdings: 130,260 books; 113,265 nonprint units; 20,637 bound periodical volumes; 125,000 fashion slides; 4712 reels of microfilm; 438 CD-ROM serials and digital monographs. Subscriptions: 4000 journals and other serials. Telecommunication Services: nj_wolfe@fitnyc.edu.

4175 ■ Illinois Institute of Art/Schaumburg - Learning Resource Center
1000 N. Plaza Dr., Ste. 100
Schaumburg, IL 60173-4913

Ph: (847)619-3450
Free: 800-314-3450
Fax: (847)619-3064
URL: http://www.artinstitutes.edu/schaumburg/
Scope: Graphic design, interior design, applied art and design, furniture history. **Services:** Interlibrary loan. **Founded:** 1985. **Holdings:** Books; slides; periodicals; videotapes; DVDs; CD-ROMs. **Subscriptions:** 175 journals and other serials.

4176 ■ Metropolitan Museum of Art - Irene Lewisohn Costume Reference Library—The Costume Institute - Irene Lewisohn Costume Reference Library.
1000 Fifth Ave.
New York, NY 10028-0198
Ph: (212)650-2723
Fax: (212)570-3970
Co. E-mail: julie.le@metmuseum.org
URL: http://www.metmuseum.org/research/libraries-and-study-centers/
URL(s): libmma.org/portal/the-irene-lewisohn-costume-reference-library/. **Scope:** History of costume, fashion, fashion designers, social history. **Services:** Copying; Library open to professional designers and research scholars by appointment. **Founded:** 1937. **Holdings:** 40,000 cataloged books and journals; 100,000 pieces of ephemera, including swatch books, fashion sketches, fashion plates, postcards, and vertical files; 50 fashion periodical subscriptions. **Subscriptions:** 70 journals and other serials. **Telecommunication Services:** watson.library@metmuseum.org.

4177 ■ Otis College of Art and Design - Millard Sheets Library
Ahmanson Bldg., 3rd Fl.
9045 Lincoln Blvd.
Goldsmith Campus
Los Angeles, CA 90045
Ph: (310)665-6930
Co. E-mail: maberry@otis.edu
URL: http://www.otis.edu/life_otis/library/index.html
Contact: Heather Cleary, Librarian

Scope: Fine arts, communication design, architecture, fashion, ceramics, photography. **Services:** Interlibrary loan; copying; library open to the public by appointment only. **Founded:** 1917. **Holdings:** 45,000 books; 2900 bound periodical volumes; 100,000 slides; 54 VF drawers of artists' ephemera files; 8 VF drawers of clipping files; 267 audiocassettes; 123 films; 150 videocassettes and cassettes; 5000 videos/DVDs; 20,000 images. **Subscriptions:** 150 journals and other serials. **Telecommunication Services:** cathcham@otis.edu; hcleary@otis.edu.

4178 ■ Parsons School of Design - Adam & Sophie Gimbel Design Library
2 W. 13th St.
New York, NY 10011
Ph: (212)229-8914

Fax: (212)229-2806
Co. E-mail: cassimar@newschool.edul
URL: http://library.newschool.edu/gimbel
Contact: Kira Appel, Director
Scope: Fine arts, architecture, costume, crafts, design, environmental design, fashion, graphic arts, photography, typography. **Services:** Interlibrary loan. **Founded:** 1896. **Holdings:** 61,000 books; 55,000 mounted picture plates; 85,000 slides; archives. **Subscriptions:** 200 journals and other serials.

4179 ■ Philadelphia University - Paul J. Gutman Library
School House Ln. and Henry Ave.
Philadelphia, PA 19144
Ph: (215)951-2840
Fax: (215)951-2574
Co. E-mail: reference@philau.edu
URL: http://www.philau.edu/library
Contact: Karen Albert, Director, Library Services
Scope: Textiles, textile manufacturing, apparel, fashion, architecture, design, business. **Services:** Interlibrary loan; copying; library open to the public for research only. **Founded:** 1945. **Holdings:** 113,600 books; 12,000 bound periodical volumes; 4900 microforms; 2000 AV items; 8000 archival items. **Subscriptions:** 929 journals and other serials; 20 newspapers. **Telecommunication Services:** mulroyk@philau.edu; helpdesk@philau.edu.

4180 ■ Southern New Hampshire University - Shapiro Library
2500 N. River Rd.
Manchester, NH 03106-1394
Ph: (603)645-9605
Fax: (603)645-9685
Co. E-mail: k.growney@snhu.edu
URL: http://www.snhu.edu/library.asp
Contact: Kathy Growney, Dean, Library Services
Scope: Economics, accounting, computer sciences, business management, finance, taxes, marketing and retailing, hotel/resort/tourism, mathematics, education. **Services:** Interlibrary loan; copying; Library open to the public. **Founded:** 1963. **Holdings:** 121,608 books; 514 bound periodical volumes; 3206 reels of microfilm; 10 VF drawers of archival materials; 347,231 microfiche. **Subscriptions:** 658 journals and other serials; 11 newspapers. **Telecommunication Services:** c.sullivan@snhu.edu.

4181 ■ Tavy Stone Fashion Library
Detroit Historical Museum
5401 Woodward Ave.
Detroit, MI 48202
Ph: (313)833-1805
Fax: (313)833-5342
Co. E-mail: joels@detroithistorical.org
URL: http://www.detroithistorical.org
Contact: Joel Stone, Curator
Scope: Fashion (antiquity to present) - American and European fashion designers, careers, advertising, merchandising, management, textiles and fabrics, cosmetics and fragrances, historic costume, fashion retailers; the business, sociological, and psychologi-

cal aspects of fashion. **Services:** Copying; library open to the public with restrictions. **Founded:** 1987. **Holdings:** 800 books; 40 VF drawers; 500 slides; 10 color swatches; 21 AV programs. **Subscriptions:** 6 journals and other serials.

4182 ■ University of British Columbia - Art, Architecture, and Planning Division
Irving K. Barber Learning Centre
1961 East Mall
Vancouver, BC, Canada V6T 1Z1
Ph: (604)822-3943
Fax: (604)822-3779
Co. E-mail: vanessa.kam@ubc.ca
URL: http://aarp.library.ubc.ca
Contact: D. Vanessa Kam, Librarian
Scope: Fine arts, architecture, community and regional planning, history of costume and dance, artistic photography, fashion design. **Services:** Library open to the public with restrictions. **Founded:** 1948. **Holdings:** 220,000 books and bound periodical volumes. **Subscriptions:** 200 journals and other serials. **Telecommunication Services:** paula.farrar@ubc.ca; aarp.library@ubc.ca.

4183 ■ University of Cincinnati - Design, Architecture, Art & Planning Library
5480 Aronoff Center for Design and Art
Cincinnati, OH 45221-0016
Ph: (513)556-1335
Co. E-mail: jennifer.krivickas@uc.edu
URL: http://www.libraries.uc.edu/libraries/daap/index.html
Contact: Jennifer Krivickas, Department Head
Scope: Architecture, art history, art education, planning, interior design, industrial design, fine arts, fashion design, urban studies, health planning, graphic design. **Services:** Interlibrary loan; copying; Library open to the public. **Founded:** 1929. **Holdings:** 100,000 books and bound periodical volumes; 11,000 serial volumes; 5000 microforms; 100 planning reports; 200,000 35mm slides; digital images. **Subscriptions:** 400 journals and other serials. **Telecommunication Services:** elizabeth.meyer@uc.edu.

4184 ■ Woodbury University Library
7500 Glenoaks Blvd.
Burbank, CA 91504-1052
Ph: (818)252-5201
Fax: (818)767-4534
Co. E-mail: jennifer.rosenfeld@woodbury.edu
URL: http://library.woodbury.edu
Contact: Nedra Peterson, Director
Scope: Business and management, International business, art, architecture, interior design, fashion marketing and design, psychology, animation. **Services:** Interlibrary loan; copying; Library open to the public for reference use only. **Founded:** 1884. **Holdings:** 65,000 books; 3070 bound periodical volumes; 17,401 slides; 2000 DVD/VHS. **Subscriptions:** 300 journals and other serials; 5 newspapers. **Telecommunication Services:** nedra.peterson@woodbury.edu.

START-UP INFORMATION

4185 ■ Design and Launch Your Online Boutique in a Week
Pub: Entrepreneur Press
Ed: Melissa Campanelli. **Released:** June 26, 2008. **Price:** $17.95. **Description:** Tips for starting an online boutique in a short amount of time are given. The books shows how to build the online boutique with designer goods or your own product, ways to create eye-catching content, online tools to handle payments and accept orders, marketing and advertising techniques, and customer service.

4186 ■ In Fashion: From Runway to Retail, Everything You Need to Know to Break Into the Fashion Industry
Pub: Crown Business Books
Ed: Annemarie Iverson. **Released:** August 10, 2010. **Price:** $16.99. **Description:** Whether your dream is to photograph models, outfit celebrities, design fashions, this book provides details into every aspect for working in the fashion industry.

4187 ■ "Money Matters: Using Sound Resources, You Can Find Capital For Your Business" in Black Enterprise (Vol. 38, November 2007, No. 4)
Pub: Earl G. Graves Publishing Co. Inc.
Ed: Carolyn M. Brown. **Description:** Profile of fashion designer Kara Saun who inspired an angel investor from Connecticut to help launch her Fall 2006 clothing line.

4188 ■ "Mount Laurel Woman Launches Venture Into Children's Used Clothing" in Philadelphia Inquirer (September 17, 2010)
Pub: Philadelphia Media Network
Ed: Maria Panaritis. **Description:** Profile of Jennifer Frisch, stay-at-home mom turned entrepreneur. Frisch started a used-clothing store Once Upon a Child after opening her franchised Plato's Closet, selling unwanted and used baby clothing and accessories at her new shop, while offering used merchandise to teens at Plato's Closet.

4189 ■ The Specialty Shop: How to Create Your Own Unique and Profitable Retail Business
Pub: AMACOM
Ed: Dorothy Finell. **Released:** February 27, 2007. **Price:** $21.95. **Description:** Advise to start retail businesses, including bakeries, gift shops, toy stores, book shops, tea houses, clothing boutiques, and other unique stores.

4190 ■ Start Your Own Fashion Accessories Business
Pub: Entrepreneur Press
Contact: Perlman Neil, President
Released: March 1, 2009. **Price:** $17.95. **Description:** Entrepreneurs wishing to start a fashion accessories business will find important information for setting up a home workshop and office, exploring the market, managing finances, publicizing and advertising the business and more.

ASSOCIATIONS AND OTHER ORGANIZATIONS

4191 ■ International Formalwear Association (IFA)
244 E Main St.
Galesburg, IL 61401
Ph: (309)721-5450
Fax: (309)342-5921
Co. E-mail: admin@formalwear.org
URL: http://www.formalwear.org
Contact: Rod Benbrook, President
Description: Specialists working to promote the formal wear industry. Conducts educational programs through seminars and exhibitions. **Founded:** 1972. **Publications:** IFA Membership Directory (Annual); International Formalwear Association--Membership Directory. **Educational Activities:** International Formalwear Association Expo (Annual). **Awards:** Black Tie Award.

4192 ■ National Retail Federation (NRF)
325 7th St. NW, Ste. 1100
Washington, DC 20004
Ph: (202)783-7971
Free: 800-673-4692
Fax: (202)737-2849
Co. E-mail: bookinquiries@nrf.com
URL: http://www.nrf.com
Contact: Terry J. Lundgren, President
E-mail: shaym@nrf.com
Description: Represents state retail associations, several dozen national retail associations, as well as large and small corporate members representing the breadth and diversity of the retail industry's establishment and employees. Conducts informational and educational conferences related to all phases of retailing including financial planning and cash management, taxation, economic forecasting, expense planning, shortage control, credit, electronic data processing, telecommunications, merchandise management, buying, traffic, security, supply, materials handling, store planning and construction, personnel administration, recruitment and training, and advertising and display. **Scope:** retail management, fashion merchandising. **Founded:** 1911. **Subscriptions:** 1000. **Publications:** NRF Foundation Focus (Quarterly); NRF Update; STORES Magazine (Monthly); Washington Retail Report (Weekly); STORES--Top 100 Retailers Issue (Annual). **Educational Activities:** Human Resources Summit (Annual); Retail's Big Show (Annual); Loss Prevention Conference & Exhibition (Annual); National Retail Federation Annual Convention & Expo (Annual). **Awards:** American Spirit Award (Annual); Gold Medal in Retailing (Annual); Leadership/Public Service Award (Annual); Gold Medal Award; International Retailer of the Year; Silver Plaque Award; Distinguished Service Award; Leadership in Public Service Award; American Spirit Award; J. Thomas Weyant Lifetime Achievement Award. **Telecommunication Services:** shaym@nrf.com.

REFERENCE WORKS

4193 ■ "Always Striving" in Women In Business (Vol. 61, December 2009, No. 6, pp. 28)
Pub: American Business Women's Association
Ed: Kathleen Leighton. **Description:** Jennifer Mull discusses her responsibilities and how she attained success as CEO of Backwoods, a gear and clothing store founded by her father in 1973. She places importance on being true to one's words and beliefs, while emphasizing the capacity to tolerate risks in business. Mull defines success as an evolving concept and believes there must always be something to strive for.

4194 ■ "Apparel" in Retail Merchandiser (Vol. 51, July-August 2011, No. 4, pp. 14)
Pub: Phoenix Media Corporation
Description: NPD Group Inc. released current sales statistics for the women's apparel market along with men's apparel. It also reported annual shoes sales for 2010. Statistical data included.

4195 ■ "Apparel Apparatchic at Kmart" in Barron's (Vol. 88, March 17, 2008, No. 11, pp. 16)
Pub: Dow Jones & Company, Inc.
Description: Kmart began a nationwide search for women to represent the company in a national advertising campaign. Contestants need to upload their photos to Kmart's website and winners will be chosen by a panel of celebrity judges. The contest aims to reverse preconceived negative notions about the store's quality and service.

4196 ■ "Are You Looking for an Environmentally Friendly Dry Cleaner?" in Inc. (Vol. 30, December 2008, No. 12, pp. 34)
Pub: Mansueto Ventures LLC
Ed: Shivani Vora. **Description:** Greenopia rates the greenness of 52 various kinds of businesses, including restaurants, nail salons, dry cleaners, and clothing stores. The guidebooks are sold through various retailers including Barnes & Noble and Amazon.com.

4197 ■ "As Seen On TV" in Canadian Business (Vol. 80, November 5, 2007, No. 22, pp. 93)
Pub: Rogers Media
Ed: Zena Olijnyk. **Description:** StarBrand Media Inc. is one of the companies providing fans with information on how and where to purchase the items that television characters are using. StarBrand created the style section found on different television shows' Websites, such as that of the Gossip Girl and Smallville. The benefits of using sites like StarBrand are evaluated.

4198 ■ "Babynut.com to Shut Down" in Bellingham Business Journal (Vol. February 2010, pp. 3)
Pub: Sound Publishing Inc.
Description: Saralee Sky and Jerry Kilgore, owners of Babynut.com will close their online store. The site offered a free online and email newsletter to help

mothers through pregnancy and the first three years of their child's life. Products being sold at clearance prices include organic and natural maternity and nursing clothing, baby and toddler clothes, books on pregnancy, and more.

4199 ■ "Better Than New" in Bellingham Business Journal (Vol. February 2010, pp. 16)
Pub: Sound Publishing Inc.

Ed: Ashley Mitchell. **Description:** Profile of family owned Better Than New clothing store that sells overstock items from department stores and clothing manufacturers. The stores location makes it easy to miss and its only advertising is a large sign posted outside. This is the sixth store owned by the couple, Keijeo and Sirba Halmekanqas.

4200 ■ "Breadwinner Tries on Designer Jeans" in Houston Business Journal (Vol. 40, December 18, 2009, No. 32, pp. 1)
Pub: American City Business Journals

Ed: Allison Wollam. **Description:** Chuck Cain, the franchisee who introduced Panera Bread to Houston, Texas has partnered with tax accountant Jim Jacobsen to introduce custom-make Tattu Jeans. As more Tattu Jeans outlets are being planned, Cain is using entrepreneurial lessons learned from Panera Bread in the new venture. Both Panera Bread and Tattu Jeans were opened by Cain during economic downturns.

4201 ■ "Bringing Charities More Bang for Their Buck" in Crain's Chicago Business (Vol. 34, May 23, 2011, No. 21, pp. 31)
Pub: Crain Communications Inc.

Ed: Lisa Bertagnoli. **Description:** Marcy-Newberry Association connects charities with manufacturers in order to use excess items such as clothing, janitorial and office supplies.

4202 ■ "Buy the Pants, Save the Planet?" in Globe & Mail (February 5, 2007, pp. B1)
Pub: CTVglobemedia Publishing Inc.

Ed: Keith McArthur. **Description:** The marketing campaign of the clothing company Diesel S.p.A. is discussed. The company has based its latest collection of T-shirt designs on the problem of global warming.

4203 ■ "Buying Chanel (All Of It)" in Conde Nast Portfolio (Vol. 2, June 2008, No. 6, pp. 34)
Pub: Conde Nast Publications
Contact: David Carey, President

Ed: Willow Duttge. **Description:** Overview of the luxury company Chanel and an estimated guess as to what the company is worth.

4204 ■ "Can Avenue be Fashionable Again? Livernois Merchants, City Want Revival" in Crain's Detroit Business (March 10, 2008)
Pub: Crain Communications, Inc.

Ed: Nancy Kaffer. **Description:** Once a busy retail district, the Avenue of Fashion, a Livernois Avenue strip between Six Mile and Eight Mile roads, is facing a community business effort being backed by city support whose aim is to restore the area to its former glory.

4205 ■ Canadian Apparel Directory
Pub: Canadian Apparel Federation
Contact: Bob Kirke, Executive Director

URL(s): www.apparel.ca. **Released:** Biennial; May/June. **Price:** $132, Members; $350, Nonmembers. **Publication includes:** Lists of Canadian industry suppliers, and manufacturers of apparel. **Entries include:** Company name, address, phone, fax, names and titles of key personnel, name and title of contact, product/service, description of company business activities. **Arrangement:** Alphabetical. **Indexes:** Trade name, product/service, geographical.

4206 ■ "A Change Would Do You Good" in Canadian Business (Vol. 80, November 19, 2007, No. 23, pp. 15)
Pub: Rogers Media

Ed: Geoff Kirbyson. **Description:** Western Glove Works will be manufacturing clothing offshore, including Sheryl Crow's jeans collection, in countries such as China and the Philippines. The company decided

to operate offshore after 86 years of existence due to the high price of manufacturing jeans in Canada. Western Glove's focus on producing celebrity-endorsed goods is discussed.

4207 ■ Chief Culture Officer: How to Create a Living, Breathing Corporation
Pub: Basic Books

Ed: Grant McCracken. **Price:** $26.95. **Description:** Business consultant argues that corporations need to focus on 'reading' what's happening in the culture around them. Otherwise, companies will suffer the consequences, as Levi Strauss did when it missed out on the rise of hip-hop (and the baggy pants that are part of that lifestyle).

4208 ■ "Clothier Delays Opening" in The Business Journal-Serving Metropolitan Kansas City (Vol. 27, November 14, 2008, No. 10, pp. 1)
Pub: American City Business Journals, Inc.

Ed: Suzanna Stagemeyer. **Description:** Jos A. Bank Clothiers Inc. has delayed the opening of its store at the Kansas City Power and Light District in Missouri for the first quarter of 2009. The company is still waiting for other tenants to open shop in the district. Comments from officials concerning the retail sector are also presented.

4209 ■ "Common Thread" in Entrepreneur (Vol. 36, March 2008, No. 3, pp. 144)
Pub: Entrepreneur Media Inc.

Ed: Sara Wilson. **Description:** Profile of Stacey Benet and her business, Alice and Olivia, and how she jumpstarted her career in the clothing industry after she wore a self-designed pair of pants that caught the attention of a Barney's New York representative is presented.

4210 ■ "Consignment Shop Closes Without Warning to Customers, Landlord" in Sun Journal (June 30, 2010)
Pub: Freedom Communications Inc.

Ed: Laura Oleniacz. **Description:** Off The Racks consignment shop located on Glenburnie Road in New Bern, North Carolina closed without warning to customers or its landlord. The consignors who donated clothing to the store were left unpaid.

4211 ■ "Consignment Shop Offers Children's Clothes, Products" in Frederick News-Post (August 19, 2010)
Pub: Federick News-Post

Ed: Ed Waters Jr. **Description:** Sweet Pea Consignments for Children offers used items for newborns to pre-teens. The shop carries name brand clothing as well as toys, books and baby products.

4212 ■ "Crowdsourcing their Way into One Big Mess" in Brandweek (Vol. 51, October 25, 2010, No. 38, pp. 26)
Pub: Nielsen Business Media, Inc.

Ed: Gregg S. Lipman. **Description:** The Gap, was counting on crowdsourcing to provide feedback for its new logo, but it did not prove positive for the retailer. However, a massive outcry of negative opinion, via crowdsourcing, may not always equal valid, constructive criticism.

4213 ■ "Designer is Walking Ad for TIBI Line" in Charlotte Observer (February 5, 2007)
Pub: Knight-Ridder/Tribune Business News

Ed: Crystal Dempsey. **Description:** Profile of Amy Smilovic, mother of two children, and clothing designer. Smilovic wears what she designs, making her a great marketing tool for her clothing line TIBI.

4214 ■ Directory of Apparel Specialty Stores
Pub: Chain Store Guide
Contact: Lisa Patterson, President

URL(s): www.chainstoreguide.com. **Released:** Annual; Latest edition 2012. **Price:** $395, Individuals Directory; $445, Individuals online lite; $1075, Individuals online pro; $1375, Individuals online pro plus. **Covers:** 5,040 apparel and sporting goods specialty retailers in the United States and Canada, operating more than 70,700 stores. Apparel retailers must have annual retail sales of at least $500,000; sporting goods specialty retailers must also have $500,000 in annual sales, with the condition that at

least 20% of product sales are from sporting goods equipment. **Entries include:** Company name, phone, and fax numbers; physical and mailing addresses; company e-mail and web addresses; Internet order processing indicator; percentage of Internet sales; type of business; listing type; product lines; total, industry, and product group sales; total selling square footage; store prototype sizes; total stores; trading areas; projected openings and remodeling; units by trade name; distribution center locations; resident buyer's name and location; mail order indicator; percentage of mail order sales; catalog names; private label indicator; private label credit card indicator; apparel price lines; average number of checkouts; year founded; public company indicator; parent company name and location; and key personnel with titles; 7,200 personnel email addresses . **Arrangement:** Geographical. **Indexes:** Alphabetical, product lines, exclusions.

4215 ■ "Doing Good: Fair Fashion" in Entrepreneur (Vol. 35, October 2007, No. 10, pp. 36)
Pub: Entrepreneur Media Inc.

Ed: J.J. Ramberg. **Description:** Indigenous Designs was launched in 1993, when organic clothing was not yet popular. However, the company has become successful in the industry, with $4 million dollars in revenue, owing to the growing environment awareness of consumers. A history of how the company was formed and an overview of their production process are provided.

4216 ■ "Don't Tweak Your Supply Chain - Rethink It End to End" in Harvard Business Review (Vol. 88, October 2010, No. 10, pp. 62)
Pub: Harvard Business School Publishing

Ed: Hau L. Lee. **Description:** Hong Kong apparel firm Esquel Apparel Ltd. is used to illustrate supply chain reorganization to improve a firm's sustainability. Discussion focuses on taking a broad approach rather than addressing individual steps or processes.

4217 ■ "Dots Sings To New Tune With Its Radio Station" in Crain's Cleveland Business (Vol. 30, June 15, 2009, No. 23, pp. 7)
Pub: Crain Communications, Inc.

Description: Dots LLC, a women's clothing retailer, has launched an online radio station on its Website. The station plays the in-store music to customers while they are shopping online.

4218 ■ "Dress Professionally Cool for Summer" in Women In Business (Vol. 62, June 2010, No. 2, pp. 38)
Pub: American Business Women's Association

Ed: Maureen Sullivan. **Description:** Summer clothing for business and career women is discussed with regard to traditional and relaxed work places. Fabric considerations, tips on choosing blazers and a list of clothes and other items that are not appropriate for the workplace are presented.

4219 ■ "Echo Vintage Clothing Fundraiser Set July 24" in Tri-City Herald (July 22, 2010)
Pub: McClatchy-Tribune

Description: Bicentennial Echo Vintage Clothing Show and Tea was held July 24, 2010 at the Echo City Hall Ballroom in Echo, Oregon. The event is held every two years to fund project in Echo and to maintain the vintage clothing collection.

4220 ■ "The Endless Flow of Russell Simmons" in Entrepreneur (Vol. 37, September 2009, No. 9, pp. 24)
Pub: Entrepreneur Media, Inc.

Ed: Josh Dean. **Description:** Entrepreneur Russell Simmons has successfully grown his businesses by focusing on underserved markets. Simons has never given up on any business strategy. He has also entered the music, clothing and television industries.

4221 ■ "Fall Fever" in Canadian Business (Vol. 81, October 13, 2008, No. 17, pp. S12)
Pub: Rogers Media Ltd.

Description: Buyer's guide of men's suits and jackets for fall are presented, including a suit by Boss Hugo Boss recommended for fun in the city after finishing work. Designers Ermenegildo, Michael Kors, and Arnold Brant are also highlighted.

4222 ■ *"Fall Wardrobe on a Budget"* in *Women In Business (Vol. 62, September 2010, No. 3, pp. 38)*
Pub: American Business Women's Association
Ed: Kathleen Leighton. **Description:** Things women should keep in mind when putting together a fall wardrobe are discussed. Women should aim for at least two jackets, five tops, four pants or skirts, two twin sets, five pairs of pantyhose, and two pair of shoes. They should also be ruthless when it comes to quality and practicality.

4223 ■ *The Fashion Designer Survival Guide*
Pub: Kaplan Publishing
Ed: Mary Gehlhar; Zac Posen. **Released:** September 1, 2005. **Description:** Professional advice from an insider to help start and run a fashion business.

4224 ■ *"Fashion Forward - Frugally"* in *Entrepreneur (Vol. 37, July 2009, No. 7, pp. 18)*
Pub: Entrepreneur Media, Inc.
Ed: Jason Daley. **Description:** Staci Deal, a Fayetteville-based franchisee of fashion brand Plato's Closet, shares her experiences on the company's growth. Deal believes that the economy, and the fact that Fayetteville is a college town, played a vital role in boosting the used clothing store's popularity. Her thoughts on being a young business owner, and the advantages of running a franchise are also given.

4225 ■ *"Fashionistas Weigh in on the Super-Thin"* in *Charlotte Observer (February 7, 2007)*
Pub: Knight-Ridder/Tribune Business News
Ed: Crystal Dempsey. **Description:** Council of Fashion Designers of America held a panel discussion regarding the weight and ages of models used to highlight clothing.

4226 ■ *"Finishing Touches: the Fashion Statement is in the Detail"* in *Black Enterprise (Vol. 37, January 2007, No. 6, pp. 106)*
Pub: Earl G. Graves Publishing Co. Inc.
Ed: Sonia Alleyne. **Description:** Men are discovering the importance of dressing for success. Paying attention to the details such as shoes, socks, cuffs, and collars are just as important as finding the right suit.

4227 ■ *"Five Reasons Why the Gap Fell Out of Fashion"* in *Globe & Mail (January 27, 2007, pp. B4)*
Pub: CTVglobemedia Publishing Inc.
Ed: Keith McArthur. **Description:** The five major market trends that have caused the decline of fashion clothing retailer Gap Inc.'s sales are discussed. The shift in brand, workplace fashion culture, competition, demographics, and consumer preferences have lead to the Gap's brand identity.

4228 ■ *"Fledgling Brands May Take the Fall With Steve & Barry's"* in *Advertising Age (Vol. 79, July 7, 2008, No. 26, pp. 6)*
Pub: Crain Communications, Inc.
Ed: Natalie Zmuda. **Description:** Steve & Barry's, a retailer that holds licensing deals with a number of designers and celebrities, may have to declare bankruptcy; this leaves the fate of the retailer's hundreds of licensing deals and exclusive celebrity lines in question.

4229 ■ *"Forget Your Pants, Calvin Klein Wants Into Your Bedroom"* in *Globe & Mail (March 31, 2007, pp. B4)*
Pub: CTVglobemedia Publishing Inc.
Ed: Barrie McKenna. **Description:** The plans of Phillips-Van Heusen Corp. to open more Calvin Klein stores for selling the new ranges of clothing, personal care products, luggage and mattresses are discussed.

4230 ■ *Fugitive Denim: A Moving Story of People and Pants in the Borderless World of Global Trade*
Pub: W.W. Norton & Company
Ed: Rachel Snyder. **Released:** April 2009. **Price:** $16.95. **Description:** In-depth study of the global production and processes of how jeans are designed, sewn, and transported as well as how the cotton for denim is grown, regulated, purchased and processed.

4231 ■ *"Green It Like You Mean It"* in *Special Events Magazine (Vol. 28, February 1, 2009, No. 2)*
Pub: Special Events Magazine
Ed: Christine Landry. **Description:** Eco-friendly party planners offer advice for planning and hosting green parties or events. Tips include information for using recycled paper products, organic food and drinks. The Eco Nouveau Fashion Show held by Serene Star Productions reused old garments to create new fashions as well as art pieces from discarded doors and window frames for the show; eco-friendly treats and gift bags were highlighted at the event.

4232 ■ *"H&M Offers a Dress for Less"* in *Canadian Business (Vol. 83, September 14, 2010, No. 15, pp. 20)*
Pub: Rogers Media Ltd.
Ed: Laura Cameron. **Description:** Swedish clothing company H&M has implemented loss leader strategy by pricing some dresses at extremely low prices. The economy has forced retailers to keep prices down despite the increasing cost of manufacturing, partly due to Chinese labor becoming more expensive. How the trend will affect apparel companies is discussed.

4233 ■ *"Haute Flyers"* in *Canadian Business (Vol. 80, November 19, 2007, No. 23, pp. 68)*
Pub: Rogers Media
Ed: Rachel Pulfer. **Description:** Duckie Brown has been nominated by the Council of Fashion Designers of America as best menswear designer in the U.S. for 2007, along with leaders Calvin Klein and Ralph Lauren. The New York-based company was formed the day after September 11, 2001, but the timing did not hamper its growth. The works and plans of owners Steven Cox and Daniel Silver are described.

4234 ■ *"Home Shows Signs of Life at Target"* in *Home Textiles Today (Vol. 31, May 24, 2011, No. 13, pp. 1)*
Pub: Reed Business Information
Contact: Jeff Greisch, President
Description: Retailer, Target, is experience a boost in sales for apparel and products for the home.

4235 ■ *"Hot Kicks, Cool Price"* in *Black Enterprise (Vol. 37, December 2006, No. 5, pp. 34)*
Pub: Earl G. Graves Publishing Co. Inc.
Ed: Topher Sanders. **Description:** Stephon Marbury of the New York Nicks introduced a new basketball shoe, the Starbury One, costing $14.98. The shoes are an addition to the Starbury clothing line and although the privately owned company would not disclose figures; stores sold out of a month's worth of inventory in merely three days.

4236 ■ *"How to Keep Your Cool and Your Friends in a Heat Wave"* in *Canadian Business (Vol. 83, August 17, 2010, No. 13-14, pp. 79)*
Pub: Rogers Media Ltd.
Ed: Angelina Chapin. **Description:** A buyer's guide of menswear clothing for businessmen is presented. The products include an antiperspirant and deodorant, men's dress shorts, shoes and bamboo fabric undershirt.

4237 ■ *"How This First Lady Moves Markets"* in *Harvard Business Review (Vol. 88, November 2010, No. 11, pp. 38)*
Pub: Harvard Business School Publishing
Description: A chart is presented demonstrating how First Lady Michelle Obama's choice of fashion designer has impacted the clothing industry.

4238 ■ *Hug Your Customers*
Pub: Hyperion Books
Ed: Jack Mitchell. **Price:** $19.95. **Description:** The CEO of Mitchells/Roberts, two very successful clothing stores, professes his belief in showering customers with attention. His secrets for long-term business success include advice about attracting a good staff, lowering marketing costs, and maintaining a higher gross margins and revenues.

4239 ■ *"Insider"* in *Canadian Business (Vol. 80, Winter 2007, No. 24, pp.)*
Pub: Rogers Media
Ed: Zena Olijnyk. **Description:** Luluemon Athletica started in 1998 after Dennis Wilson takes a yoga class and notices a demand from women for breathable clothes. The company opened their first outlet in Vancouver in November 2000 then opened their first U.S. store in 2003 until finally going public July 27, 2007 where its stocks doubled in value within days of trading.

4240 ■ *"Island Co.: Isle Style"* in *Entrepreneur (Vol. 35, October 2007, No. 10, pp. 172)*
Pub: Entrepreneur Media Inc.
Ed: Sara Wilson. **Description:** Island Co., producer of travel clothing and swimsuits was formed by Spencer Antle in 2002. Its office projects the Caribbean atmosphere, a strategy Antle used to promote the company's theme to its clients. Future plans for the company are also indicated.

4241 ■ *"It's All in the Details"* in *Canadian Business (Vol. 80, December 25, 2006, No. 1, pp. 11)*
Pub: Rogers Media
Description: The failure of several Canadian clothing retailers to disclose their labor practices is discussed.

4242 ■ *"It's So You! Consignment Chop Owner Thrilled to See Vision Come to Fruition"* in *News-Herald (August 27, 2010)*
Pub: News-Herald
Ed: Brandon C. Baker. **Description:** Profile of Laurel Howes and her It's So You! Boutique. The consignment shop is located in Willoughby's Pine Ride Plaza in Ohio. The shop targets all women, but particularly those who are not that comfortable with shopping consignment.

4243 ■ *"Izod, Loft Outlets Coming To Tanger"* in *New Hampshire Business Review (Vol. 33, March 25, 2011, No. 6, pp. 30)*
Pub: Business Publications Inc.
Description: Izod and Lots stores will open at the Tanger Outlet Center in Tilton, New Hampshire. Both stores will feature fashions and accessories.

4244 ■ *"Jeans Draw a Global Following"* in *Marketing to Women (Vol. 21, April 2008, No. 4, pp. 6)*
Pub: EPM Communications Inc.
Contact: Ira Mayer, President
E-mail: imayer@epmcom.com
Description: According to a global study by Synovate of jeans and the women who wear them uncovered trends such as brand loyalty and if given a choice 45 percent of all respondents say that if given a choice, they would wear jeans every day.

4245 ■ *"Let It Shine: Organization Helps Disadvantaged Girls See Their Worth"* in *Black Enterprise (Vol. 38, February 2008, No. 7, pp. 142)*
Pub: Earl G. Graves Publishing Co. Inc.
Ed: George Alexander. **Description:** Wilson Mourning, founder of the clothing label Honey Child, attributes her success to her mother and other positive women who helped her through her adolescence. Mourning created a mentoring organization that helps young girls in the Miami, Florida area to develop life skills.

4246 ■ *"Longtime Peoria Heights Second-Hand Clothing Shop Closing"* in *Journal Star (December 18, 2010)*
Pub: Journal Star
Ed: Scott Hilyard. **Description:** The Happy Hangar, a consignment clothing store located in Peoria Heights, Illinois is closing after 31 years of selling second-hand clothing.

4247 ■ *"Luxe Men Are In Style"* in *Brandweek (Vol. 49, April 21, 2008, No. 16, pp. 12)*
Pub: VNU Business Media, Inc.
Description: According to a recent survey by Unity Marketing, among 1,300 luxury shoppers found that men spent an average of $2,401 on fashion items

over a three-month period which is nearly $1,000 more than women. Men also spring for more luxury items such as vehicles and memberships to exclusive clubs.

4248 ■ "Luxury Still Sells Well" in Puget Sound Business Journal (Vol. 29, September 5, 2008, No. 20, pp. 1)

Pub: American City Business Journals

Ed: Jeanne Lang Jones. Description: High fashion retailers are planning to open stores in the Puget Sound area despite the economic slowdown, citing high incomes in the area despite the weak U.S. dollar.

4249 ■ "Making It Work" in Retail Merchandiser (Vol. 51, July-August 2011, No. 4, pp. 43)

Pub: Phoenix Media Corporation

Ed: Anthony DiPaolo. Description: Profile of Anthony DiPaolo and his purchase of the Work 'N Gear retail store in 2002. The brick and mortar shop sells work wear and healthcare apparel and DiPaolo believes customer respect is essential to his success.

4250 ■ "Maternity Wear Goes Green" in Marketing to Women (Vol. 21, March 2008, No. 3, pp. 3)

Pub: EPM Communications Inc.

Contact: Ira Mayer, President

E-mail: imayer@epmcom.com

Description: Mother's Work Inc. has launched a series of environmentally-friendly products made from such sustainable fibers as organic cotton and bamboo.

4251 ■ "Meet Joe Fresh" in Canadian Business (Vol. 79, November 6, 2006, No. 22, pp. 49)

Pub: Rogers Media

Ed: Calvin Leung. Description: The efforts of Joseph Mimran, a fashion designer, in improving the business of Joe Fresh style products are analyzed.

4252 ■ Men's & Boys' Wear Buyers

Pub: Briefings Media Group

Contact: Alan M. Douglas, President

E-mail: adouglas@douglaspublications.com

URL(s): www.thesalesmansguide.comwww.douglas-publications.com. Released: Annual; latest edition 2011-2012. Price: $329, Individuals directory price; $699, Individuals directory/CD combo price. Covers: 9,000 buyers and 5,100 stores in the men's and boys' retail industry. Entries include: Store name, address, phone, fax; names and titles of key personnel; e-mail; URL; financial data; branch/subsidiary name and address; products/services provided; price points and sales volume; parent company; type and number of stores for companies; corporate buying office. Arrangement: Geographical. Indexes: Store name, new listings, mail order, buying office, online retailer.

4253 ■ "Military Brides Can Get Free Wedding Gowns" in Virginian-Pilot (November 10, 2010)

Pub: The Virginia-Pilot

Ed: Jamesetta Walker. Description: Seventy-five designer wedding gowns will be given to military brides on a first-come, first-served basis at Maya Couture through the Brides Across America's wedding gown giveaway program. Gowns are valued between $500 to $3,000 and are donated by designers Maggie Sottero, Pronovias and Essense of Australia.

4254 ■ "Not All Contracts a Good Fit for Fashion Reps" in Agency Sales Magazine (Vol. 39, September-October 2009, No. 9, pp. 10)

Pub: MANA

Ed: Jack Foster. Description: Difficult situations regarding the relationship between sales representatives and their principals in the fashion industry are presented and suggestions on how to create contracts that seek to prevent potential problems are provided. Sales reps should make sure that manufacturer has a viable business that is well thought-out and adequately financed.

4255 ■ "Office Party Attire" in Women In Business (Vol. 61, October-November 2009, No. 5, pp. 27)

Pub: American Business Women's Association

Ed: Leigh Elmore. Description: Office holiday party attire should conform to factors such as time, location, scheduled events, and other company-furnished details. Observing this guideline can help in upholding the business nature of the party. Party attendees are also encouraged to network with other attendees, while tips on how to behave during the party are also presented.

4256 ■ "On a Mission: Ginch Gonch Wants You to Get Rid of Your Tighty Whities" in Canadian Business (Vol. 81, September 29, 2008, No. 16)

Pub: Rogers Media Ltd.

Ed: Michelle Magnan. Description: New Equity Capital acquired underwear maker Ginch Gonch in July 2008; founder Jason Sutherland kept his position as creative director of the company and will retain his title as 'director of stitches and inches'. The company is known for its products, which are reminiscent of the days when people wore underwear covered in cowboys and stars as kids. The company also claims that Nelly, Justin Timberlake, and Hilary Duff have worn their products.

4257 ■ "One Paddle, Two Paddle" in Hawaii Business (Vol. 53, October 2007, No. 4, pp. 65)

Pub: Hawaii Business Publishing

Ed: Kyle Galdeira. Description: Oiwi Ocean Gear's strategy may not give instant profits, but it works well for the company's goal of providing high-quality apparel for paddlers. The apparel company produces and markets swimwear, paddling jerseys and active wear. The company's strategy is compared with the selling of mass-produced clothes lower prices.

4258 ■ "Pink Label: Victoria's Sales Secret" in Advertising Age (Vol. 79, July 7, 2008, No. 26, pp. 4)

Pub: Crain Communications, Inc.

Ed: Natalie Zmuda. Description: Victoria Secret's Pink label accounted for roughly 17 percent of the retailer's total sales last year. The company is launching a Collegiate Collection which will be promoted by a campus tour program.

4259 ■ "Portland Wooing Under Armour to West Coast Facility" in Baltimore Business Journal (Vol. 27, January 29, 2010, No. 39, pp. 1)

Pub: American City Business Journals

Ed: Andy Giegerich. Description: Baltimore, Maryland sports apparel maker, Under Armour, is planning a west coast expansion with Portland, Oregon among the sites considered to house its apparel and footwear design center. Portland officials counting on the concentration of nearly 10,000 activewear workers in the city will help lure the company to the city.

4260 ■ "Prime Time for Vintage" in Daily Variety (Vol. 308, August 23, 2010, No. 35, pp. 12)

Pub: Reed Business Information Inc.

Ed: Cynthia Littleton. Description: The week of August 23 starts the busy season for owners of Los Angeles' vintage couture shops due to Emmy-related events.

4261 ■ "Pssst! Buzz About Target" in Barron's (Vol. 89, July 27, 2009, No. 30, pp. 15)

Pub: Dow Jones & Co., Inc.

Ed: Katherine Cheng. Description: Target rebutted the rumor that they will disassociate themselves from a line of clothing inspired by the television show 'Gossip Girl'. Target's spokesman says that the retailer intends to remain closely identified with the show. Target's sales should benefit from the hotly anticipated clothing line.

4262 ■ "Q&A: Joseph Ribkoff" in Canadian Business (Vol. 81, March 31, 2008, No. 5, pp. 4)

Pub: Rogers Media

Ed: Zena Olijnyk. Description: Joseph Ribkoff started his career in the garment trade by sweeping

floors and running deliveries for a dress manufacturer called Town & Country and earned $16 a week. Ribkoff says that the key to controlling costs in Canada is to invest in the latest equipment and technology to stay competitive.

4263 ■ "Research and Market Adds: 2010 US Women's and Children's Clothing Wholesale Report" in Wireless News (November 8, 2009)

Pub: Close-Up Media

Description: Highlights of the annual Research and Markets '2010 U.S. Women's and Children's Clothing Wholesale Report' include industry statistics, demographics and forecasts.

4264 ■ "Research and Markets Adds: 2011 U.S. Women's & Children's Clothing Wholesale Report" in Health & Beauty Close-Up (October 16, 2010)

Pub: Close-Up Media Inc.

Description: The Women's & Children's Clothing Wholesale Report is an annual report containing timely and accurate industry statistics, forecasts and demographics.

4265 ■ "Retail News: Children's Boutique Relocates to Conway" in Sun News (June 4, 2010)

Pub: The Sun News

Description: Little Angel's Children's Boutique and Big Oak Frame Shop have moved to downtown locations in Conway, South Carolina. Little Angel's will sell children's clothing and accessories, shoes and gifts, while the frame shop will offer custom framing along with the sale of stationary, invitations and local prints.

4266 ■ "Rule of the Masses: Reinventing Fashion Via Crowdsourcing" in WWD (Vol. 200, July 26, 2010, No. 17, pp. 1)

Pub: Conde Nast Publications

Contact: David Carey, President

Ed: Cate T. Corcoran. Description: Large apparel brands and retailers are crowdsourcing as a way to increase customer loyalty and to build their businesses.

4267 ■ "Shop Around" in Houston Chronicle (December 7, 2010, pp. 3)

Pub: Houston Chronicle

Ed: Tara Dooley. Description: Profile of Diana Candida and Maria Martinez who partnered to open Beatniks, a shop carrying vintage clothing, art from various artists, dance shoes, and jewelry.

4268 ■ "Size Obsession" in Marketing to Women (Vol. 22, August 2009, No. 8, pp. 2)

Pub: EPM Communications Inc.

Contact: Ira Mayer, President

E-mail: imayer@epmcom.com

Description: Clothing size is becoming a marketing tool for retailers who wish to seize more of the female market share. Women are more likely to purchase an item in a smaller size.

4269 ■ "Skinny Jeans Sticking Around for Fall" in Charlotte Observer (February 5, 2007)

Pub: Knight-Ridder/Tribune Business News

Ed: Crystal Dempsey. Description: Clothing designers were showing skinny jeans in the fall/winter fashion shows for 2007.

4270 ■ "S.M. Whitney Co. (1868-2010)" in Canadian Business (Vol. 83, October 12, 2010, No. 17, pp. 27)

Pub: Rogers Media Ltd.

Ed: Angelina Chapin. Description: A history of S.M. Whitney Company is presented. The cotton company was opened in 1868. The cotton is sold to textile manufacturers after crops have been picked, ginned and baled. The company closed down in 2010 after chief executive officer Barry Whitney decided to sell his last bale of cotton.

4271 ■ "The Smell of Fear: Is a Bottom Near?" in Barron's (Vol. 88, March 17, 2008, No. 11, pp. M3)

Pub: Dow Jones & Company, Inc.

Ed: Kopin Tan. Description: Liquidity problems at Bear Stearns frightened investors in markets around the world due to the fear of the prospects of a big bank's failure. Shares of health maintenance organizations got battered led by WellPoint, and Humana but longer-term investors who could weather short-term volatility may find value here. The value of J. Crew shares is also discussed.

4272 ■ *"Spell It Out" in Entrepreneur (Vol. 36, April 2008, No. 4, pp. 123)*
Pub: Entrepreneur Media, Inc.
Ed: Emily Weisberg. **Description:** IM:It is an apparel and accessories company that markets products with instant messaging (IM) acronyms and emoticons. Examples of these are 'LOL' and 'GTG'. Other details on IM:It products are discussed.

4273 ■ *"Stylish Successes" in Women In Business (Vol. 61, October-November 2009, No. 5, pp. 12)*
Pub: American Business Women's Association
Ed: Leigh Elmore; Megan L. Reese. **Description:** Amanda Horan Kennedy, Angela Samuels, Barbara Nast Saletan, and Patty Nast Canton are career women who ventured into entrepreneurship. They are deemed to possess networking and teamwork skills that ensured their success in the garment industry.

4274 ■ *"Suited for Success" in Retail Merchandiser (Vol. 51, July-August 2011, No. 4, pp. 6)*
Pub: Phoenix Media Corporation
Description: MyBestFit is a size-matching body scanner that helps consumers find the perfect size clothing for themselves, giving brick and mortar retailers an edge on ecommerce competitors.

4275 ■ *"Suiting Up; Yes, You're Smart, But Can You Look the Part" in Crain's Chicago Business (Vol. 30, February 2007, No. 6, pp. 39)*
Pub: Crain Communications, Inc.
Ed: Kate Ryan. **Description:** For investment bankers, fashion is a must. Advice for men and women included.

4276 ■ *"Timberland's CEO On Standing Up to 65,000 Angry Activists" in Harvard Business Review (Vol. 88, September 2010, No. 9, pp. 39)*
Pub: Harvard Business School Publishing
Ed: Jeff Swartz. **Description:** Timberland Company avoided a potential boycott by taking a two-way approach. It addressed a supplier issue that posed a threat to the environment, and launched an email campaign to keep Greenpeace activists informed of the development of a new supplier agreement.

4277 ■ *Too Good to be Threw: The Complete Operations Manual for Resale and Consignment Shops*
Pub: Katydid Press
Price: $69.95. **Description:** Revised edition covers all the information needed to start and run a buy-outright or consignment shop, covering anything from clothing to furniture resale.

4278 ■ *"The Transparent Supply Chain" in Harvard Business Review (Vol. 88, October 2010, No. 10, pp. 76)*
Pub: Harvard Business School Publishing
Ed: Steve New. **Description:** Examination of the use of new technologies to create a transparent supply chain, such as next-generation 2D bar codes in clothing labels that can provide data on a garment's provenance.

4279 ■ *"Trousseaus of Memories Trail Behind Wedding Gowns" in Oregonian (September 4, 2010)*
Pub: The Oregonian
Ed: Anne Saker. **Description:** Readers are asked to share stories about their wedding gowns and what that garment meant to them at the time and now.

4280 ■ *"The Ultimate Home Shopping Network" in Austin Business JournalInc. (Vol. 28, October 17, 2008, No. 31, pp. A1)*
Pub: American City Business Journals
Ed: Sandra Zaragoza. **Description:** New York-based Etcetera sells their clothing through more than 850 fashion consultants in the U.S. Central Texas is one

of the company's top markets and the company is looking to increase its fashion consultants in the area from five to about 20 since they believe there is plenty of room to expand their customer base in the area.

4281 ■ *"Under Armour Wants to Equip Athletes, Too" in Boston Business Journal (Vol. 29, July 8, 2011, No. 9, pp. 1)*
Pub: American City Business Journals Inc.
Ed: Ryan Sharrow. **Description:** Baltimore sportswear maker Under Armour advances plans to enter into the equipment field, aiming to strengthen its hold on football, basketball and lacrosse markets where it already has a strong market share. The company is now cooking up licensing deals to bolster the firm's presence among athletes.

4282 ■ *"Uptick in Clicks: Nordstrom's Online Sales Surging" in Puget Sound Business Journal (Vol. 29, August 22, 2008, No. 18, pp. 1)*
Pub: American City Business Journals
Ed: Gregg Lamm. **Description:** Nordstrom Inc.'s online division grew its sales by 15 percent in the second quarter of 2008, compared to 2007's 4.3 percent in overall decline. The company expects their online net sales to reach $700 million in 2008 capturing eight percent of overall sales.

4283 ■ *"Weaving a Stronger Fabric: Organizing a Global Sweat-Free Apparel Production Agreement" in WorkingUSA (Vol. 11, June 2008, No. 2)*
Pub: Blackwell Publishers Ltd.
Ed: Eric Dirnbach. **Description:** Tens of millions of workers working under terrible sweatshop conditions in the global apparel industry. Workers are employed at apparel contractors and have been largely unsuccessful in organizing and improving their working conditions. The major apparel manufacturers and retailers have the most power in this industry, and they have adopted corporate social responsibility programs as a false solution to the sweatshop problem. The major North American apparel unions dealt with similar sweatshop conditions a century ago by organizing the contractors and brands into joint association contracts that significantly raised standards. Taking inspiration from their example, workers and their anti-sweatshop allies need to work together to coordinate a global organizing effort that builds worker power and establishes a global production agreement that negotiates with both contractors and the brands for improved wages, benefits, and working conditions.

4284 ■ *"Web Sight: Do You See What I See?" in Entrepreneur (Vol. 35, October 2007, No. 10, pp. 58)*
Pub: Entrepreneur Media Inc.
Ed: Heather Clancy. **Description:** Owners of Trunkt, a boutique in New York that showcases independent designs, have created a new style of Website called Trunkt.org. The Website allows buyers to select the products they want to see and designers can choose anytime which of their items will be displayed on the site. An explanation of the strategy that helped bring Trunkt closer to its clients is presented.

4285 ■ *"Wedding: Style Gowns Ready to Go" in Houston Chronicle (June 3, 2010)*
Pub: Houston Chronicle
Ed: Molly Glentzer. **Description:** Wedding gowns with slender silhouettes travel well for destination weddings. Amsale, Oscar del la Renta and Monique Lhuillier dresses are highlighted.

4286 ■ *"When Dov Cries" in Canadian Business (Vol. 83, June 15, 2010, No. 10, pp. 71)*
Pub: Rogers Media Ltd.
Ed: Joe Castaldo. **Description:** American Apparel disclosed that they will have problems meeting one of its debt covenants which could trigger a chain reaction that could lead to bankruptcy. The prospects look bleak, but eccentric company founder Dov Charney, has always defied expectations.

4287 ■ *"White Cat Media Tells You Where to Get a Bargain. Now It's Shopping for $1.5 Million" in Inc. (March 2008, pp. 48)*
Pub: Gruner & Jahr USA Publishing
Ed: Athena Schindelheim. **Description:** Profile of White Cat Media which runs two shopping Websites: SheFinds.com for fashion and beauty items, and MomFinds.com for mothers. The New York City firm reported revenues for 2007 at $400,000 and is looking for funding capital in the amount of $1.7 million.

4288 ■ *Women's & Children's Wear Buyers*
Pub: Briefings Media Group
Contact: Alan M. Douglas, President
E-mail: adouglas@douglaspublications.com
URL(s): www.thesalesmansguide.comwww.douglaspublications.com. **Released:** Annual; latest edition 2011-2012. **Price:** $329, directory price; $699, directory/CD combo price. **Covers:** Over 9,000 retailers and 17,000 buyers in women's and children's wear industry. **Entries include:** Company name, address, phone, fax; e-mail; URL; names and titles of key personnel; financial data; branch or subsidiary name and address; products and/or services provided; names and titles of buyers; price points and sales volume; type and number of stores for companies; parent companies, and corporate buying offices. **Arrangement:** Geographical. **Indexes:** Store name, new listings, mail order, buying office, online retailer.

4289 ■ *"Work that Skirt!" in Entrepreneur (Vol. 37, October 2009, No. 10, pp. 17)*
Pub: Entrepreneur Media Inc.
Ed: Donnell Alexander. **Description:** Steven Villegas, also called Krash, has captured a segment of the men's clothing market with his skirts called Utilikilts. Villegas has sold 100,000 kilts since starting his business in 2000.

STATISTICAL SOURCES

4290 ■ *RMA Annual Statement Studies*
Pub: Risk Management Association
Contact: Kevin M. Blakey, President
Released: Annual. **Price:** $175.00 2006-07 edition, $105.00. **Description:** Contains composite balance sheets and income statements for more than 360 industries, including the accounting, auditing, and bookkeeping industries. Also contains five years of comparative historical data for discerning trends. Includes 16 commonly used ratios, computed for most of the size groupings for nearly every industry.

4291 ■ *Standard & Poor's Industry Surveys*
Pub: Standard & Poor's Corp.
Released: Annual. **Price:** $3633.00. **Description:** Two-volume book that examines the prospects for specific industries, including trucking. Also provides analyses of trends and problems, statistical tables and charts, and comparative company analyses.

TRADE PERIODICALS

4292 ■ *Apparel News South*
Pub: Apparel News Group
Contact: John Irwin, Manager
URL(s): www.apparelnews.net. **Released:** 5/yr. **Price:** $89, Individuals.

4293 ■ *DNR: Defining Men's Fashion*
Pub: Fairchild Publications
URL(s): www.dnrnews.com/. **Released:** Daily (morn.) **Price:** $329, Individuals; $99, Individuals online; $169, Individuals online + print; $895, Individuals online archive.

4294 ■ *Formaltimes*
Pub: International Formalwear Association
Released: Bimonthly. **Description:** Concerned with the promotion of the formalwear industry, providing specialized information on profit strategies, marketing, merchandising, advertising, sales, and other areas of interest. Includes Association news and columns titled President's Message, and Member Profile. Recurring features include reports of meetings and a calendar of events.

4295 ■ *Made to Measure: The Uniform Magazine*
Pub: Halper Publishing Co.
URL(s): www.madetomeasuremag.com. **Released:** Semiannual **Price:** $5, Single issue; $20, Single issue international.

4296 ■ *Stores: The Magazine for Retail Decision Makers*
Pub: NRF Enterprises Inc.
Contact: Ellen Davis, Director
E-mail: davise@nrf.com
URL(s): www.stores.org. **Ed:** Susan Reda. **Released:** Monthly **Price:** Free to retailers and to members of NRF; $120, Nonmembers.

TRADE SHOWS AND CONVENTIONS

4297 ■ Big and Tall Men's Apparel Needs Show
Specialty Trade Show, Inc.
3939 Hardie Rd.
Coconut Grove, FL 33133-6437
Ph: (305)663-6635
Fax: (305)661-8118
Co. E-mail: info@spectrade.com
URL: http://www.spectrade.com
URL(s): www.spectrade.com. **Frequency:** Semiannual. **Audience:** Retailers. **Principal Exhibits:** Menswear.

4298 ■ Denver Apparel and Accessory Market
Denver Merchandise Mart
451 E. 58th Ave., Ste. 4270
Denver, CO 80216-8470
Ph: (303)292-6278
Free: 800-289-6278
Fax: (303)297-8473
Co. E-mail: info@denvermart.com
URL: http://www.denvermart.com
URL(s): www.denvermart.com. **Frequency:** 5/year. **Audience:** Retailers of women's, children's, and men's apparel and accessories. **Principal Exhibits:** Women's, men's, and children's apparel and accessories. **Dates and Locations:** Merchandise Mart. **Telecommunication Services:** info@denvermart.com.

4299 ■ Florida Fashion Focus Show
Southern Apparel Exhibitors, Inc.
1856 Sheridan St.
Evanston, IL 60201
Ph: (847)475-1856
Free: 888-249-1377
Co. E-mail: info@saemiami.com
URL: http://www.saemiami.com
Contact: John Harper, President
E-mail: harper@saemiami.com
URL(s): www.floridafashionfocus.com/. **Frequency:** 5/year. **Audience:** Trade buyers. **Principal Exhibits:** Ladies ready-to-wear clothing; handbags, jewelry, and accessories. Order-writing for future delivery. **Dates and Locations:** Merchandise Mart. **Telecommunication Services:** Info@FocusTradeshow.com.

4300 ■ Mitteldeutsche Handwerksmesse; Central German Handicrafts Fair
Leipziger Messe GmbH
Messe-Allee 1
04356 Leipzig, Germany
Ph: 0341 6 78-0
Fax: 0341 6 78-8762
Co. E-mail: info@leipziger-messe.de
URL: http://www.leipziger-messe.de
Contact: Dr. Arend Oetker, Director
URL(s): www.handwerksmesse-leipzig.de. **Frequency:** Annual. **Audience:** General public. **Principal Exhibits:** Building and conversion, home, arts and crafts, health, lifestyle, food crafts, vehicles, rare handicrafts.

4301 ■ New England Apparel Club
New England Apparel Club, Inc.
75 McNeal Way, Ste. 207
Dedham, MA 02026

Ph: (781)326-9223
Fax: (781)326-6892
Co. E-mail: neacrlg@aol.com
URL(s): www.neacshow.com. **Frequency:** 5/year. **Principal Exhibits:** Clothing and related equipment, supplies, and services. **Dates and Locations:** Bayside Expo Center. **Telecommunication Services:** neacrlg@aol.com.

4302 ■ Women's and Children's Apparel and Accessories Mart
Dallas Market Center Co.
2100 Stemmons Fwy.
Dallas, TX 75207
Ph: (214)655-6100
Free: 800-DAL-MKTS
Co. E-mail: lvillarreal@dmcmail.com
URL: http://www.dallasmarketcenter.com/
Audience: Apparel and accessories and home furnishings retailers. **Principal Exhibits:** Regional Merchandising Mart servicing department and specialty store buyers nationwide.

FRANCHISES AND BUSINESS OPPORTUNITIES

4303 ■ Children's Orchard
Children's Orchard, Inc.
900 Victors Way, Ste. 200
Ann Arbor, MI 48108
Ph: (734)994-9199
Free: 800-999-5437
Fax: (734)994-9323
Description: Children's upscale/resale retail store. **No. of Franchise Units:** 93. **No. of Company-Owned Units:** 1. **Founded:** 1980. **Franchised:** 1985. **Equity Capital Needed:** $115,600-$197,000. **Franchise Fee:** $25,000. **Royalty Fee:** 5%. **Training:** Provides 12 days training at headquarters, 3 days onsite and ongoing support.

4304 ■ Compuchild
Compuchild Services of America
1800 Halifax St.
Camel, IN 46032
Ph: (317)817-9817
Free: 800-619-5437
Fax: (317)818-8184
Description: Computer education to children. **No. of Franchise Units:** 69. **No. of Company-Owned Units:** 1. **Founded:** 1994.. **Franchised:** 1995. **Equity Capital Needed:** $15,000. **Franchise Fee:** $12,500 or $17,500. **Financial Assistance:** Yes. **Training:** Yes.

4305 ■ Embroidme
2121 Vista Pky.
West Palm Beach, FL 33411
Ph: (561)640-7367
Fax: (561)478-4340
URL: http://www.embroidme.com
Description: Custom apparel and merchandise specializing in embroidered pieces. **No. of Franchise Units:** 450. **Founded:** 2000.. **Franchised:** 2000. **Equity Capital Needed:** $184,000-$187,000 total investment. **Franchise Fee:** $42,500. **Financial Assistance:** Yes. **Training:** 4 weeks of training, marketing, merchandising and support (2 weeks in FL, 2 weeks onsite) and ongoing support.

4306 ■ Pickles & Ice Cream Franchising, Inc.
5001 Spring Valley Rd., Ste. 385-W
Dallas, TX 75244
Ph: (214)742-5537
Fax: (972)980-9861
Description: Maternity clothing franchise. **No. of Franchise Units:** 4. **No. of Company-Owned Units:** 2. **Founded:** 1997.. **Franchised:** 1999. **Equity Capital Needed:** $167,200-$366,000. **Franchise Fee:** $30,000. **Royalty Fee:** 6%. **Training:** Offers 10 days at headquarters, 2 days at franchisee location with ongoing support.

COMPUTERIZED DATABASES

4307 ■ *Consumer Buying Power™*
770 Broadway
New York, NY 10003-9595
URL: http://www.claritas.com/sitereports/default.jsp
Availability: Online: The Nielsen Co. - Nielsen SiteReports. **Type:** Statistical.

LIBRARIES

4308 ■ Conde Nast Publications Library and Information Services
4 Times Sq.
New York, NY 10036
Ph: (212)286-2860
Co. E-mail: communications@condenast.com
URL: http://www.condenastdigital.com
Contact: Sarah Chubb, President
Scope: Fashion, houses, gardens, home furnishings, interior design, health, personalities, photographs. **Services:** Library not open to public. **Founded:** 1935. **Holdings:** 7000 volumes. **Subscriptions:** 200 journals and other serials; 4 newspapers.

4309 ■ Fashion Institute of Design & Merchandising - Cyril Magnin Resource and Research Center
55 Stockton St., 5th Fl.
San Francisco, CA 94108-5829
Ph: (415)675-5200
Free: 800-422-3436
Fax: (415)296-7299
URL: http://fidm.edu
Contact: Jim Glenny, Director, Library Services
Scope: Fashion design and merchandising, interior design, apparel manufacturing, advertising, merchandising, marketing. **Services:** Center not open to the public. **Founded:** 1977. **Holdings:** 4000 books; 800 AV programs; 1000 newspaper clipping files; 4000 videos, DVDs, and slides. **Subscriptions:** 200 journals and other serials.

4310 ■ Fashion Institute of Technology - Gladys Marcus Library
7th Ave. at 27th St.
E-Bldg. E502
New York, NY 10001-5992
Ph: (212)217-4340
Fax: (212)217-4371
Co. E-mail: greta_earnest@fitnyc.edu
URL: http://www.fitnyc.edu/library.asp
Contact: Prof. N.J. Wolfe, Director, Library Services
Scope: Costume, fashion, interior design, management engineering technology, fashion buying and merchandising, textiles, toy design, packaging design, advertising. **Services:** Interlibrary loan; copying; library open to the public for reference use only by appointment. **Founded:** 1944. **Holdings:** 130,260 books; 113,265 nonprint units; 20,637 bound periodical volumes; 125,000 fashion slides; 4712 reels of microfilm; 438 CD-ROM serials and digital monographs. **Subscriptions:** 4000 journals and other serials. **Telecommunication Services:** nj_wolfe@fitnyc.edu.

4311 ■ Illinois Institute of Art/Schaumburg - Learning Resource Center
1000 N. Plaza Dr., Ste. 100
Schaumburg, IL 60173-4913
Ph: (847)619-3450
Free: 800-314-3450
Fax: (847)619-3064
URL: http://www.artinstitutes.edu/schaumburg/
Scope: Graphic design, interior design, applied art and design, furniture history. **Services:** Interlibrary loan. **Founded:** 1985. **Holdings:** Books; slides; periodicals; videotapes; DVDs; CD-ROMs. **Subscriptions:** 175 journals and other serials.

4312 ■ Tavy Stone Fashion Library
Detroit Historical Museum
5401 Woodward Ave.
Detroit, MI 48202

Ph: (313)833-1805
Fax: (313)833-5342
Co. E-mail: joels@detroithistorical.org
URL: http://www.detroithistorical.org
Contact: Joel Stone, Curator

Scope: Fashion (antiquity to present) - American and European fashion designers, careers, advertising, merchandising, management, textiles and fabrics, cosmetics and fragrances, historic costume, fashion retailers; the business, sociological, and psychologi

cal aspects of fashion. **Services:** Copying; library open to the public with restrictions. **Founded:** 1987. **Holdings:** 800 books; 40 VF drawers; 500 slides; 10 color swatches; 21 AV programs. **Subscriptions:** 6 journals and other serials.

ASSOCIATIONS AND OTHER ORGANIZATIONS

4313 ■ National Coffee Association of U.S.A. (NCA)
45 Broadway, Ste. 1140
New York, NY 10006
Ph: (212)766-4007
Fax: (212)766-5815
Co. E-mail: info@ncausa.org
URL: http://www.ncausa.org
Contact: Robert F. Nelson, President
E-mail: rfnelson@ncausa.org

URL(s): www.coffeescience.org. **Description:** Green coffee importers, jobbers, brokers, and agents; instant coffee and liquid extract processors; roasters and allied coffee industries; exporters; retailers. Promotes sound business relations and mutual understanding among members of the trade, and to increase coffee consumption. Collects and publishes consumer, market and technical information on the coffee industry. **Scope:** coffee, caffeine. **Founded:** 1911. **Subscriptions:** 600. **Publications:** *CoffeeTrax* (Quarterly); *National Coffee Drinking Trends* (Annual); *US Coffee Industry Review 2005*; *National Coffee Association of U.S.A.--Membership Directory* (Annual). **Educational Activities:** National Coffee Association of U.S.A. Annual Convention (Annual).

4314 ■ Specialty Coffee Association of America (SCAA)
330 Golden Shore, No. 50
Long Beach, CA 90802
Ph: (562)624-4100
Fax: (562)624-4101
Co. E-mail: info@scaa.org
URL: http://www.scaa.org
Contact: Max Quirin, President

Description: Coffee roasters, green coffee brokers, retailers, distributors, and others involved in the gourmet coffee industry. Provides business, professional, promotional, and educational assistance in the areas of cultivation, processing, preparation, and marketing of specialty coffee; increase consumer awareness, understanding, and consumption of specialty coffee. Provides a forum for discussion of the purpose and unified character of the industry and represents members in national and regional coffee concerns. Distributes posters, surveys, articles, and other promotional information; develops coffee education curricula for culinary school programs. Maintains reference materials. Sponsors tastings of specialty coffees. **Scope:** coffee. **Founded:** 1982. **Subscriptions:** 1 books. **Publications:** *Specialty Coffee Association of America--Member Directory*. **Educational Activities:** SCAA Exposition (Annual); SCAA Planning Meeting; SCAA Symposium (Annual); SCAA Leadership Summit. **Awards:** SCAA Achievement Awards (Annual); SCAA Sustainability Award (Annual); SCAA Best New Product (Annual); Achievement Awards (Annual); TOPS (Annual); Mose Drachman Sales and Service Award (Annual).

SOURCES OF SUPPLY

4315 ■ *Automatic Merchandiser--Blue Book Buyer's Guide Issue*
Cygnus Business Media
Contact: Rich Reiff, President
URL(s): www.vendingmarketwatch.comwww.cygnus.com. **Ed:** Elliot Maras. **Released:** Annual **Publication includes:** Suppliers of products, services, and equipment to the merchandise vending, contract foodservice, and office coffee service industries. **Entries include:** Company name, address, phone, names of executives, trade and brand names, and products or services offered. **Arrangement:** Classified by type of business. **Indexes:** Alphabetical, product.

4316 ■ *Vending Times--Buyers Guide and Directory Issue*
Vending Times Inc.
Contact: Alicia Lavay-Kertes, President
E-mail: alicia@vendingtimes.net
URL(s): www.vendingtimes.com. **Released:** Annual; Latest edition 2012. **Price:** $40, Individuals includes shipping and handling. **Publication includes:** Lists of manufacturers and suppliers of equipment and products used by vending machine industry operators, including product venders, juke boxes, pinball and other games; industry trade associations. **Entries include:** Company name, address, phone, names of key personnel, description of products. **Database includes:** Specifications of major vending machines. **Arrangement:** Classified by product or service.

STATISTICAL SOURCES

4317 ■ *Standard & Poor's Industry Surveys*
Pub: Standard & Poor's Corp.
Released: Annual. **Price:** $3633.00. **Description:** Two-volume book that examines the prospects for specific industries, including trucking. Also provides analyses of trends and problems, statistical tables and charts, and comparative company analyses.

TRADE PERIODICALS

4318 ■ *Automatic Merchandiser: The Monthly Management Magazine for Vending and OCS Professionals*
Pub: Cygnus Business Media
Contact: Rich Reiff, President
URL(s): www.vendingmarketwatch.com/www.cygnusb2b.com/PropertyPub.cfm?PropertyID=100. **Released:** Monthly **Price:** Free.

4319 ■ *Tea and Coffee Trade Journal*
Pub: Lockwood Publications Inc.
Contact: Robert M. Lockwood, President
E-mail: robertlockwoodsr@lockwoodpublications.com
URL(s): www.teaandcoffee.net. **Released:** Monthly **Price:** $49, Individuals; $74, Two years; $129, Other countries airmail; $89, Other countries surface mail; $199, Two years airmail; $139, Two years surface mail.

TRADE SHOWS AND CONVENTIONS

4320 ■ Atlantic Coast Exposition - Showcasing the Vending and Food Service Industry
South Carolina Automatic Merchandising Association
PO Box 3159
Durham, NC 27715-3159
Ph: (919)383-0044
Fax: (919)383-0035
URL(s): atlanticcoastexpo.com. **Frequency:** Annual. **Audience:** Vending, food service, and OCS personnel. **Principal Exhibits:** Vending machines, office coffee service equipment, food stuffs, and related goods and services. **Telecommunication Services:** info@atlanticcoastexpo.com.

FRANCHISES AND BUSINESS OPPORTUNITIES

4321 ■ Blenz Coffee
535 Thurlow St., Ste. 300
Vancouver, BC, Canada V6E 3L2
Ph: (604)682-2995
Fax: (604)684-2542
Description: Coffee beverages and coffee beans. **No. of Franchise Units:** 25. **No. of Company-Owned Units:** 2. **Founded:** 1990.. **Franchised:** 1992. **Equity Capital Needed:** $30,000-$70,000 plus equity. **Training:** Yes.

4322 ■ Cafe Ala Carte
Cafe Ala Carte Corp.
19512 S Coquina Way
Weston, FL 33332
Ph: (949)349-1030
Fax: (954)349-3100
Description: Carts serving coffee and espresso drinks. **No. of Franchise Units:** 2. **No. of Company-Owned Units:** 13. **Founded:** 1996.. **Franchised:** 2000. **Equity Capital Needed:** $56,200-$80,800 total investment. **Franchise Fee:** $25,000. **Royalty Fee:** 8-5%. **Training:** Provides 1 week at headquarters, 1 week in Fort Lauderdale, FL with ongoing support.

4323 ■ Coffee Beanery
Coffee Beanery, Ltd.
3429 Pierson Pl.
Flushing 48433
Ph: (810)733-1020
Free: 888-385-2326
Fax: (810)733-1536
Co. E-mail: stacyp@beanerysupport.com
URL: http://www.coffeebeanery.com
Description: The Coffee Beanery retails whole bean coffees and beverages, espresso and cappuccino in a variety of styles in carts, kiosks, in-line mall stores and street front cafes. **No. of Franchise Units:** 93. **No. of Company-Owned Units:** 2. **Founded:** 1976.. **Franchised:** 1985. **Equity Capital Needed:** $74,250-$545,000. **Franchise Fee:** $27,500. **Training:** 4 weeks training at corporate headquarters plus 1 week orientation including customer service, merchandis-

ing, marketing & daily operations. Additional onsite training, site selection assistance, lease negotiation, layout & construction supervision, and on-going support via 800 line, Internet, fax, enewsletter, & field support.

4324 ■ Java Hut Drive Thru
148 Bamboo Ln.
Fallbrook, CA 92028
Ph: (760)630-4245
Description: Drive-thru coffee, tea & smoothie shop. **No. of Franchise Units:** 2. **No. of Company-Owned Units:** 2. **Founded:** 1993.. **Equity Capital Needed:** $12,000-$50,000. **Franchise Fee:** $10,000. **Training:** Yes.

4325 ■ Jo To Go Coffee
Jo to Go America, Inc.
1263 Main St., Ste. 228
Green Bay, WI 54302
Free: 866-568-6461

Fax: (920)482-5623
Description: Drive-thru specialty coffee, smoothies and bakery. **No. of Franchise Units:** 12. **No. of Company-Owned Units:** 6. **Founded:** 1998.. **Franchised:** 2001. **Equity Capital Needed:** $133,000-$409,000. **Franchise Fee:** $25,000. **Royalty Fee:** 7%. **Financial Assistance:** Third party financing available. **Training:** Provides 1 week at headquarters, 1 week at franchisee's location, 1 week at a corporate store and ongoing support.

4326 ■ Williams Fresh Cafe Inc.
202 Grand River Ave.
Brantford, ON, Canada N3T 4X9
Ph: (519)752-4850
Fax: (519)752-2671
Co. E-mail: franchiseinfo@williamsfreshcafe.com
URL: http://www.williamsfreshcafe.com
Description: Serves best cafe, coffee bar and restaurant and caters to its customers with convenient hours of operation, a comprehensive easy-to-prepare

menu, quick, modified table service and popular pricing. **No. of Franchise Units:** 40. **Founded:** 1993.. **Franchised:** 1994. **Equity Capital Needed:** $300,000-$675,000. **Franchise Fee:** $35,000. **Training:** Offers 8-12 weeks of training.

LIBRARIES

4327 ■ Noble and Associates Library
2155 W. Chesterfield Blvd.
Springfield, MO 65807
Ph: (417)875-5000
Co. E-mail: julie.tumy@noble.net
URL: http://www.noble.net
Contact: Julie Tumy, President
Scope: Food, food service, advertising, construction, agriculture. **Services:** Interlibrary loan; copying; SDI; Library not open to the public. **Holdings:** 500 books; 1000 reports. **Subscriptions:** 300 journals and other serials; 5 newspapers.

ASSOCIATIONS AND OTHER ORGANIZATIONS

4328 ■ American Hatpin Society
c/o Cathy Miller, VP
2505 Indian Creek Rd.
Diamond Bar, CA 91765-3307
Ph: (909)861-4267
Co. E-mail: info@americanhatpinsociety.com
URL: http://www.americanhatpinsociety.com
Contact: Jodi Lenocker, President
Description: Collectors of hatpins. Promotes collection, preservation, and restoration of hatpins and related fashion accessories. Serves as a clearinghouse on hatpins and their history; facilitates exchange of information among members; conducts educational programs. **Founded:** 1989. **Publications:** *American Hatpin Society Newsletter.*

4329 ■ American Numismatic Association (ANA)
818 N Cascade Ave.
Colorado Springs, CO 80903-3208
Ph: (719)632-2646
Free: 800-367-9723
Fax: (719)634-4085
Co. E-mail: ana@money.org
URL: http://www.money.org
Contact: Tom Hallenbeck, President
Description: Collectors of coins, medals, tokens, and paper money. Promotes the study, research, and publication of articles on coins, coinage, and history of money. Sponsors correspondence courses; conducts research. Maintains museum, archive, authentication service for coins, and hall of fame. Sponsors National Coin Week; operates speakers' bureau. **Founded:** 1891. **Publications:** *The Numismatist: For Collectors of Coins, Medals, Tokens and Paper Money* (Monthly); *ANA Journal Advanced Studies in Numismatics* (Quarterly); *The Numismatist: For Collectors of Coins, Medals, Tokens and Paper Money* (Monthly). **Educational Activities:** World's Fair of Money (Annual); World's Fair of Money (Annual). **Awards:** Medal of Merit; Farran Zerbe Memorial Award; Glenn Smedley Memorial Award; Lifetime Achievement Award; Exemplary Service Award; Outstanding Government Service Award; Outstanding Club Publication Awards; Ray Byrne Memorial Literary Award; Gould Memorial Literary Award; Abe Kosoff Memorial Literary Award; Outstanding Young Numismatist of the Year; Adult Advisor of the Year Award; Lelan G. Rogers Memorial Exhibit Award; B. P. Wright Memorial Exhibit Award; John S. Davenport Memorial Exhibit Award; Numismatic Error Collectors Exhibit Award; Love Token Society Exhibit Award; Edgerton-Lenker Memorial Youth Exhibit Award; James L. Betton Youth Exhibit Award; Melissa Van Grover Youth Exhibit Award; Farrun Zerbe Award (Annual); Medal of Merit (Annual); Numismatic Art Award for Excellence in Medallic Sculpture; Sidney W. Smith/William Donlon Memorial Exhibit Award; Burton Saxton/George Bauer Memorial Exhibit Award; Dr. Charles W. Crowe Memorial Exhibit Award; Gaston DiBello/Melvin and Leona Kohl Memorial Exhibit Award; Henry Christensen/John Jay Pittman Sr.

Memorial Exhibit Award; William C. Henderson/Fred Cihon Memorial Exhibit Award; Menachem Chaim and Simcha Tova Mizel Memorial Exhibit Award; Kagin Family Paper Money Youth Exhibit Award; Charles "Cheech" Litman Memorial Youth Exhibit Award.

4330 ■ American Numismatic Society (ANS)
75 Varick St., 11th Fl.
New York, NY 10038
Ph: (212)571-4470
Fax: (212)571-4479
Co. E-mail: meadows@numismatics.org
URL: http://www.numismatics.org
Contact: Ute W. Kagan, Executive Director
Description: Collectors and others interested in coins, medals, and related materials. Advances numismatic knowledge as it relates to history, art, archaeology, and economics by collecting coins, medals, tokens, decorations, and paper money. Maintains only museum devoted entirely to numismatics. Presents annual Graduate Fellowship in Numismatics. Sponsors Graduate Seminar in Numismatics, a nine-week individual study program for ten students. **Services:** Technical advice on specialized photography of numismatic material. **Founded:** 1858. **Subscriptions:** books pamphlets photographs numismatic literature. **Publications:** *American Journal of Numismatics* (Annual); *American Journal of Numismatics* (Annual); *ANS Magazine* (3/year); *Coinage of the Americas Conference; Index to American Journal of Numismatics; Numismatic Literature* (Semiannual); *Numismatic Notes and Monographs; Numismatic Studies; American Journal of Numismatics* (Annual); *American Numismatic Society Magazine* (Quarterly); *ANS Annual Report; Numismatic Literature* (Semiannual); *The Colonial Newsletter; American Numismatic Society--Numismatic Studies* (Periodic); *Ancient Coins in North American Collections* (Periodic); *Sylloge Nummorum Graecorum: The Collection of the American Numismatic Society* (Periodic). **Educational Activities:** Coinage of the Americas Conference (Annual); Graduate Seminar in Numismatics (Annual); Coinage of the Americas Conference (Annual); Educational slide programs which provide visual aids to assist in the instruction of history and art history (Annual). **Awards:** Frances M. Schwartz Fellowship; Archer M. Huntington Medal Award; J. Sanford Saltus Medal Award; Donald Groves Fund Awards; Huntington Award Medal (Annual); Saltus Medal Award (Annual); Donald Groves Fund Grants for research and publications in early American numismatics. **Telecommunication Services:** info@numismatics.org; uwk@numismatics.org.

4331 ■ American Philatelic Congress (APC)
c/o Mr. Ross A. Towle, Sec.-Treas.
400 Clayton St.
San Francisco, CA 94117-1912
Co. E-mail: rosstowle@yahoo.com
URL: http://www.americanphilateliccongress.org/index.html
Contact: Dr. Mark E. Banchik, President
Description: Promotes philatelic writing and research. **Founded:** 1935. **Publications:** *Congress Comments* (3/year); *American Philatelic Congress Book* (Annual). **Educational Activities:** Stamp Show

(Annual). **Awards:** Barr Award (Annual); Colby Award (Annual); Drossos Award (Annual); Helen August Memorial Award; Klein Award (Annual); McCoy Award (Annual); Meritorious Service Award; Wagner Award (Annual).

4332 ■ American Philatelic Society (APS)
100 Match Factory Pl.
Bellefonte, PA 16823
Ph: (814)933-3803
Free: 800-782-9580
Fax: (814)933-6128
Co. E-mail: flsente@stamps.org
URL: http://www.stamps.org/
Contact: Kenneth P. Martin, Executive Director
Description: Collectors of postage and revenue stamps, first day covers, postal history, and related philatelic items. Helps members buy and sell stamps; operates expertise service; offers stamp insurance program; circulates slide programs. Maintains hall of fame; offers correspondence courses; accredits judges for philatelic competitions. Conducts philatelic seminars. **Founded:** 1886. **Publications:** *American Philatelic Society CAC Newsletter; Philatelic Literature Review* (Quarterly); *The American Philatelist* (Monthly). **Educational Activities:** Stampshow (Annual); AmeriStamp Expo (Annual). **Awards:** Champion of Champions; Luff Award; Philatelic Hall of Fame. **Telecommunication Services:** stampshow@stamps.org; doris@stamps.org.

4333 ■ American Stamp Dealers Association (ASDA)
217-14 Northern Blvd., Ste. 205
Bayside, NY 11361
Ph: (718)224-2500
Fax: (718)224-2501
Co. E-mail: asda@asdaonline.com
URL: http://www.asdaonline.com
Contact: James E. Lee, President
Description: Dealers and wholesalers of stamps, albums and other philatelic materials. Sponsors National Stamp Collecting Week in November. **Founded:** 1914. **Publications:** *The American Stamp Dealer and Collector* (10/year); *Members Only Newsletter* (Monthly).

4334 ■ Bicycle Stamps Club (BSC)
21304 2nd Ave. SE
Bothell, WA 98021-7550
Co. E-mail: tonimaur@bigpond.com
URL: http://bicyclestamps.tripod.com
Description: Philatelists interested in collecting stamps depicting bicycles and cycling themes. **Founded:** 1980. **Publications:** *Bicycle Stamps* (Quarterly).

4335 ■ Canadian Aerophilatelic Society (CAS)
c/o Brian Wolfenden, Sec.-Treas.
203A Woodfield Dr.
Nepean, ON, Canada K2G 4P2
Co. E-mail: bjnepean@trytel.com
URL: http://www.aerophilately.ca
Contact: Chris Hargreaves, President
Description: Individuals interested in the history of Canadian and Newfoundland air mail service and

aerophilately. Promotes study of Canadian postal history and collection of aerophilatelic materials. Conducts research and educational programs; sponsors competitions. **Founded:** 1986. **Publications:** *Canadian Aerophilatelist* (Quarterly). **Awards:** Editor Award (Annual).

4336 ■ *Canadian Aerophilatelist*
c/o Brian Wolfenden, Sec.-Treas.
203A Woodfield Dr.
Nepean, ON, Canada K2G 4P2
Co. E-mail: bjnepean@trytel.com
URL: http://www.aerophilately.ca
Contact: Chris Hargreaves, President
Released: Quarterly **Price:** included in membership dues.

4337 ■ Canadian Association of Numismatic Dealers (CAND)—L'Association Canadienne Marchands Numismatiques
Winona Postal Outlet
Stoney Creek, ON, Canada L8E 5R1
Ph: (905)643-4988
Fax: (905)643-6329
Co. E-mail: email@cand.org
URL: http://www.cand.org
Contact: Michael Findlay, President
Description: Dealers in numismatic materials. Seeks to advance the numismatic collectibles industry. Facilitates communication and cooperation among members; represents members' interests. **Founded:** 1975.

4338 ■ Canadian Numismatic Research Society (CNRS)
PO Box 1351
Victoria, BC, Canada V8W 2W7
Fax: (250)598-5539
Co. E-mail: ragreene@telus.net
URL: http://www.nunet.ca/cnrs.htm
Contact: Ronald Greene, Secretary
Description: Numismatists and other individuals with an interest in coins, tokens, paper money, and medals; membership by invitation only. Seeks to advance numismatic study. Sponsors research and educational programs. **Founded:** 1963. **Publications:** *Numismatica Canada* (Annual).

4339 ■ *The Canadian Philatelist*
Sta. Q
Toronto, ON, Canada M4T 2P1
Ph: (416)921-2077
Free: 888-285-4143
Fax: (416)921-1282
Co. E-mail: info@rpsc.org
URL: http://www.rpsc.org
Contact: George Pepall, President
Released: Bimonthly **Price:** C$5, back issue for nonmembers; free for members; C$25, /year for nonmembers.

4340 ■ *The CN Journal*
5694 Hwy. No. 7 E, Ste. 432
Markham, ON, Canada L3P 1B4
Ph: (647)401-4014
Fax: (905)472-9645
Co. E-mail: info@rcna.ca
URL: http://www.canadian-numismatic.org/index.php
Contact: William Waychison, President

4341 ■ Cracker Jack Collectors Association (CJCA)
c/o Linda Farris, Membership Chair
4908 N Holborn Dr.
Muncie, IN 47304
Co. E-mail: lindajfarris@comcast.net
URL: http://www.crackerjackcollectors.com
Contact: Nancy Schultz, President
Description: Collectors of Cracker Jack prizes and related items. Promotes collection and preservation of Cracker Jack memorabilia. Gathers and disseminates information on Cracker Jack collectibles and their availability; facilitates exchange of information and promotes good fellowship among members. **Founded:** 1993.

4342 ■ Craft and Hobby Association (CHA)
319 E 54th St.
Elmwood Park, NJ 07407

Ph: (201)835-1200
Free: 800-822-0494
Fax: (201)797-0657
Co. E-mail: info@craftandhobby.org
URL: http://www.craftandhobby.org
Contact: Steven Z. Berger, President
E-mail: sberger@craftandhobby.org
URL(s): www.hobby.org, www.chashow.org. **Description:** Manufacturers, wholesalers, retailers, publishers, and allied firms in the craft and hobby industry. Promotes the interest of all companies engaged in the buying, selling, or manufacturing of craft and hobby merchandise; conceives, develops, and implements programs for members to achieve greater individual growth. Conducts seminars and educational workshops; sponsors national trade show. Compiles statistics. **Founded:** 2004. **Publications:** *HIA Show Directory* (Annual); *Directory of Manufacturer Representatives, Service Suppliers, Professional Chaft Producers, Certified Professional Demonstrators* (Biennial). **Educational Activities:** CHA Winter Convention and Trade Show (Annual).

4343 ■ Fostoria Glass Collectors (FGC)
PO Box 826
Moundsville, WV 26041
Ph: (304)845-9188
URL: http://www.fostoriacollectors.org
Contact: Jim Davis, President
Description: Collectors and admirers of handmade American glassware. Promotes appreciation of handmade American glass products. Serves as a clearinghouse on handmade American glassware and its collection; sponsors research and educational programs; participates in charitable activities; maintains museum. **Founded:** 1990. **Educational Activities:** Fostoria Glass Collectors Meeting (Monthly). **Awards:** Gift (Annual).

4344 ■ *Index to the PHSC Journal*
255 Shakespeare St.
Ottawa, ON, Canada K1L 5M7
Co. E-mail: secretary@postalhistorycanada.net
URL: http://postalhistorycanada.net
Contact: Stephane Cloutier, Secretary
Released: Annual

4345 ■ Industry Council for Tangible Assets (ICTA)
PO Box 1365
Severna Park, MD 21146-8365
Ph: (410)626-7005
Fax: (410)626-7007
Co. E-mail: eloise.ullman@ictaonline.org
URL: http://ictaonline.org
Contact: Bob Greenstein, Chairman
Description: Individuals and firms engaged in the fabrication, manufacture, importation, wholesale distribution, or retail sale of any tangible asset (precious or other metals, coins, antiques, stamps, or art objects). Cooperates in maintaining an appropriate and favorable regulatory climate in the U.S.; serves as liaison with governmental and other agencies. **Founded:** 1983. **Publications:** *ICTA Washington Wire* (Quarterly).

4346 ■ International Harvester Collectors (IHC)
c/o Emmett Webb
PO Box 35
Dublin, IN 47335-0035
Ph: (765)478-6179
Co. E-mail: ihcclub@aol.com
URL: http://www.nationalihcollectors.com
Contact: Robert Caloud, President
Description: Owners and admirers of farm machinery produced by International Harvester. Promotes preservation and restoration of International Harvester equipment. Facilitates communication among members; serves as a clearinghouse on International Harvester tractors and other farm equipment. **Founded:** 1990. **Educational Activities:** Red Power Round-up (Annual). **Awards:** International Harvester Collectors Scholarships. **Telecommunication Services:** rjihc@fctc.coop.

4347 ■ International Paperweight Society (IPS)
410 S Michigan Ave., Ste. No. 207
Chicago, IL 60605
Ph: (312)583-1177
Free: 800-538-0766
Co. E-mail: lselman@got.net
URL: http://www.paperweight.com
Contact: Larry Selman, President
Description: Promotes paperweight collecting. Conducts educational programs. Runs a speakers' bureau. **Founded:** 1993.

4348 ■ National Shaving Mug Collectors Association (NSMCA)
366 Lake Shore Dr.
Hewitt, NJ 07421
URL: http://www.nsmca.net
Contact: Don Allain, Treasurer
Description: Collectors of shaving mugs and other shaving equipment. Promotes collection of shaving paraphernalia as a hobby. Facilitates communication and trading among members; gathers and disseminates information on shaving mugs and related equipment. **Founded:** 1980.

4349 ■ *Numismatica Canada*
PO Box 1351
Victoria, BC, Canada V8W 2W7
Fax: (250)598-5539
Co. E-mail: ragreene@telus.net
URL: http://www.nunet.ca/cnrs.htm
Contact: Ronald Greene, Secretary
Released: Annual **Price:** C$20, in Canada; $20, outside Canada.

4350 ■ Numismatics International (NI)
PO Box 570842
Dallas, TX 75357-0842
Co. E-mail: johnvan@tx.rr.com
URL: http://www.numis.org
Contact: Mr. John E. Vandigriff, Chairman
Description: Numismatists, coin dealers, students, and numismatic authors in 35 countries. Works to: encourage and promote the science of numismatics; cultivate fraternal relations among collectors and numismatic students; encourage new collectors and foster the interest of youth in numismatics; stimulate and advance affiliations among collectors and kindred organizations; acquire, share, and disseminate numismatic knowledge including cultural and historical information on coins. Sponsors periodic lectures. Maintains coin collection. **Founded:** 1964. **Publications:** *NI Bulletin* (Periodic).

4351 ■ Postal History Society of Canada (PHSC)
255 Shakespeare St.
Ottawa, ON, Canada K1L 5M7
Co. E-mail: secretary@postalhistorycanada.net
URL: http://postalhistorycanada.net
Contact: Stephane Cloutier, Secretary Treasurer
Description: Postal historians and philatelists. Disseminates information on Canadian postal history. Conducts postal history mail auction. Maintains specialized study groups. **Founded:** 1972. **Publications:** *Index to the PHSC Journal* (Annual). **Awards:** Certificate of Merit (Periodic); Citation of Merit (Periodic); Frank W. Campbell Award (Periodic); Stan Shantz Award (Periodic); Frank W. Campbell Award; Stan Shantz Award.

4352 ■ Professional Currency Dealers Association (PCDA)
c/o James A. Simek, Sec.
PO Box 7157
Westchester, IL 60154
Co. E-mail: nge3@comcast.net
URL: http://www.pcdaonline.com
Contact: Sergio Sanchez, Jr., President
Description: Dealers of rare paper money and other printed media of exchange including stocks, bonds, fiscal documents, and related ephemera. Promotes the study of and interest in collectible paper media of exchange; maintains standards in commercial aspects of syngraphics. Sponsors research project to identify U.S. national banks whose large size note issues are undiscovered. **Founded:** 1985. **Educational**

Activities: Professional Currency Dealers Association Meeting (Annual). **Awards:** John Hickman National Bank Note Exhibit Award (Annual).

4353 ■ Professional Numismatists Guild (PNG)

28441 Rancho California Rd., Ste. 106
Temecula, CA 92590
Ph: (951)587-8300
Free: 800-375-4653
Fax: (951)587-8301
Co. E-mail: info@pngdealers.com
URL: http://www.pngdealers.com
Contact: Jeffrey Bernberg, President
Description: Represents coin dealers who have been involved full-time in the profession for at least five years. Establishes, promotes, and defends ethics in the hobby of numismatics. **Founded:** 1954. **Publications:** The Pleasure of Coin Collecting; What You Should Know Before You Invest in Coins. **Awards:** Abe Kosoff Founders Award (Annual); Friedberg Award; Lifetime Achievement Award; Sol Kaplan Award; Friedberg Award (Annual); Lifetime Achievement Award (Annual); Sol Kaplan Award (Annual).

4354 ■ Royal Canadian Numismatic Association (RCNA)

5694 Hwy. No. 7 E, Ste. 432
Markham, ON, Canada L3P 1B4
Ph: (647)401-4014
Fax: (905)472-9645
Co. E-mail: info@rcna.ca
URL: http://www.canadian-numismatic.org/index.php
Contact: William Waychison, President
Description: Individuals interested in coins and other Canada numismatic artifacts. Promotes collection of numismatic materials. Serves as a clearinghouse on numismatic materials and their collection and preservation; provides assistance to members. **Founded:** 1950. **Publications:** The CN Journal. **Awards:** Fellow of the CNA Award (Annual); Guy Potter Literary Award (Annual); J. Douglas Ferguson Award (Annual); Jean Bullen Award (Annual); Jerome H. Remick III Literary Award (Annual); Louise Graham Memorial Club of the Year Award (Annual).

4355 ■ Royal Philatelic Society of Canada (RPSC)—La Societe Royale de Philatelie du Canada

Sta. Q
Toronto, ON, Canada M4T 2P1
Ph: (416)921-2077
Free: 888-285-4143
Fax: (416)921-1282
Co. E-mail: info@rpsc.org
URL: http://www.rpsc.org
Contact: George Pepall, President
Description: Individuals with an interest in philately. Promotes interest in stamps and postal history. Conducts educational and social programs; facilitates exchange of information among members. Sponsors competitions. **Founded:** 1887. **Publications:** The Canadian Philatelist (Bimonthly); The Canadian Philatelist (Bimonthly). **Awards:** Fellow of the Royal Philatelic Society of Canada (Periodic); Geldert Medal (Annual). **Telecommunication Services:** president@rpsc.org.

4356 ■ Strawberry Shortcake Chat Group

138 E Main Cross St.
Greenville, KY 42345
Ph: (270)338-4318
Co. E-mail: jenniferbowles@bellsouth.net
URL: http://www.strawberrybonkers.com
Contact: Jennifer Bowles, Editor
Description: Owners and admirers of Strawberry Shortcake dolls. Promotes collection and preservation of Strawberry Shortcake dolls. Facilitates communication among members; serves as a clearinghouse on Strawberry Shortcake dolls. **Founded:** 1996.

TRADE PERIODICALS

4357 ■ American Philatelic Society CAC Newsletter

Pub: American Philatelic Society
Contact: Kenneth P. Martin, Executive Director
Ed: Jane King Fohn, Editor, jkfohn1442@aol.com. **Released:** Quarterly. **Description:** Provides service to stamp clubs affiliated with the Society.

4358 ■ Americana Philatelic News

Pub: Americana Unit
Ed: Melvin Morris, Editor. **Released:** Quarterly. **Description:** Contains information about stamps and other philatelic materials relating to the U.S., emphasizing stamps issued by countries other than the U.S. Includes news of the Americana Unit and its members. Publishes checklists of new and old stamps on a specific subject within the Americana topic. Recurring features include a schedule of activities and a list of newly-issued Americana stamps.

4359 ■ Artistamp News

Pub: Ed Varney
Ed: Ed Varney, Editor, evarney@mars.ark.com. **Released:** Semiannual. **Price:** $10 2 issues. **Description:** Contains articles on the production of stamp art editions. Provides reviews of shows and editions, profiles of artists, and mail art show and project information. Recurring features include notices of publications available.

4360 ■ Canadian Coin News

Pub: Trajan Publishing Corp.
URL(s): www.canadiancoinnews.ca/. **Released:** Biweekly **Price:** $43.95, Individuals; $76.95, Two years; $43, Canada; C$172, Other countries.

4361 ■ The Canadian Stamp News

Pub: Trajan Publishing Corp.
URL(s): www.canadianstampnews.ca. **Released:** Biweekly **Price:** $43, Individuals in Canada; $75.34, Canada in Canada, 2 years; $172, Other countries; $43.95, Individuals; $76.95, Two years.

4362 ■ Certified Coin Dealer Newsletter

Pub: Shane Downing
Contact: Shane Downing, Publisher
Released: Weekly. **Price:** $117, U.S., Canada, and Mexico; $193, U.S., Canada, and Mexico two years;. **Description:** Provides current prices and market commentary on certified coins (Mint State Grades of MS61-MS67 and PR61-PR67) of Professional Coin Grading Service (PCGS), Numismatic Guaranty Corporation of America (NGC) Weekly, ANACS, NCI, PCI, and INS.

4363 ■ The Coin Dealer Newsletter

Pub: Shane Downing
Ed: Keith M. Zaner, Editor. **Released:** Weekly, Plus a monthly and quarterly for a total of 75 newsletters. **Price:** $98, individuals. **Description:** Provides information on U.S. coinage, 1793 to present. Gives current prices and market commentary and analysis. Issues The Monthly Supplement and Complete Series Pricing Guide as an adjunct to the newsletter. Recurring features include columns titled The Market in Depth and This Week's Market.

4364 ■ Coin Prices: Complete Guide to U.S Coin Values

Pub: FW Publications
Contact: Sara Domville, President
E-mail: sara.domville@fwpubs.com
URL(s): numismaster.com/ta/inside_numis.jsp?page=CoinPricesMagazine. **Ed:** Robert R. Van Ryzin, Alan Herbert. **Released:** Bimonthly **Price:** $18.98, Individuals.

4365 ■ Coin World: World's 1 Publication for Coin Collectors

Pub: Amos Press Inc.
Contact: Bruce D. Boyd, Chief Executive Officer
URL(s): www.coinworldonline.comwww.coinworld.com. **Released:** Weekly **Price:** $19.99, Individuals; $34.99, Canada; $127.97, Canada 52 issues; $49.97, Individuals 52 issues.

4366 ■ The COINfidential Report

Pub: Bale Publications
Ed: Don Bale, Jr., Editor. **Released:** Bimonthly, except July and August. **Price:** $19.95, individuals; $99 lifetime subscription. **Description:** Features coin, stock and bullion market forecasts and analyses, plus inside information and best coin and stock bets. Recurring features include interviews, book reviews, and notices of publications available.

4367 ■ Coins Magazine

Pub: FW Publications
Contact: Sara Domville, President
E-mail: sara.domville@fwpubs.com
URL(s): numismaster.com/ta/inside_numis.jsp?page=CoinsMagazine. **Ed:** Robert R. Van Ryzin. **Released:** Monthly **Price:** $22.98, Individuals.

4368 ■ The Collectors Club Philatelist

Pub: Collectors Club
Contact: Dr. Roger S. Brody, President
E-mail: collectorsclub@verizon.net
URL(s): www.collectorsclub.org/. **Ed:** Robert P. Odenweller. **Released:** Bimonthly **Price:** $45, Members; $7, Single issue; Institutions; $7.50, Nonmembers.

4369 ■ The Colonial Newsletter

Pub: American Numismatic Society
Contact: Ute W. Kagan, Executive Director
Ed: Gary Trudgen, Editor, gtrudgen@aol.com. **Released:** 3/year. **Price:** $35; $35, members; $45, nonmembers. **Description:** Contains original research papers on the scientific and humanistic aspects of early American numismatics, especially die varieties of the American coinages produced prior to the establishment of the U.S. Mint in 1793. Also covers paper money and early tokens.

4370 ■ The Currency Dealer Newsletter

Pub: Shane Downing
Ed: Keith M. Zaner, Editor. **Released:** Monthly. **Price:** $44, individuals $44/year; $78, two years; $5, single issue. **Description:** Concerned with U.S. currency, 1861 to present. Recurring features include current wholesale price lists (from dealer-to-dealer transactions), and an analysis of a particular issue of currency with a Bid/Ask Pricing Chart.

4371 ■ David Hall's Inside View

Pub: David Hall Rare Coins
Ed: David Hall, Editor. **Released:** Monthly, 10-12/year. **Description:** Provides advisory information on collecting and investing in rare coins.

4372 ■ Lambda Philatelic Journal

Pub: Gay-Lesbian History Stamp Club
Released: Quarterly. **Price:** $15, U.S., Canada, and Mexico; $15, elsewhere. **Description:** Journal of the Gay-Lesbian History Stamp Club. Provides information and articles on stamp collecting.

4373 ■ Linn's Stamp News: World's Largest Weekly Stamp Newspaper

Pub: Linn's Stamp News
Contact: Phyllis Stegemoller, Manager
E-mail: pstegemoller@linns.com
URL(s): www.linns.com. **Ed:** Michael Baadke, Jay Bigalke. **Released:** Weekly **Price:** $59.95, Individuals print and digital; $105.99, Canada print and digital; $135.99, Other countries; $19.99, Individuals digital.

4374 ■ Numismatic News

Pub: Krause Publications Inc.
Contact: Roger Case, President
URL(s): www.numismaticnews.net/. **Ed:** David C. Harper. **Released:** 52/yr. **Price:** $29.99, Individuals; C$96.99, Canada; $146.99, Other countries.

4375 ■ The Numismatist: For Collectors of Coins, Medals, Tokens and Paper Money

Pub: American Numismatic Association
Contact: Tom Hallenbeck, President
URL(s): www.money.org/communications/the-numismatist.aspx. **Released:** Monthly **Price:** $28, Individuals online delivery; $46, Individuals mail delivery.

4376 ■ Philatelic Literature Review

Pub: American Philatelic Society
Contact: Kenneth P. Martin, Executive Director
URL(s): stamps.org/Quarterly-Journal. **Ed:** Barbara Boal. **Released:** Quarterly

4377 ■ *The Posthorn: Journal of the Scandinavian Collectors Club*
Pub: Scandinavian Collectors Club
URL(s): www.scc-online.org/memberpublications. htm. **Ed:** Paul Albright. **Released:** Quarterly **Price:** $20, Individuals.

4378 ■ *Proof Collectors Corner*
Pub: World Proof Numismatic Association
Ed: Edward J. Moschetti, Editor. **Released:** Bi-monthly. **Price:** Included in membership. **Description:** Provides information on coin collecting. Recurring features include news of research and reports of meetings, news releases on new world-wide coin issues including photos. A free coin selling and swapping section for members.

4379 ■ *Rosen Numismatic Advisory*
Pub: Numismatic Counseling Inc.
Ed: Maurice Rosen, Editor, mauricerosen@aol.com. **Released:** 6-8/year. **Description:** In-depth analysis for rare coin investors. Comprehensive coverage of all active areas, key interviews and no-holes-barred examination of controversal subjects.

4380 ■ *Scott Stamp Monthly: Scott Stamp Monthly with Scott Catalogue Update*
Pub: Scott Publishing
Contact: Bruce Boyd, President
URL(s): www.linns.com/. **Ed:** Michael Baadke. **Released:** Monthly **Price:** $99.99, Individuals print; $59.99, Two years print & digital; $49.99, Other countries; $194.99, Other countries two years, print & digital.

4381 ■ *Stamps*
Pub: American Publishing Co.
URL(s): www.magazinesubscriptionsipc.com/ipc/ipc-shop/product.asp?jrnlid=XTP. **Released:** Weekly (Sat.)

4382 ■ *World Coin News*
Pub: FW Publications
Contact: Sara Domville, President
E-mail: sara.domville@fwpubs.com
URL(s): numismaster.com/ta/inside_numis. jsp?page=WorldCoinNews. **Ed:** Maggie Pahl. **Released:** Monthly **Price:** $25.99, Individuals; $40.99, Canada; $55.99, Other countries.

TRADE SHOWS AND CONVENTIONS

4383 ■ Canadian Numismatic Association Convention
Canadian Numismatic Association
5694 Hwy., No. 7 E, Ste. 432
Markham, ON, Canada L3P 1B4
Ph: (647)401-4014
Fax: (905)472-9645
Co. E-mail: info@rcna.ca
URL: http://www.canadian-numismatic.org
Contact: William Waychison, President
E-mail: billwaychison@gmail.com
URL(s): www.canadian-numismatic.org. **Frequency:** Annual. **Audience:** Coin collectors. **Principal Exhibits:** Coins, currency, medals, and tokens. **Telecommunication Services:** mbcoin@shaw.ca.

4384 ■ National Topical Stamp Show
American Topical Association (ATA)
PO Box 8
Carterville, IL 62918-0008
Ph: (618)985-5100
Fax: (618)985-5100
Co. E-mail: americantopical@msn.com
URL: http://www.americantopicalassn.org
Contact: Vera Felts, Executive Director
URL(s): www.americantopicalassn.org. **Frequency:** Annual. **Audience:** Stamp collectors. **Principal Exhibits:** Topical stamp and 200 frames of stamp exhibits. **Telecommunication Services:** americantopical@msn.com.

4385 ■ Spring Postage Stamp Mega Event
American Stamp Dealers Association
217-14 Northern Blvd., Ste. 205
Glen Cove, NY 11361
Ph: (718)224-2500

Fax: (718)224-2501
Co. E-mail: asda@asdaonline .com
URL: http://www.asdaonline.com
URL(s): www.asdaonline.com. **Frequency:** Annual. **Audience:** Stamp collectors and the general public. **Principal Exhibits:** Stamps, philatelic supplies, and related displays. **Telecommunication Services:** asdashows@erols.com.

LIBRARIES

4386 ■ American Numismatic Society - Library
75 Varick St., Fl. 11
New York, NY 10013
Ph: (212)571-4470, x-4
Fax: (212)571-4479
Co. E-mail: library@numismatics.org
URL: http://www.numismatics.org/Library/Library
Contact: Elizabeth Hahn, Librarian
Scope: Numismatics. **Services:** Copying (limited); scanning; library open to the public with restrictions. **Founded:** 1858. **Holdings:** 100,000 books; 10,000 bound periodical volumes; 10,000 other cataloged items; 350 reels of microfilm. **Subscriptions:** 260 journals and other serials. **Telecommunication Services:** hahn@numismatics.org.

4387 ■ American Philatelic Research (APRL)
100 Match Factory Pl.
Bellefonte, PA 16823
Ph: (814)933-3803
Fax: (814)933-6128
Co. E-mail: aprl@stamps.org
URL: http://stamps.org/About-the-Library
Contact: Tara Murray, Director, Information Services Librarian
Description: Stamp collectors, students of postal history, advanced philatelists; authors, editors, and publishers of philatelic reference publications. Encourages greater use and study of philatelic literature; provides facilities for purchase, sale, and exchange of reference material; prepares bibliographies on various philatelic topics such as world postal history; conducts philatelic and postal history research; reviews philatelic books, catalogs, and periodicals. Convention/Meeting: none. **Scope:** Stamp collecting, postal history, U.S. postal records, stamp production. **Services:** Interlibrary loan; copying; scanning; library open to the public for reference use only. **Founded:** 1942. **Holdings:** 21,000 book titles; 5700 journal titles; 5000 stamp auction firms' catalogs; dealer price lists; new issue releases; clipping files; CD-ROMS. **Subscriptions:** 400 journals and other serials; 5 newspapers. **Publications:** *Philatelic Literature Review* (Quarterly). **Telecommunication Services:** tmurray@stamps.org; webmaster@ stamps.org.

4388 ■ Bick International Library
Box 854
Van Nuys, CA 91408
Ph: (818)997-6496
Fax: (818)988-4337
Co. E-mail: iibick@sbcglobal.net
URL: http://www.bick.net
Contact: Israel I. Bick, President
URL(s): bickinternational.com. **Scope:** Philately. **Services:** Library open to the public by appointment. **Founded:** 1970. **Holdings:** 200 books; 50 bound periodical volumes; other cataloged items. **Subscriptions:** 75 journals and other serials; 50 newspapers.

4389 ■ Canadian Numismatic Association Library
c/o Daniel Gosling
49 Sierra Grande Estates
52131 Range Rd. 210
Sherwood Park, AB, Canada T8G 1A2
Ph: (780)922-5743
Fax: (506)472-9645
Co. E-mail: dan@gosling.ca
URL: http://www.rcna.ca/library.php
Contact: Daniel Gosling, Librarian
Scope: Numismatics. **Services:** Library open to the public with restrictions. **Founded:** 1950. **Holdings:** 3500 books. **Subscriptions:** 15 journals and other serials; 1 newspaper. **Telecommunication Services:** info@rcna.ca.

4390 ■ Collectors Club of Chicago Library
1029 N. Dearborn St.
Chicago, IL 60610
Ph: (312)642-7981
Co. E-mail: info@askphil.org
URL: http://www.askphil.org
Contact: Edward Waterous, Chairman
Scope: Philately. **Services:** Interlibrary loan; library open to the public by appointment. **Founded:** 1945. **Holdings:** 4000 books; 2000 bound periodical volumes. **Subscriptions:** 100 journals and other serials.

4391 ■ Collectors Club Library
22 E. 35th St.
New York, NY 10016
Ph: (212)683-0559
Fax: (212)481-1269
Co. E-mail: steidley@nac.net
URL: http://www.collectorsclub.org
Contact: Mark E. Banchik, Treasurer
Scope: Philately, postal history. **Services:** Interlibrary loan (fee); copying; library open to the public for reference use only by appointment (members may borrow books). **Founded:** 1896. **Holdings:** 150,000 volumes. **Subscriptions:** 200 journals and other serials. **Telecommunication Services:** collectorsclub@ verizon.net.

4392 ■ Franklin Mint Information Research Center
US Rte. 1
Chester Heights, PA 19017
Ph: (610)459-6868
Fax: (610)459-7526
Contact: Cheryl Towne, Director
Scope: Antiques, American history, art, die-cast, decorative arts, travel, numismatics, natural history, philatelics, direct mail, collectibles, home decor, dolls. **Services:** Center not open to the public. **Founded:** 1969. **Holdings:** 45,000 volumes; 100 VF drawers of pictures and slides. **Subscriptions:** 500 journals and other serials; 6 newspapers.

4393 ■ Friends of the Western Philatelic Library
PO Box 2219
Sunnyvale, CA 94087-2219
Ph: (408)733-0336
Co. E-mail: stulev@ix.netcom.com
URL: http://www.fwpl.org
Contact: Stuart Leven, Chairperson
Scope: Stamp collecting. **Services:** Interlibrary loan; copying; Library open to the public. **Founded:** 1969. **Holdings:** 5000 books; 7000 bound periodical volumes; 12 cabinets of pamphlets and files; microfilm. **Subscriptions:** 150 journals and other serials.

4394 ■ Numismatics International Library
PO Box 570842
Dallas, TX 75357-0842
Co. E-mail: davidfg248@grandecom.net
URL: http://www.numis.org/index-5.html
Contact: David Gracey, Librarian
Scope: Coins, currency. **Services:** Interlibrary loan (fee); library open to members and other numismatic organizations. **Founded:** 1964. **Holdings:** 3000 books; slide sets.

4395 ■ Philatelic Foundation Archives and Library
70 W. 40th St., 15th Fl.
New York, NY 10018-2615
Ph: (212)221-6555
Fax: (212)221-6208
Co. E-mail: philatelicfoundation@verizon.net
URL: http://www.philatelicfoundation.org
Contact: Robert Waterman, Archivist
Scope: Philately. **Services:** Copying; library open to contributors by appointment. **Founded:** 1945. **Holdings:** 1500 books; 600 bound periodical volumes; 5000 documents and archival materials. **Subscriptions:** 25 journals and other serials; 10 newspapers.

4396 ■ Smithsonian Institution - National Postal Museum Library
2 Massachusetts Ave., NE
Washington, DC 20560-0570
Ph: (202)633-5544

Fax: (202)357-4879
Co. E-mail: askalibrarian@si.edu
URL: http://library.si.edu/libraries/postal-museum
Contact: Baasil Wilder, Librarian
Scope: Philately, stamp and postal history (domestic and foreign). **Services:** Library open to the public by appointment. **Founded:** 1993. **Holdings:** 40,000 books, journals, catalogues, and archival documents. **Subscriptions:** 250 journals and other serials. **Telecommunication Services:** wilderb@si.edu.

4397 ■ Stack's Rare Coin Company of New York - Technical Information Center
123 W. 57th St.
New York, NY 10019
Ph: (212)582-2580
Fax: (212)245-5018
Scope: Rare coins - U.S., ancient, foreign; medals and decorations. **Services:** Center open to the public by appointment. **Holdings:** 10,000 books; 5000 bound periodical volumes.

4398 ■ Women on Stamps Study Unit Library
c/o D. Kristy
515 Ocean Ave., No. 608S
Santa Monica, CA 90402
Ph: (310)394-5587

Fax: (310)899-3927
Co. E-mail: dkristy@sprintmail.com
Scope: Postage stamps; philately. **Services:** Library not open to the public but information is available on request. **Founded:** 1979. **Holdings:** Archival materials. **Subscriptions:** 70 journals and other serials.

RESEARCH CENTERS

4399 ■ American Numismatic Society (ANS)
75 Varick St., 11th Fl.
New York, NY 10038
Ph: (212)571-4470
Fax: (212)571-4479
Co. E-mail: meadows@numismatics.org
URL: http://www.numismatics.org
Contact: Ute W. Kagan, Executive Director
Description: Collectors and others interested in coins, medals, and related materials. Advances numismatic knowledge as it relates to history, art, archaeology, and economics by collecting coins, medals, tokens, decorations, and paper money. Maintains only museum devoted entirely to numismatics. Presents annual Graduate Fellowship in Numismatics. Sponsors Graduate Seminar in Numismatics, a nine-week individual study program for ten students. **Services:** Technical advice on specialized photography of numismatic material. **Founded:** 1858. **Subscriptions:** books pamphlets photographs numismatic literature. **Publications:** *American Journal of Numismatics* (Annual); *American Journal of Numismatics* (Annual); *ANS Magazine* (3/year); *Coinage of the Americas Conference*; *Index to American Journal of Numismatics*; *Numismatic Literature* (Semiannual); *Numismatic Notes and Monographs*; *Numismatic Studies*; *American Journal of Numismatics* (Annual); *American Numismatic Society Magazine* (Quarterly); *ANS Annual Report*; *Numismatic Literature* (Semiannual); *The Colonial Newsletter*; *American Numismatic Society--Numismatic Studies* (Periodic); *Ancient Coins in North American Collections* (Periodic); *Sylloge Nummorum Graecorum: The Collection of the American Numismatic Society* (Periodic). **Educational Activities:** Coinage of the Americas Conference (Annual); Graduate Seminar in Numismatics (Annual); Coinage of the Americas Conference (Annual); Educational slide programs which provide visual aids to assist in the instruction of history and art history (Annual). **Awards:** Frances M. Schwartz Fellowship; Archer M. Huntington Medal Award; J. Sanford Saltus Medal Award; Donald Groves Fund Awards; Huntington Award Medal (Annual); Saltus Medal Award (Annual); Donald Groves Fund Grants for research and publications in early American numismatics. **Telecommunication Services:** info@numismatics.org; uwk@numismatics.org.

REFERENCE WORKS

4400 ■ *"Ask Inc." in Inc. (October 2007, pp. 74)*
Pub: Gruner & Jahr USA Publishing
Description: Promoting a new comedy club using television, radio and print advertising and tracking results is discussed.

4401 ■ *"Waite, Cancer Survivor, Readies Sch'dy 'Big House' after Long Delay" in Business Review, Albany New York (October 26, 2007)*
Pub: American City Business Journals, Inc.
Ed: Michael DeMasi. **Description:** Stephen Waite, owner of Big House Brewing Company, will be opening its new nightclub called Big House Underground. The nightclub is part of a $3.25 million project Waite started in 2005, which was delayed due to his battle with tonsil cancer. Details of turning the building into a restaurant, bar and nightclub are provided.

ASSOCIATIONS AND OTHER ORGANIZATIONS

4402 ■ *Canada Numismatica*
c/o Len Kuenzig, Sec.-Treas.
Box 21018 Meadowvale RPO
Mississauga, ON, Canada L5N 6A2
Co. E-mail: len.kuenzig@sympatico.ca
URL: http://www.nunet.ca/catc.htm
Contact: Harry N. James, President
Released: Quarterly **Price:** C$15, /year.

4403 ■ Canadian Association of Token Collectors (CATC)
c/o Len Kuenzig, Sec.-Treas.
Box 21018 Meadowvale RPO
Mississauga, ON, Canada L5N 6A2
Co. E-mail: len.kuenzig@sympatico.ca
URL: http://www.nunet.ca/catc.htm
Contact: Harry N. James, President
Description: Collectors of Canadian tokens. Promotes collection of tokens and other memorabilia as a recreational pastime. Facilitates exchange of information among members; serves as a clearinghouse on the preservation, availability, and value of tokens. **Founded:** 1972. **Publications:** *Canada Numismatica* (Quarterly).

4404 ■ Cartoonists Northwest (CNW)
PO Box 31122
Seattle, WA 98103
Co. E-mail: cartoonistsnw@gmail.com
URL: http://sites.google.com/site/cartoonistnw/home
Description: Cartoonists, writers, publishers, illustrators, agents, and others interested in cartooning. Members are accepted nationwide and internationally. Provides information on all aspects of the cartooning profession to amateur, aspiring, and practicing cartoonists. Promotes cartooning as an art form. Provides networking opportunities and referral services. Conducts educational programs. **Founded:** 1981. **Awards:** Toonie Awards (Annual).

4405 ■ Haviland Collectors International Foundation (HCIF)
PO Box 5163
Buffalo Grove, IL 60089-5163
Co. E-mail: haviland@aeroinc.net
URL: http://www.havilandcollectors.com
Contact: Fred Daniels, President
Description: Owners and admirers of Haviland China objects. Promotes "the study of porcelain and pottery produced by the Haviland family in France and America". Facilitates communication and cooperation among members; serves as a clearinghouse on Haviland China; promotes China exhibits. **Founded:** 1990. **Publications:** *Haviland Quarterly* (Quarterly); *Charles Field Haviland: China Identification Guide*; *Dining with Flowers: Haviland Porcelain from 1860 to 1910*; *Porcelain Theodore Haviland*.

REFERENCE WORKS

4406 ■ *Bookman's Price Index: A Guide to the Values of Rare and Other Out of Print Books*
Pub: Cengage Learning Inc.
Contact: Ronald Dunn, President
URL(s): www.gale.cengage.com. **Ed:** Anne F. McGrath. **Released:** 3 to 4 volumes per year. **Price:**

$595, Individuals. **Covers:** Rare and collectible books offered for sale by 150 bookdealers in the United States, Canada, and the United Kingdom. **Entries include:** Book title, author's name, date and place of publication, description of book's condition, name of dealer, catalog and item number, year of catalog in which listing appeared, price; dealer's address is given in a separate list. **Arrangement:** Alphabetical by author name; separate sections for association copies, books with special bindings, and books with fore-edge paintings.

4407 ■ *Collectibles Market Guide & Price Index*
Pub: Collectors Information Bureau
Contact: Linda Kruger, Director
E-mail: lkruger@pioneermagazines.com
URL(s): www.treasuresmagazine.com. **Released:** Annual; latest edition 20th. **Price:** $24.95, Individuals suggested retail; $10, Individuals sales price. **Publication includes:** List of manufacturers of limited edition collectible plates, figurines, bells, graphics, ornaments, dolls, and steins; related associations and museums; price guide to secondary market values of limited edition collectibles. **Entries include:** Company name and address, history, current projects, values of retired editions. **Arrangement:** Membership organization. Editorial restricted to member companies. **Indexes:** Price index of collectibles. Biographies of collectibles artists; collectibles price index; feature articles; glossary; directory of secondary market dealers.

4408 ■ *Fandom Directory*
Pub: Fandata Publications
Contact: Harry A. Hopkins, President
E-mail: harry@fandata.com
URL(s): www.fandata.com. **Released:** Biennial; Latest edition 2011. **Price:** $19.95, plus $4.50 shipping. **Covers:** over 20,000 fans, fan clubs, fan magazine publishers, and fan events in the field of science fiction, fantasy, television and movies, old radio programs, computer games, comic books; location of large or rare manuscript collections; over 9,000 stores that serve fans and collectors. **Entries include:** Club, individual, or firm name, address, phone, special interest(s). **Arrangement:** Geographical. **Indexes:** Alphabetical, interest, geographical.

4409 ■ *Old-Stuff--Directory of Shops Section*
Pub: VBM Printers Inc.
Contact: Ron Miller, Publisher
E-mail: ron@oldstuffnews.com
URL(s): oldstuffnews.com. **Ed:** Donna Miller. **Released:** 6 times a year. **Price:** $20, Individuals yearly subscription; $5.50, Single issue; $35, Two years; $35, Canada. **Publication includes:** List of approximately 900 antiques shops in the northwestern United States. **Entries include:** Shop name, address, phone. **Database includes:** Calendar of events. **Arrangement:** Geographical. **Indexes:** Shops, alphabetical by city.

TRADE PERIODICALS

4410 ■ *Antique Bottle and Glass Collector*
Pub: Antique Bottle and Glass Collector
URL(s): www.glswrk-auction.com. **Ed:** Ralph Finch. **Released:** Monthly **Price:** $32, Individuals 2nd class;

$47, Individuals 1st class; $54, Individuals CAN; $95, Other countries by airmail.

4411 ■ *Antiques & Collecting Magazine*
Pub: Lightner Publishing Corp.
URL(s): www.acmagazine.com/. **Released:** Monthly **Price:** $38, Individuals; $66, Two years.

4412 ■ *Beer Cans and Brewery Collectibles*
Pub: Brewery Collectibles Club of America
Contact: Robert Fondren, President
E-mail: fondren@cox.net
Ed: Marcia Butterbaugh, Editor. **Released:** Bimonthly. **Price:** $38. **Description:** Contains information on collecting beer cans and brewery paraphernalia.

4413 ■ *Collectors News: Serving Coolectors for 50 Years*
Pub: Pioneer Communications Inc.
Contact: Jim Miller, President
E-mail: jmiller@thepioneergroup.com
URL(s): collectors-news.com. **Released:** Monthly **Price:** $26.95, Individuals.

4414 ■ *Comics Buyer's Guide*
Pub: Krause Publications Inc.
Contact: Roger Case, President
URL(s): www.cbgxtra.com. **Released:** Monthly **Price:** $24.95, Individuals; $74.95, Other countries; $59.95, Canada; $5.99, Single issue.

4415 ■ *Comics & Games Retailer: Business Management for the Comics and Gaming Industries*
Pub: Krause Publications Inc.
Contact: Roger Case, President
URL(s): www.comicsretailer.com/. **Ed:** Brent Frankenhoff. **Released:** Monthly **Price:** $151.13, Individuals; €119.95, Other countries.

4416 ■ *The Comics Journal: The Magazine of Comic News and Criticism*
Pub: Fantagraphics Books Inc.
Contact: Matt Thorn, Director
URL(s): www.tcj.com. **Ed:** Timothy Hodler, Dirk Deppey. **Released:** Monthly **Price:** $72, Individuals; $193, Other countries; $128, Canada; $36, Individuals 5 issues; $64, Canada 5 issues; $96, Other countries 5 issues.

4417 ■ *Postcard History Society*
Pub: Postcard History Society
Contact: Jim Ward, Director
Released: Quarterly. **Price:** $9. **Description:** Supplies information on the hobby of collecting postcards.

VIDEOCASSETTES/ AUDIOCASSETTES

4418 ■ *Baseball Card Collector*
Karol Media
Hanover Industrial Estates
375 Stewart Rd.
Wilkes Barre, PA 18773-7600
Ph: (570)822-8899

Free: 800-526-4773
Co. E-mail: sales@karolmedia.com
URL: http://www.karolmedia.com
Released: 1989. **Price:** $19.99. **Description:** Mel Allen narrates this guide to the buying and selling of baseball cards. Also available as a "deluxe edition," half an hour longer for $29.99. **Availability:** VHS.

4419 ■ *Big Kids Baseball Cards*
ESPN Inc.
ESPN Plz.
Bristol, CT 06010
Ph: (860)766-2000
Free: 888-549-3776
Fax: (860)766-2213
Co. E-mail: espnpr@espn.com
URL: http://espn.go.com
Contact: Steven M. Bornstein, President
Released: 1988. **Price:** $19.95. **Description:** Strategies on buying and collecting baseball cards. Includes hints on speculating on tomorrow's stars, and tips from card shark Alan "Mr. Mint" Rosen. **Availability:** VHS.

TRADE SHOWS AND CONVENTIONS

4420 ■ VEGASPEX - Las Vegas International Stamp, Coin, Antique Watch, Jewelry & Collectibles Expo
Bick International
PO Box 854
Van Nuys, CA 91408
Ph: (818)997-6496
Fax: (818)988-4337
Co. E-mail: iibick@sbcglobal.net
URL: http://www.bick.net
Frequency: Biennial. **Audience:** General public. **Principal Exhibits:** Coin, stamp, currency, collectible and antique watch collecting show. **Dates and Locations:** Tropicana Hotel.

4421 ■ Washington Gift Show
George Little Management, LLC
1133 Westchester Ave., Ste. N136
White Plains, NY 10606
Ph: (914)421-3200
Free: 800-272-SHOW
Co. E-mail: cathy_steel@glmshows.com
URL: http://www.glmshows.com
URL(s): www.washingtongiftshow.com. **Frequency:** Semiannual. **Audience:** Specialty and department store retailers, importers, and distributors. **Principal Exhibits:** Gifts, stationery, gourmet products, floral industry products and services, decorative accessories, souvenirs, crafts, jewelry, personal accessories, china, glass, fine and fashion jewelry, collectibles, and related tabletop items. **Dates and Locations:** Capital Expo Center.

FRANCHISES AND BUSINESS OPPORTUNITIES

4422 ■ All Nations Flag Co., Inc.
Patriot Enterprises LLC
118 W 5th St.
Kansas City, MO 64105
Ph: (816)842-8798
Free: 800-533-3524
Description: Custom flags and banners. **No. of Company-Owned Units:** 1. **Founded:** 1924. **Franchised:** 1996. **Equity Capital Needed:** $125,000 minimum. **Franchise Fee:** $15,000. **Training:** Yes.

LIBRARIES

4423 ■ American Matchcover Collecting Club Library
PO Box 18481
Asheville, NC 28814
Co. E-mail: bill@matchcovers.com
URL: http://www.matchcovers.net
Contact: Bill Retskin, President
Scope: Matchcovers. **Services:** Library not open to the public. **Founded:** 1986. **Holdings:** 150,000 archival items. **Subscriptions:** 600 journals and other serials.

4424 ■ Comics Magazine Association of America Library
355 Lexington Ave.
New York, NY 10017-6603
Ph: (212)661-4261
Fax: (212)370-9047
Scope: Comics magazines. **Services:** Library not open to the public. **Holdings:** 100 books; 2000 periodicals; 2 VF drawers.

4425 ■ Interlac Library
97 Woodmere Rd.
Stamford, CT 06905
Ph: (203)975-1554
URL: http://members.aol.com/interlac/
Contact: Tom Burkert
Scope: Comic books, popular culture. **Services:** Library not open to the public. **Founded:** 1976. **Holdings:** 20,000 volumes. **Subscriptions:** 20 journals and other serials.

4426 ■ Michigan State University - Special Collections Division - Russel B. Nye Popular Culture Collection
366 W. Circle Dr.
East Lansing, MI 48824
Ph: (517)432-6123, x-100
Fax: (517)353-5069
Co. E-mail: comics@msu.edu
URL: http://specialcollections.lib.msu.edu/index.jsp
Contact: Peter Berg, Director
Scope: Comic books - fiction - juvenile, detective, science fiction, western, gay and lesbian pulp fiction, romance; popular arts and entertainment; popular information. **Services:** Copying; Interlibrary loan; collections open to the public for reference use only with required identification. **Founded:** 1970. **Holdings:** 300,000 volumes. **Subscriptions:** 30 journals and other serials; 5 newspapers.

4427 ■ Museum of Western Colorado - Loyd Files Research Library
462 Ute Ave.
Grand Junction, CO 81501-2516
Ph: (970)242-0971
Fax: (970)242-3960
Co. E-mail: mmenard@westcomuseum.org
URL: http://www.museumofwesternco.com
Contact: Michael Menard, Archivist Librarian
Scope: Western Colorado, Mesa County, and Grand Junction history; genealogy; paleontology; geology; anthropology. **Services:** Copying; photographic reproduction (including scanning); center open to the public. **Founded:** 1965. **Holdings:** 3500 books and monographs; 18,000 historical and aerial photographs; 2200 audiocassettes; maps and vertical files; institutional archives; reels of microfilm; National Park Service publications on historic preservation; site inventories. **Subscriptions:** 15 journals and other serials; 7 newspapers. **Telecommunication Services:** library@westcomuseum.org.

4428 ■ Ohio State University - Cartoon Library and Museum
Wexner Ctr., Rm. 023L
27 W. 17th Ave. Mall
Columbus, OH 43210-1393
Ph: (614)292-0538
Fax: (614)292-9101
Co. E-mail: cartoons@osu.edu
URL: http://cartoons.osu.edu
Contact: Lucy Shelton Caswell
Scope: Comic strips, editorial cartoons, magazine cartoons, comic books, graphic novels, illustrations, movie posters and stills, photographs. **Services:** Copying; digital reproduction services; Library open to the public upon registration. **Founded:** 1977. **Holdings:** 36,000 books on cartoon art; more than 450,000 original cartoons; 3000 linear feet of manuscript materials; 2.5 million comic strip clippings; representative holdings of original art from editorial cartoonists, comic book artists, and comic strip artists; Association of American Editorial Cartoonists and National Cartoonists Society Archives; Newspaper Features Council Archives; Collections of San Francisco Academy of Comic Art. **Subscriptions:** 51,000 journals and other serials.

4429 ■ University of California, Los Angeles - Department of Special Collections
A1713 Young Research Library
Box 951575
Los Angeles, CA 90095-1575
Ph: (310)825-4988
Fax: (310)206-1864
Co. E-mail: speccoll-paging@library.ucla.edu
URL: http://www.library.ucla.edu/specialcollections/ researchlibrary/index.cfm
Contact: Annie A. Watanabe-Rocco, Office Manager
Scope: California and the West; children's books; literature; motion pictures; radio; television; dance; African Americans; Japanese Americans; Latinos; visual arts; photography; popular culture; printing history (especially Aldines and early Italian printing); fine press printing, fine bindings, and artists' books; fashion; Brazil; Southern California architecture; Leonardo da Vinci. **Services:** Copying (mediated); department open to the public for reference use only. **Founded:** 1946. **Holdings:** 333,000 volumes; 30 million manuscripts; 632 volumes of newspapers; 5 million photographs and negatives, ephemera, maps, works of art, architectural drawings and models, and other graphic arts material; 13,806 reels of microfilm; 4828 sound recordings; 15,285 slides; 9743 videotapes. **Subscriptions:** 212 journals and other serials.

4430 ■ University of Minnesota - Children's Literature Research Collections
113 Elmer L. Andersen Library
222 - 21st Ave., S.
Minneapolis, MN 55455
Ph: (612)624-4576
Fax: (612)626-0377
Co. E-mail: k-hoyl@umn.edu
URL: http://special.lib.umn.edu/clrc
Contact: Karen Nelson Hoyle, Curator
Scope: Children's books - first editions, manuscripts, illustrations; children's literary history and criticism; children's periodicals; American and British dime novels, periodicals, story papers, pulps; Big Little Books; comic books. **Services:** Copying (limited); Collection open for research only. **Founded:** 1949. **Holdings:** 60,000 monographs; 2600 feet of manuscripts; 1913.41 lin.ft. of illustrations; 771 reels of microfilm or 83 dime novel titles; 1732 posters; 65 audio/visual titles. **Subscriptions:** 37 journals and other serials. **Telecommunication Services:** clrc@umn.edu.

Commercial/Graphic Art Business

START-UP INFORMATION

4431 ■ *"Savvy Solutions" in Black Enterprise (Vol. 41, December 2010, No. 5, pp. 42)*
Pub: Earl G. Graves Publishing Co. Inc.
Ed: Tennille M. Robinson. **Description:** Individual asks for advice in launching a graphic design business, particularly grants available in a slow economy.

ASSOCIATIONS AND OTHER ORGANIZATIONS

4432 ■ **Advertising Production Club of New York (APC)**
Euro RSCG Life, 7th Fl.
200 Madison Ave.
New York, NY 10016
Ph: (212)251-7295
Fax: (212)726-5057
Co. E-mail: admin@apc-ny.org
URL: http://www.apc-nyc.org
Contact: George Ashbrook, President
Description: Production and traffic department personnel from advertising agencies, corporate or retail advertising departments, and publishing companies; college level graphic arts educators. Meetings include educational programs on graphic arts procedures and plant tours. Maintains employment service for members. **Founded:** 1931. **Awards:** Advertising Production Club of New York High School Scholarships (APC); Advertising Production Club Scholarship Awards; PGSF-GATF Scholarships; Thomas Cochrane Sr. Scholarship Award (Annual); Tuition-Assist Scholarship Award; APC Tuition-Assist Scholarship Awards. **Telecommunication Services:** news@apc-ny.org.

4433 ■ **American Institute of Graphic Arts (AIGA)**
164 5th Ave.
New York, NY 10010-5901
Ph: (212)807-1990
Fax: (212)807-1799
Co. E-mail: grefe@aiga.org
URL: http://www.aiga.org
Contact: Doug Powell, President
Description: Graphic designers, art directors, illustrators and packaging designers. Sponsors exhibits and projects in the public interest. Sponsors traveling exhibitions. Operates gallery. Maintains library of design books and periodicals; offers slide archives. **Founded:** 1914. **Publications:** *365: AIGA Year in Design 24* (Annual). **Educational Activities:** AIGA Design Conference (Biennial). **Awards:** Gold Medal (Annual); Corporate Leadership Award; AIGA Medal; 50 Books/50 Covers Competition.

4434 ■ **Associated Designers of Canada (ADC)—Association des Designers Canadiens**
201-192 Spadina Ave.
Toronto, ON, Canada M5T 2C2
Ph: (416)410-4209
Free: 800-361-2721
Fax: (416)703-6601
Co. E-mail: adc@designers.ca
URL: http://www.designers.ca
Contact: Phillip Silver, President
Description: Theatre designers, including set, costume, lighting, and sound. Promotes the professional advancement of members. Facilitates communication and cooperation among members. Conducts continuing professional development programs. **Founded:** 1965.

4435 ■ *Aub bas de l'echelle...pas pour toujours*
6839A rue Drolet, Bur. 305
Montreal, QC, Canada H2S 2T1
Ph: (514)270-7878
Fax: (514)270-7726
Co. E-mail: abe@aubasdelechelle.ca
URL: http://www.aubasdelechelle.ca
Contact: Pierre-Antoine Harvey, President
Released: 3/year

4436 ■ **California Society of Printmakers (CSP)**
PO Box 194202
San Francisco, CA 94119
Co. E-mail: info@caprintmakers.org
URL: http://www.caprintmakers.org
Contact: Michelle Murillo, President
Description: Fosters the appreciation of prints and printmaking; sponsors education programs, including exhibitions. **Scope:** slide registry contains works of current members. **Founded:** 1912. **Subscriptions:** archival material films. **Publications:** *California Printmaker* (Annual). **Educational Activities:** California Society of Printmakers General assembly (Annual); Membership Exhibition. **Awards:** Distinguished Artist Award (Periodic).

4437 ■ **Canadian Association of Photographers and Illustrators in Communications (CAPIC)—Association Canadienne de Photographes et Illustrateurs de Publicite**
720 Spadina Ave., Ste. 202
Toronto, ON, Canada M5S 2T9
Ph: (416)462-3677
Free: 888-252-2742
Fax: (416)929-5256
Co. E-mail: administrator@capic.org
URL: http://www.capic.org
Contact: Andre Cornellier, Chairman
Description: Photographers and illustrators employed in communications. Promotes professional and artistic advancement of members. Represents members' interests before industrial organizations; formulates standards of ethics and practice for members. **Founded:** 1978.

4438 ■ **Digital Printing and Imaging Association (DPI)**
c/o Specialty Graphic Imaging Association
10015 Main St.
Fairfax, VA 22031-3489
Ph: (703)385-1335
Free: 888-385-3588
Fax: (703)273-0456
Co. E-mail: sgia@sgia.org
URL: http://www.sgia.org
Contact: Michael E. Robertson, President
Description: Electronic printing, pre-press companies, commercial printers, service bureaus, photo labs, reprographic companies, and printer suppliers, and educational institutions. Works to advance the electronic imaging field by promoting the use of digital printing devices, responding to industry needs and concerns, and improving the industry's ability to serve its market and customers. Conducts educational programs. **Founded:** 1992. **Publications:** *RIP* (Quarterly). **Awards:** Andre Schellenberg Award (Annual); Product of the Year (Annual); Vision Award (Annual).

4439 ■ *Graphic Design*
Arts Ct.
2 Daly Ave.
Ottawa, ON, Canada K1N 6E2
Ph: (613)567-5400
Free: 877-496-4453
Fax: (613)564-4428
Co. E-mail: info@gdc.net
URL: http://www.gdc.net
Contact: Adrian Jean, President
Released: Periodic **Price:** included in membership dues.

4440 ■ *The National*
Arts Ct.
2 Daly Ave.
Ottawa, ON, Canada K1N 6E2
Ph: (613)567-5400
Free: 877-496-4453
Fax: (613)564-4428
Co. E-mail: info@gdc.net
URL: http://www.gdc.net
Contact: Adrian Jean, President
Released: Quarterly **Price:** included in membership dues.

4441 ■ **National Association of Quick Printers (NAQP)**
2250 E Devon Ave., Ste. 245
Des Plaines, IL 60018
Ph: (847)298-8680
Free: 800-234-0040
Fax: (847)298-8705
Co. E-mail: info@naqp.com
URL: http://www.naqp.com
Description: Independent printers and printing franchise businesses; industry suppliers. Seeks to bring recognition, improved quality, and increased profits to the entire quick printing field. Provides services to members; works to advance the collective interests of the printing industries at the national and international levels. **Scope:** technical manuals. **Founded:** 1975.

4442 ■ **National Oil and Acrylic Painters' Society (NOAPS)**
PO Box 676
Osage Beach, MO 65065-0676

Ph: (573)348-1764
Co. E-mail: noaps1991_usa@noaps.org
URL: http://www.noaps.org
Contact: Joe Ray Kelly, President
Description: Represents artists and others interested in exhibition and sales of original oil and acrylic paintings. **Founded:** 1991. **Publications:** *NOAPS News-letter* (Semiannual).

4443 ■ **Organization of Black Designers (OBD)**
300 M St. SW, Ste. N110
Washington, DC 20024
Ph: (202)659-3918
Co. E-mail: info@obd.org
URL: http://www.obd.org
Contact: David H. Rice, Chairman Founder
Description: African American designers holding college degrees who are practicing graphic advertising, industrial, fashion, textile, and interior design. Provides forum for discussion and educational programs, business, career and economic development. Sponsors competitions and speakers' bureau. **Scope:** design issues that impact black design professionals. **Founded:** 1994. **Subscriptions:** archival material articles. **Publications:** *DesigNation* (Biennial); *OBData*. **Educational Activities:** Desig-Nation (Annual). **Awards:** OBD Design Award (Annual); OBD Scholarship (Annual).

4444 ■ **Rank and File (RF)—Au Bas de l'Echelle**
6839A rue Drolet, Bur. 305
Montreal, QC, Canada H2S 2T1
Ph: (514)270-7878
Fax: (514)270-7726
Co. E-mail: abe@aubasdelechelle.ca
URL: http://www.aubasdelechelle.ca
Contact: Pierre-Antoine Harvey, President
Description: Promotes increased recognition of the working rights of nonsyndicated workers. Represents members' interests; gathers and disseminates information to increase public awareness of conditions faced by nonsyndicated workers. **Founded:** 1975. **Publications:** *Aub bas de l'echelle...pas pour toujours* (3/year).

4445 ■ *Regional Newsletter*
Arts Ct.
2 Daly Ave.
Ottawa, ON, Canada K1N 6E2
Ph: (613)567-5400
Free: 877-496-4453
Fax: (613)564-4428
Co. E-mail: info@gdc.net
URL: http://www.gdc.net
Contact: Adrian Jean, President
Released: Periodic

4446 ■ **Society for Environmental Graphic Design (SEGD)**
1000 Vermont Ave. NW, Ste. 400
Washington, DC 20005
Ph: (202)638-5555
Fax: (202)638-0891
Co. E-mail: segd@segd.org
URL: http://www.segd.org
Contact: Jessica London, Chief Executive Officer
Description: Designers and manufacturers of sign systems and environmental graphics. Establishes educational guidelines for professional development as well as governmental guidelines for environmental graphics programs; provides a forum for interaction and communication among members who are from a variety of design disciplines and with manufacturers; compiles and disseminates technical data. Offers members the opportunity to participate in government hearings, code reviews, and related proceedings regarding environmental graphic design. Conducts educational programs and develops resource materials. Maintains slide collection, library and educational materials. **Scope:** design. **Founded:** 1974. **Subscriptions:** 600. **Publications:** *SEGdesign* (Quarterly); *What is Exhibition Design*; *SEGD Compensation and Billing Survey*; *SEGD Green Paper: Best Practices, Strategies, and Scenarios for Sustainability in Environmental Graphic Design*; *You are Here, Graphics that Direct, Explain and Entertain* (Bimonthly). **Educational Activities:** Society for

Environmental Graphic Design Conference (Annual). **Awards:** Angel Award (Annual); Distinguished Member Award (Annual); Gold Arrow Award (Annual).

4447 ■ **Society of Graphic Designers of Canada (GDC)—Societe des designers graphiques du Canada**
Arts Ct.
2 Daly Ave.
Ottawa, ON, Canada K1N 6E2
Ph: (613)567-5400
Free: 877-496-4453
Fax: (613)564-4428
Co. E-mail: info@gdc.net
URL: http://www.gdc.net
Contact: Adrian Jean, President
Description: Graphic designers, administrators, educators, students, and organizations promoting graphic design in Canada. Provides for professional development and information exchange within the field; promotes high standards in the industry. Represents the interests of members; maintains communication with federal and provincial bodies. Sponsors shows and competitions for professional designers and students. Conducts educational programs and seminars. **Founded:** 1956. **Subscriptions:** archival material. **Publications:** *Graphic Design* (Periodic); *The National* (Quarterly); *Regional Newsletter* (Periodic). **Awards:** Society of Graphic Designers of Canada Adobe Scholarships; Society of Graphic Designers of Canada Applied Arts Scholarships; Society of Graphic Designers of Canada Veer Scholarships.

4448 ■ **Specialty Graphic Imaging Association (SPTF) - Screen Printing Technical Foundation (SPTF)**
10015 Main St.
Fairfax, VA 22031
Ph: (703)385-1335
Co. E-mail: sptf@sgia.org
URL: http://www.sgia.org/sptf
Description: Participants include corporations, institutions, and individuals interested in screen-printing. Advances the screen-printing industry. Conducts technical research and hands-on training programs to address production problems and processes. Sponsors educational programs and prepares educational materials. **Founded:** 1986.

DIRECTORIES OF EDUCATIONAL PROGRAMS

4449 ■ *Directory of Private Accredited Career Schools and Colleges of Technology*
Pub: Accrediting Commission of Career Schools and Colleges of Technology
Contact: Michale S. McComis, Executive Director
Released: On web page. **Price:** Free. **Description:** Covers 3900 accredited post-secondary programs that provide training programs in business, trade, and technical fields, including various small business endeavors. Entries offer school name, address, phone, description of courses, job placement assistance, and requirements for admission. Arrangement is alphabetical.

REFERENCE WORKS

4450 ■ *"Agfa: M-Press Leopard Debuts"* in *American Printer (Vol. 128, June 1, 2011, No. 6)*
Pub: Penton Media Inc.
Description: M-Press Leopard is a new version of the machine that offers advanced ink jet technology at a lower price point. Agfa Graphics introduced the new version that allows for new applications that require more manual handling.

4451 ■ *"Art Attack 2007 Comes to Minneapolis"* in *Art Business News (Vol. 34, November 2007, No. 11, pp. 11)*
Pub: Pfingsten Publishing, LLC
Description: Overview of Art Attack 2007, an open studio and gallery crawl in the Northeast Minneapolis Arts District which featured artists working in glass, ceramics, jewelry, mosaics, mixed media, photography, painting, pottery, sculpture, textiles and wood.

4452 ■ *"Art Miami Comes to Miami's Wynwood Art District"* in *Art Business News (Vol. 34, November 2007, No. 11, pp. 18)*
Pub: Pfingsten Publishing, LLC
Description: In December, The Art Group will hold its Art Miami fair in the Wynwood Art District; the exhibitors range from painting, sculpture, video and works on paper.

4453 ■ *"Artexpo Celebrates 30th Anniversary"* in *Art Business News (Vol. 34, November 2007, No. 11, pp. 18)*
Pub: Pfingsten Publishing, LLC
Description: In honor of its 30th anniversary Artexpo New York 2008 will be an unforgettable show offering a collection of fine-art education courses for both trade and consumer attendees and featuring a variety of artists working in all mediums.

4454 ■ *"Avanti Hosts Users Conference"* in *American Printer (Vol. 128, July 1, 2011, No. 7)*
Pub: Penton Media Inc.
Description: Avanti Computer Systems Ltd. hosted its 19th annual users conference in Washington DC. In-plant and commercial printers were in attendance.

4455 ■ *"Avoid a Tablet Generation Gap"* in *American Printer (Vol. 128, July 1, 2011, No. 7)*
Pub: Penton Media Inc.
Description: Individuals between the ages of 18-34 are the only generation that is more likely to own a laptop computer or netbook insead of a desktop computer. Statistical data included.

4456 ■ *Black Book Photography*
Pub: Black Book Marketing Group Inc.
Contact: Michael Fitzgerald, President
E-mail: mfitzgerald@blackbook.com
URL(s): www.BlackBook.com. **Released:** Annual; Latest edition 2008. **Price:** $60, Individuals Deluxe Edition - Hardcover. **Publication includes:** Over 19,000 art directors, creative directors, photographers and photographic services, design firms, advertising agencies, and other firms whose products or services are used in advertising. **Entries include:** Company name, address, phone. Principal content of publication is 4-color samples from the leading commercial photographers. **Arrangement:** Classified by product/service.

4457 ■ *"Boston Printer Celebrates 60th Anniversary"* in *American Printer (Vol. 128, August 1, 2011, No. 8)*
Pub: Penton Media Inc.
Description: Shawmut printing is celebrating its 60th anniversary. The family business plans to increase efficiency through automation, monitoring job progress online from start to finish.

4458 ■ *"Business is Unbelievable"* in *American Printer (Vol. 128, August 1, 2011, No. 8)*
Pub: Penton Media Inc.
Ed: Katherine O'Brien. **Description:** Most commercial printers have seen an increase in business over the last year.

4459 ■ *"Calendar"* in *Crain's Detroit Business (Vol. 26, January 11, 2010, No. 2, pp. 16)*
Pub: Crain Communications Inc.
Description: Listing of events includes seminars sponsored by the Detroit Economic Club as well as conferences dealing with globalization and graphic design.

4460 ■ *"Catching Creatives; Detroit Group Gets Grant to Attract 1,000 Design Pros"* in *Crain's Detroit Business (March 24, 2008)*
Pub: Crain Communications, Inc.
Ed: Sherri Begin. **Description:** Design Detroit was given a $200,000 planning grant by the Knight Foundation, an organization that strives to back initiatives that leverage talent and resources in each of the 26 U.S. cities it funds, to inspire strategies to attract up to 1,000 creative professionals to live in Detroit.

4461 ■ *"Challenges Await Quad in Going Public"* in *Milwaukee Business Journal (Vol. 27, January 29, 2010, No. 18, pp. A1)*
Pub: American City Business Journals

Ed: Rich Rovito. **Description:** Sussex, Wisconsin-based Quad/Graphics Inc.'s impending acquisition of rival Canadian World Color Press Inc. will transform it into a publicly held entity for the first time. Quad has operated as a private company for nearly 40 years and will need to adjust to changes, such as the way management shares information with Quad/Graphics' employees. Details of the merger are included.

4462 ■ *"City Slickers"* in *Canadian Business (Vol. 81, March 31, 2008, No. 5, pp. 36)*
Pub: Rogers Media

Ed: Joe Castaldo. **Description:** Richard Florida believes that the creative class drives the economy and the prosperity of countries depends on attracting and retaining these people. Florida has brought attention to developing livable and economically vibrant cities thanks in part to his promotional skills. However, he has also drawn critics who see his data on his theories as flimsy and inadequate.

4463 ■ *"ContiTech Celebrates 100 Years"* in *American Printer (Vol. 128, July 1, 2011, No. 7)*
Pub: Penton Media Inc.

Description: ContiTech celebrated 100 years in business. The firm started in 1911 after developing the first elastic printing blanket. Other milestones for the firm include its manufacturing process for compressible printing blankets, the Conti-Air brand and climate-neutral printing blankets.

4464 ■ *The Creative Business Guide to Running a Graphic Design Business*
Pub: W.W. Norton & Company, Incorporated

Ed: Cameron S. Foote. **Released:** April 2004. **Price:** $23.10. **Description:** Advice for running a graphic design firm, focusing on organizations, marketing, personnel and operations.

4465 ■ *"Crouser Offers UV Coating Price Report"* in *American Printer (Vol. 128, June 1, 2011, No. 6)*
Pub: Penton Media Inc.

Description: Crouser and Associates will offer the 'Pricing Off-Line UV Coating' report that provides background information on all three types of protective printing coatings and price guidance. The report will also offer comparisons of four popular types of offline equipment.

4466 ■ *"Customer OKs on Press"* in *American Printer (Vol. 128, August 1, 2011, No. 8)*
Pub: Penton Media Inc.

Description: Printers discuss the value of having customers meet at the plant in order to okay print colors for projects.

4467 ■ *"Design Center Shows Quality of Digital Paper"* in *American Printer (Vol. 128, June 1, 2011, No. 6)*
Pub: Penton Media Inc.

Description: Digital Design Centers allows printers to customize marketing tools in order to promote their own digital printing capabilities.

4468 ■ *"Digital Printing Walks the Plank"* in *American Printer (Vol. 128, August 1, 2011, No. 8)*
Pub: Penton Media Inc.

Description: Digital print manufacturing is discussed.

4469 ■ *"F1 Makes Room(s) for Aspiring Entrepreneur"* in *Austin Business Journal (Vol. 31, July 1, 2011, No. 17, pp. 1)*
Pub: American City Business Journals Inc.

Ed: Vicky Garza. **Description:** Formula One fan and graphic designer Danielle Crespo cashes in on the June 17, 2012 racing event in Austin, Texas via hosting a Website that allows users to book hotel rooms. She invested less than $100 and long hours on this enterprise which now has 74,000-plus visitors.

4470 ■ *Fashion & Print Directory*
Pub: Peter Glenn Publications
Contact: Gregory James Blount, President
E-mail: gjames@pgdirect.com
URL(s): www.pgdirect.com/fpintro.asp. **Ed:** Gregory James. **Released:** Annual; November; latest edition 47th. **Price:** $39.95, Individuals. **Covers:** Advertising agencies, PR firms, marketing companies, 1,000 client brand companies and related services in the U.S. and Canada. Includes photographers, marketing agency, suppliers, sources of props and rentals, fashion houses, beauty services, locations. **Entries include:** Company name, address, phone; paid listings numbering 5,000 include description of products or services, key personnel. **Arrangement:** Classified by line of business.

4471 ■ *"Feeding the Elephants While Searching for Greener Pastures"* in *American Printer (Vol. 128, July 1, 2011, No. 7)*
Pub: Penton Media Inc.

Ed: Bob Rosen. **Description:** Three steps to help printers to build a new business while facing the challenges to the existing business are outlined.

4472 ■ *"First U.S. :M-Press Tiger with Inline Screen Printing"* in *American Printer (Vol. 128, June 1, 2011, No. 6)*
Pub: Penton Media Inc.

Description: Graphic Tech located in California bought :M-Press Tiger, the first in North America with an inline screen printing unit.

4473 ■ *"Flint Group Raises Prices"* in *American Printer (Vol. 128, August 1, 2011, No. 8)*
Pub: Penton Media Inc.

Description: Due to the rising cost for raw materials, Flint Group is raising their prices for inks and coatings in North American.

4474 ■ *"Four Exhibition Considerations"* in *American Printer (Vol. 128, August 1, 2011, No. 8)*
Pub: Penton Media Inc.

Description: Four questions to ask at the Graph Expo will help printers improve their own business.

4475 ■ *"Fujifilm Invites Printers to Take the 'Onset Challenge"* in *American Printer (Vol. 128, August 1, 2011, No. 8)*
Pub: Penton Media Inc.

Description: Fujifilm North American Corporation's Graphic Systems Division offers a new five-step product selection and return-on-investment calculator for the Onset family of wide-format printers.

4476 ■ *"Gallery Street Launches ArtCandy"* in *Art Business News (Vol. 34, November 2007, No. 11, pp. 8)*
Pub: Pfingsten Publishing, LLC

Description: Fine-art reproduction house Gallery Street recently launched its new division, ArtCandy Editions; the division was created in order to help a network of artists expand the distribution of their work.

4477 ■ *"Giovanni Sanfilippo"* in *Art Business News (Vol. 34, November 2007, No. 11, pp. 14)*
Pub: Pfingsten Publishing, LLC

Description: GSG Publishing is marketing a new release of Maestro Sanfilippo's 'Timida', in a limited edition.

4478 ■ *Graphic Monthly--Estimators' & Buyers' Guide Issue*
Pub: Masthead Publishing Ltd.

URL(s): www.mastheadonline.comwww.ebguide.ca/. **Ed:** Filomena Tamburri. **Released:** Annual; Latest edition 2009-2010. **Price:** $25, Individuals. **Publication includes:** List of about 800 suppliers of graphic arts products and services, such as trade printers, art studios, film houses, binding equipment manufacturers, and printing equipment manufacturers. **Entries include:** Company name, address, phone, product or service. **Arrangement:** Classified by product/service. **Indexes:** Product/service.

4479 ■ *"Guide to Carbon Footprinting"* in *American Printer (Vol. 128, June 1, 2011, No. 6)*
Pub: Penton Media Inc.

Description: PrintCity Alliance published its new report, 'Carbon Footprint & Energy Reduction for Graphic Industry Value Chain.' The report aims to help improve the environmental performance of printers, converters, publishers, brand owners and their suppliers.

4480 ■ *"A Home's Identity in Black and White"* in *Crain's Chicago Business (Vol. 31, April 21, 2008, No. 16, pp. 35)*
Pub: Crain Communications, Inc.

Ed: Lisa Bertagnoli. **Description:** Real estate agents are finding that showing customers a written floor plan is a trend that is growing since many buyers feel that Online virtual tours distort a room. Although floor plans cost up to $500 to have drawn up, they clearly show potential buyers the exact dimensions of rooms and how they connect.

4481 ■ *"How to Save Money on Ink"* in *American Printer (Vol. 128, July 1, 2011, No. 7)*
Pub: Penton Media Inc.

Description: Tips are shared to help graphic arts and printing companies save money on raw materials. Factors to consider once the type of ink is decided are also outlined.

4482 ■ *"Improving the USPS"* in *American Printer (Vol. 128, July 1, 2011, No. 7)*
Pub: Penton Media Inc.

Description: National Postal Forum held in San Diego, California May 1-4, 2011 hosted 4,000 attendees. Highlights of the event are provided.

4483 ■ *"Industry Events 2011"* in *American Printer (Vol. 128, August 1, 2011, No. 8)*
Pub: Penton Media Inc.

Description: Listing of events of interest to graphic arts and printing businesses in presented.

4484 ■ *"Industry/Events 2011"* in *American Printer (Vol. 128, July 1, 2011, No. 7)*
Pub: Penton Media Inc.

Description: PMA, the Worldwide Community of Imaging Association launched its new CliQ with how-to tips, product reviews and monthly photo contests. PMA formed a partnership with the Consumer Electronics Association to make changes to this year's annual convention.

4485 ■ *"Inside an Online Bazaar"* in *Entrepreneur (Vol. 37, September 2009, No. 9, pp. 38)*
Pub: Entrepreneur Media Inc.

Ed: Kara Ohngren. **Description:** Etsy.com is a website that provides a marketplace for handmade products. The site has attracted more than 250,000 sellers since its launch in 2005. Site features and services are also supplied.

4486 ■ *"Interchangeable or Irreplaceable?"* in *American Printer (Vol. 128, August 1, 2011, No. 8)*
Pub: Penton Media Inc.

Description: Creating and maintaining customers is important for all graphic design and printing companies. Tips are shared to help maintain good customer satisfaction and repeat business.

4487 ■ *"IPEX Moves to London Venue"* in *American Printer (Vol. 128, July 1, 2011, No. 7)*
Pub: Penton Media Inc.

Description: IPES 2014 is being relocated to London's ExCeL International Exhibition and Conference Centre from March 26 to April 2, 2014.

4488 ■ *"JDF Integration: 3 Key Tips"* in *American Printer (Vol. 128, August 1, 2011, No. 8)*
Pub: Penton Media Inc.

Description: Three tips for implementing cross-vendor integrations are outlined.

4489 ■ *"KBA, Graphic Art System Partner on Cold Foil" in American Printer (Vol. 128, June 1, 2011, No. 6)*
Pub: Penton Media Inc.
Description: KBA North America has partnered with Graphic Art System to retrofit and equip presses with cold foil machines.

4490 ■ *"Kodak Offers Cloud-Based Operating Option" in American Printer (Vol. 128, June 1, 2011, No. 6)*
Pub: Penton Media Inc.
Description: Kodak partnered with VMware to offer its first Virtual Operating Environment option for Kodak Unified Workflow Solutions. The new feature enables cost savings, increased efficiency and failover protection.

4491 ■ *"Metallics Education" in American Printer (Vol. 128, June 1, 2011, No. 6)*
Pub: Penton Media Inc.
Description: Guide 'Curious About Print: Your Guide to the World of Curious Metallics' provides hints and tips to help printers maximize selection and reproduction, advice on working with metallic and UV inks, and recommendations for gaining quantity without sacrificing quality.

4492 ■ *"MFSA Officially Endorses Five-Day USPS Delivery" in American Printer (Vol. 128, August 1, 2011, No. 8)*
Pub: Penton Media Inc.
Description: Board of Directors of the Mailing and Fulfillment Service Association (MFSA) voted to support the US Postal Service's move to five-day delivery service.

4493 ■ *"New Approach to Mechanical Binding" in American Printer (Vol. 128, July 1, 2011, No. 7)*
Pub: Penton Media Inc.
Description: EcoBinder coil binding system from Kugler-Womako eliminates traditional plastic combs or wire spiral with the use of 22-mm wide printable paper rings.

4494 ■ *"No Straight Lines: How Video Visionary Julien 'Little X' Lutz Creates His Images" in Black Enterprise (Vol. 38, January 2008)*
Pub: Earl G. Graves Publishing Co. Inc.
Ed: Sonia Alleyne. **Description:** Profile of Julien Lutz, who turned his passion for drawing into a successful career.

4495 ■ *"OCE Boosts JetStream Productivity" in American Printer (Vol. 128, August 1, 2011, No. 8)*
Pub: Penton Media Inc.
Description: New Oce JetStream 1400 and 3000 digital full-color inkjet presses are profiled. The new models promise higher speed to grow print volume.

4496 ■ *"One World" in American Printer (Vol. 128, August 1, 2011, No. 8)*
Pub: Penton Media Inc.
Description: Graph Expo will highlight entrepreneurs focused on the connection between content, technology and business models.

4497 ■ *"Paper a la Carte" in American Printer (Vol. 128, June 1, 2011, No. 6)*
Pub: Penton Media Inc.
Description: Blurb, the online publishing platform, launched ProLine which features Mohawk Superfine and Mohawk proPhoto papers. ProLine papers offer two finishes: Pearl Photo and Uncoated.

4498 ■ *"Paper Choices Made Simple" in American Printer (Vol. 128, June 1, 2011, No. 6)*
Pub: Penton Media Inc.
Description: Choices, a new initiative by Boise, provides professional guidance to help customers and consumers make informed, effective choices for using paper.

4499 ■ *"Paper Replaces PVC for Gift Cards" in American Printer (Vol. 128, June 1, 2011, No. 6)*
Pub: Penton Media Inc.
Description: Monadnock Envi Card Stock replaces paper for gift cards, loyalty cards, membership cards, hotel keys and durable signage. This renewable wood fiber alternative to PVC card materials comes from Monadock Paper Mills.

4500 ■ *"Partnering for Success" in Art Business News (Vol. 36, October 2009, No. 10, pp. 4)*
Pub: Summit Business Media
Ed: Jennifer Dulin Wiley. **Description:** In such a volatile economy many savvy artists and gallery owners are turning to out-of-the-box partnerships for continued success; these partnerships are also pervading the Internet, especially with such social media networks as Facebook and Twitter where artists and businesses can develop a loyal following.

4501 ■ *The Pixar Touch: The Making of a Company*
Pub: Pantheon Books
Ed: David A. Price. **Released:** 2009. **Price:** $27.95.
Description: Profile of how Pixar's founders turned their computer-animated films into a successful movie studio.

4502 ■ *"Prices Continue to Rise" in American Printer (Vol. 128, June 1, 2011, No. 6)*
Pub: Penton Media Inc.
Description: Prices were increased by both Flint Group and Ashland Performance Materials by 7-10 percent and 5-15 percent respectively.

4503 ■ *"Printers to the Trade" in American Printer (Vol. 128, July 1, 2011, No. 7)*
Pub: Penton Media Inc.
Description: Wholesale printing is discussed. Two wholesale printers share insight into their success, from business philosophies in general to practices that build strong relationships.

4504 ■ *"QR Codes: OK, I Get It Now" in American Printer (Vol. 128, July 1, 2011, No. 7)*
Pub: Penton Media Inc.
Description: QR Code technology is discussed. It is up to the user to enter the proper QR Code.

4505 ■ *"The Rage Offstage at Marvel" in Barron's (Vol. 88, June 30, 2008, No. 26, pp. 19)*
Pub: Dow Jones & Co., Inc.
Ed: Bill Alpert. **Description:** Lawsuits against Marvel Entertainment and Stan Lee are pushing the claims from Peter F. Paul that Stan Lee Media was undone by the actions of the accused. Paul's associates argue that Stan Lee Media owns rights to Marvel characters and that they want half the profits that Marvel is making.

4506 ■ *"Red One and The Rain Chronicles" in Michigan Vue (Vol. 13, July-August 2008, No. 4, pp. 30)*
Pub: Entrepreneur Media Inc.
Ed: Evan Cornish. **Description:** Troy-based film school the Motion Picture Institute (MPI) implemented the latest technology by shooting the second of their trilogy, 'The Rain Chronicles', on the Red One camera. This is the first feature film in Michigan to utilize this exciting new camera, which includes proprietary software for rendering and color correction. Brian K. Johnson heads up the visual effects team as visual effects supervisor and lead CG artist. His company, Dream Conduit Studios, had to tackle the task of employing the new work flow through a post-production pipeline that would allow him to attack complex visual effects shots, many of which were shot with a moving camera, a technique rarely seen in films at this budgetary level where the camera is traditionally locked off.

4507 ■ *"Reducing the Book's Carbon Footprint" in American Printer (Vol. 128, July 1, 2011, No. 7)*
Pub: Penton Media Inc.
Description: Green Press Initiative's Book Industry Environmental Council is working to achieve a 20 percent reduction in the book industry's carbon footprint by 2020. The Council is made up of publishers, printers, paper suppliers, and non-governmental organizations.

4508 ■ *"Root, Root, Root for the P.A. Hutchison Co." in American Printer (Vol. 128, August 1, 2011, No. 8)*
Pub: Penton Media Inc.
Description: The P.A. Hutchison Company celebrate 100 years in the printing business. President and CEO Chris Hutchison presented awards to employees, however employees also presented awards to Chris and his father as Employer of the Century.

4509 ■ *RSVP: The Directory of Illustration and Design*
Pub: RSVP: The Directory of Illustration and Design
Contact: Richard Lebenson, Publisher
URL(s): www.rsvpdirectory.com. **Released:** Annual; January/February latest edition 2005. **Price:** $20, Individuals. **Covers:** about 250 illustrators and designers in the graphic arts industry. All listings are paid. **Entries include:** Name, address, phone, sample of work. **Arrangement:** Separate sections for illustrators and designers; each subdivided into color and black and white. **Indexes:** Specialty (with phone), geographical, alphabetical.

4510 ■ *"Sappi Awards Gold NA Printers of the Year Winners" in American Printer (Vol. 128, July 1, 2011, No. 7)*
Pub: Penton Media Inc.
Description: Sappi Fine Paper North America honored ten gold winners of its 14th North American Printers of the Year awards. Each gold winning printer will receive $20,000 to support marketing and brand initiatives.

4511 ■ *"Seeing the Light" in American Printer (Vol. 128, July 1, 2011, No. 7)*
Pub: Penton Media Inc.
Description: Four printing demos on sheetfed, digital, label and pad printing equipment were highlighted at the Fifth UV Days held in Stuttgart, Germany in May 2011.

4512 ■ *Seven Days in the Art World*
Pub: W.W. Norton & Company
Ed: Sarah Thornton. **Released:** 2009. **Price:** $24.95.
Description: A sociologist renders the interplay among buyers, critics, curators and makers of contemporary art.

4513 ■ *"Seven Tips for Continuous Improvement" in American Printer (Vol. 128, July 1, 2011, No. 7)*
Pub: Penton Media Inc.
Description: Seven tips are given to help any graphic arts or printing company improve by integrating lean manufacturing into operations.

4514 ■ *"Show Dates" in Art Business News (Vol. 34, November 2007, No. 11, pp. 18)*
Pub: Pfingsten Publishing, LLC
Description: Listing of conferences, trade shows and gallery openings for artists and those in the art industry.

4515 ■ *"Something Old and Something New" in American Printer (Vol. 128, August 1, 2011, No. 8)*
Pub: Penton Media Inc.
Description: Trade journalists and industry analysts were invited to Fujifilm North America Corporation's Hanover Park, Illinois facility to view it's sheetfed inkjet press. The JPress 720 is the first and only of its kind in the world.

4516 ■ *"Successful First Year for Twin Rivers" in American Printer (Vol. 128, June 1, 2011, No. 6)*
Pub: Penton Media Inc.
Description: Profile of Twin Rivers located in Maine. The firm manufactured 380,000 tons of free sheet and hybrid-groundwood papers in its first year.

4517 ■ "Ted Stahl: Executive Chairman" in Inside Business (Vol. 13, September-October 2011, No. 5, pp. NC6)
Pub: Great Lakes Publishing Co.
Ed: Miranda S. Miller. **Description:** Profile of Ted Stahl, who started working in his family's business when he was ten years old is presented. The firm makes dies for numbers and letters used on team uniforms. Another of the family firms manufactures stock and custom heat-printing products, equipment and supplies. It also educates customers on ways to decorate garments with heat printing products and offers graphics and software for customers to create their own artwork.

4518 ■ "Tic-Tac-Show" in American Printer (Vol. 128, August 1, 2011, No. 8)
Pub: Penton Media Inc.
Description: Graph Expo has become the US print industry's main event. There will be as many as 500 exhibitors at this year's event and the Graphic Arts Show Company lists over 30 co-located events as well as 53 new sessions in the seminar program's 28 education categories.

4519 ■ "Transcontinental to Exchange Assets with Quad/Graphics" in American Printer (Vol. 128, August 1, 2011, No. 8)
Pub: Penton Media Inc.
Description: Transcontinental Inc. and Quad/Graphics Inc. entered into an agreement where Transcontinental will indirectly acquire all shares of Quad Graphics Canada Inc.

4520 ■ "Try a Little Social Media" in American Printer (Vol. 128, June 1, 2011, No. 6)
Pub: Penton Media Inc.
Description: Social media helps keep Ussery Printing on customers radar. Jim David, VP of marketing for the firm, states that 350 people following them on Facebook are from the local area.

4521 ■ "Use Ink Presets to Minimize Makeready" in American Printer (Vol. 128, July 1, 2011, No. 7)
Pub: Penton Media Inc.
Description: Automatic registration systems enable most printers to be in register very quickly after press startup. If the paper, ink and press time wasted during makeready can be reduced, these savings will flow directly to the bottom line. Ink presetting as an economical solution to set color quickly is a trend that continues to gain momentum.

4522 ■ "UV Suppliers Form Strategic Alliance" in American Printer (Vol. 128, June 1, 2011, No. 6)
Pub: Penton Media Inc.
Description: British ultra-violent curing systems developer Integration Technology Ltd. formed a strategic alliance with UV technology provider IST Metz GmbH of Germany in order to offer a complete line of UV solutions for the printing industry.

4523 ■ "A Vegas Sensation Inaugural Artexpo Las Vegas" in Art Business News (Vol. 34, November 2007, No. 11, pp. 1)
Pub: Pfingsten Publishing, LLC
Ed: Jennifer Dulin. **Description:** Overview of the first Artexpo Las Vegas which featured exhibitors, artists and buyers and was a wonderful place for networking.

4524 ■ "Web to Print" in American Printer (Vol. 128, August 1, 2011, No. 8)
Pub: Penton Media Inc.
Description: Jerry Kennelly, CEO and founder of Tweak.com believes that Web-to-Design is middleware with no content. His firm offers an easy to use interface that flows right into the printer's workflow with no additional costs.

STATISTICAL SOURCES

4525 ■ RMA Annual Statement Studies
Pub: Risk Management Association
Contact: Kevin M. Blakey, President
Released: Annual. **Price:** $175.00 2006-07 edition, $105.00. **Description:** Contains composite balance sheets and income statements for more than 360

industries, including the accounting, auditing, and bookkeeping industries. Also contains five years of comparative historical data for discerning trends. Includes 16 commonly used ratios, computed for most of the size groupings for nearly every industry.

TRADE PERIODICALS

4526 ■ Applied Arts Magazine
Pub: Applied Arts Inc.
URL(s): www.appliedartsmag.com/about_us.php. **Ed:** Peter Giffen. **Released:** 6/yr. **Price:** C$60, Individuals; C$100, Two years; $75, U.S. and other countries; $150, Two years U.S. & other countries.

4527 ■ Before & After: How to Design Cool Stuff
Pub: JMS Publishing L.L.C.
URL(s): www.bamagazine.com. **Released:** Bimonthly **Price:** $48, Individuals.

4528 ■ Country Home
Pub: Meredith Corp.
URL(s): www.countryhome.com. **Released:** Monthly; 10/yr. **Price:** $4.95, Individuals newstand; $21.97, Two years.

4529 ■ Economic Edge
Pub: National Association for Printing Leadership
Released: Quarterly. **Price:** Included in membership. **Description:** Provides current economic data for the printing industry. Also covers sales growth projections, capital spending, and employment.

4530 ■ Gain: AIGA Journal of Business and Design
Pub: American Institute of Graphic Arts
Contact: Katie Baker, Director
E-mail: katie_baker@aiga.org
URL(s): www.aiga.org/content.cfm/gain. **Released:** Semiannual

4531 ■ Graphic Communicator
Pub: Graphic Communication Conference of the International Brotherhood of Teamsters
Contact: Robert Lacey, Secretary
E-mail: rlacey@gciu.org
URL(s): www.gciu.org/. **Released:** 5/yr. **Price:** $12, U.S. and Canada; $15, Other countries.

4532 ■ The Graphic Monthly
Pub: North Island Publishing
URL(s): www.graphicmonthly.ca. **Ed:** Filomena Tamburri. **Released:** Bimonthly

VIDEOCASSETTES/ AUDIOCASSETTES

4533 ■ The Application of Good Design
Instructional Video
2219 C St.
Lincoln, NE 68502
Ph: (402)475-6570
Free: 800-228-0164
Fax: (402)475-6500
Co. E-mail: feedback@insvideo.com
URL: http://www.insvideo.com
Released: 19??. **Price:** $39.95. **Description:** Outlines techniques in creating graphic designs that sell. Provides demonstrations by professional designers working on rough layouts, comprehensives, and dummies. Also discusses computer aids. **Availability:** VHS.

4534 ■ Lithography: How to Paint and Sell Lithographs
Instructional Video
2219 C St.
Lincoln, NE 68502
Ph: (402)475-6570
Free: 800-228-0164

Fax: (402)475-6500
Co. E-mail: feedback@insvideo.com
URL: http://www.insvideo.com
Released: 19??. **Price:** $19.95. **Description:** Provides information on how professional print makers plan and print original lithographs to sell. Also contains demonstrations of tools, techniques, materials, and marketing. **Availability:** VHS.

TRADE SHOWS AND CONVENTIONS

4535 ■ Graph Expo and Converting Expo
Graphic Arts Show Co. (GASC)
1899 Preston White Dr.
Reston, VA 20191-5468
Ph: (703)264-7200
Fax: (703)620-9187
Co. E-mail: info@gasc.org
URL: http://www.gasc.org
Contact: Ralph Nappi, President
URL(s): www.gasc.org. **Frequency:** Annual. **Audience:** Commercial printers, designers, publishers, typographers, converters. **Principal Exhibits:** Graphic art equipment, supplies, and services. Printing, publishing, and converting equipment.

4536 ■ Graphics of the Americas
Printing Association of Florida, Inc.
6275 Hazeltine National Dr.
Orlando, FL 32822
Ph: (407)240-8009
Free: 800-749-4855
Fax: (407)240-8333
Co. E-mail: agaither@pafgraf.org
URL: http://www.pafgraf.org
URL(s): www.graphicsoftheamericas.com. **Frequency:** Annual. **Audience:** Graphics arts trade. **Principal Exhibits:** Graphic arts and specialty printing equipment, supplies, and services. **Dates and Locations:** , Convention Center. **Telecommunication Services:** spatt@pafgraf.org.

4537 ■ Graphics Canada
dmg world media inc.
180 Duncan Mill Rd., Ste. 400
Toronto, ON, Canada M3B 1Z6
Ph: (416)385-1880
Free: 888-823-7469
Fax: (416)385-1855
Co. E-mail: corpinfo@ca.dmgworldmedia.com
URL: http://www.dmgworldmedia.com
URL(s): www.graphicscanada.com. **Price:** $15, Pre-registered for industry personnel; $25, Onsite. **Frequency:** Annual. **Audience:** People who are interested in the graphic arts and printing industry. **Principal Exhibits:** Printing and graphic art industries equipment, supplies, and services, including computer graphics, desktop publishing, and art supplies. **Telecommunication Services:** danmustata@graphicscanada.com.

CONSULTANTS

4538 ■ AT Associates (ATA)
63 Old Rutherford Ave.
Charlestown, MA 02129-3750
Ph: (617)242-6004
Co. E-mail: annette@atadesign.net
URL: http://atadesign.net
Contact: Dan Kovacevic, Designer
E-mail: dan@atadesign.net
Scope: Provider of consulting services in industrial design, model making and graphic design. **Founded:** 1976.

4539 ■ Jack J. Bulloff Consulting and Expert Witness Services
8140 Township Line Rd., Ste. 5220
Indianapolis, IN 46260-5866
Ph: (317)824-0014
Fax: (317)824-0589
Contact: Dr. Jack J. Bulloff, Owner
Scope: Chemical and environmental consultant and expert witness specializing in the following areas: occupational and environmental safety and health, hazardous chemicals and waste management/

disposal, research and development and innovation information development, environmental impact/ technology assessment, technological forecasting and planning. **Founded:** 1968.

4540 ■ CATTAN Services Group Inc.
1006 Haywood Dr.
College Station, TX 77845
Ph: (979)260-7200
Fax: (979)260-7100
Co. E-mail: cattan@cattan.com
URL: http://www.cattan.com
Contact: Thomas L. Tanel, President
E-mail: tanel@cattan.com
Scope: Consultants offering supply chain and logistics advisory; counseling and training services. Specialists in purchasing and procurement; distribution and warehousing; inventory control; traffic management and supply chain strategy. Works with client organizations to assist in personnel; organizational; procedural; policy or strategic issues. Conducts functional operational audits; interfunctional problem-solving; productivity improvement programs; facility layouts; coaching; seminars and strategic planning. Industries served: business services, distribution, oil and gas, processors and manufacturing; financial services; building owners; local; state and federal government; nonprofit organizations and utilities. **Founded:** 1987. **Seminars:** Advanced Cargo Traffic Management; Bar Coding, RFID and Automatic Identification; Effective Purchasing Negotiations; Improving Supplier Performance; Strategic Planning from a Purchasing and Supply Management Perspective; Advanced Purchasing & Supply Management Techniques; Fundamentals of International Purchasing; Fundamentals of Traffic; Improving Supplier Performance; Legal Aspects of Purchasing; Maximizing Purchasing Power; Outsourcing to Success; Warehouse Operations & Inventory Management; Strategic Sourcing; Strategic Planning from a Purchasing & Supply Management Perspective; Purchasing Techniques for Effective Buying; Logistics & Supply Chain Management; Purchasing Negotiation Process & Communication Skills.

4541 ■ Concord Associates Co.
16 Chambers Cir.
West Lebanon, NH 03784
Ph: (603)643-6768
Fax: (603)643-6768
Contact: Elliott D. Novak, President
Scope: Offers business counsel and market and marketing consulting assistance in key areas of both the consumer and professional digital imaging fields. Primary emphasis is in digital cameras; ink jet and dye sublimation printers; digital mini labs; and related or ancillary products such as flash memory cards for digital cameras. **Founded:** 1982.

4542 ■ Davis Consultants Library—W. F. Davis Consultants
179 Voelbel Rd.
Hightstown, NJ 08520-2807
Ph: (609)448-0161
Contact: William F. Davis, Owner
Scope: Offers counsel to corporations on planning, manufacturing, product development, product conception, special purpose machinery development, production methodology, profit enhancement, and manufacturing systems. Specializes in printing and bindery equipment. Clients include paper, printing, publication, graphic arts machinery, disposable products, textile, consumer products, machine tool and instrumentation industries. **Founded:** 1953.

4543 ■ Gate Group USA Inc.—Graphic Arts Technology Corp.
137 Varick St., Ste. 400
New York, NY 10013-1105
Ph: (212)989-9797
Free: 800-966-9889
Fax: (212)989-9363
Co. E-mail: gategroupusa@graphicartstech.com
URL: http://www.graphicartstech.com
Contact: Isaac M. Savitt, President
Scope: Provider of foreign trade and international marketing consulting services. S specializes in the graphic arts and printing-related industries. **Founded:** 1983. **Telecommunication Services:** info@graphicartstech.com.

4544 ■ KiBiz Inc.
432 Knollwood Dr.
Newbury Park, CA 91320-4840
Ph: (805)499-4912
Free: 800-946-2854
Fax: (805)499-8048
Co. E-mail: ki@kibizsystems.com
URL: http://www.kibizsystems.com
Contact: Allen Imbarrato, President
Scope: Training company specializing in learning technologies. Develops customized program to develop a high performance organization. Do extensive needs analysis on current level of organizational functioning. Assesses leadership skills, and develops individualized leadership development programs to improve leadership skills. Facilitates a VISIONING process to develop clear corporate mission, goals, and strategy. Does personal computer consulting to achieve optimum use of computers and network. Industries served: retail, video production, real estate development, graphic arts, advertising, telephone, communications, computer, aerospace, defense, government agencies, and health. **Founded:** 1985. **Seminars:** Winning at Work and at Life; Developing a High Performance Organization; Maximizing Productivity with Fundamental Macintosh Tools; Creating Presentations with a Computer; Break through Technology. **Special Services:** KiBizSystem 4.5; KiShop; KiPoint; KiBizSystem 5.0.; KiBiz Accounting; KiBiz Production Management; Ki Sales Automation via EDI or XML.

4545 ■ LandaJob Advertising Staffing Specialists
222 W Gregory Blvd., Ste. 304
Kansas City, MO 64114
Ph: (816)523-1881
Free: 800-931-8806
Fax: (816)523-1876
Co. E-mail: adstaff@landajobnow.com
URL: http://www.landajobnow.com
Contact: Ken Southwick, Manager
Scope: Personnel consultants and recruiters for advertising, marketing, and communications positions. Industries served: advertising, communications, marketing, graphic arts, printing and publishing. **Founded:** 1985.

4546 ■ Landor Associates—Landor Assoc
1001 Front St.
San Francisco, CA 94111-1424
Ph: (415)365-1700
Free: 888-252-6367
Fax: (415)365-3190
Co. E-mail: more_info@landor.com
URL: http://www.landor.com
Contact: Charlie Wrench, Chief Executive Officer
Scope: A global brand consulting and strategic design firm. **Founded:** 1941. **Publications:** "Brand simple" Palgrave Macmillan, 2006.

4547 ■ Sales Directors Inc.
1034 Lake St.
Oak Park, IL 60301
Ph: (708)383-4038
Fax: (708)383-4081
Co. E-mail: info@salesdirectors.com
URL: http://www.salesdirectors.com
Contact: Douglas Wyman, President
E-mail: doug@salesdirectors.com
Scope: Sales and marketing consultants for the printing and graphic arts industries. Specializes in sales training for personnel of graphic arts firms, and search/placement of sales people. **Founded:** 1979. **Publications:** "Bull's Eye Selling. A Guide to Target Account Sales"; "Twelve Steps to Success in Selling"; "Sales basics for newer sales people"; "Selling Graphic Arts in the Electronic Age"; "How To Manage a Sales Force That Sells". **Seminars:** How to Manage a Sales Force That Sells; Great Training Great Price, Personal Support Real Development.

4548 ■ Smith, Bridges & Associates
555 S Old Woodward Ave., Ste. 603
Birmingham, MI 48009-6658
Ph: (248)540-2448
Free: 800-728-0168

Fax: (248)540-2801
Contact: Peter M. Bridges, Managing Partner
E-mail: pete@smithbridges.com
Scope: Offers contingency executive search for national and regional companies and nonprofit organizations. Recruiting activity includes sourcing candidates for executive level positions with a minimum of five years industry experience and income in the 80, 000 to 160, 000 dollar range. **Founded:** 1987.

4549 ■ Miles F. Southworth, Consultant to the Graphic Arts
3100 Bronson Hill Rd.
Livonia, NY 14487-9716
Ph: (716)346-2776
Fax: (716)346-2276
Co. E-mail: mfsouth@aol.com
Contact: Miles F. Southworth, Chairman
Scope: Graphic arts consultant active in the areas of color reproduction, quality control, and total quality management, productivity audit and training. **Founded:** 1966. **Publications:** "Quality and Productivity in the Graphic Arts and How to Implement Total Quality Management," Southworth and Southworth; "Pocket Guide to Color Reproduction," 1995; "Color Separation on the Desktop," 1994. **Seminars:** As need relating to topics listed under consulting activities; 10 Steps to good color reproduction; GRACOL. Productivity and Color Quality Improvement Newspaper.

4550 ■ Strack Vaughan L.L.C.
4833 Rugby Ave., Ste. 201
Bethesda, MD 20814-3035
Ph: (301)654-7778
Fax: (301)951-0063
Contact: Steven G. Strack, Principal
Scope: Business and financial planning consultants providing services in mergers and acquisitions, strategic planning, and tax planning. Serves insurance agencies and the graphic arts industry. **Founded:** 1950.

4551 ■ Teague
2727 Western Ave., Ste. 200
Seattle, WA 98121
Ph: (206)838-4200
Fax: (206)838-4299
Co. E-mail: newbiz@teague.com
URL: http://www.teague.com
Contact: Robert Blaich, Director
Scope: Offers counsel in industrial design, graphics design, environmental and interior design, packaging design, transportation design, quality assurance and reliability and maintainability engineering. **Founded:** 1926. **Telecommunication Services:** info@teague.com; smathery@teague.com.

4552 ■ VMS Inc.
805 Airway Dr.
Allegan, MI 49010-8516
Free: 800-343-6430
URL: http://www.vms-online.com
Contact: Michael S. Walsh, President
E-mail: mike@vms-online.com

Description: Description: Wholesaler. Specializes in textbooks, videos, and computer software for vocational education. Reaches market through direct mail, telephone sales, and trade shows. Stock 3,000 text titles, publish 60. **Scope:** Provider of marketing services to clients producing training materials for vocational schools, colleges, and industry. Assists in identifying and preparing training materials, training staff to prepare training materials, packaging, and developing marketing plans. Works with traditional publishers and clients wishing to convert internal training materials for external sale. Industries served: Automotive, building and machine trades, software, graphic arts and government in the U.S. and Canada. **Founded:** 1986. **Seminars:** Product Marketing; Direct Mail; Trade Show Boothmanship; Product Evaluation. **Special Services:** Corel WordPerfect X4: Academic Version; WordPerfect Office X3 Essential Training; CorelDRAW Graphics Suite X4: Academic Version; AutoCAD LT 2010 for Windows; AutoCAD LT 2010 Student Version: 61 month License; TurboCAD Pro 16 Platinum Ed: Academic; TurboCAD PRO 16 Architectural: Academic; TurboCAD Mac PRO: Academic; TurboCAD Mac Deluxe 2D/3D: Academic; TurboFLOORPLAN 3D Home and Landscape PRO.

FRANCHISES AND BUSINESS OPPORTUNITIES

4553 ■ Greenbaum Marketing Communications
12 Sunset Way, Ste. A-104
Henderson, NV 89014
Ph: (702)898-8818
Fax: (702)898-8870
Description: Marketing/graphic design firm. **Founded:** 2004..

4554 ■ Kwik Kopy Business Centers
Kwik Kopy Business Centers, Inc. Kwik Kopy Business Centers
12715 Telge Rd.
Cypress, TX 77429
Free: 888-638-8722
Fax: (281)256-4178
Co. E-mail: franchisedevelopment@iced.net
URL: http://www.iced.net
Description: Offers business advertisement aids and printing and copying services. **No. of Franchise Units:** 16. **No. of Company-Owned Units:** 1. **Founded:** 2001.. **Franchised:** 2001. **Equity Capital Needed:** $65,000 liquid capital; $250,000 net worth. **Franchise Fee:** $35,000. **Financial Assistance:** Yes. **Training:** Owners attend classroom and field training, as well as ongoing training through workshops and conferences.

4555 ■ Sign Biz, Inc.
24681 La Plaza, Ste. 270
Dana Point, CA 92629
Ph: (949)234-0408
Free: 800-633-5580
Fax: (949)234-0426
URL: http://www.signbiz.com
Description: Visual communication stores developing digital sign making. **No. of Franchise Units:** 185. **Founded:** 1989.. **Franchised:** 1990. **Equity Capital Needed:** $45,000-$50,000 liquid. **Franchise Fee:** None. **Training:** 2 weeks initial training at corporate office and 1-2 week home study program.

COMPUTERIZED DATABASES

4556 ■ *Art Index™*
10 Estes St.
Ipswich, MA 01938-2106
Ph: (978)356-6500
Free: 800-653-2726
Fax: (978)356-6565
Co. E-mail: information@ebscohost.com
URL: http://www.ebscohost.com
Contact: Tim Collins, President
E-mail: tcollins@ebscohost.com
Availability: Online: EBSCO Publishing. **Type:** Bibliographic.

4557 ■ *Art on Screen Database™*
200 Willoughby Ave.
Brooklyn, NY 11205-3817
Ph: (718)399-4506
Fax: (718)399-4507
Co. E-mail: info@artfilm.org
URL: http://www.artfilm.org
Availability: Online: Program for Art on Film Inc. **Type:** Directory.

4558 ■ *Graphic Arts Blue Book*
Quadrant House
The Quadrant
Surrey
Sutton SM2 5AS, United Kingdom
Ph: 20 8652 3500
Fax: 20 8652 8932
Co. E-mail: rbi.subscriptions@qss-uk.com
URL: http://www.rbi.co.uk
Availability: Online: Reed Business Information Ltd. **Type:** Full-text; Directory.

4559 ■ *Impressionism and Its Sources*
1601 N Sepulveda Blvd., Ste. 374
Manhattan Beach, CA 90267
Ph: (310)406-1803
Fax: (310)406-0833
Co. E-mail: contact@tdcinteractive.com
URL: http://www.tdcinteractive.net
Availability: CD-ROM: Technology Dynamics Corp. - TDC Interactive. **Type:** Full-text.

LIBRARIES

4560 ■ Art Center College of Design - James Lemont Fogg Memorial Library
1700 Lida St.
Pasadena, CA 91103
Ph: (626)396-2233
Co. E-mail: betsy.galloway@artcenter.edu
URL: http://www.artcenter.edu
Contact: Betsy Galloway, Director, Library Services
URL(s): library.artcenter.edu. **Scope:** Fine arts, communications design, graphics/packaging, advertising design, industrial design, illustration, photography and film. **Services:** Copying; Library open to the public by appointment. **Founded:** 1930. **Holdings:** 86,000 volumes of books and periodicals; 4200 bound periodical volumes; 2086 exhibition catalogs; 32 VF drawers; 1900 Annual reports; 110,000 slides; 133 films; 10,000 videotapes and DVDs; 90,000 photographs. **Subscriptions:** 400 journals and other serials; 10 newspapers. **Telecommunication Services:** library@artcenter.edu.

4561 ■ Art Institute of Boston at Lesley University Library—AIB Library.
700 Beacon St.
Boston, MA 02215
Ph: (617)585-6670
Co. E-mail: library@lesley.edu
URL: http://www.lesley.edu/aib/studentlife/services.html
Contact: Deb Verhoff, Librarian
Scope: Art history, photography, graphics, design, humanities, graphic design, illustration, animation, humanities. **Services:** Copying; scanning; Library open to the public for reference use only. **Founded:** 1969. **Holdings:** 11,000 books; 45,000 slides; 7 VF drawers of picture reference files; 4 VF drawers of exhibition catalogs; 6 VF drawer of pamphlets; 450 videos; 10,000 photographs. **Subscriptions:** 95 journals and other serials.

4562 ■ Art Institute of Philadelphia Library
1610 Chestnut St.
Philadelphia, PA 19103
Ph: (215)405-6402
Co. E-mail: rschachter@aii.edu
URL: http://www.artinstitutes.edu/philadelphia
Contact: Ruth Schachter, Director
URL(s): www.artinstitutes.edu/philadelphia/studentlife/library.aspx. **Scope:** Visual communications, interior design, industrial design, animation, fashion marketing, fashion design, visual merchandising, photography, website design, multimedia. **Services:** Interlibrary loan; copying; library not open to the public (circulation services provided for students and faculty). **Founded:** 1974. **Holdings:** 31,000 volumes; 2000 videocassettes; audiocassettes. **Subscriptions:** 180 print subscriptions and other serials.

4563 ■ The Baltimore Museum of Art - E. Kirkbride Miller Art Research Library
10 Art Museum Dr.
Baltimore, MD 21218-3898
Ph: (443)573-1778
Fax: (443)573-1582
Co. E-mail: bmalibrary@artbma.org
URL: http://www.artbma.org/about/library.html
Contact: Doreen Bolger, Director
Scope: History of art with special strengths in: modern and contemporary art; 19th-century French art; American and British decorative arts; prints, drawings, and photography; arts of Africa, Asia, Oceania, and the Americas. **Services:** Library open to the public. **Founded:** 1930. **Holdings:** 47,530 books; 3056 bound periodical volumes; 14,600 auction catalogs; 168 drawers of vertical files (artists, museums, and dealers); manuscripts; archives; microfilm. **Subscriptions:** 100 journals and other serials; 1 newspaper.

4564 ■ California College of the Arts Libraries - Meyer Library
5212 Broadway
Oakland, CA 94618
Ph: (510)594-3658
Co. E-mail: meyerlib@cca.edu
URL: http://library.cca.edu
Contact: Donald Smith, Manager
Scope: Art, architecture, design, humanities. **Services:** Library limited to the CCA community (specialized research by appointment). **Founded:** 1907. **Holdings:** 62,000 volumes; 150,000 slides and pictures; 100 lin.ft. of archival material. **Subscriptions:** 275 journals and other serials. **Telecommunication Services:** jwoo@cca.edu.

4565 ■ Cleveland Institute of Art - Jessica R. Gund Memorial Library
11141 East Blvd., 3rd Fl.
Cleveland, OH 44106
Ph: (216)421-7440
Fax: (216)421-7439
Co. E-mail: referencehelp@cia.edu
URL: http://www.cia.edu/library/
Contact: Cristine C. Rom, Director, Library Services
Scope: Fine arts, crafts, industrial design, general design, graphic arts, new media, glass, ceramics, medical illustration, textiles, metals. **Services:** Internet access; Interlibrary loan; copying; Library open to the public. **Founded:** 1882. **Holdings:** 47,000 books; 10,000 bound periodical volumes; 125,000 slides; 9000 pictures; 37 volumes and boxes of archival materials; 4000 reels of microfilm; 15,000 microfiche; 600 videotapes, DVDs and films; 1600 sound recordings. **Subscriptions:** 145 journals and other serials; 2 newspapers. **Telecommunication Services:** crom@cia.edu; dbjorklund@cia.edu.

4566 ■ Des Moines Art Center Library
4700 Grand Ave.
Des Moines, IA 50312-2099
Ph: (515)277-4405
URL: http://www.desmoinesartcenter.org
Scope: 19th- and 20th-century painting, graphics, sculpture, architecture, drawing, photography. **Services:** Library open to the public by appointment for reference use only. **Founded:** 1948. **Holdings:** 16,750 books; 850 bound periodical volumes; 36 VF drawers of publications on individual artists; 36 VF drawers of museum catalogs, art collection catalogs, and allied materials; archives; slides. **Subscriptions:** 70 journals and other serials.

4567 ■ Free Library of Philadelphia - Art Department
1901 Vine St.
Philadelphia, PA 19103-1189
Ph: (215)686-5403
Fax: (215)563-3628
URL: http://www.freelibrary.org
Contact: Deborah Litwack, Director
Scope: Art history, African and African-American art, architecture, painting, sculpture, costume history, drawing, decorative arts, ceramics, cartoons, crafts, design, commercial art, photography, graphic arts, numismatics. **Services:** Interlibrary loan; copying. **Founded:** 1891. **Holdings:** 60,000 volumes; 35,000 pamphlets and clippings; 735 periodical titles; card index of 15,700 artists; 1500 original graphics (1491 to present); 800,000 photographs and art reproductions in loan collection; postcards; greeting cards; posters. **Subscriptions:** 220 journals and other serials.

4568 ■ Graphic Communications World Library
PO Box 1126
Port Orchard, WA 98366
Ph: (360)769-5417
Fax: (360)769-5622
URL: http://www.quoinpublishing.com
Contact: William Esler, President
Scope: Printing and graphic communications technology. **Services:** Library open to subscribers. **Founded:** 1968. **Holdings:** Figures not available. **Subscriptions:** 150 journals and other serials.

4569 ■ Hallmark Cards, Inc. - Creative Research Library
2501 McGee, No. 146
Kansas City, MO 64108
Ph: (816)274-5525
Free: 800-425-5627
Fax: (816)274-7245
Co. E-mail: hallmarkplus@hallmark.com
URL: http://www.hallmark.com
Contact: Mark Spencer, Manager
Scope: Fine art, lettering, advertising, graphic art, design, illustration, photography. **Services:** Library open to Hallmark employees only. **Founded:** 1930. **Holdings:** 18,000 books; 60 bound periodical volumes. **Subscriptions:** 150 journals and other serials; 3 newspapers.

4570 ■ Library of Congress - Prints & Photographs Division
101 Independence Ave., SE
James Madison Bldg., Rm. LM 337
Washington, DC 20540-4730
Ph: (202)707-6394
Fax: (202)707-6647
URL: http://www.loc.gov/rr/print/
Contact: Harry Katz, Director
Scope: Architecture, design, engineering, popular and applied graphic art, documentary photographs, fine prints, master photographs, posters. **Services:** Photoduplication service. **Founded:** 1897. **Holdings:** 190,000 prints and drawings; 80,000 posters; 14 million photographic prints and negatives, daguerreotypes, slides; 1.8 million prints, posters, architectural drawings, and related materials; 200,000 images (electronic).

4571 ■ Milwaukee Area Technical College - Rasche Memorial Library
Downtown Milwaukee Campus
700 W. State St.
Milwaukee, WI 53233-1443
Ph: (414)297-7030
Fax: (414)297-6798
Co. E-mail: jackson@qwise1.matc.edu
URL: http://www.matc.edu/library/matclibrary.html
Contact: Jeff Jackson, Director
Scope: Applied science and technology, graphic arts, liberal arts, health sciences. **Services:** Interlibrary loan; copying; Library open to the public. **Founded:** 1937. **Holdings:** 70,000 volumes. **Subscriptions:** 856 journals and other serials; 15 newspapers.

4572 ■ Milwaukee Art Museum - George Peckham Miller Art Research Library
700 N. Art Museum Dr.
Milwaukee, WI 53202
Ph: (414)224-3270
Co. E-mail: library@mam.org
URL: http://www.mam.org/collection/library.php
Contact: Heather Winter, Archivist Librarian
Scope: Visual arts in all forms, including painting, graphic arts, sculpture, drawing, design, and photography. **Services:** Library open to Art Museum patrons. **Founded:** 1916. **Subscriptions:** 124 journals and other serials.

4573 ■ Milwaukee Institute of Art & Design Library
273 E. Erie St.
Milwaukee, WI 53202
Ph: (414)847-3342
Fax: (414)291-8077
Co. E-mail: cynthialynch@miad.edu
URL: http://www.miad.edu
Contact: Cynthia Lynch, Director, Library Services
Scope: Artists, graphic design, art history, aesthetics, industrial design, decorative arts, photography, sculpture, painting, illustration, interior design, history, social sciences, literature, natural sciences. **Services:** Copying; Library open to the public with restrictions. **Founded:** 1977. **Holdings:** 22,920 books; 47,500 slides. **Subscriptions:** 125 journals and other serials. **Telecommunication Services:** nancysiker@miad.edu.

4574 ■ Minneapolis College of Art and Design Library
2501 Stevens Ave., S.
Minneapolis, MN 55404
Ph: (612)874-3791
Fax: (612)874-3795
Co. E-mail: library@mcad.edu
URL: http://intranet.mcad.edu/modules/library
Contact: Amy Naughton, Director, Library Services
Scope: Painting, sculpture, graphic arts, design, films and film making, photography, video, performance art. **Services:** Interlibrary loan (limited); copying; library open to the public for reference use only. **Founded:** 1916. **Holdings:** 60,000 volumes; 350 artists' books; 140,000 slides; college archives; compact discs; video cassettes, CD-ROMs. **Subscriptions:** 200 journals and other serials. **Telecommunication Services:** suzanne_degler@mcad.edu.

4575 ■ Modern Art Museum of Fort Worth Library
3200 Darnell St.
Fort Worth, TX 76107-2872
Ph: (817)738-9215
Free: 866-824-5566
Co. E-mail: info@themodern.org
URL: http://www.themodern.org
Contact: Kate Alleman, Library Assistant
Scope: 20th-century art in all countries, focusing on media consisting of painting, sculpture, and graphics. **Services:** Library not open to the public. **Founded:** 1892. **Holdings:** 10,000 books.

4576 ■ Paier College of Art, Inc. Library
20 Gorham Ave.
Hamden, CT 06514-3902
Ph: (203)287-3023
Fax: (203)287-3021
URL: http://www.paiercollegeofart.edu
Contact: Beth R. Harris, Librarian
Scope: Fine arts, graphic design, interior design, photography, illustration, general academics. **Services:** Library open to the public for research only. **Founded:** 1985. **Holdings:** 13,000 books; 71 periodical titles; 30,000 pictures; 16,000 slides. **Subscriptions:** 71 journals and other serials.

4577 ■ Parsons School of Design - Adam & Sophie Gimbel Design Library
2 W. 13th St.
New York, NY 10011
Ph: (212)229-8914
Fax: (212)229-2806
Co. E-mail: cassimar@newschool.edul
URL: http://library.newschool.edu/gimbel
Contact: Kira Appel, Director
Scope: Fine arts, architecture, costume, crafts, design, environmental design, fashion, graphic arts, photography, typography. **Services:** Interlibrary loan. **Founded:** 1896. **Holdings:** 61,000 books; 55,000 mounted picture plates; 85,000 slides; archives. **Subscriptions:** 200 journals and other serials.

4578 ■ Printing Brokerage/Buyers Association Library—PBBA Library.
PO Box 744
Palm Beach, FL 33480
Ph: (877)585-7141
Fax: (561)845-7130
Co. E-mail: info@pbbai.net
URL: http://www.pbba.org/
Contact: Merry Francen, President
Scope: Management techniques in the graphic arts industries. **Services:** Library open to the public for reference use only. **Founded:** 1984. **Holdings:** 500 books. **Subscriptions:** 25 journals and other serials. **Telecommunication Services:** merry@pbbai.net.

4579 ■ Printing Industries of America/Graphic Arts Technical Foundation - Edward H. Wadewitz Memorial Library
200 Deer Run Rd.
Sewickley, PA 15143-2324
Ph: (412)741-6860
Free: 800-910-4283
Fax: (412)741-2311
Co. E-mail: dgentile@printing.org
URL: http://www.printing.org/page/4506
Contact: Hallie Barcalow, Administrator
Scope: Printing processes, lithography, paper, ink, graphic design, desktop publishing, packaging, chemistry, physics, environmental control, safety and health, photography. **Services:** Document delivery; library open to the public by appointment. **Founded:** 1924. **Holdings:** 15,000 volumes. **Subscriptions:** 180 journals and other serials.

4580 ■ Ringling College of Art and Design - Verman Kimbrough Memorial Library
2700 N. Tamiami Trail
Sarasota, FL 34234
Ph: (941)359-7587
Free: 800-255-7695
Fax: (941)359-7632
Co. E-mail: library@ringling.edu
URL: http://www.ringling.edu
Contact: Kathleen List, Director, Library Services
Scope: Art history, interior design, graphic design, computer animation, photography, architecture, fine arts, decorative arts, illustration. **Services:** Interlibrary loan; copying; library open to artists and researchers. **Founded:** 1932. **Holdings:** 49,000 books; 110,000 art slides; 34 16mm films; 3000 videocassettes and DVDs. **Subscriptions:** 320 journals and other serials. **Telecommunication Services:** klist@ringling. edu.

4581 ■ Rochester Institute of Technology - Melbert B. Cary, Jr. Graphic Arts Collection
Wallace Memorial Library
90 Lomb Memorial Dr.
Rochester, NY 14623-5604
Ph: (585)475-2408
Fax: (585)475-6900
Co. E-mail: ahfwml@rit.edu
URL: http://library.rit.edu/cary
Contact: Steven K. Galbraith, Curator
Scope: Printing history, type specimens, typography, book arts, press books, calligraphy, papermaking, graphic arts, bookbinding. **Services:** Copying (limited); collection open to the public. **Founded:** 1969. **Holdings:** 50,000 books; 20 VF drawers of clippings; ephemera; pamphlets; 50 boxes of posters, broadsides, drawings; 400 boxes of correspondence and manuscript material. **Subscriptions:** 20 journals and other serials. **Telecommunication Services:** skgtwc@rit.edu; circwml@rit.edu.

4582 ■ School of Visual Arts - Visual Arts Library
380 2nd Ave., 22nd St., 2nd Fl.
New York, NY 10010-3994
Ph: (212)592-2660
Fax: (212)592-2655
Co. E-mail: rlobe@sva.edu
URL: http://www.schoolofvisualarts.edu/sr/index. jsp?sid0=258&sid1=290
Contact: Robert Lobe, Director, Library Services
Scope: Fine arts, graphic design, advertising, photography, film, computer graphics, humanities. **Services:** Copying; Library open to students, faculty, staff, and alumni (METRO passes honored). **Founded:** 1961. **Holdings:** 70,000 books and bound periodical volumes; 2000 pamphlets; 270,000 pictures; 152,000 slides. **Subscriptions:** 300 journals and other serials.

4583 ■ Smithsonian Institution - Smithsonian American Art Museum - National Portrait Gallery Library
750 9th St. NW, Ste. 2100
Washington, DC 20013-7012
Ph: (202)633-8230
Co. E-mail: littsd@si.edu
URL: http://www.sil.si.edu/libraries/aapg
Contact: Douglas Litts, Director
Scope: American painting, sculpture, graphic arts, biography, history, photography, portraiture; contemporary art. **Services:** Interlibrary loan; copying; Library open to the public for reference use only. **Founded:** 1937. **Holdings:** 180,000 books; exhibi-

tions catalogs; catalogues raisonnes; serials; dissertations; artists' books; ephemeral materials; auction catalogs; scrapbooks; microforms; CD-ROMs.

4584 ■ Smithsonian Institution - Smithsonian American Art Museum - Photograph Archives
MRC 970
Washington, DC 20013-7012
Ph: (202)633-8390
Fax: (202)633-8373
Co. E-mail: sapa@si.edu
URL: http://sirismm.si.edu/siris/saam.htm
Contact: Christine Hennessey
URL(s): americanart.si.edu/research/programs/archive. **Scope:** American art, painting, sculpture, graphics. **Services:** Copying; archives open to researchers by appointment. **Founded:** 1973.

4585 ■ Springfield Art Museum - Art Reference Library
1111 E. Brookside Dr.
Springfield, MO 65807
Ph: (417)837-5700
Fax: (417)837-5704
Co. E-mail: artmuseum@springfieldmo.gov
URL: http://www.springfieldmo.gov/art/
Contact: Jerry Berger, Director
Scope: Art history, painting, sculpture, graphics, decorative arts, photography. **Services:** Library open to the public. **Founded:** 1937. **Holdings:** 8000 volumes; periodicals; catalogs; AV materials. **Subscriptions:** 65 journals and other serials.

4586 ■ University of Guam - Robert F. Kennedy Memorial Library - Instructional Media Division
Tan Siu Lin Bldg.
UOG Station
Mangilao, GU 96923
Ph: (671)735-2326
Fax: (671)734-6882
Co. E-mail: millhoff@uog9.uog.edu
URL: http://www.uog.edu
Contact: Brian L. Millhoff, Coordinator, Media Services
Scope: Multimedia; graphics. **Services:** Interlibrary loan. **Holdings:** 2388 videotapes; 110 CD-ROMs; 28 laser discs; 139 audio programs tape/CD; 200 pieces of media equipment. **Telecommunication Services:** angelp@uog9.uog.edu.

4587 ■ University of Minnesota - Eric Sevareid Journalism Library—Digital Information Resource Center.
20 Murphy Hall
206 Church St., SE
Minneapolis, MN 55455
Ph: (612)625-7892
Fax: (612)626-8251
Co. E-mail: j-nybe@umn.edu
URL: http://www.lib.umn.edu/journalism/
Contact: Jan Nyberg
Scope: Mass communications, new media arts studies, newspaper journalism, broadcasting, magazine journalism, graphic arts, advertising, International communication, public relations, behavioral research, media management, visual communication. **Services:** Interlibrary loan; copying; Library open to the public. **Founded:** 1941. **Holdings:** 12,000 books; 2800 bound periodical volumes; 200 theses; 14 DVDs; CD-ROMs; 22 videotapes. **Subscriptions:** 250 journals and other serials; newspapers. **Telecommunication Services:** houls001@umn.edu; sjmclib@umn.edu.

4588 ■ University of Puerto Rico - Library System - Arts Collection
PO Box 23302
San Juan, PR 00931-3302
Ph: (787)764-0000, x3492
Fax: (787)763-5685
Co. E-mail: artes@uprrp.edu
URL: http://biblioteca.uprrp.edu/index.html
Contact: Iris Rodriguez de Parrilla
Scope: Fine arts, dance. **Services:** Copying; Library open to the public with restrictions. **Founded:** 1953. **Holdings:** 27,900 books; 205 slides; manuscripts; photographs; artist books; rare books. **Telecommunication Services:** idrodriguez@uprrp.edu.

4589 ■ Walker Art Center - Staff Reference Library
1750 Hennepin Ave.
Vineland Pl.
Minneapolis, MN 55403
Ph: (612)375-7680
Co. E-mail: rosemary.furtak@walkerart.org
URL: http://www.walkerart.org
Contact: Rosemary Furtak, Librarian
Scope: Contemporary art, art history, architecture, design, film, artists' books, graphics, photography, painting, sculpture. **Services:** Copying; internet searches; reference services; library open to the public by appointment. **Founded:** 1950. **Holdings:** 35,000 books; 550 bound periodical volumes; vertical files. **Subscriptions:** 140 journals. **Telecommunication Services:** info@walkerart.org.

4590 ■ Williams College - Chapin Library
96 School St., Apartment 3
Williamstown, MA 01267
Ph: (413)597-2462
Co. E-mail: chapin.library@williams.edu
URL: http://chapin.williams.edu
Contact: Elaine Yanow, Administrative Assistant
Scope: Education, reference. **Services:** Answers correspondence requests for bibliographical information; library open to the public with restrictions. **Founded:** 1923. **Holdings:** 50,000 volumes; 100,000 manuscripts. **Subscriptions:** 25 journals and other serials. **Telecommunication Services:** Robert.L.Volz@williams.edu; Wayne.G.Hammond@williams.edu.

RESEARCH CENTERS

4591 ■ Graphic Arts Education and Research Foundation (GAERF)
1899 Preston White Dr.
Reston, VA 20191-4367
Ph: (703)264-7200
Free: 866-381-9839
Fax: (703)620-3165
Co. E-mail: gaerf@npes.org
URL: http://www.gaerf.org
Contact: Ralph J. Nappi, President
Services: Career Focus: a graphic communications awareness campaign. **Founded:** 1983. **Publications:** Guidelines Booklet; Resource (Annual); Vanguard Annual Report. **Educational Activities:** GAERF Grants.

4592 ■ University of California, Los Angeles - Grunwald Center for the Graphic Arts
Hammer Museum of Art & Cultural Ctr.
10899 Wilshire Blvd.
Los Angeles, CA 90024
Ph: (310)443-7000
Fax: (310)443-7099
Co. E-mail: cburlingham@hammer.ucla.edu
URL: http://www.hammer.ucla.edu/collections
Contact: Ann Philbin, Director
Services: Friends of the Graphic Arts Support Group. **Founded:** 1956. **Publications:** Exhibition catalogues (Occasionally).

ASSOCIATIONS AND OTHER ORGANIZATIONS

4593 ■ Association of Alternate Postal Systems (AAPS)
1725 Oaks Way
Oklahoma City, OK 73131
Ph: (405)478-0006
Co. E-mail: aaps@cox.net
URL: http://www.aapsinc.org
Contact: Tom Seminack, President
Description: Companies in the business of delivering private postal advertising material to residences. Seeks to improve industry credibility and increase the public's awareness of the private postal industry. **Founded:** 1973. **Publications:** *Association of Alternate Postal Systems--Member Directory* (Annual); *Association of Alternate Postal Systems--Update* (Quarterly). **Educational Activities:** Alternative Delivery Conference (Annual). **Awards:** Award of Excellence (Annual); Lifetime Achievement Award (Annual).

4594 ■ Women in Packaging (WMPKG)
4290 Bells Ferry Rd., Ste. 106-17
Kennesaw, GA 30144-1300
Ph: (678)594-6872
Co. E-mail: joann@womeninpackaging.org
URL: http://womeninpackaging.org
Contact: JoAnn R. Hines, Founder
URL(s): www.womeninpackaging.org/. **Description:** Works to promote and encourage women in the packaging industry. Educates the packaging industry about the contributions of women to the industry; helps to eliminate stereotypes and discrimination in the profession; offers networking opportunities; conducts career enhancement programs; compiles statistics; maintains speakers' bureau. **Founded:** 1993. **Publications:** *Packaging Horizons Online* (Weekly); *Packaging Horizons*.

REFERENCE WORKS

4595 ■ "Contest Produce Ad Designs on a Dime" in San Diego Business Journal (Vol. 31, August 23, 2010, No. 31, pp. 1)
Pub: San Diego Business Journal
Ed: Mike Allen. **Description:** San Diego-based Prova.fm runs design contests for clients such as the U.S. Postal Service. The client then chooses the best entry from the contest. Prova.fm relies on the Internet to deliver a range of possible graphic solutions and allowing the customer to make the right selection for its business through a process called crowdsourcing.

4596 ■ *Directory of Major Mailers*
Pub: North American Publishing Co.
Contact: Ned S. Borowsky, President
URL(s): www.majormailers.com. **Ed:** Cheryl Cagle. **Released:** Annual; latest edition 2012. **Price:** $299, Individuals Print; plus shipping and handling; $599, Individuals online; $799, Individuals print and CD-ROM; plus shipping and handling; $14.95, Individuals

print; $14.95, Individuals CD-ROM. **Covers:** About 7,000 mailers and 19,000 mailing efforts. **Entries include:** Company name, address, phone, fax; names and titles of key personnel, marketing and production, product/service, and mailing campaigns from the previous year. **Arrangement:** Alphabetical. **Indexes:** Geographical, product/service, mailing formats.

4597 ■ "The Question: Who Do You Think Is the Most Genuine?" in Advertising Age (Vol. 79, July 7, 2008, No. 26, pp. 4)
Pub: Crain Communications, Inc.
Ed: Ken Wheaton. **Description:** According to a survey conducted by Harris Interactive Reputation Quotient, Johnson & Johnson was deemed the most genuine brand. Google came in second followed by UPS.

TRADE PERIODICALS

4598 ■ *Fastline--Bluegrass Truck Edition*
Pub: Fastline
URL(s): www.fastline.com/v100/index.aspx. **Released:** 13/yr. **Price:** $20, Individuals; $35, Two years; $45, Canada and Mexico; $95, Other countries.

4599 ■ *Fastline--Florida Truck Edition*
Pub: Fastline
URL(s): www.fastline.com/v100/index.aspx. **Released:** 13/yr. **Price:** $20, Individuals; $35, Two years; $45, Canada and Mexico; $95, Other countries.

4600 ■ *Fastline--Georgia Truck Edition*
Pub: Fastline
URL(s): www.fastline.com/v100/index.aspx. **Released:** 13/yr. **Price:** $20, Individuals; $35, Two years; $45, Canada and Mexico; $95, Other countries.

4601 ■ *Fastline--Tennessee Truck Edition*
Pub: Fastline
URL(s): www.fastline.com/v100/index.aspx. **Released:** Monthly **Price:** $20, Individuals; $35, Two years; $45, Canada and Mexico; $95, Other countries; $40, Individuals 3 years.

4602 ■ *Fastline--Tri-State Truck Edition*
Pub: Fastline
URL(s): www.fastline.com/v100/index.aspx. **Released:** 13/yr. **Price:** $20, Individuals; $35, Two years; $45, Canada and Mexico; $95, Other countries.

4603 ■ *Food & Beverage Packaging: The Information Source for Food and Drug Packagers*
Pub: BNP Media
Contact: Al Reser, President
URL(s): www.foodandbeveragepackaging.com. **Released:** Monthly

4604 ■ *Mailing Systems Technology (MAST)*
Pub: RB Publishing Co.
Contact: Shelby Murphy, Editor
URL(s): mailingsystemstechnology.com/me2/default. asp. **Ed:** Dan O'Rourke.

4605 ■ *Postal Bulletin: The Official Source of Updates to Postal Service Policies and Procedures*
Pub: U.S. Government Printing Office
URL(s): www.usps.com/cpim/ftp/bulletin/pb.htm. **Released:** 26/yr. **Price:** $163, Individuals; $228, Other countries.

TRADE SHOWS AND CONVENTIONS

4606 ■ National Association of Postmasters of the United States Convention
National Association of Postmasters of the United States
8 Herbert St.
Alexandria, VA 22305-2600
Ph: (703)683-9027
Fax: (703)683-6820
Co. E-mail: napusinfo@napus.org
URL: http://www.napus.org
Contact: Bob Rapoza, President
URL(s): www.napus.org. **Price:** $150, Pre-registered and onsite; $75, Pre-registered and onsite children below 17 . **Frequency:** Annual. **Audience:** Postmasters. **Principal Exhibits:** Office supplies and materials for the postal service. **Telecommunication Services:** napusinfo@napus.org.

FRANCHISES AND BUSINESS OPPORTUNITIES

4607 ■ Mail Boxes Etc. - MBEC Communications, Inc.
MBEC Communications, Inc.
1115 North Service Rd. W, Unit 1
Oakville, ON, Canada L6M 2V9
Ph: (905)338-9754
Free: 800-661-6232
Fax: (905)338-7491
Co. E-mail: customerservice@theupsstore.ca
URL: http://www.mbe.ca
Description: With over 4,000 locations worldwide and over 260 centers operating in Canada, MBE is one of the largest and fastest growing business and communications service franchise. Services include expert packing services, shipping, worldwide courier services, black and white and color photocopies, electronic document services, digital color printing, fax sending and receiving, computer rental, word processing, Internet/email access and mail receiving services. **No. of Franchise Units:** 351. **Founded:** 1990.. **Franchised:** 1991. **Equity Capital Needed:** $146,150-$179,550 plus working capital. **Franchise Fee:** $35,900. **Royalty Fee:** 6% of gross. **Training:** Complete pre-opening support provided, including

site selection, lease negotiation, design and construction, training, marketing, as well as ongoing operational and marketing field support.

4608 ■ Navis Pack & Ship Centers

Annex Brands, Inc.
7580 Metropolitan Dr., Ste. 200
San Diego, CA 92108-4417
Ph: (619)563-4800
Free: 800-456-1525
Fax: (619)563-9850
Co. E-mail: ryan@postalannex.com
URL: http://www.postalannex.com

Description: Packaging and shipping industry. **No. of Franchise Units:** 46. **Founded:** 1984.. **Franchised:** 2001. **Equity Capital Needed:** $500,000 liquid capital; $200,000 net worth; actual $96,950-$172,650. **Franchise Fee:** $29,500. **Financial Assistance:** Yes. **Training:** Offers 3 weeks training and certification course.

4609 ■ Navis Pack and Ship Centers

15 Romina Dr.
Concord, ON, Canada L4K 4Z7
Ph: (905)760-0834
Free: 888-996-2847
Fax: (905)660-6224
URL: http://www.goNavis.com

Description: Business-to-business franchises offering custom crating and specialty packaging for high value and fragile goods that need to be shipped safely. We service commercial, retail and consumer customers, and we specialize in protecting and safely shipping artwork, antiques and commercial goods. Navis franchises operate from light industrial warehouse facilities of 2,000 to 3,000 square feet. Listed on Franchise500 as well as Fast55 fastest growing franchises. **No. of Franchise Units:** 5. **Franchised:** 1982. **Equity Capital Needed:** $95,000-$160,000. **Franchise Fee:** $38,500. **Training:** Yes.

4610 ■ Packaging and Shipping Specialists

5211 85th St., Ste. 104
Lubbock, TX 79424
Ph: (806)794-0202
Free: 800-877-8884
Fax: (806)794-9997
Co. E-mail: mike@packship.com
URL: http://www.packship.com

Description: Business center, including copying and shipping services. **No. of Franchise Units:** 904. **No. of Company-Owned Units:** 1. **Founded:** 1981.. **Franchised:** 1987. **Equity Capital Needed:** $50,000. **Franchise Fee:** $28,900. **Training:** In classroom and on-the-job training.

4611 ■ Pak Mail

7173 S Havan St., Ste. 600
Centennial, CO 80112
Ph: (800)833-2821
Fax: (800)336-7363
Co. E-mail: sales@pakmail.org
URL: http://www.pakmail.com

Description: One-stop shop offers the customer a convenient location to send packages, make copies, send or receive a fax or rent a private mailbox. **No. of Franchise Units:** 500. **Founded:** 1983.. **Franchised:** 1984. **Equity Capital Needed:** $130,000-$164,300 total investment. **Franchise Fee:** $29,950. **Financial Assistance:** Yes. **Training:** Provides training, education & ongoing support to build your business.

4612 ■ Pak Mail Centres Ltd. (Toronto, Canada)

501 Passmore Ave., Ste, 30
Toronto, ON, Canada M1V 5G4
Ph: (416)335-6245
Free: 800-387-8335

Fax: (416)335-9080
Co. E-mail: info@pakmailcanada.com
URL: http://www.pakmailcanada.com

Description: Offers mailing services like customer packaging, domestic and international shipping by means of courier, truck, planes, train and ocean freight. **No. of Franchise Units:** 10. **No. of Company-Owned Units:** 1. **Founded:** 1983.. **Franchised:** 1996. **Equity Capital Needed:** $114,000-$140,000. **Franchise Fee:** $25,000. **Training:** Offers 4 weeks initial and ongoing support.

4613 ■ Postal Connections of America

Templar Franchise Company
275 E. Douglas Ave., Ste. 115
El Cajon, CA 92020
Ph: (619)294-7550
Free: 800-767-8257
Fax: (619)294-4550
Co. E-mail: info@postalconnections.com
URL: http://www.postalconnections.com.

Description: Postal Connections stores offer packaging, shipping, mail receiving & forwarding, copies, printing, scanning & storage of digital documents, eBay auction support, office & packing supplies, crate & freight shipping and more. **No. of Franchise Units:** 99. **Founded:** 1985.. **Franchised:** 1996. **Equity Capital Needed:** $119,000-$153,900, average initial investment. **Franchise Fee:** $23,900. **Financial Assistance:** Yes. **Training:** Extensive training prior to & after opening. Franchisee's receive 5 days live action training in a regional training store, Unique Act video training program & 4 days onsite.

4614 ■ Postalannex+

Annex Brands, Inc.
7580 Metropolitan Dr., Ste. 200
San Diego, CA 92108-4417
Ph: (619)563-4800
Free: 800-456-1525
Fax: (619)563-9850
Co. E-mail: ryan@postalannex.com
URL: http://www.postalannex.com

Description: Provides postal, communication, and business services in the convenience of a store setting. Services rendered include mailbox rental, mail check, express money services, passport photos, metered mail, word processing, secretarial services, packaging and packaging supplies, laminating, copy services, office supplies, printing, business cards and stationery, binding, and notary. Also provides a fax network and telephone message center. **No. of Franchise Units:** 321. **Founded:** 1985.. **Franchised:** 1986. **Equity Capital Needed:** $200,000 net worth; $50,000 liquid assets; actual cost $138,800-$200,050. **Franchise Fee:** $29,950. **Financial Assistance:** Yes. **Training:** 2 week training at home office, plus 1 week at location. Ongoing training and support provided.

4615 ■ PostNet

PostNet Intl. Franchise Corp.
1819 Wazee St.
Denver, CO 80202
Ph: (303)771-7100
Free: 800-338-7401
Fax: (303)771-7133
Co. E-mail: info@postnet.net
URL: http://www.postnet.net

Description: PostNet International offers site location assistance based on proven criteria, high tech design layout, development services, stateof-the-art equipment, startup inventory, full color promotional materials, plus 800 line, fax, Internet and regional support. Centers offer shipping, packaging, private mailboxes, fax, office/packaging supplies, printing, voice mail and the latest information and communication services available. **No. of Franchise Units:** 900. **Founded:** 1985.. **Franchised:** 1993. **Equity Capital Needed:** $175,875-$197,600, total investment includes working capital. **Franchise Fee:** $29,900. **Fi-**

nancial **Assistance:** Yes. **Training:** In-depth 3-step training process includes classroom, onsite and follow-up. Continuous ongoing support provided.

4616 ■ Sunshine Pack & Ship

7580 Metropolitan Dr., Ste. 200
San Diego, CA 92108-4417
Ph: (619)563-4800
Free: 800-456-1525
Fax: (619)563-9850
Co. E-mail: info@annexbrands.com
URL: http://www.sunshinepackandship.com

Description: Packing, shipping & eBay drop-off stores. **No. of Franchise Units:** 27. **No. of Company-Owned Units:** 2. **Founded:** 1993.. **Franchised:** 2000. **Equity Capital Needed:** $69,000-$123,000. **Franchise Fee:** $19,900. **Royalty Fee:** 5%. **Financial Assistance:** Limited third party financing available. **Training:** Offers 40 hours at headquarters, 40 hours at franchisees location and additional training as needed.

4617 ■ The UPS Store

1115 North Service Rd.W, Unit 1
Oakville, ON, Canada L6M 2V9
Ph: (905)338-9754
Free: 800-661-6232
Fax: (905)338-7491
Co. E-mail: development@theupsstore.ca
URL: http://www.theupsstore.ca

Description: Offering one-stop convenience for small business: digital print and photocopies (colour & B/W), document finishing, worldwide courier services, packaging services & supplies, fax services, computer rental, WIFI and mail receiving services. **No. of Franchise Units:** 350. **Founded:** 1990.. **Equity Capital Needed:** $146,150-$179,550. **Franchise Fee:** $35,000.

4618 ■ The UPS Store / Mail Boxes Etc.

6060 Cornerstone Ct., W
San Diego, CA 92121-3795
Ph: (858)597-8513
Free: 877-623-7253
Fax: (858)546-7492
Co. E-mail: usafranchise@mbe.com
URL: http://www.theupsstore.com

Description: Retail shipping, postal and business services. **No. of Franchise Units:** 4,342. **Founded:** 1980.. **Franchised:** 1980. **Equity Capital Needed:** $176,066-$331,353. **Franchise Fee:** $29,950. **Royalty Fee:** 5%. **Financial Assistance:** Third party and limited in-house financing available. **Training:** Offers 2 weeks at headquarters, 2 weeks at franchisee's location and ongoing support.

4619 ■ Worldwide Express

CGI Franchise Systems, Inc.
2828 Raith St., Ste. 400
Dallas, TX 75201
Ph: (214)720-2400
Free: 800-758-SHIP
Fax: (214)720-2446
URL: http://www.wwex.com

Description: Discounted air express services. **No. of Franchise Units:** 208. **Founded:** 1991.. **Franchised:** 1994. **Franchise Fee:** $28,125-$315,000. **Training:** Training available at headquarters and onsite.

RESEARCH CENTERS

4620 ■ University of Colorado at Boulder - Center for Advanced Manufacturing and Packaging of Microwave, Optical and Digital Electronics (CAMPmode)

University of Colorado
Boulder, CO 80309-0427
Ph: (303)492-7750
Fax: (303)492-3498
Co. E-mail: mahajan@spot.colorado.edu
URL: http://www.nsf.gov/eng/iip/iucrc/directory/camp.jsp

Contact: Prof. Roop L. Mahajan, Director
Founded: 1995.

ASSOCIATIONS AND OTHER ORGANIZATIONS

4621 ■ **National Association of Recording Merchandisers (NARM)**
9 Eves Dr., Ste. 120
Marlton, NJ 08053
Ph: (856)596-2221
Fax: (856)596-3268
Co. E-mail: donio@narm.com
URL: http://www.narm.com
Contact: Rachelle Friedman, Chairman
Description: Serves the music and other prerecorded entertainment software industry as a forum for insight and dialogue; members include retailers, wholesalers, distributors, entertainment software suppliers, and suppliers of related products and services. **Scope:** merchandising, loss prevention, classical music, EDI. **Founded:** 1958. **Publications:** *NARM Convention Official Guide* (Annual); *NARM News Bits* (Monthly); *NARM Research Briefs* (Monthly); *NARM Membership Directory and Buyer's Guide* (Annual). **Educational Activities:** Insights and Sounds (Annual). **Awards:** Marketing Awards; Harry Chapin Memorial Humanitarian Award; Presidential Award for Sustained Executive Achievement.

REFERENCE WORKS

4622 ■ *The Rhythm of Success: How an Immigrant Produced His Own American Dream*
Pub: Penguin Group USA Inc.
Ed: Emilio Estefan. **Released:** January 10, 2010. **Price:** $24.95. **Description:** Emilio Estefan, husband to singer Gloria Estefan and founder of the Latin pop legend Miami Sound Machine, is the classic example of the American dream. He shares his guiding principles that entrepreneurs need to start and grow a business.

4623 ■ *"Scoring Music" in Canadian Business (Vol. 81, December 8, 2008, No. 21, pp. S3)*
Pub: Rogers Media Ltd.
Ed: Jay Somerset. **Description:** Boyd Devereaux, who plays with the Toronto Maple Leafs, collaborates with musicians through his record label Elevation Records. Devereaux won a Stanley Cup with the Detroit Red Wings in 2002 and has released five limited edition discs through Elevation records.

4624 ■ *"Sound Fundamentals" in Hispanic Business (September 2007, pp. 12, 14, 16)*
Pub: Hispanic Business
Ed: Michael T. Mena. **Description:** Profile of Ozomatli, a Los Angeles-based multicultural, multi-ethnic musical group that has topped Billboard's Latin Pop chart without relying on record sales. Members explain how they run the group like a small business.

TRADE PERIODICALS

4625 ■ *Music Inc.: For Progresive Music Retailers*
Pub: Maher Publications Inc.
Contact: James Petrillo, President
URL(s): www.musicincmag.com/magazine.html. **Released:** 11/yr. **Price:** $17, Individuals.

4626 ■ *Turok's Choice*
Pub: Paul Turok
Ed: Paul Turok, Editor. **Released:** 11/year. **Price:** $14.95, individuals; $19, Canada and Mexico; $23, elsewhere. **Description:** Publishes reviews of classical compact discs.

FRANCHISES AND BUSINESS OPPORTUNITIES

4627 ■ **CD Tradepost**
826 S Kansas Ave.
Topeka, KS 66612
Ph: (785)233-0675
Fax: (785)232-4444
Description: Used CDs, videos & video games. **No. of Franchise Units:** 5. **No. of Company-Owned Units:** 14. **Founded:** 1998.. **Franchised:** 2002. **Equity Capital Needed:** $98,000-$159,000. **Franchise Fee:** $30,000. **Royalty Fee:** 5-6%. **Training:** Provides 2 weeks at headquarters with ongoing support including grand opening support.

LIBRARIES

4628 ■ **Chicago Public Library - Visual & Performing Arts Division - Music Information Center**
Harold Washington Library Center
400 S. State St., 8th Fl.
Chicago, IL 60605
Ph: (312)747-4850
URL: http://www.chipublib.org/branch/details/library/harold-washington/p/Vpa
Contact: Brian Bannon, Commissioner
Scope: History and theory of music, biographies of musicians and composers, music education, opera, musical comedy, sacred music, popular music, discography, music business, musical instruments, vocal and instrumental pedagogy, music therapy, folk music, composition and orchestration, arranging. **Services:** Interlibrary loan; copying; listening/viewing Center; practice rooms; music chamber; Center open to the public. **Founded:** 1915. **Holdings:** 49,800 books; 8025 bound periodical volumes; 67,000 bound volumes of music; 30,000 pieces of music; 15 VF drawers of pamphlets and clippings; 6102 microfiche of music; 2220 reels of microfilm of periodicals; 169,000 phonograph records, compact discs, audiocassettes; 3900 music videos; 334 laserdiscs; 4250 photographs; 51,957 uncatalogued scores. **Subscriptions:** 561 journals and other serials.

ASSOCIATIONS AND OTHER ORGANIZATIONS

4629 ■ **Association of Professional Computer Consultants (APCC)**
2323 Yonge St., Ste. 400
Toronto, ON, Canada M4P 2C9
Ph: (416)545-5275
Free: 888-487-2722
Co. E-mail: information@apcconline.com
URL: http://www.apcconline.com
Description: Promotes the interests of Independent Computer Consultants. **Founded:** 1985. **Subscriptions:** articles. **Publications:** *Gateway* (Periodic).

4630 ■ **British Columbia Technology Industries Association (BC TIA)**
1188 W Georgia St., Ste. 900
Vancouver, BC, Canada V6E 4A2
Ph: (604)683-6159
Fax: (604)683-3879
Co. E-mail: info@bctia.org
URL: http://www.bctia.org
Contact: Bill Tam, President
Description: Fosters the growth and development of the Province's technology industries and member companies. Provides programs, services and activities designed to meet the needs and interests of members in the areas of networking, education, public awareness, and government relations. Offers a forum for members to review industry issues, acquire new business knowledge from leading industry professionals, to supply input on existing and proposed legislation and generally work together to advance the industry's interests. **Founded:** 1993. **Publications:** *Impact* (Annual).

4631 ■ **Canadian Image Processing and Pattern Recognition Society (CIPPRS)—Association Canadienne de Traitement d'Images et de Reconnaissance des Formes (ACTIRF)**
University of Western Ontario
Middlesex College 379
Dept. of Computer Science
London, ON, Canada N6A 5B7
Ph: (519)661-2111
Fax: (519)661-3515
Co. E-mail: cipprs@csd.uwo.ca
URL: http://www.gel.ulaval.ca
Contact: Prof. John Barron, Treasurer
URL(s): www.cipprs.org. **Description:** Strives to advance the theory and practice of signal and image processing for pattern analysis and classification, scene or speech understanding and recognition, computer vision, on-line and off-line document analysis and recognition, robotic perception, intelligent autonomous systems, biomedical imaging, neural networks and modeling, remote sensing, specialized architecture and industrial applications. **Scope:** image and signal processing. **Founded:** 1978. **Subscriptions:** articles. **Publications:** *Vision Interface.* **Educational Activities:** Computer and Robot Vision (Annual). **Awards:** Doctoral Dissertation Award (Annual); Distinguished Service Awards; CIPPS Distinguished Service Awards (Annual).

4632 ■ *Gateway*
2323 Yonge St., Ste. 400
Toronto, ON, Canada M4P 2C9
Ph: (416)545-5275
Free: 888-487-2722
Co. E-mail: information@apcconline.com
URL: http://www.apcconline.com
Released: Periodic **Price:** free.

4633 ■ *Impact*
1188 W Georgia St., Ste. 900
Vancouver, BC, Canada V6E 4A2
Ph: (604)683-6159
Fax: (604)683-3879
Co. E-mail: info@bctia.org
URL: http://www.bctia.org
Contact: Bill Tam, President
Released: Annual

4634 ■ **International Association for Computer Information Systems (IACIS)**
c/o Richard McCarthy, Pres.
Quinnipiac University
School of Business
275 Mt. Carmel Ave.
Hamden, CT 06518
Co. E-mail: richard.mccarthy@quinnipiac.edu
URL: http://www.iacis.org
Contact: Richard McCarthy, President
Description: Educators and computer professionals. Seeks to promote the knowledge, use, and teaching of computers, and technology; dedicated to the improvement of information systems and computer professionals. **Scope:** computers, technology, education. **Founded:** 1960. **Subscriptions:** 43 software. **Publications:** *IACIS Newsletter* (Semiannual); *Journal of Computer Information Systems* (Quarterly). **Awards:** Computer Educator of the Year; Ben Braun Award for Excellence (Annual); Computer Educator of the Year (Annual).

4635 ■ **TechServe Alliance**
1420 King St., Ste. 610
Alexandria, VA 22314
Ph: (703)838-2050
Fax: (703)838-3610
Co. E-mail: staff@techservealliance.org
URL: http://www.techservealliance.org
Contact: Susan Thaden, President
Description: Businesses that provide the services of highly technical professionals, such as computer programmers, systems analysts, engineers, to clients in need of temporary technical support. Promotes legal and economic environment favorable to the technical services industry, including protection of a firm's freedom to choose either employees or independent contractors when supplying services to clients. Encourages professional standards in the industry; serves as a support mechanism for members. Provides industry-specific educational informa-tion and insurance discounts. **Founded:** 1987. **Publications:** *Directory of Members Firms* (Periodic); *NACCB Monitor* (Quarterly); *NACCB Newsletter* (Quarterly).

4636 ■ **Vision Interface**
University of Western Ontario
Middlesex College 379
Dept. of Computer Science
London, ON, Canada N6A 5B7
Ph: (519)661-2111
Fax: (519)661-3515
Co. E-mail: cipprs@csd.uwo.ca
URL: http://www.gel.ulaval.ca
Contact: Prof. John Barron, Treasurer

REFERENCE WORKS

4637 ■ *"Arctic IT Honored" in Alaska Business Monthly (Vol. 27, October 2011, No. 10, pp. 10)*
Pub: Alaska Business Publishing Company
Ed: Nancy Pounds. **Description:** Arctic Information Technology Inc. was named to Everything Channel's 2011 Computer Reseller News (CRN) Next-Generation 250 list. The firm provides business software and network infrastructure solutions.

4638 ■ *"Auctions and Bidding: a Guide for Computer Scientists" in ACM Computing Surveys (Vol. 43, Summer 2011, No. 2, pp. 10)*
Pub: Association for Computing Machinery
Ed: Simon Parsons, Juan A. Rodriguez-Aguilar, Mark Klein. **Description:** There are various actions: single dimensional, multi-dimensional, single-sided, double-sided, first-price, second-price, English, Dutch, Japanese, sealed-bid, and these have been extensively discussed and analyzed in economics literature. This literature is surveyed from a computer science perspective, primarily from the viewpoint of computer scientists who are interested in learning about auction theory, and to provide pointers into the economics literature for those who want a deeper technical understanding. In addition, since auctions are an increasingly important topic in computer science, the article also looks at work on auctions from the computer science literature. The aim is to identify what both bodies of work tell us about creating electronic auctions.

4639 ■ *"Burton Group Answers Industry Need for Practical Data Center Advice" in Canadian Corporate News (May 14, 2007)*
Pub: Comtex News Network Inc.
Description: Burton Group, an IT research firm focused on in-depth technical analysis of enterprise IT infrastructures, launched a new service providing practical advice for IT professionals facing critical data center decisions which due to technological advances can be more efficient while reducing costs.

4640 ■ *"Consumer Trust in E-Commerce Web Sites: a Meta-Study" in ACM Computing*

Surveys (Vol. 43, Fall 2011, No. 3, pp. 14)
Pub: Association for Computing Machinery
Ed: Patricia Beatty, Ian Reay, Scott Dick, James Miller. **Description:** Trust is at once an elusive, imprecise concept, and a critical attribute that must be engineered into e-commerce systems. Engineering trust is examined.

4641 ■ "Discrete Wavelet Transform-Based Time Series Analysis and Mining" in ACM Computing Surveys (Vol. 43, Summer 2011, No. 2, pp. 6)
Pub: Association for Computing Machinery
Ed: Pimwadee Chaovalit, Aryya Gangopadhyay, George Karabatis, Zhiyuan Chen. **Description:** Time series are recorded values of an interesting phenomenon such as stock prices, household items, or patient heart rates over a period of time. Time series data mining focuses on discovering interesting patterns in such data. An introduction to a wavelet-based times series data analysis is provided with a systematic survey of various analysis techniques that use discrete wavelet transformation (DWT) in time series data mining, and outlines the benefits of this approach demonstrated by previous studies performed on diverse application domains, including image classification, multimedia retrieval, and computer network anomaly detection.

4642 ■ "The Failure Detector Abstraction" in ACM Computing Surveys (Vol. 43, Summer 2011, No. 2, pp. 9)
Pub: Association for Computing Machinery
Ed: Felix C. Freiling, Rachid Guerraoui, Petr Kuznetsov. **Description:** A failure detector is a fundamental abstraction in distributed computing. This article surveys this abstraction through two dimensions. First it studies failure detectors as building blocks to simplify the design of reliable distributed algorithms, particularly how failure detectors can factor out timing assumptions to detect failures in distributed agreement algorithms. Second, failure detectors as computability benchmarks are studied. Some limitations of the failure detector abstraction along each of the dimensions is also highlighted.

4643 ■ "Free Speech Vs. Privacy in Data Mining" in Information Today (Vol. 28, September 2011, No. 8, pp. 22)
Pub: Information Today, Inc.
Ed: George H. Pike. **Description:** The U.S. Constitution does not explicitly guarantee the right of privacy. Organizations and businesses that require obtaining and disseminating information can be caught in the middle of privacy rights. The long-term impact on data mining, Internet marketing, and Internet privacy issues are examined.

4644 ■ "Human Activity Analysis: a Review" in ACM Computing Surveys (Vol. 43, Fall 2011, No. 3, pp. 16)
Pub: Association for Computing Machinery
Ed: J.K. Aggarwal, M.S. Ryoo. **Description:** Human activity recognition is an important area of computer vision research and is studied in this report.

4645 ■ "Implementing Statically Typed Object-Oriented Programming Languages" in ACM Computing Surveys (Vol. 43, Fall 2011, No. 3, pp. 18)
Pub: Association for Computing Machinery
Ed: Roland Ducournau. **Description:** Object-oriented programming represents an original implementation issue due to its philosophy of making the program behavior depend on the dynamic type of objects. A review of the various implementation techniques available in static typing and in the three cases of single inheritance, multiple inheritance, and multiple subtyping are reviewed.

4646 ■ "Lighter Than Air" in Game Developer (Vol. 18, November 1, 2011, No. 10, pp. 38)
Pub: Think Services
Ed: Andy Firth. **Description:** Floating point performance tips and tricks are outlined. Floating point allows freedom of representation when implementing algorithms and is both intuitive to set up and simple

to work with; hardware is also improved so that it is faster to use floating point math as opposed to integer in many environments.

4647 ■ "Machine Transliteration Survey" in ACM Computing Surveys (Vol. 43, Fall 2011, No. 3, pp. 17)
Pub: Association for Computing Machinery
Ed: Sarvnaz Karimi, Falk Scholer, Andrew Turpin. **Description:** Machine transliteration is the process of automatically transforming the script of a word from a source language to a target language, while preserving pronunciation. The development of algorithms specifically for machine transliteration began over a decade ago based on the phonetics of source and target languages, followed by approaches using statistical and language-specific methods. In this survey, the key methodologies introduced in transliteration literature are reviewed. The approaches are categorized based on the resources and algorithms used, and the effectiveness is compared.

4648 ■ "Nampa Police Department: Electronic Systems Just One Tool in Business Security Toolbox" in Idaho Business Review (October 29, 2010)
Pub: Dolan Media Newswires
Ed: Brad Carlson. **Description:** Police departments and private security firms can help small businesses with hard security and business consultants can assist with internal audit security and fraud prevention.

4649 ■ "Our Hoarder Mentality: Blame the Hard Disk" in PC Magazine (Vol. 30, November 2011, No. 11, pp. 46)
Pub: Ziff-Davis Inc.
Contact: Vivek Shah, Chief Executive Officer
Ed: John C. Dvorak. **Description:** Computer programmers, once referred to as computer users, are slowly being replaced by passive consumers of products and content of tablets and handheld mobile phones and devices of the future. Understanding is garnered as this article examines this industry trend.

4650 ■ Pro Windows Small Business Server 2003
Pub: Apress L.P.
Ed: Tony Campbell. **Released:** July 2006. **Price:** $39.99. **Description:** Profile of Microsoft's Windows Small Business Server, designed for companies with 50 or fewer employees.

4651 ■ "The State of the Art in End-User Software Engineering" in ACM Computing Surveys (Vol. 43, Fall 2011, No. 3, pp. 21)
Pub: Association for Computing Machinery
Description: Most programs today are not written by professional software developers but by people with expertise in other domains working towards goals for which they need computational support. A discussion of empirical research about end-user software engineering activities and the technologies designed to support them is presented. Several crosscutting issues in the design of EUSE tools, including the roles of risk, reward, and domain complexity, and self-efficacy in the design of EUSE tools and the potential of educating users about software engineering principles are also examined.

4652 ■ "Strict Intersection Types for the Lambda Calculus" in ACM Computing Surveys (Vol. 43, Fall 2011, No. 3, pp. 20)
Pub: Association for Computing Machinery
Ed: Steffen Van Bakel. **Description:** The usefulness and elegance of strict intersection types for the Lambda Calculus, that are strict in the sense that they are the representatives of equivalence classes of types in the BCD-system is shown. Focus in directed on the essential intersection type assignment; this system is almost syntax directed, and the article will show that all major properties hold that are known to hold for other intersection systems, like the approximation theorem, the characterization of (head/strong) normalization, completeness of type assignment using filter semantics, strong normalization for cut-elimination and the principal pair property. In part, the proofs for these properties are new. A brief comparison of the essential system with other existing systems is given.

4653 ■ "A Survey of Combinatorial Testing" in ACM Computing Surveys (Vol. 43, Summer 2011, No. 2, pp. 11)
Pub: Association for Computing Machinery
Ed: Changhai Nie, Hareton Leung. **Description:** Combinatorial Testing (CT) can detect failures triggered by interactions of parameters in the Software Under Test (SUT) with a covering array test suite generated by some sampling mechanisms. Basic concepts and notations of CT are covered.

4654 ■ "A Survey of Comparison-Based System-Level Diagnosis" in ACM Computing Surveys (Vol. 43, Fall 2011, No. 3, pp. 22)
Pub: Association for Computing Machinery
Ed: Elias P. Duarte Jr., Roverli P. Ziwich, Luiz C.P. Albini. **Description:** The growing complexity and dependability requirements of hardware, software, and networks demand efficient techniques for discovering disruptive behavior in those systems. Comparison-based diagnosis is a realistic approach to detect faulty units based on the outputs of tasks executed by system units. This survey integrates the vast amount of research efforts that have been produced in this field.

4655 ■ "A Survey of DHT Security Techniques" in ACM Computing Surveys (Vol. 43, Summer 2011, No. 2, pp. 8)
Pub: Association for Computing Machinery
Ed: Guido Urdaneta, Guillaume Pierre, Maarten Van Steen. **Description:** Peer-to-peer networks based on distributed hash tables (DHTs) have received considerable attention since their introduction in 2001. Unfortunately, DHT-based systems have been shown to be difficult to protect against security attacks. An overview of techniques reported in literature for making DHT-based systems resistant to the three most important attacks that can be launched by malicious nodes participating in the DHT is given: the Sybil attack, the Eclipse attack, and routing and storage attacks.

4656 ■ "What is the Future of Disk Drives, Death or Rebirth?" in ACM Computing Surveys (Vol. 43, Fall 2011, No. 3, pp. 23)
Pub: Association for Computing Machinery
Ed: Yuhui Deng. **Description:** Disk drives have experienced dramatic development to meet performance requirements since the IBM 1301 disk drive was announced in 1961. However, the performance gap between memory and disk drives has widened to 6 orders of magnitude and continues to widen by about 50 percent per year. Challenges and opportunities facing these storage devices are explored.

TRADE PERIODICALS

4657 ■ Association for Computing Machinery
Pub: Special Interest Group on Data Communication
Ed: Martha Steenstrup, Editor. **Released:** Quarterly. **Price:** $50. **Description:** Serves as a forum for computing professionals in the data communications field. Focuses on network architecture, including the Internet, network protocols, and distributed systems.

4658 ■ Computer Link Magazine
Pub: Millennium Publishing Inc.
URL(s): techny.com/. **Released:** Monthly **Price:** $20, Free.

4659 ■ Consultants News
Pub: Kennedy Information Inc.
Contact: Wayne E. Cooper, President
Released: Monthly. **Price:** $349, U.S. and Canada; $399, elsewhere. **Description:** The authoritative voice of the consulting industry, covering news, analysis, practice advice, proprietary data and opinion.

4660 ■ DCLNews
Pub: Data Conversion Laboratory
Contact: Mark Gross, President
Released: Monthly. **Price:** Included in membership;. **Description:** E-journal providing you insider information on XML and SGML, along with the latest technology and e-publishing news.

4661 ■ *Information Technology Adviser*
Pub: Progressive Business Publications
Ed: Robin Nelson, Editor. **Released:** Semimonthly. **Price:** $299, individuals. **Description:** Presents information to keep IT/IS managers up to date on how technology cuts costs, boosts productivity, and makes companies more successful. Recurring features include interviews, news of research, a calendar of events, news of educational opportunities, and a column titled Sharpen Your Judgment.

4662 ■ *Maximum PC*
Pub: Future Network USA
URL(s): maximumpc.com. **Ed:** Michael Brown, Gordon Mah Ung. **Released:** Monthly **Price:** $14.95, Individuals; $24.95, Individuals 12 CDs; $29.95, Other countries; $49.95, Other countries two years; $1.95, Single issue.

4663 ■ *Media Computing*
Pub: Dreamscape Productions
Ed: Sheridan Tatsuno, Editor, statsuno@aol.com. **Released:** Monthly. **Price:** $495, institutions in the U.S. and Canada; $550, institutions elsewhere. **Description:** Supplies analysis of multimedia, internet, intranet, and web computing issues. Recurring features include interviews and reports of meetings.

4664 ■ *Microprocessor Report*
Pub: MicroDesign Resources
Released: 17x/yr. **Price:** $695, U.S. and Canada for print version; $495, U.S. and Canada pounds;. **Description:** The leading technical publication for the microprocessor industry. Dedicated to providing unbiased, in-depth, critical analysis of new high-performance microprocessor developments. This newsletter is exclusively subscriber-supported.

4665 ■ *Online: The Leading Magazine for Information Professionals*
Pub: Online, A Division of Information Today Inc.
URL(s): www.infotoday.com/online/default.shtml. **Ed:** Marydee Ojala. **Released:** Bimonthly **Price:** $124.95, Individuals; $235, Two years; $141, Canada and Mexico; $167, Other countries.

4666 ■ *PATCA Journal*
Pub: Professional and Technical Consultants Association
Ed: Stan Turnbull, Editor, stant@ix.netcom.com. **Released:** Quarterly. **Price:** Included in membership. **Description:** Acts as a forum for the exchange of information on consulting and consulting practices. Provides professional support for member independent consultants active in business, industry, and government. Recurring features include book reviews, seminar announcements, interviews, letters to the editor, news of educational opportunities, and member profiles.

4667 ■ *Productivity Software*
Pub: Worldwide Videotex
Released: Monthly. **Price:** $150. **Description:** Provides information on computer software.

TRADE SHOWS AND CONVENTIONS

4668 ■ Computer Fest
ShowFest Productions, Inc.
75 Dufflaw Rd., Ste. 202
Toronto, ON, Canada M6A 2W4
Ph: (416)782-0063
Fax: (416)782-3178
URL(s): www.compfest.com. **Price:** $9, For individual; $21, For family; $5, For senior; Children 10 and under admitted free. **Frequency:** Semiannual. **Audience:** General public and industry professionals. **Principal Exhibits:** Computer equipment, supplies, and services. **Telecommunication Services:** ryhan@compfest.com.

4669 ■ ON DEMAND Digital Printing & Publishing Strategy Conference and Exposition
Advanstar Communications
641 Lexington Ave., 8th Fl.
New York, NY 10022
Ph: (212)951-6600

Free: 800-346-0085
Fax: (212)951-6793
Co. E-mail: info@advantstar.com
URL: http://www.advanstar.com
Contact: Robert Krakoff, President
URL(s): www.ondemandexpo.com. **Frequency:** Annual. **Audience:** Corporate executives, print providers, government users. **Principal Exhibits:** Addresses the digitalization of workflow in the printing and publishing marketplace. **Telecommunication Services:** sfrank@advanstar.com.

CONSULTANTS

4670 ■ Richard I. Anderson—Riander
101 Spear St., Ste. 203
San Francisco, CA 94105
Ph: (415)412-1858
Co. E-mail: riander@well.com
URL: http://www.well.com/user/riander
Scope: Provides guidance to organizations seeking to increase the influence of user-centered design, ethnographic research, multidisciplinary collaboration, on business strategy, organizational process, product conceptualization and design. **Seminars:** User-Centered Design/Usability Engineering, May, 2000; Addressing Organizational Obstacles to and Achieving Greater Business Benefits; User-Centered Design; Ethnographic Research; Multidisciplinary Collaboration; Managing User Experience Groups; Meeting the Needs of a Multidisciplinary Profession; User Experience Managers and Executives Speak; Changing the Role User Experience Plays in Your Business.

4671 ■ COTC Technologies Inc.—COTC-TrenzSoft
172 E Industrial Blvd.
Pueblo, CO 81007-4406
Ph: (719)547-0938
Free: 888-547-0938
Fax: (719)547-1105
Contact: Tom Renz, Chief Executive Officer
E-mail: tom@cotc-consulting.com
Scope: Provides software consulting services to organizations that require assistance with their HP3000 computer system. Provides systems analysis, programming, operations support, and system management. Also provides PC software and hardware support and consulting. Additionally provides various training for the HP3000 computer system. Industries served: healthcare, aerospace procurement, aerospace proposal activities, and HP3000 computer systems. **Founded:** 2006.

4672 ■ Executive Analytics & Design Inc.
10 Malcolm X Blvd.
Boston, MA 02119
Ph: (617)445-5200
Fax: (617)445-5224
URL: http://www.eadfinancialit.com
Contact: Josie Haywood, Manager
E-mail: josie@eadfinancialit.com
Scope: A technology consulting firm, specializing in custom financial solutions, that provides systems, software and website development solutions. Provides services including o-the-shelf accounting software selection, custom software development, financial management consulting, project management and financial and technology outsourcing. **Founded:** 1996. **Seminars:** Technology and Networking for Better Business Performance.

4673 ■ Hardy Stevenson and Associates Ltd.
364 Davenport Rd.
Toronto, ON, Canada M5R 1K6
Ph: (416)944-8444
Free: 877-267-7794
Fax: (416)944-0900
Co. E-mail: hsa@hardystevenson.com
URL: http://www.hardystevenson.com
Contact: Glynn Gomes, Principal
Scope: Firm specialize in land use and environmental planning social economic impact assessment facilitation, conflict resolution community relations, public consultation strategic planning policy and project management consulting. **Founded:** 1990.

4674 ■ Strategic Systems & Products Corp.
320 Decker Dr., Ste. 100
Irving, TX 75062
Ph: (972)719-2543
Fax: (972)719-2540
Co. E-mail: sales@sspcorp.com
URL: http://www.sspcorp.com
Contact: Carlos A. Martinez, President
E-mail: carlos.martinez@sspcorp.com
Scope: Specializes in the implementation and support of application development, project management and e-business consulting services to the exploration and production business unit of petroleum companies. **Founded:** 1998.

4675 ■ Weich & Bilotti Inc.
600 Worcester Rd., 4th Fl.
Framingham, MA 01702
Ph: (508)663-1600
Fax: (508)663-1682
Co. E-mail: info@weich-bilotti.com
Contact: Mervyn D. Weich, Director
E-mail: mweich@weich-bilotti.com
Scope: Specializes in business plans, venture capital, computer information systems, turnaround/interim management, retail consulting, start-up process, college recruiting and IS and IT personnel. **Founded:** 1995.

FRANCHISES AND BUSINESS OPPORTUNITIES

4676 ■ Rescuecom
2560 Burnet Ave.
Syracuse, NY 13206
Free: 800-RES-CUE7
Fax: (315)433-5228
URL: http://www.rescuecom.com
Description: Computer consulting and repair services. **No. of Franchise Units:** 40. **No. of Company-Owned Units:** 6. **Founded:** 1985.. **Franchised:** 1997. **Franchise Fee:** $1,495-$18,800. **Financial Assistance:** Yes. **Training:** Yes.

4677 ■ Silution Franchise Corp.
1472 E Walnut St.
Pasadena, CA 91106
Ph: (626)535-0560
Free: 877-745-8846
Fax: (626)535-0566
URL: http://www.silution.com
Description: Computer services & support. **Founded:** 1998.. **Franchised:** 2006. **Equity Capital Needed:** $39,950-$71,800. **Franchise Fee:** $22,000. **Royalty Fee:** 10%. **Training:** Provides 5 days at headquarters, 1 day at franchisee's location with ongoing support.

LIBRARIES

4678 ■ AT & T Middletown Technical Library
200 Laurel Ave., S.
Middletown, NJ 07748
Ph: (732)420-5092
URL: http://www.research.att.com/
Scope: Computer science, data communications, telecommunications. **Services:** Interlibrary loan; copying; library not open to the public. **Founded:** 1986. **Holdings:** 20,000 books; 5000 bound periodical volumes; 200 U.S. and foreign standards. **Subscriptions:** 500 journals and other serials.

4679 ■ Colorado Technical University Library
4435 N. Chestnut St.
Colorado Springs, CO 80907-3812
Ph: (719)590-6708
Fax: (719)598-3740
Co. E-mail: aphillips@coloradotech.edu
URL: http://www.coloradotech.edu
Contact: Amy Phillips, Librarian
Scope: Computer science, logistics, electronics, electrical engineering, business management, quality, computer engineering. **Services:** Interlibrary loan; copying; library open to the public with restrictions. **Holdings:** 32,000 books; 60 microfiche titles; 400

videocassettes. **Subscriptions:** 2400 journals and other serials (print and Internet); 4 newspapers. **Telecommunication Services:** library@coloradotech. edu.

4680 ■ DeVry University Library
2149 W. Dunlap Ave.
Phoenix, AZ 85021
Ph: (602)749-4500
URL: http://www.devry.edu
Scope: Electronics, bio/med technology, game programming, computer languages, business operations, computers, accounting, electronic engineering, telecommunications, Internet. **Services:** Copying; virtual reference service; library open to the public for reference use only. **Founded:** 1925. **Holdings:** 25,000 books; 25 CD audio books; 3 cabinets of microfiche; 800 videotapes; 250 DVDs; 500 CD-ROMs; 250 computer disks. **Subscriptions:** 100 journals and other serials; 10 newspapers.

4681 ■ Walt Disney World - Global Business Technology Strategy Library
Team Disney 336-N
1375 Buena Vista Dr.
Lake Buena Vista, FL 32830-1000
Ph: (407)828-4250
Fax: (407)827-8260
Co. E-mail: david.w.hartman@disney.com
URL: http://disneyworld.disney.go.com/wdw
Contact: David Hartman, Librarian
Scope: Computer science, human resources, general business. **Services:** Center not open to the public.

Founded: 1986. **Holdings:** 4000 books, videos, DVDs, and CDs; 100 AV equipment. **Subscriptions:** 200 journals and other serials; 3 newspapers.

4682 ■ District of Columbia Public Library - Technology and Science Division
Martin Luther King Memorial Library
901 G St., NW, Rm. 220
Washington, DC 20001
Ph: (202)727-1175
Fax: (202)727-1129
Co. E-mail: commentssuggestions.dcpl@dc.gov
URL: http://www.dclibrary.org
Contact: Diane Henry, Assistant Director
Scope: Automobile and appliance repair, botany, cookery, general science, geology, genetics, manufacturing, nutrition, paleontology, pet care, printing, zoology, mathematics, computer science, biology, domestic arts, earth science, chemistry and chemical technology, physics, engineering, agriculture, gardening, medicine, psychiatry, astronomy, consumer information, health, veterinary science, physical anthropology. **Services:** Interlibrary loan; copying; free Wi-Fi access; library open to the public. **Founded:** 1907. **Holdings:** 92,127 books; 2500 bound periodical volumes; 5755 microforms; 65 VF drawers. **Subscriptions:** 300 journals and other serials. **Telecommunication Services:** mlkjrlibrary@dc. gov.

4683 ■ Goldey Beacom College - J. Wilbur Hirons Library
4701 Limestone Rd.
Joseph West Jones College Center
Wilmington, DE 19808

Ph: (302)225-6247
Fax: (302)998-6189
Co. E-mail: stewarp@gbc.edu
URL: http://www.gbc.edu/library/
Contact: Pamela Stewart, Director, Library Services
Scope: Business, management, accounting, business administration, marketing, computer science. **Services:** Interlibrary loan; copying; library open to the public for reference use only. **Founded:** 1969. **Holdings:** 60,000 books; 19,500 bound periodical volumes; transparencies; maps; 786 AV programs; 1234 reels of microfilm; 44,637 microfiche; 700 corporation annual reports. **Subscriptions:** 250 journals and other serials; 6 newspapers. **Telecommunication Services:** hirons@gbc.edu.

4684 ■ Intel Corporation Library
1900 Prairie City Rd.
FM5-50
Folsom, CA 95630
Ph: (916)356-8080
Fax: (916)356-6890
URL: http://www.intel.com/
Contact: Cary O'Keeffe, Specialist
Scope: Semiconductor industry, business, microcomputer components and systems, telecommunications. **Services:** Library not open to the public. **Founded:** 1985. **Holdings:** 1000 books. **Subscriptions:** 100 journals and other serials.

ASSOCIATIONS AND OTHER ORGANIZATIONS

4685 ■ Automated Storage/Retrieval Systems (AS/RS)
8720 Red Oak Blvd., Ste. 201
Charlotte, NC 28217-3996
Ph: (704)676-1190
Free: 800-345-1815
Fax: (704)676-1199
Co. E-mail: publications@mhia.org
URL: http://www.mhia.org
Contact: Mike Ogle, Manager
E-mail: mogle@mhia.org
Description: Companies manufacturing automated storage/retrieval systems. Develops and promotes standard nomenclature, codes for equipment operations, fire prevention, and personnel safety; assists and coordinates efforts of related trade associations pertaining to total systems. Develops and promotes a code of ethics; prepares and distributes publicity and educational materials. Cooperates with private and governmental groups that establish standards or safety codes. Sponsors educational programs and maintains speaker's bureau. **Publications:** *AS/RS Roster of Members* (Periodic).

4686 ■ Information Storage Industry Consortium (INSIC)
12396 World Trade Dr., Ste. 201
San Diego, CA 92128
Ph: (858)279-7230
Fax: (858)279-8591
Co. E-mail: insic@insic.org
URL: http://www.insic.org
Contact: Dr. Paul D. Frank, Executive Director
Description: Brings together companies and universities involved in computer data storage research, united to accomplish mutual goals. Creates and manages joint precompetitive research programs among its members. Performs studies to develop long-term roadmaps for various data storage technologies. **Founded:** 1991.

4687 ■ Order Fulfillment Council - Material Handling Industry of America
8720 Red Oak Blvd., Ste. 201
Charlotte, NC 28217-3992
Ph: (704)676-1190
Fax: (704)676-1199
URL: http://www.mhia.org/industrygroups/ofc
Contact: Larry E. Strayhorn, Executive Chairman of the Board
Description: Trade associations comprising storage industries. Compiles statistics; sponsors research and educational programs. **Founded:** 1986. **Publications:** *Storage and Handling Idea Book.* **Awards:** Material Handling Education Foundation Annual Scholarship (Annual).

4688 ■ PRISM International
1418 Aversboro Rd., Ste. 201
Garner, NC 27529
Ph: (919)771-0657

Fax: (919)771-0457
Co. E-mail: jim@prismintl.org
URL: http://www.prismintl.org
Contact: Jim Teske, President
Description: Represents owners and operators of commercial information management facilities, which include: commercial record centers, media vaults, imaging service bureaus, confidential destruction vendors, digital archiving operations, vendors to the industry, self-vended records and data repositories, government records repositories and educators. Seeks to provide operating guidelines, education, and research in the industry. Promotes professional quality of services offered by commercial and non-commercial information management organizations; facilitates exchange of technical and management information; provides conferences and educational events in the United States, Europe and Asia; works to advocate for and improve public image of commercial information management industry. **Founded:** 1980.

REFERENCE WORKS

4689 ■ "3Par: Storing Up Value" in Barron's (Vol. 90, August 30, 2010, No. 35, pp. 30)
Pub: Barron's Editorial & Corporate Headquarters
Ed: Mark Veverka. **Description:** Dell and Hewlett Packard are both bidding for data storage company 3Par. The acquisition would help Dell and Hewlett Packard provide customers with a one-stop shop as customers move to a private cloud in the Internet.

4690 ■ "Also Check Out.." in Black Enterprise (Vol. 38, October 2007, No. 3, pp. 64)
Pub: Earl G. Graves Publishing Co. Inc.
Description: Profile of Lenovo's Think Vantage Rescue and Recovery system that performs backup files for CD/DVDs.

4691 ■ "Attivio Brings Order to Data" in Information Today (Vol. 26, February 2009, No. 2, pp. 14)
Pub: Information Today, Inc.
Ed: Marji McClure. **Description:** Profile of Attivio, the high tech firm offering next-generation software that helps businesses to consolidate data and eliminate enterprise silos.

4692 ■ "Beam My Data Up" in Canadian Business (Vol. 80, February 12, 2007, No. 4, pp. 42)
Pub: Rogers Media
Ed: Marlene Rego. **Description:** Innovations in the field of teleportation since its invention by Gilles Brassard in 1992 is discussed.

4693 ■ "Best Managed Companies (Canada)" in Canadian Business (Vol. 82, Summer 2009, No. 8, pp. 38)
Pub: Rogers Media
Ed: Calvin Leung. **Description:** Agrium Inc. and Barrick Gold Corporation are among those that are found to be the best managed companies in Canada. Best managed companies also include software firm Open Text Corporation, which has grown annual sales by

75 percent and annual profits by 160 percent since 1995. Open Text markets software that allow firms to manage word-based data, and has 46,000 customers in 114 countries.

4694 ■ The Big Switch: Rewiring the World, From Edison to Google
Pub: W.W. Norton & Company
Ed: Nicholas Carr. **Released:** 2009. **Price:** $25.95.
Description: Companies such as Google, Microsoft, and Amazon.com are building huge centers in order to create massive data centers. Together these centers form a giant computing grid that will deliver the digital universe to scientific labs, companies and homes in the future. This trend could bring about a new, darker phase for the Internet, one where these networks could operate as a fearsome entity that will dominate the lives of individuals worldwide.

4695 ■ "Burton Group Answers Industry Need for Practical Data Center Advice" in Canadian Corporate News (May 14, 2007)
Pub: Comtex News Network Inc.
Description: Burton Group, an IT research firm focused on in-depth technical analysis of enterprise IT infrastructures, launched a new service providing practical advice for IT professionals facing critical data center decisions which due to technological advances can be more efficient while reducing costs.

4696 ■ "Cerner Works the Business Circuit" in Business Journal-Serving Metropolitan Kansas City (Vol. 26, October 5, 2007, No. 4, pp. 1)
Pub: American City Business Journals, Inc.
Ed: Rob Roberts. **Description:** Cerner Corporation is embracing the coming of the electronic medical record exchange by creating a regional health information organization (RHIO) called the CareEntrust. The RHIO convinced health insurers to share claims data with patients and clinicians. At the Center Health Conference, held October 7 to 10, Cerner will demonstrate the software it developed for CareEntrust to the 40,000 healthcare and information technology professionals.

4697 ■ "Clouds in the Forecast" in Information Today (Vol. 28, September 2011, No. 8, pp. 10)
Pub: Information Today, Inc.
Ed: Paula J. Hane. **Description:** Cloud computing is software, applications, and data stored remotely and accessed via the Internet with output displayed on a client device. Recent developments in cloud computing are explored.

4698 ■ "Cloudy Future for VMware?" in Barron's (Vol. 90, September 13, 2010, No. 37, pp. 21)
Pub: Barron's Editorial & Corporate Headquarters
Ed: Jonathan R. Laing. **Description:** VMWare dominated the virtualization market for years, but it may be ending as it faces more competition from rivals that offer cloud computing services. The company's stocks are also expensive and are vulnerable to the smallest mishap.

4699 ■ *"CMS Products and Avecto Team for Business Security Product Solutions"* in *Wireless News (November 11, 2009)*
Pub: Close-Up Media
Description: CMS Products, a provider of data security, backup, content management and disaster recovery, has agreed on a strategic partnership with Avect, a provider in least privilege management. The partnership will allow the companies to bundle their products.

4700 ■ *Contingency Planning and Disaster Recovery: A Small Business Guide*
Pub: John Wiley & Sons, Incorporated
Ed: Donna R. Childs, Stefan Dietrich. **Released:** October 2002. **Description:** Four keys issues to help a business plan for disasters include: preparation, response, recovery, and sample IT solutions in order to secure property and confidential data files and covers the six types of disasters: human errors, equipment failures, third-party failures, environmental hazards, fires and other structural catastrophes, and terrorism and sabotage.

4701 ■ *"County Tract Pitched for Data Center"* in *Baltimore Business Journal (Vol. 28, July 23, 2010, No. 11, pp. 1)*
Pub: Baltimore Business Journal
Ed: Scott Dance. **Description:** One hundred acres of land in Woodlawn, Maryland is set to be sold for use in the construction of a data center for the U.S. Social Security Administration. Baltimore County has submitted a bid for the $750M construction project.

4702 ■ *"Data Center Plan Bearing Fruit From Apple, Spec Center"* in *Charlotte Business Journal (Vol. 25, October 15, 2010, No. 30, pp. 1)*
Pub: Charlotte Business Journal
Ed: Ken Elkins. **Description:** Apple Inc. is planning to expand its server farm at the North Carolina Data Center Corridor in Catawba County. T5 Partners, on the other hand, will build a shell building to house a server on the site. Infocrossing Inc. will also build an open data center in the area.

4703 ■ *"Data Firm Growth 'Opportunistic"* in *Tampa Bay Business Journal (Vol. 30, January 29, 2010, No. 6, pp. 1)*
Pub: American City Business Journals
Ed: Michael Hinman. **Description:** E Solutions Corporation is experiencing growth amid the economic downturn, with its Park Tower data center occupancy in Tampa Florida expanding from 14,000 square feet to 20,000 square feet. Details on the increased operations fueled by demand for information storage and management services offered by the company are discussed.

4704 ■ *"Data Security is No. 1 Compliance Concern"* in *HRMagazine (Vol. 53, October 2008, No. 10, pp. 32)*
Pub: Society for Human Resource Management
Contact: Henry G. Jackson, President
E-mail: hjackson@shrm.org
Ed: Aliah D. Wright. **Description:** Electronic data protection and data privacy are the leading ethics and compliance issues faced by companies today.

4705 ■ *"Discrete Wavelet Transform-Based Time Series Analysis and Mining"* in *ACM Computing Surveys (Vol. 43, Summer 2011, No. 2, pp. 6)*
Pub: Association for Computing Machinery
Ed: Pimwadee Chaovalit, Aryya Gangopadhyay, George Karabatis, Zhiyuan Chen. **Description:** Time series are recorded values of an interesting phenomenon such as stock prices, household items, or patient heart rates over a period of time. Time series data mining focuses on discovering interesting patterns in such data. An introduction to a wavelet-based times series data analysis is provided with a systematic survey of various analysis techniques that use discrete wavelet transformation (DWT) in time series data mining, and outlines the benefits of this approach demonstrated by previous studies performed on diverse application domains, including image classification, multimedia retrieval, and computer network anomaly detection.

4706 ■ *"E-Medical Records Save Money, Time in Ann Arbor"* in *Crain's Detroit Business (Vol. 24, January 21, 2008, No. 3, pp. 6)*
Pub: Crain Communications Inc. - Detroit
Ed: Jay Greene. **Description:** Ann Arbor Area Health Information Exchange is improving patient outcomes by sharing clinical and administrative data in electronic medical record systems.

4707 ■ *"EBSCO Adds New Features to EBSCOhost Content Viewer"* in *Information Today (Vol. 26, February 2009, No. 2, pp. 31)*
Pub: Information Today, Inc.
Description: EBSCOhost Content Viewer historical digital archive collection provides a visual overview of a displayed document, highlighting search keywords on the page as well as providing a document map that shows the number of times a given keyword is mentioned in a periodical, monograph, article, or other document. For periodical content, the viewer lets users browse multiple issues in a volume without leaving the interface; features include zoom and pan technology similar to online maps.

4708 ■ *"Ex Libris Rosetta Hits the Market"* in *Information Today (Vol. 26, February 2009, No. 2, pp. 30)*
Pub: Information Today, Inc.
Description: Ex Libris Rosetta, the latest version of the Ex Libris Group's Digital Preservation System supports the acquisition, validation, ingest, storage, management, preservation, and dissemination of digital objects, allowing libraries the infrastructure and technology to preserve and facilitate access to digital collections. The firm's Ex Libris Rosseta Charter Program helps users develop strategic collaboration between Ex Libris and its customers to improve the product.

4709 ■ *"The Failure Detector Abstraction"* in *ACM Computing Surveys (Vol. 43, Summer 2011, No. 2, pp. 9)*
Pub: Association for Computing Machinery
Ed: Felix C. Freiling, Rachid Guerraoui, Petr Kuznetsov. **Description:** A failure detector is a fundamental abstraction in distributed computing. This article surveys this abstraction through two dimensions. First it studies failure detectors as building blocks to simplify the design of reliable distributed algorithms, particularly how failure detectors can factor out timing assumptions to detect failures in distributed agreement algorithms. Second, failure detectors as computability benchmarks are studied. Some limitations of the failure detector abstraction along each of the dimensions is also highlighted.

4710 ■ *"The Fort"* in *Hawaii Business (Vol. 53, November 2007, No. 5, pp. 19)*
Pub: Hawaii Business Publishing
Ed: Jason Ubay. **Description:** DRFortress' flagship data center The Fort located at Honolulu's Airport Industrial Park provides companies a place to store their servers in an ultra-secure environment. Anything stored in here that requires power has a back up and in case of an outage generators can supply power up to 80 hrs. The Fort caters to major carriers and Internet service providers.

4711 ■ *"Free Speech Vs. Privacy in Data Mining"* in *Information Today (Vol. 28, September 2011, No. 8, pp. 22)*
Pub: Information Today, Inc.
Ed: George H. Pike. **Description:** The U.S. Constitution does not explicitly guarantee the right of privacy. Organizations and businesses that require obtaining and disseminating information can be caught in the middle of privacy rights. The long-term impact on data mining, Internet marketing, and Internet privacy issues are examined.

4712 ■ *"Health IT Regulations Generate Static Among Providers"* in *Philadelphia Business Journal (Vol. 28, January 29, 2010, No. 50, pp. 1)*
Pub: American City Business Journals
Ed: John George. **Description:** US Centers for Medicaid and Medicare Services and the Office of the National Coordinator for Health Information

Technology have proposed rules regarding the meaningful use of electronic health records. The rules must be complied with by hospitals and physicians to qualify for federal stimulus funds.

4713 ■ *"Help Wanted: 100 Hospitals IT Workers"* in *Business Courier (Vol. 27, October 8, 2010, No. 23, pp. 1)*
Pub: Business Courier
Ed: James Ritchie. **Description:** Hospitals in the Greater Cincinnati area are expected to hire more than 100 information technology (IT) workers to help digitize medical records. Financial incentives from the health care reform bill encouraged investments in electronic medical record systems, increasing the demand for IT workers that would help make information exchange across the healthcare system easier.

4714 ■ *"How to Play the Tech Mergers"* in *Barron's (Vol. 90, August 30, 2010, No. 35, pp. 18)*
Pub: Barron's Editorial & Corporate Headquarters
Ed: Tiernan Ray. **Description:** The intense bidding by Hewlett-Packard and Dell for 3Par was foreseen in a previous Barron's cover story and 3Par's stock has nearly tripled since reported. Other possible acquisition targets in the tech industry include Brocade Communication Systems, NetApp, Xyratex, and Isilon Systems.

4715 ■ *"Image Conscious"* in *Canadian Business (Vol. 81, March 17, 2008, No. 4, pp. 36)*
Pub: Rogers Media
Ed: Andrew Wahl. **Description:** Idee Inc. is testing an Internet search engine for images that does not rely on tags but compares its visual data to a database of other images. The company was founded and managed by Leila Boujnane as an off-shoot of their risk-management software firm. Their software has already been used by image companies to track copyrighted images and to find images within their own archives.

4716 ■ *Information Industry Directory*
Pub: Cengage Learning Inc.
Contact: Ronald Dunn, President
URL(s): www.gale.cengage.com. **Released:** Annual; Latest edition 38th; April, 2013. **Price:** $1160, Individuals. **Covers:** Approximately 12,000 organizations, systems, and services involved in the production and distribution of information in electronic form: database producers and their products online host services, transactional services, library and information networks, bibliographic utilities, library management systems, information retrieval software, mailing list services, fee-based information on demand services, document delivery sources, data collection and analysis centers and firms, and related consultants, service companies, professional and trade associations, publishers, and research activities. **Entries include:** Name of parent organization, name of system of service, address, phone, toll-free phone, fax, telex, email address, year founded name of unit head, size of staff, names of any affiliated organizations, financial information. Internet access information, general description of electronic product, system, or service, subjects covered or areas of service offered, sources of data for the system, type and quantity of stored information in all forms, publications and microform products and services, computer-based products and services, other services, clientele served, availability and restrictions, name of contact. **Arrangement:** Alphabetical. **Indexes:** Master, database name, software name, publication/microform title, function/service, personal name, subject, geographical.

4717 ■ *Information Sources: The IIA Annual Membership Directory*
Pub: Software and Information Industry Association
Contact: Kenneth Wasch, President
URL(s): www.siia.net. **Released:** Continuous **Covers:** More than 800 companies involved in the creation, distribution, and use of information products, services, and technology. Entries are prepared by companies described. **Entries include:** Company name, address, phone, names of executives, international partners, regional offices, trade and brand

names, and description of products and services. **Arrangement:** Alphabetical. **Indexes:** Product, personal name, trade name, geographical, corporate parents, international and niche markets.

4718 ■ *Information Technology for the Small Business: How to Make IT Work For Your Company*
Pub: TAB Computer Systems, Incorporated

Ed: T.J. Benoit. **Released:** June 2006. **Price:** $17.95. **Description:** Basics of information technology to help small companies maximize benefits are covered. Topics include pitfalls to avoid, email and Internet use, data backup, recovery and overall IT organization.

4719 ■ *"Media Software and Data Services" in MarketingMagazine (Vol. 115, September 27, 2010, No. 13, pp. 78)*
Pub: Rogers Publishing Ltd.

Description: Media software and data services information in Canada is presented.

4720 ■ *"Mimosa Systems Gains 150,000 New NearPoint Users" in Information Today (Vol. 26, February 2009, No. 2, pp. 31)*
Pub: Information Today, Inc.

Description: Mimosa System's NearPoint archive solution features email and file archiving, e-discovery, archive virtualization, and disaster recovery capabilities.

4721 ■ *"New Database Brings Doctors Out of the Dark" in Business Courier (Vol. 26, October 23, 2009, No. 26, pp. 1)*
Pub: American City Business Journals, Inc.

Ed: James Ritchie. **Description:** A database created by managed care consulting firm Praesentia allows doctors in Cincinnati to compare average reimbursements from health insurance companies to doctors in different areas. Specialist doctors in the city are paid an average of $172.25 for every office consultation.

4722 ■ *"New Wave of Business Security Products Ushers in the Kaspersky Anti-Malware Protection System" in Internet Wire (October 26, 2010)*
Pub: Comtex

Description: Kaspersky Anti-Malware System provides anti-malware protection that requires minimal in-house resources for small businesses. The system offers a full range of tightly integrated end-to-end protection solutions, ensuring unified protection across an entire network, from endpoint and mobile device protection to file server, mail server, network storage and gateway protection. It provides flexible centralized management, immediate threat visibility and a level of responsiveness not seen in other anti-malware approaches.

4723 ■ *"New Ways To Think About Data Loss: Data Loss Is Costly and Painful" in Franchising World (Vol. 42, August 2010, No. 8, pp. 21)*
Pub: International Franchise Association

Ed: Ken Colburn. **Description:** Information for maintaining data securely for franchised organizations, including smart phones, tablets, copiers, computers and more is given.

4724 ■ *Pro Windows Small Business Server 2003*
Pub: Apress L.P.

Ed: Tony Campbell. **Released:** July 2006. **Price:** $39.99. **Description:** Profile of Microsoft's Windows Small Business Server, designed for companies with 50 or fewer employees.

4725 ■ *"Put Your Data to Work in the Marketplace" in Harvard Business Review (Vol. 86, September 2008, No. 9, pp. 34)*
Pub: Harvard Business School Press

Ed: Thomas C. Redman. **Description:** Nine strategies are presented for data asset marketing including exploiting asymmetries, unbundling, repackaging, and offering new content.

4726 ■ *"Scanning Dell's Shopping List" in Barron's (Vol. 89, July 13, 2009, No. 28, pp. 24)*
Pub: Dow Jones & Co., Inc.

Ed: Mark Veverka. **Description:** It is believed that Dell will be looking for companies to acquire since they poached an experienced mergers-and-acquisitions executive. In addition Dell's CEO is reportedly telling people he plans to go shopping. Dell executives have also stated an interest in data storage.

4727 ■ *"Serials Solutions Launches 360 Resource Manager Consortium Edition" in Information Today (Vol. 26, February 2009, No. 2, pp. 32)*
Pub: Information Today, Inc.

Description: Serials Solutions new Serials Solutions 360 Resource Manager Consortium Edition helps consortia, groups and member libraries with their e-resource management services. The products allows users to consolidate e-resource metadata and acquisition information into one place, which enables groups to manage holdings, subscriptions, licensing, contacts, and cost information and to streamline delivery of information to members.

4728 ■ *Strategies for Growth in SMEs: The Role of Information and Information Systems*
Pub: Elsevier Science & Technology Books

Ed: Margi Levy, Philip Powell. **Released:** December 2004. **Price:** $62.95. **Description:** Role of information and information systems in the growth of small and medium-sized enterprises in the U.S.

4729 ■ *"A Survey of DHT Security Techniques" in ACM Computing Surveys (Vol. 43, Summer 2011, No. 2, pp. 8)*
Pub: Association for Computing Machinery

Ed: Guido Urdaneta, Guillaume Pierre, Maarten Van Steen. **Description:** Peer-to-peer networks based on distributed hash tables (DHTs) have received considerable attention since their introduction in 2001. Unfortunately, DHT-based systems have been shown to be difficult to protect against security attacks. An overview of techniques reported in literature for making DHT-based systems resistant to the three most important attacks that can be launched by malicious nodes participating in the DHT is given: the Sybil attack, the Eclipse attack, and routing and storage attacks.

4730 ■ *"Tech Data Launches Unified Communications and Network Security Specialized Business Units" in Wireless News (October 22, 2009)*
Pub: Close-Up Media

Description: Responding to the growing demand for unified communications and network security, Tech Data announced the formation of two new Specialized Business Units.

4731 ■ *"The Total Cost of Ignorance: Avoiding Top Tech Mistakes" in Black Enterprise (Vol. 38, October 2007, No. 3, pp. 64)*
Pub: Earl G. Graves Publishing Co. Inc.

Ed: Alwin A.D. Jones. **Description:** Cost of data loss for any small business can be devastating; lack of security is another mistake companies make when it comes to technology.

4732 ■ *"Wegmans Uses Database for Recall" in Supermarket News (Vol. 56, September 22, 2008, No. 38)*
Pub: Penton Business Media, Inc.

Ed: Carol Angrisani. **Description:** Wegmans used data obtained through its loyalty card that, in turn, sent automated telephone calls to every customer who had purchased tainted pet food when Mars Petcare recalled dog food products.

4733 ■ *"What is the Future of Disk Drives, Death or Rebirth?" in ACM Computing Surveys (Vol. 43, Fall 2011, No. 3, pp. 23)*
Pub: Association for Computing Machinery

Ed: Yuhui Deng. **Description:** Disk drives have experienced dramatic development to meet performance requirements since the IBM 1301 disk drive

was announced in 1961. However, the performance gap between memory and disk drives has widened to 6 orders of magnitude and continues to widen by about 50 percent per year. Challenges and opportunities facing these storage devices are explored.

4734 ■ *"Z-Tech Lands Contract with CMS" in Black Enterprise (Vol. 37, October 2006, No. 3, pp. 36)*
Pub: Earl G. Graves Publishing Co. Inc.

Ed: Glenn Townes. **Description:** Z-Tech Corp., a Maryland-based company providing database design and warehousing, was awarded a five-year government contract with the Centers for Medicare and Medicaid Services' Chronic Care Improvement Program worth $20 million.

TRADE PERIODICALS

4735 ■ *DSSCourse*
Pub: Data Storage Systems Center

Ed: Meg A. Papa, Editor. **Released:** 2/year. **Price:** Free. **Description:** Reports on research conducted at the Center as well as the activities of faculty and students. Recurring features include notices of publications available and news of seminars and workshops.

4736 ■ *Journal of Database Management*
Contact: Dinesh Batra, Associate Editor

URL(s): www.igi-pub.com/journals/details.asp?id=198. **Released:** Quarterly **Price:** $210, Individuals print only; $860, Institutions print and free online; $595, Institutions online only; $595, Institutions print only.

4737 ■ *Online: The Leading Magazine for Information Professionals*
Pub: Online, A Division of Information Today Inc.

URL(s): www.infotoday.com/online/default.shtml. **Ed:** Marydee Ojala. **Released:** Bimonthly **Price:** $124.95, Individuals; $235, Two years; $141, Canada and Mexico; $167, Other countries.

4738 ■ *SIGIR Forum*
Pub: Association for Computing Machinery Special Interest Group on Array Programming Languages

Ed: Peter Anick, Editor. **Released:** 2/year. **Price:** $30, Included in membership; $30, nonmembers; $15, students. **Description:** Concerned with how machines may be used in the storage, retrieval, and dissemination of information, including news and information relating to retrieval theory, programming, file preparation, searching strategy, output schemes, systems evaluation, and development of equipment best suited for these tasks. Also contains proceedings of annual international SIGIR conferences.

VIDEOCASSETTES/ AUDIOCASSETTES

4739 ■ *Communications: The Wired World*
The Cinema Guild
115 W 30th St., Ste. 800
New York, NY 10001
Ph: (212)685-6242
Free: 800-723-5522
Fax: (212)685-4717
Co. E-mail: info@cinemaguild.com
URL: http://www.cinemaguild.com

Released: 198?. **Description:** The methods we will use to store and disseminate information in the future are examined. Developments considered for the future include instant transmission of diagnostic data to any hospital, robot manufacturing plants, and homemakers shopping electronically. **Availability:** 3/4 U; Special order formats.

TRADE SHOWS AND CONVENTIONS

4740 ■ COMDEX
Ziff-Davis Inc.
28 E 28th St.
New York, NY 10016-7939
Ph: (212)503-3500

Fax: (212)503-4599
Co. E-mail: randy_zane@ziffdavis.com
URL: http://www.ziffdavis.com
Contact: Vivek Shah, Chief Executive Officer
URL(s): www.comdex.com/. **Frequency:** Annual. **Audience:** Volume resellers and value-adders of small computers and related items; only a virtual trade show since 2003. **Principal Exhibits:** Small computer systems, related peripherals, software, accessories, services, and supplies. **Dates and Locations:** , Sands Expo and Convention Center.

COMPUTERIZED DATABASES

4741 ■ Business Wire
44 Montgomery St., 39th Fl.
San Francisco, CA 94104
Ph: (415)986-4422
Free: 800-227-0845
Fax: (415)788-5335
Co. E-mail: SF_sales_group@bizwire.com
URL: http://www.businesswire.com
Availability: Online: ProQuest LLC - Dialog; Dow Jones & Company Inc.; Mzinga Inc.; LexisNexis Group; Bloomberg L.P. **Type:** Full-text.

4742 ■ Computer Database
10650 Toebben Dr.
Independence, KY 41051
Free: 800-354-9706
Fax: (800)487-8488
Co. E-mail: investors@cengage.com
URL: http://www.gale.cengage.com
Contact: Ronald Dunn, President
Availability: Online: ProQuest LLC-Dialog; ProQuest LLC - Dialog; Cengage Learning Inc. **Type:** Bibliographic; Full-text.

4743 ■ Computer and Information Systems Abstracts
789 E Eisenhower Pky.
Ann Arbor, MI 48103
Ph: (734)761-4700
Fax: (734)997-4222
Co. E-mail: info@proquest.com
URL: http://www.csa.com
Availability: Online: ProQuest LLC - CSA; STN International; STN International. **Type:** Bibliographic.

4744 ■ Computerworld
One Exeter Plz., 15th Fl.
Boston, MA 02116

Ph: (617)534-1200
Co. E-mail: idgcorpcom@idg.com
URL: http://www.idg.com
Availability: Online: International Data Group Inc.; LexisNexis Group. **Type:** Full-text.

4745 ■ Gartner Online
56 Top Gallant Rd.
Stamford, CT 06904-7747
Ph: (203)964-0096
Fax: (203)316-6488
Co. E-mail: info@gartner.com
URL: http://www.gartner.com
Contact: Tony Friscia, President
E-mail: tfriscia@amrresearch.com
Availability: Online: Gartner Inc. **Type:** Numeric.

4746 ■ TecTrends™
PO Box 8120
Berkeley, CA 94707
Ph: (510)525-6220
Co. E-mail: tectrendsinfo@tectrends.com
URL: http://www.tectrends.com
Availability: Online: ProQuest LLC-Dialog; ProQuest LLC - Dialog; Information Sources Inc. - TecTrends. **Type:** Bibliographic; Directory.

LIBRARIES

4747 ■ University of Minnesota - Business Library
Wilson Library, Basement Level
309 19th Ave., S.
Minneapolis, MN 55455
Ph: (612)624-5073
Fax: (612)626-9353
Co. E-mail: busref@umn.edu
URL: http://busref.lib.umn.edu
Contact: Judy Wells
Scope: Business, finance and investments, marketing, accounting, management information systems, human resources & industrial relations, advertising, medical industry leadership, computer hardware and software, insurance, management science, transportation. **Services:** Interlibrary loan; copying; reference collection open to the public for reference use only. **Founded:** 1968. **Holdings:** 6511 volumes; 108,420 microforms. **Subscriptions:** 8530 journals and other serials. **Telecommunication Services:** lily@umn.edu.

4748 ■ University of Minnesota - Charles Babbage Institute - Center for the History of Information Technology
211 Andersen Library
222 21st Ave., S.
Minneapolis, MN 55455
Ph: (612)624-5050
Fax: (612)625-8054
Co. E-mail: cbi@umn.edu
URL: http://www.cbi.umn.edu
Contact: Thomas J. Misa, PhD, Director
Scope: History - information and technology, information storage and retrieval systems, computers, programming languages, computing; software industry; computer industry; Burroughs Corporation; Control Data Corporation. **Services:** Copying; collection open to researchers. **Founded:** 1979. **Holdings:** 600 volumes; 5500 lin.ft. of documents, oral interview transcripts, records; 300,000 photographs and other AV material; 1062 microforms. **Subscriptions:** 3 journals and other serials. **Telecommunication Services:** tmisa@umn.edu.

RESEARCH CENTERS

4749 ■ Boston University - Multimedia Communications Laboratory (MCL)
Department of Electrical & Computer Engineering
8 St. Mary's St.
Boston, MA 02215
Ph: (617)353-9877
Fax: (617)353-6440
Co. E-mail: tdcl@bu.edu
URL: http://hulk.bu.edu
Contact: Prof. Thomas D.C. Little, Director
Founded: 1991. **Publications:** *MCL Technical reports*. **Educational Activities:** MCL Research seminars. **Awards:** MCL Research assistantships, academic.

4750 ■ University of Florida - Database Systems Research Center
CSE Bldg., Rm. E452, Box 116125
Gainesville, FL 32611-6125
Ph: (352)392-1200
Fax: (352)392-1220
Co. E-mail: jhammer@cise.ufl.edu
URL: http://www.cise.ufl.edu/dbcenter/
Contact: Dr. Joachim Hammer, Director (Acting)
Services: Editorial services: to technical journals. **Founded:** 1977. **Publications:** *Database Systems Research Center Journal* (5/year); *Database Systems Research Center Conference proceedings* (10/year). **Educational Activities:** Research workshops, offered to industrial companies, government organizations, and academic institutions; Technical seminars.

ASSOCIATIONS AND OTHER ORGANIZATIONS

4751 ■ AFCOM
742 E Chapman Ave.
Orange, CA 92866
Ph: (714)643-8110
Fax: (714)997-9743
Co. E-mail: afcom@afcom.com
URL: http://www.afcom.com
Contact: Tom Roberts, President
Description: Data center, networking and enterprise systems management professionals from medium and large scale mainframe, midrange and client/server data centers worldwide. Works to meet the professional needs of the enterprise system management community. Provides information and support through educational events, research and assistance hotlines, and surveys. **Founded:** 1980. **Publications:** *AFCOM's Fall Program Proceedings* (Annual); *Annual Survey of Data Processing Operations Salaries* (Annual); *The Communique* (Monthly); *DCM Magazine* (Bimonthly); *Digest of Conference Sessions* (Annual); *Enterprise Management Issues* (Bimonthly). **Educational Activities:** Educational Conference (Semiannual); Focus on Enterprise Systems (Annual); Focus on Enterprise Systems (Annual). **Awards:** AFCOM Scholarship Fund at NTID (Annual); Enterprise Systems Manager of the Year Award (Annual); NTID Scholarship (Annual).

4752 ■ ASTD—American Society for Training and Development (ASTD)
1640 King St.
Alexandria, VA 22314-2746
Ph: (703)683-8100
Free: 800-628-2783
Fax: (703)683-1523
Co. E-mail: customercare@astd.org
URL: http://www.astd.org
Contact: Tony Bingham, President
E-mail: tbingham@astd.org
Description: Represents workplace learning and performance professionals. **Scope:** training and development, workplace performance. **Founded:** 1943. **Subscriptions:** 5000. **Publications:** *TD Magazine*; *ASTD Buyer's Guide* (Annual); *ASTD Buyer's Guide* (Annual); *Info-Line: Tips, Tools, and Intelligence for Trainers* (Monthly); *Learning Circuits* (Monthly); *T and D Magazine*; *TD Magazine* (Monthly); *Member Information Exchange (MIX)*; *TRAINET*; *Training Resources: ASTD Buyer's Guide* (Annual); *Buyer's Guide & Consultant Directory*; *American Society for Training and Development-- Training Video Directory*; *ASTD Buyer's Guide and Consultants Directory*; *Who's Who in Training and Development* (Annual); *ASTD Buyer's Guide and Consultants Directory*; *American Society Training and Development Buyer's Guide and Consultant Directory* (Annual); *Technical Training: Learning Technology for Performance Improvement*; *ASTD Buyer's Guide & Consultant Directory* (Annual); *Infoline Plus* (Monthly). **Educational Activities:** International Exposition (Annual); TechKnowledge Conference & Exposition (Annual); American Society for Training

and Development Conference; TechKnowledge Conference and Exposition (Annual). **Awards:** ASTD BEST Award; Awards in the Advancing ASTD's Vision; Awards in the Advancing Workplace Learning and Performance; Excellence in Practice; Dissertation Award; Torch Award; Gordon M. Bliss Memorial Award; Distinguished Contribution to Workplace Learning and Performance Award. **Telecommunication Services:** subscriberservice@astd.org.

4753 ■ Capital PC User Group (CPCUG)
19209 Mt. Airey Rd.
Brookeville, MD 20833
Ph: (301)560-6442
Fax: (301)760-3303
Co. E-mail: admin@cpcug.org
URL: http://www.cpcug.org
Contact: Dennis Courtney, President
Description: An educational and support group for users of IBM personal computers and compatible computers. Objectives are to: provide a forum for members of the IBM PC and compatible equipment; increase understanding and utilization of the personal computer; encourage experimentation and research on current and potential uses of personal computers; exchange information and experience for the benefit of all concerned; provide an opportunity for both formal and informal education in computer applications and hardware and software technologies. Provides speakers, instructors, materials, and experienced consultants to local educational institutions and nonprofit groups. Conducts charitable program. Sponsors special interest groups. Although it operates primarily in the Washington, DC, area, membership is international. **Scope:** computers. **Founded:** 1982. **Subscriptions:** 3000 books periodicals software.

4754 ■ Computer Assisted Language Instruction Consortium (CALICO)
Texas State University
214 Centennial Hall
601 University Dr.
San Marcos, TX 78666
Ph: (512)245-1417
Fax: (512)245-9089
Co. E-mail: info@calico.org
URL: http://calico.org
Contact: Ms. Esther Horn, Manager
Description: Individuals, corporations, and institutions from the academic, business, research, manufacturing, and government sectors. Seeks to apply primarily computer-related technology to the teaching, learning, and processing of first and second languages. Acts as clearinghouse; facilitates and coordinates information sharing. Conducts software fairs, workshops, and annual conferences on the application of computer-assisted language instruction. **Scope:** educational technology, computer-assisted language learning. **Founded:** 1983. **Subscriptions:** 20 business records monographs periodicals. **Publications:** *CALICO Resource Guide*; *CALICO Monograph Series*. **Awards:** Outstanding Article (Annual); Outstanding Graduate Student (Annual).

4755 ■ International Association for Computer Information Systems (IACIS)
c/o Richard McCarthy, Pres.
Quinnipiac University
School of Business
275 Mt. Carmel Ave.
Hamden, CT 06518
Co. E-mail: richard.mccarthy@quinnipiac.edu
URL: http://www.iacis.org
Contact: Richard McCarthy, President
Description: Educators and computer professionals. Seeks to promote the knowledge, use, and teaching of computers, and technology; dedicated to the improvement of information systems and computer professionals. **Scope:** computers, technology, education. **Founded:** 1960. **Subscriptions:** 43 software. **Publications:** *IACIS Newsletter* (Semiannual); *Journal of Computer Information Systems* (Quarterly). **Awards:** Computer Educator of the Year; Ben Braun Award for Excellence (Annual); Computer Educator of the Year (Annual).

4756 ■ Jobs for the Future (JFF)
88 Broad St., 8th Fl.
Boston, MA 02110
Ph: (617)728-4446
Fax: (617)728-4857
Co. E-mail: info@jff.org
URL: http://www.jff.org
Contact: Norma DeGraffenreid, Receptionist
Description: Seeks to integrate quality education and work opportunities. Offers technical assistance and training to educators, executives, and policy makers. Conducts research and disseminates results on trends in learning among students and employees. **Founded:** 1983. **Publications:** *Newswire* (Bimonthly).

4757 ■ Learning Resources Network (LERN)
PO Box 9
River Falls, WI 54022
Ph: (715)426-9777
Free: 800-678-5376
Fax: (888)234-8633
Co. E-mail: info@lern.org
URL: http://www.lern.org
Contact: William A. Draves, President
Description: Represents college and university affiliated groups, community education organizations, associations, recreation departments, and learning networks; continuing professional educators and individuals interested in lifelong learning. Objectives are: to help people and communities start adult learning programs; to provide technical assistance to existing adult learning organizations; to promote alternative education and social change at the national level. Serves as a national technical assistance network in adult learning and noncredit programming. Provides speakers and technical assistance to members and nonmembers. Sponsors seminars; compiles statistics. **Scope:** Provides programming, management support, and marketing techniques for adult education providers, including online classes and in-house seminars. **Services:** Consulting and membership services. **Founded:** 1974. **Subscriptions:** 50200

archival material books reports. **Publications:** "Course Trends"; "Marketing Recreation Classes"; "LERN"; "Creating and Sustaining Partnerships"; "Continuing Education: The Essentials"; "Teaching Online"; "Generational Learning Styles"; "Nine Shift"; "Marketing Manual"; "Contract Training Manual"; "How To Teach Adults"; "Developing Successful New Programs". **Educational Activities:** LERN Conferences (Annual); Seminars and institutes; Learning Resources Network Conference (Annual). **Awards:** Sam Brightman Award (Annual). **Seminars:** Negotiation: Strategies to Get More and Give More; Designing Brochures for Results; Developing Your One-Year Marketing Plan; Building an Information-Age Organization. **Telecommunication Services:** draves@lern. org.

4758 ■ Society for Applied Learning Technology (SALT)
50 Culpeper St.
Warrenton, VA 20186
Ph: (540)347-0055
Fax: (540)349-3169
Co. E-mail: info@salt.org
URL: http://www.salt.org
Contact: Raymond G. Fox, President
Description: Senior executives from military, academic, and industrial organizations which design, manufacture, or use training technology, including computer assisted instruction, simulators, trainers, audio-visual instruction delivery devices, and job performance aids. Objectives are to contribute to the development of the highest standards and practices in the application of technology to training; to assist individuals, agencies, and institutions in applying training technology to the definition and solution of social problems; to facilitate the exchange of information and experience; to promote understanding and knowledge in actual and potential uses of technology in the field of training; to provide an effective educational channel among scientists, managers, and users of training technology in the private and public sectors in order to assure adequate skills, understanding, and effective management of training technology. Maintains special interest groups. **Founded:** 1972. **Publications:** *Conference Proceedings* (Annual); *Journal of Educational Technology Systems* (Quarterly); *Journal of Instruction Delivery Systems* (Quarterly); *Journal of Instruction Delivery Systems* (Quarterly); *Journal of Interactive Instruction Development* (Quarterly). **Educational Activities:** Interactive Technologies (Annual); New Learning Technologies (Annual); SALT Education Technology (Annual).

REFERENCE WORKS

4759 ■ *"MindLeaders' Online Training Courses Come to ePath Learning" in Information Today (Vol. 26, February 2009, No. 2, pp. 4)*
Pub: Information Today, Inc.
Description: MindLeaders has partnered with ePath Learning to provide clients with over 2,200 new online courses. ePath's integrated Learning Management Service (iLMS) allows organizations to create online training programs for employees.

TRADE PERIODICALS

4760 ■ *Alpha Forum*
Pub: Alpha Forum Inc.
Ed: Tom Marcellus, Editor. **Released:** Monthly. **Price:** $59, individuals in the U.S.; $69, individuals elsewhere. **Description:** Contains tips, techniques, and application articles for Alpha Software's Alpha Four.

4761 ■ *Computer Science Education*
Pub: Routledge Journals Taylor & Francis Group
URL(s): www.tandf.co.uk/journals/titles/08993408. asp. **Released:** Quarterly **Price:** $232, Individuals print only; $739, Institutions online only; $822, Institutions print and online.

4762 ■ *Computer Science Index*
Pub: EBSCO Publishing
Contact: Tim Collins, President
E-mail: tcollins@ebscohost.com
URL(s): www.ebsco.com/home/whatsnew/csi.asp-www.epnet.com.

4763 ■ *DCLNews*
Pub: Data Conversion Laboratory
Contact: Mark Gross, President
Released: Monthly. **Price:** Included in membership;. **Description:** E-journal providing you insider information on XML and SGML, along with the latest technology and e-publishing news.

4764 ■ *Educational Technology Magazine: Magazine for Managers of Change in Education*
Pub: Educational Technology Publ
Contact: Barney Quint, Manager
URL(s): bookstoread.com/etp. **Released:** 6/yr. **Price:** $259, Individuals; $289, Other countries.

4765 ■ *Learning and Leading with Technology*
Pub: International Society for Technology in Education
Contact: Holly Jobe, President
URL(s): www.iste.org/learn/publications/learning-and-leading.aspx. **Ed:** Kate Conley. **Released:** 8/year.

4766 ■ *Media Computing*
Pub: Dreamscape Productions
Ed: Sheridan Tatsuno, Editor, statsuno@aol.com. **Released:** Monthly. **Price:** $495, institutions in the U.S. and Canada; $550, institutions elsewhere. **Description:** Supplies analysis of multimedia, internet, intranet, and web computing issues. Recurring features include interviews and reports of meetings.

4767 ■ *Online: The Leading Magazine for Information Professionals*
Pub: Online, A Division of Information Today Inc.
URL(s): www.infotoday.com/online/default.shtml. **Ed:** Marydee Ojala. **Released:** Bimonthly **Price:** $124.95, Individuals; $235, Two years; $141, Canada and Mexico; $167, Other countries.

4768 ■ *Smart Access*
Pub: Pinnacle Publishing Inc. Lawrence Ragan Communications, Inc.
Ed: Farlon Grove, Editor. **Released:** Monthly. **Price:** $149, individuals in the U.S.;; $169, individuals elsewhere. **Description:** Contains tips, techniques, and application articles for Microsoft Corporation's Microsoft Access. Also includes an accompanying source code disk.

4769 ■ *TechTrends*
Pub: Association for Educational Communications and Technology
Contact: Ward Cates, President
E-mail: wcates@smarter-by-design.com
URL(s): www.aect.org/intranet/publications/index.as-pwww.springer.com/education+%26+language/learning+%26+instruction/jou rnal/11528. **Released:** Bimonthly **Price:** Free to AECT members; $111, Institutions print and electronic; $133, Institutions print and enhanced access.

VIDEOCASSETTES/ AUDIOCASSETTES

4770 ■ *Adult Learning Video? You've Got to Be Kidding!*
ASTD
1640 King St.
Alexandria, VA 22314-2746
Ph: (703)683-8100
Free: 800-628-2783
Fax: (703)683-1523
Co. E-mail: customercare@astd.org
URL: http://www.astd.org
Contact: Tony Bingham, President
E-mail: tbingham@astd.org
Released: 1989. **Description:** A look at the seven steps to becoming an all-star trainer in business and industry. Describes how to use the principles of learning theory to improve training sessions. Focuses on the issues of the adult learner, including fear of failure, new technology vs. past experience, and bureaucractic systems. **Availability:** VHS; 3/4 U.

4771 ■ *Computer Applications: Lifestyle*
Encyclopedia Britannica
331 N. LaSalle St.
Chicago, IL 60654
Ph: (312)347-7159
Free: 800-323-1229
Fax: (312)294-2104
URL: http://www.britannica.com
Released: 1982. **Description:** A look at how computers are affecting the job, life at home and the marketplace. **Availability:** VHS; 3/4 U.

4772 ■ *A Crash Course on the Internet*
Tapeworm Video Distributors
25876 The Old Road #141
Stevenson Ranch, CA 91381
Ph: (661)257-4904
Fax: (661)257-4820
Co. E-mail: sales@tapeworm.com
URL: http://www.tapeworm.com
Released: 19??. **Price:** $69.95. **Description:** Presents a thorough explanation of many facets of the Internet, including definitions, file transfers, and plug-in installations. **Availability:** VHS.

4773 ■ *Industrial Computer Control*
Williams Learning Network
15400 Calhoun Dr.
Rockville, MD 20855-2762
Fax: (301)315-6880
Co. E-mail: mait@willearn.com
URL: http://www.willearn.com
Released: 19??. **Description:** Four-module, 42-section comprehensive industrial training program aimed at training industrial technicians to maintain state-of-the-art computer-based instrumentation and control equipment, including digital instrumentation, programmable controllers, distributed control systems, and other types of computer-controlled equipment. Comes with five student guides, five textbooks, and an instructor guide. **Availability:** VHS.

4774 ■ *Instrument Technician Training Program (ITTP)*
ISA -The International Society of Automation (ISA)
67 Alexander Dr.
Research Triangle Park, NC 27709
Ph: (919)549-8411
Fax: (919)549-8288
Co. E-mail: info@isa.org
URL: http://www.isa.org
Contact: Robert Renner, Director
Released: 1982. **Description:** Twenty-two modules provide basic information on the maintenance and repair of pneumatic instruments, electronic instruments, and microprocessors and digital systems. **Availability:** 3/4 U; Special order formats.

4775 ■ *Shake Hands with Your Computer*
Educational Video Network
1401 19th St.
Huntsville, TX 77340
Ph: (936)295-5767
Free: 800-762-0060
Fax: (936)294-0233
URL: http://www.evndirect.com
Released: 19??. **Price:** $59.95. **Description:** Teaches basic computer skills in layman's terms. **Availability:** VHS.

TRADE SHOWS AND CONVENTIONS

4776 ■ *COMDEX*
Ziff-Davis Inc.
28 E 28th St.
New York, NY 10016-7939
Ph: (212)503-3500
Fax: (212)503-4599
Co. E-mail: randy_zane@ziffdavis.com
URL: http://www.ziffdavis.com
Contact: Vivek Shah, Chief Executive Officer
URL(s): www.comdex.com/. **Frequency:** Annual. **Audience:** Volume resellers and value-adders of small computers and related items; only a virtual trade show since 2003. **Principal Exhibits:** Small computer

systems, related peripherals, software, accessories, services, and supplies. **Dates and Locations:** , Sands Expo and Convention Center.

4777 ■ Michigan Association for Computer Users in Learning Conference

Michigan Association for Computer Users in Learning
3410 Belle Chase Way, Ste. 100
Lansing, MI 48911
Ph: (517)882-1403
Fax: (517)882-2362
Co. E-mail: macul@macul.org
URL: http://www.macul.org
Contact: Ric Wiltse, Executive Director
URL(s): www.macul.org. **Frequency:** Annual. **Audience:** Educational technology professionals. **Principal Exhibits:** Computer and educational equipment, supplies, and services.

FRANCHISES AND BUSINESS OPPORTUNITIES

4778 ■ CMIT Solutions

500 N Capital of TX Highway, Bldg. 6, Ste. 200
Austin, TX 78746
Ph: (512)477-6667
Free: 800-710-2648
Fax: (512)692-3711
URL: http://www.cmitsolutions.com
Description: Offers IT service and computer support to small businesses. Franchise can be home-based, as we service the client at their place of business. **No. of Franchise Units:** 137. **Founded:** 1994. **Franchised:** 1998. **Equity Capital Needed:** $124,800-$150,950 total investment. **Franchise Fee:** $49,500. **Royalty Fee:** 6%. **Financial Assistance:** Limited third party financing available. **Training:** Offers 3 weeks training at headquarters, 1 week onsite with ongoing support.

4779 ■ Compuchild

Compuchild Services of America
1800 Halifax St.
Camel, IN 46032
Ph: (317)817-9817
Free: 800-619-5437
Fax: (317)818-8184
Description: Computer education to children. **No. of Franchise Units:** 69. **No. of Company-Owned Units:** 1. **Founded:** 1994. **Franchised:** 1995. **Equity Capital Needed:** $15,000. **Franchise Fee:** $12,500 or $17,500. **Financial Assistance:** Yes. **Training:** Yes.

4780 ■ Computer Explorers

ICED
PO Box 1511
Cypress, TX 77410
Ph: (888)638-8722
Fax: (281)256-4178
URL: http://www.computerexplorers.com
Description: Turnkey educational technology franchise. Home office based business providing educational technology solutions for childcare centers, preschools, public and private schools, recreation and community centers. Provides trained technology resource teachers who plan and guide the lessons for students ages 3 to adult. Also offers training for professional development. No retail site is established. **No. of Franchise Units:** 65. **Founded:** 1983. **Franchised:** 1989. **Equity Capital Needed:** $30,000. **Franchise Fee:** $35,000. **Financial Assistance:** Yes. **Training:** Provides 2 week instruction at training facility in Texas and ongoing training and support.

4781 ■ Executrain Corporation

2500 Northwinds Pkwy., Ste. 460
Alpharetta, GA 30009
Ph: (770)667-7700
Fax: (770)521-6084
Description: Specializes in the education of business professionals, teaching clients how to use popular business related software through hands-on classroom training. **No. of Franchise Units:** 166. **Founded:** 1984. **Franchised:** 1986. **Equity Capital Needed:** $500,000. **Franchise Fee:** Varies by territory. **Financial Assistance:** Yes. **Training:** Yes.

4782 ■ New Horizons Computer Learning Centers, Inc.

New Horizons Worldwide, Inc.
1900 S State College Blvd., Ste. 120
Anaheim, CA 92806
Ph: (714)940-8188
Fax: (714)938-6008
Co. E-mail: na.franchising@newhorizons.com
URL: http://www.newhorizons.com
Description: Complete PC, Macintosh, Novell and Unix training company. Provides 1 and 2 day classes to businesses and individuals at the center or at the client's location. **No. of Franchise Units:** 300. **No. of Company-Owned Units:** 2. **Founded:** 1982. **Franchised:** 1992. **Equity Capital Needed:** $350,000-$500,000. **Franchise Fee:** $60,00-$75,000-$125,000. **Financial Assistance:** Yes. **Training:** Training provided at corporate headquarters with ongoing support.

4783 ■ PC Kidz

PO Box 133002
Tyler, TX 75713
Free: 888-311-5259
Fax: (903)726-7014
Description: Children's computer education. **No. of Franchise Units:** 12. **No. of Company-Owned Units:** 3. **Founded:** 2001. **Franchised:** 2005. **Equity Capital Needed:** $19,800-$91,300. **Franchise Fee:** $15,000-$45,000. **Royalty Fee:** 7%. **Training:** Offers 4 days at headquarters, 3 days onsite, onsite at child care facilities (part of 4 days at HQ) with ongoing support.

COMPUTERIZED DATABASES

4784 ■ Business Wire

44 Montgomery St., 39th Fl.
San Francisco, CA 94104
Ph: (415)986-4422
Free: 800-227-0845
Fax: (415)788-5335
Co. E-mail: SF_sales_group@bizwire.com
URL: http://www.businesswire.com
Availability: Online: ProQuest LLC - Dialog; Dow Jones & Company Inc.; Mzinga Inc.; LexisNexis Group; Bloomberg L.P. **Type:** Full-text.

4785 ■ Computer Database

10650 Toebben Dr.
Independence, KY 41051
Free: 800-354-9706
Fax: (800)487-8488
Co. E-mail: investors@cengage.com
URL: http://www.gale.cengage.com
Contact: Ronald Dunn, President
Availability: Online: ProQuest LLC-Dialog; ProQuest LLC - Dialog; Cengage Learning Inc. **Type:** Bibliographic; Full-text.

4786 ■ Computer and Information Systems Abstracts

789 E Eisenhower Pky.
Ann Arbor, MI 48103
Ph: (734)761-4700
Fax: (734)997-4222
Co. E-mail: info@proquest.com
URL: http://www.csa.com
Availability: Online: ProQuest LLC - CSA; STN International; STN International. **Type:** Bibliographic.

4787 ■ Computerworld

One Exeter Plz., 15th Fl.
Boston, MA 02116
Ph: (617)534-1200
Co. E-mail: idgcorpcom@idg.com
URL: http://www.idg.com
Availability: Online: International Data Group Inc.; LexisNexis Group. **Type:** Full-text.

4788 ■ TecTrends™

PO Box 8120
Berkeley, CA 94707
Ph: (510)525-6220
Co. E-mail: tectrendsinfo@tectrends.com
URL: http://www.tectrends.com
Availability: Online: ProQuest LLC-Dialog; ProQuest LLC - Dialog; Information Sources Inc. - TecTrends. **Type:** Bibliographic; Directory.

RESEARCH CENTERS

4789 ■ Los Alamos National Laboratory - Advanced Computing Laboratory (ACL)

TA-3, Bldg. SM-2011, Rm. 202
Los Alamos, NM 87545
Ph: (505)665-2000
Fax: (505)665-4939
URL: http://www.ccs.lanl.gov/ccs1/
Contact: Richard Graham, Leader
Services: Technology transfer agreements with universities, industry, vendors, and funding agencies. **Founded:** 1989. **Publications:** *Journal of the Advanced Computer Laboratory.* **Educational Activities:** Classes, workshops, and seminars, on high performance computing; Cyber security student program, in summer; ACL Seminar series.

4790 ■ Massachusetts Institute of Technology - Center for Collective Intelligence (CCI)

5 Cambridge Ctr., NE25-753
Sloan School of Management
Cambridge, MA 02142
Ph: (617)253-6843
Fax: (617)253-2242
Co. E-mail: rjl@mit.edu
URL: http://cci.mit.edu
Contact: Robert Halperin, Executive Director
E-mail: rrhalp@mit.edu
Founded: 1989. **Publications:** *CCI Working papers* (Occasionally). **Educational Activities:** CCI Seminars and conferences.

4791 ■ Michigan State University - Software Engineering and Network Systems Laboratory (SENS)

3115 Engineering Bldg.
East Lansing, MI 48224
Ph: (517)355-8344
Fax: (517)432-1061
Co. E-mail: chengb@cse.msu.edu
URL: http://www.cse.msu.edu/sens
Contact: Dr. Betty H.C. Cheng, Director
Founded: 1990. **Educational Activities:** IEEE International Conference on Requirements Engineering; IEEE International Conference on Software Engineering; International Software Engineering Week; Workshop on Industrial Strength Formal Specification Techniques.

4792 ■ Rice University - Computer and Information Technology Institute (CITI)

MS-39
Houston, TX 77251-1892
Ph: (713)348-5823
Fax: (866)596-1062
Co. E-mail: vardi@rice.edu
URL: http://www.k2i.rice.edu
Contact: Jan E. Odegard, Executive Director
E-mail: odegard@rice.edu
Services: Electronic Software Distribution System: for access to public domain and licensable software. **Founded:** 1986. **Publications:** *CITI Technical reports.* **Educational Activities:** Artificial Intelligence Symposium; Compaq/Rice High Performance Software Symposium; Graduate and undergraduate student training; Short courses and research symposia; U.S. Army Conference on Applied Statistics, on Applied Statistics. **Telecommunication Services:** k2i@rice.edu.

4793 ■ University of Michigan - Collaboratory for Research on Electronic Work (CREW)

School of Information N, Rm. 2226
1075 Beal Ave.
Ann Arbor, MI 48109-2112
Ph: (734)764-6131

Fax: (734)647-8045
Co. E-mail: finholt@umich.edu
URL: http://crew.umich.edu/
Contact: Thomas A. Finholt, Director
Founded: 1985. **Publications:** *Technical Report Series*. **Educational Activities:** Seminars, colloquia, conferences, and workshops.

ASSOCIATIONS AND OTHER ORGANIZATIONS

4794 ■ **International Society of Certified Electronics Technicians (ISCET)**
3608 Pershing Ave.
Fort Worth, TX 76107-4527
Ph: (817)921-9101
Free: 800-946-0201
Fax: (817)921-3741
Co. E-mail: info@iscet.org
URL: http://www.iscet.org
Contact: Dan Mundy, President
E-mail: dmundy@earthlink.net
Description: Technicians in 50 countries who have been certified by the society. Seeks to provide a fraternal bond among certified electronics technicians, raise their public image and improve the effectiveness of industry education programs for technicians. Offers training programs in new electronics information. Maintains library of service literature for consumer electronic equipment, including manuals and schematics for out-of-date equipment. Offers all FCC licenses. Sponsors testing program for certification of electronics technicians in the fields of audio, communications, computer, consumer, industrial, medical electronics, radar, radio-television and video. **Founded:** 1965. **Publications:** *ISCET Update* (Quarterly). **Educational Activities:** National Professional Service Convention and Trade Show (Annual). **Awards:** Technician of the Year; Technician of the Year Award.

4795 ■ **National Electronics Service Dealers Association (NESDA)**
3608 Pershing Ave.
Fort Worth, TX 76107-4527
Ph: (817)921-9061
Fax: (817)921-3741
Co. E-mail: mack@nesda.com
URL: http://www.nesda.com
Contact: Mack Blakely, Executive Director
Description: Local and state electronic service associations and companies. Supplies technical service information on business management training to electronic service dealers. Offers certification and training programs through International Society of Certified Electronics Technicians. Conducts technical service and business management seminars. **Founded:** 1963. **Publications:** *ProService Directory and Yearbook* (Annual). **Awards:** NESDA Awards; Associate Leadership Excellence Award (Annual); Best Local Publication (Annual); Everett Pershing Memorial Membership Award (Annual); Leo Shumavon Award (Annual); National Friend of Service (Annual); Outstanding Associate President Award (Annual); Outstanding Committee Chairperson Award (Annual); Person of the Year (Annual); M.L. Fineburgh, Sr., Award of Excellence (Annual); Richard Mildenberger Outstanding NESDA Officer (Annual).

EDUCATIONAL PROGRAMS

4796 ■ **Penn Foster Career School**
925 Oak St.
Scranton, PA 18515

Ph: (570)961-4033
Free: 800-275-4410
Fax: (570)702-8380
Co. E-mail: infoims@pennfoster.com
URL: http://www.pennfoster.edu
Contact: Richard W. Ferrin, President
URL(s): www.pennfoster.com, www.educationdirect.com. **Description:** Home-study school offering a small business management program. **Founded:** 1958. **Telecommunication Services:** info@pennfoster.com.

DIRECTORIES OF EDUCATIONAL PROGRAMS

4797 ■ *Directory of Private Accredited Career Schools and Colleges of Technology*
Pub: Accrediting Commission of Career Schools and Colleges of Technology
Contact: Michale S. McComis, Executive Director
Released: On web page. **Price:** Free. **Description:** Covers 3900 accredited post-secondary programs that provide training programs in business, trade, and technical fields, including various small business endeavors. Entries offer school name, address, phone, description of courses, job placement assistance, and requirements for admission. Arrangement is alphabetical.

REFERENCE WORKS

4798 ■ *Cisco Network Design Solutions for Small-Medium Businesses*
Pub: Cisco Press
Ed: Peter Rybaczyk. **Released:** August 2004. **Price:** $55.00. **Description:** Solutions for computer networking professionals using computer networks within a small to medium-sized business. Topics cover not only core networking issues and solutions, but security, IP telephony, unified communications, customer relations management, wireless LANs, and more.

4799 ■ *"CMS Products and Avecto Team for Business Security Product Solutions" in Wireless News (November 11, 2009)*
Pub: Close-Up Media
Description: CMS Products, a provider of data security, backup, content management and disaster recovery, has agreed on a strategic partnership with Avect, a provider in least privilege management. The partnership will allow the companies to bundle their products.

4800 ■ *"iMozi Integrates Esprida LiveControl for Advanced DVD Kiosk Hardware" in Wireless News (December 20, 2010)*
Pub: Close-Up Media Inc.
Description: Provider of self-service entertainment technology, iMozi Canada has partnered with Esprida to make its automated DVD Kiosk solutions Esprida-enabled. Esprida develops remote device management solutions and will offer enhanced capabilities and to improve customer experience for users.

4801 ■ *"PCI Express Powers Machine Vision" in Canadian Electronics (Vol. 23, February 2008, No. 1, pp. 8)*
Pub: CLB Media Inc.
Ed: Inder Kohli. **Description:** PCI Express is an innovative peripheral bus that can be used in industrial computing. The peripheral bus delivers a high-bandwidth, scaleable, point-to-point path from peripheral cards to the computing core. Features and functions of PCI Express are described in detail.

4802 ■ *Power Up Your Small-Medium Business: A Guide to Enabling Network Technologies*
Pub: Cisco Press
Ed: Robyn Aber. **Released:** March 2004. **Price:** $39.95 (US), $57.95 (Canadian). **Description:** Network technologies geared to small and medium-size business, focusing on access, IP telephony, wireless technologies, security, and computer network management.

TRADE PERIODICALS

4803 ■ *Association for Computing Machinery*
Pub: Special Interest Group on Data Communication
Ed: Martha Steenstrup, Editor. **Released:** Quarterly. **Price:** $50. **Description:** Serves as a forum for computing professionals in the data communications field. Focuses on network architecture, including the Internet, network protocols, and distributed systems.

4804 ■ *Electronic Products*
Contact: Christina Nickolas, Editor
E-mail: cnickolas@hearst.com
URL(s): www.electronicproducts.com. **Ed:** Christina Nickolas. **Released:** Monthly **Price:** $12, Individuals.

4805 ■ *The High-Tech News*
Pub: ETA International
Ed: Bryan Allen, Editor, bryan@eta-i.org. **Released:** Monthly. **Description:** Serves member technicians with news of the Association and the electronics industry, including items on service, education, employment, management, and events. Contains information on membership, management, telecommunications, and business and technical training programs. Recurring features include editorials, news of research, letters to the editor, book reviews, and a calendar of events.

4806 ■ *Microprocessor Report*
Pub: MicroDesign Resources
Released: 17x/yr. **Price:** $695, U.S. and Canada for print version; $495, U.S. and Canada pounds;. **Description:** The leading technical publication for the microprocessor industry. Dedicated to providing unbiased, in-depth, critical analysis of new high-performance microprocessor developments. This newsletter is exclusively subscriber-supported.

VIDEOCASSETTES/AUDIOCASSETTES

4807 ■ *Apple II Repair, Maintenance and Expansion*
Bergwall Productions, Inc.
1 Dickinson Drive, Brandywine Building 5, Ste. 105
Chadds Ford, PA 19317

Ph: (610)361-0334
Free: 800-934-8696
Fax: (610)361-0092
URL: http://www.bergwall.com
Released: 1987. **Price:** $249.00. **Description:** Many different repair techniques and applications for the Apple II are explored. **Availability:** VHS.

4808 ■ *Troubleshooting the IBM PC*
Bergwall Productions, Inc.
1 DIckinson Drive, Brandywine BUilding 5, Ste. 105
Chadds Ford, PA 19317
Ph: (610)361-0334
Free: 800-934-8696
Fax: (610)361-0092
URL: http://www.bergwall.com
Released: 1987. **Price:** $269.00. **Description:** Complete guide to isolating and repairing the problems of an IBM PC. **Availability:** VHS.

4809 ■ *Troubleshooting the IBM PC II*
Bergwall Productions, Inc.
1 DIckinson Drive, Brandywine BUilding 5, Ste. 105
Chadds Ford, PA 19317
Ph: (610)361-0334
Free: 800-934-8696
Fax: (610)361-0092
URL: http://www.bergwall.com
Released: 1987. **Price:** $359.00. **Description:** More information on IBM PC problems and solutions is given. **Availability:** VHS.

TRADE SHOWS AND CONVENTIONS

4810 ■ COMDEX
Ziff-Davis Inc.
28 E 28th St.
New York, NY 10016-7939
Ph: (212)503-3500
Fax: (212)503-4599
Co. E-mail: randy_zane@ziffdavis.com
URL: http://www.ziffdavis.com
Contact: Vivek Shah, Chief Executive Officer
URL(s): www.comdex.com/. **Frequency:** Annual. **Audience:** Volume resellers and value-adders of small computers and related items; only a virtual trade show since 2003. **Principal Exhibits:** Small computer systems, related peripherals, software, accessories, services, and supplies. **Dates and Locations:** , Sands Expo and Convention Center.

FRANCHISES AND BUSINESS OPPORTUNITIES

4811 ■ Cm It Solutions
500 N Capital of TX Hwy., Bldg. 6, Ste. 200
Austin, TX 78746
Ph: (800)399-2648
Fax: (512)692-3711
Co. E-mail: franchise@computermoms.com
URL: http://www.computermoms.com
Description: Computer support services: system maintenance, problem resolution, upgrades, network design, and training needs to business to business owners and professionals. **No. of Franchise Units:** 125. **Founded:** 1994.. **Franchised:** 1998. **Equity Capital Needed:** $100,000-$125,000. **Franchise Fee:** $44,950 plus terr. fee. **Training:** Training includes 2 weeks at corporate office, business coaching, support website and telephone line, email exchange, newsgroups, meetings and conferences.

4812 ■ Computer Medics of America, Inc.
2260 N Green Forest Dr.
Palmer, AK 99645
Ph: (907)694-0371
Fax: (800)665-8568
Co. E-mail: marketing@computermedicsofamerica.com
URL: http://www.computermedicsofamerica.com
Description: Mobile repair computer services. **No. of Franchise Units:** 54. **No. of Company-Owned Units:** 2. **Founded:** 2000.. **Franchised:** 2003. **Equity Capital Needed:** $10,300-$60,000. **Franchise Fee:**

$7,000-$23,000. **Financial Assistance:** Financial assistance available for franchise fee. **Training:** Includes 1 week training at headquarters and ongoing support.

4813 ■ Computer Troubleshooters
Computer Troubleshooters USA, Inc.
2296 Henderson Mill Rd. NE, Ste. 405
Atlanta, GA 30345
Ph: (877)704-1702
Fax: (770)234-6162
Co. E-mail: info@comptroub.com
URL: http://www.comptroub.com
Description: Onsite computer service franchise, with over 340 locations in 18 countries. Provide IT services to small businesses and residential users in their area. **No. of Franchise Units:** 460. **No. of Company-Owned Units:** 1. **Founded:** 1997.. **Franchised:** 1997. **Equity Capital Needed:** $29,000 estimated start-up costs. **Franchise Fee:** $14,500. **Training:** Yes.

4814 ■ Concerto Networks
PO Box 9326
San Diego, CA 92169-0326
Ph: (858)386-4177
Free: 888-565-9198
Co. E-mail: info@concertonetworks.com
URL: http://www.concertonetworks.com
Description: Onsite Simple Office Solutions. **No. of Franchise Units:** 38. **Founded:** 2002.. **Franchised:** 2003. **Equity Capital Needed:** $12,500. **Franchise Fee:** $1,250-$12,500. **Royalty Fee:** $199/month. **Training:** Yes. **Telecommunication Services:** franchiseinfo@concertonetworks.com.

4815 ■ Data Doctors
Data Doctors Franchise Systems, Inc.
Description: Computer sales and services, including web services. **No. of Franchise Units:** 69. **No. of Company-Owned Units:** 8. **Founded:** 1988.. **Franchised:** 2002. **Equity Capital Needed:** $122,065-$178,415. **Franchise Fee:** $35,000. **Royalty Fee:** 5%. **Training:** Initial 11 day training at headquarters, 1 week onsite prior to opening and 1 week following opening and ongoing support.

4816 ■ Debugit Computer Services
922 Rte. 70, W
Marlton, NJ 08053
Ph: (856)489-9704
Description: Computer maintenance services. **No. of Company-Owned Units:** 1. **Founded:** 2000. **Franchised:** 2005. **Equity Capital Needed:** $127,000-$163,500. **Franchise Fee:** $30,000. **Royalty Fee:** 7%. **Training:** 5 days at headquarters, 3 days at franchisee's location and ongoing.

4817 ■ Expetec Technology Services
Expetec Corp.
12 2nd Ave., SW
Aberdeen, SD 57401
Free: 888-209-2292
Fax: (605)225-5176
Co. E-mail: sales@cdfs.com
URL: http://www.expetec.biz
Description: Provides computer repair and technology services. **No. of Franchise Units:** 40. **No. of Company-Owned Units:** 1. **Founded:** 1992.. **Franchised:** 1996. **Equity Capital Needed:** $82,000-$121,000. **Franchise Fee:** $45,000. **Financial Assistance:** Yes. **Training:** Provides training on franchise management, customer service, marketing & advertising.

4818 ■ Fast-teks On-site Computer Services
15310 Amberly Dr., Ste. 185
Tampa, FL 33647
Ph: (800)262-1671
Fax: (813)932-2485
URL: http://www.fastteks.com
Description: Onsite computer repair services. **No. of Franchise Units:** 249. **Founded:** 2003.. **Franchised:** 2004. **Equity Capital Needed:** $36,460-$62,260. **Franchise Fee:** $19,750-$42,250. **Royalty Fee:** 8%. **Financial Assistance:** Third party financing available. **Training:** Offers 2 days training at headquarters and 2 days onsite with ongoing support provided.

4819 ■ Friendly Computers
Big L's, Inc.
3616 North Rancho
Las Vegas, NV 89130
Ph: (702)458-2780
Free: 800-656-3115
Fax: (702)869-2780
URL: http://www.friendlycomputers.com/franchise
Description: Onsite service and sales of computers to homes and businesses within a given territory. **No. of Franchise Units:** 52. **No. of Company-Owned Units:** 1. **Founded:** 1992.. **Franchised:** 2000. **Equity Capital Needed:** $47,500-$176,980. **Franchise Fee:** $15,000-$25,000. **Financial Assistance:** Yes. **Training:** 1 Week training at Corporate Store and an additional week of training at franchisees location.

4820 ■ Geeks On The Way
1223 Macleod Tr., SE
Calgary, AB, Canada L6T 4Z2
Ph: (403)283-3316
Fax: (403)206-7270
Co. E-mail: franchise@geeksontheway.com
URL: http://www.geeksontheway.com
Description: Provides quality computer support from removing viruses and spy ware to diagnosing and replacing defective hardware to maintaining corporate networks. **No. of Company-Owned Units:** 4. **Founded:** 2001.. **Franchised:** 2006. **Equity Capital Needed:** $43,400. **Franchise Fee:** $15,000. **Training:** Provides 2 weeks then weekly consultations for one year.

4821 ■ Nerd Force
97 New Drop Plz.
Staten Island, NY 10306
Free: 800-979-6373
Fax: (718)370-6731
Description: Onsite tech support services. **No. of Franchise Units:** 24. **No. of Company-Owned Units:** 3. **Founded:** 2003. **Franchised:** 2007. **Equity Capital Needed:** $34,100-$59,000. **Franchise Fee:** $14,000. **Royalty Fee:** $100/week. **Training:** Provides 1 week at headquarters, 1 week at franchisee's location and ongoing support.

4822 ■ Teamlogic IT
Franchise Services, Inc.
26722 Plaza Dr.
Mission Viejo, CA 92691
Ph: (949)582-6300
Free: 866-TEA-MLOG
Fax: (949)582-6301
Co. E-mail: franchise.sales@teamlogicIT.com
URL: http://www.teamlogicIT.com
Description: Offers computer consultation, maintenance & repair service to small & mid-sized businesses. **No. of Franchise Units:** 46. **Founded:** 2004.. **Franchised:** 2005. **Equity Capital Needed:** $120,000 total investment. **Franchise Fee:** $35,000. **Financial Assistance:** Yes. **Training:** Yes.

LIBRARIES

4823 ■ DeVry University, Chicago Campus Library
3300 N. Campbell Ave.
Chicago, IL 60618
Ph: (773)929-8500
Fax: (773)697-2714
Co. E-mail: jrossi@devry.edu
URL: http://www.chi.devry.edu/Library.html
Contact: Jason Rossi
Scope: Business, electronics, computer science, telecommunications. **Services:** Interlibrary loan; copying; center open to the public for reference use only. **Holdings:** 20,000 volumes. **Subscriptions:** 70 journals and other serials.

4824 ■ DeVry University, Columbus Campus Library
1350 Alum Creek Dr.
Columbus, OH 43209-2705
Ph: (614)253-7291
Free: 800-426-2206

Fax: (614)252-4108
Co. E-mail: bweaver@devry.edu
URL: http://www.cols.devry.edu/library.html
Contact: Bruce Weaver, Director
Scope: Electronics technology, computer science, business operations, accounting. **Services:** Library open to the students. **Founded:** 1970. **Holdings:** 23,000 volumes. **Subscriptions:** 50 journals and other serials. **Telecommunication Services:** oriley@devry.edu.

4825 ■ DeVry University - James E. Lovan Library
11224 Holmes Rd.
Kansas City, MO 64131
Ph: (816)941-0430, x5220
Fax: (816)941-0896
Co. E-mail: bcaldarello@devry.edu
URL: http://www.kc.devry.edu/Library.html
Contact: Beth Caldarello, Director, Library Services
Scope: Electronics, computer information systems, business, accounting, telecommunications. **Services:** Copying; Center open to the public for reference use only. **Founded:** 1931. **Holdings:** 15,500 books; 450 videos; 750 CD-ROMs. **Subscriptions:** 1500 journals and other serials.

4826 ■ DeVry University Library Services
4800 Regent Blvd.
Irving, TX 75063-2440
Ph: (972)929-9347
Fax: (972)929-6778
Co. E-mail: gferdman@devry.edu
URL: http://www.dal.devry.edu/Library.html
Contact: Glenn Ferdman, Librarian

URL(s): www.librarydb.devry.edu. **Scope:** Electronics, computer science, electronic engineering, business information, telecommunications, accounting, information technology, electrical engineering. **Services:** Copying; information services for handicapped; center open to the public for reference use only. **Founded:** 1969. **Holdings:** 15,300 books; 875 videotapes; computer software. **Subscriptions:** 57 journals and other serials. **Telecommunication Services:** devrylib@devry.edu.

4827 ■ Walt Disney World - Global Business Technology Strategy Library
Team Disney 336-N
1375 Buena Vista Dr.
Lake Buena Vista, FL 32830-1000
Ph: (407)828-4250

Fax: (407)827-8260
Co. E-mail: david.w.hartman@disney.com
URL: http://disneyworld.disney.go.com/wdw
Contact: David Hartman, Librarian
Scope: Computer science, human resources, general business. **Services:** Center not open to the public. **Founded:** 1986. **Holdings:** 4000 books, videos, DVDs, and CDs; 100 AV equipment. **Subscriptions:** 200 journals and other serials; 3 newspapers.

4828 ■ IBM Corporation - Burlington Technical Library
967-B, 1000 River St.
Essex Junction, VT 05452-4299
Ph: (802)769-6519
Fax: (802)769-6501
Co. E-mail: karenlyn@us.ibm.com
URL: http://www.ibm.com/us/en/
Contact: Karen Kromer Lynch, Director, Library Services
Scope: Semiconductor manufacturing, chemistry, computing, solid-state electronics, physics, business and professional, project management, programming, management science, mathematics. **Services:** Interlibrary loan; Center not open to the public. **Founded:** 1965. **Holdings:** 10,000 books; 100 reels of microfilm. **Subscriptions:** 160 journals and other serials.

START-UP INFORMATION

4829 ■ *"Probability Processing Chip: Lyric Semiconductor" in Inc. (Volume 32, December 2010, No. 10, pp. 52)*
Pub: Inc. Magazine

Ed: Christine Lagorio. **Description:** Lyric Semiconductor, a start up located in Cambridge, Massachusetts, has developed a computer chip that also uses values that fall between zero and one, resulting in a chip that can process information using probabilities, considering many possible answers that find the best fit.

ASSOCIATIONS AND OTHER ORGANIZATIONS

4830 ■ **Association for Women in Computing (AWC)**
PO Box 2768
Oakland, CA 94602
Co. E-mail: info@awc-hq.org
URL: http://www.awc-hq.org
Contact: Jill Sweeney, President

Description: Individuals interested in promoting the education, professional development, and advancement of women in computing. **Founded:** 1978. **Awards:** Augusta Ada Lovelace Award; Augusta Ada Lovelace Award (Annual); President's Award (Annual).

4831 ■ **Black Data Processing Associates (BDPA)**
9500 Arena Dr., Ste. 350
Largo, MD 20774
Ph: (301)584-3135
Free: 800-727-BDPA
Fax: (301)560-8300
Co. E-mail: office@bdpa.org
URL: http://www.bdpa.org
Contact: Monique F. Berry, President

Description: Represents persons employed in the information processing industry, including electronic data processing, electronic word processing and data communications; others interested in information processing. Seeks to accumulate and share information processing knowledge and business expertise to increase the career and business potential of minorities in the information processing field. Conducts professional seminars, workshops, tutoring services and community introductions to data processing. Makes annual donation to the United Negro College Fund. **Founded:** 1975. **Educational Activities:** Looking at Tomorrow Today (Annual). **Awards:** Dr. Jesse L. Bemley Scholarship Award (Annual).

4832 ■ **Blissymbolics Communication International (BCI)**
1630 Lawrence Ave. W, Ste. 104
Toronto, ON, Canada M6L 1C5
Ph: (416)644-8291

Fax: (416)244-6543
Co. E-mail: bci@blissymbolics.org
URL: http://www.blissymbolics.org
Contact: Mats Lundalv, President

Description: Promotes appropriate use of Blissymbol applications in software, publications, and educational materials. Conducts research and educational programs. **Scope:** augmentative communication, alternative communication. **Founded:** 1975. **Subscriptions:** archival material books.

4833 ■ **British Columbia Technology Industries Association (BC TIA)**
1188 W Georgia St., Ste. 900
Vancouver, BC, Canada V6E 4A2
Ph: (604)683-6159
Fax: (604)683-3879
Co. E-mail: info@bctia.org
URL: http://www.bctia.org
Contact: Bill Tam, President

Description: Fosters the growth and development of the Province's technology industries and member companies. Provides programs, services and activities designed to meet the needs and interests of members in the areas of networking, education, public awareness, and government relations. Offers a forum for members to review industry issues, acquire new business knowledge from leading industry professionals, to supply input on existing and proposed legislation and generally work together to advance the industry's interests. **Founded:** 1993. **Publications:** *Impact* (Annual).

4834 ■ **Canadian Image Processing and Pattern Recognition Society (CIPPRS)—Association Canadienne de Traitement d'Images et de Reconnaissance des Formes (ACTIRF)**
University of Western Ontario
Middlesex College 379
Dept. of Computer Science
London, ON, Canada N6A 5B7
Ph: (519)661-2111
Fax: (519)661-3515
Co. E-mail: cipprs@csd.uwo.ca
URL: http://www.gel.ulaval.ca
Contact: Prof. John Barron, Treasurer

URL(s): www.cipprs.org. **Description:** Strives to advance the theory and practice of signal and image processing for pattern analysis and classification, scene or speech understanding and recognition, computer vision, on-line and off-line document analysis and recognition, robotic perception, intelligent autonomous systems, biomedical imaging, neural networks and modeling, remote sensing, specialized architecture and industrial applications. **Scope:** image and signal processing. **Founded:** 1978. **Subscriptions:** articles. **Publications:** *Vision Interface.* **Educational Activities:** Computer and Robot Vision (Annual). **Awards:** Doctoral Dissertation Award (Annual); Distinguished Service Awards; CIPPS Distinguished Service Award (Annual).

4835 ■ *Impact*
1188 W Georgia St., Ste. 900
Vancouver, BC, Canada V6E 4A2

Ph: (604)683-6159
Fax: (604)683-3879
Co. E-mail: info@bctia.org
URL: http://www.bctia.org
Contact: Bill Tam, President
Released: Annual

4836 ■ **Institute for Certification of Computing Professionals (ICCP)**
2400 E Devon Ave., Ste. 281
Des Plaines, IL 60018-4610
Ph: (847)299-4227
Free: 800-843-8227
Fax: (847)299-4280
Co. E-mail: office2@iccp.org
URL: http://www.iccp.org
Contact: John Whitehouse, Director

Description: Professional societies. Promotes the development of computer examinations which are of high quality, directed toward information technology professionals, and designed to encourage competence and professionalism. Individuals passing the exams automatically become members of the Institute for Certification of Computing Professionals and become certified as CCP or ACP. Has developed code of ethics and good practice to which those taking the exams promise to adhere. Maintains speakers' bureau; compiles statistics. **Founded:** 1973. **Publications:** *Certified Business Intelligence Professional; ICCP Complete Guide to Professional Computing; ICCP Examinations Review Manual for Conference ExamCram Sessions; Official Exam Review Outline.*

4837 ■ **I.T. Financial Management Association (ITFMA)**
PO Box 30188
Santa Barbara, CA 93130
Ph: (805)687-7390
Fax: (805)687-7382
Co. E-mail: info@itfma.com
URL: http://www.itfma.com
Contact: Terence Quinlan, Director

Description: Individuals and corporations interested in the financial management of information technology (IT) organizations. Works for the education and improvement of members and the industry. Offers certification in IT financial management. Conducts peer studies, in-house seminars, and chargeback system reviews. Operates educational programs. **Founded:** 1988. **Publications:** *Journal of IS Financial Management* (Triennial); *Journal of IT Financial Management* (Triennial). **Awards:** Decade of Contribution Award (Annual); Education Certification (Annual).

4838 ■ **TechServe Alliance**
1420 King St., Ste. 610
Alexandria, VA 22314
Ph: (703)838-2050
Fax: (703)838-3610
Co. E-mail: staff@techservealliance.org
URL: http://www.techservealliance.org
Contact: Susan Thaden, President

Description: Businesses that provide the services of highly technical professionals, such as computer programmers, systems analysts, engineers, to clients in need of temporary technical support. Promotes legal and economic environment favorable to the technical services industry, including protection of a firm's freedom to choose either employees or independent contractors when supplying services to clients. Encourages professional standards in the industry; serves as a support mechanism for members. Provides industry-specific educational information and insurance discounts. **Founded:** 1987. **Publications:** *Directory of Members Firms* (Periodic); *NACCB Monitor* (Quarterly); *NACCB Newsletter* (Quarterly).

4839 ■ Vision Interface
University of Western Ontario
Middlesex College 379
Dept. of Computer Science
London, ON, Canada N6A 5B7
Ph: (519)661-2111
Fax: (519)661-3515
Co. E-mail: cipprs@csd.uwo.ca
URL: http://www.gel.ulaval.ca
Contact: Prof. John Barron, Treasurer

DIRECTORIES OF EDUCATIONAL PROGRAMS

4840 ■ Directory of Private Accredited Career Schools and Colleges of Technology
Pub: Accrediting Commission of Career Schools and Colleges of Technology
Contact: Michale S. McComis, Executive Director
Released: On web page. **Price:** Free. **Description:** Covers 3900 accredited post-secondary programs that provide training programs in business, trade, and technical fields, including various small business endeavors. Entries offer school name, address, phone, description of courses, job placement assistance, and requirements for admission. Arrangement is alphabetical.

REFERENCE WORKS

4841 ■ "AMT's Partner Program Enables New Security Business Models" in Internet Wire (August 12, 2010)
Pub: Comtex

Description: AMT, technical provider of physical access control Software as a Service (Saas) solutions, has developed a new Partner Program that allows partners to outsource any technical abilities lacking to AMT with no upfront fees.

4842 ■ "Auctions and Bidding: a Guide for Computer Scientists" in ACM Computing Surveys (Vol. 43, Summer 2011, No. 2, pp. 10)
Pub: Association for Computing Machinery

Ed: Simon Parsons, Juan A. Rodriguez-Aguilar, Mark Klein. **Description:** There are various actions: single dimensional, multi-dimensional, single-sided, double-sided, first-price, second-price, English, Dutch, Japanese, sealed-bid, and these have been extensively discussed and analyzed in economics literature. This literature is surveyed from a computer science perspective, primarily from the viewpoint of computer scientists who are interested in learning about auction theory, and to provide pointers into the economics literature for those who want a deeper technical understanding. In addition, since auctions are an increasingly important topic in computer science, the article also looks at work on auctions from the computer science literature. The aim is to identify what both bodies of work tell us about creating electronic auctions.

4843 ■ "Beam My Data Up" in Canadian Business (Vol. 80, February 12, 2007, No. 4, pp. 42)
Pub: Rogers Media

Ed: Marlene Rego. **Description:** Innovations in the field of teleportation since its invention by Gilles Brassard in 1992 is discussed.

4844 ■ "Burton Group Answers Industry Need for Practical Data Center Advice" in

Canadian Corporate News (May 14, 2007)
Pub: Comtex News Network Inc.

Description: Burton Group, an IT research firm focused on in-depth technical analysis of enterprise IT infrastructures, launched a new service providing practical advice for IT professionals facing critical data center decisions that due to technological advances can be more efficient while reducing costs.

4845 ■ "ChemSW Software Development Services Available for Outsourcing" in Information Today (Vol. 26, February 2009, No. 2, pp. 30)
Pub: Information Today, Inc.

Description: ChemSW software development services include requirements analysis, specification development, design, development, testing, and system documentation as an IT outsourcing solution. The company can also develop software tracking systems for satellite stockrooms, provide asset management integration solutions and more.

4846 ■ Cisco Network Design Solutions for Small-Medium Businesses
Pub: Cisco Press

Ed: Peter Rybaczyk. **Released:** August 2004. **Price:** $55.00. **Description:** Solutions for computer networking professionals using computer networks within a small to medium-sized business. Topics cover not only core networking issues and solutions, but security, IP telephony, unified communications, customer relations management, wireless LANs, and more.

4847 ■ "Cloudy Future for VMware?" in Barron's (Vol. 90, September 13, 2010, No. 37, pp. 21)
Pub: Barron's Editorial & Corporate Headquarters

Ed: Jonathan R. Laing. **Description:** VMWare dominated the virtualization market for years, but it may be ending as it faces more competition from rivals that offer cloud computing services. The company's stocks are also expensive and are vulnerable to the smallest mishap.

4848 ■ "Consumer Trust in E-Commerce Web Sites: a Meta-Study" in ACM Computing Surveys (Vol. 43, Fall 2011, No. 3, pp. 14)
Pub: Association for Computing Machinery

Ed: Patricia Beatty, Ian Reay, Scott Dick, James Miller. **Description:** Trust is at once an elusive, imprecise concept, and a critical attribute that must be engineered into e-commerce systems. Engineering trust is examined.

4849 ■ "Data Center Plan Bearing Fruit From Apple, Spec Center" in Charlotte Business Journal (Vol. 25, October 15, 2010, No. 30, pp. 1)
Pub: Charlotte Business Journal

Ed: Ken Elkins. **Description:** Apple Inc. is planning to expand its server farm at the North Carolina Data Center Corridor in Catawba County. T5 Partners, on the other hand, will build a shell building to house a server on the site. Infocrossing Inc. will also build an open data center in the area.

4850 ■ "Data Firm Growth 'Opportunistic'" in Tampa Bay Business Journal (Vol. 30, January 29, 2010, No. 6, pp. 1)
Pub: American City Business Journals

Ed: Michael Hinman. **Description:** E Solutions Corporation is experiencing growth amid the economic downturn, with its Park Tower data center occupancy in Tampa Florida expanding from 14,000 square feet to 20,000 square feet. Details on the increased operations fueled by demand for information storage and management services offered by the company are discussed.

4851 ■ "Discrete Wavelet Transform-Based Time Series Analysis and Mining" in ACM Computing Surveys (Vol. 43, Summer 2011, No. 2, pp. 6)
Pub: Association for Computing Machinery

Ed: Pimwadee Chaovalit, Aryya Gangopadhyay, George Karabatis, Zhiyuan Chen. **Description:** Time series are recorded values of an interesting phenomenon such as stock prices, household items, or

patient heart rates over a period of time. Time series data mining focuses on discovering interesting patterns in such data. An introduction to a wavelet-based times series data analysis is provided with a systematic survey of various analysis techniques that use discrete wavelet transformation (DWT) in time series data mining, and outlines the benefits of this approach demonstrated by previous studies performed on diverse application domains, including image classification, multimedia retrieval, and computer network anomaly detection.

4852 ■ "Experts Take the Temp of Obama Plan" in The Business Journal-Serving Metropolitan Kansas City (Vol. 27, November 14, 2008, No. 10)
Pub: American City Business Journals, Inc.

Ed: Rob Roberts. **Description:** Kansas City, Missouri-based employee benefits experts say president-elect Barack Obama's health care reform plan is on track. Insurance for children and capitalization for health information technology are seen as priority areas. The plan is aimed at reducing the number of uninsured people in the United States.

4853 ■ "The Failure Detector Abstraction" in ACM Computing Surveys (Vol. 43, Summer 2011, No. 2, pp. 9)
Pub: Association for Computing Machinery

Ed: Felix C. Freiling, Rachid Guerraoui, Petr Kuznetsov. **Description:** A failure detector is a fundamental abstraction in distributed computing. This article surveys this abstraction through two dimensions. First it studies failure detectors as building blocks to simplify the design of reliable distributed algorithms, particularly how failure detectors can factor out timing assumptions to detect failures in distributed agreement algorithms. Second, failure detectors as computability benchmarks are studied. Some limitations of the failure detector abstraction along each of the dimensions is also highlighted.

4854 ■ Faulkner Information Services
Pub: Faulkner Information Services Inc.
Contact: Tom Hogan, President

URL(s): www.faulkner.com. **Released:** Monthly; Updates; base volumes available with subscription. **Description:** The "Faulkner FACCTs" series includes separate reference services for many areas of data processing, communications, and related fields (the full information service is available as well). Titles include: "Enterprise Computing"; "Enterprise Communications"; "Local Area Networks"; "Telecommunications"; "Converging Communications Technologies"; "Large and Midrange Systems and Software"; "Micro Systems and Software"; "The Internet"; "Wireless Communications". **Entries include:** All reports contain company name, address, phone, fax, URL if available, and product list or description. Some reports also contain sales reports, financial data, products carried or distributed, and/or distribution statistics. Some comprise technology overviews or "how-to" guides.

4855 ■ Graduate Assistantship Directory in Computing
Pub: Association for Computing Machinery
Contact: Wendy Hall, President

URL(s): www.acm.org/gad/credit_new.html. **Entries include:** Institution name, address, name and title of contact, degrees offered, area of expertise, financial aid offered, stipend amount, department facilities (hardware and software), school enrollment, required exams, admission deadlines. **Database covers:** Fellowships and assistantships in the computer sciences offered at U.S. and Canadian educational institutions. **Arrangement:** Geographical.

4856 ■ "Health IT Regulations Generate Static Among Providers" in Philadelphia Business Journal (Vol. 28, January 29, 2010, No. 50, pp. 1)
Pub: American City Business Journals

Ed: John George. **Description:** US Centers for Medicaid and Medicare Services and the Office of the National Coordinator for Health Information Technology have proposed rules regarding the meaningful use of electronic health records. The rules must be complied with by hospitals and physicians to qualify for federal stimulus funds.

4857 ■ *"Help Wanted: 100 Hospitals IT Workers" in Business Courier (Vol. 27, October 8, 2010, No. 23, pp. 1)*

Pub: Business Courier

Ed: James Ritchie. **Description:** Hospitals in the Greater Cincinnati area are expected to hire more than 100 information technology (IT) workers to help digitize medical records. Financial incentives from the health care reform bill encouraged investments in electronic medical record systems, increasing the demand for IT workers that would help make information exchange across the healthcare system easier.

4858 ■ *"Human Activity Analysis: a Review" in ACM Computing Surveys (Vol. 43, Fall 2011, No. 3, pp. 16)*

Pub: Association for Computing Machinery

Ed: J.K. Aggarwal, M.S. Ryoo. **Description:** Human activity recognition is an important area of computer vision research and is studied in this report.

4859 ■ *"Identity Crisis: The Battle For Your Data" in Canadian Business (Vol. 81, March 17, 2008, No. 4, pp. 12)*

Pub: Rogers Media

Description: Nigel Brown explains that businesses must protect their data through encryption and tightening up access to data. Brown also points out that banks and merchants bear most of the costs for identity fraud and leaves individuals with a lot of pain and heartache in clearing their name.

4860 ■ *"Image Conscious" in Canadian Business (Vol. 81, March 17, 2008, No. 4, pp. 36)*

Pub: Rogers Media

Ed: Andrew Wahl. **Description:** Idee Inc. is testing an Internet search engine for images that does not rely on tags but compares its visual data to a database of other images. The company was founded and managed by Leila Boujnane as an off-shoot of their risk-management software firm. Their software has already been used by image companies to track copyrighted images and to find images within their own archives.

4861 ■ *"iMozi Integrates Esprida LiveControl for Advanced DVD Kiosk Hardware" in Wireless News (December 20, 2010)*

Pub: Close-Up Media Inc.

Description: Provider of self-service entertainment technology, iMozi Canada has partnered with Esprida to make its automated DVD Kiosk solutions Esprida-enabled. Esprida develops remote device management solutions and will offer enhanced capabilities and to improve customer experience for users.

4862 ■ *"Implementing Statically Typed Object-Oriented Programming Languages" in ACM Computing Surveys (Vol. 43, Fall 2011, No. 3, pp. 18)*

Pub: Association for Computing Machinery

Ed: Roland Ducournau. **Description:** Object-oriented programming represents an original implementation issue due to its philosophy of making the program behavior depend on the dynamic type of objects. A review of the various implementation techniques available in static typing and in the three cases of single inheritance, multiple inheritance, and multiple subtyping are reviewed.

4863 ■ *"In the Mobikey of Life" in Canadian Business (Vol. 81, July 21, 2008, No. 11, pp. 42)*

Pub: Rogers Media Ltd.

Ed: John Gray. **Description:** Toronto-based Route1 has created a data security software system that allows employees to access files and programs stored in the head office without permanently transferring data to the actual computer being used. Mobikey technology is useful in protecting laptops of chief executive officers, which contain confidential financial and customer data.

4864 ■ *"Lighter Than Air" in Game Developer (Vol. 18, November 1, 2011, No. 10, pp. 38)*

Pub: Think Services

Ed: Andy Firth. **Description:** Floating point performance tips and tricks are outlined. Floating point allows freedom of representation when implementing algorithms and is both intuitive to set up and simple to work with; hardware is also improved so that it is faster to use floating point math as opposed to integer in many environments.

4865 ■ *"Machine Transliteration Survey" in ACM Computing Surveys (Vol. 43, Fall 2011, No. 3, pp. 17)*

Pub: Association for Computing Machinery

Ed: Sarvnaz Karimi, Falk Scholer, Andrew Turpin. **Description:** Machine transliteration is the process of automatically transforming the script of a word from a source language to a target language, while preserving pronunciation. The development of algorithms specifically for machine transliteration began over a decade ago based on the phonetics of source and target languages, followed by approaches using statistical and language-specific methods. In this survey, the key methodologies introduced in transliteration literature are reviewed. The approaches are categorized based on the resources and algorithms used, and the effectiveness is compared.

4866 ■ *"Make It Easy" in Entrepreneur (Vol. 36, May 2008, No. 5, pp. 49)*

Pub: Entrepreneur Media, Inc.

Ed: Mike Hogan. **Description:** Zoho has a Planner that keep contacts, notes and reminders and a DB & Reports feature for reports, data analysis and pricing comparisons. WebEx WebOffice Workgroup supports document management and templates for contacts lists, time sheets and sales tracking. Other online data manages are presented.

4867 ■ *"Media Software and Data Services" in MarketingMagazine (Vol. 115, September 27, 2010, No. 13, pp. 78)*

Pub: Rogers Publishing Ltd.

Description: Media software and data services information in Canada is presented.

4868 ■ *"New Database Brings Doctors Out of the Dark" in Business Courier (Vol. 26, October 23, 2009, No. 26, pp. 1)*

Pub: American City Business Journals, Inc.

Ed: James Ritchie. **Description:** A database created by managed care consulting firm Praesentia allows doctors in Cincinnati to compare average reimbursements from health insurance companies to doctors in different areas. Specialist doctors in the city are paid an average of $172.25 for every office consultation.

4869 ■ *"New Ways To Think About Data Loss: Data Loss Is Costly and Painful" in Franchising World (Vol. 42, August 2010, No. 8, pp. 21)*

Pub: International Franchise Association

Ed: Ken Colburn. **Description:** Information for maintaining data securely for franchised organizations, including smart phones, tablets, copiers, computers and more is given.

4870 ■ *"Our Hoarder Mentality: Blame the Hard Disk" in PC Magazine (Vol. 30, November 2011, No. 11, pp. 46)*

Pub: Ziff-Davis Inc.

Contact: Vivek Shah, Chief Executive Officer

Ed: John C. Dvorak. **Description:** Computer programmers, once referred to as computer users, are slowly being replaced by passive consumers of products and content of tablets and handheld mobile phones and devices of the future. Understanding is garnered as this article examines this industry trend.

4871 ■ *"Panda Security for Business 4.05" in SC Magazine (Vol. 21, July 2010, No. 7, pp. 50)*

Pub: Haymarket Media Inc.

Description: Profile of Panda Security for Business, software offering endpoint security protection for computer desktops and servers is presented.

4872 ■ *"Power Up Your Small-Medium Business: A Guide to Enabling Network Technologies*

Pub: Cisco Press

Ed: Robyn Aber. **Released:** March 2004. **Price:** $39.95 (US), $57.95 (Canadian). **Description:** Network technologies geared to small and medium-size business, focusing on access, IP telephony, wireless technologies, security, and computer network management.

4873 ■ *"Save the Date" in Barron's (Vol. 90, September 13, 2010, No. 37, pp. 35)*

Pub: Barron's Editorial & Corporate Headquarters

Ed: Mark Veverka. **Description:** Mark Hurd is the new Co-President of Oracle after being forced out at Hewlett-Packard where he faced a harassment complaint. HP fired Hurd due to expense account malfeasance. Hurd is also set to speak at an Oracle trade show in San Francisco on September 20, 2010.

4874 ■ *"The State of the Art in End-User Software Engineering" in ACM Computing Surveys (Vol. 43, Fall 2011, No. 3, pp. 21)*

Pub: Association for Computing Machinery

Description: Most programs today are not written by professional software developers but by people with expertise in other domains working towards goals for which they need computational support. A discussion of empirical research about end-user software engineering activities and the technologies designed to support them is presented. Several crosscutting issues in the design of EUSE tools, including the roles of risk, reward, and domain complexity, and self-efficacy in the design of EUSE tools and the potential of educating users about software engineering principles are also examined.

4875 ■ *"Strict Intersection Types for the Lambda Calculus" in ACM Computing Surveys (Vol. 43, Fall 2011, No. 3, pp. 20)*

Pub: Association for Computing Machinery

Ed: Steffen Van Bakel. **Description:** The usefulness and elegance of strict intersection types for the Lambda Calculus, that are strict in the sense that they are the representatives of equivalence classes of types in the BCD-system is shown. Focus in directed on the essential intersection type assignment; this system is almost syntax directed, and the article will show that all major properties hold that are known to hold for other intersection systems, like the approximation theorem, the characterization of (head/strong) normalization, completeness of type assignment using filter semantics, strong normalization for cut-elimination and the principal pair property. In part, the proofs for these properties are new. A brief comparison of the essential system with other existing systems is given.

4876 ■ *"A Survey of Combinatorial Testing" in ACM Computing Surveys (Vol. 43, Summer 2011, No. 2, pp. 11)*

Pub: Association for Computing Machinery

Ed: Changhai Nie, Hareton Leung. **Description:** Combinatorial Testing (CT) can detect failures triggered by interactions of parameters in the Software Under Test (SUT) with a covering array test suite generated by some sampling mechanisms. Basic concepts and notations of CT are covered.

4877 ■ *"A Survey of Comparison-Based System-Level Diagnosis" in ACM Computing Surveys (Vol. 43, Fall 2011, No. 3, pp. 22)*

Pub: Association for Computing Machinery

Ed: Elias P. Duarte Jr., Roverli P. Ziwich, Luiz C.P. Albini. **Description:** The growing complexity and dependability requirements of hardware, software, and networks demand efficient techniques for discovering disruptive behavior in those systems. Comparison-based diagnosis is a realistic approach to detect faulty units based on the outputs of tasks executed by system units. This survey integrates the vast amount of research efforts that have been produced in this field.

4878 ■ *"A Survey of DHT Security Techniques" in ACM Computing Surveys (Vol.*

43, Summer 2011, No. 2, pp. 8)
Pub: Association for Computing Machinery
Ed: Guido Urdaneta, Guillaume Pierre, Maarten Van Steen. Description: Peer-to-peer networks based on distributed hash tables (DHTs) have received considerable attention since their introduction in 2001. Unfortunately, DHT-based systems have been shown to be difficult to protect against security attacks. An overview of techniques reported in literature for making DHT-based systems resistant to the three most important attacks that can be launched by malicious nodes participating in the DHT is given: the Sybil attack, the Eclipse attack, and routing and storage attacks.

4879 ■ "Tektronix Buys Arbor Networks for Security Business" in eWeek (August 9, 2010)
Pub: Ziff Davis Enterprise
Description: Tektronix Communications, provider of communications test and network intelligence solutions will acquire Arbor Networks. The deal will help Tektronix build a brand in security. Details of the transaction are included.

4880 ■ "What is the Future of Disk Drives, Death or Rebirth?" in ACM Computing Surveys (Vol. 43, Fall 2011, No. 3, pp. 23)
Pub: Association for Computing Machinery
Ed: Yuhui Deng. **Description:** Disk drives have experienced dramatic development to meet performance requirements since the IBM 1301 disk drive was announced in 1961. However, the performance gap between memory and disk drives has widened to 6 orders of magnitude and continues to widen by about 50 percent per year. Challenges and opportunities facing these storage devices are explored.

4881 ■ "Xtium Has Its Head in the Clouds" in Philadelphia Business Journal (Vol. 30, September 23, 2011, No. 32, pp. 1)
Pub: American City Business Journals Inc.
Ed: Peter Key. **Description:** Philadelphia-based cloud computing firm Xtium LLC received an $11.5 million first-round investment from Boston-Massachusetts-based OpenView Venture Partners. Catering to midsize businesses and unit of bigger firms, Xtium offers disaster-recovery, hosting, and managed-information-technology-infrastructure services.

4882 ■ "Z-Tech Lands Contract with CMS" in Black Enterprise (Vol. 37, October 2006, No. 3, pp. 36)
Pub: Earl G. Graves Publishing Co. Inc.
Ed: Glenn Townes. **Description:** Z-Tech Corp., a Maryland-based company providing database design and warehousing, was awarded a five-year government contract with the Centers for Medicare and Medicaid Services' Chronic Care Improvement Program worth $20 million.

STATISTICAL SOURCES

4883 ■ RMA Annual Statement Studies
Pub: Risk Management Association
Contact: Kevin M. Blakey, President
Released: Annual. **Price:** $175.00 2006-07 edition, $105.00. **Description:** Contains composite balance sheets and income statements for more than 360 industries, including the accounting, auditing, and bookkeeping industries. Also contains five years of comparative historical data for discerning trends. Includes 16 commonly used ratios, computed for most of the size groupings for nearly every industry.

4884 ■ Standard & Poor's Industry Surveys
Pub: Standard & Poor's Corp.
Released: Annual. **Price:** $3633.00. **Description:** Two-volume book that examines the prospects for specific industries, including trucking. Also provides analyses of trends and problems, statistical tables and charts, and comparative company analyses.

TRADE PERIODICALS

4885 ■ Computerworld
Pub: 101 Communications
Contact: Neil Vitale, President
URL(s): www.computerworld.com. **Released:** Weekly **Price:** $129, Individuals; $129, Canada; $295, Other

countries; $250, Individuals Mexico/Central/South America; $29, Individuals digital edition.

4886 ■ Computing Reviews
Pub: Association for Computing Machinery
Contact: Wendy Hall, President
URL(s): www.reviews.com. **Released:** Monthly **Price:** $3085, Institutions PhD or equivalent; $2015, Institutions MS or equivalent; $1345, Institutions BA or equivalent; $3015, Institutions other non-profit; $7180, Institutions large corporate; $5360, Institutions medium corporate; $4180, Institutions small corporate.

4887 ■ Datamation: The Emerging Technologies Magazine for Today's IS
Pub: Reed Business Information
Contact: Jeff Greisch, President
URL(s): www.datamation.com. **Released:** Semimonthly

4888 ■ Dr. Dobb's Journal: The World of Software Development
Pub: UBM PLC
Contact: David Levin, Chief Executive Officer
URL(s): drdobbs.com. **Ed:** Michael Swaine. **Released:** Monthly **Price:** $25, Individuals; $99.95, Individuals CD-ROM library.

4889 ■ The Independent
Pub: Independent Computer Consultants Association
Released: Bimonthly. **Price:** Included in membership. **Description:** Supports the Association by seeking to promote professionalism among member computer consultants, to increase awareness of products and services available, and to disseminate news and information about Association activities and benefits. Reports legislative and regulatory developments as well as information on marketing and business materials available. Recurring features include reports of meetings, news of educational opportunities, book reviews, and a calendar of events.

4890 ■ InfoWorld: Defining Technology for Business
Pub: InfoWorld Media Group
Contact: James Treacy, President
URL(s): www.infoworld.com/. **Released:** Weekly **Price:** $180, Individuals.

4891 ■ International Journal of Computers and Applications
Pub: ACTA Press
Contact: M. H. Hamza, President
URL(s): www.actapress.com/Content_of_Journal.aspx?journalID=144. **Released:** 4/yr. **Price:** $685, Individuals online or hardcopy.

4892 ■ International Journal of Intelligent Systems
Pub: John Wiley & Sons Inc.
Contact: Stephen M. Smith, President
URL(s): onlinelibrary.wiley.com/journal/10.1002/(-ISSN)1098-111X. **Ed:** Ronald R. Yager. **Released:** Monthly **Price:** $3985, Institutions print and online; $4153, Institutions, Canada and Mexico print and online; £1899, Institutions print only; $3465, Institutions print only; $3633, Institutions, Canada and Mexico print only; $3717, Institutions, other countries print only; €2399, Institutions print only; £2185, Institutions print and online; €2760, Institutions, other countries print and online; $4237, Institutions, other countries print and online.

4893 ■ IT Forecaster
Pub: International Data Corp.
Released: Weekly. **Description:** Provides news of original research and explains important trends in the worldwide information technology industry. Analyzes, segments, and sizes worldwide computer markets. Remarks: available online only.

4894 ■ Journal of Database Management
Contact: Dinesh Batra, Associate Editor
URL(s): www.igi-pub.com/journals/details.asp?id=198. **Released:** Quarterly **Price:** $210, Individuals print only; $860, Institutions print and free online; $595, Institutions online only; $595, Institutions print only.

4895 ■ MIS Quarterly
Pub: MIS Research Center
URL(s): www.misq.org/. **Released:** Quarterly; (March, June, September, and December). **Price:** $115, Individuals print; $130, Other countries print; $225, Institutions library; print; $250, Institutions, other countries print; $215, Individuals print and online; $230, Other countries print and online; $100, Individuals online only.

4896 ■ Online: The Leading Magazine for Information Professionals
Pub: Online, A Division of Information Today Inc.
URL(s): www.infotoday.com/online/default.shtml. **Ed:** Marydee Ojala. **Released:** Bimonthly **Price:** $124.95, Individuals; $235, Two years; $141, Canada and Mexico; $167, Other countries.

4897 ■ PC AI Online: Where Intelligent Technology Meets the Real World
Pub: Knowledge Technology Inc.
URL(s): www.pcai.com. **Released:** Bimonthly

4898 ■ SIGACT News
Pub: Association for Computing Machinery
Contact: Wendy Hall, President
Ed: Mumey Brendan, Editor. **Released:** Quarterly. **Price:** Included in membership. **Description:** Provides information on the practical and theoretical aspects of design, analysis, and application of algorithms, data structures, systems and languages for algebraic and symbolic mathematical computation.

4899 ■ SIGPLAN Notices
Pub: Special Interest Group on Programming Languages
Contact: Jan Vitek, Chairman
Ed: Michael Berman, Editor. **Released:** Monthly. **Price:** $35, Included in membership; $57, nonmembers; $10, students. **Description:** Examines all aspects of programming languages and programming languages processors. Utilizes practical and theoretical approaches to such areas as programming methodology; language definition and design; principles and techniques of computer implementation; general purpose and application-oriented languages; and teaching of programming languages. Recurring features include standards information and proceedings of SIGPLAN symposia.

4900 ■ SIGSOFT Software Engineering Notes
Pub: Association for Computing Machinery
Contact: Wendy Hall, President
Ed: Will Tracz, Editor, will.tracz@lmco.com. **Released:** Quarterly. **Price:** Included in membership. **Description:** Tracks developments in programming and software maintenance processes, as well as the use of computers to provide and maintain timely, higher quality, cost-effective, and durable software. Contains proceedings of software engineering workshops and symposia.

VIDEOCASSETTES/AUDIOCASSETTES

4901 ■ Career Possibilities: Computer Programming
Silver Mine Video Inc.
31316 Via Colinas, Ste. 104
Westlake Village, CA 91362-6715
Ph: (818)707-0300
Fax: (818)707-1606
Co. E-mail: quksil@aol.com
URL: http://www.quicksilverrecords.zoomshare.com
Contact: Howard L. Silver, President
Released: 1984. **Price:** $29.95. **Description:** Examines all the aspects of computer programming: the fields where programmers are needed, a programmer's responsibilities and a look into the future of computer programming. **Availability:** VHS.

TRADE SHOWS AND CONVENTIONS

4902 ■ COMDEX
Ziff-Davis Inc.
28 E 28th St.
New York, NY 10016-7939

Ph: (212)503-3500
Fax: (212)503-4599
Co. E-mail: randy_zane@ziffdavis.com
URL: http://www.ziffdavis.com
Contact: Vivek Shah, Chief Executive Officer
URL(s): www.comdex.com/. **Frequency:** Annual. **Audience:** Volume resellers and value-adders of small computers and related items; only a virtual trade show since 2003. **Principal Exhibits:** Small computer systems, related peripherals, software, accessories, services, and supplies. **Dates and Locations:** , Sands Expo and Convention Center.

CONSULTANTS

4903 ■ **Beeline Learning Solutions (BLS)**
14911 Quorum Dr., Ste. 120
Dallas, TX 75254
Ph: (972)813-0465
Fax: (972)386-8667
Co. E-mail: info@consultingpartners.com
URL: http://www.beeline.com
Contact: Dominic Nagy, Manager
E-mail: dominic.nagy@consultingpartners.com
Scope: Consulting firm offering technology, content, and services addressing recruitment and sourcing, talent management, and learning and performance optimization. Solutions offered include contingent workforce solutions, vendor management software, talent management solutions, recruitment process outsourcing, performance management, applicant tracking, learning management and eLearning. **Founded:** 1990. **Special Services:** Beeline®.

4904 ■ **Broadsword Solutions Corp.**
3795 Dorothy Ln.
Waterford, MI 48329
Ph: (248)341-3367
Free: 888-715-4423
Fax: (248)341-3672
Co. E-mail: info@broadswordsolutions.com
URL: http://www.broadswordsolutions.com
Contact: Jeff Dalton, President
E-mail: jeff@broadswordsolutions.com
Scope: Firm helps small and medium-sized organizations build software with solutions such as Agile CMMI and Traditional CMMI Consulting. **Founded:** 2004. **Seminars:** CMMI Accelerator Boxed Set v2.1. **Special Services:** AgileCMMI.

4905 ■ **Meg Consulting Group L.L.C.**
35452 Edgeton Ct., Ste. 204
Farmington Hills, MI 48335
Ph: (248)477-1186
Fax: (248)579-0226
Co. E-mail: support@megcg.com
URL: http://www.megcg.com
Contact: Mohit Sethi, Owner
Scope: Offers business consulting services in custom and boxed software solutions and network design. Provides significant cost savings, simplified infrastructure management, and mitigated business disruption risk - all needed to increase business agility and successfully compete in today's dynamic marketplace. Helps identify and improve parts of the network that need improvement for higher level of customer quality of experience (QoE) and reduced churn.

4906 ■ **Sterling-Hoffman**
425 University Ave., Ste. 800
Toronto, ON, Canada M5G 1T6
Ph: (416)979-6701
Free: 888-758-0942
Fax: (416)979-3030
Co. E-mail: customerservice@sterlinghoffman.com
URL: http://www.sterlinghoffman.com
Contact: Angel Mehta, Chief Executive Officer
E-mail: amehta@sterlinghoffman.com
Scope: A retained search firm for emerging software companies needing high-performance sales, marketing and business development executives. **Founded:** 1975. **Publications:** "Missed the Number? Send Your CEO a Japanese Death Poem"; "Want to Win? Forget YOU Exist"; "Secrets from the Farm: On Fear, Honor, and Building Companies"; "Bruce Lee says your new VP Sales will Fail"; "'Tragic Flaws: Why Software Companies Really Fail". **Seminars:** What CEOs want HR to know, Toronto.

4907 ■ **Wheeler and Young Inc.**
33 Peter St.
Markham, ON, Canada L3P 2A5
Ph: (905)471-5709
Fax: (905)471-9989
Co. E-mail: wheeler@ericwheeler.ca
URL: http://www.ericwheeler.ca
Contact: Eric S. Wheeler, Managing Partner
E-mail: ewheeler@yorku.ca
Scope: Provider of consulting services to high-tech companies on the implementation of software development processes; quality management systems (including ISO 9000 compliance) and business management systems. Offers business management and knowledge-management services to organizations. Industries served: Knowledge-based industries, including software and hardware development, medical and legal professionals, information service providers. **Founded:** 1994.

COMPUTERIZED DATABASES

4908 ■ *Computer Database*
10650 Toebben Dr.
Independence, KY 41051
Free: 800-354-9706
Fax: (800)487-8488
Co. E-mail: investors@cengage.com
URL: http://www.gale.cengage.com
Contact: Ronald Dunn, President
Availability: Online: ProQuest LLC-Dialog; ProQuest LLC - Dialog; Cengage Learning Inc. **Type:** Bibliographic; Full-text.

LIBRARIES

4909 ■ **Boston University - Corporate Education Center Library**
1 Executive Dr., Ste. 301
Chelmsford, MA 01824-2558
Ph: (978)649-8200
Free: 800-288-7246
Fax: (978)649-62145
Co. E-mail: info@corpedgroup.com
URL: http://www.corpedgroup.com/
Scope: Software engineering, business administration and management, computer programming languages, program methodology, project management, computer science, social work. **Services:** Interlibrary loan; copying; SDI; Library open to the public by appointment. **Founded:** 1980. **Holdings:** 5000 books. **Subscriptions:** 150 journals and other serials; 10 newspapers.

4910 ■ **Computer Sciences Corporation Corporate Library**
3170 Fairview Park Dr.
Falls Church, VA 22042-4516
Ph: (703)876-1000
Fax: (310)322-3685
URL: http://www.csc.com
Scope: Data processing, communications, information retrieval, programming, systems analysis, business, management, operations research, systems integration, outsourcing, company background information. **Services:** Interlibrary loan; copying; library not open to the public. **Founded:** 1962. **Holdings:** 150 books. **Subscriptions:** 70 journals and other serials.

4911 ■ **Walt Disney World - Global Business Technology Strategy Library**
Team Disney 336-N
1375 Buena Vista Dr.
Lake Buena Vista, FL 32830-1000
Ph: (407)828-4250
Fax: (407)827-8260
Co. E-mail: david.w.hartman@disney.com
URL: http://disneyworld.disney.go.com/wdw
Contact: David Hartman, Librarian
Scope: Computer science, human resources, general business. **Services:** Center not open to the public. **Founded:** 1986. **Holdings:** 4000 books, videos, DVDs, and CDs; 100 AV equipment. **Subscriptions:** 200 journals and other serials; 3 newspapers.

4912 ■ **Ernst & Young LLP - Center for Business Knowledge Library**
8484 Westpark Dr.
McLean, VA 22102
Ph: (703)747-1000
Fax: (703)747-0123
URL: http://www.ey.com
Scope: Data communication, computers and data processing. **Services:** Interlibrary loan; Library not open to the public. **Founded:** 1990. **Holdings:** 300 volumes. **Subscriptions:** 200 journals and other serials.

4913 ■ **IBM Corporation - Burlington Technical Library**
967-B, 1000 River St.
Essex Junction, VT 05452-4299
Ph: (802)769-6519
Fax: (802)769-6501
Co. E-mail: karenlyn@us.ibm.com
URL: http://www.ibm.com/us/en/
Contact: Karen Kromer Lynch, Director, Library Services
Scope: Semiconductor manufacturing, chemistry, computing, solid-state electronics, physics, business and professional, project management, programming, management science, mathematics. **Services:** Interlibrary loan; Center not open to the public. **Founded:** 1965. **Holdings:** 10,000 books; 100 reels of microfilm. **Subscriptions:** 160 journals and other serials.

4914 ■ **IBM Corporation - Library/Information Resource Center**
Dept. LVUS, B/908 Z/9819
11400 Burnet Rd.
Austin, TX 78758
Ph: (512)823-0404
Co. E-mail: gillen@us.ibm.com
URL: http://www.ibm.com/us/en/
Contact: Bev Gerzcvske, Manager
Scope: Computer architecture, RISC, personal computing, telecommunications, management, human factors, communications. **Services:** Interlibrary loan; Library not open to the public. **Founded:** 1967. **Holdings:** 11,000 books; 500 bound periodical volumes; 400 videotapes; 200 audiocassettes; 2000 reels of microfilm. **Subscriptions:** 300 journals, newsletters, and other serials; 15 newspapers. **Telecommunication Services:** auslib@us.ibm.com; llevitan@us.ibm.com.

4915 ■ **International Data Corp. Library**
5 Speen St.
Framingham, MA 01701
Ph: (508)872-8200
URL: http://www.idc.com
Contact: Kirk Campbell, President
Scope: Computer technology, management. **Services:** Interlibrary loan; Center not open to the public. **Founded:** 1970. **Holdings:** 2200 books; 50 Annual reports; 235 subject files; 12 CD-ROMs. **Subscriptions:** 200 journals and other serials.

4916 ■ **Kansas State University, Salina - Libraries**
2310 Centennial Rd.
Technology Center Bldg.
Salina, KS 67401-8058
Ph: (785)826-2637
Free: 800-248-5782
Fax: (785)826-2937
Co. E-mail: astarkey@k-state.edu
URL: http://www.sal.ksu.edu/library/index.html
Contact: Alysia Starkey, Director, Library Services
Scope: Computers, electronics, environmental, aeronautics, civil and mechanical engineering. **Services:** Interlibrary loan; copying; library open to the public. **Founded:** 1965. **Holdings:** 26,000 books; videotapes collection; 300 electronic databases. **Subscriptions:** 300 journals and other serials; 9 newspapers. **Telecommunication Services:** libhelp@salina.k-state.edu.

4917 ■ **Lockheed Martin Manassas Library**
105/029
9500 Godwin Dr.
Manassas, VA 20110
Ph: (703)367-6508

Fax: (703)367-4698
Co. E-mail: manassas.library@lmco.com
URL: http://www.lockheedmartin.com
Contact: Jennifer Hatfield, Manager
Scope: Computer systems and technology; signal processing; electronics; sonar. **Services:** Interlibrary loan. **Holdings:** 10,000 books; 2000 bound periodical volumes; 100 reports. **Subscriptions:** 200 journals and other serials; 10 newspapers.

4918 ■ MAGNET Information Resource Center—Manufacturing Advocacy & Growth Network.
1768 E 25th St.
Cleveland, OH 44114-4420
Ph: (216)391-7002
Free: 800-669-2267
Co. E-mail: info@magnetwork.org
URL: http://www.camp.org
Scope: Manufacturing technology; ECOMM, EDI, CAD/CAM, Business Systems. **Services:** SDI; Library open to members. **Founded:** 1989. **Holdings:** 2000 books; 200 periodical titles; 1000 archival reports; CD-ROMs. **Subscriptions:** 200 journals and other serials.

4919 ■ Mayo Biomedical Imaging Resource Library
Mayo Clinic
200 First St., SW
Rochester, MN 55905
Ph: (507)284-2511
Co. E-mail: robb.richard@mayo.edu
URL: http://mayoresearch.mayo.edu/mayo/research/
    robb_lab/
Contact: Richard A. Robb, PhD, Director
Scope: Biomedical imaging, visualization science, software systems, workstations, networks, computer graphics, virtual reality. **Services:** Interlibrary loan; library open to the public. **Founded:** 1970. **Holdings:** 100 books; 200 bound periodical volumes; 100 reports; 35 patents. **Subscriptions:** 20 journals and other serials; 5 newspapers.

4920 ■ Sargent & Lundy Engineers - Computer Software Library
55 E. Monroe St.
Chicago, IL 60603
Ph: (312)269-2000
Fax: (312)269-3680
Co. E-mail: thinkingpower@sargentlundy.com
URL: http://www.sargentlundy.com
Contact: John Wittenauer, Director, Information
    Technology
Scope: Computer applications. **Services:** Copying; library open to the public by appointment. **Holdings:** 250 books; 723 computer program manuals; 70 VF drawers of computer program documentation; microfiche. **Subscriptions:** 27 journals and other serials. **Telecommunication Services:** john.p.wittenauer@ sargentlundy.com.

4921 ■ UNISYS Corporation Corporate Library
One Unisys Way
Blue Bell, PA 19424
Ph: (215)986-2324
Fax: (215)986-6733
URL: http://www.unisys.com/unisys/
Contact: Susan H. Hahn, Manager
Scope: Business, computer science, computer industry, computer services, computer security. **Services:** Library not open to the public. **Founded:** 1952. **Holdings:** 9000 books; 200 audiobooks, 350 videocassettes. **Subscriptions:** 100 journals and other serials; 6 newspapers.

4922 ■ UNISYS Corporation - West Coast Information Center
25725 Jeronimo Rd., MS-260
Mission Viejo, CA 92691
Ph: (714)380-5061
Fax: (714)380-5138
URL: http://www.unisys.com/unisys
Contact: M. Patricia Feeney, Manager, Information
    Technology
Scope: Computer architecture, computer programming, software design, hardware engineering design, data communications, management. **Services:** Interlibrary loan; center open to the public at librarian's discretion. **Founded:** 1974. **Holdings:** 5000 books; 3500 technical reports; 3000 other cataloged items. **Subscriptions:** 225 journals and other serials.

4923 ■ Xerox Corporation - Wilsonville Library
Box 1000, M/S 63-531
Wilsonville, OR 97070
Ph: (503)685-3986
Fax: (503)685-2296
Co. E-mail: linda.appel@opbu.xerox.com
Contact: Linda K. Appel, Librarian
Scope: Color computer printers, programming, electronics, business and management. **Services:** Interlibrary loan; SDI. **Founded:** 1978. **Holdings:** 4000 books. **Subscriptions:** 100 journals and other serials; 9 newspapers.

RESEARCH CENTERS

4924 ■ Massachusetts Institute of Technology - Laboratory for Computer Science - Programming Methodology Group (PMG)
32 Vasaar St., 32-G942
Cambridge, MA 02139
Ph: (617)253-5886
Fax: (617)253-8460
Co. E-mail: liskov@csail.mit.edu
URL: http://www.pmg.lcs.mit.edu/
Contact: Prof. Barbara Liskov, Leader
Telecommunication Services: liskov@lcs.mit.edu.

4925 ■ Ohio State University - Advanced Computing Center for the Arts and Design (ACCAD)
1224 Kinnear Rd.
Columbus, OH 43212-1154
Ph: (614)292-3416
Fax: (614)292-7776
Co. E-mail: mpalazzi@accad.ohio-state.edu
URL: http://accad.osu.edu
Contact: Prof. Maria Palazzi, Director
Founded: 1986. **Publications:** *Newsletter On-line.* **Educational Activities:** Digital Animation: A Technology Mentoring Program for Young Women (Annual), free summer program for 8th and 9th grade young women to learn computer animation; Open House (Annual), held in the beginning of May. **Telecommunication Services:** accad@accad.osu.edu.

4926 ■ University at Albany, State University of New York - Institute for Informatics, Logics, and Security Studies (ILS)
SUNY, Social Science Bldg., Rm. 262
Albany, NY 12222
Ph: (518)442-2605
Fax: (518)442-2606
Co. E-mail: nvm@cs.albany.edu
URL: http://www.ils.albany.edu
Contact: Prof. Neil V. Murray, Director
Founded: 1991. **Publications:** *ILS Technical reports.* **Educational Activities:** ILS Conferences.

4927 ■ University of California, Irvine - Distributed Real-time Ever Available Microcomputing Laboratory (DREAM) ●
4111 Engineering Hall
Irvine, CA 92697
Ph: (949)824-5542
Fax: (949)824-4148
Co. E-mail: khkim@uci.edu
URL: http://dream.eng.uci.edu/
Contact: Prof. Kane Kim, Director

4928 ■ University of Georgia - Center for Remote Sensing and Mapping Science (CRMS)
Geography-Geology Bldg., Rm. 209a
Department of Geography
Athens, GA 30602-2503
Ph: (706)542-2379
Fax: (706)542-2388
Co. E-mail: mmadden@uga.edu
URL: http://www.crms.uga.edu
Contact: Prof. Marguerite Madden, Director
Founded: 1984.

4929 ■ University of Southern California - Information Sciences Institute (ISI)
4676 Admiralty Way, Ste. 1001
Marina del Rey, CA 90292
Ph: (310)822-1511
Fax: (310)823-6714
Co. E-mail: schorr@isi.edu
URL: http://www3.isi.edu/home
Contact: Prof. Herbert Schorr, Executive Director
Founded: 1972.

START-UP INFORMATION

4930 ■ *The Mousedriver Chronicles*
Pub: Perseus Books Group
Ed: John Lusk; Kyle Harrison. **Released:** 2003.
Price: $16.95. **Description:** Entrepreneurial voyage through the startup business of two ivy-league business school graduates and the lessons they learned while developing their idea of a computer mouse that looks like a golf driver into the marketplace. The book is an inspiration for those looking to turn an idea into a company.

ASSOCIATIONS AND OTHER ORGANIZATIONS

4931 ■ **Information Technology Industry Council (ITI)**
1101 K St. NW, Ste. 610
Washington, DC 20005
Ph: (202)737-8888
Fax: (202)638-4922
Co. E-mail: info@itic.org
URL: http://www.itic.org
Contact: Dean Garfield, President
Description: Represents manufacturers of information technology products. Serves as secretariat and technology for ANSI-accredited standards committee x3 information technology group. Conducts public policy programs; compiles industry statistics. **Founded:** 1916. **Publications:** *Washington Letter* (Biweekly). **Awards:** Public Policy Award (Annual). **Telecommunication Services:** rdawson@itic.org.

4932 ■ **Transaction Processing Performance Council (TPC)**
PO Box 29920
San Francisco, CA 94129-0920
Ph: (415)561-6272
Fax: (415)561-6120
Co. E-mail: info@tpc.org
URL: http://www.tpc.org
Contact: Omri Serlin, Founder
Description: Represents computer hardware and software companies, computer users and vendors, and industry organizations. Defines transaction processing and database benchmarks. Disseminates objective, verifiable TPC performance data to the industry. Conducts activities such as Benchmark development and maintenance, publication and dissemination of TPC results. **Founded:** 1988. **Publications:** *Benchmark Status Report* (Bimonthly). **Educational Activities:** Transaction Processing Performance Council Meeting (Bimonthly).

DIRECTORIES OF EDUCATIONAL PROGRAMS

4933 ■ *Directory of Private Accredited Career Schools and Colleges of Technology*
Pub: Accrediting Commission of Career Schools and Colleges of Technology
Contact: Michale S. McComis, Executive Director
Released: On web page. **Price:** Free. **Description:** Covers 3900 accredited post-secondary programs

that provide training programs in business, trade, and technical fields, including various small business endeavors. Entries offer school name, address, phone, description of courses, job placement assistance, and requirements for admission. Arrangement is alphabetical.

REFERENCE WORKS

4934 ■ *"3Par: Storing Up Value" in Barron's (Vol. 90, August 30, 2010, No. 35, pp. 30)*
Pub: Barron's Editorial & Corporate Headquarters
Ed: Mark Veverka. **Description:** Dell and Hewlett Packard are both bidding for data storage company 3Par. The acquisition would help Dell and Hewlett Packard provide customers with a one-stop shop as customers move to a private cloud in the Internet.

4935 ■ *Achieving Planned Innovation: A Proven System for Creating Successful New Products and Services*
Pub: Simon and Schuster
Ed: Frank R. Bacon. **Released:** August 2007. **Price:** $16.95. **Description:** Planned innovation is a disciplined and practical step-by-step sequence of procedures for reaching the intended destination point: successful products. This easy-to-read book explains the system along with an action-oriented program for continuous success in new-product innovations. Five steps outlined include: a disciplined reasoning process; lasting market orientation; proper selection criteria that reflect both strategic and tactical business objectives and goals along with dynamic matching of resources to present and future opportunities, and positive and negative requirements before making major expenditures; and proper organizational staffing. The author explains what to do and evaluating the potential of any new product or service, ranging from ventures in retail distribution to the manufacture of goods as diverse as bicycles, motorcycles, aerospace communication and navigation equipment, small business computers, food packaging, and medical products.

4936 ■ *"Agricharts Launches New Mobile App for Ag Market" in Farm Industry News (December 1, 2011)*
Pub: Penton Business Media Inc.
Description: AgriCharts provides market data, agribusiness Website hosting and technology solutions for the agricultural industry. AgriCharts is a division of Barchart.com Inc. and announced the release of a new mobile applications that offers real-time or delayed platform for viewing quotes, charts and analysis of grains, livestock and other commodity markets.

4937 ■ *"Also Check Out.." in Black Enterprise (Vol. 38, October 2007, No. 3, pp. 64)*
Pub: Earl G. Graves Publishing Co. Inc.
Description: Profile of Lenovo's Think Vantage Rescue and Recovery system that performs backup files for CD/DVDs.

4938 ■ *"Aptitudes for Apps" in Boston Business Journal (Vol. 31, July 1, 2011, No. 23, pp. 3)*
Pub: Boston Business Journal
Ed: Kyle Alspach. **Description:** Startups Apperian Inc. and Kinvey Inc. are aiming to accelerate the

development and deployment of mobile applications and have received fund pledges from Boston-area venture capital firms.

4939 ■ *"Avanti Hosts Users Conference" in American Printer (Vol. 128, July 1, 2011, No. 7)*
Pub: Penton Media Inc.
Description: Avanti Computer Systems Ltd. hosted its 19th annual users conference in Washington DC. In-plant and commercial printers were in attendance.

4940 ■ *The Big Switch*
Pub: W. W. Norton & Company, Inc.
Ed: Nicholas Carr. **Released:** January 19, 2009. **Price:** $16.95 paperback. **Description:** Today companies are dismantling private computer systems and tapping into services provided via the Internet. This shift is remaking the computer industry, bringing competitors such as Google to the forefront ant threatening traditional companies like Microsoft and Dell. The book weaves together history, economics, and technology to explain why computing is changing and what it means for the future.

4941 ■ *"Buyer's Guide: Room for Improvement" in Entrepreneur (Vol. 35, October 2007, No. 10, pp. 62)*
Pub: Entrepreneur Media Inc.
Ed: Amanda C. Kooser. **Description:** Buyers guide for wireless routers is presented. Price, features and availability of the Belkin N1 Vision, Buffalo Wireless-N Nfinit Router, D-Link Xtreme Gigabit Router DIR 655, Linksys Wireless-N Gigabit Security Router, Netgear RangeMax Next Wireless-N Router and Zyxel NBG-460N are provided.

4942 ■ *Cisco Network Design Solutions for Small-Medium Businesses*
Pub: Cisco Press
Ed: Peter Rybaczyk. **Released:** August 2004. **Price:** $55.00. **Description:** Solutions for computer networking professionals using computer networks within a small to medium-sized business. Topics cover not only core networking issues and solutions, but security, IP telephony, unified communications, customer relations management, wireless LANs, and more.

4943 ■ *"Clouds in the Forecast" in Information Today (Vol. 28, September 2011, No. 8, pp. 10)*
Pub: Information Today, Inc.
Ed: Paula J. Hane. **Description:** Cloud computing is software, applications, and data stored remotely and accessed via the Internet with output displayed on a client device. Recent developments in cloud computing are explored.

4944 ■ *Computing Technology Industry Association--Membership Directory*
Pub: Computing Technology Industry Association
URL(s): www.comptia.org. **Released:** Annual; winter. **Covers:** 7,500 member computer hardware and software manufacturers, distributors, associate members, and resellers. **Entries include:** For manufacturers and distributors--Company name, ad-

dress, phone, fax, name and title of contact, products. For resellers--Personal name, company name, address, phone, fax, vertical markets served and CPU brands sold. **Arrangement:** Alphabetical. **Indexes:** Company name, geographical, vertical market, CPU, contact name.

4945 ■ "Cyberwise" in Black Enterprise (Vol. 41, December 2010, No. 5, pp. 50)
Pub: Earl G. Graves Publishing Co. Inc.
Ed: Marica Wade Talbert. **Description:** Information is given regarding single platforms that can be used to develop applications for iPhone, Android, Blackberry, and Nokia.

4946 ■ "Death of the PC" in Canadian Business (Vol. 83, October 12, 2010, No. 17, pp. 44)
Pub: Rogers Media Ltd.
Ed: Joe Castaldo. **Description:** The future of the personal computer (PC) is looking bleak as consumers are relying more on new mobile devices instead of their PC. A 'Wall Street Journal' article published in September 2010 reported that the iPad had cannibalized sales of laptops by as much as 50 percent. The emergence of tablet computers running alternative operating systems is also explained.

4947 ■ "The Digital Revolution is Over. Long Live the Digital Revolution!" in Business Strategy Review (Vol. 21, Spring 2010, No. 1, pp. 74)
Pub: Wiley-Blackwell
Ed: Gianvito Lanzolla, Jamie Anderson. **Description:** Many businesses are now involved in the digital marketplace. The authors argue that the new reality of numerous companies offering overlapping products means that it is critical for managers to understand digital convergence and to observe the imperatives for remaining competitive.

4948 ■ "Etextbook Space Heats Up" in Information Today (Vol. 28, November 2011, No. 10, pp. 10)
Pub: Information Today, Inc.
Ed: Paula J. Hane. **Description:** The use of etextbooks is expected to grow with the use of mobile devices and tablets. A new group of activists is asking students, faculty members and others to sign a petition urging higher education leaders to prioritize affordable textbooks or free ebooks over the traditional, expensive new books required for classes.

4949 ■ "Facebook Purchased Push Pop Press" in Information Today (Vol. 28, October 2011, No. 9, pp. 12)
Pub: Information Today, Inc.
Description: Facebook purchased Push Pop Press, a digital publishing company that developed a multitouch interface for ebook publishing on the iPad.

4950 ■ Faulkner Information Services
Pub: Faulkner Information Services Inc.
Contact: Tom Hogan, President
URL(s): www.faulkner.com. **Released:** Monthly; Updates; base volumes available with subscription. **Description:** The "Faulkner FACCTs" series includes separate reference services for many areas of data processing, communications, and related fields (the full information service is available as well). Titles include: "Enterprise Computing"; "Enterprise Communications"; "Local Area Networks"; "Telecommunications"; "Converging Communications Technologies"; "Large and Midrange Systems and Software"; "Micro Systems and Software"; "The Internet"; "Wireless Communications". **Entries include:** All reports contain company name, address, phone, fax, URL if available, and product list or description. Some reports also contain sales reports, financial data, products carried or distributed, and/or distribution statistics. Some comprise technology overviews or "how-to" guides.

4951 ■ "Featherweight Contenders: Thin and Light, But Heavy On Features" in Inc. (Vol. 33, October 2011, No. 8, pp. 44)
Pub: Inc. Magazine
Ed: John Brandon. **Description:** Profiles of ultraportable notebooks include Sony Z Series VPCZ212GX/B, Samsung Series 9 NP900X1B, ASUS U36SJC, and Macbook Air.

4952 ■ "For Apple, It's Showtime Again" in Barron's (Vol. 90, August 30, 2010, No. 35, pp. 29)
Pub: Barron's Editorial & Corporate Headquarters
Ed: Eric J. Savitz. **Description:** Speculations on what Apple Inc. will unveil at its product launch event are presented. These products include a possible new iPhone Nano, a new update to its Apple TV, and possibly a deal with the Beatles to distribute their songs over iTunes.

4953 ■ "Funny Business" in Canadian Business (Vol. 82, April 27, 2009, No. 7, pp. 27)
Pub: Rogers Media
Ed: Rachel Pulfer. **Description:** Companies are advised to use humor in marketing to drive more revenue. IBM Canada, for example, commissioned Second City Communications for a marketing campaign that involved humor. While IBM Canada declined to give sales or traffic figures, firm executives rank the marketing campaign as an overall success.

4954 ■ "gdgt: The New Online Home for Gadget Fans" in Hispanic Business (July-August 2009, pp. 15)
Pub: Hispanic Business
Ed: Jeremy Nisen. **Description:** Profile of the new online Website for gadget lovers. The site combines a leek interface, gadget database, and social networking-type features which highlights devices for the consumer.

4955 ■ "Googly Eyed" in Entrepreneur (Vol. 36, February 2008, No. 2, pp. 48)
Pub: Entrepreneur Media Inc.
Ed: Mike Hogan. **Description:** Linux has developed desktops that boot into the Google toolbar and applications. These desktops include: Zonbu, Everex gPCTC2502, and Asus Eee PC 4G mini laptop. Details on the applications of these desktops are discussed.

4956 ■ "Hewlett-Packard Mini: Ultra-Portable, and Affordable" in Hispanic Business (July-August 2009, pp. 36)
Pub: Hispanic Business
Ed: Jeremy Nisen. **Description:** Hewlett-Packard's 1151 NR computers works a lot like a smartphone online, it can dial up fast speeds on Verizon's 3G network almost anywhere.

4957 ■ "Holiday Sales Look Uncertain for Microsoft and PC Sellers" in Puget Sound Business Journal (Vol. 29, November 28, 2008, No. 32)
Pub: American City Business Journals
Ed: Todd Bishop. **Description:** Personal computer makers face uncertain holiday sales for 2008 as a result of the weak U.S. economy and a shift toward low-cost computers. Personal computer shipments for the fourth quarter 2008 are forecast to drop 1 percent compared to the same quarter 2007.

4958 ■ "Homing In On the Future" in Black Enterprise (Vol. 38, October 2007, No. 3, pp. 61)
Pub: Earl G. Graves Publishing Co. Inc.
Ed: Sean Drakes. **Description:** More and more people are wanting new homes wired automated systems that integrate multiple home devices such as computers, audio/visual entertainment, security, communications, utilities, and lighting and environmental controls.

4959 ■ "How Dell Will Dial for Dollars" in Austin Business JournalInc. (Vol. 29, December 4, 2009, No. 39, pp. 1)
Pub: American City Business Journals
Ed: Christopher Calnan. **Description:** Dell Inc. revealed plans to launch a Mini3i smartphone in China which could enable revenue sharing by bundling with wireless service subscription. Dell's smartphone plan is similar to the netbook business, which Dell sold with service provided by AT&T Inc.

4960 ■ How to Get Rich
Pub: Ebury Press
Ed: Felix Dennis. **Released:** 2008. **Price:** $25.95. **Description:** Publisher of Maxim, The Week, and Stuff magazines, discusses the mistakes he made running his companies. He didn't understand that people who buy computer gaming magazines wanted a free game with each copy, as one of his rivals was offering. And he laments not diversifying into television and exploiting the Internet.

4961 ■ "How to Play the Tech Mergers" in Barron's (Vol. 90, August 30, 2010, No. 35, pp. 18)
Pub: Barron's Editorial & Corporate Headquarters
Ed: Tiernan Ray. **Description:** The intense bidding by Hewlett-Packard and Dell for 3Par was foreseen in a previous Barron's cover story and 3Par's stock has nearly tripled since reported. Other possible acquisition targets in the tech industry include Brocade Communication Systems, NetApp, Xyratex, and Isilon Systems.

4962 ■ IBM on Demand Technology for the Growing Business: How to Optimize Your Computing Environment for Today and Tomorrow
Pub: Maximum Press
Ed: Jim Hoskins. **Released:** June 2005. **Price:** $29. 95. **Description:** IBM is offering computer solutions to small companies entering the On Demand trend in business.

4963 ■ Information Technology for the Small Business: How to Make IT Work For Your Company
Pub: TAB Computer Systems, Incorporated
Ed: T.J. Benoit. **Released:** June 2006. **Price:** $17. 95. **Description:** Basics of information technology to help small companies maximize benefits are covered. Topics include pitfalls to avoid, email and Internet use, data backup, recovery and overall IT organization.

4964 ■ "Intel: Tax Breaks Key" in Business Journal Portland (Vol. 27, October 22, 2010, No. 34, pp. 1)
Pub: Portland Business Journal
Ed: Erik Siemers. **Description:** Intel Corporation believes that state tax incentives will be critical, especially in the purchase of manufacturing equipment, as they build a new chip factory in Hillsboro, Oregon. The tax breaks would help Intel avoid paying 10 times more in property taxes compared to average Washington County firms. Critics argue that Intel has about $15 billion in cash assets, and can afford the factory without the tax breaks.

4965 ■ "It Was a Very Good Year..To Be Ted Rogers" in Canadian Business (Vol. 80, Winter 2007, No. 24, pp. 121)
Pub: Rogers Media
Ed: Andrew Wahl. **Description:** Ted Rogers had a banner year in 2007 as Rogers Communications Inc. (RCI) took in huge profits from its phone and wireless business and his personal wealth grew sixty-seven percent to $7.6 billion. Rogers has record of betting on technologies that get the best returns relative to the investment in the marketplace such as its use of the GSM network and its cable hybrid fiber coaxial network.

4966 ■ "Keeping Up With the Joneses: Outfitting Your Company With Up-To-Date Technology is Vital" in Black Enterprise (November 2007)
Pub: Earl G. Graves Publishing Co. Inc.
Ed: Sonya A. Donaldson. **Description:** Small businesses, whether home-based or not, need to keep up with new technological developments including hardware, software, and the Internet.

4967 ■ "Kids, Computers and the Social Networking Evolution" in Canadian Business (Vol. 81, October 27, 2008, No. 18, pp. 93)
Pub: Rogers Media Ltd.
Ed: Penny Milton. **Description:** Social networking was found to help educate students in countries like the U.S., Canada and Mexico. Schools that embrace

social networking teach students how to use computers safely and responsibility in order to counter threats to children on the Internet.

4968 ■ *"Microsoft Releases Office Security Updates" in Mac World (Vol. 27, November 2010, No. 11, pp. 66)*

Pub: Mac Publishing

Ed: David Dahlquist. **Description:** Office for Mac and Mac Business Unit are Microsoft's pair of security- and stability-enhancing updates for Office 2008 and Office 2004. The software will improve the stability and compatibility and fixes vulnerabilities that would allow attackers to overwrite Mac's memory with malicious code.

4969 ■ *Mobile Office: The Essential Small Business Guide to Office Technology*

Pub: Double Storey Books

Ed: Arthur Goldstruck, Steven Ambrose. **Released:** September 1, 2009. **Price:** $6.95. **Description:** Essential pocket guide for startup businesses and entrepreneurs which provides information to create a mobile office in order to maximize business potential while using current technologies.

4970 ■ *"Mobility: So Happy Together" in Entrepreneur (Vol. 35, October 2007, No. 10, pp. 64)*

Pub: Entrepreneur Media Inc.

Ed: Heather Clancy. **Description:** Joshua Burnett, CEO and founder of 9ci, uses index cards to keep track of what he needs to do despite the fact that he has a notebook computer, cell phone and PDA. Kim Hahn, a media entrepreneur, prefers jotting her ideas down in a spiral notebook, has a team that would organize her records for her, and a personal assistant that would keep track of changes to her schedule. Reasons why these entrepreneurs use old-fashioned methods along with new technology are given.

4971 ■ *"Motors and Motion Control" in Canadian Electronics (Vol. 23, February 2008, No. 1, pp. 23)*

Pub: CLB Media Inc.

Description: A new version of MicroMo Electronics Inc.'s Smoovy Series 0303..B has been added to MicroMo's DC motor product line. United Electronic Industries, on the other hand, has introduced the new UEIPAC series of programmable automation controllers that can offer solutions to various applications such as unmanned vehicle controllers. Features and functions of other new motors and motion control devices are given.

4972 ■ *"My Favorite Tool for Organizing Data" in Inc. (Vol. 33, November 2011, No. 9, pp. 46)*

Pub: Inc. Magazine

Ed: Abram Brown. **Description:** Intelligence software firm uses Roambi, a Web-based service that turns spreadsheet data into interactive files for iPhones and iPads.

4973 ■ *"Nat'l Instruments Connects with Lego" in Austin Business JournalInc. (Vol. 28, August 22, 2008, No. 23, pp. 1)*

Pub: American City Business Journals

Ed: Laura Hipp. **Description:** Austin-based National Instruments Corporation has teamed with Lego Group from Denmark to create a robot that can be built by children and can be used to perform tasks. Lego WeDo, their latest product, uses computer connection to power its movements. The educational benefits of the new product are discussed.

4974 ■ *"The New Breed of Wi-Fi Only Tablets: No Data Plan Required" in Inc. (Vol. 33, September 2011, No. 7, pp. 52)*

Pub: Inc. Magazine

Ed: John Brandon. **Description:** New Wi-Fi only tablets are available from Samsung, Hewlett Packard, Asus and Acer. A description of offerings from these companies is included.

4975 ■ *"New Ways To Think About Data Loss: Data Loss Is Costly and Painful" in*

Franchising World (Vol. 42, August 2010, No. 8, pp. 21)

Pub: International Franchise Association

Ed: Ken Colburn. **Description:** Information for maintaining data securely for franchised organizations, including smart phones, tablets, copiers, computers and more is given.

4976 ■ *"Not Your Father's Whiteboard" in Inc. (Vol. 33, November 2011, No. 9, pp. 50)*

Pub: Inc. Magazine

Ed: Adam Baer. **Description:** Sharp's new interactive whiteboard is really a 70-inch touch screen monitor with software for importing presentations from any Windows 7 computer.

4977 ■ *"Note-Taking App, Supercharged" in Inc. (Vol. 33, October 2011, No. 8, pp. 48)*

Pub: Inc. Magazine

Ed: Adam Baer. **Description:** Note Taker HD is an iPad app that lets the user text by typing with finger or stylus with various colors, fonts and sizes; Extensive Notes creates notes, records audio memos, and takes photos and videos; Evernote allows users to create notes, take snapshots, and record voice memos.

4978 ■ *"One Laptop Per Child Weighs Going For-Profit" in Boston Business Journal (Vol. 31, May 20, 2011, No. 17, pp. 1)*

Pub: Boston Business Journal

Ed: Mary Moore. **Description:** Nonprofit organization One Laptop Per Child is thinking of shifting into a for-profit structure in order to raise as much as $10 million in capital to achieve its goal of distributing more XO laptops to poor children worldwide. The organization has distributed 2 million computers since 2008 with Uruguay, Peru and Rwanda as its biggest markets.

4979 ■ *"Our Hoarder Mentality: Blame the Hard Disk" in PC Magazine (Vol. 30, November 2011, No. 11, pp. 46)*

Pub: Ziff-Davis Inc.

Contact: Vivek Shah, Chief Executive Officer

Ed: John C. Dvorak. **Description:** Computer programmers, once referred to as computer users, are slowly being replaced by passive consumers of products and content of tablets and handheld mobile phones and devices of the future. Understanding is garnered as this article examines this industry trend.

4980 ■ *"Panda Security for Business 4.05" in SC Magazine (Vol. 21, July 2010, No. 7, pp. 50)*

Pub: Haymarket Media Inc.

Description: Profile of Panda Security for Business, software offering endpoint security protection for computer desktops and servers is presented.

4981 ■ *"PC Connection Acquires Cloud Software Provider" in New Hampshire Business Review (Vol. 33, March 25, 2011, No. 6, pp. 8)*

Pub: Business Publications Inc.

Description: Merrimack-based PC Connection Inc. acquired ValCom Technology, a provider of cloud-based IT service management software. Details of the deal are included.

4982 ■ *"PC Running Slowly? How to Rev Up Your Machine" in Inc. (Vol. 33, November 2011, No. 9, pp. 46)*

Pub: Inc. Magazine

Ed: John Brandon. **Description:** Software that keeps PCs tuned up and running smoothing are profiled: AUSLO6ICS BOOSTSPEED 5, $50; Tuneup Utilities 2011, $40; Slimware Slimcleaner 1.9, free; and IOBIT Advanced Systemcare Pro 4, $20 a year.

4983 ■ *"PCI Express Powers Machine Vision" in Canadian Electronics (Vol. 23, February 2008, No. 1, pp. 8)*

Pub: CLB Media Inc.

Ed: Inder Kohli. **Description:** PCI Express is an innovative peripheral bus that can be used in industrial computing. The peripheral bus delivers a high-

bandwidth, scaleable, point-to-point path from peripheral cards to the computing core. Features and functions of PCI Express are described in detail.

4984 ■ *"Port of Call" in Entrepreneur (Vol. 35, November 2007, No. 11, pp. 66)*

Pub: Entrepreneur Media Inc.

Ed: Amanda C. Kooser. **Description:** List of the latest USB (universal serial bus) devices for upgrading technology for a small business is presented.

4985 ■ *Power Up Your Small-Medium Business: A Guide to Enabling Network Technologies*

Pub: Cisco Press

Ed: Robyn Aber. **Released:** March 2004. **Price:** $39.95 (US), $57.95 (Canadian). **Description:** Network technologies geared to small and medium-size business, focusing on access, IP telephony, wireless technologies, security, and computer network management.

4986 ■ *Practical Tech for Your Business*

Pub: Kiplinger Books and Tapes

Ed: Michael J. Martinez. **Released:** 2002. **Description:** Advice is offered to help small business owners choose the right technology for their company. The guide tells how to get started, network via the Internet, create an office network, use database software, and conduct business using mobile technology.

4987 ■ *"Press Release: Trimble Introduces CFX-750 Display" in Farm Industry News (January 4, 2011)*

Pub: Penton Business Media Inc.

Description: Trimble is offering a touch screen display called the CFX-750. The new 8-inch full-color display allows farmers to choose the specific guidance, steering and precision agriculture capabilities that best fit their farm's particular needs. The display can be upgraded as business needs change, including the addition of GLONASS capabilities, or the addition of section and rate control for crop inputs such as seed, chemicals and fertilizer.

4988 ■ *Pro Windows Small Business Server 2003*

Pub: Apress L.P.

Ed: Tony Campbell. **Released:** July 2006. **Price:** $39.99. **Description:** Profile of Microsoft's Windows Small Business Server, designed for companies with 50 or fewer employees.

4989 ■ *"Quickoffice's MobileFiles Pro App Enables Excel Editing On-the-Go" in Information Today (Vol. 26, February 2009, No. 2, pp. 31)*

Pub: Information Today, Inc.

Description: Quickoffice Inc. introduced MobileFiles Pro, which features editable Microsoft Office functionality for the iPone and iPod touch. The application allows users to edit and save Microsoft Excel files in .xls format, transfer files to and from PC and Mac desktops via Wi-Fi, and access and synchronize with Apple MobileMe accounts.

4990 ■ *"Remote Control: Working From Wherever" in Inc. (February 2008, pp. 46-47)*

Pub: Gruner & Jahr USA Publishing

Ed: Ryan Underwood. **Description:** New technology allows workers to perform tasks from anywhere via the Internet. Profiles of products to help connect to your office from afar include, LogMein Pro, a Web-based service that allowsaccess to a computer from anywhere; Xdrive, an online service that allows users to store and swap files; Basecamp, a Web-based tools that works like a secure version of MySpace; MojoPac Freedom, is software that allows users to copy their computer's desktop to a removable hard drive and plug into any PC; WatchGuard Firebox X Core e-Series UTM Bundle, hardware that blocks hackers and viruses while allowing employees to work remotely; TightVNC, a free open-source software that lets you control another computer via the Internet.

4991 ■ *Resource Directory*

Pub: Closing the Gap Inc.

Contact: MaryAnn Harty, Manager

URL(s): www.closingthegap.com. **Released:** Annual; February/March. **Price:** $16.95, Individuals plus $4 shipping; $36, one-year subscription; $50, online subscription; $40, Students online subscription; $52, Canada one-year subscription. **Covers:** About 300 suppliers of computer hardware and software designed for use by persons with disabilities. **Entries include:** Company or organization name, address, phone, description of products. **Arrangement:** Alphabetical. **Indexes:** Product/service, subject, supplier name.

4992 ■ *Running Your Small Business on a Mac*
Pub: Pearson Technology Group Canada
Ed: Doug Hanley. **Released:** November 2006. **Price:** $39.99. **Description:** Tips for using a Mac computer for small business is presented. The book offers shortcuts to iWork and email.

4993 ■ *"Samsung's Metamorphosis" in Austin Business Journal (Vol. 31, May 20, 2011, No. 11, pp. 1)*
Pub: American City Business Journals Inc.
Ed: Christopher Calnan. **Description:** Samsung Austin Semiconductor LP, a developer of semiconductors for smartphones and tablet computers, plans to diversify its offerings to include niche products: flash memory devices and microprocessing devices. In light of this strategy, Samsung Austin will be hiring 300 engineers as part of a $3.6 billion expansion of its plant.

4994 ■ *"Save the Date" in Barron's (Vol. 90, September 13, 2010, No. 37, pp. 35)*
Pub: Barron's Editorial & Corporate Headquarters
Ed: Mark Veverka. **Description:** Mark Hurd is the new Co-President of Oracle after being forced out at Hewlett-Packard where he faced a harassment complaint. HP fired Hurd due to expense account malfeasance. Hurd is also set to speak at an Oracle trade show in San Francisco on September 20, 2010.

4995 ■ *The Small Business Owner's Manual: Everything You Need to Know to Start Up and Run Your Business*
Pub: Career Press, Incorporated
Ed: Joe Kennedy. **Released:** June 2005. **Price:** $19.99 (US), $26.95 (Canadian). **Description:** Comprehensive guide for starting a small business, focusing on twelve ways to obtain financing, business plans, selling and advertising products and services, hiring and firing employees, setting up a Web site, business law, accounting issues, insurance, equipment, computers, banks, financing, customer credit and collection, leasing, and more.

4996 ■ *"A Souped-Up Digital Pen" in Inc. (Vol. 33, November 2011, No. 9, pp. 50)*
Pub: Inc. Magazine
Ed: Adam Baer. **Description:** Wacom's Inkling is a digital pen designed to record drawings and can save layers of sketches and add or remove them at a later date. Animation of these drawings can also be played. Files can be saved on the receiver which has a 2GB memory and they can then be transferred to a computer.

4997 ■ *"Taiwan Technology Initiatives Foster Growth" in Canadian Electronics (Vol. 23, February 2008, No. 1, pp. 28)*
Pub: CLB Media Inc.
Description: A study conducted by the Market Intelligence Center shows that currently, Taiwan is the world's larges producer of information technology products such as motherboards, servers, and LCD monitors. In 2006, Taiwan's LED industry reached a production value of NTD 21 billion. This push into the LED sector shows the Ministry of Economic Affairs' plan to target industries that are environmentally friendly.

4998 ■ *"Taking the Steps Into the Clouds" in New Hampshire Business Review (Vol. 33, March 25, 2011, No. 6, pp. 19)*
Pub: Business Publications Inc.
Ed: Tim Wessels. **Description:** Cloud services include Internet and Web security, spam filtering, message archiving, work group collaboration, IT asset management, help desk and disaster recovery backup.

4999 ■ *"Tap the iPad and Mobile Internet Device Market" in Franchising World (Vol. 42, September 2010, No. 9, pp. 43)*
Pub: International Franchise Association
Ed: John Thomson. **Description:** The iPad and other mobile Internet devices will help franchise owners interact with customers. It will be a good marketing tool for these businesses.

5000 ■ *"Tech Tax Heroes Go from Political Neophytes to Savvy Fundraisers" in Baltimore Business Journal (Vol. 27, November 20, 2009, No. 28)*
Pub: American City Business Journals
Ed: Scott Dance. **Description:** A group of computer services and information technology executives in Maryland have arranged a private dinner that will function as a fundraiser for Governor Martin O'Malley and Lieutenant Governor Anthony Brown. The event is seen as an effort to ensure the industry's involvement in the state after fighting for the repeal of the tech tax in 2007.

5001 ■ *"TomTom GO910: On the Road Again" in Black Enterprise (Vol. 37, January 2007, No. 6, pp. 52)*
Pub: Earl G. Graves Publishing Co. Inc.
Ed: Stephanie Young. **Description:** TomTom GO 910 is a GPS navigator that offers detailed maps of the U.S., Canada, and Europe. Consumers view their routes by a customizable LCD screen showing everything from the quickest to the shortest routes available or how to avoid toll roads. Business travelers may find this product invaluable as it also functions as a cell phone and connects to a variety of other multi-media devices.

5002 ■ *"Two Local Firms Make Inc. List: Minority Business" in Indianapolis Business Journal (Vol. 31, August 30, 2010, No. 26, pp. 13A)*
Pub: Indianapolis Business Journal Corporation
Description: Smart IT staffing agency and Entap Inc., an IT outsourcing firm were among the top ten fastest growing black-owned businesses in the U.S. by Inc. magazine.

5003 ■ *"U.S. Trade Body Clears Apple in Patent Case" in Wall Street Journal Eastern Edition (November 23 , 2011, pp. C1)*
Pub: Dow Jones & Company Inc. Enterprise Media Group
Contact: Clare Hart, President
Ed: Matt Jarzemsky, Paul Mozur. **Description:** HTC Corporation alleged in its patent-infringement case against Apple Inc. that Apple violated patents of S3 Graphics Inc., a company which was acquired by HTC Corporation. Now the International Trade Commission has issued a ruling saying that Apple did not violate the patents.

5004 ■ *"What is the Future of Disk Drives, Death or Rebirth?" in ACM Computing Surveys (Vol. 43, Fall 2011, No. 3, pp. 23)*
Pub: Association for Computing Machinery
Ed: Yuhui Deng. **Description:** Disk drives have experienced dramatic development to meet performance requirements since the IBM 1301 disk drive was announced in 1961. However, the performance gap between memory and disk drives has widened to 6 orders of magnitude and continues to widen by about 50 percent per year. Challenges and opportunities facing these storage devices are explored.

5005 ■ *"Will mCommerce Make Black Friday Green?" in Retail Merchandiser (Vol. 51, September-October 2011, No. 5, pp. 8)*
Pub: Phoenix Media Corporation
Ed: Scott Miller. **Description:** Retailers speculate the possibilities of mobile commerce and are implementing strategies at their stores. Consumers using mobile devices accounted for only 0.1 percent of visits to retail Websites on Black Friday 2009 and rose to 5.6 percent in 2010; numbers are expected to rise for 2011.

5006 ■ *"Work for Play: Careers in Video Game Development" in Occupational Outlook Quarterly (Vol. 55, Fall 2011, No. 3, pp. 2)*
Pub: U.S. Bureau of Labor Statistics
Ed: Drew Liming, Dennis Vilorio. **Description:** Game developers make a living creating the games the public enjoys playing. The video gaming industry reported sales over $10 billion in 2009 and employed 32,000 people in 34 states. Career options in video game development are featured.

5007 ■ *"Xbox 360 Excels as a Media Hub" in Hispanic Business (October 2009, pp. 40)*
Pub: Hispanic Business
Ed: Jeremy Nisen. **Description:** Xbox 360 video game console from Microsoft offers games, amazing graphics and state-of-the-art accessories. The trend towards purchase of the Xbox includes more than teenagers.

5008 ■ *"Xtium Has Its Head in the Clouds" in Philadelphia Business Journal (Vol. 30, September 23, 2011, No. 32, pp. 1)*
Pub: American City Business Journals Inc.
Ed: Peter Key. **Description:** Philadelphia-based cloud computing firm Xtium LLC received an $11.5 million first-round investment from Boston-Massachusetts-based OpenView Venture Partners. Catering to midsize businesses and unit of bigger firms, Xtium offers disaster-recovery, hosting, and managed-information-technology-infrastructure services.

STATISTICAL SOURCES

5009 ■ *RMA Annual Statement Studies*
Pub: Risk Management Association
Contact: Kevin M. Blakey, President
Released: Annual. **Price:** $175.00 2006-07 edition, $105.00. **Description:** Contains composite balance sheets and income statements for more than 360 industries, including the accounting, auditing, and bookkeeping industries. Also contains five years of comparative historical data for discerning trends. Includes 16 commonly used ratios, computed for most of the size groupings for nearly every industry.

5010 ■ *Standard & Poor's Industry Surveys*
Pub: Standard & Poor's Corp.
Released: Annual. **Price:** $3633.00. **Description:** Two-volume book that examines the prospects for specific industries, including trucking. Also provides analyses of trends and problems, statistical tables and charts, and comparative company analyses.

TRADE PERIODICALS

5011 ■ *Computer Link Magazine*
Pub: Millennium Publishing Inc.
URL(s): techny.com/. **Released:** Monthly **Price:** $20, Free.

5012 ■ *DCLNews*
Pub: Data Conversion Laboratory
Contact: Mark Gross, President
Released: Monthly. **Price:** Included in membership;. **Description:** E-journal providing you insider information on XML and SGML, along with the latest technology and e-publishing news.

5013 ■ *Maximum PC*
Pub: Future Network USA
URL(s): maximumpc.com. **Ed:** Michael Brown, Gordon Mah Ung. **Released:** Monthly **Price:** $14.95, Individuals; $24.95, Individuals 12 CDs; $29.95, Other countries; $49.95, Other countries two years; $1.95, Single issue.

5014 ■ *Media Computing*
Pub: Dreamscape Productions
Ed: Sheridan Tatsuno, Editor, statsuno@aol.com. **Released:** Monthly. **Price:** $495, institutions in the U.S. and Canada; $550, institutions elsewhere. **Description:** Supplies analysis of multimedia, internet, intranet, and web computing issues. Recurring features include interviews and reports of meetings.

5015 ■ *Microprocessor Report*
Pub: MicroDesign Resources
Released: 17x/yr. **Price:** $695, U.S. and Canada for print version; $495, U.S. and Canada pounds;. **Description:** The leading technical publication for the microprocessor industry. Dedicated to providing unbiased, in-depth, critical analysis of new high-performance microprocessor developments. This newsletter is exclusively subscriber-supported.

5016 ■ *Multimedia Internet@Schools: A Practical Journal of Multimedia, CD-ROM, Online, & Internet in K-12*
Pub: Information Today Inc.
Contact: Thomas H. Hogan, President
E-mail: ctuthill@infotoday.com
URL(s): www.mmischools.com/. **Ed:** David Hoffman. **Released:** Bimonthly **Price:** $45.95, U.S.; $64, Canada and Mexico; $73, Other countries; $94, Two years; $144, Individuals 3 years.

5017 ■ *Online: The Leading Magazine for Information Professionals*
Pub: Online, A Division of Information Today Inc.
URL(s): www.infotoday.com/online/default.shtml. **Ed:** Marydee Ojala. **Released:** Bimonthly **Price:** $124.95, Individuals; $235, Two years; $141, Canada and Mexico; $167, Other countries.

TRADE SHOWS AND CONVENTIONS

5018 ■ COMDEX
Ziff-Davis Inc.
28 E 28th St.
New York, NY 10016-7939
Ph: (212)503-3500
Fax: (212)503-4599
Co. E-mail: randy_zane@ziffdavis.com
URL: http://www.ziffdavis.com
Contact: Vivek Shah, Chief Executive Officer
URL(s): www.comdex.com/. **Frequency:** Annual. **Audience:** Volume resellers and value-adders of small computers and related items; only a virtual trade show since 2003. **Principal Exhibits:** Small computer systems, related peripherals, software, accessories, services, and supplies. **Dates and Locations:** , Sands Expo and Convention Center.

5019 ■ Computer Game Developers' Conference
UBM LLC
240 West 35th Street
New York, CA 94403
Ph: (650)513-4300
Free: 800-842-0798
Fax: (650)513-4618
URL: http://www.cmp.com
URL(s): www.gdconf.com. **Frequency:** Annual. **Principal Exhibits:** Equipment, supplies, and services for developers and producers of computer games. **Telecommunication Services:** pchapnick@cmp.com.

5020 ■ Expo Comm Wireless Korea
E.J. Krause & Associates, Inc.
6550 Rock Spring Dr., Ste. 500
Bethesda, MD 20817
Ph: (301)493-5500
Fax: (301)493-5705
Co. E-mail: info@ejkrause.com
URL: http://www.ejkrause.com
Contact: Sharon Deutch, Director
E-mail: deutch@ejkrause.com
Frequency: Annual. **Principal Exhibits:** Equipment, supplies, and services for computers. **Telecommunication Services:** owens@ejkrause.com.

FRANCHISES AND BUSINESS OPPORTUNITIES

5021 ■ Computer Renaissance
JMG, Inc.
Description: Computer stores that buy, sell, and trade new and used computer equipment. **No. of Franchise Units:** 31. **Founded:** 1988.. **Franchised:** 1993. **Equity Capital Needed:** Liquid capital of $193,000-$283,800. **Franchise Fee:** $27,500. **Financial Assistance:** Yes. **Training:** Includes 2 weeks training at headquarters, 1 week at franchisee's location and ongoing support.

5022 ■ Data Doctors
Data Doctors Franchise Systems, Inc.
Description: Computer sales and services, including web services. **No. of Franchise Units:** 69. **No. of Company-Owned Units:** 8. **Founded:** 1988.. **Franchised:** 2002. **Equity Capital Needed:** $122,065-$178,415. **Franchise Fee:** $35,000. **Royalty Fee:** 5%. **Training:** Initial 11 day training at headquarters, 1 week onsite prior to opening and 1 week following opening and ongoing support.

5023 ■ Palm Tree Computer Systems
Palm Tree Franchise Corp.
119 N Central Ave.
Oviedo, FL 32765
Ph: (407)796-5001
Description: Retail computer store. **No. of Franchise Units:** 3. **No. of Company-Owned Units:** 1. **Founded:** 1996.. **Franchised:** 2006. **Equity Capital Needed:** $116,300-$285,500. **Training:** Yes.

COMPUTERIZED DATABASES

5024 ■ *Computer Database*
10650 Toebben Dr.
Independence, KY 41051
Free: 800-354-9706
Fax: (800)487-8488
Co. E-mail: investors@cengage.com
URL: http://www.gale.cengage.com
Contact: Ronald Dunn, President
Availability: Online: ProQuest LLC-Dialog; ProQuest LLC - Dialog; Cengage Learning Inc. **Type:** Bibliographic; Full-text.

5025 ■ *CRN Direct*
600 Community Dr.
Manhasset, NY 11030
Ph: (516)562-5000
Fax: (516)562-7830
Co. E-mail: inquiries@ubm-us.com
URL: http://www.ubmtechnology.com
Availability: Online: UBM plc-UBM Tech. **Type:** Full-text.

5026 ■ *INSPEC® Ondisc - Technology*
Michael Faraday House
6 Hills Way
Stevenage SG1 2AY, United Kingdom
Ph: 1438 313 311
Fax: 1438 765 526
Co. E-mail: postmaster@theiet.org
URL: http://www.theiet.org
Contact: Nigel Fine, Chief Executive Officer
Availability: CD-ROM: Institution of Engineering and Technology. **Type:** Bibliographic.

LIBRARIES

5027 ■ Walt Disney World - Global Business Technology Strategy Library
Team Disney 336-N
1375 Buena Vista Dr.
Lake Buena Vista, FL 32830-1000
Ph: (407)828-4250
Fax: (407)827-8260
Co. E-mail: david.w.hartman@disney.com
URL: http://disneyworld.disney.go.com/wdw
Contact: David Hartman, Librarian
Scope: Computer science, human resources, general business. **Services:** Center not open to the public. **Founded:** 1986. **Holdings:** 4000 books, videos, DVDs, and CDs; 100 AV equipment. **Subscriptions:** 200 journals and other serials; 3 newspapers.

5028 ■ Fujitsu Microelectronics, Inc. - FMI Library
1250 E. Arques Ave., No. 333
Sunnyvale, CA 94085-5401
Ph: (408)746-6000
Free: 800-831-3183
Fax: (408)992-2674
Co. E-mail: fsa_inquiry@us.fujitsu.com
URL: http://www.fujitsu.com/us
Scope: Semiconductor industry and products, computer industry and products, telecommunications, electronics industry. **Services:** Interlibrary loan; SDI; Library not open to the public. **Founded:** 1990. **Holdings:** 500 books and conference proceedings; 250 market research reports and newsletters; CD-ROMs. **Subscriptions:** 70 journals and other serials; 2 newspapers. **Telecommunication Services:** inquiry@fma.fujitsu.com.

Computer System Integrators

START-UP INFORMATION

5029 ■ *"Probability Processing Chip: Lyric Semiconductor"* in Inc. (Volume 32, December 2010, No. 10, pp. 52)

Pub: Inc. Magazine

Ed: Christine Lagorio. **Description:** Lyric Semiconductor, a start up located in Cambridge, Massachusetts, has developed a computer chip that also uses values that fall between zero and one, resulting in a chip that can process information using probabilities, considering many possible answers that find the best fit.

ASSOCIATIONS AND OTHER ORGANIZATIONS

5030 ■ **British Columbia Technology Industries Association (BC TIA)**
1188 W Georgia St., Ste. 900
Vancouver, BC, Canada V6E 4A2
Ph: (604)683-6159
Fax: (604)683-3879
Co. E-mail: info@bctia.org
URL: http://www.bctia.org
Contact: Bill Tam, President
Description: Fosters the growth and development of the Province's technology industries and member companies. Provides programs, services and activities designed to meet the needs and interests of members in the areas of networking, education, public awareness, and government relations. Offers a forum for members to review industry issues, acquire new business knowledge from leading industry professionals, to supply input on existing and proposed legislation and generally work together to advance the industry's interests. **Founded:** 1993. **Publications:** *Impact* (Annual).

5031 ■ **Impact**
1188 W Georgia St., Ste. 900
Vancouver, BC, Canada V6E 4A2
Ph: (604)683-6159
Fax: (604)683-3879
Co. E-mail: info@bctia.org
URL: http://www.bctia.org
Contact: Bill Tam, President
Released: Annual

REFERENCE WORKS

5032 ■ *"ChemSW Software Development Services Available for Outsourcing"* in Information Today (Vol. 26, February 2009, No. 2, pp. 30)

Pub: Information Today, Inc.

Description: ChemSW software development services include requirements analysis, specification development, design, development, testing, and system documentation as an IT outsourcing solution. The company can also develop software tracking systems for satellite stockrooms, provide asset management integration solutions and more.

5033 ■ *Cisco Network Design Solutions for Small-Medium Businesses*
Pub: Cisco Press

Ed: Peter Rybaczyk. **Released:** August 2004. **Price:** $55.00. **Description:** Solutions for computer networking professionals using computer networks within a small to medium-sized business. Topics cover not only core networking issues and solutions, but security, IP telephony, unified communications, customer relations management, wireless LANs, and more.

5034 ■ *Information Industry Directory*
Pub: Cengage Learning Inc.
Contact: Ronald Dunn, President
URL(s): www.gale.cengage.com. **Released:** Annual; Latest edition 38th; April, 2013. **Price:** $1160, Individuals. **Covers:** Approximately 12,000 organizations, systems, and services involved in the production and distribution of information in electronic form: database producers and their products online host services, transactional services, library and information networks, bibliographic utilities, library management systems, information retrieval software, mailing list services, fee-based information on demand services, document delivery sources, data collection and analysis centers and firms, and related consultants, service companies, professional and trade associations, publishers, and research activities. **Entries include:** Name of parent organization, name of system of service, address, phone, toll-free phone, fax, telex, email address, year founded name of unit head, size of staff, names of any affiliated organizations, financial information. Internet access information, general description of electronic product, system, or service, subjects covered or areas of service offered, sources of data for the system, type and quantity of stored information in all forms, publications and microform products and services, computer-based products and services, other services, clientele served, availability and restrictions, name of contact. **Arrangement:** Alphabetical. **Indexes:** Master, database name, software name, publication/microform title, function/service, personal name, subject, geographical.

5035 ■ *Information Sources: The IIA Annual Membership Directory*
Pub: Software and Information Industry Association
Contact: Kenneth Wasch, President
URL(s): www.siia.net. **Released:** Continuous **Covers:** More than 800 companies involved in the creation, distribution, and use of information products, services, and technology. Entries are prepared by companies described. **Entries include:** Company name, address, phone, names of executives, international partners, regional offices, trade and brand names, and description of products and services. **Arrangement:** Alphabetical. **Indexes:** Product, personal name, trade name, geographical, corporate parents, international and niche markets.

5036 ■ *"PCI Express Powers Machine Vision"* in Canadian Electronics (Vol. 23, February 2008, No. 1, pp. 8)
Pub: CLB Media Inc.

Ed: Inder Kohli. **Description:** PCI Express is an innovative peripheral bus that can be used in industrial computing. The peripheral bus delivers a high-bandwidth, scaleable, point-to-point path from peripheral cards to the computing core. Features and functions of PCI Express are described in detail.

5037 ■ *Power Up Your Small-Medium Business: A Guide to Enabling Network Technologies*
Pub: Cisco Press

Ed: Robyn Aber. **Released:** March 2004. **Price:** $39.95 (US), $57.95 (Canadian). **Description:** Network technologies geared to small and medium-size business, focusing on access, IP telephony, wireless technologies, security, and computer network management.

5038 ■ *Pro Windows Small Business Server 2003*
Pub: Apress L.P.

Ed: Tony Campbell. **Released:** July 2006. **Price:** $39.99. **Description:** Profile of Microsoft's Windows Small Business Server, designed for companies with 50 or fewer employees.

5039 ■ *"Tech Data Launches Unified Communications and Network Security Specialized Business Units"* in Wireless News (October 22, 2009)
Pub: Close-Up Media

Description: Responding to the growing demand for unified communications and network security, Tech Data announced the formation of two new Specialized Business Units.

5040 ■ *"The Web Gets Real"* in Canadian Business (Vol. 79, July 17, 2006, No. 14-15, pp. 19)
Pub: Rogers Media

Ed: Andrew Wahl. **Description:** Ron Lake's efforts of bringing the virtual and physical worlds more closely together by using Geographic Markup Language (GML) are presented.

5041 ■ *"Xtium Has Its Head in the Clouds"* in Philadelphia Business Journal (Vol. 30, September 23, 2011, No. 32, pp. 1)
Pub: American City Business Journals Inc.

Ed: Peter Key. **Description:** Philadelphia-based cloud computing firm Xtium LLC received an $11.5 million first-round investment from Boston-Massachusetts-based OpenView Venture Partners. Catering to midsize businesses and unit of bigger firms, Xtium offers disaster-recovery, hosting, and managed-information-technology-infrastructure services.

TRADE PERIODICALS

5042 ■ *ClieNT Server News*
Pub: G2 Computer Intelligence Inc.

Ed: Maureen O'Gara, Editor, ogara@g2news.com. **Released:** Weekly. **Price:** $595. **Description:** Provides news on Windows 2000, XPad NT, and NT and Microsoft. Covers software and hardware roll-outs, developments of marketing strategies and client server moves competitive to Windows XP 2000 and

NT. Recurring features include letters to the editor, news of research, and interviews. Remarks: Available in Acrobat, HTML, and ASCII.

5043 ■ *ePostal News*

Pub: G2 Computer Intelligence Inc.
Ed: Maureen O'Gara, Editor, ogara@g2news.com. **Released:** Weekly. **Price:** $595. **Description:** Reports news on digital media and e-commerce, e-business, Internet security, and Internet Post and e-mail matters.

5044 ■ *International Journal of Intelligent Systems*

Pub: John Wiley & Sons Inc.
Contact: Stephen M. Smith, President
URL(s): onlinelibrary.wiley.com/journal/10.1002/(-ISSN)1098-111X. **Ed:** Ronald R. Yager. **Released:** Monthly **Price:** $3985, Institutions print and online; $4153, Institutions, Canada and Mexico print and online; £1899, Institutions print only; $3465, Institutions print only; $3633, Institutions, Canada and Mexico print only; $3717, Institutions, other countries print only; €2399, Institutions print only; £2185, Institutions print and online; €2760, Institutions, other countries print and online; $4237, Institutions, other countries print and online.

5045 ■ *Microprocessor Report*

Pub: MicroDesign Resources
Released: 17x/yr. **Price:** $695, U.S. and Canada for print version; $495, U.S. and Canada pounds;. **Description:** The leading technical publication for the microprocessor industry. Dedicated to providing unbiased, in-depth, critical analysis of new high-performance microprocessor developments. This newsletter is exclusively subscriber-supported.

5046 ■ *Online: The Leading Magazine for Information Professionals*

Pub: Online, A Division of Information Today Inc.
URL(s): www.infotoday.com/online/default.shtml. **Ed:** Marydee Ojala. **Released:** Bimonthly **Price:** $124.95, Individuals; $235, Two years; $141, Canada and Mexico; $167, Other countries.

TRADE SHOWS AND CONVENTIONS

5047 ■ COMDEX

Ziff-Davis Inc.
28 E 28th St.
New York, NY 10016-7939
Ph: (212)503-3500
Fax: (212)503-4599
Co. E-mail: randy_zane@ziffdavis.com
URL: http://www.ziffdavis.com
Contact: Vivek Shah, Chief Executive Officer
URL(s): www.comdex.com/. **Frequency:** Annual. **Audience:** Volume resellers and value-adders of small computers and related items; only a virtual trade show since 2003. **Principal Exhibits:** Small computer systems, related peripherals, software, accessories, services, and supplies. **Dates and Locations:** , Sands Expo and Convention Center.

CONSULTANTS

5048 ■ Advanced Computer Consulting Inc.

17-24 Parsons Blvd.
Whitestone, NY 11357
Ph: (718)746-0900
Fax: (718)746-2099
Contact: Dr. Gus A. Galatianos, President
E-mail: accidrg@aol.com
Scope: Services include management consulting, technology assessment, strategic systems planning, feasibility studies, computer and communications hardware and software evaluations, systems analysis through implementation, project management, systems integration, and computer training. Industries served include banking, defense, distribution, healthcare, insurance and manufacturing. **Founded:** 1987. **Publications:** "Distributed DDBMS: Problems and Prospects," Scientific Computing &Automation Magazine, Nov, 1992; "Expert Systems Give PCs a Piece of Mind," Office Technology Management Magazine, Dec, 1991. **Seminars:** Principles of Software Engineering; Principles of Database Systems; Principles of Artificial Intelligence and Expert Systems; Principles of Object-oriented Programming and C Plus Plus.

5049 ■ The Centech Group Inc.

6402 Arlington Blvd., 10th Fl.
Falls Church, VA 22042
Ph: (703)525-4444
Free: 800-938-1026
Fax: (703)525-2349
Co. E-mail: clientinterest@centechgroup.com
URL: http://www.centechgroup.com
Contact: Fernando V. Galaviz, President
E-mail: galavizf@centechgroup.com
Scope: Provider of a variety of computer and information systems services. Work involves program management support, computer systems analysis and integration, software engineering and development, network services, imaging, document conversion, manufacturing and engineering, LAN/WAN; work-flow, and document management and data warehousing, including analysis, design, and implementation, information systems modernization and integration, is a lot to be said for the company you keep, whether it is your customers, your partners or your team members (employees) and information engineering. **Founded:** 1988.

5050 ■ Computer Integrations Inc.

1670 Bayview Ave.
Toronto, ON, Canada 647147
Ph: (416)485-4712
Fax: (416)481-4220
Contact: Ivo Zivkov, President
E-mail: izivkov@onramp.ca
Scope: Specializes in the integration of hardware software products from different vendors as well as custom software development. Provides the following services feasibility study cost benefit analysis participating in RFP preparation and evaluation project design, development, and management installation planning application integration user needs analysis vendor selection, hardware and software; software hardware integration and configuration technical support, maintenance installation assistance training program for trainer and end users phone support for trainer information resource management and documentation preparation. Industries served computer and retail companies. **Founded:** 1988.

5051 ■ COTC Technologies Inc.—COTC-TrenzSoft

172 E Industrial Blvd.
Pueblo, CO 81007-4406
Ph: (719)547-0938
Free: 888-547-0938
Fax: (719)547-1105
Contact: Tom Renz, Chief Executive Officer
E-mail: tom@cotc-consulting.com
Scope: Provides software consulting services to organizations that require assistance with their HP3000 computer system. Provides systems analysis, programming, operations support, and system management. Also provides PC software and hardware support and consulting. Additionally provides various training for the HP3000 computer system. Industries served: healthcare, aerospace procurement, aerospace proposal activities, and HP3000 computer systems. **Founded:** 2006.

5052 ■ Pathways Unlimited Inc.

1331 S Knoxville Ave.
Tulsa, OK 74112-5805
Ph: (918)744-7482
Fax: (918)744-8909
Co. E-mail: sales@pathways-unlimited.com
Contact: Gary L. Stice, President
Scope: Specializes in database publishing. Serving as a Microsoft fox pro development partner, data publishing systems have been developed to input and process directory information seamlessly from databases and lotus into publishing systems. Serves the publishing industry. **Founded:** 1994. **Telecommunication Services:** pathwaysor@aol.com.

5053 ■ Saffire Systems & Development Inc.—Saffire Productions

2919 Lucky John Dr.
Park City, UT 84060
Ph: (435)649-4146
Fax: (435)647-5708
Co. E-mail: info@saffiresystems.com
URL: http://www.saffiresystems.com
Contact: George Dymalski, Vice President
E-mail: gdd@saffiresystems.com
Scope: Diverse consulting firm that provides system integration, including software and utility development, training and technical writing. Serves private industries as well as government agencies. Woman owned firm. **Founded:** 1988. **Publications:** "Interleaf Tips & Tricks," Onward Press, Santa Fe, NM; "The Interleaf Exercise Book," Onward Press, Santa Fe, NM. **Seminars:** Desktop publishing. **Special Services:** HAGNET.

5054 ■ STN Inc.

4200 Forbes Blvd., Ste. 206
Lanham, MD 20706
Ph: (410)721-4004
Free: 800-321-1969
Fax: (410)721-9011
Co. E-mail: ask@stn.com
URL: http://www.stn.com
Contact: Marcia Owens-Fowler, President
Scope: Computer systems consultants specializing in custom software for multi-user computers. All work based on the UNIX environment, with C language and database management system expertise on staff. Provides a full range of solutions, from computer hardware, software and services, to LAN and WAN technology and Internet assistance. Serves private industry and government agencies worldwide. **Founded:** 1981. **Publications:** "File Pro Developers Reference Manual". **Seminars:** Browser-Based filePro On Your Local Area Network, 2009; Advanced filePro Input and Output Techniques, Sep, 2008; filePro for Database Managers and Programmers New To filePro, Jul, 2008. **Special Services:** filePro®; WorkLine™; MoveTrac™; LeadTrac™; MoveBill™.

5055 ■ Sygenex Inc.—Sygenex

4770 Eastgate Mall
San Diego, CA 92121-1970
Ph: (858)535-5530
Fax: (858)452-0271
Co. E-mail: sygenex@orincon.com
Contact: Robert J. Stevens, President
Scope: Supplier of advanced technology products and services in key niches essential to the United States intelligence community and its partners. Engaged in the research, design, development, manufacture and integration of advanced technology systems, products and services. **Founded:** 1984.

FRANCHISES AND BUSINESS OPPORTUNITIES

5056 ■ Silution Franchise Corp.

1472 E Walnut St.
Pasadena, CA 91106
Ph: (626)535-0560
Free: 877-745-8846
Fax: (626)535-0566
URL: http://www.silution.com
Description: Computer services & support. **Founded:** 1998.. **Franchised:** 2006. **Equity Capital Needed:** $39,950-$71,800. **Franchise Fee:** $22,000. **Royalty Fee:** 10%. **Training:** Provides 5 days at headquarters, 1 day at franchisee's location with ongoing support.

5057 ■ Vehicle Tracking Solutions

10 E 5th St.
Deer Park, NY 11729
Ph: (631)586-7400
Fax: (866)873-0066
Co. E-mail: jmcjr@VTSN.com
URL: http://www.VTSN.com
Description: Companies that have fleets of vehicles use VTS Systems and software to gauge the productivity of their vehicles. **No. of Franchise Units:** 9. **No. of Company-Owned Units:** 3. **Founded:** 2001..

Franchised: 2007. **Equity Capital Needed:** $58,150-$64,600. **Franchise Fee:** $24,900. **Financial Assistance:** Financing available for startup costs. **Training:** 1 week training program provided at headquarters followed by 2 days onsite.

COMPUTERIZED DATABASES

5058 ■ *Business Wire*
44 Montgomery St., 39th Fl.
San Francisco, CA 94104
Ph: (415)986-4422
Free: 800-227-0845
Fax: (415)788-5335
Co. E-mail: SF_sales_group@bizwire.com
URL: http://www.businesswire.com
Availability: Online: ProQuest LLC - Dialog; Dow Jones & Company Inc.; Mzinga Inc.; LexisNexis Group; Bloomberg L.P. **Type:** Full-text.

5059 ■ *Computer Database*
10650 Toebben Dr.
Independence, KY 41051
Free: 800-354-9706
Fax: (800)487-8488
Co. E-mail: investors@cengage.com
URL: http://www.gale.cengage.com
Contact: Ronald Dunn, President
Availability: Online: ProQuest LLC-Dialog; ProQuest LLC - Dialog; Cengage Learning Inc. **Type:** Bibliographic; Full-text.

5060 ■ *Computer and Information Systems Abstracts*
789 E Eisenhower Pky.
Ann Arbor, MI 48103
Ph: (734)761-4700
Fax: (734)997-4222
Co. E-mail: info@proquest.com
URL: http://www.csa.com
Availability: Online: ProQuest LLC - CSA; STN International; STN International. **Type:** Bibliographic.

5061 ■ *Computerworld*
One Exeter Plz., 15th Fl.
Boston, MA 02116
Ph: (617)534-1200
Co. E-mail: idgcorpcom@idg.com
URL: http://www.idg.com
Availability: Online: International Data Group Inc.; LexisNexis Group. **Type:** Full-text.

5062 ■ *TecTrends™*
PO Box 8120
Berkeley, CA 94707
Ph: (510)525-6220
Co. E-mail: tectrendsinfo@tectrends.com
URL: http://www.tectrends.com
Availability: Online: ProQuest LLC-Dialog; ProQuest LLC - Dialog; Information Sources Inc. - TecTrends. **Type:** Bibliographic; Directory.

LIBRARIES

5063 ■ Agilent Technologies - Santa Clara Site Library
5301 Stevens Creek Blvd.
MS 55/27
Santa Clara, CA 95051
Ph: (408)345-8886
Free: 877-424-4536
Fax: (408)345-8474
Co. E-mail: contact_us@agilent.com
URL: http://www.home.agilent.com
Contact: Diana Robba
Scope: Electronics, business, computer science, biological sciences. **Services:** Interlibrary loan; copying; library not open to the public. **Founded:** 1975. **Holdings:** 4000 books. **Subscriptions:** 160 journals and other serials; 2 newspapers.

5064 ■ AMS - Knowledge Center Library
4050 Legato Rd.
Fairfax, VA 22033
Ph: (703)267-5669

Fax: (703)276-5094
Co. E-mail: AMS_know@mail.amsinc.com
Contact: Nancy Gregory, Librarian
Scope: Business, economics, computers, data processing, software engineering, computer programming, telecommunications. **Services:** Interlibrary loan; Library open to the public by appointment. **Founded:** 1978. **Holdings:** 3500 volumes; CD-ROMs. **Subscriptions:** 200 journals and other serials.

5065 ■ CitiBank Technical Library
820 Stillwater Rd., 2nd Fl.
West Sacramento, CA 95605-1629
Ph: (916)374-7486
Free: 800-374-9700
Co. E-mail: mjones3@calfed.com
URL: http://www.citibank.com/domain/calfed_converts.htm
Contact: Michael Jones, Librarian, Technical Services
Scope: Computer systems, telecommunications. **Services:** Library not open to the public. **Founded:** 1986. **Holdings:** 500 books; 4000 mainframe computer documents. **Subscriptions:** 10 journals and other serials.

5066 ■ Computer Sciences Corporation Corporate Library
3170 Fairview Park Dr.
Falls Church, VA 22042-4516
Ph: (703)876-1000
Fax: (310)322-3685
URL: http://www.csc.com
Scope: Data processing, communications, information retrieval, programming, systems analysis, business, management, operations research, systems integration, outsourcing, company background information. **Services:** Interlibrary loan; copying; library not open to the public. **Founded:** 1962. **Holdings:** 150 books. **Subscriptions:** 70 journals and other serials.

5067 ■ Hewlett-Packard Company - Roseville Research Library
8000 Foothills Blvd.
MS 5621
Roseville, CA 95747
Ph: (916)785-5548
Fax: (916)785-3266
URL: http://www.hp.com
Contact: Rick Shallenberger, Analyst
Scope: Computer science, electrical engineering, computer networking, business. **Services:** Interlibrary loan; copying; SDI; library not open to the public. **Holdings:** 2000 books. **Subscriptions:** 125 journals and other serials.

5068 ■ Northrop Grumman Mission Systems - Technology Library
12011 Sunset Hills Rd.
Reston, VA 20190
Ph: (703)345-7738
Fax: (703)345-7735
Co. E-mail: norma.j.draper@ngc.com
URL: http://www.is.northropgrumman.com
Contact: Norma Draper, Librarian, Technical Services
Scope: Systems engineering, information technology, computer science, systems integration. **Services:** Interlibrary loan; library not open to the public. **Founded:** 1965. **Holdings:** 500 books and technical reports. **Subscriptions:** 35 journals and other serials.

RESEARCH CENTERS

5069 ■ HEC Montreal - Information Systems Research Group—HEC Montreal - Groupe de recherche en systèmes d'information (GReSI)
3000 Chemin de la Cote-Sainte-Catherine
Montreal, QC, Canada H3T 2A7
Ph: (514)340-6852

Fax: (514)340-6132
Co. E-mail: guy.pare@hec.ca
URL: http://www2.hec.ca/gresi
Contact: Prof. Guy Paré, Director
Founded: 1986. **Publications:** *Cahiers du GReSI*. **Educational Activities:** Information Systems Research Group Conferences (Bimonthly).

5070 ■ National Research Council Canada - Institute for Information Technology (IIT)
46 Dinnen Dr.
Fredericton, NB, Canada E3B 9W4
Ph: (506)451-2500
Fax: (506)452-4031
Co. E-mail: andrew.reddick@nrc-cnrc.gc.ca
URL: http://www.nrc-cnrc.gc.ca/eng/ibp/iit.html
Contact: Lorna Brown, Manager
E-mail: lorna.brown@nrc-cnrc.gc.ca
Services: Business mentoring; Licensing opportunities; Research and development support; Strategic partnerships. **Founded:** 1990. **Publications:** *NRC Annual Report*. **Educational Activities:** Colloquium series (Monthly). **Telecommunication Services:** info.iit-iti@nrc-cnrc.gc.ca.

5071 ■ Stanford University - Information Systems Laboratory (ISL)
350 Serra Mall
Department of Electrical Engineering
Stanford, CA 94305-9510
Ph: (650)723-3473
Fax: (650)723-8473
Co. E-mail: abbas@ee.stanford.edu
URL: http://isl.stanford.edu
Contact: Prof. Abbas El Gamal, Director
Founded: 1960.

5072 ■ University of Illinois at Urbana-Champaign - Center for Reliable and High Performance Computing (CHRC)
Coordinated Science Laboratory
1308 W Main St.
Urbana, IL 61801
Ph: (217)333-6201
Fax: (217)244-5685
Co. E-mail: patel@crhc.uiuc.edu
URL: http://www.crhc.illinois.edu
Contact: Prof. Janak H. Patel, Director
Founded: 1988.

5073 ■ University of Maryland at College Park - Institute for Advanced Computer Studies (UMIACS)
3143 A.V. Williams Bldg.
College Park, MD 20740
Ph: (301)405-6722
Fax: (301)314-9658
Co. E-mail: varshney@umiacs.umd.edu
URL: http://www.umiacs.umd.edu
Contact: Prof. Amitabh Varshney, Director
Founded: 1985. **Publications:** *Technical report series*.

5074 ■ University of Maryland at College Park - Institute for Systems Research (ISR)
2173 A.V. Williams Bldg.
College Park, MD 20742
Ph: (301)405-6615
Fax: (301)314-9920
Co. E-mail: rebeccac@isr.umd.edu
URL: http://www.isr.umd.edu
Contact: Prof. Reza Ghodssi, Director
E-mail: ghodssi@umd.edu
Services: Research Review Day: annual free showcase event of research held in the spring. **Founded:** 1985. **Publications:** *Institute for Systems Research Technical Reports*; *ISR Newsletter* (Quarterly). **Educational Activities:** Colloquia; ISR Seminars; ISR Workshops; Industrial Review Meeting (Annual); Systems Symposium (Annual), generally held in the spring semester, sponsorship from industrial partners. **Awards:** ISR Fellowships; ISR Graduate Assistantships.

5075 ■ Washington University in St. Louis - Computer and Communications Research Center (CCRC)
CB 1045

Department of Computer Science & Engineering
Saint Louis, MO 63130-4899
Ph: (314)935-6107
Fax: (314)935-7302

Co. E-mail: jbf@wustl.edu
URL: http://www.ccrc.wustl.edu
Contact: Prof. Mark A. Franklin, Director

Founded: 1980.

REFERENCE WORKS

5076 ■ *"Cerner Works the Business Circuit' in Business Journal-Serving Metropolitan Kansas City (Vol. 26, October 5, 2007, No. 4, pp. 1)*

Pub: American City Business Journals, Inc.

Ed: Rob Roberts. **Description:** Cerner Corporation is embracing the coming of the electronic medical record exchange by creating a regional health information organization (RHIO) called the CareEntrust. The RHIO convinced health insurers to share claims data with patients and clinicians. At the Center Health Conference, held October 7 to 10, Cerner will demonstrate the software it developed for CareEntrust to the 40,000 healthcare and information technology professionals.

5077 ■ *"The Keeper of Records" in Black Enterprise (Vol. 41, December 2010, No. 5, pp. 54)*

Pub: Earl G. Graves Publishing Co. Inc.

Ed: Denise Campbell. **Description:** Medical billing and coding, submission of claims to health insurance companies and Medicare or Medicaid for payment is one of the fastest growing disciplines in healthcare.

TRADE PERIODICALS

5078 ■ *Office Technology*

URL(s): www.bta.org/?page=OfficeTechnology. **Released:** Monthly **Price:** $100, Individuals; $115, Other countries; $45, /year for individuals in U.S.; $50, /year for individuals in Canada.

5079 ■ *Print Solutions: Award-Winning Coverage of the Printing Industry*

Pub: Print Services and Distribution Association

Contact: Robert O'Connell, President

URL(s): www.printsolutionsmag.com. **Ed:** John Delavan. **Released:** Monthly **Price:** Free to members; $29, Nonmembers.

TRADE SHOWS AND CONVENTIONS

5080 ■ **Business & Technology Solutions Show**

Illinois Certified Public Accounting Society
550 W Jackson, Ste. 900
Chicago, IL 60661-5716
Ph: (312)933-0407
Free: 800-993-0407
Fax: (312)993-9954
URL: http://www.icpas.org
Contact: Teresa Bates, Coordinator, Conferences

URL(s): www.icpas.org. **Frequency:** Annual. **Audience:** Certified public accountants and their clients, business owners and managers, and others from the financial and business community. **Principal Exhib-**

its: Computers, office equipment, software publishing and educational supplies, and financial services. **Dates and Locations:** , Donald E. Stephens Convention Center.

5081 ■ **COMDEX**

Ziff-Davis Inc.
28 E 28th St.
New York, NY 10016-7939
Ph: (212)503-3500
Fax: (212)503-4599
Co. E-mail: randy_zane@ziffdavis.com
URL: http://www.ziffdavis.com
Contact: Vivek Shah, Chief Executive Officer

URL(s): www.comdex.com/. **Frequency:** Annual. **Audience:** Volume resellers and value-adders of small computers and related items; only a virtual trade show since 2003. **Principal Exhibits:** Small computer systems, related peripherals, software, accessories, services, and supplies. **Dates and Locations:** , Sands Expo and Convention Center.

CONSULTANTS

5082 ■ **Bass & Co.**

9800 Thunderhill Ct.
Great Falls, VA 22066
Ph: (703)759-4720
Fax: (703)759-0465
Contact: Shirley A. Bass, President
E-mail: shirley@bassandco.com

Scope: Offers business consulting on selection and implementation of microcomputer-based accounting systems. Also offers consulting on Federal Acquisition Regulation (FAR) compliance for accounting, purchasing, and estimating systems. Practice includes litigation support, policy and procedure development, DCAA audit assistance, incurred cost submissions and proposal pricing. Industries served: Government contractors, nonprofits, and general service businesses. **Founded:** 1991. **Publications:** "The Sba Loan Programs". **Seminars:** Accounting for Government Contracts; Doing Business With the Federal Government; Cost Proposals for Federal Government Contracts; Selecting and Implementing an Accounting System; Financing Alternatives for Small Businesses.

5083 ■ **Health Management Systems Inc.**

401 Park Ave. S
New York, NY 10016-8008
Ph: (212)857-5000
Free: 877-467-0184
Fax: (212)857-5004
Co. E-mail: info@hms.com
URL: http://www.hmsy.com
Contact: Bill Lucia, President

Scope: Provides cost containment solutions for government-funded, commercial, and private entities. Services to make the healthcare system better by improving access, impacting outcomes, containing costs, recovering dollars and creating efficiencies. Services include the following areas: Coordination of Benefits, Program Integrity, Eligibility and Enrollment, Customer Service Operations and Pharmacy Ser-

vices. **Founded:** 1985. **Publications:** "Credit Balance Recovery"; "Preparing for a Historic 2009"; "Introducing the New HMS".

5084 ■ **Kluger and Associates Inc.**

70 Mitchell Blvd., Ste. 106
San Rafael, CA 94903-2019
Ph: (415)479-7900
Free: 800-776-5060
Fax: (415)472-3534
Contact: Andrew M. Kluger, President
E-mail: akluger@pacbell.net

Scope: Provides professional practice management specialization in accounting and billing services. Industries served health care. **Founded:** 1980.

5085 ■ **McLeod Associates Inc.**

3 Mayfair Ln.
Westport, CT 06880
Ph: (203)227-3767
Fax: (203)227-9554
Co. E-mail: bernicestine@mcleodassociatesinc.com
URL: http://www.mcleodassociatesinc.com
Contact: Bernicestine E. McLeod, Chief Executive Officer
E-mail: bemcleo@attglobal.net

Scope: Management information systems consulting firm specializes in providing computer-related project management, education, database design and development, systems analysis and design, systems and application programming services in the mainframe, workstation, and client/server environments. Offers expertise in implementing user oriented computer solutions to facilitate business objectives in all environments. Application areas include accounts receivable, order entry, billing, leasing, credit, and inventory management/control. Firm also specializes in workgroup applications, for example, Lotus Notes as well as personal computer software products (word processors, database managers, spreadsheets). Industries served: manufacturing, distribution, retail, hospital, financial services. **Founded:** 1981.

LIBRARIES

5086 ■ **International Data Corp. - IDC Library**

2131 Landings Dr.
Mountain View, CA 94043
Ph: (650)962-6481
Fax: (650)691-0518
Co. E-mail: slake@idc.com
URL: http://www.idc.com
Contact: Sara Lake, Director, Library Services

Scope: Information technology. **Services:** Center not open to the public. **Founded:** 1990. **Holdings:** 350 books; 250 subject files. **Subscriptions:** 70 journals and other serials.

5087 ■ **International Data Corp. Library**

5 Speen St.
Framingham, MA 01701
Ph: (508)872-8200
URL: http://www.idc.com
Contact: Kirk Campbell, President

Scope: Computer technology, management. **Services:** Interlibrary loan; Center not open to the public.

Founded: 1970. **Holdings:** 2200 books; 50 Annual reports; 235 subject files; 12 CD-ROMs. **Subscriptions:** 200 journals and other serials.

RESEARCH CENTERS

5088 ■ **University of Tennessee at Chattanooga - Center of Excellence in Applied Computational Science and Engineering (CEACSE)**
701 E M.L. King Blvd.
Chattanooga, TN 37403

Ph: (423)425-5493
Fax: (423)425-5517
Co. E-mail: henry-mcdonald@utc.edu
URL: http://www.utc.edu/Research/CEACSE
Contact: Dr. H. McDonald, Director

5089 ■ **University of Texas at Arlington - Center for Information Technologies Management (CITM)**
Department of Information Systems & Operations
   Management, Box 19437
Arlington, TX 76019-0437

Ph: (817)272-3546
Fax: (817)272-5801
Co. E-mail: pobeck@uta.edu
URL: http://www2.uta.edu/infosys/citm/
Contact: Phil Beck, Director

Services: Consulting for industry in information systems, management science, production and operations management, and statistics; Coordinates research activities to complement the needs of local industry. **Founded:** 1984. **Educational Activities:** Disaster Recovery Institute seminars (3/year).

REFERENCE WORKS

5090 ■ *"55-Alive! Wants To Be MySpace for the Baby Boomer Set. Can It Raise $250,000?' in Inc. (October 2007, pp. 50)*
Pub: Gruner & Jahr USA Publishing
Description: Profile of 55-Alive! The online community created especially for individuals over the age of 50. The Website offers blogs, a dating section, listings for recreational vehicles for sale, movie reviews, advertising and articles of interest to users.

5091 ■ *"And the Money Comes Rolling In" in Inc. (Vol. 31, January-February 2009, No. 1, pp. 62)*
Pub: Mansueto Ventures LLC
Ed: Max Chafkin. **Description:** Profile of Markus Frind, founder of the online dating service in British Columbia called Plenty of Fish. Frind works one hour a day and earns $10 million a year by keeping things simple.

5092 ■ *"Ask Inc." in Inc. (October 2007, pp. 73-74)*
Pub: Gruner & Jahr USA Publishing
Description: An online marketing research firm investigates the use of online communities such as MySpace and Second life in order to recruit individuals to answer surveys.

5093 ■ *"On Target" in Canadian Business (Vol. 81, July 22, 2008, No. 12-13, pp. 45)*
Pub: Rogers Media Ltd.
Ed: Calvin Leung. **Description:** Companies such as LavalifePRIME, a dating website devoted to singles 45 and older, discuss the value of marketing and services aimed at Canada's older consumers. One-third of Canada's 33 million people are 50-plus, controlling 77 percent of the countries wealth.

TRADE SHOWS AND CONVENTIONS

5094 ■ **COMDEX**
Ziff-Davis Inc.
28 E 28th St.
New York, NY 10016-7939
Ph: (212)503-3500
Fax: (212)503-4599
Co. E-mail: randy_zane@ziffdavis.com
URL: http://www.ziffdavis.com
Contact: Vivek Shah, Chief Executive Officer
URL(s): www.comdex.com/. **Frequency:** Annual. **Audience:** Volume resellers and value-adders of small computers and related items; only a virtual trade show since 2003. **Principal Exhibits:** Small computer systems, related peripherals, software, accessories, services, and supplies. **Dates and Locations:** , Sands Expo and Convention Center.

FRANCHISES AND BUSINESS OPPORTUNITIES

5095 ■ **The Right One**
200 Cordwainer Dr., Ste. 102
Norwell, MA 02061
Ph: (781)982-4522
Fax: (781)982-0455
URL: http://www.therightone.com

Description: Dating service. **No. of Franchise Units:** 15. **No. of Company-Owned Units:** 12. **Founded:** 1990.. **Franchised:** 1999. **Equity Capital Needed:** $98,400-$254,000. **Franchise Fee:** $50,000-$150,000. **Royalty Fee:** 6%. **Training:** 1 week at headquarters, 1 week at franchisees location, 2 weeks at existing locations and ongoing support.

ASSOCIATIONS AND OTHER ORGANIZATIONS

5096 ■ *Canadian Foodservice Industry Operations Report*
316 Bloor St. W
Toronto, ON, Canada M5S 1W5
Ph: (416)923-8416
Free: 800-387-5649
Fax: (416)923-1450
Co. E-mail: info@crfa.ca
URL: http://www.crfa.ca
Contact: Garth Whyte, President
Released: Biennial

5097 ■ Canadian Restaurant and Foodservices Association (CRFA)—Association Canadienne des Restaurateurs et des Services Alimentaires
316 Bloor St. W
Toronto, ON, Canada M5S 1W5
Ph: (416)923-8416
Free: 800-387-5649
Fax: (416)923-1450
Co. E-mail: info@crfa.ca
URL: http://www.crfa.ca
Contact: Garth Whyte, President
Description: Restaurant and food service corporations, hotels, caterers, and food service suppliers and educators. Seeks to create a favorable business environment for members. Represents members' interests before government; conducts trade research. Makes available group buying programs and other services to members; owns and operates three industry trade shows. **Scope:** hospitality industries. **Founded:** 1944. **Subscriptions:** books periodicals. **Publications:** *Foodservice Facts* (Annual); *Legislation Guide* (Quarterly); *Canadian Foodservice Industry Operations Report* (Biennial); *CRFA National Hospitality News.* **Educational Activities:** Canadian Food and Beverage Show (Annual); ApEx; Canadian International Food and Beverage Show (Annual).

5098 ■ *Foodservice Facts*
316 Bloor St. W
Toronto, ON, Canada M5S 1W5
Ph: (416)923-8416
Free: 800-387-5649
Fax: (416)923-1450
Co. E-mail: info@crfa.ca
URL: http://www.crfa.ca
Contact: Garth Whyte, President
Released: Annual

5099 ■ *Legislation Guide*
316 Bloor St. W
Toronto, ON, Canada M5S 1W5
Ph: (416)923-8416
Free: 800-387-5649
Fax: (416)923-1450
Co. E-mail: info@crfa.ca
URL: http://www.crfa.ca
Contact: Garth Whyte, President
Released: Quarterly

5100 ■ National Association of Concessionaires (NAC)
35 E Wacker Dr., Ste. 1816
Chicago, IL 60601
Ph: (312)236-3858
Fax: (312)236-7809
Co. E-mail: info@naconline.org
URL: http://www.naconline.org
Contact: Dan Borschke, Executive Director
Description: Represents popcorn processors, manufacturers, and merchandisers; operators of food and beverage concessions in theaters, amusement parks, sports arenas, and other recreational facilities; equipment manufacturers and suppliers. Works to professionalize the concession industry. Provides information services and audiovisual training programs for concession managers and employees. Maintains certification program for concession industry. **Founded:** 1944. **Publications:** *Concession Profession* (Semiannual); *Concessionworks* (Semiannual). **Educational Activities:** National Association of Concessionaires Convention (Annual).

5101 ■ National Restaurant Association
2055 L St. NW
Washington, DC 20036
Ph: (202)331-5900
Free: 800-424-5156
Fax: (202)331-2429
Co. E-mail: info@restaurant.org
URL: http://www.restaurant.org
Contact: Dawn Sweeney, President
E-mail: dsweeney@restaurant.org
Description: Represents restaurants, cafeterias, clubs, contract foodservice management, drive-ins, caterers, institutional food services and other members of the foodservice industry; also represents establishments belonging to non-affiliated state and local restaurant associations in governmental affairs. Supports foodservice education and research in several educational institutions. Is affiliated with the Educational Foundation of the National Restaurant Association to provide training and education for operators, food and equipment manufacturers, distributors and educators. Has 300,000 member locations. **Scope:** restaurant management, cookery, menus. **Founded:** 1919. **Subscriptions:** 5000 periodicals. **Publications:** *National Restaurant Association--Washington Report* (Semimonthly); *Restaurant Industry Operations Report*; *Restaurants USA: The Monthly Magazine of the National Restaurant Assn* (Monthly); *Who's Who in the Foodservice Industry*; *Restaurant Information Abstracts* (Biweekly). **Awards:** Restaurant Good Neighbor Award (Annual); Hennessy Awards.

5102 ■ Outdoor Amusement Business Association (OABA)
1035 S Semoran Blvd., Ste. 1045A
Winter Park, FL 32792
Ph: (407)681-9444
Free: 800-517-OABA
Fax: (407)681-9445
Co. E-mail: oaba@oaba.org
URL: http://www.oaba.org
Contact: Robert W. Johnson, President
Description: Represents executives and employees of carnivals and fairs; ride owners; independent food

and games concessionaires; manufacturers and suppliers of equipment. Promotes and lobbies on behalf of the interests of the outdoor amusement industry; provides a center for dissemination of information. **Founded:** 1965. **Publications:** *Midway Marquee* (Annual).

5103 ■ Western Fairs Association (WFA)
1776 Tribute Rd., Ste. 210
Sacramento, CA 95815-4495
Ph: (916)927-3100
Fax: (916)927-6397
Co. E-mail: wfa@fairsnet.org
URL: http://www.fairsnet.org
Contact: Stephen J. Chambers, Executive Director
Description: State and county fairs, carnival operators, food concessionaires, entertainment agents, and commercial exhibitors. Seeks to improve conditions in the fair industry by maintaining good relations with governmental agencies. Maintains hall of fame. Compiles statistics. **Scope:** fair management, fair financing, horse racing, breeding, other agricultural and fair subjects. **Founded:** 1945. **Subscriptions:** archival material articles books papers photographs reports. **Publications:** *WFA Newsletter* (Quarterly); *Western Fairs Association--Date List and Membership Directory* (Annual). **Awards:** Merrit Award (Annual).

REFERENCE WORKS

5104 ■ *Concession Profession*
Pub: National Association of Concessionaires
URL(s): www.naconline.org/programs_services/index.cfm?pg=pubs.htm. **Ed:** Charles A. Winans. **Released:** Biennial; Latest edition 2010-2011. **Covers:** About 900 member equipment manufacturers, suppliers, jobber/distributors, popcorn processors, theaters, amusement parks, stadiums, rinks, and other concession operators in the United States and Canada. **Entries include:** For operators--Company name, address, phone, name of contact. For manufacturers and suppliers--Company name, address, phone, names and titles of up to four executives, brief description of service or products. **Arrangement:** Classified by type of concession or business activity. **Indexes:** Name, geographical.

5105 ■ *"Working the Streets" in Baltimore Business Journal (Vol. 28, July 30, 2010, No. 12, pp. 1)*
Pub: Baltimore Business Journal
Ed: Amanda Pino. **Description:** Reports show that street vendors are popping up on new corners in Baltimore, Maryland, with city-inspected stainless steel food carts in tow. Applications for street vending licenses shot up at the end of 2009 and into this summer. It is believed that pinning down the exact number of vendors operating at any one point is difficult.

TRADE PERIODICALS

5106 ■ *Tourist Attractions & Parks Magazine*
Pub: Kane Communications Inc.
Contact: Scott Borowsky, Editor
E-mail: scborowsky@kanec.com
URL(s): www.tapmag.com. **Ed:** Scott C. Borowsky. **Released:** 7/yr. **Price:** $49, Individuals; $55, Two years; $55, Other countries; $61, Other countries 2 years.

TRADE SHOWS AND CONVENTIONS

5107 ■ International Association of Fairs and Expositions Trade Show
International Association of Fairs and Expositions (IAFE)
3043 E. Cairo St.
Springfield, MO 65802
Ph: (417)862-5771
Free: 800-516-0313
Fax: (417)862-0156
Co. E-mail: iafe@fairsandexpos.com
URL: http://www.fairsandexpos.com
Contact: Jim Tucker, Chief Executive Officer
E-mail: jimt@fairsandexpos.com
URL(s): www.fairsandexpos.com. **Frequency:** Annual. **Audience:** Fair managers, staffs, and board members; carnival owners and staffs; concessionaires; talent and other agencies related to the fair industry. **Principal Exhibits:** Talent agencies, concessionaires, novelties, amusement devices, insurance, ribbons, plaques, attractions, and equipment. Products and services for the fair industry. **Dates and Locations:** , Hilton Hotel. **Telecommunication Services:** iafe@fairsandexpos.com.

FRANCHISES AND BUSINESS OPPORTUNITIES

5108 ■ Camille's Sidewalk Cafe
Camille's Franchise System, LLC
8801 S Yale Ave., Ste. 400
Tulsa, OK 74137-3575
Ph: (918)488-9727
Free: 800-230-7004
Fax: (918)497-1916
Description: Sidewalk cafe serving wraps and sandwiches. **No. of Franchise Units:** 21. **No. of Company-Owned Units:** 1. **Founded:** 1996.. **Franchised:** 1999. **Equity Capital Needed:** $214,000-$280,000. **Franchise Fee:** $25,000. **Financial Assistance:** Yes. **Training:** Yes.

5109 ■ Carvel Ice Cream
Focus Brands, Inc.
200 Glenridge Point Pky., Ste. 200
Atlanta, GA 30342
Ph: (404)255-3250

Fax: (404)255-4978
URL: http://www.carvel.com
Description: Custom ice cream desserts and novelties. **No. of Franchise Units:** 449. **No. of Company-Owned Units:** 15. **Founded:** 1934.. **Franchised:** 1947. **Equity Capital Needed:** $100,000 liquid cash; $300,000 net worth. **Franchise Fee:** $30,000. **Training:** 2 week ice cream training school; access to the Carvel Development Network (real estate brokers, architects, lenders, contractors, etc.); Design & construction support & assistance; Grand opening support and toll-free hotline available.

5110 ■ The Different Twist Pretzel Co.
6052 Rte. 8
Bakerstown, PA 15007
Ph: (724)443-8010
Fax: (724)443-7287
Description: Soft pretzels in ten flavors. **No. of Franchise Units:** 15. **Founded:** 1992.. **Franchised:** 1992. **Equity Capital Needed:** $40,000-$80,000. **Franchise Fee:** $5,000. **Training:** Yes.

5111 ■ Pretzelmaker, Inc.
Global Franchise Group
1346 Oakbrook Dr., Ste. 170
Norcross, GA 30093
Ph: (880)524-6444
Fax: (770)514-4903
URL: http://www.theathletesfoot.com
Description: Franchises concession stands featuring pretzels. **No. of Franchise Units:** 350. **Founded:** 1991.. **Franchised:** 1992. **Equity Capital Needed:** $250,000 net worth; $85,000 liquid. **Franchise Fee:** $25,000. **Training:** Yes.

5112 ■ Willy Dog
120 Clarence St., Ste. 1141
Kingston, ON, Canada K7L 4Y5
Ph: (613)389-6118
Fax: (613)389-6138
Co. E-mail: sales@willydogs.com
URL: http://www.willydogs.com
Description: Hot dog cart resembling giant hot dog. **No. of Franchise Units:** 115. **No. of Company-Owned Units:** 5. **Founded:** 1989.. **Franchised:** 1993. **Equity Capital Needed:** $6,500. **Franchise Fee:** $6,500. **Training:** Yes.

LIBRARIES

5113 ■ American Beverage Association Information Center
1101 16th St., NW
Washington, DC 20036

Ph: (202)463-6732
Fax: (202)659-5349
Co. E-mail: info@ameribev.org
URL: http://www.ameribev.org/
Contact: Susan K. Neely, President
Scope: Beverage industry. **Services:** Library open to the public for reference use only. **Founded:** 1919. **Holdings:** 500 books, articles, papers, and historical materials. **Subscriptions:** 115 journals and other serials.

5114 ■ American Institute of Food Distribution, Inc. - Information and Research Center—The Food Institute.
1 Broadway Plaza, 2nd Fl.
Elmwood Park, NJ 07407
Ph: (201)791-5570
Fax: (201)791-5222
Co. E-mail: jkastrinsky@foodinstitute.com
URL: http://www.foodinstitute.com/
Contact: Brian Todd, President
Scope: Food industry. **Services:** Center open to the public on fee basis. **Founded:** 1928. **Subscriptions:** 400 journals and other serials. **Publications:** *Food Business Mergers and Acquisitions*. **Telecommunication Services:** food1@foodinstitute.com.

5115 ■ Noble and Associates Library
2155 W. Chesterfield Blvd.
Springfield, MO 65807
Ph: (417)875-5000
Co. E-mail: julie.tumy@noble.net
URL: http://www.noble.net
Contact: Julie Tumy, President
Scope: Food, food service, advertising, construction, agriculture. **Services:** Interlibrary loan; copying; SDI; Library not open to the public. **Holdings:** 500 books; 1000 reports. **Subscriptions:** 300 journals and other serials; 5 newspapers.

RESEARCH CENTERS

5116 ■ National Food Laboratory (NFL)
365 N Canyons Pky., Ste. 201
Livermore, CA 94551
Ph: (925)828-1440
Fax: (925)243-0117
Co. E-mail: watersk@thenfl.com
URL: http://www.thenfl.com
Contact: Kevin Waters, President
Founded: 1985.

START-UP INFORMATION

5117 ■ *"Five Low-Cost Home Based Startups"* *in Women Entrepreneur (December 16, 2008)*
Pub: Entrepreneur Media Inc.
Ed: Lesley Spencer Pyle. **Description:** During tough economic times, small businesses have an advantage over large companies because they can adjust to economic conditions more easily and without having to go through corporate red tape that can slow the implementation process. A budding entrepreneur may find success by taking inventory of his or her skills, experience, expertise and passions and utilizing those qualities to start a business. Five low-cost home-based startups are profiled. These include starting an online store, a virtual assistant service, web designer, sales representative and a home staging counselor.

5118 ■ *"Online Fortunes" in Small Business Opportunities (Fall 2008)*
Pub: Entrepreneur Media Inc.
Description: Fifty hot, e-commerce enterprises for the aspiring entrepreneur to consider are featured; virtual assistants, marketing services, party planning, travel services, researching, web design and development, importing as well as creating an online store are among the businesses featured.

ASSOCIATIONS AND OTHER ORGANIZATIONS

5119 ■ **National Concierge Association (NCA)**
2920 Idaho Ave. N
Minneapolis, MN 55427
Ph: (612)317-2932
Fax: (612)317-2910
Co. E-mail: info@ncakey.org
URL: http://www.ncakey.org
Contact: Sara-ann G. Kasner, President
Description: Represents concierges of all types and affiliated hospitality related businesses whose exceptional products and services are of benefit to concierge clientele. **Founded:** 1998. **Publications:** *National Concierge Association Brochure*; *NCA Keynotes* (Biennial). **Educational Activities:** National Concierge Association Conference (Annual). **Awards:** Concierge Outstanding Service (Annual); NCA Chapter of the Year (Annual); NCA Partner of the Year (Annual).

REFERENCE WORKS

5120 ■ *"Anybody Out There?' in Canadian Business (Vol. 81, July 21 2008, No. 11, pp. 31)*
Pub: Rogers Media Ltd.
Ed: Andrew Wahl. **Description:** Virtual offices or shared office services provide solutions to companies that can no longer accommodate additional workspaces. The alternative working arrangement allows the company to have a kind of distributed work system. The disadvantages of employing virtual offices are presented.

5121 ■ *"At Your Service: Corporate Concierges Come in Three Varieties" in Incentive (August 25, 2008)*
Pub: Nielson Business Media
Ed: Nathan Adkisson. **Description:** Companies are offering corporate concierge services to handle tasks for new employees as a sign-on benefit. Concierge of Boston has six employees that focus on fulfilling the needs of individuals.

5122 ■ *"Attending to the Needs of the Too Busy" in New York Times (Vol. 158, October 1, 2008, No. 54450, pp. 7)*
Pub: New York Times Co./Globe Newspaper Co.
Ed: Ken Belson. **Description:** Profiles of individuals working as concierges to meet the needs of their clients are presented.

5123 ■ *The Concierge Manual: A Step-by-Step Guide to Starting Your Own Concierge Service or Lifestyle Management Company*
Pub: New Road Publishing
Ed: Katharine C. Giovanni. **Released:** September 9, 2010. **Price:** $23.00. **Description:** Answering some of the biggest questions about the logistics of running a concierge business, this guide provides all the tools necessary to create a successful concierge, lifestyle management, errand service, or personal assistant company.

5124 ■ *"Concierges Get New Marching Orders" in New York Times (Vol. 158, January 11, 2009, No. 54552, pp. 1)*
Pub: New York Times Co./Globe Newspaper Co.
Ed: Vivian S. Toy. **Description:** Effects of the slowing economy are felt by individuals working as concierges.

5125 ■ *"Fitness Made Fun" in Playthings (Vol. 106, September 1, 2008, No. 8, pp. 12)*
Pub: Reed Business Information
Contact: Jeff Greisch, President
Ed: Karyn M. Peterson. **Description:** Nintendo Wii has developed the Wii Fit game that allows gamers to engage in over forty physical activities through its Balance Board accessory, an engineered platform that senses weight and shifts in movement and balance. It also offers virtual trainers to talk participants through the activities and keeps track of the progress of multiple users.

5126 ■ *"Mobility: So Happy Together" in Entrepreneur (Vol. 35, October 2007, No. 10, pp. 64)*
Pub: Entrepreneur Media Inc.
Ed: Heather Clancy. **Description:** Joshua Burnett, CEO and founder of 9ci, uses index cards to keep track of what he needs to do despite the fact that he has a notebook computer, cell phone and PDA. Kim Hahn, a media entrepreneur, prefers jotting her ideas down in a spiral notebook, has a team that would organize her records for her, and a personal assistant that would keep track of changes to her schedule. Reasons why these entrepreneurs use old-fashioned methods along with new technology are given.

5127 ■ *"Opportunity Knocks" in Small Business Opportunities (September 2008)*
Pub: Entrepreneur Media Inc.
Description: Profile of YourOffice USA, a franchise that provides home-based and small businesses cost-effective and efficient support through 'virtual' offices that are available as much or as little as the client needs it; they also supply necessary tools such as a professional business address, private mailbox service, personalized telephone answering and more that supports clients who want to look, act and operate with an advanced business image.

5128 ■ *"The Personal Touch: Entrepreneur Turns Good Taste, Love of Luxury Into Lucrative Venture" in Black Enterprise (October 2007)*
Pub: Earl G. Graves Publishing Co. Inc.
Ed: Tamara E. Holmes. **Description:** Profile of Chaka Fattah Jr. who turned his taste for luxurious things into a successful luxury travel and concierge service catering to business owners, corporate executives, athletes, and entertainers.

5129 ■ *"Professional Help: Cross That Off Your To-Do List" in Inc. (November 2007, pp. 89-90, 92)*
Pub: Gruner & Jahr USA Publishing
Ed: Alison Stein Wellner. **Description:** Small business owners are finding that it pays to hire someone to takeover the personal tasks of daily living, including hiring a personal assistant, chauffeur, chef, stylist, pet caregiver, or concierge service.

5130 ■ *"The Way I Work" in Inc. (March 2008, pp. 102-104, 106)*
Pub: Gruner & Jahr USA Publishing
Ed: Hannah Clark Steiman. **Description:** Profile of Howard Lefkowitz, CEO of Vegas.com, a Website that allows visitors to book flights, reserve hotel rooms, buy show tickets, make spa appointments, and coordinate any and all aspects of a trip to Las Vegas. The firm also runs brick-and-mortar box offices and concierge desks at various cities.

START-UP INFORMATION

5131 ■ *202 Things You Can Buy and Sell for Big Profits*
Pub: Entrepreneur Press
Ed: James Stephenson; Jason R. Rich. **Released:** July 2008. **Price:** $19.95. **Description:** Become an entrepreneur at selling new and used products. This handbook will help individuals cash in on the boom in reselling new and used products online. A new section defines ways to set realistic goals while distinguishing between 'get-rich schemes' and long term, viable businesses. A discussion about targeting and reaching the right customer base is included, along with finding and obtaining the service support needed for starting a new business.

5132 ■ *The Complete Idiot's Guide to Starting and Running a Thrift Store*
Pub: Alpha Publishing House
Ed: Ravel Buckley, Carol Costa. **Released:** January 5, 2010. **Price:** $18.95. **Description:** Thrift stores saw a 35 percent increase in sales during the falling economy in 2008. Despite the low startup costs, launching and running a thrift store is complicated. Two experts cover the entire process, including setting up a store on a nonprofit basis, choosing a location, funding, donations for saleable items, recruiting and managing staff, sorting items, pricing, and recycling donations.

5133 ■ *eBay Business the Smart Way*
Pub: AMACOM
Ed: Joseph T. Sinclair. **Released:** June 6, 2007. **Price:** $17.95. **Description:** eBay commands ninety percent of all online auction business. Computer and software expert and online entrepreneur shares information to help online sellers get started and move merchandise on eBay. Tips include the best ways to build credibility, find products to sell, manage inventory, create a storefront Website, and more.

5134 ■ *EBay Business Start-up Kit: 100s of Live Links to All the Information and Tools You Need*
Pub: NOLO
Ed: Richard Stim. **Released:** July 2008. **Price:** $24.99. **Description:** Interactive kit that connects user directly to EBay is presented.

5135 ■ *"Mount Laurel Woman Launches Venture Into Children's Used Clothing" in Philadelphia Inquirer (September 17, 2010)*
Pub: Philadelphia Media Network
Ed: Maria Panaritis. **Description:** Profile of Jennifer Frisch, stay-at-home mom turned entrepreneur. Frisch started a used-clothing store Once Upon a Child after opening her franchised Plato's Closet, selling unwanted and used baby clothing and accessories at her new shop, while offering used merchandise to teens at Plato's Closet.

ASSOCIATIONS AND OTHER ORGANIZATIONS

5136 ■ **NARTS - The Association of Resale Professionals**
PO Box 80707
St. Clair Shores, MI 48080-5707

Ph: (586)294-6700
Free: 800-544-0751
Fax: (586)294-6776
Co. E-mail: info@narts.org
URL: http://www.narts.org
Contact: Adele Meyer, Executive Director
Description: Owners, managers, professionals, and other individuals involved in the resale and thrift shop industry. Works for the exchange of ideas and information among members, develops public recognition and knowledge of the field, and promotes professionalism in the industry. Helps members to become more professional and to increase profits. Offers educational materials. **Scope:** resale, advertising, marketing. **Founded:** 1984. **Subscriptions:** audio recordings books. **Publications:** *Your NARTS Network* (Monthly); *The Budget Guide to Retail Store Planning and Design*; *Operating Survey*; *Retail in Detail*. **Awards:** Affiliate Member Award (Annual); Educational Service Award (Annual); Outstanding Service Award (Annual); Renee River Award; Affiliate Member Award; Educational Service Award; Outstanding Service Award; Renee River Award.

REFERENCE WORKS

5137 ■ *"Auction Company Grows with Much Smaller Sites" in Automotive News (Vol. 86, October 31, 2011, No. 6488, pp. 23)*
Pub: Crain Communications Inc.
Ed: Arlena Sawyers. **Description:** Auction Broadcasting Company has launched auction sites and is expanding into new areas. The family-owned business will provide auctions half the size traditionally used. The firm reports that 40 percent of the General Motors factory-owned vehicles sold on consignment were purchased by online buyers, up 30 percent over 2010.

5138 ■ *"Cash in Your Attic: Is Your Junk Someone Else's Treasure?" in Black Enterprise (Vol. 37, November 2006, No. 4, pp. 156)*
Pub: Earl G. Graves Publishing Co. Inc.
Ed: Angela P. Moore-Thorpe. **Description:** Selling items accumulated over the years or purchased at auctions or garage sales can be a lucrative way to make extra cash. Advice and resources on auctions, collecting, and consignment shops included.

5139 ■ *"Consignment Shop Closes Without Warning to Customers, Landlord" in Sun Journal (June 30, 2010)*
Pub: Freedom Communications Inc.
Ed: Laura Oleniacz. **Description:** Off The Racks consignment shop located on Glenburnie Road in New Bern, North Carolina closed without warning to customers or its landlord. The consignors who donated clothing to the store were left unpaid.

5140 ■ *"Consignment Shop Offers Children's Clothes, Products" in Frederick News-Post (August 19, 2010)*
Pub: Federick News-Post
Ed: Ed Waters Jr. **Description:** Sweet Pea Consignments for Children offers used items for newborns to pre-teens. The shop carries name brand clothing as well as toys, books and baby products.

5141 ■ *The Ebay Seller's Tax and Legal Answer Book*
Pub: AMACOM
Ed: Cliff Ennico. **Released:** April 30, 2007. **Price:** $19.95. **Description:** Helps sellers using Ebay to file taxes properly, while saving money.

5142 ■ *Ebay the Smart Way: Selling, Burying, and Profiting on the Web's Number One Auction Site*
Pub: AMACOM
Ed: Joseph T. Sinclair. **Released:** May 2007. **Price:** $17.95. **Description:** Resource to help individuals sell, buy and profit using the Internet auction site Ebay.

5143 ■ *"Get Sold On eBay" in Entrepreneur (Vol. 36, March 2008, No. 3, pp. 94)*
Pub: Entrepreneur Media Inc.
Ed: Marcia Layton Turner. **Description:** Entrepreneurs are increasingly using eBay to sell products. Some tips to start selling products through eBay include: starting with used items, developing a niche to sell specific products, and researching product pricing. Other tips with regard to starting an eBay business are covered.

5144 ■ *How to Market and Sell Your Art, Music, Photographs, and Handmade Crafts Online*
Pub: Atlantic Publishing Group, Inc.
Ed: Lee Rowley. **Released:** May 2008. **Price:** $24.95. **Description:** The book provides all the basics for starting and running an online store selling arts, crafts, photography or music. There are more than 300 Websites listed to help anyone market and promote their arts and/or crafts online.

5145 ■ *"It's So You! Consignment Chop Owner Thrilled to See Vision Come to Fruition" in News-Herald (August 27, 2010)*
Pub: News-Herald
Ed: Brandon C. Baker. **Description:** Profile of Laurel Howes and her It's So You! Boutique. The consignment shop is located in Willoughby's Pine Ride Plaza in Ohio. The shop targets all women, but particularly those who are not that comfortable with shopping consignment.

5146 ■ *"Longtime Peoria Heights Second-Hand Clothing Shop Closing" in Journal Star (December 18, 2010)*
Pub: Journal Star
Ed: Scott Hilyard. **Description:** The Happy Hangar, a consignment clothing store located in Peoria Heights, Illinois is closing after 31 years of selling second-hand clothing.

5147 ■ *"Power Up" in Entrepreneur (Vol. 35, November 2007, No. 11, pp. 140)*
Pub: Entrepreneur Media Inc.
Ed: Amanda C. Kooser. **Description:** PowerSeller is a status in the Internet company eBay, wherein sellers average at least $1,000 in sales per month for

three consecutive months. There are five tiers in the PowerSeller status, which ranges from Bronze to Titanium. Launching startups at eBay can help entrepreneurs pick up a wide customer base, but getting and maintaining PowerSeller status is a challenge.

5148 ▪ *"Shore Total Office Liquidates Massive Supply of Bank Furniture and Used Furniture" in Internet Wire (June 21, 2010)*
Pub: Comtex
Description: Shore Total Office, located in San Diego, California, is liquidating quality bank furniture and used furniture to customers hoping to outfit their facilities with stylish new furnishings. Shore Total Office is a leading supplier of high quality office furniture and designs.

5149 ▪ *Too Good to be Threw: The Complete Operations Manual for Resale and Consignment Shops*
Pub: Katydid Press
Price: $69.95. **Description:** Revised edition covers all the information needfed to start and run a buy-outright or consignment shop, covering anything from clothing to furniture resale.

5150 ▪ *"Understanding Persuasive Online Sales Messages from eBay Auctions" in Business Communication Quarterly (December 2007, pp. 482)*
Pub: SAGE Publications USA
Contact: Blaise R. Simqu, President
Ed: Barbara Jo White, Daniel Clapper, Rita Noel, Jenny Fortier, Pierre Grabolosa. **Description:** eBay product listings were studied to determine the requirements of persuasive sales writing. Potential sellers should use the proper keywords and make an authentic description with authentic photographs of the item being auctioned.

TRADE PERIODICALS

5151 ▪ *Swap Meet Magazine*
Pub: Forum Publishing Co.
Contact: Justo Rey, President
URL(s): www.magazinesubscriptions.com/swap-meet-magazine-subscription.htmlwww.forum123.com/

inc/sdetail/172. **Released:** Monthly **Price:** $29.97, Individuals 1 year (12 issues); $59.94, Two years. **Covers:** Over 5,000 manufacturers and importers of jewelry, electronics, clothing, cosmetics, watches, novelties, and other items that are sold to merchandise retailers and flee market vendors at wholesale prices. **Entries include:** Company name, address, phone, products or services.

FRANCHISES AND BUSINESS OPPORTUNITIES

5152 ▪ **Once Upon a Child**
Winmark Corp.
605 Hwy. 169 N, Ste. 400
Minneapolis, MN 55441-6536
Ph: (763)520-8500
Free: 800-433-2540
Fax: (763)520-8410
Co. E-mail: winmark.information@winmarkcorporation.com
URL: http://www.winmarkcorporation.com
Description: Franchises consignment shops featuring children's products including toys, books, furniture, and apparel. **No. of Franchise Units:** 247. **Founded:** 1985. **Franchised:** 1993. **Equity Capital Needed:** $221,300-$312,600; approximately 30% cash requirement. **Franchise Fee:** $25,000. **Training:** Yes.

5153 ▪ **Plato's Closet**
Winmark Corp.
605 Hwy. 169 N, Ste. 400
Minneapolis, MN 55441-6536
Ph: (763)520-8500
Free: 800-433-2540
Fax: (763)520-8410
Co. E-mail: winmark.information@winmarkcorporation.com
URL: http://www.winmarkcorporation.com
Description: Teen and young adult apparel and accessories consignment. **No. of Franchise Units:** 324. **Founded:** 1998.. **Franchised:** 1999. **Equity Capital Needed:** $230,700-$386,150; approximately

30 percent cash required. **Franchise Fee:** $25,000. **Training:** Training program includes product acquisition, fashion trends, inventory management, and proprietary point-of-sale computer system. Annual franchise conferences, owner only website, and on-site business consultations.

5154 ▪ **Play it Again Sports**
Winmark Corp.
605 Hwy. 169 N, Ste. 400
Minneapolis, MN 55441-6536
Ph: (763)520-8500
Free: 800-433-2540
Fax: (763)520-8410
Co. E-mail: winmark.information@winmarkcorporation.com
URL: http://www.winmarkcorporation.com
Description: Sells new and used sports equipment and clothing. Franchisees purchase discount inventory through closeouts and overruns and accept used equipment in trade from customers, reducing retail prices by 40-60%. **No. of Franchise Units:** 325. **Founded:** 1983.. **Franchised:** 1988. **Equity Capital Needed:** $244,800-$391,900; Approximately 30% cash requirement. **Franchise Fee:** $25,000. **Training:** Training includes product acquisition, inventory management, staff hiring and training, customer service, advertising and marketing, and merchandising. Ongoing regional meetings and national training conferences held annually.

5155 ▪ **Terri's New & Consigned Furnishings**
Consign & Design Franchise Corp.
4747 E. Elliot Rd., Ste. 29-700
Phoenix, AZ 85044
Ph: (480)969-1121
Fax: (480)969-5052
URL: http://www.shopterris.com
Description: Upscale home furnishings on consignment. **No. of Franchise Units:** 8. **No. of Company-Owned Units:** 8. **Founded:** 1979.. **Franchised:** 1993. **Equity Capital Needed:** $100,000. **Franchise Fee:** $10,000-$40,000. **Training:** Yes.

START-UP INFORMATION

5156 ■ "Builder Comes Back Home" in Houston Business Journal (Vol. 40, September 18, 2009, No. 19, pp. 1A)
Pub: American City Business Journals
Ed: Allison Wollam. **Description:** Jason Hammonds, who has been previously involved in the local home building market in Texas, has launched a new home building company called J. Kyle Homes. The new company has chosen Cinco Ranch, a neo-traditional styled neighborhood in Katy, Texas to build its first housing community.

5157 ■ "Building a Business: Directbuild Helps Clients Build Their Own Home" in Small Business Opportunities (Winter 2007)
Pub: Harris Publications Inc.
Description: Mike New, founder of Directbuild, a franchise company that helps individuals with no construction knowledge build their own home.

5158 ■ "Driving Home Success: Stamped Asphalt for Driveways and Paths is Hottest New Trend" in Small Business Opportunities (Winter 2007)
Pub: Harris Publications Inc.
Description: Profile of technology that turns asphalt into three-dimensional replicas of hand-laid brick, slate, cobblestone and other design effects. Profiles of franchise opportunities in this industry are included.

5159 ■ How to Open and Operate a Financially Successful Construction Company
Pub: Atlantic Publishing Group, Inc.
Ed: Tanya R. Davis. **Released:** April 2008. **Price:** $39.95 paperback. **Description:** Construction businesses are predicted to be one of the fastest growing industries in the U.S. economy, according to the U.S. Bureau of Labor Statistics. A comprehensive guide is offered detailing the practical side of starting and growing a construction firm. The step-by-step guide provides sample business forms, leases, contracts, worksheets and checklists for planning and running the day-to-day operations.

ASSOCIATIONS AND OTHER ORGANIZATIONS

5160 ■ Advantage Steel
3760 14th Ave., Ste. 200
Markham, ON, Canada L3R 3T7
Ph: (905)946-0864
Fax: (905)946-8574
Co. E-mail: info@cisc-icca.ca
URL: http://www.cisc-icca.ca
Contact: Stephen Benson, Chairman
Released: Quarterly

5161 ■ American Council for Construction Education (ACCE)
1717 N Loop 1604 E, Ste. 320
San Antonio, TX 78232-1570
Ph: (210)495-6161
Fax: (210)495-6168
Co. E-mail: acce@acce-hq.org
URL: http://www.acce-hq.org
Contact: Prof. James Goddard, President
Description: Represents construction-oriented associations, corporations, and individuals. Promotes and improves construction education at the postsecondary level. Engages in accrediting construction education programs offered by colleges and universities nationwide. Maintains procedures consistent with the accrediting policies of the Council for Higher Education Accreditation and reports the results of its activities and list the colleges and universities with accredited programs of study in construction. Reviews at regular intervals the criteria, standards, and procedures that the council has adopted to evaluate programs in construction education. Provides visiting teams for campus program evaluations; compiles statistics. **Founded:** 1974.

5162 ■ American Institute of Constructors (AIC)
700 N Fairfax St., Ste. 510
Alexandria, VA 22314
Ph: (703)683-4999
Fax: (571)527-3105
URL: http://www.professionalconstructor.org
Contact: Tanya Matthews, President
URL(s): www.professionalconstructor.org/contactus/.
Description: Professionals engaged in construction practice, education, and research. Serves as the certifying body for the professional constructor. Promotes the study and advances the practice of construction. Facilitates the exchange of information and ideas relating to construction. Conducts educational programs. **Founded:** 1971. **Publications:** *Roster of Members* (Annual); *American Professional Constructor* (Biennial); *Constructor Certification Exam Study Guide Level II.* **Awards:** AIC Award (Annual); Jack Kinnaman AIC Leadership Award (Annual); Victor C. Smith Professional Constructor Award (Annual); Walter Nashert, Sr. Award (Annual).

5163 ■ American Society of Professional Estimators (ASPE)
2525 Perimeter Place Dr., Ste. 103
Nashville, TN 37214
Ph: (615)316-9200
Free: 888-EST-MATE
Fax: (615)316-9800
Co. E-mail: psmith@aspenational.org
URL: http://www.aspenational.org
Contact: Paulette R. Rutlen, President
E-mail: prrutlen@cox.net
Description: Construction cost estimators. Develops professional and ethical standards in construction estimating. Offers continuing education to established professionals; provides certification for estimators. **Founded:** 1956. **Publications:** *American Society of Professional Estimators--Membership Directory and Buyers' Guide* (Annual); *Standard Estimating Practice Manual.* **Awards:** Estimator of the Year (Annual). **Telecommunication Services:** info@aspenational.org.

5164 ■ American Sports Builders Association (ASBA)
8480 Baltimore National Pike, No. 307
Ellicott City, MD 21043
Ph: (410)730-9595
Free: 866-501-2722
Fax: (410)730-8833
Co. E-mail: info@sportsbuilders.org
URL: http://sportsbuilders.org
Contact: Mark Brogan, Chairman
Description: Contractors who install running tracks, synthetic turf fields, tennis courts and indoor sports surfaces; manufacturers who supply basic materials for construction; accessory suppliers, designers, architects, and consultants of facilities. Provides guidelines for tennis court construction, running track construction, fencing, synthetic turf field construction and lighting. Offers certification and awards programs. **Founded:** 1965. **Publications:** *Tennis and Track Construction Guidelines* (Periodic); *Buyers Guide for Tennis Court Construction* (Periodic); *Running Tracks: A Construction and Maintenance Manual* (Semiannual). **Awards:** Outstanding Indoor Tennis Facility Award (Annual); Outstanding Outdoor Tennis Facility Award (Annual); Outstanding Track/Facility Award (Annual); Outstanding Residential Tennis Court/Facility Award (Annual).

5165 ■ Architectural Glass and Metal Contractors Association (AGMCA)
619 Liverpool Rd.
Pickering, ON, Canada L1W 1R1
Ph: (905)420-7272
Fax: (905)420-7288
Co. E-mail: info@agmca.ca
URL: http://www.agmca.ca
Description: Architectural glass and metal contractors. Promotes advancement of the building industries; seeks to insure adherence to high standards of ethics and practice among members. Represents members' interests before industrial organizations, government agencies, and the public. Facilitates communication and cooperation among members; serves as a clearinghouse on the architectural glass and metal industries. **Founded:** 1979.

5166 ■ Associated Builders and Contractors (ABC)
4250 N Fairfax Dr., 9th Fl.
Arlington, VA 22203-1607
Ph: (703)812-2000
Fax: (703)812-8201
Co. E-mail: gotquestions@abc.org
URL: http://www.abc.org
Contact: Michael D. Bellaman, President
Description: Construction contractors, subcontractors, suppliers and associates. Aims to foster and perpetuate the principles of rewarding construction workers and management on the basis of merit. Sponsors management education programs and craft training; also sponsors apprenticeship and skill training programs. Disseminates technological and labor relations information. **Founded:** 1950. **Awards:** Excellence in Construction Awards; Beam Club Man on the Year (Annual); Contractor of the Year (An-

nual); Excellence in Construction (Annual); Beam Club Member of the Year; National Safety Excellence Awards; STEP Platinum; John Trimmer Excellence in Teaching Award; CURT Construction Industry Safety Excellence Awards.

5167 ■ Associated Builders and Contractors (ABC) - National Mechanical Contractors Council (NMCC)
4250 N Fairfax Dr., 9th Fl.
Arlington, VA 22203-1607
Ph: (703)812-2000
Co. E-mail: gotquestions@abc.org
URL: http://www.abc.org
Contact: Greg Hoberock, Chairman
Description: A council of Associated Builders and Contractors. Seeks to meet the needs of workers in sheet metal, plumbing, heating, ventilation, and air conditioning. **Founded:** 1983. **Publications:** *Construction Executive.* **Educational Activities:** Mechanical Contractors Conference (Annual).

5168 ■ Associated General Contractors of America (AGC)
2300 Wilson Blvd., Ste. 400
Arlington, VA 22201
Ph: (703)548-3118
Free: 800-242-1767
Fax: (703)548-3119
Co. E-mail: info@agc.org
URL: http://www.agc.org
Contact: Ted Aadland, President
Description: General construction contractors; subcontractors; industry suppliers; service firms. Provides market services through its divisions. Conducts special conferences and seminars designed specifically for construction firms. Compiles statistics on job accidents reported by member firms. Maintains 65 committees, including joint cooperative committees with other associations and liaison committees with federal agencies. **Founded:** 1918. **Publications:** *Constructor: The Construction Management Magazine* (Bimonthly); *Associated General Contractors of America--News and Views* (Biweekly); *AGC Membership Directory and Buyers' Guide* (Annual). **Educational Activities:** Construction Exposition (Annual). **Awards:** Build/America Awards (Annual); Willis Safety Awards (Annual); AGC Foundation Outstanding Educator Awards; AGC Education and Research Fund Scholarships.

5169 ■ Associated Schools of Construction (ASC)
PO Box 1312
Fort Collins, CO 80522
Ph: (970)222-4459
Fax: (970)223-3859
Co. E-mail: sue.asc@gmail.com
URL: http://www.ascweb.org
Contact: Jay P. Christofferson, President
Description: Represents colleges and universities offering a program leading to an undergraduate or advanced degree with major emphasis on construction. Aims to establish objectives for the development of construction education and to assist institutions of higher education in establishing construction education and management programs. Compiles statistics. **Founded:** 1965. **Publications:** *Proceedings of the Annual Meeting* (Annual); *International Journal of Construction Education and Research* (Triennial). **Awards:** Lifetime Achievement (Periodic); National Excellence Teaching Award (Annual); Outstanding Educator (Annual); Outstanding Researcher (Annual); Regional Excellence Teaching Award (Annual).

5170 ■ Associated Specialty Contractors (ASC)
3 Bethesda Metro Ctr., Ste. 1100
Bethesda, MD 20814
Co. E-mail: dgw@necanet.org
URL: http://www.assoc-spec-con.org
Contact: D. L. Smith, Chairman
Description: Works to promote efficient management and productivity. Coordinates the work of specialized branches of the industry in management information, research, public information, government relations and construction relations. Serves as a liaison among specialty trade associations in the areas of public relations, government relations, and

with other organizations. Seeks to avoid unnecessary duplication of effort and expense or conflicting programs among affiliates. Identifies areas of interest and problems shared by members, and develops positions and approaches on such problems. **Founded:** 1955. **Publications:** *Contract Documents.*

5171 ■ Canadian Construction Association (CCA)—Association Canadienne de la Construction
275 Slater St., 19th Fl.
Ottawa, ON, Canada K1P 5H9
Ph: (613)236-9455
Fax: (613)236-9526
Co. E-mail: cca@cca-acc.com
URL: http://www.cca-acc.com
Contact: Dianna Fournier, Executive Director
Description: Construction companies and building contractors. Promotes growth and development of the building industries. Serves as a forum for the discussion of construction industry issues; establishes voluntary standards of ethics, materials, and practice for use by members. Facilitates communication and cooperation among members; represents the commercial, labor, and regulatory interests of the construction industry; sponsors promotional programs. **Founded:** 1918. **Awards:** Environmental Achievement Award (Periodic); Montgomery Memorial Trophy (Periodic); Robert G. Saunders Memorial Trophy (Periodic); Robert Stollery Award (Annual).

5172 ■ Canadian Home Builders' Association (CHBA)
150 Laurier Ave. W, Ste. 500
Ottawa, ON, Canada K1P 5J4
Ph: (613)230-3060
Free: 800-387-2422
Fax: (613)232-8214
Co. E-mail: chba@chba.ca
URL: http://www.chba.ca
Contact: Lynda Barrett, Director
Description: Home builders and contractors. Promotes growth and development of the residential building industries. Represents members' interests. **Founded:** 1943. **Publications:** *The National* (Quarterly).

5173 ■ Canadian Institute of Steel Construction (CISC)—Institut canadien de la construction en acier
3760 14th Ave., Ste. 200
Markham, ON, Canada L3R 3T7
Ph: (905)946-0864
Fax: (905)946-8574
Co. E-mail: info@cisc-icca.ca
URL: http://www.cisc-icca.ca
Contact: Stephen Benson, Chairman
Description: Represents the structural steel, open-web steel joist and steel platework fabricating industries; operates as a technical, marketing and government relations organization. **Founded:** 1930. **Publications:** *Advantage Steel* (Quarterly); *Handbook of Steel Construction*; *Design and Construction of Composite Floor Systems.*

5174 ■ Ceilings and Interior Systems Construction Association (CISCA)
405 Illinois Ave., Unit 2B
St. Charles, IL 60174
Ph: (630)584-1919
Fax: (866)560-8537
Co. E-mail: cisca@cisca.org
URL: http://www.cisca.org
Contact: Shawn Burnum, President
Description: International trade association for the advancement of the interior commercial construction industry. Provides quality education, resources and a forum for communication among its members. **Founded:** 1949. **Publications:** *Ceiling Systems.* **Awards:** Construction Excellence Award (Annual).

5175 ■ *Chapter Specifiers*
120 Carlton St., Ste. 312
Toronto, ON, Canada M5A 4K2
Ph: (416)777-2198
Free: 800-668-5684

Fax: (416)777-2197
Co. E-mail: info@csc-dcc.ca
URL: http://www.csc-dcc.ca
Contact: Bruce Gillham, President
Released: 10/year

5176 ■ *Construction Canada*
120 Carlton St., Ste. 312
Toronto, ON, Canada M5A 4K2
Ph: (416)777-2198
Free: 800-668-5684
Fax: (416)777-2197
Co. E-mail: info@csc-dcc.ca
URL: http://www.csc-dcc.ca
Contact: Bruce Gillham, President
Released: Bimonthly

5177 ■ Construction Financial Management Association (CFMA)
100 Village Blvd., Ste. 200
Princeton, NJ 08540
Ph: (609)452-8000
Free: 888-421-9996
Fax: (609)452-0474
Co. E-mail: sbinstock@cfma.org
URL: http://www.cfma.org
Contact: Stuart Binstock, President
Description: Contractors, subcontractors, architects, real estate developers and engineers; associate members are equipment and material suppliers, accountants, lawyers, bankers and others involved with the financial management of the construction industry. Provides a forum for the exchange of ideas; coordinates educational programs dedicated to improving the professional standards of financial management in the construction industry. Offers expanded national programs, technical assistance and industry representation. Conducts research programs; maintains speakers' bureau and placement service; compiles statistics. **Scope:** industry analysis. **Founded:** 1981. **Subscriptions:** 9. **Publications:** *CFMA Building Profits; Construction Industry Annual Financial Survey; CFMA Building Profits* (Bimonthly); *The Source* (Annual); *CFMA's Information Technology Survey for the Construction Industry* (Biennial); *C.F.M.A. Building Profits: The Magazine for Construction Financial Professionals* (Bimonthly). **Educational Activities:** Construction Financial Management Association Annual Conference and Exhibition (Annual). **Awards:** Cindy P. Dennis Scholarship Fund; Danny Parrish Leadership Award (Annual); Debra Hahn Memorial Award (Annual); Joe Quigley Memorial Award (Annual). **Telecommunication Services:** info@cfma. org.

5178 ■ Construction Management Association of America (CMAA)
7926 Jones Branch Dr., Ste. 800
McLean, VA 22102
Ph: (703)356-2622
Fax: (703)356-6388
Co. E-mail: info@cmaanet.org
URL: http://www.cmaanet.org
Contact: Bruce D'Agostino, President
Description: Promotes the growth and development of construction management as a professional service; encourages high professional standards. Conducts conferences and forums on construction management topics. Sponsors a professional certification program. **Founded:** 1981. **Publications:** *CM Advisor; CMAA Documents: Standard CM Services and Practice* (Annual). **Awards:** Person of the Year Award (Annual); Project Achievement Awards (Annual).

5179 ■ Construction Owners Association of America (COAA)
5000 Austell Powder Springs Rd., Ste. 217
Austell, GA 30106
Ph: (770)433-0820
Free: 800-994-2622
Fax: (404)577-3551
Co. E-mail: coaa@coaa.org
URL: http://www.coaa.org
Contact: Ted Argyle, President
Description: Represents public and private owners and developers of construction projects all across America. Aims to make a significant and lasting

impact on the construction industry by educating its membership and by providing a collective voice for owners and developers of construction projects. **Founded:** 1994. **Publications:** *The Owner's Perspective* (Semiannual). **Educational Activities:** Construction Owners Leadership Conference (Semiannual); Conference Owners Spring Leadership Conference (Semiannual). **Awards:** Construction Owners Project Leadership Award (Annual).

5180 ■ Construction Specifications Canada (CSC)
120 Carlton St., Ste. 312
Toronto, ON, Canada M5A 4K2
Ph: (416)777-2198
Free: 800-668-5684
Fax: (416)777-2197
Co. E-mail: info@csc-dcc.ca
URL: http://www.csc-dcc.ca
Contact: Bruce Gillham, President
Description: Construction companies, workers, engineers, and writers of building standards and specifications. Promotes continuing professional development of members; seeks to insure adherence to high standards of practice in the building industries. Conducts educational programs; makes available vocational training courses. Develops industry standards. Represents members' interests before industry organizations and government agencies; advises government agencies responsible for promulgating building codes and construction specifications. Makes available discount insurance and vehicle leasing programs to members. **Founded:** 1954. **Publications:** *Construction Specifications Canada--Directory* (Annual); *Chapter Specifiers* (10/year); *Construction Canada* (Bimonthly); *News in Brief* (Semiannual); *National Master Specification (NMS)*. **Awards:** Award of Merit; Chapter Certificate of Appreciation (Periodic); President's Award (Annual); Lloyd Boddy Chapter of the Year Award.

5181 ■ Construction Specifications Institute (CSI)
110 S Union St., Ste. 100
Alexandria, VA 22314-3351
Free: 800-689-2900
Fax: (703)236-4600
Co. E-mail: csi@csinet.org
URL: http://www.csinet.org
Contact: Paul R. Bertram, Jr., President
Description: Individuals concerned with the specifications and documents used for construction projects. Membership includes architects, professional engineers, specifiers, contractors, product manufacturers, teachers and research workers in architectural and engineering fields, and building maintenance engineers. Advances construction technology through communication, service, education, and research. Certifies construction specifiers and others involved in construction and allied industries. Maintains 20 committees including Certification, Credentials, Specifications Competition, and Technical Documents. Sponsors competitions; maintains speakers' bureau; offers seminars. **Scope:** architecture, construction. **Founded:** 1948. **Subscriptions:** biographical archives. **Publications:** *The Construction Specifier* (Monthly); *NewsBrief* (Weekly). **Awards:** Distinguished Service Award; CSI Fellowship; Honorary Membership; Organizational Certificate of Appreciation; President's Plaques; Electronic Innovation Commendation; Student Liaison Award; Continuing Publication Commendation; Robert P. Brosseau Award for the Advancement of CSI; J. Norman Hunter Award for Construction Document Education; Ben John Small Award for Specifications Writing; Dale C. Moll Quality Management Award.

5182 ■ Energy and Environmental Building Association (EEBA)
6520 Edenvale Blvd., Ste. 112
Eden Prairie, MN 55346
Ph: (952)881-1098
Fax: (952)881-3048
Co. E-mail: inquiry@eeba.org
URL: http://www.eeba.org
Contact: Kathleen Guidera, Executive Director
Description: Professional association of builders, architects, consultants, designers, researchers, educators, government agencies, suppliers, and

manufactures. Promotes the awareness, education, and development of energy-efficient and environmentally responsible buildings and communities. **Founded:** 1982. **Publications:** *EEBA News* (Quarterly). **Educational Activities:** Excellence in Building Conference (Annual); Excellence in Building Conference (Annual).

5183 ■ Engineering Contractors Association (ECA)
8310 Florence Ave.
Downey, CA 90240
Ph: (562)861-0929
Free: 800-293-2240
Fax: (562)923-6179
Co. E-mail: info.eca@verizon.net
URL: http://www.ecaonline.net
Contact: Wes May, Executive Director
Description: Engineering construction contractors and suppliers. Represents members in labor and legislation matters and negotiates disputes within the industry. **Scope:** Serves the general engineering construction industry in matters of labor relations, government relations, legislative direction and public relations. Seeks to create a networking forum through association membership meetings, conventions, seminars, committee activities, and educational resources. Industries served: heavy construction contractors specializing in water, sewer and storm drain pipeline construction, road building, paving and grading. **Founded:** 1976. **Publications:** "Injury and Illness Prevention Program". **Seminars:** Trench Safety Class; Safety in Construction.

5184 ■ International Masonry Institute (IMI)
The James Brice House
42 East St.
Annapolis, MD 21401
Ph: (410)280-1305
Free: 800-803-0295
Fax: (301)261-2855
Co. E-mail: masonryquestions@imiweb.org
URL: http://www.imiweb.org
Contact: James Boland, Co-Chairman
Description: Joint labor/management trust fund of the International Union of Bricklayers and Allied Craftworkers and union masonry contractors. Aims for the advancement of quality masonry construction through national and regional training, promotion, advertising and labor management relations programs in the U.S. and Canada. Provides support and materials for local/regional masonry promotion groups in the U.S. and Canada, and cooperates with national groups and organizations promoting the industry. Sponsors craft training and research programs. Offers educational programs. Maintains museum. **Scope:** masonry construction, design, installation. **Founded:** 1970. **Subscriptions:** books clippings periodicals reports. **Publications:** *IMI Today* (Bimonthly). **Educational Activities:** Mason Industry Educational Conference (Annual). **Awards:** Golden Trowel Award (Periodic); Golden Trowel Awards.

5185 ■ *Just the Fax*
No. 601-280 Albert St.
Ottawa, ON, Canada K1P 5G8
Ph: (613)232-0492
Fax: (613)235-2793
Co. E-mail: mcac@mcac.ca
URL: http://mcac.ca
Contact: Richard McKeagan, President
Released: Weekly

5186 ■ Mechanical Contractors Association of Canada (MCAC)
No. 601-280 Albert St.
Ottawa, ON, Canada K1P 5G8
Ph: (613)232-0492
Fax: (613)235-2793
Co. E-mail: mcac@mcac.ca
URL: http://mcac.ca
Contact: Richard McKeagan, President
Description: Mechanical contractors and providers of related services. Promotes growth and development of members' businesses; works to ensure high standards of ethics and practice in the mechanical contracting industry. Formulates standards of practice in mechanical contracting; facilitates exchange of information among members; represents members'

interests before government agencies, industrial associations, and the public. **Founded:** 1895. **Publications:** *Just the Fax* (Weekly); *National Bulletin* (Periodic). **Awards:** Life Membership (Annual); Outstanding Achievement (Annual). **Telecommunication Services:** rick@mcac.ca.

5187 ■ *The National*
150 Laurier Ave. W, Ste. 500
Ottawa, ON, Canada K1P 5J4
Ph: (613)230-3060
Free: 800-387-2422
Fax: (613)232-8214
Co. E-mail: chba@chba.ca
URL: http://www.chba.ca
Contact: Lynda Barrett, Director
Released: Quarterly

5188 ■ National Association of Home Builders - Leading Suppliers Council
1201 15th St. NW
Washington, DC 20005-2800
Ph: (202)266-8200
Free: 800-368-5242
Fax: (202)266-8400
Co. E-mail: cday@nahb.org
URL: http://www.nahb.org/page.aspx/category/sectionID=469
Contact: Barry Rutenberg, Chairman
Description: Manufacturers of goods and services for the American housing industry. Provides support for the effort of the industry to fill the housing needs of American families. **Founded:** 1964.

5189 ■ National Association of Home Builders (MBSC) - Modular Building Systems Council (MBSC)
c/o National Association of Home Builders
1201 15th St. NW
Washington, DC 20005
Ph: (202)266-8200
Free: 800-368-5242
Fax: (202)266-8400
URL: http://www.nahb.org/page.aspx/category/sectionID=809
Contact: Barry Rutenberg, Chairman of the Board
Description: Operates under the Building Systems Council of NAHB. Modular building manufacturers. Monitors state and federal housing legislation that impacts the building industry. Provides a forum for communication, networking and recruiting for those involved in manufacturing modular building systems. Addresses and solves problems specific to the council; offers consumer leads service. **Scope:** housing, building/construction, mortgage finance, business management, housing policy, regulatory issues, smart growth. **Founded:** 1942. **Subscriptions:** 35000 archival material audiovisuals books clippings periodicals. **Publications:** *Builder Magazine* (Monthly); *Land Development Magazine* (Quarterly); *Nation's Building News* (Semimonthly). **Educational Activities:** International Builders' Show (Annual). **Awards:** Remodeler of the Year Award (Annual); Best in American Living Awards.

5190 ■ National Association of Women in Construction (NAWIC)
327 S Adams St.
Fort Worth, TX 76104
Ph: (817)877-5551
Free: 800-552-3506
Fax: (817)877-0324
Co. E-mail: nawic@nawic.org
URL: http://www.nawic.org
Contact: Tamie Taylor, President
E-mail: karar@nawic.org
Description: Seeks to enhance the success of women in the construction industry. **Founded:** 1955. **Publications:** *The NAWIC Image*; *The NAWIC Image*; *Women's Business Enterprise Directory*. **Awards:** Crystal Vision Awards (Annual); Construction Trades Scholarships; National Association of Women in Construction Founders Undergraduate Scholarships.

5191 ■ *National Bulletin*
No. 601-280 Albert St.
Ottawa, ON, Canada K1P 5G8
Ph: (613)232-0492

Fax: (613)235-2793
Co. E-mail: mcac@mcac.ca
URL: http://mcac.ca
Contact: Richard McKeagan, President
Released: Periodic

5192 ■ National Demolition Association
16 N Franklin St., Ste. 203
Doylestown, PA 18901-3536
Ph: (215)348-4949
Free: 800-541-2412
Fax: (215)348-8422
Co. E-mail: drachel@rachelcontracting.com
URL: http://www.demolitionassociation.com
Contact: Don Rachel, President
E-mail: drachel@rachelcontracting.com
Description: Demolition contractors and equipment manufacturers. Seeks to foster goodwill and to encourage the exchange of ideas among the public and members. **Scope:** demolition. **Founded:** 1972. **Subscriptions:** 500 articles books papers periodicals. **Publications:** *Demolition Safety Manual* (Annual); *Demolition Age* (Monthly). **Educational Activities:** National Demolition Association Annual Convention (Annual); National Association of Demolition Contractors Annual Convention (Annual). **Awards:** Lifetime Achievement Award (Annual). **Telecommunication Services:** info@demolitionassociation.com.

5193 ■ National Frame Builders Association (NFBA)
4700 W Lake Ave.
Glenview, IL 60025
Free: 800-557-6957
Fax: (847)375-6495
Co. E-mail: info@nfba.org
URL: http://www.nfba.org
Contact: Larry Edema, Chairman
Description: Construction contractors specializing in post frame structures for agricultural, residential, industrial and commercial uses. Seeks to enhance the image of the industry and improve management and construction techniques. Conducts educational programs on safety and other vital matters. **Founded:** 1971. **Publications:** *Frame Building News* (5/year); *Frame Building News--Membership Directory Issue* (Annual). **Awards:** Bernon G. Perkins (Annual); Building of the Year (Annual); Crew Foreman of the Month Award (Monthly); Gail Miller Distinguished Safety Award (Annual).

5194 ■ National Housing Endowment
1201 15th St. NW
Washington, DC 20005
Free: 800-368-5242
Fax: (202)266-8177
Co. E-mail: nhe@nahb.com
URL: http://www.nationalhousingendowment.org
Contact: Bruce S. Silver, President
Description: Works to 'build a foundation' to help make the American dream of homeownership a reality for present and future generations. Provides a permanent source of funds to address long-term industry concerns at the national level. Helps the industry to develop more effective approaches to home building. Enhances the ways to educate and train future generations of leaders in residential construction and increase the body of knowledge on housing issues. Supports innovative and effective programs that further Education, Training, and Research. **Founded:** 1987. **Publications:** *Blueprint.* **Awards:** Lee S. Evans/National Housing Endowment Scholarships; Herman J. Smith Scholarships; Builders Achievement Award for Community Service (Annual); Home Builders Care Project of the Year (Annual); Various Scholarships Awards (Annual).

5195 ■ National Insulation Association (NIA)
12100 Sunset Hills Rd., Ste. 330
Reston, VA 20190
Ph: (703)464-6422
Fax: (703)464-5896
Co. E-mail: mjones@insulation.org
URL: http://www.insulation.org
Contact: Alec Rexroat, President
Description: Insulation contractors, distributors, and manufacturers. **Founded:** 1953. **Publications:** *National Insulation Association--Membership Directory*

and *Resource Guide* (Annual); *Insulation Outlook* (Monthly); *Insulation Outlook* (Monthly); *National Industries and Commercial Standards Manual*; *NIA News* (Monthly); *Safety Handbook*; *Insulation Outlook: Business Solutions for Expanding or Relocating Companies*; *Asbestos Abatement Industry Directory.* **Educational Activities:** National Insulation Association Annual Convention (Annual); National Insulation Association Convention (Annual).

5196 ■ News in Brief
120 Carlton St., Ste. 312
Toronto, ON, Canada M5A 4K2
Ph: (416)777-2198
Free: 800-668-5684
Fax: (416)777-2197
Co. E-mail: info@csc-dcc.ca
URL: http://www.csc-dcc.ca
Contact: Bruce Gillham, President
Released: Semiannual

5197 ■ North American Building Material Distribution Association (NBMDA)
401 N Michigan Ave.
Chicago, IL 60611
Ph: (312)321-6845
Free: 888-747-7862
Fax: (312)644-0310
Co. E-mail: info@nbmda.org
URL: http://www.nbmda.org
Contact: Bill Delaney, President
Description: Building material distributors and manufacturers operating in more than 1500 locations. Represents the industry when appropriate. Distributes member and industry information; provides networking opportunities to distributors and manufacturers in the building material industry. Maintains education foundation; provides charitable programs. **Founded:** 1952. **Publications:** *North American Building Material Distribution Association--Membership Directory* (Annual); *NBMDA Membership and Product Directory* (Annual); *The Sales Trainer: A Bi-Monthly Digest of Marketing Techniques for Aggressive Salespeople* (Bimonthly). **Educational Activities:** North American Building Material Distribution Association Convention (Annual).

5198 ■ Professional Construction Estimators Association of America (PCEA)
PO Box 680336
Charlotte, NC 28216
Ph: (704)489-1494
Free: 877-521-7232
Fax: (704)489-1495
Co. E-mail: pcea@pcea.org
URL: http://www.pcea.org
Contact: Lance Pollock, President
Description: Professional construction estimators. Objectives are to further recognition of construction estimating as a professional field of endeavor; to collect and disseminate information; to research and solve problems related to the construction industry; to establish educational programs for youth and promote construction estimating as a career; to maintain ethical standards. **Founded:** 1956. **Publications:** *National PCEA Directory* (Annual). **Awards:** Rudy Barnes Award (Annual); Ted G. Wilson Scholarship (Annual); Bill Helms Chapter of the Year (Annual); Ted C. Wilson Memorial Scholarships; Rudolph John Barnes Award.

5199 ■ Professional Women in Construction (PWC)
315 E 56th St.
New York, NY 10022-3730
Ph: (212)486-4712
Fax: (212)486-0228
Co. E-mail: pwc@pwcusa.org
URL: http://www.pwcusa.org
Contact: Lenore Janis, President
Description: Management-level women and men in construction and allied industries; owners, suppliers, architects, engineers, field personnel, office personnel and bonding/surety personnel. Provides a forum for exchange of ideas and promotion of political and legislative action, education and job opportunities for women in construction and related fields; forms liaisons with other trade and professional groups; develops research programs. Strives to reform

abuses and to assure justice and equity within the construction industry. Sponsors mini-workshops. Maintains Action Line, which provides members with current information on pertinent legislation and on the association's activities and job referrals. **Founded:** 1980. **Publications:** *e-PWC* (Quarterly). **Educational Activities:** Professional Women in Construction Tradeshow (Annual). **Awards:** Project of the Year (Annual); Salute to Women of Achievement (Annual).

5200 ■ Women Construction Owners and Executives U.S.A. (WCOE USA)
1004 Duke St.
Alexandria, VA 22314
Free: 800-788-3548
Fax: (202)330-5151
Co. E-mail: info@wcoeusa.org
URL: http://www.wcoeusa.org
Contact: Rosana Privitera Biondo, President
Description: Promotes the interests of women construction owners and executives. Provides legislation, business, educational, and networking opportunities. **Founded:** 1984. **Awards:** President's Phoenix Award (Annual).

EDUCATIONAL PROGRAMS

5201 ■ Construction Contracting
Seminar Information Service, Inc.
20 Executive Park, Ste. 120
Irvine, CA 92614
Ph: (949)261-9104
Free: 877-SEM-INFO
Fax: (949)261-1963
Co. E-mail: info@seminarinformation.com
URL: http://www.seminarinformation.com
Price: $1,845.00. **Description:** Gain an understanding of the entire contracting process to deal effectively with all parties involved. **Dates and Locations:** Atlanta, GA; Chicago, IL; Washington, DC; and San Diego, CA.

DIRECTORIES OF EDUCATIONAL PROGRAMS

5202 ■ *Directory of Private Accredited Career Schools and Colleges of Technology*
Pub: Accrediting Commission of Career Schools and Colleges of Technology
Contact: Michale S. McComis, Executive Director
Released: On web page. **Price:** Free. **Description:** Covers 3900 accredited post-secondary programs that provide training programs in business, trade, and technical fields, including various small business endeavors. Entries offer school name, address, phone, description of courses, job placement assistance, and requirements for admission. Arrangement is alphabetical.

REFERENCE WORKS

5203 ■ *"3CDC's Biggest Year" in Business Courier (Vol. 26, December 18, 2009, No. 34, pp. 1)*
Pub: American City Business Journals, Inc.
Ed: Lucy May. **Description:** Cincinnati Center City Development Corporation (3CDC) will make 2010 its biggest year with nearly $164 million projects in the works. Historic tax credits and continued help from the city have allowed the private nonprofit organization to finance mega projects such as the $43 million renovation and expansion of Washington Park. Other projects that 3CDC will start or complete in 2010 are presented.

5204 ■ *"21st Century Filling Station" in Austin Business JournalInc. (Vol. 29, December 11, 2009, No. 40, pp. 1)*
Pub: American City Business Journals
Ed: Jacob Dirr. **Description:** Clean Energy Fuels Corporation announced plans for the construction of a $1 million, 17,000 square foot compressed natural gas fueling station at or near the Austin-Bergstrom International Airport (ABIA). Clean Energy Fuels hopes to encourage cab and shuttle companies in the ABIA to switch from gasoline to natural gas.

5205 ■ "$100 Million Complex To Be Built..On a Bridge" in Business Courier (Vol. 27, November 12, 2010, No. 28, pp. 1)

Pub: Business Courier

Ed: Lucy May. Description: A development firm closed a deal with the Newport Southbank Bridge Company for a $100M entertainment complex that will be built on tope of the Purple People Bridge. The proposed project will cover 150,000 square feet with attractions such as restaurants, a boutique hotel, and pubs.

5206 ■ "$100 Million Plan for Jefferson Arms" in Saint Louis Business Journal (Vol. 32, October 14, 2011, No. 7, pp. 1)

Pub: Saint Louis Business Journal

Ed: Evan Binns. Description: Teach for America is planning a $100 million renovation project of the former Jefferson Arms hotel in St. Louis, Missouri. The organization has signed a letter of intent to occupy the space. Financing of the project will be mainly through tax credits.

5207 ■ "$100 Million in Projects Jeopardized" in Business Courier (Vol. 24, March 28, 2008, No. 51, pp. 1)

Pub: American City Business Journals, Inc.

Ed: Dan Monk. Description: Ohio's historic preservation tax credit program may be reinstated after some companies planned to sue over its stoppage. The Ohio Department of Development said the program was halted because it exceeded the allocated budget for the credit. $34 million in credits are at stake for more than two dozen local projects if the program is reinstated.

5208 ■ "217 Homes Planned for Former Crystal Cream Site" in Sacramento Business Journal (Vol. 25, August 8, 2008, No. 23, pp. 1)

Pub: American City Business Journals, Inc.

Ed: Michael Shaw. Description: MetroNova Development LLC plans to develop housing at the former Crystal Cream & Butter Co. site near downtown Sacramento. The developer expects to sell the new loft houses for about $300,000 without public subsidies. Views and other information on the planned development project, is presented.

5209 ■ "$161.9M 'Pit Stop' Fix-Up Will Create About 1,600 Jobs" in Orlando Business Journal (Vol. 26, January 22, 2010, No. 34, pp. 1)

Pub: American City Business Journals

Ed: Anjali Fluker. Description: State of Florida will be providing $161.9 million to renovate eight service plazas starting November 2010. The project is expected to create 1,600 jobs across the state and is expected to be completed by 2012. Details on bid advertisements and facilities slated for improvement are discussed.

5210 ■ "2010: Important Year Ahead for Waterfront" in Bellingham Business Journal (Vol. March 2010, pp. 2)

Pub: Sound Publishing Inc.

Ed: Isaac Bonnell. Description: A tentative timeline has been established for the environmental impact statement (EIS) slated for completion in May 2010. The plan for the Waterfront District includes detailed economic and architectural analysis of the feasibility of reusing remaining structures and retaining some industrial icons.

5211 ■ ABC Today--Associated Builders and Contractors National Membership Directory Issue

Pub: Associated Builders and Contractors Inc.

Contact: Kirk Pickerel, President

E-mail: pickerel@abc.org

URL(s): www.abc.org. Released: Annual; December. Price: $150, plus $7.00 shipping. Publication includes: List of approximately 19,000 member construction contractors and suppliers. Entries include: Company name, address, phone, name of principal executive, code to volume of business, business specialty. Arrangement: Classified by chapter, then by work specialty.

5212 ■ "Adventures at Hydronicahh" in Contractor (Vol. 56, September 2009, No. 9, pp. 52)

Pub: Penton Media, Inc.

Ed: Mark Eatherton. Description: Installation of the heating system of a lakeview room are described. The room's radiant windows are powered by electricity from a solar PV array and a propane-powered hydrogen fuel cell. The system will be programmed to use the most energy available.

5213 ■ "Advertisers Hooked on Horns, their Playground" in Austin Business JournalInc. (Vol. 28, July 25, 2008, No. 19, pp. A1)

Pub: American City Business Journals

Ed: Sandra Zaragoza. Description: Renovation of the D.K. Royal-Texas Memorial Stadium has increased its advertising revenue from $570,000 in 1993 to $10 in 2008. Sponsorship has grown in the past years due to the revenue-sharing agreement, a ten-year contract through 2015 between the University of Texas and IMG College Sports.

5214 ■ "Affordable Housing on the Rise" in Philadelphia Business Journal (Vol. 28, October 23, 2009, No. 36, pp. 1)

Pub: American City Business Journals

Ed: Natalie Kostelni. Description: Philadelphia, Pennsylvania led an affordable housing boom with more than 800 new affordable housing units in the works in spite of the recession. The converging of developers and federal stimulus money has driven the sudden increase with the launching of several projects across the city.

5215 ■ "Agricultural Community Implements Green Technologies, Building Team" in Contractor (Vol. 56, September 2009, No. 9, pp. 5)

Pub: Penton Media, Inc.

Ed: Candace Ruolo. Description: John DeWald and Associates has initiated a residential development project which uses green technologies in Illinois. The community features a community center, organic farm and recreational trails. Comments from executives are also provided.

5216 ■ "Aircraft Maker May Land Here" in Austin Business Journal (Vol. 31, April 15, 2011, No. 6, pp. 1)

Pub: American City Business Journals Inc.

Ed: Jacob Dirr. Description: Icon Aircraft Inc. is planning to build a manufacturing facility in Austin, Texas. The company needs 100,000 square feet of space in a new or renovated plant. Executive comments are included.

5217 ■ "All About The Benjamins" in Canadian Business (Vol. 81, September 29, 2008, No. 16, pp. 92)

Pub: Rogers Media Ltd.

Ed: David Baines. Description: Discusses real estate developer Royal Indian Raj International Corp., a company that planned to build a $3 billion 'smart city' near the Bangalore airport; to this day nothing has ever been built. The company was incorporated in 1999 by Manoj C. Benjamin one investor, Bill Zack, has been sued by the developer for libel due to his website that calls the company a scam. Benjamin has had a previous case of fraud issued against him as well as a string of liabilities and lawsuits.

5218 ■ American Society of Professional Estimators--Membership Directory and Buyers' Guide

Pub: American Society of Professional Estimators

Contact: Paulette R. Rutlen, President

E-mail: prrutlen@cox.net

URL(s): www.aspenational.com. Released: Annual; Latest edition 2010-2011. Covers: 3,000 members allied to the building industry as construction estimators. Entries include: Name, address, phone, business address and phone, category of membership. Arrangement: Classified by numbered chapter. Indexes: Alphabetical.

5219 ■ "Amid Recession, Companies Still Value Supplier Diversity Programs" in Hispanic Business (July-August 2009, pp. 34)

Pub: Hispanic Business

Ed: Joshua Molina. Description: The decline of traditionally strong industries, from automotive manufacturing to construction, has shaken today's economy and has forced small businesses, especially suppliers and minority-owned firms, turn to diversity programs in order to make changes.

5220 ■ "Analysts: Intel Site May Be Last Major U.S.-Built Fab" in Business Journal-Serving Phoenix and the Valley of the Sun (Oct. 19, 2007)

Pub: American City Business Journals, Inc.

Ed: Ty Young. Description: Intel's million-square-foot manufacturing facility, called Fab 32, is expected to open in 2007. The plant will mass-produce the 45-nanometer microchip. Industry analysts believe Fab 32 may be the last of its kind to be built in the U.S., as construction costs are higher in America than in other countries. Intel's future in Chandler is examined.

5221 ■ "Analysts Not Fazed By Constellation's Halt to New Nuclear Plants" in Baltimore Business Journal (Vol. 28, October 22, 2010, No. 24)

Pub: Baltimore Business Journal

Ed: Scott Dance. Description: Wall Street analysts believe that Constellation Energy Group Inc.'s decision to pull out of the nuclear construction business would not change their outlook on the company. New nuclear power had been one of Constellation's long-term goals, but the company pulled the plug on the project. It is believed that most investors were not expecting any payoff from the venture.

5222 ■ "Are We There Yet?" in Business Courier (Vol. 24, April 4, 2008, No. 52, pp. 1)

Pub: American City Business Journals, Inc.

Ed: Lucy May; Dan Monk. Description: Groundbreaking for The Banks project happened in April 2, 2008, however, the future of the development remains uncertain due to some unresolved issues such as financing. Developers Harold A. Dawson Co. and Carter still have to pass final financing documents to Hamilton County and Cincinnati. The issue of financial commitment for the central riverfront project is examined.

5223 ■ "Areva Diversifies Further Into Wind" in Wall Street Journal Eastern Edition (November 29, 2011, pp. B7)

Pub: Dow Jones & Company Inc. Enterprise Media Group

Contact: Clare Hart, President

Ed: Max Colchester, Noemie Bisserbe. Description: French engineering company Areva SA is diversifying and moving away from nuclear energy projects. One sign of that is its recent discussion to construct 120 wind turbines to be located at two German wind farms. Such a deal, if signed, would be worth about US$1.59 billion.

5224 ■ "As Tradesmen Age, New Workers In Short Supply" in Boston Business Journal (Vol. 27, November 9, 2007, No. 41, pp. 1)

Pub: American City Business Journals Inc.

Ed: Jackie Noblett. Description: It is becoming more difficult to find young people who have the skills for installation and maintenance businesses. Some businesses are unable to complete contracts on time due to lack of staff. Unions are making efforts to address the expected shortfall of laborers in the coming years through apprenticeship programs.

5225 ■ "Athletes' Performance Building $10 Million Facility In ASU Park" in The Business Journal - Serving Phoenix and the Valley of the Sun (Vol. 28, August 8, 2008, No. 49, pp. 1)

Pub: American City Business Journals, Inc.

Ed: Jan Buchholz. Description: Athletes' Performance's planned facility at Arizona State University is scheduled to begin in November 2008 and expected to be completed by September 2009. The new building will almost double the company's training space as it will expand from around 19,000 square feet to 35,000 square feet.

5226 ■ *"Austin Homes are Overpriced, Study Says"* in *Austin Business JournalInc. (Vol. 29, January 1, 2010, No. 43, pp. 1)*
Pub: American City Business Journals
Ed: Kate Harrington. **Description:** Study by Forbes. com shows that Austin-Round Rock metropolitan statistical area ranked 10th on the list of cities with the most over-priced homes. For instance, the average price for a single-family home pegged at $188,000.

5227 ■ *"Austin Ponders Annexing Fl Racetrack"* in *Austin Business Journal (Vol. 31, July 8, 2011, No. 18, pp. 1)*
Pub: American City Business Journals Inc.
Ed: Vicky Garza. **Description:** City planners in Austin, Texas are studying the feasibility of annexing the land under and around the Circuit of the Americas Formula One Racetrack being constructed east of the city. The annexation could generate at least $13 million in financial gain over 25 years from property taxes alone.

5228 ■ *"BABs in Bond Land"* in *Barron's (Vol. 89, July 6, 2009, No. 27, pp. 14)*
Pub: Dow Jones & Co., Inc.
Ed: Jim McTague. **Description:** American Recovery and Reinvestment Act has created taxable Build America Bonds (BAB) to finance new construction projects. The issuance of the two varieties of taxable BABs is expected to benefit the municipal bond market.

5229 ■ *"Bad News for Canada: U.S. New-Home Starts Sink"* in *Globe & Mail (February 17, 2007, pp. B7)*
Pub: CTVglobemedia Publishing Inc.
Ed: Tavia Grant. **Description:** The new-home construction in the United States dropped by 14.3 percent in January 2007. The sinking construction activity shows significant impact on the Canadian factories and lumber companies.

5230 ■ *"Bankruptcies"* in *Crain's Detroit Business (Vol. 24, March 24, 2008, No. 12, pp. 6)*
Pub: Crain Communications, Inc.
Description: Current list of business that filed for Chapter 7 or 11 protection in U.S. Bankruptcy Court in Detroit include a construction company, a medical care company, a physical therapy firm and a communications firm.

5231 ■ *"Banks Could Greet Tenants in One Year"* in *Business Courier (Vol. 26, October 16, 2009, No. 25, pp. 1)*
Pub: American City Business Journals, Inc.
Ed: Lucy May. **Description:** The Banks project's initial phase is expected to start in 60 days, which may mean that the project's first tenant could move in by the end of 2010 or beginning of 2011. Carter, an Atlanta-based firm has partnered with Dawson Company in this riverfront development. The first phase will include 80,000 square feet of retail and 300 apartments.

5232 ■ *"Be Proactive - Closely Review Contracts"* in *Contractor (Vol. 56, July 2009, No. 7, pp. 19)*
Pub: Penton Media, Inc.
Ed: Al Schwartz. **Description:** Contract disputes can make construction suffer big financial losses or even cause a new subcontractor to fail. Subcontractors should scour the plans and specifications for any references to work that might remotely come under their scope and to cross out any line in the contract that does not accurately reflect the work that they agreed to.

5233 ■ *"Be Wary of Dual-Flush Conversion Kits"* in *Contractor (Vol. 56, September 2009, No. 9, pp. 66)*
Pub: Penton Media, Inc.
Ed: John Koeller; Bill Gauley. **Description:** Recommendation of untested dual-flush conversion devices for tank-type toilets in the United States have been

questioned. The products are being advertised as having the ability to convert single-flush to a dual-flush toilet. No evidence of water conservation from using such devices has been recorded.

5234 ■ *"Behind the Scenes: Companies at the Heart of Everyday Life"* in *Inc. (March 2008, pp. 34-35)*
Pub: Gruner & Jahr USA Publishing
Ed: Athena Schindelheim. **Description:** Profiles of companies used to improve road conditions at the Bedford, New Hampshire Toll Plaza are presented. General Traffic Equipment provides LED traffic lights; TRMI, provided 8-foot strips treadles that count the number of axles that drive over them; E-Z Pass system is an antenna from Mark IV Industries that uses radio-frequency identification (RFID) technology to scan a small device attached to a car's windshield; and Transport Data Systems installed cameras that snap photos of passengers and license plates in order to catch individuals who try to dodge fees.

5235 ■ *"Belmont Annexation Approved"* in *Charlotte Observer (February 7, 2007)*
Pub: Knight-Ridder/Tribune Business News
Ed: Jefferson George. **Description:** Belmont, North Carolina City Council approved annexation of nearly 64 acres. The land will be used to develop a residential community.

5236 ■ *"Bigger TIF Makes Development Inroads"* in *The Business Journal-Serving Metropolitan Kansas City (Vol. 26, July 11, 2008, No. 44)*
Pub: American City Business Journals, Inc.
Ed: Rob Roberts. **Description:** On July 9, 2008 the Tax Increment Financing Commission voted to expand a TIF district to Tiffany Springs Road. The plan for the TIF district close to Kansas City International Airport is to include a-half mile of the road. The impacts of the expansion on construction projects and on the road network are analyzed.

5237 ■ *"BIM and LPS Improve Project Management"* in *Contractor (Vol. 57, January 2010, No. 1, pp. 56)*
Pub: Penton Media, Inc.
Ed: Dennis Sowards. **Description:** Building Information Modeling helps reduce workspace conflicts and construction problems that are not seen in typical design efforts for mechanical contractors. The Last Planner System in Lean Construction also helps improve productivity in project management.

5238 ■ *"BIM and You: Know Its Benefits and Risks"* in *Contractor (Vol. 57, January 2010, No. 1, pp. 46)*
Pub: Penton Media, Inc.
Ed: Susan Linden McGreevy. **Description:** Building Information Modeling is intended to be 'collaborative' and this could raise legal issues if a contractor sends an electronic bid and it is filtered out. Other legal issues that mechanical contractors need to consider before using this technology are discussed.

5239 ■ *"Block Plans Office Park Along K-10 Corridor"* in *The Business Journal-Serving Metropolitan Kansas City (Vol. 27, October 3, 2008)*
Pub: American City Business Journals, Inc.
Ed: Rob Roberts. **Description:** Kansas City, Missouri-based Block and Co. is planning to build four office buildings at the corner of College Boulevard and Ridgeview Road in Olathe. Features of the planned development are provided. Comments from executives are also presented.

5240 ■ *"Block Pulls Plug On Riverside Deal"* in *The Business Journal-Serving Metropolitan Kansas City (Vol. 27, October 10, 2008, No. 4)*
Pub: American City Business Journals, Inc.
Ed: Rob Roberts. **Description:** Real estate developer Ken Block has backed out from a $300 million Riverside industrial project. Block says he has already invested $1 million of his own money into the deal. Details regarding the project are given.

5241 ■ *"Bond Hill Cinema Site To See New Life"* in *Business Courier (Vol. 27, October 29, 2010, No. 26, pp. 1)*
Pub: Business Courier
Ed: Dan Monk. **Description:** Avondale, Ohio's Corinthian Baptist Church will redevelop the 30-acre former Showcase Cinema property to a mixed-use site that could feature a college, senior home, and retail. Corinthian Baptist, which is one of the largest African-American churches in the region, is also planning to relocate the church.

5242 ■ *"Bond OK Could Bring Back the Housing Battle?"* in *Charlotte Business Journal (Vol. 25, November 5, 2010, No. 33, pp. 1)*
Pub: Charlotte Business Journal
Ed: Susan Stabley. **Description:** The approval of the $15 million housing bond in Charlotte, North Carolina could bring back the debates on housing in the region. Protesters have opposed affordable housing developments that were proposed in the area since 2008. Other information on the recently approved housing bond and on other real estate issues in North Carolina is presented.

5243 ■ *"Bridging the Bay"* in *Business Journal Serving Greater Tampa Bay (Vol. 30, November 5, 2010, No. 46, pp. 1)*
Pub: Tampa Bay Business Journal
Ed: Mark Holan. **Description:** The Florida Department of Transportation has launched a study to design the proposed addition to the Howard Frankland Bridge. The bridge would be designed to accommodate more than personal vehicles.

5244 ■ *"Brookfield Eyes 'New World'"* in *Globe & Mail (February 6, 2007, pp. B1)*
Pub: CTVglobemedia Publishing Inc.
Ed: Sinclair Stewart; Elizabeth Church. **Description:** The efforts of Brookfield Asset Management Inc. to acquire American paper company, Longview Fibre Co., and Australian construction company Multiplex Ltd. are discussed.

5245 ■ *"Builder's Bankruptcy Fans Fears"* in *Crain's Cleveland Business (Vol. 28, October 22, 2007, No. 42, pp. 1)*
Pub: Crain Communications, Inc.
Ed: Stan Bullard. **Description:** Whitlatch & Co., Northeast Ohio's largest builder by unit volume in the early 1990s, has filed for Chapter 11 bankruptcy. This is causing builders and others in the real estate industry to wonder how long and severe the housing slump will be and which companies will survive.

5246 ■ *"Builder's Comeback Highlights Uptick in Demand for New Homes"* in *Boston Business Journal (Vol. 29, June 3, 2011, No. 4, pp. 1)*
Pub: American City Business Journals Inc.
Ed: Gary Haber. **Description:** The return of builder Michael Canock after a series of credit crisis and the funding for his new projects are discussed in light of the recent upsurge in the home-building industry in the Baltimore area. New single-family homes numbered 318 in first quarter 2011 which is a 20 percent increase from first quarter 2010.

5247 ■ *"Builders Land Rutenberg Deal"* in *Charlotte Observer (February 2, 2007)*
Pub: Knight-Ridder/Tribune Business News
Ed: Bob Fliss. **Description:** Jim and Larry Sanders purchased a franchise from builder, Arthur Rutenberg Homes. The brothers will build custom homes in the area.

5248 ■ *"Builders, Unions Aim to Cut Costs; Pushing Changes to Regain Share of Residential Market; Seek Council's Help"* in *Crain's New York Business*
Pub: Crain Communications, Inc.
Ed: Erik Engquist. **Description:** Union contractors and workers are worried about a decline in their market share for housing so they intend to ask the City Council to impose new safety and benefit standards on all contractors to avoid being undercut by nonunion competitors.

5249 ■ *"Building Targeted for Marriott in Violation"* in *Business Journal-Milwaukee (Vol. 28, December 24, 2010, No. 12, pp. A1)*
Pub: Milwaukee Business Journal
Ed: Sean Ryan. **Description:** Milwaukee, Wisconsin's Department of Neighborhood Services has ordered structural improvements and safeguards for the Pioneer Building after three violations from structural failures were found. Pioneer was among the five buildings wanted by Jackson Street Management LLC to demolish for the new Marriott Hotel.

5250 ■ *"A Burning Issue: Lives Are at Stake Every Day"* in *Contractor (Vol. 56, October 2009, No. 10, pp. 29)*
Pub: Penton Media, Inc.
Ed: Julius A. Ballanco; Stanley Wolfson. **Description:** American Society of Plumbing Engineers has been accused of being biased for supporting rules that require residential fire sprinklers although the society's members will not receive any benefit from their installation. The organization trains and certifies plumbing engineers who design life-saving fire protection systems.

5251 ■ *"Buy Now?"* in *Hawaii Business (Vol. 53, March 2008, No. 9, pp. 32)*
Pub: Hawaii Business Publishing
Ed: David K. Choo. **Description:** Discusses the Honolulu Board of REALTORS which said that the last two months of 2007 saw double-digit housing sales drop, with December figures showing 30.6 percent and 22.9 percent decline in sales of single-family homes and condominiums, respectively. Forecasts on Hawaii's real estate market for 2008 are discussed.

5252 ■ *"Cadillac Tower Largest to Start in a Decade"* in *Globe & Mail (March 28, 2006, pp. B5)*
Pub: CTVglobemedia Publishing Inc.
Ed: Elizabeth Church. **Description:** The plans of Cadillac Fairview Corporation Ltd. to build office towers, in downtown Canada, are presented.

5253 ■ *"Cal-ISO Plans $125 Million Facility"* in *Sacramento Business Journal (Vol. 25, August 1, 2008, No. 22, pp. 1)*
Pub: American City Business Journals, Inc.
Ed: Celia Lamb; Michael Shaw. **Description:** Sacramento, California-based nonprofit organization California Independent System Operator (ISO) is planning to build a new headquarters in Folsom. The new building would double its current leased space to 227,000 square feet. The ISO will seek tax-exempt bond financing for the project.

5254 ■ *"Can HOAs Stop You From Going Green?"* in *Contractor (Vol. 56, July 2009, No. 7, pp. 39)*
Pub: Penton Media, Inc.
Ed: Susan Linden McGreevy. **Description:** There have been cases concerning homeowners' associations objections to the installation of wind turbines and solar panels. Precedence with the courts show that they will look at several factors when deciding to uphold restrictions on property use including whether the item encroaches on the rights of others, is likely to adversely affect property values, and also the state of enforcement.

5255 ■ *"Canada's Largest Bakery Officially Opened Today"* in *Ecology,Environment & Conservation Business (October 15, 2011, pp. 7)*
Pub: HighBeam Research
Description: Maple Leaf Foods opened Canada's largest commercial bakery in Hamilton, Ontario. The firm's 385,000 square foot Trillium bakery benefits from efficient design flow and best-in-class technologies.

5256 ■ *"Capital Metro May Soon Seek Contractor to Replace Star Tran"* in *Austin Business Journal (Vol. 31, June 10, 2011, No. 14, pp. 1)*
Pub: American City Business Journals Inc.
Ed: Vicky Garza. **Description:** Capital Metropolitan Transportation Authority may be forced to contract out its bus services provided by StarTran Inc. as early

as September 2012 following legislation approved by the Texas legislature. The bill originates in a report by the Sunset Advisory Commission. Details are included.

5257 ■ *"Casino Minority Spend: $80 Million"* in *Business Courier (Vol. 27, August 20, 2010, No. 16, pp. 1)*
Pub: Business Courier
Ed: Lucy May. **Description:** Real estate developers are planning to invest $80 million to build the Harrah's casino project in Cincinnati, Ohio. Rock Ventures LLC is seeking a 20 percent inclusion rate in the project.

5258 ■ *"Chicago Public School District Builds Green"* in *Contractor (Vol. 56, October 2009, No. 10, pp. 5)*
Pub: Penton Media, Inc.
Ed: Candace Roulo. **Description:** Chicago Public Schools district has already built six U.S. Green Building Council LEED certified schools and one addition in five years and will continue to build new green buildings. The district has an Environmental Action Plan that strives to reduce energy usage, improve indoor air quality, and reduce contribution to climate change.

5259 ■ *"Children's Hospital to Build in New Berlin"* in *The Business Journal-Milwaukee (Vol. 25, August 1, 2008, No. 45, pp. A1)*
Pub: American City Business Journals, Inc.
Ed: Corrinne Hess. **Description:** Children's Hospital of Wisconsin plans a clinic in the 35-acre medical office park in New Berlin, Wisconsin, owned by Froedtert Memorial Lutheran Hospital and Medical College of Wisconsin Real Estate Ventures LLC. The hospital will be the first major tenant in the park, to be built by Irgens Development Partners LLC.

5260 ■ *"Children's Hospital to Grow"* in *Austin Business Journal (Vol. 31, July 22, 2011, No. 20, pp. A1)*
Pub: American City Business Journals Inc.
Ed: Sandra Zaragoza. **Description:** Austin, Texas-based Dell Children's Medical Center is set to embark on a tower expansion. The plan will accommodate more patients and make room for the hospital's growing specialty program.

5261 ■ *"Chinese Solar Panel Manufacturer Scopes Out Austin"* in *Austin Business JournalInc. (Vol. 29, October 30, 2009, No. 34, pp. 1)*
Pub: American City Business Journals
Ed: Jacob Dirr. **Description:** China's Yingli Green Energy Holding Company Ltd. is looking for a site in order to construct a $20 million photovoltaic panel plant. Both Austin and San Antonio are vying to house the manufacturing hub. The project could create about 300 jobs and give Austin a chance to become a player in the solar energy market. Other solar companies are also considering Central Texas as an option to set up shop.

5262 ■ *"Christ Hospital to Expand"* in *Business Courier (Vol. 27, June 25, 2010, No. 8, pp. 3)*
Pub: Business Courier
Ed: Dan Monk, James Ritchie. **Description:** Christ Hospital intends to invest more than $300 million and generate 200 jobs in an expansion of its Mount Auburn campus in Cincinnati, Ohio. About $22 million in retail activity can be created by the hospital expansion, which will also include a replacement garage and new surgery facilities.

5263 ■ *"Cincinnati's Senior Moment"* in *Business Courier (Vol. 27, June 11, 2010, No. 6, pp. 1)*
Pub: Business Courier
Ed: James Ritchie. **Description:** It is believed that the high demand in housing that will accompany the aging population has yet to arrive, and is not due for years to come. The next few years could lead to leaner times for long-standing independent-living properties and a slow climb for newer centers looking to build occupancy.

5264 ■ *"City Eyeing Tax Breaks for Arena"* in *Boston Business Journal (Vol. 29, June 3, 2011, No. 4, pp. 1)*
Pub: American City Business Journals Inc.
Ed: Daniel J. Sernovitz. **Description:** Baltimore City is opting to give millions of dollars in tax breaks and construction loans to a group of private investors led by William Hackerman who is proposing to build a new arena and hotel at the Baltimore Convention Center. The project will cost $500 million with the state putting up another $400 million for the center's expansion.

5265 ■ *"City Seeks More Minorities"* in *Austin Business JournalInc. (Vol. 28, November 7, 2008, No. 34, pp. A1)*
Pub: American City Business Journals
Ed: Jean Kwon. **Description:** Austin, Texas is planning to increase the participation of minority- and women-owned businesses in government contracts. Contractors are required to show 'good faith' to comply with the specified goals. The city is planning to effect the changes in the construction and professional services sector.

5266 ■ *"City Sets Yamhill Makeover"* in *The Business Journal-Portland (Vol. 25, July 4, 2008, No. 17, pp. 1)*
Pub: American City Business Journals, Inc.
Ed: Andy Giegerich. **Description:** City government is scheduled to redevelop Peterson's property on Yamhill Street in Portland. The redevelopment is seen as a way to better developing commercial properties in the area. Problems associated with the project, which include cost and developer selection, are also discussed.

5267 ■ *"City Struggles to Iron Out Tangled Transportation"* in *Crain's New York Business (Vol. 24, January 14, 2008, No. 2, pp. 33)*
Pub: Crain Communications, Inc.
Ed: Judith Messina. **Description:** Discusses the possible solutions to improve lower Manhattan's transportation infrastructure including the construction of three new transit centers, an expansion in ferry service and the plan to get parked buses off the street.

5268 ■ *"CityLink Project On Hold"* in *Business Courier (Vol. 24, November 9, 2008, No. 30, pp. 3)*
Pub: American City Business Journals, Inc.
Ed: Dan Monk. **Description:** Developers of the CityLink project have indicated that it will be at least a year before they start the planned social services mall at 800 Bank West End. According to Tim Senff, Citylink CEO, the company wants to build bridges before constructing the buildings. The project's critics are still considering whether to appeal a court ruling regarding the facility's compliance with the city's zoning code.

5269 ■ *"Civil Council Almost On Board With Light Rail Plan"* in *The Business Journal-Serving Metropolitan Kansas City (September 5, 2008)*
Pub: American City Business Journals, Inc.
Ed: Steve Vockrodt. **Description:** Civic Council of Greater Kansas City has taken back its demand for the city to show a 10-year financial plan to win its endorsement of a light rail plan. The council said it will accept a five-year financial plan for the project. Details of the light rail plan are also presented.

5270 ■ *"Clean Wind Energy Tower Transitions from R&D Stage Company"* in *Professional Services Close-Up (September 30, 2011)*
Pub: Close-Up Media
Description: Clean Wind Energy designed and is developing large downdraft towers that use benevolent, non-toxic natural elements to generate electricity and clean water. The firm is closing its internally staffed engineering office in Warrenton, Virginia and transitioning a development team to oversee and coordinate industry consultants and advisors to construct their first dual renewable energy tower.

5271 ■ *"Clock Ticking for Hotel Berry" in Sacramento Business Journal (Vol. 25, July 25, 2008, No. 21, pp. 1)*
Pub: American City Business Journals, Inc.
Ed: Michael Shaw. **Description:** Federal tax credits worth $13.6 million have been awarded to boost the renovation project for the aging Hotel Berry in downtown Sacramento, California. The owners of the hotel have five months before the expiration of the tax credits to raise the remaining funding for the $20 million renovation.

5272 ■ *"Collateral Damage" in Business Courier (Vol. 26, October 16, 2009, No. 25, pp. 1)*
Pub: American City Business Journals, Inc.
Ed: Jon Newberry. **Description:** Non-union construction firms representing Ohio Valley Associated Builders and Contractors Inc. have filed cases against unionized shops claiming violations of wage law in Ohio. Defendants say the violations are minor, however, they believe they are caught in the middle of the group's campaign to change the state's wage law.

5273 ■ *"Columbia Sale Narrowed To Two Developers" in The Business Journal-Milwaukee (Vol. 25, July 18, 2008, No. 43, pp. A1)*
Pub: American City Business Journals, Inc.
Ed: Corrinne Hess. **Description:** Officials of Columbia St. Mary's Inc plan to pick one of two real-estate developers who will buy the 8-acre property of the Columbia Hospital which the company will move away from when their new hospital has been constructed. The hospital on Newport Ave. has been on the market since 2001.

5274 ■ *"Combo Dorm-Field House Built to Attain LEED Gold" in Contractor (Vol. 56, September 2009, No. 9, pp. 1)*
Pub: Penton Media, Inc.
Ed: Candace Roulo; Robert P. Mader. **Description:** North Central College in Illinois has built a new dormitory that is expected to attain Leadership in Energy and Environmental Design Gold certification from the United States Green Building Council. The structure features a geo-exchange heat pump system and radiant floor heat. A description of the facility is also provided.

5275 ■ *"Commercial Builders Take It on the Chin" in Crain's Chicago Business (Vol. 31, April 28, 2008, No. 17, pp. 16)*
Pub: Crain Communications, Inc.
Ed: Alby Gallun. **Description:** Although the health care development sector has seen growth, the rest of Chicago's local commercial building industry has seen steep declines in the first quarter of this year. According to McGraw-Hill Construction, Chicago-area non-residential construction starts totaled $731 million in the quarter, a 60 percent drop from the year-earlier period. Volume in the retail, office and hotel markets fell by nearly 70 percent.

5276 ■ *"Condo Markdown" in Boston Business Journal (Vol. 27, November 30, 2007, No. 44, pp. 1)*
Pub: American City Business Journals Inc.
Ed: Michelle Hillman. **Description:** Boston real estate market is softening, and condominium developers such as Beacon Communities LLC are sending out various incentives like markdowns and unit upgrades. Developers have also held auctions and even offered brand new cars to lure buyers. Other perks being offered by various Boston developers are discussed.

5277 ■ *"Condominium Sales Fall to a Seven-Year Low" in Crain's Chicago Business (Vol. 31, November 10, 2008, No. 45, pp. 2)*
Pub: Crain Communications, Inc.
Ed: Alby Gallun. **Description:** Downtown Chicago condominium market is experiencing the lowest number of sales in years due to the tightening of the mortgage lending market, the Wall Street crisis and the downturn in the economy. The supply of new condos is soaring, the result of the building boom of 2005 and 2006; many developers are finding it dif-

ficult to pay off construction loans and fear foreclosure on their properties. Additional information and statistical data related to the downtown condominium market is provided.

5278 ■ *"Construction Companies Think Smaller, Find Niches as Projects Become Fewer" in Crain's Detroit Business (March 10, 2008)*
Pub: Crain Communications, Inc.
Ed: Daniel Duggan. **Description:** Due to the decline in development projects, construction firms are facing stronger competition for bids and are relying on their good track records or developing expertise in specific niches to get the job.

5279 ■ *"Contracting Firm Sees Timing Right for Expansion" in Tampa Bay Business Journal (Vol. 29, November 13, 2009, No. 47, pp. 1)*
Pub: American City Business Journals
Ed: Janet Leiser. **Description:** Construction management company Moss & Associates LLC of Fort Lauderdale, Florida has launched its expansion to Tampa Bay. Moss & Associates has started the construction of the Marlins stadium in Miami, Florida's Little Havana section. It also plans to diversify by embarking on other government development, such as health care facilities and airports.

5280 ■ *"Contractors Debate Maximizing Green Opportunities, Education" in Contractor (Vol. 56, November 2009, No. 11, pp. 3)*
Pub: Penton Media, Inc.
Ed: Robert P. Mader. **Description:** Attendees at the Mechanical Service Co ntractors Association convention were urged to get involved with their local U.S. Green Building Council chapter by one presenter. Another presenter says that one green opportunity for contractors is the commissioning of new buildings.

5281 ■ *"Contractors Must be Lead Certified by April 2010" in Contractor (Vol. 57, February 2010, No. 2, pp. 3)*
Pub: Penton Media, Inc.
Description: Contractors should be trained and certified to comply with the U.S. Environmental Protection Agency's Lead Renovation, Repair, and Painting regulation if they work on housing built before 1978 by April 2010. Contractors with previous lead abatement training must be trained and certified under this new program.

5282 ■ *"Contractors Scramble for Jobs" in Business Journal Portland (Vol. 26, December 18, 2009, No. 41, pp. 1)*
Pub: American City Business Journals Inc.
Ed: Andy Giegerich. **Description:** Contractors in Portland area are expected to bid for capital construction projects that will be funded by municipalities in the said area. Contracts for companies that work on materials handling, road improvement, and public safety structure projects will be issued.

5283 ■ *"Contractors: Slots MBE Goal a Test" in Baltimore Business Journal (Vol. 27, November 20, 2009, No. 28, pp. 1)*
Pub: American City Business Journals
Ed: Scott Dance. **Description:** Slot machine manufacturers in Maryland have been searching minority business enterprises (MBEs) that will provide maintenance and delivery services to the machines. MBEs will also build the stands where the machines will be mounted.

5284 ■ *"Convenience Store Expanding" in Clovis News Journal (November 9, 2010)*
Pub: Freedom Communications Inc.
Description: Allsup's convenience store on North Prince Street in Clovis, New Mexico will expand its facilities. The current building is being demolished to make way for the new construction.

5285 ■ *"Corporate Park Retrofits for Water Savings" in Contractor (Vol. 56, October 2009, No. 10, pp. 5)*
Pub: Penton Media, Inc.
Description: Merrit Corporate Park in Norwalk, Connecticut has been interested in improving building efficiency and one of its buildings has been retrofit-

ted with water-efficient plumbing systems which will allow them to save as much as two million gallons of water. ADP Service Corp. helped the park upgrade their plumbing system.

5286 ■ *"Corporex Checks Into Hotel Niche" in Business Courier (Vol. 24, October 12, 2008, No. 26, pp. 1)*
Pub: American City Business Journals, Inc.
Ed: Laura Baverman. **Description:** Corporex Companies Inc. is investing $900 million on select-service hotels ranging from $12 million to $20 million each, with eight hotels under construction and nine sites under contract.

5287 ■ *"Corus Eases Off Ailing Condo Market; Office Developers Get Majority of 1Q Loans" in Crain's Chicago Business (April 28, 2008)*
Pub: Crain Communications, Inc.
Ed: H. Lee Murphy. **Description:** Corus Bankshares Inc., a specialist in lending for the condominium high-rise construction market, is diversifying its portfolio by making loans to office developers and expects to be investing in hotels through the rest of the year. Corus' $7.57 billion loan portfolio is also discussed in detail as well as the company's earnings and share price. Statistical data included.

5288 ■ *"Could This Be Your Next Office Building?" in Austin Business Journal (Vol. 31, May 13, 2011, No. 10, pp. A1)*
Pub: American City Business Journals Inc.
Ed: Cody Lyon. **Description:** Falcon Containers moved to a 51-acre site in Far East Austin, Texas and started construction of a 2,500-square-foot headquarters made from eight 40-foot shipping containers. Falcon's CEO Stephen Shang plans to use his headquarters building as a showroom to attract upscale, urban hipsters. Insights on the construction's environmental and social impact are shared.

5289 ■ *"Councilman May Revive Labor Bill" in Baltimore Business Journal (Vol. 28, August 13, 2010, No. 14, pp. 1)*
Pub: Baltimore Business Journal
Ed: Daniel J. Sernovitz. **Description:** Baltimore, Maryland Councilman Bill Henry has started reviving controversial legislation that would force developers and contractors to give preference to union labor. The legislation requires contractors to give preference to city workers in order to lower Baltimore's unemployment rate.

5290 ■ *"County Tract Pitched for Data Center" in Baltimore Business Journal (Vol. 28, July 23, 2010, No. 11, pp. 1)*
Pub: Baltimore Business Journal
Ed: Scott Dance. **Description:** One hundred acres of land in Woodlawn, Maryland is set to be sold for use in the construction of a data center for the U.S. Social Security Administration. Baltimore County has submitted a bid for the $750M construction project.

5291 ■ *"Covington's Business Owners Get Bridge Relief" in Business Courier (Vol. 27, October 29, 2010, No. 26, pp. 1)*
Pub: Business Courier
Ed: Dan Monk. **Description:** Engineers of Brent Spence Bridge have developed a new 'second chance' exit that preserves highway access to Covington, Kentucky's main business districts. It is believed that the planned ramp off Interstate 75 represents a compromise between highway planners, who wish to maintain continuous traffic for interstate users.

5292 ■ *"Creativity is Essential in Sagging Relocation Market" in Crain's Cleveland Business (Vol. 28, November 5, 2007, No. 44, pp. 19)*
Pub: Crain Communications, Inc.
Ed: Christine Gordillo. **Description:** Since Northeast Ohio was headquarters to a number of Fortune 500 companies, residential real estate builders and brokers could count on corporate relocation clients for a steady stream of business. Today, corporations have become more cautious when relocating talent

due to the costs involved which has forced industry experts to be more patient and more creative in the ways they attract out-of-town buyers who are likely to be a sure sell.

5293 ■ "A Crystal Ball" in Business Journal Portland (Vol. 27, December 31, 2010, No. 44, pp. 1)
Pub: Portland Business Journal
Ed: Wendy Culverwell. **Description:** McMenamins Pubs and Breweries has resumed construction of its Crystal Hotel project. The company has been working to convert a former bath house into a 51-room hotel. The hotel is expected to open in 2011.

5294 ■ "Customer Service Center Will Rise in Indian Land" in Charlotte Observer (February 4, 2007)
Pub: Knight-Ridder/Tribune Business News
Ed: Taylor Bright. **Description:** Kennametal is building a new customer service center in Lancaster County, North Carolina. Kennametal makes metal tools and parts, specializing in metals highly resistant to heat.

5295 ■ "D.A.G. Sues to Stay on Job" in Business Courier (Vol. 24, November 9, 2008, No. 30, pp. 4)
Pub: American City Business Journals, Inc.
Ed: Jon Newberry. **Description:** D.A.G. Construction Co. filed a breach of contract lawsuit against the Cincinnati Metropolitan Housing Authority. The company asked the Hamilton County Pleas Court to stop the housing authority from taking over a $10 million senior housing project. According to the company, the agency displaced D.A.G. and its subcontractors without warning.

5296 ■ "Data Center Plan Bearing Fruit From Apple, Spec Center" in Charlotte Business Journal (Vol. 25, October 15, 2010, No. 30, pp. 1)
Pub: Charlotte Business Journal
Ed: Ken Elkins. **Description:** Apple Inc. is planning to expand its server farm at the North Carolina Data Center Corridor in Catawba County. T5 Partners, on the other hand, will build a shell building to house a server on the site. Infocrossing Inc. will also build an open data center in the area.

5297 ■ "Decorated Marine Sues Contractor" in Wall Street Journal Eastern Edition (November 29, 2011, pp. A4)
Pub: Dow Jones & Company Inc. Enterprise Media Group
Contact: Clare Hart, President
Ed: Julian E. Barnes. **Description:** Marine Devon Maylie, who was awarded the Congressional Medal of Honor for bravery, has filed a lawsuit against defense contractor BAE Systems PLC claiming that the company prevented his hiring by another firm by saying he has a mental condition and a drinking problem. Maylie says that this was in retaliation for his objections to the company's plan to sell the Pakistani military high-tech sniper scopes.

5298 ■ "Deltona to Get First Movie Theater, Shopping Center" in Orlando Business Journal (Vol. 26, December 4, 2009, No. 26, pp. 1)
Pub: American City Business Journals
Ed: Anjali Fluker. **Description:** Epic Theaters Inc. revealed plans to build a new 900,000 square foot retail center anchored by a 12-screen movie theater in the city of Deltona in Volusia County, Florida by 2010. The project, dubbed Deltona Village, would provide the city with its first movie theater and shopping center.

5299 ■ "Design Programs for HVAC Sizing Solutions" in Contractor (Vol. 57, January 2010, No. 1, pp. 44)
Pub: Penton Media, Inc.
Ed: William Feldman; Patti Feldman. **Description:** Rhvac 8 is an HVAC design program that lets users calculate peak heating and cooling load requirements for rooms, zones, systems, and entire buildings. The HVAC Pipe Sizer software for the iPhone enables quick sizing of a simple piping system.

5300 ■ "Detroit Residential Market Slows; Bright Spots Emerge" in Crain's Detroit Business (Vol. 24, October 6, 2008, No. 40, pp. 11)
Pub: Crain Communications, Inc.
Ed: Daniel Duggan. **Description:** Discusses the state of the residential real estate market in Detroit; although condominium projects receive the most attention, deals for single-family homes are taking place in greater numbers due to financing issues. Buyers can purchase a single family home with a 3.5 percent down payment compared to 20 percent for some condo deals because of the number of first-time homebuyer programs under the Federal Housing Administration.

5301 ■ "Developer Banks On East Submarket, Slowdown Not a Hinderance" in The Business Journal-Serving Greater Tampa Bay (August 1, 2008)
Pub: American City Business Journals, Inc.
Ed: Janet Leiser. **Description:** CLW Industrial Group and Cobalt Industrial REIT II have teamed up to develop a 14-acre area in northeast Hillsborough County, Florida. The $15 million industrial park project includes the 175,000-square-foot New Tampa Commerce Center, scheduled for completion in the first quarter of 2009.

5302 ■ "Developer Tries to Bring Homes to Buda" in Austin Business JournalInc. (Vol. 28, December 26, 2008, No. 41, pp. 1)
Pub: American City Business Journals
Ed: Kate Harrington. **Description:** Real estate developer Jeremiah Venture LP is planning a residential, single-family development on about 600 acres near Buda, Texas. The company also plans to construct a membrane waste treatment plant, and has applied to do land application. However, several groups have come forward to ask for more information on the application due to concerns about soil density.

5303 ■ "Developers Await Hotel" in The Business Journal-Portland (Vol. 25, July 11, 2008, No. 18, pp. 1)
Pub: American City Business Journals, Inc.
Ed: Wendy Culverwell. **Description:** Developers are eager to start the construction of a new hotel at the Oregon Convention Center in Portland, Oregon as hey say that the project will help boost the convention center neighborhood. The project, called The Westin Portland at the Convention Center, is partly handled by Ashforth Pacific Inc.

5304 ■ "Developers Compete for APG Project" in Baltimore Business Journal (Vol. 27, October 16, 2009, No. 23, pp. 1)
Pub: American City Business Journals
Ed: Daniel J. Sernovitz. **Description:** Corporate Office Properties Trust has lost the case in Delaware bankruptcy court to prevent rival St. John Properties Inc. from going ahead with its plans to develop the 400 acres at Aberdeen Proving Ground (APG) in Maryland. Both developers have competed for the right to develop the two million square foot business park in APG.

5305 ■ "Developers Give Big to Mayor's Bid" in Boston Business Journal (Vol. 29, August 26, 2011, No. 16, pp. 1)
Pub: American City Business Journals Inc.
Ed: Scott Dance. **Description:** Mayor Stephanie Rawlings-Blake received thousands of dollars in her political campaign from companies of real estate developers who are vying to build key development projects in Baltimore, Maryland. Rawlings-Blake created a major fundraising advantage over other mayoral candidates with the help of those contributions.

5306 ■ "Developers Give City Dwellings a Modern Spin" in Crain's Cleveland Business (Vol. 28, November 5, 2007, No. 44, pp. 18)
Pub: Crain Communications, Inc.
Description: Cleveland is increasingly becoming a canvas for fresh, cutting-edge design due to several recent projects, some at prominent sites.

5307 ■ "Developers Poised to Pull Trigers" in Boston Business Journal (Vol. 30, November 12, 2010, No. 42, pp. 1)
Pub: Boston Business Journal
Ed: Craig M. Douglas. **Description:** Large residential projects are expected to break ground in Boston, Massachusetts in 2011, as real estate developers expect growth for the industry. Real estate experts expect more than 2,000 rental units to be available by 2011. Information on key real estate projects in Boston is presented.

5308 ■ "Developers Vie for UWM Dorm" in The Business Journal-Milwaukee (Vol. 25, July 11, 2008, No. 42, pp. A1)
Pub: American City Business Journals, Inc.
Ed: Rich Kirchen. **Description:** Eight developers are competing to build a 500- to 700-student residence hall for the University of Wisconsin-Milwaukee. The residence hall will probably be developed within two miles of the main campus. It was revealed that the university's real estate foundation will select the successful bidder on July 25, 2008, and construction will begin by January 2009.

5309 ■ "Docs Might Hold Cure for Real Estate, Banks" in Baltimore Business Journal (Vol. 28, November 5, 2010, No. 26, pp. 1)
Pub: Baltimore Business Journal
Ed: Gary Haber. **Description:** Health care providers, including physicians are purchasing their office space instead of renting it as banks lower interest rates to 6 percent on mortgages for medical offices. The rise in demand offers relief to the commercial real estate market. It has also resulted in a boom in building new medical offices.

5310 ■ "Donated Sprinkler System Honors Fallen Firefighter" in Contractor (Vol. 56, July 2009, No. 7, pp. 3)
Pub: Penton Media, Inc.
Ed: Steve Spaulding. **Description:** Capital City District Habitat for Humanity has constructed a home with a residential fire sprinkler system in honor of Ted Abriel, a firefighter who died on the job. Albany Fire Protection donated the labor for the installation of the fire sprinkler system.

5311 ■ "Downtown Light Rail Plans Up in the Air" in Business Journal Serving Greater Tampa Bay (Vol. 30, October 22, 2010, No. 44, pp. 1)
Pub: Tampa Bay Business Journal
Ed: Mark Holan. **Description:** Construction of Tampa's $2 billion light rail transit is suspended pending the result of the November 2, 2010 referendum. The routes, usage, and financing of the light rail project will be decided on the referendum. Whether the light rail will be elevated is also discussed.

5312 ■ "Drawn to York County: Less-Expensive Homes, Good Schools Attract Charlotteans" in Charlotte Observer (February 4, 2007)
Pub: Knight-Ridder/Tribune Business News
Ed: Taylor Bright. **Description:** York County, North Carolina offers low-priced homes and good schools, making it attractive to workers and small business.

5313 ■ "East Coast Solar" in Contractor (Vol. 57, February 2010, No. 2, pp. 17)
Pub: Penton Media, Inc.
Ed: Dave Yates. **Description:** U.S. Department of Energy's Solar Decathlon lets 20 college student-led teams from around the world compete to design and build a solar-powered home. A mechanical contractor discusses his work as an advisor during the competition.

5314 ■ "Eclipse to Hire 50 for Airp;ort Hangar" in Business Review, Albany New York (Vol. 34, November 9, 2007, No. 32, pp. 3)
Pub: American City Business Journals, Inc.
Ed: Robin K. Cooper. **Description:** Eclipse Aviation, a jet manufacturer will hire fifty workers who will operate its new maintenance hangar at Albany International Airport. The company was expected to hire around twenty-five employees after it announced its

plan to open one of the seven U.S. Factory Service Centers in 2005. Denise Zieske, the airport Economic Development Manager, expects the hangar construction to be completed by December 2007.

5315 ■ "Eco Smart Home Will Showcase Green Technology" in Contractor (Vol. 56, September 2009, No. 9, pp. 3)
Pub: Penton Media, Inc.
Ed: Steve Spaulding. **Description:** Eco Smart World Wide is building the Eco Smart Demonstration House to promote the latest in sustainable, renewable and high-efficiency practices and products. The company will use insulated concrete forms in the construction of the building. Features and dimensions of the structure are also presented.

5316 ■ "Economy Hammers Local Builders" in Business Courier (Vol. 24, February 8, 2008, No. 44, pp. 1)
Pub: American City Business Journals, Inc.
Ed: Laura Baverman. **Description:** Home builders in Cincinnati, Ohio, have lower revenue and smaller workforces as a result of the housing crisis and economic slowdown. Only four out of the top 25 home builders registered revenue gains, average revenue for 2007 is down 21 percent from 2006 levels, and employment declined by 37 percent from 2006.

5317 ■ "El Paso Firm Rides Boom to the Top" in Hispanic Business (Vol. 30, July-August 2008, No. 7-8, pp. 28)
Pub: Hispanic Business, Inc.
Ed: Jeremy Nisen. **Description:** VEMAC, a commercial construction management and general contracting firm that is experiencing success despite the plummeting construction market is discussed. VEMAC's success is attributed to the Pentagons' $5 billion investment in construction for the benefit of new personnel and their families to be transferred to Fort Bliss, a U.S. army base adjacent to El Paso.

5318 ■ "Energy Sparks Job Growth" in The Business Journal-Serving Greater Tampa Bay (Vol. 28, August 8, 2008, No. 33, pp. 1)
Pub: American City Business Journals, Inc.
Ed: Margie Manning. **Description:** Energy infrastructure projects in Tampa Bay, Florida, are increasing the demand for labor in the area. Energy projects requiring an increase in labor include TECO Energy Inc.'s plan for a natural gas pipeline in the area and the installation of energy management system in Bank of America's branches in the area.

5319 ■ "Entrepreneurship: As Cool As It Gets" in Canadian Business (Vol. 80, January 29, 2007, No. 3, pp. 10)
Pub: Rogers Media
Ed: Norman de Bono. **Description:** The proposed construction of a restaurant with ice in Dubai by the Canadian firm Iceculture Inc. for the Sharaf Group is discussed. The growth of the clientele of Iceculture Inc. is described.

5320 ■ "EPA 'Finalizes' WaterSense for Homes" in Contractor (Vol. 57, January 2010, No. 1, pp. 70)
Pub: Penton Media, Inc.
Ed: Bob Mader. **Description:** U.S. Environmental Protection Agency released its 'final' version of the WaterSense for Homes standard. The standard's provisions that affect plumbing contractors includes the specification that everything has to be leak tested and final service pressure cannot exceed 60 psi.

5321 ■ "EPA to Tighten Energy Star Standards for 2011" in Contractor (Vol. 56, September 2009, No. 9, pp. 6)
Pub: Penton Media, Inc.
Description: United States Environmental Protection Agency will tighten standards for its Energy Star for Homes program in 2011. The green trend in the construction industry has been cited as reason for the plan. The agency is adding requirements for energy-efficient equipment and building techniques.

5322 ■ Equipment World's Top Bid
Pub: Randall-Reilly Publishing Co.
Contact: Michael Reilly, President
E-mail: mreilly@rrpub.com.
URL(s): www.randallreilly.com. **Released:** Annual; Latest edition 2008. **Price:** $395, Individuals annual;

$269, Individuals semi-annual; $395, Individuals CD-ROM; $189, Individuals serial number book. **Publication includes:** List of suppliers of new, used, and surplus construction equipment and services. **Entries include:** Company name, address, phone, description of products or services offered. **Arrangement:** Classified by product or service. **Indexes:** Product or service, geographical.

5323 ■ "Everett Dowling" in Hawaii Business (Vol. 54, August 2008, No. 2, pp. 32)
Pub: Hawaii Business Publishing
Ed: Jason Ubay. **Description:** Real estate developer Everett Dowling, president of Dowling Company Inc., talks about the company's sustainable management and services. The company's office has been retrofitted to earn a Leadership in Energy and Environmental Design (LEED) certification. Dowling believes that real estate development can be part of the sustainable solution.

5324 ■ "Everett Hospice Planned" in Puget Sound Business Journal (Vol. 29, September 26, 2008, No. 23, pp. 1)
Pub: American City Business Journals
Ed: Peter Neurath. **Description:** Providence Senior and Community Services is pursuing a purchase-and-sales agreement for land in Everett to build a $9.7 million 20-bed hospice facility. The organization plans to break ground on the new facility in 2009.

5325 ■ "Federal Buildings to Achieve Zero-Net Energy by 2030" in Contractor (Vol. 56, December 2009, No. 12, pp. 5)
Pub: Penton Media, Inc.
Ed: Candace Roulo. **Description:** United States president Barack Obama has issued sustainable goals for federal buildings. Federal agencies are also required to increase energy efficiency, conserve water and support sustainable communities. Obama has also announced a $3.4 billion investment in a smart energy creed.

5326 ■ "Feldman Pushing Past 'Pain' of Cost Overruns, Delays at Colonie Center" in Business Review, Albany New York (November 9, 2007)
Pub: American City Business Journals, Inc.
Ed: Michael DeMasi. **Description:** Details of major improvements at Colonie Center are presented. The total cost for these projects increased by $15 million, and the construction of the nearly ten-story theater in the mall is experiencing delays. According to Larry Feldman, chairman of Feldman Mall Properties, which owns a minority stake in the mall, the cost overruns have pushed the company's renovation costs to around $85 million.

5327 ■ "Fewer People Dying At Work" in Sacramento Business Journal (Vol. 25, August 29, 2008, No. 26, pp. 1)
Pub: American City Business Journals, Inc.
Ed: Kathy Robertson. **Description:** Statistics show that workplace deaths in California dropped by 24 percent in 2007 compared with the previous year. Much of the decline was observed in the construction industry, where a slowing economy affected employment and dangerous work. The number of workplace deaths in the state also declined in all major categories except fires and explosions.

5328 ■ "Financing for NNSA Plant Is a Work in Progress" in The Business Journal-Serving Metropolitan Kansas City (October 24, 2008)
Pub: American City Business Journals, Inc.
Ed: Rob Roberts. **Description:** The Kansas City Council approved a development plan for a $500 million nuclear weapons parts plant in south Kansas City. The US Congress approved a $59 million annual lease payment to the plant's developer. Financing for the construction of the plant remains in question as the plant's developers have to shoulder construction costs.

5329 ■ "Firm Takes 'Local' Worldwide" in Hispanic Business (July-August 2007, pp. 48)
Pub: Hispanic Business
Ed: Keith Rosenblum. **Description:** Willy A. Bermello tells how he has expanded his architectural, engineering and construction firm globally.

5330 ■ "Firms Sue Doracon to Recoup More Than $1M in Unpaid Bills" in Baltimore Business Journal (Vol. 28, July 9, 2010, No. 9, pp. 1)
Pub: Baltimore Business Journal
Ed: Scott Dance. **Description:** Concrete supplier Paul J. Rach Inc., Selective Insurance Company, and equipment leasing firm Colonial Pacific Leasing Corporation intend to sue Baltimore, Maryland-based Doracon Contracting Inc. for $1 million in unpaid bills. Doracon owed Colonial Pacific $794,000 and the equipment is still in Doracon's possession. Selective Insurance and Paul J. Rach respectively seek $132,000 and $88,000.

5331 ■ "First-Time Homebuyer Credit May Add Some Momentum to Market" in Crain's Cleveland Business (Vol. 30, May 18, 2009, No. 20)
Pub: Crain Communications, Inc.
Ed: Stan Bullard. **Description:** Federal tax credits for first-time homebuyers have increased the number of homes being sold. Details of the tax credit are defined.

5332 ■ "Fogg Planning Twinsburg Warehouse Project" in Crain's Cleveland Business (Vol. 28, November 26, 2007, No. 47, pp. 6)
Pub: Crain Communications, Inc.
Ed: Stan Bullard. **Description:** Discusses such projects as the proposed 205,000-square-foot distribution center in the works by Ray Fogg Corporate Properties LLC as well as other industrial real estate developments that are looking to target tenants that need larger spaces.

5333 ■ "Food Bank to Move, Double in Size" in Austin Business Journal (Vol. 31, July 8, 2011, No. 18, pp. 1)
Pub: American City Business Journals Inc.
Ed: Sandra Zaragoza. **Description:** The Capital Area Food Bank (CAFB) of Texas intends to construct a 125,000-square-foot hub on the land it purchased in East Texas. The hub will accommodate administrative offices, warehouse and refrigeration space, and a production kitchen.

5334 ■ "For Kenwood, Cavalry Could Be Close" in Business Courier (Vol. 26, October 2, 2009, No. 23, pp. 1)
Pub: American City Business Journals, Inc.
Ed: Dan Monk. **Description:** New York-based Black-Rock Inc. is believed to be participating in the settlement liens at Kenwood Towne Place, a mixed-use development site in Cincinnati, Ohio. BlackRock may play a key role as an advisor or investor representative to an unnamed investors.

5335 ■ "Fred Weber CEO Tom Dunne: Sales Talks Confidential" in Saint Louis Business Journal (Vol. 32, September 23, 2011, No. 4, pp. 1)
Pub: Saint Louis Business Journal
Ed: Evan Binns. **Description:** Fred Weber Inc. CEO Tom Dunne Sr. signed a letter of confidentiality as part of an inquiry made by interested party to the construction company. However, Dunne denied the company is in a fire sale and has been continuing to bid for work and has not stopped securing projects.

5336 ■ "From Malls to Steel Plants" in Crain's Chicago Business (Vol. 31, April 28, 2008, No. 17, pp. 30)
Pub: Crain Communications, Inc.
Ed: Samantha Stainburn. **Description:** Profile of the company Graycor Inc. which started out as a sand-blasting and concrete-breaking firm but has grown into four businesses due to innovation and acquisitions. Graycor's businesses include: Graycor Industrial Constructors Inc., which builds and renovates power plants and steel mills; Graycor Construction Co., which erects stores, medical centers and office buildings; Graycor Blasting Co., which uses explosives and blasts tunnels for industrial cleaning, and Graycor International Inc., which provides construction services in Mexico.

5337 ■ *"Funding Drought Stalls Biotech Incubators"* in *Saint Louis Business Journal (Vol. 31, July 29, 2011, No. 49, pp. 1)*
Pub: Saint Louis Business Journal
Ed: Angela Mueller. **Description:** Economic slowdown took its toll on cash-strapped startups that fill incubators such as the Bio-Research and Development Growth (BRDG) Park in Creve Coeur, Missouri and the Center for Emerging Technologies in Midtown St. Louis. BRDG put a hold on construction of of its two buildings.

5338 ■ *"Funkhouser Wants Region to Get On Board Light Rail"* in *Business Journal-Serving Metropolitan Kansas City (November 30, 2007)*
Pub: American City Business Journals, Inc.
Ed: Suzanna Stagemeyer. **Description:** Mark Funhouser, Mayor of Kansas City, is planning to construct a regional multimodal public transit system. A previous light rail plan was rescinded due to logistical, financial and legal problems. Details of the light transit plans are discussed.

5339 ■ *"Gables Unveils Plan for Downtown Tower"* in *Austin Business JournalInc. (Vol. 28, August 8, 2008, No. 21, pp. A1)*
Pub: American City Business Journals
Ed: Jean Kwon. **Description:** Gables Residential plans to develop a residential tower with 220 units and 15,000 square feet of retail and commercial spaces in the Warehouse District in Ohio. The development is expected to start in late 2009 and be completed in 18 to 24 months.

5340 ■ *"Gateway Delays Start"* in *The Business Journal-Serving Metropolitan Kansas City (Vol. 27, October 31, 2008, No. 8, pp. 1)*
Pub: American City Business Journals, Inc.
Ed: Rob Roberts. **Description:** Economic problems caused, in part, by the Wall Street crisis has resulted in the setback of a proposed mixed-use redevelopment project, The Gateway. The $307 million project, which includes the Kansas Aquarium, will be delayed due to financing problems. Details of the project are given.

5341 ■ *"Generation Y Driving Portland Multifamily Market"* in *Daily Journal of Commerce, Portland (October 29, 2010)*
Pub: Dolan Media Newswires
Ed: Nick Bjork. **Description:** Generation Y, young adults between the ages of 18-30, are interested in multifamily residents in the Portland, Oregon area. Developers in the area, particularly North Portland, have recognized this trend and are looking into multifamily investments.

5342 ■ *"Germans Win Solar Decathlon - Again"* in *Contractor (Vol. 56, November 2009, No. 11, pp. 1)*
Pub: Penton Media, Inc.
Ed: Robert P. Mader. **Description:** Students from Technische Universtat Darmstadt won the U.S. Department of Energy's Solar Decathlon by designing and building the most attractive and efficient solar-powered home. The winner's design produced a surplus of power even during three days of rain and photovoltaic panels covered nearly every exterior surface.

5343 ■ *"Get Online Quick in the Office Or in the Field"* in *Contractor (Vol. 56, October 2009, No. 10, pp. 47)*
Pub: Penton Media, Inc.
Ed: William Feldman; Patti Feldman. **Description:** Contractors can set up a web site in minutes using the www.1and1.com website. Verizon's Novatel MIFI 2372 HSPA personal hotspot device lets contractors go online in the field. The StarTech scalable business management system helps contractors manage daily operations.

5344 ■ *"Getting in the Game"* in *Baltimore Business Journal (Vol. 27, October 16, 2009, No. 23, pp. 1)*
Pub: American City Business Journals
Ed: Ryan Sharrow. **Description:** Crystal Palace FC USA is finalizing a deal with a North Carolina development team to build a 7,000 seat stadium by early

2012 in spite of efforts by Baltimore Mayor Sheila Dixon to bring in professional soccer's DC United. The planned stadium is in the Carroll Camden Industrial area near M&T Bank Stadium. Plans for the new stadium are included.

5345 ■ *"Ghazi Insists Downtown Project Still On"* in *The Business Journal-Milwaukee (Vol. 25, August 1, 2008, No. 45, pp. A1)*
Pub: American City Business Journals, Inc.
Ed: Rich Kirchen. **Description:** Afshin Ghazi remains confident that his $200 million Catalyst project in downtown Milwaukee, Wisconsin, will push through despite financial disputes delaying his EpiCentre project in Charlotte, North Carolina. He added that the Catalyst is on schedule for groundbreaking in the spring of 2009.

5346 ■ *"Giant Garages Could Rise Up Downtown"* in *Business Courier (Vol. 27, October 22, 2010, No. 25, pp. 1)*
Pub: Business Courier
Ed: Dan Monk. **Description:** More than 2,500 new parking spaces could rise up to the eastern edge of downtown Cincinnati, Ohio as public and private investors collect resources for new garage projects. These projects are expected to accommodate almost 1,500 monthly parkers who will lose access at Broadway Commons due to the construction of Harrah's casino.

5347 ■ *"GL Homes Buys 1,000 Acres in Former Agricultural Reserve"* in *Miami Daily Business Review (March 26, 2008)*
Pub: ALM Media Inc.
Ed: Polyana da Costa. **Description:** One of the nation's largest home builders, GL Homes, purchased over 1,000 acres of agricultural land in Southern Palm Beach County, Florida. Plans for 554 residential units are detailed.

5348 ■ *"Glendale Pumping $29 Million Into Redevelopment"* in *The Business Journal - Serving Phoenix and the Valley of the Sun (Vol. 28, August 1, 2008, No. 48, pp. 1)*
Pub: American City Business Journals, Inc.
Ed: Mike Sunnucks. **Description:** Glendale City is planning to invest $29 million to improve city infrastructure like roadways and water and sewer lines over the next five years. Glendale's city council is also planning to hold a workshop on the redevelopment projects in September 2008. Other views and information on the redevelopment project, are presented.

5349 ■ *"GM's Decision to Boot Dealer Prompts Sale"* in *Baltimore Business Journal (Vol. 27, November 6, 2009, No. 26, pp. 1)*
Pub: American City Business Journals
Ed: Daniel J. Sernovitz. **Description:** General Motors Corporation's (GM) decision to strip Baltimore's Anderson Automotive Group Inc. of its GM franchise has prompted the owner, Bruce Mortimer, to close the automotive dealership and sell the land to a developer. The new project could make way for new homes, a shopping center and supermarket.

5350 ■ *"Good Track Record Helps Developer Secure Construction Loan for Offices"* in *Miami Daily Business Review (March 26, 2008)*
Pub: ALM Media Inc.
Description: Luis Lamar, developer, has secured a $64.75 million construction loan to construct a Class A office building in Kendall, Florida. Details of the loan and proposed construction are presented.

5351 ■ *"Got to be Smarter than the Average Bear"* in *Contractor (Vol. 56, September 2009, No. 9, pp. 82)*
Pub: Penton Media, Inc.
Ed: Bob Mader. **Description:** International Association of Plumbing and Mechanical Officials Green Technical Committee has debated the need for contractors to have certifications in installing green plumbing. Some have argued that qualifications would discourage homeowners from improving their properties. Comments from executives are also included.

5352 ■ *"Grainger Show Highlights Building Green, Economy"* in *Contractor (Vol. 57, February 2010, No. 2, pp. 3)*
Pub: Penton Media, Inc.
Ed: Candace Roulo. **Description:** chief U.S. economist told attendees of the Grainger's 2010 Total MRO Solutions National Customer Show that the economic recovery would be subdued. Mechanical contractors who attended the event also learned about building sustainable, green products, and technologies, and economic and business challenges.

5353 ■ *"Green Energy Exec Hits State Policy"* in *Boston Business Journal (Vol. 30, December 3, 2010, No. 45, pp. 1)*
Pub: Boston Business Journal
Ed: Kyle Alspach. **Description:** American Superconductor Corporation President Dan McGahn believes that the state government of Massachusetts is not proactive enough to develop the state into a manufacturing hub for wind power technology. McGahn believes that while Governor Deval Patrick campaigned for wind turbines in the state, his administration does not have the focus required to build the turbines in the state.

5354 ■ *"Groundbreaking 2.0"* in *Philadelphia Business Journal (Vol. 30, September 23, 2011, No. 32, pp. 1)*
Pub: American City Business Journals Inc.
Ed: Natalie Kostelni. **Description:** University Place Associates, the developer of 2.0 University Place in West Philadelphia, Pennsylvania, will break ground on a five-story, 97,000-square-foot office building in December 2011. The decision follows the Citizenship and Immigration Services signing of a 15-year lease as anchor tenant.

5355 ■ *"'Groundhog Day' B & B Likely Will Be Converted Into One In Real Life"* in *Chicago Tribune (October 21, 2008)*
Pub: McClatchy-Tribune Information Services
Ed: Carolyn Starks. **Description:** Everton Martin and Karla Stewart Martin have purchased the Victorian house that was featured as a bed-and-breakfast in the 1993 hit move 'Groundhog Day'; the couple was initially unaware of the structure's celebrity status when they purchased it with the hope of fulfilling their dream of owning a bed-and-breakfast.

5356 ■ *"Growing Pains"* in *Crain's Cleveland Business (Vol. 30, June 22, 2009, No. 24, pp. 3)*
Pub: Crain Communications, Inc.
Ed: Shannon Mortland. **Description:** Judson's latest retirement community, called South Franklin Circle, is near completion despite a faltering economy and delays. Details of the project are explored.

5357 ■ *"Habitat, Home Depot Expand Building Programs"* in *Contractor (Vol. 56, September 2009, No. 9, pp. 16)*
Pub: Penton Media, Inc.
Description: Habitat for Humanity International and The Home Depot Foundation are planning to expand their Partners in Sustainable Building program. The program will provide funds to help Habitat affiliates build 5,000 homes. Comments from executives are also included.

5358 ■ *"Hard Rock on Pike"* in *Puget Sound Business Journal (Vol. 29, September 5, 2008, No. 20, pp. 1)*
Pub: American City Business Journals
Ed: Jeanne Lang Jones. **Description:** A branch of the Hard Rock Cafe is opening in 2009 in the Liberty Building on Pike Street in downtown Seattle, Washington. The location is being renovated as a green building; the restaurant and concert venue will seat 300 patrons and has a rooftop deck and memorabilia shop.

5359 ■ *"Hard Times for Hard Money"* in *Sacramento Business Journal (Vol. 25, July 18, 2008, No. 20, pp. 1)*
Pub: American City Business Journals, Inc.
Ed: Michael Shaw. **Description:** Three private lenders who supplied $1 million sued VLD Realty, its associated companies and owners Volodymyr and Le-

onid Dubinsky accusing them of default after a plan to build two subdivisions fell through. Investigators are finding that borrowers and lenders ignored most rules on private investments on real estate.

5360 ■ *"He Has a Sky-High Outlook on His Business" in Charlotte Observer (February 4, 2007)*
Pub: Knight-Ridder/Tribune Business News
Ed: Stella M. Hopkins. **Description:** Profile of Chuck Boyle, former Army pilot; Boyle patrols over construction sites in the Charlotte, North Carolina area. The firm's team of engineers and geologists specialize in services such as: rock blasting, roads, testing concrete and other construction materials, and more.

5361 ■ *"Health-Care Highway" in Saint Louis Business Journal (Vol. 32, October 14, 2011, No. 7, pp. 1)*
Pub: Saint Louis Business Journal
Ed: Angela Mueller. **Description:** Around $2.6 billion will be invested in health care facilities along the Highway 64/40 corridor in St. Louis, Missouri. Mercy Hospital is planning to invest $19 million in a virtual care center. St. Elizabeth's Hospital on the other hand, will purchase 105 acres in the corridor.

5362 ■ *"Health Centers Plan Expansion" in Crain's Detroit Business (Vol. 25, June 15, 2009, No. 24, pp. 3)*
Pub: Crain Communications Inc. - Detroit
Ed: Jay Greene. **Description:** Detroit has five federally qualified health centers that plan to receive over $3 million in federal stimulus money that will be used to expand projects that will care for uninsured patients.

5363 ■ *"Heavy Industry" in Business North Carolina (Vol. 28, February 2008, No. 2, pp. 54)*
Pub: Business North Carolina
Ed: Arthur O. Murray. **Description:** Volvo Construction Equipment factory in Asheville, North Carolina expanded its factory that builds road-construction machinery.

5364 ■ *"Henry Ford Health Leases Lab Space at TechTown" in Crain's Detroit Business (Vol. 24, March 31, 2008, No. 13, pp. 5)*
Pub: Crain Communications, Inc.
Ed: Tom Henderson. **Description:** Henry Ford Health System has signed a seven-year lease at TechTown, the high-tech incubator and research park affiliated with Wayne State University, to take over 14,000 square feet of space for four research groups and laboratories. Construction has already begun and Henry Ford officials hope to take occupancy as early as June 1.

5365 ■ *"High Hopes: Ralph Mitchell's Picks Have Growth Potential" in Black Enterprise (Vol. 37, February 2007, No. 7, pp. 42)*
Pub: Earl G. Graves Publishing Co. Inc.
Ed: Carolyn M. Brown. **Description:** Ralph Mitchell, president and senior financial advisor of Braintree-Carthage Financial Group, offers three recommendations: Toll Brothers, Home Depot, and Lowe's.

5366 ■ *"Higher Thread Count for Metropole" in Business Courier (Vol. 26, September 25, 2009, No. 22, pp. 1)*
Pub: American City Business Journals, Inc.
Ed: Lisa Biank Fasig, Lucy May. **Description:** Cincinnati Center City Development Corporation is under contract to buy the 225-unit apartment building called Metropole Apartments and 21c Museum Hotel is the lead candidate for the space. Advocates of some residents of the low-income rental complex complain that this move could leave them homeless.

5367 ■ *"Historic Tax Credit Plan Gains Support" in Baltimore Business Journal (Vol. 27, January 8, 2010, No. 36, pp. 1)*
Pub: American City Business Journals
Ed: Heather Harlan Warnack. **Description:** Maryland Governor Martin O'Malley plans to push legislation in the General Assembly to extend for three more years the tax credit program for rehabilitation of obsolete buildings. The Maryland Heritage Structure Rehabilitation Tax Credit Program has declined from almost

$75 million in expenses in 2001 to roughly $5 million in 2010 fiscal year. Details on the projects that benefited from the program are explored.

5368 ■ *"HOK Sport May Build Own Practice" in The Business Journal-Serving Metropolitan Kansas City (Vol. 26, August 29, 2008, No. 51, pp. 1)*
Pub: American City Business Journals, Inc.
Ed: Rob Roberts. **Description:** HOK Sport Venue Event is considering a spin-off from its parent company, HOK Group Inc. HOK Sport spokeswoman Gina Leo confirms that the firm is exploring structures, including a management buyout. Some of HOK Sport Venue Event's Minnesota projects are discussed.

5369 ■ *"Hollander 95 Project Getting Bigger" in Boston Business Journal (Vol. 29, September 23, 2011, No. 20, pp. 1)*
Pub: American City Business Journals Inc.
Ed: Gary Haber. **Description:** Hollander 95 Business Park is in for a huge change as its new owners plan a $50 million expansion which calls for building as many as eight more buildings or a total of more than 500,000 square feed. FRP Development bought the site for $4.35 million at a foreclosure sale in July 2010 and is now seeking city approval for an Industrial Planned Unit Development designation.

5370 ■ *"Home Builder, Four Others, Face Sentencing" in Business Courier (Vol. 27, November 26, 2010, No. 30, pp. 1)*
Pub: Business Courier
Ed: Jon Newberry. **Description:** Home builder Bernie Kurlemann was convicted on November 10, 2010 on six felony counts and faces up to 65 years in prison due to his part in a 2006 Warren County mortgage fraud scheme. Four other business people have pleaded guilty to related charges, and all are awaiting sentencing in early 2011.

5371 ■ *"A Home of Her Own" in Hawaii Business (Vol. 53, October 2007, No. 4, pp. 51)*
Pub: Hawaii Business Publishing
Ed: Maria Torres-Kitamura. **Description:** It was observed that the number of single women in Hawaii purchasing their own home has increased, as that in the whole United States where the percentage has increased from 14 percent in 1995 to 22 percent in 2006. However, First Hawaiian Bank's Wendy Lum thinks that the trend will not continue in Hawaii due to lending restrictions. The factors that women consider in buying a home of their own are presented.

5372 ■ *"Home Prices Sag" in Crain's Chicago Business (Vol. 31, April 28, 2008, No. 17, pp. 3)*
Pub: Crain Communications, Inc.
Ed: Alby Gallun. **Description:** Since the slump in the housing market is continuing with no sign of recovery, Chicago-area home prices are poised for an even steeper drop this year. In 2007, the region's home prices fell nearly 5 percent and according to a forecast by Fiserv Inc., they will decline 8.1 percent this year and another 2.2 percent in 2009. Statistical data included.

5373 ■ *"Home Sprinklers Blocked in Texas, Long Beach, California" in Contractor (Vol. 56, July 2009, No. 7, pp. 1)*
Pub: Penton Media, Inc.
Ed: Robert P. Mader. **Description:** Long Beach, California has exempted older residential high rises and large apartment complexes from a rule to install fire sprinkler systems. Texas has also prohibited municipalities from enacting residential sprinkler ordinances.

5374 ■ *"Homebuilders Continue to be Our Nemesis" in Contractor (Vol. 56, July 2009, No. 7, pp. 50)*
Pub: Penton Media, Inc.
Ed: Bob Mader. **Description:** Homebuilders rank high on the greed scale along with Wall Street brokers. There is this one instance when a builder gave copies of another contractor's quotes that have

just been blackened out and another instance when one builder let other bidders visit a site while the current mechanical contractor is working.

5375 ■ *"Homing In On the Future" in Black Enterprise (Vol. 38, October 2007, No. 3, pp. 61)*
Pub: Earl G. Graves Publishing Co. Inc.
Ed: Sean Drakes. **Description:** More and more people are wanting new homes wired automated systems that integrate multiple home devices such as computers, audio/visual entertainment, security, communications, utilities, and lighting and environmental controls.

5376 ■ *"Honcoop Honored as BIAWC's Builder of the Year" in Bellingham Business Journal (Vol. February 2010, pp. 17)*
Pub: Sound Publishing Inc.
Description: Gary Honcoop, co-owner and president of Roosendaal-Honcoop Construction Inc. was honored by the Building Industry Association of Whatcom County as Builder of the Year. The construction company was founded in 1979.

5377 ■ *"Hospital to Get $72M Makeover" in Austin Business JournalInc. (Vol. 29, January 15, 2010, No. 45, pp. 1)*
Pub: American City Business Journals
Ed: Sandra Zaragoza. **Description:** St. David's South Austin Medical Center, formerly St. David's South Austin Hospital, is undertaking an expansion and renovation project worth $72 million. Meanwhile, CEO Erol Akdamar has resigned to serve as CEO of Medical City Hospital in Dallas, Texas. A new CEO and a general contractor for the project are yet to be chosen by the hospital.

5378 ■ *"Hospital Jobs" in Baltimore Business Journal (Vol. 28, June 25, 2010, No. 7, pp. 1)*
Pub: Baltimore Business Journal
Ed: Scott Graham. **Description:** Greater Baltimore, Maryland has four hospitals that are in the middle of transforming their campuses with new facilities for treating various patients. Construction at Mercy Medical Center, Johns Hopkins Hospital, Franklin Square Hospital and Anne Rundle Hospital has helped bring the construction industry back to life. Insights into the hiring plans of these hospitals are also included.

5379 ■ *"Hospital Pegged for Lakeway" in Austin Business JournalInc. (Vol. 28, August 8, 2008, No. 21, pp. A1)*
Pub: American City Business Journals
Ed: Kate Harrington. **Description:** Views and information on the development of the Lakeway Regional Medical Center in Texas, are presented. The hospital, which is expected to cost more than $250 million, will include 244,000 square feet of medical space. Shops, offices, hike-and-bike trails are also planned around hospital.

5380 ■ *"Hotel Woes Reflect Area Struggle" in Business Journal Serving Greater Tampa Bay (Vol. 30, December 3, 2010, No. 50, pp. 1)*
Pub: Tampa Bay Business Journal
Ed: Mark Holan. **Description:** Quality Inn and Suites in East Tampa, Florida has struggled against the sluggish economy but remained open to guests despite facing a foreclosure. The hotel project is the center of East Tampa's redevelopment plans and public officials defend the $650,000 investment in public amenities near the building.

5381 ■ *"Housing Slide Picks Up Speed" in Crain's Chicago Business (Vol. 31, April 21, 2008, No. 16, pp. 2)*
Pub: Crain Communications, Inc.
Ed: Eddie Baeb. **Description:** According to Tracy Cross & Associates Inc., a real estate consultancy, sales of new homes in the Chicago area dropped 61 percent from the year-earlier period which is more bad news for homebuilders, contractors and real estate agents who are eager for an indication that market conditions are improving.

5382 ■ *"How I Did It: Mel Zuckerman" in Inc. (December 2007, pp. 140-142)*
Pub: Gruner & Jahr USA Publishing
Ed: Daniel McGinn. **Description:** Profile of Mel Zuckerman, who tells how transformed his life as a middle-

aged, overweight homebuilder to a healthy addition to the fitness and spa industry with his posh Canyon Ranch retreats.

5383 ■ *"Hydronicahh - Everything in Modulation"* **in Contractor (Vol. 56, December 2009, No. 12, pp. 24)**
Pub: Penton Media, Inc.
Ed: Mark Eatherton. **Description:** Management and the environmental impact of a home hydronic system are discussed. Radiant windows have the potential to reduce energy consumption. A variable speed delta T pump is required for the construction of a hydronic wood pit.

5384 ■ *"IAPMO GTC Votes to Limit Showers to 2.0-GPM"* **in Contractor (Vol. 56, September 2009, No. 9, pp. 1)**
Pub: Penton Media, Inc.
Ed: Robert P. Mader. **Description:** Green Technical Committee of the International Association of Plumbing and Mechanical Officials has voted to limit showers to 2.0 GPM. It is also developing a Green Plumbing and Mechanical Supplement. Comments from executives are also supplied.

5385 ■ *"ICC Works on Prescriptive Green Construction Code"* **in Contractor (Vol. 56, October 2009, No. 10, pp. 1)**
Pub: Penton Media, Inc.
Ed: Robert P. Mader. **Description:** International Code Council launched an initiative to create a green construction code that focuses on existing commercial buildings. The initiative's timeline will include public meetings leading up to a final draft that will be available in 2010.

5386 ■ *"Illinois Residential Building Legislation Includes New HVAC Requirements"* **in Contractor (Vol. 56, July 2009, No. 7, pp. 3)**
Pub: Penton Media, Inc.
Ed: Candace Roulo. **Description:** Illinois' Energy Efficient Building Act will require all new buildings and houses to conform to the International Energy Conservation Code. The code includes a duct leakage requirement followed by a post-construction test to verify leakage rates and requires programmable thermostats on all houses.

5387 ■ *"IMRA's Ultrafast Lasers Bring Precision, profits; Ann Arbor Company Eyes Expansion"* **in Crain's Detroit Business (March 10, 2008)**
Pub: Crain Communications, Inc.
Ed: Tom Henderson. **Description:** IMRA America Inc. plans to expand its headquarters and has applied for permits to build a fourth building that will house research and development facilities and allow the company more room for manufacturing; the company plans to add about 20 more employees that would include research scientists, manufacturing and assembly workers, engineers and salespeople. The growth is due mainly to a new technology of ultrafast fiber lasers that reduce side effects for those getting eye surgeries and help manufacturers of computer chips to reduce their size and cost.

5388 ■ *"Incentives Debate Rages On Unabated"* **in The Business Journal-Serving Metropolitan Kansas City (Vol. 26, September 5, 2008, No. 52)**
Pub: American City Business Journals, Inc.
Ed: Rob Roberts. **Description:** Debate on the new economic development and incentives policy adopted by the Kansas City Council is still on. The city's Planned Industrial Expansion Authority has rejected a standard property tax abatement proposal. The real estate development community has opposed the rejection of proposed the tax incentives policy.

5389 ■ *"Increased Competition Prompts Detroit Hotels to Make Upgrades"* **in Crain's Detroit Business (Vol. 24, March 31, 2008, No. 13, pp. 1)**
Pub: Crain Communications, Inc.
Ed: Daniel Duggan. **Description:** Five Detroit hotels have recently undergone upgrades or are preparing for major construction projects due to a more competitive hospitality market in the city.

5390 ■ *"Increasing Building Work at Ryan Cos."* **in Crain's Chicago Business (Vol. 34, May 23, 2011, No. 21, pp. 6)**
Pub: Crain Communications Inc.
Ed: Eddie Baeb. **Description:** Profile of Tim Hennelly, who is working to make Ryan Company known as a pure builder rather than a developer-builder.

5391 ■ *"Independence Station Utilizes Sustainable Technologies"* **in Contractor (Vol. 56, September 2009, No. 9, pp. 3)**
Pub: Penton Media, Inc.
Ed: Candace Ruolo. **Description:** Independence Station building in Oregon is seen to receive the most LEED points ever awarded by the United States Green Building Council. The building will use an ice-based cooling storage system, biofuel cogeneration system and phovoltaic system. Other building features and dimensions are also supplied.

5392 ■ *"Independence's Day Keeps on Getting Brighter"* **in Business Courier (Vol. 27, June 11, 2010, No. 6, pp. 1)**
Pub: Business Courier
Ed: Lucy May. **Description:** Reports show that residential and commercial development continues in Independence, Kentucky despite the recession, with a 144-unit apartment complex under construction. The city recorded 152 new-home closings in 2009, or 25 percent of all new homes closed in Boone, Campbell, and Kenton counties.

5393 ■ *Innovation in Small Construction Firms*
Pub: Taylor & Francis Group
Contact: Peter Rigby, Chief Executive Officer
Ed: Peter Barrett. **Released:** March 2008. **Price:** $120.00. **Description:** Examination into the ways construction firms can introduce innovation into working practices in order to meet the demands of this rapidly changing industry.

5394 ■ *"Intel: Tax Breaks Key"* **in Business Journal Portland (Vol. 27, October 22, 2010, No. 34, pp. 1)**
Pub: Portland Business Journal
Ed: Erik Siemers. **Description:** Intel Corporation believes that state tax incentives will be critical, especially in the purchase of manufacturing equipment, as they build a new chip factory in Hillsboro, Oregon. The tax breaks would help Intel avoid paying 10 times more in property taxes compared to average Washington County firms. Critics argue that Intel has about $15 billion in cash assets, and can afford the factory without the tax breaks.

5395 ■ *"Iogen in Talks to Build Ethanol Plant in Canada"* **in Globe & Mail (March 21, 2007, pp. B7)**
Pub: CTVglobemedia Publishing Inc.
Ed: Shawn McCarthy. **Description:** Ottawa based Iogen Corp. is planning to construct a cellulosic ethanol plant in Saskatchewan region. The company will be investing an estimated $500 million for this purpose.

5396 ■ *"It's Not Easy Being Small"* **in Baltimore Business Journal (Vol. 27, October 9, 2009, No. 22, pp. 1)**
Pub: American City Business Journals
Ed: Scott Dance. **Description:** A look at how small businesses were left out of the stimulus-funded federal contracts in Maryland. Small contractors were not listed in the federal contracts database USAspending.gov and none were hired for work in the state.

5397 ■ *"It's What You Know. It's Who You Know. It's China"* **in Inc. (Vol. 33, October 2011, No. 8, pp. 80)**
Pub: Inc. Magazine
Ed: David H. Freedman. **Description:** Michael Lee will be the first American entrepreneur to build big in China. The company is piloting two large commercial real estate developments, one in New York City the other in Nanjing, China.

5398 ■ *"J.C. Evans Seeks Bankruptcy Protection"* **in Austin Business Journal (Vol. 31, August 12, 2011, No. 23, pp. A1)**
Pub: American City Business Journals Inc.
Ed: Vicky Garza. **Description:** J.C. Evans Construction Holdings Inc., as well as its affiliated companies, has filed for Chapter 11 bankruptcy following its continued financial breakdown which it blames on the tough economy. Details are included.

5399 ■ *"Jennifer Hernandez Helps Developers Transform Contaminated Properties"* **in Hispanic Business (Vol. 30, April 2008, No. 4, pp. 32)**
Pub: Hispanic Business
Ed: Hildy Medina. **Description:** Jennifer Hernandez is a partner and head of the law firm of Holland & Knight's environmental practice which specializes in the restoration of polluted land where former industrial and commercial buildings once stood, known as brownfields. Brownfield redevelopment can be lucrative but costly due to the cleaning up of contaminated land and challenging because of federal and state environmental laws.

5400 ■ *"Joint Venture Plans Bronzeville Project"* **in Business Journal-Milwaukee (Vol. 25, October 5, 2007, No. 1, pp. A1)**
Pub: American City Business Journals, Inc.
Ed: Rich Kirchen. **Description:** Proposal for construction of an apartment building and possible expansion of Northtown Mall in Milwaukee, Wisconsin is being planned by developers in the city's Bronzeville area. The project for rehabilitating the existing mall and building of a 50-unit apartment would amount to about $12.5 million.

5401 ■ *"Kenosha 'Lifestyle Center' Delayed"* **in The Business Journal-Milwaukee (Vol. 25, August 8, 2008, No. 46, pp. A1)**
Pub: American City Business Journals, Inc.
Ed: Rich Kirchen. **Description:** Quality Centers of Orlando, Florida has postponed construction plans for the Kenosha Town Center in Kenosha County, Wisconsin to 2009 due to the economic downturn and lending concerns. The $200-million, 750,000-square-foot retail and residential center will be located near the corner of Wisconsin Highway 50 and I-94.

5402 ■ *"Kimball Hill Files for Chapter 11"* **in Crain's Chicago Business (Vol. 31, April 28, 2008, No. 17, pp. 12)**
Pub: Crain Communications, Inc.
Description: Homebuilder Kimball Hill filed for Chapter 11 bankruptcy protection after months of negotiations with lenders. The firm plans to continue operations as it restructures its debt.

5403 ■ *"Kroger Forges Ahead with Fuel Centers"* **in Business Courier (Vol. 26, December 25, 2009, No. 35, pp. 1)**
Pub: American City Business Journals, Inc.
Ed: Jon Newberry. **Description:** Cincinnati-based grocery chain Kroger Company plans to construct more fuel centers near supermarkets and food stores despite declining profit margins in gasoline sales. Statistical data included.

5404 ■ *"KXAN Seeks Larger Studio, Office Space"* **in Austin Business Journal (Vol. 31, May 27, 2011, No. 12, pp. A1)**
Pub: American City Business Journals Inc.
Ed: Cody Lyon. **Description:** Austin NBC affiliate KXAN Television is opting to sell its property north of downtown and relocate to another site. The station is now inspecting possible sites to house its broadcasting facility and employees totaling as many as 200 people. Estimated cost of the construction of the studios and offices is $13 million plus another million in moving the equipment.

5405 ■ *"LA Passes HET Ordinance, California Greens Code"* **in Contractor (Vol. 56, September 2009, No. 9, pp. 1)**
Pub: Penton Media, Inc.
Ed: Candace Ruolo. **Description:** Los Angeles City Council has passed a Water Efficiency Requirements ordinance. The law mandates lower low-flow plumb-

ing requirements for plumbing fixtures installed in new buildings and retrofits. Under the ordinance, a toilet's maximum flush volume may not exceed 1.28-gpf.

5406 ■ "Land Swap Key to Ending Royal Oak Project Impasse" in Crain's Detroit Business (Vol. 25, June 8, 2009, No. 23, pp. 20)
Pub: Crain Communications Inc. - Detroit
Ed: Chad Halcom. **Description:** Details of the new construction of the LA Fitness health club near Woodward and Washington Avenues in Royal Oak, Michigan are discussed.

5407 ■ "Large Homes can be Energy Efficient Too" in Contractor (Vol. 56, October 2009, No. 10, pp. 5)
Pub: Penton Media, Inc.
Ed: Candace Roulo. **Description:** Eco Estate at Briggs Chaney subdivision in Silver Spring, Maryland has model houses that use sustainable technologies and products and the homes that will be built on the subdivision will feature some of the technologies featured on the model home. The energy efficient HVAC system of the model homes are discussed.

5408 ■ "The Latest on E-Verify" in Contractor (Vol. 56, September 2009, No. 9, pp. 58)
Pub: Penton Media, Inc.
Ed: Susan McGreevy. **Description:** United States government has required federal contractors to use its E-Verify program to verify the eligibility of incoming and existent employees. The use of the program is seen to eliminate Social Security mismatches.

5409 ■ "Latest Falls, Ontario Hotel Will Be 25-Story Westin" in Business First Buffalo (October 19, 2007, pp. 1)
Pub: American City Business Journals, Inc.
Ed: James Fink. **Description:** Niagara Falls, Ontario-based Canadian Niagara Hotels has announced the construction of a Westin Hotel on Robinson Street that is 25-stories high and has 518 suites starting in 2008. The scope of the $120 million construction project is expected to be completed in 2010.

5410 ■ "Latest Volley Tries to Press Port Group" in Business Courier (Vol. 26, November 20, 2009, No. 30, pp. 1)
Pub: American City Business Journals, Inc.
Ed: Dan Monk. **Description:** Subcontractors filed a new legal argument to force the Port of Greater Cincinnati Development Authority to pursue default claim against Bank of America. The bank issued letters of credit to guarantee bond payments in addition to holding the mortgage of the Kenwood Towne Place. Details of the claim are discussed.

5411 ■ "Laugh or Cry?" in Barron's (Vol. 88, March 24, 2008, No. 12, pp. 7)
Pub: Dow Jones & Company, Inc.
Ed: Alan Abelson. **Description:** Discusses the American economy which is just starting to feel the effect of the credit and housing crises. JPMorgan Chase purchased Bear Stearns for $2 a share, much lower than its share price of $60, while quasi-government entities Fannie Mae and Freddie Mac are starting to run into trouble.

5412 ■ "Legislature Passes Increased Tax Credit for Urban Brownfield Projects" in Crain's Detroit Business (Vol. 24, March 31, 2008, No. 13)
Pub: Crain Communications, Inc.
Ed: Amy Lane. **Description:** Discusses the bill passed by the Legislature that creates a tax credit of up to 20 percent for projects in urban development areas.

5413 ■ "Legoland Florida Theme Park Construction to Start in May" in Orlando Business Journal (Vol. 26, January 29, 2010, No. 35, pp. 1)
Pub: American City Business Journals
Ed: Richard Bilbao. **Description:** Merlin Entertainments Group purchased the closed Cypress Garden theme park in Winter Haven, Florida for $22.3 million and plans to spend a reported $100 million or more

to begin transforming it into the world's largest Legoland. Winter Haven businesses are expecting a windfall from the theme park's constructions workers.

5414 ■ "Lenders" in The Business Journal - Serving Phoenix and the Valley of the Sun (Vol. 28, July 25, 2008, No. 47, pp. 1)
Pub: American City Business Journals, Inc.
Ed: Jan Buchholz. **Description:** Private equity lender Investor Mortgage Holdings Inc. has continued growing despite the crisis surrounding the real estate and financial industries and has accumulated a $700 million loan portfolio. Private lending has become increasingly important in financing real estate deals as commercial credit has dried up.

5415 ■ "Lending Door Slams" in Puget Sound Business Journal (Vol. 29, October 24, 2008, No. 27, pp. 1)
Pub: American City Business Journals
Ed: Jeanne Lang Jones, Kirsten Grind. **Description:** KeyBank's closure of its Puget Sound unit that services single-family homebuilders is part of a nationwide shutdown that includes similar closures in other cities. Bank of America is adopting more conservative terms for homebuilding loans while Union Bank of California is still offering credit for market rate housing.

5416 ■ "Long Live Rock" in Inc. (November 2007, pp. 130)
Pub: Gruner & Jahr USA Publishing
Ed: Nitasha Tiku. **Description:** Profile of a family business using chemistry to recycle concrete products.

5417 ■ "Loop 360 Offices Planned" in Austin Business JournalInc. (Vol. 28, December 5, 2008, No. 38, pp. A1)
Pub: American City Business Journals
Ed: Kate Harrington. **Description:** Nearly 356,000 square feet of office space is planned in the South Capital of Texas Highway Corridor, also known as Loop 360 in Austin. Riverside Developers plans to wait until the economy improves before starting construction.

5418 ■ "Major Advances in Heat Pump Technology" in Contractor (Vol. 57, January 2010, No. 1, pp. 42)
Pub: Penton Media, Inc.
Ed: Mark Eatherton. **Description:** Tax credits make ground-source heat pump technology more economically feasible. Suggestions on how to choose the right ground-source heat pump technology to install in a house are discussed.

5419 ■ "Major Renovation Planned for Southridge" in Business Journal-Milwaukee (Vol. 28, November 12, 2010, No. 6, pp. A1)
Pub: Milwaukee Business Journal
Ed: Stacy Vogel Davis. **Description:** Simon Property Group plans to invest more than $20 million in upgrading and renovating Southridge Mall in Milwaukee County, Wisconsin. The project, which is partially financed by a $10 million grant from the Village of Greendale, could boost the property's value by $52.5 million.

5420 ■ "Mann to Lead Builders" in Charlotte Observer (January 31, 2007)
Pub: Knight-Ridder/Tribune Business News
Ed: Allen Norwood. **Description:** Elliot Mann of Standard Pacific Homes was sworn in as president of Home Builders Association of Charlotte, North Carolina.

5421 ■ "Marine Act Amendments Gain Parliamentary Approval" in Canadian Sailings (July 7, 2008)
Pub: UBM Global Trade
Contact: Leonard J. Corallo, President
Ed: Alex Binkley. **Description:** Changes to the Canada Marine Act provides better borrowing deals as well as an ability to tap into federal infrastructure funding for environmental protection measures, security improvements and other site enhancements.

5422 ■ "Martin Marietta Expands Rock Solid Port Manatee Presence" in Tampa Bay Business Journal (Vol. 30, January 8, 2010, No. 3, pp. 1)
Pub: American City Business Journals
Ed: Jane Meinhardt. **Description:** Raleigh, North Carolina-based Martin Marietta Materials Inc. has been granted by Florida's Manatee County Port Authority with a 30-year, $42 million contract. Through the contract, an aggregate terminal will be built by Martin Marietta at the port. Construction work is anticipated to start in earl 2010 with terminal operations commencing by late summer 2010.

5423 ■ "McDonald's Founders Fund $80 Million Project" in The Business Journal - Serving Phoenix and the Valley of the Sun (Vol. 28, September 12, 2008, No. 53, pp. 1)
Pub: American City Business Journals, Inc.
Ed: Jan Buchholz. **Description:** Construction will begin in early 2009 on an $80 million Ray and Joan Kroc Community Center in Phoenix, Arizona. It will be located adjacent to the Salvation Army, which received a $1.9 billion contribution from Joan Kroc after her death in 2003. This fund will be divided to construct 30 community centers across the country.

5424 ■ "Medical Office Developers To Merge November 1" in The Business Journal - Serving Phoenix and the Valley of the Sun (Vol. 29, September 26, 2008, No. 4, pp. 1)
Pub: American City Business Journals, Inc.
Ed: Angela Gonzales. **Description:** Ensemble Real Estate Services LLC and DevMan Co. will merge effective November 1, 2008 and will call the firm Ensemble DevMan of Arizona after the merger. The two companies will combine their resources and expertise on planned projects that include the Phoenix Children's Hospital's Specialty Clinic and Banner Ironwood Medical Office Building.

5425 ■ "Mequon Plan On Tracks, Bucks Housing Trend" in The Business Journal-Milwaukee (Vol. 25, September 26, 2008, No. 53, pp. A1)
Pub: American City Business Journals, Inc.
Ed: Pete Millard. **Description:** Insight Development Group plans to build condominium units and single-family homes despite the residential market downturn. The Orchard Glen project, a planned development in Mequon, is a $22 million project which will include 38 condos and 12 single-family homes. Details of the project are provided.

5426 ■ "Merchants Association Working on Deal for Large Wholesale Warehouse" in Austin Business JournalInc. (September 19, 2008)
Pub: American City Business Journals
Ed: Jean Kwon. **Description:** Greater Austin Merchants Association planning to buy a former Dell Outlet Factory in Austin, Texas and convert it into a warehouse for convenience stores and gas stations.

5427 ■ Metal Construction News--Metal Architecture Building Systems Product File and Directory Issue
Pub: Modern Trade Communications Inc.
URL(s): www.moderntrade.com. **Ed:** Shawn Zuver. **Released:** Annual; January. **Price:** C$60, Canada and Mexico; $140, Other countries. **Publication includes:** List of more than 990 manufacturers and suppliers of building components and accessories, insulation, doors and frames, mechanical products, cranes, manufacturing and construction equipment; nearly 90 steel erectors; and about 35 industry associations. **Entries include:** Company or association name, address, phone, contacts. Listings for associations also include trade show and convention dates; erector listings include geographic areas served; other listings include product information. **Arrangement:** Separate alphabetical sections for manufacturers/suppliers, erectors, and associations. **Indexes:** Product (manufacturers and suppliers).

5428 ■ "Midtown Tampa Bay Taking Shape" in The Business Journal-Serving Greater

Tampa Bay (Vol. 28, September 12, 2008, No. 38, pp. 1)
Pub: American City Business Journals, Inc.
Ed: Janet Leiser. **Description:** Midtown Tampa Bay's 610,000 square foot shopping and entertainment center is being planned in Florida and is to replace the Tampa Bay One project proposed years earlier. The retail center is to be developed by Bromley Cos. and Opus South Corp. and is expected to have five buildings. Other details about the plan are discussed.

5429 ■ *"Military Center a Go" in Austin Business JournalInc. (Vol. 29, December 11, 2009, No. 40, pp. 1)*
Pub: American City Business Journals
Ed: Kate Harrington. **Description:** The $40 million Armed Forces Guard and Reserve Center project at Austin-Bergstrom International Airport has resumed work after a delay of several years. The project is in both the House and Senate versions of the fiscal 2010 Military Construction and Veterans Appropriations Bill that would earmark $16.5 million for the center and $5.7 million for the maintenance facility. Details of construction plans are covered.

5430 ■ *"Minnesota ABC Event Looks at Government Contracting" in Finance and Commerce Daily Newspaper (November 23, 2010)*
Pub: Dolan Media Newswires
Ed: Brian Johnson. **Description:** Minnesota Associated Builders and Contractors hosted an event focusing on doing business with government agencies. Topics included bidding work, awarding jobs, paperwork, guidelines, certifications and upcoming projects.

5431 ■ *"Minor-League Baseball's Sliders Plan Stock Offering" in Crain's Detroit Business (Vol. 25, June 15, 2009, No. 24, pp. 3)*
Pub: Crain Communications Inc. - Detroit
Ed: Bill Shea. **Description:** New minor-league baseball team is raising funds to build a new stadium in Waterford Township, Michigan because banks are unwilling to provide loans for the project. Owners of the Midwest Sliders in Ypsilanti, Michigan are waiting for the federal Securities and Exchange Commission to approve a Regulation A public offering.

5432 ■ *"A Model Development" in Crain's Cleveland Business (Vol. 28, October 1, 2007, No. 39, pp. 12)*
Pub: Crain Communications, Inc.
Description: Profile a Forest City Enterprises Inc., a firm that is developing a project in New Mexico called Mesa del Sol. The Albuquerque development is being seen as the vanguard of master-planned communities with its high-tech economic development center which is expected to become the site of 60,000 jobs, 38,000 homes and a town center.

5433 ■ *"Modular Home Center Opens in Arcadia" in Charlotte Observer (February 1, 2007)*
Pub: Knight-Ridder/Tribune Business News
Ed: John Lawhorne. **Description:** Arcadia Home Center features modular homes constructed on a steel frame; regulations regarding the manufacture and moving of these homes are included.

5434 ■ *"The Money Train: How Public Projects Shape Our Economic Future" in Hawaii Business (Vol. 54, September 2008, No. 3, pp. 31)*
Pub: Hawaii Business Publishing
Ed: Jason Ubay. **Description:** Public projects impact the construction industry as such projects create jobs and new infrastructure that can lead to private developments. Details on the government contracts and construction projects in Hawaii and their rising costs and impact on the state's economy are discussed.

5435 ■ *"More Contractors Unpaid" in Puget Sound Business Journal (Vol. 29, October 3, 2008, No. 24, pp. 1)*
Pub: American City Business Journals
Ed: Brad Berton. **Description:** An 80 percent rise in the filing of mechanics' liens was reported in Seattle, Washington. It is believed that financial problems are

spreading to construction companies and contractors as home sales slide and builders default on construction loans. Delinquencies of single-family construction homes has increased.

5436 ■ *"More Details Emerge on Maersk Plan" in Charlotte Business Journal (Vol. 25, August 13, 2010, No. 21, pp. 1)*
Pub: Charlotte Business Journal
Ed: Will Boye. **Description:** Children Klen Properties has announced the details of its redevelopment plan for a property in Charlotte, North Carolina. The plan includes office and retail space and residential units. The construction of a hotel has also been proposed.

5437 ■ *"More Gains in the Pipeline" in Barron's (Vol. 89, August 3, 2009, No. 31, pp. M5)*
Pub: Dow Jones & Co., Inc.
Ed: Fleming Meeks. **Description:** Shares of El Paso Corp. could recover as the company concludes a deal with a private-equity group to fund pipeline construction. The company's shares are trading at $10.06 and could move up to $12 as bad news has already been priced into the stock.

5438 ■ *"Museum Center to Exhibit New Look" in Business Courier (Vol. 24, February 22, 2008, No. 46, pp. 1)*
Pub: American City Business Journals, Inc.
Ed: Dan Monk. **Description:** Discusses a $120 million renovation is being planned for the Cincinnati Museum Center complex at Union Terminal. The project aims to build a 14-acre park and office spaces in the area. Details of the Museum Center's renovation plans are given.

5439 ■ *"A Necessary Balancing Act: Bookkeeping" in Contractor (Vol. 56, November 2009, No. 11, pp. 22)*
Pub: Penton Media, Inc.
Ed: Al Schwartz. **Description:** Pros and cons of getting a bookkeeper or a certified public accountant for the subcontractor are discussed. A bookkeeper can help a subcontractor get new accounting software up and running while an accountant will more than likely keep after the books at regular intervals throughout the year.

5440 ■ *"New-Home Sales Grab a Foothold With Q2 Boost" in Sacramento Business Journal (Vol. 25, July 11, 2008, No. 19, pp. 1)*
Pub: American City Business Journals, Inc.
Ed: Michael Shaw. **Description:** Statistics show that homebuilders in Sacramento, California experienced an increase in new-home sales during the second quarter of 2008. It was also reported that builders moved more homes without slashing prices significantly. Barry Grant, president of KB Home's Sacramento division, believes that the improvement is caused by the stability in the supply of resale homes.

5441 ■ *"New Hydronic Heating Technologies Work" in Contractor (Vol. 57, January 2010, No. 1, pp. 58)*
Pub: Penton Media, Inc.
Ed: Carol Fey. **Description:** Technology behind hydronic heating systems is reviewed. These technologies include radiant and geothermal hydronic heating. System requirements for installing these greener forms of heating are discussed.

5442 ■ *"New ICA, Ex-Builder Tangle Over Construction" in Boston Business Journal (Vol. 27, October 12, 2007, No. 37, pp. 1)*
Pub: American City Business Journals Inc.
Ed: Michelle Hillman. **Description:** Now-defunct George B.H. Macomber Company is suing the Institute of Contemporary Art (ICA) in Boston, Massachusetts as it believes that it has done extra work worth more than $6.6 million that was not included in the original contract with the construction of the museum. A series of setbacks and minor repairs has caused delays in the opening of the ICA, which was further complicated when Macomber began having financial difficulties.

5443 ■ *"New State Rules Require Cranes and Operators to be Certified" in Bellingham Business Journal (Vol. February 2010, pp. 11)*
Pub: Sound Publishing Inc.
Ed: Isaac Bonnell. **Description:** All construction cranes in Washington state must be inspected annually to be certified for use. The move is part of a larger L&I crane safety program that also requires crane operators to pass a written exam and a skill test.

5444 ■ *"New Stores, New Headquarters in Schenectady for Golub Corporation" in Business Review, Albany New York (November 23, 2007)*
Pub: American City Business Journals, Inc.
Ed: Michael DeMasi. **Description:** Details of Golub Corporation's expansion plan are presented. The supermarket chain, which has 116 stores in six northeastern states, plans to open thirty more stores within the next three or four years. The company will also build 524,000 square feet of warehouse space which will help in supplying new stores. Its corporate headquarters will also move to a vacant lot in Schenectady, New York.

5445 ■ *"Newcomers Join Roster of Indoor Sports Venues" in Business Review, Albany New York (Vol. 34, October 12, 2007, No. 28, pp. 1)*
Pub: American City Business Journals, Inc.
Ed: Adam Sichko. **Description:** Indoor sports scene in Albany, New York is growing, with several indoor training facilities with a special attention to baseball and softball being built. These facilities include the $2.2 million Extra Innings facility in Ballston Corporate Technology Park and the Warning Track facility on Route 9 in Malta. The market for indoor sports, which is seen as saturated, is analyzed.

5446 ■ *"The Next Chapter" in Business Courier (Vol. 26, November 20, 2009, No. 30, pp. 1)*
Pub: American City Business Journals, Inc.
Ed: Lucy May. **Description:** Eric Browne and Mel Gravely purchased controlling interest in TriVersity Construction Group from CM-GC CEO Schulyer Murdoch and MBJ Consultants President Monroe Barnes. One third of the company was still owned by Cincinnati-based Messer and TriVersity and will continue to be a certified minority business enterprise.

5447 ■ *"The Next Government Bailout?" in Barron's (Vol. 88, March 10, 2008, No. 10, pp. 21)*
Pub: Dow Jones & Company, Inc.
Ed: Jonathan Laing. **Description:** Fannie Mae may need a government bailout as it faces huge hits brought about by the effects of the housing crisis. The shares of the government-sponsored enterprise have dropped 65 percent since the housing crisis began.

5448 ■ *"Next Stage of Green Building will be Water Efficiency" in Contractor (Vol. 56, July 2009, No. 7, pp. 41)*
Pub: Penton Media, Inc.
Description: One market report says that water efficiency and conservation will become critical factors in green design, construction, and product selection in the next five years from 2009. The report outlines how critical it will be for the construction industry to address responsible water practices in the future.

5449 ■ *"N.H. Near the LEED in Green Space" in New Hampshire Business Review (Vol. 33, March 25, 2011, No. 6, pp. 30)*
Pub: Business Publications Inc.
Description: New Hamphire's architects, contractors and suppliers are among the leaders with LEED-certified space per capita.

5450 ■ *"Nine Sectors to Watch: Construction" in Canadian Business (Vol. 81, December 24, 2007, No. 1, pp. 48)*
Pub: Rogers Media
Ed: Jeff Sanford. **Description:** Infrastructure deficit of C$123 billion, and still growing, was recently reported by the Federation of Canadian Municipalities. Details on plans for infrastructure projects and forecasts on the construction sector for 2008 are discussed.

5451 ■ *"No Rooms for the Inn In This High-Rise" in Chicago Tribune (October 4, 2008)*

Pub: McClatchy-Tribune Information Services

Ed: Ameet Sachdev; Jim Kirk. **Description:** Construction has stalled for several hotel expansion projects due to the economy which has caused a decline in occupancy and little growth in average daily room rates in downtown Chicago because consumers and businesses are becoming more cautious in the amount of money they spend on travel.

5452 ■ *"Noah's Park: $150M Project Eyed in Ky." in Business Courier (Vol. 27, November 19, 2010, No. 29, pp. 1)*

Pub: Business Courier

Ed: Lucy May. **Description:** Grant County, Kentucky has been abuzz with speculation about a $150M Noah's Ark-themed project being planned for Williamstown, Kentucky. The theme park's planned location is halfway between Cincinnati, Ohio and Louisville, Kentucky and about 40 minutes south of the Answers in Genesis Creation Museum in Petersburg.

5453 ■ *"Nonprofit to Grow" in Austin Business JournalInc. (Vol. 29, January 22, 2010, No. 46, pp. 1)*

Pub: American City Business Journals

Ed: Sandra Zaragoza. **Description:** Southwest Key Programs Inc. received a $2.1 million grant from the U.S. Economic Development Administration to help finance the building of a $3.6 million 'Social Enterprise Complex'. The complex is expected to create at least 100 jobs in East Austin, Texas. Details of the plan for the complex are presented.

5454 ■ *"Northwest Washington Fair Building Larger Horse Arena" in Bellingham Business Journal (Vol. March 2010, pp. 6)*

Pub: Sound Publishing Inc.

Description: Northwest Washington Fair is building a new equestrian arena that will provide larger show space for the horse community. The existing arena will function as a warm-up arena when hosting large shows.

5455 ■ *"Not Enough Room" in Austin Business JournalInc. (Vol. 29, November 13, 2009, No. 36, pp. A1)*

Pub: American City Business Journals

Ed: Jacob Dirr. **Description:** Hotel and convention business in downtown Austin, Texas lost nearly $5.3 million when Dell Inc. relocated its annual convention to Las Vegas. However, lack of capital caused the postponement of various hotel projects which need to be finished in order to attract well-attended conventions. Makeover projects on Austin's Waller Creek and Sixth Street are discussed.

5456 ■ *"Novi Eyed for $11 Million, 100-Bed Medilodge" in Crain's Detroit Business (Vol. 25, June 1, 2009, No. 22, pp. M032)*

Pub: Crain Communications Inc. - Detroit

Description: Novi, Michigan is one of the cities being considered for construction of a new 110-bed skilled nursing facility. Details of the project are included.

5457 ■ *"O'Reilly Will Soup Up KC Warehouse" in The Business Journal-Serving Metropolitan Kansas City (Vol. 26, August 15, 2008, No. 49)*

Pub: American City Business Journals, Inc.

Ed: Rob Roberts. **Description:** O'Reilly Automotive Inc. plans to construct a 215,000-square foot warehouse in Kansas City. The move is expected to triple the size of the company's distribution center. Other views and information on the planned warehouse construction, are presented.

5458 ■ *"Orlando Health to Build $24M Proton Therapy Facility" in Orlando Business Journal (Vol. 26, January 22, 2010, No. 34, pp. 1)*

Pub: American City Business Journals

Ed: Melanie Stawicki Azam. **Description:** Orlando Health is planning to construct a $24 million proton therapy facility at its MD Anderson Cancer Center Orlando in Florida. The facility, which aims for a 2011

opening, will be using radiation for more accurate targeting of tumors and avoiding the damage to surrounding tissues and organs.

5459 ■ *"Our Company is Dedicated to the Environment, But We Work With Vendors that Aren't" in Inc. (March 2008, pp. 78)*

Pub: Gruner & Jahr USA Publishing

Ed: Myra Goodman. **Description:** Insight into working with vendors, such as construction and janitorial contractors, to comploy with your company's environmental policies is given.

5460 ■ *"Overseas Marketing Key to Success of Chicago Spire" in Commercial Property News (March 17, 2008)*

Pub: Nielsen Company

Description: New construction of the Chicago Spire, a condominium project located on Lake Michigan's shore, is being marketed to would-be clients in Asia where Chicago is viewed as an emerging world city.

5461 ■ *"Pain Ahead as Profit Pressure Increases" in Crain's Chicago Business (Vol. 31, May 5, 2008, No. 18, pp. 4)*

Pub: Crain Communications, Inc.

Ed: Daniel Rome Levine. **Description:** Interview with David Klaskin, the chairman and chief investment officer at Oak Ridge Investments LLC, who discusses the outlook for the economy and corporate earnings, particularly in the housing and auto industries, the impact of economic stimulus checks, the weakness of the dollar and recommendations of stocks that individual investors may find helpful.

5462 ■ *"P&L Building Owner Nears Start of $157M Condo Plan" in Business Journal-Serving Metropolitan Kansas City (November 23, 2007)*

Pub: American City Business Journals, Inc.

Ed: Jim Davis. **Description:** The owner of Power and Light Building is ready to begin a $157 million plan to refurbish the Kansas City landmark and redevelop a property right next to it after receiving tax increment refinancing for the project.

5463 ■ *"Pavilions Poised for Image Overhaul" in The Business Journal - Serving Phoenix and the Valley of the Sun (Vol. 28, August 22, 2008)*

Pub: American City Business Journals, Inc.

Ed: Jan Buchholz. **Description:** DeRitto Partners Inc. is expected to push through with plans for a major renovation of the 1.1 million-square foot Scottsdale Pavilions in Scottsdale, Arizona. An aggressive marketing campaign is planned to be included in the renovation, which aims to address high vacancy rates and competition. Views and information on the planned renovation are presented.

5464 ■ *"Peter Gilgan" in Canadian Business (Vol. 82, April 27, 2009, No. 7, pp. 58)*

Pub: Rogers Media

Ed: Calvin Leung. **Description:** Mattamy Homes Ltd. president and chief executive officer Peter Gilgan believes that their business model of building communities in an organized way brings advantages to the firm and for their customers. He also believes in adopting their product prices to new market realities. Gilgan considers the approvals regime in Ontario his biggest challenge in the last 20 years.

5465 ■ *"Pierre's Ice Cream" in Ice Cream Reporter (Vol. 23, October 20, 2010, No. 11, pp. 8)*

Pub: Ice Cream Reporter

Description: Pierre's Ice Cream has started work on its new $8 million manufacturing facility in Cleveland, Ohio.

5466 ■ *"Pinellas Leaders Want First Leg of Light Rail" in The Business Journal-Serving Greater Tampa Bay (Vol. 28, August 8, 2008, No. 33)*

Pub: American City Business Journals, Inc.

Ed: Larry Halstead. **Description:** Proposed routes for the first leg of the planned light railway system in the Tampa Bay, Florida area are being presented as the Tampa Bay Area Regional Transportation Author-

ity is about to make its master plan for the project. A sales tax for transit is being proposed to fund the project, as well as an expansion of the accompanying bus system.

5467 ■ *"Pipeline Dreams" in Canadian Business (Vol. 80, October 22, 2007, No. 21, pp. 19)*

Pub: Rogers Media

Ed: Rachel Pulfer. **Description:** Northwest Mackenzie Valley Pipeline has been under review by the National Energy Board since 2004. Hearings on the construction of the gas pipeline will wrap up in 2008. Pius Rolheiser, the spokesman of Imperial Oil Company Inc. believes the change of government in the area will not affect the negotiations on the pipeline construction.

5468 ■ *"Placer Land Sells for $12 Million" in Sacramento Business Journal (Vol. 25, July 25, 2008, No. 21, pp. 1)*

Pub: American City Business Journals, Inc.

Ed: Michael Shaw; Celia Lamb. **Description:** Reynen & Bardis Communities Inc., a Sacramento, California-based homebuilder, has purchased the Antonio Mountain Ranch in Placer County, California shortly before the property's scheduled foreclosure on June 27, 2008. Placer County Recorder's data show that the purchase price of the 808-acre wetland-rich property is $12 million.

5469 ■ *"Plans for $160M Condo Resort in Wisconsin Dells Moves Forward" in Commercial Property News (March 18, 2008)*

Pub: Nielsen Company

Description: Plans for the Grand Cambrian Resort in the Wisconsin Dells is discussed. The luxury condominium resort will include condos, townhomes, and condo-hotel style residences, two water parts, meeting space and indoor entertainment space, as well as a spa, four restaurants and retail offerings.

5470 ■ *"Playing Defense" in Crain's Chicago Business (Vol. 31, November 10, 2008, No. 45, pp. 4)*

Pub: Crain Communications, Inc.

Ed: Monee Fields-White. **Description:** Chicago's money managers are increasingly investing in local companies such as Caterpillar Inc., a maker of construction and mining equipment, Kraft Foods Inc. and Baxter International Inc., a manufacturer of medical products, in an attempt to bolster their portfolios. These companies have a history of surviving tough economic times.

5471 ■ *"Port Authority Taking Heat in Kenwood Mess" in Business Courier (Vol. 26, September 18, 2009, No. 21, pp. 1)*

Pub: American City Business Journals, Inc.

Ed: Dan Monk. **Description:** Port of Greater Cincinnati Development Authority is being criticized for not requiring payment and performance bonds to ensure that contractors would be paid. The criticism occurred after the general contractor for the project to build a parking garage at Kenwood Towne Plaza stopped paying its subcontractors.

5472 ■ *"Possible Green Light On Transit" in The Business Journal-Milwaukee (Vol. 25, July 25, 2008, No. 44, pp. A1)*

Pub: American City Business Journals, Inc.

Ed: David Doege. **Description:** $50 million in federal funding is being sought by Wisconsin's Milwaukee County Executive Scott Walker for the creation of two bus rapid transit lines, and is to be added to the unspent Milwaukee area federal funds worth $91.5 million. The new transit line will have new higher-speed buses and fewer stops than the traditional line.

5473 ■ *"Power Partnerships" in Business Courier (Vol. 27, October 22, 2010, No. 25, pp. 1)*

Pub: Business Courier

Ed: Lucy May. **Description:** The $400 million Harrah's casino and the $47 million redevelopment and expansion of Washington Park are project aimed at boosting the economy in downtown Cincinnati, Ohio. These projects will be done in cooperation with the

National Association for the Advancement of Colored People. Insights into the role of minority-owned businesses in regional economic development are explored.

5474 ■ *"'Pre-Sale' for Planned Could Mich Tower" in Crain's Chicago Business (Vol. 31, March 24, 2008, No. 12, pp. 14)*
Pub: Crain Communications, Inc.
Ed: Eddie Baeb. **Description:** Condominium developer William Warman is planning to build a mixed-use tower at 300 North Michigan Avenue which would include a hotel, retail space, apartments and a parking garage. Mr. Warman is looking for investors to buy part or all of the space in order to make it easier to land financing.

5475 ■ *"Prince of the City" in Canadian Business (Vol. 80, November 19, 2007, No. 23, pp. 62)*
Pub: Rogers Media
Ed: Rachel Pulfer. **Description:** Robert Fung and the Salilent Group aim to revive the poverty-stricken communities in Vancouver by transforming the city's old buildings into designer condominiums using city incentives. Fung and his partners have increased property values in the most unlikely neighborhoods by creating luxury real estate. Fung's recommendations on Vancouver's real estate development are given.

5476 ■ *"Project Could Forge Path to Jobs, Growth" in Business Courier (Vol. 26, September 11, 2009, No. 20, pp. 1)*
Pub: American City Business Journals, Inc.
Ed: Lucy May. **Description:** The planned 13.5 mile Mill Creek Greenway Trail extension could create 445 jobs and bring $52 million to the economy of Cincinnati, Ohio. The trail extension would cost $24 million and would be used for recreational purposes.

5477 ■ *"Prominent Hispanic Businessman Signs with Choice Hotels" in Hispanic Business (March 2008, pp. 36)*
Pub: Hispanic Business
Ed: Melinda Burns. **Description:** Profile of John C. Lopez, who has signed an agreement with Choice Hotels International to build five new Cambria Suites in the U.S.; cost of the project will total $14 million.

5478 ■ *"Prominent Hispanic Businessman Signs With Choice Hotels" in Hispanic Business (Vol. 30, March 2008, No. 3, pp. 36)*
Pub: Hispanic Business
Ed: Melinda Burns. **Description:** Chairman of the board of Lopez Food Inc., John C. Lopez signs the agreement with Choice Hotels International to build five new Cambria suites in the USA. This is his first hotel venture and also the first Hispanic franchisee to enter into business with Choice Hotels.

5479 ■ *"Proposal Ruffles Builders" in Austin Business JournalInc. (Vol. 29, November 20, 2009, No. 37, pp. 1)*
Pub: American City Business Journals
Ed: Jacob Dirr. **Description:** A proposal that requires heating, ventilation and cooling equipment checking for a new commercial building having an area of at least 10,000 square feet might cost 25 cents to 50 cents per square foot for the owners. This may lead to higher housing costs. Both the Building and Fire Code Board of Appeals and the Mechanical Plumbing and Solar Board have recommended the plan.

5480 ■ *"PSU Launches $90 Million Project" in The Business Journal-Portland (Vol. 25, July 18, 2008, No. 19, pp. 1)*
Pub: American City Business Journals, Inc.
Ed: Aliza Earnshaw. **Description:** Portland State University (PSU) has launched a $90-million project for a new business school building, which is to be located at Southwest Market and Southwest Park. The business school is expected to move in to its new 130,000-suqare-foot building by 2013. PSU business school needs to raise $30 million for the project.

5481 ■ *"Public Bathroom Pressure Woes Resolved" in Contractor (Vol. 56, September 2009, No. 9, pp. 44)*
Pub: Penton Media, Inc.
Ed: Dave Yates. **Description:** Design and construction of a public bathroom's plumbing system in the United States are discussed. Installed plumbing fixtures with flush valves would not function properly. The installation of Grundfos SQE variable-speed pumps has resolved problems with the bathroom's water pressure.

5482 ■ *"Pulp Friction: Spin Off Mills to Boost Wood Products" in Globe & Mail (February 18, 2006, pp. B3)*
Pub: CTVglobemedia Publishing Inc.
Ed: Peter Kennedy. **Description:** The reasons behind the decision of chief executive officer Jim Shepherd of Canfor Corp. to sell pulp mills are presented.

5483 ■ *"Pulte May Be Bouncing Back From Stock-Price Doldrums" in Crain's Detroit Business (Vol. 23, October 8, 2007, No. 41, pp. 4)*
Pub: Crain Communications Inc. - Detroit
Ed: Daniel Duggan. **Description:** Pulte Homes saw a jump in its stocks due to Citigroup's analysts rating Pulte and other builders higher due to strong balance sheets.

5484 ■ *"Real Estate Ambitions" in Black Enterprise (Vol. 37, January 2007, No. 6, pp. 101)*
Pub: Earl G. Graves Publishing Co. Inc.
Description: National Real Estate Investors Association is a nonprofit trade association for both advanced as well as novice real estate investors that offers information on builders to contractors to banks. When looking to become a real estate investor utilize this organization, talk to various investors like the president of your local chapter, let people know your aspirations, and see if you can find a partner who has experience in the field. Resources included.

5485 ■ *"Realities May Blur Vision" in The Business Journal-Serving Metropolitan Kansas City (Vol. 27, September 19, 2008, No. 1, pp. 1)*
Pub: American City Business Journals, Inc.
Ed: Rob Roberts. **Description:** Vision Metcalf is a study how Kansas City that depicts how Metcalf Avenue could look like if redeveloped. Redevelopment plans for the Metcalf corridor include a 20-story mixed-use building on a vacant car dealership. The challenges that the redevelopment plans will face are also analyzed.

5486 ■ *"Recovery on Tap for 2010?" in Orlando Business Journal (Vol. 26, January 1, 2010, No. 31, pp. 1)*
Pub: American City Business Journals
Ed: Melanie Stawicki Azam, Richard Bilbao, Christopher Boyd, Anjali Fluker. **Description:** Economic forecasts for Central Florida's leading business sectors in 2010 are presented. These sectors include housing, film and TV, sports business, law, restaurants, aviation, tourism and hospitality, banking and finance, commercial real estate, retail, health care, insurance, higher education, and manufacturing. According to some local executives, Central Florida's economy will slowly recover in 2010.

5487 ■ *"Redcorp Ventures Ltd.: Tulsequah Camp Construction Begins" in Canadian Corporate News (May 16, 2007)*
Pub: Comtex News Network Inc.
Description: Redfern Reources Ltd., a subsidiary of Redcorp Ventures Ltd., announced that Modular Transportable Solutions LLC was selected to design and manufacture its prefabricated, modular construction camp, cookhouse, administration buildings, and mine dry at the Tulsequah Mine location in northwest British Columbia due to the virtually indestructible design of the units that withstand extreme weather conditions.

5488 ■ *"A Renewal in Rentals" in Barron's (Vol. 88, March 17, 2008, No. 11, pp. 17)*
Pub: Dow Jones & Company, Inc.
Description: Discusses the projected entry of the estimated 82 million echo-boomers into the rentals market and the influx of immigrants and displaced homeowners which could turn apartments into lucrative investments again. While apartment-building completions rose slowly since 2003, demand is expected to increase steeply until 2015.

5489 ■ *"Restoring Grandeur" in Business Courier (Vol. 26, December 4, 2009, No. 32, pp. 1)*
Pub: American City Business Journals, Inc.
Ed: Dan Monk. **Description:** Eagle Realty Group intends to spend more than $10 to restore the historic 12-story Phelps apartment building in Lytle Park in Cincinnati. Its president, Mario San Marco, expressed the need to invest in the building in order to maintain operations. The building could be restored into a hotel catering to executives and consultants.

5490 ■ *"Retail Center Pitched" in Business Courier (Vol. 27, June 18, 2010, No. 7, pp. 1)*
Pub: Business Courier
Ed: Dan Monk. **Description:** Jeffrey R. Anderson Real Estate Inc.'s plan for a retail center in Butler County, Ohio could have three department stores in the 1.1 million-square-foot property. An outdoor sports retailer is also part of the plans.

5491 ■ *"Retail Center Planned for Canton Site" in Boston Business Journal (Vol. 29, May 20, 2011, No. 2, pp. 1)*
Pub: American City Business Journals Inc.
Ed: Daniel J. Sernovitz. **Description:** A real estate development team is planning to build a shopping center at Canton Crossing in Baltimore, Maryland and is near closing the deal with ExxonMobil Corporation who owns the waterfront site.

5492 ■ *"ReVenture Plan Appears Close to Landing Key Legislative Deal" in Charlotte Business Journal (Vol. 25, July 9, 2010, No. 16, pp. 1)*
Pub: Charlotte Business Journal
Ed: John Downey. **Description:** North Carolina lawmakers acted on special legislation that would boost development of Forsite Development 667-acre ReVenture Energy Park. The legislation could also improve chances that Duke Energy Carolinas will contract to purchase the power from the planned 50-megawatt biomass power plant located at the park. How utilities would benefit from the legislation is also discussed.

5493 ■ *"Rise in Occupancy Rate Fuels Area Hotel Building Boom" in Crain's Detroit Business (Vol. 24, March 10, 2008, No. 10, pp. 14)*
Pub: Crain Communications, Inc.
Ed: Jonathan Eppley. **Description:** Due to a rise in the region's yearly occupancy rate, a number of new hotel construction and renovation projects are slated for the Detroit area.

5494 ■ *"A Rise in Rental Units" in Philadelphia Business Journal (Vol. 30, October 7, 2011, No. 34, pp. 1)*
Pub: American City Business Journals Inc.
Ed: Natalie Kostelni. **Description:** Housing developers have been stepping up the construction of new apartment complexes throughout the suburbs of Pennsylvania in order to capture growing demand for rental properties. BPG Properties Ltd. has nearly 1,000 new apartments under construction.

5495 ■ *"Ritz Kapalua Sells 93 Suites for $176M to Fund Renovation" in Commercial Property News (March 17, 2008)*
Pub: Nielsen Company
Description: Ritz-Carlton, Kapalua in Lahaina, Hawaii sold ninety-three of its units in order to fund renovations of 463 rooms and suites along with construction of a new spa and fitness center, new and expanded restaurants and pools and an environmental education center for children.

5496 ■ *"Rivals Blow In" in Crain's Cleveland Business (Vol. 30, June 1, 2009, No. 21, pp. 1)*
Pub: Crain Communications, Inc.
Ed: Chuck Soder. **Description:** U.S. and Canadian competitors are hoping to start construction of offshore wind farm project proposed by Cuyahoga County's Great Lakes Energy Development Task Force. Details of the project are included.

5497 ■ *"River Plan in Disarray" in Business Journal Portland (Vol. 26, December 4, 2009, No. 39, pp. 1)*
Pub: American City Business Journals Inc.
Ed: Andy Giegerich. **Description:** Portland's proposed rules on a waterfront development plan for the Willamette River calls for fees intended for river bank preservation, a move that could drive industrial manufacturers away. The manufacturers, under the Working Waterfront Coalition, claim that the proposals could increase riverfront building costs by 15 percent.

5498 ■ *"Roger Hickel Contracting: Smoothing the Road for Owners" in Alaska Business Monthly (Vol. 27, October 2011, No. 10, pp. 114)*
Pub: Alaska Business Publishing Company
Ed: Gail West. **Description:** Profile of Roger Hickel and his contracting company that reports nearly $60 million annually in gross revenue. The firm focuses on customer service.

5499 ■ *"Ronald Taketa" in Hawaii Business (Vol. 54, September 2008, No. 3, pp. 28)*
Pub: Hawaii Business Publishing
Ed: Shara Enay. **Description:** Interview with Ronald Taketa of the Hawaii Carpenters Union who states that the economic downturn has affected the construction industry as 20 percent of the union's 7,800 members are unemployed. He shares his thoughts about the industry's economic situation, the union's advertisements, and his role as a leader of the union.

5500 ■ *"RT Seeking Ways to Finance Expansion" in Sacramento Business Journal (Vol. 28, July 29, 2011, No. 22, pp. 1)*
Pub: Sacramento Business Journal
Ed: Melanie Turner. **Description:** Sacramento Regional Transit District is considering ways to finance all its capital projects outlined in a 30-year transit master plan which would cost more than $7 billion to complete. Current funding sources include developer fees and state and federal assistance and fares. Part of the master plan is a light-rail line to Sacramento International Airport.

5501 ■ *"Saratoga Eagle Project Quenches Thirst To Grow" in Business Review, Albany New York (Vol. 34, November 30, 2007, No. 35, pp. 3)*
Pub: American City Business Journals, Inc.
Ed: Robin K. Cooper. **Description:** Saratoga Eagle Sales and Service will be searching for contractors for the construction of its new beverage distribution center at the WJ Grande Industrial Park in Saratoga Springs, New York. The $8 million, 107,000 square foot facility is part of Saratoga Eagle's expansion plan. The company's growth in the Capital Region market and $1.3 million tax break are discussed.

5502 ■ *"Schlitterbahn Broadens" in Austin Business Journallnc. (Vol. 28, September 19, 2008, No. 27, pp. A1)*
Pub: American City Business Journals
Ed: Kate Harrington. **Description:** Schlitterbahn is planning to introduce a Christmas-themed event this winter 2008 in its water amusement park that will keep it open from November to January. The company is also constructing its first out-of-Texas park, which is a $170 million, 376-acre project in Kansas City, Missouri. Other details about Schlitterbahn's expansion are discussed.

5503 ■ *"A Second Chance at Road Dollars" in Orlando Business Journal (Vol. 26, February 5, 2010, No. 36, pp. 1)*
Pub: American City Business Journals
Ed: Bill Orben. **Description:** Nearly $10 million worth of construction projects in Central Florida would give construction companies that missed the initial round of federal stimulus-funded local road building projects another opportunity. Cost savings in the initial round of road projects enabled Orange, Osceola, and Seminole Counties to secure additional projects.

5504 ■ *"Seeing Green in Going Green" in The Business Journal-Serving Greater Tampa Bay*

(Vol. 28, July 4, 2008, No. 28, pp. 1)
Pub: American City Business Journals, Inc.
Ed: Janet Leiser. **Description:** Atlanta, Georgia-based developer IDI Corp. is pushing for Leadership in Energy and Environmental Design certification for the warehouse that is currently under construction at Madison Business Center along Port Sutton and U.S. 41. The industrial building is the first in Tampa Bay to seek certification for LEED as set by the U.S. Green Building Council.

5505 ■ *"Self-Employment in the United States" in Montly Labor Review (Vol. 133, September 2010, No. 9, pp. 17)*
Pub: Bureau of Labor Statistics
Description: Self employment in 2009 in the U.S. continued to be more common among men, Whites, Asians, and older workers and in the agriculture, construction, and services industries.

5506 ■ *"Sellers Face Excess Land Dilemma" in Crain's Cleveland Business (Vol. 28, November 12, 2007, No. 45, pp. 1)*
Pub: Crain Communications, Inc.
Ed: Stan Bullard. **Description:** Overview on the way in which the housing slump is effecting builders, land developers and lot prices. Statistical data included.

5507 ■ *Shedworking: The Alternative Workplace Revolution*
Pub: Frances Lincoln Limited
Ed: Alex Johnson. **Released:** June 10, 2010. **Price:** $29.95. **Description:** Shedworking is an alternative office space for those working at home. The book features shedworkers and shedbuilders from around the world who are leading this alternative workplace revolution and why this trend is working.

5508 ■ *"Sixty-Acre Vision for North Suburbs" in Business Courier (Vol. 24, April 4, 2008, No. 52, pp. 1)*
Pub: American City Business Journals, Inc.
Ed: Laura Baverman. **Description:** Al Neyer Inc. plans for a mixed-use development at the 60-acre site it has recently purchased. The mixed-use project could cost up to $100 million, and will include medical offices, residential buildings, and corporate offices. Details of Al Neyer's plans for the site are given.

5509 ■ *"Sneak Preview: Alamo Revamp" in Austin Business Journallnc. (Vol. 28, December 12, 2008, No. 39, pp. 1)*
Pub: American City Business Journals
Ed: Sandra Zaragoza. **Description:** Austin, Texas-based Alamo Drafthouse Cinemas is planning to build a new Circle C Ranch. The new theater will showcase digital projectors and the latest sound systems to show 3-D movies. The company is in lease negotiations with developer Stratus Properties Inc.

5510 ■ *"Son of Sandman: Can Tom Gaglardi Really Outdo His Old Man?" in Canadian Business (Vol. 80, Winter 2007, No. 24, pp. 106)*
Pub: Rogers Media
Ed: Calvin Leung. **Description:** Bob Gaglardi of Northland Properties started to learn about his family's business by working at a construction site at one of the high-rise buildings in downtown Vancouver. Gaglardi wants to expand their Moxie's restaurant chain and increase the market share of their Sandman hotel by 2018.

5511 ■ *"South Lake Hospital Starting $47M Patient Tower" in Orlando Business Journal (Vol. 26, December 4, 2009, No. 26, pp. 1)*
Pub: American City Business Journals
Ed: Melanie Stawicki Azam. **Description:** Clermont, Florida's South Lake Hospital has divulged intentions to issue $50.9 million in bonds in order to fund construction of the $47 million patient tower. The three-story, 124,000 square foot tower would add eighteen inpatient rooms, a new lobby and expanded pharmacy, diagnostic and lab services, and treatment areas.

5512 ■ *"South Loop Site Lands a Buyer" in Crain's Chicago Business (Vol. 31, March 24, 2008, No. 12, pp. 1)*
Pub: Crain Communications, Inc.
Ed: Alby Gallun. **Description:** Russland Capital Group, a little-known condominium developer from Skokie, recently purchased a 6.5-acre riverside property in the site known as Franklin Point for $40 million.

5513 ■ *"State Center Lease Deal High for Md." in Baltimore Business Journal (Vol. 28, August 6, 2010, No. 13, pp. 1)*
Pub: Baltimore Business Journal
Ed: Daniel J. Sernovitz. **Description:** The proposed $1.5 billion State Center development project in Midtown Baltimore might cause the State of Maryland to pay the most expensive rental rates in the city. The state will have to pay an effective rental rate of $34 per square foot, including expenses, on the leasing. Other details of the redevelopment project are discussed.

5514 ■ *"State Printing Plant on the Move" in Sacramento Business Journal (Vol. 25, August 29, 2008, No. 26, pp. 1)*
Pub: American City Business Journals, Inc.
Ed: Michael Shaw; Celia Lamb. **Description:** California is planning to replace its printing plant on Richards Boulevard and 7th Street with a newly built or leased facility in the Sacramento area. It was revealed that the project will meet the state's standards for new buildings. It is believed that the new site will require 15 acres or more depending on requirements.

5515 ■ *"State Weighs Tearing Down Hoan" in The Business Journal-Milwaukee (Vol. 25, August 22, 2008, No. 48, pp. A1)*
Pub: American City Business Journals, Inc.
Ed: Pete Millard. **Description:** Department of Transportation of Wisconsin is studying the feasibility of tearing the Daniel Hoan Memorial Bridge down because rehabilitating the bridge is costly. Rebuilding the Interstate 794 at street level could be less expensive. The potential plans for the bridge are discussed further.

5516 ■ *"Still No Arena Financing Plan" in Sacramento Business Journal (Vol. 28, May 27, 2011, No. 13, pp. 1)*
Pub: Sacramento Business Journal
Ed: Kelly Johnson. **Description:** The government of Sacramento, California has yet to devise a plan to finance the construction of a proposed stadium. The arena is estimated to cost $387 million. A brief description of the facility is also included.

5517 ■ *"Stimulus 'Loser' Won't Build Plant in Mass." in Boston Business Journal (Vol. 30, November 5, 2010, No. 41, pp. 1)*
Pub: Boston Business Journal
Ed: Kyle Alspach. **Description:** Boston-Power Inc. no longer plans to build an electric vehicle battery plant in Massachusetts after it failed to obtain stimulus funds from the federal government. The company is instead looking to build a lithium-ion battery plant in China and possibly Europe.

5518 ■ *"Stone Company Slated to Expand Here" in Austin Business Journallnc. (Vol. 28, September 12, 2008, No. 26, pp. 1)*
Pub: American City Business Journals
Ed: Jean Kwon. **Description:** Architectural Granite & Marble Inc. has a $6 million investment that moved the company from 2,500 square feet of space to a 10,000 square foot office in Southwest Austin, Texas. The investment will also provide for the company's expansion in Nashville, Tennessee and San Antonio, Texas.

5519 ■ *"Stung by Recession, Hemmer Regroups with New Strategy" in Business Courier (Vol. 27, June 4, 2010, No. 5, pp. 1)*
Pub: Business Courier
Ed: Lucy May. **Description:** Paul Hemmer Companies reduced its work force and outsourced operations such as marketing and architecture, in order for the commercial and construction firm to survive the

recession. Hammer's total core revenue in 2009 dropped to less than $30 million forcing the closure of its Chicago office.

5520 ■ *"Sundt, DPR Score $470 Million Biotech Project"* in *The Business Journal - Serving Phoenix and the Valley of the Sun (Vol. 29, September 19, 2008, No. 3, pp. 1)*
Pub: American City Business Journals, Inc.
Ed: Jan Buchholz. **Description:** Sundt Inc. and DPR Construction Inc. were awarded the winning joint-venture contract to develop the second phase of the Arizona Biomedical Collaborative on the Phoenix Biomedical Campus. Both firms declined to comment, but an employee of the Arizona Board of Regents confirmed that the firms won the bidding. Views and information on the development project are presented.

5521 ■ *"Sunriver Venture Hits Snag"* in *The Business Journal-Portland (Vol. 25, August 1, 2008, No. 21, pp. 1)*
Pub: American City Business Journals, Inc.
Ed: Robin J. Moody. **Description:** Portland, Oregon based-Sunwest Management Inc. has divided its Sunriver resort community to make way for a redevelopment plan. Sunwest owner Jon Harder and three partners formed SilverStar Destinations LLC to broker the purchase and redevelopment of the property. Details and description of the redevelopment project are also presented.

5522 ■ *"Surplus Store Rebuilding Again"* in *Spokesman-Review (November 17, 2010)*
Pub: Spokesman Review
Ed: Chelsea Bannach. **Description:** Retail business owner, David Arnold Sr., is rebuilding his Army Surplus store in Spokane, Washington after a truck crashed into the building.

5523 ■ *"Survey: Don't Expect Big Results From Stimulus"* in *Crain's Detroit Business (Vol. 25, June 1, 2009, No. 22)*
Pub: Crain Communications Inc. - Detroit
Ed: Nancy Kaffer, Chad Halcom. **Description:** In a recent survey, Michigan business owners, operators or managers showed that 48 percent of respondents oppose the President's stimulus package and believe it will have little or no effect on the economy.

5524 ■ *"Sustainability Is Top Priority for GreenTown Chicago"* in *Contractor (Vol. 56, November 2009, No. 11, pp. 1)*
Pub: Penton Media, Inc.
Ed: Candace Roulo. **Description:** GreenTown Chicago 2009 conference tackled energy-efficient practices and technologies, green design and building, and sustainable policies. Water conservation was also a topic at the conference and one mayor who made a presentation said that reducing the water loss in the system is a priority in the city's endeavor.

5525 ■ *"Swope: Breakup Won't Delay Job"* in *The Business Journal-Serving Metropolitan Kansas City (Vol. 26, August 22, 2008, No. 50, pp. 1)*
Pub: American City Business Journals, Inc.
Ed: Rob Roberts. **Description:** Swope Community Builders said that the Kansas City Redevelopment Project will not be delayed by the breakup of their partnership with Sherman Associates Inc. Swopes will be the sole master developer of the project.

5526 ■ *"Tax Abatement Changes Seen as Home Run for Cleveland Condo Market"* in *Crain's Cleveland Business (Vol. 30, June 15, 2009, No. 23)*
Pub: Crain Communications, Inc.
Ed: Jay Miller. **Description:** Condominium ownership became a bit more affordable for Cleveland residents since changes in both state and local tax abatement policy changes. The tax credits are examined.

5527 ■ *"Tax Credit Crunch"* in *Miami Daily Business Review (March 26, 2008)*
Pub: ALM Media Inc.
Ed: Paula Iuspa-Abbott. **Description:** Uncertainty is growing over the future of the low-income housing project in South Florida and the tax credit program that helps fuel the projects.

5528 ■ *"Tax Deal Yields Polaris Offices"* in *Business First-Columbus (October 26, 2007, pp. A1)*
Pub: American City Business Journals, Inc.
Ed: Brian R. Ball. **Description:** Speculation on a possible office building construction is increasing with the expansion of tax incentives to build at the Polaris Centers of Commerce. Details of community reinvestment in the Columbus, Ohio area along with possible 15-year 100 percent tax abatements for Polaris office buildings are discussed.

5529 ■ *"Taylor Tests Land Grant Program"* in *Austin Business Journal (Vol. 31, June 3, 2011, No. 13, pp. 1)*
Pub: American City Business Journals Inc.
Ed: Vicky Garza. **Description:** Taylor Economic Development Corporation implemented a land grant program called Build On Our Lot to lure businesses to Taylor City, Austin, Texas. They are targeting small businesses, especially those in the renewable energy, advanced manufacturing, technical services and food products. Program details are included.

5530 ■ *"Testing Firm to Add Jobs"* in *Business Courier (Vol. 26, December 11, 2009, No. 33, pp. 1)*
Pub: American City Business Journals, Inc.
Ed: Dan Monk. **Description:** Cincinnati-based Q Laboratories announced plans to add dozens of jobs with the $1.6 million stimulus assisted expansion. The company hired Michael Lichtenberg & Sons Construction Co. to build a new 9,000 square foot laboratory building.

5531 ■ *"Texas State Poised for Boom"* in *Austin Business JournalInc. (Vol. 29, January 29, 2010, No. 47, pp. 1)*
Pub: American City Business Journals
Ed: Sandra Zaragoza. **Description:** Texas State University, San Marcos has seen its student population grow to 30,800 and the university is set for $633 million in construction projects to address demand for student housing and building expansions and renovations. Details on the buildings and student housing plans for the projects are provided.

5532 ■ *"That Empty Feeling"* in *Crain's Cleveland Business (Vol. 28, October 15, 2007, No. 41, pp. 1)*
Pub: Crain Communications, Inc.
Ed: Stan Bullard. **Description:** Townhouses, cluster homes and condominiums lured both buyers and builders for most of this decade but now that market is suffering to an even greater degree than the single-family home market. Statistical data included.

5533 ■ *"Things Fall Apart"* in *Canadian Business (Vol. 80, October 8, 2007, No. 20, pp. 187)*
Pub: Rogers Media
Ed: Jeff Sanford. **Description:** Infrastructure crisis in Canada and in other countries in North America is examined. Incidents that demonstrate this crisis, such as the collapse of a bridge in Minneapolis and the collapse of an overpass in Quebec, Canada are presented. It is estimated that the reconstruction in the country will cost between C$44 billion and C$200 billion.

5534 ■ *"This Just In"* in *Crain's Detroit Business (Vol. 25, June 22, 2009, No. 25, pp. 1)*
Pub: Crain Communications Inc. - Detroit
Description: Yamasaki Associates, an architectural firm has been sued for non payment of wages to four employees. Yamasaki spokesperson stated the economy has affected the company and it is focusing marketing efforts on areas encouraged by recovery funding.

5535 ■ *"Threat of New Office Space Records Rent Hikes"* in *Globe & Mail (March 21, 2007, pp. B4)*
Pub: CTVglobemedia Publishing Inc.
Ed: Elizabeth Church. **Description:** The increasing commercial rent prices in the Toronto region amid the high office building construction market are discussed.

5536 ■ *"Times are Tough, I Figure I'm Tougher"* in *Inc. (Vol. 33, September 2011, No. 7, pp. 92)*
Pub: Inc. Magazine
Ed: April Joyner. **Description:** Profile of Frank Campanaro and his company, Trillacorpe Construction located in Bingham Farms, Michigan. Campanaro has partnered with other companies that have bonding in reserve and lets them take the lion's share.

5537 ■ *"Top 100 Consolidate Gains"* in *Hispanic Business (Vol. 30, July-August 2008, No. 7-8, pp. 30)*
Pub: Hispanic Business, Inc.
Ed: Richard Kaplan. **Description:** Data developed by HispanTelligence on the increase in revenue posted by the top 100 fastest-growing U.S. Hispanic firms over the last five years is reported. Despite the economic downturn, the service sector, IT and health suppliers showed an increase in revenue whereas construction companies showed a marginal slump in revenue growth.

5538 ■ *"Traffic Slows at O'Hare; As Airlines Cut Flights, City Tries to Push Expansion Forward"* in *Crain's Chicago Business (April 28, 2008)*
Pub: Crain Communications, Inc.
Ed: Paul Merrion; John Pletz. **Description:** O'Hare International Airport is seeing a decline in passenger traffic just as the city of Chicago presses cash-strapped airlines to fund the second phase of the airport's expansion which would include the extension of one runway, the relocation of two others and the construction of a new western terminal.

5539 ■ *"Trisun Healthcare Eager to Add Centers"* in *Austin Business JournalInc. (Vol. 28, August 22, 2008, No. 23, pp. 1)*
Pub: American City Business Journals
Ed: Kate Harrington. **Description:** Austin-based nursing and rehabilitation centers operator Trisun Healthcare plans to build more facilities as part of a growth strategy that can expand beyond Texas. Trisun has 16 facilities along the corridor from San Antonio to Temple, and projects to have three more in Texas in 2008.

5540 ■ *"Troubled Project In Court"* in *The Business Journal-Portland (Vol. 25, July 25, 2008, No. 20, pp. 1)*
Pub: American City Business Journals, Inc.
Ed: Wendy Culverwell. **Description:** Views and information on Salpare Bay's Hayden Island project, as well as on financing problems and cases associated with the project, are presented. Construction of luxurious waterside condominiums stopped last fall, after the discovery of financing problems and subcontractors and other parties started filing claims and counterclaims.

5541 ■ *"The Turkey Has Landed"* in *Canadian Business (Vol. 79, November 20, 2006, No. 23, pp. 38)*
Pub: Rogers Media
Ed: Erik Heinrich. **Description:** The design and construction of Toronto Pearson International Airport to handle domestic, international and transborder flights in one facility is discussed.

5542 ■ *"UA Turns Ann Arbor Green"* in *Contractor (Vol. 56, September 2009, No. 9, pp. 5)*
Pub: Penton Media, Inc.
Ed: Robert P. Mader. **Description:** Instructors at the United Association of Plumbers and Steamfitters have studied the latest in green and sustainable construction and service at the Washtenaw Community College in Michigan. Classes included building information modeling, hydronic heating and cooling and advanced HVACR troubleshooting. The UA is currently focusing on green training.

5543 ■ *"The Ultimate Comfort System"* in *Contractor (Vol. 56, July 2009, No. 7, pp. 30)*
Pub: Penton Media, Inc.
Ed: Mark Eatherton. **Description:** Retrofitting of a hydronic heating system to an existing home is presented. The project approaches near net-zero energy production.

5544 ■ *"UMKC, Hospital Drill Down on Deal"* *in The Business Journal-Serving Metropolitan Kansas City (Vol. 26, July 18, 2008, No. 45, pp. 1)*

Pub: American City Business Journals, Inc.

Ed: Rob Roberts. **Description:** University of Missouri Kansas City and Children's Mercy Hospital are negotiating the hospital's potential acquisition of the university's School of Dentistry building. The deal would transfer the 240,000-square foot dental school building to Children's Mercy. Plans for a new dental school building for the UMKC are also presented.

5545 ■ *"USF Plans $30M Sports Complex"* *in Tampa Bay Business Journal (Vol. 29, October 23, 2009, No. 44, pp. 1)*

Pub: American City Business Journals

Ed: Jane Meinhardt. **Description:** University of South Florida (USF) is going to build a new sports complex with the aid of a $30 million loan from BB&T. The project, which is also comprised of new and renovated athletic facilities on USF's Tampa campus, is projected to create more than $37 million in revenue in its first year. Revenues from the said facilities are expected to achieve an annual growth of at least four percent.

5546 ■ *"VA Seeking Bidders for Ft. Howard"* *in Baltimore Business Journal (Vol. 28, June 25, 2010, No. 7, pp. 1)*

Pub: Baltimore Business Journal

Ed: Daniel J. Sernovitz. **Description:** The Veterans Affairs Maryland Health Care Systems has requested proposals from developers to build a retirement community at Fort Howard in Baltimore County. The historic site, which has about 36 mostly vacant buildings, could become the home to hundreds of war veterans. Details of the proposed development are discussed.

5547 ■ *"Vernon Revamp"* *in Business Courier (Vol. 26, October 9, 2009, No. 24, pp. 1)*

Pub: American City Business Journals, Inc.

Ed: Dan Monk. **Description:** Al Neyer Inc. will redevelop the Vernon Manor Hotel as an office building for the Cincinnati Children's Hospital Medical Center. The project will cost $35 million and would generate a new investment vehicle for black investors who plan to raise $2.7 million in private offerings to claim majority ownership of the property after its renovations.

5548 ■ *"Vision for Camden in Better Focus"* *in Philadelphia Business Journal (Vol. 30, September 30, 2011, No. 33, pp. 1)*

Pub: American City Business Journals Inc.

Ed: Natalie Kostelni. **Description:** More than $500 million worth of projects aimed at redeveloping the downtown and waterfront areas of Camden, New Jersey are being planned. These include the construction of residential, commercial, and education buildings.

5549 ■ *"Wal-Mart Proposed for Timmerman Plaza"* *in Business Journal-Milwaukee (Vol. 28, December 31, 2010, No. 14, pp. A1)*

Pub: Milwaukee Business Journal

Ed: Sean Ryan. **Description:** Dickson, Tennessee-based Gatlin Development Company Inc. owner Franklin C. Gatlin III revealed plans for a new Wal-Mart store in Timmerman Plaza in Milwaukee, Wisconsin. Wal-Mart plans to open up approximately 18 new stores in southeast Wisconsin in 2012 and the Timmerman project is the first of four that Gatlin will submit for city approval.

5550 ■ *"Was Mandating Solar Power Water Heaters For New Homes Good Policy?"* *in Hawaii Business (Vol. 54, August 2008, No. 2, pp. 28)*

Pub: Hawaii Business Publishing

Description: Senator Gary L. Kooser of District 7 Kauai-Niihau believes that the mandating of energy-efficient water heaters for new single-family homes starting in 2010 will help cut Hawaii's oil consumption. Ron Richmond of the Hawaii Solar Energy Association says that the content of SB 644 has nega-

tive consequences as it allows for choice of energy and not just solar, and it also eliminates tax credits for new homebuyers.

5551 ■ *"Water Conservation Helps GC's Building Attain LEED Gold Status"* *in Contractor (Vol. 56, September 2009, No. 9, pp. 5)*

Pub: Penton Media, Inc.

Description: Green contractor Marshall Erdman has built a new office building using green design. The facility is seen to become a prime Leadership in Energy and Environmental Design (LEED) building model. Details of the building's design and features are also provided.

5552 ■ *"Water Park, Convention Center Plan Matures"* *in Austin Business JournalInc. (Vol. 28, July 18, 2008, No. 18, pp. 1)*

Pub: American City Business Journals

Ed: Kate Harrington. **Description:** Plans for the proposed water park in Cedar Park in Austin, Texas is moving forward as it grows in size from 40 to 90 acres, with first phase of construction to begin in early 2009.

5553 ■ *"Watershed Solution"* *in Business Courier (Vol. 24, December 14, 2008, No. 35, pp. 1)*

Pub: American City Business Journals, Inc.

Ed: Dan Monk. **Description:** Discusses the Metropolitan Sewer District of Greater Cincinnati which is planning to spend around $128 million for its 20-year green-infrastructure improvement projects. Part of the project involves construction of green roofs, rain gardens and restored wetlands to manage water overflows.

5554 ■ *"Wayne, Oakland Counties Create Own 'Medical Corridor"* *in Crain's Detroit Business (Vol. 24, October 6, 2008, No. 40, pp. 8)*

Pub: Crain Communications, Inc.

Ed: Jay Greene. **Description:** Woodward Medical Corridor that runs along Woodward Avenue and currently encompasses twelve hospitals and is rapidly growing with additional physician offices, advanced oncology centers and new hospitals. Beaumont Hospital is building a $160 million proton-beam therapy cancer center on its Royal Oak campus in a joint venture with Procure Treatment Centers of Bloomington Ind. That is expected to open in 2010 and will employ approximately 145 new workers.

5555 ■ *"What Happens in Vegas Could Happen in Baltimore, Too"* *in Boston Business Journal (Vol. 29, June 17, 2011, No. 6, pp. 1)*

Pub: American City Business Journals Inc.

Ed: Daniel J. Sernovitz. **Description:** At least 36 companies expressed their interest in developing a casino in South Baltimore following the state commission's announcement for bids. Developers have until July 28, 2011 to submit their proposals. Baltimore's strong economy is the major factor for the interest, yet the fact that blackjack and poker are outlawed in Maryland could be a drawback.

5556 ■ *"What Homes Do Retirees Want?"* *in Canadian Business (Vol. 79, July 17, 2006, No. 14-15, pp.)*

Pub: Rogers Media

Ed: Joe Cataldo. **Description:** The obstacles and challenges faced by homebuilders in Canada as well as the approach adopted by them to appeal to the mature homebuilders segment, is discussed.

5557 ■ *"What Players in the Midmarket Are Talking About"* *in Mergers & Acquisitions: The Dealmaker's Journal (March 1, 2008)*

Pub: SourceMedia, Inc.

Description: Sports Properties Acquisition Corp. went public at the end of January; according to the company's prospectus, it is not limiting its focus to just teams, it is also considering deals for stadium construction companies, sports leagues, facilities, sports-related advertising and licensing of products, in addition to other related segments.

5558 ■ *"What's Good Faith Got to Do With Contracts?"* *in Contractor (Vol. 56, November 2009, No. 11, pp. 41)*

Pub: Penton Media, Inc.

Ed: Susan Linden McGreevy. **Description:** Uniform Commercial Code makes the obligation to act in good faith a term of every commercial transaction. The code generally applies to the sale of goods and not to construction contracts but parties to a construction contract have the right to expect people to act in good faith and forego actions not related to the contract itself.

5559 ■ *"Where Are the Vultures?"* *in Mergers & Acquisitions: The Dealmaker's Journal (March 1, 2008)*

Pub: SourceMedia, Inc.

Ed: Ken MacFadyen. **Description:** Although the real estate market is distressed, not many acquisitions are being made by distress private equity investors; this is due, in part, to the difficulty in assessing real estate industry firms since it is a sector which is so localized.

5560 ■ *"Will Home Buyers Pay for Green Features?"* *in Contractor (Vol. 56, October 2009, No. 10, pp. 70)*

Pub: Penton Media, Inc.

Ed: Bob Mader. **Description:** National Association of Home Builders commissioned a survey which shows that homeowners are interested in green as long as they do no have to pay much for it. The association did not allow a board member to read the survey which raises questions about how the questions were phrased and how the sample was selected.

5561 ■ *"Will Workers Be Left To Build It Here?"* *in Boston Business Journal (Vol. 31, June 3, 2011, No. 19, pp. 1)*

Pub: Boston Business Journal

Ed: Kyle Alspach. **Description:** Lack of skilled workers has resulted in delayed expansion of local manufacturing operations in Massachusetts. Acme Packet Inc. expects to add only 10 jobs by the end of 2011.

5562 ■ *"With Building Plans in Flux, County Could Sell Key Site"* *in Crain's Cleveland Business (Vol. 28, October 8, 2007, No. 40, pp. 1)*

Pub: Crain Communications, Inc.

Ed: Jay Miller. **Description:** Due to such issues as financial and administrative problems, Cuyahoga County commissioners have pushed back the construction timeline for a planned county administration center and are saying that they are considering selling the site in downtown Cleveland to developers who would erect a new office building that another large tenant could occupy.

5563 ■ *"Yates Helps Turn Log Home Green"* *in Contractor (Vol. 56, November 2009, No. 11, pp. 1)*

Pub: Penton Media, Inc.

Description: Dave Yates of F.W. Behler Inc. helped homeowners from James Creek, Pennsylvania achieve energy efficiency on the heating system of their log cabin. The mechanical system installed on the cabin had high-temp 'THW' water-to-water geothermal system by ClimateMaster, two twin-coil indirect water heaters, and several pre-assembled, pre-engineered Hydronex panels by Watts Radiant.

5564 ■ *"Your Place: Housing Developers Try to Read Generation Y"* *in Philadelphia Inquirer (December 2, 2010)*

Pub: Philadelphia Media Network Inc.

Ed: Al Heavens. **Description:** Results of a survey conducted with Generation Y individuals are examined, focusing on housing developments and whether this particular generation prefers suburban or rural lifestyles. Generation Y encompasses people ages 18 to 32 years old. Statistical data included.

5565 ■ *"Yudelson Challenges San Antonio Groups"* *in Contractor (Vol. 56, October 2009, No. 10, pp. 6)*

Pub: Penton Media, Inc.

Description: Green building consultant and author Jerry Yudelson made a presentation for the Central Texas Green Building Council and Leadership San

Antonio where he discussed the European approach to sustainability and how it can be used for designing green buildings. Yudelson also discussed how to use sustainable practices for planning 25 years into the future.

5566 ■ "ZF Revving Up Jobs, Growth" in Business Courier (Vol. 26, November 6, 2009, No. 28, pp. 1)
Pub: American City Business Journals, Inc.
Ed: Jon Newberry. Description: Proposed $96 million expansion of German-owned automotive supplier ZF Steering systems LLC is anticipated to generate 299 jobs in Boone County, Kentucky. ZF might invest $90 million in equipment, while the rest will go to building and improvements.

STATISTICAL SOURCES

5567 ■ Means Labor Rates for the Construction Industry
Pub: R. S. Means Co., Inc.
Released: Annual. Price: $379.95 (paper).

5568 ■ RMA Annual Statement Studies
Pub: Risk Management Association
Contact: Kevin M. Blakey, President
Released: Annual. Price: $175.00 2006-07 edition, $105.00. Description: Contains composite balance sheets and income statements for more than 360 industries, including the accounting, auditing, and bookkeeping industries. Also contains five years of comparative historical data for discerning trends. Includes 16 commonly used ratios, computed for most of the size groupings for nearly every industry.

5569 ■ Standard & Poor's Industry Surveys
Pub: Standard & Poor's Corp.
Released: Annual. Price: $3633.00. Description: Two-volume book that examines the prospects for specific industries, including trucking. Also provides analyses of trends and problems, statistical tables and charts, and comparative company analyses.

TRADE PERIODICALS

5570 ■ AMD Newsletter
Pub: Association of Millwork Distributors
Released: Monthly. Price: Included in membership; $40, nonmembers. Description: Reports on Association activities, government rulings, home building statistics, activities of members, and various other subjects of interest to sash and door jobbers.

5571 ■ AppendX
Pub: Appendx
URL(s): www.appendx.org. Released: Annual

5572 ■ Architects' Guide to Glass, Metal & Glazing
Pub: Key Communications Inc.
Contact: Debra Levy, President
E-mail: deb@glass.com
URL(s): www.glassguides.com/. Ed: Tara Taffera, Megan Headley, Ellen Rogers, Charles Cumpston. Released: 6/yr. Price: $19, Individuals one day; $39, Individuals one month; $259, Individuals.

5573 ■ Architectural Designs
Pub: Architectural Designs Inc.
Contact: Joel Davis, President
URL(s): www.architecturaldesigns.com/. Released: Quarterly

5574 ■ Builder: The Magazine of the National Association of Home Builders
Pub: Hanley Wood L.L.C.
Contact: Patrick J. Carroll, President
E-mail: pcarroll@hanleywood.com
URL(s): www.hanleywood.com/default.aspx?page=magazineswww.builderonline.com. Released: 13/yr. Price: $29.95, U.S. and Canada; $54.95, U.S. and Canada 2 years; $192, Other countries.

5575 ■ Building Standards
Pub: International Code Council
Ed: Greg Layne, Editor, glayne@icbo.org. Released: 6/year. Price: $25; $40 2 years; $55 3 years. Description: Provides articles of interest to building of-

ficials, architects, engineers, and others in the construction industry. The newsletter is part of Building Standards magazine subscription.

5576 ■ California Builder & Engineer
Pub: California Builder & Engineer Inc.
URL(s): www.acppubs.com/page_subscribe.html. Released: Biweekly Price: $30, Individuals; $2, Single issue.

5577 ■ CE News
Pub: Mercor Media
URL(s): www.cenews.com. Ed: Bob Drake. Released: Monthly

5578 ■ C.F.M.A. Building Profits: The Magazine for Construction Financial Professionals
Pub: Construction Financial Management Association
Contact: Stuart Binstock, President
URL(s): www.cfma.org/. Released: Bimonthly Price: $320, Individuals contractor; $420, Individuals industry service provider.

5579 ■ CM Advisor
Pub: Construction Management Association of America
Contact: Bruce D'Agostino, President
Ed: Dannelle Prezioso, Editor, dprezioso@cmaanet.org. Released: Bimonthly. Price: Included in membership. Description: Provides information on construction management and its technical, legal, and legislative issues. Recurring features include letters to the editor, news of research, a calendar of events, reports of meetings, news of educational opportunities, book reviews, notices of publications available, and columns titled Government Affairs and For Your Information.

5580 ■ Construction Briefings
Pub: Thomson West
Contact: Kathryn M. Downing, President
Ed: Lisa C. Weltsch, Editor, lisa.weltsch@westgroup.com. Released: Monthly. Price: $1464.00. Description: Covers issues in construction contracting.

5581 ■ Construction Contracts Law Report
Pub: Thomson West
Contact: Kathryn M. Downing, President
Ed: Richard L. Shea, Editor, richard.shea@westgroup.com. Released: Biweekly. Price: $1679.04 year. Description: Contains news, insight, and analysis of construction industry developments and cases.

5582 ■ Construction Division Newsletter
Pub: NSC Press
Contact: Janet Froetscher, President
E-mail: janet.froetscher@nsc.org
Ed: Laura Coyne, Editor. Released: Bimonthly. Price: $15, members; $19, nonmembers. Description: Focuses on industrial and occupational safety in the construction industry. Carries items on such topics as safe work practices and products; accident prevention; and successful industrial safety programs and policies. Remarks: Available online only.

5583 ■ Construction Executive: The Magazine for the Business of Construction
Pub: Associated Builders and Contractors Inc.
Contact: Kirk Pickerel, President
E-mail: pickerel@abc.org
URL(s): www.constructionexec.com. Released: Monthly

5584 ■ Construction Litigation Reporter
Pub: Thomson West
Contact: Kathryn M. Downing, President
Ed: Marc Schneier, Editor. Released: 11/year. Price: $1322.96, individuals. Description: Consists of articles, case digests, and commentary covering recent litigation in the construction field. Recurring features include lists of expert witnesses.

5585 ■ Construction Reports: Housing Starts (C20)
Pub: U.S. Government Printing Office
URL(s): www.census.gov/prod/www/abs/c22.html. Released: Monthly Price: $16, Individuals; $22.40, Other countries; $4.25, Single issue; $5.95, Other countries single issue.

5586 ■ Construction Specifications Institute--Newsdigest
Pub: The Construction Specifications Institute
Ed: Dan Merriman, Editor, dmerriman@csinet.org. Released: Monthly. Price: Included in membership; $48, nonmembers. Description: Covers the technical and certification programs offered by the Institute, which is 'dedicated to the advancement of construction technology through service, education, and research.' Also reports on regional and chapter activities and carries items on educational programs related to the construction industry. Recurring features include news of members, a calendar of events, listings of new publications available through the Institute, and columns titled Board Flash, Convention Briefs, and T.I.E. (Technical Information and Education Activities).

5587 ■ The Construction Specifier: Solutions for the Construction Industry
Pub: The Construction Specifications Institute
URL(s): www.csinet.org/www.constructionspecifier.com/. Released: Monthly

5588 ■ Constructor: The Construction Management Magazine
Pub: Associated General Contractors of America
Contact: Ted Aadland, President
URL(s): constructor.agc.org/. Released: Bimonthly Price: $95, Individuals.

5589 ■ Construire
Pub: Association de la construction du Quebec
URL(s): www.acq.org/index.php?option=com_content&task=view&id=50&Itemid=2361. Released: Bimonthly

5590 ■ Contractors Hot Line Monthly: The One-of-A-Kind Locating and Pricing Guide for Construction Equipment
Pub: Heartland Communications Group Inc.
Contact: Gale W. McKinney, II, President
E-mail: gale@hlipublishing.com
URL(s): www.hlipublishing.com/store/construction-magazines/contractorshot-li ne-monthly. Released: Monthly Price: $15.95, Single issue.

5591 ■ Current Housing Reports: H-130, Market Absorption of Apartments
Pub: U.S. Government Printing Office
URL(s): www.census.gov/prod/www/abs/apart.html. Released: Quarterly Price: $18, Individuals; $25.20, Other countries.

5592 ■ Design Cost Data: Cost Estimating Magazine for Design and Construction
Pub: DC & D Technologies Inc.
Contact: David Castelli, Manager
URL(s): www.dcd.com. Released: Bimonthly Price: $94, Individuals silver; $157, Two years silver; $149, Individuals gold; $239, Two years gold.

5593 ■ ECA Magazine
Pub: Engineering Contractors Association
Contact: Wes May, Executive Director
URL(s): www.ecaonline.net/ECA_Magazinex.html. Released: Monthly

5594 ■ Environmental Building News
Pub: Building Green Inc.
Ed: Alexander T. Wilson, Editor, alex@buildinggreen.com. Released: Monthly. Price: $99, individuals U.S.; $199 for organization; $169, two years U.S. Description: Covers the building trade with an environmental slant. Covers nontoxic materials, better landscaping and water use, and resources for energy conservation in a technical manner.

5595 ■ *Fine Homebuilding*
Pub: Taunton Press Inc.
Contact: John Lively, Chief Executive Officer
URL(s): www.finehomebuilding.com. **Ed:** Kevin Ireton. **Released:** 8/yr. **Price:** $37.95, U.S.; $65.95, U.S. two years; $93.95, U.S. three years; $40.95, Canada; $45.95, Other countries.

5596 ■ *Heavy Equipment Guide*
Pub: Baum Publications Ltd.
URL(s): heg.baumpub.com/. **Released:** 10/yr. **Price:** Free.

5597 ■ *Housing Economics*
Pub: Economics Dept.
Released: Monthly. **Description:** Presents statistical data on the housing industry and includes news of governmental agency actions, business and economic trends, and housing trends. Analyzes the interrelationship between housing and the economy as well as between the industry and government policy. Recurring features include building permit activity, employment rates, and housing opportunity index.

5598 ■ *Interior Construction*
Pub: Ceilings and Interior Systems Construction Association
Contact: Shawn Burnum, President
E-mail: shawn.burnum@pcg.com
URL(s): www.cisca.org/i4a/pages/index.cfm?pageid=1. **Released:** Bimonthly **Price:** $75, Nonmembers; $40, Members.

5599 ■ *Intermountain Contractor*
Pub: McGraw-Hill Inc.
URL(s): intermountain.construction.com/. **Ed:** Melissa Leslie. **Released:** Weekly **Price:** $40, Individuals.

5600 ■ *Journal of Construction Accounting and Taxation*
Pub: Research Institute of America
Contact: Peter Warwick, President
URL(s): ria.thomson.com/estore/detail.aspx?ID=WJCA. **Released:** Bimonthly

5601 ■ *Metal Architecture*
Pub: Modern Trade Communications Inc.
URL(s): www.metalarchitecture.com. **Released:** Monthly **Price:** $75, Canada and Mexico; $150, Other countries; $45, Individuals.

5602 ■ *Midwest Contractor*
Pub: Reed Construction Data Inc.
Contact: Iain Melville, Chief Executive Officer
URL(s): www.acppubs.com/. **Released:** Semimonthly

5603 ■ *The NAWIC Image*
Pub: National Association of Women in Construction
Contact: Tamie Taylor, President
E-mail: karar@nawic.org
Ed: Leona P. Dalavai, Editor, leonad@nawic.org. **Released:** 6/year. **Price:** $50, nonmembers. **Description:** Fosters career advancement for women in construction. Features women business owners, training for construction trades and educational programs. Recurring features include columns titled Issues and Trends, Road to Success, Chapter Highlights, Members on the Move, and Q&A.

5604 ■ *Panel World*
Pub: Hatton-Brown Publishers Inc.
Contact: Cindy Sparks, Manager
E-mail: cindy@hattonbrown.com
URL(s): www.panelworldmag.com/. **Released:** Bimonthly

5605 ■ *Pavement: The International Journal of the Asphalt Aftermarket*
Pub: Cygnus Business Media
Contact: Rich Reiff, President
URL(s): www.cygnusb2b.com/PropertyPub.cfm?PropertyID=109www.forconstructionpros.com/magazine/pvm. **Ed:** Allan Heydorn. **Released:** 8/yr. **Price:** Free.

5606 ■ *Practice Periodical on Structural Design and Construction*
Pub: American Society of Civil Engineers Architectural Engineering Institute
Contact: D. Wayne Klotz, President
URL(s): ascelibrary.org/sco. **Released:** Quarterly **Price:** $420, Institutions print & online; $440, Institutions, other countries print & online; $368, Institutions print; $388, Institutions, other countries print; $323, U.S. and other countries online; $105, Members print & online; $125, Members international; print & online; $92, Members print; $112, Members international; print; $81, U.S. and other countries online only.

5607 ■ *Professional Builder: The Magazine of the Housing and Light Construction Industry*
Pub: SGC Horizon LLC
URL(s): www.housingzone.com/professionalbuilder. **Ed:** David Barista. **Released:** Monthly **Price:** Free.

5608 ■ *Remodeling*
Pub: Hanley Wood L.L.C.
Contact: Patrick J. Carroll, President
E-mail: pcarroll@hanleywood.com
URL(s): www.remodeling.hw.net. **Released:** 13/yr. **Price:** $24.95, Individuals; $39.95, Individuals Canadian residents; $192, Individuals international residents.

5609 ■ *Roofing Contractor*
Pub: BNP Media
Contact: Al Reser, President
URL(s): www.roofingcontractor.com/. **Released:** Monthly **Price:** $25, Free to qualified subscribers; $5, Individuals; $5, Single issue.

5610 ■ *Rural Builder*
Pub: FW Publications
Contact: Sara Domville, President
E-mail: sara.domville@fwpubs.com
URL(s): www.ruralbuilder.com/ruralbuilder/. **Released:** 7/yr. **Price:** Free.

5611 ■ *Solar Today*
Pub: American Solar Energy Society
Contact: Chuck Kutscher, Director
URL(s): www.solartoday.org. **Ed:** Regina Johnson. **Released:** Bimonthly; 6/yr. **Price:** included in membership dues; $29, /year for nonmembers.

5612 ■ *System-Built Advantage*
Pub: National Association of Home Builders
Ed: Barbara Martin, Editor. **Released:** Monthly. **Price:** Included in membership. **Description:** Carries industry and Council news for manufacturers of systems-built housing and suppliers. Recurring features include legislative updates, a calendar of events, news of research, announcements of educational opportunities, and meeting reports.

5613 ■ *Timber Framing: Journal of the Timber Framers Guild*
Pub: Timber Framers Guild
Contact: Joel McCarty, Executive Director
URL(s): www.timberframersguild.org/pubpg.html. **Ed:** Ken Rower. **Released:** Quarterly **Price:** $25, Free with membership; $25, Nonmembers.

5614 ■ *Traditional Building: Historical Products for Public Architecture*
Pub: Historical Trends Corp.
URL(s): www.traditional-building.com. **Ed:** Clem Labine. **Released:** Bimonthly **Price:** $21.95, Individuals; $65, Canada; $35.95, Two years.

5615 ■ *Wood Design & Building*
Pub: Canadian Wood Council
Contact: Michael Giroux, President
E-mail: mgiroux@cwc.ca
URL(s): www.cwc.ca/. **Released:** Quarterly **Price:** $24, Individuals; $40, Two years; $55, Two years other countries; $35, Other countries; $50, Canada 3 years; $70, Other countries 3 years.

5616 ■ *Words From Woody*
Pub: David W. Wood
Ed: David W. Wood, Editor. **Released:** Quarterly. **Price:** $24.95; $39.95, two years. **Description:** Contains information of interest to construction-related firms. Also includes business and marketing tips.

VIDEOCASSETTES/ AUDIOCASSETTES

5617 ■ *Construction Systems Technology*
Bergwall Productions, Inc.
1 DIckinson Drive, Brandywine BUilding 5, Ste. 105
Chadds Ford, PA 19317
Ph: (610)361-0334
Free: 800-934-8696
Fax: (610)361-0092
URL: http://www.bergwall.com
Released: 1989. **Price:** $369.00. **Description:** Modern construction technologies and methodologies are examined. **Availability:** VHS.

5618 ■ *Safety Orientation for Construction Contractors*
DuPont Safety Resources
PO Box 80013
Wilmington, DE 19880-0013
Free: 800-532-7233
Fax: (888)644-7233
URL: http://www2.dupont.com/Sustainable_Solutions/en_US/practice_areas/safety_consultants/index.html
Released: 1993. **Price:** $475.00. **Description:** Designed to raise and promote safety consciousness among construction contractors and their employees. Includes an administrator's guide and personal handbooks outlining site safety rules and work practices. **Availability:** VHS.

5619 ■ *The 3-Point Contact*
Film Library/National Safety Council California Chapter
4553 Glencoe Ave., Ste. 150
Marina Del Rey, CA 90292
Ph: (310)827-9781
Free: 800-421-9585
Fax: (310)827-9861
Co. E-mail: California@nsc.org
URL: http://www.nsc.org/nsc_near_you/FindYourLocalChapter/Pages/California.aspx
Released: 198?. **Description:** This program demonstrates the safest ways to mount and dismount heavy construction equipment. **Availability:** VHS; 3/4 U; Special order formats.

TRADE SHOWS AND CONVENTIONS

5620 ■ AEC-ST
Ecobuild Federal, LCC
1645 Falmouth Rd., Ste. 1A
Centerville, MA 02632
Ph: (508)790-4751
Free: 800-996-3863
Fax: (508)790-4750
Co. E-mail: support@aecst.com
URL: http://www.aececobuild.com/
URL(s): www.aecst.com/. **Frequency:** Annual. **Audience:** Design and construction professionals, engineers, government officials, facility managers. **Principal Exhibits:** Sustainable and environmental design, energy efficiency, green building, best practices and expert strategies, building information modeling, future of IT trends.

5621 ■ The Builders' Show
National Association of Home Builders of the U.S.
1201 15th St. NW
Washington, DC 20005
Ph: (202)266-8200
Free: 800-368-5242

Fax: (202)822-0586
Co. E-mail: info@nahb.com
Contact: Robert F. Nielsen, Chairman of the Board
URL(s): www.buildershow.com. **Frequency:** Annual.
Audience: Trade. **Principal Exhibits:** Building products, equipment, and services.

5622 ■ CONEXPO-CON/AGG
International Concrete and Aggregates Group (ICAG)
900 Spring St.
Silver Spring, MD 20910
Ph: (301)587-3140
Free: 800-867-6060
Fax: (301)587-4260
URL(s): www.conexpoconagg.com. **Frequency:** Annual. **Audience:** Construction and related equipment contractors, manufacturers, distributors, engineers, and government officials. **Principal Exhibits:** Construction and construction materials industry equipment, supplies, and services. **Telecommunication Services:** info@conexpoconagg.com.

5623 ■ Indiana's Midwest Builders Convention
Indiana Builders Association
101 W. Ohio St., Ste. 1111
Indianapolis, IN 46204
Ph: (317)917-1100
Free: 800-377-6334
Fax: (317)917-0335
Co. E-mail: info@buildindiana.org
URL: http://www.buildindiana.org
Contact: Rick Wajda, Chief Executive Officer
E-mail: rick@buildindiana.org
URL(s): buildindiana.org. **Frequency:** Annual. **Audience:** Builders, remodelers, and subcontractors. **Principal Exhibits:** Building supplies, including windows, doors, and insulation; title insurance information. **Dates and Locations:** , Convention Center.

5624 ■ Michigan Construction & Design Tradeshow
Construction Specifications Institute
URL(s): www.cam-online.com. **Frequency:** Annual. **Audience:** Trade professionals. **Principal Exhibits:** Construction industry equipment, supplies, and services. **Telecommunication Services:** marketing@cam-online.com.

5625 ■ Power Show Ohio
Ohio-Michigan Equipment Dealers Association (OMEDA)
PO Box 68
Dublin, OH 43017
Ph: (614)889-1309
Fax: (614)889-0463
Co. E-mail: info@amgllcusa.com
URL: http://www.omeda.org
Contact: L. Kim Rominger, Chief Executive Officer
Frequency: Annual. **Audience:** Trade professionals and general public. **Principal Exhibits:** Construction equipment, agricultural equipment, and outdoor power equipment. **Dates and Locations:** , Ohio Exposition Center.

CONSULTANTS

5626 ■ A/R/C Associates Inc.
601 N Fern Creek Ave., Ste. 100
Orlando, FL 32803-4899
Ph: (407)896-7875
Fax: (407)898-6043
Co. E-mail: info@arc-arc.com
URL: http://www.arc-arc.com
Contact: Donald G. Dorner, President
Scope: Architectural firm with specialized capacities in roof consulting and construction technology. Services include: Facility evaluation reports, construction document preparation, bidding and negotiation, construction contract observation and contract administration; roof consulting-roof investigation and analysis, roof inspection and maintenance scheduling, roof litigation and expert testimony, and historical roof preservation and restoration. **Founded:** 1982.

5627 ■ Breen & Associates Inc.
PO Box 120424
Arlington, TX 76012
Ph: (817)275-4711
Fax: (817)275-4711
Co. E-mail: jbreen504@aol.com
Contact: James E. Breen, President
E-mail: jbreen504@aol.com
Scope: Building construction consultants offering complete inspection services of residential and commercial structures (includes structural, equipment and systems). Clients include real estate brokers, investors (real estate) and builders/developers. **Founded:** 1978.

5628 ■ Capital Project Management Inc. (CPMI)
1777 Sentry Pky. W, Abington Hall, Ste. 100
Blue Bell, PA 19422-2210
Ph: (267)464-0500
Free: 888-260-2626
Fax: (267)464-0400
Co. E-mail: cpmi@cpmiteam.com
URL: http://www.cpmiteam.com
Contact: William M. Wolf, Jr., Principal
E-mail: wwolf@cpmiteam.com
Scope: Engineering consulting firm specializing in contract dispute analysis and resolution; project management oversight; project controls; and surety evaluations. Specializes in analyzing and resolving construction and manufacturing contract disputes. Evaluates technical, schedule and cost issues; develops dispute resolution strategies; assists in settlement negotiations and provides expert witness testimony. **Founded:** 1996. **Publications:** "Dealing with Mid-Course Adjustments in Project Planning and Scheduling, and Resultant Claims"; "The ABCs of DRBs"; "Identifying Concurrent Delay"; "When the Best-Laid Plans Go Astray"; "Techniques and Methods for Assessing Delays". **Seminars:** Demystifying Scheduling, New York, Mar, 2007; Handling Construction Risks2006, Allocate Now or Litigate Later, New York, Apr, 2006; 2005 CPM Case Law - Year in Review and One Slice In Time: Two Competing Perspectives for Analyzing Project Delay, Orlando, Apr, 2006.

5629 ■ CMD Group
30 Technology Pkwy., No. 100
Norcross, GA 30092
Ph: (770)417-4000
Fax: (770)417-4002
Co. E-mail: chris.caset@cmdg.com
Contact: Jen Gallam, President
Scope: Provider of products and services including national, regional and local construction data, building product information, construction cost data, market analytics and advertising channels to construction industry professionals in the US and Canada. Offers information on commercial construction, architects and specifiers and CAD and technical information for manufacturer's building products.

5630 ■ Commercial Cost Control Inc.
3523 Princeton Corners Ln.
Marietta, GA 30062
Ph: (770)971-2557
Fax: (817)656-3310
Co. E-mail: info@commercialcostcontrol.com
URL: http://www.commercialcostcontrol.com
Contact: Calvin Boybstun, Partner
Scope: A construction audit firm dedicated to providing value to clients by reducing or recovering capital and expense cost items while maintaining sensitivity to the partnership between clients and their vendors. Services include construction audit services, lease audit services, subtenant portfolio audits, utility audit and consultation, bill verification, rate audits, deregulation opportunity assessments and accounts payable audit services. **Founded:** 1996.

5631 ■ Construction Experts Inc. (CEI)
2419 Sacada Cir.
Encinitas, CA 92023-1832

Ph: (760)634-2474
Co. E-mail: info@constructionguy.com
URL: http://www.constructionguy.com
Contact: Robert R. George, President
E-mail: bob@constructionclasses.com
Scope: Provider of consultation, assistance and guidance to construction companies in the process of developing in-house construction training programs for both craft and supervisory workers. Provides self-paced and paced online courses for educational institutions and non-profit industry organizations. **Founded:** 1994. **Publications:** "Scheduling for Estimators"; "The Cost of Training Construction People"; "Eichleay Formula Calculations". **Seminars:** Training Programs for Construction; Introduction to Construction Estimating; Construction Blueprint Reading; Eichleay Formula Calculations; How to Estimate the Cost of Training.

5632 ■ Construction Interface Services Inc.
2 N Front St., 5th Fl.
Wilmington, NC 28401
Ph: (910)762-4165
Free: 888-899-6312
Fax: (910)762-4703
Co. E-mail: info@constructor.com
URL: http://www.constructor.com
Contact: John Bahr, President
E-mail: jlb@constructor.com
Scope: Provider of project management consulting services and seminars to contractors, attorneys, sureties, lending institutions, owners and design professionals. **Founded:** 1991. **Seminars:** Training and seminars on scheduling, productivity, cost control, documentation, negotiation, change order preparation and claims management.

5633 ■ Construction Testing Inc. (CTI)
925 N Jerome St.
Allentown, PA 18109-1925
Ph: (610)433-6871
Fax: (610)433-7594
Contact: Dolores J. Demyan, President
Scope: Specializing in testing and inspection of concrete, soil structural steel, aggregates, concrete masonry units and mortar, structural clay brick, bituminous concrete, and high strength non-shrink grout. **Founded:** 1991.

5634 ■ Corporate Facility Services Inc. (CFS)
9 Daffodil Ln.
San Carlos, CA 94070-1552
Ph: (650)610-9111
Fax: (650)610-9119
Co. E-mail: info@corpfacserv.com
URL: http://www.corpfacserv.com
Contact: David Bourland, President
E-mail: david.bourland@corpfacserv.com
Scope: Provider of project management services for construction, furniture and relocation projects in Silicon Valley and the San Francisco Bay Area. Services provided include: planning and budgeting; assessing current and future facility requirements; exploring and analyzing logical approaches; articulating objectives on behalf of management; directing the conceptual design process and developing budget estimates documenting plans for evaluation by management. **Founded:** 1993.

5635 ■ Draper & Associates
5665 New Northside Dr., Ste. 100
Atlanta, GA 30328-4617
Ph: (404)256-3601
Free: 800-257-0691
Fax: (404)256-3922
Co. E-mail: crivers@draperandassociates.com
URL: http://www.draperandassociates.com
Contact: Gary W. Draper, President
Scope: Provider of construction project management services. Has managed projects ranging from single facility renovations to billion-dollar multi-project environments. **Founded:** 1972. **Publications:** "Our Economy Stinks. Your Projects Don't Have To," Sep, 2009; "The Demolition of Bowen Homes," Jul, 2009; "The Art of Listening," Jul, 2009; "Another Meeting," May, 2009; "Giving Hope to All Atlantans," May, 2009; "Do You Need an Upgrade," May, 2009. **Seminars:** Champagne Services of a Beer Budget, Sep, 2009.

5636 ■ Empire Building Diagnostics Inc.
2 Main St.
Depew, NY 14043
Ph: (716)685-4588
Fax: (716)685-6055
Co. E-mail: empire@ebdinc.com
URL: http://www.ebdinc.com
Contact: Carolann Pagano, Principal
E-mail: carolannp@ebdinc.com
Scope: Consulting firm that provides a full range of pre-renovation contracting services. Specializes in asbestos abatement, asbestos inspections/consulting, asbestos emergency response, lead testing and abatement, third party representation, project management/specification, concrete/CMU saw cutting/removal, radon testing/consulting, site and structure demolition, industrial services and contracting, commercial cleaning, indoor air quality and tank removal and soil remediation. **Founded:** 1988.

5637 ■ Engineering and Technical Consultants Inc.
46040 Center Oak Plz., Ste. 100
Sterling, VA 20166
Ph: (703)450-6220
Fax: (703)444-2285
Co. E-mail: info@etc-web.com
URL: http://www.etc-web.com
Contact: Joseph D. Shuffleton, President
E-mail: jshuff@etc-web.com
Scope: Provider of evaluations, intrusive evaluation, design and specifications, solicitation and review of bids, construction monitoring, administration, forensic investigation, testing, document review, research and negotiations services. **Founded:** 1982.

5638 ■ Environmental & Engineering Services Inc.
687 NW 5th St.
Corvallis, OR 97330
Ph: (541)754-1062
Fax: (541)753-3948
Co. E-mail: kelly.guenther@eesinet.com
URL: http://www.eesinet.com
Contact: Steve Barney, Principal
Scope: Provider of mechanical, electrical engineering and commissioning services, with a special emphasis in renovation and energy upgrades. Offers a wide range of HVAC, electrical and controls engineering services including feasibility assessments, master planning, budgeting, cost analysis, design, computer aided drafting, energy use modeling, facility management and construction management. **Founded:** 1979.

5639 ■ Fanning, Fanning & Associates Inc.—FFA Inc.
2555 74th St.
Lubbock, TX 79423
Ph: (806)745-2533
Fax: (806)745-3596
Co. E-mail: nfanning@fanningfanning.com
URL: http://www.fanningfanning.com
Contact: William White, Manager
E-mail: bwhite@fanningfanning.com
Scope: Specializes in engineering services including mechanical, electrical, plumbing design and plant layout, HVAC, energy conservation and management, utilities, fire protection and alarms, central heating and cooling plants and communications for institutional, commercial and industrial buildings. Offers design services for drawings, specifications and bid documents, master planning, engineering reports, estimates, analysis, feasibility studies and construction phase services.

5640 ■ Fard Engineers Inc.
309 Lennon Ln., Ste. 200
Walnut Creek, CA 94598
Ph: (925)932-5505
Fax: (925)932-0555
Co. E-mail: mailbox@fard.com
URL: http://www.fard.com
Contact: Max E. Saiidnia, President
Scope: Designs mechanical and electrical systems for all types of buildings. Serves the construction industry in California, Oregon, Arizona, Washington and Nevada. Specialized in apartment buildings, senior housing complexes and school renovation. **Founded:** 1988. **Special Services:** Autocad and Paradox.

5641 ■ Franz Wolf Design and Construction Consultants
96 MacGregor Dr.
Mahopac, NY 10541-2779
Ph: (845)628-5159
Fax: (206)781-1911
Contact: Franz Wolf, Owner
Scope: Architectural consultant offers a wide range of particular and specialized areas of design and construction consulting. Particular expertise available in planning and master planning (sites, buildings, interior space planning, design and review); architectural (interior and exterior from concept to finish); building and zoning codes; and handicapped, local, state and federal laws. Industries served: owners, businesses, corporations, builders, contractors, entrepreneurs, law firms, architects, interior designers, and engineers. **Founded:** 1991. **Seminars:** NYC code sessions by NY state code division; NY state energy sessions.

5642 ■ GHT Ltd.
1010 N Glebe Rd., Ste. 200
Arlington, VA 22201-4749
Ph: (703)243-1200
Fax: (703)276-1376
Co. E-mail: ght@ghtltd.com
URL: http://www.ghtltd.com
Contact: Robert M. Menuet, Principal
E-mail: rmenuet@ghtltd.com
Scope: Provider of design services in mechanical engineering. Offers telecommunications and security engineering services. Provides life safety engineering services and utilities planning services. Provides estimates of life expectancy and replacement or upgrade costs for mechanical and electrical equipment and systems. **Founded:** 1965. **Publications:** "Critical spaces keep the pace of business humming," May, 2004; "To avoid staticlater, hire right telecom consultant," Oct, 2007. **Special Services:** LEED®.

5643 ■ Greacen Consulting Engineers Inc.
919 Old Hwy. 8 NW, Ste. 200
Saint Paul, MN 55112
Ph: (651)633-1318
Fax: (651)633-1885
Contact: Ed Greacen, Principal
Scope: Specializes in plumbing, heating, ventilating, air conditioning and project management. Designs domestic water and water treatment systems, fire protection, fuel and gas piping, humidification and de-humidification systems, variable air volume (VAV), fan-powered VAV, and retrofit systems for Indoor Air Quality (IAQ). **Founded:** 1999.

5644 ■ Hatch Associates—Hatch
Sheridan Science and Technology Pk., 2800 Speakman Dr.
Mississauga, ON, Canada L5K 2R7
Ph: (905)855-7600
Fax: (905)855-8270
Co. E-mail: tomreid@hatch.ca
URL: http://www.hatch.ca
Contact: Kurt A. Strobele, Chief Executive Officer
Scope: Provides process and business consulting, information technology, engineering and project and construction management services to the mining, metallurgical, manufacturing, energy and infrastructure industries. **Founded:** 1955. **Telecommunication Services:** hatch@hatch.ca.

5645 ■ Historic Exterior Paint Colors Consulting—Historic House Colors
3661 Waldenwood Dr.
Ann Arbor, MI 48105
Ph: (734)668-0298
Co. E-mail: robs@umich.edu
URL: http://www.historichousecolors.com
Contact: Robert Schweitzer, Owner
E-mail: robs@umich.edu
Scope: Provider of exterior paint color consulting services. Provides services for historic, contemporary, new, commercial and residential services; museums. **Publications:** "Proof that Paint Color Lends Detail," Arts and Crafts Homes, 2006; "Bungalow Colors-Exteriors," Gibbs-Smith Publishers, 2002; "Color Scheming," Design NJ, 2002; "Colonial Revival Homes," Victorian Homes, Feb, 2003; "America's Favorite Homes"; "Color a New World," 60s Ranch Color Makeover, Romantic Homes, Aug, 2001; "How Shall I Paint my House," American Bungalow, 1999; "Color Concepts and Bungalow Basics," Cottages & Bungalows.

5646 ■ H.H. Holmes Testing Laboratories Inc.
170 Shepard Ave.
Wheeling, IL 60090
Ph: (847)541-4040
Fax: (847)537-9098
Co. E-mail: scott@hhholmestesting.com
URL: http://www.hhholmestesting.com
Contact: Scott R. Nelson, President
E-mail: scott@hhholmestesting.com
Scope: Offers soil, packaging and construction materials testing on-site and in laboratory. Provides reports and engineering recommendations. Laboratory services include: Full range of construction materials testing and research in soils, concrete, aggregate, asphalt, masonry, steel, paper, corrugated, wood, metals and plastics testing for retail, industrial and medical applications. **Founded:** 1936.

5647 ■ Home Builders Network (HBN)
205 E Ridgeville Blvd., Ste. C
Mount Airy, MD 21771
Ph: (301)829-6549
Free: 800-823-4344
Fax: (301)829-8907
Co. E-mail: info@hbnnet.com
URL: http://www.hbnnet.com
Contact: William Watkins, Partner
Scope: Provides a wide array of consulting services to homebuilder clients. Focus is on product, pricing, sales process management, optimization of capital and maintaining proper land positions. **Founded:** 1991. **Publications:** "Documents Contracts and Worksheets for Home Builders," Jun, 1998. **Seminars:** The Value-Driven Builder; Price it Right; Sales Are About; Spec for Success; The Builders Guide to Marketing Success; The Design Advantage; The New and Improved Builder Money Making Machine; Strategies and Tactics for a Competitive Market; The Art of War; Negotiation for Profit Creating the Customer; Beating the Competition Marketing Success; Creating the Brand Image; Lots of Opportunity-Land and Spec Houses; The Rd to Success; The Sequence of Success; Its About Time; Making a Difference in the Marketplace. **Telecommunication Services:** mail@hbnnet.com.

5648 ■ The Home Star Group
4646 N Hermitage Ave.
Chicago, IL 60640-4506
Ph: (773)878-7078
Fax: (773)878-7255
Co. E-mail: homestar1@aol.com
Contact: Ronald L. Gan, President
Scope: A full service construction consulting firm specializing in analyzing and reorganizing construction projects that not progressing as planned. Provides project analysis, financial analysis, project recovery services and litigation support.

5649 ■ Irvine Team—IrvineDCS Team L.L.C.Irvine Associates Architects Inc.;
4900 Woodway Dr., Ste. 1100
Houston, TX 77056
Ph: (713)840-1880
Fax: (713)840-1891
Co. E-mail: rmonsour@irvineteam.com
URL: http://www.irvineteam.com
Contact: Dennis Irvine, President
E-mail: dirvine@irvineteam.com
Scope: A design and construction strategy company that directs from concept to completion, incorporating project management and quality assurance services. Projects have included theaters, museums, civic facilities, health care and institutional entities, and large churches. Offers a range of strategic services to support design and construction, including project leadership, cost strategy development and manage-

ment, procurement and sourcing, scheduling, project control/construction management, and project accounting. **Founded:** 2002.

5650 ■ IRZ Consulting L.L.C.
505 E Main St.
Hermiston, OR 97838
Ph: (541)567-0252
Free: 800-823-7352
Fax: (541)567-4239
Co. E-mail: irz@irz.com
URL: http://www.irz.com
Contact: Farahmand A. Ziari, President
E-mail: fziari@irz.com
Scope: A full-service irrigation engineering and consulting firm that specializes in large scale irrigation development, design and construction management. **Founded:** 1984. **Seminars:** Umatilla Sub-Basin Replacement Water (SB 1069) Workshop, Oct, 2008.

5651 ■ C. E. Jackson, Jr.
1103 Virginia Ave.
McComb, MS 39649-1226
Ph: (601)684-1107
Fax: (601)684-4232
Co. E-mail: cejjrpe@telepak.net
URL: http://www.telapex.com/~cejjrpe/resour01.htm
Contact: C.E. Jackson, Jr., President
E-mail: cejjrpe@telepak.net
Scope: Construction consulting services in construction safety, civil engineering, construction management, electrical safety, construction engineering, OSHA regulations, arbitration/mediation, public safety, demolition, steel erection, trenching/excavation, highway work-zone safety, and construction equipment safety.

5652 ■ JDE Construction Management Ltd.
14321-112 Ave.
Edmonton, AB, Canada T5M 2W3
Ph: (780)429-4849
Free: 800-667-4849
Fax: (780)429-4843
Co. E-mail: jde@jdecm.com
Contact: John Dawson-Edwards, President
E-mail: john@jdecm.com
Scope: Construction consultants. Specializes in providing solutions that encourage the prevention, mitigation, and equitable settlement of construction disputes.

5653 ■ Kalin Associates Inc.
1121 Washington St.
Newton, MA 02465
Ph: (617)964-5477
Free: 800-565-2546
Fax: (617)964-5788
Co. E-mail: mark@kalinassociates.com
URL: http://www.kalinassociates.com
Contact: Mark J. Kalin, President
E-mail: mkalin@kalinassociates.com
Scope: Independent specifications firm specializing in preparation of technical specifications and bidding documents for construction projects, and preparation of guide specifications for building product manufacturers. Related service include development of master specifications for agencies and design firms; computer automation of technical documents; specification coordination for large projects. **Founded:** 1984. **Publications:** "Specifying Green Building Products," Rs Means, 2002. **Seminars:** Integrating BIM and Specifications at Ecobuild, Washington, DC.

5654 ■ Kohn Engineering
4220 Mountain Rd.
Macungie, PA 18062
Ph: (610)967-4766
Fax: (610)967-6468
Co. E-mail: don@kohnengineering.com
URL: http://www.kohnengineering.com
Contact: Don Kohn, Principal
E-mail: don@kohnengineering.com
Scope: Offers fire protection consulting. Provides a wide range of fire protection consulting services that includes design, code interpretation, expert witness, project management, fire safety program develop-

ment, and hazard identification. Provides cost effective solutions to fire protection problems. **Founded:** 1995. **Seminars:** Fire Protection in Nuclear Power Plants.

5655 ■ Kora Management Ltd.
200-2005 Sheppard Ave. E
Toronto, ON, Canada M2J 5B4
Ph: (705)675-2251
Free: 866-705-4447
Fax: (705)675-6302
Co. E-mail: mrspeigel@koramgt.com
URL: http://www.koramgt.com
Contact: Mitchell R. Speigel, President
E-mail: mrspeigel@koramgt.com
Scope: Specializes in construction, real estate development, management advice and dispute resolution services. Specializes in property management, administration and on-site construction. Offers services in five languages throughout North and South America. Provides personal and commercial loans; recruiting and financial consulting globally. **Founded:** 1995.

5656 ■ Lawrence Siegel-Consultant (LSC)
5292 Eliots Oak Rd.
Columbia, MD 21044
Ph: (410)997-9210
Fax: (410)997-0927
Co. E-mail: consult@lscourt.com
URL: http://www.lscourt.com
Contact: Lawrence Siegel, President
E-mail: lscourt@cs.com
Scope: Serves government agencies and architects with needs assessment, security analysis and design, facility planning, master planning, feasibility and pre-design, facility programming. **Founded:** 1975. **Publications:** "The Image Of Justice"; "Space Management and the Courts"; "Some Issues inCourt Security," The Court Manager, 1997.

5657 ■ Lee and Baldauf Consulting Engineers Inc.
12980 Pandora Dr., Ste. 201
Dallas, TX 75238
Ph: (214)342-0399
Fax: (214)342-2600
Co. E-mail: hlee@lbce.com
Contact: Harry A. Lee, President
E-mail: hlee@lbce.com
Scope: Provides structural engineering services to architects and owners in the commercial, institutional and industrial building markets. **Founded:** 1993.

5658 ■ Lundquist, Killeen, Potvin and Bender Inc.—LKPB Engineers Inc.
1935 W County Road B2, Ste. 300
Saint Paul, MN 55113-2722
Ph: (651)633-1223
Fax: (651)633-1355
Co. E-mail: nbart@lkpb.com
URL: http://www.lkpb.com
Contact: Allen V. Theisen, Manager
Scope: Provider of services in heating, ventilation, plumbing, piping, refrigeration, air conditioning, fire protection, lighting design and fixture selection, communications, electrical power distribution, security, life safety system design, energy conservation analysis, design and implementation. **Founded:** 1969.

5659 ■ Maharishi Global Construction L.L.C.
500 N 3rd St., Ste. 110
Fairfield, IA 52556
Ph: (641)472-7570
Co. E-mail: vedicarchitecture@maharishi.net
URL: http://www.vedicarchitecture.org
Contact: Doug Greenfield, President
Scope: Consulting services to designers and builders of homes and institutional and commercial buildings, pre-designed homes and office buildings providing drawings and specifications. **Founded:** 1997. **Publications:** "Austin House and Home," Jul, 2000.

5660 ■ Materials Advisory Group Inc.
9457 S University Blvd., Ste. 245
Littleton, CO 80126
Ph: (303)757-6284

Fax: (303)757-3363
Contact: Keith A. Jones, President
Scope: Mining, mineral and construction materials consultants whose services include business sales, acquisitions, divestitures, valuations, succession planning, management consulting, marketing and market research. **Founded:** 1987.

5661 ■ McKay/Moore Consultants L.L.C.
7323 11th Ave. NW
Seattle, WA 98117-4142
Ph: (206)781-0676
Free: 888-680-4987
Fax: (888)680-4987
Co. E-mail: mckaymoore@strabo.com
URL: http://www.mckaymoore.com
Contact: Patricia Moore, Owner
E-mail: mckaymoore@strabo.com
Scope: Provider of cost estimating/consulting services for all disciplines of a construction project - architectural, structural, mechanical, electrical, and civil. Services include: value engineering cost support, expert witness, and cost estimate review/quality; control and administrative support services. **Founded:** 1996. **Publications:** "Estimating Mechanical Systems". **Seminars:** Port of Seattle Engineering Department Estimating; Plywood Manufacturing.

5662 ■ MDA Engineering Inc.—Mechanical Design Associates Inc.
1415 Holland Rd.
Maumee, OH 43537
Ph: (419)893-3141
Fax: (419)893-0687
Co. E-mail: info@mdaengr.com
URL: http://www.mdaengr.com
Contact: Kevin P. Lafferty, President
E-mail: klafferty@mdaengr.com
Scope: Provider of mechanical, electrical and telecommunications engineering services. Engineers systems for new building construction, building renovations and industrial process support. Services include: Commercial, municipal, educational, industrial, research and development and healthcare facilities. Offers a spectrum of mechanical engineering and consulting services. **Founded:** 1976.

5663 ■ Mueser Rutledge Consulting Engineers (MRCE)
14 Penn Plz., 225 W 34th St., 2nd Fl.
New York, NY 10122-0002
Ph: (917)339-9300
Fax: (917)339-9400
Co. E-mail: mhuguet@mrce.com
URL: http://www.mrce.com
Contact: Francis J. Arland, Partner
E-mail: farland@mrce.com
Scope: Geotechnical and structural foundation engineering services provided for: Foundation design: Building foundations; transportation structures; special structures and excavation support; temporary structures; claim support; underpinning. Geotechnical services: investigations, analysis and recommendations; field observation and testing; groundwater control and waste containment; ground improvement. Instrumentation: marine and water-related structures; waterfront development studies; piers, wharves and bulkheads; outfalls and intakes; cellular cofferdams; dams and dikes; waste water treatment plants. **Founded:** 1910. **Publications:** "Deep Foundations in Washington, DC," 2006; "Urban Sites present firms with foundation challenges," 2006; "Woodrow Wilson Bridge Cofferdams," 2005; "Slurry Trench Design and Construction in Difficult Conditions," 2005; "Lessons Learned from Installation of ACIP Piles in Various Geologic Settings of the NYC Region," 2004; "Auger Cast Piles Founded in Compressible Bearing Stratum," 2004; "Design and Construction of the Watauga Raw Water Facility in Karstic Limestone near the City of Johnson City, TN"; "Construction Dewatering and Groundwater Control"; "90 Years of Foundation Engineering The Last 15 Years"; "A Tale of Two Towers," Civil Engineering Magazine, Jun, 2004; "Cantilever Frozen Ground Structure to Support 18M Deep Excavation"; "North American Tunneling," Apr, 2004; "Marine Foundations of Bridges in the Northeastern USA"; "Superjet Grouting A New Technology for In situ Soil Improvement," 2000. **Seminars:** Proceedings of the Deep Foundation Institutes Marine

Foundations; Underground Construction In Urban Environments; DFI Specialty; Marine Foundations: Proceedings of the Deep Foundation Institutes Marine Foundations Committee Specialty.

5664 ■ The Panigas Group of Companies
946 Edgeley Blvd.
Concord, ON, Canada L4K 4V4
Ph: (416)798-7199
Free: 866-726-4427
Fax: (905)669-4385
Contact: Lou Panigas, President
E-mail: lou_panigas@panigas.com
Scope: Firm provides services in design, signage and construction to the retail industry. Experience in feasibility studies, conceptual development of building and marketing parameters, site planning and civic coordination, base building design signage, communication and fixture design, full coordination of construction, construction documents and contract administration and post construction services. **Founded:** 1972.

5665 ■ PJ Materials Consultants Ltd.
11 Wagoners Trl.
Guelph, ON, Canada N1G 3M9
Ph: (519)767-0702
Fax: (519)821-2870
URL: http://www.pjmc.net
Contact: Paul Jeffs, Proprietor
E-mail: pjeffs@pjmc.net
Scope: Provider of a wide range of specialist concrete and masonry consultant services for concrete and masonry structures. Services include: provision of materials technology expertise and technical training. Provides technical consulting services for the design, specification, construction, restoration and protection of concrete and masonry structures. **Founded:** 1989. **Seminars:** Restoration and Conservation of Masonry Structures; Concrete in the Arabian Peninsular Today; Concrete Slabs on Grade; Modern Concrete Materials and Practices; Modern Concrete Materials and Practices.

5666 ■ Revay and Associates Ltd.
4333 St. Catherine St. W, Ste. 500
Montreal, QC, Canada H3Z 1P9
Ph: (514)932-2188
Fax: (514)939-0776
Co. E-mail: montreal@revay.com
URL: http://www.revay.com
Contact: Stephen G. Revay, President
E-mail: sgrevay@revay.com
Scope: Services include construction claims preparation; project management services; cost estimating; planning and scheduling; risk analysis; dispute resolution services; in-depth surveys and studies for the government and the construction industry. **Founded:** 1970.

5667 ■ Richmond Sterling Inc.
2870 Pharr Ct. S, Ste. 2007
Atlanta, GA 30305
Ph: (404)525-9606
Fax: (404)525-4416
Co. E-mail: contact@richmondsterling.com
URL: http://www.richmondsterling.com
Contact: Paul N. Marston, President
E-mail: pnm@richmondsterling.com
Scope: Provider of construction consulting services. It offers project and cost management, budgeting, and scheduling solutions. **Founded:** 1995.

5668 ■ Saunders Construction Inc.
6950 S Jordan Rd.
Centennial, CO 80112
Ph: (303)699-9000
Co. E-mail: businessdevelopment@saundersci.com
URL: http://www.saundersci.com
Contact: Gregory A. Schmidt, President
Scope: Specializes in serving healthcare providers and organizations with practice mergers/acquisition/divestiture, practice valuation, strategic planning, compensation, and development of business plans. **Founded:** 1972. **Seminars:** Pilot Leadership Training, Jan, 2008.

5669 ■ Shoreline General Contractors Inc.
3828 Herman Ave.
San Diego, CA 92104-3714
Ph: (619)283-2024
Fax: (619)283-2032
Contact: Lloyd Palmaymesa, President
Scope: General building contractors involved from the initial concept, through design, contracting and completion of a project. **Founded:** 1993.

5670 ■ Smith-Emery Co.—Smith-Emery Company Inc.
791 E Washington Blvd.
Los Angeles, CA 90021-3043
Ph: (213)749-3411
Fax: (213)741-8620
Co. E-mail: mktla@smithemery.com
URL: http://www.smithemery.com
Contact: Jim Partridge, President
E-mail: jpartridge@smithemery.com
Scope: Provider of construction testing and inspection services. Acts as a single source of testing and inspection for all construction related services in the commercial building market, from the soil to the roof. Offers inspection, testing and failure analysis services including post tensioning, curtain wall testing, masonry inspection and tests, flatness testing, flat jack testing, batch plant inspection, seismic evaluation, on destructive examinations, laboratory mock ups, concrete placement, construction materials testing, concrete compression tests, roofing inspections and tests, wood structure inspection, reinforcing steel placement, gypsum inspection, and metallurgical lab testing. **Founded:** 1904.

5671 ■ Space Management Programs Inc.
55 W Wacker Dr., Ste. 600
Chicago, IL 60601-1609
Ph: (312)263-0700
Fax: (312)263-1228
Contact: Michael J. Cohen, President
E-mail: mcohen@ghk.net
Scope: A facilities and technology consulting firm experienced in all aspects of design and corporate relocation. Available for site evaluation, strategic planning through the writing of briefs, or architectural programs through space planning, design and construction documents. **Founded:** 1973.

5672 ■ Steinmann Facility Development Consultants (SFDC)
9702 N Lake Blvd.
Kings Beach, CA 96143
Ph: (530)546-4428
Fax: (530)546-0422
Co. E-mail: sfdc@jimsteinmann.com
URL: http://www.jimsteinmann.com
Contact: Garner Grayson, Principal
Scope: Provider of facility programming and planning consulting services to government and private sector space users. Specializes in needs assessment, facility programming, pre architectural planning, strategic planning, justice system planning, industrial engineering, design/build development and project management. **Founded:** 1972.

5673 ■ Stueven Engineering Consultants
140 W 3rd Ave.
Escondido, CA 92025
Ph: (760)735-8577
Fax: (760)735-8578
Co. E-mail: sb@stueven-engineering.com
URL: http://www.stueven-engineering.com
Contact: Harold J. Stueven, President
E-mail: hjs@stueven-engineering.com
Scope: Provider of services in professional engineering, planning, design, and construction support services for mechanical and plumbing systems. **Founded:** 1994.

5674 ■ Swanson Associates
6705 Highway 290 W, Ste. 502-126
Austin, TX 78735
Ph: (512)288-9097
Fax: (512)288-9096
Co. E-mail: gps@flash.net
URL: http://www.geoswan.com
Contact: George Paul Swanson, Owner
E-mail: gps@flash.net
Scope: Environmentally-conscience construction firm services include non-toxic, breathing construction consulting; natural low impact energy and site utility development consulting; CADD custom and stock natural building design plans; site supervision, construction management and general contracting. **Founded:** 1979. **Publications:** "Dome Scrapbook," 1981. **Seminars:** Sustainable Development and Concrete Technology; Traditional Straw/Clay Slip form Construction; Natural design and construction; Benefits of natural building design.

5675 ■ TechniScan Inc.
155 S Madison St., Ste. 228
Denver, CO 80209-3013
Ph: (303)329-0535
Free: 800-266-8565
Fax: (303)377-2740
Co. E-mail: inquiries@techniscan.com
URL: http://www.techniscan.com
Contact: David G. Davis, President
E-mail: david.g.davis@techniscan.com
Scope: An architecturally based consulting practice that performs diagnostic scanning, remedial repair and design, project management, and expert witness services for roofing and curtain wall systems. **Founded:** 1986. **Seminars:** Roofing asset portfolio. **Special Services:** TechniScan®.

5676 ■ Tempest Co.
13326 A St.
Omaha, NE 68144-3641
Ph: (402)334-3332
Free: 888-334-3332
Fax: (402)334-9033
Co. E-mail: inquire@tempestcompany.com
URL: http://www.tempestcompany.com
Contact: Don L. Short, II, President
E-mail: donshort@tempestcompany.com
Scope: A construction consulting firm specializing in management consulting, marketing and proposal preparation, strategic bidding and estimating and bidding practices. Services include: Estimating, scheduling, project controls, construction consulting and expert services such as arbitration. **Founded:** 1981. **Publications:** "Some Estimates Are Wishful Thinking"; "The Nine Secrets of Estimating"; "Fallacy of the Contract Schedule of Values"; "CPM Scheduling Will Work For Your Project"; "Controlling Capital Costs Prior to Construction".

5677 ■ Robert G. Thomas Jr.
1417 Sadler Rd., Ste. 269
Fernandina Beach, FL 32034
Ph: (904)343-2365
Co. E-mail: rgt@rgthomas.com
URL: http://www.eifs.com
Contact: Robert G. Thomas, Manager
Scope: Provider of insulation, weatherproofing and a finished surface in a single integrated product. **Founded:** 1980. **Publications:** "EIFS Design Handbook"; "EIFS New Construction Inspection Guide"; "EIFS Existing Construction Inspection Maintenance and Repair Guide"; "EIFS Homeowners Guide".

5678 ■ R. L. Townsend & Associates Inc.
3941 Legacy Dr., Ste. 204-218A
Plano, TX 75023
Ph: (972)208-1222
Free: 800-559-4471
Fax: (214)853-5287
Co. E-mail: info@rltownsend.com
URL: http://www.rltownsend.com
Contact: Rich L. Townsend, President
E-mail: rltownsend@rltownsend.com
Scope: Provider of construction contract cost control advisory and audit services to owner organizations. Its clients include design and construction management firms and construction contractors. **Founded:** 2009. **Publications:** "Contracting for Construction Projects," Rich Townsend, Jun, 1993. **Seminars:** Auditing Construction Activity, Austin, 2009; Controlling Construction Costs, Madison, 2009; Controlling

Construction Costs, Madison, 2007; Managing Construction Projects, Madison, 2007; Effective Auditing of Construction Activity, Orlando, 2007.

5679 ■ Joe Turner
3525 Sandybrook Ln.
Napa, CA 94558
Ph: (707)224-6344
Free: 888-754-6900
Fax: (707)224-6392
Co. E-mail: jmturner@joeturner.com
URL: http://www.joeturner.com
Contact: Joe Turner, Owner
Scope: Provider of customer service consulting, materials, software and training for the new home industry. Specializes in construction defect litigation. Specific problem solving, including recruiting, validating employment information, meeting with homeowners and strategic assessment are available. Produces homeowner manuals for builders and developers. **Founded:** 1982. **Seminars:** TeamTraks.

5680 ■ US Aquatics Inc.
124 Bridge Ave.
Delano, MN 55328
Ph: (763)972-5897
Fax: (763)972-5864
Co. E-mail: info@usaquaticsinc.com
URL: http://www.usaquaticsinc.com
Contact: Ryan Johnson, Manager
Scope: It is an engineering/design firm specializing in aquatic design. They provide following services: Facility Assessment, Feasibility Study, Construction Documents, Contract Administration, Construction Administration, Plan Review, Performance Contracts, CPO Instruction. **Founded:** 1991.

FRANCHISES AND BUSINESS OPPORTUNITIES

5681 ■ A-1 Concrete Leveling Inc.
388 S Main St., Ste. 402
Akron, OH 44311
Free: 888-675-3835
Fax: (330)253-1261
Description: Concrete leveling service. **No. of Franchise Units:** 47. **Founded:** 1992. **Franchised:** 1993. **Equity Capital Needed:** $115,500-$145,900 total investment. **Franchise Fee:** $85,000. **Royalty Fee:** 6%. **Financial Assistance:** Limited in-house and third party financing available. **Training:** Provides 1 week at headquarters, 2 weeks of onsite and ongoing support including newsletter, meetings toll-free phone line, Internet, security/safety procedures, and field operations/evaluations.

5682 ■ ABC Seamless Siding
ABC Inc.
3001 Fiechtner Dr.
Fargo, ND 58103
Ph: (701)293-5952
Free: 800-732-6577
Fax: (701)293-3107
Co. E-mail: info@abcseamless.com
URL: http://www.abcseamless.com
Description: Sales and installation of seamless steel and steel gutters. **No. of Franchise Units:** 109. **No. of Company-Owned Units:** 9. **Founded:** 1973.. **Franchised:** 1978. **Equity Capital Needed:** $81,000-$207,500. **Franchise Fee:** $12,000+. **Financial Assistance:** Yes. **Training:** Yes.

5683 ■ Andy OnCall
Franchise Dept.
921 E Main St.
Chattanooga, TN 37408
Free: 877-263-9662
Fax: (423)622-0580
Co. E-mail: info@andyoncall.com
URL: http://www.andyoncall.com
Description: Manage independent contractors to fulfill homeowners' small job needs; management and organizational skills, no construction experience needed, strong and growing demand for service in marketplace. **No. of Franchise Units:** 54. **Founded:** 1993. **Franchised:** 1999. **Equity Capital Needed:** $48,150-$62,050. **Franchise Fee:** $25,000 or

$30,000 based on pop. **Financial Assistance:** Yes. **Training:** Training at corporate office, onsite, and ongoing support in all areas of business.

5684 ■ The BrickKicker
RonLen Enterprises Inc.
849 N Ellsworth St.
Naperville, IL 60563
Free: 888-339-5425
Fax: (630)420-2270
Co. E-mail: linda@brickkicker.com
URL: http://www.brickkicker.com
Description: Building inspection service. **No. of Franchise Units:** 152. **Founded:** 1989.. **Franchised:** 1995. **Equity Capital Needed:** $15,000-$40,000. **Franchise Fee:** $9,000-$40,000. **Financial Assistance:** Yes. **Training:** Yes.

5685 ■ Case Handyman & Remodeling Services LLC
Case Design/Remodeling Inc.
North Plz., Ste. 40
4701 Sangamore Rd.
Bethesda, MD 20816
Ph: (301)229-4600
Free: 800-426-9434
Fax: (301)229-2089
Co. E-mail: info@casehandyman.com
URL: http://www.casehandyman.com
Description: Handyman services. **No. of Franchise Units:** 57. **No. of Company-Owned Units:** 4. **Founded:** 1992. **Franchised:** 1997. **Equity Capital Needed:** $105,000-$150,000. **Franchise Fee:** $25,000. **Royalty Fee:** 4-6%. **Training:** Includes 3 weeks training at headquarters, 2 days at franchisee's location and ongoing support.

5686 ■ Epcon Communities
500 Stonehenge Pky.
Columbus, OH 43017
Ph: (614)761-1010
Fax: (614)761-2672
URL: http://www.epmarkinc.com
Description: Franchiser of condo communities. **No. of Franchise Units:** 200+. **Founded:** 1986.. **Franchised:** 1995. **Equity Capital Needed:** $1,000,000. **Franchise Fee:** $50,000. **Royalty Fee:** $2,500 per unit. **Training:** Available at headquarters, onsite and with ongoing support. Provides additional training at sales conference (2 days) and construction conference (2 days).

5687 ■ Handyman Connection
Mamar, Inc.
10250 Alliance Rd., Ste.100
Cincinnati, OH 45242
Ph: (513)771-3003
Free: 800-466-5530
Fax: (513)771-6439
Co. E-mail: soaks@handymanconnection.com
URL: http://www.handymanconnection.com
Description: Small to medium home repairs and remodeling. **No. of Franchise Units:** 160. **No. of Company-Owned Units:** 1. **Founded:** 1990.. **Franchised:** 1993. **Equity Capital Needed:** $90,000-$125,000. **Franchise Fee:** $25,000-$40,000. **Training:** 2 weeks at corporate training center and 1 week grand opening onsite.

5688 ■ Handyman Matters Franchise Corp.
Handyman Matters, Inc.
12567 W Cedar Dr., Ste. 150
Lakewood, CO 80228
Ph: (866)808-8401
Free: 888-448-3451
Fax: (303)942-5993
Co. E-mail: info@HandymanMatters.com
URL: http://www.HandymanMatters.com
Description: Repairs, maintains, and improves properties including carpentry, plumbing, electrical, drywall, painting, roofing & flooring. **No. of Franchise Units:** 121. **Founded:** 1997.. **Franchised:** 2001. **Equity Capital Needed:** $48,930-$89,425. **Franchise Fee:** $30,000. **Training:** Offers 1-2 weeks training at corporate office and 1 week onsite.

5689 ■ Hickory Dickory Decks
115 Dundas St., W
Hamilton, ON, Canada L9H 7L6

Ph: (905)689-4774
Free: 800-263-4774
Fax: (905)689-9753
Co. E-mail: hddoffice@gmail.com
URL: http://www.hickorydickorydecks.com
Description: Custom builders of decks and gazebos. **No. of Franchise Units:** 32. **No. of Company-Owned Units:** 15. **Founded:** 1987. **Franchised:** 1999. **Equity Capital Needed:** $50,000-$100,000. **Franchise Fee:** $25,000. **Training:** Provides 3 weeks training.

5690 ■ Janbury
Synergy Franchising LLC
Sawyer Oaks Professional Park
5674 Marquesas Ctr.
Sarasota, FL 34233
Ph: (941)927-9400
Fax: (941)927-9401
Description: Construction support/cleaning service. **No. of Franchise Units:** 2. **No. of Company-Owned Units:** 1. **Founded:** 2001.. **Franchised:** 2006. **Equity Capital Needed:** $156,900-$271,000. **Franchise Fee:** $45,000. **Royalty Fee:** 7%. **Training:** Includes 1 week training at headquarters, 1 week at franchisee's location and ongoing support.

5691 ■ Maintenance Made Simple
4919 Albemarle Rd. Suite 203
Charlotte, NC 28205
Ph: (704)584-9999
Free: 866-778-6283
Description: Handyman and home improvement services. **No. of Franchise Units:** 32. **Founded:** 2003.. **Franchised:** 2003. **Equity Capital Needed:** $69,900-$114,900. **Franchise Fee:** $30,000. **Royalty Fee:** 7%. **Training:** Yes.

5692 ■ National Franchise Resources, Inc.
Hoey Construction Co.
3310 Southwest Blvd.
Tulsa, OK 74107
Ph: (918)270-4886
Fax: (918)270-4889
Description: Franchise design build general contractor. **Founded:** 1979.. **Training:** No.

5693 ■ Perma-Jack Co.
9066 Watson Rd.
St. Louis, MO 63126-2234
Ph: (314)843-1957
Free: 800-843-1888
Description: Franchises a fast, patented building foundation stabilizing system. **No. of Franchise Units:** 38. **Founded:** 1974.. **Equity Capital Needed:** $25,000-$200,000. **Franchise Fee:** None. **Training:** Yes.

5694 ■ Sealmaster
InFrasys Inc.
2520 S Campbell St.
Sandusky, OH 44870
Ph: (419)626-4375
Free: 800-395-7325
Fax: (419)626-5477
Co. E-mail: info@sealmaster.net
URL: http://www.sealmaster.net
Description: Manufacture pavement sealers and supply a complete line of pavement maintenance products and equipment including crack fillers, traffic paints, sport surfaces and tools. **No. of Franchise Units:** 32. **No. of Company-Owned Units:** 1. **Founded:** 1969.. **Franchised:** 1993. **Equity Capital Needed:** $500,000-$700,000 total investment required; possible startup equipment. **Franchise Fee:** $35,000. **Financial Assistance:** Yes. **Training:** Technical and administrative training, operations manual. Scheduled consulting visits by operations experts.

5695 ■ Tile Outlet Always in Stock   ●
3329 Fitzgerald Rd., Ste. 1
Rancho Cordova, CA 95742
Ph: (916)861-0855
Free: 888-328-4374

Fax: (916)861-0859
Co. E-mail: info@tileoutlet.net
URL: http://www.tileoutlet.net
Description: Discount retail tile store selling granite counters, tile, slate, travertine, marble and related products. Our customers include the general public, contractors and builders. The corporate office directly imports products and sells to our franchisees to allow them to focus on selling. Great overhead, high profit margin business with no previous experience required. **No. of Franchise Units:** 44. **No. of Company-Owned Units:** 6. **Founded:** 2001.. **Franchised:** 2002. **Equity Capital Needed:** $59,850-$104,600, franchise fee for additional units $15,000. **Franchise Fee:** $20,000 for 1st. **Training:** Provides 3 days of complete training at our corporate facility, 5 days of onsite training at your location and unlimited ongoing support through phone, fax, email, web page and in person visits.

5696 ■ UBuildlt
UBuildit Holdings, LLC.
Description: Building or remodeling general contractors. **No. of Franchise Units:** 31. **Founded:** 1988.. **Franchised:** 1998. **Equity Capital Needed:** $100,000-$225,000. **Franchise Fee:** $37,500. **Training:** Pretraining business start-up assistance, 2 week training and ongoing support.

COMPUTERIZED DATABASES

5697 ■ *Construction Labor Report™*
1801 S Bell St.
Arlington, VA 22202
Free: 800-372-1033
Co. E-mail: customercare@bna.com
URL: http://www.bna.com
Availability: Online: Bloomberg LP-Bloomberg BNA; Thomson Reuters - Westlaw. **Type:** Full-text.

5698 ■ *Residential Building Permits*
60 E 42nd St.
New York, NY 10165
Ph: (212)986-9300
Fax: (212)986-5857
Co. E-mail: data@haver.com
URL: http://www.haver.com
Availability: Online: Haver Analytics - HaverSelect. **Type:** Time Series.

COMPUTER SYSTEMS/ SOFTWARE

5699 ■ *Activant*
5 Independence Pointe
Greenville, SC 29602-2383
Ph: (864)234-7676
Free: 800-569-6309
Fax: (864)987-6400
Co. E-mail: ecs-inc@activant.com
URL: http://www.activant.com
Description: Available for IBM computers. System provides a construction management system with accounting capabilities.

LIBRARIES

5700 ■ Associated General Contractors of America - James L. Allhands Memorial Library
333 John Carlyle St., Ste. 200
Alexandria, VA 22314
Ph: (703)837-5308
Fax: (703)548-3119
Co. E-mail: dayd@agc.org
URL: http://www.agc.org/
Contact: Dennis Day, Director, Public Affairs
Scope: History of construction industry. **Services:** Interlibrary loan; Library open to the public by appointment. **Founded:** 1963. **Holdings:** 400 books. **Subscriptions:** 4 newspapers. **Telecommunication Services:** info@agc.org.

5701 ■ Boston Architectural Center - Alfred Shaw and Edward Durell Stone Library
320 Newbury St., 6th Fl.
Boston, MA 02115
Ph: (617)585-0155
Free: 877-585-0100
Fax: (617)585-0151
Co. E-mail: library@the-bac.edu
URL: http://the-bac.edu/resources/library
Contact: Susan Lewis, Director, Library Services
Scope: Architectural design and history, building technology, urban planning, urban design, landscape architecture, photography, interior design, energy conservation, solar energy. **Services:** Copying; library open to the public for reference only. **Founded:** 1966. **Holdings:** 44,000 books; 800 bound periodical volumes; 800 student theses; 40,000 slides; 500 other cataloged items; archives. **Subscriptions:** 120 journals and other serials. **Telecommunication Services:** susan.lewis@the-bac.edu.

5702 ■ California Real Estate Services Division Library
707 3rd St., Ste. 6-100
West Sacramento, CA 95605
Ph: (916)376-1900
Fax: (916)376-1895
Co. E-mail: dbrakowi@dgs.ca.gov
URL: http://www.dgs.ca.gov/resd
Scope: Construction industry standards, architecture, electrical and mechanical engineering, building products, interior design. **Services:** Interlibrary loan; copying; Library open to other state agencies. **Founded:** 1958. **Holdings:** 400 books; 30 bound periodical volumes; 1500 catalogs; titles 1-26 of the California Code of Regulations. **Subscriptions:** 30 journals and other serials.

5703 ■ Canada National Research Council - CISTI Institute for Research in Construction Branch
1200 Montreal Rd., Bldg. M-55
Ottawa, ON, Canada K1A 0R6
Ph: (613)993-9101
Free: 800-668-1222
Fax: (613)993-7619
Co. E-mail: info.cisti@nrc-cnrc.gc.ca
URL: http://www.nrc-cnrc.gc.ca/eng/ibp/irc.html
Contact: Mike Culhane, Manager
Scope: Construction, acoustics, building services, fire research, building codes, building structures, materials, infrastructure, indoor environment. **Services:** Interlibrary loan; copying; branch open to the public. **Founded:** 1948. **Holdings:** 100,000 books; 200,000 reports. **Subscriptions:** 700 journals and other serials. **Telecommunication Services:** mike. culhane@nrc-cnrc.gc.ca.

5704 ■ Canadian Home Builders' Association - Saskatchewan Library
11-3012 Louise St.
Saskatoon, SK, Canada S7J 3L8
Ph: (306)955-5188
Free: 888-955-5188
Fax: (306)373-3735
Co. E-mail: info@chbasaskatchewan.com
URL: http://www.chbasaskatchewan.com
Contact: Alan H.J. Thomarat, Chief Executive Officer
Scope: Home construction. **Services:** Copying; library open to the public. **Holdings:** 100 books; 20 reports; slides; videocassettes.

5705 ■ Foundation of the Wall & Ceiling Industry - John H. Hampshire Memorial Library
513 W. Broad St., Ste. 210
Falls Church, VA 22046
Ph: (703)538-1600
Fax: (703)534-8307
Co. E-mail: smith@awci.org
URL: http://www.awci.org/thefoundation.shtml
Contact: Don Smith, Technical Director
Scope: Construction - specifications and standards, management, and law; asbestos removal; fire standards; insulation. **Services:** Copying; Library open to

the public. **Founded:** 1981. **Holdings:** 10,000 volumes; 3000 books; 500 unbound reports; manufacturers' catalogs. **Subscriptions:** 100 journals and other serials.

5706 ■ Hanley-Wood, LLC Library
426 S. Westgate St.
Addison, IL 60101-4546
Ph: (630)543-0870
Fax: (630)543-3112
URL: http://www.hanleywood.com
Scope: Concrete, cement, masonry, construction, home building. **Services:** Interlibrary loan; copying. **Founded:** 1971. **Holdings:** 3000 books; 120 bound periodical volumes. **Subscriptions:** 100 journals and other serials.

5707 ■ Harrington College of Design - Design Library
200 W. Madison St., 2nd Fl.
Chicago, IL 60606-3433
Ph: (312)697-3318
Free: 866-590-4423
Fax: (312)939-8005
Co. E-mail: elaine@interiordesign.edu
URL: http://www.harrington.edu
Contact: Elaine Lowenthal, Director, Library Services
Scope: Architecture, design, building materials, furniture, decorative arts, modern design. **Services:** Interlibrary loan; copying; library open to the public by appointment for reference use only and with referral from another library . **Founded:** 1974. **Holdings:** 22,000 books; 900 bound periodical volumes; 23,000 slides; 450 videotapes; 35,000 digital images. **Subscriptions:** 125 journals and other serials.

5708 ■ Hill International, Inc. Library
303 Lippincott Ctr.
Marlton, NJ 08053
Ph: (856)810-6200
Fax: (856)810-1309
URL: http://www.hillintl.com/
Contact: Irvin E. Richter, Chief Executive Officer
Scope: Construction claims avoidance and resolution. **Services:** Interlibrary loan; Library not open to the public. **Founded:** 1976. **Holdings:** Comprehensive case histories of claims.

5709 ■ Intertek Testing Services - Warnock Hersey Library
1500 Brigantine Dr.
Coquitlam, BC, Canada V3K 7C1
Ph: (604)520-3321
Fax: (604)524-9186
Co. E-mail: lawrence.gibson@intertek.com
URL: http://www.intertek.com/
Scope: Building codes, electrical codes, plumbing codes, standards. **Services:** Library open to potential clients at librarian's discretion. **Holdings:** Standards; codes; handbooks; manuals; directories. **Subscriptions:** 20 journals and other serials.

5710 ■ Missouri Historical Society Archives - Architecture Collection
PO Box 11940
St. Louis, MO 63112-0040
Ph: (314)746-4599
Fax: (314)454-3162
Co. E-mail: archives@mohistory.org
URL: http://www.mohistory.org
Contact: Christopher Gordon, Archivist
Scope: Construction. **Services:** Copying; collection open to the public by appointment. **Founded:** 1993. **Holdings:** Drawings of 2500 different projects; research file specifications; job files; models. **Telecommunication Services:** library@mohistory.org.

5711 ■ Murphy/Jahn Library
35 E. Wacker Dr., 3rd Fl.
Chicago, IL 60601
Ph: (312)427-7300
Fax: (312)332-0274
Co. E-mail: library@murphyjahn.com
URL: http://www.murphyjahn.com/
Contact: Joseph A. Stypka, Director
Scope: Architecture, codes, construction products. **Services:** Library open to the public by appointment. **Founded:** 1968. **Holdings:** 7000 books and articles; 4 bound periodical volumes; 7000 product catalogs;

1900 construction consultant. **Subscriptions:** 200 journals and other serials; 2 newspapers. **Telecommunication Services:** info@jahn-us.com.

5712 ■ Noble and Associates Library
2155 W. Chesterfield Blvd.
Springfield, MO 65807
Ph: (417)875-5000
Co. E-mail: julie.tumy@noble.net
URL: http://www.noble.net
Contact: Julie Tumy, President
Scope: Food, food service, advertising, construction, agriculture. **Services:** Interlibrary loan; copying; SDI; Library not open to the public. **Holdings:** 500 books; 1000 reports. **Subscriptions:** 300 journals and other serials; 5 newspapers.

5713 ■ North Carolina State University - Libraries - D.H. Hill Library Special Collections Research Center
Rm. 1128, East Wing
2 Broughton Dr.
Raleigh, NC 27695-7111
Ph: (919)515-2273
Fax: (919)515-1787
Co. E-mail: eleanor_brown@ncsu.edu
URL: http://www.lib.ncsu.edu/specialcollections/
Contact: Eli Brown, Director
Scope: Architecture and design, engineering and technology, history of science, natural resources, textiles, history of NCSU, plant and forestry genetics and genomics, history of computing and simulation, veterinary medicine, entomology, animal welfare. **Services:** Copying; digitization; Library open to the public. **Founded:** 1995. **Holdings:** 32,000 books; 7665 lin.ft. of manuscripts; 6778 lin.ft. of University archives. **Telecommunication Services:** special_collections@ncsu.edu.

5714 ■ Pacific Energy Center - Energy Resource Center
851 Howard St.
San Francisco, CA 94103
Ph: (415)973-7206
Free: 800-468-4743
Fax: (415)896-1290
Co. E-mail: mxv6@pge.com
URL: http://www.pge.com/pec
Contact: Marlene Vogelsang, Specialist
Scope: Energy conservation, sustainable design, renewables, architecture, design, lighting, HVAC systems. **Services:** Copying; library open to the public. **Founded:** 1992. **Holdings:** 3000 books; reports. **Subscriptions:** 120 journals and other serials.

5715 ■ Portland Cement Association Library
5420 Old Orchard Rd.
Skokie, IL 60077
Ph: (847)966-6200
Fax: (847)966-8389
Co. E-mail: library@cement.org
URL: http://www.cement.org/library
Contact: Connie Field, Director
Scope: Concrete technology, cement chemistry, structural engineering, civil engineering, construction. **Services:** Interlibrary loan; copying; web access; document delivery; research services available to nonmembers on fee basis. **Founded:** 1938. **Holdings:** 10,000 books; 13,500 bound periodical volumes; 40,000 technical reports; 100,000 abstracts; 300 CD publications; 70,000 images. **Subscriptions:** 200 journals and other serials. **Telecommunication Services:** info@cement.org.

5716 ■ Societe d'Habitation du Quebec - Centre de Documentation
500, boul. Rene-Levesque Quest, 5e etage
Montreal, QC, Canada H2Z 1W7
Ph: (514)873-8775
Free: 800-463-4315
Fax: (514)873-8340
Co. E-mail: sdih@shq.gouv.qc.ca
URL: http://www.habitation.gouv.qc.ca/en/index.html
Contact: Barbara Maass, Librarian
Scope: Housing, residential construction, architecture, urban planning. **Services:** Interlibrary loan; copying; library open to the public by appointment.

Founded: 1987. **Holdings:** 15,000 books and reports; 150 audio/visual materials. **Subscriptions:** 360 journals and other serials.

5717 ■ U.S. Dept. of Housing and Urban Development Library
451 7th St. SW, Rm. 8141
Washington, DC 20410
Ph: (202)708-2370
URL: http://www.hud.gov/library/index.cfm
URL(s): www.hud.gov/offices/adm/library. **Scope:** Housing, community development, urban planning, sociology, law, mortgage and construction finance, architecture, land use, environmental concerns. **Services:** Interlibrary loan; copying (limited); Library open to the public. **Founded:** 1934. **Holdings:** 680,000 items. **Subscriptions:** 2200 journals and other serials.

5718 ■ U.S. National Park Service - Blue Ridge Parkway Archives
199 Hemphill Knob Rd.
Asheville, NC 28803-8686
Ph: (828)271-4779
Fax: (828)271-4313
URL: http://www.nps.gov/blri
Contact: Jackie Holt, Curator
Scope: Blue Ridge Parkway - history, development, design, construction, landscape, resource management. **Services:** Archives open to researchers by appointment only. **Founded:** 1990. **Holdings:** 350,000 archives.

5719 ■ University of Nevada, Las Vegas - Architecture Studies Library
Box 454049
4505 Maryland Pkwy.
Las Vegas, NV 89154-4049
Ph: (702)895-1959
Fax: (702)895-1975
Co. E-mail: caroline.smith@unlv.edu
URL: http://www.library.unlv.edu/arch/index.html
Contact: Caroline Smith, Director
Scope: Architecture - history, design, theory, and criticism; landscape architecture; interior design; construction; urban planning. **Services:** Interlibrary loan; copying; scanners; Library open to the public. **Founded:** 1997. **Holdings:** 25,000 volumes; 600 videos/DVDs; archives; microfiche and microfilm. **Subscriptions:** 150 journals and other serials.

5720 ■ USG Corporation - USG Research and Technology Center Library
700 N. Hwy. 45
Libertyville, IL 60048
Ph: (847)970-5036
Fax: (847)214-1466
Co. E-mail: jsteffen@usg.com
Contact: Joy Steffen, Coordinator, Information
Scope: Building materials, gypsum products, acoustical products. **Services:** Interlibrary loan; copying; SDI. **Founded:** 1961. **Holdings:** 6862 books; 1150 bound periodical volumes; 1846 pamphlets; 32,240 laboratory reports; 987 reels of microfilm; 970 microfiche; 10,000 patents. **Subscriptions:** 125 journals and other serials.

5721 ■ Virginia Tech University - Art & Architecture Library
100 Cowgill Hall
Blacksburg, VA 24061
Ph: (540)231-9271
Fax: (540)231-9263
Co. E-mail: tomlin@vt.edu
URL: http://www.lib.vt.edu/artarch/index.html
Contact: Patrick Tomlin
Scope: Architecture, art, art history, building construction, landscape architecture. **Services:** Interlibrary loan; copying; Library open to the public. **Holdings:** 78,000 volumes; 400 architectural drawing sets; 900 multimedia items, including DVDs, videotapes, and slides. **Subscriptions:** 200 journals and other serials.

5722 ■ H.B. Zachry Company - Central Records and Library
PO Box 240130
San Antonio, TX 78224-0130
Ph: (210)922-1213

Fax: (210)927-8060
Contact: Leroy Rome, Director
Scope: Construction specifications, industrial relations, tax laws, electronic data processing, accounting procedures, building codes. **Services:** Interlibrary loan; copying; library open to the public by permission. **Holdings:** 1500 books; 60 bound periodical volumes; film; maps. **Subscriptions:** 135 journals and other serials.

RESEARCH CENTERS

5723 ■ Concordia University - Centre for Building Studies (CBS)—Concordia University - Centre d'études sur le bâtimentbâtiment
Department of Bldg., Civil & Environmental Engineering, Rm. EV-6.139
1455 de Maisonneuve Blvd. W
Montreal, QC, Canada H3G 1M8
Ph: (514)848-2424
Fax: (514)848-7965
Co. E-mail: zmeur@bcee.concordia.ca
URL: http://www.bcee.concordia.ca/research-and-facilities/research-network-centres/cent re-for-building-studies
Contact: Prof. Radu Zmeureanu, Director
Services: Research development and information transfer services. **Founded:** 1977. **Publications:** *CBS Annual Report*; *CBS Research papers*. **Educational Activities:** Master's and doctoral degrees, in building engineering through the U.S. Department of of Building, Civil and Environment Engineering; eSim2002 Conference.

5724 ■ National Institute of Building Sciences (NIBS)
1090 Vermont Ave. NW, Ste. 700
Washington, DC 20005-4905
Ph: (202)289-7800
Free: 877-222-5667
Fax: (202)289-1092
Co. E-mail: hgreen@nibs.org
URL: http://www.nibs.org
Contact: Henry L. Green, President
Description: Individuals and organizations, including architects, engineers, builders, contractors, realtors, universities, and all levels of government interested in the building industry. Works to promote a favorable and coherent building regulatory environment and encourage new technology in the building industry. **Founded:** 1974. **Publications:** *Building Sciences Newsletter* (Bimonthly); *CCB Bulletin* (Quarterly); *Building Sciences* (Bimonthly); *Directory of Online Databases for Building and Construction*; *National Institute of Building Sciences--Directory of Building Community Organizations*; *Asbestos Operations and Maintenance Work Practices Manual* (Periodic); *Construction Criteria Base (CCB)*. **Educational Activities:** BETEC Symposia, in spring and fall; Workshops and seminars on seismic design, moisture control, and building envelope energy issues. **Awards:** BSSC Exceptional Service Award (Annual); BSSC Honor Award (Annual); Institute Honor Award (Annual); Institute Member Award (Annual); President's Award (Annual); BSSC Exceptional Service Award (Annual); BSSC Honor Award (Annual); NIBS Honor Award (Annual); NIBS Member Award (Annual); President's Award (Annual); BSSC Exceptional Service Award; BSSC Honor Award; Honor Award; Member Award; President's Award. **Telecommunication Services:** nibs@nibs.org.

5725 ■ University of Hartford - Construction Institute
260 Girard Ave., 2nd Fl.
Hartford, CT 06105
Ph: (860)768-5659
Fax: (860)768-5662
Co. E-mail: wcianci@construction.org
URL: http://www.construction.org
Contact: William H. Cianci, Executive Director
Services: Provides information: to industry and public officials. **Founded:** 1975. **Publications:** *Construction Institute Newsletter*. **Educational Activities:** Construction Institute Forums (8/year); Construction Institute Seminars and conferences, on critical

industry issues September to June; Construction Institute Training, to help industry professionals improve management skills, add to their technical knowledge, develop personnel, and increase productivity.

5726 ■ University of Illinois at Urbana-Champaign - Building Research Council
School of Architecture
1 Saint Mary's Rd.
Champaign, IL 61820
Ph: (217)333-4698

Fax: (217)244-2204
Co. E-mail: dfournie@illinois.edu
URL: http://brc.arch.uiuc.edu
Contact: Donald Fournier, Chairperson
Founded: 1944. **Publications:** *SEDAC Newsletter* (Monthly). **Educational Activities:** High performance building analyses; Weatherization training and building energy assessments. **Awards:** Building Research Council Graduate research assistantships.

5727 ■ University of Texas at Arlington - Construction Research Center (CRC)
PO Box 19347
Arlington, TX 76019-0347

Ph: (817)272-3701
Fax: (817)272-7575
Co. E-mail: matthys@uta.edu
URL: http://www.uta.edu/ce/crc
Contact: John H. Matthys, Director

Founded: 1972. **Educational Activities:** CRC Seminars (10/year), open to builders, architects, engineers, contractors, and other personnel of the construction industry. **Telecommunication Services:** crc@uta.edu.

ASSOCIATIONS AND OTHER ORGANIZATIONS

5728 ■ Electronics Representatives Association
300 W Adams St., Ste. 617
Chicago, IL 60606
Ph: (312)527-3050
Fax: (312)527-3783
Co. E-mail: info@era.org
URL: http://www.era.org
Contact: Mark Conley, President
Description: Professional field sales organizations selling components and materials; computer, instrumentation and data communications products; audiovisual, security, land/mobile communications and commercial sound components and consumer products to the electronics industry. Sponsors insurance programs and educational conference for members. **Publications:** *Electronics Industry Showcase* (Annual); *Lines Available* (Weekly); *Representor* (Quarterly); *Locator of Professional Field Sales Organizations* (Annual); *The Locator--The Electronics Representatives Directory/Electronics Industry Calendar* (Annual). **Educational Activities:** Electronic Distribution Show and Conference (Annual).

5729 ■ National Electronics Service Dealers Association (NESDA)
3608 Pershing Ave.
Fort Worth, TX 76107-4527
Ph: (817)921-9061
Fax: (817)921-3741
Co. E-mail: mack@nesda.com
URL: http://www.nesda.com
Contact: Mack Blakely, Executive Director
Description: Local and state electronic service associations and companies. Supplies technical service information on business management training to electronic service dealers. Offers certification and training programs through International Society of Certified Electronics Technicians. Conducts technical service and business management seminars. **Founded:** 1963. **Publications:** *ProService Directory and Yearbook* (Annual). **Awards:** NESDA Awards; Associate Leadership Excellence Award (Annual); Best Local Publication (Annual); Everett Pershing Memorial Membership Award (Annual); Leo Shumavon Award (Annual); National Friend of Service (Annual); Outstanding Associate President Award (Annual); Outstanding Committee Chairperson Award (Annual); Person of the Year (Annual); M.L. Fineburgh, Sr., Award of Excellence (Annual); Richard Mildenberger Outstanding NESDA Officer (Annual).

REFERENCE WORKS

5730 ■ "After Price Cuts, Competition GPS Makers Lose Direction" in Brandweek (Vol. 49, April 21, 2008, No. 16, pp. 16)
Pub: VNU Business Media, Inc.
Ed: Steve Miller. **Description:** Garmin and TomTom, two of the leaders in portable navigation devices, have seen lowering revenues due to dramatic price cuts and unexpected competition from the broadening availability of personal navigation on mobile phones. TomTom has trimmed its sales outlook for its first quarter while Garmin's stock dropped 40 percent since February.

5731 ■ Appliance--Appliance Industry Purchasing Section Issue
Pub: Dana Chase Publications Inc.
URL(s): www.appliancemagazine.com. **Ed:** David Chase. **Released:** Annual; January. **Publication includes:** Suppliers to manufacturers of consumer, commercial, and business appliances. Membership directories for the following associations: Air-Conditioning and Refrigeration Institute, Association of Home Appliance Manufacturers, Commercial Refrigerator Manufacturers Association, Computer and Business Equipment Manufacturers Association, Consumer Electronics Group/Electronic Industries Association, Gas Appliance Manufacturers Association, Cookware Manufacturers Association, National Association of Food Equipment Manufacturers, National Housewares Manufacturers Association, Power Tool Institute, and Vacuum Cleaner Manufacturers Association. **Entries include:** Company name, address, phone, fax, and products. **Arrangement:** Classified by product. **Indexes:** Manufacturer, product heading.

5732 ■ "Bag It" in Entrepreneur (Vol. 36, May 2008, No. 5, pp. 48)
Pub: Entrepreneur Media, Inc.
Ed: Amanda C. Kooser. **Description:** Buyer's guide featuring bags and carrying cases for laptops is presented. Prices and attributes of the bags are provided.

5733 ■ "Best Buy's CEO On Learning to Love Social Media" in Harvard Business Review (Vol. 88, December 2010, No. 12, pp. 43)
Pub: Harvard Business School Publishing
Ed: Brian J. Dunn. **Description:** Effective utilization of online social networks to enhance brand identity, connect with consumers, and address bad publicity scenarios is examined.

5734 ■ "The Big Picture" in Canadian Business (Vol. 79, Winter 2006, No. 24, pp. 142)
Pub: Rogers Media
Ed: Andy Holloway. **Description:** The features of the new range of high-definition television sets released by Matushita Electric Corporation of America are described. The pricing of the television sets is discussed.

5735 ■ "Bon Voyager" in Entrepreneur (Vol. 36, April 2008, No. 4, pp. 58)
Pub: Entrepreneur Media, Inc.
Ed: Heather Clancy. **Description:** LG Voyager, especially made for Verizon Wireless, is a smart phone that is being compared to Apple iPhone. The Voyager has a 2.8-inch external touchscreen and has a clamshell design, which features an internal keyboard. It does not have Wi-Fi support like iPhone, but it has 3G support. Other differences between the two phones are discussed.

5736 ■ "Canon Focuses on New Moms" in Marketing to Women (Vol. 21, January 2008, No. 1, pp. 3)
Pub: EPM Communications Inc.
Contact: Ira Mayer, President
E-mail: imayer@epmcom.com
Description: Canon launches a photo contest aimed at spotlighting baby's first pictures in an attempt to connect with new mothers.

5737 ■ "Clusters Last Stand?" in Canadian Electronics (Vol. 23, February 2008, No. 1, pp. 6)
Pub: CLB Media Inc.
Description: Survival of technology clusters was the focus of Strategic Microelectronics Council's conference entitled, 'The Power of Community: Building Technology Clusters in Canada'. Clusters can help foster growth in the microelectronics sector, and it was recognized that government intervention is needed to maintain these clusters.

5738 ■ "Consumer Electronics: Brick and Mortar Vs. Online" in Retail Merchandiser (Vol. 51, September-October 2011, No. 5, pp. 15)
Pub: Phoenix Media Corporation
Description: Brick and mortar retailers with Web-sites are discovering that the Internet is used more for research than purchasing when it comes to electronics products. According to a recent study conducted by The NPD Group shows that 56 percent of consumers research televisions online before purchasing, but only 19 percent actually buy them online.

5739 ■ "Craig Muhlhauser" in Canadian Business (Vol. 81, September 15, 2008, No. 14-15, pp. 6)
Pub: Rogers Media Ltd.
Ed: Andrew Wahl. **Description:** Interview with Craig Muhlhauser who is the CEO of Celestica, a manufacturing company that provides services for the electronics sector; Muhlhauser discusses the company's restructuring program, which he feels was the secret to their surprising first-quarter results. Muhlhauser states that the company is operating with more forward visibility and that understanding the opportunities during the current economic situation presents the biggest challenge.

5740 ■ "Customers Turned Off? Not at Best Buy" in Barron's (Vol. 88, March 24, 2008, No. 12, pp. 29)
Pub: Dow Jones & Company, Inc.
Ed: Sandra Ward. **Description:** Shares of Best Buy, trading at $42.41 each, are expected to rise to an average of $52 a share due to the company's solid fundamentals. The company's shares have fallen 20 percent from their 52-week high and are attractive given the company's bright prospects in the video game sector and high-definition video.

5741 ■ "Dear Diary, Arbitron is Dumping You" in Business Courier (Vol. 26, September 25,

2009, No. 22, pp. 1)
Pub: American City Business Journals, Inc.
Ed: Dan Monk. **Description:** Arbitron Inc. is replacing hand-written ratings diaries with Portable People Meters or electronic sensors that measure local radio audiences. The technology counts all exposure to radio and stations; those that penetrate the workplace will see success, while the more 'niche' oriented formats will have a more difficult time.

5742 ■ *"Digital Edge: Stay Tuned" in Entrepreneur (Vol. 35, October 2007, No. 10, pp. 56)*
Pub: Entrepreneur Media Inc.
Ed: Mike Hogan. **Description:** Future of set-top boxes, particularly the digital video recorders is promising. TiVo HD, for example, already receives content from Websites, while companies such as Diego and Microsoft are soon to release similar devices. The potential applications of television and computer convergence are provided.

5743 ■ *"Digital Power Management and the PMBus" in Canadian Electronics (Vol. 23, June-July 2008, No. 4, pp. 8)*
Pub: Action Communication Inc.
Ed: Torbjorn Hohnberg. **Description:** PMBus is an interface that can be applied to a variety of devices including power management devices. Information on digital power management products using this interface are also provided.

5744 ■ *"The Easy Route" in Entrepreneur (Vol. 36, April 2008, No. 4, pp. 60)*
Pub: Entrepreneur Media, Inc.
Ed: Amanda C. Kooser. **Description:** Buyer's guide of wireless office routers is presented. All products included in the list use the latest draft-n technology. Price and availability of the products are provided.

5745 ■ *"EDCO Doling Out Capital Along Border" in Austin Business JournalInc. (Vol. 28, August 1, 2008, No. 20, pp. 1)*
Pub: American City Business Journals
Ed: Sandra Zaragoza. **Description:** Non-profit business incubator Economic Development Catalyst Organization Ventures is searching for promising start-up companies. The company is targeting startups in green energy, technology and consumer markets. EDCO has partnered with consumer electronics repair company CherryFusion and technology firm MiniDonations.

5746 ■ *"Electronic Design and a Greener Environment" in Canadian Electronics (Vol. 23, June-July 2008, No. 4, pp. 6)*
Pub: Action Communication Inc.
Ed: Nicholas Deeble. **Description:** Companies seeking to minimize their environmental impact are using Design methodologies of Cadence Design Systems Ltd. The company's Low Power Format and Low Power Design Flow help reduce carbon dioxide emissions.

5747 ■ *"Electronics Recycler Poised to Grow" in Austin Business Journal (Vol. 31, July 22, 2011, No. 20, pp. A1)*
Pub: American City Business Journals Inc.
Ed: Cody Lyon. **Description:** Electronic Recycling and Trading Inc. has leased 138,000 square feet of space in North Austin, Texas. The company requires more space for bigger equipment.

5748 ■ *"Five Things..For Photo Fun" in Hawaii Business (Vol. 53, October 2007, No. 4, pp. 20)*
Pub: Hawaii Business Publishing
Ed: Cathy S. Cruz-George. **Description:** Featured is a buyers guide of products used for capturing or displaying digital photos; products featured include the Digital Photo Wallet and Light Affection.

5749 ■ *"Game On! African Americans Get a Shot at $17.9 Billion Video Game Industry" in Black Enterprise (Vol. 38, July 2008, No. 12, pp. 56)*
Pub: Earl G. Graves Publishing Co. Inc.
Ed: Carolyn M. Brown. **Description:** Despite the economic crisis, consumers are still purchasing the hottest video games and hardware. Tips for African

American developers who want to become a part of this industry that lacks content targeting this demographic are offered.

5750 ■ *"HR Tech on the Go" in Workforce Management (Vol. 88, November 16, 2009, No. 12, pp. 1)*
Pub: Crain Communications Inc.
Ed: Ed Frauenheim. **Description:** Examination of the necessity of mobile access of human resources software applications that allow managers to recruit, schedule and train employees via their mobile devices; some industry leaders believe that mobile HR applications are vital while others see this new technology as hype.

5751 ■ *"Industry/Events 2011" in American Printer (Vol. 128, July 1, 2011, No. 7)*
Pub: Penton Media Inc.
Description: PMA, the Worldwide Community of Imaging Association launched its new CliQ with how-to tips, product reviews and monthly photo contests. PMA formed a partnership with the Consumer Electronics Association to make changes to this year's annual convention.

5752 ■ *"IPod Killers?" in Canadian Business (Vol. 79, November 20, 2006, No. 23, pp. 68)*
Pub: Rogers Media
Ed: Gerry Blackwell. **Description:** The features of Apple iPod that distinguishes it from other MP3 players available in the market are discussed.

5753 ■ *"Kodiak Bucks Bear Market" in Austin Business JournalInc. (Vol. 29, December 18, 2009, No. 41, pp. 1)*
Pub: American City Business Journals
Ed: Kate Harrington. **Description:** Austin, Texas-based Kodiak Assembly Solutions LLC, a company that installs components into printed circuit boards for product or evaluation tool kit prototyping purposes, will expand despite the recession. It will relocate from a 28,000 square foot space to a 42,000 square foot space in North Austin. The firm will also increase its workforce by 20 employees.

5754 ■ *"LED Screen Technology Takes Centre Stage" in Canadian Electronics (Vol. 23, June-July 2008, No. 4, pp. 17)*
Pub: Action Communication Inc.
Ed: Ed Whitaker. **Description:** Display technologies based on light emitting diodes are becoming more popular due to their flexibility, versatility and reproducibility of displays. These are being increasingly used in different applications, such as advertising and concerts.

5755 ■ *"Manufacturing Behind the Great Wall: What Works, What Doesn't" in Canadian Electronics (Vol. 23, February 2008, No. 1, pp. 6)*
Pub: CLB Media Inc.
Ed: Michel Jullian. **Description:** Electronic component producers are increasingly transitioning their manufacturing operations to China in order to take advantage of the growing Chinese manufacturing industry. It is believed that manufacturers have to carefully consider whether their run sizes are appropriate for Chinese manufacturing before moving their operations.

5756 ■ *"Meet the Jetsons" in Entrepreneur (Vol. 35, November 2007, No. 11, pp. 21)*
Pub: Entrepreneur Media Inc.
Ed: Amanda C. Kooser. **Description:** An overview of modern home devices is presented, including an organic light-emitting diode (OLED) wall display with changeable artwork, networked appliances like refrigerators, biometric door locks, and a television that can serve as a computer monitor.

5757 ■ *"Miller's Crossroad" in Canadian Business (Vol. 83, September 14, 2010, No. 15, pp. 58)*
Pub: Rogers Media Ltd.
Ed: Joe Castaldo. **Description:** Future Electronics founder and billionaire Robert Miller shares the secret of Future's unique operating model, which is based

on inventory and market research. Miller attributes much of the company's success to its privately held status that enables quick movement against competitors.

5758 ■ *"Mosaid Grants First Wireless Parent License To Matsushita" in Canadian Electronics (Vol. 23, June-July 2008, No. 5, pp. 1)*
Pub: Action Communication Inc.
Description: Matsushita Electric Industrial Co. Ltd. has been granted a six-and-a-half-year license by Mosaid Technologies Inc. to manufacture the latter's products. The patent portfolio license agreement covers Mosaid's Wi-Fi, Wi-Max, CDMA-enabled notebook computers and other products.

5759 ■ *"Motors and Motion Control" in Canadian Electronics (Vol. 23, February 2008, No. 1, pp. 23)*
Pub: CLB Media Inc.
Description: A new version of MicroMo Electronics Inc.'s Smoovy Series 0303..B has been added to MicroMo's DC motor product line. United Electronic Industries, on the other hand, has introduced the new UEIPAC series of programmable automation controllers that can offer solutions to various applications such as unmanned vehicle controllers. Features and functions of other new motors and motion control devices are given.

5760 ■ *National Electronic Distributors Association--Membership Directory*
Pub: National Electronic Distributors Association
Contact: Brian McNally, President
URL(s): www.nedassoc.org. **Released:** Annual; summer; latest edition 2003-2004. **Covers:** Approximately 150 member distributors and 150 member manufacturers of electronics products, plus 1,100 branch offices. **Entries include:** Company name, address, branch locations, phones, names of principal executives, size of firm, products handled, territory served, product cross-reference of distributors, geographical listing, e-mail and web site addresses. **Arrangement:** Alphabetical. **Indexes:** Geographical (includes about 1,100 branches), product category (includes distributors).

5761 ■ *"Network TV" in Canadian Business (Vol. 79, September 11, 2006, No. 18, pp. 136)*
Pub: Rogers Media
Ed: Gerry Blackwell. **Description:** The functions and features of the new Mediasmart LCD TV offered by Hewlett-Packard are discussed.

5762 ■ *"Now See This" in Entrepreneur (Vol. 36, April 2008, No. 4, pp. 53)*
Pub: Entrepreneur Media, Inc.
Ed: Mike Hogan. **Description:** New high definition (HD) products are to be introduced in 2008 at the Consumer Electronics Show and the Macworld Conference & Expo. HD lineup from companies such as Dell Inc. and Hewlett-Packard Co. are discussed.

5763 ■ *"Nvidia Shares Clobbered After Gloomy Warning" in Barron's (Vol. 88, July 7, 2008, No. 27, pp. 25)*
Pub: Dow Jones & Co., Inc.
Ed: Eric J. Savitz. **Description:** Shares of graphics chip manufacturer Nvidia suffered a 30 percent drop in its share price after the company warned that revenue and gross margin forecasts for the quarter ending July 27, 2008 will be below expectations. Stan Glasgow, chief operating officer of Sony Electronics, believes the US economic slowdown will not affect demand for the company's products. Statistical data included.

5764 ■ *"Pressed for Time" in Marketing to Women (Vol. 21, March 2008, No. 3, pp. 1)*
Pub: EPM Communications Inc.
Contact: Ira Mayer, President
E-mail: imayer@epmcom.com

Description: Statistical data concerning the tools women use for time management which include gadgets as well as traditional media such as calendars.

5765 ■ *"Products and Services" in Canadian Electronics (Vol. 23, August 2008, No. 5, pp. 46)*
Pub: Action Communication Inc.
Description: Directory of companies under the alphabetical listing of electronic equipment and allied components that they offer is presented.

5766 ■ *"Providing Expertise Required to Develop Microsystems" in Canadian Electronics (Vol. 23, February 2008, No. 1, pp. 6)*
Pub: CLB Media Inc.
Ed: Ian McWalter. **Description:** CMC Microsystems, formerly Canadian Microelectronics Corporation, is focused on empowering microelectronics and Microsystems research in Canada. Microsystems offers the basis for innovations in the fields of science, environment, technology, automotives, energy, aerospace and communications technology. CMC's strategy in developing Microsystems in Canada is described.

5767 ■ *"Provinces Tackle E-Waste Problem" in Canadian Electronics (Vol. 23, June-July 2008, No. 4, pp. 1)*
Pub: Action Communication Inc.
Ed: Ken Manchen. **Description:** Canadian provinces are implementing measures concerning the safe and environmentally friendly disposal of electronic waste. Alberta, British Columbia, Nova Scotia, and Saskatchewan impose an e-waste recycling fee on electronic equipment purchases.

5768 ■ *"RIM Gets Smart" in Canadian Business (Vol. 79, October 23, 2006, No. 21, pp. 157)*
Pub: Rogers Media
Ed: Gerry Blackwell. **Description:** Details of the features of Blackberry Pearl, the new personal digital assistant from Research in Motion Inc., are presented.

5769 ■ *"Samsung 'Holding Breath'" in Austin Business JournalInc. (Vol. 29, January 29, 2010, No. 47, pp. 1)*
Pub: American City Business Journals
Ed: Jacob Dirr. **Description:** Samsung Austin Semiconductor LLC entered into an incentives agreement with the State of Texas in 2005, which involved $230 million in tax breaks and public financing. Terms of the agreement have been met, but some are questioning whether the company will be able to meet its goals for the Austin operations in 2010.

5770 ■ *"Sources" in Canadian Electronics (Vol. 23, August 2008, No. 5, pp. 12)*
Pub: Action Communication Inc.
Description: Directory of electronic manufacturers, distributors and representatives in Canada is provided. The list presents distributors and representatives under each manufacturer.

5771 ■ *"STMicroelectronics" in Canadian Electronics (Vol. 23, February 2008, No. 1, pp. 1)*
Pub: CLB Media Inc.
Description: STMicroelectronics, a semiconductor maker, revealed that it plans to acquire Genesis Microchip Inc. Genesis develops image and video processing systems. It was reported that the acquisition has been approved by Genesis' Board of Directors. It is expected that Genesis will enhance STMicroelectronics' technological capabilities.

5772 ■ *"Taiwan Technology Initiatives Foster Growth" in Canadian Electronics (Vol. 23, February 2008, No. 1, pp. 28)*
Pub: CLB Media Inc.
Description: A study conducted by the Market Intelligence Center shows that currently, Taiwan is the world's larges producer of information technology products such as motherboards, servers, and LCD monitors. In 2006, Taiwan's LED industry reached a production value of NTD 21 billion. This push into the LED sector shows the Ministry of Economic Affairs' plan to target industries that are environmentally friendly.

5773 ■ *"Thumbing Around" in Canadian Business (Vol. 79, October 9, 2006, No. 20, pp. 143)*
Pub: Rogers Media
Ed: Gerry Blackwell. **Description:** The features, functions of Cruzer Titanium, a serial bus standard to interface device developed by SanDisk Corporation are discussed.

5774 ■ *"TomTom GO910: On the Road Again" in Black Enterprise (Vol. 37, January 2007, No. 6, pp. 52)*
Pub: Earl G. Graves Publishing Co. Inc.
Ed: Stephanie Young. **Description:** TomTom GO 910 is a GPS navigator that offers detailed maps of the U.S., Canada, and Europe. Consumers view their routes by a customizable LCD screen showing everything from the quickest to the shortest routes available or how to avoid toll roads. Business travelers may find this product invaluable as it also functions as a cell phone and connects to a variety of other multi-media devices.

5775 ■ *"Tony Hawk Carves a New Niche" in Entrepreneur (Vol. 37, October 2009, No. 10, pp. 26)*
Pub: Entrepreneur Media, Inc.
Ed: Gary Cohn. **Description:** Professional skateboarder Tony Hawk discusses the growth of Birdhouse, the skateboard company he founded. He is excited about the release of Tony Hawk Ride, a videogame with a skateboard controller.

5776 ■ *"VTech Targets Tots With a Wee Wii" in Advertising Age (Vol. 79, September 8, 2008, No. 33, pp. 14)*
Pub: Crain Communications, Inc.
Ed: Beth Snyder Bulik. **Description:** V-Motion is a video-game console targeting 3-to-7-year-olds and is manufactured by educational toy company VTech. The company is marketing the product as a kind of Wii for preschoolers and hopes to build a formidable brand presence in the kids' electronics market.

5777 ■ *"Wattles Plugs Back Into State" in Business Journal Portland (Vol. 27, November 19, 2010, No. 38, pp. 1)*
Pub: Portland Business Journal
Ed: Wendy Culverwell. **Description:** Denver, Colorado-based Ultimate Electronics Inc.'s first store in Oregon was opened in Portland and the 46th store in the chain of electronic superstores is expected to employ 70-80 workers. The venture is the latest for Mark Wattles, one of Oregon's most successful entrepreneurs, who acquired Ultimate from bankruptcy.

5778 ■ *"Winning With Women" in Marketing to Women (Vol. 22, August 2009, No. 8, pp. 6)*
Pub: EPM Communications Inc.
Contact: Ira Mayer, President
E-mail: imayer@epmcom.com
Description: Women shoppers are buying more utilitarian categories despite the overall fall in consumer electronics sales. Among the top five purchases women will defer in the next three months are personal consumer electronics, such as MP3 players and digital cameras, as well as home entertainment items.

5779 ■ *"A Wireless Makes 8 Store-In-Store Kiosk Acquisitions" in Wireless News (October 16, 2010)*
Pub: Close-Up Media Inc.
Description: A Wireless, a retailer for Verizon Wireless has acquired eight of Verizon's retail kiosks that are positioned in home appliance and electronics stores.

STATISTICAL SOURCES

5780 ■ *RMA Annual Statement Studies*
Pub: Risk Management Association
Contact: Kevin M. Blakey, President
Released: Annual. **Price:** $175.00 2006-07 edition, $105.00. **Description:** Contains composite balance sheets and income statements for more than 360 industries, including the accounting, auditing, and bookkeeping industries. Also contains five years of comparative historical data for discerning trends. Includes 16 commonly used ratios, computed for most of the size groupings for nearly every industry.

TRADE PERIODICALS

5781 ■ *Wireless Week*
Pub: Wireless Week
Contact: Monica Allewen,
URL(s): www.wirelessweek.com. **Released:** Weekly **Price:** Free.

TRADE SHOWS AND CONVENTIONS

5782 ■ **National Professional Service Convention and Trade Show**
International Society of Certified Electronics Technicians (ISCET)
3608 Pershing Ave.
Fort Worth, TX 76107-4527
Ph: (817)921-9101
Free: 800-946-0201
Fax: (817)921-3741
Co. E-mail: info@iscet.org
URL: http://www.iscet.org
Contact: Dan Mundy, President
E-mail: dmundy@earthlink.net
URL(s): www.nesda.com. **Frequency:** Annual. **Audience:** Electronic product servicers, dealers. **Principal Exhibits:** Electronics, receivers, recorders, and supplies; software; telecommunications equipment; computers; videocassette recorders; parts and accessories, business forms, warranty companies, and magazines/associations.

FRANCHISES AND BUSINESS OPPORTUNITIES

5783 ■ **Handypro Handyman Service**
HandyPro Franchise, Inc.
995 S Main St.
Plymouth, MI 48170
Ph: (734)254-9160
Fax: (734)254-9171
Description: Professional handyman services. **No. of Franchise Units:** 14. **No. of Company-Owned Units:** 2. **Founded:** 1993.. **Franchised:** 2001. **Equity Capital Needed:** $65,500-$107,500. **Franchise Fee:** $25,000. **Training:** Yes.

5784 ■ **K & N Mobile Distribution Systems**
K & N Electric Franchising, Inc.
4909 Rondo Dr.
Ft. Worth, TX 76106
Free: 800-433-2170
Fax: (817)624-3721
Description: Distribution and sale of electrical products and fasteners from a "mobile warehouse." Six-month, money-back guarantee in applicable states. **No. of Franchise Units:** 12. **No. of Company-Owned Units:** 13. **Founded:** 1972.. **Equity Capital Needed:** $87,000. **Franchise Fee:** $10,000. **Training:** Initial 10-day training course is conducted at corporate headquarters. Trainer accompanies franchisee during the first 3-10 days in the field. During the first year, a trainer rides with the franchisee at least 2 days per quarter. After the franchisee has been in business for 1 year, a corporate representative will spend 4 or more days with the franchisee each year.

5785 ■ **RadioShack**
RadioShack Dealer Franchise
RadioShack Riverfrt Campus
300 RadioShack Cr
Ft. Worth, TX 76102
Ph: (817)415-9138
Description: Retail electronics. **No. of Franchise Units:** 1,300. **No. of Company-Owned Units:** 4,500. **Founded:** 1921. **Franchised:** 1968. **Equity Capital Needed:** $198,175-$346,851 initial investment. **Franchise Fee:** $39,900. **Training:** Offers 1 week training at franchisee's location, local workshops, annual convention and ongoing support.

5786 ■ Rapid Refill Ink
Rapid Refill Ink Intl., Corp.
18732 Lake Dr. E
Chanhassen, MN 55317
Ph: (952)238-1000
Free: 877-880-4465
Fax: (952)238-1009
Description: Remanufacturing of inkjet & laser toner cartridges. **No. of Franchise Units:** 92. **No. of Company-Owned Units:** 1. **Founded:** 2002.. **Franchised:** 2004. **Equity Capital Needed:** $23,200-$142,400. **Franchise Fee:** $15,000-$30,000. **Royalty Fee:** 6%. **Financial Assistance:** Limited in-house and third party financing available. **Training:** Provides 2 weeks training at headquarters, including 3 days business training.

COMPUTERIZED DATABASES

5787 ■ INSPEC® Ondisc - Technology
Michael Faraday House
6 Hills Way
Stevenage SG1 2AY, United Kingdom
Ph: 1438 313 311
Fax: 1438 765 526
Co. E-mail: postmaster@theiet.org
URL: http://www.theiet.org
Contact: Nigel Fine, Chief Executive Officer
Availability: CD-ROM: Institution of Engineering and Technology. **Type:** Bibliographic.

LIBRARIES

5788 ■ Agilent Technologies - Santa Clara Site Library
5301 Stevens Creek Blvd.
MS 55/27
Santa Clara, CA 95051
Ph: (408)345-8886
Free: 877-424-4536
Fax: (408)345-8474
Co. E-mail: contact_us@agilent.com
URL: http://www.home.agilent.com
Contact: Diana Robba
Scope: Electronics, business, computer science, biological sciences. **Services:** Interlibrary loan; copying; library not open to the public. **Founded:** 1975. **Holdings:** 4000 books. **Subscriptions:** 160 journals and other serials; 2 newspapers.

5789 ■ Fujitsu Microelectronics, Inc. - FMI Library
1250 E. Arques Ave., No. 333
Sunnyvale, CA 94085-5401
Ph: (408)746-6000
Free: 800-831-3183
Fax: (408)992-2674
Co. E-mail: fsa_inquiry@us.fujitsu.com
URL: http://www.fujitsu.com/us
Scope: Semiconductor industry and products, computer industry and products, telecommunications, electronics industry. **Services:** Interlibrary loan; SDI; Library not open to the public. **Founded:** 1990. **Holdings:** 500 books and conference proceedings; 250 market research reports and newsletters; CD-ROMs. **Subscriptions:** 70 journals and other serials; 2 newspapers. **Telecommunication Services:** inquiry@fma.fujitsu.com.

ASSOCIATIONS AND OTHER ORGANIZATIONS

5790 ■ **Food Marketing Institute (FMI)**
2345 Crystal Dr.Ste. 800
Arlington, VA 22202
Ph: (202)452-8444
Fax: (202)429-4519
Co. E-mail: fmi@fmi.org
URL: http://www.fmi.org
Contact: Leslie G. Sarasin, President
Description: Grocery retailers and wholesalers. Maintains liaison with government and consumers. Conducts 30 educational conferences and seminars per year. Conducts research programs; compiles statistics. **Founded:** 1977. **Publications:** *Facts About Supermarket Development* (Annual); *Food Marketing Industry Speaks* (Annual); *FMI Annual Financial Review*; *Food Retailing Industry Speaks*; *Operating Results of Independent Supermarkets*; *Advantage* (Monthly); *FMI Newsletter*; *Food Storage Information*; *FMI News: Aisle by Aisle* (Monthly); *Information Systems Directory* (Biennial). **Educational Activities:** Trade workshops and seminars, about thirty per year; FMI Annual Convention; GEO India (Biennial); MARKETECHNICS (Annual); Productivity Convention & Expo; Supermarket Industry Convention and Educational Exposition (Annual). **Awards:** William H. Albers Industry Relations Award; Esther Peterson Consumer Service Award; Sidney R. Rabb Award.

5791 ■ **National Association of Convenience Stores (NACS)**
1600 Duke St., 7th Fl.
Alexandria, VA 22314
Ph: (703)684-3600
Free: 800-966-6227
Fax: (703)836-4564
Co. E-mail: information@nacsonline.com
URL: http://www.nacsonline.com
Contact: Henry Armour, Chief Executive Officer
E-mail: harmour@nacsonline.com
Description: Represents retail stores that sell gasoline, fast foods, soft drinks, dairy products, beer, cigarettes, publications, grocery items, snacks and nonfood items and are usually open seven days per week for longer hours than conventional supermarkets. Serves the convenience and fuel retailing industry by providing industry knowledge, connections and advocacy to ensure the competitive viability of its members' businesses. Conducts educational and legislative activities and sponsors management seminars. **Scope:** convenience store industry. **Founded:** 1961. **Subscriptions:** 500 periodicals reports video recordings. **Publications:** *Compensation Survey* (Annual); *NACS Magazine* (Monthly); *NACS*; *National Association of Convenience Stores--Membership and Services Directory* (Annual); *State of the Industry Report/Factbook* (Annual); *National Association of Convenience Stores--Membership and Services Directory* (Annual). **Educational Activities:** National Association of Convenience Stores Convention (Annual); NACS Show (Annual). **Awards:** Global

Scholarship (Annual); Jim Yates Scholarship (Annual). **Telecommunication Services:** nacs@nacsonline.com; bremoyer@nacsonline.com.

5792 ■ **National Grocers Association (NGA)**
1005 N Glebe Rd., Ste. 250
Arlington, VA 22201-5758
Ph: (703)516-0700
Fax: (703)812-1821
Co. E-mail: info@nationalgrocers.org
URL: http://www.nationalgrocers.org
Contact: Thomas K. Zaucha, President
Description: Independent food retailers; wholesale food distributors servicing 29,000 food stores. Promotes industry interests and works to advance understanding, trade and cooperation among all sectors of the food industry. Represents members' interests before the government. Aids in the development of programs designed to improve the productivity and efficiency of the food distribution industry. Offers services in areas such as store planning and engineering, personnel selection and training, operations and advertising. Sponsors seminars and in-house training. Maintains liaison with Women Grocers of America, which serves as an advisory arm. **Founded:** 1980. **Publications:** *Congressional or Regulatory Update* (Periodic). **Educational Activities:** Supermarket Synergy Showcase (Annual); NGA Show (Annual); America's Supermarket Showcase (Annual). **Awards:** Clarence G. Adamy Great American Award; Spirit of America Award. **Telecommunication Services:** feedback@nationalgrocers.org.

REFERENCE WORKS

5793 ■ *"7-Eleven Considers Private Label Ice Cream"* in Ice Cream Reporter (Vol. 22, December 20, 2008, No. 1, pp. 1)
Pub: Ice Cream Reporter
Description: 7-Eleven is considering the introduction of a private label of snack foods, including ice cream desserts.

5794 ■ *"Amcon Distributing Co."* in Arkansas Business (Vol. 26, November 9, 2009, No. 45, pp. 13)
Pub: Journal Publishing Inc.
Description: Amcon Distributing Co., a consumer products company, has bought the convenience store distribution assets of Discount Distributors from its parent, Harps Food Stores Inc., significantly increasing its wholesale distribution presence in the northwest Arkansas market. The acquisition will be funded through Amcon's existing credit facilities.

5795 ■ *"Ampm Focus Has BP Working Overtime; New Convenience-Store Brand Comes to Chicago"* in Crain's Chicago Business (April 28, 2008)
Pub: Crain Communications, Inc.
Ed: John T. Slania. **Description:** Britian's oil giant BP PLC is opening its ampm convenience stores in the Chicago market and has already begun converting most of its 78 Chicago-area gas stations to

ampms. The company has also started to franchise the stores to independent operators. BP is promoting the brand with both traditional and unconventional marketing techniques such s real or simulated 3D snacks embedded in bus shelter ads and an in-store Guitar Hero contest featuring finalists from a recent contest at the House of Blues.

5796 ■ *"Casey's Buys Second Marion Convenience Store"* in Gazette (December 14, 2010)
Pub: Gazette
Ed: Dave DeWitte. **Description:** Casey's General Stores Inc. has acquired a Short Stop convenience store on Marion's west side in Iowa. The new store includes a car and truck wash.

5797 ■ *"Clean Bathrooms Are Big Key to Convenience Store's Success"* in Marketing to Women (Vol. 23, January 2010, No. 1, pp. 3)
Pub: EPM Communications Inc.
Contact: Ira Mayer, President
E-mail: imayer@epmcom.com
Description: Buc-ee's, a Texas-based convenience store chain, is attributing its large female consumer base to the cleanliness of its bathrooms. The chain actually markets itself specifically to female consumers.

5798 ■ *"Convenience Store Deal for Cardtronics"* in American Banker (Vol. 174, July 28, 2009, No. 143, pp. 12)
Pub: SourceMedia, Inc.
Description: Royal Buying Group, Inc., a convenience store marketing company, has agreed to recommend automated teller machine services from Cardtronics Inc., to its clients.

5799 ■ *"Convenience Store Expanding"* in Clovis News Journal (November 9, 2010)
Pub: Freedom Communications Inc.
Description: Allsup's convenience store on North Prince Street in Clovis, New Mexico will expand its facilities. The current building is being demolished to make way for the new construction.

5800 ■ *"Convenience Store Owners Will Request New Zoning Once More"* in Daily Republic (November 1, 2010)
Pub: McClatchy Tribune Information Services
Ed: Tom Lawrence. **Description:** Zoning change has been requested for a proposed convenience store in Mitchell, South Dakota. Details are included.

5801 ■ *"December 19 Is a Great Day to be Terrible"* in Internet Wire (December 15, 2009)
Pub: Comtex News Network, Inc.
Description: Overview of the plans to market the grand opening of the newest Terrible Herbst location in Las Vegas, Nevada. Terrible Herbst is a complete convenience destination offering a gas station, convenience store, car wash and lube center.

5802 ■ *Directory of Supermarket, Grocery & Convenience Store Chains*
Pub: Chain Store Guide
Contact: Lisa Patterson, President
URL(s): www.chainstoreguide.com. **Released:** Annual; Latest edition 2011. **Price:** $425, Individuals Directory; $495, Individuals Online lite; $1175, Individuals Online pro; $1475, Individuals online pro plus. **Covers:** Over 3,269 supermarket, grocery, and convenience store chains operating 71,000 stores in the United States and Canada. **Entries include:** For supermarkets/groceries--company name, address, phone, fax, e-mail and web address; total annual sales; grocery sales; Internet order processing indicator; total units; number of units by type; number of units by trade name; number of units franchised to and from; total selling square feet; prototype sizes; average number of checkouts; projected number of units by specialty department; primary wholesaler type, name and location; parent company name and location; subsidiary name and location; divisional and branch office locations; warehouse locations; year founded; public company indicator; key personnel with titles. For convenience stores--company name, address, phone and fax numbers, web and e-mail addresses; total annual sales; convenience store sales; gasoline sales percentage; Internet order processing indicator; total units; number of units by trade name; number of units franchised to and from; total selling square footage; prototype sizes; average number of checkouts; projected number of openings and remodeling; packaged liquor indicators; trading areas; distribution center locations; number of units by specialty department; primary wholesaler type, name and location; parent company, subsidiary, warehouse, divisional and branch office names and locations; year founded; public company indicator; key personnel with titles. **Arrangement:** Geographical with sections for supermarkets and convenience stores. **Indexes:** Top 200 chains, trading area, alphabetical, exclusions.

5803 ■ *"Green and Clean"* in *Retail Merchandiser (Vol. 51, July-August 2011, No. 4, pp. 56)*
Pub: Phoenix Media Corporation
Description: Green Valley Grocery partnered with Paragon Solutions consulting firm to make their stores environmentally green.

5804 ■ *"Hy-Vee Plans Expansion, Convenience Store in Cedar Rapids"* in *Gazette (November 26, 2010)*
Pub: Gazette
Ed: George Ford. **Description:** Hy-Vee Inc. is awaiting approval to expand its supermarket in Cedar Rapids, Iowa. Hy-Vee is a food and drug store chain will construct a convenience store and gas station on the site.

5805 ■ *"In the Fast Lane"* in *Chain Store Age (Vol. 85, November 2009, No. 11, pp. 44)*
Pub: Chain Store Age
Ed: Samantha Murphy. **Description:** Quick Chek, which operates some 120 convenience stores in New Jersey and southern New York, is testing a new self-checkout system in order to examine how speed affects its in-store experience.

5806 ■ *"Javo Beverage to Feature On-Demand Coffee System"* in *GlobeNewswire (October 20, 2009)*
Pub: Comtex News Network, Inc.
Description: During the National Association of Convenience Store Show (NACS) at the Las Vegas Convention Center, Javo Beverage Company, Inc., a leading provider of premium dispensable coffee and tea-based beverages to the foodservice industry, will introduce its on-demand hot coffee system as well as a new line of products for the convenience store industry.

5807 ■ *"Killings Remind Convenience Store Workers of Job's Potential Risks"* in *Waterloo Courier (November 19, 2010)*
Pub: Gazette
Ed: Tina Hinz. **Description:** Potential risks for convenience store workers is stressed citing shootings in area shops; safety plans are important for these stores.

5808 ■ *"McD's Picks a Soda Fight; Takes on 7-Eleven With $1 Pop as Economy Softens"* in *Crain's Chicago Business (April 14, 2008)*
Pub: Crain Communications, Inc.
Ed: David Sterrett. **Description:** McDonald's Corp. is urging franchise owners to slash prices on large soft drinks to one dollar this summer to win customers from convenience store chains like 7-Eleven.

5809 ■ *"Merchants Association Working on Deal for Large Wholesale Warehouse"* in *Austin Business JournalInc. (September 19, 2008)*
Pub: American City Business Journals
Ed: Jean Kwon. **Description:** Greater Austin Merchants Association planning to buy a former Dell Outlet Factory in Austin, Texas and convert it into a warehouse for convenience stores and gas stations.

5810 ■ *"MillerCoors Needs the Quickie Mart"* in *Crain's Chicago Business (Vol. 32, November 16, 2009, No. 46, pp. 2)*
Pub: Crain Communications, Inc.
Ed: David Sterrett. **Description:** Power Marts convenience store owner Sam Odeh says that Chicago-based MillerCoors LLC has done a poor job at promoting its brand, keeping its signs up to date and stocking the shelves at his stores. He complains that the company's service has been awful and the marketing pathetic. Convenience stores accounted for more than $14 billion in beer sales in the past year.

5811 ■ *Progressive Grocer's Marketing Guidebook: The Comprehensive Source for Grocery, Drug and Mass Merchant Insights*
Pub: Trade Dimensions
Contact: Lynda Gutierrez, Director
URL(s): www.tradedimensions.com. **Released:** Annual; Latest edition 2011. **Covers:** Over 1,000 U.S. and Canadian supermarket chains, large independents and wholesalers; also includes 350 specialty distributors include smaller food wholesalers, food brokers, non-food distributors, and candy/tobacco/media distributors and over 15,000 key executives and buyers. **Entries include:** For retailers and wholesalers--Company name, address, phone, email and websites, number of stores operated or served, areas of operation, major grocery supplier, three-year financial summary, buying policies, private label information, lists of executives, buyers, and merchandisers. For specialty distributors--Name, address, phone, list of key personnel including buyers' categories, list of items handled, URL. **Arrangement:** Alphabetical by hierarchy, geographical by eight regions and 50 market areas. **Indexes:** Grocery related organizations, chain and wholesalers, state index, store operating name/parent company reference.

5812 ■ *"QuikTrip Makes Fortune 'Best' List"* in *Tulsa World (January 22, 2010)*
Pub: Tulsa World
Ed: Kyle Arnold. **Description:** According to a list released by Fortune Magazine, QuikTrip Corp. is once again ranked among the best companies in the country to work for due to the core values and culture held by the company's management.

5813 ■ *"Shout and Devour"* in *Tulsa World (November 7, 2009)*
Pub: Tulsa World
Ed: Kyle Arnold. **Description:** Profile of convenience store Shout and Sack whose owners have distanced themselves from the corporate fray of the chain stores by offering homemade lunches served at a counter; the store recently gained national exposure that highlighted the popularity despite a market share heavily dominated by franchises and chains.

5814 ■ *"Some Atlantic Beach Leaders Leery About Convenience Store Safety Measure"* in *Florida Times-Union (November 3, 2010)*
Pub: Florida Times-Union
Ed: Drew Dixon. **Description:** Jacksonville, Florida authorities are proposing a new ordinance that would require convenience stores to upgrade safety measures to protect store workers and customers from robbery and other crimes.

5815 ■ *"TMC Development Closes $1.1 Million Real Estate Purchase"* in *Internet Wire (September 17, 2009)*
Pub: Comtex News Network, Inc.
Description: TMC Development announced the closing of a $1.1 million real estate purchase for Mansa, LLC dba Kwikee Mart, a Napa-based convenience store; TMC helped the company secure a Small Business Administration 504 loan in order to purchase the acquisition of a 3,464 square foot building. SBA created the 504 loan program to provide financing for growing small and medium-sized businesses.

5816 ■ *Trade Dimensions--Directory of Convenience Stores: The Book of C-Store Market Facts*
Pub: Trade Dimensions
Contact: Lynda Gutierrez, Director
URL(s): www.tradedimensions.com. **Released:** Annual; Latest edition 2009. **Price:** $290, Individuals print; $645, Individuals CD. **Covers:** Over 1,600 U.S. and Canadian convenience store companies, each having four or more convenience stores. **Entries include:** Company name, address, phone, fax, email, website; URL; operating names; financial data; key personnel; number of stores operated; number of stores selling gasoline; number of stores franchised; number of stores selling fast food, number of stores with ATMs; names of grocery wholesalers, gasoline suppliers; candy, tobacco, and other distributors. **Database includes:** Ranking of the leading convenience store companies and a 10-year sales summary. **Arrangement:** Geographical (in 50 market areas). **Indexes:** Organization name, store operating name, major grocery supplier.

5817 ■ *"Walmart, Target Moving to Convenience Store Near You"* in *Hardware Retailing (Vol. 199, November 2010, No. 5, pp. 60)*
Pub: North American Retail Hardware Association
Contact: Mike O'Hara, President
Description: Walmart has plans to move into small convenience stores in Chicago, Detroit, San Francisco, and Los Angeles.

STATISTICAL SOURCES

5818 ■ *RMA Annual Statement Studies*
Pub: Risk Management Association
Contact: Kevin M. Blakey, President
Released: Annual. **Price:** $175.00 2006-07 edition, $105.00. **Description:** Contains composite balance sheets and income statements for more than 360 industries, including the accounting, auditing, and bookkeeping industries. Also contains five years of comparative historical data for discerning trends. Includes 16 commonly used ratios, computed for most of the size groupings for nearly every industry.

5819 ■ *Standard & Poor's Industry Surveys*
Pub: Standard & Poor's Corp.
Released: Annual. **Price:** $3633.00. **Description:** Two-volume book that examines the prospects for specific industries, including trucking. Also provides analyses of trends and problems, statistical tables and charts, and comparative company analyses.

TRADE PERIODICALS

5820 ■ *Grocery Headquarters*
Pub: Macfadden Communications Group L.L.C.
URL(s): www.groceryheadquarters.com. **Ed:** Tom Weir. **Released:** Monthly

5821 ■ *NACS*
Pub: National Association of Convenience Stores
Contact: Henry Armour, Chief Executive Officer
E-mail: harmour@nacsonline.com
Ed: Pressley Erin, Editor, ssmall@cstorecentral.com. **Released:** Monthly. **Price:** Included in membership. **Description:** Reports on key industry trends and innovative practices of convenience store companies. Recurring features include news of research, a calendar of events, reports of meetings, news of educational opportunities, and notices of publications available.

5822 ■ VFDA Update
Pub: Virginia Food Dealers Association Inc.
Ed: Nadine Kadlubowski, Editor. **Released:** Monthly.
Price: Included in membership. **Description:** Carries news and items of interest to those in retail food industries.

FRANCHISES AND BUSINESS OPPORTUNITIES

5823 ■ 7-Eleven Inc.
1722 Routh St., Ste. 1000
Dallas, TX 75201-2504
Ph: (972)828-7011
Free: 800-255-0711
URL: http://www.7-eleven.com
Contact: Joseph M. DePinto, President
Description: Convenience store. **Founded:** 1927.
Training: Provides 6 weeks training and ongoing support.

5824 ■ Circle K
1130 W Warner Rd.
Tempe, AZ 85284
Ph: (602)728-8000
Fax: (602)728-5248
Description: Convenience store. **No. of Franchise Units:** 452. **No. of Company-Owned Units:** 3,045.
Founded: 1991.. **Franchised:** 1995. **Equity Capital Needed:** $172,500-$1,407,250. **Franchise Fee:** $25,000. **Royalty Fee:** 3.7-4.5%. **Financial Assistance:** Limited third party financing available.
Training: 2 weeks training at headquarters, 2 weeks at franchisee's location and ongoing support.

5825 ■ Express Mart Franchising Corp.
Petr-All Petroleum Corp.
6567 Kinne Rd.
DeWitt, NY 13214
Ph: (315)446-0125
Description: Convenience stores the franchise is a license to utilize the franchisor's service name "Express Mart," related service mark and logotype,

as well as the franchisor's system for identification, layout and operation of convenience stores. Features pre-packaged and prepared foods, beverages, sundries, motor fuels and convenience store goods at a single approved location. **No. of Franchise Units:** 21. **No. of Company-Owned Units:** 44.
Founded: 1975.. **Franchised:** 1987. **Equity Capital Needed:** $86,000-$450,000. **Franchise Fee:** $15,000. **Training:** Provides comprehensive training: 1 week of classroom training in Phase I, and 1 week of in-store training in Phase II. Phase I deals with gasoline merchandising, convenience-store merchandising, alcohol management, inventory and loss control, recruiting, hiring, interviewing and customer relations. Phase II is onsite training on all applications.

5826 ■ Just-A-Buck
Just-A-Buck Licensing, Inc
563 Temple Hill Rd.
New Windsor, NY 12553
Ph: (845)561-7411
Fax: (845)561-7433
Co. E-mail: rs@spryal.net
URL: http://www.just-a-buck.com

Description: Dollar store. **No. of Franchise Units:** 21. **No. of Company-Owned Units:** 6. **Founded:** 1988.. **Franchised:** 1992. **Equity Capital Needed:** Minimum initial liquid capital required $50,000. **Franchise Fee:** $25,000. **Financial Assistance:** Yes.
Training: Provides corporate and onsite training.

5827 ■ Street Corner
McColla Enterprises Ltd.
2945 SW Wanamaker Dr.
Topeka, KS 66614
Ph: (782)272-8529
Fax: (785)272-2384
URL: http://www.streetcornernews.com

Description: A convenience store and newsstand.
No. of Franchise Units: 52. **Founded:** 1988. **Franchised:** 1995. **Equity Capital Needed:** $40,000

liquid required. **Franchise Fee:** $19,900. **Training:** Training available at headquarters upon request, 1 week at franchisee's location and ongoing support.

5828 ■ White Hen Pantry, Inc.
Clark Retail Enterprises Inc.
1722 Routh St., Ste. 1000
Dallas, TX 75201
Ph: (630)366-3100
Fax: (630)366-3447
Description: Convenience food store of approximately 2,500 square feet. Up-front parking for 10-15 cars. Stores are usually open 24 hours (some operate a lesser number of hours) for 365 days a year. Product line includes a service deli, fresh bakery, fresh produce and a wide variety of staples. **No. of Franchise Units:** 260. **Founded:** 1965.. **Franchised:** 1965. **Equity Capital Needed:** $40,000-$45,000, not including franchise fee. **Franchise Fee:** $25,000. **Financial Assistance:** Yes. **Training:** 3 weeks of classroom and in-store training precede store opening. Follow-up training provided after taking over store. Detailed operations manuals provided.

LIBRARIES

5829 ■ National Association of Convenience Stores - NACS Information Center
1600 Duke St.
Alexandria, VA 22314-3436
Ph: (703)684-3600
Free: 800-966-6227
Fax: (703)836-4564
Co. E-mail: nacs@nacsonline.com
URL: http://www.nacsonline.com
Contact: Henry Armour, President
Scope: Convenience stores, retail trade, petroleum marketing, food service. **Services:** Center open to the public by appointment only. **Founded:** 1988.
Holdings: 600 books; 200 video cassettes; archives.
Subscriptions: 100 journals and other serials. **Telecommunication Services:** harmour@nacsonline.com.

ASSOCIATIONS AND OTHER ORGANIZATIONS

5830 ■ American Culinary Federation (ACF)
180 Center Place Way
St. Augustine, FL 32095
Ph: (904)824-4468
Free: 800-624-9458
Fax: (904)825-4758
Co. E-mail: acf@acfchefs.net
URL: http://www.acfchefs.org
Contact: Michael Ty, President
Description: Aims to promote the culinary profession and provide on-going educational training and networking for members. Provides opportunities for competition, professional recognition, and access to educational forums with other culinary experts at local, regional, national, and international events. Operates the National Apprenticeship Program for Cooks and pastry cooks. Offers programs that address certification of the individual chef's skills, accreditation of culinary programs, apprenticeship of cooks and pastry cooks, professional development, and the fight against childhood hunger. **Scope:** hospitality industry. **Founded:** 1929. **Subscriptions:** books. **Publications:** *The Culinary Insider* (Biweekly); *National Culinary Review* (Monthly); *Sizzle* (Quarterly); *Culinary Olympic Cookbook.* **Educational Activities:** American Culinary Federation Convention (Annual). **Awards:** Chef Educator of the Year Award (Annual); Chef of the Year Award (Annual); Chef Professionalism Award (Annual); Hermann G. Rusch Chef's Achievement Award (Annual); Pastry Chef of the Year Award (Annual); Student Chef of the Year Award (Annual); American Culinary Classic; American Culinary Federation Chair's Scholarship Grants; Balestreri/Cutino Scholarships; Chaine des Rotisseurs Scholarships; Julia Child Memorial Scholarships; Linda Cullen Memorial Scholarships; Stanley "Doc" Jensen Scholarships; Andrew Macrina Scholarships; Ray and Gertrude Marshall Scholarships; Hermann G. Rusch Scholarships; Spice Box Grants; Tomato Fest Scholarship Grants. **Telecommunication Services:** academy@acfchefs.net.

5831 ■ International Association of Culinary Professionals (IACP)
1221 Avenue of the Americas, 42nd Fl.
New York, NY 10020
Ph: (646)358-4957
Free: 866-358-4951
Fax: (866)358-2524
Co. E-mail: info@iacp.com
URL: http://www.iacp.com
Contact: Doug Duda, President
Description: Represents cooking school owners, food writers, chefs, caterers, culinary specialists, directors, teachers, cookbook authors, food stylists, food photographers, student/apprentices, and individuals in related industries in 20 countries. Promotes the interests of cooking schools, teachers, and culinary professionals. Encourages the exchange of information and education. Promotes professional standards and accreditation procedures. Maintains a Foundation to award culinary scholarships and

grants. **Founded:** 1978. **Publications:** *Frontburner* (Monthly); *International Association of Culinary Professionals Food Forum Quarterly* (Quarterly). **Awards:** Bert Greene Award (Annual); IACP Awards of Excellence (Annual); IACP Cookbook Awards (Annual); Cookbook Awards.

5832 ■ International Council on Hotel, Restaurant, and Institutional Education (CHRIE)
2810 N Parham Rd., Ste. 230
Richmond, VA 23294
Ph: (804)346-4800
Fax: (804)346-5009
Co. E-mail: publications@chrie.org
URL: http://www.chrie.org
Contact: Susan Fournier, President
E-mail: susan.fournier@ritz.edu
Description: Schools and colleges offering specialized education and training in hospitals, recreation, tourism and hotel, restaurant, and institutional administration; individuals, executives, and students. Provides networking opportunities and professional development. **Founded:** 1946. **Publications:** *A Guide to College Programs in Hospitality, Tourism, & Culinary Arts* (Biennial); *Guide to Hospitality Education* (Semiannual); *Hosteur Magazine* (Biennial); *The Journal of Hospitality and Tourism Education* (Quarterly); *The Journal of Hospitality and Tourism Research* (3/year); *Membership Directory and Research Guide* (Annual); *Journal of Hospitality & Tourism Research* (Quarterly); *Council on Hotel, Restaurant and Institutional Education--Member Directory and Resource Guide* (Biennial). **Awards:** Chef Herman Breithaupt Award; Stevenson W. Fletcher Achievement Award; Industry Recognition Award; W. Bradford Wiley Memorial Best Research Paper of the Year Award; Howard B. Meek Award; John Wiley and Sons Lifetime Research Achievement Award; John Wiley and Sons Award for Innovation in Teaching. **Telecommunication Services:** kmccarty@chrie.org.

5833 ■ National Restaurant Association Educational Foundation (NRAEF)
175 W Jackson Blvd., Ste. 1500
Chicago, IL 60604-2814
Ph: (312)715-1010
Free: 800-765-2122
Fax: (312)583-9841
Co. E-mail: info@restaurant.org
URL: http://www.nraef.org
Contact: Mary M. Adolf, President
E-mail: madolf@nraef.org
Description: Serves as an educational foundation supported by the National Restaurant Association and all segments of the foodservice industry including restaurateurs, foodservice companies, food and equipment manufacturers, distributors and trade associations. Advances the professional standards of the industry through education and research. Offers video training programs, management courses and careers information. Conducts research and maintains hall of fame. **Founded:** 1987. **Publications:** *Foodservice/Hospitality College Directory* (Irregular); *Directory of Computer Hardware and Software for the Food Service Industry.* **Awards:** College of

Diplomates Award; Al Schuman Ecolab Undergraduate Entrepreneurial Scholarships; Thad and Alice Eure Ambassador of Hospitality Award. **Telecommunication Services:** lmckee@nraef.org; scholars@nraef.org.

REFERENCE WORKS

5834 ■ "Beyond Grits: The Many Varieties of Southern Cuisine" in Women In Business (Vol. 62, June 2010, No. 2, pp. 14)
Pub: American Business Women's Association
Ed: Debbie Gold. **Description:** Southern cuisine is believed to be associated with grits, but the cuisine is not always with grits and offers varieties from Europe, Native American and African cooking. Southern cuisine varieties include soul food, Creole food, Cajun food and Low Country food. Examples are provided.

5835 ■ "A Failed Promise: A Dream Job Gone..or Just Delayed?" in Restaurant Business (Vol. 107, September 2008, No. 9, pp. 34)
Pub: Ideal Media
Ed: Patricia Cobe, Joan M. Lang, Dana Tanyeri. **Description:** Profile of Jeremy Lycanwas, executive chef who taught at the California Culinary Academy. Lycanwas tells of accepting a position as executive chef from his mentor, and later started his own restaurant.

5836 ■ "Holy Wasabi! Sushi Not Just For Parents Anymore" in Chicago Tribune (March 13, 2008)
Pub: McClatchy-Tribune Information Services
Ed: Christopher Borrelli. **Description:** Wicker Park cooking school, The Kid's Table, specializes in cooking classes for pre-teens; Elena Marre who owns the school was surprised when she was asked to plan a children's party in which she would teach a course in sushi making. More and more adolescents and small children are eating sushi.

5837 ■ "Intrepid Souls: Meet a Few Who've Made the Big Leap" in Crain's Chicago Business (Vol. 31, November 10, 2008, No. 45, pp. 26)
Pub: Crain Communications, Inc.
Ed: Meredith Landry. **Description:** Advice is given from entrepreneurs who have launched businesses in the last year despite the economic crisis. Among the types of businesses featured are a cooking school, a child day-care center, a children's clothing store and an Internet-based company.

5838 ■ "It's all Kosher at Downtown Eatery/Bakery" in AZ Daily Star (July 10, 2008)
Pub: Arizona Daily Star
Ed: Valerie Vinyard. **Description:** Rabbi James Botwright and partner Wayne Anderson are profiled. Details of how the partners opened their bakery and eatery in Tucson, Arizona. Botwright, who attended culinary school in San Francisco, learned much from his grandfather who was a pastry chef.

5839 ■ *Martha, Inc.*
Pub: John Wiley and Sons, Inc.
Ed: Christopher Byron. **Released:** 2002. **Price:** $28.
00. **Description:** Profile of Martha Stewart's rise from working class to a billionaire businesswoman is presented. The book covers Stewart's power struggles and personal conflicts as well as her triumphs.

5840 ■ *"Nurturing Talent for Tomorrow" in Restaurants and Institutions (Vol. 118, September 15, 2008, No. 14, pp. 90)*
Pub: Reed Business Information
Contact: Jeff Greisch, President
Description: Hormel Foods Corporation and The Culinary Institute of America (CIA) have teamed to develop The Culinary Enrichment and Innovation Program that supports future culinary leaders by providing creative and competitive staff development. Sixteen students attend four three-day sessions at the CIA's campus in Hyde Park, New York; sessions include classroom teaching, one-on-one interaction with leading culinarians, and hands-on kitchen time.

5841 ■ *The Pampered Chef*
Pub: Doubleday Broadway Publishing Group
Ed: Doris Christopher. **Price:** $24.95.

TRADE PERIODICALS

5842 ■ *Bon Appetit: America's Food and Entertaining Magazine*
Pub: Conde Nast Publications
Contact: David Carey, President
URL(s): www.bonappetit.com/. **Released:** Monthly **Price:** $12, Individuals plus 3 shipping & handling; $21, Individuals plus 6 shipping & handling.

5843 ■ *Cooking for Profit*
Pub: CP Publishing Inc.
Contact: Craig Culver, President
URL(s): www.cookingforprofit.com/home.html. **Released:** Monthly **Price:** $30, Individuals; $55, Two years; $52, Canada; $98, Canada 2 years; $85, Other countries; $160, Other countries 2 years.

5844 ■ *ESSENCE*
Pub: Canadian Federation of Chefs & Cooks
Ed: Julius Pokomandy, Editor. **Released:** Quarterly. **Price:** Included in membership; $15, nonmembers. **Description:** Promotes national culinary events, information from chefs, skills upgrading, and product information. Recurring features include letters to the editor, interviews, news of research, a calendar of events, reports of meetings, and news of educational opportunities.

5845 ■ *No Salt Week-The Newsletter*
Pub: Prosperity & Profits Unlimited, Distribution Services
Ed: A. Doyle, Editor. **Released:** Annual. **Price:** $2, U.S.; $3, Canada; $4, elsewhere. **Description:** Presents possibilities for herb and spice blends that contain no added salt. Also contains ideas for cooking and much more.

FRANCHISES AND BUSINESS OPPORTUNITIES

5846 ■ Batter Up Kids Culinary Center
4403 Canyonside Trail
Austin, TX 78731
Ph: (512)342-8682
Free: 866-345-8682
Fax: (512)343-8810
Description: Children's culinary program. **No. of Company-Owned Units:** 1. **Founded:** 1991. **Franchised:** 2006. **Equity Capital Needed:** $178,100-$256,000 total investment; $70,000 net worth. **Franchise Fee:** $25,000. **Royalty Fee:** 4%. **Training:** Provides 4-5 days at headquarters, 4-5 days at franchisee's location with ongoing support.

LIBRARIES

5847 ■ Atlantic Cape Community College - William Spangler Library
Mays Landing Campus
5100 Black Horse Pike
Mays Landing, NJ 08330-2623

Ph: (609)343-4951
Co. E-mail: wilinski@atlantic.edu
URL: http://www.atlantic.edu/library/index.htm
Contact: Grant Wilinski, Director
Scope: Business, criminal justice, culinary arts, dance, education, English, general studies, geography, history, hospitality, Library vocabulary, nursing, psychology, sociology. **Services:** Interlibrary loan; copying; library open to the public. **Founded:** 1966. **Holdings:** 71,000 books; audio and video materials. **Subscriptions:** 56 journals and other serials; 3 newspapers.

5848 ■ California Culinary Academy Library
350 Rhode Island St.
San Francisco, CA 94103
Ph: (415)771-3500
Free: 888-897-3222
Co. E-mail: bgk@baychef.com
URL: http://www.chefs.edu/San-Francisco
Scope: Culinary arts, nutrition, restaurant and hospitality industry. **Services:** Library open to the public by special appointment only. **Founded:** 1989. **Holdings:** 3500 books. **Subscriptions:** 90 journals and other serials.

5849 ■ Canadian Restaurant & Foodservices Association Resource Centre
316 Bloor St., W.
Toronto, ON, Canada M5S 1W5
Ph: (416)923-8416
Free: 800-387-5649
Fax: (416)923-1450
Co. E-mail: info@crfa.ca
URL: http://www.crfa.ca/research/
Contact: Prasanthi Vasanthakumar, Communications Specialist
Scope: Food service, quantity cooking, legislation, administration, management, statistics, training, customer attitude surveys. **Services:** Copying; center open to the public on fee basis. **Founded:** 1972. **Holdings:** 1000 books. **Subscriptions:** 100 journals and other serials. **Telecommunication Services:** research@crfa.ca.

5850 ■ City College of San Francisco - Department - Culinary Arts and Hospitality Studies Alice Statler Library
50 Phelan Ave.
Statler Wing, Rm. 10
San Francisco, CA 94112
Ph: (415)239-3460
Co. E-mail: aniosi@ccsf.edu
URL: http://www.ccsf.edu/NEW/en/library/about-library/library-locations/statler.html
Contact: Andrea Niosi, Librarian
Scope: Public hospitality industries - hotels, motels, restaurants, catering services, cookery and nutrition; tourism; beverages. **Services:** Copying; Wi-Fi; library open to the public for reference use only. **Founded:** 1964. **Holdings:** 10,000 books; 3500 pamphlets; 900 menus; videotapes; archives. **Subscriptions:** 80 journals and other serials. **Telecommunication Services:** astatler@ccsf.edu.

5851 ■ Culinary Institute of America - Conrad N. Hilton Library
1946 Campus Dr.
Hyde Park, NY 12538-1499
Ph: (845)452-9600
URL: http://www.ciachef.edu/newyork/library/
URL(s): library.culinary.edu/. **Scope:** Cookery, food service, restaurant management, hospitality. **Services:** Interlibrary loan; copying; Library open to the public by appointment. **Founded:** 1972. **Holdings:** 86,000 volumes; 30,000 menus; 4500 DVDs and videos. **Subscriptions:** 280 journals and other serials.

5852 ■ Indianapolis-Marion County Public Library - Business, Science and Technology Service Section
40 E. St. Clair St.
Indianapolis, IN 46204
Ph: (317)275-4100

Fax: (317)269-1768
Co. E-mail: ofields@imcpl.org
URL: http://www.imcpl.org/
Contact: Mark Leggett, Manager
Scope: Science, engineering, space science, agriculture, electronics, computer science, building, health, cookery, television, accounting, advertising, economics, business, insurance, investment, management. **Services:** Interlibrary loan; copying. **Founded:** 1921. **Holdings:** 65,000 titles; 10 VF drawers. **Subscriptions:** 950 journals and other serials.

5853 ■ Johnson & Wales University - Harborside Culinary Library
321 Harborside Blvd.
Providence, RI 02905
Ph: (401)598-1282
Co. E-mail: bjanson@jwu.edu
URL: http://www.jwu.edu
Contact: Barbara Janson, Librarian
Scope: Cookbooks, food service, menu planning, nutrition, professional management, catering and banquets, household manuals, canning, preserving and freezing, hotel and motel management. **Services:** Copying; Library open to the public. **Founded:** 1979. **Holdings:** 10,000 books; 700 menus. **Subscriptions:** 100 journals and other serials.

5854 ■ Lamar University - Mary and John Gray Library - Justice Cookery Collection
7th Fl., Room 701
211 Redbird Ln.
Beaumont, TX 77710-0021
Ph: (409)880-7787
Fax: (409)880-2318
Co. E-mail: penny.clark@lamar.edu
URL: http://library.lamar.edu
Contact: David Carroll, Director, Library Services
Scope: Southeast Texas - settlement, politics, trails, environment and conservation, mining and petroleum industries, shipping, air and rail transportation, performing arts. **Services:** Photoduplication; imaging; library open to the public. **Founded:** 1923. **Holdings:** 3000 volumes. **Subscriptions:** 2700 journals and other serials; 11 newspapers. **Telecommunication Services:** charlotte.holliman@lamar.edu.

5855 ■ Prince Edward Island Food Technology Centre - Information Services
PO Box 2000
Charlottetown, PE, Canada C1A 7N8
Ph: (902)368-5548
Fax: (902)368-5548
Co. E-mail: peiftc@gov.pe.ca
URL: http://www.biofoodtech.ca/
Contact: Kathy MacEwen, Library Technician
Scope: Agriculture, food, technology, food research. **Services:** Interlibrary loan; library open to the public by permission only. **Founded:** 1987. **Holdings:** 200 books; 9 bound periodical volumes. **Subscriptions:** 38 journals and other serials. **Telecommunication Services:** ftcweb@gov.pe.ca; kmmacewe@gov.pe.ca.

5856 ■ Paul Smith's College of Arts and Sciences - Joan Weill Adirondack Library
Rte. 86 and 30
Paul Smiths, NY 12970-0265
Ph: (518)327-6313
Free: 800-421-2605
Fax: (518)327-6016
Co. E-mail: library@paulsmiths.edu
URL: http://www.paulsmiths.edu/library
Contact: Neil Surprenant, Director, Library Services
Scope: Hotel and restaurant management, chef training, culinary arts, forestry, urban tree management, environmental science, forest recreation, surveying, ecotourism, natural resources management, fisheries management, business management. **Services:** Interlibrary loan; copying; library open to the public with restrictions. **Founded:** 1946. **Holdings:** 54,000 books; pamphlets. **Subscriptions:** 504 journals and other serials; 7 newspapers. **Telecommunication Services:** nsurprenant@paulsmiths.edu.

5857 ■ Societe Culinaire - Philanthropique
305 E. 47th St., Ste. 11B
New York, NY 10017
Ph: (212)308-0628

Fax: (212)308-0588
Co. E-mail: salon@societeculinaire.com
URL: http://www.societeculinaire.com
Contact: Jean-Pierre Stoehr, President
Scope: Professional cooking. **Services:** Library open to members only. **Holdings:** Cookbooks. **Telecommunication Services:** info@societeculinaire.com.

5858 ■ University of Denver - Penrose Library Special Collections and Archives
2150 E. Evans Ave.
Denver, CO 80208-0287
Ph: (303)871-3428

Fax: (303)871-2290
Co. E-mail: archives@du.edu
URL: http://library.du.edu/site/about/specialCollections/specialCollections.php
Contact: Steven Fisher
Scope: University of Denver archives, cookery, Judaica, dance, Civil War. **Services:** Interlibrary loan; copying; collections open to the public. **Founded:** 1864. **Holdings:** 30,000 books. 15,000 lin. ft. of archives. **Telecommunication Services:** steven. fisher@du.edu.

5859 ■ University of Nebraska--Kearney - Nebraska Career and Technical Education Resource Center
West Center, E212

Kearney, NE 68849
Ph: (308)865-8462
Fax: (308)865-8669
Co. E-mail: klesathmj@unk.edu
URL: http://www.unk.edu
Contact: Mary Jo Klesath

Scope: Vocational education, family and consumer science, tech prep, applied academics, gender equity, industrial technology, career education, business education, agriculture, marketing, health occupations. **Services:** Interlibrary loan; Library open to the public. **Founded:** 1973. **Holdings:** 7000 books; 500 audio/visual materials; curriculum guides; games; kits.

ASSOCIATIONS AND OTHER ORGANIZATIONS

5860 ■ Copyright Clearance Center (CCC)
222 Rosewood Dr.
Danvers, MA 01923-4520
Ph: (978)750-8400
Fax: (978)646-8600
Co. E-mail: info@copyright.com
URL: http://www.copyright.com
Contact: Tracey L. Armstrong, President
Description: Facilitates compliance with U.S. copyright law. Provides licensing systems for the reproduction and distribution of copyrighted materials in print and electronic formats throughout the world. Manages rights relating to over 1.75 million works and represents more than 9600 publishers and hundreds of thousands of authors and other creators, directly or through their representatives. **Scope:** An international licensing organization, representing authors, publishers and creators from around the world, licenses the rights to books, journals, newspapers, websites, eBooks, images, blogs and more. Works with thought leaders, government agencies and policy makers to streamline copyright licensing across the globe. **Founded:** 1978. **Seminars:** 110th Semiannual Cancer Seminar of the California Tumor Tissue Registry, 2006. **Special Services:** Rightsphere®.

5861 ■ International Reprographic Association (IRgA)
c/o Robert Roperti
Jiffy Reprographics Inc
411 South Garden Ave.
Clearwater, FL 33756
Ph: (727)442-7125
Fax: (727)443-6179
Co. E-mail: roperti@jiffyreprographics.com
URL: http://www.irga.com
Contact: Robert Roperti, President
Description: Commercial blue print and photocopy firms, engineering supply stores, and materials and equipment suppliers. Conducts annual photo-tech, marketing, management, and business planning seminars. **Founded:** 1927. **Publications:** *IRgA News Digest* (Monthly); *Repro Report* (Bimonthly). **Awards:** George K. Bukovsky Award (Annual).

REFERENCE WORKS

5862 ■ "Funny Business" in Canadian Business (Vol. 82, April 27, 2009, No. 7, pp. 27)
Pub: Rogers Media

Ed: Rachel Pulfer. **Description:** Companies are advised to use humor in marketing to drive more revenue. IBM Canada, for example, commissioned Second City Communications for a marketing campaign that involved humor. While IBM Canada declined to give sales or traffic figures, firm executives rank the marketing campaign as an overall success.

5863 ■ "Xerox Diverts Waste from Landfills" in Canadian Electronics (Vol. 23, February 2008, No. 1, pp. 1)
Pub: CLB Media Inc.

Description: Xerox Corporation revealed that it was able to divert more than two billion pounds of electronic waste from landfills through waste-free initiatives. The company's program, which was launched in 1991, covers waste avoidance in imaging supplies and parts reuse. Environmental priorities are also integrated into manufacturing operations.

STATISTICAL SOURCES

5864 ■ RMA Annual Statement Studies
Pub: Risk Management Association
Contact: Kevin M. Blakey, President

Released: Annual. **Price:** $175.00 2006-07 edition, $105.00. **Description:** Contains composite balance sheets and income statements for more than 360 industries, including the accounting, auditing, and bookkeeping industries. Also contains five years of comparative historical data for discerning trends. Includes 16 commonly used ratios, computed for most of the size groupings for nearly every industry.

TRADE PERIODICALS

5865 ■ NAQP News
Pub: PrintImage International
Contact: Steven D. Johnson, President

Released: Monthly. **Price:** Included in membership. **Description:** Features information on the newest technologies in electronic publishing, color copying, mailing services, and computer hardware and software. Includes association news, advice on management and marketing methods, government issues affecting the industry, and an ideas exchange forum.

5866 ■ Quick Printing: The Information Source for Commercial Copyshops & Printshops
Pub: Cygnus Business Media
Contact: Rich Reiff, President

URL(s): www.myprintresource.com/magazinewww.cygnusb2b.com/PropertyPub.cfm?PropertyID=158. **Ed:** Karen Lowery Hall. **Released:** Monthly **Price:** Free.

TRADE SHOWS AND CONVENTIONS

5867 ■ International Reprographic Association Annual Convention and Trade Show
International Reprographic Association
401 N Michigan Ave., Ste. 2200
Chicago, IL 60611
Ph: (312)245-1026
Free: 800-833-4742
Fax: (312)673-6724
Co. E-mail: info@irga.com
URL: http://www.irga.com
URL(s): www.irga.com. **Frequency:** Annual. **Audience:** Reprographic professionals. **Principal Exhibits:** Reprographic equipment, supplies, and services for color graphics, reprographic and digital imaging service supplies.

5868 ■ Print Ontario
IAPHC, Inc.
IAPHC Corporate HQ
Maple Grove, MN 55311-7549
Co. E-mail: headquarters@iaphc.org
URL: http://www.iaphc.org
URL(s): www.printontario.com. **Price:** $7, Preregistered; $15, Onsite. **Frequency:** Biennial. **Audience:** Small and mid-size commercial printers, instant printers, implant shops, brokers and forms distributors. **Principal Exhibits:** Press manufactures, bindery equipment, high speed photocopiers, color copiers, paper manufactures, ink manufactures, trade business, manufactures, trade labels. **Dates and Locations:** , Exhibition Place.

CONSULTANTS

5869 ■ Concord Associates Co.
16 Chambers Cir.
West Lebanon, NH 03784
Ph: (603)643-6768
Fax: (603)643-6768
Contact: Elliott D. Novak, President
Scope: Offers business counsel and market and marketing consulting assistance in key areas of both the consumer and professional digital imaging fields. Primary emphasis is in digital cameras; ink jet and dye sublimation printers; digital mini labs; and related or ancillary products such as flash memory cards for digital cameras. **Founded:** 1982.

FRANCHISES AND BUSINESS OPPORTUNITIES

5870 ■ Kwik Kopy Business Centers
Kwik Kopy Business Centers, Inc. Kwik Kopy Business Centers
12715 Telge Rd.
Cypress, TX 77429
Free: 888-638-8722
Fax: (281)256-4178
Co. E-mail: franchisedevelopment@iced.net
URL: http://www.iced.net
Description: Offers business advertisement aids and printing and copying services. **No. of Franchise Units:** 16. **No. of Company-Owned Units:** 1. **Founded:** 2001.. **Franchised:** 2001. **Equity Capital Needed:** $65,000 liquid capital; $250,000 net worth. **Franchise Fee:** $35,000. **Financial Assistance:** Yes. **Training:** Owners attend classroom and field training, as well as ongoing training through workshops and conferences.

5871 ■ Pip Printing and Document Services
26722 Plz. Dr., Ste. 200
Mission Viejo, CA 92691
Ph: (800)894-7498
Fax: (800)747-0679
URL: http://www.pip.com
Description: Offers complete range of business including multi-color printing, high-volume copying, desktop publishing, layout, design and finishing on newsletters, brochures, bound presentations, business stationery and forms. **No. of Franchise Units:** 285. **Founded:** 1965.. **Franchised:** 1968. **Equity Capital Needed:** Minimum cash investment $83,000 living expenses; Total investment $232,850-$465,840. **Franchise Fee:** $20,000. **Financial Assistance:** Yes. **Training:** 2 1/2 weeks of training at PIP University and field visit within the first six months of operation.

5872 ■ Postal Connections of America
Templar Franchise Company
275 E. Douglas Ave., Ste. 115
El Cajon, CA 92020
Ph: (619)294-7550
Free: 800-767-8257
Fax: (619)294-4550
Co. E-mail: info@postalconnections.com
URL: http://www.postalconnections.com.
Description: Postal Connections stores offer packaging, shipping, mail receiving & forwarding, copies, printing, scanning & storage of digital documents, eBay auction support, office & packing supplies, crate & freight shipping and more. **No. of Franchise Units:** 99. **Founded:** 1985.. **Franchised:** 1996. **Equity Capital Needed:** $119,000-$153,900, average initial investment. **Franchise Fee:** $23,900. **Financial Assistance:** Yes. **Training:** Extensive training prior to & after opening. Franchisee's receive 5 days live action training in a regional training store, Unique Act video training program & 4 days onsite.

5873 ■ Sir Speedy Inc.—Sir Speedy
26722 Plz. Dr.
Mission Viejo, CA 92691-6390
Ph: (949)348-5000
Free: 800-747-7733
Fax: (949)348-5066
Co. E-mail: markting@sirspeedy.com
URL: http://www.sirspeedy.com
Contact: Rich Lowe, President
Description: Franchisor of printing, copying, graphic design and digital networking centers. **No. of Franchise Units:** 237. **Founded:** 1968. **Franchised:** 1968. **Equity Capital Needed:** $221,040-$271,040; net worth $450,000. **Franchise Fee:** $25,000. **Royalty Fee:** 4-6%. **Training:** Available at headquarters 2 weeks, 2 weeks at franchisee's location, at regional meeings 1-3 days, and ongoing support.

5874 ■ Sure Print & Copy Centers
12465 82nd Ave.
Surrey, BC, Canada V3W 3E8
Ph: (604)594-8334
Free: 800-914-7873
Fax: (604)594-8320
Co. E-mail: info@surecopy.com
URL: http://www.surecopy.com
Description: A print and copy service provider. **No. of Franchise Units:** 90. **No. of Company-Owned Units:** 3. **Founded:** 1984.. **Franchised:** 1990. **Equity Capital Needed:** $50,000 cash minimum $15,000 working capital. **Franchise Fee:** $20,000. **Training:** Full training and guidance provided prior to start-up and on an ongoing basis as required. **Telecommunication Services:** sure@surecopy.com.

LIBRARIES

5875 ■ Xerox Corporation - Technical Information Center
800 Philips Rd.
Mail Stop 0105-66C
Webster, NY 14580
Ph: (716)422-3505
Fax: (716)265-5722
URL: http://www.xerox.com
Contact: Laura R. Tucker, Manager
Scope: Xerography, electrophotography, reprography, electronics, chemistry, physics, photography, materials and processes, computer science. **Services:** Interlibrary loan; SDI; center open to the public by appointment. **Founded:** 1960. **Holdings:** 17,318 books; 10,728 microfilm reels/rolls; 126,531 internal reports; 16,937 external reports; 55 VF drawers; 5500 reels of microfilm; 455,426 microfiche; 3,793,423 patents. **Subscriptions:** 90 journals and other serials.

ASSOCIATIONS AND OTHER ORGANIZATIONS

5876 ■ Canadian Cosmetic, Toiletry and Fragrance Association (CCTFA)—Association Canadienne des Cosmetiques, Produits de Toilette et Parfums
420 Britannia Rd. E, Ste. 102
Mississauga, ON, Canada L4Z 3L5
Ph: (905)890-5161
Fax: (905)890-2607
Co. E-mail: cctfa@cctfa.ca
URL: http://www.cctfa.ca/site/cctfa
Description: Manufacturers of personal care products, cosmetics, and perfumes. Seeks to advance the cosmetics and toiletries industries. Represents members before labor and industrial organizations, government agencies, and the public. Sponsors cosmetic safety research. **Founded:** 1928. **Publications:** *CCTFA News and Events Newsletter* (Monthly).

5877 ■ CCTFA News and Events Newsletter
420 Britannia Rd. E, Ste. 102
Mississauga, ON, Canada L4Z 3L5
Ph: (905)890-5161
Fax: (905)890-2607
Co. E-mail: cctfa@cctfa.ca
URL: http://www.cctfa.ca/site/cctfa
Released: Monthly

5878 ■ Cosmetic Executive Women (CEW)
286 Madison Ave., 19th Fl.
New York, NY 10017
Ph: (212)685-5955
Fax: (212)685-3334
Co. E-mail: cjacobson@cew.org
URL: http://cew.org
Contact: Carlotta Jacobson, President
Description: Women in the cosmetic and allied industries. Unites women executives in the cosmetic field for industry awareness and business advancement. Promotes products, people, professional development and philanthropy. **Founded:** 1954. **Publications:** *Membership Roster* (Periodic). **Educational Activities:** Product Demonstration (Annual). **Awards:** Beauty Awards (Annual); Cosmetic Executive Women Achiever Award (Annual).

5879 ■ Cosmetic Industry Buyers and Suppliers (CIBS)
c/o Rafael Cruz
830 Terry Rd.
Hauppauge, NY 11788
Co. E-mail: cibsmail@cibsonline.com
URL: http://www.cibsonline.com
Contact: Charles Marchese, President
Description: Buyers and suppliers of essential oils, chemicals, packaging, and finished goods relative to the cosmetic industry. Enhances growth, stability, prosperity, and protection of the American cosmetic industry through close personal contact and the exchange of ideas and experiences. **Founded:** 1948.

5880 ■ Cosmetic Ingredient Review (CIR)
1101 17th St. NW, Ste. 412
Washington, DC 20036-4702
Ph: (202)331-0651
Fax: (202)331-0088
Co. E-mail: cirinfo@cir-safety.org
URL: http://www.cir-safety.org
Contact: Wilma F. Bergfeld, Chairperson
Description: A cosmetic industry self-regulatory organization sponsored by the Cosmetic, Toiletry, and Fragrance Association. Seeks to assure the safety of ingredients used in cosmetics. Reviews scientific data on the safety of ingredients used in cosmetics; documents validity of tests used to study ingredients. **Scope:** unpublished safety data used in ingredient reports. **Founded:** 1976. **Publications:** *CIR Annual Report* (Annual); *Ingredient Report*; *Final Reports on Cosmetic Ingredient Safety Assessments* (Quarterly). **Educational Activities:** Expert Panel (Quarterly).

5881 ■ International Spa Association (ISPA)
2365 Harrodsburg Rd., Ste. A325
Lexington, KY 40504
Ph: (859)226-4326
Free: 888-651-4772
Fax: (859)226-4445
Co. E-mail: ispa@ispastaff.com
URL: http://www.experienceispa.com
Contact: Ms. Lynne Walker McNees, President
Description: Professional association and voice of the spa industry. Forms and maintains alliances that educate, set standards, provide resources, influence policy and build coalitions for the industry. Raises awareness of the spa industry and educates the public and industry professionals about the benefits of the spa experience. **Founded:** 1991. **Publications:** *LiveSpa*; *Pulse* (Bimonthly). **Educational Activities:** International Spa Association Conference (Annual). **Awards:** Mary Tabacchi Scholarship (Annual).

5882 ■ National Beauty Culturists' League (NBCL)
25 Logan Cir. NW
Washington, DC 20005-3725
Ph: (202)332-2695
Fax: (202)332-0940
Co. E-mail: nbcl@bellsouth.net
URL: http://www.nbcl.org
Contact: Dr. Katie B. Catalon, President
Description: Beauticians, cosmetologists, and beauty products manufacturers. Encourages standardized, scientific, and approved methods of hair, scalp, and skin treatments. Offers scholarships and plans to establish a research center. Sponsors: National Institute of Cosmetology, a training course in operating and designing and business techniques. Maintains hall of fame; conducts research program. **Founded:** 1919. **Educational Activities:** National Beauty Culturists' League Annual Trade Show (Annual).

5883 ■ National - Interstate Council of State Boards of Cosmetology (NIC)
7622 Briarwood Cir.
Little Rock, AR 72205
Ph: (501)227-8262
Fax: (501)227-8212
Co. E-mail: dnorton@nictesting.org
URL: http://www.nictesting.org
Contact: Kay Kendrick, President
Description: Persons commissioned by 50 state governments as administrators of cosmetology laws and examiners of applicants for licenses to practice cosmetology. **Founded:** 1956. **Educational Activities:** National - Interstate Council of State Boards of Cosmetology Seminar (Annual).

5884 ■ Personal Care Product Council
1101 17th St. NW, Ste. 300
Washington, DC 20036-4702
Ph: (202)331-1770
Fax: (202)331-1969
Co. E-mail: membership@personalcarecouncil.org
URL: http://www.personalcarecouncil.org
Contact: Lezlee Westine, President
Description: Manufacturers and distributors of finished cosmetics, fragrances, and personal care products; suppliers of raw materials and services. Provides scientific, legal, regulatory, and legislative services. Coordinates public service, educational, and public affairs activities. **Founded:** 1894. **Publications:** *CTFA News* (Biweekly); *International Color Handbook*; *International Resource Manual*.

REFERENCE WORKS

5885 ■ *Avon: Building the World's Premier Company for Women*
Pub: John Wiley & Sons, Incorporated
Ed: Laura Klepacki. **Released:** May 2006. **Price:** $16.95. **Description:** Profile of Avon and how it grew from a small business selling door-to-door to one of the largest cosmetics companies in the world.

5886 ■ *Business as Usual*
Pub: HarperBusiness
Ed: Anita Roddick. **Released:** 2005. **Price:** $12.95. **Description:** Founder of The Body Shop shares her story and gives her opinion on everything from cynical cosmetic companies to destructive consultants.

5887 ■ *"Eco-Preneuring" in Small Business Opportunities (Jan. 2008)*
Pub: Harris Publications Inc.
Description: Iceland Naturally is a joint marketing effort among tourism and business interests hoping to increase demand for Icelandic products including frozen seafood, bottled water, agriculture, and tourism in North America.

5888 ■ *"Every Little Bit Helps" in Black Enterprise (Vol. 38, November 2007, No. 4, pp. 102)*
Pub: Earl G. Graves Publishing Co. Inc.
Ed: Tennille M. Robinson. **Description:** After a career in the cosmetics industry, Tricialee Riley is marketing

and advertising her new venture, the Polish Bar, a salon offering manicures, pedicures, makeup application, and waxing.

5889 ▪ *"Greening the Manscape" in Canadian Business (Vol. 81, October 13, 2008, No. 17, pp. S19)*
Pub: Rogers Media Ltd.
Ed: David Lackie. **Description:** Buyer's guide of environmentally friendly grooming products for men is provided. Improved formulations have solved the problems of having synthetic ingredients in grooming products. Details about a face scrub, after shave conditioner, and a nourishing cream made of 91 percent organic ingredients are given, including prices.

5890 ▪ *"How I Did It: It Just Came Naturally" in Inc. (November 2007, pp. 110-112)*
Pub: Gruner & Jahr USA Publishing
Ed: Athena Schindelheim. **Description:** Profile of Bobbi Brown, CEO and founder of Bobbi Brown Cosmetics, designed to highlight a woman's natural look. Brown opened her first freestanding retail store recently that houses a makeup artistry school in the back.

5891 ▪ *"Identify and Conquer" in Black Enterprise (Vol. 38, December 2007, No. 5, pp. 76)*
Pub: Earl G. Graves Publishing Co. Inc.
Ed: Tennille M. Robinson. **Description:** Twenty-two-year-old entrepreneur wants to expand her wholesale body oil and skincare products business.

5892 ▪ *Lessons of a Lipstick Queen: Finding and Developing the Great Idea That Can Change Your Life*
Pub: Simon and Schuster Inc.
Contact: Carolyn Reidy, President
E-mail: carolyn.reidy@simonandschuster.com
Ed: Poppy King. **Released:** May 1, 2009. **Price:** $14.00. **Description:** Poppy King tells how she started her lipstick brand at age eighteen. She reveals how she managed to launch her business using a good idea and finding financing, marketing the product and how she became successful.

5893 ▪ *"Master of His Domain" in Canadian Business (Vol. 81, December 8, 2008, No. 21, pp. S17)*
Pub: Rogers Media Ltd.
Ed: Andy Holloway. **Description:** L'Oreal Canada chief executive Javier San Juan believes in being close to consumers and travels to one of his company's fifteen locations in Canada about once a month. San Juan's job is to build the L'Oreal brand in Canada.

5894 ▪ *More Than a Pink Cadillac*
Pub: McGraw-Hill
Ed: Jim Underwood. **Released:** 2002. **Price:** $23.95. **Description:** Profile of Mary Kay Ash who turned her $5,000 investment into a billion-dollar corporation. Ash's nine principles that form the foundation of her company's global success are outlined. Stories from her sales force leaders share ideas for motivating employees, impressing customers and building a successful company. The book emphasizes the leadership skills required to drive performance in any successful enterprise.

5895 ▪ *"Natural Attraction: Bath and Body Products Maker Delivers Wholesome Goodness" in Black Enterprise (Vol. 38, November 2007, No. 4)*
Pub: Earl G. Graves Publishing Co. Inc.
Ed: Kaylyn Kendall Dines. **Description:** Profile of Dawn Fitch, creator of Pooka Inc., manufacturer of handmade bath and body products that contain no preservatives. Sales are expected to reach $750,000 for 2007.

5896 ▪ *The Perfect Scent: A Year Inside the Perfume Industry in Paris and New York*
Pub: Henry Holt and Co.
Contact: Michael Naumann, President
Ed: Chandler Burr. **Released:** 2009. **Price:** $25.00. **Description:** An insiders glimpse at the development of two new fragrances from Hermes and Coty.

5897 ▪ *"Style Me Pretty on My Wedding Day - Final Chance to Enter" in Benzinga.com (October 29, 2011)*
Pub: Benzinga.com
Ed: Benzinga Staff. **Description:** Style Me Pretty and Christian Dior have partnered to award one bride the chance to have a personal Dior makeup artist for their wedding day.

5898 ▪ *"Want a Facial With That Steak?' in Charlotte Observer (February 5, 2007)*
Pub: Knight-Ridder/Tribune Business News
Ed: Jen Aronoff. **Description:** Profile of Burke Myotherapy Massage & Spa and Schell's Bistro. Lynn Shell moved her massage therapy business into a 106-year old home that had been used as a restaurant. She opened her own eatery on the first floor and offers massage therapy upstairs.

5899 ▪ *Who's Who--Personal Care Products Council Membership Directory*
Pub: Personal Care Products Council
Contact: LezLee Westine, President
E-mail: westinel@personalcarecouncil.org
URL(s): www.personalcarecouncil.org. **Released:** Annual; Latest edition 2012. **Covers:** More than 1,000 member companies. **Entries include:** Company name, address, phone, telex/TWX number, Internet site, names and titles of key personnel, parent company name, affiliates and subsidiaries, products and services, designation as manufacturer, distributor, supplier, or private-label manufacturer. **Arrangement:** Alphabetical within membership categories. **Indexes:** Company name.

TRADE PERIODICALS

5900 ▪ *Cosmetics & Toiletries: The International Magazine of Cosmetic Technology*
Contact: Jane Evison, Account Manager
E-mail: jane-evison@btconnect.com
URL(s): www.cosmeticsandtoiletries.com. **Released:** Monthly **Price:** $98, Individuals; $137, Canada; $189, Other countries; $169, Two years; $231, Canada two years; $330, Other countries two years.

5901 ▪ *The Food & Drug Letter*
Pub: Washington Business Information Inc.
Released: Biweekly. **Price:** $1,245, individuals. **Description:** Seeks to provide a detailed analysis of federal regulatory activity relating to food, drugs, and cosmetics. Interprets policy and regulatory changes, focusing on the impact of specific actions on industry in both the long and short term. .

5902 ▪ *For Formulation Chemists Only*
Pub: CITA International
URL(s): www.citainternational.com/knowledge21.org/trade-journals-publications/for-formulation-chemists-only/. **Released:** Quarterly **Price:** $100, Individuals online.

5903 ▪ *The Rose Sheet*
Pub: Elsevier Business Intelligence
URL(s): www.therosesheet.com/fdc/weekly/rose/toc.htm. **Released:** Weekly (Mon.) **Price:** $1395, Individuals print & online.

5904 ▪ *Skin Inc.: Professional Skin Care*
Contact: Melinda Taschetta-Millane, Editor-in-Chief
E-mail: taschetta_millane@allured.com
URL(s): www.skininc.com/. **Released:** Monthly **Price:** $49, Individuals; $57, Canada; $98, Other countries.

VIDEOCASSETTES/ AUDIOCASSETTES

5905 ▪ *Cosmetic and Personal Services*
Morris Video
12881 Knott St.
Garden Grove, CA 92841
Ph: (310)533-4800
Fax: (310)320-3171
Released: 1985. **Price:** $24.95. **Description:** Occupations involving cosmetology, hair styling and manicures are covered. **Availability:** VHS.

5906 ▪ *Puttin' on Your Lips*
Tapeworm Video Distributors
25876 The Old Road #141
Stevenson Ranch, CA 91381
Ph: (661)257-4904
Fax: (661)257-4820
Co. E-mail: sales@tapeworm.com
URL: http://www.tapeworm.com
Released: 1997. **Price:** $14.95. **Description:** Demonstrates proper make-up application techniques. **Availability:** VHS.

TRADE SHOWS AND CONVENTIONS

5907 ▪ **American Association of Cosmetology Schools Annual Conference - AACS Annual Convention & Expo**
American Association of Cosmetology Schools (AACS)
9927 E Bell Rd., Ste. 110
Scottsdale, AZ 85260
Ph: (480)281-0431
Free: 800-831-1086
Fax: (480)905-0993
Co. E-mail: jim@beautyschools.org
URL: http://www.beautyschools.org
Contact: Jim Cox, Executive Director
E-mail: jim@beautyschools.org
URL(s): www.beautyschools.org. **Price:** $500, Members online registration; $500, Non-members online registration. **Frequency:** Annual. **Audience:** School owners. **Principal Exhibits:** Beauty supplies and products, and cosmetology services. **Telecommunication Services:** dilsah@beautyschools.org.

5908 ▪ **Beauty Fair**
The Finnish Fair Corp.
PO Box 21
FIN-00521 Helsinki, Finland
Ph: 358 40 4503250
Fax: 358 9 142358
Co. E-mail: info@finnexpo.fi
URL: http://web.finnexpo.fi/en/Yritys/finnishfair/Pages/default.aspx
URL(s): www.finnexpo.fi. **Frequency:** Annual. **Audience:** General public. **Principal Exhibits:** Beauty and fashion, cosmetics and services; hair products and services; clothing, showes, bags, accessories, jewelry, education, and publications.

5909 ▪ **Extracts - A Division of New York International Gift Fair**
George Little Management, LLC
1133 Westchester Ave., Ste. N136
White Plains, NY 10606
Ph: (914)421-3200
Free: 800-272-SHOW
Co. E-mail: cathy_steel@glmshows.com
URL: http://www.glmshows.com
URL(s): www.extractsny.com. **Frequency:** Semiannual. **Audience:** Specialty, chain and department stores, gift and drug stores, mail order catalog houses, cosmetic companies, home furnishings/decorative accessory retailers. **Principal Exhibits:** Personal care products, aromatherapy products, body lotions, bath and shower gels, soaps, fragrances, botanicals, potpourri, candles, home fragrance products, bath accessories, and small appliances. **Telecommunication Services:** customerrelations@glmshows.com.

5910 ▪ **National Beauty Show - HAIRWORLD**
National Cosmetology Association
15825 N. 71st St., Ste. 100
Scottsdale, AZ 85254
Ph: (480)281-0424
Free: 800-468-2274
Fax: (480)905-0708
Co. E-mail: info@probeauty.org
URL: http://www.probeauty.org/nca/
Frequency: Annual. **Audience:** Salon owners and cosmetologists. **Principal Exhibits:** Hair products, cosmetics, and jewelry.

FRANCHISES AND BUSINESS OPPORTUNITIES

5911 ■ Caryl Baker Visage
31 Wingold Ave.
Toronto, ON, Canada M6B 1P8
Ph: (416)789-7191
Fax: (416)789-2594
Co. E-mail: info@carylbakervisage.com
URL: http://www.carylbakervisage.com
Description: A professional salon selling a comprehensive line of cosmetics and skin care products with a selection of services designed to pamper a wide range of clientele. Locations available in major shopping centers across Canada. **No. of Franchise Units:** 30. **Founded:** 1969.. **Franchised:** 1974. **Equity Capital Needed:** $220,000-$270,000. **Franchise Fee:** $20,000. **Training:** 9-12 weeks and ongoing training and support.

5912 ■ FACES
Faces, Inc.
30 Machintosh Blvd., Unit 6
Vaughan, ON, Canada L4K 4P1
Ph: (905)760-0110
Fax: (905)760-0901
URL: http://www.faces-cosmetics.com
Description: Retail cosmetics business featuring in-mall, stand-alone boutiques and in-line stores selling FACES own extensive, affordable and distinct brand of prestige color cosmetics and bath and body care. **No. of Franchise Units:** 57. **No. of Company-Owned Units:** 12. **Founded:** 1974.. **Franchised:** 1976. **Equity Capital Needed:** Approximate total cost of turn-key business is from $180,000-$380,000 U.S. **Franchise Fee:** $25,000. **Financial Assistance:** Yes. **Training:** FACES Academy is a 2 week, comprehensive training program at FACES head office in Toronto. Courses in beauty health theory, cosmetic product knowledge, business and counter sales management, cosmetic application and retail sales strategies will earn franchisees Retail Cosmetic Management certification.

5913 ■ Faces Cosmetics
3010 LBJ Fwy., Ste. 1200
Dallas, TX 75234
Free: 877-773-2237
Co. E-mail: Jennifer@faces-cosmetics.com
URL: http://www.faces-cosmetics.com
Description: Retailer of cosmetics, skincare and anti-aging products and services for make-up, aesthetics and mini-spa treatments. Provides a turn-key package including a fully-equipped boutique with complete inventory. **No. of Franchise Units:** 45. **No. of Company-Owned Units:** 11. **No. of Operating Units:** 56. **Founded:** 1976.. **Franchised:** 1976. **Equity Capital Needed:** $219,500-$372,500. **Franchise Fee:** $27,500. **Royalty Fee:** 6%. **Training:** Initial training and ongoing support.

5914 ■ Ideal Image
1 Urban Ctr.
4830 W Kennedy Blvd., Ste. 440
Tampa, FL 33609
Ph: (813)286-8100
Fax: (866)866-4390
URL: http://www.idealimage.com
Description: Laser hair removal. **No. of Franchise Units:** 60. **No. of Company-Owned Units:** 7. **Founded:** 2001.. **Franchised:** 2004. **Equity Capital Needed:** $551,300-$903,400. **Franchise Fee:** $25,000-$35,000. **Royalty Fee:** 9%. **Training:** Offers 2-4 weeks at headquarters, onsite as needed, and i-Learn online training ongoing.

5915 ■ Merle Norman Cosmetics Studio
Merle Norman Cosmetics
9130 Bellanca Ave.
Los Angeles 90045
Ph: (310)641-3000
Free: 800-406-3753
Fax: (310)641-7144
URL: http://www.merlenorman.com
Description: Offers a complete line of Merle Norman cosmetics along with professional cosmetic advice from trained consultants. Locations feature unique interior designs and are situated in major shopping

centers and strip malls. **No. of Franchise Units:** 2,000. **No. of Company-Owned Units:** 6. **Founded:** 1931.. **Franchised:** 1989. **Equity Capital Needed:** Varies. **Franchise Fee:** None. **Financial Assistance:** Yes. **Training:** Offers 2 week home office training and ongoing field support.

5916 ■ Top of the Line Fragrances
T.O.L. Franchise Group, Inc.
Description: Cosmetics and fragrances. **No. of Franchise Units:** 11. **Founded:** 1983.. **Franchised:** 1987. **Equity Capital Needed:** $164,800-$237-800. **Franchise Fee:** $20,000. **Royalty Fee:** 5%. **Training:** Offered at franchisee's location for 7-10 days with ongoing support.

5917 ■ Women's Health Boutique
Women's Health Boutique Franchise System, Inc.
12715 Telge Rd.
Cypress, TX 77429
Free: 888-708-9982
Fax: (281)256-4100
Co. E-mail: w-h-bsales@w-h-b.com
URL: http://www.w-h-b.com
Description: Products and services related to pre and postnatal care, post-mastectomy, compression therapy, hair loss, incontinence, and skin care. **No. of Franchise Units:** 13. **Founded:** 1991.. **Franchised:** 1994. **Equity Capital Needed:** $49,000 minimum start-up cash. **Training:** Yes.

LIBRARIES

5918 ■ Avon Products, Inc. Research Library
777 Third Ave.
New York, NY 10017
Ph: (212)282-7000
Free: 800-445-2866
Fax: (914)369-2803
Co. E-mail: dearavon@avon.com
URL: http://www.avoncompany.com/
Scope: Cosmetics, packaging, toxicology, dermatology, pharmacology, chemistry, engineering, microbiology. **Services:** Interlibrary loan; SDI; library open to the public for reference use only on request. **Founded:** 1934. **Holdings:** 6500 books; 5000 bound periodical volumes; 6000 U.S. and foreign patents. **Subscriptions:** 300 journals and other serials.

5919 ■ Clairol Research Library
1 Blachley Rd.
Stamford, CT 06922
Free: 800-252-4765
URL: http://www.clairol.com
Scope: Chemistry and technology of cosmetics, hair dyes and dyeing, personal care. **Services:** Library open to the public with restrictions. **Holdings:** 10,000 books; 6000 bound periodical volumes; 30 titles on microfilm. **Subscriptions:** 350 journals and other serials.

5920 ■ Colgate Palmolive Company Technology Information Center
909 River Rd.
Piscataway, NJ 08854
Ph: (732)878-7574
Fax: (732)878-7128
URL: http://www.colgate.com
Contact: Miranda D. Scott, Associate
Scope: Soaps and detergents, fats and oils, dentifrices, cosmetics, perfumes and essential oils, environmental pollution, foods, chemistry. **Services:** Interlibrary loan; copying; SDI. **Founded:** 1936. **Holdings:** 20,000 books; 10,000 bound periodical volumes; 16,000 periodical volumes on 4000 reels of microfilm; 250 VF drawers of internal reports; 10 VF drawers of archival materials. **Subscriptions:** 300 journals and other serials.

5921 ■ Gillette Company Technical Information Center
37 A St.
Needham, MA 02492-9120
Ph: (781)292-8406
Free: 800 -445 5388

Fax: (617)463-2815
Co. E-mail: susan_fox@gillette.com
URL: http://www.gillette.com
Contact: Susan R. Fox, Specialist
Scope: Chemistry, hair, skin, cosmetics, materials, polymers, plastics, electrochemistry. **Services:** Interlibrary loan; Center not open to the public. **Founded:** 1968. **Holdings:** 12,000 books; 8000 reports; 350 patents. **Subscriptions:** 150 journals and other serials.

5922 ■ Mary Kay Inc. Information Resources
16251 N. Dallas Pkwy.
Addison, TX 75001
Ph: (972)687-5527
Fax: (972)687-1643
Co. E-mail: cecilia.armas@mkcorp.com
Contact: Lynn F. Johnson
Scope: Cosmetics, dermatology, toxicology, chemistry, business, marketing. **Services:** Interlibrary loan. **Founded:** 1976. **Holdings:** 2000 books; 500 bound periodical volumes. **Subscriptions:** 250 journals and other serials.

5923 ■ Revlon Research Center Library
2121 Rte. 27
Edison, NJ 08818
Ph: (732)287-1400
Fax: (732)287-7270
URL: http://www.revlon.com/
Contact: Ann Van Dine, Librarian
Scope: Cosmetics, soaps, chemistry, perfumery, dermatology, pharmacology, microbiology, aerosols. **Services:** Interlibrary loan; copying; SDI; library open to the public by appointment for reference only. **Founded:** 1955. **Holdings:** 11,000 books; 4000 bound periodical volumes. **Subscriptions:** 100 journals and other serials.

5924 ■ Tavy Stone Fashion Library
Detroit Historical Museum
5401 Woodward Ave.
Detroit, MI 48202
Ph: (313)833-1805
Fax: (313)833-5342
Co. E-mail: joels@detroithistorical.org
URL: http://www.detroithistorical.org
Contact: Joel Stone, Curator
Scope: Fashion (antiquity to present) - American and European fashion designers, careers, advertising, merchandising, management, textiles and fabrics, cosmetics and fragrances, historic costume, fashion retailers; the business, sociological, and psychological aspects of fashion. **Services:** Copying; library open to the public with restrictions. **Founded:** 1987. **Holdings:** 800 books; 40 VF drawers; 500 slides; 10 color swatches; 21 AV programs. **Subscriptions:** 6 journals and other serials.

5925 ■ Unilever HPC NA Research Library
40 Merritt Blvd.
Trumbull, CT 06611
Ph: (203)377-8300
Fax: (203)381-4355
Co. E-mail: mary.m.davis@unilever.com
URL: http://www.unilever.com
Contact: Mary Davis, Librarian
Scope: Cosmetic science, dermatology. **Founded:** 1959. **Holdings:** 5000 books; 2000 bound periodical volumes. **Subscriptions:** 250 journals and other serials.

5926 ■ U.S. Food & Drug Administration osciences Library - CFSAN Branch Library—FDA.
5100 Paint Branch Pkwy.
HFS-678
College Park, MD 20740
Ph: (301)436-2163
Fax: (301)436-2653
Co. E-mail: cfsanlib@fda.hhs.gov
Contact: Lee S. Bernstein, Manager
Scope: Chemistry, analytical chemistry, toxicology, food technology, nutrition, medicine, biology, cosmetics. **Services:** Interlibrary loan; Library open to the public. **Founded:** 1961. **Holdings:** 1000 books; 500 reports, documents, pamphlets; 16,000 cartridges of microfilm. **Subscriptions:** 100 journals and other serials.

ASSOCIATIONS AND OTHER ORGANIZATIONS

5927 ■ Costume Society of America (CSA)
390 Amwell Rd., Ste. 402
Hillsborough, NJ 08844
Ph: (908)359-1471
Free: 800-272-9447
Fax: (908)450-1118
Co. E-mail: national.office@costumesocietyamerica.
com
URL: http://www.costumesocietyamerica.com
Contact: Robin Campbell, President
Description: Represents museum and historical society personnel; college/university faculty of costume history, retailing, material culture, apparel design, social-psychological aspects, economics; theatre/film fashion designers; conservators; costume and textile collectors/dealers; and re-enactors. Focuses on the scholarly study of all aspects of dress and appearance. Promotes the study of dress through education, research, preservation, and design. Supports scholarship and its dissemination through research papers and publications; collects and disseminates information on the preservation, interpretation, and exhibition of costumes; provides referrals for the identification and conservation of costumes, sponsors international study tours. **Founded:** 1973. **Publications:** *Dress: The Journal of The Costume Society of America* (Annual); *CSA E-News* (Monthly); *CSA News* (3/year); *DRESS* (Annual); *Costume Society of America Membership Directory* (Annual). **Educational Activities:** Costume Society of America Meeting (Annual). **Awards:** College and University Collection Grant (Biennial); Costume Design Award (Biennial); Evelyn Welch Livingstone Award (Annual); Fellow (Annual); Grant to Support Costume in Small Museums (Annual); Millia Davenport Publication Award (Annual); Scholars Roundtable (Annual); Stella Blum Research Grant (Annual); Travel Research Grants (Biennial); Adele Filene Student Travel Award (Annual); Travel Research Grants; Evelyn Welch Livingstone Grant; Small Museums Collection Care Grant; Millia Davenport Publication Award; Stella Blum Research Grant; Richard Martin Award for Excellence in the Exhibition of Costume (Biennial); Richard Martin Award for Excellence in the Exhibition of Costume.

5928 ■ National Costumers Association (NCA)
121 N Bosart Ave.
Indianapolis, IN 46201
Ph: (317)351-1940
Free: 800-NCA-1321
Fax: (317)351-1941
Co. E-mail: office@costumers.org
URL: http://www.costumers.org
Contact: Janie Westendorf, President
Description: Designers, producers, and renters of costumes for all occasions. Works to establish and maintain professional and ethical standards of business in the costume industry. Encourages and promotes a greater and more diversified use of costumes in all fields of human activity. Offers Play

Plot, Book services; conducts educational programs during conventions; buyer's group discounts, website listing, book service, and debt recovery source. **Scope:** costume design. **Founded:** 1923. **Publications:** *National Costumers Magazine*; *Operations Guide Book* (Periodic). **Educational Activities:** Halloween Dance Apparel and Costume Show (Annual). **Awards:** Memorial Award; National Costumers Association Scholarships.

REFERENCE WORKS

5929 ■ "Ghouls, Goblins, and Harry Potter: Cashing In On Halloween" in Inc. (Vol. 33, October 2011, No. 8, pp. 24)
Pub: Inc. Magazine
Ed: Darren Dahl. **Description:** Costume Craze, an online costume retailer reports $13.2 million in sales last year. Originally the family business started out as a software company called StaticAdvantage, but switched gears.

5930 ■ "Scream Therapy: A Chain of New York City Beauty Stores Perfect Halloween Pop-Ups" in Inc. (Vol. 33, October 2011, No. 8, pp. 99)
Pub: Inc. Magazine
Ed: Amy Barrett. **Description:** Ricky's Halloween stores will open 30 temporary stores for about two months, 28 of which are permanent beauty supply shops the rest of the year.

TRADE SHOWS AND CONVENTIONS

5931 ■ National Costumers Association Annual Convention
National Costumers Association
121 N. Bosart Ave.
Indianapolis, IN 46201
Ph: (317)351-1940
Fax: (317)351-1941
Co. E-mail: office@costumers.org
URL: http://www.costumers.org
Contact: Janie Westendorf, President
URL(s): www.costumers.org. **Price:** $175, Preregistered, members; $200, Onsite registered, members; $225, Pre-registered, non-members; $250, Onsite registered, non-members. **Frequency:** Annual. **Principal Exhibits:** Exhibits for designers, producers and renters of costumes for all occasions including parties and dance. **Telecommunication Services:** office@costumers.org.

FRANCHISES AND BUSINESS OPPORTUNITIES

5932 ■ Halloween Express
100 Progress Way
Owenton, KY 40359
Ph: (513)300-0000

Fax: (513)677-8641
Description: Costumes, masks, and make-up. **No. of Franchise Units:** 135. **No. of Company-Owned Units:** 7. **Founded:** 1992.. **Equity Capital Needed:** $75,000 plus. **Franchise Fee:** $10,000. **Training:** Train and assist you in setting up your business, including site selection and guidance throughout the lease process.

LIBRARIES

5933 ■ BMV Archives: Butterick, McCall's, Vogue - Patterns Archives
11 Penn Plaza, 18th Fl.
New York, NY 10001-2000
Ph: (212)620-2790
Fax: (212)465-6962
Co. E-mail: sherryh@mccallpattern.com
Contact: Lillian Esposito, Manager, Promotions
Scope: Vogue/Butterick costume and marketing history. **Services:** Archives open to students and researchers by appointment, for reference use only. **Founded:** 1863. **Holdings:** 200 books; 1500 bound periodical volumes; 1300 cubic feet of archival materials; 100 cubic feet of pictures, clippings, posters. **Subscriptions:** 10 journals and other serials. **Telecommunication Services:** consumerservices@butterick.com.

5934 ■ Carnegie Library of Pittsburgh - Music Department
4400 Forbes Ave.
Pittsburgh, PA 15213
Ph: (412)622-3105
Fax: (412)687-8982
Co. E-mail: musicdept@carnegielibrary.org
URL: http://www.clpgh.org/locations/music
Contact: Kathryn Logan, Department Head
Scope: Music, art, architecture, interior design, collectibles, dance. **Services:** Reference and reader's assistance; department open to the public. **Founded:** 1938. **Holdings:** 110,000 music books and scores; 63,000 art books; 1500 dance books; 30,000 sound recordings; 1200 videocassettes; 280,000 mounted pictures; 54,000 slides; 69 VF drawers; 1700 videos and DVDs. **Subscriptions:** 320 journals and other serials.

5935 ■ Fashion Institute of Design & Merchandising - Orange County Library
17590 Gillette Ave.
Irvine, CA 92614-5610
Ph: (949)851-6200
Free: 888-974-3436
Fax: (949)851-6808
URL: http://fidm.com
Scope: Apparel manufacturing management, cosmetics and fragrance merchandising, fashion design, interior design, merchandise marketing, textile design, visual presentation and space design. **Services:** Copying; library open to the public by appointment. **Founded:** 1980. **Holdings:** 3000 books; 130 bound periodical volumes; 40 pamphlet headings;

475 videotapes; 135 slide sets; 300 retail catalogs; 100 Annual reports; 50 CD-ROMs. **Subscriptions:** 80 journals and other serials; 8 newspapers.

5936 ■ Fashion Institute of Technology - Gladys Marcus Library
7th Ave. at 27th St.
E-Bldg. E502
New York, NY 10001-5992
Ph: (212)217-4340
Fax: (212)217-4371
Co. E-mail: greta_earnest@fitnyc.edu
URL: http://www.fitnyc.edu/library.asp
Contact: Prof. N.J. Wolfe, Director, Library Services
Scope: Costume, fashion, interior design, management engineering technology, fashion buying and merchandising, textiles, toy design, packaging design, advertising. **Services:** Interlibrary loan; copying; library open to the public for reference use only by appointment. **Founded:** 1944. **Holdings:** 130,260 books; 113,265 nonprint units; 20,637 bound periodical volumes; 125,000 fashion slides; 4712 reels of microfilm; 438 CD-ROM serials and digital monographs. **Subscriptions:** 4000 journals and other serials. **Telecommunication Services:** nj_wolfe@fitnyc.edu.

5937 ■ Wayne Finkelman Research Library at Western Costume Company
11041 Vanowen St.
North Hollywood, CA 91605
Ph: (818)760-0900
Fax: (818)508-2190
Co. E-mail: wccmail@westerncostume.com
URL: http://westerncostume.com
Contact: Bobi Garland, Director
Scope: Clothing, military and civilian uniforms, insignia, medals and decorations, police uniforms, occupational clothing, sports clothing, ecclesiastical clothing, costume, fashion, folk dress. **Services:** Copying; library open to the public on a fee basis. **Founded:** 1915. **Holdings:** 15,000 volumes; 130 VF drawers; bound periodical volumes. **Subscriptions:** 60 journals and other serials. **Telecommunication Services:** research@westerncostume.com.

5938 ■ Guthrie Theater Foundation - Staff Reference Library
818 S. 2nd St.
Minneapolis, MN 55415
Ph: (612)377-2224
Free: 1 87744STAGE
Fax: (612)225-6004
Co. E-mail: joh@guthrietheater.org
URL: http://www.guthrietheater.org
Contact: Jo Holcomb, Librarian
Scope: Costume design and history, decorative arts, architecture, history of theater, actors and acting, stage lighting and design, technical production, dramatic literature and critical works, poetry, music, general history and geography. **Services:** Library not open to the public. **Founded:** 1972. **Holdings:** 4500 books; 3900 plays; 8 VF drawers of slides; 12 VF drawers of photographs of past productions; 10 VF drawers of scripts from past productions. **Subscriptions:** 6 journals and other serials.

5939 ■ Kansas State University - Richard L.D. and Marjorie J. Morse Department of Special Collections
506 Hale Library
Manhattan, KS 66506
Ph: (785)532-7456
Fax: (785)532-7415
Co. E-mail: rarebooks@k-state.edu
URL: http://www.lib.k-state.edu/depts/spec/index.html
Contact: Roger C. Adams, Librarian, Special Collections
Scope: Cookery, Kanzana, literature, agriculture, military history, milling and grain science, botany, prairie ecology, Oz, science fiction/fantasy, historic

costumes and textiles. **Services:** Collections open to the public. **Founded:** 1966. **Holdings:** 100,000 volumes. **Telecommunication Services:** rcadams@k-state.edu.

5940 ■ Los Angeles County Museum of Art - Balch Art Research Library
5905 Wilshire Blvd.
Los Angeles, CA 90036
Ph: (323)857-6118
Co. E-mail: library@lacma.org
URL: http://www.lacma.org
Contact: Alexis Curry, Librarian
Scope: Art, photography, costumes and textiles, prints and drawings, conservation, European art, American art, Asian art, South and Southeast Asian art, ancient and Islamic art, Latin American art, Craft and Folk Art. **Services:** Interlibrary loan; copying; library open to the public by appointment only. **Founded:** 1965. **Holdings:** 175,000 books; 450 current periodical; 24,107 microfiche; 74 reels of microfilm; current auction catalogs; 150 VF drawers of artist ephemera. **Telecommunication Services:** acury@lacma.org.

5941 ■ Metropolitan Museum of Art - Irene Lewisohn Costume Reference Library—The Costume Institute - Irene Lewisohn Costume Reference Library.
1000 Fifth Ave.
New York, NY 10028-0198
Ph: (212)650-2723
Fax: (212)570-3970
Co. E-mail: julie.le@metmuseum.org
URL: http://www.metmuseum.org/research/libraries-and-study-centers/
URL(s): libmma.org/portal/the-irene-lewisohn-costume-reference-library/. **Scope:** History of costume, fashion, fashion designers, social history. **Services:** Copying; Library open to professional designers and research scholars by appointment. **Founded:** 1937. **Holdings:** 40,000 cataloged books and journals; 100,000 pieces of ephemera, including swatch books, fashion sketches, fashion plates, postcards, and vertical files; 50 fashion periodical subscriptions. **Subscriptions:** 70 journals and other serials. **Telecommunication Services:** watson.library@metmuseum.org.

5942 ■ Minneapolis College of Art and Design Library
2501 Stevens Ave., S.
Minneapolis, MN 55404
Ph: (612)874-3791
Fax: (612)874-3795
Co. E-mail: library@mcad.edu
URL: http://intranet.mcad.edu/modules/library
Contact: Amy Naughton, Director, Library Services
Scope: Painting, sculpture, graphic arts, design, films and film making, photography, video, performance art. **Services:** Interlibrary loan (limited); copying; library open to the public for reference use only. **Founded:** 1916. **Holdings:** 60,000 volumes; 350 artists' books; 140,000 slides; college archives; compact discs; video cassettes, CD-ROMs. **Subscriptions:** 200 journals and other serials. **Telecommunication Services:** suzanne_degler@mcad.edu.

5943 ■ Museum of the City of New York - Department of Collections Access
1220 5th Ave.
New York, NY 10029
Ph: (212)534-1672, x3399
Fax: (917)492-3960
Co. E-mail: research@mcny.org
URL: http://www.mcny.org
Contact: Lindsay Turley, Archivist Specialist, Manuscripts
Scope: New York City's history, diversity, opportunity, and perpetual transformation. **Services:** Scanning; collection open to qualified scholars and researchers by appointment. **Founded:** 1926. **Holdings:** Books; pamphlets; manuscripts; photography; prints; drawings.

5944 ■ Newark Public Library - Reference Center
Main Library, 2nd Fl.
5 Washington St.
Newark, NJ 07101-0630
Ph: (973)733-7779
Fax: (973)733-5648
Co. E-mail: reference@npl.org
URL: http://www.npl.org
Contact: Wilma J. Grey, Director, Library Services
URL(s): www.npl.org/pages/collections/refdesk.html.
Scope: Art and art history, theory, and practice; architecture; biography; bibliography; business; costume; decorative arts; historical stock prices; history; literature and literary criticism; music and music history; religion; social science. **Services:** Interlibrary loan; copying; public fax; Center open to the public. **Founded:** 1888. **Holdings:** 300,000 books; 1500 periodical titles (including 19th-century journals); 6.7 million patents; 15,500 scores and song books; 7500 compact discs. **Subscriptions:** 170 journals and other serials. **Telecommunication Services:** wgrey@npl.org.

5945 ■ Eugene O'Neill Theater Center - Leibling-Wood Library - Monte Cristo Cottage Collection
325 Pequot Ave.
New London, CT 06320
Ph: (860)443-5378
Fax: (860)443-9653
Co. E-mail: montecristo@theoneill.org
URL: http://www.theoneill.org/monte-cristo-cottage
Contact: Preston Whiteway, Executive Director
Scope: Drama, dramatic literature, costume design, theater memorabilia. **Services:** Copying; collection open to the public. **Founded:** 1967. **Holdings:** 5000 books; playbills; theater scrapbooks; photographic stills; manuscripts; letters; set and costume designs; television manuscripts; clipping files; periodicals. **Telecommunication Services:** theaterlives@theoneill.org.

5946 ■ University of Wisconsin--Madison - Ruth Ketterer Harris Library - Helen Louise Allen Textile Collection
1300 Linden Dr., Rm. 378
School of Human Ecology
Madison, WI 53706-1524
Ph: (608)262-1162
Fax: (608)265-5099
Co. E-mail: hlatc@mail.sohe.wisc.edu
URL: http://textilecollection.wisc.edu/harrislibrary.html
Contact: Mark Nelson, Director
Scope: Textiles (history), folk art, costume, design. **Services:** Copying; Library open to the public with restrictions (non-circulating). **Founded:** 1993. **Holdings:** 4000 books, pamphlets, and journals; 1000 periodical volumes; folios. **Subscriptions:** 30 journals and other serials. **Telecommunication Services:** harrislibrary@mail.sohe.wisc.edu.

5947 ■ Yale University - Drama Collection—Robert B. Haas Family Arts Library.
180 York St.
New Haven, CT 06520-8318
Ph: (203)432-2645
Fax: (203)432-0549
Co. E-mail: allen.townsend@yale.edu
URL: http://www.library.yale.edu/arts/arts_collections.html#drama
Contact: Allen Townsend, Director
Scope: Plays by American, British, and foreign playwrights; history of the theater; theater architecture; drama criticism; costume and set design; stage lighting; acting; direction; production; theater administration. **Services:** Interlibrary loan; copying; audio and video cassette players; Library open to the public for reference use only (circulation limited to Yale University card holders). **Founded:** 1925. **Holdings:** 20,000 volumes; 150 production books; 300 masters' theses; 130 dissertations; 120 scrapbooks of clippings. All unpublished material is under the responsibility of Special collections/Arts Library. **Subscriptions:** 44 journals and other serials; 3 newspapers.

START-UP INFORMATION

5948 ■ *Craft Inc: Turn Your Creative Hobby into a Business*
Pub: Chronicle Books LLC

Ed: Meg Mateo Ilasco. **Released:** September 2007. **Price:** $16.95. **Description:** Guide to help any crafter turn their hobby into a successful business. The book covers all aspects including pricing, sales and marketing, trade shows, as well as interviews with successful craft artisans Jonathan Adler, Lotta Jansdotter, Denyse Schmidt and Jill Bliss.

5949 ■ *How to Start a Faux Painting or Mural Business, Second Edition*
Pub: Allworth Press

Ed: Rebecca Pittman. **Released:** October 1, 2010. **Price:** $24.95. **Description:** Updated and expanded to cover better ways to advertise, innovative supplies (such as Venetian plasters and stained cements), unique bidding and studio setups required for new plasters and varnishes.

5950 ■ *How to Start a Home-Based Craft Business, 5th Ed.*
Pub: Globe Pequot Press

Ed: Kenn Oberrecht. **Released:** July 2007. **Price:** $18.95. **Description:** Step-by-step guide for starting and growing a home-based craft business.

5951 ■ *How to Start a Home-Based Craft Business, 5th Edition*
Pub: Globe Pequot Press

Ed: Kenn Oberrecht. **Released:** July 2007. **Price:** $18.95. **Description:** Advice for starting a home-based craft business is given, including sources for finding supplies on the Internet, writing a business plan, publicity, zoning ordinances, and more.

5952 ■ *Scrapbooking for Profit: Cashing in on Retail, Home-Based and Internet Opportunities*
Pub: Allworth Press

Ed: Rebecca Pittman. **Released:** June 2005. **Price:** $19.95 (US), $22.95 (Canadian). **Description:** Eleven strategies for starting a scrapbooking business, including brick-and-mortar stores, home-based businesses, and online retail and wholesale outlets.

5953 ■ *Setting Up Your Ceramic Studio: Ideas and Plans from Working Artists*
Pub: Lark Books

Ed: Virginia Scotchie. **Released:** March 2005. **Price:** $45.00. **Description:** Floor plans and advice for setting up a creative ceramics studio are provided, focusing on equipment, workflow, and safety issues.

5954 ■ *Will Work for Fun: 3 Simple Steps for Turning Any Hobby or Interest into Cash*
Pub: John Wiley and Sons, Inc.

Ed: Allan R. Bechtold. **Released:** May 2008. **Price:** $24.95. **Description:** Tips for turning any hobby or interest into a lucrative business are shared.

ASSOCIATIONS AND OTHER ORGANIZATIONS

5955 ■ **Aid to Artisans (ATA)**
1030 New Britain Ave., Ste. 102
West Hartford, CT 06110
Ph: (860)756-5550
Fax: (860)756-5558
Co. E-mail: info@aidtoartisans.org
URL: http://www.aidtoartisans.org
Contact: Alfredo Espinosa, President

Description: Offers practical assistance worldwide to artisans. Fosters artistic traditions and cultural vitality to improve livelihood and keep communities healthy, strong and growing. Works with its artisan partners to develop products with the appeal to compete successfully in new markets around the world and to improve their business skills so that the changes achieved are enduring. **Founded:** 1976. **Publications:** *Artisans of Haiti.* **Awards:** Aid to Artisans Award for Artisan Advocate (Annual); Aid to Artisans Award for Innovation in Craft (Annual); Aid to Artisans Award for Preservation of Craft (Annual).

5956 ■ **American Craft Council (ACC)**
1224 Marshall St. NE, Ste. 200
Minneapolis, MN 55413-1089
Ph: (612)206-3100
Free: 800-836-3470
Fax: (612)355-2330
Co. E-mail: council@craftcouncil.org
URL: http://www.craftcouncil.org
Contact: Chris Amundsen, Executive Director
E-mail: camundsen@craftcouncil.org

Description: Promotes understanding and appreciation of contemporary American craft. **Scope:** 20th century American craft. **Founded:** 1943. **Subscriptions:** 10000 books periodicals video recordings. **Publications:** *American Craft* (Bimonthly); *American Craft--News Section* (Bimonthly); *American Craft* (Bimonthly); *American Craft--American Craft Guide to Craft Galleries & Shops USA Issue*; *American Craft Council--Crafts Fair Directory.* **Educational Activities:** ACC Craft Fair Sarasota (Annual); ACC Craft Show Baltimore (Annual); ACC Craft Show San Francisco (Annual). **Awards:** American Craft Council Fellow (Annual); American Craft Council Fellows; Gold Medal; Aileen Osborn Webb Award (Annual).

5957 ■ **American Society of Artists (ASA)**
PO Box 1326
Palatine, IL 60078
Ph: (312)751-2500
Co. E-mail: asoa@webtv.net
URL: http://community-2.webtv.net/ASOA/ASA

Description: Professional artists and craftspeople. Maintains art referral service and information exchange service. Sponsors art and craft festivals and a Lecture and Demonstration Service; the Special Arts Services Division aids disabled individuals to either practice or enjoy the visual arts. Presents demonstrations in visual arts to better acquaint the public with various processes in different media. **Scope:** art. **Founded:** 1972. **Subscriptions:** books. **Publications:** *Art Lovers Art and Craft Fair Bulletin* (Quarterly).

5958 ■ **Guild of American Papercutters (GAP)**
PO Box 384
Somerset, PA 15501-0384
Co. E-mail: patty.kile@yahoo.com
URL: http://www.papercutters.org
Contact: Marie-Helene Grabman, President
Description: Unites fellow papercutters to share ideas, display artwork, and increase public appreciation and awareness of this art form. Offers demonstrations and exhibits. **Founded:** 1988. **Educational Activities:** Collection.

5959 ■ **Handweavers Guild of America (HGA)**
1255 Buford Hwy., Ste. 211
Suwanee, GA 30024
Ph: (678)730-0010
Fax: (678)730-0836
Co. E-mail: hga@weavespindye.org
URL: http://www.weavespindye.org
Contact: Sandra Bowles, Executive Director
Description: Individuals, weaving arts guilds, educational institutions, teachers, suppliers, and libraries. Seeks to promote participation and interest in handcrafted textiles; encourage the development of places to work, sell, exhibit, and teach; bring about cooperation among agencies and individuals interested in the textile arts, fiber arts and related fields. **Founded:** 1969. **Publications:** *Shuttle Spindle & Dyepot* (Quarterly); *Shuttle Spindle and Dyepot* (Quarterly); *Shuttle, Spindle & Dyepot, Shuttle Spindle and Dyepot* (Quarterly); *Handweavers Guild of America--Suppliers Directory; Education Directory; Speakers Bureau Directory.* **Educational Activities:** Convergence (Biennial). **Awards:** Certificates of Excellence (Biennial); HGA and Dendel Scholarship (Annual); Convergence Assistantship Grants; Mearl K. Gable II Memorial Grants; Handweavers Guild of America and Dendel Scholarships; Silvio and Eugenio Petrini Grants; HGA Award. **Telecommunication Services:** weavespindye@compuserve.com.

5960 ■ **Indian Arts and Crafts Association (IACA)**
4010 Carlisle Blvd. NE, Ste. C
Albuquerque, NM 87107
Ph: (505)265-9149
Fax: (505)265-8251
Co. E-mail: info@iaca.com
URL: http://www.iaca.com
Contact: Joseph P. Zeller, President
Description: Indian craftspeople and artists, museums, dealers, collectors, and others. Works to promote, preserve, protect, and enhance the understanding of authentic American Indian arts and crafts. Sets code of ethics for members and standards for the industry. Conducts consumer education seminars, meetings, and display programs; works with related government groups. Operates speakers' bureau. **Founded:** 1974. **Publications:** *IACA Journal* (Quarterly); *Indian Arts and Crafts Association--Directory*

(Annual); *Membership Directory/Buyer's Guide* (Annual). **Educational Activities:** Wholesale Market (Semiannual). **Awards:** Artist of the Year (Annual).

5961 ■ Knifemakers' Guild (KG)

2914 Winters Ln.
La Grange, KY 40031-8543
Ph: (502)222-1397
Fax: (502)222-2676
Co. E-mail: gil@hibbenknives.com
URL: http://www.knifemakersguild.com
Contact: Gil Hibben, President

Description: Knifemakers and interested others. Promotes knives and knifemakers; provides technical assistance to knifemakers; encourages ethical and professional business conduct. **Founded:** 1970.

5962 ■ The Knitting Guild Association (TKGA)

1100-H Brandywine Blvd.
Zanesville, OH 43701-7303
Ph: (740)452-4541
Fax: (740)452-2552
Co. E-mail: tkga@tkga.com
URL: http://www.tkga.com
Contact: Ms. Penny Sitler, Executive Director

Description: Represents shop owners and individuals interested in knitting. Provides education and a means of communication to those wishing to improve the quality of workmanship and creativity of their knitting projects. **Founded:** 1984. **Publications:** *Convention Brochure* (Annual); *Seminar Brochure* (Quarterly). **Awards:** Design Competition (Annual); Memorial Scholarship Award (Annual).

5963 ■ Smocking Arts Guild of America (SAGA)

PO Box 2846
Grapevine, TX 76099
Free: 800-520-3101
Fax: (817)886-0393
Co. E-mail: president@smocking.org
URL: http://www.smocking.org
Contact: Liz Perch, President

Description: Needleart enthusiasts, designers, instructors, business owners, and others interested in smocking, embroidery, fine hand sewing, and/or fine machine sewing. Works to preserve and foster the art of smocking and related needlework through education communication and quality workmanship. Conducts artisan program in four areas of study including smocking, embroidery and heirloom stitching. Offers correspondence courses. **Founded:** 1979.

REFERENCE WORKS

5964 ■ 202 Things You Can Make and Sell for Big Profits

Pub: Entrepreneur Press

Ed: James Stephenson. **Released:** September 2005. **Price:** $19.95. **Description:** Instructions for 202 products that can be made and sold over the Internet.

5965 ■ American Craft--News Section

Pub: American Craft Council
Contact: Chris Amundsen, Executive Director
E-mail: camundsen@craftcouncil.org

URL(s): www.craftcouncil.org. **Ed:** Lois Moran, Pat Dandignac, Beverly Sanders. **Released:** Bimonthly **Price:** $5, per issue; $40, per year. **Publication includes:** List of exhibitions, sales, workshops, seminars, conferences, and competitions for contemporary American craftspersons. **Entries include:** Event name, dates, location; name of gallery, museum, or sponsoring organization. For shows and sales--Whether juried, deadline for applications, fees, contact name and address, media accepted. For workshops, courses, conferences, etc.--Contact name and address, guest artist presiding, dates of events. **Arrangement:** Classified by type of event, then geographical.

5966 ■ "Arario Gallery Opens First American Space" in Art Business News (Vol. 34,

November 2007, No. 11, pp. 14)
Pub: Pfingsten Publishing, LLC

Description: Opening a new space in New York's Chelsea gallery district is Arario Gallery, a leader in the field of Asian contemporary art; the gallery will feature new works by Chinese artists at its opening.

5967 ■ "Art Attack 2007 Comes to Minneapolis" in Art Business News (Vol. 34, November 2007, No. 11, pp. 11)

Pub: Pfingsten Publishing, LLC

Description: Overview of Art Attack 2007, an open studio and gallery crawl in the Northeast Minneapolis Arts District which featured artists working in glass, ceramics, jewelry, mosaics, mixed media, photography, painting, pottery, sculpture, textiles and wood.

5968 ■ "Art Miami Comes to Miami's Wynwood Art District" in Art Business News (Vol. 34, November 2007, No. 11, pp. 18)

Pub: Pfingsten Publishing, LLC

Description: In December, The Art Group will hold its Art Miami fair in the Wynwood Art District; the exhibitors range from painting, sculpture, video and works on paper.

5969 ■ "Artexpo Celebrates 30th Anniversary" in Art Business News (Vol. 34, November 2007, No. 11, pp. 18)

Pub: Pfingsten Publishing, LLC

Description: In honor of its 30th anniversary Artexpo New York 2008 will be an unforgettable show offering a collection of fine-art education courses for both trade and consumer attendees and featuring a variety of artists working in all mediums.

5970 ■ ASA Artisan

Pub: American Society of Artists

URL(s): community-2.webtv.net/ASOA/ASAASSOCI-ATESHIP/index.html. **Released:** Quarterly **Publication includes:** Lists of shows and competitions accepting fine art, art and craft work and other information for and about members. **Entries include:** Show or competition name, location, sponsor, name and address of contact, dates, requirements, supple exhibit info, etc. Principal content of publication is information for and about ASA members. **Arrangement:** Chronological.

5971 ■ "Ask Inc." in Inc. (January 2008, pp. 61)

Pub: Gruner & Jahr USA Publishing

Description: Information to help crafter of custom quilts made from old T-shirts, baby clothes, jeans, and neckties to market her items on a small budget.

5972 ■ "Carving Passion, Talent Help Couple Craft Business on Wood-Rich Land" in Crain's Cleveland Business (October 8, 2007)

Pub: Crain Communications, Inc.

Ed: Sharon Schnall. **Description:** Profile of Wood-carved Art Gallery & Studio, a family-owned business which includes several ventures of the husband-and-wife team, Jim Stadtlander and Diane Harto.

5973 ■ "Catching Creatives; Detroit Group Gets Grant to Attract 1,000 Design Pros" in Crain's Detroit Business (March 24, 2008)

Pub: Crain Communications, Inc.

Ed: Sherri Begin. **Description:** Design Detroit was given a $200,000 planning grant by the Knight Foundation, an organization that strives to back initiatives that leverage talent and resources in each of the 26 U.S. cities it funds, to inspire strategies to attract up to 1,000 creative professionals to live in Detroit.

5974 ■ "City Slickers" in Canadian Business (Vol. 81, March 31, 2008, No. 5, pp. 36)

Pub: Rogers Media

Ed: Joe Castaldo. **Description:** Richard Florida believes that the creative class drives the economy and the prosperity of countries depends on attracting and retaining these people. Florida has brought attention to developing livable and economically vibrant cities thanks in part to his promotional skills. However, he has also drawn critics who see his data on his theories as flimsy and inadequate.

5975 ■ The Craft Business Answer Book: Starting, Managing, and Marketing a Home-Based Art, Crafts, Design Business

Pub: M. Evans and Company, Incorporated

Ed: Barbara Brabec. **Released:** August 2006. **Price:** $16.95. **Description:** Expert advice for starting a home-based art or crafts business is offered.

5976 ■ Craft, Inc.

Pub: Chronicle Books LLC

Ed: Meg Mateo Ilasco. **Released:** August 2007. **Price:** $16.95. **Description:** Business primer for entrepreneurial crafters wishing to turn their hobbies into a small business, including tips for developing products, naming the company, writing a business plan, applying for licenses, and paying taxes.

5977 ■ The Crafts Report--Shows & Fairs Column

Pub: The Crafts Report News, Editorial & Advertising Offices

URL(s): www.craftsreport.com. **Ed:** Bernadette Finnerty. **Released:** Monthly **Publication includes:** List of forthcoming arts and crafts shows, articles for craft industry. **Entries include:** Show name, name and address of contact, sizes, fees, attendance. **Database includes:** Articles for craft industry. **Arrangement:** Chronological.

5978 ■ "A Decent Proposal" in Hawaii Business (Vol. 53, March 2008, No. 9, pp. 52)

Pub: Hawaii Business Publishing

Ed: Jacy L. Youn. **Description:** Bonnie Cooper and Brian Joy own Big Rock Manufacturing Inc., a stone manufacturing company, which sells carved rocks and bowls, lava benches, waterfalls, and Buddhas. Details about the company's growth are discussed.

5979 ■ "Doing Good: Cause and Effect" in Entrepreneur (Vol. 36, February 2008, No. 2, pp. 23)

Pub: Entrepreneur Media Inc.

Description: Lisa Knoppe established Art for a Cause LLC that employs people with mental and physical disabilities. The company makes hand-painted tools and furniture to be sold at gift retailers and hardware stores.

5980 ■ "A Doll That Looks Like You: Will Custom Toys Take Off?" in Inc. (Volume 32, December 2010, No. 10, pp. 144)

Pub: Inc. Magazine

Ed: Shivani Vora. **Description:** Profiles of various companies that provide custom items that look like people.

5981 ■ Earn Cash Crafting at Home: An MBA At-Home Mom Explains Step-by-Step Her Fun, Proven, Money-Making, Own-Your-Own Business Formula

Pub: Dark Horse, Incorporated

Ed: Maria Colman. **Released:** March 2006. **Price:** $10.00. **Description:** Manual offering advice to start and run an at-home craft business.

5982 ■ Enterprising Women in Urban Zimbabwe: Gender, Microbusiness, and Globalization

Pub: Indiana University Press
Contact: Janet Rabinowitch, Director
E-mail: jrabinow@indiana.edu

Ed: Mary Johnson Osirim. **Released:** April 1, 2009. **Price:** $39.95. **Description:** An investigation into the business and personal experiences of women entrepreneurs in the microenterprise sector in Zimbabwe. Many of these women work as market traders, crocheters, seamstresses, and hairdressers.

5983 ■ "From Craft Biz To Wholesale Giant" in Women Entrepreneur (January 19, 2009)

Pub: Entrepreneur Media Inc.

Ed: Maria Falconer. **Description:** Advice is given on how to turn a small craft business into a full-time venture; tips to help one transition from a part-time designer to a full-time wholesaler and brand are also included.

5984 ■ *"Gallery Street Launches ArtCandy" in Art Business News (Vol. 34, November 2007, No. 11, pp. 8)*
Pub: Pfingsten Publishing, LLC
Description: Fine-art reproduction house Gallery Street recently launched its new division, ArtCandy Editions; the division was created in order to help a network of artists expand the distribution of their work.

5985 ■ *"Getting It Sold" in Black Enterprise (Vol. 38, November 2007, No. 4, pp. 54)*
Pub: Earl G. Graves Publishing Co. Inc.
Ed: Tennille M. Robinson. **Description:** Artist is given advice for marketing and selling paintings, as well as getting artwork published.

5986 ■ *"Greg Lueck: Glass Blowing" in Inc. (Volume 32, December 2010, No. 10, pp. 36)*
Pub: Inc. Magazine
Ed: April Joyner. **Description:** Profile of Greg Lueck, partner and COO of Centerstance, a tech consulting firm in Portland, Oregon. Lueck opened Firehouse Glass, a studio that provides workspace and equipment for glass blowers. He says glass blowing serves as a welcome counterbalance to the cerebral work he does at the office.

5987 ■ *How to Market and Sell Your Art, Music, Photographs, and Handmade Crafts Online*
Pub: Atlantic Publishing Group, Inc.
Ed: Lee Rowley. **Released:** May 2008. **Price:** $24.95. **Description:** The book provides all the basics for starting and running an online store selling arts, crafts, photography or music. There are more than 300 Websites listed to help anyone market and promote their arts and/or crafts online.

5988 ■ *"Innovation Can Be Imperative for Those in Hands-On Trades" in Crain's Cleveland Business (Vol. 28, November 12, 2007, No. 45)*
Pub: Crain Communications, Inc.
Ed: Harriet Tramer. **Description:** Discusses the importance of networking and innovative marketing concerning those in art and restoration trades.

5989 ■ *"Inside an Online Bazaar" in Entrepreneur (Vol. 37, September 2009, No. 9, pp. 38)*
Pub: Entrepreneur Media Inc.
Ed: Kara Ohngren. **Description:** Etsy.com is a website that provides a marketplace for handmade products. The site has attracted more than 250,000 sellers since its launch in 2005. Site features and services are also supplied.

5990 ■ *"Jo-Ann Fabric and Craft Stores Joins ArtFire.com to Offer Free Online Craft Marketplace" in Internet Wire (January 26, 2010)*
Pub: Comtex News Network, Inc.
Description: Jo-Ann Fabric and Craft Stores has entered into a partnership with ArtFire.com which will provide sewers and crafters all the tools they need in order to make and sell their products from an online venue.

5991 ■ *"Let the Light Shine" in Retail Merchandiser (Vol. 51, July-August 2011, No. 4, pp. 74)*
Pub: Phoenix Media Corporation
Description: For over 25 years, The Thomas Kinkade Company has been producing art that is collected by both old and young, and is the only company that publishes Thomas Kinkade art.

5992 ■ *Martha, Inc.*
Pub: John Wiley and Sons, Inc.
Ed: Christopher Byron. **Released:** 2002. **Price:** $28.00. **Description:** Profile of Martha Stewart's rise from working class to a billionaire businesswoman is presented. The book covers Stewart's power struggles and personal conflicts as well as her triumphs.

5993 ■ *"Midas Touch" in Entrepreneur (Vol. 36, April 2008, No. 4, pp. 160)*
Pub: Entrepreneur Media, Inc.
Ed: Sara Wilson. **Description:** Lana Fertelmeister is a model-turned-jewelry designer. Her company, Lana Jewelry, designs fine jewelry for women. Her jewelry line is available in more than 100 stores worldwide and has been worn by celebrities like Cameron Diaz and Sandra Bullock.

5994 ■ *"Off the Wall: Keith Collins' Larger-Than-Life Designs" in Black Enterprise (Vol. 37, February 2007, No. 7, pp. 138)*
Pub: Earl G. Graves Publishing Co. Inc.
Description: Profile of Keith Collins, an entrepreneur who makes carpets for the likes of Jay Leno, Nicolas Cage, Arnold Schwartzenegger, Janet Jackson, and Will Smith. Collins is passionate about this ancient art form and saw a future in it despite the negative feedback from those around him.

5995 ■ *"Partnering for Success" in Art Business News (Vol. 36, October 2009, No. 10, pp. 4)*
Pub: Summit Business Media
Ed: Jennifer Dulin Wiley. **Description:** In such a volatile economy many savvy artists and gallery owners are turning to out-of-the-box partnerships for continued success; these partnerships are also pervading the Internet, especially with such social media networks as Facebook and Twitter where artists and businesses can develop a loyal following.

5996 ■ *"Pick A Name, Not Just Any Name" in Women Entrepreneur (December 17, 2008)*
Pub: Entrepreneur Media Inc.
Ed: Maria Falconer. **Description:** Craft business owners must choose a name that sounds personal since customers who buy hand-made products want to feel that they are buying from an individual rather than an institution. Tips for choosing a name are provided.

5997 ■ *Seven Days in the Art World*
Pub: W.W. Norton & Company
Ed: Sarah Thornton. **Released:** 2009. **Price:** $24.95. **Description:** A sociologist renders the interplay among buyers, critics, curators and makers of contemporary art.

5998 ■ *"Show Dates" in Art Business News (Vol. 34, November 2007, No. 11, pp. 18)*
Pub: Pfingsten Publishing, LLC
Description: Listing of conferences, trade shows and gallery openings for artists and those in the art industry.

5999 ■ *"Ted Stahl: Executive Chairman" in Inside Business (Vol. 13, September-October 2011, No. 5, pp. NC6)*
Pub: Great Lakes Publishing Co.
Ed: Miranda S. Miller. **Description:** Profile of Ted Stahl, who started working in his family's business when he was ten years old is presented. The firm makes dies for numbers and letters used on team uniforms. Another of the family firms manufactures stock and custom heat-printing products, equipment and supplies. It also educates customers on ways to decorate garments with heat printing products and offers graphics and software for customers to create their own artwork.

6000 ■ *"A Vegas Sensation Inaugural Artexpo Las Vegas" in Art Business News (Vol. 34, November 2007, No. 11, pp. 1)*
Pub: Pfingsten Publishing, LLC
Ed: Jennifer Dulin. **Description:** Overview of the first Artexpo Las Vegas which featured exhibitors, artists and buyers and was a wonderful place for networking.

TRADE PERIODICALS

6001 ■ *American Ceramic Society Bulletin*
Pub: American Ceramic Society
Contact: Charles Spahr, Executive Director
E-mail: cspahr@ceramics.org
URL(s): ceramics.org/. **Ed:** Peter Wray. **Released:** Monthly **Price:** $95, U.S. and Canada non-members; $150, Other countries non-members.

6002 ■ *Ceramics Monthly*
Pub: American Ceramic Society
Contact: Charles Spahr, Executive Director
E-mail: cspahr@ceramics.org
URL(s): ceramicartsdaily.org/ceramics-monthly/. **Ed:** Cynthia Griffith, Sherman Hall. **Released:** 10/yr. **Price:** $34.95, Individuals; $40, Canada; $60, Other countries; $59.95, Two years; $75, Canada two years; $99, Other countries two years.

6003 ■ *The China Painter*
Pub: World Organization of China Painters
Contact: Pat Dickerson, Executive Director
URL(s): www.theshop.net/wocporg/magazine/magazine.html. **Ed:** Pat Dickerson. **Released:** Bimonthly **Price:** $34, Individuals; $39, Other countries.

6004 ■ *Chip Chats*
Pub: National Wood Carvers Association
URL(s): www.chipchats.org. **Released:** Bimonthly **Price:** $16, Individuals; $22, Other countries.

6005 ■ *CityArt Magazine: A Contemporary Review of the Visual Arts*
Pub: Fleisher Fine Arts Inc.
URL(s): www.artfocustoronto.presspublisher.us/. **Released:** 3/yr. **Price:** $15, Canada 7% GST.

6006 ■ *Country Home*
Pub: Meredith Corp.
URL(s): www.countryhome.com. **Released:** Monthly; 10/yr. **Price:** $4.95, Individuals newstand; $21.97, Two years.

6007 ■ *The Crafts Fair Guide*
Pub: The Crafts Fair Guide
Contact: Lee Spiegel, Publisher
URL(s): www.craftsfairguide.com. **Released:** Quarterly **Price:** $48.95, Individuals; $87.95, Two years.

6008 ■ *Crafts 'n things*
Pub: Amos Press Inc.
Contact: Bruce D. Boyd, Chief Executive Officer
URL(s): www.craftsnthings.com. **Ed:** Abby Foster. **Released:** 6/yr. **Price:** $21.97, Individuals print and online; $19.97, Individuals online only; $29.47, Canada print and online; $36.97, Other countries print and online.

6009 ■ *Crafts News*
Pub: The Crafts Center
Released: Quarterly. **Price:** $50. **Description:** Features practical and timely news on market and trade information, sources of microcredit, successful artisan products, artisan advocacy issues, and crafts-related publications and events worldwide.

6010 ■ *Crafts--Newsletter*
Pub: Craft Council of Newfoundland and Labrador
Ed: Sandy Newton, Editor, sandy@nfld.com. **Released:** Monthly. **Price:** Included in membership. Contains news and information of the Association.

6011 ■ *CWB Custom Woodworking Business: Environmental Studies*
Contact: Bill Esler, Associate Publisher
E-mail: besler@vancepublishing.com
URL(s): www.vancepublishing.com/. **Ed:** Karen Koenig. **Released:** Monthly

6012 ■ *Doll World*
Pub: House of White Birches
Contact: David McKee, Chief Executive Officer
URL(s): www.dollworldmagazine.com. **Ed:** Vicki Steensma. **Released:** Bimonthly

6013 ■ *European Clinical Laboratory*
Pub: International Scientific Communications Inc.
Contact: William N. Wham, Publisher
E-mail: iscpubs@iscpubs.com
URL(s): www.iscpubs.comwww.iscpubs.com/publications/#eu. **Released:** Bimonthly; 6 times.

6014 ■ *Fine Woodworking*
Pub: Taunton Press Inc.
Contact: John Lively, Chief Executive Officer
URL(s): www.finewoodworking.com. **Ed:** Timothy D. Schreiner. **Released:** 7/yr. **Price:** $34.95, U.S. and Canada; $59.95, U.S. and Canada two years; $83.95, U.S. and Canada three years.

6015 ■ Fired Arts & Crafts: The Bible of the Ceramic Hobbyists Since 1955
Contact: Joyce Greenholdt, Editor
E-mail: joyceg@jonespublishing.com

URL(s): www.firedartsandcrafts.com/. **Ed:** Joyce Greenholdt. **Released:** Monthly **Price:** $39.95, Individuals; $74.95, Two years; $84.95, Individuals 3 years.

6016 ■ The Home Shop Machinist
Pub: The Home Shop Machinist

URL(s): www.homeshopmachinist.net. **Released:** Bimonthly **Price:** $29.95, Individuals.

6017 ■ Loomsong
Pub: Atlantic Spinners & Handweavers Nova Scotia Museum

Ed: Fran Nowakowski, Editor, fcn@dal.ca. **Released:** Monthly, 10/year. **Price:** Included in membership. **Description:** Discusses weaving and spinning. Recurring features include a calendar of events, reports of meetings, news of educational opportunities, book reviews.

6018 ■ Machinist's Workshop
Pub: Village Press Publications
Contact: Dave Moore, President
E-mail: davemoore@villagepress.com

URL(s): www.homeshopmachinist.net/. **Ed:** George Bulliss. **Released:** Bimonthly **Price:** $26.95, Individuals.

6019 ■ Modern Woodworking
Pub: BNP Media
Contact: Al Reser, President

URL(s): www.modernwoodworking.com.

6020 ■ National Guild of Decoupeurs--Dialogue
Pub: National Guild of Decoupeurs

Ed: Marion D. Peer, Editor, mdpeer@aol.com. **Released:** 4/year. **Price:** $40, Included in membership. **Description:** Publishes 'how to' articles on decoupage. Recurring features include news of the activities of the Guild.

6021 ■ Painting
Pub: Amos Press Inc.
Contact: Bruce D. Boyd, Chief Executive Officer

URL(s): paintingmagazine.net. **Released:** Bimonthly **Price:** $24.95, Individuals online only; $26.95, Individuals print and online; $34.45, Canada print and online; $41.95, Other countries print and online.

6022 ■ PaintWorks
Pub: All American Crafts Inc.
Contact: Gerald Cohen, President

URL(s): www.paintworksmag.com. **Ed:** Linda R. Heller. **Released:** 7/yr. **Price:** $29.97, Individuals; $45.97, Canada; $53.97, Out of country; $49.97, Two years; $81.97, Canada two years; $97.97, Out of country two years.

6023 ■ Paper Crafts Magazine: More Project-More Skills-More Fun
Pub: Primedia Special Interest Publications

URL(s): www.papercraftsmag.com/. **Ed:** Susan Opel. **Released:** 8/yr. **Price:** $16.97, Individuals; $29.97, Two years; $22.97, Canada; $28.97, Other countries.

6024 ■ Scentouri News
Pub: Scentouri

Ed: A. Doyle, Editor. **Description:** Contains recipes and suggestions for making potpourri. Distributed by Prosperity & Profits Unlimited.

6025 ■ Selling Christmas Decorations
Pub: Edgell Communications Inc.
Contact: Gerald C. Ryerson, President
E-mail: gryerson@edgellmail.com

URL(s): sellingchristmas.edgl.com/home. **Ed:** Dorothy Creamer. **Released:** Quarterly

6026 ■ Soft Dolls & Animals
Pub: Scott Advertising & Publishing Co.
Contact: Jeanette Foxe, Manager
E-mail: jfoxe@scottpublications.com

URL(s): scottpublications.com/catalog/product_info.php/products_id/149. **Released:** Bimonthly **Price:** $29.95, Individuals; $53.90, Two years; $41.95, Out of country non-US; $77.90, Two years non-US.

6027 ■ This Time
Pub: Homeworkers Organized for More Employment
Contact: Lucy Paulin, Founder

Released: Quarterly. **Price:** $5. **Description:** Provides information about H.O.M.E. Furthers the purpose of the organization, which is to provide supplemental income for low-income families through sale of their crafts through the organization. Reports on the education, social service, job training, home building, shelters for the homeless, and a food bank the organization promotes.

6028 ■ Threads
Pub: Taunton Press Inc.
Contact: John Lively, Chief Executive Officer

URL(s): www.threadsmagazine.com. **Released:** Bimonthly **Price:** $32.95, Individuals; $54.95, U.S. and Canada two years; $78.95, U.S. and Canada 3/yr.

6029 ■ Tole World: Creative Designs for Decorative Painting
Pub: EGW.com Inc.

URL(s): www.egw.com/index.html. **Released:** Bimonthly **Price:** $17, Individuals.

6030 ■ WoodenBoat: The Magazine for Wooden Boat Owners, Builders, and Designers
Pub: Woodenboat Publications Inc.
Contact: James Miller, President

URL(s): www.woodenboat.com/. **Ed:** Matthew Murphy. **Released:** Bimonthly **Price:** $32, Individuals; $59, Two years; $85, Individuals three years; $37, Canada; $69, Canada two years; $45, Other countries.

6031 ■ Woodshop News: The News Magazine for Professional Woodworkers
Pub: Dominion Enterprises
Contact: Jack Ross, President

URL(s): www.woodshopnews.com. **Ed:** Tod Riggio. **Released:** Monthly **Price:** $21.95, Individuals; $33.95, Canada; $35.95, Other countries; $35.95, Two years; $59.95, Canada 2 years; $63.95, Other countries 2 years.

6032 ■ Woodsmith
Pub: August Home Publishing
Contact: Donald Peschke, President

URL(s): www.woodsmith.comwww.augusthome.com/brands/woodsmith/. **Ed:** Terry J. Strohman. **Released:** Bimonthly **Price:** $33, Two years; C$37, Canada includes additional postage & GST; $36, Other countries includes additional postage; $22, Individuals.

6033 ■ Wool Gathering
Pub: Schoolhouse Press

Ed: Meg Swansen, Editor. **Released:** Semiannual. **Price:** $25, other countries airmail; $30, elsewhere. **Description:** Provides hand-knitters with original designs by Elizabeth Zimmermann and Meg Swansen. Includes reviews of knitting trends, information on wools, book reviews, and video news.

VIDEOCASSETTES/ AUDIOCASSETTES

6034 ■ Lithography: How to Paint and Sell Lithographs
Instructional Video
2219 C St.
Lincoln, NE 68502
Ph: (402)475-6570
Free: 800-228-0164

Fax: (402)475-6500
Co. E-mail: feedback@insvideo.com
URL: http://www.insvideo.com
Released: 19??. **Price:** $19.95. **Description:** Provides information on how professional print makers plan and print original lithographs to sell. Also contains demonstrations of tools, techniques, materials, and marketing. **Availability:** VHS.

6035 ■ Maskmaking with Clay
Crystal Productions
1812 Johns Dr.
Box 2159
Glenview, IL 60025-6519
Ph: (847)657-8144
Free: 800-255-8629
Fax: (847)657-8149
Co. E-mail: custserv@crystalproductions.com
URL: http://www.crystalproductions.com
Released: 1997. **Price:** $24.95. **Description:** Demonstrates complete techniques and materials for creating masks from clay. **Availability:** VHS.

6036 ■ With These Hands
Time-Life Video and Television
1450 Palmyra Ave.
Richmond, VA 23227-4420
Ph: (804)266-6330
Free: 800-950-7887
Fax: (757)427-7905
URL: http://www.timelife.com
Released: 1979. **Description:** This program contains footage of craftspeople at work. Potters Toshiko Takaezu and Paul Soldner, sculptors Peter Voulkos, Harry Nohr, Clayton Bailey, and J.B. Blunk, fiber artist Dorian Zachai, and glass blower James Tanner tell why they do what they do. **Availability:** VHS; 3/4 U; Special order formats.

TRADE SHOWS AND CONVENTIONS

6037 ■ Annual Dickens Christmas Show and Festivals Week
Leisure Time Unlimited, Inc.
708 Main St.
Myrtle Beach, SC 29577
Ph: (843)448-9483
Free: 800-261-5591
Fax: (843)626-1513
Co. E-mail: ltushows@sc.rr.com
URL: http://www.leisuretimeunlimited.com/
Contact: Brooke P. Baker, Show Manager
E-mail: dickensshow@sc.rr.com

URL(s): www.dickenschristmasshow.com/. **Price:** $8.50, adult; $4, children, ages 2-12; $13, multi-day ticket. **Frequency:** Annual. **Audience:** General public. **Principal Exhibits:** Crafts, art, paintings, gifts, and Christmas related items. **Dates and Locations:** , Convention Center. **Telecommunication Services:** dickensshow@sc.rr.com

6038 ■ Atlanta International Gift and Home Furnishing Market
AMC Inc.
240 Peachtree St. NW, Ste. 2200
Atlanta, GA 30303-1327
Ph: (404)220-3000
Free: 800-285-6278
Fax: (404)220-3030
URL(s): www.americasmart.com. **Frequency:** Semiannual. **Audience:** Buyers. **Principal Exhibits:** Gifts, stationery, souvenirs, home accents, furniture, Americana, home textiles, designer gifts, homemade gifts, holiday merchandise, florals, and jewelry. **Dates and Locations:** , Market Center.

6039 ■ Atlantic Craft Trade Show
Nova Scotia Department of Economic Development
1660 Hollis St., Suite 600
Halifax, NS, Canada B3J 3C8
Ph: (902)424-0377
Fax: (902)424-7008
URL: http://www.gov.ns.ca/econ
URL(s): www.actshow.ca. **Frequency:** Annual. **Audience:** Craft, giftware, and apparel trade professionals. **Principal Exhibits:** Crafts and giftware, includ-

ing porcelain, silver and pewter ware, jewelry, hand knits, hooked rugs, hand blown glass, toys; apparel, wood, and food products. **Dates and Locations:** World Trade and Convention Center. **Telecommunication Services:** acts@gov.ns.ca.

6040 ■ Border Security Expo
E.J. Krause & Associates, Inc.
6550 Rock Spring Dr., Ste. 500
Bethesda, MD 20817
Ph: (301)493-5500
Fax: (301)493-5705
Co. E-mail: info@ejkrause.com
URL: http://www.ejkrause.com
Contact: Sharon Deutch, Director
E-mail: deutch@ejkrause.com
URL(s): www.bordersecurityexpo.com/. **Price:** $695, industry; $195, government. **Frequency:** Annual. **Audience:** Law enforcement personnel, government officials. **Principal Exhibits:** GPS systems, wireless communications, law enforcement training, fingerprinting technology, voice recognition systems, documentation checking, guards and bomb sniffing dogs, motion detectors, intelligence sharing, unmanned ground vehicles, armored vehicles, surveillance cameras, sensors, radar systems, scanning systems, control monitors, barriers, biohazard detection systems.

6041 ■ CHA Winter Convention and Trade Show
Craft and Hobby Association (CHA)
319 E 54th St.
Elmwood Park, NJ 07407
Ph: (201)835-1200
Free: 800-822-0494
Fax: (201)797-0657
Co. E-mail: info@craftandhobby.org
URL: http://www.craftandhobby.org
Contact: Steven Z. Berger, President
E-mail: sberger@craftandhobby.org
URL(s): www.chashow.org. **Price:** Pre-registered, members; $25. **Frequency:** Annual. **Audience:** Owners, corporate officers and buyers from craft, hobby, DIY stores, general merchandise stores, wholesalers, and professional crafters. **Principal Exhibits:** Crafts, ceramics, floral accessories, dollhouse miniatures, aromatics, art materials and frames, jewelry findings, fabrics, needlework and quilting supplies, home decor, rubber stamps, stencils and scrapbooking supplies.

6042 ■ Charlotte Gift and Jewelry Show
Charlotte Gift and Jewelry Show
3710 Latrobe Dr., Ste. 110
Charlotte, NC 28211
Ph: (704)365-4152
Fax: (704)365-4154
Co. E-mail: michael@charlottegiftshow.com
URL: http://www.charlottegiftshow.com
URL(s): www.charlottegiftshow.com. **Frequency:** Quarterly. **Audience:** Trade buyers. **Principal Exhibits:** Gifts, housewares, jewelry, crafts, silk plants and flowers, tabletop, glassware, collectibles, accessories, home decorating accessories, basketry, and other related products. **Dates and Locations:** Merchandise Mart. **Telecommunication Services:** michael@charlottegiftshow.com.

6043 ■ Christmas Gift and Hobby Show
HSI Show Productions
PO Box 502797
Indianapolis, IN 46250
Ph: (317)576-9933
Free: 800-215-1700
Fax: (317)576-9955
Co. E-mail: info@hsishows.com
URL: http://www.hsishows.com
URL(s): www.christmasgiftandhobbyshow.com. **Price:** $10; $7, senior admission; $6, groups of twenty or more; free for children 12 and under. **Frequency:** Annual. **Audience:** General public. **Principal Exhibits:** Art, crafts, and giftware. **Dates and Locations:** , Indiana State Fairgrounds. **Telecommunication Services:** info@hsishows.com.

6044 ■ Connecticut Craft Show
Sugarloaf Mountain Works, Inc.
19807 Executive Park Circle
Germantown, MD 20874
Ph: (301)990-1400
Free: 800-210-9900
Fax: (301)253-9620
Co. E-mail: sugarloafinfo@sugarloaffest.com
URL: http://www.sugarloafcrafts.com
URL(s): www.sugarloafcrafts.com. **Frequency:** Annual. **Audience:** General public. **Principal Exhibits:** Arts and crafts.

6045 ■ The Craftmen's Christmas Classic Arts & Crafts Festival
Gilmore Enterprises
3514-A Drawbridge Pkwy.
Greensboro, NC 27410-8584
Ph: (336)282-5550
Co. E-mail: contact@gilmoreshows.com
URL: http://www.gilmoreshows.com
URL(s): www.gilmoreshows.com/craftsmens_classics_greensboro_christmas.shtml. **Frequency:** Annual. **Audience:** Trade and general public. **Principal Exhibits:** Original arts and crafts. **Dates and Locations:** Coliseum Exhibit Hall. **Telecommunication Services:** contact@gilmoreshows.com.

6046 ■ Craftsmen's Classic Arts & Crafts Festival-Columbia
Gilmore Enterprises
3514-A Drawbridge Pkwy.
Greensboro, NC 27410-8584
Ph: (336)282-5550
Co. E-mail: contact@gilmoreshows.com
URL: http://www.gilmoreshows.com
URL(s): www.gilmoreshows.com/craftsmens_classics_columbia_christmas.shtml. **Frequency:** Annual. **Audience:** Trade and general public. **Principal Exhibits:** Original arts and crafts, hand made and presented by their creator. **Dates and Locations:** SC State Fair Grounds. **Telecommunication Services:** contact@gilmoreshows.com.

6047 ■ The Craftsmen's Classic Arts & Crafts Festival--Greensboro
Gilmore Enterprises
3514-A Drawbridge Pkwy.
Greensboro, NC 27410-8584
Ph: (336)282-5550
Co. E-mail: contact@gilmoreshows.com
URL: http://www.gilmoreshows.com
URL(s): www.gilmoreshows.com/craftsmens_classics_greensboro_spring.shtml. **Frequency:** Annual. **Audience:** General public. **Principal Exhibits:** Originals arts and crafts. **Dates and Locations:** Greensboro Coliseum Special Events Center. **Telecommunication Services:** contact@gilmoreshows.com.

6048 ■ The Craftsmen's Classic Arts & Crafts Festival--Myrtle Beach
Gilmore Enterprises
3514-A Drawbridge Pkwy.
Greensboro, NC 27410-8584
Ph: (336)282-5550
Co. E-mail: contact@gilmoreshows.com
URL: http://www.gilmoreshows.com
URL(s): www.gilmoreshows.com/craftsmens_classics_myrtle_summer.shtml. **Price:** $7, for adults; $1, for children between age 6-12; free for under 6 years. **Frequency:** Annual. **Audience:** Trade and general public. **Principal Exhibits:** Original arts and crafts. **Dates and Locations:** The Myrtle Beach Convention Center. **Telecommunication Services:** info@gilmoreshows.com.

6049 ■ Handmade - A Division of the New York International Gift Fair
George Little Management, LLC
1133 Westchester Ave., Ste. N136
White Plains, NY 10606
Ph: (914)421-3200

Free: 800-272-SHOW
Co. E-mail: cathy_steel@glmshows.com
URL: http://www.glmshows.com
URL(s): www.nyigf.com. **Frequency:** Semiannual. **Audience:** Buyers of specialty, department, jewelry, and stationery stores; gift shops, interior designers, importers/distributors of home products, mail order catalogs. **Principal Exhibits:** Handmade merchandise, including functional and decorative home furnishings, fashion accessories, jewelry plus an array of other unique craft objects. All merchandise is selected by a panel of craft professionals for uniqueness, originality and marketability. **Dates and Locations:** Jacob K. Javits Convention Center.

6050 ■ Handmade - A Division of the San Francisco International Gift Fair
George Little Management, LLC
1133 Westchester Ave., Ste. N136
White Plains, NY 10606
Ph: (914)421-3200
Free: 800-272-SHOW
Co. E-mail: cathy_steel@glmshows.com
URL: http://www.glmshows.com
URL(s): www.sfigf.com. **Frequency:** Semiannual. **Audience:** Specialty, department, stationery, juvenile, and jewelry stores, interior designers, gift shops, mail order catalogs, importers/distributors of home products. **Principal Exhibits:** Handmade merchandise, including functional and decorative home furnishings, fashion accessories, jewelry plus an array of other unique craft objects. All merchandise is selected by a panel of craft professionals for uniqueness, originality and marketability.

6051 ■ Holiday Fair
Textile Hall Corp.
PO Box 5823
Greenville, SC 29606
Ph: (864)233-2562
Fax: (864)233-0619
Co. E-mail: atmei@textilehall.com
Contact: Butler Mullins, Director
E-mail: bmullins@textilehall.com
URL(s): www.holidayfairgreenville.com/index.html. **Price:** $6, adult general admission; $5, group rate (15 or more) general admission; $4, seniors (60 or over) general admission; $3, seniors group rate (15 or more) general admission. **Frequency:** Annual. **Audience:** General public. **Principal Exhibits:** Arts and crafts. **Dates and Locations:** , Palmetto International Exposition Center. **Telecommunication Services:** kwarner@carolinafirstcenter.com.

6052 ■ Home Entertainment Show
Trigger Agency
3539 Clipper Mill Rd.
Baltimore, MD 21211
Free: 800-830-3976
Fax: (410)878-9911
Co. E-mail: info@triggeragency.com
URL: http://www.triggeragency.com/
Contact: Greg Nivens, President
E-mail: gnivens@triggeragency.com
URL(s): www.mooreamarketing.com. **Price:** $32, Pre-registered 3-day pass; $37, Onsite 3-day pass; $22, Pre-registered 1-day pass; $27, Onsite 1-day pass. **Frequency:** Biennial. **Audience:** Consumers, trade and press. **Principal Exhibits:** Home theater and high-fidelity audio equipment, supplies, and services. **Telecommunication Services:** gnivens@mooreamarketing.com.

6053 ■ Memories Expo
Offinger Management Co.
1100-H Brandywine Blvd.
Zanesville, OH 43701-7303
Ph: (740)452-4541
Free: 888-878-6334
Fax: (740)452-2552
Co. E-mail: omc.info@offinger.com
URL: http://www.offinger.com
URL(s): www.memoriesexpo.com. **Price:** $10, Non-members one day; $15, Non-members. **Frequency:** 5/year. **Audience:** Trade and public. **Principal Exhibits:** Scrapbook supplies. **Telecommunication Services:** memories@offinger.com.

6054 ■ Mid-South Jewelry & Accessories Fair Fall
Helen Brett Enterprises, Inc.
5111 Academy Dr.
Lisle, IL 60532-2171
Ph: (630)241-9865
Fax: (630)241-9870
URL: http://www.gift2jewelry.com
URL(s): www.gift2jewelry.com. **Frequency:** Semiannual. **Audience:** Wholesaler buyers. **Principal Exhibits:** Fine/costume jewelry, apparel, leathers, silks, beaded items, home decor, novelties.

6055 ■ Society of Craft Designers Educational Seminar (SCD)
Offinger Management Co.
1100-H Brandywine Blvd.
Zanesville, OH 43701-7303
Ph: (740)452-4541
Free: 888-878-6334
Fax: (740)452-2552
Co. E-mail: omc@offinger.com
URL: http://www.offinger.com
URL(s): www.craftdesigners.org. **Frequency:** Annual. **Audience:** Designers, manufacturers, editors, and publishers. **Principal Exhibits:** Craft designer showcases and education. **Telecommunication Services:** scd@offinger.com.

6056 ■ Southern Christmas Show
Southern Shows, Inc.
PO Box 36859
Charlotte, NC 28236
Ph: (704)376-6594
Free: 800-849-0248
Fax: (704)376-6345
Co. E-mail: sabernethy@southernshows.com
URL: http://www.southernshows.com
Contact: David J. Zimmerman, President
E-mail: dzimmerman@southernshows.com
URL(s): www.southernshows.com. **Price:** $8, Preregistered; $7, Onsite; $6.50, Pre-registered for groups of 20 or more; $3, for ages 6-12. **Frequency:** Annual. **Audience:** General public. **Principal Exhibits:** Christmas gifts, crafts, arts, foods, and educational materials, Christmas tree lane, and decorating competitions, and Santa Claus. **Dates and Locations:** , The Park Expo and Conference Center. **Telecommunication Services:** ccipriano@southernshows.com.

6057 ■ Sugarloaf Art Fair Novi, Spring
Sugarloaf Mountain Works, Inc.
19807 Executive Park Circle
Germantown, MD 20874
Ph: (301)990-1400
Free: 800-210-9900
Fax: (301)253-9620
Co. E-mail: sugarloafinfo@sugarloaffest.com
URL: http://www.sugarloafcrafts.com
URL(s): sugarloafcrafts.com. **Price:** $6, Onsite. **Frequency:** Annual. **Audience:** Women ages 25 through 54. **Principal Exhibits:** Arts and crafts.

6058 ■ Sugarloaf Crafts Festival Gaithersburg, Fall
Sugarloaf Mountain Works, Inc.
19807 Executive Park Circle
Germantown, MD 20874
Ph: (301)990-1400
Free: 800-210-9900
Fax: (301)253-9620
Co. E-mail: sugarloafinfo@sugarloaffest.com
URL: http://www.sugarloafcrafts.com
URL(s): www.sugarloafcrafts.com. **Price:** $7, Onsite under 12 free. **Frequency:** Annual. **Audience:** Women ages 25 through 54. **Principal Exhibits:** Arts and crafts.

6059 ■ Sugarloaf Crafts Festival Gaithersburg, Spring
Sugarloaf Mountain Works, Inc.
19807 Executive Park Circle
Germantown, MD 20874
Ph: (301)990-1400
Free: 800-210-9900

Fax: (301)253-9620
Co. E-mail: sugarloafinfo@sugarloaffest.com
URL: http://www.sugarloafcrafts.com
URL(s): www.sugarloafcrafts.com. **Frequency:** Annual. **Audience:** Women ages 25 through 54. **Principal Exhibits:** Arts and crafts.

6060 ■ Sugarloaf Crafts Festival Manassas, Fall
Sugarloaf Mountain Works, Inc.
19807 Executive Park Circle
Germantown, MD 20874
Ph: (301)990-1400
Free: 800-210-9900
Fax: (301)253-9620
Co. E-mail: sugarloafinfo@sugarloaffest.com
URL: http://www.sugarloafcrafts.com
URL(s): www.sugarloafcrafts.com. **Price:** $7, Onsite under 12 free. **Frequency:** Annual. **Audience:** Women ages 25 through 54. **Principal Exhibits:** Arts and crafts.

6061 ■ Sugarloaf Crafts Festival Philadelphia
Sugarloaf Mountain Works, Inc.
19807 Executive Park Circle
Germantown, MD 20874
Ph: (301)990-1400
Free: 800-210-9900
Fax: (301)253-9620
Co. E-mail: sugarloafinfo@sugarloaffest.com
URL: http://www.sugarloafcrafts.com
URL(s): sugarloafcrafts.com. **Price:** $7, free for children under 12. **Frequency:** Semiannual. **Audience:** Women ages 25 through 54. **Principal Exhibits:** Arts and crafts.

6062 ■ Sugarloaf Crafts Festival Somerset, Fall
Sugarloaf Mountain Works, Inc.
19807 Executive Park Circle
Germantown, MD 20874
Ph: (301)990-1400
Free: 800-210-9900
Fax: (301)253-9620
Co. E-mail: sugarloafinfo@sugarloaffest.com
URL: http://www.sugarloafcrafts.com
URL(s): www.sugarloafcrafts.com. **Price:** $8, Onsite free for under 12 years. **Frequency:** Annual. **Audience:** Women ages 25 through 54. **Principal Exhibits:** Arts and crafts.

6063 ■ Sugarloaf Crafts Festival Somerset, Spring
Sugarloaf Mountain Works, Inc.
19807 Executive Park Circle
Germantown, MD 20874
Ph: (301)990-1400
Free: 800-210-9900
Fax: (301)253-9620
Co. E-mail: sugarloafinfo@sugarloaffest.com
URL: http://www.sugarloafcrafts.com
URL(s): sugarloafcrafts.com. **Price:** $8, Onsite. **Frequency:** Semiannual. **Audience:** Women ages 25 through 54. **Principal Exhibits:** Arts and crafts.

6064 ■ Sugarloaf Crafts Festival Timonium, Fall
Sugarloaf Mountain Works, Inc.
19807 Executive Park Circle
Germantown, MD 20874
Ph: (301)990-1400
Free: 800-210-9900
Fax: (301)253-9620
Co. E-mail: sugarloafinfo@sugarloaffest.com
URL: http://www.sugarloafcrafts.com
URL(s): www.sugarloafcrafts.com. **Price:** $8, Onsite free for under 12 years; free for under 12 years. **Frequency:** Annual. **Audience:** Women ages 25 through 54. **Principal Exhibits:** Arts and crafts.

6065 ■ Sugarloaf Crafts Festival Timonium, Spring
Sugarloaf Mountain Works, Inc.
19807 Executive Park Circle
Germantown, MD 20874
Ph: (301)990-1400
Free: 800-210-9900

Fax: (301)253-9620
Co. E-mail: sugarloafinfo@sugarloaffest.com
URL: http://www.sugarloafcrafts.com
URL(s): sugarloafcrafts.com. **Frequency:** Annual. **Audience:** Women ages 25 through 54. **Principal Exhibits:** Arts and crafts.

6066 ■ TNNA Winter Trade Show
The National NeedleArts Association
1100-H Brandywine Blvd.
Zanesville, OH 43701
Ph: (740)455-6773
Free: 800-889-8662
Fax: (740)452-2552
Co. E-mail: tnna.info@offinger.com
URL: http://www.tnna.org
URL(s): www.tnna.org. **Frequency:** Semiannual. **Audience:** Trade-retail buyers of needle art products. **Principal Exhibits:** Upscale needle art products such as needlepoint, knitting, counted thread, embroidery, and crochet supplies as well as related products such as buttons, beads, trims, frames, fibers, books, etc. **Telecommunication Services:** tnna.info@offinger.com.

FRANCHISES AND BUSINESS OPPORTUNITIES

6067 ■ Crock A Doodle
299 Wayne Gretzy Pkwy.
Brantford, ON, Canada N3R 8A5
Ph: (519)752-8080
Co. E-mail: franchise@crockadoodle.com
URL: http://www.imaginelovingwhatyoudo.com
Description: Provides a variety of pottery painting events and activities for groups of all kinds. For women, we offer a calendar full of pottery-painting workshops and classes, as well as creative activities for girls' nights, bridal showers and special occasions. For children, we offer birthday parties, seasonal events and pottery-painting classes, as well as creative programming for camps, schools, teams and groups. The opportunity extends throughout the community to corporate team builders, fundraisers and community events of all kinds. **No. of Franchise Units:** 10. **No. of Company-Owned Units:** 2. **Founded:** 2002. **Franchised:** 2004. **Equity Capital Needed:** Total investment from $75,000. **Franchise Fee:** $20,000. **Training:** Provides 2 weeks plus ongoing support.

6068 ■ The Painted Penguin, LLC
6115 Monroe Ct.
Morton Grove, IL 60053
Ph: (847)681-0005
Fax: (847)432-3437
Co. E-mail: franchise@thepaintedpenguin.com
URL: http://www.thepaintedpenguin.com
Description: Offers the opportunity to get in on the ground floor of the booming craft industry with a well respected, growth oriented franchise that combines business ownership with a fun environment. **No. of Franchise Units:** 1. **No. of Company-Owned Units:** 2. **Founded:** 2000.. **Franchised:** 2003. **Equity Capital Needed:** $115,000-$199,000. **Franchise Fee:** $35,000. **Training:** Comprehensive training, marketing guidance, site selection assistance and other on-going support.

COMPUTERIZED DATABASES

6069 ■ Art on Screen Database™
200 Willoughby Ave.
Brooklyn, NY 11205-3817
Ph: (718)399-4506
Fax: (718)399-4507
Co. E-mail: info@artfilm.org
URL: http://www.artfilm.org
Availability: Online: Program for Art on Film Inc. **Type:** Directory.

6070 ■ Consumer InSite<svs>
610 Opperman Dr.
Eagen, MN 55122

Free: 800-477-4300
Co. E-mail: gale.contentlicensing@cengage.com
URL: http://www.insite2.gale.com
Availability: Online: Cengage Learning Inc. - Gale - InSite2. **Type:** Full-text.

6071 ■ *Humanities Full Text™*
10 Estes St.
Ipswich, MA 01938-2106
Ph: (978)356-6500
Free: 800-653-2726
Fax: (978)356-6565
Co. E-mail: information@ebscohost.com
URL: http://www.ebscohost.com
Contact: Tim Collins, President
E-mail: tcollins@ebscohost.com
Availability: Online: EBSCO Publishing. **Type:** Full-text; Bibliographic.

LIBRARIES

6072 ■ American Craft Council Library
1224 Marshall St. NE, Ste. 200
Minneapolis, MN 55413
Ph: (612)206-3100
Fax: (612)355-2330
Co. E-mail: library@craftcouncil.org
URL: http://www.craftcouncil.org/library
Contact: Jessica Shaykett, Librarian

URL(s): www.craftcouncil.org. **Scope:** 20th-century contemporary fine crafts - fiber, clay, metal, wood, glass, enamel, plastics, mixed media; decorative arts; design. **Services:** Copying; library open to the public (Monday to Friday). **Founded:** 1956. **Holdings:** 6400 books; 700 bound periodical volumes; 7000 exhibition catalogs; 200 videocassettes. **Subscriptions:** 100 journals and other serials.

6073 ■ American Society of Artists, Inc. - Resource Center
Box 1326
Palatine, IL 60078
Ph: (312)751-2500
Co. E-mail: asoa@webtv.net
URL: http://community-2.webtv.net/ASOA/ASA/
URL(s): www.americansocietyofartists.us. **Scope:** Art, crafts, supplies. **Services:** Lectures; demonstrations; seminars; workshops. **Founded:** 1978. **Holdings:** 50 volumes; 43 VF drawers. **Subscriptions:** 11 journals and other serials. **Telecommunication Services:** asoaartists@aol.com; contact@americansocietyofartists.us.

6074 ■ California College of the Arts Libraries - Meyer Library
5212 Broadway
Oakland, CA 94618

Ph: (510)594-3658
Co. E-mail: meyerlib@cca.edu
URL: http://library.cca.edu
Contact: Donald Smith, Manager
Scope: Art, architecture, design, humanities. **Services:** Library limited to the CCA community (specialized research by appointment). **Founded:** 1907. **Holdings:** 62,000 volumes; 150,000 slides and pictures; 100 lin.ft. of archival material. **Subscriptions:** 275 journals and other serials. **Telecommunication Services:** jwoo@cca.edu.

6075 ■ Cleveland Institute of Art - Jessica R. Gund Memorial Library
11141 East Blvd., 3rd Fl.
Cleveland, OH 44106
Ph: (216)421-7440
Fax: (216)421-7439
Co. E-mail: referencehelp@cia.edu
URL: http://www.cia.edu/library/
Contact: Cristine C. Rom, Director, Library Services
Scope: Fine arts, crafts, industrial design, general design, graphic arts, new media, glass, ceramics, medical illustration, textiles, metals. **Services:** Internet access; Interlibrary loan; copying; Library open to the public. **Founded:** 1882. **Holdings:** 47,000 books; 10,000 bound periodical volumes; 125,000 slides; 9000 pictures; 37 volumes and boxes of archival materials; 4000 reels of microfilm; 15,000 microfiche; 600 videotapes, DVDs and films; 1600 sound recordings. **Subscriptions:** 145 journals and other serials; 2 newspapers. **Telecommunication Services:** crom@cia.edu; dbjorklund@cia.edu.

6076 ■ Haystack Mountain School of Crafts Library
PO Box 518
Deer Isle, ME 04627-0518
Ph: (207)348-2306
Fax: (207)348-2307
Co. E-mail: haystack@haystack-mtn.org
URL: http://www.haystack-mtn.org/
Contact: Lissa Hunter, President
Scope: Fine arts, ceramics, weaving, glassblowing, flat glass, jewelry, surface and textile design, wood, blacksmithing, printmaking, papermaking, weaving. **Services:** Library open to the public on a limited basis. **Holdings:** 1000 books. **Subscriptions:** 20 journals and other serials.

6077 ■ Manitoba Crafts Museum & Library - Gladys Chown Memorial Library
1B-183 Kennedy St.
Winnipeg, MB, Canada R3C 1S6
Ph: (204)487-6117
Co. E-mail: info@mcml.ca
URL: http://www.mcml.ca
Contact: Andrea Reichert, Curator
Scope: Crafts - weaving, pottery, embroidery, knitting, crochet, quilting, paper, wood, Inuit and Aboriji-

nal, polymer clay, lace; craft design; color theory; history of craft. **Services:** Copying; Library open to the public. **Founded:** 1928. **Holdings:** 3500 volumes; 2000 slides; 9000 artifacts. **Subscriptions:** 4 journals and other serials.

6078 ■ Museum of Contemporary Craft Library
724 NW Davis St.
Portland, OR 97209
Ph: (503)223-2654
Fax: (503)223-0190
Co. E-mail: info@museumofcontemporarycraft.org
URL: http://www.museumofcontemporarycraft.org/
Contact: Linda Brower, Treasurer
Scope: Ceramics and pottery, weaving and textiles, Pacific Northwest craftsmen, contemporary designers, metalwork and jewelry, contemporary glass, sculpture, woodworking, architecture. **Services:** Library open during Museum hours. **Founded:** 1937. **Holdings:** 420 books; 74 bound and 125 unbound periodical volumes. **Telecommunication Services:** nnathan@museumofcontemporarycraft.org.

6079 ■ Parsons School of Design - Adam & Sophie Gimbel Design Library
2 W. 13th St.
New York, NY 10011
Ph: (212)229-8914
Fax: (212)229-2806
Co. E-mail: cassimar@newschool.edul
URL: http://library.newschool.edu/gimbel
Contact: Kira Appel, Director
Scope: Fine arts, architecture, costume, crafts, design, environmental design, fashion, graphic arts, photography, typography. **Services:** Interlibrary loan. **Founded:** 1896. **Holdings:** 61,000 books; 55,000 mounted picture plates; 85,000 slides; archives. **Subscriptions:** 200 journals and other serials.

6080 ■ University of Hartford - William H. Mortensen Library - Anne Bunce Cheney Art Collection
200 Bloomfield Ave.
West Hartford, CT 06117
Ph: (860)768-4397
Fax: (860)768-5298
Co. E-mail: bigazzi@hartford.edu
URL: http://library.hartford.edu/about_libraries/info_pol/coll_cheney.aspx
Contact: Anna B. Bigazzi, Librarian, Art
Scope: Art history, architecture, art education, applied art, decorative arts, crafts, photography, typography. **Services:** Interlibrary loan; copying; Library open to the public. **Founded:** 1963. **Holdings:** 24,000 books; 3200 bound periodical volumes; 19,000 mounted reproductions; 2500 pamphlets; CD-ROMs; videos. **Subscriptions:** 70 journals and other serials.

START-UP INFORMATION

6081 ■ *Careers for Self-Starters and Other Entrepreneurial Types*
Pub: McGraw-Hill Companies Inc.
Contact: Deven Sharma, President
Ed: Blythe Camenson. **Released:** September 2004. **Price:** $9.99 (US). **Description:** Advice to entrepreneurs wishing to start their own small company. Tips for turning hobbies into job skills are included.

6082 ■ *The Craft Business Answer Book: Starting, Managing, and Marketing a Home-Based Art, Crafts, Design Business*
Pub: M. Evans and Company, Incorporated
Ed: Barbara Brabec. **Released:** August 2006. **Price:** $16.95. **Description:** Expert advice for starting a home-based art or crafts business is offered.

6083 ■ *Craft Inc: Turn Your Creative Hobby into a Business*
Pub: Chronicle Books LLC
Ed: Meg Mateo Ilasco. **Released:** September 2007. **Price:** $16.95. **Description:** Guide to help any crafter turn their hobby into a successful business. The book covers all aspects including pricing, sales and marketing, trade shows, as well as interviews with successful craft artisans Jonathan Adler, Lotta Jansdotter, Denyse Schmidt and Jill Bliss.

6084 ■ *Earn Cash Crafting at Home: An MBA At-Home Mom Explains Step-by-Step Her Fun, Proven, Money-Making, Own-Your-Own Business Formula*
Pub: Dark Horse, Incorporated
Ed: Maria Colman. **Released:** March 2006. **Price:** $10.00. **Description:** Manual offering advice to start and run an at-home craft business.

6085 ■ *How to Start a Home-Based Craft Business, 5th Ed.*
Pub: Globe Pequot Press
Ed: Kenn Oberrecht. **Released:** July 2007. **Price:** $18.95. **Description:** Step-by-step guide for starting and growing a home-based craft business.

6086 ■ *How to Start a Home-Based Craft Business, 5th Edition*
Pub: Globe Pequot Press
Ed: Kenn Oberrecht. **Released:** July 2007. **Price:** $18.95. **Description:** Advice for starting a home-based craft business is given, including sources for finding supplies on the Internet, writing a business plan, publicity, zoning ordinances, and more.

6087 ■ *Scrapbooking for Profit: Cashing in on Retail, Home-Based and Internet Opportunities*
Pub: Allworth Press
Ed: Rebecca Pittman. **Released:** June 2005. **Price:** $19.95 (US), $22.95 (Canadian). **Description:** Eleven strategies for starting a scrapbooking business, including brick-and-mortar stores, home-based businesses, and online retail and wholesale outlets.

6088 ■ *Setting Up Your Ceramic Studio: Ideas and Plans from Working Artists*
Pub: Lark Books
Ed: Virginia Scotchie. **Released:** March 2005. **Price:** $45.00. **Description:** Floor plans and advice for setting up a creative ceramics studio are provided, focusing on equipment, workflow, and safety issues.

6089 ■ *Soul Proprietor: 101 Lessons from a Lifestyle Entrepreneur*
Pub: Crossing Press, Incorporated
Ed: Jane Pollak. **Released:** September 2004. **Description:** More than 100 tips and stores to inspire and guide any would-be entrepreneur to earn a living from a favorite hobby or passion.

6090 ■ *Will Work for Fun: 3 Simple Steps for Turning Any Hobby or Interest into Cash*
Pub: John Wiley and Sons, Inc.
Ed: Allan R. Bechtold. **Released:** May 2008. **Price:** $24.95. **Description:** Tips for turning any hobby or interest into a lucrative business are shared.

ASSOCIATIONS AND OTHER ORGANIZATIONS

6091 ■ **American Craft Council (ACC)**
1224 Marshall St. NE, Ste. 200
Minneapolis, MN 55413-1089
Ph: (612)206-3100
Free: 800-836-3470
Fax: (612)355-2330
Co. E-mail: council@craftcouncil.org
URL: http://www.craftcouncil.org
Contact: Chris Amundsen, Executive Director
E-mail: camundsen@craftcouncil.org
Description: Promotes understanding and appreciation of contemporary American craft. **Scope:** 20th century American craft. **Founded:** 1943. **Subscriptions:** 10000 books periodicals video recordings. **Publications:** *American Craft* (Bimonthly); *American Craft--News Section* (Bimonthly); *American Craft* (Bimonthly); *American Craft--American Craft Guide to Craft Galleries & Shops USA Issue*; *American Craft Council--Crafts Fair Directory*. **Educational Activities:** ACC Craft Fair Sarasota (Annual); ACC Craft Show Baltimore (Annual); ACC Craft Show San Francisco (Annual). **Awards:** American Craft Council Fellow (Annual); American Craft Council Fellows; Gold Medal; Aileen Osborn Webb Award (Annual).

6092 ■ **American Sewing Guild (ASG)**
9660 Hillcroft, Ste. 510
Houston, TX 77096
Ph: (713)729-3000
Fax: (713)721-9230
Co. E-mail: ddias@asg.org
URL: http://www.asg.org
Contact: Margo Martin, Executive Director
Description: Home sewers and people interested in sewing. Provides current sewing information and advice through lectures, demonstrations, classes, seminars, and fashion shows. Seeks to improve communication between home sewers and sewing industry. Encourages the development of neighborhood

workshop groups. **Founded:** 1978. **Awards:** Community Service Volunteer of the Year (Annual); Member of the Year (Annual).

6093 ■ **Canadian Craft and Hobby Association (CCHA)**
PO Box 101
Orangeville, ON, Canada L9W 2Z5
Ph: (519)940-5969
Free: 866-386-8853
Fax: (519)941-0492
Co. E-mail: paul.laplante@asi-tapedots.com
URL: http://www.cdncraft.org
Contact: Paul Laplante, President
Description: Hobbyists and craftspeople. Promotes recreational and commercial participation in the production of craft objects. Facilitates communication and cooperation among members; provides support and services to craftspeople; conducts promotional activities. **Founded:** 1980. **Publications:** *Canadian Craft and Hobby Association--Membership Directory* (Annual); *Canadian Craft Trade* (Semiannual).

6094 ■ *Canadian Craft Trade*
PO Box 101
Orangeville, ON, Canada L9W 2Z5
Ph: (519)940-5969
Free: 866-386-8853
Fax: (519)941-0492
Co. E-mail: paul.laplante@asi-tapedots.com
URL: http://www.cdncraft.org
Contact: Paul Laplante, President
Released: Semiannual **Price:** free.

6095 ■ **Craft and Hobby Association (CHA)**
319 E 54th St.
Elmwood Park, NJ 07407
Ph: (201)835-1200
Free: 800-822-0494
Fax: (201)797-0657
Co. E-mail: info@craftandhobby.org
URL: http://www.craftandhobby.org
Contact: Steven Z. Berger, President
E-mail: sberger@craftandhobby.org
URL(s): www.hobby.org, www.chashow.org. **Description:** Manufacturers, wholesalers, retailers, publishers, and allied firms in the craft and hobby industry. Promotes the interest of all companies engaged in the buying, selling, or manufacturing of craft and hobby merchandise; conceives, develops, and implements programs for members to achieve greater individual growth. Conducts seminars and educational workshops; sponsors national trade show. Compiles statistics. **Founded:** 2004. **Publications:** *HIA Show Directory* (Annual); *Directory of Manufacturer Representatives, Service Suppliers, Professional Chaft Producers, Certified Professional Demonstrators* (Biennial). **Educational Activities:** CHA Winter Convention and Trade Show (Annual).

6096 ■ **Embroiderers' Guild of America (EGA)**
1355 Bardstown Rd., Ste. 157
Louisville, KY 40202
Ph: (502)589-6956

Fax: (502)584-7900
Co. E-mail: egahq@egausa.org
URL: http://www.egausa.org
Contact: Lorie Welker, President
Description: People interested in the art of needle-work. Aims to set and maintain high standards of design, color, and workmanship in all kinds of embroidery. Sponsors exhibitions; offers examinations for teaching certification; serves as an information source for needlework in the U.S. Conducts classes and correspondence on all types of needle-work. Presents certificate for successful completion of Master Craftsman Programs. **Scope:** embroidery, needlework, art history, design. **Founded:** 1958. **Subscriptions:** 2200 articles audiovisuals books monographs periodicals video recordings. **Publications:** *Needle Arts* (Quarterly); *Inside EGA* (Quarterly). **Awards:** Educators' Award of Excellence (Annual); Gold Thread Award (Annual); Research Fellowship (Annual).

6097 ■ Indian Arts and Crafts Association (IACA)
4010 Carlisle Blvd. NE, Ste. C
Albuquerque, NM 87107
Ph: (505)265-9149
Fax: (505)265-8251
Co. E-mail: info@iaca.com
URL: http://www.iaca.com
Contact: Joseph P. Zeller, President
Description: Indian craftspeople and artists, museums, dealers, collectors, and others. Works to promote, preserve, protect, and enhance the understanding of authentic American Indian arts and crafts. Sets code of ethics for members and standards for the industry. Conducts consumer education seminars, meetings, and display programs; works with related government groups. Operates speakers' bureau. **Founded:** 1974. **Publications:** *IACA Journal* (Quarterly); *Indian Arts and Crafts Association--Directory* (Annual); *Membership Directory/Buyer's Guide* (Annual). **Educational Activities:** Wholesale Market (Semiannual). **Awards:** Artist of the Year (Annual).

6098 ■ The National Needle Arts Association (TNNA)
1100-H Brandywine Blvd.
Zanesville, OH 43701-7303
Ph: (740)455-6773
Free: 800-889-8662
Fax: (740)452-2552
Co. E-mail: tnna.info@offinger.com
URL: http://www.tnna.org
Contact: Joel Woodcock, President
Description: Manufacturers, retailers and distributors of upscale needle art products (needlepoint, embroidery, cross stitch, crochet, knitting, books and accessories). Advances its community of professional businesses by encouraging the passion for needle arts though education, industry knowledge exchange and a strong marketplace. **Founded:** 1975. **Publications:** *Directory of Exhibitors* (Semiannual); *TNNA Today.* **Awards:** Excellence in Needlework Award (Annual).

REFERENCE WORKS

6099 ■ *202 Things You Can Make and Sell for Big Profits*
Pub: Entrepreneur Press
Ed: James Stephenson. **Released:** September 2005. **Price:** $19.95. **Description:** Instructions for 202 products that can be made and sold over the Internet.

6100 ■ *"Ask Inc."* in Inc. (January 2008, pp. 61)
Pub: Gruner & Jahr USA Publishing
Description: Information to help crafter of custom quilts made from old T-shirts, baby clothes, jeans, and neckties to market her items on a small budget.

6101 ■ *Craft, Inc.*
Pub: Chronicle Books LLC
Ed: Meg Mateo Ilasco. **Released:** August 2007. **Price:** $16.95. **Description:** Business primer for entrepreneurial crafters wishing to turn their hobbies

into a small business, including tips for developing products, naming the company, writing a business plan, applying for licenses, and paying taxes.

6102 ■ *The Crafts Report--Shows & Fairs Column*
Pub: The Crafts Report News, Editorial & Advertising Offices
URL(s): www.craftsreport.com. **Ed:** Bernadette Finnerty. **Released:** Monthly **Publication includes:** List of forthcoming arts and crafts shows, articles for craft industry. **Entries include:** Show name, name and address of contact, sizes, fees, attendance. **Database includes:** Articles for craft industry. **Arrangement:** Chronological.

6103 ■ *"A Curious Appeal (Market for Scientific Toys)"* in Playthings (Vol. 106, October 1, 2008, No. 9, pp. 26)
Pub: Reed Business Information
Contact: Jeff Greisch, President
Ed: Pamela Brill. **Description:** Science and nature toys are still popular with children. Kits allow kids to make candy, soap, grow miniature gardens, catch bugs and more. These hands-on kits have manufacturers watching trends to create more toys in this category.

6104 ■ *"Fabric, Craft Store Opens in North Bibb"* in Macon Telegraph (July 17, 2010)
Pub: Macon Telegraph
Ed: Linda S. Morris. **Description:** Ohio-based Jo-Ann Fabrics and Craft Stores opened a new shop in Macon, Georgia. The store will feature items for crafters, hobbyists, needle artists and seamstresses.

6105 ■ *"Greg Lueck: Glass Blowing"* in Inc. (Volume 32, December 2010, No. 10, pp. 36)
Pub: Inc. Magazine
Ed: April Joyner. **Description:** Profile of Greg Lueck, partner and COO of Centerstance, a tech consulting firm in Portland, Oregon. Lueck opened Firehouse Glass, a studio that provides workspace and equipment for glass blowers. He says glass blowing serves as a welcome counterbalance to the cerebral work he does at the office.

6106 ■ *"Hobbies Hold Fast"* in Playthings (Vol. 106, November 1, 2008, No. 1, pp. 6)
Pub: Reed Business Information
Contact: Jeff Greisch, President
Ed: Karyn M. Peterson. **Description:** Profile of the 24th Annual iHobby Expo is presented. The event is a combined trade and consumer show offering a look at the latest releases in die-cast collectibles, model railroads and aircraft, slot cars, remote control vehicles, rocketry, robotics, military toys, wood/plastic model kits, games, etc.

6107 ■ *Hobby Merchandiser Annual Trade Directory*
Pub: Hobby Publications, Inc.
Contact: Sandy Alberti, Director
URL(s): www.hobbymerchandiser.comwww.hobby-pub.com/. **Released:** Annual; December. **Covers:** Manufacturers, wholesalers, industry suppliers, and publishers of books and periodicals in the hobby trade industry. **Entries include:** For manufacturers--Company name, address, phone, name and title of contact. For wholesalers--Company name, address, phone, specialty, geographical area covered. For publishers--Company name, address, phone, name and title of contact; types of books, periodicals, or other media published or produced. For industry suppliers--Company name, address, phone, name and title of contact, product. **Arrangement:** Manufacturers, publishers, and suppliers are alphabetical; wholesalers are geographical. **Indexes:** Product.

6108 ■ *How to Market and Sell Your Art, Music, Photographs, and Handmade Crafts Online*
Pub: Atlantic Publishing Group, Inc.
Ed: Lee Rowley. **Released:** May 2008. **Price:** $24.95. **Description:** The book provides all the basics for starting and running an online store selling arts, crafts, photography or music. There are more than 300 Websites listed to help anyone market and promote their arts and/or crafts online.

6109 ■ *"Jo-Ann Fabric and Craft Stores Joins ArtFire.com to Offer Free Online Craft Marketplace"* in Internet Wire (January 26, 2010)
Pub: Comtex News Network, Inc.
Description: Jo-Ann Fabric and Craft Stores has entered into a partnership with ArtFire.com which will provide sewers and crafters all the tools they need in order to make and sell their products from an online venue.

6110 ■ *"Jo-Ann Launches Quilt Your Colors Contest to Celebrate National Sewing Month"* in Internet Wire (September 10, 2010)
Pub: Comtex
Description: Jo-Ann Fabric and Craft Stores featured a contest to create a quilt in order to promote National Sewing Month.

6111 ■ *Martha, Inc.*
Pub: John Wiley and Sons, Inc.
Ed: Christopher Byron. **Released:** 2002. **Price:** $28.00. **Description:** Profile of Martha Stewart's rise from working class to a billionaire businesswoman is presented. The book covers Stewart's power struggles and personal conflicts as well as her triumphs.

6112 ■ *"Paper Cache"* in Playthings (Vol. 106, October 1, 2008, No. 9, pp. 9)
Pub: Reed Business Information
Contact: Jeff Greisch, President
Ed: Karyn M. Peterson. **Description:** New toys in the paper play category are capturing children's imaginations with pirate ships and fairy houses and more they can build or design themselves. Hands-on paper and cardboard-based kits offer options for all ages.

6113 ■ *"Remodeled Stores Help Fabric Retailer Stitch Up Profit Growth"* in Investor's Business Daily (January 7, 2010, pp. A06)
Pub: Investor's Business Daily
Ed: Marilyn Much. **Description:** Overview of the successful plan implemented by Darrell Webb for Jo-Ann Fabric and Craft stores to stimulate growth and generate revenue; changes include better inventory controls and remodeling; statistical data included.

6114 ■ *"Retail Briefs - Dollar Store Opens in Long Leaf Mall"* in Star-News (November 5, 2010)
Pub: Star-News Media
Ed: Judy Royal. **Description:** Dollar Delight$ opened a new shop in Long Leaf Mall in Wilmington, North Carolina. The store will carry gift bags, balloons, party supplies, greeting cards, school supplies, health and beauty products, hardware, baby items, toys, Christmas goods, crafts, housewares and jewelry in its inventory.

6115 ■ *"Sewing Is a Life Skill; Teaching To Sew Is An Art"* in Virginia-Pilot (August 31, 2010)
Pub: Virginian-Pilot
Ed: Jamesetta Walker. **Description:** In conjunction with National Sewing Month, the American Sewing Guild is sponsoring a two-day workshop featuring Stephanie Kimura.

6116 ■ *"Sewing Shoppe Is All His"* in News & Observer (October 8, 2010)
Pub: News & Observer
Ed: Sue Stock. **Description:** Profile of My Sewing Shoppe, authorized sales and service dealers for Pfaff and Singer sewing machines, and also sells items for sewing, embroider and quilting. The store is located in Raleigh, North Carolina area.

6117 ■ *"Up, Up and Away"* in Small Business Opportunities (November 2007)
Pub: Harris Publications Inc.
Ed: Stan Roberts. **Description:** Profile of Miniature Aircraft USA, a mail order business providing kits to build flying machines priced from $500 to $2,500.

STATISTICAL SOURCES

6118 ■ RMA Annual Statement Studies
Pub: Risk Management Association
Contact: Kevin M. Blakey, President
Released: Annual. **Price:** $175.00 2006-07 edition, $105.00. **Description:** Contains composite balance sheets and income statements for more than 360 industries, including the accounting, auditing, and bookkeeping industries. Also contains five years of comparative historical data for discerning trends. Includes 16 commonly used ratios, computed for most of the size groupings for nearly every industry.

6119 ■ Size of Craft/Hobby Industry
Pub: MarketResearch.com
Released: 1992. **Price:** $500.00. **Description:** Report from the Hobby Industries of America (HIA) evaluating 1990 and 1991 sales volumes by six main craft categories, including art materials, florals and naturals, frames, hard crafts, needlecrafts, and sewing and notions. Also contains copies of all research materials, including questionnaires and regional data for manufacturers, retailers, and consumers.

TRADE PERIODICALS

6120 ■ American Craft
Pub: American Craft Council
Contact: Chris Amundsen, Executive Director
E-mail: camundsen@craftcouncil.org
URL(s): www.craftcouncil.org/magazine. **Released:** Bimonthly **Price:** $25, Individuals; $40, Other countries.

6121 ■ Annie's Plastic Canvas Magazine
Pub: The Needlecraft Shop L.L.C.
URL(s): www.anniesplasticcanvas.com/. **Released:** Bimonthly **Price:** $20, Individuals plus postage and processing; $25, Canada plus postage and processing.

6122 ■ Antique Bottle and Glass Collector
Pub: Antique Bottle and Glass Collector
URL(s): www.glswrk-auction.com. **Ed:** Ralph Finch. **Released:** Monthly **Price:** $32, Individuals 2nd class; $47, Individuals 1st class; $54, Individuals CAN; $95, Other countries by airmail.

6123 ■ Bead and Button
Pub: Kalmbach Publishing Co.
Contact: Gerald Butch Boettcher, President
E-mail: gboettcher@kalmbach.com
URL(s): www.beadandbutton.com. **Ed:** Ann Dee Allen. **Released:** Bimonthly **Price:** $28.95, Individuals; $42.95, Other countries; $55.95, Individuals 12 issues; $83.95, Other countries 12 issues; $79.95, Individuals 18 issues; $121.95, Other countries 18 issues.

6124 ■ Ceramics Monthly
Pub: American Ceramic Society
Contact: Charles Spahr, Executive Director
E-mail: cspahr@ceramics.org
URL(s): ceramicartsdaily.org/ceramics-monthly/. **Ed:** Cynthia Griffith, Sherman Hall. **Released:** 10/yr. **Price:** $34.95, Individuals; $40, Canada; $60, Other countries; $59.95, Two years; $75, Canada two years; $99, Other countries two years.

6125 ■ Country Home
Pub: Meredith Corp.
URL(s): www.countryhome.com. **Released:** Monthly; 10/yr. **Price:** $4.95, Individuals newstand; $21.97, Two years.

6126 ■ Craft Train News
Pub: Wm. K. Walthers Inc.
Description: Contains information such as prices and detailed descriptions on new model railroad products.

6127 ■ Crafts 'n things
Pub: Amos Press Inc.
Contact: Bruce D. Boyd, Chief Executive Officer
URL(s): www.craftsnthings.com. **Ed:** Abby Foster. **Released:** 6/yr. **Price:** $21.97, Individuals print and online; $19.97, Individuals online only; $29.47, Canada print and online; $36.97, Other countries print and online.

6128 ■ Discover Mid-America
Pub: Discovery Publications Inc.
URL(s): www.discoverypub.com. **Released:** Monthly

6129 ■ Doll Costuming
URL(s): www.jonespublishing.comwww.dollcostuming.net. **Released:** 6/yr. **Price:** $20, Individuals; $74.95, Two years; $89.95, Individuals 3 years.

6130 ■ Dragon Magazine
URL(s): www.wizards.comwww.wizards.com/default.asp?x=dnd/news/20051215b. **Released:** Monthly

6131 ■ Fine Woodworking
Pub: Taunton Press Inc.
Contact: John Lively, Chief Executive Officer
URL(s): www.finewoodworking.com. **Ed:** Timothy D. Schreiner. **Released:** 7/yr. **Price:** $34.95, U.S. and Canada; $59.95, U.S. and Canada two years; $83.95, U.S. and Canada three years.

6132 ■ Fired Arts & Crafts: The Bible of the Ceramic Hobbyists Since 1955
Contact: Joyce Greenholdt, Editor
E-mail: joyceg@jonespublishing.com
URL(s): www.firedartsandcrafts.com/. **Ed:** Joyce Greenholdt. **Released:** Monthly **Price:** $39.95, Individuals; $74.95, Two years; $84.95, Individuals 3 years.

6133 ■ Garden Railways
Pub: Kalmbach Publishing Co.
Contact: Gerald Butch Boettcher, President
E-mail: gboettcher@kalmbach.com
URL(s): grw.trains.com. **Ed:** Marc Horovitz. **Released:** Bimonthly **Price:** $29.95, Individuals; $39.95, Other countries; $56, Individuals 12 issues; $76, Other countries 12 issues; $80, Individuals 18 issues; $110, Other countries 18 issues; $37.95, Canada 6 issues; $69.95, Canada 12 issues; $99.95, Canada 18 issues.

6134 ■ Glass Craftsman
Pub: Arts & Media Inc.
URL(s): www.glasscraftsman.com. **Released:** Bimonthly **Price:** $19.95, Individuals; $39.95, Two years; $15.95, Other countries digital only; $29.90, Other countries digital, 2 years; $27.95, Other countries; $54.95, Other countries 2 years.

6135 ■ Glass Patterns Quarterly
Pub: Glass Patterns Quarterly Inc.
URL(s): www.glasspatterns.com. **Released:** Quarterly **Price:** $24, Individuals; $29, Other countries; $59, Other countries via air; $43, Two years; $53, Other countries 2 years; $118, Other countries 2 years, via air; $61, Individuals 3 years; $76, Other countries 3 years; $170, Other countries 3 years, via air.

6136 ■ Hobby Merchandiser
Pub: Hobby Publications Inc.
URL(s): www.hobbymerchandiser.com/. **Released:** 15/yr. **Price:** $20, Individuals; $35, Other countries surface mail; $120, Other countries airmail; $20, Individuals renewal.

6137 ■ Model Airplane News: The World's Premier R/C Modeling Magazine
Pub: Air Age Publishing Inc.
URL(s): www.modelairplanenews.com/. **Released:** Monthly **Price:** $24.95, Individuals.

6138 ■ Model Railroader
Pub: Kalmbach Publishing Co.
Contact: Gerald Butch Boettcher, President
E-mail: gboettcher@kalmbach.com
URL(s): mrr.trains.com. **Released:** Monthly **Price:** $42.95, Individuals; $77.95, Two years; $107.95, Individuals 3 years; $52.95, Canada; $97.95, Canada 2 years; $137.95, Canada 3 years.

6139 ■ Model Retailer: Resources for Successful Hobby Retailing
Pub: Kalmbach Publishing Co.
Contact: Gerald Butch Boettcher, President
E-mail: gboettcher@kalmbach.com
URL(s): www.modelretailer.com. **Ed:** Hal Miller. **Released:** Monthly **Price:** $85, Individuals; $85, Other countries surface mail.

6140 ■ Needlework Retailer
Pub: Yarn Tree Design Inc.
URL(s): yarntree.comneedleworkretailer.com/. **Released:** Bimonthly

6141 ■ Out Your Backdoor
Pub: Out Your Backdoor
URL(s): www.outyourbackdoor.com. **Ed:** Jeff Potter. **Released:** Monthly

6142 ■ Railroad Model Craftsman
Pub: Carstens Publications Inc.
Contact: Harold Carstens, President
URL(s): www.rrmodelcraftsman.com. **Ed:** William C. Schaumburg. **Released:** Monthly **Price:** $37.95, Individuals; $50, Other countries including Canada; $69.95, Two years; $94, Two years other countries.

6143 ■ Scrap & Stamp Arts
Pub: Scott Advertising & Publishing Co.
Contact: Jeanette Foxe, Manager
E-mail: jfoxe@scottpublications.com
URL(s): scottpublications.com/ssa/. **Released:** 8/yr. **Price:** $29.90, Individuals; $55, Two years; $45.90, Out of country; $87, Two years other countries.

6144 ■ Soft Dolls & Animals
Pub: Scott Advertising & Publishing Co.
Contact: Jeanette Foxe, Manager
E-mail: jfoxe@scottpublications.com
URL(s): scottpublications.com/catalog/product_info.php/products_id/149. **Released:** Bimonthly **Price:** $29.95, Individuals; $53.90, Two years; $41.95, Out of country non-US; $77.90, Two years non-US.

6145 ■ Uncoverings: The Research Papers of the American Quilt Study Group
Pub: American Quilt Study Group
Contact: Mary G. Persyn, President
URL(s): www.americanquiltstudygroup.org/publications.asp. **Ed:** Laurel Horton. **Released:** Annual **Price:** $20, Single issue.

VIDEOCASSETTES/AUDIOCASSETTES

6146 ■ Angel Crafts Video Vol. 1
Tapeworm Video Distributors
25876 The Old Road #141
Stevenson Ranch, CA 91381
Ph: (661)257-4904
Fax: (661)257-4820
Co. E-mail: sales@tapeworm.com
URL: http://www.tapeworm.com
Released: 1996. **Price:** $19.95. **Description:** Kathy Peterson provides instruction for creating six heirloom angels. **Availability:** VHS.

6147 ■ Crafts in Less Than 10 Minutes Video Vol. 1
Tapeworm Video Distributors
25876 The Old Road #141
Stevenson Ranch, CA 91381
Ph: (661)257-4904
Fax: (661)257-4820
Co. E-mail: sales@tapeworm.com
URL: http://www.tapeworm.com
Released: 1996. **Price:** $19.95. **Description:** Kathy Peterson provides instruction for creating nine fast and easy craft projects. **Availability:** VHS.

6148 ■ Kids Make Puppets: Easy Scarf Marionettes
Tapeworm Video Distributors
25876 The Old Road #141
Stevenson Ranch, CA 91381
Ph: (661)257-4904
Fax: (661)257-4820
Co. E-mail: sales@tapeworm.com
URL: http://www.tapeworm.com
Released: 19??. **Price:** $14.95. **Description:** Provides instruction for making marionettes from materials found at home. **Availability:** VHS.

6149 ■ Pets Crafts Video Vol. 1
Tapeworm Video Distributors
25876 The Old Road #141
Stevenson Ranch, CA 91381

Ph: (661)257-4904
Fax: (661)257-4820
Co. E-mail: sales@tapeworm.com
URL: http://www.tapeworm.com
Released: 1996. **Price:** $19.95. **Description:** Kathy Peterson provides instruction for creating seven pet projects. **Availability:** VHS.

6150 ■ Santa Crafts Video Vol. 1
Tapeworm Video Distributors
25876 The Old Road #141
Stevenson Ranch, CA 91381
Ph: (661)257-4904
Fax: (661)257-4820
Co. E-mail: sales@tapeworm.com
URL: http://www.tapeworm.com
Released: 1996. **Price:** $19.95. **Description:** Kathy Peterson provides instruction for creating five heirloom Santas. **Availability:** VHS.

6151 ■ The Secrets of Magic and Illusion
MPI Home Video
16101 S. 108th Ave.
Orland Park, IL 60467
Ph: (708)460-0555
Free: 800-323-0442
Fax: (708)873-3177
URL: http://www.mpihomevideo.com
Released: 1997. **Price:** $19.98. **Description:** Reveals the secrets of famous illusions including the Sword Suspension, Cards and Coins, and the Chinese Linking Rings. **Availability:** VHS.

6152 ■ Victorian Crafts Video Vol. 1
Tapeworm Video Distributors
25876 The Old Road #141
Stevenson Ranch, CA 91381
Ph: (661)257-4904
Fax: (661)257-4820
Co. E-mail: sales@tapeworm.com
URL: http://www.tapeworm.com
Released: 1996. **Price:** $19.95. **Description:** Kathy Peterson provides instruction for creating seven Victorian heirlooms. **Availability:** VHS.

TRADE SHOWS AND CONVENTIONS

6153 ■ Annual Dickens Christmas Show and Festivals Week
Leisure Time Unlimited, Inc.
708 Main St.
Myrtle Beach, SC 29577
Ph: (843)448-9483
Free: 800-261-5591
Fax: (843)626-1513
Co. E-mail: ltushows@sc.rr.com
URL: http://www.leisuretimeunlimited.com/
Contact: Brooke P. Baker, Show Manager
E-mail: dickensshow@sc.rr.com
URL(s): www.dickenschristmasshow.com/. **Price:** $8.50, adult; $4, children, ages 2-12; $13, multi-day ticket. **Frequency:** Annual. **Audience:** General public. **Principal Exhibits:** Crafts, art, paintings, gifts, and Christmas related items. **Dates and Locations:** , Convention Center. **Telecommunication Services:** dickensshow@sc.rr.com.

6154 ■ Atlantic Craft Trade Show
Nova Scotia Department of Economic Development
1660 Hollis St., Suite 600
Halifax, NS, Canada B3J 3C8
Ph: (902)424-0377
Fax: (902)424-7008
URL: http://www.gov.ns.ca/econ
URL(s): www.actshow.ca. **Frequency:** Annual. **Audience:** Craft, giftware, and apparel trade professionals. **Principal Exhibits:** Crafts and giftware, including porcelain, silver and pewter ware, jewelry, hand knits, hooked rugs, hand blown glass, toys; apparel, wood, and food products. **Dates and Locations:** World Trade and Convention Center. **Telecommunication Services:** acts@gov.ns.ca.

6155 ■ CHA Winter Convention and Trade Show
Craft and Hobby Association (CHA)
319 E 54th St.
Elmwood Park, NJ 07407
Ph: (201)835-1200
Free: 800-822-0494
Fax: (201)797-0657
Co. E-mail: info@craftandhobby.org
URL: http://www.craftandhobby.org
Contact: Steven Z. Berger, President
E-mail: sberger@craftandhobby.org
URL(s): www.chashow.org. **Price:** Pre-registered, members; $25. **Frequency:** Annual. **Audience:** Owners, corporate officers and buyers from craft, hobby, DIY stores, general merchandise stores, wholesalers, and professional crafters. **Principal Exhibits:** Crafts, ceramics, floral accessories, dollhouse miniatures, aromatics, art materials and frames, jewelry findings, fabrics, needlework and quilting supplies, home decor, rubber stamps, stencils and scrapbooking supplies.

6156 ■ Christmas Gift and Hobby Show
HSI Show Productions
PO Box 502797
Indianapolis, IN 46250
Ph: (317)576-9933
Free: 800-215-1700
Fax: (317)576-9955
Co. E-mail: info@hsishows.com
URL: http://www.hsishows.com
URL(s): www.christmasgiftandhobbyshow.com. **Price:** $10; $7, senior admission; $6, groups of twenty or more; free for children 12 and under. **Frequency:** Annual. **Audience:** General public. **Principal Exhibits:** Art, crafts, and giftware. **Dates and Locations:** , Indiana State Fairgrounds. **Telecommunication Services:** info@hsishows.com.

6157 ■ Holiday Fair
Textile Hall Corp.
PO Box 5823
Greenville, SC 29606
Ph: (864)233-2562
Fax: (864)233-0619
Co. E-mail: atmei@textilehall.com
Contact: Butler Mullins, Director
E-mail: bmullins@textilehall.com
URL(s): www.holidayfairgreenville.com/index.html. **Price:** $6, adult general admission; $5, group rate (15 or more) general admission; $4, seniors (60 or over) general admission; $3, seniors group rate (15 or more) general admission. **Frequency:** Annual. **Audience:** General public. **Principal Exhibits:** Arts and crafts. **Dates and Locations:** , Palmetto International Exposition Center. **Telecommunication Services:** kwarner@carolinafirstcenter.com.

6158 ■ Home Entertainment Show
Trigger Agency
3539 Clipper Mill Rd.
Baltimore, MD 21211
Free: 800-830-3976
Fax: (410)878-9911
Co. E-mail: info@triggeragency.com
URL: http://www.triggeragency.com/
Contact: Greg Nivens, President
E-mail: gnivens@triggeragency.com
URL(s): www.mooreamarketing.com. **Price:** $32, Pre-registered 3-day pass; $37, Onsite 3-day pass; $22, Pre-registered 1-day pass; $27, Onsite 1-day pass. **Frequency:** Biennial. **Audience:** Consumers, trade and press. **Principal Exhibits:** Home theater and high-fidelity audio equipment, supplies, and services. **Telecommunication Services:** gnivens@mooreamarketing.com.

6159 ■ iHobby Expo
Peak Management Solutions
PO Box 315
Butler, NJ 07405-0315
Ph: (973)283-4680

Fax: (973)838-7124
URL: http://www.rchta.org
Contact: Pat Koziol, Executive Director
E-mail: pkoziol@rchta.org
URL(s): www.ihobbyexpo.com. **Price:** $10, seniors over 65; $12, adults. **Frequency:** Annual. **Audience:** Hobby retailers, distributors, general public. **Principal Exhibits:** Model kits and hobby equipment, supplies, and services, radio control products and accessories, model railroad products and accessories, aerodynamics, games, rockets, die cast, adhesives, plastic models, miniatures, tools, slot cars, astronomy, paints, publications, apparel, collectables, kites, science/educational, videos, and speciality items.

6160 ■ Memories Expo
Offinger Management Co.
1100-H Brandywine Blvd.
Zanesville, OH 43701-7303
Ph: (740)452-4541
Free: 888-878-6334
Fax: (740)452-2552
Co. E-mail: omc.info@offinger.com
URL: http://www.offinger.com
URL(s): www.memoriesexpo.com. **Price:** $10, Non-members one day; $15, Non-members. **Frequency:** 5/year. **Audience:** Trade and public. **Principal Exhibits:** Scrapbook supplies. **Telecommunication Services:** memories@offinger.com.

6161 ■ Society of Craft Designers Educational Seminar (SCD)
Offinger Management Co.
1100-H Brandywine Blvd.
Zanesville, OH 43701-7303
Ph: (740)452-4541
Free: 888-878-6334
Fax: (740)452-2552
Co. E-mail: omc.info@offinger.com
URL: http://www.offinger.com
URL(s): www.craftdesigners.org. **Frequency:** Annual. **Audience:** Designers, manufacturers, editors, and publishers. **Principal Exhibits:** Craft designer showcases and education. **Telecommunication Services:** scd@offinger.com.

FRANCHISES AND BUSINESS OPPORTUNITIES

6162 ■ Hobbytown USA
Hobby Town Unlimited Inc.
1233 Libra Dr.
Lincoln, NE 68512
Ph: (402)434-5064
Free: 800-858-7370
Fax: (402)434-5055
Co. E-mail: nichole@hobbytown.com
URL: http://www.hobbytown.com
Description: full-line hobby stores featuring model railroading, models, radio controlled vehicles, games, collectible cards, die cast, toys, gifts, accessories and more. provides store owners with a comprehensive package of systems and services to be competitive in the hobby and entertainment industries. **No. of Franchise Units:** 175. **Founded:** 1980.. **Franchised:** 1986. **Equity Capital Needed:** $75,000-$200,000 cash investment; total investment $250,000-$350,000. **Franchise Fee:** $19,500 ($15,000 veterans). **Financial Assistance:** 30-V, FRA handbook. **Training:** 3 week comprehensive training program, including home office and onsite field training.

6163 ■ Pinch a Penny Inc.
PO Box 6025
Clearwater, FL 33758
Ph: (727)785-8841
Free: 888-557-3669
Fax: (727)784-9314
Co. E-mail: info@pinchapenny.com
URL: http://www.pinchapenny.com
Contact: John Thomas, President
URL(s): www.pinchapenny.com/franchise. **Description:** Swimming pool supplies & spa supplies. **No. of Franchise Units:** 213. **No. of Company-Owned Units:** 2. **Founded:** 1975. **Franchised:** 1976. **Equity Capital Needed:** $180,000-$350,000. **Franchise**

Fee: $30,000. **Financial Assistance:** For new stores for a limited time. **Training:** Offers 4 weeks training in Clearwater, FL.

6164 ■ Remote Control Hobbies
5435 Boatworks Dr., Ste. 1
Littleton, CO 80126
Ph: (303)804-0470
Fax: (303)531-5273
Description: Remote control hobby vehicles, parts & accessories. **No. of Franchise Units:** 12. **Founded:** 2003.. **Franchised:** 2004. **Equity Capital Needed:** $111,900-$315,900. **Franchise Fee:** $18,000-$22,000. **Royalty Fee:** 2.5%. **Training:** Provides 7 weeks training at headquarters, 6 weeks onsite with ongoing support.

LIBRARIES

6165 ■ American Craft Council Library
1224 Marshall St. NE, Ste. 200
Minneapolis, MN 55413
Ph: (612)206-3100
Fax: (612)355-2330
Co. E-mail: library@craftcouncil.org
URL: http://www.craftcouncil.org/library
Contact: Jessica Shaykett, Librarian
URL(s): www.craftcouncil.org. **Scope:** 20th-century contemporary fine crafts - fiber, clay, metal, wood, glass, enamel, plastics, mixed media; decorative arts; design. **Services:** Copying; library open to the public (Monday to Friday). **Founded:** 1956. **Holdings:** 6400 books; 700 bound periodical volumes; 7000 exhibition catalogs; 200 videocassettes. **Subscriptions:** 100 journals and other serials.

6166 ■ American Museum of Magic - Lund Memorial Library
107 E. Michigan Ave.
Marshall, MI 49068
Ph: (269)781-7570
Co. E-mail: info@americanmuseumofmagic.org
URL: http://www.americanmuseumofmagic.org
Scope: Conjuring, confidence games, superstition. **Services:** Library open to the public with restrictions. **Founded:** 1978. **Holdings:** 15,000 books; 30,000 magazines; 150,000 letters; 3000 posters; newspaper clippings; programs; photographs; films; manuscripts. **Subscriptions:** 25 journals and other serials.

6167 ■ American Society of Artists, Inc. - Resource Center
Box 1326
Palatine, IL 60078
Ph: (312)751-2500
Co. E-mail: asoa@webtv.net
URL: http://community-2.webtv.net/ASOA/ASA/
URL(s): www.americansocietyofartists.us. **Scope:** Art, crafts, supplies. **Services:** Lectures; demonstrations; seminars; workshops. **Founded:** 1978. **Holdings:** 50 volumes; 43 VF drawers. **Subscriptions:** 11 journals and other serials. **Telecommunication Services:** asoaartists@aol.com; contact@americansocietyofartists.us.

6168 ■ California College of the Arts Libraries - Meyer Library
5212 Broadway
Oakland, CA 94618
Ph: (510)594-3658
Co. E-mail: meyerlib@cca.edu
URL: http://library.cca.edu
Contact: Donald Smith, Manager
Scope: Art, architecture, design, humanities. **Services:** Library limited to the CCA community (specialized research by appointment). **Founded:** 1907. **Holdings:** 62,000 volumes; 150,000 slides and pictures; 100 lin.ft. of archival material. **Subscriptions:** 275 journals and other serials. **Telecommunication Services:** jwoo@cca.edu.

6169 ■ Craft Council of Newfoundland and Labrador Library
Devon House Craft Ctr.
59 Duckworth St.
St. John's, NL, Canada A1C 1E6
Ph: (709)753-2749

Fax: (709)753-2766
Co. E-mail: info@craftcouncil.nl.ca
URL: http://www.craftcouncil.nl.ca
Scope: Craft promotion and development. **Services:** Copying; library open to the public. **Holdings:** 400 books; 20 serials; 50 reports. **Subscriptions:** 10 journals and other serials.

6170 ■ Ferrum College - Blue Ridge Heritage Archive
20 Museum Dr.
Ferrum College
Ferrum, VA 24088-9001
Ph: (540)365-4412
Co. E-mail: bri@ferrum.edu
URL: http://www.blueridgeinstitute.org
Contact: Vaughan Webb, Assistant Director
Scope: Folk culture, legends, crafts, music, and customs of Virginia, especially the Blue Ridge Mountain area, 1780 to present. **Services:** Copying; archive open to the public by appointment. **Founded:** 1973. **Holdings:** 4000 musical performances; 500 photographic images; videotapes; audio tapes; CDs; DVDs; phonograph records; manuscripts; films; books; correspondence; transcripts.

6171 ■ Haystack Mountain School of Crafts Library
PO Box 518
Deer Isle, ME 04627-0518
Ph: (207)348-2306
Fax: (207)348-2307
Co. E-mail: haystack@haystack-mtn.org
URL: http://www.haystack-mtn.org/
Contact: Lissa Hunter, President
Scope: Fine arts, ceramics, weaving, glassblowing, flat glass, jewelry, surface and textile design, wood, blacksmithing, printmaking, papermaking, weaving. **Services:** Library open to the public on a limited basis. **Holdings:** 1000 books. **Subscriptions:** 20 journals and other serials.

6172 ■ John Michael Kohler Arts Center Resource Center
608 New York Ave.
Box 489
Sheboygan, WI 53081
Ph: (920)458-6144, x-147
Fax: (920)458-4473
Co. E-mail: rc@jmkac.org
URL: http://www.jmkac.org
Contact: Alison Loewen, Librarian Archivist
Scope: Art environments; self-taught vernacular art; contemporary art, contemporary crafts, non-traditional photography. **Services:** Onsite assistance available by appointment; reference and research services, including image reproduction services, available by phone or email. **Founded:** 1968. **Holdings:** 5000 monographs; 150 serials; 90,000 images of Arts Center programming including permanent collection objects and works in exhibitions. **Subscriptions:** 50 serials.

6173 ■ Manitoba Crafts Museum & Library - Gladys Chown Memorial Library
1B-183 Kennedy St.
Winnipeg, MB, Canada R3C 1S6
Ph: (204)487-6117
Co. E-mail: info@mcml.ca
URL: http://www.mcml.ca
Contact: Andrea Reichert, Curator
Scope: Crafts - weaving, pottery, embroidery, knitting, crochet, quilting, paper, wood, Inuit and Aborijinal, polymer clay, lace; craft design; color theory; history of craft. **Services:** Copying; Library open to the public. **Founded:** 1928. **Holdings:** 3500 volumes; 2000 slides; 9000 artifacts. **Subscriptions:** 4 journals and other serials.

6174 ■ Museum of Contemporary Craft Library
724 NW Davis St.
Portland, OR 97209
Ph: (503)223-2654

Fax: (503)223-0190
Co. E-mail: info@museumofcontemporarycraft.org
URL: http://www.museumofcontemporarycraft.org/
Contact: Linda Brower, Treasurer
Scope: Ceramics and pottery, weaving and textiles, Pacific Northwest craftsmen, contemporary designers, metalwork and jewelry, contemporary glass, sculpture, woodworking, architecture. **Services:** Library open during Museum hours. **Founded:** 1937. **Holdings:** 420 books; 74 bound and 125 unbound periodical volumes. **Telecommunication Services:** nnathan@museumofcontemporarycraft.org.

6175 ■ Oregon College of Art and Craft Library
8245 SW Barnes Rd.
Portland, OR 97225
Ph: (503)297-5544
Free: 800-390-0632
Fax: (503)297-9651
Co. E-mail: library@ocac.edu
URL: http://ocac.edu/campus-life/library
Contact: Lori Johnson, Director, Library Services
Scope: Textiles, ceramics, woodworking, drawing and design, metals, book arts, photography, calligraphy, painting, sculpture, art history, art criticism. **Services:** Interlibrary loan; library open to the public. **Founded:** 1907. **Holdings:** 9000 books; 28,000 slides. **Subscriptions:** 90 journals and other serials. **Telecommunication Services:** ljohnson@ocac.edu.

6176 ■ San Francisco Public Library - Bernard Osher Foundation - Art, Music & Recreation Center
100 Larkin St., 4th Fl.
San Francisco, CA 94102
Ph: (415)557-4525
Fax: (415)557-4524
Co. E-mail: info@sfpl.org
URL: http://www.sfpl.org
Contact: Mark Hall, Manager
URL(s): sfpl.org/index.php?pg=0200001401. **Scope:** Arts - visual, graphic; sports and recreation; photography; architecture; arts and crafts; performing arts; music - orchestral, chamber, opera, popular, folk, jazz. **Services:** Center open to the public. **Holdings:** Books; serials; scores. **Telecommunication Services:** artmusicrec@sfpl.org.

6177 ■ University of Hartford - William H. Mortensen Library - Anne Bunce Cheney Art Collection
200 Bloomfield Ave.
West Hartford, CT 06117
Ph: (860)768-4397
Fax: (860)768-5298
Co. E-mail: bigazzi@hartford.edu
URL: http://library.hartford.edu/about_libraries/info_
  pol/coll_cheney.aspx
Contact: Anna B. Bigazzi, Librarian, Art
Scope: Art history, architecture, art education, applied art, decorative arts, crafts, photography, typography. **Services:** Interlibrary loan; copying; Library open to the public. **Founded:** 1963. **Holdings:** 24,000 books; 3200 bound periodical volumes; 19,000 mounted reproductions; 2500 pamphlets; CD-ROMs; videos. **Subscriptions:** 70 journals and other serials.

RESEARCH CENTERS

6178 ■ Canadian Crafts Federation (CCF)—Fédération canadienne des métiers d'art (FCMA)
PO Box 1231
Fredericton, NB, Canada E3B 5C8
Ph: (506)464-9560
Fax: (506)457-6010
Co. E-mail: info@canadiancraftsfederation.ca
URL: http://canadiancraftsfederation.typepad.com/
  canadian-crafts-federatn
Contact: Deborah Dumka, President
Founded: 1998. **Telecommunication Services:** dumkasanford@telus.net.

6179 ■ Museum of International Folk Art (MOIFA)—El Museo de Arte Popular Internacional
PO Box 2087
Santa Fe, NM 87504-2087
Ph: (505)476-1200
Fax: (505)476-1300

Co. E-mail: marsha.bol@state.nm.us
URL: http://www.internationalfolkart.org
Contact: Marsha C. Bol, Director
Founded: 1953. **Publications:** *Exhibition Catalogs*; *Reports Curriculum for K-12*. **Educational Activities:** Docent-led tours (Daily), for the public, artist demonstrations; MOIFA Exhibitions (Weekly), of traditional arts; Gallery talks (Periodic); Lecture/film series, in relation to exhibits, family and school programs; Public school outreach programs; Staff development programs; Workshops, demonstrations; Teacher Training Institute for Elementary Teachers. **Telecommunication Services:** internationalfolkart@gmail.com.

START-UP INFORMATION

6180 ■ Setting Up Your Ceramic Studio: Ideas and Plans from Working Artists
Pub: Lark Books

Ed: Virginia Scotchie. **Released:** March 2005. **Price:** $45.00. **Description:** Floor plans and advice for setting up a creative ceramics studio are provided, focusing on equipment, workflow, and safety issues.

TRADE PERIODICALS

6181 ■ Small Business Opportunities: Money Making Ideas for Entrepreneurs
Pub: Harris Publications Inc.

URL(s): www.sbomag.com/. **Ed:** Susan Rakowski. **Released:** Bimonthly; (plus 4 special editions). **Price:** $14.97, U.S. and Canada; $29.94, Other countries.

TRADE SHOWS AND CONVENTIONS

6182 ■ American Quilt Study Group Seminar
American Quilt Study Group (AQSG)
1610 L St.
Lincoln, NE 68508-2509
Ph: (402)477-1181
Fax: (402)477-1181
Co. E-mail: aqsg2@americanquiltstudygroup.org
URL: http://www.americanquiltstudygroup.org
Contact: Mary G. Persyn, President

URL(s): www.americanquiltstudygroup.org. **Frequency:** Annual. **Principal Exhibits:** Quilt-related articles.

6183 ■ Handmade - A Division of the San Francisco International Gift Fair
George Little Management, LLC
1133 Westchester Ave., Ste. N136
White Plains, NY 10606
Ph: (914)421-3200
Free: 800-272-SHOW
Co. E-mail: cathy_steel@glmshows.com
URL: http://www.glmshows.com

URL(s): www.sfigf.com. **Frequency:** Semiannual. **Audience:** Specialty, department, stationery, juvenile, and jewelry stores, interior designers, gift shops, mail order catalogs, importers/distributors of home products. **Principal Exhibits:** Handmade merchandise, including functional and decorative home furnishings, fashion accessories, jewelry plus an array of other unique craft objects. All merchandise is selected by a panel of craft professionals for uniqueness, originality and marketability.

FRANCHISES AND BUSINESS OPPORTUNITIES

6184 ■ Color Me Mine Franchising, Inc.
Versent Inc.
3722 San Fernando Rd.
Glendale, CA 91204
Ph: (818)291-5900
Free: 888-265-6764
Fax: (818)240-9712

Description: Paint-your-own ceramics studio. **No. of Franchise Units:** 142. **Founded:** 1992.. **Franchised:** 1996. **Equity Capital Needed:** $50,000 of a total investment of an estimated $145,000. **Franchise Fee:** $30,000. **Financial Assistance:** Yes. **Training:** Yes.

6185 ■ Dream Dinners Inc.
PO Box 889
Snohomish, WA 98291
Ph: (425)397-3511
Fax: (425)397-7211

Description: Do-it-yourself home meal preparation. **No. of Franchise Units:** 234. **No. of Company-Owned Units:** 2. **Founded:** 2002.. **Franchised:** 2003. **Equity Capital Needed:** $245,000-$367,000. **Franchise Fee:** $35,000. **Royalty Fee:** 6%. **Training:** Provides 1 week at headquarters, 2 days at franchisees location with ongoing support.

6186 ■ GourMade Franchise
7060 Koll Center Pky., Ste. 320
Pleasanton, CA 94566
Ph: (925)846-4774
Fax: (925)484-3324

Description: Meal assembly and meals-to-go. **No. of Company-Owned Units:** 1. **Founded:** 2004.. **Franchised:** 2006. **Equity Capital Needed:** $141,000-$256,000. **Franchise Fee:** $20,000. **Royalty Fee:** 5%.

6187 ■ Mr. Food No-Fuss Meals
NFM Franchise, LLC
1770 NW 64th St., Ste. 500
Ft. Lauderdale, FL 33309
Ph: (954)938-0400
Fax: (954)938-2005

Description: Make-and-take meal assembly. **No. of Franchise Units:** 6. **No. of Company-Owned Units:** 1. **Founded:** 2004.. **Franchised:** 2006. **Equity Capital Needed:** $350,000 net worth, including $75,000 in liquid assets. **Franchise Fee:** $35,000. **Training:** Yes.

6188 ■ Super Suppers
6100 Camp Bowie Blvd.
Fort Worth, TX 76132
Ph: (817)732-6100
Fax: (817)732-6106

Description: Do-it-yourself home meal preparation. **No. of Franchise Units:** 206. **No. of Company-Owned Units:** 1. **Founded:** 1986.. **Franchised:** 2004. **Equity Capital Needed:** $175,400-$263,200. **Franchise Fee:** $35,000. **Royalty Fee:** 5%. **Training:** Offers 1 week at headquarters, 3 days at franchisees location, regional seminars and ongoing support.

6189 ■ Wacky Bear Factory Express
5953 W Park Ave., Ste. L13
Houma, LA 70360
Ph: (985)872-1212
Fax: (985)872-1357

Description: Custom stuffed toy animals & related accessories. **No. of Company-Owned Units:** 3. **Founded:** 2000.. **Franchised:** 2004. **Equity Capital Needed:** $150,500-$187,500. **Franchise Fee:** $30,000. **Royalty Fee:** 4%. **Training:** Training includes 2 weeks at headquarters and ongoing support.

DIRECTORIES OF EDUCATIONAL PROGRAMS

6190 ■ *International Association of Credit Card Investigators--Membership Directory*
Pub: International Association of Financial Crimes Investigators
Contact: George E. Curtis, Director
URL(s): www.iafci.org. **Released:** Annual **Covers:** Approximately 3,500 firms and individuals involved in investigating fraudulent credit card use who are members of the International Association of Credit Card Investigators. **Entries include:** Contact information. **Arrangement:** Alphabetical by name. **Indexes:** Geographical; alphabetical by firm name.

REFERENCE WORKS

6191 ■ *All About Credit*
Pub: Kaplan Publishing
Ed: Deborah McNaughton. **Released:** April 1999. **Price:** $15.95. **Description:** Debt solution to specific credit problems for individuals denied credit, trying to mortgage a home, problems with creditors, and bankruptcy.

6192 ■ *"At Wine Kiosk, Show ID, Face Camera, Swipe Card and Blow" in Pittsburgh Post-Gazette (November 28, 2010)*
Pub: Pittsburgh-Post Gazette
Ed: Dennis B. Roddy. **Description:** New technology installed on wine kiosks enables sellers to abide by the law. This technology tests blood alcohol levels and warns people if they have recently used a mouthwash before testing.

6193 ■ *BIN Number Directory of All Visa/Mastercard Issuing Banks*
Pub: Fraud & Theft Information Bureau
Contact: Pearl Sax, Owner
E-mail: pearlsax@fraudandtheftinfo.com
URL(s): www.fraudandtheftinfo.com. **Ed:** Pearl Sax. **Released:** Annual; January. **Price:** $1175, Individuals postpaid print edition; $5075, Individuals on CD-ROM, postpaid. **Covers:** About 30,000 banks worldwide issuing Visa and Mastercard credit cards. **Entries include:** Name of issuing bank, bank identification number, address, phone. BIN numbers, the digits on credit cards that identify a credit card holder's issuing bank are also called prefix numbers and ISO numbers. Directory is used by merchants to prevent fraud by verifying that customer is actually the cardholder. **Arrangement:** Numerical.

6194 ■ *Chain of Blame: How Wall Street Caused the Mortgage and Credit Crisis*
Pub: John Wiley & Sons, Inc.
Ed: Paul Muolo, Mathew Padilla. **Released:** 2009. **Price:** $27.95. **Description:** The book describes how risky loans given irresponsibly put big investment banks at the center of the subprime crisis.

6195 ■ *"Collection Industry Fights Stigma, Lagging Payments" in Crain's Cleveland Business (Vol. 30, June 8, 2009, No. 22, pp. 15)*
Pub: Crain Communications, Inc.
Ed: Joel Hammond. **Description:** John Murray, co-owner and president of JP Recovery Services Inc. in Rocky River, Ohio discusses the burden of the collection industry during a financial crisis like a recession. Statistical data included.

6196 ■ *"Cost of Business Banking May Soon Go Up" in Baltimore Business Journal (Vol. 28, October 29, 2010, No. 25, pp. 1)*
Pub: Baltimore Business Journal
Ed: Gary Haber. **Description:** Experts in the financial industry expect banks to charge credit card transactions, especially to small business owners and consumers to recover about $11 million in lost revenue annually. Banks are expected to charge old fees and new ones, including $5 to $10 a month for a checking account.

6197 ■ *"Credit Card Crackdown" in Business Journal-Portland (Vol. 24, November 23, 2007, No. 38, pp. 1)*
Pub: American City Business Journals, Inc.
Ed: Andy Giegerich. **Description:** Oregon's U.S. Senator Ron Wyden is sponsoring Credit Card Safety Act of 2007, a bill that requires credit card companies to reduce the jargon of credit card agreements and require the Federal Reserve Board to launch a public education campaign among credit card users. The legislation will also impose a rating system for credit card contracts with five being the safest for consumers to use.

6198 ■ *"Curbing the Debt Collector" in Business Journal-Portland (Vol. 24, October 5, 2007, No. 32, pp. 1)*
Pub: American City Business Journals, Inc.
Ed: Andy Giegerich. **Description:** Republican representative Sal Esquivel, who had a bad personal experience with a Houston collector, is developing legislation that would give the state attorney general's office enforcement powers over debt collecting agencies. The existing Oregon legislation concerning the debt collection industry is also discussed.

6199 ■ *"Economic Trends for Small Business" in Small Business Economic Trends (April 2008, pp. 1)*
Pub: National Federation of Independent Business
Ed: William C. Dunkelberg, Holly Wade. **Description:** Summary of economic trends for small businesses in the U.S. is presented. Economic indicators such as capital spending, inventories and sales, inflation, and profits are given. Analysis of credit markets is also provided.

6200 ■ *"End of the Beginning" in Canadian Business (Vol. 81, November 10, 2008, No. 19, pp. 17)*
Pub: Rogers Media Ltd.
Ed: David Wolf. **Description:** The freeze in the money markets and historic decline in equity markets around the world finally forced governments into aggressive coordinated action. The asset price inflation brought on by cheap credit will now work in reverse and the tightening of credit will be difficult economically. Canada is exposed to the fallout everywhere, given that the U.S, the U.K. and Japan buy 30 percent of Canada's output.

6201 ■ *"Fees Fueling Frustration for Region's Gas Retailers" in Business First Buffalo (December 7, 2007, pp. 1)*
Pub: American City Business Journals, Inc.
Ed: David Bertola. **Description:** Credit card fees are a major cause of concern to gas retailers along with higher gasoline prices. Statistical details included.

6202 ■ *The Girl's Guide to Building a Million-Dollar Business*
Pub: AMACOM
Ed: Susan Wilson Solovic. **Released:** 2008. **Price:** $21.95. **Description:** Success plan for women business owners; the book includes tips for determination, managing changing relationships, keeping employees and customers happy, getting and maintaining credit, overcoming gender bias, and creating a good business plan and solid brand.

6203 ■ *"A New FICO Scoring Model: Get Ready For Changes That Could Affect Your Score" in Black Enterprise (Vol. 38, March 2008, No. 8)*
Pub: Earl G. Graves Publishing Co. Inc.
Ed: Sheiresa McRae. **Description:** Fair Isaac Corporation, creator of the FICO credit score has developed a new scoring model that provides a more accurate way for lenders to determine a borrower's creditworthiness.

6204 ■ *"New Money" in Entrepreneur (Vol. 36, February 2008, No. 2, pp. 62)*
Pub: Entrepreneur Media Inc.
Ed: C.J. Prince. **Description:** Tips on how to handle business finance, with regard to the tightened credit standards imposed by leading institutions, are provided. These include: selling receivables, margining blue chips, and selling purchase orders.

6205 ■ *"New Rule Rankles In Jersey" in Philadelphia Business Journal (Vol. 30, September 16, 2011, No. 31, pp. 1)*
Pub: American City Business Journals Inc.
Ed: Jeff Blumenthal. **Description:** A new rule in New Jersey which taxes out-of-state companies that conduct business in the state earned the ire of several banks, mortgage lenders and credit card companies and prompted opponents to threaten to file lawsuits. The new rule is an amendment to New Jersey Division of Taxation's corporate business tax regulation and is retroactive to 2002. Details are given.

6206 ■ *"Prepaid Cards and State Unclaimed Property Laws" in Franchise Law Journal (Vol. 27, Summer 2007, No. 1, pp. 23)*
Pub: American Bar Association
Contact: Carolyn Lamm, President
Ed: Phillip W. Bohl, Kathryn J. Bergstrom, Kevin J. Moran. **Description:** Unredeemed value of electronic

prepaid stored-value credit cards for retail purchases is known as breakage. Laws governing unclaimed property as it relates to these gift cards is covered.

6207 ■ "Small Business Credit Conditions" in Small Business Economic Trends (April 2008, pp. 12)
Pub: National Federation of Independent Business
Ed: William C. Dunkelberg, Holly Wade. Description: Graphs and tables that present the credit conditions of small businesses in the U.S. are provided. The tables include figures on availability of loans, interest rates, and expected credit conditions.

6208 ■ "Small Business Credit Conditions" in Small Business Economic Trends (February 2008, pp. 12)
Pub: National Federation of Independent Business
Ed: William C. Dunkelberg, Holly Wade. Description: Graphs and tables that present the credit conditions of small businesses in the U.S. are provided. The tables include figures on availability of loans, interest rates, and expected credit conditions.

6209 ■ "Small Business Credit Conditions" in Small Business Economic Trends (January 2008, pp. 12)
Pub: National Federation of Independent Business
Description: Graphs representing loan availability and interest rates among U.S. small businesses surveyed from January 1986 to December 2007 are given. Tables showing regular borrowers, availability of loans, satisfied borrowing needs, expected credit conditions, relative interest rate paid by regular borrowers, and actual interest rate paid on short-term loans by borrowers are also presented.

6210 ■ "State Targets Credit Fixers" in Business Journal-Portland (Vol. 24, October 12, 2007, No. 33, pp. 1)
Pub: American City Business Journals, Inc.
Ed: Andy Giegerich, Justin Matlick. Description: Number of companies that offer quick fix to consumers is growing; the State of Oregon is considering rules to target them. A group working on a study in the state's mortgage lending regulations could craft bills to be examined for legislative session in February 2008.

6211 ■ "Summary. Economic Trends for Small Business" in Small Business Economic Trends (March 2008, pp. 1)
Pub: National Federation of Independent Business
Ed: William C. Dunkelberg, Holly Wade. Description: Summary of economic trends for small businesses in the U.S. is provided. Economic indicators such as capital spending, inventories and sales, inflation, and profits are given. Analysis of credit markets is also provided.

6212 ■ "Summary. Economic Trends for Small Business" in Small Business Economic Trends (February 2008, pp. 1)
Pub: National Federation of Independent Business
Ed: William C. Dunkelberg, Holly Wade. Description: Summary of economic trends for small businesses in the U.S. is provided. Economic indicators such as capital spending, inventories and sales, inflation, and profits are given. Analysis of credit markets is also provided.

6213 ■ "Survival Guide: There Can Be an Upside to Managing a Downturn" in Canadian Business (Vol. 81, November 10, 2008, No. 19, pp. 54)
Pub: Rogers Media Ltd.
Ed: Sharda Prashad. Description: Canada-based Foxy is already limiting its exposure to retailers who could be a credit problem in case of recession. Retirement Life Communities is entering into fixed-rate and fixed-term loans for them to have sufficient financing to grow. Business owners need to realize that customers want more for less.

6214 ■ "Travel Rewards Take Off" in Inc. (Vol. 33, October 2011, No. 8, pp. 46)
Pub: Inc. Magazine
Ed: Matthew DeLuca. Description: Credit card companies are offering travel reward cards with special perks, including sign-up bonuses; three such cards are described.

6215 ■ The Trillion Dollar Meltdown: Easy Money, High Rollers, and the Great Credit Crash
Pub: Public Affairs
Ed: Charles R. Morris. Released: 2009. Price: $22.95. Description: Former banker believes that Wall Street and the financial community have too much power in America. He estimates that writedowns and defaults of residential mortgages, commercial mortgages, junk bonds, leveraged loans, credit cards, and complex securitized bonds could reach $1 trillion.

6216 ■ The Visa Approval Backlog and Its Impact on American Small Business: Congressional Hearing
Pub: DIANE Publishing Company
Ed: Donald A. Manzullo. Released: July 2006. Price: $30.00. Description: Information regarding the Congressional hearing involving the Visa approval backlog is discussed.

TRADE PERIODICALS

6217 ■ Bankcard Barometer
Pub: RAM Research Group
Ed: Robert B. McKinley, Editor. Released: Monthly. Price: $1295, individuals. Description: Provides proprietary statistical data on specific U.S. credit card issuers, including gross receivables, gross accounts, delinquency rate (30/60 day), attrition rate (voluntary/involuntary), charge-offs, recoveries, acquisitions, average balance for standard and gold accounts, number of standard and gold cards, average cash advance for gold and standard accounts, active accounts, interest income, number of business cards, non-interest income, card/merchant processor, bankruptcy losses, fraud losses, average portfolio A.P.R.

6218 ■ Bankcard Update
Pub: RAM Research Group
Ed: Robert B. McKinley, Editor. Released: Monthly. Price: $1295, individuals. Description: Focuses on the pricing and marketing of bank credit cards. Covers standard, gold, secured, and business bank credit cards from more than 1,000 issuers (500 monitored on a monthly basis) and provides national and regional breakouts. Recurring features include news of research and departments titled Top 10 Issuer

Scorecard, National Top 25 Low-Card Survey, Weighted and Unweighted A.P.R./Fee Averages for Standard and Gold Cards, Average Delinquency Rates, Average Charge-Off Rates, Average Balance Per Account, Average Volume Per Account, Average Bankruptcy Losses, Late Payment Fees,.

6219 ■ Cardfax
Pub: SourceMedia Inc.
Ed: Andrea McKenna Findlay, Editor. Released: Daily. Description: Contains news of the credit and debit card industry. Emphasizes company plans, ventures, programs, performance, competition, and legal and regulatory issues.

VIDEOCASSETTES/ AUDIOCASSETTES

6220 ■ Credit Card Basics: Play Now Pay Forever
Cambridge Educational
c/o Films Media Group
132 West 31st Street, 17th Floor
Ste. 124
New York, NY 10001
Free: 800-257-5126
Fax: (609)671-0266
Co. E-mail: custserve@films.com
URL: http://www.cambridgeol.com
Released: 1992. Price: $79.00. Description: Defines terms and explains procedures associated with credit. Emphasizes the need to keep accounts current in order to maintain a good credit rating. Availability: VHS.

6221 ■ Credit Cards: Living with Plastic
The Learning Seed
641 W. Lake St., Ste. 301
Chicago, IL 60661
Free: 800-634-4941
Fax: (800)998-0854
Co. E-mail: info@learningseed.com
URL: http://www.learningseed.com
Released: 199?. Price: $89.00. Description: How to evaluate and "shop" for the credit card that best fits your needs. Discusses how to match a credit card to your spending patterns, grace periods, computing interest, annual percentage rates, yearly fees, and cardholders' legal rights. Availability: VHS.

6222 ■ Credit Connection
Commonwealth Films, Inc.
223 Commonwealth Ave.
Boston, MA 02116
Ph: (617)262-5634
Fax: (617)262-6948
Co. E-mail: info@commonwealthfilms.com
URL: http://www.commonwealthfilms.com
Released: 1986. Price: $295.00. Description: Increase your knowledge of the use of credit in the business world. Availability: VHS; 3/4 U.

LIBRARIES

6223 ■ Loan Brokers Association Information Services
917 S. Park St.
Owosso, MI 48867-4422
Contact: Ben Campbell, Director
Scope: Loan brokers, loan consulting, credit repair, lending, credit cards, venture capital. Services: Copying; SDI; library to members or by permission.

START-UP INFORMATION

6224 ■ *How to Start a Bankruptcy Forms Processing Service*
Pub: Graphico Publishing Company
Ed: Victoria Ring. **Released:** September 2004. **Price:** $39.00. **Description:** Due to the increase in bankruptcy filings, attorneys are outsourcing related jobs in order to reduce overhead.

ASSOCIATIONS AND OTHER ORGANIZATIONS

6225 ■ American Financial Services Association (AFSA)
919 18th St. NW, Ste. 300
Washington, DC 20006-5526
Ph: (202)296-5544
Fax: (202)223-0321
Co. E-mail: cstinebert@afsamail.org
URL: http://www.afsaonline.org
Contact: Chris Stinebert, President
URL(s): www.americanfinsvcs.org. **Description:** Represents companies whose business is primarily direct credit lending to consumers and/or the purchase of sales finance paper on consumer goods. Has members that have insurance and retail subsidiaries; some are themselves subsidiaries of highly diversified parent corporations. Encourages the business of financing individuals and families for necessary and useful purposes at reasonable charges, including interest; promotes consumer understanding of basic money management principles as well as constructive uses of consumer credit. Includes educational services such as films, textbooks and study units for the classroom and budgeting guides for individuals and families. Compiles statistical reports; offers seminars. **Founded:** 1916. **Publications:** *Credit* (Monthly); *Independent Operations*; *Credit* (Bimonthly); *Spotlight* (Monthly); *Credit Executive Letter*. **Awards:** Distinguished Service Award (Annual). **Telecommunication Services:** afsa@afsamail.org.

6226 ■ Credit Professionals International (CPI)
10726 Manchester Rd., Ste. 210
St. Louis, MO 63122
Ph: (314)821-9393
Fax: (314)821-7171
Co. E-mail: creditpro@creditprofessionals.org
URL: http://www.creditprofessionals.org
Contact: Diane Radcliff, President
Description: Represents individuals employed in credit or collection departments of business firms or professional offices. Conducts educational program in credit work. Sponsors Career Club composed of members who have been involved in credit work for at least 25 years. **Founded:** 1937. **Publications:** *The Credit Professional* (Annual). **Awards:** Credit Professional of the Year (Annual).

6227 ■ Credit Research Foundation (CRF)
1812 Baltimore Blvd., Ste. H
Westminster, MD 21157
Ph: (443)821-3000
Fax: (443)821-3627
URL: http://www.crfonline.org
Contact: Karren Salter, Chairwoman
Description: Represents credit, financial, and working capital executives of manufacturing and banking concerns. Aims to create a better understanding of the impact of credit on the economy. Plans, supervises, and administers research and educational programs. Conducts surveys on economic conditions, trends, policies, practices, theory, systems, and methodology. Sponsors formal educational programs in credit and financial management. Maintains library on credit, collections, and management. **Founded:** 1947. **Publications:** *Credit Professional's Handbook*; *CRF News* (Quarterly); *National Summary of Domestic Trade Receivables* (Quarterly).

6228 ■ National Association of Credit Management (NACM)
8840 Columbia 100 Pkwy.
Columbia, MD 21045-2158
Ph: (410)740-5560
Free: 800-955-8815
Fax: (410)740-5574
Co. E-mail: nacm_national@nacm.org
URL: http://www.nacm.org
Contact: Susan Delloiacono, Director
Description: Credit and financial executives representing manufacturers, wholesalers, financial institutions, insurance companies, utilities, and other businesses interested in business credit. Promotes sound credit practices and legislation. Conducts Graduate School of Credit and Financial Management at Dartmouth College, Hanover, NH. **Founded:** 1896. **Publications:** *Business Credit* (9/year); *Credit Executives Handbook*; *Manual of Credit and Commercial Laws* (Annual); *Business Credit: The Publication for Credit and Finance Professionals*. **Educational Activities:** Credit Congress and Exposition (Annual); Credit Congress and Exposition (Annual). **Awards:** Certified Credit Executive (Annual); Mentor of the Year (Annual); O. D. Glaus Credit Executive of the Year; Alice M.H. McGregor Award of Exceptional Achievement. **Telecommunication Services:** nacm-info@nacm.org; nacm_info@nacm.org.

6229 ■ National Foundation for Credit Counseling (NFCC)
2000 M St. NW, Ste. 505
Washington, DC 20036
Free: 800-388-2227
URL: http://www.nfcc.org
Contact: Susan C. Keating, President
Description: Umbrella group for 200 member services operating over 1,500 offices throughout the United States and Canada. Promotes the wise use of credit through education, counseling and debt repayment programs. Member agencies provide teaching units and other money management educational materials to high schools, universities, employee assistance programs and community groups. Sponsors confidential credit and budget and homeownership counseling. **Scope:** consumer credit. **Founded:** 1951. **Subscriptions:** articles. **Awards:** Pace Awards (Annual).

REFERENCE WORKS

6230 ■ *All About Credit*
Pub: Kaplan Publishing
Ed: Deborah McNaughton. **Released:** April 1999. **Price:** $15.95. **Description:** Debt solution to specific credit problems for individuals denied credit, trying to mortgage a home, problems with creditors, and bankruptcy.

6231 ■ *"The Best Option for All" in American Executive (Vol. 7, September 2009, No. 5, pp. 170)*
Pub: RedCoat Publishing, Inc.
Ed: Ashley McGown. **Description:** Plaza Associates, a collections agency that conducts business primarily in the accounts receivable management sector, is the first in the industry to purchase 100 percent of the company from the founders through the formation of a leveraged Employee Stock Ownership Plan (ESOP).

6232 ■ *Chain of Blame: How Wall Street Caused the Mortgage and Credit Crisis*
Pub: John Wiley & Sons, Inc.
Ed: Paul Muolo, Mathew Padilla. **Released:** 2009. **Price:** $27.95. **Description:** The book describes how risky loans given irresponsibly put big investment banks at the center of the subprime crisis.

6233 ■ *"Collection Agencies Industry Rankings" in Collections and Credit Risk (Vol. 14, September 1, 2009, No. 8, pp. 18)*
Pub: SourceMedia, Inc.
Description: Ranking of the top collection agencies in the United States in terms of the revenue generated in 2007 and 2088; statistical data included.

6234 ■ *"Collection Agencies Industry Rankings" in Collections and Credit Risk (Vol. 14, September 1, 2009, No. 8, pp. 18)*
Pub: SourceMedia, Inc.
Description: Ranking of the top collection agencies in the United States in terms of the revenue generated in 2007 and 2088; statistical data included.

6235 ■ *"Collection Agency Issues Whitepaper on Legal and Ethical Methods of Collecting on Overdue Accounts" in Internet Wire (July 20, 2009)*
Pub: Comtex News Network, Inc.
Description: American Profit Recovery, a collection agency based in Massachusetts and Michigan, has updated and reissued a whitepaper on what businesses can and cannot do regarding conversing with their customers in an attempt to collect on overdue accounts and payments. A detailed summary on the federal laws associated with collecting on overdue accounts is outlined in such a way that any business owner, manager, or responsible party can easily understand.

6236 ■ *"Collection Industry Fights Stigma, Lagging Payments"* in Crain's Cleveland Business (Vol. 30, June 8, 2009, No. 22, pp. 15)

Pub: Crain Communications, Inc.

Ed: Joel Hammond. **Description:** John Murray, co-owner and president of JP Recovery Services Inc. in Rocky River, Ohio discusses the burden of the collection industry during a financial crisis like a recession. Statistical data included.

6237 ■ *"Credit Card Crackdown"* in Business Journal-Portland (Vol. 24, November 23, 2007, No. 38, pp. 1)

Pub: American City Business Journals, Inc.

Ed: Andy Giegerich. **Description:** Oregon's U.S. Senator Ron Wyden is sponsoring Credit Card Safety Act of 2007, a bill that requires credit card companies to reduce the jargon of credit card agreements and require the Federal Reserve Board to launch a public education campaign among credit card users. The legislation will also impose a rating system for credit card contracts with five being the safest for consumers to use.

6238 ■ *"Curbing the Debt Collector"* in Business Journal-Portland (Vol. 24, October 5, 2007, No. 32, pp. 1)

Pub: American City Business Journals, Inc.

Ed: Andy Giegerich. **Description:** Republican representative Sal Esquivel, who had a bad personal experience with a Houston collector, is developing legislation that would give the state attorney general's office enforcement powers over debt collecting agencies. The existing Oregon legislation concerning the debt collection industry is also discussed.

6239 ■ *"Debt Buyers Industry Rankings"* in Collections and Credit Risk (Vol. 14, September 1, 2009, No. 8, pp. 19)

Pub: SourceMedia, Inc.

Description: Ranking of the top debt buyers in the United States in terms of the revenue generated in 2007 and 2088; statistical data included.

6240 ■ *"Economic Trends for Small Business"* in Small Business Economic Trends (April 2008, pp. 1)

Pub: National Federation of Independent Business

Ed: William C. Dunkelberg, Holly Wade. **Description:** Summary of economic trends for small businesses in the U.S. is presented. Economic indicators such as capital spending, inventories and sales, inflation, and profits are given. Analysis of credit markets is also provided.

6241 ■ *"End of the Beginning"* in Canadian Business (Vol. 81, November 10, 2008, No. 19, pp. 17)

Pub: Rogers Media Ltd.

Ed: David Wolf. **Description:** The freeze in the money markets and historic decline in equity markets around the world finally forced governments into aggressive coordinated action. The asset price inflation brought on by cheap credit will now work in reverse and the tightening of credit will be difficult economically. Canada is exposed to the fallout everywhere, given that the U.S, the U.K. and Japan buy 30 percent of Canada's output.

6242 ■ *Get Your Credit Straight: A Sister's Guide to Ditching Your Debt, Mending Your Credit, and Building a Strong Financial Future*

Pub: Broadway Books

Contact: David Drake, Manager

E-mail: ddrake@randomhouse.com

Ed: Glinda Bridgforth. **Price:** $19.95. **Description:** Third book in the series is aimed primarily at African American women and offers helpful and understandable information for a larger audience. The sidebars on how women in particular tend to get into credit trouble and ways they can increase their financial knowledge and reign in their spending habits are especially notable.

6243 ■ *Grow Your Money: 101 Easy Tips to Plan, Save and Invest*

Pub: HarperBusiness

Ed: Jonathan D. Pond. **Released:** December 2007. **Price:** $26.95. **Description:** In what should be required reading for anyone entering the work world, the author offers helpful investment and financial definitions, debt-management strategies, retirement and home ownerships considerations and more.

6244 ■ *"The Letter of the Law"* in Collections and Credit Risk (Vol. 14, November 1, 2009, No. 9, pp. 40)

Pub: SourceMedia, Inc.

Ed: Michelle Dunn. **Description:** Analyzes the regulatory landscape regarding debt collection and the ways in which those in the field are dealing with a tough economy, unclear laws and the newest regulations.

6245 ■ *"A New FICO Scoring Model: Get Ready For Changes That Could Affect Your Score"* in Black Enterprise (Vol. 38, March 2008, No. 8)

Pub: Earl G. Graves Publishing Co. Inc.

Ed: Sheiresa McRae. **Description:** Fair Isaac Corporation, creator of the FICO credit score has developed a new scoring model that provides a more accurate way for lenders to determine a borrower's creditworthiness.

6246 ■ *"New Money"* in Entrepreneur (Vol. 36, February 2008, No. 2, pp. 62)

Pub: Entrepreneur Media Inc.

Ed: C.J. Prince. **Description:** Tips on how to handle business finance, with regard to the tightened credit standards imposed by leading institutions, are provided. These include: selling receivables, margining blue chips, and selling purchase orders.

6247 ■ *"Portfolio Recovery Associates Expands Its Hampton Call Center"* in Internet Wire (January 20, 2010)

Pub: Comtex News Network, Inc.

Description: Entering into a lease amendment in order to expand its Hampton, Virginia call center and extend its lease agreement, Portfolio Recovery Associates, Inc., a company that collects, purchases and manages defaulted consumer debt, plans to upgrade the existing space enabling them to draw on local talent.

6248 ■ *"Research and Markets Adds Report: Credit and Collection Practices 2009"* in Wireless News (August 12, 2009)

Pub: Close-Up Media

Description: Research and Markets announced the addition of the 'Credit and Collection Practices 2009' report which will highlight credit and collection industry practices and technologies. The report also includes an overview of the best practices in the field.

6249 ■ *"'Rocket Docket' Leaves Memphis Debtors Behind"* in Commercial Appeal (November 28, 2009)

Pub: Commercial Appeal

Ed: Bartholomew Sullivan. **Description:** According to an investigation by the Scripps Howard News Service, Memphians lodged 807 formal complaints about debt-collection practices to the Federal Trade Commission in a 2 1/2 -year period ending in July; Nearly 1/3 of the complaints involved some type of error with the debt in question. The majority of the complaints were leveled at NCO Group, which also generated the most complaints around the country.

6250 ■ *"Small Business Credit Conditions"* in Small Business Economic Trends (April 2008, pp. 12)

Pub: National Federation of Independent Business

Ed: William C. Dunkelberg, Holly Wade. **Description:** Graphs and tables that present the credit conditions of small businesses in the U.S. are provided. The tables include figures on availability of loans, interest rates, and expected credit conditions.

6251 ■ *"Small Business Credit Conditions"* in Small Business Economic Trends (February 2008, pp. 12)

Pub: National Federation of Independent Business

Ed: William C. Dunkelberg, Holly Wade. **Description:** Graphs and tables that present the credit conditions of small businesses in the U.S. are provided. The tables include figures on availability of loans, interest rates, and expected credit conditions.

6252 ■ *"Small Business Credit Conditions"* in Small Business Economic Trends (January 2008, pp. 12)

Pub: National Federation of Independent Business

Description: Graphs representing loan availability and interest rates among U.S. small businesses surveyed from January 1986 to December 2007 are given. Tables showing regular borrowers, availability of loans, satisfied borrowing needs, expected credit conditions, relative interest rate paid by regular borrowers, and actual interest rate paid on short-term loans by borrowers are also presented.

6253 ■ *"State Targets Credit Fixers"* in Business Journal-Portland (Vol. 24, October 12, 2007, No. 33, pp. 1)

Pub: American City Business Journals, Inc.

Ed: Andy Giegerich, Justin Matlick. **Description:** Number of companies that offer quick fix to consumers is growing; the State of Oregon is considering rules to target them. A group working on a study in the state's mortgage lending regulations could craft bills to be examined for legislative session in February 2008.

6254 ■ *"Summary. Economic Trends for Small Business"* in Small Business Economic Trends (March 2008, pp. 1)

Pub: National Federation of Independent Business

Ed: William C. Dunkelberg, Holly Wade. **Description:** Summary of economic trends for small businesses in the U.S. is provided. Economic indicators such as capital spending, inventories and sales, inflation, and profits are given. Analysis of credit markets is also provided.

6255 ■ *"Summary. Economic Trends for Small Business"* in Small Business Economic Trends (February 2008, pp. 1)

Pub: National Federation of Independent Business

Ed: William C. Dunkelberg, Holly Wade. **Description:** Summary of economic trends for small businesses in the U.S. is provided. Economic indicators such as capital spending, inventories and sales, inflation, and profits are given. Analysis of credit markets is also provided.

6256 ■ *"The Survey Says"* in Collections and Credit Risk (Vol. 14, September 1, 2009, No. 8, pp. 16)

Pub: SourceMedia, Inc.

Ed: Bill Grabarek; Darren Waggoner. **Description:** Revenue for the top accounts receivable management firms rose nearly 20 percent in 2008 despite lower liquidation rates, a poor economy and riskier, albeit cheaper debt portfolios; the trend may continue this year as collection agencies expect revenue, on average, to increase 5.8 percent. Debt buyers, however, found that their revenue fell nearly 7 percent in 2008 and expect it to fall another 12 percent this year.

6257 ■ *"Survival Guide: There Can Be an Upside to Managing a Downturn"* in Canadian Business (Vol. 81, November 10, 2008, No. 19, pp. 54)

Pub: Rogers Media Ltd.

Ed: Sharda Prashad. **Description:** Canada-based Foxy is already limiting its exposure to retailers who could be a credit problem in case of recession. Retirement Life Communities is entering into fixed-rate and fixed-term loans for them to have sufficient financing to grow. Business owners need to realize that customers want more for less.

6258 ■ *"Taking Collections"* in Investment Dealers' Digest (Vol. 75, October 9, 2009, No. 38, pp. 19)

Pub: SourceMedia, Inc.

Ed: Aleksandrs Rozens. **Description:** Although the nation's debt-collection industry has grown with increased reliance by consumers on credit, valuations of these firms have lessened due to the economy which has hurt some of the success of these firms in obtaining the debt back from consumers who are experiencing trying economic times.

6259 ■ *The Trillion Dollar Meltdown: Easy Money, High Rollers, and the Great Credit Crash*

Pub: Public Affairs

Ed: Charles R. Morris. **Released:** 2009. **Price:** $22.95. **Description:** Former banker believes that Wall Street and the financial community have too much power in America. He estimates that writedowns and defaults of residential mortgages, commercial mortgages, junk bonds, leveraged loans, credit cards, and complex securitized bonds could reach $1 trillion.

TRADE PERIODICALS

6260 ■ *Notables*

Pub: National Foundation for Credit Counseling

Contact: Lydia Sermons-Ward, Executive Editor

E-mail: lsward@nfcc.org

Released: Monthly. **Description:** Covers issues concerning consumer credit counseling, family finances, and debt counseling. Recurring features include news of research, reports of meetings, and notices of publications available.

LIBRARIES

6261 ■ Loan Brokers Association Information Services

917 S. Park St.

Owosso, MI 48867-4422

Contact: Ben Campbell, Director

Scope: Loan brokers, loan consulting, credit repair, lending, credit cards, venture capital. **Services:** Copying; SDI; library to members or by permission.

6262 ■ National Foundation for Credit Counseling Library

2000 M St. NW, Ste. 505

Washington, DC 20036

Ph: (202)677-4300

Co. E-mail: dadlis@nfcc.org

URL: http://www.nfcc.org/

Contact: Debra Adlis, Chief Financial Officer Senior Vice President

Scope: Consumer credit, credit counseling, credit research and education. **Services:** Library not open to the public. **Holdings:** Brochures and pamphlets.

START-UP INFORMATION

6263 ■ *How to Start a Bankruptcy Forms Processing Service*
Pub: Graphico Publishing Company
Ed: Victoria Ring. **Released:** September 2004. **Price:** $39.00. **Description:** Due to the increase in bankruptcy filings, attorneys are outsourcing related jobs in order to reduce overhead.

ASSOCIATIONS AND OTHER ORGANIZATIONS

6264 ■ **ACA International**
4040 W 70th St.
Minneapolis, MN 55439
Ph: (952)926-6547
Fax: (612)926-1624
Co. E-mail: aca@acainternational.org
URL: http://www.acainternational.org
Contact: Michael V. Shoop, President
E-mail: mshoop@pfccollects.com
Description: Collection services handling overdue accounts for retail, professional, and commercial credit grantors. Maintains specialized programs in the areas of healthcare, checks, and government which provide services for members who work with credit grantors in these areas. Conducts research. Offers specialized education; compiles statistics. **Publications:** *Collector* (Monthly); *Consumer Trends* (Monthly); *Cred-Alert* (Monthly); *Management Trends* (Bimonthly); *ACA International--Membership Roster* (Annual); *Collector: The Official Publication of the ACA International* (Monthly). **Educational Activities:** American Collectors Association Convention (Annual). **Awards:** ACA Academy Scholar and Fellow Degrees (Annual); Enterprises Award of Merit (Annual); Fred Kirschner Instructor Achievement Award (Annual); Honorary Membership (Annual); International Foundation Fellow Award (Annual); James K. Erickson Continuous Service (Annual); Member of the Year (Annual); Red Coat (Membership) Award (Annual); Unit Certificate of Excellence (Annual); Unit Leader of the Year (Annual); Member of the Year Award; James K. Erickson Continuous Service Award; International Fellowship of Certified Collection Executives; Enterprises Award of Merit; Fred Kirschner Instructor Achievement Award; Honorary Membership; International Foundation Fellow Award; Unit Leader of the Year; Charles F. Lindemann Certified Instructor of the Year (Annual); Charles F. Lindemann Certified Instructor of the Year.

6265 ■ **Consumer Data Industry Association (CDIA)**
1090 Vermont Ave. NW, Ste. 200
Washington, DC 20005-4964
Ph: (202)371-0910
Fax: (202)371-0134
Co. E-mail: cdia@cdiaonline.org
URL: http://www.cdiaonline.org
Description: Serves as international association of credit reporting and collection service offices. Maintains hall of fame and biographical archives; conducts specialized educational programs. Offers computerized services and compiles statistics. **Founded:** 1906.

6266 ■ **Credit Professionals International (CPI)**
10726 Manchester Rd., Ste. 210
St. Louis, MO 63122
Ph: (314)821-9393
Fax: (314)821-7171
Co. E-mail: creditpro@creditprofessionals.org
URL: http://www.creditprofessionals.org
Contact: Diane Radcliff, President
Description: Represents individuals employed in credit or collection departments of business firms or professional offices. Conducts educational program in credit work. Sponsors Career Club composed of members who have been involved in credit work for at least 25 years. **Founded:** 1937. **Publications:** *The Credit Professional* (Annual). **Awards:** Credit Professional of the Year (Annual).

6267 ■ **International Association of Commercial Collectors (IACC)**
4040 W 70th St.
Minneapolis, MN 55435
Ph: (952)925-0760
Free: 800-859-9526
Fax: (952)926-1624
Co. E-mail: iacc@commercialcollector.com
URL: http://www.commercialcollector.com
Contact: Tammy Schoenberg, Executive Director
Description: Debt collection professionals who are specialists in the recovery of commercial accounts receivable. **Founded:** 1970. **Publications:** *Scope* (Monthly); *Commercial Collection Guidelines for Credit Grantors.*

6268 ■ **International Association of Financial Crimes Investigators (IAFCI)**
1020 Suncast Ln., Ste. 102
El Dorado Hills, CA 95762
Ph: (916)939-5000
Fax: (916)939-0395
Co. E-mail: admin@iafci.org
URL: http://www.iafci.org
Contact: George E. Curtis, Director
Description: Special agents, investigators, and investigation supervisors who investigate criminal violations of credit card laws and prosecute offenders; law enforcement officers, prosecutors, or related officials who investigate, apprehend, and prosecute credit card offenders; employees of card issuing institutions who are responsible for credit card security and investigations; management personnel of companies performing services for the credit card industry. Aids in the establishment of effective credit card security programs; suppresses fraudulent use of credit cards; and detects and proceeds with the apprehension of credit card thieves. Emphasizes a professional approach to the investigative function, a free exchange of criminal intelligence, and a vigorous prosecution policy. Encourages members to use existing federal and local criminal statutes and to seek more effective legislation in areas where it is lacking. Provides workshops and training conferences to acquaint law enforcement bodies and the membership with technological advances in the industry. **Founded:** 1968. **Publications:** *IAFCI News* (Quarterly); *International Association of Financial Crimes Investigators: Membership Directory*; *International Association of Credit Card Investigators--Membership Directory* (Annual); *International Association of Financial Crimes Investigators--Membership Directory* (Annual). **Educational Activities:** International Association of Financial Crimes Investigators Conference (Annual).

6269 ■ **National Association of Credit Management (NACM)**
8840 Columbia 100 Pkwy.
Columbia, MD 21045-2158
Ph: (410)740-5560
Free: 800-955-8815
Fax: (410)740-5574
Co. E-mail: nacm_national@nacm.org
URL: http://www.nacm.org
Contact: Susan Delloiacono, Director
Description: Credit and financial executives representing manufacturers, wholesalers, financial institutions, insurance companies, utilities, and other businesses interested in business credit. Promotes sound credit practices and legislation. Conducts Graduate School of Credit and Financial Management at Dartmouth College, Hanover, NH. **Founded:** 1896. **Publications:** *Business Credit* (9/year); *Credit Executives Handbook*; *Manual of Credit and Commercial Laws* (Annual); *Business Credit: The Publication for Credit and Finance Professionals.* **Educational Activities:** Credit Congress and Exposition (Annual); Credit Congress and Exposition (Annual). **Awards:** Certified Credit Executive (Annual); Mentor of the Year (Annual); O. D. Glaus Credit Executive of the Year; Alice M.H. McGregor Award of Exceptional Achievement. **Telecommunication Services:** nacm-info@nacm. org; nacm_info@nacm.org.

DIRECTORIES OF EDUCATIONAL PROGRAMS

6270 ■ *International Association of Credit Card Investigators--Membership Directory*
Pub: International Association of Financial Crimes Investigators
Contact: George E. Curtis, Director
URL(s): www.iafci.org. **Released:** Annual **Covers:** Approximately 3,500 firms and individuals involved in investigating fraudulent credit card use who are members of the International Association of Credit Card Investigators. **Entries include:** Contact information. **Arrangement:** Alphabetical by name. **Indexes:** Geographical; alphabetical by firm name.

REFERENCE WORKS

6271 ■ *"11th Circuit: Don't Break the Law to Comply with It" in Miami Daily Business Review (October 21, 2009)*
Pub: Incisive Media
Contact: Lee Feldman, Manager
E-mail: lee.feldman@incisivemedia.com
Ed: Janet L. Conley. **Description:** Niagara Credit Solutions argued with a three-judge panel that the

company broke the rule saying debt collectors must identify themselves so that they could comply with a rule barring debt collectors from communicating about a debt with third parties.

6272 ■ ACA International--Membership Roster
Pub: ACA International
Contact: Michael V. Shoop, President
E-mail: mshoop@pfccollects.com

URL(s): www.acainternational.com. **Ed:** Tim Dressen. **Released:** Annual; Latest edition 2008. **Publication includes:** List of about 3,600 debt collection agencies, 1,000 credit grantors and 700 collection attorneys, and services in 55 countries. **Entries include:** Firm name, address, phone, fax, URL, e-mail, names and names and titles of key personnel. **Arrangement:** Geographical.

6273 ■ "All-Star Advice 2010" in Black Enterprise (Vol. 41, October 2010, No. 3, pp. 97)
Pub: Earl G. Graves Publishing Co. Inc.

Ed: Renita Burns, Sheiresa Ngo, Marcia Wade Talbert. **Description:** Financial experts share tips on real estate, investing, taxes, insurance and debt management.

6274 ■ "B2B Commercial Collection Agency Accounts Fall" in Managing Credit, Receivables & Collections (November 2010, No. 10-11, pp. 9)
Pub: Institute of Management & Administration

Description: A fall in the number of Business-To-Business collection accounts reflects the pace of the global economic recovery.

6275 ■ "Banks, Retailers Squabble Over Fees" in Baltimore Business Journal (Vol. 28, June 18, 2010, No. 6, pp. 1)
Pub: Baltimore Business Journal

Ed: Gary Haber. **Description:** How an amendment to the financial regulatory reform bill would affect the bankers' and retailers' conflict over interchange fees is discussed. Interchange fees are paid for by retailers every time consumers make purchases through debit cards. Industry estimates indicate that approximately $50 million in such fees are paid by retailers.

6276 ■ "Barred Collection Agency Sued by Colorado AG" in Collections & Credit Risk (Vol. 15, August 1, 2010, No. 7, pp. 7)
Pub: SourceMedia Inc.

Description: Collection agency run by Chad Lee received notice that it is barred from collecting in the State of Colorado by Attorney General John Suther's office. A ruling cited that the firm engages in harassment or abuse and/or threats of violence, made false representations as to its legal status of debts, made false and misleading representations of nonpayment of debts that would result in arrest, and that Lee failed to disclose his previous felony conviction.

6277 ■ "The Best Option for All" in American Executive (Vol. 7, September 2009, No. 5, pp. 170)
Pub: RedCoat Publishing, Inc.

Ed: Ashley McGown. **Description:** Plaza Associates, a collections agency that conducts business primarily in the accounts receivable management sector, is the first in the industry to purchase 100 percent of the company from the founders through the formation of a leveraged Employee Stock Ownership Plan (ESOP).

6278 ■ "Boosting Your Merchant Management Services With Wireless Technology" in Franchising World (Vol. 42, August 2010, No. 8, pp. 27)
Pub: International Franchise Association

Ed: Michael S. Slominski. **Description:** Franchises should have the capability to accept credit cards away from their businesses. This technology will increase sales.

6279 ■ "Boring Bonds Gain Pizzazz as Investors Flock to Debt Issues" in Baltimore Business Journal (Vol. 28, June 11, 2010, No. 5, pp. 1)
Pub: Baltimore Business Journal

Ed: Gary Haber. **Description:** Companies and nonprofit organizations have increased the pace of bond offerings in order to take advantage of the bonds' appeal among willing investors. Companies mostly issued corporate bonds to replace existing debt at lower interest rates and save them money from interest payments.

6280 ■ Chain of Blame: How Wall Street Caused the Mortgage and Credit Crisis
Pub: John Wiley & Sons, Inc.

Ed: Paul Muolo, Mathew Padilla. **Released:** 2009. **Price:** $27.95. **Description:** The book describes how risky loans given irresponsibly put big investment banks at the center of the subprime crisis.

6281 ■ "China's Dagong Show" in Canadian Business (Vol. 83, August 17, 2010, No. 13-14, pp. 15)
Pub: Rogers Media Ltd.

Ed: Matthew McClearn. **Description:** Beijing, China-based Dagong Global Credit Rating has downgraded US credit ratings, as well as other developed countries such as Canada, while granting higher ratings to China, Russia and Brazil. However, there is a perceived disconnection between Dagong's ratings and its official pronouncements.

6282 ■ "Clock Ticks On Columbia Sussex Debt" in Business Courier (Vol. 27, July 30, 2010, No. 13, pp. 1)
Pub: Business Courier

Ed: Dan Monk. **Description:** Cincinnati, Ohio-based Columbia Sussex Corporation has made plans to restructure a $1 billion loan bundle that was scheduled to mature in October 2010. The privately held hotel has strived in a weak hotel market to keep pace with its $3 billion debt load.

6283 ■ "Collection Agencies Industry Rankings" in Collections and Credit Risk (Vol. 14, September 1, 2009, No. 8, pp. 18)
Pub: SourceMedia, Inc.

Description: Ranking of the top collection agencies in the United States in terms of the revenue generated in 2007 and 2088; statistical data included.

6284 ■ "Collection Agencies Industry Rankings" in Collections and Credit Risk (Vol. 14, September 1, 2009, No. 8, pp. 18)
Pub: SourceMedia, Inc.

Description: Ranking of the top collection agencies in the United States in terms of the revenue generated in 2007 and 2088; statistical data included.

6285 ■ "Collection Agency Issues Whitepaper on Legal and Ethical Methods of Collecting on Overdue Accounts" in Internet Wire (July 20, 2009)
Pub: Comtex News Network, Inc.

Description: American Profit Recovery, a collection agency based in Massachusetts and Michigan, has updated and reissued a whitepaper on what businesses can and cannot do regarding conversing with their customers in an attempt to collect on overdue accounts and payments. A detailed summary on the federal laws associated with collecting on overdue accounts is outlined in such a way that any business owner, manager, or responsible party can easily understand.

6286 ■ "Collection Industry Fights Stigma, Lagging Payments" in Crain's Cleveland Business (Vol. 30, June 8, 2009, No. 22, pp. 15)
Pub: Crain Communications, Inc.

Ed: Joel Hammond. **Description:** John Murray, co-owner and president of JP Recovery Services Inc. in Rocky River, Ohio discusses the burden of the collection industry during a financial crisis like a recession. Statistical data included.

6287 ■ "Companies Warned About California Collection Agency" in Cardline (Vol. 10, June 4, 2010, No. 23, pp. 3)
Pub: SourceMedia Inc.

Description: Maxwell, Turner & Associates has received an F-rating from the Better Business Bureau of Central California, citing 32 unanswered complaints in less than a year.

6288 ■ Complete Idiot's Guide to Starting an Ebay Business
Pub: Penguin Books USA Inc.

Ed: Barbara Weltman, Malcolm Katt. **Released:** February 2008. **Price:** $19.95 (US), $29.00 (Canadian). **Description:** Guide for starting an eBay business includes information on products to sell, how to price merchandise, and details for working with services like PayPal, and how to organize fulfillment services.

6289 ■ "Cost of Business Banking May Soon Go Up" in Baltimore Business Journal (Vol. 28, October 29, 2010, No. 25, pp. 1)
Pub: Baltimore Business Journal

Ed: Gary Haber. **Description:** Experts in the financial industry expect banks to charge credit card transactions, especially to small business owners and consumers to recover about $11 million in lost revenue annually. Banks are expected to charge old fees and new ones, including $5 to $10 a month for a checking account.

6290 ■ "Credit Card Crackdown" in Business Journal-Portland (Vol. 24, November 23, 2007, No. 38, pp. 1)
Pub: American City Business Journals, Inc.

Ed: Andy Giegerich. **Description:** Oregon's U.S. Senator Ron Wyden is sponsoring Credit Card Safety Act of 2007, a bill that requires credit card companies to reduce the jargon of credit card agreements and require the Federal Reserve Board to launch a public education campaign among credit card users. The legislation will also impose a rating system for credit card contracts with five being the safest for consumers to use.

6291 ■ "Credit Reporting Myths and Reality" in Black Enterprise (Vol. 41, December 2010, No. 5, pp. 34)
Pub: Earl G. Graves Publishing Co. Inc.

Ed: Denise Campbell. **Description:** It is critical to understand all the factors affecting credit scores before making any major purchase.

6292 ■ "Curbing the Debt Collector" in Business Journal-Portland (Vol. 24, October 5, 2007, No. 32, pp. 1)
Pub: American City Business Journals, Inc.

Ed: Andy Giegerich. **Description:** Republican representative Sal Esquivel, who had a bad personal experience with a Houston collector, is developing legislation that would give the state attorney general's office enforcement powers over debt collecting agencies. The existing Oregon legislation concerning the debt collection industry is also discussed.

6293 ■ "Death Spiral" in Business Journal Serving Greater Tampa Bay (Vol. 30, October 29, 2010, No. 45, pp. 1)
Pub: Tampa Bay Business Journal

Ed: Margie Manning. **Description:** Bay Cities Bank has started working on the loan portfolio of its acquisition, Progress Bank of Florida. Regulators closed Progress Bank in October 2010 after capital collapsed due to charge-offs and increases in the provision for future loan losses.

6294 ■ "Debt Buyers Industry Rankings" in Collections and Credit Risk (Vol. 14, September 1, 2009, No. 8, pp. 19)
Pub: SourceMedia, Inc.

Description: Ranking of the top debt buyers in the United States in terms of the revenue generated in 2007 and 2088; statistical data included.

6295 ■ "Debt-Collection Agency to Lay Off 368 in Hampton Center" in Virginian-Pilot

(December 4, 2010)
Pub: Virginian-Pilot
Ed: Tom Shean. **Description:** NCO Financial Systems Inc., provider of debt-collection and outsourcing services will permanently lay off 368 workers at its Hampton call center in 2011.

6296 ■ *"Delinquent Properties on the Rise" in Business Courier (Vol. 27, June 11, 2010, No. 6, pp. 1)*
Pub: Business Courier
Ed: Dan Monk. **Description:** Reports show that Cincinnati now ranks in the U.S. Top 20 for its delinquency rate on securitized commercial real estate loans. In December 2009, the region ranked 28th out of 50 cities studied by Trepp LLC. As of May 30, 2010, more than $378 million in commercial mortgage-backed security loans were more than 60 days past due.

6297 ■ *"Developer Wins Bout with Bank in Roundabout Way" in Tampa Bay Business Journal (Vol. 30, January 29, 2010, No. 6, pp. 1)*
Pub: American City Business Journals
Ed: Janet Leiser. **Description:** Developer Donald E. Phillips of Phillips Development and Realty LLC won against the foreclosure filed by First Horizon National Corporation, which is demanding the company to fully pay its $2.9 million loan. Phillips requested that his company pay monthly mortgage and extend the loan's maturity date.

6298 ■ *"Direct Recovery Associates Debt Collection Agency Beats Industry Record" in Internet Wire (June 24, 2010)*
Pub: Comtex
Description: Direct Recovery Associates Inc. was named as one of the highest collection records in the industry, which has consistently improved over 18 years. The firm is an international attorney-based debt collection agency.

6299 ■ *"Direct Recovery Associates, Inc. Debt Collection Agency Founder Featured in China Daily" in Internet Wire (November 9, 2010)*
Pub: Comtex
Description: Richard Hart, founder of Direct Recovery Associates, was featured in an article published in the China Daily. The article discussed the increased credit and debt collection demands involving the U.S. and China.

6300 ■ *"Doctors, Health Insurers Squabble Over Who Sends Patients the Bill" in Baltimore Business Journal (Vol. 27, February 6, 2010)*
Pub: American City Business Journals
Ed: Scott Graham. **Description:** Issue of allowing patients to send reimbursement checks to physicians who are not part of their health insurer's provider network is being debated in Maryland. Details on the proposed Maryland bill and the arguments presented by doctors and insurers are outlined.

6301 ■ *"EBay Income: How ANYONE of Any Age, Location, and/or Background Can Build a Highly Profitable Online Business with eBay*
Pub: Atlantic Publishing Company
Released: December 1, 2010. **Price:** $24.95. **Description:** A complete overview of eBay is given and guides any small company through the entire process of creating the auction and auction strategies, photography, writing copy, text and formatting, multiple sales, programming tricks, PayPal, accounting, creating marketing, merchandising, managing email lists, advertising plans, taxes and sales tax, best time to list items and for how long, sniping programs, international customers, opening a storefront, electronic commerce, buy-it now pricing, keywords, Google marketing and eBay secrets.

6302 ■ *"Economic Trends for Small Business" in Small Business Economic Trends (April 2008, pp. 1)*
Pub: National Federation of Independent Business
Ed: William C. Dunkelberg, Holly Wade. **Description:** Summary of economic trends for small businesses in the U.S. is presented. Economic indicators

such as capital spending, inventories and sales, inflation, and profits are given. Analysis of credit markets is also provided.

6303 ■ *"End of the Beginning" in Canadian Business (Vol. 81, November 10, 2008, No. 19, pp. 17)*
Pub: Rogers Media Ltd.
Ed: David Wolf. **Description:** The freeze in the money markets and historic decline in equity markets around the world finally forced governments into aggressive coordinated action. The asset price inflation brought on by cheap credit will now work in reverse and the tightening of credit will be difficult economically. Canada is exposed to the fallout everywhere, given that the U.S., the U.K. and Japan buy 30 percent of Canada's output.

6304 ■ *"Ethics Commission May Hire Collection Agency" in Tulsa World (August 21, 2010)*
Pub: World Publishing
Ed: Barbara Hoberock. **Description:** Oklahoma Ethics Commission is considering a more to hire a collection agency or law firm in order to collect fees from candidates owing money for filing late financial reports.

6305 ■ *"Fight Ensues Over Irreplaceable Gowns" in Tampa Bay Business Journal (Vol. 30, January 15, 2010, No. 4, pp. 1)*
Pub: American City Business Journals
Ed: Janet Leiser. **Description:** People's Princess Charitable Foundation Inc. founder Maureen Rorech Dunkel has sought Chapter 11 bankruptcy protection before a state court decides on the fate of the five of 13 Princess Diana Gowns. Dunkel and the nonprofit were sued by Patricia Sullivan of HRH Venture LLC who claimed they defaulted on $1.5 million in loans.

6306 ■ *"Firms Sue Doracon to Recoup More Than $1M in Unpaid Bills" in Baltimore Business Journal (Vol. 28, July 9, 2010, No. 9, pp. 1)*
Pub: Baltimore Business Journal
Ed: Scott Dance. **Description:** Concrete supplier Paul J. Rach Inc., Selective Insurance Company, and equipment leasing firm Colonial Pacific Leasing Corporation intend to sue Baltimore, Maryland-based Doracon Contracting Inc. for $1 million in unpaid bills. Doracon owed Colonial Pacific $794,000 and the equipment is still in Doracon's possession. Selective Insurance and Paul J. Rach respectively seek $132,000 and $88,000.

6307 ■ *Get Your Credit Straight: A Sister's Guide to Ditching Your Debt, Mending Your Credit, and Building a Strong Financial Future*
Pub: Broadway Books
Contact: David Drake, Manager
E-mail: ddrake@randomhouse.com
Ed: Glinda Bridgforth. **Price:** $19.95. **Description:** Third book in the series is aimed primarily at African American women and offers helpful and understandable information for a wider audience. The sidebars on how women in particular tend to get into credit trouble and ways they can increase their financial knowledge and reign in their spending habits are especially notable.

6308 ■ *"The Great Deleveraging" in Canadian Business (Vol. 81, October 13, 2008, No. 17, pp. 45)*
Pub: Rogers Media Ltd.
Ed: Jeff Sanford. **Description:** 'Hell Week' of financial crisis on Wall Street is believed to have started with the downgrade of AIG Inc.'s credit rating. AIG is a major player in the credit derivatives market, and its bankruptcy would have affected firms on Wall Street.

6309 ■ *"High-End Jeweler Loses Street Sparkle" in Houston Business Journal (Vol. 40, November 27, 2009, No. 29, pp. 1)*
Pub: American City Business Journals
Ed: Allison Wollam. **Description:** High-end jeweler Bailey Banks & Biddle's 7,000 square foot prototype store in Houston, Texas' CityCentre will be ceasing operations despite its parent company's filing for

Chapter 11 protection from creditors. According to the bankruptcy filing, parent company Finlay Enterprises Inc. of New York intends to auction off its business and assets. Finlay has 67 Bailey Banks locations throughout the US.

6310 ■ *"Hospitals Feel Pain from Slow Economy" in Business Courier (Vol. 27, September 3, 2010, No. 18, pp. 1)*
Pub: Business Courier
Ed: James Ritchie. **Description:** Hospitals in Cincinnati, Ohio have suffered from decreased revenues owing to the economic crises. Declining patient volumes and bad debt have also adversely impacted hospitals.

6311 ■ *"Illinois Regulators Revoke Collection Agency's License" in Collections & Credit Risk (Vol. 15, August 1, 2010, No. 7, pp. 13)*
Pub: SourceMedia Inc.
Description: Creditors Service Bureau of Springfield, Illinois had its license revoked by a state regulatory agency and was fined $55,000 because the owner and president, Craig W. Lewis, did not turn over portions of collected funds to clients.

6312 ■ *"The Letter of the Law" in Collections and Credit Risk (Vol. 14, November 1, 2009, No. 9, pp. 40)*
Pub: SourceMedia, Inc.
Ed: Michelle Dunn. **Description:** Analyzes the regulatory landscape regarding debt collection and the ways in which those in the field are dealing with a tough economy, unclear laws and the newest regulations.

6313 ■ *"Making Automated Royalty Payments Work for Your Franchise" in Franchising World (Vol. 42, October 2010, No. 10, pp. 30)*
Pub: International Franchise Association
Ed: J.P. O'Brien. **Description:** In the past, royalty payments were sent by franchisees through regular postal mail and accompanied by a single slip of paper with handwritten notes indicating the month's revenue numbers and royalty amounts.

6314 ■ *"Media Industry Collection Agency Completes Acquisition" in Collections & Credit Risk (Vol. 15, December 1, 2010, No. 11, pp. 22)*
Pub: SourceMedia Inc.
Description: Media Receivable Management Inc. (MRM) will take over the collection operations at Borden, Jones & Mitchell, in Miami, Florida. MRM clients are basically magazine and electronic media publishers.

6315 ■ *"More Ad Shops Link Payment to Results" in Boston Business Journal (Vol. 30, November 12, 2010, No. 42, pp. 1)*
Pub: Boston Business Journal
Ed: Lisa van der Pool. **Description:** A growing number of advertising firms are proposing a 'value-based' payment scheme where they are paid a base fee plus a bonus if certain sales goals or other targets are met. The proposed shift in payment scheme is seen as reminiscent of the dot-com boom about ten years ago. Advertising firms are traditionally paid by the hour.

6316 ■ *"A New FICO Scoring Model: Get Ready For Changes That Could Affect Your Score" in Black Enterprise (Vol. 38, March 2008, No. 8)*
Pub: Earl G. Graves Publishing Co. Inc.
Ed: Sheiresa McRae. **Description:** Fair Isaac Corporation, creator of the FICO credit score has developed a new scoring model that provides a more accurate way for lenders to determine a borrower's creditworthiness.

6317 ■ *"New Money" in Entrepreneur (Vol. 36, February 2008, No. 2, pp. 62)*
Pub: Entrepreneur Media Inc.
Ed: C.J. Prince. **Description:** Tips on how to handle business finance, with regard to the tightened credit standards imposed by leading institutions, are provided. These include: selling receivables, margining blue chips, and selling purchase orders.

6318 ■ *"New York Collection Agency's Bribery Case Resolved"* in *Collections & Credit Risk (Vol. 15, August 1, 2010, No. 7, pp. 19)*
Pub: SourceMedia Inc.
Description: Criminal conviction and civil settlement in a bribery case and Medicaid scam involving H.I.S. Holdings Inc. and owner Deborah Kantor is examined.

6319 ■ *"Ohio Collection Agency Settles Second Lawsuit"* in *Collections & Credit Risk (Vol. 15, July 1, 2010, No. 6, pp. 9)*
Pub: SourceMedia Inc.
Description: National Enterprise Systems, will pay $75,000 for illegal and abusive collection charged in a lawsuit filed by West Virginia's Attorney General's office. Money will be used to reimburse students and consumers who paid the illegal fees to the company.

6320 ■ *"Pay Me! How to Get the Money You're Owed When No One Seems to Have Any"* in *Entrepreneur (Vol. 37, July 2009, No. 7, pp. 49)*
Pub: Entrepreneur Media, Inc.
Ed: Randy B. Hecht. **Description:** How certain collections scenarios with clients, who have already fallen behind on their payments, should be handled is discussed. During a down economy, business owners should properly manage collection and billing because this can actually strengthen client relationships. Insights on hiring a collections agency are also presented.

6321 ■ *"Portfolio Recovery Associates Expands Its Hampton Call Center"* in *Internet Wire (January 20, 2010)*
Pub: Comtex News Network, Inc.
Description: Entering into a lease amendment in order to expand its Hampton, Virginia call center and extend its lease agreement, Portfolio Recovery Associates, Inc., a company that collects, purchases and manages defaulted consumer debt, plans to upgrade the existing space enabling them to draw on local talent.

6322 ■ *Practical Debt Collecting for Small Companies and Traders*
Pub: Meadow Books
Ed: Robin Evelegh. **Released:** December 2006. **Price:** $12.99. **Description:** Credit and collection guide for small companies.

6323 ■ *"Regulators Revoke Mann Bracken's Collection Agency Licenses"* in *Collections & Credit Risk (Vol. 15, September 1, 2010, No. 8, pp. 19)*
Pub: SourceMedia Inc.
Description: Maryland regulators have revoked the collections licenses of defunct law firm Mann Bracken LLP.

6324 ■ *"Research and Markets Adds Report: Credit and Collection Practices 2009"* in *Wireless News (August 12, 2009)*
Pub: Close-Up Media
Description: Research and Markets announced the addition of the 'Credit and Collection Practices 2009' report which will highlight credit and collection industry practices and technologies. The report also includes an overview of the best practices in the field.

6325 ■ *"'Rocket Docket' Leaves Memphis Debtors Behind"* in *Commercial Appeal (November 28, 2009)*
Pub: Commercial Appeal
Ed: Bartholomew Sullivan. **Description:** According to an investigation by the Scripps Howard News Service, Memphians lodged 807 formal complaints about debt-collection practices to the Federal Trade Commission in a 2 1/2 -year period ending in July; Nearly 1/3 of the complaints involved some type of error with the debt in question. The majority of the complaints were leveled at NCO Group, which also generated the most complaints around the country.

6326 ■ *"Small Business Credit Conditions"* in *Small Business Economic Trends (April 2008, pp. 12)*
Pub: National Federation of Independent Business
Ed: William C. Dunkelberg, Holly Wade. **Description:** Graphs and tables that present the credit condi-

tions of small businesses in the U.S. are provided. The tables include figures on availability of loans, interest rates, and expected credit conditions.

6327 ■ *"Small Business Credit Conditions"* in *Small Business Economic Trends (February 2008, pp. 12)*
Pub: National Federation of Independent Business
Ed: William C. Dunkelberg, Holly Wade. **Description:** Graphs and tables that present the credit conditions of small businesses in the U.S. are provided. The tables include figures on availability of loans, interest rates, and expected credit conditions.

6328 ■ *"Small Business Credit Conditions"* in *Small Business Economic Trends (January 2008, pp. 12)*
Pub: National Federation of Independent Business
Description: Graphs representing loan availability and interest rates among U.S. small businesses surveyed from January 1986 to December 2007 are given. Tables showing regular borrowers, availability of loans, satisfied borrowing needs, expected credit conditions, relative interest rate paid by regular borrowers, and actual interest rate paid on short-term loans by borrowers are also presented.

6329 ■ *"Small Business Credit Conditions"* in *Small Business Economic Trends (September 2010, pp. 12)*
Pub: National Federation of Independent Business
Ed: William C. Dunkelberg, Holly Wade. **Description:** Graphs representing loan availability and interest rates among U.S. small businesses surveyed from January 1986 to August 2010 are given. Tables showing regular borrowers, availability of loans, satisfied borrowing needs, expected credit conditions, relative interest rate paid by regular borrowers, and actual interest rate paid on short-term loans by borrowers are also presented.

6330 ■ *"Small Business Credit Conditions"* in *Small Business Economic Trends (July 2010, pp. 12)*
Pub: National Federation of Independent Business
Description: Graphs representing loan availability and interest rates among U.S. small businesses surveyed from January 1986 to June 2010 are given. Tables showing regular borrowers, availability of loans, satisfied borrowing needs, expected credit conditions, relative interest rate paid by regular borrowers, and actual interest rate paid on short-term loans by borrowers are also presented.

6331 ■ *"State Targets Credit Fixers"* in *Business Journal-Portland (Vol. 24, October 12, 2007, No. 33, pp. 1)*
Pub: American City Business Journals, Inc.
Ed: Andy Giegerich, Justin Matlick. **Description:** Number of companies that offer quick fix to consumers is growing; the State of Oregon is considering rules to target them. A group working on a study in the state's mortgage lending regulations could craft bills to be examined for legislative session in February 2008.

6332 ■ *"Summary. Economic Trends for Small Business"* in *Small Business Economic Trends (March 2008, pp. 1)*
Pub: National Federation of Independent Business
Ed: William C. Dunkelberg, Holly Wade. **Description:** Summary of economic trends for small businesses in the U.S. is provided. Economic indicators such as capital spending, inventories and sales, inflation, and profits are given. Analysis of credit markets is also provided.

6333 ■ *"Summary. Economic Trends for Small Business"* in *Small Business Economic Trends (February 2008, pp. 1)*
Pub: National Federation of Independent Business
Ed: William C. Dunkelberg, Holly Wade. **Description:** Summary of economic trends for small businesses in the U.S. is provided. Economic indicators such as capital spending, inventories and sales, inflation, and profits are given. Analysis of credit markets is also provided.

6334 ■ *"The Survey Says"* in *Collections and Credit Risk (Vol. 14, September 1, 2009, No. 8, pp. 16)*
Pub: SourceMedia, Inc.
Ed: Bill Grabarek; Darren Waggoner. **Description:** Revenue for the top accounts receivable management firms rose nearly 20 percent in 2008 despite lower liquidation rates, a poor economy and riskier, albeit cheaper debt portfolios; the trend may continue this year as collection agencies expect revenue, on average, to increase 5.8 percent. Debt buyers, however, found that their revenue fell nearly 7 percent in 2008 and expect it to fall another 12 percent this year.

6335 ■ *"Survival Guide: There Can Be an Upside to Managing a Downturn"* in *Canadian Business (Vol. 81, November 10, 2008, No. 19, pp. 54)*
Pub: Rogers Media Ltd.
Ed: Sharda Prashad. **Description:** Canada-based Foxy is already limiting its exposure to retailers who could be a credit problem in case of recession. Retirement Life Communities is entering into fixed-rate and fixed-term loans for them to have sufficient financing to grow. Business owners need to realize that customers want more for less.

6336 ■ *"Taking Collections"* in *Investment Dealers' Digest (Vol. 75, October 9, 2009, No. 38, pp. 19)*
Pub: SourceMedia, Inc.
Ed: Aleksandrs Rozens. **Description:** Although the nation's debt-collection industry has grown with increased reliance by consumers on credit, valuations of these firms have lessened due to the economy which has hurt some of the success of these firms in obtaining the debt back from consumers who are experiencing trying economic times.

6337 ■ *"Tampa Bay's CMBS Exposure Looms Large"* in *Tampa Bay Business Journal (Vol. 30, December 4, 2009, No. 50, pp. 1)*
Pub: American City Business Journals
Ed: Margie Manning. **Description:** Tampa, Florida's metropolitan statistical area have listed 50 to 601 commercial mortgage-backed securities loans as delinquent with a total delinquent loan balance of $439 million. The total was 9.7 percent of the $4.5 billion loans outstanding and was higher than the delinquency rate in New York and Los Angeles.

6338 ■ *"Travel Rewards Take Off"* in *Inc. (Vol. 33, October 2011, No. 8, pp. 46)*
Pub: Inc. Magazine
Ed: Matthew DeLuca. **Description:** Credit card companies are offering travel reward cards with special perks, including sign-up bonuses; three such cards are described.

6339 ■ *The Trillion Dollar Meltdown: Easy Money, High Rollers, and the Great Credit Crash*
Pub: Public Affairs
Ed: Charles R. Morris. **Released:** 2009. **Price:** $22.95. **Description:** Former banker believes that Wall Street and the financial community have too much power in America. He estimates that writedowns and defaults of residential mortgages, commercial mortgages, junk bonds, leveraged loans, credit cards, and complex securitized bonds could reach $1 trillion.

6340 ■ *Ultimate Credit and Collection Handbook*
Pub: Entrepreneur Press
Ed: Michelle Dunn. **Released:** August 2006. **Price:** $36.95. **Description:** Entrepreneurial experts offer advice for successful credit and collection procedures.

6341 ■ *"Unfair Distraction of Employees"* in *Business Owner (Vol. 35, March-April 2011, No. 2, pp. 8)*
Pub: DL Perkins Company
Description: Fair Credit Collection Practices Act makes it illegal for collectors to contact a debtor at his or her place of employment if the collector is made aware that it is against personnel policy of the employer for the worker to take such a call.

6342 ■ *"Unlicensed Utah Collection Agency Settles with Idaho Department of Finance" in Idaho Business Review, Boise (July 15, 2010)*
Pub: Idaho Business Review
Description: Federal Recovery Acceptance Inc., doing business as Paramount Acceptance in Utah, agreed to pay penalties and expenses after the firm was investigated by the state for improprieties. The firm was charged with conducting unlicensed collection activity.

6343 ■ *The Visa Approval Backlog and Its Impact on American Small Business: Congressional Hearing*
Pub: DIANE Publishing Company
Ed: Donald A. Manzullo. **Released:** July 2006. **Price:** $30.00. **Description:** Information regarding the Congressional hearing involving the Visa approval backlog is discussed.

6344 ■ *"Welcome Back" in Canadian Business (Vol. 82, April 27, 2009, No. 7, pp. 25)*
Pub: Rogers Media
Ed: Sarka Halas. **Description:** Some Canadian companies such as Gennum Corporation have taken advantage of corporate sale-leasebacks to raise money at a time when credit is hard to acquire. Corporate sale-leasebacks allow companies to sell their property assets while remaining as tenants of the building. Sale-leasebacks allow firms to increase capital while avoiding the disruptions that may result with moving.

6345 ■ *"What the Future Holds for Consumers" in Black Enterprise (Vol. 41, August 2010, No. 1, pp. 47)*
Pub: Earl G. Graves Publishing Co. Inc.
Ed: Sheiresa Ngo. **Description:** The way people purchase goods and service has changed with technology. With an increased focus on security (as well as privacy and fairness) the U.S. Congress began regulating the credit card industry with the Fair Credit Reporting Act of 1970 and the Credit Card Accountability, Responsibility, and Disclosure (CARD) Act of 2009.

6346 ■ *"When Dov Cries" in Canadian Business (Vol. 83, June 15, 2010, No. 10, pp. 71)*
Pub: Rogers Media Ltd.
Ed: Joe Castaldo. **Description:** American Apparel disclosed that they will have problems meeting one of its debt covenants which could trigger a chain reaction that could lead to bankruptcy. The prospects look bleak, but eccentric company founder Dov Charney, has always defied expectations.

STATISTICAL SOURCES

6347 ■ *U.S. Credit Bureau and Collections Agencies: An Industry Analysis*
Pub: MarketResearch.com
Released: 2003. **Price:** $1595.00. **Description:** This newly updated bestseller by Marketdata examines the growth businesses of credit reporting services and debt collection agencies.

TRADE PERIODICALS

6348 ■ *Collections & Credit Risk: The Monthly Magazine for Collections and Credit Policy Professionals*
Pub: SourceMedia Inc.
Contact: Douglas J. Manoni, Chief Executive Officer
E-mail: doug.manoni@sourcemedia.com
URL(s): www.collectionscreditrisk.com/. **Released:** Monthly **Price:** $119, Individuals; C$148, Individuals; $213, Two years; $376, Two years in Canada.

6349 ■ *Collector: The Official Publication of the ACA International*
Pub: ACA International
Contact: Michael V. Shoop, President
E-mail: mshoop@pfccollects.com
URL(s): www.acainternational.org/. **Released:** Monthly **Price:** $35, Members; $70, Nonmembers; $45, Canada members; $90, Canada non-members; $60, Other countries members; $120, Other countries non-members.

FRANCHISES AND BUSINESS OPPORTUNITIES

6350 ■ **National Tenant Network**
PO Box 1664
Lake Grove, OR 97035
Ph: (503)635-1238
Description: Residential and commercial tenant performance reporting. **No. of Franchise Units:** 25. **No. of Company-Owned Units:** 2. **Founded:** 1980.. **Franchised:** 1987. **Equity Capital Needed:** $75,000-$120,000. **Franchise Fee:** $30,000 plus $40,000. **Financial Assistance:** Yes. **Training:** Yes.

COMPUTER SYSTEMS/ SOFTWARE

6351 ■ *Collection-Master*
170 Changebridge Rd., Ste. A4-2
Montville, NJ 07045

Ph: (973)575-5646
Free: 800-435-7257
Fax: (781)207-0219
Co. E-mail: cmaster@collectionsoftware.com
URL: http://www.collectionsoftware.com
Description: Available for IBM computers and compatibles. System provides collection agencies with data management and word processing.

6352 ■ *Collection Resource System*
4035 Ridge Top Rd., Ste. 600
Fairfax, VA 22030
Ph: (703)934-9060
Free: 800-222-1722
Fax: (703)293-7510
URL: http://www.crsoftwareinc.com
Description: Contact CR Software.

6353 ■ *Comtronic Debtmaster: Software for Debt Collection*
205 N Harris Ave.
Cle Elum, WA 98922
Ph: (509)573-4300
Fax: (509)674-2383
Co. E-mail: sales@comtronic.com
URL: http://www.comtronic.com
Description: Debt collector software with varied capabilities such as collector work schedules, account assignments, and general ledger accounting.

LIBRARIES

6354 ■ **Loan Brokers Association Information Services**
917 S. Park St.
Owosso, MI 48867-4422
Contact: Ben Campbell, Director
Scope: Loan brokers, loan consulting, credit repair, lending, credit cards, venture capital. **Services:** Copying; SDI; library to members or by permission.

6355 ■ **RMA Information Center**
1 Liberty Pl.
1801 Market St., Ste. 300
Philadelphia, PA 19103-1628
Ph: (215)446-4000
Fax: (215)446-4101
Co. E-mail: rmainfo@rmahq.org
URL: http://www.rmahq.org
Contact: Allen King, Specialist
Scope: Banking and finance, lending/credit, industry/ analysis. **Services:** Library not open to the public. **Holdings:** 1500 books. **Subscriptions:** 150 journals and other serials. **Telecommunication Services:** aking@rmahq.org; customers@rmahq.org.

ASSOCIATIONS AND OTHER ORGANIZATIONS

6356 ■ National Association of Flood and Storm Water Management Agencies (NAFSMA)
1333 H St. NW, West Tower, 10th Fl.
Washington, DC 20005
Ph: (202)289-8625
Fax: (202)530-3389
Co. E-mail: info@nafsma.org
URL: http://www.nafsma.org
Contact: Jim Fiedler, President
Description: State, county, and local governments; special districts concerned with management of water resources. Objectives are to reduce or eliminate flooding and provide for improved storm water management and conservation of watersheds. **Founded:** 1978. **Publications:** *NAFSMA Bulletin* (Periodic); *NAFSMA Newsletter* (Monthly); *Survey of Local Storm Water Utilities.*

6357 ■ Natural Hazards Research and Applications Information Center
University of Colorado
483 UCB
Boulder, CO 80309-0482
Ph: (303)492-6818
Fax: (303)492-2151
Co. E-mail: hazctr@colorado.edu
URL: http://www.colorado.edu/hazards
Contact: Kathleen Tierney, Director
Description: Advances and communicates knowledge on hazards mitigation and disaster preparedness, response, and recovery. Fosters information sharing and integration of activities among researchers, practitioners, and policy makers from around the world; supports and conducts research; and provides educational opportunities for the next generation of hazards scholars and professionals. **Scope:** economic, social, and behavioral aspects of natural hazards and extreme events. **Founded:** 1977. **Subscriptions:** 28000 articles books periodicals reports. **Publications:** *Disaster Research* (Biweekly); *Natural Hazards Observer* (Bimonthly); *Quick Response Research Reports Series* (Periodic); *Special Publications Series* (Periodic); *Topical Bibliographies Series* (Periodic); *Environment and Behavior Monograph Series* (Periodic). **Educational Activities:** Hazards Research and Applications Workshop (Annual). **Awards:** Mary Fran Myers (Annual).

TRADE PERIODICALS

6358 ■ *Cleaning & Restoration*
Pub: Restoration Industry Association
Contact: Frank L. Headen, President
E-mail: fheaden@firstrestoration.com
URL(s): www.restorationindustry.org/content/cr-magazine. **Released:** Monthly **Price:** $69, Nonmembers; $79, Nonmembers Canada; $99, Nonmembers international.

6359 ■ *Natural Hazards Observer*
Pub: Natural Hazards Research and Applications Information Center
Ed: Christa Rabenold, Editor. **Released:** Bimonthly. **Description:** Discusses methods of mitigating the effects of all natural hazards on humans, especially earthquakes, floods, hurricanes, and some technological hazards. Emphasizes research into land use planning, disaster contingency planning, and reconstruction. Recurring features include reports of relevant legislative and government actions, announcements of research grants awarded, lists of new publications, hazard maps and videos, and schedules of workshops, conferences, and significant programs.

TRADE SHOWS AND CONVENTIONS

6360 ■ Can Clean
Canadian Sanitation Supply Association—CSSA
910 Dundas St. W.
Whitby, ON, Canada L1P 1P7
Ph: (905)665-8001
Free: 800-684-8273
Fax: (905)430-6418
Co. E-mail: cssa@cssa.com
URL: http://www.cssa.com
Contact: Ken Hilder, President
URL(s): www.cssa.com. **Price:** $40, Pre-registered. **Frequency:** Annual. **Audience:** Distributors and end-users of sanitary maintenance products. **Principal Exhibits:** Sanitary maintenance products. **Dates and Locations:** April 30 - May 1, Mississauga, ON, Canada, International Centre.

6361 ■ Restoration Industry Association Annual Convention and Exhibition
Restoration Industry Association (RIA)
12339 Carroll Ave.
Rockville, MD 20852
Ph: (301)231-6505
Free: 800-272-7012
Fax: (301)231-6569
Co. E-mail: tshaw@restorationindustry.org
URL: http://www.ascr.org
Contact: Frank L. Headen, President
E-mail: fheaden@firstrestoration.com
URL(s): www.restorationindustry.org. **Frequency:** Annual. **Audience:** Owners and managers of cleaning and restoration firms. **Principal Exhibits:** Carpet, upholstery, and draperies cleaning and restoration equipment, duct cleaning supplies and services.

FRANCHISES AND BUSINESS OPPORTUNITIES

6362 ■ Deck Renewal Systems USA
2369 Promenade Way
Dayton, OH 45342
Ph: (937)434-3256
Free: 800-430-4711
Fax: (937)434-2931
URL: http://www.deckrenewalsystems.com
Description: Wood restoration. **No. of Franchise Units:** 3. **Founded:** 1993. **Franchised:** 2006. **Equity Capital Needed:** $29,000. **Franchise Fee:** $29,000. **Royalty Fee:** 5%. **Training:** 1 week training at headquarters, 1 week at franchisee's location and ongoing support.

6363 ■ Disaster Kleenup Int'l.
1555 Mittel Blvd., Ste. 5
Wood Dale, IL 60191
Ph: (630)350-3000
Free: 800-567-8047
Fax: (630)350-9354
Co. E-mail: info@disasterkleenup.com
URL: http://www.disasterkleenup.com
Description: Insurance restoration services. **No. of Franchise Units:** 264. **Founded:** 1974.. **Franchised:** 1994. **Equity Capital Needed:** $7,145-$117,535. **Franchise Fee:** $5,000-$43,785. **Royalty Fee:** $625-$2,100/month. **Training:** Offers 1 day and ongoing training, including 2-5 days national & regional conferences & meetings.

6364 ■ Servpro
Servpro Industries, Inc.
801 Industrial Blvd.
Gallatin, TN 37066
Ph: (615)451-0600
Free: 800-826-9586
Fax: (615)451-1602
Co. E-mail: franchise@servpronet.com
URL: http://www.servpro.com
Description: A completely diversified cleaning and restoration business, with multiple income opportunities. The insurance restoration market (fire, smoke and water damage) is their main focus. Specialize in commercial & residential cleaning. **No. of Franchise Units:** 1,600. **Founded:** 1967.. **Franchised:** 1969. **Equity Capital Needed:** $133,050-$181,450. **Franchise Fee:** $42,000. **Training:** Intensive home study curriculum, manuals and videos. Provides 2 weeks training in state of the art national training facility, 1 week set up/opening assistance, and trainer assistance. Ongoing support, convention, regional and area meetings, formal business reviews, newsletters, bulletins, and more.

Dance School

ASSOCIATIONS AND OTHER ORGANIZATIONS

6365 ■ **American Dance Guild (ADG)**
240 W 14th St.
New York, NY 10011-7218
Ph: (212)627-9407
Co. E-mail: gloria.mclean@earthlink.net
URL: http://www.americandanceguild.org
Contact: Gloria McLean, President

Description: Serves the dance professional by providing: a networking system between dance artists and dance educators; an informed voice on behalf of the dance field to governmental, educational and corporate institutions and the general public; international dance festivals, conferences and dance film festivals; educational publications and videos; the ADG Fannie Weiss Scholarship; the ADG Harkness Resource for Dance Study. **Scope:** dance. **Founded:** 1956. **Subscriptions:** 300 books periodicals video recordings. **Publications:** *ADG Newsletter* (Semiannual); *Souvenir Journal* (Annual). **Educational Activities:** American Dance Guild Conference (Annual). **Awards:** Award of Artistry (Annual); Fannie Weiss Student Scholarship (Annual); American Dance Guild Annual Award; Fannie Weiss Student Scholarship. **Telecommunication Services:** americandanceguild@hotmail.com.

6366 ■ **American Dance Therapy Association (ADTA)**
10632 Little Patuxent Pkwy., Ste. 108
Columbia, MD 21044
Ph: (410)997-4040
Fax: (410)997-4048
URL: http://www.adta.org
Contact: Sharon Goodill, President

Description: Individuals professionally practicing dance therapy, students interested in becoming dance therapists, university departments with dance therapy programs, and individuals in related therapeutic fields. Establishes and maintains high standards of professional education and competence in dance therapy. Acts as information center; develops guidelines for educational programs and for approval of programs; maintains registry of qualified dance therapists. Maintains Marian Chace Memorial Fund to be used for educational, literary, or scientific projects related to dance in the field of mental health. **Founded:** 1966. **Publications:** *American Dance Therapy Association--Membership Directory* (Annual); *Conference Proceedings*; *Dance Therapy Bibliography*; *American Journal of Dance Therapy* (Semiannual); *Dance Therapy Notebook*; *Capturing the Essence of Chase: A Teacher's Journey Schmais*; *Metamorphosis in Movement: Mart Stark Whitehouse - a Video Retrospective*.

6367 ■ **American Society for the Alexander Technique (AMSAT)**
PO Box 2307
Dayton, OH 45401-2307
Ph: (937)586-3732
Free: 800-473-0620
Fax: (937)586-3699
Co. E-mail: info@amsatonline.org
URL: http://www.amsatonline.org
Contact: Kathryn Miranda, Chairperson

Description: Individuals who have completed a three-year training course and have been certified by the society; students currently enrolled in an approved AmSAT teacher training course. Promotes and trains teachers of the Alexander Technique. Created by Australian actor F. M. Alexander (1863-1955), the technique employs reeducation of habitual movement patterns so the body is used efficiently with the least amount of "wear and tear". Seeks to: promote proficiency, knowledge, and skill in the field of psycho-physical reeducation; encourage education and study in the Alexander Technique; approve the establishment and continuation of teacher training courses. Promotes communication and the interchange of skills and information between the society and other organizations of teachers in the Alexander Technique; works to achieve reciprocal memberships between such organizations. Promotes and conducts research. Compiles information regarding teacher members and members of affiliated societies and disseminates this information to the public. Maintains speakers' bureau. **Founded:** 1987. **Publications:** *AMSAT News* (Quarterly); *Teaching Members List* (Annual); *List of Certified Training Courses* (Annual). **Educational Activities:** American Society for the Alexander Technique Meeting (Annual); Teacher Refresher Course (Annual).

6368 ■ **Cecchetti Council of America (CCA)**
23393 Meadows Ave.
Flat Rock, MI 48134
Ph: (734)379-6710
Fax: (734)379-3886
Co. E-mail: info@cecchetti.org
URL: http://www.cecchetti.org
Contact: Julie Merkle, President

Description: Teachers of ballet and ballet dancers. Aims to raise the quality of ballet teaching and to promote the Cecchetti method of ballet training. (Named for Cavalier Enrico Cecchetti, 1850-1928, Italian ballet dancer and teacher.) Uses the teachings and writings of Cecchetti in a sequence of grades measured to the degree of difficulty and physical development; provides a system of accredited examinations to test the student's proficiency within those grades. Holds exams regularly for teachers and students; conducts refresher courses. Maintains close liaison with Cecchetti Society Branch of the Imperial Society of Teachers of Dancing. **Founded:** 1939. **Publications:** *National CCA Newsletter* (Semiannual). **Educational Activities:** International Summer School (Annual). **Awards:** CCA Virgiline Smith Teacher Scholarship (Annual).

6369 ■ **Country Dance and Song Society (CDSS)**
116 Pleasant St., Ste. 345
Easthampton, MA 01027-2759
Ph: (413)203-5467
Fax: (413)203-5471
Co. E-mail: office@cdss.org
URL: http://www.cdss.org
Contact: David Millstone, President

Description: Amateur and professional musicians; dance historians and recreational dancers. Promotes modern use of English and Anglo-American folk dances, songs, and music. Holds 11 week-long adult camps per year and 3 week-long family camps. **Founded:** 1915. **Publications:** *Country Dance and Song Society--Group Directory* (Annual); *Country Dance and Song Society--Newsletter* (Bimonthly); *A Choice Selection of American Country Dances of the Revolutionary Era*; *Legacy: 50 Years of Dance and Song*; *The Playford Ball: 103 Early English Country Dances*; *Twenty-four Early American Country Dances: Cotillions and Reels*.

6370 ■ **Cross-Cultural Dance Resources (CCDR)—CCDR**
518 S Agassiz St.
Flagstaff, AZ 86001-5711
Ph: (928)774-8108
Fax: (928)774-8108
Co. E-mail: ccdr-researchcenter@ccdr.org
URL: http://www.ccdr.org
Contact: Pegge Vissicaro, Managing Director

Description: Promotes dance performances; preserves and researches dance materials; fosters a dynamic environment for dance events; provides rehearsal space. Offers consultation in areas such as dance theory and methods, ethnomusicology, cultural dynamics, and ethics. Awards internships. Sponsors concerts, visiting artists, and lecture demonstrations. Maintains museum of musical instruments and costumes. Archive includes material of Gertrude Prokosch Kurath, Eleanor King. **Scope:** performance, especially dance, Eleanor King Collection, Gertrude Prokosch Kurath collection. **Founded:** 1981. **Subscriptions:** 14000 artwork audiovisuals books clippings monographs periodicals. **Publications:** *Tibet Week in Flagstaff*; *Half a Century of Dance Research: Essays by Gertrude Prokosch Kurath*.

6371 ■ **Dance Affiliates**
4701 Bath St., Bldg. 46B
Philadelphia, PA 19137-2235
Ph: (215)636-9000
Fax: (215)672-2912
Co. E-mail: info@danceaffiliates.org
URL: http://danceaffiliates.org/index.php
Contact: F. Randolph Swartz, Art Director

Description: Selects and prepares the U.S. team for participation in the annual International Ballet Competition (the "Olympics of Dance"). Works to establish the U.S. as a major force in ballet; to stimulate interest in international competitions and festivals; to encourage young American dancers to strive for world-class excellence; and to build an ongoing program to finance and support further international competitions. Raises funds from private and corporate sources; secures federal grants and sells promotional items. Sponsors trips to observe performing arts in other countries. **Founded:** 1979. **Educational Activities:** International Competition (Annual).

6372 ■ **Dance Educators of America (DEA)**
340 5th Ave.
Pelham, NY 10803
Ph: (914)636-3200
Free: 800-229-3868

Fax: (914)636-5895
Co. E-mail: diane.bush@dancedea.com
URL: http://www.deadance.com
Description: Qualified dance teachers who pass an examination and subscribe to a code of ethics and advertising rules and regulations. Works to further and promote the education of teachers in the performing arts and stage arts and of dance in all its forms. Conducts training schools at New York and Las Vegas. **Scope:** ballet, tap, jazz, modern, acrobatic. **Founded:** 1932. **Publications:** *To Teach Is To Learn Twice.* **Educational Activities:** Dance Educators of America Seminar; Dance Educators of America Seminar.

6373 ▪ Dance Notation Bureau (DNB)
111 John St., Ste. 704
New York, NY 10038
Ph: (212)571-7011
Fax: (212)571-7012
Co. E-mail: dnbinfo@dancenotation.org
URL: http://www.dancenotation.org
Contact: Lynne Weber, Executive Director
Description: Documents and preserves dance works through the use of graphic notation. Conducts research into movement-related analysis techniques and programs. Maintains extension at Ohio State University, Columbus. Maintains placement service; assists choreographers in copyrighting, licensing, and restaging of their dance works. Offers service for dance reconstructors and circulating library materials to members. Maintains archive of original Labanotated dance scores in the world. **Scope:** dance and movement. **Founded:** 1940. **Subscriptions:** 3000 archival material articles audio recordings books periodicals video recordings. **Educational Activities:** Professional Advisory Committee (Biennial). **Awards:** Dance Service Award (Annual).

6374 ▪ International Association for Creative Dance (IACD)
103 Princeton Ave.
Providence, RI 02907
Ph: (401)521-0546
Co. E-mail: doug.dance@juno.com
URL: http://www.dancecreative.org
Contact: Douglas R. Victor, Founder
Description: Represents individuals with an interest in Mettler-based creative dance. Works to advance the field of creative dance and sponsors opportunities for the study and teaching of creative dance. **Founded:** 1996. **Educational Activities:** Creative Dance Congress (Annual).

6375 ▪ International Council of Kinetography Laban (ICKL)
c/o Susan Gingrasso, Treas.
4308 Heffron St.
Stevens Point, WI 54481-5338
Co. E-mail: treasurer@ickl.org
URL: http://www.ickl.org
Contact: Richard Allan Ploch, Secretary
Description: Professional dancers, teachers, and others in 20 countries using the Labanotation system for recording dance movements. Supports Kinetography Laban/Labanotation by: guiding the unified development of the system; encouraging consistent standards of practice; acting as the authoritative body with regard to orthography; promoting research into notation matters likely to increase the efficiency and usage of the system. Maintains archive of papers and conference reports. **Founded:** 1959.

6376 ▪ International Tap Association (ITA)
PO Box 150574
Austin, TX 78715
Ph: (303)443-7989
URL: http://www.tapdance.org
Contact: Acia Gray, President
Description: Represents the interests of tap dancers, performers, studios, choreographers, teachers, scholars, historians, students, and other tap enthusiasts. Promotes understanding, preservation, and development of tap dance as an art form. Encourages the creation of new tap performance venues and touring circuits. Preserves the history of tap

through archival documentation and research. Establishes support mechanisms and communication networks for tap. **Founded:** 1987. **Publications:** *On Tap* (5/year).

6377 ▪ National Association of Schools of Dance (NASD)
11250 Roger Bacon Dr., Ste. 21
Reston, VA 20190-5248
Ph: (703)437-0700
Fax: (703)437-6312
Co. E-mail: info@arts-accredit.org
URL: http://nasd.arts-accredit.org
Contact: Samuel Hope, Executive Director
Description: Serves as accrediting agency for educational programs in dance. Provides prospective students with current, accurate information about schools offering instruction in dance. Seeks to establish standards in the field regarding budget, class time requirements, faculty qualifications, faculty-student ratios, and library and physical facilities. Fosters public understanding and acceptance of the educational disciplines inherent in the creative arts in the nation's system of higher education. Encourages high-quality teaching, as well as varied and experimental methods and theories of dance instruction. Provides national representation in matters pertaining to dance and affecting member institutions and their goals. Encourages the collaboration of individuals and professional dance groups in formulating curricula and standards. Offers members general assistance and counseling in program development and encourages self-evaluation and continuing efforts toward improvement. Evaluates dance schools and dance instruction programs through voluntary accreditation processes; assures students and parents that accredited programs offer competent instructors and adequate curricula and facilities. **Founded:** 1981. **Publications:** *NASD Handbook* (Biennial).

6378 ▪ National Ballroom and Entertainment Association (NBEA)
2799 Locust Rd.
Decorah, IA 52101-7600
Ph: (563)382-3871
Co. E-mail: nbea@q.com
URL: http://www.nbea.com
Contact: Larry Bowers, President
Description: Represents owners and operators of ballrooms; entertainment members are band leaders and others in positions related to live music dancing. **Founded:** 1947.

6379 ▪ National Dance Association (NDA)
1900 Association Dr.
Reston, VA 20191-1502
Ph: (703)476-3400
Free: 800-213-7193
Fax: (703)476-9527
Co. E-mail: lhelms@aahperd.org
URL: http://www.aahperd.org/nda
Contact: Freddie Thompson-Esters, President
Description: Dance educators, choreographers, schools and dance/arts administrators, researchers, performers, dance medicine/science specialists, technologists, therapists and others associated with dance/arts education. Works with 160 federal and state agencies, arts and education associations, foundations, and businesses and corporations to ensure that: (1) quality dance/arts education is available to all Americans regardless of age, sex, ability, interest, or culture; and (2) quality dance/arts education becomes a part of U.S. education for all children. **Founded:** 1932. **Publications:** *Spotlight on Dance*; *Dance Directory*; *Dance Movement Therapy: A Healing Book*; *The National Standards for Dance Education*; *Seeing While Being Seen: Dance Photography & the Creative Process.* **Educational Activities:** Dancing with the Mouse Technology/Dance Conference (Semiannual). **Awards:** Dance Educators of the Year (Annual); Heritage Award (Annual); NDA Scholar/Artist Award (Annual); NDA Student Literary Award (Annual); Outstanding Dance Student Award (Annual); Heritage Award; Scholar/Artist Award; K-12 Dance Educator of the Year; Student Literary Award; Outstanding Student Recognition Awards. **Telecommunication Services:** nda@aahperd.org.

6380 ▪ Royal Academy of Dance (RAD)
3211 S Lake Dr., Ste. R317
Milwaukee, WI 53235
Ph: (414)747-9060
Fax: (414)747-9062
Co. E-mail: info@radusa.org
URL: http://www.radusa.org
Description: International examining body working to maintain a high standard of classical ballet training. Provides teachers with an examination syllabus. Conducts teachers' courses and summer schools for children and teachers. **Scope:** dance, ballet education. **Founded:** 1920. **Subscriptions:** archival material books periodicals photographs video recordings. **Educational Activities:** Teachers' Workshop (Annual).

REFERENCE WORKS

6381 ▪ *Dance Magazine College Guide*
Pub: Dance Magazine Inc.
Contact: Dan Lenz, Director
E-mail: dlenz@dancemagazine.com
URL(s): www.dancemagazine.com. **Ed:** Karen Hildebrand. **Released:** Annual; Latest edition 2011. **Price:** $29.95, Individuals plus shipping and handling. **Covers:** Approximately 600 college-level dance programs. **Entries include:** College name, address, phone, and name of contact for dance department; degrees offered; degree requirements; facilities; special programs; admission requirements; tuition and fees; financial aid available. Also includes articles on issues in dance education. **Arrangement:** Alphabetical, geographical. **Indexes:** College or University name.

6382 ▪ *National Guild of Community Schools of the Arts--Membership Directory*
Pub: National Guild for Community Arts Education
Contact: Mr. Jonathan Herman, Executive Director
URL(s): www.nationalguild.org. **Released:** Annual; August. **Covers:** Over 320 member schools, including community schools, social service centers, and collegiate divisions with programs in music, dance, drama, visual arts, and creative writing; about 150 individual members, business affiliate members, trustees, and board members; coverage includes Canada. **Entries include:** For schools--School name, address, phone, fax, e-mail addresses, website addresses, name and title of director, year established, year and status of NGCSA membership, number of branches (affiliate programs), areas of instruction, organizational affiliations, profile of school guild membership, special programs and classes, number of students. For individuals--Name, title, affiliation, address. For business affiliates--Name, address, phone, fax, e-mail, website, name and title of main contacts, description of products and services. **Arrangement:** Institutions are geographical; individuals and business affiliates are alphabetical. **Indexes:** Regional chapter; school director; geographical.

6383 ▪ *"Shop Around" in Houston Chronicle (December 7, 2010, pp. 3)*
Pub: Houston Chronicle
Ed: Tara Dooley. **Description:** Profile of Diana Candida and Maria Martinez who partnered to open Beatniks, a shop carrying vintage clothing, art from various artists, dance shoes, and jewelry.

6384 ▪ *"Toes for Business" in Hispanic Business (October 2007, pp. 10, 12)*
Pub: Hispanic Business
Ed: Gabriel Rodriguez. **Description:** Prima ballerinas, Lorena and Lorna Feijoo, have increased box office sales by at least 30 to 40 percent. A discussion with Pedro Pablo Pena, artistic director of the Miami Hispanic Ballet Corps and founder of the first Choreographic Workshop of Havana is included.

TRADE PERIODICALS

6385 ▪ *AAHPERD Update*
Pub: American Alliance for Health, Physical Education, Recreation and Dance
Contact: Ang Chen, President
Ed: Getchen O'Brien, Editor. **Released:** 6/year. **Price:** $45, individuals; $48.15, Canada; $53, other countries. **Description:** Provides news and informa-

tion on the Alliance. Discusses current issues and research in the areas of health, physical education, recreation, dance, fitness, and adapted physical education. Recurring features include a calendar of events, reports of meetings, news of educational opportunities, job listings, notices of publications available, and columns titled President's Message, Membership Corner, and From the EVP's Desk.

6386 ■ Ballet Review
Pub: Dance Research Foundation Inc.
URL(s): www.balletreview.com/. **Released:** Quarterly **Price:** $23, Individuals; $5.95, Single issue; $9, Individuals back issues; $42, Individuals.

6387 ■ Country Dance and Song Society Newsletter
Pub: Country Dance and Song Society
Contact: Caroline Batson, Editor-in-Chief
Released: 6/year. **Price:** Included in membership. **Description:** Promotes the study and enjoyment of traditional Anglo-American and English folk dances, songs, and music. Carries Society news, reports from dance centers across the country, book reviews, and recordings.

6388 ■ Dance International
Pub: Vancouver Ballet Society
URL(s): www.danceinternational.org/. **Released:** Quarterly **Price:** $41, U.S.; $69, Two years within USA; $26, Canada; $66, U.S. library/institution; $46, Canada library/institution; $48, Other countries beyond North America; $86, Other countries library/institution, beyond North America.

6389 ■ Dance Magazine
Pub: Dance Magazine Inc.
Contact: Dan Lenz, Director
E-mail: dlenz@dancemagazine.com
URL(s): www.dancemagazine.com. **Ed:** Jennifer Stahl. **Released:** Monthly **Price:** $34.95, Individuals; $64.90, Two years; $46.95, Canada; $88.90, Canada 2 years; $66.95, Other countries; $128.90, Other countries 2 years.

6390 ■ Spotlight on Dance
Pub: National Dance Association
Contact: Freddie Thompson-Esters, President
Released: 3/year. **Price:** Included in membership. **Description:** Promotes the development of sound philosophies and policies in all forms of dance and dance education. Reports on dance research, current information on dance education, professional preparation, and certification.

VIDEOCASSETTES/ AUDIOCASSETTES

6391 ■ Advanced Progressions for Across the Floor
Stagestep
4701 Bath St., #46B
Philadelphia, PA 19137
Ph: (215)636-9000
Free: 800-523-0960
Fax: (267)672-2912
Co. E-mail: stagestep@stagestep.com
URL: http://stagestep.com
Released: 19??. **Price:** $39.95. **Description:** Cathy Roe demonstrates a number of dance progressions, including time steps, jumps, and kicks. **Availability:** VHS.

6392 ■ Ballet 101
Tapeworm Video Distributors
25876 The Old Road #141
Stevenson Ranch, CA 91381
Ph: (661)257-4904
Fax: (661)257-4820
Co. E-mail: sales@tapeworm.com
URL: http://www.tapeworm.com
Released: 1997. **Price:** $19.95. **Description:** Introduces basic ballet warm-up exercises and technique. Based on a University of California major program. **Availability:** VHS.

6393 ■ Bellydance! Fast Moves
Tapeworm Video Distributors
25876 The Old Road #141
Stevenson Ranch, CA 91381
Ph: (661)257-4904
Fax: (661)257-4820
Co. E-mail: sales@tapeworm.com
URL: http://www.tapeworm.com
Released: 1996. **Description:** Presents beginner through intermediate movements and combinations designed to increase vitality. **Availability:** VHS.

6394 ■ Bellydance! Slow Moves
Tapeworm Video Distributors
25876 The Old Road #141
Stevenson Ranch, CA 91381
Ph: (661)257-4904
Fax: (661)257-4820
Co. E-mail: sales@tapeworm.com
URL: http://www.tapeworm.com
Released: 1996. **Description:** Presents beginner through intermediate movements and combinations designed to tone and reduce stress. **Availability:** VHS.

6395 ■ Beyond Routine
Stagestep
4701 Bath St., #46B
Philadelphia, PA 19137
Ph: (215)636-9000
Free: 800-523-0960
Fax: (267)672-2912
Co. E-mail: stagestep@stagestep.com
URL: http://stagestep.com
Released: 19??. **Price:** $49.95. **Description:** Joffrey Ballet dancers deconstruct a theatre dance production number to demonstrate the elements involved. "Happy Feet" from the ballet "A Shoestring Revue" is used as the example. **Availability:** VHS.

6396 ■ Bob Rizzo's Dance New York: Jazz
Stagestep
4701 Bath St., #46B
Philadelphia, PA 19137
Ph: (215)636-9000
Free: 800-523-0960
Fax: (267)672-2912
Co. E-mail: stagestep@stagestep.com
URL: http://stagestep.com
Released: 19??. **Price:** $39.95. **Description:** Bob Rizzo teaches three jazz routines for beginner through advanced dancers. **Availability:** VHS.

6397 ■ Bob Rizzo's Dance New York: Lyrical
Stagestep
4701 Bath St., #46B
Philadelphia, PA 19137
Ph: (215)636-9000
Free: 800-523-0960
Fax: (267)672-2912
Co. E-mail: stagestep@stagestep.com
URL: http://stagestep.com
Released: 19??. **Price:** $39.95. **Description:** Ray Leeper teaches three lyrical routines for beginner through advanced dancers. **Availability:** VHS.

6398 ■ Bob Rizzo's Dance New York: Tap
Stagestep
4701 Bath St., #46B
Philadelphia, PA 19137
Ph: (215)636-9000
Free: 800-523-0960
Fax: (267)672-2912
Co. E-mail: stagestep@stagestep.com
URL: http://stagestep.com
Released: 19??. **Price:** $39.95. **Description:** Alan Onickel teaches three tap routines for beginner through advanced dancers. **Availability:** VHS.

6399 ■ Creating the Dancer's Body
Stagestep
4701 Bath St., #46B
Philadelphia, PA 19137
Ph: (215)636-9000
Free: 800-523-0960

Fax: (267)672-2912
Co. E-mail: stagestep@stagestep.com
URL: http://stagestep.com
Released: 19??. **Price:** $39.95. **Description:** Cathy Roe demonstrates exercises for dancers intended to improve muscular strength and endurance. **Availability:** VHS.

6400 ■ Dances for Drill and Dance Teams
Stagestep
4701 Bath St., #46B
Philadelphia, PA 19137
Ph: (215)636-9000
Free: 800-523-0960
Fax: (267)672-2912
Co. E-mail: stagestep@stagestep.com
URL: http://stagestep.com
Released: 19??. **Price:** $39.95. **Description:** Presents three routines for drill teams and other large dancing groups. Jazz-funk, precision, and lyrical styles are used. **Availability:** VHS.

6401 ■ Dancing in Hollywood: A Guide for the Professional Dancer
Stagestep
4701 Bath St., #46B
Philadelphia, PA 19137
Ph: (215)636-9000
Free: 800-523-0960
Fax: (267)672-2912
Co. E-mail: stagestep@stagestep.com
URL: http://stagestep.com
Released: 19??. **Price:** $34.95. **Description:** Provides tips and techniques for becoming a professional dancer in Hollywood, including how to prepare a resume and get a dance agent. **Availability:** VHS.

6402 ■ Dynamic Dance: Principles of Choreography
Stagestep
4701 Bath St., #46B
Philadelphia, PA 19137
Ph: (215)636-9000
Free: 800-523-0960
Fax: (267)672-2912
Co. E-mail: stagestep@stagestep.com
URL: http://stagestep.com
Released: 19??. **Price:** $34.95. **Description:** Provides instruction on how to use the basic principles of choreography to create powerful modern and jazz dance routines. **Availability:** VHS.

6403 ■ Eight Great Steps to Choreography
Stagestep
4701 Bath St., #46B
Philadelphia, PA 19137
Ph: (215)636-9000
Free: 800-523-0960
Fax: (267)672-2912
Co. E-mail: stagestep@stagestep.com
URL: http://stagestep.com
Released: 19??. **Price:** $49.95. **Description:** Students from the Joffrey Ballet School demonstrate eight choreographic concepts, including the use of patterns, pace, and orchestration. **Availability:** VHS.

6404 ■ Flatfooting Workshop
Stagestep
4701 Bath St., #46B
Philadelphia, PA 19137
Ph: (215)636-9000
Free: 800-523-0960
Fax: (267)672-2912
Co. E-mail: stagestep@stagestep.com
URL: http://stagestep.com
Released: 19??. **Price:** $50.00. **Description:** Presents 27 flatfooting steps, beginning with the basics and moving through to an advanced level. Features Ira Bernstein in three dancing samples. **Availability:** VHS.

6405 ■ Funk, Funk & More Funk
Stagestep
4701 Bath St., #46B
Philadelphia, PA 19137
Ph: (215)636-9000
Free: 800-523-0960

Fax: (267)672-2912
Co. E-mail: stagestep@stagestep.com
URL: http://stagestep.com
Released: 19??. **Price:** $39.95. **Description:** Cathy Roe and Lyn Cramer present three high energy dances for beginners, intermediate, and advanced dancers. **Availability:** VHS.

6406 ■ *Irish Dance*
Leslie T. McClure
PO Box 1223
Pebble Beach, CA 93953
Ph: (831)656-0553
Fax: (831)656-0555
Co. E-mail: leslie@411videoinfo.com
URL: http://www.411videoinfo.com
Released: 1997. **Price:** $12.99. **Description:** Two-volume set celebrates authentic Irish dance, culture, and tradition. **Availability:** VHS.

6407 ■ *Jazzin' across the Floor*
Stagestep
4701 Bath St., #46B
Philadelphia, PA 19137
Ph: (215)636-9000
Free: 800-523-0960
Fax: (267)672-2912
Co. E-mail: stagestep@stagestep.com
URL: http://stagestep.com
Released: 19??. **Price:** $39.95. **Description:** Instructor Bob Rizzo provides step-by-step instruction for jazz and lyrical dance. **Availability:** VHS.

6408 ■ *Leonard Reed's Shim Sham Shimmy*
Stagestep
4701 Bath St., #46B
Philadelphia, PA 19137
Ph: (215)636-9000
Free: 800-523-0960
Fax: (267)672-2912
Co. E-mail: stagestep@stagestep.com
URL: http://stagestep.com
Released: 19??. **Price:** $48.00. **Description:** Tap instructor Rusty Frank teaches the Shim Sham Shimmy, the Freeze Chorus, and the Shim Sham II. **Availability:** VHS.

6409 ■ *Lifts for Your Choreography: From Beginner to Spectacular, Vol. 1*
Stagestep
4701 Bath St., #46B
Philadelphia, PA 19137
Ph: (215)636-9000
Free: 800-523-0960
Fax: (267)672-2912
Co. E-mail: stagestep@stagestep.com
URL: http://stagestep.com
Released: 19??. **Price:** $34.95. **Description:** Presents a variety of easy dance lifts and explains how they are incorporated into routines. **Availability:** VHS.

6410 ■ *Rommett Floor-Barre Technique: A Method to Develop and Refine Ballet Technique*
Stagestep
4701 Bath St., #46B
Philadelphia, PA 19137
Ph: (215)636-9000
Free: 800-523-0960
Fax: (267)672-2912
Co. E-mail: stagestep@stagestep.com
URL: http://stagestep.com
Released: 19??. **Price:** $53.00. **Description:** Zena Rommett combines ballet and anatomical principles to develop a teaching method that helps dancers increase vitality, prevent injury, and more. **Availability:** VHS.

6411 ■ *Suhaila Unveiled*
Tapeworm Video Distributors
25876 The Old Road #141
Stevenson Ranch, CA 91381
Ph: (661)257-4904
Fax: (661)257-4820
Co. E-mail: sales@tapeworm.com
URL: http://www.tapeworm.com
Released: 1996. **Description:** Suhaila Salimpour performs exotic dances. **Availability:** VHS.

6412 ■ *Tap Dancin'*
Stagestep
4701 Bath St., #46B
Philadelphia, PA 19137
Ph: (215)636-9000
Free: 800-523-0960
Fax: (267)672-2912
Co. E-mail: stagestep@stagestep.com
URL: http://stagestep.com
Released: 19??. **Price:** $26.95. **Description:** Judy Ann Bassing demonstrates two tap routines, with each step presented independently. **Availability:** VHS.

6413 ■ *Tappin' across the Floor*
Stagestep
4701 Bath St., #46B
Philadelphia, PA 19137
Ph: (215)636-9000
Free: 800-523-0960
Fax: (267)672-2912
Co. E-mail: stagestep@stagestep.com
URL: http://stagestep.com
Released: 19??. **Price:** $39.95. **Description:** Instructor Jimmy Kichler presents more than 30 tap progressions, suitable for the beginner or the professional. **Availability:** VHS.

6414 ■ *Tappin' Rhythm*
Stagestep
4701 Bath St., #46B
Philadelphia, PA 19137
Ph: (215)636-9000
Free: 800-523-0960
Fax: (267)672-2912
Co. E-mail: stagestep@stagestep.com
URL: http://stagestep.com
Released: 19??. **Price:** $39.95. **Description:** Charles Kelley demonstrates more than 50 tap steps, including the Waltz Clog, Cramproll, and Heel Grind. **Availability:** VHS.

FRANCHISES AND BUSINESS OPPORTUNITIES

6415 ■ Fred Astaire Dance Studios, Inc.
Fred Astaire Dance of N.A. Inc.
10 Bliss Rd.
Longmeadow, MA 01106
Ph: (413)567-3200
Fax: (413)565-2298
Description: Adult ballroom dance instruction. **No. of Franchise Units:** 144. **Founded:** 1947.. **Franchised:** 1952. **Equity Capital Needed:** $125,000. **Franchise Fee:** $87,500-$191,000 which includes an initial franchise. **Training:** Yes.

6416 ■ Webby Dance Company
H & R Dance, Inc.
190 Pomona Ave.
Long Beach, CA 90803
Ph: (513)438-4466
Free: 888-243-2623
Fax: (513)438-3466
Description: Mobile dance business. **No. of Franchise Units:** 4. **No. of Company-Owned Units:** 2. **Founded:** 1975.. **Franchised:** 1999. **Equity Capital Needed:** $22,700-$31,000. **Franchise Fee:** $15,000. **Training:** Yes.

LIBRARIES

6417 ■ Beverly Hills Public Library - Fine Arts Division
444 N. Rexford Dr.
Beverly Hills, CA 90210
Ph: (310)288-2244
Co. E-mail: reference@beverlyhills.org
URL: http://www.beverlyhills.org/exploring/beverlyhillspubliclibrary/
Contact: Jeri Byrne, Librarian, Art
Scope: Art, film, theater, dance, music, photography. **Services:** Interlibrary loan; copying; collection open to the public for reference only. **Founded:** 1970. **Holdings:** 22,000 books/exhibition catalogs; 19,000

slides. **Subscriptions:** 120 journals and other serials. **Telecommunication Services:** nhuntcoffey@beverlyHills.org .

6418 ■ Dance Films Association, Inc.
48 W. 21st St., No. 907
New York, NY 10010
Ph: (212)727-0764
Fax: (212)727-0764
Co. E-mail: info@dancefilms.org
URL: http://dancefilms.org
Contact: Christy Park, Executive Director
Scope: Dance on film and videotape. **Services:** Public and members may view DVDs and VHS in the Library. **Founded:** 1956. **Holdings:** Films/video on dance; articles; journals; programs; videos.

6419 ■ Los Angeles Public Library - Arts, Music and Recreation Department
Tom Bradley Wing, Level 2
630 W. 5th St.
Los Angeles, CA 90071
Ph: (213)228-7225
Fax: (213)228-7239
URL: http://www.lapl.org/central/art.html
Contact: Youngsil Lee, Department Manager
Scope: Art, architecture, music, opera, sports and recreation, film, photography, dance, costume, urban planning, gardening, circus. **Services:** Interlibrary loan; copying; department open to the public. **Founded:** 1872. **Holdings:** 166,000 volumes; 155,000 clippings; 34,000 scores; 220,000 mounted pictures; 3000 music CDs. **Subscriptions:** 600 journals and other serials.

6420 ■ New York Public Library - The Research Libraries - Jerome Robbins Dance Division
40 Lincoln Center Plaza, 3rd Fl.
New York, NY 10023-7498
Ph: (212)870-1657
Fax: (212)870-1869
Co. E-mail: dance@nypl.org
URL: http://www.nypl.org/locations/lpa/jerome-robbins-dance-division
Contact: Jan Schmidt, Curator
Scope: All forms of dance. **Services:** Copying; collection open to the public. **Founded:** 1944. **Holdings:** 42,000 books; 2200 original drawings and stage designs; manuscripts (1 million items); 1700 reels of microfilm; 38,500 reels of videotape and film; 3270 hours of oral history tapes; 2200 scrapbooks; 25,800 files of clippings and reviews; 325,800 photographs and negatives; 4500 posters; 6000 prints; 100,800 programs. **Subscriptions:** 247 journals and other serials.

6421 ■ St. Norbert Arts Centre Archives
PO Box 175
Winnipeg, MB, Canada R3V 1L6
Ph: (204)269-0564
Fax: (204)261-1927
Co. E-mail: snac@snac.mb.ca
URL: http://www.snac.mb.ca
Contact: Louise May, Director
Scope: Art - visual art, music, theater, and dance. **Services:** Archives open to the public. **Founded:** 1996. **Holdings:** Graphic materials; textual records.

6422 ■ Toronto Reference Library - Performing Arts Centre
789 Yonge St., 5th Fl.
Toronto, ON, Canada M4W 2G8
Ph: (416)393-7131
Fax: (416)393-7147
Co. E-mail: mmilne@torontopubliclibrary.ca
Contact: Mary Shantz, Manager
Scope: Music, dance, film, theatre. **Services:** Library open to the public. **Founded:** 1915. **Holdings:** 17,000 LPs; 12,000 CDs; 47,000 music scores; 11,000 photographs; 4000 original stage drawings; prints; engravings; Canadian theatre and concert programs; clippings; archival materials; Canadian sheet music; microfiche; microfilm. **Subscriptions:** 150 journals and other serials.

6423 ■ University of Cincinnati - College Conservatory of Music - Gorno Memorial Music Library
600 Carl Blegen Library
Cincinnati, OH 45221-0152
Ph: (513)556-1970
Fax: (513)556-3777
Co. E-mail: mark.palkovic@uc.edu
URL: http://www.libraries.uc.edu/libraries/ccm/index.
html
Contact: Mark Palkovic, Director, Library Services
Scope: Music performance, history, and theory; musicology; dance; theater arts; music education. **Services:** Interlibrary loan; copying; Library open to the public for reference use only. **Founded:** 1949. **Holdings:** 40,500 bound volumes; 74,000 scores; 57,000 sound recordings; 6000 microforms; 3000 media materials. **Subscriptions:** 550 journals and other serials. **Telecommunication Services:** paul.cauthen@uc.edu.

6424 ■ University of North Carolina at Greensboro - Special Collections & Rare Books, Jackson Library - Dance Collection
PO Box 26170
Greensboro, NC 27402-6170
Ph: (336)334-5246
Free: 888-245-0180
Fax: (336)334-5399
Co. E-mail: carolyn_shankle@uncg.edu
URL: http://library.uncg.edu/info/depts/scua
Contact: William K. Finley
Scope: History of the dance, modern dance, dance notation. **Services:** Collection open to the public for research. **Telecommunication Services:** bill_finley@uncg.edu.

6425 ■ University of North Carolina School of the Arts - Semans Library
UNC School of the Arts
1533 S. Main St.
Winston-Salem, NC 27127
Ph: (336)770-3270
Fax: (336)770-3271
Co. E-mail: rebeccab@uncsa.edu
URL: http://www.uncsa.edu/library
Contact: Christia Thomason
Scope: Music, art and design, theater, film, dance, humanities. **Services:** Interlibrary loan; Library open to the public. **Founded:** 1965. **Holdings:** 111,000 books; 9000 bound periodical volumes; 50,000 music scores; 45,000 sound recordings; 5200 DVDs and videos. **Subscriptions:** 470 journals and other serials; 25 newspapers.

RESEARCH CENTERS

6426 ■ Laban/Bartenieff Institute of Movement Studies Inc. (LIMS)
11 E 4th St.
New York, NY 10003
Ph: (212)643-8888
Fax: (212)643-8888
Co. E-mail: anabella@limsonline.org
URL: http://www.limsonline.org
Contact: Virginia Reed, President
Description: Professional movement educators, dancers, choreographers, dance therapists, behavioral researchers, teachers, fitness and athletic trainers, health practitioners, and students. Devoted to the study of human movement. Studies the role of movement in human behavior through training, research, and practical application. Offers certificate program in Laban movement studies, workshops, and seminars. Supports research and development projects of practicing movement analysts. **Scope:** movement, psychology, art. **Founded:** 1978. **Subscriptions:** 250 archival material books. **Publications:** *Movement Studies* (Annual); *Movement Studies* (Annual); *Movement News*; *Journal of Laban Movement Studies*. **Educational Activities:** Bartenieff Program, experiential approach to somatic movement; Laban In the Performing Arts at Bratislava in Movement; Certification Program in Laban Movement Studies. **Telecommunication Services:** info@limsonline.org.

6427 ■ Congress on Research in Dance (CORD)
3416 Primm Ln.
Birmingham, AL 35216
Ph: (205)823-5517
Fax: (205)823-2760
Co. E-mail: ashanti@cordance.org
URL: http://www.cordance.org
Contact: Marta Savigliano, President
Description: Represents colleges, universities, and libraries around the world as well as from the United States. Works to encourage research in all aspects of dance and related fields. Fosters the exchange of ideas, resources, and methodologies through publications, international and regional conferences, and workshops. Promotes the accessibility of research materials. Works with other professional organizations to provide members unique opportunities to network with others in and outside the field of dance. Provides vehicles for the dissemination of scholarship over the years; has provided and continues to provide leadership in dance scholarship by defining the standards for the field. **Founded:** 1965. **Publications:** *Annual conference proceeding*; *CORD Newsletter* (Semiannual); *Dance Research Journal* (Semiannual); *Membership Directory*; *CORD Conference Proceedings*; *Dance Research Journal* (Semiannual). **Educational Activities:** National and regional conferences (Annual); CORD Workshops. **Awards:** Award for Outstanding Publications (Annual); Graduate Student Research Award (Annual); Outstanding Contribution to Dance Research (Annual); Outstanding Leadership in Dance Research (Annual); Outstanding Service to Dance Research (Annual); Trust for Dance Scholarship (Annual). **Telecommunication Services:** membership@cordance.org.

START-UP INFORMATION

6428 ■ *Culinary Careers: How to Get Your Dream Job in Food with Advice from Top Culinary Professionals*
Pub: Crown Business Books
Ed: Rick Smilow, Anne E. McBride. **Released:** May 4, 2010. **Price:** $16.99. **Description:** Top culinary experts offer advice for working in or owning a food service firm.

6429 ■ *"Franchises with an Eye on Chicago" in Crain's Chicago Business (Vol. 34, March 14, 2011, No. 11, pp. 20)*
Pub: Crain Communications Inc.
Description: Profiles of franchise companies seeking franchisees for the Chicago area include: Extreme Pita, a sandwich shop; Hand and Stone, offering massage, facial and waxing services; Molly Maid, home-cleaning service; Primrose Schools, private accredited schools for children 6 months to 6 hears and after-school programs; Protect Painters, residential and light-commercial painting contractor; and Wingstop, a restaurant offering chicken wings in nine flavors, fries and side dishes.

6430 ■ *Start and Run a Delicatessen: Small Business Starters Series*
Pub: How To Books
Ed: Deborah Penrith. **Released:** November 9, 2010. **Price:** $30.00. **Description:** Information for starting and running a successful delicatessen is provided. Insight is offered into selecting a location, researching the market, writing a business plan and more.

6431 ■ *Start Small, Finish Big*
Pub: Business Plus/Warner Business Books
Ed: Fred DeLuca with John P. Hayes. **Released:** April 2009. **Price:** $16.95. **Description:** Fred DeLuca is profiled; after founding the multi-billion dollar chain of Subway sandwich restaurants, DeLuca is committed to helping microentrepreneurs, people who start successful small businesses with less than $1,000.

ASSOCIATIONS AND OTHER ORGANIZATIONS

6432 ■ *Canadian Foodservice Industry Operations Report*
316 Bloor St. W
Toronto, ON, Canada M5S 1W5
Ph: (416)923-8416
Free: 800-387-5649
Fax: (416)923-1450
Co. E-mail: info@crfa.ca
URL: http://www.crfa.ca
Contact: Garth Whyte, President
Released: Biennial

6433 ■ **Canadian Restaurant and Foodservices Association (CRFA)—Association Canadienne des Restaurateurs et des Services Alimentaires**
316 Bloor St. W
Toronto, ON, Canada M5S 1W5
Ph: (416)923-8416
Free: 800-387-5649
Fax: (416)923-1450
Co. E-mail: info@crfa.ca
URL: http://www.crfa.ca
Contact: Garth Whyte, President
Description: Restaurant and food service corporations, hotels, caterers, and food service suppliers and educators. Seeks to create a favorable business environment for members. Represents members' interests before government; conducts trade research. Makes available group buying programs and other services to members; owns and operates three industry trade shows. **Scope:** hospitality industries. **Founded:** 1944. **Subscriptions:** books periodicals. **Publications:** *Foodservice Facts* (Annual); *Legislation Guide* (Quarterly); *Canadian Foodservice Industry Operations Report* (Biennial); *CRFA National Hospitality News.* **Educational Activities:** Canadian Food and Beverage Show (Annual); ApEx; Canadian International Food and Beverage Show (Annual).

6434 ■ *Foodservice Facts*
316 Bloor St. W
Toronto, ON, Canada M5S 1W5
Ph: (416)923-8416
Free: 800-387-5649
Fax: (416)923-1450
Co. E-mail: info@crfa.ca
URL: http://www.crfa.ca
Contact: Garth Whyte, President
Released: Annual

6435 ■ **International Dairy-Deli-Bakery Association (IDDBA)**
PO Box 5528
Madison, WI 53705-0528
Ph: (608)310-5000
Fax: (608)238-6330
Co. E-mail: iddba@iddba.org
URL: http://www.iddba.org
Contact: Steve Beekhuizen, President
Description: Companies and organizations engaged in the production, processing, packaging, marketing, promotion, and/or selling of cheese and cheese products, bakery, or delicatessen and delicatessen-related items. Aims to further the relationship between manufacturing, production, marketing and distribution channels utilized in the delivery of deli, dairy, and bakery foods to the marketplace. Develops and disseminates information concerning deli, dairy, and bakery foods. **Founded:** 1964. **Publications:** *Dairy-Deli-Bake Digest* (Monthly); *IDDBA and You* (Monthly); *Trainer's Tool Kit*; *Who's Who in Dairy-Deli-Bakery* (Periodic); *Dairy-Deli-Bake Digest*; *Who's Who in Dairy-Deli Bakery*; *WrapUp*; *IDDBA Legis-Letter*. **Educational Activities:** Dairy-Deli-Bake (Annual); Dairy-Deli-Bake Seminar and Expo (Annual). **Awards:** International Dairy-Deli-Bakery Association Undergraduate Scholarships; Undergraduate/Graduate Scholarships (Annual).

6436 ■ *Legislation Guide*
316 Bloor St. W
Toronto, ON, Canada M5S 1W5
Ph: (416)923-8416
Free: 800-387-5649
Fax: (416)923-1450
Co. E-mail: info@crfa.ca
URL: http://www.crfa.ca
Contact: Garth Whyte, President
Released: Quarterly

6437 ■ **National Restaurant Association**
2055 L St. NW
Washington, DC 20036
Ph: (202)331-5900
Free: 800-424-5156
Fax: (202)331-2429
Co. E-mail: info@restaurant.org
URL: http://www.restaurant.org
Contact: Dawn Sweeney, President
E-mail: dsweeney@restaurant.org
Description: Represents restaurants, cafeterias, clubs, contract foodservice management, drive-ins, caterers, institutional food services and other members of the foodservice industry; also represents establishments belonging to non-affiliated state and local restaurant associations in governmental affairs. Supports foodservice education and research in several educational institutions. Is affiliated with the Educational Foundation of the National Restaurant Association to provide training and education for operators, food and equipment manufacturers, distributors and educators. Has 300,000 member locations. **Scope:** restaurant management, cookery, menus. **Founded:** 1919. **Subscriptions:** 5000 periodicals. **Publications:** *National Restaurant Association--Washington Report* (Semimonthly); *Restaurant Industry Operations Report*; *Restaurants USA: The Monthly Magazine of the National Restaurant Assn* (Monthly); *Who's Who in the Foodservice Industry*; *Restaurant Information Abstracts* (Biweekly). **Awards:** Restaurant Good Neighbor Award (Annual); Hennessy Awards.

REFERENCE WORKS

6438 ■ *"Burger Market Sizzling with Newcomers" in Boston Business Journal (Vol. 29, June 10, 2011, No. 5, pp. 1)*
Pub: American City Business Journals Inc.
Ed: Ryan Sharrow. **Description:** The burger trend in Maryland is on the rise with burger joints either opening up or expanding into several branches. Startup costs for this kind of business range between $250,000 to $400,000. With a growth rate of roughly 17 percent in 2009, this so-called better burger segment of the burger categories is expected to dominate the market for quite some time.

6439 ■ *Eastern Perishable Products Association--Membership Directory*
Pub: Eastern Perishable Products Association Inc.
URL(s): www.eppainc.org. **Released:** Continuous **Price:** Free available to members only. **Covers:** About 400 member manufacturers, retailers, brokers,

and distributors of perishable products located primarily in the New York metropolitan area (including New Jersey, Pennsylvania and Connecticut). **Entries include:** Company name, address, phone, name of contact, product or service provided. **Arrangement:** Alphabetical Company name, company type, contact Alpa last name.

TRADE PERIODICALS

6440 ■ *ConcepTrac*

Pub: Technomic Information Services

Ed: Eric Giandelone, Editor, egiandelone@technomic.com. **Released:** Monthly. **Price:** $395, individuals. **Description:** Provides news on chain restaurant development. Includes information on decor, atmosphere, service styles, cooking preparation methods, and unit economics.

VIDEOCASSETTES/ AUDIOCASSETTES

6441 ■ *Be Safe, Not Sorry*

International Dairy-Deli-Bakery Association (IDDBA)
PO Box 5528
Madison, WI 53705-0528
Ph: (608)310-5000
Fax: (608)238-6330
Co. E-mail: iddba@iddba.org
URL: http://www.iddba.org
Contact: Steve Beekhuizen, President
Released: 19??. **Price:** $160.00. **Description:** Deli food safety training course. **Availability:** VHS.

6442 ■ *Center on Profit*

International Dairy-Deli-Bakery Association (IDDBA)
PO Box 5528
Madison, WI 53705-0528
Ph: (608)310-5000
Fax: (608)238-6330
Co. E-mail: iddba@iddba.org
URL: http://www.iddba.org
Contact: Steve Beekhuizen, President
Released: 19??. **Price:** $160.00. **Description:** Teaches managers how to reduce unknown shrink, write effective orders and schedules, plus calculate deli items' profit and gross margin contribution to margin. **Availability:** VHS.

6443 ■ *A Classic Guide to Custom Deli Trays*

International Dairy-Deli-Bakery Association (IDDBA)
PO Box 5528
Madison, WI 53705-0528
Ph: (608)310-5000
Fax: (608)238-6330
Co. E-mail: iddba@iddba.org
URL: http://www.iddba.org
Contact: Steve Beekhuizen, President
Released: 19??. **Price:** $100.00. **Description:** Merchandising and training video. **Availability:** VHS.

6444 ■ *Clean, Fresh & Friendly*

International Dairy-Deli-Bakery Association (IDDBA)
PO Box 5528
Madison, WI 53705-0528
Ph: (608)310-5000
Fax: (608)238-6330
Co. E-mail: iddba@iddba.org
URL: http://www.iddba.org
Contact: Steve Beekhuizen, President
Released: 19??. **Price:** $160.00. **Description:** Deli customer service training video. **Availability:** VHS.

6445 ■ *Deli Meats 101*

International Dairy-Deli-Bakery Association (IDDBA)
PO Box 5528
Madison, WI 53705-0528
Ph: (608)310-5000
Fax: (608)238-6330
Co. E-mail: iddba@iddba.org
URL: http://www.iddba.org
Contact: Steve Beekhuizen, President
Released: 19??. **Price:** $50.00. **Description:** Discusses why deli sliced meats are a high turn product; different kinds of deli ham, turkey and beef products; and information to speak knowledgeably about them. **Availability:** VHS.

6446 ■ *Deli Meats & Poultry: Classic Tastes for Today's Consumer*

International Dairy-Deli-Bakery Association (IDDBA)
PO Box 5528
Madison, WI 53705-0528
Ph: (608)310-5000
Fax: (608)238-6330
Co. E-mail: iddba@iddba.org
URL: http://www.iddba.org
Contact: Steve Beekhuizen, President
Released: 19??. **Price:** $100.00. **Description:** Merchandising and training video. **Availability:** VHS.

6447 ■ *Know What You're Selling*

International Dairy-Deli-Bakery Association (IDDBA)
PO Box 5528
Madison, WI 53705-0528
Ph: (608)310-5000
Fax: (608)238-6330
Co. E-mail: iddba@iddba.org
URL: http://www.iddba.org
Contact: Steve Beekhuizen, President
Released: 19??. **Price:** $160.00. **Description:** Deli product knowledge training video. **Availability:** VHS.

6448 ■ *Successful Food Demonstration & Sampling*

International Dairy-Deli-Bakery Association (IDDBA)
PO Box 5528
Madison, WI 53705-0528
Ph: (608)310-5000
Fax: (608)238-6330
Co. E-mail: iddba@iddba.org
URL: http://www.iddba.org
Contact: Steve Beekhuizen, President
Released: 19??. **Price:** $100.00. **Description:** Presents ways supermarket dairy, deli, bakery and food-service employees can sell more through food demonstrations and sampling. **Availability:** VHS.

TRADE SHOWS AND CONVENTIONS

6449 ■ *Dairy-Deli-Bake Seminar and Expo*

International Dairy-Deli-Bakery Association (IDDBA)
PO Box 5528
Madison, WI 53705-0528
Ph: (608)310-5000
Fax: (608)238-6330
Co. E-mail: iddba@iddba.org
URL: http://www.iddba.org
Contact: Steve Beekhuizen, President
URL(s): www.iddba.org. **Frequency:** Annual. **Audience:** Retailers, wholesalers, distributors, brokers, and manufacturers of the dairy, deli, and bakery industry. **Principal Exhibits:** Dairy, deli, and bakery products, packaging, and equipment.

6450 ■ *International Restaurant & Foodservice Show of New York*

Reed Exhibitions North American Headquarters
383 Main Ave.
Norwalk, CT 06851
Ph: (203)840-4800
Fax: (203)840-5805
Co. E-mail: inquiry@reedexpo.com
URL: http://www.reedexpo.com
URL(s): www.internationalrestaurantny.com/. **Frequency:** Annual. **Principal Exhibits:** Equipment, supplies, and services for the food products, foodservice, restaurant, and institutional food service industries. **Dates and Locations:** , Jacob K. Javits Convention Center.

CONSULTANTS

6451 ■ *Erin Services Inc.*

111 Travelers Way
Saint Simons Island, GA 31522-5632
Ph: (912)638-9916

Fax: (912)638-5701
Co. E-mail: dennisd@ns.technonet.com
Contact: Dennis J. Donnelly, III, President
E-mail: dennis179@yahoo.com

Scope: Offers assistance in technical proposal production, marketing, and research. Industries served: Food service, janitorial, landscaping, hospitality, and lodging, parks, and recreational. **Founded:** 1990.

6452 ■ *Riedel Marketing Group (RMG)*

5327 E Pinchot Ave.
Phoenix, AZ 85018-2963
Ph: (602)840-4948
Fax: (602)840-4928
Co. E-mail: ajr@4rmg.com
URL: http://www.4rmg.com
Contact: Timothy D. Riedel, President

Scope: The house wares and food service industry strategic marketing planning experts. Help manufacturers of house wares and food products solve marketing problems and identify and exploit marketing opportunities. Provides a full-range of strategic marketing planning services including development of marketing strategy, development of fact-based sales presentations, category management, definition of market opportunities and new product development exclusively to the house wares and food service industries. **Founded:** 1991. **Publications:** "Your Key Consumer: Her Take on the International Home & Housewares Show," Mar, 2008; "What's Hot, What's Not: The Consumer Speaks," Mar, 2006; "HIPsters SPEAK: What We Love to Buy and Why," Apr, 2005; "Influentials: Who They Are and Why You Should Care," Jun, 2004; "The Seven Secrets to Selling More Housewares," Jan, 2003. **Seminars:** Consumers Speak: What We Love to Buy and Why, What Do Those Consumers Think; The Seven Secrets to Selling More House wares; **Special Services:** Home Trend Influentials Panel.

FRANCHISES AND BUSINESS OPPORTUNITIES

6453 ■ *Atlantic City Sub Shops Inc.*

124 Warf Rd.
Egg Harbor Twp., NJ 08234
Ph: (609)926-4560
Fax: (609)641-2121

Description: Sandwich shop. **No. of Franchise Units:** 1. **No. of Company-Owned Units:** 2. **Founded:** 1968.. **Franchised:** 1990. **Equity Capital Needed:** $100,000-$275,000. **Franchise Fee:** $15,000. **Royalty Fee:** 5%. **Training:** Yes.

6454 ■ *Baker Bros. American Deli*

BB Franchising, Inc.
5500 Greenville Ave., Ste. 1102
Dallas, TX 75206
Ph: (214)696-8780
Fax: (214)696-8809

Description: Sandwich shop. **No. of Franchise Units:** 8. **No. of Company-Owned Units:** 8. **Founded:** 1998.. **Franchised:** 2000. **Equity Capital Needed:** $1,500,000 net worth; $750,000 liquid assets. **Franchise Fee:** $25,000. **Training:** Yes.

6455 ■ *Big Town Hero*

Hero Systems, Inc.
333 SW Taylor St., Ste. 200
Portland, OR 97204
Ph: (503)228-4376
Fax: (503)228-8778

Description: Sandwiches, salads, soups, fresh bread and baked goods from scratch. Fast and friendly. **No. of Franchise Units:** 34. **Founded:** 1983.. **Franchised:** 1989. **Equity Capital Needed:** $75,000-$175,000. **Franchise Fee:** $20,000. **Training:** Yes.

6456 ■ *Blendz Franchise System, Inc.*

267 E Campbell Ave., Ste., 200
Campbell, CA 95008
Free: 866-425-3639

Fax: (408)273-6766
Description: Tossed-to-order salads, panini, smoothies and soups. **No. of Franchise Units:** 11. **Founded:** 2002.. **Franchised:** 2005. **Equity Capital Needed:** $277,100-$350,400. **Franchise Fee:** $25,000. **Training:** Yes.

6457 ■ Camille's Sidewalk Cafe
Camille's Franchise System, LLC
8801 S Yale Ave., Ste. 400
Tulsa, OK 74137-3575
Ph: (918)488-9727
Free: 800-230-7004
Fax: (918)497-1916
Description: Sidewalk cafe serving wraps and sandwiches. **No. of Franchise Units:** 21. **No. of Company-Owned Units:** 1. **Founded:** 1996.. **Franchised:** 1999. **Equity Capital Needed:** $214,000-$280,000. **Franchise Fee:** $25,000. **Financial Assistance:** Yes. **Training:** Yes.

6458 ■ Capt. Sub
Grinner Food Systems
105 Walker St.
Truro, NS, Canada B2N 5G9
Ph: (902)820-3108
Fax: (902)820-3109
Co. E-mail: d.crane@grinners.ca
URL: http://www.captsub.ca
Description: The franchise specializes in delicious oven roasted submarine sandwiches. **No. of Franchise Units:** 27. **No. of Company-Owned Units:** 2. **Founded:** 1972.. **Franchised:** 1972. **Equity Capital Needed:** $120,000-$160,000 total investment; $40,000-$70,000 start-up capital required. **Franchise Fee:** $20,000. **Training:** Offers management and staff on start-up.

6459 ■ Cheba Hut Roasted Subs
600 S Sherwood St.
Fort Collins, CO 80521
Ph: (970)420-7082
URL: http://www.chebahut.com
Description: Toasted sandwiches & salads. **No. of Franchise Units:** 14. **Founded:** 1998. **Franchised:** 2002. **Equity Capital Needed:** $149,500-$304,500. **Franchise Fee:** $30,000. **Royalty Fee:** 4%. **Financial Assistance:** Third party financing available. **Training:** Available 14 days at headquarters, 7 days onsite and ongoing support.

6460 ■ Chedd's Gourmet Grilled Cheese
1906 Pearl St.
Denver, CO 80203
Ph: (303)948-1520
Fax: (303)948-8801
Co. E-mail: info@chedds.com
URL: http://www.chedds.com
Description: Gourmet grilled cheese sandwiches. **No. of Company-Owned Units:** 2. **Founded:** 2003.. **Franchised:** 2007. **Equity Capital Needed:** $126,500-$323,500. **Franchise Fee:** $35,000. **Royalty Fee:** 6%. **Training:** Provides 2-3 weeks training at headquarters, 1 week at franchisee's location and ongoing support.

6461 ■ Coffee Time Donuts Inc.
77 Progress Ave.
Toronto, ON, Canada M1P 2Y7
Ph: (416)288-8515
Fax: (416)288-8895
Co. E-mail: franchising@coffeetime.ca
URL: http://www.coffeetime.ca
Description: The menu includes donuts, muffins, croissants, pastries and gourmet blend coffee, soups, chili, salads, sandwiches and various hot and cold beverages. store, serving customers in a warm and efficient manner and fostering good employee relationships. **No. of Franchise Units:** 184. **No. of Company-Owned Units:** 16. **Founded:** 1982.. **Franchised:** 1986. **Equity Capital Needed:** $100,000-$360,000. **Training:** Yes.

6462 ■ Coney Beach
8801 S Yale, Ste. 400
Tulsa, OK 74137
Ph: (918)488-9727

Fax: (918)497-1916
Description: Hot dogs, hamburgers & fries. **No. of Franchise Units:** 4. **No. of Company-Owned Units:** 1. **Founded:** 2006.. **Franchised:** 2007. **Equity Capital Needed:** $240,500-$493,000. **Franchise Fee:** $25,000. **Royalty Fee:** 6%. **Financial Assistance:** Limited third party financing available.

6463 ■ Cousins Subs
Cousins Subs Systems, Inc.
N83 W13400 Leon Rd.
Menomonee Falls, WI 53051
Ph: (262)253-7700
Fax: (262)253-7710
Co. E-mail: betterfranchise@cousinssubs.com
URL: http://www.cousinssubs.com
Description: Submarine sandwich operation, with over 20 years of expertise. Volume-oriented, fast-service concept in an upscale, in-line, strip or free-standing location, some with drive-up windows. Franchising opportunities available for single, multi-unit and area developer franchisees, seminars and training classes. A corporate area representative meets with each franchise location management 3 times per month to maintain communications and assist in problem solving. **No. of Franchise Units:** 141. **No. of Company-Owned Units:** 16. **Founded:** 1972.. **Franchised:** 1985. **Equity Capital Needed:** $80,000 cash, $106,700-$288,300 total investment. **Franchise Fee:** $25,000. **Training:** Includes a store building seminar for site selection, lease negotiation and construction 30 days of hands-on training, plus 10 days of opening assistance and training. National and local store marketing support.

6464 ■ Doc Green's Gourmet Salads
782 Ponce de Leon Ave.
Atlanta, GA 30306
Ph: (404)844-3225
Fax: (404)446-1755
Description: Salads, flatbread sandwiches & bistro fare. **No. of Franchise Units:** 12. **No. of Company-Owned Units:** 1. **Founded:** 2003. **Franchised:** 2004. **Equity Capital Needed:** $367,000-$655,000. **Franchise Fee:** $25,000. **Royalty Fee:** 5%. **Training:** Offers 2 1/2 weeks training at headquarters, 1 week at franchisee's location and ongoing support.

6465 ■ Earl of Sandwich LLC (Orlando, Florida)
4700 Millenia Blvd., Ste. 400
Orlando, FL 32839
Ph: (877)426-3275
Fax: (407)992-2987
Co. E-mail: info@earlofsandwichusa.com
URL: http://www.earlofsandwichusa.com
Description: Sandwiches, wraps, salads, and desserts. **No. of Franchise Units:** 6. **No. of Company-Owned Units:** 2. **Founded:** 2003.. **Franchised:** 2005. **Equity Capital Needed:** $375,000-$400,000. **Franchise Fee:** $25,000. **Royalty Fee:** 6%. **Financial Assistance:** Third party financing available. **Telecommunication Services:** franchise@earlofsandwichusa.com.

6466 ■ East Coast Subs
RCLC Enterprises, Inc.
949 E Pioneer Rd., St. 2B
Draper, UT 84020
Ph: (801)352-1400
Fax: (801)619-4038
Description: Sandwiches and Philly subs. **No. of Franchise Units:** 2. **No. of Company-Owned Units:** 2. **Founded:** 1991.. **Franchised:** 2005. **Equity Capital Needed:** $90,500-$113,500. **Franchise Fee:** $12,500. **Training:** Yes.

6467 ■ Erbert & Gerbert's Subs & Clubs
Erbert & Gerbert's & Friends
5828 Arndt
Eau Claire, WI 54701
Ph: (715)833-1375
Fax: (715)833-8523
Description: Offers top-quality, gourmet submarine and club sandwiches on bread baked fresh onsite. A delivery service complements eat-in and carry-out services. **No. of Franchise Units:** 52. **No. of Company-Owned Units:** 1. **Founded:** 1988.. **Franchised:** 1992. **Equity Capital Needed:** Net worth of

$300,000, $75,000 liquid. **Franchise Fee:** $26,500. **Training:** 3 week training with control and quality standards covered in the first weekly section. The second week involves administrative and management training required for cost control, payroll, financial management, etc. This is followed by 1 week of training at the time of start-up in the franchisees store.

6468 ■ Frankitude
21 NW Miami Ct.
Miami, FL 33128
Ph: (305)371-9875
Free: 877-275-8778
Description: Hot dogs, salads, panini, and wraps. **No. of Franchise Units:** 1. **No. of Company-Owned Units:** 1. **Founded:** 2006.. **Franchised:** 2006. **Equity Capital Needed:** $170,200-$325,000 (Express/kiosk option available). **Franchise Fee:** $25,000. **Royalty Fee:** 6%. **Training:** Offers 2 weeks training at headquarters, 1 week plus, onsite and ongoing support.

6469 ■ Frullati Cafe & Bakery
Kahala Corp.
9311 E Via De Ventura
Scottsdale, AZ 85258
Ph: (480)362-4800
Free: 800-438-2590
Fax: (480)362-4812
Description: Deli sandwiches, smoothies, salads, soups, etc. **No. of Franchise Units:** 32. **Founded:** 1994. **Franchised:** 1994. **Equity Capital Needed:** $150,900-$511,300. **Franchise Fee:** $30,000. **Royalty Fee:** 6%. **Financial Assistance:** Limited third party financing available. **Training:** Provides 1 week at headquarters, 2 weeks at franchise's location and ongoing support.

6470 ■ Groucho's Deli
Groucho's Franchise System, LLC
Description: Subs & salads. **No. of Franchise Units:** 25. **No. of Company-Owned Units:** 1. **Founded:** 1941. **Franchised:** 2001. **Equity Capital Needed:** $72,700-$310,030. **Franchise Fee:** $10,000-$20,000. **Royalty Fee:** 5.25%. **Training:** Available at headquarters: 134-166 hours. Available at franchisee's location and ongoing support.

6471 ■ Jersey Mike's Subs
Jersey Mike's Franchise Systems, Inc.
2251 Landmark Pl.
Manasquan, NJ 08736
Ph: (732)223-4044
Free: 800-321-7676
Fax: (732)292-8256
Co. E-mail: sales@jerseymikes.com
URL: http://www.jerseymikes.com
Description: Restaurants that serve sandwiches and related items. **No. of Franchise Units:** 483. **No. of Company-Owned Units:** 24. **Founded:** 1956.. **Franchised:** 1987. **Equity Capital Needed:** $100,000 start-up cost; $215,000-$394,000 total investment. **Franchise Fee:** $18,500. **Training:** Offers 9 week training program with ongoing support.

6472 ■ Jimmy John's Gourmet Sandwiches
2212 Fox Dr.
Champaign, IL 61820
Ph: (847)888-7070
Free: 800-546-6904
Fax: (217)359-2956
URL: http://www.jimmyjohns.com
Description: Gourmet sandwich shops, which make, sell and deliver an up-scale signature line of French bread subs and wheat club sandwiches. Stores require small investment and can be located in strip centers, downtown store frontages and food courts in malls. management. **No. of Franchise Units:** 1,208. **No. of Company-Owned Units:** 26. **Founded:** 1983.. **Franchised:** 1993. **Equity Capital Needed:** $300,000 net worth; $80,000 liquid assets. **Franchise Fee:** $35,000. **Training:** Provides 3 week training course in Champaign, IL.

6473 ■ Larry's Giant Subs
4479 Deerwood Lake Pkwy.
Jacksonville, FL 32216
Ph: (904)739-9069

Fax: (904)739-1218
Co. E-mail: Bigone@larryssubs.com
URL: http://www.larryssubs.com

Description: An up-scale, New York-style submarine sandwich shop, featuring 50 varieties of subs and numerous salads. Features easy operation, no experience necessary, non-cooking environment and low royalty. Full training in corporate shop. Additional training at your franchise location. **No. of Franchise Units:** 66. **No. of Company-Owned Units:** 6. **Founded:** 1982.. **Franchised:** 1986. **Equity Capital Needed:** $159,000-$225,000. **Franchise Fee:** $20,000. **Royalty Fee:** 6%. **Financial Assistance:** Third party financing available. **Training:** Provides 3 weeks at corporate headquarters, 1-2 weeks onsite with ongoing support.

6474 ■ Lenny's Sub Shop
Lenny's Franchisor, LLC
8295 Tournament Dr., Ste. 200
Memphis, TN 38125
Ph: (901)753-4002
Fax: (901)753-4395

Description: Subs & philly cheesesteak sandwiches. **No. of Franchise Units:** 150. **No. of Company-Owned Units:** 10. **Founded:** 1998.. **Franchised:** 2001. **Equity Capital Needed:** $250,000 investment. **Franchise Fee:** $25,000. **Financial Assistance:** Yes. **Training:** Yes.

6475 ■ Little King
Little King, Inc.
11811 "I" St.
Omaha, NE 68137
Ph: (402)330-8019
Free: 800-788-9978
Fax: (402)330-3221

Description: Subs and deli-style sandwiches. **No. of Franchise Units:** 15. **Founded:** 1968.. **Franchised:** 1978. **Equity Capital Needed:** $145,000-$200,000 start-up & minimum net worth of $250,000. **Franchise Fee:** $19,000. **Financial Assistance:** Yes. **Training:** Offers 15 days in Omaha and 7-10 days when opening.

6476 ■ Maid-Rite Sandwich Shoppes
Maid-Rite Corp.
2951 86th St.
Des Moines, IA 50322
Ph: (515)276-5448
Fax: (515)276-5449

Description: Fast casual dining franchise. **No. of Franchise Units:** 77. **No. of Company-Owned Units:** 3. **Founded:** 1926.. **Franchised:** 1926. **Equity Capital Needed:** $100,000 liquid / $500,000 net worth. **Franchise Fee:** $35,000. **Training:** Yes.

6477 ■ McAlister's Deli
McAlister's Corp.
731 S Pear Orchard, Ste. 51
Ridgeland, MS 39157
Ph: (601)519-8985
Free: 888-855-3354
Fax: (601)957-0964

Description: Southern style deli. **No. of Franchise Units:** 271. **No. of Company-Owned Units:** 36. **Founded:** 1989.. **Franchised:** 1994. **Equity Capital Needed:** $600,000-$700,000. **Franchise Fee:** $35,000. **Training:** Yes.

6478 ■ Miami Subs Grill
Miami Subs Capital Partners 1
6300 NW 31st Ave.
Ft. Lauderdale, FL 33309
Ph: (954)973-0000
Fax: (954)973-7616

Description: Quick service, made to order menu. **No. of Franchise Units:** 40. **Founded:** 1983.. **Franchised:** 1986. **Equity Capital Needed:** $75,000-$550,000. **Franchise Fee:** $20,000-$30,000. **Training:** Yes.

6479 ■ Mikes Restaurants Inc.
8250 Decarie Blvd., Ste. 310
Montreal, QC, Canada H4P 2P5
Ph: (514)341-5544
Free: 866-341-9782

Fax: (514)341-5635
URL: http://www.mikes.ca

Description: Restaurant serving delicious Italian pizza, sandwiches and pasta. **No. of Franchise Units:** 83. **No. of Company-Owned Units:** 2. **Founded:** 1967.. **Franchised:** 1968. **Equity Capital Needed:** $300,000-$700,000. **Franchise Fee:** $45,000, includes training. **Training:** Provides 10 weeks training.

6480 ■ Mr. Goodcents Franchise Systems Inc.
8997 Commerce Dr.
De Soto, KS 66018
Ph: (913)583-8400
Fax: (913)583-3500

Description: Quick service submarine sandwiches and pasta. **No. of Franchise Units:** 92. **No. of Company-Owned Units:** 3. **Founded:** 1988. **Franchised:** 1990. **Equity Capital Needed:** $161,650-$274,300. **Franchise Fee:** $10,000-$20,000. **Royalty Fee:** 5%. **Financial Assistance:** Third party financing available. **Training:** Offers 5 days training at headquarters, 20 days at franchisee's location and ongoing support.

6481 ■ Mr. Goodcents Subs & Pastas
Mr. Goodcents Franchise Systems, Inc.
8997 Commerce Dr.
DeSoto, KS 66018
Ph: (913)583-8400
Free: 800-648-2368
Fax: (913)583-3500
Co. E-mail: frandev@mrgoodcents.com
URL: http://www.mrgoodcents.com

Description: Quick service restaurant serving lunch and dinner featuring submarine sandwiches with fresh meat and cheese on bread. **No. of Franchise Units:** 100. **No. of Company-Owned Units:** 1. **Founded:** 1989.. **Franchised:** 1990. **Equity Capital Needed:** $75,000. **Franchise Fee:** $20,000. **Training:** 30 days of comprehensive in-house training.

6482 ■ Mr. Pickle's Sandwich Shop
670 Auburn-Folsom Rd., Ste. 106-571
Auburn, CA 95603
Ph: (916)746-7727
Fax: (916)746-7787

Description: Sandwiches, soups, and salads. **No. of Franchise Units:** 24. **Founded:** 1996. **Franchised:** 2006. **Equity Capital Needed:** $249,000 (Express/kiosk option available). **Franchise Fee:** $25,000. **Royalty Fee:** None. **Training:** 2 weeks training included at franchisee's location and ongoing support.

6483 ■ Mr. Pita
Papa Romano's Enterprises, Inc.
24901 Northwestern Hwy., Ste. 444
Southfield, MI 48075
Ph: (248)888-7242
Free: 866-738-7482
Fax: (248)888-0011

Description: Deli serving pita sandwiches, soups, and salads. **No. of Franchise Units:** 29. **Founded:** 1993.. **Franchised:** 1994. **Equity Capital Needed:** $80,000 liquid; $250,000. **Franchise Fee:** $25,000. **Financial Assistance:** Yes. **Training:** Yes.

6484 ■ Must Be Heaven Franchise Corp.
107 W Alamo
Brenham, TX 77833
Ph: (979)830-8536
Fax: (979)836-9913
Co. E-mail: franchise@mustbeheaven.com
URL: http://www.mustbeheaven.com

Description: Soup, sandwiches, salads, pies and ice cream. **No. of Franchise Units:** 10. **Founded:** 1987.. **Franchised:** 1999. **Equity Capital Needed:** $75,000-$100,000. **Franchise Fee:** $30,000. **Training:** Yes.

6485 ■ Mustard Cafe
41 Auto Center Drive, Ste. 103
Foothill Ranch, CA 92610
Ph: (949)716-1000

Description: Sandwiches, soups, and salads. **No. of Franchise Units:** 5. **No. of Company-Owned Units:** 1. **Founded:** 2002. **Franchised:** 2004. **Equity Capital Needed:** $338,000-$536,500. **Franchise**

Fee: $25,000. **Royalty Fee:** 5%. **Training:** Offers 2 weeks training at headquarters, 4 weeks at franchisee's location and ongoing support.

6486 ■ The Original SoupMan
1110 South Ave., Ste. 300
Staten Island, NY 10314
Ph: (877)768-7626

Description: Soups. **No. of Franchise Units:** 16. **No. of Company-Owned Units:** 2. **Founded:** 1984.. **Franchised:** 2005. **Equity Capital Needed:** $79,500-$198,500. **Franchise Fee:** $30,000. **Royalty Fee:** 5%.

6487 ■ Penn Station East Coast Subs
Penn Station, Inc. ·
1226 US Hwy. 50
Milford, OH 45150
Ph: (513)474-5957
Fax: (513)474-7116

Description: Retail sale of various cheesecake and submarine sandwiches, fresh-cut fries and fresh-squeezed lemonade. **No. of Franchise Units:** 183. **No. of Company-Owned Units:** 2. **Founded:** 1985.. **Franchised:** 1987. **Equity Capital Needed:** $100,000 liquidity. **Franchise Fee:** $25,000. **Training:** Yes.

6488 ■ Perfecto's Caffe
Perfecto's Caffe Development LLC
79 N Main St.
Andover, MA 01810
Ph: (978)749-7022
Fax: (978)749-9433

Description: Bagels, muffins, coffee, wraps, salads, and cookies. **No. of Franchise Units:** 2. **No. of Company-Owned Units:** 2. **Founded:** 1993. **Franchised:** 2005. **Equity Capital Needed:** $175,000-$275,000, initial investment. **Franchise Fee:** $20,000. **Training:** Yes.

6489 ■ Port of Subs
Port-of-Subs Inc.
5365 Mae Anne Ave., Ste. A-29
Reno, NV 89523-1841
Ph: (775)747-0555
Free: 800-245-0245
Fax: (775)747-1510
Co. E-mail: jwallace@portofsubs.com
URL: http://www.portofsubs.com

Description: Submarine sandwich franchise, featuring unique front-line method of preparing specialty sandwiches, soups, salads and party platters. Bread is baked fresh daily on premises. **No. of Franchise Units:** 115. **No. of Company-Owned Units:** 25. **Founded:** 1972.. **Franchised:** 1985. **Equity Capital Needed:** $80,000 liquid assets, $250,000 net worth. **Franchise Fee:** $20,000. **Training:** Offers 2 weeks of training, plus 2 weeks in the franchisee's unit during initial opening.

6490 ■ Quizno's Subs
The Quizno's Corp.
1001 17th St., Ste. 175
Denver, CO 80202-2212
Ph: (720)359-3300
Free: 800-335-4782

Description: Italian deli theme, specializing in subs, soups, salads and pasta. **No. of Franchise Units:** 2,772. **No. of Company-Owned Units:** 62. **Founded:** 1981. **Franchised:** 1991. **Equity Capital Needed:** $157,547-$217,527, estimated initial investment for new store. **Franchise Fee:** $5,000-$12,500. **Financial Assistance:** Yes. **Training:** Twenty two day training program includes classroom and in-store training. Grand opening and initial onsite assistance.

6491 ■ Schlotzsky's
Focus Brands Inc.
Franchise Licensing Dept.
200 Glenridge Point Pky., Ste. 200
Atlanta, GA 30342
Ph: (404)255-3250
Free: 800-846-2867
Fax: (800)335-4329

Description: Fast, casual restaurant. **No. of Franchise Units:** 353. **No. of Company-Owned Units:** 38. **Founded:** 1971.. **Franchised:** 1977. **Equity**

Capital Needed: $600,000 liquidity; $1,500,000 net worth (3 store minimum required). **Franchise Fee:** $30,000. **Training:** Yes.

6492 ■ Smash Hit Subs

Orion Food Systems L.L.C.
2930 W Maple St.
Sioux Falls, SD 57107-0745
Ph: (800)336-1320
Free: 800-648-6227
Fax: (605)336-0141
URL: http://www.hotstufffoods.com
Description: Sub sandwiches. **No. of Franchise Units:** 1,300. **No. of Company-Owned Units:** 12. **Founded:** 1984.. **Franchised:** 1986. **Equity Capital Needed:** $25,000. **Franchise Fee:** $4,950. **Financial Assistance:** Yes. **Training:** Yes.

6493 ■ Subway

Doctor's Associates Inc.
Franchise Sales Dept.
325 Bic Dr.
Milford, CT 06460
Ph: (203)877-4281
Free: 800-888-4848
Fax: (203)783-7325
Co. E-mail: franchise@subway.com
URL: http://www.subway.com
Description: Submarine sandwich category with fresh, great tasting, made-for-you sandwiches and salads, many of which have 6 grams of fat or less. Offering a healthful alternative to fatty fast food has made Subway a popular destination for health-conscious consumers. **No. of Franchise Units:** 33,000. **No. of Company-Owned Units:** 1. **Founded:** 1974.. **Franchised:** 1974. **Equity Capital Needed:** $114,800-$258,300 total investment. **Franchise Fee:** $15,000. **Financial Assistance:** 30-V, FRA handbook. **Training:** Provides training and assistance to franchisee's in all areas of business operation.

6494 ■ Sweet Peppers Deli

Sweet peppers Franchise Systems, LLC
PO Box 1368
Columbus, OH 39703
Ph: (662)327-6982
Free: 888-222-9550
Fax: (662)327-1672
Description: Fast casual, deli-style restaurant. **No. of Franchise Units:** 14. **No. of Company-Owned Units:** 5. **Founded:** 1984.. **Franchised:** 2002. **Equity Capital Needed:** $200,000. **Franchise Fee:** $25,000. **Training:** Yes.

6495 ■ Togo's Eatery

Togo's Franchisor, LLC
18 N San Pedro St
San Jose, CA 95110
Ph: (408)280-6569

Free: 877-718-6467
Fax: (866)394-4902
Co. E-mail: franchisesales@togos.com
URL: http://www.togos.com
Description: Fast-food sandwiches. Only Resales are available in the United States. **No. of Franchise Units:** 245. **No. of Company-Owned Units:** 1. **Founded:** 1971.. **Franchised:** 1977. **Equity Capital Needed:** $300,000 net worth; $150,000 liquid; $256,650-$417,300 total investment. **Franchise Fee:** $25,000 10 year term; $40,000 20 year term. **Training:** Offers 2 weeks of onsite training, with periodic follow-up.

6496 ■ Tubby's Sub Shops, Inc.

30551 Edison Dr.
Roseville, MI 48066
Ph: (586)293-5099
Fax: (586)293-5088
Description: Specialty submarine sandwich shop, featuring grilled sandwiches, soups, salads and ice cream. **No. of Franchise Units:** 75. **No. of Company-Owned Units:** 2. **Founded:** 1968.. **Franchised:** 1978. **Equity Capital Needed:** $500,000 net worth; $75,000 cash/assets convertible to cash. **Franchise Fee:** $5,000-$13,000 (varies by type of store). **Training:** Classroom sessions where very facet of your business is covered. Additional onsite assistance is given just prior to opening and during your first few weeks of operation.

6497 ■ Uno Chicago Grill

Pizzeria Uno Corp.
100 Charles Park Rd.
Boston, MA 02132
Ph: (617)218-5272
Free: 877-855-8667
Fax: (617)218-5376
Description: Full service casual theme restaurant. **No. of Franchise Units:** 86. **No. of Company-Owned Units:** 124. **Founded:** 1943.. **Franchised:** 1979. **Equity Capital Needed:** $1,000,000 net worth per location; $700,000 liquidity. **Franchise Fee:** $40,000. **Training:** Yes.

6498 ■ W.G. Grinders

Grinders Inc.
9002 Cotter St.
Lewis Center, OH 43035
Ph: (614)578-6701
Fax: (614)766-4030
Description: Upscale quick service gourmet deli. **No. of Franchise Units:** 13. **No. of Company-Owned Units:** 8. **Founded:** 1989.. **Franchised:** 1995. **Equity Capital Needed:** $239,000-$314,000 estimated initial investment required. **Franchise Fee:** $15,000 thru 2011. **Financial Assistance:** Yes. **Training:** Yes.

6499 ■ Which Wich Superior Sandwiches

Which Wich Franchise, Inc.
1310 Elm St., Ste. 180LL
Dallas, TX 75202
Ph: (214)747-WICH
Fax: (214)242-4329
Description: Modern sandwich concept. **No. of Franchise Units:** 136. **No. of Company-Owned Units:** 1. **Founded:** 2003. **Franchised:** 2005. **Equity Capital Needed:** $195,000-$488,750. **Franchise Fee:** $30,000. **Royalty Fee:** 6%. **Financial Assistance:** Third party financing available. **Training:** Provides 3 weeks training at headquarters, 1-2 weeks at franchisee's location and ongoing support.

6500 ■ Zero's Subs

2859 Virginia Beach Blvd., Ste. 105
Virginia Beach, VA 23452
Ph: (757)486-8338
Free: 800-588-0782
Fax: (818)545-9132
Co. E-mail: zeros@zeros.com
URL: http://www.zeros.com
Description: A Fast-food, sit-down and to-go restaurant, serving Italian submarine sandwiches and pizzas. **No. of Franchise Units:** 70. **Founded:** 1967.. **Franchised:** 1996. **Equity Capital Needed:** $137,880-$242,300. **Franchise Fee:** $20,000. **Training:** Yes.

LIBRARIES

6501 ■ American Institute of Food Distribution, Inc. - Information and Research Center—The Food Institute.

1 Broadway Plaza, 2nd Fl.
Elmwood Park, NJ 07407
Ph: (201)791-5570
Fax: (201)791-5222
Co. E-mail: jkastrinsky@foodinstitute.com
URL: http://www.foodinstitute.com/
Contact: Brian Todd, President
Scope: Food industry. **Services:** Center open to the public on fee basis. **Founded:** 1928. **Subscriptions:** 400 journals and other serials. **Publications:** *Food Business Mergers and Acquisitions*. **Telecommunication Services:** food1@foodinstitute.com.

6502 ■ Noble and Associates Library

2155 W. Chesterfield Blvd.
Springfield, MO 65807
Ph: (417)875-5000
Co. E-mail: julie.tumy@noble.net
URL: http://www.noble.net
Contact: Julie Tumy, President
Scope: Food, food service, advertising, construction, agriculture. **Services:** Interlibrary loan; copying; SDI; Library not open to the public. **Holdings:** 500 books; 1000 reports. **Subscriptions:** 300 journals and other serials; 5 newspapers.

START-UP INFORMATION

6503 ■ *How to Start and Run a Small Book Publishing Company: A Small Business Guide to Self-Publishing and Independent Publishing*
Pub: HCM Publishing
Ed: Peter I. Hupalo. **Released:** August 30, 2002. **Price:** $18.95. **Description:** The book teaches all aspects of starting and running a small book publishing company. Topics covered include: inventory accounting in the book trade, just-in-time inventory management, turnkey fulfillment solutions, tax deductible costs, basics of sales and use tax, book pricing, standards in terms of the book industry, working with distributors and wholesalers, cover design and book layout, book promotion and marketing, how to select profitable authors to publish, printing process, printing on demand, the power of a strong backlist, and how to value copyright.

ASSOCIATIONS AND OTHER ORGANIZATIONS

6504 ■ Association of Proposal Management Professionals (APMP)
PO Box 77272
Washington, DC 20013-8272
Ph: (202)450-2549
URL: http://www.apmp.org
Contact: Rick Harris, Executive Director

Description: Proposal managers, proposal planners, proposal writers, consultants, desktop publishers and marketing managers. Encourages unity and cooperation among industry professionals. Seeks to broaden member knowledge and skills through developmental, educational and social activities. Maintains speakers' bureau. Provides current information and developments in the field. **Founded:** 1989. **Awards:** APMP Fellows Award (Annual).

6505 ■ Macrocosm USA
PO Box 185
Cambria, CA 93428
Ph: (805)927-2515
Co. E-mail: brockway@macronet.org
URL: http://www.macronet.org
Contact: Sandi Brockway, President
E-mail: brockway@macronet.org

Description: Publishes reader/directories for educators, journalists, students, and activists. Compiles and edits materials into utilitarian formats such as handbooks, databases, a databank, and newsletters. Networks people, projects, and organizations. Self-serve, searchable directory, calendar, and forums online. **Founded:** 1989. **Publications:** *Macrocosm USA: Possibilities For A New Progressive Era.*

6506 ■ Small Publishers Association of North America (SPAN)
PO Box 9725
Colorado Springs, CO 80932-0725
Ph: (719)924-5534

Fax: (719)213-2602
Co. E-mail: brad@spannet.org
URL: http://www.spannet.org
Contact: Brad Poulson, Executive Director
Description: For self-publishers, authors and small presses. Works to advance the image and profits of independent publishers through education and marketing. Offers continuing education, co-op buying power and sales and networking opportunities, plus discounts on many products and services. Publishes monthly newsletter. **Founded:** 1996. **Telecommunication Services:** span@spannet.org.

EDUCATIONAL PROGRAMS

6507 ■ Becoming a Publications Manager
EEI Communications
8945 Guilford Rd., Ste. 145
Columbia, MD 21046
Ph: (410)309-8200
Free: 888-253-2762
Fax: (410)630-3980
Co. E-mail: train@eeicom.com
URL: http://www.eeicom.com/eei-training-services
Price: $425.00. **Description:** For new managers, this seminar covers defining responsibilities, managing workflow, organizational and recruitment skills, providing feedback, and utilizing technology. **Dates and Locations:** Alexandria, VA.

6508 ■ Design for Print
EEI Communications
8945 Guilford Rd., Ste. 145
Columbia, MD 21046
Ph: (410)309-8200
Free: 888-253-2762
Fax: (410)630-3980
Co. E-mail: train@eeicom.com
URL: http://www.eeicom.com/eei-training-services
Price: $745.00. **Description:** Covers basic design principles, utilizing color and typography, composition, and preparing files for the printing process. **Dates and Locations:** Silver Spring, MD; Alexandria, VA; Hunt Valley, MD; and Columbia, MD.

6509 ■ Visual Thinking II: Color Theory
EEI Communications
8945 Guilford Rd., Ste. 145
Columbia, MD 21046
Ph: (410)309-8200
Free: 888-253-2762
Fax: (410)630-3980
Co. E-mail: train@eeicom.com
URL: http://www.eeicom.com/eei-training-services
Price: $1,395.00. **Description:** Covers the design elements of color, including the color wheel, the seven color contrasts, and the psychological aspects of color. **Dates and Locations:** Silver Spring, MD; Alexandria, VA; Hunt Valley, MD; and Columbia, MD.

REFERENCE WORKS

6510 ■ *"Career Transition" in Crain's Detroit Business (Vol. 26, January 4, 2010, No. 1, pp. 14)*
Pub: Crain Communications Inc.
Description: Profile of Nicole Longhini-McElroy who has opted to radically change her career path from

working in the manufacturing sector to becoming a self-published author of 'Charmed Adventures', a book series created to engage children in creative thought.

6511 ■ *"Freelance Writer Creates L.I. Bridal Blog" in Long Island Business News (September 10, 2010)*
Pub: Dolan Media Newswires
Ed: Gregory Zeller. **Description:** Profile of Claudia Copquin, freelance journalist who created a blog for brides on the Internet.

6512 ■ *Freelancing for Journalists*
Pub: Routledge
Ed: Diana Harris. **Released:** January 1, 2010. **Price:** $110.00. **Description:** Comprehensive guide showing the specific skills required for those wishing to freelance in newspapers, magazines, radio, television, and as online journalists.

6513 ■ *From Entrepreneur to Infopreneur: Make Money with Books, E-Books, and Other Information Products*
Pub: John Wiley & Sons, Incorporated
Ed: Stephanie Chandler. **Released:** November 2006. **Price:** $19.95. **Description:** Infopreneurs sell information online in the forms of books, e-books, special reports, audio and video products, seminars, and more.

6514 ■ *"Getting It Sold" in Black Enterprise (Vol. 38, November 2007, No. 4, pp. 54)*
Pub: Earl G. Graves Publishing Co. Inc.
Ed: Tennille M. Robinson. **Description:** Artist is given advice for marketing and selling paintings, as well as getting artwork published.

6515 ■ *How to Start a Home-Based Writing Business, 5th Edition*
Pub: Globe Pequot Press
Ed: Lucy Parker. **Released:** December 2007. **Price:** $18.95. **Description:** Guide for starting and running a home-based writing business.

6516 ■ *"Interactive Stores a Big Part of Borders' Turnaround Plan" in Crain's Detroit Business (Vol. 24, February 18, 2008, No. 7, pp. 4)*
Pub: Crain Communications Inc. - Detroit
Description: Borders Group Inc. is using digital technology and interactive media as a part of the firm's turnaround plan. The digital store will allow shoppers to create CDs, download audio books, publish their own works, print photos and search family genealogy.

6517 ■ *Literary Market Place: The Directory of the American Book Publishing Industry*
Pub: Information Today Inc.
Contact: Thomas H. Hogan, President
E-mail: ctuthill@infotoday.com
URL(s): books.infotoday.com. **Released:** Annual; Latest edition 2012. **Price:** $339, Individuals 2-volume set/softbound plus $25 shipping/handling; $305.10, Individuals first time standing order. **Covers:** Over 12,500 firms or organizations offering services related

to the publishing industry, including book publishers in the United States and Canada who issued three or more books during the preceding year, plus a small press section of publishers who publish less than three titles per year or those who are self-published. Also included: book printers and binders; book clubs; book trade and literary associations; selected syndicates, newspapers, periodicals, and radio and TV programs that use book reviews or book publishing news; translators and literary agents. **Entries include:** For publishers--Company name, address, phone, address for orders, principal executives, editorial directors, and managers, date founded, number of titles in previous year, number of backlist titles in print, types of books published, ISBN prefixes, representatives, imprints, and affiliations. For suppliers, etc.--Listings usually show firm name, address, phone, executives, services, etc. **Arrangement:** Classified by line of business. **Indexes:** Principal index is 35,000-item combined index of publishers, publications, and personnel; several sections have geographical and/or subject indexes; translators are indexed by source and target language.

6518 ■ "Online Self-Publishing Services" in Black Enterprise (Vol. 37, November 2006, No. 4, pp. 90)
Pub: Earl G. Graves Publishing Co. Inc.
Description: Profiles of five online self-publishing services.

6519 ■ "Paper a la Carte" in American Printer (Vol. 128, June 1, 2011, No. 6)
Pub: Penton Media Inc.
Description: Blurb, the online publishing platform, launched ProLine which features Mohawk Superfine and Mohawk proPhoto papers. ProLine papers offer two finishes: Pearl Photo and Uncoated.

6520 ■ "Pretentious and Loving It" in Entrepreneur (Vol. 37, August 2009, No. 8, pp. 34)
Pub: Entrepreneur Media, Inc.
Ed: Eric Mahoney. **Description:** Pitchfork.com features reviews of albums from independent artists. Their most innovative section is Pitchfork.tv, featuring videos of bands, and Forkcast along with their Features section that contains articles about bands and their histories.

6521 ■ The Publishing Game: Publish a Book in 30 Days
Pub: Peanut Butter and Jelly Press LLC
Ed: Fern Reiss. **Released:** January 31, 2003. **Price:** $19.95. **Description:** Excellent resource for individuals wanting to write a book and become their own publisher.

6522 ■ "Savvy Solutions" in Black Enterprise (Vol. 41, November 2010, No. 4, pp. 42)
Pub: Earl G. Graves Publishing Co. Inc.
Ed: Tennile M. Robinson. **Description:** Society of Children's Book Writers and Illustrators offers members many benefits, including directories of agencies looking for new writers of books.

6523 ■ The Self-Publishing Manual: How To Write, Print, and Sell Your Own Book
Pub: Para Publishing
Ed: Dan Poynter. **Released:** 2007. **Price:** $19.95. **Description:** The book provides a complete course in writing, publishing, marketing, promoting, and distributing books. Poynter offers a step-by-step study of the publishing industry and explains various book-marketing techniques.

6524 ■ "The Way I Work: Kim Kleeman" in Inc. (October 2007, pp. 110-112, 114)
Pub: Gruner & Jahr USA Publishing
Ed: Leigh Buchanan. **Description:** Profile of Kim Kleemna, founder and president of Shakespear-eSquared, a firm that develops educational materials, including lesson plans, teacher guides, activity workbooks, and discussion guides for large publishers. Kleeman talks about the challenges she faces running her nearly all-women company while maintaining a balance with her family.

TRADE PERIODICALS

6525 ■ Economic Edge
Pub: National Association for Printing Leadership
Released: Quarterly. **Price:** Included in membership. **Description:** Provides current economic data for the printing industry. Also covers sales growth projections, capital spending, and employment.

6526 ■ How To Be Your Own Publisher Update
Pub: Bibliotheca Press
Ed: A. Doyle, Editor. **Released:** Annual. **Price:** $12.95, U.S.; $15.95, Canada; $19.95, other countries. **Description:** Acts as a reference for self publishers. Distributed by Prosperity & Profits Unlimited Distribution Services, PO Box 416, Denver, CO, 80201.

6527 ■ Independent Publisher Online: The Voice of The Independent Publishing Industry
Pub: Jenkins Group Inc.
Contact: James J. Kalajian, President
E-mail: jjk@bookpublishing.com
URL(s): www.independentpublisher.com/. **Released:** Monthly **Price:** Free.

6528 ■ The Kleper Report on Digital Publishing
Pub: Graphic Dimensions
Ed: Michael Kleper, Editor, mkleper@printerport.com. **Released:** 6/year. **Price:** $24.95, individuals $150/year, U.S. and Canada; $225 elsewhere;. **Description:** Reviews software program packages for desktop, electronic, and digital publishing, imaging, multimedia, and Web publishing.

6529 ■ KMWorld: Creating and Managing the Knowledge-Based Enterprise
Pub: Information Today Inc.
Contact: Thomas H. Hogan, President
E-mail: ctuthill@infotoday.com
URL(s): www.infotoday.com/contacts.shtml#kmworld.
Released: Monthly

6530 ■ Min's b2b
Pub: Phillips Business Information Inc. Access Intelligence L.L.C.
Contact: Heather Farley, President
E-mail: hfarley@accessintel.com
Ed: Jeremy Greenfield, Editor. **Released:** Biweekly. **Description:** Provides news on business relations and strategies and tactics to increase online publishing and new media business.

6531 ■ Oregon Publisher
Pub: Oregon Newspaper Publishers Association
Contact: LeRoy Yorgason, Publisher
E-mail: leroy@orenews.com
Ed: David Merrill, Editor, dmerrill@orenews.com. **Released:** Every other month. **Price:** Included in membership. **Description:** Covers journalism and publishing topics.

VIDEOCASSETTES/ AUDIOCASSETTES

6532 ■ Desktop Design 1: Basic Electronic Graphic Techniques
Cambridge Educational
c/o Films Media Group
132 West 31st Street, 17th Floor
Ste. 124
New York, NY 10001
Free: 800-257-5126
Fax: (609)671-0266
Co. E-mail: custserve@films.com
URL: http://www.cambridgeol.com
Released: 19??. **Price:** $39.95. **Description:** Presents basic electronic design techniques and principles through a series of step-by-step projects. **Availability:** VHS.

6533 ■ Desktop Design 2: Creative Design with PostScript Drawing Software
Cambridge Educational
c/o Films Media Group
132 West 31st Street, 17th Floor
Ste. 124
New York, NY 10001
Free: 800-257-5126
Fax: (609)671-0266
Co. E-mail: custserve@films.com
URL: http://www.cambridgeol.com
Released: 19??. **Price:** $39.95. **Description:** Step-by-step project introduces major applications of Adobe Illustrator 88 and Aldus FreeHand. Covers charts and graphs, logo design, advertising, illustration, font creation, and a magazine cover. **Availability:** VHS.

6534 ■ Desktop Design 3: Creative Design with Page-Layout Software
Cambridge Educational
c/o Films Media Group
132 West 31st Street, 17th Floor
Ste. 124
New York, NY 10001
Free: 800-257-5126
Fax: (609)671-0266
Co. E-mail: custserve@films.com
URL: http://www.cambridgeol.com
Released: 19??. **Price:** $39.95. **Description:** Illustrates the use of Aldus Pagemaker; Ready, Set, Go!; and Quark XPress for newsletters, brochures, and full-page ad layout. Includes tips and tricks. **Availability:** VHS.

TRADE SHOWS AND CONVENTIONS

6535 ■ ON DEMAND Digital Printing & Publishing Strategy Conference and Exposition
Advanstar Communications
641 Lexington Ave., 8th Fl.
New York, NY 10022
Ph: (212)951-6600
Free: 800-346-0085
Fax: (212)951-6793
Co. E-mail: info@advantstar.com
URL: http://www.advanstar.com
Contact: Robert Krakoff, President
URL(s): www.ondemandexpo.com. **Frequency:** Annual. **Audience:** Corporate executives, print providers, government users. **Principal Exhibits:** Addresses the digitalization of workflow in the printing and publishing marketplace. **Telecommunication Services:** sfrank@advantstar.com.

6536 ■ Seybold San Francisco Conference and Exposition
Keith Reed Media Events
303 Vintage Park Dr.
Foster City, CA 94404
Ph: (650)578-6897
Free: 800-488-2883
Fax: (650)525-0193
Co. E-mail: mtrask@zdcf.com
URL(s): www.seybold365.com. **Frequency:** Annual. **Audience:** Computer publishing trade. **Principal Exhibits:** Equipment, supplies, and services for computer publishing. **Dates and Locations:** , Moscone Center.

CONSULTANTS

6537 ■ Barb Gordon Graphic Design
14107 Wilden Dr.
Urbandale, IA 50323
Ph: (515)278-9738
Co. E-mail: bgordon@myarbonne.com
URL: http://www.barbgordon.com
Contact: Barbara J. Gordon, Principal
E-mail: gordon@dwx.com
Scope: Consultant offers training in desktop publishing and in popular graphics software. Training is generally presented in-house and is available on a

one-to-one basis. Industries served: graphic artists. **Founded:** 1977. **Telecommunication Services:** gordon@dwx.com.

6538 ■ Editorial Code and Data Inc. (ECDI)
814 Wolverine Dr., Ste. 2
Walled Lake, MI 48390
Ph: (248)926-5187
Fax: (248)926-6047
Co. E-mail: monique.magee@gmail.com
URL: http://www.marketsize.com
Contact: Monique D. Magee, President
E-mail: monique@marketsize.com

Scope: Provider of data and computer services primarily to the publishing industry, with specialization in statistical data drawn from government sources. Services include data acquisition, analysis, formatting, and typesetting, archiving of computer data on CD-ROM, custom data display, search, and printing software, information brokering services, and related services such as design, writing, and data processing design. Industries served: publishing, in-house printing, non-profit organizations, government agencies, utilities, and manufacturing. **Founded:** 1990. **Publications:** "Market Share Reporter"; "Encyclopedia of Products & Industries"; "Economic Indicators Handbook"; "American Salaries and Wages Survey"; "Dun and Bradstreet & Gale: Industrial Handbook"; "Reference American Cost of Living Survey".

6539 ■ Intercollegiate Broadcasting System Inc. (IBS)
367 Windsor Hwy.
New Windsor, NY 12553-7900
Ph: (845)565-0003
Fax: (845)565-7446
Co. E-mail: ibs@ibsradio.org
URL: http://www.collegebroadcasters.us/content/index.html
Contact: Fritz Kass, Chief Operating Officer

URL(s): www.frontiernet.net/~ibs/ibshome.html. **Description:** Radio stations at schools, colleges, and universities. Offers educational, informational, and consulting services. Compiles statistics; conducts research and seminars. **Scope:** Communications media specialists with focus on Macintosh computing, desktop publishing, graphic production layout, database, spreadsheet, and training. Possesses particular expertise on AV systems and setups. Serves private industries as well as government agencies. **Founded:** 1970. **Publications:** *Radio Newsletter* (Monthly); *The Journal of College Radio* (Quarterly). **Educational Activities:** Intercollegiate Broadcasting System Convention (Annual). **Telecommunication Services:** ibshq@aol.com.

6540 ■ The Live Oak Press L.L.C.
445 Burgess Dr.
Menlo Park, CA 94306-0036
Ph: (650)853-0197
Fax: (815)366-8205
URL: http://www.liveoakpress.com
Contact: David M. Hamilton, President
E-mail: mhamilton@liveoakpress.com

Scope: Manages design and implementation of publishing programs. Also offers complete book and magazine preparation and publishing consulting, including web resources, advertising, concept development, manuscript, design, development and production through finished product. Specializes in high-technology clients and electronic publishing. **Founded:** 1970. **Publications:** "The Tools of My Trade"; "To the Yukon with Jack London"; "Earthquakes and Young Volcanoes"; "The Lost Cement Mine"; "Inner Voyage"; "Studies in the Development of Consciousness"; "Dialectical Realism: Studies on a Philosophy of Growth"; "Mammoth Lakes Sierra"; "Deepest Valley"; "Mammoth Gold"; "Old Mammoth". **Seminars:** Internet publishing Seminar.

6541 ■ Lovelady Consulting
1100 Martin Ridge Rd.
Roswell, GA 30076-2852
Ph: (770)992-1545
Free: 888-263-7640

Fax: (888)263-7640
URL: http://www.loveladyconsulting.com
Contact: Carol Lovelady, Owner
E-mail: clovelady@venturalady.com
Scope: Specialist on electronic publishing and office automation applications, offers consultation, design and training. Specializes in Ventura, Page Maker, Corel Draw, quark press, graphics and related applications. Develops customized corporate training programs. Serves private industries as well as government agencies. **Founded:** 1986. **Publications:** "Adobe Acrobat 9 Quick start Guide"; "Adobe Acrobat 9 How-To's"; "How to Do Everything with Acrobat 9"; "Corel Ventura 10"; "CorelDraw X4 Upgrade"; "CorelDraw X4 Full Version"; "Adobe Acrobat 9 Professional Upgrade"; "Adobe Acrobat 9 Standard Upgrade"; "CorelDraw Graphics Suite X3"; "Adobe Acrobat 8 Quick Start Guide"; "How To Do Everything with Acrobat 7"; "Acrobat 8 Upgrade from Standard to Professional". **Seminars:** Corel Ventura 10 Introduction, 2007; Adobe Acrobat Advanced; Corel Ventura 10 Transition; CorelDRAW X3 Introduction, 2007; CorelDRAW X3 Advanced; Adobe Acrobat Advanced; Corel Database Publisher 8/10; Ventura Tips and Tricks, 2005; Adobe In Design Introduction, 2005; Corel Database Publisher 8/10; CorelDRAW 11/12 Introduction; Ventura Tips & Tricks; Corel PhotoPAINT Introduction. **Special Services:** CorelDraw X4 or X3; Adobe Acrobat 8 or 9; Corel Ventura 10; CorelDRAW 11/12; Corel Ventura 10.

6542 ■ LPD Enterprises—LPD Press & Rio Grande Books
925 Salamanca St. NW
Los Ranchos de Albuquerque, NM 87107-5647
Ph: (505)344-9382
Fax: (505)345-5129
Co. E-mail: info@nmsantos.com
URL: http://www.nmsantos.com
Contact: Barbara J. Awalt, Director
Scope: Offers services in public relations, publications, desktop and electronic publishing, management, and organizational development. Specializes in serving small- to medium-sized businesses, nonprofit organizations and educational institutions. **Founded:** 1984. **Publications:** "Shoes for Santo Nino"; "Genizaro & the Artist"; "Old West Trivia"; "Tale of Pronghorned Cantaloupe"; "Saints of the Pueblos"; "A Century of Masters"; "Visions Underground"; "Avenging Victorio". **Seminars:** Balloon Safety.

6543 ■ Nicholas J. Naclerio and Associates Inc.
7463 Cross Gate Ln.
Alexandria, VA 22315-4620
Ph: (703)451-7557
Contact: Nicholas J. Naclerio, Owner
E-mail: njnaclerio@cs.com
Scope: Provider of administrative and personnel, and information management consulting to business and government in such areas as document creation and office automation, desktop publishing, database design, career development programs, and organizational development. Also, offers hands-on microcomputer training on all popular software for both IBM and Macintosh computers including Lotus Suite, Microsoft Office, Word Perfect and the Internet. **Founded:** 1978.

6544 ■ Nostradamus Advertising
884 W End Ave., Ste. 2
New York, NY 10025
Ph: (212)581-1362
Fax: (212)662-8625
Co. E-mail: nos@nostradamus.net
URL: http://www.nostradamus.net
Contact: Barry Nostradamus Sher, President
Scope: Provides graphic design, advertising and marketing services to small companies and organizations. Other services include consulting; designing direct mail for politicians; creating and updating Websites, book design and communication services. Serves government agencies. **Founded:** 1974.

6545 ■ PubCom/i-Imagery Design—BJ Chagnon Corp.
7417 Holly Ave.
Takoma Park, MD 20912-4219
Ph: (301)585-8805

Fax: (301)585-7289
Co. E-mail: info@pubcom.com
URL: http://www.pubcom.com
Contact: Jan Harp, Manager
E-mail: jan@pubcom.com
Scope: Specializes in cross media publishing for print, multimedia, and the Internet. Provides training in desktop publishing and website design. Also offers system analyses, installation, and software for publishing multimedia and website development. Industries served graphic arts, publishing, typesetting, nonprofits, government, corporations, and federal contractors in the mid Atlantic states. **Founded:** 1987. **Seminars:** Advertising 101 for Small Businesses, 2006; Marketing on a Small Budget, 2006; Strategies for Promoting your Exhibit Booth, 2006; Beginner and advanced hands-on training in desktop publishing; Cross-Media Publishing with Adobe In Design: Publishing for Press and Web; 508 Compliance with Adobe In Design; Management of Multi-Tiered Enterprise Websites and Intranets; New Directions in Publishing Technology.

6546 ■ SketchPad Graphic Design—SketchPad Publications
812 Mountain View St.
Fillmore, CA 93015
Ph: (805)524-2740
Co. E-mail: info@sketch.com
URL: http://www.sketch.com
Contact: Norma Holt, Director
E-mail: holt@sketch.com
Scope: Provider of desktop publishing, including text capture, graphic capture, typesetting, layout, design, photographs and printing, color separation, file management, software and hardware usage. Also designs and hosts web pages. Industries served: public and private sector in Ventura County and rest of U.S. via mail and facsimile. **Founded:** 1986. **Publications:** "Please Let Me Fly". **Seminars:** Desktop publishing; Ventura Publisher and PageMaker. **Telecommunication Services:** designer@sketch.com.

6547 ■ Stillman H. Publishers Inc.
21405 Woodchuck Ln.
Boca Raton, FL 33428
Ph: (561)482-6343
Contact: Herbert Stillman, President
Scope: Offers consulting services in the following areas: management, start ups, profit maximization, world wide negotiating, interim management, corporate debt resolution. **Founded:** 1984.

6548 ■ Systems Service Enterprises Inc. (SSE)
77 W Port Plz., Ste. 500
Saint Louis, MO 63146-3126
Ph: (314)439-4700
Fax: (314)439-4799
URL: http://www.sseinc.com
Contact: Elizabeth E. Niedringhaus, President
E-mail: eeniedringhaus@sseinc.com
Scope: Provides services like advisory services, custom solutions, custom elearning and mobile learning. Provides solutions that transform workforce effectiveness and foster organizational change that is measurable. Enables to implement strategic initiatives across organizations with custom learning solutions that simply work. **Founded:** 1966. **Publications:** "IT Budget Got your Stomach in Knots"; "We Have a Guy Who Does That"; "Tight Economy Forced a Hold on IT Spending? Now What?"; "Considering Telecommute Questions to Answer"; "Is Your IT MOOSE Spending Too Loose"; "Exponential Growth of Spyware in Q4"; "The Cloud Got You Feeling Foggy?"; "Are your Employees Set up to BYOT?"; "Mobile Device Security for Small Businesses";"When Disaster Strikes"; "The Cloud Part II: Let the Light Shine Thru"; "The Cloud Part III: Finding the Right Fit"; "Knowing the Tricks of the Trade"; "93 percent of Firms with Major Data Losses File for Bankruptcy"; "70 percent of Security Threats Originate Inside Your Office"; "Save Money, Save the Environment, and Go Green IT"; "99 percent of Computers Worldwide are Vulnerable to Online Attacks". **Special Services:** Pretecht™; SSEwinEngine™; SSElearn Portal™; SSEanalytics™.

LIBRARIES

**6549 ■ Printing Industries of America/
Graphic Arts Technical Foundation - Edward
H. Wadewitz Memorial Library**
200 Deer Run Rd.
Sewickley, PA 15143-2324

Ph: (412)741-6860
Free: 800-910-4283
Fax: (412)741-2311
Co. E-mail: dgentile@printing.org
URL: http://www.printing.org/page/4506
Contact: Hallie Barcalow, Administrator

Scope: Printing processes, lithography, paper, ink,
graphic design, desktop publishing, packaging,
chemistry, physics, environmental control, safety and
health, photography. **Services:** Document delivery;
library open to the public by appointment. **Founded:**
1924. **Holdings:** 15,000 volumes. **Subscriptions:**
180 journals and other serials.

TRADE PERIODICALS

6550 ■ *Audiotex News*
Pub: Audiotex News
Contact: Carol Morse, Editor
E-mail: carol@audiotex.news.com

Released: Monthly. **Description:** Covers news, trends, regulations, and information on the 900/800 pay-per-call business. Recurring features include interviews, news of research, calendar of events, reports of meetings, book reviews, and notices of publications available.

6551 ■ *Telephone IP News*
Pub: Worldwide Videotex

Released: Monthly. **Price:** $165, U.S. and Canada; $180, elsewhere outside North America; $25, single. **Description:** Provides information provider (IP) industry news for various telephone services, such as 900, 970, and 976 numbers. Covers new products, public service commission rulings, and marketing strategies.

LIBRARIES

6552 ■ Manitoba Telecom Services Corporate Library
333 Main St.
Winnipeg, MB, Canada R3C 3V6
Ph: (204)941-6344
Fax: (204)944-0830
URL: http://www.mts.ca
Contact: Tanya L. Evancio, Librarian
Scope: Telecommunications industry. **Services:** Library not open to the public. **Founded:** 1977. **Holdings:** 2000 books. **Subscriptions:** 100 journals and other serials.

6553 ■ U.S. Federal Communications Commission Library
445 12th St. SW, Rm. TW-8505
Washington, DC 20554
Ph: (202)418-0450
Free: 888-225-5322
Fax: (202)418-2805
Co. E-mail: ecclibrary@fcc.gov
URL: http://www.fcc.gov
Contact: Ms. Gloria Thomas, Librarian, Reference Senior Librarian
Scope: Telecommunications, electrical engineering, law, economics, public utility regulation, public administration, management, statistics. **Services:** SDI; Library not open to the public. **Founded:** 1934. **Holdings:** 45,000 books; 123 bound periodical volumes; 6200 VF materials; 3000 reels of microfilm. **Subscriptions:** 305 journals and other serials. **Telecommunication Services:** fccinfo@fcc.gov.

ASSOCIATIONS AND OTHER ORGANIZATIONS

6554 ■ American Disc Jockey Association (ADJA)
20118 N 67th Ave., Ste. 300-605
Glendale, AZ 85308
Free: 888-723-5776
Fax: (866)310-4676
URL: http://www.adja.org
Description: Mobile and night club disc jockeys. Seeks to promote the disc jockey as a professional form of entertainment; improves the industry by establishing standards, procedures, and benefits. Assists and trains members; provides forums for professional disc jockeys; conducts educational, charitable, and research programs. **Scope:** scripting, networking, wedding ceremonies, taxes, contracts, Latin music, ballroom dancing, country music, multi system operations, internet marketing, digital DJ technologies content requests. **Founded:** 1992. **Subscriptions:** 36 archival material articles audiovisuals business records periodicals video recordings. **Publications:** *Mobile Beat* (Annual). **Awards:** Peter Merry Leadership Award (Annual); Chapter of the Year (Annual); Michael Butler Humanitarian Award (Annual).

6555 ■ Canadian Disc Jockey Association (CDJA)
1008 Manchester Rd.
London, ON, Canada N6H 5J1
Ph: (519)287-3600
Free: 877-472-0653
Fax: (519)472-0242
Co. E-mail: chairperson@cdja.ca
URL: http://www.cdja.ca
Contact: Darryl Thompson, Chairman of the Board
Description: Disc jockeys and others promote excellence in service through education, information, networking, and support. Promotes professional development among members. Facilitates exchange of information among members; represents members' interests. **Founded:** 1976. **Publications:** *CUED-UP Street*; *DJ Pulse* (Quarterly). **Awards:** National President's Award; National President's Award (Annual).

6556 ■ *CUED-UP Street*
1008 Manchester Rd.
London, ON, Canada N6H 5J1
Ph: (519)287-3600
Free: 877-472-0653
Fax: (519)472-0242
Co. E-mail: chairperson@cdja.ca
URL: http://www.cdja.ca
Contact: Darryl Thompson, Chairman of the Board

6557 ■ *DJ Pulse*
1008 Manchester Rd.
London, ON, Canada N6H 5J1
Ph: (519)287-3600
Free: 877-472-0653
Fax: (519)472-0242
Co. E-mail: chairperson@cdja.ca
URL: http://www.cdja.ca
Contact: Darryl Thompson, Chairman of the Board
Released: Quarterly **Price:** included in membership dues.

TRADE PERIODICALS

6558 ■ *DJ Times: The International Magazine for the Professional Mobile and Club DJ*
Pub: Testa Communications
Contact: Vincent P. Testa, President
URL(s): djtimes.com/djt. **Released:** Monthly **Price:** $14.85, Individuals; $29.70, Two years.

START-UP INFORMATION

6559 ■ *"Franchises with an Eye on Chicago"*
in Crain's Chicago Business (Vol. 34, March
14, 2011, No. 11, pp. 20)
Pub: Crain Communications Inc.
Description: Profiles of franchise companies seeking franchisees for the Chicago area include: Extreme Pita, a sandwich shop; Hand and Stone, offering massage, facial and waxing services; Molly Maid, home-cleaning service; Primrose Schools, private accredited schools for children 6 months to 6 hears and after-school programs; Protect Painters, residential and light-commercial painting contractor; and Wingstop, a restaurant offering chicken wings in nine flavors, fries and side dishes.

6560 ■ *"Green Clean Machine" in Small*
Business Opportunities (Winter 2010)
Pub: Harris Publications Inc.
Description: Eco-friendly maid franchise plans to grow its $62 million sales base. Profile of Maid Brigade, a green-cleaning franchise is planning to expand across the country.

6561 ■ *Housecleaning Business: Organize*
Your Business - Get Clients and Referrals -
Set Rates and Services
Pub: Globe Pequot Press
Ed: Laura Jorstad, Melinda Morse. **Released:** June 1, 2009. **Price:** $18.95. **Description:** This book shares insight into starting a housecleaning businesses. It shows how to develop a service manual, screen clients, serve customers, select cleaning products, competition, how to up a home office, using the Internet to grow the business and offering green cleaning options to clients.

ASSOCIATIONS AND OTHER ORGANIZATIONS

6562 ■ **Canadian Association of**
Environmental Management
(CAEM)—Association Canadienne de Gestion
Environnementale
Aberdeen Hospital
835 E River Rd.
New Glasgow, NS, Canada B2G 3S6
Ph: (902)725-7600
Fax: (902)755-3975
Co. E-mail: rosemary.gillis-bowers@pcha.nshealth.ca
URL: http://www.thecanadiangroup.com/caha/index.htm
Contact: Rosemary Gillis-Bowers, President (Acting)
    Secretary Treasurer
Description: Environmental managers. Seeks to advance the environmental (housekeeping) profession; promotes adherence to high standards of ethics and practice by members. Represents members' interests; facilitates communication and cooperation among members. **Founded:** 1971. **Publications:** *The Quarterly* (Quarterly). **Awards:** CAH Certification (Annual).

6563 ■ *The Quarterly*
Aberdeen Hospital
835 E River Rd.
New Glasgow, NS, Canada B2G 3S6
Ph: (902)725-7600
Fax: (902)755-3975
Co. E-mail: rosemary.gillis-bowers@pcha.nshealth.ca
URL: http://www.thecanadiangroup.com/caha/index.htm
Contact: Rosemary Gillis-Bowers, President (Acting)
Released: Quarterly **Price:** free for members; C$20, /year for nonmembers.

REFERENCE WORKS

6564 ■ *"Domestic Workers Organize!" in*
WorkingUSA (Vol. 11, December 2008, No. 4,
pp. 413)
Pub: Blackwell Publishers Ltd.
Ed: Eileen Boris, Premilla Nadasen. **Description:** History of domestic workers in the U.S. is examined. The article challenges the long-standing assumption that these, primarily women of color cleaners, nannies, and elder care providers are unable to organize and assesses the possibilities and limitations of recent organizing efforts. The nature of the occupation, its location in the home, the isolated character of the work, informal arrangements with employers, and exclusions from labor law protection, has fostered community-based, social movement organizing to build coalitions, reform legislation and draw public attention to the plight of domestic workers.

6565 ■ *International Sanitary Supply*
Association--Membership Directory
Contact: John Garfinkel, Executive Director
URL(s): www.issa.com. **Ed:** Michael McQueen. **Released:** Annual; spring. **Covers:** About 5,500 member associates, manufacturers, manufacturers' representatives, distributors, publishers, and wholesalers of industrial and institutional cleaning and maintenance chemicals, equipment, and supplies; international coverage. **Entries include:** Company name, address, phone, names of key personnel, line of business; manufacturer listings include product information, email and website. **Database includes:** List of publishers of trade periodicals. **Arrangement:** Geographical. **Indexes:** Alphabetical, product.

6566 ■ *"What Moms Want" in Marketing to*
Women (Vol. 21, February 2008, No. 2, pp. 6)
Pub: EPM Communications Inc.
Contact: Ira Mayer, President
E-mail: imayer@epmcom.com
Description: According to a survey conducted by Eureka's Spa, moms would rather have an experience gift than flowers or chocolate. The top five dream gifts include a spa day, a weekend getaway, maid service, a bathroom makeover or a getaway weekend with girlfriends.

TRADE PERIODICALS

6567 ■ *Services: The Magazine for the*
Building Service Contracting Industry
Pub: Building Service Contractors Association Int'l.
URL(s): www.servicesmag.org/. **Ed:** Lisa Kopochinski. **Released:** Bimonthly **Price:** $24, Members; $30,

Nonmembers; $48, Other countries members; $54, Other countries non-members.

CONSULTANTS

6568 ■ **Cleaning Consultant Services Inc.**
(CCS)
3693 E Marginal Way S
Seattle, WA 98134
Ph: (206)682-9748
Fax: (206)622-6876
Co. E-mail: wgriffin@cleaningconsultants.com
URL: http://www.cleaningbusiness.com
Contact: William R. Griffin, President
E-mail: wgriffin@cleaningconsultants.com
URL(s): www.cleaningbusiness.com. **Description:** Description: Publishes books on floor care, carpet care, self-employment, window washing, custodial training and many other areas related to the cleaning industry. Reaches market through direct mail, reviews and listings, telephone sales, ads, catalogs and trade shows. **Scope:** Provider of engineering and consulting services. It deals with claim and dispute resolution, program and material development, and cleaning services. **Founded:** 1973. **Publications:** "Raising the Bar with Science, Training and Upward Mobility," Jan, 2010; "Technology Revolutionizes the Cleaning Process "Cleaning for Health" is the New Mantra," Distribution Sales and Management Magazine, May, 2003; "Bill Griffin's Crystal Balls-Cleaning Trends in the Usa 2001," Floor Care is Hot in 2001," Mar, 2001; "Inclean Magazine (Australia), Feb, 2001; "Maintaining Swimming Pools, Spas, Whirlpool Tubs and Saunas," Executive House keeping, Feb, 2001; "Whats New with Floor Care," 2001. **Seminars:** Stone Maintenance Technician (SMT) IICRC Certification Course; Carpet Cleaning Technician; Apprentice/Basic Skills; Organizing Custodial Operations for Maximum Efficiency: How to Sell & Price Contract Cleaning; Starting a House cleaning Business; Rugs & Carpet Cleaning; How to Start and Operate a Successful Cleaning Business; Cleaning Schools in the 2000and Beyond; Bringing About and Working Through Change; Organizing Custodial Operations for Maximum Efficiency; Floor Care Technician (FCT)11 CPC Certified Course; Administering Cleaning Service Contracts. **Telecommunication Services:** ccs@cleaningconsultants.com; marketing@cleaningconsultants.com.

FRANCHISES AND BUSINESS OPPORTUNITIES

6569 ■ **BearCom Building Services**
BearCom Building Services, Inc.
7022 S 400 West
Midvale, UT 84047
Ph: (801)569-9500
Free: 888-569-9533
Fax: (801)569-8400

Description: Commercial cleaning. **No. of Franchise Units:** 62. **No. of Company-Owned Units:** 1. **Founded:** 1979.. **Franchised:** 1990. **Equity Capital**

Needed: $12,787-$39,287 plus. **Franchise Fee:** $9,995 plus. **Financial Assistance:** Yes. **Training:** Offers 24 hours training with ongoing support.

6570 ■ The Cleaning Authority
7230 Lee Deforest Dr.
Columbia, MD 21046
Ph: (410)740-1900
Free: 877-504-6221
URL: http://www.thecleaningauthority.com
Description: Cleaning service. **No. of Franchise Units:** 160. **No. of Company-Owned Units:** 1. **Founded:** 1978.. **Franchised:** 1996. **Equity Capital Needed:** $90,000 -$110,000. **Franchise Fee:** $30,000-$50,000. **Training:** 2 week home office training; onsite visits, quarterly newsletter, ongoing training sessions.

6571 ■ Cleaning Consultant Services Inc.
PO Box 1273
Seattle, WA 98111
Ph: (206)682-9748
Description: Support services to those who own, manage and/or supervise cleaning operations. **No. of Franchise Units:** 2. **No. of Company-Owned Units:** 3. **Founded:** 1976.. **Franchised:** 1978. **Equity Capital Needed:** $7,500. **Franchise Fee:** $2,500. **Training:** 2-3 days at out training site in Seattle, WA.

6572 ■ CottageCare Canada
816 Willow Park Dr. SE, Ste. 105
Calgary, AB, Canada T2J 5S1
Ph: (403)225-3441
Free: 800-718-8200
Fax: (403)225-3502
Co. E-mail: housecleaning@cottagecare.ca
URL: http://www.cottagecare.com
Description: Cottage Care Canada are into general housecleaning services. **No. of Franchise Units:** 6. **No. of Operating Units:** 61. **Founded:** 1996.. **Franchised:** 1996. **Equity Capital Needed:** $75,000-$100,000. **Franchise Fee:** $19,500. **Training:** Provides 2 weeks training prior to start-up and ongoing support.

6573 ■ CottageCare, Inc.
6323 W 110th St.
Overland Park, KS 66211
Ph: (913)469-8778
Free: 800-469-6303
Fax: (913)469-0822
URL: http://www.cottagecare.com
Description: Big business approach to housecleaning. Franchisor markets and signs-up new customers. Franchisee operates business and has a staff that cleans. Jumbo territories with availability of multiple offices in each territory. **No. of Franchise Units:** 32. **No. of Company-Owned Units:** 8. **Founded:** 1988.. **Franchised:** 1989. **Equity Capital Needed:** $69,500 total investment. **Franchise Fee:** $17,500-$19,500. **Royalty Fee:** 5.5%. **Training:** Provides training at headquarters for 10 days and ongoing support.

6574 ■ Home Cleaning Centers of America
4851 W 134th St., Unit D
Leawood, KS 66209
Ph: (913)327-5227
Fax: (913)327-5272
Co. E-mail: Mcalhoon@homecleaningcenters.com
URL: http://www.homecleaningcenters.com
Description: Home and office cleaning service. **No. of Franchise Units:** 34. **Founded:** 1981.. **Franchised:** 1984. **Equity Capital Needed:** $35,000-$45,000. **Franchise Fee:** $12,500. **Training:** Begins with a 1 week training in Denver. Then franchisee will be monitored and supported by a "District Manager" who also has owned and managed a franchise. All decisions are made by "Policy Committee" comprised of franchise owners. That is followed up with an Annual Franchise Meeting.

6575 ■ Jani-King Canada
23 Cornwallis St.
Kentville, NS, Canada B4N 2E2
Ph: (902)678-3200
Free: 800-565-1873

Fax: (902)678-3500
Co. E-mail: info@janiking.ca
URL: http://www.janiking.com/franchise
Description: Commercial cleaning franchise. **No. of Franchise Units:** 593. **No. of Company-Owned Units:** 22. **Founded:** 1969.. **Franchised:** 1974. **Franchise Fee:** Varies with plan purchased. **Training:** Initial and ongoing support provided.

6576 ■ Maid Brigade
Maid Brigade, Inc.
4 Concourse Pky., Ste. 200
Atlanta, GA 30328
Ph: (800)722-6243
Fax: (770)391-9092
Co. E-mail: franrec@maidbrigade.com
URL: http://www.maidbrigade.com
Description: Cleaning service serving from 20,000 to 150,000 qualified households. We provide unparalleled support, business development, and the latest technology in the industry. If lifestyle, safe investment, quick-start, building equity and generating income are important to you contact us. **No. of Franchise Units:** 413. **Founded:** 1979.. **Franchised:** 1981. **Equity Capital Needed:** $87,000-$132,500. **Franchise Fee:** $29,500-$58,500. **Financial Assistance:** Yes. **Training:** Pre-opening throughout the life of your business, support never stops. New training DVDs, manuals, on-line training, home office training, onsite training, bulletin board, e-mail, councils, conferences, technical support, etc. Our support staff is comprised of former successful Maid Brigade franchisees.

6577 ■ Maid to Perfection
Maid to Perfection Global, Inc.
3111 Innovation Dr.
St. Cloud, FL 34769
Ph: (407)870-2474
Fax: (407)932-0587
Co. E-mail: MAIDSVC@aol.com
URL: http://www.maidtoperfectioncorp.com
Description: Maid to Perfection provides customized cleaning designed for today's sophisticated customer, making service easy to sell. A residential and commercial business. Proven record of offering choices and diversification to franchisees, which leads to higher profits. Unmatched operational format ensures continuous growth. Your business plan adjusts to your market to meet your goals. Success Magazine ranked Maid To Perfection 1 for franchise support & satisfaction 1999. **No. of Franchise Units:** 305. **Founded:** 1980. **Franchised:** 1990. **Equity Capital Needed:** $54,937-$62,635. **Franchise Fee:** $15,000. **Financial Assistance:** Yes. **Training:** 6-8 week business start-up planning, 5 day HQ training, includes live in-home estimating, 5 day office setup and field training, training manuals and CD, 11 instructional videos, advertising materials and assistance, computer program available, 800 helpline, national convention, monthly newsletters, ongoing support.

6578 ■ Maid to Sparkle Inc.
2151 Carbon Hill Drive
Midlothian, VA 23113
Ph: (804)382-7749
Fax: (804)272-0723
Description: Maid services. **No. of Franchise Units:** 2. **No. of Company-Owned Units:** 2. **Founded:** 1998.. **Franchised:** 2003. **Equity Capital Needed:** $15,000. **Franchise Fee:** $20,000. **Financial Assistance:** Yes. **Training:** Provides 1 week training at headquarters, 1 week onsite and ongoing support.

6579 ■ Maidpro
180 Canal St.
Boston, MA 02114
Ph: (617)742-8787
Free: 888-MAI-DPRO
Fax: (617)720-0700
Co. E-mail: chuck@maidpro.com
URL: http://www.maidpro.com
Description: Maid services. **No. of Franchise Units:** 109. **No. of Company-Owned Units:** 1. **Founded:** 1991.. **Franchised:** 1997. **Equity Capital Needed:** $18,709-$103,959. **Franchise Fee:** $7,900. **Training:** Includes 6-8 weeks in training and ongoing support.

6580 ■ Maids Etc.
4907 Hollenden Dr., Ste. 208
Raleigh, NC 27616
Ph: (919)834-8215
Free: 877-624-3738
Co. E-mail: info@maidsetc.com
URL: http://www.maidsetc.com
Description: It's time to clean up with MAIDS ETC. and create your own future in residential and commercial cleaning, which is experiencing explosive growth. We are the 'full service people' offering full-service residential and commercial bull's-eye cleaning systems. We provide our owner-operators with training, consultation, operational support and access to the latest technological advances. **No. of Franchise Units:** 15. **No. of Company-Owned Units:** 3. **Founded:** 1989. **Franchised:** 2003. **Equity Capital Needed:** $36,500-$56,500. **Franchise Fee:** $9,995. **Training:** 6 week business start-up training, 5 day headquarter training and 5 day onsite office setup and field training, start-up equipment and supplies, 800 assist line, computer software, and advertisement materials.

6581 ■ The Maids Home Service
The Maids International, Inc.
9394 W Dodge Rd.
Omaha, NE 68114
Free: 800-843-6243
Fax: (402)558-4112
Co. E-mail: FranchiseInfo@maids.com
URL: http://www.maids.com
Description: Residential maid service franchise. **No. of Franchise Units:** 1,026. **No. of Company-Owned Units:** 29. **Founded:** 1979. **Franchised:** 1981. **Equity Capital Needed:** $93,545-$121,295. **Franchise Fee:** $10,000. **Royalty Fee:** 3.9%-6.9%. **Financial Assistance:** Third party financing available. **Training:** Includes 10 days training at corporate headquarters, 5 days at franchisee's location and 7-10 weeks phone consultation (before and after corporate training) and ongoing support.

6582 ■ Maid2Clean
3054 Dundas St., W
Toronto, ON, Canada M6P 1Z7
Ph: (905)877-0777
Free: 877-265-6243
Fax: (905)702-8801
Co. E-mail: sales@maid2clean.ca
URL: http://www.maid2clean.ca
Description: Domestic housekeeping, cleaning and ironing services provided to private residential homes. **No. of Franchise Units:** 60. **Founded:** 1993.. **Franchised:** 1999. **Equity Capital Needed:** $29,500. **Franchise Fee:** $19,500. **Training:** Provides 2 days training and ongoing support.

6583 ■ Merry Maids
3839 Forest Hill-Irene Rd.
Memphis, TN 38125
Ph: (800)798-8000
Fax: (901)597-7580
Co. E-mail: franchisesales@mmhomeoffice.com
URL: http://www.merrymaids.com
Description: Residential cleaning service. Entrepreneur Magazine has ranked Merry Maids first in the industry for 9 consecutive yrs. Black Enterprise magazine ranked Merry Maids one of the Fabulous 15 Low Cost franchises! The company's commitment to training and support is unmatched. Merry Maids provides comprehensive software and equipment and supply package. Products and supplies available online. Member of the ServiceMaster Quality Service Network. **No. of Franchise Units:** 725. **No. of Company-Owned Units:** 220. **Founded:** 1979. **Franchised:** 1980. **Equity Capital Needed:** $55,350-$78,450 Total capital requirement. **Franchise Fee:** $33,500-$47,500. **Financial Assistance:** Yes. **Training:** 8 day HQ training; all start-up equipment and supplies for 2 teams Buddy Program, educational programs, 800 number for assistance, national TV ads, free website for each franchise, weekly intranet bulletin board, newsletters, regional meetings, national convention, proprietary intranet website, 17 field regional coordinators.

6584 ■ Merry Maids of Canada

ServiceMaster
5462 Timberlea Blvd.
Mississauga, ON, Canada L4W 2T7
Ph: (905)670-0000
Free: 800-263-5928
Fax: (905)670-0077
Co. E-mail: thould@smclean.com
URL: http://www.merrymaids.com
Description: Residential cleaning service with a majority of workers being women. **No. of Franchise Units:** 72. **No. of Company-Owned Units:** 100. **Founded:** 1979.. **Franchised:** 1980. **Equity Capital Needed:** $35,000-$60,000. **Franchise Fee:** $28,000-$35,000. **Training:** Training includes 10 days at Merry Maids University and ongoing support from Canadian home office included.

6585 ■ Mini Maid

3020 Canton Rd., Ste. 13
Marietta, GA 30066-3800
Ph: (770)794-9938
Fax: (770)794-1877
Description: Maid services. **No. of Franchise Units:** 85. **No. of Company-Owned Units:** 10. **Founded:** 1973.. **Equity Capital Needed:** $28,000. **Franchise Fee:** $15,500. **Training:** Yes.

6586 ■ Mint Condition Franchising, Inc.

Mint Condition, Inc.
1057 521 Corporate Center Dr., Ste. 165
Fort Mill, SC 29707
Ph: (803)548-6121
Fax: (803)548-4578
Co. E-mail: info@mintconditioninc.com
URL: http://www.mintconditioninc.com
Description: A Mint Condition Franchise gives you immediate access to a proven and successful model. Our Franchisees are provided with an initial customer base, training, equipment packages, billing and collections from customers, and field support. I invite you to ask about our unique contract guarantees. **No. of Franchise Units:** 234. **No. of Company-Owned Units:** 1. **Franchised:** 1996. **Equity Capital Needed:** $1,000-$20,900 start-up cash; $4,384-$45,100 total initial investment Masters available. **Franchise Fee:** $3,000-$22,000. **Financial Assistance:** Yes. **Training:** Training includes both classroom and field support. Our extensive training includes cleaning techniques and standards, customer service, sales and marketing, personnel, floor care maintenance.

6587 ■ Molly Maid, Inc.

Service Brands Intl.
3948 Ranchero Dr.
Ann Arbor, MI 48108
Ph: (734)822-6800
Fax: (734)822-6666
Co. E-mail: info@mollymaid.com
URL: http://www.mollymaid.com
Description: Maid service industry. Since 1979, they have cleaned more than 10 million homes in 5 countries. MOLLY MAID has received awards for franchise excellence, and has a stellar reputation nationwide. Learn more about MOLLY MAID by browsing through their web site or feel free to give them a call at 800-665-5962. **No. of Franchise Units:**

618. **Founded:** 1979.. **Franchised:** 1984. **Equity Capital Needed:** Total investment $150,000-$175,000, including working capital. **Franchise Fee:** $14,900. **Royalty Fee:** 6.5% -3% to declining royalty. **Training:** 6-8 pre-train program, followed by a week at the home office and week at a Regional Training Center. Industry-leading software, a dedicated support staff, publications and national meetings are available.

6588 ■ Mr. Handyman

Service Brands Intl.
3948 Ranchero Dr.
Ann Arbor, MI 48108
Ph: (734)822-6535
Free: 800-289-4600
Fax: (734)822-6666
Co. E-mail: info@mrhandyman.com
URL: http://www.mrhandyman.com
Description: Mr. Handyman caters to U.S. homeowners and commercial customers needing property repairs. Mr. Handyman is the solution for millions of time-starved, two-income families needing assistance in maintaining their households. There are hundreds of to-do lists on refrigerator doors waiting for Mr. Handyman. Learn more about Mr. Handyman by browsing their web site or give them a call at 800-289-4600. **No. of Franchise Units:** 203. **Founded:** 1996.. **Franchised:** 2000. **Equity Capital Needed:** $120,000-$130,000. **Franchise Fee:** $19,900. **Financial Assistance:** Yes. **Training:** Yes.

6589 ■ MTOclean Inc.

Maids to Order of Ohio, Inc.
7100 E Pleasant Valley Rd., Ste. 300
Independence, OH 44131
Free: 877-392-6278
Fax: (216)674-0650
Co. E-mail: kgolubski@mtoclean.com
URL: http://www.mtoclean.com
Description: Maid service. **No. of Franchise Units:** 35. **Founded:** 1988. **Franchised:** 1992. **Equity Capital Needed:** $17,300-$86,600 working capital. **Franchise Fee:** $5,000-$9,900. **Royalty Fee:** 3-6%. **Financial Assistance:** In-house financing available. **Training:** Training provided at corporate headquarters for 1 week, 1-2 days at franchisee's location and ongoing support.

6590 ■ Nature Stone

O.C.R. Products Inc.
15 N Park St.
Bedford, OH 44146
Ph: (440)786-9100
Free: 800-358-0583
Fax: (440)786-1927
Co. E-mail: jteresi@naturestonefloors.com
URL: http://www.naturestonefloors.com
Description: Franchisee will receive a franchise to own and operate a Nature Stone business, involving the sale and installation of a line of flooring and concrete resurfacing products used as a floor surface for garages, patios, driveways, basements, pool decks, and related surfaces, for an initial term of 5 years with the right, upon payment of a renewal fee and compliance with other conditions, to renew for up to three additional 5 year renewal terms. **No. of Franchise Units:** 41. **No. of Company-Owned**

Units: 3. **Founded:** 1989.. **Franchised:** 2005. **Equity Capital Needed:** $141,500-$398,630. **Franchise Fee:** $24,950-$34,950. **Training:** Yes.

6591 ■ Royal Maid Enterprises

Enterprise House
1574 Pointe Tarpon Blvd.
Tarpon Springs, FL 34689
Ph: (727)943-9521
Co. E-mail: rmaids@knology.net
URL: http://www.royalmaidservice.com
No. of Franchise Units: 36. **Founded:** 1992.. **Equity Capital Needed:** $39,000-$60,000. **Franchise Fee:** From $25,000. **Training:** Offers 6-8 week business start up planning, 5 day office set up and on site training including in home estimating and field training and ongoing support.

6592 ■ ServiceMaster Residential and Commercial Services, L.P.

ServiceMaster Clean
3839 Forest Hill-Irene Rd.
Memphis, TN 38125
Ph: (901)597-7500
Fax: (901)597-7580
Co. E-mail: smfranchiseinfo@smclean.com
URL: http://www.ownafranchise.com
Description: Provides heavy cleaning services for homes, including carpet, upholstery, draperies, windows and disaster restoration. Janitorial services are also provided for the commercial market. Provides all the research, equipment, supplies, initial and continuous training franchisees need. **No. of Franchise Units:** 4,500. **Founded:** 1947.. **Franchised:** 1952. **Equity Capital Needed:** $47,860-$161,125. **Franchise Fee:** $24,900-$79,200. **Financial Assistance:** Financing available. **Training:** 2 weeks training at corporate headquarters; monthly newsletters; local and national conferences. Regional operations managers assist the franchisees in the growth and development of their business. All of the departments within ServiceMaster have at least one person who handles franchise relations. Each distributor has owned and operated his/her own ServiceMaster for at least 5 years, as have the regional operations managers.

6593 ■ Servpro

Servpro Industries, Inc.
801 Industrial Blvd.
Gallatin, TN 37066
Ph: (615)451-0600
Free: 800-826-9586
Fax: (615)451-1602
Co. E-mail: franchise@servpronet.com
URL: http://www.servpro.com
Description: A completely diversified cleaning and restoration business, with multiple income opportunities. The insurance restoration market (fire, smoke and water damage) is their main focus. Specialize in commercial & residential cleaning. **No. of Franchise Units:** 1,600. **Founded:** 1967.. **Franchised:** 1969. **Equity Capital Needed:** $133,050-$181,450. **Franchise Fee:** $42,000. **Training:** Intensive home study curriculum, manuals and videos. Provides 2 weeks training in state of the art national training facility, 1 week set up/opening assistance, and trainer assistance. Ongoing support, convention, regional and area meetings, formal business reviews, newsletters, bulletins, and more.

ASSOCIATIONS AND OTHER ORGANIZATIONS

6594 ■ American Driver and Traffic Safety Education Association (ADTSEA)
Highway Safety Services, LLC
1434 Trim Tree Rd.
Indiana, PA 15701
Ph: (724)801-8246
Free: 877-485-7172
Fax: (724)349-5042
Co. E-mail: office@adtsea.org
URL: http://www.adtsea.org/adtsea
Contact: Connie Sessoms, Jr., President
URL(s): www.adtsea.org. **Description:** Professional organization of teachers and supervisors interested in improving driver and traffic safety education in colleges and secondary and elementary schools. Awards honorary memberships to retired persons distinguished in the field. Provides assistance to state departments of education, colleges and universities, state associations, and local school districts. **Founded:** 1956. **Publications:** *Journal of Traffic Safety Education* (Quarterly); *Washington Wire* (Periodic). **Telecommunication Services:** office@advertisingsea.org.

6595 ■ Governors Highway Safety Association (GHSA)
444 N Capitol St. NW, Ste. 722
Washington, DC 20001
Ph: (202)789-0942
Fax: (202)789-0946
Co. E-mail: headquarters@ghsa.org
URL: http://www.ghsa.org
Contact: Troy E. Costales, Chairman
Description: Represents the interests of state and territorial officials who administer the Highway Safety Act of 1966. (The Highway Safety Act requires that states receiving highway safety grants under 23 U.S. Code 402 may not receive program approval unless the governor of each state or territory is responsible for administration of the program.) Works to reduce highway fatalities and automobile accidents; enforces the 55 mph speed limit; develops and maintains driver education and pedestrian and bicycle safety programs; manages alcohol safety and occupant protection programs. Conducts research through grant programs. Provides highway safety training in such areas as judicial training, engineering, traffic engineering, and traffic safety engineering. **Founded:** 1969. **Publications:** *Directions in Highway Safety* (Quarterly). **Educational Activities:** Governors Highway Safety Association Convention (Annual); Lifesavers (Annual). **Awards:** James J. Howard Highway Safety Trailblazer Award (Annual); Peter K. O'Rourke Special Achievement Award (Annual).

TRADE PERIODICALS

6596 ■ Dual News
Pub: Driving School Association of Americas
Ed: George R. Hensel, Editor, grhensel@aol.com.
Released: Quarterly. **Price:** Free. **Description:** Focuses on traffic safety, automobile care (repair and maintenance), teaching methods, and driving, in general. Recurring features include news of research and columns titled Legislation Pertaining to Driving, Teaching Methods, and President's Corner.

6597 ■ Highway Safety Directions
Pub: Highway Safety Research Center
Ed: Katy Jones. **Released:** Biennial. **Price:** Free. **Description:** Reports on research being done by the University of North Carolina Highway Safety Research Center, including alcohol and highway safety, motor vehicle inspection, accident investigation and analysis, driver behavior, and education and licensing. Carries news on adult and child passenger safety, including seat belts and child seats, passenger protection laws, and statewide passenger safety efforts.

6598 ■ In Motion
Pub: General Learning Communications
Contact: John E. Cimba, President
URL(s): www.glcomm.com/. **Released:** Annual **Price:** Free to schools.

VIDEOCASSETTES/ AUDIOCASSETTES

6599 ■ At the Wheel
National Film Board of Canada
1123 Broadway, Ste. 307
New York, NY 10010
Ph: (212)629-8890
Free: 800-542-2164
Fax: (212)629-8502
URL: http://www.nfb.ca
Released: 1989. **Price:** $400.00. **Description:** This video series documents the consequences and after-effects of a serious automobile crash. **Availability:** VHS; 3/4 U.

6600 ■ Defensive Driving Techniques
Gun Video
4585 Murphy Canyon Rd.
San Diego, CA 92123
Ph: (858)569-4000
Free: 800-942-8273
Fax: (858)569-0505
Co. E-mail: info2@gunvideo.com
URL: http://www.gunvideo.com
Released: 19??. **Price:** $49.95. **Description:** Advice on high-speed driving from expert instructors. **Availability:** VHS.

6601 ■ General Driving Safety
Gulf Publishing Co.
2 Greenway Plz., Ste. 1020
Houston, TX 77046-0208
Ph: (713)529-4301
Free: 800-231-6275
Fax: (713)520-4433
Co. E-mail: advertising@gulfpub.com
URL: http://www.gulfpub.com
Contact: John Royall, President
Released: 19??. **Description:** Eleven-part series that provides instruction on driving safety, including information on road conditions and speed, drunk driving, accidents, sleepiness and driving, mountain driving, skidding, convoys, safety devices, seat belts, fire-resistant clothing, and backing up. **Availability:** VHS; 3/4 U.

TRADE SHOWS AND CONVENTIONS

6602 ■ Driving School Association of America Annual Conference
Driving School Association of America
3125 Wilmington Pike
Kettering, OH 45429
Free: 800-270-3722
Fax: (937)290-0696
Co. E-mail: info@thedssa.org
URL: http://www.thedssa.org
Contact: Sharon Postigo Fife, President
URL(s): www.thedsaa.org/conference.asp. **Price:** $400, first delegate; $375, additional delegates; $175. **Frequency:** Annual. **Audience:** social functions only. **Principal Exhibits:** Automobile safety products related to driver training and traffic safety. **Telecommunication Services:** info@thedssa.org.

FRANCHISES AND BUSINESS OPPORTUNITIES

6603 ■ All Star Franchising, LLC
All Star Driver Education, Inc.
1011 S Main St.
Ann Arbor, MI 48104
Ph: (734)665-7374
Free: 800-967-7719
Fax: (734)665-7680
Description: Driver education. **No. of Company-Owned Units:** 30. **Founded:** 1997.. **Franchised:** 2007. **Equity Capital Needed:** $83,700-$199,900. **Franchise Fee:** $30,000. **Financial Assistance:** Yes. **Training:** Yes.

LIBRARIES

6604 ■ Alabama Department of Transportation - Research & Development Bureau - Research Library
1409 Coliseum Blvd.
Montgomery, AL 36110
Ph: (334)253-6940
Fax: (334)264-2042
Co. E-mail: brownje@dot.state.al.us
URL: http://www.dot.state.al.us/rdweb/Index.htm
Contact: Jeffrey W. Brown
Scope: Transportation. **Services:** Interlibrary loan; Library not open to the public. **Founded:** 1953. **Holdings:** 1000 books; 5000 reports. **Subscriptions:** 8 journals and other serials.

6605 ■ American Automobile Association Research Library—AAA Research Library.
1000 AAA Dr.
Heathrow, FL 32746-5060
Ph: (407)444-7965

Fax: (407)444-7759
Co. E-mail: rinesta@aaasouth.com
URL: http://www.aaasouth.com
Contact: Renaldo Inesta, Division Manager
Scope: Travel guide books; market studies; highway and traffic safety; driver education; automobiles - history, statistics, insurance. **Services:** Interlibrary loan; Library open to researchers with permission. **Founded:** 1955. **Holdings:** 10,000 books; 20 VF drawers of pamphlets; reports. **Subscriptions:** 100 journals and other serials.

6606 ■ California State Department of Motor Vehicles - Licensing Operations Division - Research and Development Branch - Traffic Safety Research Library
2415 1st Ave., MS F-126
Sacramento, CA 95818
Ph: (916)657-3079
Free: 800-368-4327
Fax: (916)657-8589
Co. E-mail: dluong@dvm.ca.gov
Contact: Douglas Luong, Analyst
Scope: Automobile transportation. **Services:** Copying; library not open to the public. **Holdings:** 500 books; 10,000 bound periodical volumes; reports; manuscripts. **Subscriptions:** 20 journals and other serials.

6607 ■ ConnDOT Library and Information Center
2800 Berlin Tpke.
Newington, CT 06111-4116
Ph: (860)594-2000
Fax: (860)594-3039
Co. E-mail: drew.coleman@ct.gov
URL: http://www.ct.gov/dot/site/default.asp
Contact: Betty Ambler, Librarian
Scope: Transportation. **Services:** Interlibrary loan; copying; library open to the public by appointment. **Founded:** 1983. **Holdings:** 10,000 books; 10,000 reports; videos.

6608 ■ Kansas Department of Transportation Library—KDOT Library.
700 SW Harrison St.
Eisenhower State Office Bldg., 4th Fl. W.
Topeka, KS 66603-3745
Ph: (785)291-3854
Fax: (785)291-3717
Co. E-mail: library@ksdot.org
Contact: Marie Manthe, Librarian
Scope: Transportation. **Services:** Interlibrary loan; Library open to the public. **Founded:** 1963. **Holdings:** 3000 books; 20,000 reports; 175 CD-ROMs; 100 videos. **Subscriptions:** 100 journals and other serials.

6609 ■ Kentucky Transportation Center Library
University of Kentucky
176 Raymond Bldg.
Lexington, KY 40506-0281
Ph: (859)257-2155
Free: 800-432-0719
Fax: (859)257-1815
Co. E-mail: lwhayne@engr.uky.edu
URL: http://www.kyt2.com/
Contact: Laura Whayne, Librarian
Scope: Transportation. **Services:** Interlibrary loan; copying; Library open to the public. **Founded:** 1980. **Holdings:** 6000 books; 9000 reports; 800 videotapes. **Subscriptions:** 300 journals and other serials. **Telecommunication Services:** vbrock@engr.uky.edu.

6610 ■ Missouri Highway and Transportation Department - Division of Materials Library
105 W. Capitol Ave.
Jefferson City, MO 65102-0270
Ph: (573)751-6735
Free: 888-275 6636

Fax: (573)526-5636
Co. E-mail: michael.meyerhoff@mail.modot.state.mo.us
URL: http://www.modot.org/
Contact: Mona Scott
Scope: Transportation. **Services:** Library not open to the public. **Holdings:** Figures not available.

6611 ■ Montana Department of Transportation Library
2701 Prospect Ave.
Helena, MT 59620-1001
Ph: (406)444-6338
Free: 800-335-7592
Fax: (406)444-6204
Co. E-mail: ssillick@mt.gov
URL: http://www.mdt.mt.gov/research/unique/services.shtml
Contact: Susan Sillick
Scope: Transportation. **Services:** Interlibrary loan; copying. **Holdings:** 10,000 items; reports; CD-ROMs; video. **Subscriptions:** 10 journals and other serials. **Telecommunication Services:** mdtresearch@mt.gov.

6612 ■ New Jersey Department of Transportation Research Library
1035 Parkway Ave.
Trenton, NJ 08625-0600
Ph: (609)530-5289
Fax: (609)530-2052
Co. E-mail: library@dot.state.nj.us
URL: http://www.state.nj.us/transportation/refdata/library/
Contact: Carol Paszamant, Librarian
Scope: Transportation. **Services:** Interlibrary loan; copying; library open to the public by appointment. **Founded:** 1962. **Holdings:** 300 books; 11,000 reports. **Subscriptions:** 50 journals and other serials.

6613 ■ North Carolina Department of Transportation, Research and Development Library
PO Box 25201
Raleigh, NC 27611
Ph: (919)715-2463
Fax: (919)715-0137
Co. E-mail: rhhall@dot.state.nc.us
URL: http://www.ncdot.org/
Contact: Bob Hall
Scope: Transportation. **Services:** Interlibrary loan; copying; Library open to the public for reference use only. **Holdings:** 11,209 books; 20,021 reports; 132 videos. **Subscriptions:** 57 journals and other serials.

6614 ■ North Dakota Department of Transportation - Materials and Research Division Library
608 East Blvd.
Bismarck, ND 58505-0700
Ph: (701)328-2500
Free: 855-637-6237
Fax: (701)328-0310
Co. E-mail: gweisger@nd.gov
URL: http://www.dot.nd.gov
Contact: Gerri Weisgerber, Manager, Administration
Scope: Transportation. **Services:** Library not open to the public. **Founded:** 1970. **Holdings:** 6600 reports. **Subscriptions:** 5 journals and other serials.

6615 ■ South Carolina Department of Transportation Library
955 Park St., Rm. 110
Columbia, SC 29202
Ph: (803)737-9897
Free: 855-467-2368

Fax: (803)737-0824
Co. E-mail: adcockda@dot.state.sc.us
URL: http://www.dot.state.sc.us
Contact: Ann Adcock, Manager
Scope: Transportation, engineering, mass transit. **Services:** Interlibrary loan; transportation related research; library open to the public. **Founded:** 1998. **Holdings:** 5500 books; 90 bound periodical volumes; 1900 reports; 250 videos. **Subscriptions:** 41 journals and other serials; 10 newspapers. **Telecommunication Services:** SCDOT_contact@scdot.org.

6616 ■ U.S. National Highway Traffic Safety Administration - Technical Information Services
1200 New Jersey Ave., SE
Washington, DC 20590
Ph: (888)327-4236
Fax: (202)493-2833
Co. E-mail: tis@nhtsa.dot.gov
URL: http://www.nhtsa.dot.gov/cars/problems/trd/?name=
Contact: Shirlene D. Ball, Analyst
Scope: Motor vehicle safety, highway traffic safety, alcohol countermeasures for driving safety, vehicle occupant protection, emergency medical services. **Services:** Copying; TIS open to the public. **Founded:** 1967. **Holdings:** 200 books; 52,000 agency and related publications and reports; 920,000 microfiche. **Subscriptions:** 40 journals and other serials.

6617 ■ Vermont Agency of Transportation, Policy and Planning Division Library
1 National Drive
c, VT 05633-0001
Ph: (802)828-3960
Fax: (802)828-3983
URL: http://www.aot.state.vt.us
Contact: Sandy Aja
Scope: Transportation. **Holdings:** Figures not available.

RESEARCH CENTERS

6618 ■ Indiana University Bloomington - Center for Health and Safety Studies
1025 E 7th, HPER Rm. 116
Bloomington, IN 47405
Ph: (812)855-2429
Fax: (812)855-3936
Co. E-mail: torabi@indiana.edu
URL: http://www.research.iu.edu/centers/chss.html
Contact: Dr. Mohammad R. Torabi, Chairperson
Services: Health and safety consulting to industry and government. **Founded:** 1965. **Educational Activities:** Conferences on health and safety issues (Occasionally).

6619 ■ University of North Carolina at Chapel Hill - Highway Safety Research Center (HSRC)
730 Martin Luther King Jr. Blvd., CB 3430
Chapel Hill, NC 27599-3430
Ph: (919)962-2202
Free: 800-672-4527
Fax: (919)962-8710
Co. E-mail: david_harkey@unc.edu
URL: http://www.hsrc.unc.edu/index.cfm
Contact: David L. Harkey, Director
Founded: 1965. **Publications:** *Highway Safety Directions* (Occasionally). **Educational Activities:** Annual series of traffic records workshops; Occupant protection workshops (Occasionally), for health and safety professionals, law enforcement officials, and researchers; Safe Routes to School Course (Occasionally), for planners; Transportation Research Board (Annual). **Telecommunication Services:** info@hsrc.unc.edu.

ASSOCIATIONS AND OTHER ORGANIZATIONS

6620 ■ American Association of Colleges of Pharmacy (AACP)
1727 King St.
Alexandria, VA 22314
Ph: (703)739-2330
Fax: (703)836-8982
Co. E-mail: mail@aacp.org
URL: http://www.aacp.org
Contact: Lucinda L. Maine, Chief Executive Officer
URL(s): www.aacp.org/news/Pages/default.aspx. **Description:** College of pharmacy programs accredited by American Council on Pharmaceutical Education; corporations and individuals. Compiles statistics. **Founded:** 1900. **Publications:** *American Journal of Pharmaceutical Education* (Quarterly); *AACP E-lert*; *Prescription for a Rewarding Career* (Periodic); *Roster of Faculty and Professional Staff* (Annual); *Roster of Teaching Personnel in Colleges of Pharmacy* (Annual); *American Association of Colleges of Pharmacy--Roster of Teaching Personnel in Colleges and Schools of Pharmacy* (Annual); *Pharmacy School Admission Requirements* (Annual); *American Journal of Pharmaceutical Education*; *Roster of Faculty and Professional Staff in Colleges and Schools of Pharmacy* (Annual); *American Association of Colleges of Pharmacy--Graduate Programs in the Pharmaceutical Sciences* (Annual). **Awards:** Paul Dawson Biotechnology Award (Annual); The Volwiler Research Achievement Award (Annual).

6621 ■ American Association of Pharmacy Technicians (AAPT)
PO Box 1447
Greensboro, NC 27402
Ph: (336)333-9356
Free: 877-368-4771
Fax: (336)333-9068
Co. E-mail: aapt@pharmacytechnician.com
URL: http://www.pharmacytechnician.com
Contact: Ms. Ann Oberg, President
Description: Pharmacy technicians. Promotes professional advancement of members. Represents members before health care and public organizations; conducts continuing professional development courses; publicizes the role of the pharmacy technician as an "integral part of the patient care team". **Awards:** AAPT Founders Award (Annual).

6622 ■ American College of Apothecaries (ACA)
2830 Summer Oaks Dr.
Bartlett, TN 38134
Ph: (901)383-8119
Free: 800-828-5933
Fax: (901)383-8882
Co. E-mail: aca@acainfo.org
URL: http://www.americancollegeofapothecaries.com
Contact: Nelson L. Showalter, President
E-mail: nshow@comcast.net
Description: Professional society of pharmacists owning and operating ethical prescription pharmacies, including hospital pharmacists, pharmacy students, and faculty of colleges of pharmacy. Translates, transforms, and disseminates knowledge, research data, and recent developments in the pharmaceutical industry and public health. Offers continuing education courses and certificate program. Conducts research programs; sponsors charitable program; compiles statistics; operates speakers' bureau. **Founded:** 1940. **Publications:** *American College of Apothecaries Newsletter* (Monthly); *American College of Apothecaries--Patron's Newsletter* (Monthly); *American College of Apothecaries-- Physician's Newsletter* (Monthly); *Voice of the Pharmacist* (Quarterly); *Voice of the Pharmacist Newsletter*; *Voice of the Pharmacist Newsletter*. **Awards:** J. Leon Lascoff Memorial Award; Albert E. Rosica, Jr. Memorial Award.

6623 ■ American Foundation for Pharmaceutical Education (AFPE)
1 Church St., Ste. 400
Rockville, MD 20850
Ph: (301)738-2160
Fax: (301)738-2161
Co. E-mail: info@afpenet.org
URL: http://www.afpenet.org
Contact: Robert M. Bachman, President
Description: Established by pharmaceutical and drug trade associations to improve pharmaceutical education, colleges of pharmacy, and pharmacy student performance. Accepts and administers gifts, legacies, bequests, and funds and makes disbursements for fellowships and the promotion of pharmaceutical education. **Founded:** 1942. **Awards:** American Foundation for Pharmaceutical Education Gateway Research Scholarships; American Foundation for Pharmaceutical Education Pre-Doctoral Fellowships in the Pharmaceutical Sciences; Clinical Pharmacy Post-Pharm.D. Fellowships in the Biomedical Research Sciences; Minority Pharmacy Faculty New Investigator Grants; Minority Student Gateway to Research Scholarships; Minority Student Pre-Doctoral Fellowship Program; Pharmacy Faculty Fellowships in Community Pharmacy Practice; Pharmacy Faculty Fellowships in Geriatric Pharmacy/ Geriatric Pharmaceutical Science; Pharmacy Faculty New Investigator Grants Program.

6624 ■ American Institute of the History of Pharmacy (AIHP)
777 Highland Ave.
Madison, WI 53705-2222
Ph: (608)262-5378
Fax: (608)262-3397
Co. E-mail: aihp@aihp.org
URL: http://www.pharmacy.wisc.edu/aihp
Contact: Dr. Gregory J. Higby, Executive Director
Description: Pharmacists, firms, and organizations interested in historical and social aspects of the pharmaceutical field. Maintains pharmaceutical Americana collection; conducts research programs. **Founded:** 1941. **Publications:** *Current Newsletter*; *AIHP Notes* (Quarterly); *Pharmacy in History* (Quarterly); *AIHP Pamphlets*; *AIHP Papers*; *Pharmacy in History* (Quarterly); *Pharmacy in History* (Quarterly). **Educational Activities:** American Institute of the History of Pharmacy Meeting (Annual); Conferences and historical seminars (Occasionally); Business Meetings (Annual). **Awards:** AIHP Student Certificate Program (Annual); Fischelis Grants (Annual); Grants for graduate students in history of pharmacy; Grant-in-Aid Toward Thesis Expenses Related to the History of Pharmacy (Annual). **Telecommunication Services:** bdfisher@aihp.org.

6625 ■ American Society of Consultant Pharmacists (ASCP)
1321 Duke St.
Alexandria, VA 22314-3563
Ph: (703)739-1300
Free: 800-355-2727
Fax: (703)739-1321
Co. E-mail: info@ascp.com
URL: http://www.ascp.com
Contact: Penny S. Shelton, President
Description: Provides leadership, education, advocacy and resources enabling consultant and senior care pharmacists to enhance quality of care and quality of life for older individuals through the provision of pharmaceutical care and the promotion of healthy aging. Excels in the areas of: knowledge and skills in geriatric pharmacotherapy; expertise in long-term care settings for the frail at-risk elderly and other residents; and patient-centered advocate for seniors at-risk for medication related problems. Improves drug therapy and quality of life of geriatric patients and other individuals residing in a variety of environments, including nursing facilities, subacute care and assisted living facilities, psychiatric hospitals, hospice programs, and in home and community settings. **Founded:** 1969. **Publications:** *UPDATE* (Monthly); *Clinical Consult*; *The Consultant Pharmacist* (Monthly); *American Society of Consultant Pharmacists - Update*. **Educational Activities:** Midyear (Annual); Senior Care Pharmacy (Annual); American Society of Consultant Pharmacists Annual Meeting and Exhibition (Annual); MD-ASCP Mid-Atlantic Conference (Annual); Midwest Regional Conference (Annual). **Awards:** Leadership in Education Award (Annual); Richard S. Berman Service Award (Annual); George F. Archambault Award (Annual); Leadership in Education Award; Armon Neel Senior Care Pharmacist Award (Annual); Richard S. Berman Service Award.

6626 ■ American Society of Health-System Pharmacists (ASHP)
7272 Wisconsin Ave.
Bethesda, MD 20814
Ph: (301)664-8700
Free: 866-279-0681
Fax: (301)657-1251
Co. E-mail: custserv@ashp.org
URL: http://www.ashp.org
Contact: Diane B. Ginsburg, President
Description: Professional society of pharmacists employed by hospitals, HMOs, clinics, and other health systems. Provides personnel placement service for members; sponsors professional and personal liability program. Conducts educational and exhibit programs. Maintains 30 practice interest areas, special sections for home care practitioners and clinical specialists, and research and education

foundation. **Scope:** medicine, pharmacy. **Founded:** 1942. **Subscriptions:** 3200 books periodicals. **Publications:** *American Journal of Health-System Pharmacy* (Semimonthly); *American Journal of Health System Pharmacy* (Semimonthly); *ASHP Newsletter* (Monthly); *ASHP Intersections* (Quarterly); *Drug Information Fulltext*; *International Pharmaceutical Abstracts* (Semimonthly); *MedTeach™/MedTeach™ for Windows*; *Drug Information Fulltext (DIF)*; *International Pharmaceutical Abstracts (IPA)*; *Handbook on Injectable Drugs*; *ASHP Handbook on Injectable Drugs* (Biennial); *AHFS Drug Information (AHFS-DI)*; *Drug Information Fulltext/IPA*; *International Pharmaceutical Abstracts: Key to the World's Literature of Pharmacy*; *Drug Information Fulltext® (DIFT)*; *IPA on TOXLINE Plus*; *AHFS Drug Information on Statl-Ref*; *Manual for Pharmacy Technicians*; *Pharmacy Technician Certification Review and Practice Exam.* **Educational Activities:** Midyear Clinical Meeting (Annual); American Society of Health-System Pharmacists Midyear Clinical Meeting. **Awards:** Donald E. Francke Medal (Annual); Distinguished Leadership Award; ASHP Student Research Awards; Award for Distinguished Leadership of Health-System Pharmacy Practice (Annual); Board of Director's Award of Honor (Annual); Harvey A.K. Whitney Lecture Award (Annual); Board of Director's Award of Honor; Donald E. Francke Medal; Harvey A.K. Whitney Lecture Award; John W. Webb Lecture Awards.

6627 ■ American Society for Pharmacy Law (ASPL)

3085 Stevenson Dr., Ste. 200
Springfield, IL 62703-4270
Ph: (217)529-6948
Fax: (217)529-9120
Co. E-mail: nchatara@associationcentral.org
URL: http://www.aspl.org
Contact: Nathela Chatara, Executive Director
E-mail: nchatara@associationcentral.org
Description: Pharmacists, lawyers, and students. Aims are to: further legal knowledge; communicate accurate legal information to pharmacists; foster knowledge and education pertaining to the rights and duties of pharmacists; distribute information of interest to members; provide a forum for exchange of information pertaining to pharmacy law. **Founded:** 1974. **Publications:** *Pharma-Law eNews* (Monthly); *Rx Ipsa Loquitur* (Bimonthly). **Educational Activities:** Developments in Pharmacy Law (Annual); National Pharmacy and other Organizations (Annual); Developments in Pharmacy Law (Annual). **Awards:** Larry Simonsmeizr Award (Annual); Joseph L. Fink III Founders Award (Periodic). **Telecommunication Services:** info@aspl.org.

6628 ■ Canadian Pharmaceutical Journal

1785 Alta Vista Dr.
Ottawa, ON, Canada K1G 3Y6
Ph: (613)523-7877
Free: 800-917-9489
Fax: (613)523-0445
Co. E-mail: info@pharmacists.ca
URL: http://www.pharmacists.ca/
Contact: Jody Shkrobo, President
E-mail: jshkrobot@gmail.com
Released: 10/year **Price:** included in membership dues.

6629 ■ Canadian Pharmacists Association (CPhA)—Association Pharmaciens Du Canada

1785 Alta Vista Dr.
Ottawa, ON, Canada K1G 3Y6
Ph: (613)523-7877
Free: 800-917-9489
Fax: (613)523-0445
Co. E-mail: info@pharmacists.ca
URL: http://www.pharmacists.ca/
Contact: Jody Shkrobo, President
E-mail: jshkrobot@gmail.com
Description: Pharmacists in Canada. Works to provide leadership for the pharmacy profession. Monitors government health care policies and legislation; lobbies for the interests of pharmacists. Maintains liaison with government departments, pharmaceutical manufacturers, and health care organizations. Conducts education and research programs.

Founded: 1907. **Publications:** *Provincial Drug Benefit Programs* (Semiannual); *Compendium of Pharmaceuticals and Specialties* (Annual); *Impact*; *Canadian Pharmacists Journal*; *Canadian Pharmaceutical Journal* (10/year); *Compendium of Pharmaceuticals and Specialties* (Annual); *Sterile Preparations*; *Pharmacy Directory* (Annual). **Awards:** Centennial Award; Canadian Pharmacist of the Year; New Practitioner Award; International Leadership Award; Dean George A. Burbidge Award; Canadian Pharmacist of the Year (Annual); CPhA New Practitioner Award (Annual); Patient Care Achievement Award for Health Promotion; Patient Care Achievement Award for Innovation; Patient Care Achievement Award for Specialty Practice.

6630 ■ Chain Drug Marketing Association (CDMA)

43157 W Nine Mile Rd.
Novi, MI 48376-0995
Ph: (248)449-9300
Free: 800-935-2362
Fax: (248)449-9396
Co. E-mail: support@chaindrug.com
URL: http://www.chaindrug.com
Contact: Jim Devine, President
Description: Drug store chains located throughout the world. Represents members in the market for merchandise; keeps them abreast of trends in relevant fields. **Founded:** 1926. **Educational Activities:** CDMA Fall Show (Semiannual).

6631 ■ Compendium of Pharmaceuticals and Specialties

1785 Alta Vista Dr.
Ottawa, ON, Canada K1G 3Y6
Ph: (613)523-7877
Free: 800-917-9489
Fax: (613)523-0445
Co. E-mail: info@pharmacists.ca
URL: http://www.pharmacists.ca/
Contact: Jody Shkrobo, President
E-mail: jshkrobot@gmail.com
Released: Annual

6632 ■ Foreign Pharmacy Graduate Examination Committee (FPGEC)

Natl. Assn. of Boards of Pharmacy
1600 Feehanville Dr.
Mount Prospect, IL 60056
Ph: (847)391-4406
Fax: (847)391-4502
Co. E-mail: custserv@nabp.net
URL: http://www.nabp.net/programs/examination/fpgec
Contact: Malcolm J. Broussard, Chairperson
Description: A committee of the National Association of Boards of Pharmacy. Provides information to foreign pharmacy graduates regarding entry into the U.S. pharmacy profession and health care systems. Evaluates qualifications of foreign pharmacy graduates. Gathers and disseminates data on foreign graduates; maintains information on foreign pharmacy schools in order to produce an examination that measures academic competence with regard to U.S. pharmacy school standards. **Founded:** 1982. **Publications:** *National Pharmacy Compliance News* (Quarterly); *State Newsletter Program* (Quarterly). **Educational Activities:** Foreign Pharmacy Graduate Equivalency Examination Administration (Biennial).

6633 ■ Generic Pharmaceutical Association (GPhA)

777 6th St. NW, Ste. 510
Washington, DC 20001
Ph: (202)249-7100
URL: http://www.gphaonline.org
Contact: Ralph G. Neas, President
Description: Promotes the common interests of the members and the general welfare of the pharmaceutical industry; prepares and disseminates among members and others, accurate and reliable information concerning the industry, products, needs and requirements; participates in international, federal, state and municipal legislative, regulatory and administrative proceedings with respect to law, rules and orders affecting the pharmaceutical industry; participates in scientific research and product development with intent to increase consumer access to

generic products; and raises awareness and visibility of the significant benefits and value of generic drugs to the consumers. **Founded:** 2001.

6634 ■ Healthcare Distribution Management Association (HDMA)

901 N Glebe Rd., Ste. 1000
Arlington, VA 22203
Ph: (703)787-0000
Fax: (703)812-5282
Co. E-mail: lkanfer@hdmanet.org
URL: http://www.healthcaredistribution.org
Contact: David Moody, Chairman
Description: Wholesalers and manufacturers of drug and health care products and industry service providers. Seeks to secure safe and effective distribution of healthcare products, create and exchange industry knowledge affecting the future of distribution management, and influence standards and business processes that produce efficient health care commerce. Compiles statistics; sponsors research and specialized education programs. **Scope:** distribution, logistics, pharmacy, wholesale marketing. **Founded:** 1876. **Subscriptions:** 1000. **Educational Activities:** Business Partners Exchange (Annual); Distribution Management and Expo (Annual); Leadership Forum (Annual). **Awards:** Diana Award (Annual); iBusiness Solutions (Annual); Innovation for Success (Annual); Nexus Award (Annual); DIANA Award; Nexus Award for Lifetime Achievement; Distribution Management Award; Technology Award.

6635 ■ International Academy of Compounding Pharmacists (IACP)

4638 Riverstone Blvd.
Missouri City, TX 77459
Ph: (281)933-8400
Free: 800-927-4227
Fax: (281)495-0602
Co. E-mail: iacpinfo@iacprx.org
URL: http://www.iacprx.org
Contact: Scott Karolchyk, President
Description: Pharmacists who compound custom medications to meet unique patient needs. Seeks to "enhance credibility and respect of the compounding pharmacy practice to the health care community and its patients"; promotes empowerment of compounding pharmacists. Develops and enforces codes of ethics and practice for members; facilitates cooperation and exchange of information among members; sponsors research and educational programs. **Founded:** 1991. **Publications:** *The eLink* (Weekly); *The Pharmacists' Link* (Quarterly). **Educational Activities:** Compounders on Capital Hill (Annual).

6636 ■ International Federation of Pharmaceutical Wholesalers (IFPW)

10569 Crestwood Dr.
Manassas, VA 20109
Ph: (703)331-3714
Fax: (703)331-3715
Co. E-mail: info@ifpw.com
URL: http://www.ifpw.com
Contact: Eric V. Zwisler, Vice Chairman
Description: Wholesalers and distributors of pharmaceutical products. Promotes efficient delivery of pharmaceuticals to hospitals, physicians, and pharmacists; seeks to increase public awareness of the role played by members in the health care system. Facilitates cooperation and exchange of information among members; represents members' commercial and regulatory interests; sponsors educational and promotional programs.

6637 ■ National Association of Chain Drug Stores (NACDS)

1776 Wilson Blvd., Ste. 200
Arlington, VA 22209
Ph: (703)549-3001
Fax: (703)836-4869
Co. E-mail: contactus@nacds.org
URL: http://www.nacds.org
Contact: Gregory D. Wasson, Chairman
Description: Represents the concerns of community pharmacies in Washington, in state capitals, and across the country. Members are more than 210 chain community pharmacy companies. Collectively, community pharmacy comprises the largest component of pharmacy practice with over 107,000 FTE

pharmacists. **Scope:** industry history, trends, statistics, pharmacy and OTC statistics, pharmacy and retail management, managed care. **Founded:** 1933. **Subscriptions:** 10000 audio recordings books periodicals reports video recordings. **Publications:** *National Association of Chain Drug Stores-- Communications Directory* (Annual); *National Association of Chain Drug Stores - Communications Directory.* **Educational Activities:** Marketplace (Annual); NACDS Marketplace Conference (Annual); NACDS Pharmacy & Technology Conference (Annual); Pharmacy Conference and Managed Care Forum (Annual). **Awards:** Harold W. Pratt Award (Annual); Robert B. Begley Award; Sheldon W. Fantle Lifetime Achievement Honor Award (Annual); Harold W. Pratt Award; Robert B. Begley Award; Sheldon W. Fantle Lifetime Achievement Honor Award.

6638 ■ National Community Pharmacists Association (NCPA)

100 Daingerfield Rd.
Alexandria, VA 22314
Ph: (703)683-8200
Free: 800-544-7447
Fax: (703)683-3619
Co. E-mail: info@ncpanet.org
URL: http://www.ncpanet.org
Contact: Robert Greenwood, President

Description: Owners and managers of independent drugstores and pharmacists employed in community pharmacies offering pharmacy service. Provides support for undergraduate pharmacy education through National Community Pharmacists Association Foundation. **Founded:** 1898. **Publications:** *America's Pharmacist* (Monthly); *NCPA Newsletter* (Semimonthly); *NCPA Newsletter*, *NCPA Newsletter*, *America's Pharmacist: The Voice of the Community Pharmacists* (Monthly). **Educational Activities:** NCPA Convention and Trade Exposition; NCPA Annual Convention and Trade Exposition (Annual). **Awards:** National Community Pharmacists Association Presidential Scholarships; National Community Pharmacists Association Summer Internship Programs; Neil Pruitt, Sr. Memorial Scholarships; J.C. and Rheba Cobb Memorial Scholarships; Willard B. Simmons Sr. Memorial Scholarships.

6639 ■ Pharmaceutical Care Management Association (PCMA)

601 Pennsylvania Ave. NW, Ste. 740 S
Washington, DC 20004
Ph: (202)207-3610
URL: http://www.pcmanet.org
Contact: George Paz, Chairman

Description: Represents managed care pharmacy, Pharmaceutical Benefits Management companies (PBMs) and their healthcare partners in pharmaceutical care. Promotes education, legislation, practice standards, and research to foster quality, affordable pharmaceutical care. **Founded:** 1975. **Awards:** Excellence in Pharmaceutical Care (Annual); Latiolais Honor Medal (Annual); Outstanding Individual and Company (Annual).

6640 ■ Pharmaceutical Research and Manufacturers of America (PhRMA)

950 F St. NW, Ste. 300
Washington, DC 20004
Ph: (202)835-3400
Fax: (202)835-3414
Co. E-mail: info@phrma.org
URL: http://www.phrma.org
Contact: John J. Castellani, President
E-mail: jjastellani@phrma.org

Description: Research based manufacturers of ethical pharmaceutical and biological products that are distributed under their own labels. Encourages high standards for quality control and good manufacturing practices; researches toward the development of new and better medical products; enactment of uniform and reasonable drug legislation for the protection of public health. Disseminates information on governmental regulations and policies, but does not maintain or supply information on specific products, prices, distribution, promotion, or sales policies of its individual members. Has established the Pharmaceutical Manufacturers Association Foundation to promote public health through scientific and medical research. **Scope:** scientific, legislative, business,

economic aspects of the pharmaceutical industry. **Founded:** 1958. **Subscriptions:** 1600 books periodicals. **Publications:** *BuySafeDrugs.info.* **Awards:** Discoverers' Award.

6641 ■ Sterile Preparations

1785 Alta Vista Dr.
Ottawa, ON, Canada K1G 3Y6
Ph: (613)523-7877
Free: 800-917-9489
Fax: (613)523-0445
Co. E-mail: info@pharmacists.ca
URL: http://www.pharmacists.ca/
Contact: Jody Shkrobo, President
E-mail: jshkrobot@gmail.com
Price: C$39.95, for members; C$69.95, for nonmembers.

REFERENCE WORKS

6642 ■ "Analysts Not Too Sad Over Gemunder" in Business Courier (Vol. 27, August 6, 2010, No. 14, pp. 1)

Pub: Business Courier

Ed: James Ritchie. **Description:** Analysts and investors do not understand why Omnicare chief executive officer (CEO) Joel Gemunder suddenly retired after nearly thirty years with the Covington, Kentucky company. They believe that new leadership might invigorate the firm, which provides pharmacy and related services to the long-term care industry.

6643 ■ "Angiotech to Buy Top Medical Devices Company" in Globe & Mail (February 1, 2006, pp. B1)

Pub: CTVglobemedia Publishing Inc.

Ed: Leonard Zehr. **Description:** The details on Angiotech Pharmaceuticals Inc.'s acquisition of American Medical Instruments Holdings Inc. are presented.

6644 ■ "ART Announces New Distribution Arrangement with GE Healthcare for eXplore Optix" in Canadian Corporate News (May 14, 2007)

Pub: Comtex News Network Inc.

Description: ART Advanced Research Technologies Inc., a medical device company and a leader in optical molecular imaging products for the pharmaceutical and healthcare industries, announced that it signed an agreement with GE Healthcare regarding worldwide distribution of its eXplore Optix preclinical optical molecular imaging system.

6645 ■ "At the Drugstore, the Nurse Will See You Now" in Globe & Mail (April 13, 2007, pp. B1)

Pub: CTVglobemedia Publishing Inc.

Ed: Marina Strauss. **Description:** The appointment of several health professionals including nurse, podiatrists, etc. by Rexall Co. at its drugstores to face competition from rivals, is discussed.

6646 ■ "Auxilium Drug's New Use: Putting Squeeze On Cellulite" in Philadelphia Business Journal (Vol. 30, September 16, 2011, No. 31, pp. 1)

Pub: American City Business Journals Inc.

Ed: John George. **Description:** Auxilium Pharmaceuticals and BioSpecifics Technologies are getting on with their plans of finding new uses for their drug Xiaflex, a possible treatment for cellulite. The two firms have dismissed their pending litigations and mapped out an amended licensing agreement for their search for the potential uses of the drug.

6647 ■ "Best Growth Stocks" in Canadian Business (Vol. 82, Summer 2009, No. 8, pp. 28)

Pub: Rogers Media

Ed: Calvin Leung. **Description:** Canadian stocks that are considered as the best growth stocks, and whose price-earnings ratio is less than their earnings growth rate, are suggested. Suggestions include pharmaceutical firm Paladin Labs, which was found to have 13 consecutive years of revenue growth. Paladin Labs acquires or licenses niche drugs and markets them in Canada.

6648 ■ "Changing Prescriptions" in Business North Carolina (Vol. 28, March 2008, No. 3, pp. 52)

Pub: Business North Carolina

Description: Profile of Moose Drug Company, founded by Archibald Walter Moose in 1882. Family owners share how they focus on pharmacoeconomics (cost-benefit analyses of drugs or drug therapy) and customer service.

6649 ■ ComputerTalk for the Pharmacist--Buyers Guide Issue

Pub: ComputerTalk Associates Inc.
Contact: William A. Lockwood, Jr., President
E-mail: wal@computertalk.com

URL(s): www.computertalk.com/. **Released:** Annual; Latest edition 2012. **Publication includes:** List of more than 50 retail pharmacy data processing system suppliers. All listings are paid. **Entries include:** Company, name, address, phone; number of installations, entry-level system configuration and price, software available, expandability, additional costs, length and cost of training period, largest system installed, map showing states where systems are marketed, supplier's statement. **Database includes:** Table summarizing contents of listings. **Arrangement:** Alphabetical. **Indexes:** Geographical (code indicates whether location of installation, sales or service office, or distributor), alphabetical (including addresses and phone numbers of headquarters and sales offices or distributors).

6650 ■ "Despite Hot Toys, Holiday Sales Predicted To Be Ho-Ho-Hum" in Drug Store News (Vol. 29, November 12, 2007, No. 14, pp. 78)

Pub: Drug Store News

Ed: Doug Desjardins. **Description:** Summer toy recalls have retailers worried about holiday sales in 2007. Mattel was heavily impacted from the recall of millions of toys manufactured in China.

6651 ■ "A Different Kind of Waiting List" in Canadian Business (Vol. 80, April 9, 2007, No. 8, pp. 17)

Pub: Rogers Media

Ed: Erin Pooley. **Description:** The adverse impact on drug companies' profitability due to regulatory delays in approving drugs is discussed.

6652 ■ Directory of Drug Store & HBC Chains

Pub: Chain Store Guide
Contact: Lisa Patterson, President

URL(s): www.chainstoreguide.com/. **Released:** Annual; Latest edition 2012. **Price:** $395, Individuals print; $445, Individuals online lite; $1375, Individuals online pro; $1075, Individuals online pro. **Covers:** More than 1,200 drug store chains operation two or more units, including mass merchants and grocers with pharmacies; 215 wholesale drug companies in the United States and Canada. **Entries include:** For retailers--company name; phone and fax numbers; physical and mailing addresses; company e-mail and web addresses; listing type; number of stores; product lines; percentage of sales by product line; total sales; prescription drug sales; percentage of prescriptions filled with generic drugs; number of prescriptions filled daily; percentage of prescriptions filled with private third party, cash, and Medicaid; number of stores by type; mail order pharmacy indicator; managed care division indicator; projected openings and remodeling; store prototype sizes; total selling square footage; trading area; franchise group headquarters' name and location; distribution center and primary wholesaler names and locations; number of specialty departments; packaged liquor indicators; private label indicators; computerized pharmacy indicator; average number of checkouts; year founded; public company indicator; parent company name and location; regional and divisional office locations; headquarters personnel with titles. For wholesalers--company name, address, phone, and fax; e-mail and web addresses; listing type; product lines; percentage of sales by product line; total sales; percentage of sales by customer type; total stores served; number of member and non-member stores served; trading area; group store trading names; wholesaler type; distribution center locations; private label indicator; year founded; public company indicator; headquarters personnel with titles. **Arrangement:** Separate geographical sections for retailers and wholesalers. **Indexes:** Alphabetical, exclusions.

6653 ■ *"Eckerd Sales Spell Relief for Coutu"* **in Globe & Mail (January 18, 2006, pp. B4)**
Pub: CTVglobemedia Publishing Inc.
Ed: Bertrand Marotte. **Description:** The details on Eckerd Corp., which posted rise in sales by 2.7 percent in December 2005, are presented. Eckerd Corp. is a unit of Jean Coutu Group (PJC) Inc.

6654 ■ *"Elder Care, Rx Drugs Reforms Top Zoeller's Agenda"* **in Times (December 21, 2010)**
Pub: The Times
Ed: Sarah Tompkins. **Description:** Indiana Attorney General Greg Zoeller is hoping to develop a program in the state that will help regulate care for the elderly; freeze medical licenses for doctors involved in criminal investigations; address illegal drug use; and to establish a program to help individuals dispose of old prescription medications easily at pharmacies.

6655 ■ *"Engine of Growth: U.S. Industry Funk hasn't Hurt Cummins or Its Investors"* **in Barron's (Vol. 88, July 14, 2008, No. 28, pp. 43)**
Pub: Dow Jones & Co., Inc.
Ed: Shirley A. Lazo. **Description:** Engine maker Cummins increased its quarterly common dividend by 40 percent to 17.5 cents per share from 12.5 cents. CVS Caremark's dividend saw a hike of 18.4 percent from 9.5 cents to 11.25 cents per share while its competitor Walgreen is continuing its 75th straight year of dividend distribution and its 33rd straight year of dividend hikes.

6656 ■ *"Executive Decision: Just What the Doctor Ordered"* **in Globe & Mail (February 11, 2006, pp. B3)**
Pub: CTVglobemedia Publishing Inc.
Ed: Leonard Zehr. **Description:** The leadership ability of chief executive William Hunter of Angiotech Pharmaceuticals Inc., who acquired American Medical Instruments Holdings Inc. for $785 million, is discussed.

6657 ■ *"The Grass is Greener"* **in Canadian Business (Vol. 79, August 14, 2006, No. 16-17, pp. 43)**
Pub: Rogers Media
Ed: Thomas Watson. **Description:** Owner of New Image Plans LLC, Joe White, shares his views on the Canadian market for the marijuana drug.

6658 ■ *"Healthy Dose of Vitality"* **in Business Courier (Vol. 24, February 29, 2008, No. 47, pp. 1)**
Pub: American City Business Journals, Inc.
Ed: Dan Monk. **Description:** Healthy Advice plans to become a leading consumer brand and expand to pharmacies and hospitals. The growth opportunities for healthy Advice are discussed.

6659 ■ *"Key FDA Approval Yanked for Avastin"* **in Wall Street Journal Eastern Edition (November 19 , 2011, pp. B1)**
Pub: Dow Jones & Company Inc.
Ed: Thomas M. Burton, Jennifer Corbett Dooren. **Description:** Avastin, a drug manufactured by Genetech Inc. and used in the treatment of metastatic breast cancer in women, has had its approval by the US Food and Drug Administration withdrawn by the agency, which says there is no evidence the widely-used drug is successful in increasing the longevity of breast cancer patients.

6660 ■ *"Luster Lost"* **in Saint Louis Business Journal (Vol. 32, September 16, 2011, No. 3, pp. 1)**
Pub: Saint Louis Business Journal
Ed: E.B. Solomont. **Description:** Express Cripts shares have plunged 22.71 percent since late July amid regulatory concerns, as the luster of the second-largest deal announced for 2011 wore off. Express Scripts has become the largest pharmacy benefit manager in the country after the $29 billion deal to take rival Medco Health Solutions.

6661 ■ *Medical and Health Information Directory: A Guide to Organizations, Agencies, Institutions, Programs, Publications, Services, and Other Resources Concerned with Clinical Medicine. . .*
Pub: Cengage Learning Inc.
Contact: Ronald Dunn, President
URL(s): www.gale.cengage.com. **Released:** Annual; Latest edition April 2011. **Price:** $1190, Individuals set; $501, Individuals per volume. **Covers:** In volume 1, more than 33,000 medical and health oriented associations, organizations, institutions, and government agencies, including health maintenance organizations (HMOs), preferred provider organizations (PPOs), insurance companies, pharmaceutical companies, research centers, and medical and allied health schools. In Volume 2, over 20,000 medical book publishers; medical periodicals, directories, audiovisual producers and services, medical libraries and information centers, electronic resources, and health-related internet search engines. In Volume 3, more than 40,500 clinics, treatment centers, care programs, and counseling/diagnostic services for 34 subject areas. **Entries include:** Institution, service, or firm name, address, phone, fax, email and URL; many include names of key personnel and, when pertinent, descriptive annotation. Volume 3 was formerly listed separately as Health Services Directory. **Arrangement:** Classified by organization activity, service, etc. **Indexes:** Each volume has a complete alphabetical name and keyword index.

6662 ■ *"MPI Expansion Goes Back to Family Roots"* **in Crain's Detroit Business (Vol. 25, June 1, 2009, No. 22, pp. M007)**
Pub: Crain Communications Inc. - Detroit
Ed: Sherri Begin Welch. **Description:** William Parfet, grandson of Upjohn Company founder, is expanding MPI Research's clinical and early clinical research operations into two buildings in Kalamazoo, land which was once part of his grandfather's farm.

6663 ■ *National Drug Code Directory*
Pub: U.S. Food and Drug Administration
URL(s): www.fda.gov/cder. **Released:** Irregular; Latest edition 2011. **Publication includes:** List of manufacturers of commercially marketed human prescription drugs. **Entries include:** Drug company name, address, labeler code, product name, description of product, National Drug Code (NDC) number. Principal content of publication is a listing of about 32,000 drug products. **Arrangement:** Alphabetical. **Indexes:** NDC number, drug class, drug name.

6664 ■ *"Retail in Austin Strong, Will Continue to Be"* **in Austin Business JournalInc. (Vol. 29, January 22, 2010, No. 46, pp. 1)**
Pub: American City Business Journals
Ed: Jacob Dirr. **Description:** Retail sector in Austin, Texas has outpaced the national average in value, mid-tier, high-end and drugs retail sectors, according to a report by Pitney Bowes. The national consulting firm's report has projected growth in every sector until the end of fiscal 2012. Data regarding other sectors is also included.

6665 ■ *"Shire Seeking New Digs for Headquarters"* **in Philadelphia Business Journal (Vol. 30, September 2, 2011, No. 29, pp. 1)**
Pub: American City Business Journals Inc.
Ed: Natalie Kostelni. **Description:** Dublin, Ireland-based Shire PLC announced plans to relocate its North American headquarters from Chesterbrook Corporate Center in Wayne, Pennsylvania and currently evaluating their options. The specialty biopharmaceutical firm is also considering a move to New Jersey or Delaware.

6666 ■ *"Sinai Doctor Seeks FDA OK for Drug"* **in Baltimore Business Journal (Vol. 28, July 16, 2010, No. 10, pp. 1)**
Pub: Baltimore Business Journal
Ed: Emily Mullin. **Description:** Paul Gurbel, Sinai Hospital Center for Thrombosis Research director, is seeking an FDA approval of Brilinta, a drug which he helped create and test. Gurbel says that the approval

could bring the drug to market as early as December 2010. The drug is expected to rival Bristol-Myers' Plavix, which generated almost $6.2 billion in 2009.

6667 ■ *"Turning Trust Into Success"* **in Retail Merchandiser (Vol. 51, July-August 2011, No. 4, pp. 52)**
Pub: Phoenix Media Corporation
Ed: Karen Kondilis. **Description:** Shopko Stores employs tenured and trustworthy pharmacists and believes it is the core to their success.

6668 ■ *"Walgreen Takes Up Doctoring"* **in Crain's Chicago Business (Vol. 31, March 31, 2008, No. 13, pp. 18)**
Pub: Crain Communications, Inc.
Ed: Mark Bruno. **Description:** Walgreen Co. has agreed to acquire two firms that provide on-site medical and pharmaceutical services to large companies. Walgreen feels that these facilities mark the future of health care for a number of large corporations.

6669 ■ *"We Are Not a Marketing Company"* **in Boston Business Journal (Vol. 31, June 10, 2011, No. 20, pp. 1)**
Pub: Boston Business Journal
Ed: Julie M. Donnelly. **Description:** Vertex Pharmaceuticals Inc. is marketing its new Hepatitis C treatment, Incivek. The company hired people to connect patients to the drug. Vertex is also set to move to a new facility in Boston, Massachusetts.

6670 ■ *"Wielding a Big Ax"* **in Barron's (Vol. 89, July 13, 2009, No. 28, pp. 26)**
Pub: Dow Jones & Co., Inc.
Ed: Shirley A. Lazo. **Description:** Weyerhaeuser cut their quarterly common payout by 80 percent from 25 cents to a nickel a share which they say will help them preserve their long-term value and improve their performance. Paccar also cut their quarterly dividend by half to nine cents a share. Walgreen however, boosted their quarterly dividend by 22.2 percent to 13.75 cents a share.

SOURCES OF SUPPLY

6671 ■ *Scott's Canadian Pharmacists Directory*
Business Information Group
Contact: Bruce Creighton, President
URL(s): www.businessinformationgroup.ca/medical/cndpharmdirect.asp. **Released:** Biennial; Latest edition 2009. **Price:** $239, Individuals Plus S/H + Applicable Taxes; $209, Individuals Web pinpointer; $499, Individuals Web profiler; $1699, Individuals Web prospector (unlimited); $199, Individuals Web profiler (additional seat); $1199, Individuals Web prospector (unlimited). **Covers:** Approximately 18,000 pharmacists, university pharmacy faculty members, pharmacy suppliers, and drug and poison information centers in Canada, chain drug stores, independent. **Entries include:** Name, address, phone, names and titles of key personnel, biographical data (for pharmacists), geographical area served. **Arrangement:** For pharmacists--Same information available in geographical and alphabetical sections. For others--Classified by line of business, then alphabetical.

STATISTICAL SOURCES

6672 ■ *RMA Annual Statement Studies*
Pub: Risk Management Association
Contact: Kevin M. Blakey, President
Released: Annual. **Price:** $175.00 2006-07 edition, $105.00. **Description:** Contains composite balance sheets and income statements for more than 360 industries, including the accounting, auditing, and bookkeeping industries. Also contains five years of comparative historical data for discerning trends. Includes 16 commonly used ratios, computed for most of the size groupings for nearly every industry.

6673 ■ *Standard & Poor's Industry Surveys*
Pub: Standard & Poor's Corp.
Released: Annual. **Price:** $3633.00. **Description:** Two-volume book that examines the prospects for specific industries, including trucking. Also provides analyses of trends and problems, statistical tables and charts, and comparative company analyses.

TRADE PERIODICALS

6674 ■ *America's Pharmacist: The Voice of the Community Pharmacists*
Pub: National Community Pharmacists Association
Contact: Robert Greenwood, President
URL(s): www.americaspharmacist.net/aboutus.html.
Released: Monthly

6675 ■ *Community Pharmacist*
Pub: ELF Publications Inc.
Contact: Molly Casey, Director
E-mail: mcasey@elfpublications.com
URL(s): www.elfpublications.com. **Released:** Bimonthly

6676 ■ *The Consultant Pharmacist*
Pub: American Society of Consultant Pharmacists
Contact: Penny S. Shelton, President
URL(s): www.ascp.com/publications/tcp/. **Released:** Monthly **Price:** $105, Individuals; $150, Elsewhere; $130, Institutions; $190, Institutions elsewhere.

6677 ■ *Drug Discovery/Technology News*
Pub: Business Communications Company Inc.
Ed: Steve Edwards, Editor, salaned@aol.com. **Released:** Monthly. **Price:** $450; $821, two years; $1,160 3/years. **Description:** Covers developments in the drug industry. Recurring features include a column titled Industry News.

6678 ■ *Drug Topics: The Newsmagazine for Pharmacists*
Pub: Advanstar Communications
Contact: Robert Krakoff, President
URL(s): drugtopics.modernmedicine.com. **Released:** Bimonthly

6679 ■ *FDA Week*
Pub: Inside Washington Publishers
Contact: Korila Malecha, Manager
Ed: Donna Haseley, Editor. **Released:** Weekly (Fri.). **Price:** $595, U.S. and Canada; $645, elsewhere. **Description:** Reports on Food and Drug Administration policy, regulation, and enforcement.

6680 ■ *HealthCare Distributor*
Pub: ELF Publications Inc.
Contact: Molly Casey, Director
E-mail: mcasey@elfpublications.com
URL(s): www.elfpublications.com/. **Released:** Bimonthly **Price:** $29.95, Individuals; $80, Elsewhere.

6681 ■ *Impact*
Pub: Canadian Pharmacists Association
Contact: Jody Shkrobo, President
E-mail: jshkrobot@gmail.com
Ed: Louie Chatelain, Editor, lchatelain@pharmacists.ca. **Released:** 4/year. **Price:** Included in membership; $27.50. **Description:** Tracks activities of the Association; provides information on national and provincial programs, projects and regulatory changes. Recurring features include letters to the editor, news of research, a calendar of events, reports of meetings, and news of educational opportunities.

6682 ■ *Journal of the American Pharmacists Association*
Pub: American Pharmacists Association
Contact: Thomas E. Menighan, Chief Executive Officer
E-mail: tmenighan@aphanet.org
URL(s): www.aphanet.org/www.pharmacist.com/AM/Template.cfm?Section=JAPhA2. **Ed:** L. Michael Posey. **Released:** Bimonthly **Price:** $495, Institutions print and online; $395, Institutions online only.

6683 ■ *Journal of Pharmaceutical Sciences*
Pub: American Pharmacists Association
Contact: Thomas E. Menighan, Chief Executive Officer
E-mail: tmenighan@aphanet.org
URL(s): onlinelibrary.wiley.com/journal/10.1002/(-ISSN)1520-6017. **Ed:** Bradley D. Anderson, Harry Brittain. **Released:** Monthly **Price:** $351, Individuals print; $408, Other countries print; $1859, Institutions print only; $1916, Institutions, other countries print only; $2139, Institutions print and online; $2196, Institutions, other countries print and online.

6684 ■ *NCPA Newsletter*
Pub: National Community Pharmacists Association
Contact: Robert Greenwood, President
Released: Semimonthly. **Price:** Included in membership; $50, nonmembers. **Description:** Reports on topics affecting independents, including developments within the pharmaceutical industry, regulatory and legislative activity, and pricing and import information. Recurring features include reports of meetings, news of educational opportunities, notices of publications available, and news of NARD activities and events.

6685 ■ *Pharmaceutical Approvals Monthly*
Pub: F-D-C Reports Inc.
Contact: Jaimie Kelley, Managing Editor
Ed: Jon Dobson, Editor. **Released:** Monthly. **Price:** $975. **Description:** Reports on current and future drug/pharmaceutical approvals. Also provides lists of drugs pending FDA approval.

6686 ■ *Pharmacy Times: Practical Information for Today's Pharmacist*
Pub: Ascend Integrated Media
URL(s): www.pharmacytimes.com. **Released:** Monthly; 1 OTC supplement.

6687 ■ *Pharmacy Today*
Pub: American Pharmacists Association
Contact: Carli Richard
Released: Monthly. **Price:** Included in membership; $200, nonmembers U.S.; $250, nonmembers other. **Description:** Reports news and opinions of interest to pharmacists. Includes comprehensive coverage of pharmacotherapeutic, legislative, and socioeconomic news of every segment of the pharmacy profession.

6688 ■ *Pharmacy Week*
Pub: Pharmacy Week
Contact: Paul Barnes, Publisher
Released: Weekly. **Price:** Free. **Description:** Employment newsletter for pharmacists.

6689 ■ *The Pink Sheet*
Pub: F-D-C Reports Inc.
Contact: Jaimie Kelley, Managing Editor
Ed: M. Nielsen Hobbs, Editor. **Released:** Weekly, 50x/yr. **Price:** $2,145 print and web. **Description:** Provides in-depth news and analysis about developments affecting prescription medicines, including FDA, FTC, and HCFA policies and actions, as well as federal and state legislation affecting the drug industry. Coverage includes FDA recalls and seizures, mergers and acquisitions, biotechnology startups, new product activity, and company research and development.

6690 ■ *Validation Times*
Pub: Washington Information Source
Contact: Kenneth Reid, Editor
Released: Monthly, plus weekly email updates. **Price:** $1,021, U.S. and Canada. **Description:** Covers pre-approval and post-approval regulatory news on pharmaceutical products and biologics. Recurring features include letters to the editor, interviews, news of research, and a calendar of events.

6691 ■ *Voice of the Pharmacist Newsletter*
Pub: American College of Apothecaries
Contact: Nelson L. Showalter, President
E-mail: nshow@comcast.net
Ed: Dr. D.C. Huffman, Jr., Editor. **Released:** Quarterly. **Price:** Included in membership; $40, nonmembers. **Description:** Examines current issues and opportunities affecting the retail, hospital, and consultant practices of pharmacy. Discusses controversial issues, often with commentary by pharmacists. Recurring features include editorials, news of research, and letters to the editor.

TRADE SHOWS AND CONVENTIONS

6692 ■ American Society of Consultant Pharmacists Annual Meeting and Exhibition
American Society of Consultant Pharmacists (ASCP)
1321 Duke St.
Alexandria, VA 22314-3563
Ph: (703)739-1300

Free: 800-355-2727
Fax: (703)739-1321
Co. E-mail: info@ascp.com
URL: http://www.ascp.com
Contact: Penny S. Shelton, President
URL(s): www.ascp.com. **Frequency:** Annual. **Audience:** Pharmacists in the long-term care field, allied professionals, and general public. **Principal Exhibits:** Pharmaceuticals, drug distribution systems, packaging equipment, computers, durable medical equipment, and medical supplies. **Telecommunication Services:** info@ascp.com.

6693 ■ Florida Pharmacy Association Annual Meeting and Convention
Florida Pharmacy Association (FPA)
610 N Adams St.
Tallahassee, FL 32301
Ph: (850)222-2400
Fax: (850)561-6758
Co. E-mail: mtg584@aol.com
URL: http://www.pharmview.com
Contact: Michael Jackson, Executive Vice President
URL(s): www.pharmview.com. **Frequency:** Annual. **Audience:** Trade professionals and general public. **Principal Exhibits:** Pharmaceuticals and other product lines and services provided for and by pharmacists. **Dates and Locations:** , Sandestin Beach Hilton Resort.

6694 ■ NCPA Annual Convention and Trade Exposition
National Community Pharmacists Association (NCPA)
100 Daingerfield Rd.
Alexandria, VA 22314
Ph: (703)683-8200
Free: 800-544-7447
Fax: (703)683-3619
Co. E-mail: info@ncpanet.org
URL: http://www.ncpanet.org
Contact: Robert Greenwood, President
URL(s): www.ncpanet.org. **Frequency:** Annual. **Audience:** Pharmacy owners and managers. **Principal Exhibits:** Pharmaceutical and related equipment, supplies, and services. **Telecommunication Services:** info@ncpanet.org.

6695 ■ PDA Annual Meeting
PDA (PDA)
Bethesda Towers
Bethesda, MD 20814
Ph: (301)656-5900
Fax: (301)986-0296
Co. E-mail: brown@pda.org
URL: http://www.pda.org
Contact: Richard M. Johnson, President
E-mail: johnson@pda.org
URL(s): www.pda.org. **Price:** $1450, Members before early-bird date; $1900, Non-members before early-bird date; $1650, Members after early-bird date; $2100, Non-members after early-bird date. **Frequency:** Annual. **Audience:** Pharmaceutical manufacturers. **Principal Exhibits:** Supplies and services related to pharmaceuticals manufacturing the science and technology.

6696 ■ Texas Pharmacy Association Annual Meeting and Exhibit
Texas Pharmacy Association (TPA)
12007 Research Blvd., Ste. 201
Austin, TX 78759
Ph: (512)836-8350
Free: 800-505-5463
Fax: (512)836-0308
Co. E-mail: JDaSilva@texaspharmacy.org
URL: http://www.texaspharmacy.org
Contact: Joe DaSilva, Chief Executive Officer
E-mail: jdasilva@texaspharmacy.org
URL(s): www.texaspharmacy.org. **Frequency:** Annual. **Audience:** Pharmacists, students. **Principal Exhibits:** Pharmaceuticals and various services provided to pharmacists.

CONSULTANTS

6697 ■ Thole Associates—Thole Enterprises
1400 Shadwell Cir.
Lake Mary, FL 32746-4344
Ph: (407)333-2174
Fax: (407)333-2174
Contact: Jerome L. Thole, President
Scope: Consulting organization specializing in food and drug store merchandising and operations. In addition to serving retailers, the firm provides consulting service to wholesalers and manufacturers as well. Areas of expertise include store operations, store conditions, operating cost control, customer service training, research, and budget control and scheduling. Industries served: retail food supermarket and drug companies. **Founded:** 1988. **Seminars:** How to Improve Customer Service-Without Sacrificing Productivity; Customer Satisfaction-Develop a Strategy for Success; How to Control Expense in Tough Economic Times.

FRANCHISES AND BUSINESS OPPORTUNITIES

6698 ■ Medicap Pharmacy
Medicap Pharmacies, Inc.
1 Rider Trail Plaza Dr.
Earth City, MO 63045
Ph: (800)445-2244
Description: Professional pharmacy that typically operates in an 800-1,000 square foot location. Ninety percent of the business is prescription and the remaining 10% consists of over-the-counter medications. New store start-ups and conversion of full-line drug stores and independent pharmacies to the Medicap concept. continued support. **No. of Franchise Units:** 201. **Founded:** 1971.. **Franchised:** 1974. **Equity Capital Needed:** Equity capital $10,000-$55,000; total investment $22,100-$414,700. **Franchise Fee:** $15,000 new/$8,500 converted. **Financial Assistance:** Yes. **Training:** 3 days of orientation at corporate office and 3 days of onsite training, plus continued support.

6699 ■ Medicine Shoppe Canada
10104 103 Avenue NW, Ste. 1600
Edmonton, AB, Canada T5J 0H8
Free: 800-267-8877
Fax: (780)425-3980
Co. E-mail: info@medicineshoppe.ca
URL: http://www.futureofpharmacy.com
Description: Franchise of retail pharmacies. Focuses on patient care, health screenings and risk assessments. **No. of Franchise Units:** 174. **Founded:** 1992.. **Franchised:** 1992. **Equity Capital Needed:** $175,000-$200,000. **Franchise Fee:** $9,000-$25,000. **Training:** Yes.

6700 ■ Medicine Shoppe International, Inc.
Cardinal Health
7000 Cardinal Pl.
Dublin, OH 43017
Ph: (614)757-5000
Free: 800-234-8701
Fax: (614)757-6000
Co. E-mail: info@cardinal.com
URL: http://www.cardinal.com
Description: Retail professional pharmacy and health care. **No. of Franchise Units:** 927. **Founded:** 1970.. **Franchised:** 1970. **Equity Capital Needed:** $74,300-$253,400. **Franchise Fee:** $10,000-$18,000. **Royalty Fee:** 2-5.5%. **Financial Assistance:** In-house financing available. **Training:** Provides 6 days training at headquarters, at franchisee's location twice a year, regional meetings and seminars and ongoing support.

6701 ■ Shoppers Drug Mart
Pharamaprix
243 Consumers Rd.
North York, ON, Canada M2J 4W8
Ph: (416)490-2690
Fax: (416)490-2700
URL: http://www.shoppersdrugmart.ca
Description: Licensing of retail drug stores with licenses available only to qualified registered pharmacists. **No. of Franchise Units:** 1,090. **Founded:** 1962.. **Franchise Fee:** Provided by franchiser (minimum of $25,000 in Quebec). **Training:** Yes.

COMPUTERIZED DATABASES

6702 ■ *Clinical Pharmacology™*
302 Knights Run Ave., Ste. 800
Tampa, FL 33602
Ph: (813)258-4747
Free: 800-375-0943
Fax: (813)259-1585
Co. E-mail: info@goldstandard.com
URL: http://www.goldstandard.com
Availability: Online: ; Elsevier - Gold Standard. CD-ROM: North American Center for Continuing Medical Eduation LLC-CME LLC; American Society of Health-System Pharmacists; Elsevier - Gold Standard. **Type:** Full-text; Image.

6703 ■ *Compendium of Pharmaceuticals and Specialties (CPS)*
1785 Alta Vista Dr.
Ottawa, ON, Canada K1G 3Y6
Ph: (613)523-7877
Free: 800-917-9489
Fax: (613)523-0445
Co. E-mail: info@pharmacists.ca
URL: http://www.pharmacists.ca
Availability: Online: Canadian Pharmacists Association. **Type:** Full-text; Image.

6704 ■ *International Pharmaceutical Abstracts (IPA)*
3501 Market St.
Philadelphia, PA 19104
Ph: (215)386-0100
Free: 800-336-4474
Fax: (215)386-2911
Co. E-mail: general.info@thomsonreuters.com
URL: http://science.thomsonreuters.com
Availability: Online: ProQuest LLC - CSA; ProQuest LLC - Dialog; German Institute of Medical Documentation and Information; EBSCO Publishing; STN International; Wolters Kluwer Health - Ovid. CD-ROM: Wolters Kluwer Health - Ovid. **Type:** Bibliographic.

6705 ■ *KINETIDEX® System*
777 E Eisenhower Pky.
Ann Arbor, MI 48108
Co. E-mail: info@truvenhealth.com
URL: http://www.truvenhealth.com
Availability: Online: Truven Health Analytics Inc. **Type:** Full-text; Numeric.

6706 ■ *State Health Care Regulatory Developments™*
1801 S Bell St.
Arlington, VA 22202
Free: 800-372-1033
Co. E-mail: customercare@bna.com
URL: http://www.bna.com
Availability: Online: Bloomberg LP-Bloomberg BNA; Thomson Reuters - Westlaw. **Type:** Full-text.

LIBRARIES

6707 ■ American Pharmacists Association - Foundation Library
2215 Constitution Ave., NW
Washington, DC 20037
Ph: (202)429-7524
Fax: (202)783-2351
Co. E-mail: gnorheim@aphanet.org
URL: http://www.pharmacist.com
Contact: Gwen Norheim
Scope: Pharmacy, pharmacology, medicine, pharmaceutical care. **Services:** Library open to the public by appointment. **Founded:** 1934. **Holdings:** 2000 books; 7000 bound periodical volumes. **Subscriptions:** 225 journals and other serials. **Telecommunication Services:** infocenter@aphanet.org.

6708 ■ Amgen, Inc. - Amgen Libraries
One Amgen Center Dr., 14-1-A
Thousand Oaks, CA 91320-1789
Ph: (805)447-1000
Fax: (805)447-1010
Co. E-mail: larrym@amgen.com
URL: http://www.amgen.com
Contact: Larry Markworth
Scope: Biotechnology, molecular biology, pharmaceutical industry. **Services:** Interlibrary loan; SDI; group open to the public by appointment. **Founded:** 1981. **Holdings:** 7000 books; 50 reports; patents on microfilm and CDs. **Subscriptions:** 400 journals and other serials; 10 newspapers.

6709 ■ Anderson Area Medical Center Library
800 N. Fant St.
Anderson, SC 29621
Ph: (864)261-1253
Fax: (864)261-1552
URL: http://www.anmedhealth.org
Contact: Beth Addis
Scope: Medicine, nursing. **Services:** Interlibrary loan. **Holdings:** 750 books. **Subscriptions:** 125 journals and other serials; 2 newspapers.

6710 ■ AstraZeneca Pharmaceuticals LP Library and Information Services
PO Box 15437
Wilmington, DE 19850-5437
Ph: (302)886-3000
Free: 800-236-9933
URL: http://www.astrazeneca-us.com/
Scope: Pharmacology, pharmacy, chemistry, bioscience, medicine, pharmaceutical industry. **Services:** Interlibrary loan. **Holdings:** 3500 books; 4750 bound periodical volumes. **Subscriptions:** 360 journals and other serials.

6711 ■ Block Drug Company - Research and Development Library
257 Cornelison Ave.
Jersey City, NJ 07302
Ph: (201)434-3000
Fax: (201)434-0842
Co. E-mail: karen_berryman@BlockDrug.com
Contact: Karen Berryman, Librarian, Technical Services
Scope: Dentistry, medicine, pharmacology, dermatology. **Services:** SDI; Library not open to the public. **Founded:** 1960. **Holdings:** 2000 books. **Subscriptions:** 350 journals and other serials; 2 newspapers.

6712 ■ Emmanuel College - Cardinal Cushing Library
400 The Fenway
Boston, MA 02115
Ph: (617)735-9927
Co. E-mail: tuohyc@emmanuel.edu
URL: http://www1.emmanuel.edu/library/
Contact: Dr. Susan von Daum Tholl, Director
Scope: Theology, pastoral ministry, religious history, women's studies, arts, humanities, education. **Services:** Interlibrary loan; library open to the public. **Founded:** 1964. **Holdings:** 130,000 volumes. **Subscriptions:** 2000 journals and other serials.

6713 ■ Fisons Corporation Limited - Information Resources Centre
2235 Sheppard Ave. E.
Atria 11, 18th Fl.
Pickering, ON, Canada M2J 5B5
Ph: (416)497-8444
Fax: (416)498-2869
Contact: David Thompson, Manager
Scope: Pharmaceuticals. **Services:** Copying; online searching. **Holdings:** Figures not available.

6714 ■ GlaxoSmithKline Information and Library Services
5 Moore Dr.
Research Triangle Park, NC 27709
Ph: (919)483-5395
Free: 888-825-5249

Fax: (919)483-5328
URL: http://us.gsk.com
Contact: Alberta McKay, Manager, Information
  Services
Scope: Organic chemistry, medicine, biochemistry, pharmacology, microbiology, toxicology, business. **Services:** Document delivery; copying; SDI. **Founded:** 1929. **Holdings:** 14,331 books; 34,039 bound periodical volumes. **Subscriptions:** 1300 journals and other serials; 5 newspapers.

6715 ■ GlaxoSmithKline - U.S. Medical Information Library FP1045
1 Franklin Plaza
Philadelphia, PA 19102-1225
Free: 888-825-5249
Fax: (215)751-5211
Co. E-mail: betty.j.kelley@gsk.com
URL: http://www.gsk.com/
Contact: Betty-Jane Kelley, Librarian
Scope: Medicine, pharmaceutical science, chemistry, biology, business, regulatory affairs. **Services:** Library not open to the public. **Holdings:** 3500 books; 9000 bound periodical volumes. **Subscriptions:** 400 journals and other serials.

6716 ■ Johnson & Johnson Pharmaceutical Research & Development - Hartman Library
920 Rte. 202
Mailstop E1756
Raritan, NJ 08869
Co. E-mail: glblpharmardcom@prdus.jnj.com
URL: http://www.jnjpharmarnd.com
Scope: Medicine, pharmacy, endocrinology, biological sciences, chemistry. **Founded:** 1944. **Holdings:** 5000 books; 20,000 bound periodical volumes; 300 reels of microfilm. **Subscriptions:** 600 journals and other serials.

6717 ■ Keller and Heckman LLP - Law Firm Library
1001 G St. NW, Ste. 500 W.
Washington, DC 20001
Ph: (202)434-4100
Fax: (202)434-4646
URL: http://www.khlaw.com
Scope: Food and drug, the environment, telecommunications, transportation, intellectual property, International trade. **Services:** Interlibrary loan; Library not open to the public. **Founded:** 1962. **Holdings:** 8000 books. **Subscriptions:** 140 journals and other serials; 8 newspapers.

6718 ■ Lexington Medical Center - LMC Health Library
2720 Sunset Blvd.
West Columbia, SC 29169
Ph: (803)791-2000
Fax: (803)791-2623
Co. E-mail: librarian@lexhealth.org
URL: http://www.lexmed.com/about/community-involvement/health-library.aspx
Scope: Medical science, psychology, nutrition, childcare, sports medicine, health care law, general health. **Holdings:** 1000 books; 500 audiocassettes; 200 journals.

6719 ■ Maryland Pharmacists Association Library
1800 Washington Blvd.
Baltimore, MD 21230
Ph: (410)727-0746
Fax: (410)727-2253
Co. E-mail: hrschiff@mdpha.com
URL: http://marylandpharmacist.org
Contact: Howard Schiff, Executive Director
Scope: Pharmacy, allied health sciences. **Services:** Library not open to the public. **Founded:** 1882. **Holdings:** 1000 volumes. **Subscriptions:** 1 journal.

6720 ■ McKenna Long & Aldridge LLP Law Library
1900 K St. NW, Lower Level
Washington, DC 20006-1108
Ph: (202)496-7500

Fax: (202)496-7756
Co. E-mail: tpapson@mckennalong.com
URL: http://www.mckennalong.com
Scope: Law - government contracts, environmental, litigation, food and drug, International, health care, labor, insurance, energy. **Services:** Interlibrary loan; Library not open to the public. **Founded:** 1940. **Holdings:** 15,000 books; 5000 bound periodical volumes. **Subscriptions:** 400 journals and other serials.

6721 ■ McNeil Consumer and Specialty Pharmaceuticals - Pharmaceutical Research Center
7050 Camp Hill Rd.
Fort Washington, PA 19034-2799
Ph: (215)273-7603
Fax: (215)273-4082
Co. E-mail: hhohman@mccus.jnj.com
Contact: Helen J. Hohman
Scope: Pharmaceutics, medicine, chemistry, marketing, finance, nutritionals. **Services:** Interlibrary loan; center not open to the public. **Founded:** 1980. **Holdings:** 600 books. **Subscriptions:** 300 journals and other serials; 5 newspapers.

6722 ■ Merck Frosst Canada Ltd. - Research Library and Information Centre
16711 Trans Canada Hwy.
Kirkland, QC, Canada H9H 3L1
Ph: (514)428-2666
Free: 800-567-2594
Fax: (514)428-8635
Co. E-mail: josee_schepper@merck.com
URL: http://www.merckfrosst.ca
Contact: Josee Schepper, Manager
Scope: Biochemistry, chemistry, molecular biology, pharmacology, pharmacy, biology. **Services:** Interlibrary loan; library open to professionals based on need to access. **Founded:** 1938. **Holdings:** 3000 books; 10,000 bound periodical volumes. **Subscriptions:** 300 journals and other serials; 1300 e-journals; 4 newspapers.

6723 ■ National Association of Boards of Pharmacy Library
1600 Feehanville Dr.
Mount Prospect, IL 60056
Ph: (847)391-4406
Fax: (847)391-4502
Co. E-mail: exec-office@nabp.net
URL: http://www.nabp.net
Contact: Carmen A. Catizone, Executive Director
Scope: Pharmacy - law and regulation, education, licensure. **Founded:** 1904. **Holdings:** Figures not available.

6724 ■ National Association of Chain Drug Stores Resource Center
413 N. Lee St.
Alexandria, VA 22314-1417
Ph: (703)549-3001
URL: http://www.nacds.org
Contact: Larry J. Merlo, Chairperson
Scope: Industry-related topics; community pharmacy. **Services:** Interlibrary loan; library open to the public at director's discretion. **Founded:** 1933. **Holdings:** 10,000 volumes; 1000 videocassettes; 500 audiocassettes. **Subscriptions:** 150 journals and other serials.

6725 ■ Oak Ridge National Laboratory - Toxicology Information Response Center
1060 Commerce Park, MS-6480
Oak Ridge, TN 37830
Ph: (865)576-1746
Fax: (423)574-9888
Co. E-mail: slusherkg@ornl.gov
URL: http://www.ornl.gov/sci/techresources/tirc/hmepg.shtml
Contact: Kim Slusher
Scope: Toxicology, pharmacology, veterinary toxicology, heavy metals, pesticides, chemistry, biology, medicine, industrial hygiene. **Services:** SDI; center open to the public. **Founded:** 1971. **Holdings:** 10,000 search files; 250 microfiche of published bibliographies. **Subscriptions:** 300 journals and other serials.

6726 ■ Sanofi-Synthelabo Inc. - Virtual Information Center
90 Park Ave.
New York, NY 10016
Ph: (212)551-4105
Fax: (212)551-4908
Contact: Donna A. Brown
Scope: Pharmaceuticals, clinical medicine. **Services:** Library open to the public by appointment. **Founded:** 1927. **Holdings:** 300 books and bound periodical volumes. **Subscriptions:** 120 journals and other serials.

6727 ■ Sanofi-Synthelabo - Research Division - Research Information Services
9 Great Valley Pkwy.
Malvern, PA 19355
Ph: (610)889-8652
Fax: (610)889-8988
Contact: Don Miles, Director
Scope: Biomedicine, biochemistry, clinical medicine, chemistry, pharmacology, toxicology. **Services:** Interlibrary loan; copying; SDI. **Founded:** 1987. **Holdings:** 4000 books; 1000 bound periodical volumes; 6000 reels of microfilm; 2000 nonbook items. **Subscriptions:** 300 journals and other serials.

6728 ■ Schering-Plough Healthcare, Inc. - R & D Library
3030 Jackson Ave.
Memphis, TN 38151-0001
Ph: (901)320-2702
Fax: (901)320-3017
Co. E-mail: martha.hurst@spcorp.com
Contact: Martha Hurst, Librarian
Scope: Pharmacology, toxicology, medicine, chemistry, pharmaceutical technology. **Services:** Interlibrary loan; Library open to the public by permission only. **Holdings:** 1600 books; 1800 bound periodical volumes; 3000 reprints. **Subscriptions:** 150 journals and other serials. **Telecommunication Services:** carolyn.cotton@spcorp.com.

6729 ■ Sentron Medical Inc. - Senmed Medical Ventures Library
4445 Lake Forest Dr., No. 600
Cincinnati, OH 45242-3798
Ph: (513)563-3240
Fax: (513)563-3261
URL: http://www.senmed.com/organization.htm
Contact: Rosanne Wohlwender
Scope: Biotechnology, medical devices and diagnostics, technology transfer, pharmaceuticals, venture capital, licensing. **Services:** Library not open to the public. **Founded:** 1987. **Holdings:** 800 books; 50 reports. **Subscriptions:** 100 journals and other serials; 2 newspapers.

6730 ■ Southwest Health Center Medical Library
1400 East Side Rd.
Platteville, WI 53818
Ph: (608)348-2331
Fax: (608)342-5011
Co. E-mail: library@southwesthealth.org
URL: http://www.southwesthealth.org/index.php
Scope: Medicine, nursing, and allied health sciences. **Services:** Interlibrary loan; copying; library open to the public. **Founded:** 1975. **Holdings:** 500 books. **Subscriptions:** 80 journals and other serials.

6731 ■ Thomson Physicians World - Knowledge Management & Medical Library
150 Meadowlands Pkwy.
Secaucus, NJ 07094
Ph: (201)271-6105
Free: 800-223-8978
Fax: (201)865-9247
Co. E-mail: pw.contact@pwnj.thomson.com
URL: http://www.physiciansworld.com
Contact: Maria V. Kwonn, Director
Scope: Medicine, pharmaceuticals, medical education, clinicals. **Services:** Interlibrary loan; library not open to the public. **Founded:** 1976. **Holdings:** 1200 books; 1400 bound periodical volumes. **Subscriptions:** 110 journals and other serials. **Telecommunication Services:** mkwon@mail.pwcq.com.

6732 ■ Tri-Meridian, Inc. - MEDSEARCH Division Library
PO Box 7664
Wilmington, NC 28406
Ph: (910)793-6456
Fax: (910)793-8280
Co. E-mail: michaels2@worldnet.att.net
Contact: Debbra D. Michaels, Director

Scope: Medicine, pharmaceuticals, consumer health, nursing, allied health. **Services:** Interlibrary loan; Library not open to the public. **Founded:** 1983. **Holdings:** 150 books. **Subscriptions:** 10 journals and other serials.

RESEARCH CENTERS

6733 ■ University of Maryland at Baltimore - Center on Drugs and Public Policy (CDPP)
School of Pharmacy
220 Arch St.
Baltimore, MD 21201
Ph: (410)706-0133
Fax: (410)706-5394
Co. E-mail: fpalumbo@rx.umaryland.edu
URL: http://www.pharmacy.umaryland.edu/cdpp
Contact: Francis B. Palumbo, Executive Director
Founded: 1987. **Educational Activities:** CDPP Conferences. **Telecommunication Services:** cdpp@rx.umaryland.edu.

6734 ■ University of Tennessee - Drug Information Center
875 Monroe Ave., Ste. 116
Memphis, TN 38163
Ph: (901)448-5555
Fax: (901)448-5419
Co. E-mail: ksuda@utmem.edu
URL: http://www.uthsc.edu/pharmacy/dcp/dic
Contact: Dr. Katie Suda, Director
Founded: 1972. **Educational Activities:** Drug Information Clerkship, offered to doctoral candidates; Drug Information Course, for doctoral students. **Telecommunication Services:** utdic@utmem.edu.

START-UP INFORMATION

6735 ■ *Coin Laundries - Road to Financial Independence: A Complete Guide to Starting and Operating Profitable Self-Service Laundries*
Pub: Mountain Publishing Company

Ed: Emerson G. Higdon. **Released:** June 2001. **Description:** Guide to starting and operating a self-service laundry.

ASSOCIATIONS AND OTHER ORGANIZATIONS

6736 ■ **Coin Laundry Association (CLA)**
1 S 660 Midwest Rd., Ste. 205
Oakbrook Terrace, IL 60181
Ph: (630)953-7920
Free: 800-570-5629
Fax: (630)953-7925
Co. E-mail: info@coinlaundry.org
URL: http://coinlaundry.org
Contact: Brian Wallace, President

URL(s): www.coinlaundry.org. **Description:** Manufacturers of equipment or supplies used in self-service (coin-operated) laundry or dry cleaning establishments; distributors of equipment services and supplies; owners and operators of self-service laundry and/or dry cleaning stores. Compiles statistics. **Scope:** management. **Founded:** 1960. **Subscriptions:** archival material business records monographs periodicals video recordings. **Publications:** *CLA Member Journal; The Official Voice of the Coin Laundry Industry* (Monthly); *CLA Management Guidelines* (Quarterly); *The Journal of the Coin Laundry Industry* (Monthly). **Educational Activities:** Regional Educational Workshops (Annual).

6737 ■ **Drycleaning and Laundry Institute International (DLI)**
14700 Sweitzer Ln.
Laurel, MD 20707
Ph: (301)622-1900
Free: 800-638-2627
Fax: (240)295-0685
Co. E-mail: techline@dlionline.org
URL: http://www.ifi.org
Contact: Rick Kasperbauer, Chairman

Description: Retail and industrial drycleaners, hospital laundries, linen supply and drapery services, distributors and manufacturers of supplies and machinery, dry-cleaning and laundry associations, and individual launders in 43 countries. Provides washability and dry-cleanability testing for manufacturers of fabrics and related products; offers quality testing and consulting services; conducts research for members. Organizes courses in dry-cleaning, laundering, management, and maintenance. Maintains consulting service, speakers' bureau, research facilities, and library. **Founded:** 1972. **Publications:** *Fabricare* (Bimonthly).

6738 ■ **Multi-Housing Laundry Association (MLA)**
1500 Sunday Dr., Ste. 102
Raleigh, NC 27607
Ph: (919)861-5579
Fax: (919)787-4916
Co. E-mail: nshore@mla-online.com
URL: http://www.mla-online.com
Contact: Dave DeMarsh, President

Description: Operating and supplier companies. Strives to provide tenants with professionally operated laundry facilities. Sponsors annual convention and trade show. **Founded:** 1959. **Educational Activities:** Multi-Housing Laundry Association Conference (Semiannual).

6739 ■ **Textile Care Allied Trades Association (TCATA)**
271 Rte. 46 W, No. D203
Fairfield, NJ 07004
Ph: (973)244-1790
Fax: (973)244-4455
Co. E-mail: info@tcata.org
URL: http://www.tcata.org/i4a/pages/index.
cfm?pageid=1
Contact: David Cotter, Chief Executive Officer

Description: Represents Manufacturers and distributors of laundry and dry-cleaning machinery, and supplies. **Founded:** 1920. **Publications:** *Roster and Buyers Guide* (Annual). **Educational Activities:** Clean Show - World Educational Congress for Laundering and Drycleaning (Biennial). **Awards:** TCATA College Scholarship Program; Dean Allen Education Scholarship.

REFERENCE WORKS

6740 ■ *"Are You Looking for an Environmentally Friendly Dry Cleaner?" in Inc. (Vol. 30, December 2008, No. 12, pp. 34)*
Pub: Mansueto Ventures LLC

Ed: Shivani Vora. **Description:** Greenopia rates the greenness of 52 various kinds of businesses, including restaurants, nail salons, dry cleaners, and clothing stores. The guidebooks are sold through various retailers including Barnes & Noble and Amazon.com.

6741 ■ **Coin Laundry Association Supplier Directory**
Pub: Coin Laundry Association

URL(s): www.coinlaundry.org. **Ed:** Michael Sokolowski, Bob Nieman. **Released:** Annual; August. **Covers:** about 500 manufacturers and suppliers of products and services to the coin laundry and dry cleaning industries. **Entries include:** Name of firm, address, phone, e-mail, URL, products or services; distributors show area served. **Arrangement:** Manufacturers are alphabetical; distributors are geographical.

6742 ■ *"'Green' Cleaner Buys Local Firm" in Puget Sound Business Journal (Vol. 29,*

December 19, 2008, No. 35, pp. 3)
Pub: American City Business Journals

Ed: Greg Lamm. **Description:** Washington-based Blue Sky Cleaners has purchased Four Seasons Cleaners. The green company also purchased Queen Anne store and Four Seasons' routes fro Snohomish County through Seattle.

6743 ■ *"Nation of Islam Businessman Who Became Manager for Muhammad Ali Dies" in Chicago Tribune (August 28, 2008)*
Pub: McClatchy-Tribune Information Services

Ed: Trevor Jensen. **Description:** Profile of Jabir Herbert Muhammad who died on August 25, after heart surgery; Muhammad lived nearly all his life on Chicago's South Side and ran a number of small businesses including a bakery and a dry cleaners before becoming the manager to famed boxer Mohammad Ali.

STATISTICAL SOURCES

6744 ■ *RMA Annual Statement Studies*
Pub: Risk Management Association
Contact: Kevin M. Blakey, President

Released: Annual. **Price:** $175.00 2006-07 edition, $105.00. **Description:** Contains composite balance sheets and income statements for more than 360 industries, including the accounting, auditing, and bookkeeping industries. Also contains five years of comparative historical data for discerning trends. Includes 16 commonly used ratios, computed for most of the size groupings for nearly every industry.

TRADE PERIODICALS

6745 ■ *American Coin-Op*
Pub: American Trade Magazines Crain Associated Enterprises Inc.

URL(s): www.americancoinop.com/. **Ed:** Paul Partyka. **Released:** Monthly

6746 ■ *American Drycleaner: The Industry's Number One Magazine*
Pub: American Trade Magazines Crain Associated Enterprises Inc.

URL(s): www.americandrycleaner.com/. **Released:** Monthly

6747 ■ *CLA Member Journal*
Pub: Coin Laundry Association
Contact: Brian Wallace, President

Released: Quarterly. **Price:** Included in membership. **Description:** Provides management and technical information for members of the self-service (coin-operated) laundry and drycleaning industry.

6748 ■ *Cycles*
Pub: Service Directions Inc.

Released: Semiannual. **Price:** Free. **Description:** Describes new laundry equipment, advances in laundryroom management, and analyzes problems in residential laundryrooms. Recurring features include interviews.

6749 ■ *Drycleaners News: The News and Management Magazine*
Pub: Zackin Publications Inc.
URL(s): www.dcn-online.com/dcn/. **Ed:** Mark Del-Franco. **Released:** Monthly **Price:** $36, Individuals.

6750 ■ *Fabricare*
Pub: Drycleaning & Laundry Institute
Contact: Jillian Handman, Editor
Released: Monthly. **Price:** Included in membership. **Description:** Informs drycleaners and launderers of industry developments and Institute activities. Carries legislative updates, technical data, management ideas, and tips on problem fabrics and garments.

6751 ■ *Fabricare Canada*
Pub: Fabricare Canada
URL(s): www.fabricarecanada.com. **Released:** Bimonthly **Price:** $25, Other countries.

6752 ■ *The National Clothesline*
Pub: BPS Communications
URL(s): www.natclo.com/. **Ed:** Hal Horning. **Released:** Monthly

TRADE SHOWS AND CONVENTIONS

6753 ■ Clean Show - World Educational Congress for Laundering and Drycleaning
Association of Institutional Linen Management
2161 Lexington Rd., Ste. 2
Richmond, KY 40475
Ph: (859)624-0177
Free: 800-669-0863
Fax: (859)624-3580
URL: http://www.almnet.org
Contact: Barbara Bowen, President
E-mail: barbbowen@adelphia.net
URL(s): www.cleanshow.com. **Price:** $45, Pre-registered; $70, Onsite. **Frequency:** Biennial. **Audience:** Laundering and dry cleaning personnel, equipment manufacturers, suppliers and industry professionals. **Principal Exhibits:** Laundry and dry cleaning equipment, supplies, and services. **Telecommunication Services:** info@cleanshow.com.

6754 ■ FABRICARE - Great Western Exhibit
California Cleaners Association
2520 Venture Oaks Way, Ste. 150
Sacramento, CA 95833
Ph: (916)239-4070
Fax: (916)924-7323
Co. E-mail: info@camgmt.com
URL: http://www.calcleaners.com
URL(s): www.fabricareshow.com/. **Frequency:** Biennial. **Audience:** Dry cleaning and laundry plant owners, managers, employees, and investors. **Principal Exhibits:** Laundry and dry cleaning equipment, supplies, and services. **Dates and Locations:** Convention Center.

CONSULTANTS

6755 ■ Colburn & Guyette Consulting Partners Inc.
201 Oak St., Ste. 12
Pembroke, MA 02359
Ph: (781)826-5522
Free: 800-343-3310
Fax: (781)826-5523
URL: http://www.colburnguyette.com
Contact: Peter McGillicuddy, Manager
Scope: They Provide Operations and Design Studies/Programs, Vendor RFP Development and Selection, Pre-Design Concepts/Schematic Design, Accurate Cost Estimation Equipment Plans, 3D Renderings, Automated 3D Design Tours, Detailed Renderings, Elevations and Colored Floor Plans, Utility Requirements Plans Design Team Coordination, Complete Detail Plans and Specifications, LEED Foodservice Technologies, Cook-Chill Technology and Systems "Clean Air" Ventilation Systems, Refrigeration and Heat Reclaim Systems, Waste and Warewashing Systems, Tray and Meal Delivery Systems

Laundries, Design Build Teaming Arrangements, Design and Construction Team Coordination. **Founded:** 1950.

FRANCHISES AND BUSINESS OPPORTUNITIES

6756 ■ Comet Cleaners
Comet Cleaners Franchise Group
406 W Division St.
Arlington, TX 76011
Ph: (817)461-3555
Fax: (817)861-4779
Co. E-mail: info@cometcleaners.com
URL: http://www.cometcleaners.com
Description: Dry cleaning and laundry packages. 1-to-2 weeks. **No. of Franchise Units:** 246. **Founded:** 1941.. **Franchised:** 1967. **Equity Capital Needed:** Minimum net worth $150,000; typical investment $500,000. **Franchise Fee:** $15,000-$30,000. **Training:** Yes.

6757 ■ Door-To-Door Dry Cleaning
8400 E Prentice Ave., Ste. 1500
Greenwood Village, CO 80111
Free: 877-769-3667
Fax: (866)731-5471
Description: Dry cleaning delivery. **No. of Franchise Units:** 28. **Founded:** 2004.. **Franchised:** 2006. **Equity Capital Needed:** $40,950-$57,700. **Franchise Fee:** $25,000. **Royalty Fee:** 5-7%. **Training:** Provides 1 week training at headquarters, 1 week onsite and ongoing support.

6758 ■ Dove Cleaners & Cadet Cleaners
1560 Yonge St.
Toronto, ON, Canada M4T 289
Ph: (416)413-7900
Fax: (416)413-0619
Co. E-mail: sam@dovecorp.com
URL: http://www.dovecleaners.com
Description: Named "Best Dry Cleaner" by Flare, Toronto Life and 680 News, Dove Cleaners is Toronto's leading dry cleaner. Franchises operate as depot locations with all cleaning performed off-site at Dove's central processing plant using state-of-the-art equipment and only hypo-allergenic detergents. Dove is an ISO registered company offering free pick-up and delivery to customers via call-in and online ordering service. **No. of Franchise Units:** 98. **No. of Company-Owned Units:** 1. **Founded:** 1994. **Franchised:** 2000. **Equity Capital Needed:** $30,000. **Franchise Fee:** $30,000.

6759 ■ Dry Cleaning To-Your-Door
1121 NW Bayshore Dr.
Waldport, OR 97394
Free: 800-318-1800
Fax: (541)563-6938
Description: Dry cleaning business. **No. of Franchise Units:** 85. **Founded:** 1994.. **Franchised:** 1996. **Equity Capital Needed:** $10,000-$16,000. **Franchise Fee:** $29,450. **Training:** Yes.

6760 ■ ImageFirst Healthcare Laundry Specialists
5 Radnor Corporate Center, Ste. 503
100 Matsonford Rd.
Radnor, PA 19087
Ph: (800)932-7472
Fax: (484)253-7210
Co. E-mail: dburnette@myimagefirst.com
URL: http://www.imagefirstmedical.com
Description: ImageFIRST provides laundry services on a rental basis for dentists, physicians and medical clinics. The main services offered are delivering, washing, picking up, monitoring usage and managing inventories. **No. of Franchise Units:** 21. **No. of Company-Owned Units:** 10. **Founded:** 1967.. **Franchised:** 1997. **Equity Capital Needed:** $50,00-$150,000. **Franchise Fee:** $30,000. **Training:** 4 weeks onsite marketing and sales assistance.

6761 ■ Lapels Dry Cleaning
Next Step Franchising
962 Washington St.
Hanover, MA 02339

Ph: (866)695-2735
URL: http://www.lapelsdrycleaning.com
Description: Dry cleaning retail stores. **No. of Franchise Units:** 47. **Founded:** 2000.. **Franchised:** 2001. **Equity Capital Needed:** $20,000-$100,000. **Franchise Fee:** $20,000-$30,000. **Financial Assistance:** Yes. **Training:** Full training with ongoing support.

6762 ■ Martinizing Dry Cleaning
Martin Franchises Inc.
422 Wards Corner Rd.
Loveland, OH 45140-6964
Ph: (513)351-6211
Free: 800-827-0207
Fax: (513)731-0918
URL: http://www.martinizing.com
Description: Dry cleaning stores. **No. of Franchise Units:** 459. **Founded:** 1949.. **Franchised:** 1949. **Equity Capital Needed:** $250,000 minimum net worth; $400,000 typical investment. **Franchise Fee:** $40,000. **Training:** Comprehensive managerial and technical training in classroom as well as franchisees store; equipment shakedown and ongoing service hotline; grand opening marketing package and ongoing local store and market wide promotional programs; field and operations assistance; ongoing support staff only a toll-free call away.

6763 ■ Nu-Look 1-Hour Cleaners
NLF, Inc.
5970 SW 18th St., Ste. 331
Boca Raton, FL 33433-7197
Ph: (561)362-4190
Free: 866-533-0146
Fax: (561)362-4229
Description: Retail dry cleaner. **No. of Franchise Units:** 13. **Founded:** 1967. **Franchised:** 1969. **Equity Capital Needed:** $195,000. **Franchise Fee:** $20,000. **Royalty Fee:** 2%. **Financial Assistance:** Third party financing available. **Training:** Offers 2 weeks at headquarters, 2 weeks at franchisee's location and ongoing support.

6764 ■ Oxxo Care Cleaners
1874 N Young Cir.
Hollywood, FL 33020
Ph: (954)927-7410
Fax: (954)927-7357
Co. E-mail: info@oxxousa.com
URL: http://www.oxxousa.com
Description: State of the art dry cleaners. This is not your traditional drycleaners. We have eliminated the antiquated equipment and hazardous chemicals. Oxxo brings a successful venture directly from Europe that sets us apart from all other cleaners. Our unique boutique style air conditioning garment care centers use the most technologically advanced equipment, environmentally safe cleaning solutions, hand ironing, and offer a 24 hours a day and 7 days a week pick up and drop off through a 24-hour ATM garment retrieval system. **No. of Franchise Units:** 36. **No. of Company-Owned Units:** 4. **Founded:** 2001.. **Franchised:** 2002. **Equity Capital Needed:** $225,000 net worth; $150,000 liquid capital. **Franchise Fee:** $30,000. **Financial Assistance:** Yes. **Training:** Training is provided in all areas. Technical training in classroom, Training center, as well as franchisee's store. Training in customer service, marketing, quality control, maintenance and ongoing support.

6765 ■ Pressed 4 Time
8 Clock Tower Pl., Ste. 110
Maynard, MA 01754
Ph: (800)423-8711
Fax: (978)823-8301
Co. E-mail: franchiseinfo@pressed4time.com
URL: http://www.pressed4time.com
Description: Dry cleaning and shoe repair pick-up and delivery service, serving executives and staff at local businesses. A high repeat business, a low stress operation (5-day workweek, and local cleaning plants do the actual cleaning). **No. of Franchise Units:** 165. **Founded:** 1987.. **Franchised:** 1990. **Equity Capital Needed:** $35,910-$44,810. **Franchise Fee:** $29,900. **Training:** Includes 2 days at the corporate offices, including 1 day of hands-on operations, the corporate vehicle and 1 day of intensive classroom training,

covering start-up, record keeping, administration, dry cleaning, operations and sales. Also, 2 days of training in the franchisees territory, consisting of marketing training in the field to establish initial accounts.

6766 ■ Zips Dry Cleaners
Zips Franchising LLC
7500 Greenway Center Dr., Ste. 400
Greenbelt, MD 20770
Ph: (301)313-0389
Fax: (301)345-2895

Description: One price, same day service dry cleaning. **No. of Franchise Units:** 35. **No. of Company-Owned Units:** 1. **Founded:** 1996.. **Franchised:** 2006. **Equity Capital Needed:** $616,150-$778,500. **Franchise Fee:** $50,000. **Royalty Fee:** 6%. **Financial Assistance:** Third party financing available. **Training:** Yes.

LIBRARIES

6767 ■ Drycleaning and Laundry Institute International Library
14700 Sweitzer Ln.
Silver Spring, MD 20707
Ph: (301)622-1900
Free: 800-638-2627
Fax: (240)295-0685
Co. E-mail: techline@ifi.org
URL: http://www.ifi.org/index.html
Scope: Chemistry, textiles, dry cleaning, laundering.
Services: Library open to the public by appointment only. **Holdings:** Reference materials; CD-ROMs.

RESEARCH CENTERS

6768 ■ Drycleaning and Laundry Institute International (DLI)
14700 Sweitzer Ln.

Laurel, MD 20707
Ph: (301)622-1900
Free: 800-638-2627
Fax: (240)295-0685
Co. E-mail: techline@ifi.org
URL: http://www.ifi.org
Contact: Charlie Smith, President

Services: Counseling for members on sales, advertising, engineering methods, washroom formulas, drycleaning technology, and textiles maintenance. **Founded:** 1972. **Publications:** *Fabric Bulletins* (Bimonthly); *Fabricare* (Monthly); *Fabricare Resources* (Bimonthly); *Industry Focus* (Bimonthly); *Shirt Laundry Procedures* (Bimonthly); *Technical Bulletins* (Bimonthly). **Educational Activities:** Educational facilities for members; Laundering and drycleaning clinics. **Awards:** Summer internships for textile chemistry/science major students and grants to universities.

START-UP INFORMATION

6769 ■ *How to Start a Home-Based Writing Business, 5th Edition*
Pub: Globe Pequot Press
Ed: Lucy Parker. **Released:** December 2007. **Price:** $18.95. **Description:** Guide for starting and running a home-based writing business.

ASSOCIATIONS AND OTHER ORGANIZATIONS

6770 ■ *Active Voice*
505-27 Carlton St.
Toronto, ON, Canada M5B 1L2
Ph: (416)975-1379
Free: 866-226-3348
Fax: (416)975-1637
Co. E-mail: info@editors.ca
URL: http://www.editors.ca
Contact: Greg Ioannou, President
Released: Bimonthly

6771 ■ American Book Producers Association (ABPA)
151 W 19th St., 3rd Fl.
New York, NY 10011-4116
Ph: (917)741-1919
Fax: (212)675-1364
Co. E-mail: office@abpaonline.org
URL: http://www.abpaonline.org
Contact: Richard Rothschild, President
Description: Book producing companies that develop the concepts for books and, based on a contractual agreement with a publisher, may produce finished books or production-ready film, camera-ready mechanicals, finished manuscripts, art and layouts. Aims to increase the book industry's awareness of members' capabilities and the state of the book producers' art. Facilitates exchange of information for the purpose of improving business and establishing trade standards. **Founded:** 1980. **Publications:** *American Book Producers Association--Newsletter* (Monthly); *American Book Producers Association--Directory of Members* (Annual).

6772 ■ American Society of Journalists and Authors (ASJA)
Times Square
1501 Broadway, Ste. 403
New York, NY 10036
Ph: (212)997-0947
Fax: (212)937-2315
Co. E-mail: asjaoffice@asja.org
URL: http://www.asja.org
Contact: Alexandra Owens, Executive Director
Description: Represents freelance writers of nonfiction magazine articles and books. Seeks to elevate the professional and economic position of nonfiction writers, provide a forum for discussion of common problems among writers and editors, and promote a code of ethics for writers and editors. Operates writer referral service for individuals, institutions, or companies seeking writers for special projects; sponsors

Llewellyn Miller Fund to aid professional writers who no longer able to work due to age, disability, or extraordinary professional crisis. **Founded:** 1948. **Publications:** *American Society of Journalists and Authors--Directory of Writers* (Annual); *ASJA Monthly* (Monthly); *The ASJA Guide to Freelance Writing.* **Awards:** Outstanding Article Award; Arlene Eisenberg Memorial Fund (Annual); ASJA Outstanding Articles Awards (Annual); ASJA Outstanding Book Awards (Annual); Career Achievement Award (Annual); Extraordinary Service Award (Annual); June Roth Memorial Awards (Triennial); Robert C. Anderson Memorial (Annual); Outstanding Book Award: General Nonfiction; Donald Robinson Memorial Award for Investigative Journalism Article (Annual).

6773 ■ Asian American Writers' Workshop (AAWW)
110-112 W 27th St., 6th Fl.
New York, NY 10001
Ph: (212)494-0061
Fax: (212)494-0062
Co. E-mail: desk@aaww.org
URL: http://www.aaww.org
Contact: Ken Chen, Director
Description: Dedicated to the creation, development, publication, and dissemination of Asian American literature. **Founded:** 1991. **Publications:** *Asian Pacific American Journal* (Semiannual). **Awards:** Asian American Literary Awards; Asian American Literary Awards (Annual).

6774 ■ Association of Teachers of Technical Writing (ATTW)
Texas Tech University
Lubbock, TX 79409
URL: http://www.attw.org
Description: Teachers and students of technical communication at all levels and all types of educational institutions; technical communicators from government and industry. Serves as a forum of communication among technical writing teachers and acts as a liaison with other professional organizations. Provides current bibliographies of teaching/learning materials and reports of current research in the teaching of technical writing. **Founded:** 1973. **Publications:** *Technical Communication Quarterly* (Quarterly).

6775 ■ Association of Writers and Writing Programs (AWP)
George Mason University
Fairfax, VA 22030-4444
Ph: (703)993-4301
Fax: (703)993-4302
Co. E-mail: awp@awpwriter.org
URL: http://www.awpwriter.org
Contact: Ron Tanner, President
URL(s): www.awpwriter.org/careers/joblist.htm. **Description:** Writers; students and teachers in creative writing programs in university departments of English; editors, publishers, and freelance creative and professional writers. Fosters literary talent and achievement; advocates the craft of writing as primary to a liberal and humane education; provides publications and services to the makers and readers of contempo-

rary literature. Operates career services and job listings; sponsors literary competitions. **Scope:** creative writing. **Founded:** 1967. **Subscriptions:** 28 articles. **Publications:** *AWP Job List; The Writer's Chronicle* (Periodic); *AWP Job List; The AWP Official Guide to Writing Programs* (Annual); *AWP Official Guide to Writing Programs* (Biennial). **Educational Activities:** Association of Writers and Writing Programs Conference and Bookfair (Annual); Association of Writers & Writing Programs Annual Conference. **Awards:** AWP Award Series (Annual); Donald Hall Prize for Poetry; Grace Paley Prize for Short Fiction; AWP Prize for Creative Nonfiction; AWP Prize for the Novel. **Telecommunication Services:** services@awpwriter.org; conference@awpwriter.org.

6776 ■ Bay Area Independent Publishers Association (BAIPA)
PO Box E
Corte Madera, CA 94976
Ph: (415)456-0247
Free: 866-622-1325
Co. E-mail: board@baipa.org
URL: http://www.baipa.org
Contact: Judy Baker, President
Description: Promotes authors interested in independent publishing as an alternative to the commercial publishing system; printers, artists, typists, and others in allied fields. Aims to become a comprehensive source of self-publishing information and to develop knowledge and expertise to better assist members in promoting, marketing, and publishing their works. Acts as a liaison and clearinghouse of information and provides guidance in all aspects of self-publishing, including copy preparation, book production, and marketing and sales. **Founded:** 1979. **Publications:** *SPEX; SPEX* (Monthly). **Awards:** Jack Mason Award (Annual). **Telecommunication Services:** info@baipa.net.

6777 ■ Boating Writers International (BWI)
108 9th St.
Wilmette, IL 60091
Ph: (847)736-4142
Co. E-mail: info@bwi.org
URL: http://www.bwi.org
Contact: John Wooldridge, President
Description: Individuals in numerous countries including newspaper, magazine, radio, and television writers and photographers covering boating, fishing, and outdoor recreation and public relations. Seeks to: cover boating as a competitive as well as recreational sport; promote boating safety; encourage enjoyment of other outdoor water sports. **Founded:** 1970. **Publications:** *BWI Journal* (11/year). **Educational Activities:** Boating Writers International Meeting (Annual). **Awards:** BWI Writing Awards (Annual).

6778 ■ Bowling Writers Association of America (BWAA)
621 Six Flags Dr.
Arlington, TX 76011
Free: 800-343-1329
Co. E-mail: bwaa@bowlingwriters.com
URL: http://www.bowlingwriters.com
Contact: Joan Romeo, President
Description: Reporters of bowling news. **Founded:** 1937. **Publications:** *BWAA Newsletter* (Semiannual).

Educational Activities: Bowling Writers Association of America Conference (Annual). **Awards:** Kegel Bowler of the Month; Bowler of the Year; Collegiate Bowlers of the Year; Senior Bowler of the Year; Amateur Bowler of the Year; Chuck Pezzano Scholarships; Chuck Pezzano Scholarships; BWAA Hall of Fame (Annual); BWAA Meritorious Service (Annual); Chuck Pezzano Scholarships (Annual); Kegel Bowler of the Month (Monthly); Mort Luby Sr. Hall of Fame Award; Alberta Crowe Meritorious Service Award.

6779 ■ Broad Universe (BU)
51 Watkins Ln.
Walnut Creek, CA 94596
Co. E-mail: info@broaduniverse.org
URL: http://www.broaduniverse.org
Contact: Phoebe Wray, President
Description: Promotes science fiction, fantasy, and horror written by women. **Founded:** 2000.

6780 ■ CAJ Media
Box 280
Brantford, ON, Canada N3T 5M8
Ph: (613)526-8061
Fax: (613)521-3904
Co. E-mail: canadianjour@magma.ca
URL: http://www.caj.ca
Contact: John Dickins, Executive Director
Released: 3/year **Price:** C$14.98, /year.

6781 ■ Canadian Association of Journalists (CAJ)—L'Association Canadienne des Journalistes
Box 280
Brantford, ON, Canada N3T 5M8
Ph: (613)526-8061
Fax: (613)521-3904
Co. E-mail: canadianjour@magma.ca
URL: http://www.caj.ca
Contact: John Dickins, Executive Director
Description: Professional organization representing the interests of journalists in Canada. Promotes high professional standards. Disseminates information. **Founded:** 1978. **Publications:** CAJ Media (3/year); Directory of Canadian Journalists. **Awards:** Code of Silence Award; Awards for Investigative Journalism; Code of Silence Award (Annual); Investigative Journalist Award (Annual).

6782 ■ Canadian Copyright Institute (CCI)
192 Spadina Ave., Ste. 107
Toronto, ON, Canada M5T 2C2
Ph: (416)975-1756
Fax: (416)975-1839
Co. E-mail: info@thecci.ca
URL: http://www.canadiancopyrightinstitute.ca
Contact: Anne McClelland, Administrator
Description: Creators, producers, and distributors of copyrighted works. Encourages a more complete understanding of copyright laws among members and the public. Consults with government and judicial bodies regarding reform of copyright laws. Conducts and sponsors research on copyright laws worldwide. Works with organizations pursuing similar goals to improve copyright legislation and enforcement. **Founded:** 1965. **Publications:** Copyright Reform Legislation Reporting Service (Periodic).

6783 ■ Canadian Writers Foundation (CWF)—La Fondation des ecrivains canadiens
Kanata Sta.
Ottawa, ON, Canada K2K 1X4
Ph: (613)256-6937
Fax: (613)256-5457
Co. E-mail: info@canadianwritersfoundation.org
URL: http://www.canadianwritersfoundation.org
Contact: Marianne Scott, President
Description: Provides ongoing assistance to notable senior Canadian writers who have made a significant contribution to Canadian writing and are experiencing extreme financial distress. **Founded:** 1931.

6784 ■ Communications Workers of America/ Canada (CWA)—Syndicat des Communications d'Amerique (SCA)
7B-1050 Baxter Rd.
Ottawa, ON, Canada K2C 3P1
Ph: (613)820-9777

Free: 877-486-4292
Fax: (613)820-8188
Co. E-mail: info@cwa-scacanada.ca
URL: http://www.cwa-scacanada.ca
Contact: Arnold Amber, Chairman
Description: Primarily union of journalists and media workers in Canada, as well as social workers and employees in the manufacturing industry. **Founded:** 1995. **Publications:** TNG Canada Today (Monthly).

6785 ■ Copyright Reform Legislation Reporting Service
192 Spadina Ave., Ste. 107
Toronto, ON, Canada M5T 2C2
Ph: (416)975-1756
Fax: (416)975-1839
Co. E-mail: info@thecci.ca
URL: http://www.canadiancopyrightinstitute.ca
Contact: Anne McClelland, Administrator
Released: Periodic **Price:** C$650, /year for members; C$750, /year for nonmembers.

6786 ■ Crime Writers of Canada (CWC)
2160 Colonel William Pkwy.
Oakville, ON, Canada L6M 0B8
Co. E-mail: info@crimewriterscanada.com
URL: http://www.crimewriterscanada.com
Contact: Garry Ryan, President
Description: Canadian crime writers, associated professionals, and others with serious interest in Canadian crime writing. Promotes Canadian crime writing and increases awareness of Canadian crime writers from coast to coast. **Founded:** 1982. **Publications:** Fingerprints (Quarterly); Dishes to Die For; In Cold Blood (Semiannual). **Awards:** Arthur Ellis Awards; Arthur Ellis Awards (Annual).

6787 ■ Editorial Freelancers Association (EFA)
71 W 23rd St., 4th Fl.
New York, NY 10010-4102
Ph: (212)929-5400
Free: 866-929-5439
Fax: (212)929-5439
Co. E-mail: office@the-efa.org
URL: http://www.the-efa.org
Contact: Margaret Moser, Executive
Description: Represents persons who work full or part-time as freelance writers or editorial freelancers. Promotes professionalism and facilitates the exchange of information and support. Conducts professional training seminars; and offers job listings. **Founded:** 1970. **Publications:** The Freelancer (Bimonthly).

6788 ■ Editors' Association of Canada (EAC)—Association canadienne des reviseurs
505-27 Carlton St.
Toronto, ON, Canada M5B 1L2
Ph: (416)975-1379
Free: 866-226-3348
Fax: (416)975-1637
Co. E-mail: info@editors.ca
URL: http://www.editors.ca
Contact: Greg Ioannou, President
Description: Editors, proofreaders, copy editors, and researchers working on both English and French language printed materials. Promotes advancement of the profession of editing, and of members' capabilities. Conducts professional development courses for members; makes available to members job hotline services and discount long-term disability, extended health, and dental and life insurance. Sets and enforces editorial standards of practice; establishes payment levels and conditions of employment for editorial work. Cooperates with other organizations pursuing similar goals. **Founded:** 1978. **Publications:** Active Voice (Bimonthly). **Awards:** Claudette Upton Scholarship (Annual); President's Award for Volunteer Service (Annual); Tom Fairley Award for Editorial Excellence (Annual); Lee d'Anjou Volunteer of the Year (Annual); Tom Fairley Award for Editorial Excellence.

6789 ■ Federation of BC Writers
Station Terminal
Vancouver, BC, Canada V6B 2Z3

Ph: (604)683-2057
Co. E-mail: info@bcwriters.ca
URL: http://www.bcwriters.ca
Contact: Sylvia Taylor, Executive Director
Description: Contributes to a supportive environment for writing in the community. **Founded:** 1976.

6790 ■ Fingerprints
2160 Colonel William Pkwy.
Oakville, ON, Canada L6M 0B8
Co. E-mail: info@crimewriterscanada.com
URL: http://www.crimewriterscanada.com
Contact: Garry Ryan, President
Released: Quarterly

6791 ■ Horror Writers Association (HWA)—Horror Writers of America
244 5th Ave., Ste. 2767
New York, NY 10001
Co. E-mail: hwa@horror.org
URL: http://www.horror.org
Contact: Rocky Wood, President
Description: Horror writers, including creators of comic strips, screenplays, and role-playing games, who have sold at least one work at professional rates are active members; horror writers who have sold something but not at professional rates are affiliate members. Non-writing professionals are associate members. Seeks to assist aspiring and accomplished horror writers in advancing their art and careers. Facilitates networking among members; gathers and disseminates information on horror fiction markets; serves as liaison between members and writers' agents and publishers. **Scope:** horror, writing, publishing. **Founded:** 1987. **Subscriptions:** archival material. **Publications:** Handbook/Directory (Annual). **Educational Activities:** Bram Stoker Awards Ceremony (Annual); Horror Writers Association Conference (Annual). **Awards:** Bram Stoker Awards; Bram Stoker Awards for Superior Achievement (Annual); Bram Stoker Lifetime Achievement Award (Annual); HWA Specialty Press Award (Annual).

6792 ■ The Inside Edge
460 Sarsons Rd.
Kelowna, BC, Canada V1W 1C2
Ph: (250)764-2143
Fax: (250)764-2145
Co. E-mail: nasja@shaw.ca
URL: http://www.nasja.org
Contact: Phil Johnson, President
Released: Quinquenial **Price:** included in membership dues; $52, for nonmembers.

6793 ■ International Black Writers and Authors (IBWA)
PO Box 43576
Los Angeles, CA 90043
Ph: (213)964-3721
Co. E-mail: ibwa_la@yahoo.com
URL: http://ibwa.tripod.com
Description: Seeks to discover and support new black writers. Conducts research and monthly seminars in poetry, fiction, nonfiction, music, and jazz. Provides writing services and children's services. Maintains speakers' bureau. Offers referral service. Plans to establish hall of fame, biographical archives, and museum. **Scope:** writing, Black history, Black art, writing resources. **Founded:** 1974. **Subscriptions:** 500 articles books periodicals. **Publications:** In Touch Newsletter (Monthly).

6794 ■ International Food, Wine and Travel Writers Association (IFWTWA)
1142 S Diamond Bar Blvd., No. 177
Diamond Bar, CA 91765-2203
Ph: (909)860-6914
Free: 877-439-8929
Fax: (909)396-0014
Co. E-mail: admin@ifwtwa.org
URL: http://www.ifwtwa.org
Contact: Ms. Patricia A. Anis, Executive Director
URL(s): www.global-writes.com. **Description:** Professional food, wine, and travel journalists, photographers, broadcasters and industry professionals in 28 countries; associate members are organizations in the hospitality industries. Seeks to bring recognition to those in the food, wine, and travel industry who have met the association's criteria. Offers scholar-

ships in culinary arts and sciences journalism (food-wine-travel). **Founded:** 1956. **Publications:** *Global Writes* (Weekly); *International Food, Wine and Travel Writers Association--Membership Roster* (Annual); *Membership Benefits* (Annual); *Press Pass* (Monthly); *International Food, Wine, and Travel Writers Association--Membership Roster* (Annual); *New Asian Cuisine: Fabulous Recipes from Celebrity Chefs*. **Educational Activities:** Board Retreat (Annual).

6795 ■ **International Foodservice Editorial Council (IFEC)**
PO Box 491
Hyde Park, NY 12538
Ph: (845)229-6973
Fax: (845)229-6973
Co. E-mail: ifec@ifeconline.com
URL: http://ifeconline.com
Contact: Megan McKenna, President
Description: Key communicators within the U.S. foodservice industry, including top editors and marketing and public relations personnel for leading food companies and foodservice educational institutions. Organized to sound the marketing directions of the industry on all levels; seeks to improve communications. **Founded:** 1956. **Awards:** International Foodservice Editorial Council Scholarships; IFEC Foodservice Communications Scholarships (Annual); Professional Development Awards (Annual).

6796 ■ **Investigative Reporters and Editors (IRE)—IRE**
Missouri School of Journalism
Columbia, MO 65211
Ph: (573)882-2042
Fax: (573)882-5431
Co. E-mail: info@ire.org
URL: http://www.ire.org
Contact: Manny Garcia, President
Description: Persons who report or edit in-depth journalism; journalism educators and students. Provides educational services, including computer-assisted reporting through its National Institute for Computer-Assisted Reporting. **Scope:** investigative reporting. **Founded:** 1975. **Subscriptions:** 20000 clippings video recordings. **Publications:** *The IRE Journal*; *Beat Book Series* (Quarterly); *IRE Journal* (Bimonthly); *IRE Members Directory* (Annual); *Uplink* (Bimonthly). **Educational Activities:** Investigative Reporters and Editors Conference (Annual); Computer-Assisted Reporting Boot Camp (Periodic). **Awards:** IRE Awards (Annual); FOI Award (Annual); Thomas Renner Award for Outstanding Crime Reporting (Annual). **Telecommunication Services:** journal@ire.org.

6797 ■ *NASJA Directory*
460 Sarsons Rd.
Kelowna, BC, Canada V1W 1C2
Ph: (250)764-2143
Fax: (250)764-2145
Co. E-mail: nasja@shaw.ca
URL: http://www.nasja.org
Contact: Phil Johnson, President
Released: Annual

6798 ■ **National Writers Association (NWA)**
10940 S Parker Rd., No. 508
Parker, CO 80134
Ph: (303)841-0246
Fax: (303)841-2607
Co. E-mail: natlwritersassn@hotmail.com
URL: http://www.nationalwriters.com
Description: Professional full- or part-time freelance writers who specialize in business writing. Aims to serve as a marketplace whereby business editors can easily locate competent writing talent. Establishes communication among editors and writers. **Founded:** 1945. **Publications:** *Authorship*; *Professional Freelance Writers Directory* (Annual); *Authorship* (Quarterly). **Awards:** Novel Manuscript Award; Poetry Award; Short Story Award; Nonfiction Contest.

6799 ■ **North American Snowsports Journalists Association (NASJA)**
460 Sarsons Rd.
Kelowna, BC, Canada V1W 1C2
Ph: (250)764-2143

Fax: (250)764-2145
Co. E-mail: nasja@shaw.ca
URL: http://www.nasja.org
Contact: Phil Johnson, President
Description: Newspaper, magazine, book, television, radio writers and broadcasters, and photographers who report on skiing and other snow sports. Covers skiing and other snow sports. **Founded:** 1963. **Publications:** *The Inside Edge* (Quinquenial); *NASJA Directory* (Annual). **Awards:** Lifetime Achievement Award; Carson White Golden Quill Award (Annual); Harold Hirsch Award (Annual); Lifetime Achievement Award (Annual); Outstanding Competitor Award (Annual); Carson White Golden Quill Award; Harold S. Hirsch Award for Column Writing; Harold S. Hirsch Award for Excellence in Broadcasting; Harold S. Hirsch Award for Excellence in Snow Sports Photography; Paul Robbins Outstanding Competitor Award.

6800 ■ **Novelists, Inc. (NINC)**
PO Box 2037
Manhattan, KS 66505
Fax: (785)837-1877
Co. E-mail: ninc@varney.com
URL: http://www.ninc.com
Contact: Lou Aronica, President
Description: Works to serve the needs of multi-published writers of popular fiction. **Founded:** 1989.

6801 ■ **Outdoor Writers Association of America (OWAA)**
615 Oak St., Ste. 201
Missoula, MT 59801
Ph: (406)728-7434
Fax: (406)728-7445
Co. E-mail: info@owaa.org
URL: http://www.owaa.org
Contact: Mark Taylor, President
URL(s): owaa.org/index.htm. **Description:** Professional organization of newspaper, magazine, radio, television and motion picture writers and photographers (both staff and free-lance) concerned with outdoor recreation and conservation. Conducts surveys for educational and industrial organizations; compiles market data for writer members and offers liaison aid in writer assignments. **Founded:** 1927. **Publications:** *National Outdoor Writers Directory* (Annual). **Awards:** Bodie McDowell Scholarships; Excellence in Craft Award (Annual); J. Hammond Brown Memorial Award (Annual); John Madson Fellowship (Annual). **Telecommunication Services:** owaa@montana.com.

6802 ■ **Quebec Writers' Federation (QWF)**
1200 Atwater Ave.
Westmount, QC, Canada H3Z 1X4
Ph: (514)933-0878
Co. E-mail: admin@qwf.org
URL: http://www.qwf.org
Contact: Lori Schubert, Executive Director
Description: Works toward ensuring a lasting place for English literature and practitioners on the Quebec cultural scene. **Awards:** QWF Literary Awards.

6803 ■ **Sisters in Crime (SinC)**
PO Box 442124
Lawrence, KS 66044
Ph: (785)842-1325
Fax: (785)842-1034
Co. E-mail: sinc@sistersincrime.org
URL: http://www.sistersincrime.org
Contact: Marcia Talley, President
Description: Represents writers, librarians, editors, booksellers, agents and publishers. Promotes the professional development and advancement of women crime writers. **Founded:** 1986. **Publications:** *Sisters in Crime Newsletter* (Quarterly); *Sisters in Crime*. **Educational Activities:** Bloody Words (Annual). **Telecommunication Services:** sistersincrime@juno.com.

6804 ■ **Society for Technical Communication (STC)**
9401 Lee Hwy., Ste. 300
Fairfax, VA 22031
Ph: (703)522-4114

Fax: (703)522-2075
URL: http://www.stc.org
Contact: Dr. Hillary Hart, President
Description: Writers, editors, educators, scientists, engineers, artists, publishers, and others professionally engaged in or interested in the field of technical communication; companies, corporations, organizations, and agencies interested in the aims of the society. Seeks to advance the theory and practice of technical communication in all media. Sponsors high school writing contests. **Scope:** An individual membership organization dedicated to advancing the arts and sciences of technical communication. Members include technical writers and editors, content developers, documentation specialists, technical illustrators, instructional designers, academics, information architects, usability and human factors professionals, visual designers, web designers and developers, and translators. Provides support to teachers and students of technical communication through programs, scholarships, grants and loans, annual conferences, and seminars. Also provides information about events and courses related to technical communication. **Founded:** 1957. **Publications:** "Managing Writers: A Real World Guide to Managing Technical Documentation," 2009; "Advertising Rates," 2009; "The Current Economy: What's a Technical Communicator to Do," Oct, 2008; "Breaking Through the Glass Ceiling," May, 2008; "The Tipping Point Theory," Mar, 2008; "Recession Obsession," Feb, 2008; "English Technical Writing Guide," 2008; "Publishing Fundamentals: Unstructured Frame Maker 8," 2008; "Hello, My Name is Doug and I'm a Workaholic," Oct, 2007; "Results of original research"; "Original contributions to technical communication theory". **Educational Activities:** Society for Technical Communication Conference (Annual). **Awards:** International Technical Art Competition; International Technical Publications Competition; International Online Communication Competition; Marian Norby Scholarships; STC Scholarships. **Seminars:** Web-Telephone; Salary Database.

6805 ■ *TNG Canada Today*
7B-1050 Baxter Rd.
Ottawa, ON, Canada K2C 3P1
Ph: (613)820-9777
Free: 877-486-4292
Fax: (613)820-8188
Co. E-mail: info@cwa-scacanada.ca
URL: http://www.cwa-scacanada.ca
Contact: Arnold Amber, Chairman
Released: Monthly

6806 ■ **United States Harness Writers' Association (USHWA)**
c/o Jerry Connors, Sec.
PO Box 1314
Mechanicsburg, PA 17055
Ph: (717)651-5889
Co. E-mail: ushwa@paonline.com
URL: http://www.ushwa.org
Contact: Steve Wolf, President
Description: Writers, reporters, editors, broadcasters, columnists, and cartoonists who cover harness racing for the press. Seeks to further the interests of light harness racing. Maintains hall of fame and charitable program. Votes on national awards. **Founded:** 1947. **Educational Activities:** United States Harness Writers' Association Dinner (Annual). **Awards:** Proximity Achievement Award; Rising Star Award; Living Hall of Fame; USHWAn of the Year; Dan Patch Awards; Amateur Driver (Annual); Driver of the Year (Annual); Owner of the Year (Annual); Proximity Award (Annual); Rising Star (Annual); USHWAn of the Year (Annual); Bob Zellner USHWAn of the Year; William R. Haughton Good Guy Award; Writer's Corner Hall of Fame.

6807 ■ **Women Writing the West (WWW)**
8547 E Arapahoe Rd., No. J-541
Greenwood Village, CO 80112-1436
Co. E-mail: info@womenwritingthewest.org
URL: http://www.womenwritingthewest.org
Contact: Pam Tartaglio, President
Description: Serves as a forum for writers and other professionals writing and promoting the Women's West founded by Sybil Downing and Jerrie Hurd. Promotes the legacy of earlier women writers who

depicted the life during the hard and dangerous times of the Western American era. **Awards:** WILLA Literary Award (Annual).

EDUCATIONAL PROGRAMS

6808 ■ Copywriting I (Onsite)
EEI Communications
8945 Guilford Rd., Ste. 145
Columbia, MD 21046
Ph: (410)309-8200
Free: 888-253-2762
Fax: (410)630-3980
Co. E-mail: train@eeicom.com
URL: http://www.eeicom.com/eei-training-services
Price: $797.00. **Description:** Topics include understanding your audience, defining your purpose, communication methods, and effective writing structures. **Dates and Locations:** Silver Spring, MD.

6809 ■ Copywriting II (Onsite)
EEI Communications
66 Canal Center Plz., Ste. 200
Alexandria, VA 22314
Ph: (703)683-7453
Free: 888-253-2762
Fax: (703)683-7310
Co. E-mail: train@eeicom.com
URL: http://www.eeicom.com/training
Price: $497.00. **Description:** Geared towards the experienced writer, this seminar covers forming ideas and brainstorming, impact writing, and improving the creative process. **Dates and Locations:** Silver Spring, MD.

6810 ■ The Designing Editor
EEI Communications
8945 Guilford Rd., Ste. 145
Columbia, MD 21046
Ph: (410)309-8200
Free: 888-253-2762
Fax: (410)630-3980
Co. E-mail: train@eeicom.com
URL: http://www.eeicom.com/eei-training-services
Price: $745.00. **Description:** Seminar for editors who must also perform design tasks; covers the basics of effective design, including the design process, page layout, design evaluation techniques, and related issues. **Dates and Locations:** Alexandria, VA.

6811 ■ Intensive Review of Grammar (Onsite)
EEI Communications
8945 Guilford Rd., Ste. 145
Columbia, MD 21046
Ph: (410)309-8200
Free: 888-253-2762
Fax: (410)630-3980
Co. E-mail: train@eeicom.com
URL: http://www.eeicom.com/eei-training-services
Price: $797.00. **Description:** Seminar for writers and editors; covers the advanced elements of grammar and usage, including adverbs and adjectives, restrictive and nonrestrictive clauses, dependent and independent clauses, tricky punctuation rules, pronoun/antecedent agreement, and subject/verb agreement. **Dates and Locations:** Silver Spring, MD; and Alexandria, VA.

6812 ■ Scientific Editing (Onsite)
EEI Communications
8945 Guilford Rd., Ste. 145
Columbia, MD 21046
Ph: (410)309-8200
Free: 888-253-2762
Fax: (410)630-3980
Co. E-mail: train@eeicom.com
URL: http://www.eeicom.com/eei-training-services
Price: $797.00. **Description:** Covers techniques for editing scientific and technical prose, including convincing writers to revise their manuscript; reducing author reliance on jargon and wordiness; locating and using scientific editing resources; meeting title, abstract, and keyword requirements; editing math and scientific data in graphs, diagrams, and illustrations; handling units, measurements, and numbers; and using scientific and engineering symbols. **Dates and Locations:** Silver Spring, MD.

DIRECTORIES OF EDUCATIONAL PROGRAMS

6813 ■ Contemporary Women Poets
Pub: St. James Press
Contact: Patrick C. Sommers, President
E-mail: pat.sommers@cengage.com
URL(s): www.gale.cengage.com. **Ed:** Pamela L. Shelton. **Released:** Latest edition October 2007. **Covers:** 250 prominent women poets writing and publishing in the English language and including some foreign-language authors. **Entries include:** Biographical data, list of publications, author's comments when available, signed essay about the author. **Arrangement:** Alphabetical. **Indexes:** Nationality, title.

6814 ■ FACSNET
Pub: Foundation for American Communications—FACS
URL(s): www.facsnet.org. **Entries include:** For experts--Name, address, phone, E-mail address. For others--Contact information. **Database covers:** Internet resources for journalists, including traditional news beats, seminars, institutes, conferences, and experts in the field.

6815 ■ Who's Who in the Media and Communications
Pub: Marquis Who's Who L.L.C.
Contact: James A. Finkelstein, President
URL(s): www.marquiswhoswho.com. **Covers:** More than 18,500 professionals in print journalism, broadcasting, publishing, television, public relations, advertising, radio, telecommunications, interactive multimedia, and education. **Entries include:** Biographical data.

REFERENCE WORKS

6816 ■ American Society of Journalists and Authors--Directory
Pub: American Society of Journalists & Authors
Contact: Salley Shannon, President
URL(s): www.asja.org. **Released:** Annual; January. **Price:** $98, Individuals. **Covers:** 1,000 member freelance nonfiction writers. **Entries include:** Writer's name, home and office addresses and phone numbers, specialties, areas of expertise; name, address and phone of agent; memberships; books; periodicals to which contributed; awards. **Arrangement:** Alphabetical. **Indexes:** Subject specialty, type of material written, geographical.

6817 ■ The AWP Official Guide to Writing Programs
Pub: Association of Writers and Writing Programs
Contact: Ron Tanner, President
URL(s): www.awpwriter.org/bookshelf/guide.htmguide.awpwriter.org/. **Released:** Annual; February of even years; Latest edition 11th. **Price:** $28.45, Individuals including shipping and handling. **Covers:** About 300 graduate and 400 undergraduate programs in creative writing; approximately 250 writers' conferences, festivals, and centers; coverage includes Canada and the United Kingdom. **Entries include:** Institution name, department name, contact name and address; web site, description of program, including degree or other credit offered; description of faculty, including titles of their publications; tuition, fees and dates. **Arrangement:** Alphabetical. **Indexes:** Geographical, degree.

6818 ■ Be a Brilliant Business Writer: Write Well, Write Fast, and Whip the Competition
Pub: Crown Business Books
Ed: Jane Curry, Diana Young. **Released:** October 5, 2010. **Price:** $13.99. **Description:** Tools for mastering the art of persuasive writing in every document created, from email and client letters to reports and presentations, this book will help any writer convey their message with clarity and power, increase productivity by reducing rewrites, and provide the correct tone for navigating office politics.

6819 ■ Editorial Freelancers Association--Membership Directory
Pub: Editorial Freelancers Association Inc.
Contact: Trudy Balch, Secretary
E-mail: tbalch@pobox.com
URL(s): www.the-efa.org. **Released:** Annual; spring. **Covers:** 1,100 member editorial freelancers. **Entries include:** Personal name, address, phone, services provided, specialties. **Arrangement:** Alphabetical. **Indexes:** Product/service, special interest, geographical, computer skills.

6820 ■ "Freelance Writer Creates L.I. Bridal Blog" in Long Island Business News (September 10, 2010)
Pub: Dolan Media Newswires
Ed: Gregory Zeller. **Description:** Profile of Claudia Copquin, freelance journalist who created a blog for brides on the Internet.

6821 ■ Freelancing for Journalists
Pub: Routledge
Ed: Diana Harris. **Released:** January 1, 2010. **Price:** $110.00. **Description:** Comprehensive guide showing the specific skills required for those wishing to freelance in newspapers, magazines, radio, television, and as online journalists.

6822 ■ International Literary Market Place: The Directory of the International Book Publishing Industry
Pub: Information Today Inc.
Contact: Thomas H. Hogan, President
E-mail: ctuthill@infotoday.com
URL(s): www.literarymarketplace.combooks.infotoday.com. **Released:** Annual; Latest edition 2012. **Price:** $289, Individuals softbound; $260.10, Individuals first time standing order. **Covers:** Over 10,500 publishers in over 180 countries outside the United States and Canada, and about 1,499 trade and professional organizations related to publishing abroad; includes major printers, binders, typesetters, book manufacturers, book dealers, libraries, literary agencies, translators, book clubs, reference books and journals, periodicals, prizes, and international reference section. **Entries include:** For publishers--Name, address, phone, fax, telex, names and titles of key personnel, branches, type of publications, subjects, ISBN prefix. Listings for others include similar information but less detail. **Arrangement:** Classified by business activities, then geographical. **Indexes:** Company name, subject, type of publication.

6823 ■ Midwest Travel Writers Association--Membership Directory
Pub: Midwest Travel Writers Association
Contact: Mary Lu Laffey, President
URL(s): www.mtwa.org. **Released:** Annual; February. **Price:** $50; $65, book & CD. **Covers:** Over 100 travel writers, editors, and representatives of the travel and tourism industry, located in 13 Midwestern states. **Entries include:** Name, spouse's name, address, phone; title, year membership began, publications, professional affiliations, writing specialties. **Database includes:** List of MTWA meeting sites, writing specialities, bylaws, membership requirements, stock photos available. **Arrangement:** Alphabetical. **Indexes:** Geographical.

6824 ■ My So-Called Freelance Life: How to Survive and Thrive as a Creative Professional for Hire
Pub: Seal Press
Contact: Charlie Winton, Manager
Ed: Michelle Goodman. **Released:** October 1, 2008. **Price:** $15.95. **Description:** Guidebook for women wishing to start a freelancing business; tips, advice, how-to's and all the information needed to survive working from home are included.

6825 ■ "A Network of One: Local Writer Adds Web Interviews to Creative Output" in La Crosse Tribune (September 14, 2009)
Pub: La Crosse Tribune
Ed: Geri Parlin. **Description:** Profile of Andrew Revels, a freelance and aspiring writer, who has created a website in order to help gain attention for his own writing as well as for other local artists, musi-

cians and comedians. His latest endeavor includes interviewing local talent and broadcasting the interviews on his site each week.

6826 ■ "Pretentious and Loving It" in Entrepreneur (Vol. 37, August 2009, No. 8, pp. 34)
Pub: Entrepreneur Media, Inc.
Ed: Eric Mahoney. **Description:** Pitchfork.com features reviews of albums from independent artists. Their most innovative section is Pitchfork.tv, featuring videos of bands, and Forkcast along with their Features section that contains articles about bands and their histories.

6827 ■ Professional Freelance Writers Directory
Pub: National Writers Association
URL(s): www.nationalwriters.com. **Released:** Annual **Price:** Free. **Entries include:** Name, address, phone (home and business numbers), special fields of writing competence, titles of books published by royalty firms, mention of contributions to specific magazines, journals, newspapers or anthologies, recent awards received, relevant activities and skills (photography, etc.). **Database covers:** About 200 professional members selected from the club's membership on the basis of significant articles or books, or production of plays or movies. **Arrangement:** Alphabetical. **Indexes:** By author alphabetical, by state, by subject.

6828 ■ Publishers Directory
Pub: Cengage Learning Inc.
Contact: Ronald Dunn, President
URL(s): www.gale.cengage.com. **Released:** Annual; Latest edition 37th; March, 2012. **Price:** $756, Individuals. **Covers:** Over 20,000 new and established, commercial and nonprofit, private and alternative, corporate and association, government and institution publishing programs and their distributors; includes producers of books, classroom materials, prints, reports, and databases. **Entries include:** Firm name, address, phone, fax, company e-mail address, URL, year founded, ISBN prefix, Standard Address Number, whether firm participates in the Cataloging in Publication program of the Library of Congress, names of principal executives, personal e-mail addresses, number of titles in print, description of firm and its main subject interests, discount and returns policies, affiliated and parent companies, mergers and amalgamations, principal markets, imprints and divisions, alternate formats products are offered; distributors also list firms for which they distribute, special services, terms to publishers and regional offices. **Arrangement:** Alphabetical; distributors listed separately. **Indexes:** Subject, geographical, publisher, imprints, and distributor. **Availability:** Online: Cengage Learning Inc.; LexisNexis Group. **Type:** Directory.

6829 ■ "Savvy Solutions" in Black Enterprise (Vol. 41, November 2010, No. 4, pp. 42)
Pub: Earl G. Graves Publishing Co. Inc.
Ed: Tennille M. Robinson. **Description:** Society of Children's Book Writers and Illustrators offers members many benefits, including directories of agencies looking for new writers of books.

6830 ■ Short Story Writers
Pub: Magill's Choice
Contact: Rose Bonas, Manager
URL(s): www.salempress.com. **Ed:** Frank N. Magill, Charles E. May. **Released:** Published October 2007. **Price:** $217, Individuals 3 volumes. **Covers:** 102 short story writers of the 19th and 20th centuries. **Entries include:** Writer name, principal works of short fiction, other literary forms produced, notable career and technical achievements related to the short story form, brief biography, glossary. **Arrangement:** Alphabetical. **Indexes:** Author surname, title.

6831 ■ "Welcome to a New Kind of Cubicle Culture" in Boston Business Journal (Vol. 29, August 19, 2011, No. 15, pp. 1)
Pub: American City Business Journals Inc.
Ed: Alexander Jackson. **Description:** Beehive Baltimore offers a co-working space where independent freelancers and entrepreneurs can work. There are two other companies that provide the same service and the value of these services to these

professional is that it provides them with an office that is both convenient and affordable aside from letting them network with peers.

TRADE PERIODICALS

6832 ■ American Society of Journalists and Authors Newsletter
Pub: American Society of Journalists & Authors
Ed: Barbara DeMarco Barrett, Editor, newsletter@asja.org. **Released:** Monthly, July and August issues clubbed. **Description:** Reports on the business meetings of the Society and provides market news as well as news of members, publishers, editors, and association chapters. Recurring features include professional market reports and discussions of magazines, books, and other media.

6833 ■ Authorship
Pub: National Writers Association
Ed: Sandy Whelchel, Editor. **Released:** Quarterly. **Price:** $18, nonmembers. **Description:** Contains information about the freelance writing and publishing fields. Carries market news, lists of editors and publishers against whom many have registered complaints, and updates on publications that have gone out of business or are no longer considering freelance submissions. Recurring features include news of members, editorials, letters to the editor, book reviews, and columns titled Director's Corner and Business Writing News.

6834 ■ AWP Job List
Pub: Association of Writers and Writing Programs
Contact: Ron Tanner, President
Ed: David Sherwin, Editor, awpchron@mason.gmu.edu. **Released:** Monthly, 7/year. **Price:** Included in membership. **Description:** Lists job opportunities for writers, both in academia and in the business sector.

6835 ■ Children's Book Insider
Pub: Children's Book Insider L.L.C.
Contact: Laura Backes, Editor
E-mail: laura@write4kids.com
Released: Monthly. **Price:** $29.95, individuals; $26.95 online. **Description:** Discusses writing and selling books and stories for children. Recurring features include interviews, news of educational opportunities, job listings, and columns titled Writing Workshop, Market News, and Trends.

6836 ■ Fiction Writer's Guideline
Pub: Fiction Writer's Connection
Contact: Blythe Camenson, Director
E-mail: bcamenson@aol.com
Released: Enewsletter. **Description:** Offers practical advice and support on writing and getting published. Recurring features include interviews, book reviews, and Advice From agents and editors and Writing Tips.

6837 ■ Freelance Writer's Report
Pub: CNW Publishing, Editing and Promotion Inc.
Contact: Dana K. Cassell, Director
E-mail: dana@writers-editors.com
Ed: Dana K. Cassell, Editor, danakcnw@ncia.net. **Released:** Monthly. **Price:** Included in membership. **Description:** Offers up-to-date news and information concerning effective marketing/production techniques, writing tips, self-promotion, and other topics of interest 'to freelance writers who intend to earn a good income from their work and improve the quality of their work.' Recurring features include interviews, book reviews, news of writing seminars, conferences, and market news. **Remarks:** Members of the Florida Freelance Writers Association receive an extra association section (4 pages).

6838 ■ The Freelancer
Pub: Editorial Freelancers Association Inc.
Contact: Trudy Balch, Secretary
E-mail: tbalch@pobox.com
Ed: Mary Ratcliffe, Editor, gamut@mratcliffe.com. **Released:** Bimonthly. **Price:** Included in membership; $20, nonmembers. **Description:** Publishes news of the concerns and activities of EFA, whose members 'provide freelance editorial services to the publishing and communications industries.' Recurring features include letters to the editor, news of members, book reviews, a calendar of events,

columns on usage and business, reports on on general meetings, news of member, and columns titled Grammatical Gleanings and Tax Tips.

6839 ■ How To Be Your Own Publisher Update
Pub: Bibliotheca Press
Ed: A. Doyle, Editor. **Released:** Annual. **Price:** $12.95, U.S.; $15.95, Canada; $19.95, other countries. **Description:** Acts as a reference for self publishers. Distributed by Prosperity & Profits Unlimited Distribution Services, PO Box 416, Denver, CO, 80201.

6840 ■ International Women's Writing Guild--Network
Pub: Tenth House Enterprises
Contact: Elizabeth Julia Stoumen, President
E-mail: elizabethjulia88@aol.com
Ed: Tatiana Stoumen, Editor. **Released:** Bimonthly. **Price:** Included in membership. **Description:** Carries a variety of items for women who write both for personal growth and professionally. Announces opportunities for retreat, publication, and awards. Recurring features include Guild and member news; writing conferences, and workshops; letters; and contests, environmental news, market and publication information.

6841 ■ Journal of Technical Writing and Communication
Pub: Baywood Publishing Company Inc.
Contact: Stuart Cohen, President
URL(s): www.baywood.com/journals/PreviewJournals.asp?id=0047-2816. **Ed:** Charles H. Sides, Elizabeth Tebeaux. **Released:** Quarterly **Price:** $402, Institutions; $381, Institutions online.

6842 ■ NABJ Update
Pub: National Association of Black Journalists
Ed: Ernie Suggs, Editor. **Released:** 6/year. **Description:** Reports on activities of the National Association of Black Journalists.

6843 ■ NAHWW Newsletter
Pub: National Association of Home and Workshop Writers
Ed: Richard Day, Editor. **Released:** Quarterly. **Price:** Included in membership. **Description:** Promotes communication among member writers by sharing information on publishers, marketing conditions, and mutual problems. Offers how-to tips, do-it-yourself field growth projections, and news of association activities. Recurring features include letters from members, book reviews, jokes, and columns titled Market Report and Resources.

6844 ■ New Writer's Magazine
Pub: New Writer's Magazine
URL(s): www.marketlist.com/new-writer's-magazine/dt/2267/#. **Ed:** George S. Haborak. **Released:** Bimonthly **Price:** $25, Individuals.

6845 ■ Poetalk
Pub: Bay Area Poets Coalition Inc.
Contact: John B. Rowe, President
Released: Quarterly. **Price:** $15, Included in membership; $6, nonmembers; $12, institutions. **Description:** Publishes quality work by beginner and experienced poets.

6846 ■ PWAContact
Pub: Professional Writers Association of Canada
Ed: Phil Moscovitch, Editor. **Released:** Quarterly. **Description:** Provides news and information to help further the careers of professional freelance writers in Canada. Examines copyright changes and implications and discusses available markets, industry news, computer programs and technology, and various aspects of the writing profession. Recurring features include letters to the editor, reports of meetings, a calendar of events, and columns titled New Tech, Professional Practice, and Copyright. **Remarks:** PWAC members receive a special section titled PWAC Inside, which provides an insider's view and tips about working for specific magazines, information on new publications, awards, chapter updates, and a column titled Red Flag.

6847 ■ *Travel Publicity Leads*
Pub: Scott American Corp.
Contact: Frank Scott, Editor
Released: Weekly. **Price:** $400, individuals by mail or fax. **Description:** Summarizes the information, trip invitations, data, and interviews travel writers and broadcasters desire. Provides global editorial placement opportunities for PR specialists at travel service providers, worldwide, and their PR firms. Includes an annual compilation of editorial calendars of worldwide travel media, with key-worded and time-sequenced topics.

6848 ■ *Travel Writer*
Pub: Society of American Travel Writers
Released: 10/year. **Description:** Advises and provides information for travel writers.

6849 ■ *Washington Writer*
Pub: Washington Independent Writers
Contact: Claude Berube, President
E-mail: editor@washwriter.org
Released: Monthly, July/August issue combined. **Price:** Included in membership; $45, nonmembers. **Description:** Carries information for freelance writers about current issues of interest, including developments in the book and magazine publishing businesses, new markets, and alerts concerning unfair editorial practices. Recurring features include a calendar of events, news of members, announcements of workshops, conference reports, and columns titled Bylines, Resources, Small Groups, and Classified Ads. Remarks: Subscribers must live outside the Washington metropolitan area. Members of the organization receive the newsletter as part of their membership.

6850 ■ *The Writer Magazine: The Pioneer (Oldest) Magazine for Writers*
Pub: Kalmbach Publishing Co.
Contact: Gerald Butch Boettcher, President
E-mail: gboettcher@kalmbach.com
URL(s): www.writermag.com. **Ed:** Jeff Reich. **Released:** Monthly **Price:** $32.95, Individuals; $42.95, Canada; $61, Two years; $44.95, Other countries.

6851 ■ *Writer's Digest*
Pub: FW Publications
Contact: Sara Domville, President
E-mail: sara.domville@fwpubs.com
URL(s): www.writersdigest.com. **Released:** 8/yr.
Price: $19.96, Individuals; $29.96, Canada including GST/HST; $31.96, Other countries surface delivery.

6852 ■ *Writers' Union of Canada Newsletter*
Pub: Writers' Union of Canada
Contact: Kelly Duffin, Executive Director
Released: Quarterly, 6/year. **Price:** Included in membership. **Description:** Informs members of the activities of the Union.

VIDEOCASSETTES/ AUDIOCASSETTES

6853 ■ *Get Published*
Instructional Video
2219 C St.
Lincoln, NE 68502
Ph: (402)475-6570
Free: 800-228-0164
Fax: (402)475-6500
Co. E-mail: feedback@insvideo.com
URL: http://www.insvideo.com
Released: 19??. **Price:** $149.95. **Description:** New York literary and film agent Peter Miller furnishes information on what it takes to get published, includes advise on selling fiction, defending author's rights, and developing non-fiction book proposals. He also discusses industry practices, procedures, and the television and motion picture markets. **Availability:** VHS.

6854 ■ *Jane Rule. . .Writing*
The Cinema Guild
115 W 30th St., Ste. 800
New York, NY 10001
Ph: (212)685-6242
Free: 800-723-5522

Fax: (212)685-4717
Co. E-mail: info@cinemaguild.com
URL: http://www.cinemaguild.com
Released: 1996. **Price:** $250. **Description:** Documentary features novelist Jane Rule discussing her philosophy of creative writing. **Availability:** VHS.

CONSULTANTS

6855 ■ Career Pro—Career Pro Resume Service
7825 Midlothian Tpke., Ste. 220
Richmond, VA 23235-5247
Ph: (804)323-0120
Free: 800-513-1666
Fax: (804)560-4098
Contact: John M. O'Connor, President
Scope: Firm provides professional resume and cover letter writing deliverable in Word or HTML format.

6856 ■ Carelli & Associates
17 Reid Pl.
Delmar, NY 12054
Ph: (518)439-0233
Fax: (518)439-3006
Co. E-mail: truthaboutsupervision@yahoo.com
URL: http://www.carelli.com
Contact: Anne O Brien Carelli, Owner
E-mail: anneobriencarelli@yahoo.com
Scope: Provider of writing and editing services to industry and businesses, health care and educational institutions, and government agencies. Also provides program management in creating and disseminating publications and in implementing related training. Assists organizations in designing and implementing team-based management. Offers supervisory skills training and problem-solving work sessions for managers. Individual Consultation are provided for managers, CEOs, potential supervisors including 360 degree assessments. **Founded:** 1988. **Publications:** "The Truth About Supervision: Coaching, Teamwork, Interviewing, Appraisals, 360 degree Assessments, and Recognition". **Seminars:** Supervisory Skills Training Series; Problem-Solving Work Sessions for Managers; Effective Leadership.

6857 ■ The Center for Technical Communication—Bob Bly Copywriter
590 Delcina Dr.
River Vale, NJ 07675
Ph: (201)505-9451
Fax: (201)385-1138
Co. E-mail: rwbly@bly.com
URL: http://www.bly.com
Contact: Bob Bly, President
E-mail: rwbly@bly.com
Scope: An independent consultant and copywriter specializing in business-to-business, industrial, hi-tech, and direct response advertising, marketing, publicity, and promotion. Writes marketing plans, ad campaigns, sales brochures, publicity materials, direct response ads, sales letters, and direct mail packages for clients nationwide. Industries served: publishing, business-to-business products or services, software or computers, electronics, financial, healthcare, medical equipment, industrial equipment, chemicals, consulting, and professional services. **Founded:** 1982. **Publications:** "The Bulletproof Book Proposal "; "Finding A Good Idea For Your Book"; "A Fine Position to Be In"; "What to Do When Your Book Goes Out of Print"; "How To Write a Good Advertisement"; "31 -derfully Simple Ways To Make Your Ads Generate More Inquiries"; "On Target Advertising"; "How to Write More Effective Product Brochures "; "Classy Outfit...Classy Brochure?"; "Improving Your Listening Skills"; "Improving Your Interpersonal Skills"; "10 Ways To Get More Done in Less Time"; "How to Give a Successful Presentation". **Seminars:** Active Listening; Become an Instant Guru; Get More Done In Less Time: How To Double Your Personal Productivity; How To Write A Nonfiction Book And Get It Published; How To Succeed as a Freelance Writer; The 1-Hour E-Zine Writing Formula; World's Best-Kept Copywriting Secrets; What's Working in Direct Mail Today; What's Working in E-Mail Marketing Today; Copywriting for Non-Copywriters; Effective Business Writing; Effective Technical Writing; How To Write Copy That Sells; Selling Your Services.

6858 ■ Great Western Association Management Inc.
7995 E Prentice Ave., Ste. 100
Greenwood Village, CO 80111
Ph: (303)770-2220
Fax: (303)770-1614
Co. E-mail: info83@gwami.com
URL: http://www.gwami.com
Contact: Karen M. Wojdyla, President
E-mail: kwojdyla@gwami.com
Scope: Provider of clients with products and services to effectively manage existing and startup, for- and not-for-profit organizations. Clients select from a menu of services including association development and public relations, conferences and seminars, financial management, membership communications, and governance. Expertise also includes association strategic planning, compliance, lobbying, meeting planning, fundraising, marketing and communications. Serves national, regional and state organizations. **Founded:** 1983. **Seminars:** Site selection; Creative program development; Contract negotiations; On-site conference management; Trade show management; Travel and logistics.

6859 ■ Harian Creative Enterprises—Harian Creative Books
47 Hyde Blvd.
Ballston Spa, NY 12020
Ph: (518)885-6699
Fax: (518)885-7397
Contact: Shirley Garrett, Director
Description: Description: Publishes fiction, poetry and monographs on writing, the arts, education and culture. Offers conferences, workshops, lecturing, and teaching. Accepts solicited manuscripts only. Reaches market through direct mail, trade sales and wholesalers and distributors. Does not accept unsolicited manuscripts. **Scope:** Literary service for writers and publishers, offering counsel on the writing and completion of literary projects, including titling, book and jacket design and editorial work. Industries served: Education, culture, and art and entertainment. **Founded:** 1967. **Seminars:** The Workshop Under the Sky.

LIBRARIES

6860 ■ Cleveland Public Library - Literature Department
Main Bldg., 2nd Fl.
325 Superior Ave.
Cleveland, OH 44114-1271
Ph: (216)623-2881
Co. E-mail: literature@cpl.org
URL: http://www.cpl.org/thelibrary/subjectscollections/literature.aspx
Contact: Amy Dawson, Manager
Scope: Fiction, drama and theater, film, radio, television, poetry, essays, humor, oratory and public speaking, craft of writing, literary criticism and biography, classical Greek and Latin, linguistics, journalism, book trade, printing, publishing, Library and information science. **Services:** Department open to the public. **Founded:** 1869. **Holdings:** 500,000 volumes; 11,368 bound periodical volumes; 23,000 theater programs and playbills; 16,000 titles of microform editions of plays and miscellanea; 190 vertical files. **Subscriptions:** 825 journals and other serials.

6861 ■ National Press Club - Eric Friedheim Library & News Information Center
529 14th St. NW, 13th Fl.
Washington, DC 20045
Ph: (202)662-7523
Co. E-mail: bshankle@press.org
URL: http://press.org/library
Contact: Julie Schoo, Director, Library Services
Scope: Current events; journalism - craft, history; print and broadcast media. **Services:** Copying; audio cassette copying (fee); library open to members. **Founded:** 1984. **Holdings:** 2500 books; NPC luncheon audiocassettes & videotapes; newsletters; microfilm; CDs. **Subscriptions:** 250 newspapers, magazines, journals, and newsletters.

ASSOCIATIONS AND OTHER ORGANIZATIONS

6862 ■ Independent Electrical Contractors (IEC)
4401 Ford Ave., Ste. 1100
Alexandria, VA 22302-1432
Ph: (703)549-7351
Free: 800-456-4324
Fax: (703)549-7448
Co. E-mail: info@ieci.org
URL: http://www.ieci.org
Contact: Bobby J. Tutor, President
Description: Independent electrical contractors, small and large, primarily oPEN shop. Promotes the interests of members; works to eliminate "unwise and unfair business practices" and to protect its members against "unfair or unjust taxes and legislative enactments." Sponsors electrical apprenticeship programs; conducts educational programs on cost control and personnel motivation. Represents independent electrical contractors to the National Electrical Code panel. Conducts surveys on volume of sales and purchases and on type of products used. Has formulated National Pattern Standards for Apprentice Training for Electricians. **Founded:** 1957. **Publications:** *IEC Insights* (8/year).

6863 ■ National Association of Electrical Distributors (NAED)
1181 Corporate Lake Dr.
St. Louis, MO 63132-1716
Ph: (314)991-9000
Free: 888-791-2512
Fax: (314)991-3060
Co. E-mail: customerservice@naed.org
URL: http://www.naed.org
Contact: Clarence Martin, Chairman
Description: Serves as wholesale distributors of electrical supplies and apparatus. Aims to serve and protect the electrical distribution channel; maintains several committees. **Founded:** 1908. **Publications:** *The Electrical Distributor* (Monthly); *NAED Newsline* (Weekly); *Performance Analysis Report*. **Educational Activities:** National Electrical Leadership Summit (Annual). **Awards:** Arthur W. Hooper Achievement Award (Annual); Associate Service Award (Annual); Distributor Distinguished Service Award (Annual); Industry Award of Merit (Annual).

6864 ■ National Electrical Contractors Association (NECA)
3 Bethesda Metro Ctr., Ste. 1100
Bethesda, MD 20814
Ph: (301)657-3110
Fax: (301)215-4500
Co. E-mail: neca@necanet.org
URL: http://www.necanet.org
Contact: John Grau, Chief Executive Officer
URL(s): www.ecmag.com. **Description:** Contractors erecting, installing, repairing, servicing, and maintaining electric wiring, equipment, and appliances. Provides management services and labor relations programs for electrical contractors; conducts semi-

nars for contractor sales and training. Conducts research and educational programs; compiles statistics. Sponsors honorary society, the Academy of Electrical Contracting. **Founded:** 1901. **Publications:** *Electrical Contractor*; *Electrical Contractor* (Monthly); *Electrical Contractor Magazine* (Monthly); *Electrical Maintenance Pays Dividends*; *NECA Manual of Labor Units*; *This is NECA*; *Electrical Contractor--Electrical Product Literature File Issue*; *A Comparison of Operational Cost of Union vs. Non-Union Contractors*. **Educational Activities:** National Electrical Contractors Association Meeting (Annual); The NECA Show (Annual). **Awards:** Coggeshall Award (Annual); Comstock (Annual); Industry Partner (Annual); James H. McGraw (Annual).

6865 ■ National Electrical Manufacturers Association (NEMA)—Associated Manufacturers of Electrical and Supplies
1300 N 17th St., Ste. 1752
Rosslyn, VA 22209
Ph: (703)841-3200
Fax: (703)841-5900
Co. E-mail: communications@nema.org
URL: http://www.nema.org
Contact: Evan R. Gaddis, President
Description: Aims to maintain and improve quality and reliability of products; insure safety standards in manufacture and use of products; organize and act upon members' interests in productivity, competition from overseas suppliers, energy conservation and efficiency, marketing opportunities, economic matters, and product liability. Develops product standards covering such matters as nomenclature, ratings, performance, testing, and dimensions; actively participates in regional and international standards process for electrical products; participates in developing National Electrical Code and National Electrical Safety Codes, and advocates their acceptance by state and local authorities; conducts regulatory and legislative analyses on issues of concern to electrical manufacturers; compiles and issues market data of all kinds, and statistical data on such factors as sales, new orders, unfilled orders, cancellations, production, and inventories. **Founded:** 1926. **Publications:** *Electroindustry*; *electroindustry* (Monthly); *National Electrical Manufacturers Association--Publications and Materials Catalog* (Semiannual); *Electrical Standards and Product Guide* (Annual). **Awards:** Bernard H. Falk Award (Annual); Kite and Key Award (Annual).

6866 ■ National Electrical Manufacturers Representatives Association (NEMRA)
28 Deer St., Ste. 302
Portsmouth, NH 03801
Ph: (914)524-8650
Free: 800-446-3672
Fax: (914)524-8655
Co. E-mail: nemra@nemra.org
URL: http://www.nemra.org
Contact: Kenneth W. Hooper, President
Description: North American trade association dedicated to promoting continuing education, professionalism, and the use of independent manufacturers representatives in the electrical industry. Offers

professional development programs in business management and sales training, and offers a proprietary computer system for independent electrical representatives. Sponsors educational programs; compiles statistics; and holds an annual networking conference for its representative members and their manufacturers. **Founded:** 1969. **Publications:** *National Electrical Manufacturers Representatives Association--Locator* (Annual); *NEMRA Locator* (Annual). **Awards:** NEMRA Educational Scholarship Foundation; NEMRA Educational Scholarship Fund Awards (Annual); Thomas F. Preston Manufacturer of the Year Award.

EDUCATIONAL PROGRAMS

6867 ■ Arc Flash Protection & Electrical Safety 70E (In-House Training)
American Trainco, Inc.
9785 S Maroon Cir., Ste. 300
Englewood, CO 80112
Free: 877-978-7246
Fax: (303)531-4565
Co. E-mail: Sales@AmericanTrainco.com
URL: http://wwww.americantrainco.com
Price: $990.00. **Description:** A two-day training course designed to save lives, eliminate injuries, and prevent damage to plants, buildings, and equipment. **Dates and Locations:** Cities throughout the United States.

6868 ■ Electrical Ladder Drawings, Schematics and Diagrams (Onsite)
American Trainco, Inc.
9785 S Maroon Cir., Ste. 300
Englewood, CO 80112
Free: 877-978-7246
Fax: (303)531-4565
Co. E-mail: Sales@AmericanTrainco.com
URL: http://wwww.americantrainco.com
Price: $990.00. **Description:** A two-day course for everyone in industrial plants, public facilities, and commercial buildings. **Dates and Locations:** Cities throughout the United States.

6869 ■ Electrical Troubleshooting and Preventive Maintenance (Onsite)
American Trainco, Inc.
9785 S Maroon Cir., Ste. 300
Englewood, CO 80112
Free: 877-978-7246
Fax: (303)531-4565
Co. E-mail: Sales@AmericanTrainco.com
URL: http://wwww.americantrainco.com
Price: $990.00. **Description:** A two-day course for everyday building, plant, and facility maintenance. **Dates and Locations:** Cities throughout the United States.

6870 ■ Generators and Emergency Power (Onsite)
American Trainco, Inc.
9785 S Maroon Cir., Ste. 300
Englewood, CO 80112
Free: 877-978-7246

Fax: (303)531-4565
Co. E-mail: Sales@AmericanTrainco.com
URL: http://www.AmericanTrainco.com
Price: $990.00. **Description:** A two-day seminar specifically designed to help understand the types, applications, operation, maintenance, and testing of onsite power generation systems. **Dates and Locations:** Cities throughout the United States.

6871 ■ Hands-On PLCs: Operation, Installation, Maintenance and Troubleshooting
American Trainco, Inc.
9785 S Maroon Cir., Ste. 300
Englewood, CO 80112
Free: 877-978-7246
Fax: (303)531-4565
Co. E-mail: Sales@AmericanTrainco.com
URL: http://www.americantrainco.com
Price: $980.00. **Description:** An intensive, two-day course for those needing 'hands-on' work experience with programmable logic controllers. **Dates and Locations:** Cities throughout the United States.

6872 ■ Uninterruptable Power Supply Systems for First Responders (In-House Training)
American Trainco, Inc.
9785 S Maroon Cir., Ste. 300
Englewood, CO 80112
Free: 877-978-7246
Fax: (303)531-4565
Co. E-mail: Sales@AmericanTrainco.com
URL: http://www.americantrainco.com
Price: $990.00. **Description:** Understanding the application, installation, operation, and troubleshooting of UPS systems and storage batteries. **Dates and Locations:** Oakland, CA; Orange County, CA; Baton Rouge, LA; Boston, MA; Long Island, NY; Columbus, OH; Oklahoma City, OK.

6873 ■ Variable Frequency Drives (Onsite)
American Trainco, Inc.
9785 S Maroon Cir., Ste. 300
Englewood, CO 80112
Free: 877-978-7246
Fax: (303)531-4565
Co. E-mail: Sales@AmericanTrainco.com
URL: http://www.americantrainco.com
Price: $990.00. **Description:** A practical two-day seminar for maintenance technicians. **Dates and Locations:** Cities throughout the United States.

DIRECTORIES OF EDUCATIONAL PROGRAMS

6874 ■ *Directory of Private Accredited Career Schools and Colleges of Technology*
Pub: Accrediting Commission of Career Schools and Colleges of Technology
Contact: Michale S. McComis, Executive Director
Released: On web page. **Price:** Free. **Description:** Covers 3900 accredited post-secondary programs that provide training programs in business, trade, and technical fields, including various small business endeavors. Entries offer school name, address, phone, description of courses, job placement assistance, and requirements for admission. Arrangement is alphabetical.

REFERENCE WORKS

6875 ■ *"Acing the Test" in Contractor (Vol. 57, January 2010, No. 1, pp. 32)*
Pub: Penton Media, Inc.
Ed: Robert P. Mader. **Description:** A ward winning mechanical system retrofitting of a middle school in Ohio is discussed. The school now operates at 37,800 Btu/sq. ft and reduced a significant amount of pollutants from being emitted into the environment.

6876 ■ *"Advances in Pump Technology - Part Two" in Contractor (Vol. 57, February 2010, No. 2, pp. 22)*
Pub: Penton Media, Inc.
Ed: Mark Eatherton. **Description:** Chinese and Japanese companies have come up with refrigerant based heat pump products that are air based which

will significantly lower the installed cost of heat pump based systems. Some of these newer models have variable speed, soft start compressors and have the ability to perform high-efficiency heat pump operation on a modulating basis.

6877 ■ *"Be Proactive - Closely Review Contracts" in Contractor (Vol. 56, July 2009, No. 7, pp. 19)*
Pub: Penton Media, Inc.
Ed: Al Schwartz. **Description:** Contract disputes can make subcontractors suffer big financial losses or even cause a new subcontractor to fail. Subcontractors should scour the plans and specifications for any references to work that might remotely come under their scope and to cross out any line in the contract that does not accurately reflect the work that they agreed to.

6878 ■ *"BIM and You: Know Its Benefits and Risks" in Contractor (Vol. 57, January 2010, No. 1, pp. 46)*
Pub: Penton Media, Inc.
Ed: Susan Linden McGreevy. **Description:** Building Information Modeling is intended to be 'collaborative' and this could raise legal issues if a contractor sends an electronic bid and it is filtered out. Other legal issues that mechanical contractors need to consider before using this technology are discussed.

6879 ■ *Buyer's Guide & Membership Directory*
Pub: Independent Electrical Contractors Inc.
Contact: Larry Mullins, Chief Executive Officer
E-mail: lmullins@ieci.org
URL(s): www.ieci.org. **Released:** Annual **Covers:** Member electrical contracting firms, electrical manufacturers, and distributors. **Entries include:** Name of company, address, names of principals. **Arrangement:** Geographical.

6880 ■ *"Chicago Public School District Builds Green" in Contractor (Vol. 56, October 2009, No. 10, pp. 5)*
Pub: Penton Media, Inc.
Ed: Candace Roulo. **Description:** Chicago Public Schools district has already built six U.S. Green Building Council LEED certified schools and one addition in five years and will continue to build new green buildings. The district has an Environmental Action Plan that strives to reduce energy usage, improve indoor air quality, and reduce contribution to climate change.

6881 ■ *"Contractors Fret Over Credit, People, Government" in Contractor (Vol. 57, February 2010, No. 2, pp. 7)*
Pub: Penton Media, Inc.
Ed: Robert P. Mader. **Description:** Telephone interviews with 22 plumbing and HVAC contractors reveal that only two had sales increases for 2009 and that overall, contractors were down anywhere from seven to 25 percent. In the repair/service market, the residential sector was holding its own but the commercial portion was lagging behind.

6882 ■ *"The Customer Is Right Even If He's Wrong" in Contractor (Vol. 57, February 2010, No. 2, pp. 12)*
Pub: Penton Media, Inc.
Ed: Al Schwarz. **Description:** Mechanical contractors should note that customers will make a judgment based upon the impression that they form on their first meeting. Contractors can maintain a professional image by washing their trucks and having the personnel dress uniformly. Contractors have every right to demand that employees clean up and make a better impression on customers.

6883 ■ *"East Coast Solar" in Contractor (Vol. 57, February 2010, No. 2, pp. 17)*
Pub: Penton Media, Inc.
Ed: Dave Yates. **Description:** U.S. Department of Energy's Solar Decathlon lets 20 college student-led teams from around the world compete to design and build a solar-powered home. A mechanical contractor discusses his work as an advisor during the competition.

6884 ■ *Electrical Construction Equipment Directory*
Pub: Underwriters Laboratories
Contact: Keith E. Williams, President
URL(s): www.ul.com. **Released:** Annual; Latest edition 2011. **Covers:** Companies that have qualified to use the UL listing mark or classification marking on or in connection with products that have been found to be in compliance with UL's requirements. Coverage includes foreign companies that manufacture for distribution in the United States. **Entries include:** Company name, city, ZIP code, UL file number, and type of product. **Database includes:** Section listing a limited number of trade names or trademarks authorized to use UL certification without mention of company name. **Arrangement:** Classified by type of product. **Indexes:** Company name.

6885 ■ *"EPA to Tighten Energy Star Standards for 2011" in Contractor (Vol. 56, September 2009, No. 9, pp. 6)*
Pub: Penton Media, Inc.
Description: United States Environmental Protection Agency will tighten standards for its Energy Star for Homes program in 2011. The green trend in the construction industry has been cited as reason for the plan. The agency is adding requirements for energy-efficient equipment and building techniques.

6886 ■ *"Federal Buildings to Achieve Zero-Net Energy by 2030" in Contractor (Vol. 56, December 2009, No. 12, pp. 5)*
Pub: Penton Media, Inc.
Ed: Candace Roulo. **Description:** United States president Barack Obama has issued sustainable goals for federal buildings. Federal agencies are also required to increase energy efficiency, conserve water and support sustainable communities. Obama has also announced a $3.4 billion investment in a smart energy creed.

6887 ■ *"FSU's OGZEB Is Test Bed for Sustainable Technology" in Contractor (Vol. 56, October 2009, No. 10, pp. 1)*
Pub: Penton Media, Inc.
Ed: Candace Roulo. **Description:** Florida State University has one of 14 off-grid zero emissions buildings (OGZEB) in the U.S.; it was built to research sustainable and alternative energy systems. The building produces electricity from 30 photovoltaic panels and it also has three AET water heating solar panels on the roof.

6888 ■ *"Get Online Quick in the Office Or in the Field" in Contractor (Vol. 56, October 2009, No. 10, pp. 47)*
Pub: Penton Media, Inc.
Ed: William Feldman; Patti Feldman. **Description:** Contractors can set up a web site in minutes using the www.1and1.com website. Verizon's Novatel MIFI 2372 HSPA personal hotspot device lets contractors go online in the field. The StarTech scalable business management system helps contractors manage daily operations.

6889 ■ *"Grainger Show Highlights Building Green, Economy" in Contractor (Vol. 57, February 2010, No. 2, pp. 3)*
Pub: Penton Media, Inc.
Ed: Candace Roulo. **Description:** chief U.S. economist told attendees of the Grainger's 2010 Total MRO Solutions National Customer Show that the economic recovery would be subdued. Mechanical contractors who attended the event also learned about building sustainable, green products, and technologies, and economic and business challenges.

6890 ■ *"Hansen Mechanical Performs Boiler Upgrade at Brookfield Zoo" in Contractor (Vol. 57, February 2010, No. 2, pp. 7)*
Pub: Penton Media, Inc.
Description: Hansen Mechanical installed a donated boiler in the Brookfield Zoo from Weil-McLain. The boilers were installed in the zoo's 'The Swamp' and 'The Living Coast' exhibits.

6891 ■ *"Housing Slide Picks Up Speed" in Crain's Chicago Business (Vol. 31, April 21,*

2008, No. 16, pp. 2)
Pub: Crain Communications, Inc.
Ed: Eddie Baeb. **Description:** According to Tracy Cross & Associates Inc., a real estate consultancy, sales of new homes in the Chicago area dropped 61 percent from the year-earlier period which is more bad news for homebuilders, contractors and real estate agents who are eager for an indication that market conditions are improving.

6892 ■ *"The Latest on E-Verify" in Contractor (Vol. 56, September 2009, No. 9, pp. 58)*
Pub: Penton Media, Inc.
Ed: Susan McGreevy. **Description:** United States government has required federal contractors to use its E-Verify program to verify the eligibility of incoming and existent employees. The use of the program is seen to eliminate Social Security mismatches.

6893 ■ *"Major Advances in Heat Pump Technology" in Contractor (Vol. 57, January 2010, No. 1, pp. 42)*
Pub: Penton Media, Inc.
Ed: Mark Eatherton. **Description:** Tax credits make ground-source heat pump technology more economically feasible. Suggestions on how to choose the right ground-source heat pump technology to install in a house are discussed.

6894 ■ *"Minnesota State Park Building Exemplifies Sustainability" in Contractor (Vol. 56, November 2009, No. 11, pp. 5)*
Pub: Penton Media, Inc.
Ed: Candace Roulo. **Description:** Camden State Park's newly remodeled information/office building in Lynd, Minnesota features a 10 kw wind turbine which is capable of offsetting most of the facility's electricity and a geothermal heat pump system. The heat pump is a 4-ton vertical closed-loop ground source heat pump by ClimateMaster.

6895 ■ *"Most Popular Tools? The Survey Says" in Contractor (Vol. 57, February 2010, No. 2, pp. 1)*
Pub: Penton Media, Inc.
Ed: Robert P. Mader. **Description:** According to a survey of individuals in the field, mechanical contractors are purchasing more of their tools at home centers and they are also increasingly working in the service, repair, and retrofit markets. The survey also found that the reciprocating saw is the most used corded power tool. Additional purchasing habits of mechanical contractors are listed.

6896 ■ *National Electrical Manufacturers Representatives Association--Locator*
Pub: National Electrical Manufacturers Representatives Association
Contact: Kenneth W. Hooper, President
URL(s): www.nemra.orgwww.nemra.org/locator.cfm.
Released: Annual; September. **Price:** Free. **Covers:** Approximately 1,000 electrical manufacturers representatives companies. **Entries include:** Company name, address, phone, telex, fax, number of employees, geographical area served, subsidiary and branch names and locations, products. **Arrangement:** Geographical. **Indexes:** Company name.

6897 ■ *"A Necessary Balancing Act: Bookkeeping" in Contractor (Vol. 56, November 2009, No. 11, pp. 22)*
Pub: Penton Media, Inc.
Ed: Al Schwartz. **Description:** Pros and cons of getting a bookkeeper or a certified public accountant for the subcontractor are discussed. A bookkeeper can help a subcontractor get new accounting software up and running while an accountant will more than likely keep the books at regular intervals throughout the year.

6898 ■ *"New Hydronic Heating Technologies Work" in Contractor (Vol. 57, January 2010, No. 1, pp. 58)*
Pub: Penton Media, Inc.
Ed: Carol Fey. **Description:** Technology behind hydronic heating systems is reviewed. These technologies include radiant and geothermal hydronic heating. System requirements for installing these greener forms of heating are discussed.

6899 ■ *"San Diego Museum Receives LEED Certification" in Contractor (Vol. 57, January 2010, No. 1, pp. 14)*
Pub: Penton Media, Inc.
Description: San Diego Natural History Museum received an LEED certification for existing buildings. The certification process began when they committed to displaying the Dead Sea Scrolls in 2007 and they had to upgrade their buildings' air quality and to control for air moisture, temperature, and volume. They reduced their energy consumption by upwards of 20 percent.

6900 ■ *"Selling a Job When There's Buyer's Remorse" in Contractor (Vol. 56, December 2009, No. 12, pp. 37)*
Pub: Penton Media, Inc.
Ed: H. Kent Craig. **Description:** Advice on how contractors should manage low-profit jobs in the United States are presented. Efforts should be made to try and find at least one quality field foreman or superintendent. Contractors should also try to respectfully renegotiate the terms of the job.

6901 ■ *"Software Solutions Increase Productivity" in Contractor (Vol. 57, February 2010, No. 2, pp. 26)*
Pub: Penton Media, Inc.
Ed: William Feldman; Patti Feldman. **Description:** Singletouch is a real-time data capture solution for mechanical and other contractors that work in jobs that require materials and workload tracking. Contractors get information on extreme weather and sudden changes in the cost of materials. The OptimumHVAC optimization software by Optimum Energy is designed to optimize energy savings in commercial buildings.

6902 ■ *"Sustainability Is Top Priority for GreenTown Chicago" in Contractor (Vol. 56, November 2009, No. 11, pp. 1)*
Pub: Penton Media, Inc.
Ed: Candace Roulo. **Description:** GreenTown Chicago 2009 conference tackled energy-efficient practices and technologies, green design and building, and sustainable policies. Water conservation was also a topic at the conference and one mayor who made a presentation said that reducing the water loss in the system is a priority in the city's endeavor.

6903 ■ *"Synthetic Drywall Rots Mechanical Parts" in Contractor (Vol. 56, December 2009, No. 12, pp. 50)*
Pub: Penton Media, Inc.
Ed: Bob Mader. **Description:** Chinese-made synthetic drywalls have been found to corrode mechanical and electrical products in homes. Drywalls always contain a certain amount of sulfur. The hydrogen sulfide gas component of synthetic drywalls causes copper and silver sulfide corrosion.

6904 ■ *"Tracking Your Fleet Can Increase Bottom Line" in Contractor (Vol. 56, November 2009, No. 11, pp. 26)*
Pub: Penton Media, Inc.
Ed: Candace Roulo. **Description:** GPS fleet management system can help boost a contractor's profits, employee productivity, and efficiency. These are available as a handheld device or a cell phone that employees carry around or as a piece of hardware installed in a vehicle. These lets managers track assets and communicate with employees about jobs.

6905 ■ *"Trade Craft: Take Pride in Your Trade, Demand Excellence" in Contractor (Vol. 56, October 2009, No. 10, pp. 24)*
Pub: Penton Media, Inc.
Ed: Al Schwartz. **Description:** There is a need for teaching, developing, and encouraging trade craft. An apprentice plumber is not only versed in the mechanical aspects of the trade but he also has a working knowledge of algebra, trigonometry, chemistry, and thermal dynamics. Contractors should be demanding on their personnel regarding their trade craft and should only keep and train the very best people they can hire.

6906 ■ *"Yudelson Challenges San Antonio Groups" in Contractor (Vol. 56, October 2009,*

No. 10, pp. 6)
Pub: Penton Media, Inc.
Description: Green building consultant and author Jerry Yudelson made a presentation for the Central Texas Green Building Council and Leadership San Antonio where he discussed the European approach to sustainability and how it can be used for designing green buildings. Yudelson also discussed how to use sustainable practices for planning 25 years into the future.

STATISTICAL SOURCES

6907 ■ *RMA Annual Statement Studies*
Pub: Risk Management Association
Contact: Kevin M. Blakey, President
Released: Annual. **Price:** $175.00 2006-07 edition, $105.00. **Description:** Contains composite balance sheets and income statements for more than 360 industries, including the accounting, auditing, and bookkeeping industries. Also contains five years of comparative historical data for discerning trends. Includes 16 commonly used ratios, computed for most of the size groupings for nearly every industry.

TRADE PERIODICALS

6908 ■ *Electrical Contractor*
Pub: National Electrical Contractors Association
Contact: John Grau, Chief Executive Officer
URL(s): www.ecmag.com. **Ed:** Andrea Klee. **Released:** Monthly **Price:** $5, Single issue.

6909 ■ *Electrical Wholesaling*
Pub: Penton
Contact: Raymond E. Maloney, President
URL(s): ewweb.com. **Released:** Monthly

6910 ■ *IAEI News*
Pub: International Association of Electrical Inspectors
Contact: David Clements, Chief Executive Officer
Ed: P.H. Cox, Editor. **Released:** Bimonthly. **Price:** Included in membership; $50, nonmembers. **Description:** Concerned with electrical safety and inspection. Supplies explanations of the more complicated sections of the National Electrical Code and information on electrical devices, materials, and methods. Provides news of the Association and of related organizations. Recurring features include editorials, news of research, articles on sections of the National Electrical Code (NEC), code editors responses to questions on NEC, letters to the editor, listings of new publications and products, and a calendar of events.

6911 ■ *TED The Electrical Distributor Magazine: Official Publication of the National Association of Electrical Distributors (NAED)*
Pub: National Association of Electrical Distributors Inc.
URL(s): www.tedmag.com. **Ed:** Misty Byers. **Released:** Monthly **Price:** $32, Individuals; $45, Other countries.

VIDEOCASSETTES/ AUDIOCASSETTES

6912 ■ *Low Voltage Safety*
Film Library/National Safety Council California Chapter
4553 Glencoe Ave., Ste. 150
Marina Del Rey, CA 90292
Ph: (310)827-9781
Free: 800-421-9585
Fax: (310)827-9861
Co. E-mail: California@nsc.org
URL: http://www.nsc.org/nsc_near_you/FindYourLocalChapter/Pages/California.aspx
Released: 198?. **Description:** This tape describes the safety precautions electricians should take when working with 660 volts or less. **Availability:** VHS; 3/4 U.

TRADE SHOWS AND CONVENTIONS

6913 ■ North Carolina RV and Camping Show
Affinity Events/Affinity, Inc.
6420 Sycamore Ln., Ste. 100
Maple Grove, MN 55369
Free: 800-848-6247
Fax: (763)383-4499
URL: http://www.agievents.com
URL(s): www.afievents.com. **Price:** $10, adults. **Frequency:** Annual. **Audience:** RV and camping enthusiasts. **Principal Exhibits:** Motor home, mini-homes, travel trailers, folding campers, and fifth wheels.

6914 ■ Upper Midwest Electrical Expo
North Central Electrical League
2901 Metro Dr., Ste. 203
Bloomington, MN 55425-1556
Ph: (952)854-4405
Free: 800-925-4985
URL: http://www.ncel.org
URL(s): www.ncel.org. **Frequency:** Biennial. **Audience:** Electrical contractors, distributors, utilities, industrial plant engineers, consulting engineers, and purchasing agents. **Principal Exhibits:** Electrical equipment, supplies, and services. **Dates and Locations:** , Convention Center.

CONSULTANTS

6915 ■ Environmental & Engineering Services Inc.
687 NW 5th St.
Corvallis, OR 97330
Ph: (541)754-1062
Fax: (541)753-3948
Co. E-mail: kelly.guenther@eesinet.com
URL: http://www.eesinet.com
Contact: Steve Barney, Principal
Scope: Provider of mechanical, electrical engineering and commissioning services, with a special emphasis in renovation and energy upgrades. Offers a wide range of HVAC, electrical and controls engineering services including feasibility assessments, master planning, budgeting, cost analysis, design, computer aided drafting, energy use modeling, facility management and construction management. **Founded:** 1979.

6916 ■ GHT Ltd.
1010 N Glebe Rd., Ste. 200
Arlington, VA 22201-4749
Ph: (703)243-1200
Fax: (703)276-1376
Co. E-mail: ght@ghtltd.com
URL: http://www.ghtltd.com
Contact: Robert M. Menuet, Principal
E-mail: rmenuet@ghtltd.com
Scope: Provider of design services in mechanical engineering. Offers telecommunications and security engineering services. Provides life safety engineering services and utilities planning services. Provides estimates of life expectancy and replacement or upgrade costs for mechanical and electrical equipment and systems. **Founded:** 1965. **Publications:**

"Critical spaces keep the pace of business humming," May, 2004; "To avoid staticlater, hire right telecom consultant," Oct, 2007. **Special Services:** LEED®.

6917 ■ Lundquist, Killeen, Potvin and Bender Inc.—LKPB Engineers Inc.
1935 W County Road B2, Ste. 300
Saint Paul, MN 55113-2722
Ph: (651)633-1223
Fax: (651)633-1355
Co. E-mail: nbart@lkpb.com
URL: http://www.lkpb.com
Contact: Allen V. Theisen, Manager
Scope: Provider of services in heating, ventilation, plumbing, piping, refrigeration, air conditioning, fire protection, lighting design and fixture selection, communications, electrical power distribution, security, life safety system design, energy conservation analysis, design and implementation. **Founded:** 1969.

FRANCHISES AND BUSINESS OPPORTUNITIES

6918 ■ Handyman Connection
Mamar, Inc.
10250 Alliance Rd., Ste.100
Cincinnati, OH 45242
Ph: (513)771-3003
Free: 800-466-5530
Fax: (513)771-6439
Co. E-mail: soaks@handymanconnection.com
URL: http://www.handymanconnection.com
Description: Small to medium home repairs and remodeling. **No. of Franchise Units:** 160. **No. of Company-Owned Units:** 1. **Founded:** 1990.. **Franchised:** 1993. **Equity Capital Needed:** $90,000-$125,000. **Franchise Fee:** $25,000-$40,000. **Training:** 2 weeks at corporate training center and 1 week grand opening onsite.

6919 ■ Mr. Electric
The Dwywer Group
Franchise Sales
1020 N University Parks Dr.
Waco, TX 76707
Free: 800-805-0575
Fax: (800)378-9480
Description: Residential and commercial electrical repair and service franchise. **No. of Franchise Units:** 165. **Franchised:** 1994. **Equity Capital Needed:** $73,400-$171,000 total investment. **Franchise Fee:** $28,000. **Financial Assistance:** Yes. **Training:** Complete management, marketing sales and start-up training, with annual national conferences, regional training and ongoing support.

6920 ■ Mr. Electric, Canada
1010 N. University Dr.
Waco, TX 76707
Ph: (800)805-0575
Free: 800-483-5809
Co. E-mail: ronnie.musick@dwyergroup.com
URL: http://www.mrelectric.com
Description: Residential and commercial electrical repair, installation, and maintenance and services. **No. of Franchise Units:** 27. **Founded:** 1994.. **Franchised:** 1994. **Equity Capital Needed:** $35,000 investment required; $35,000 start-up capital re-

quired. **Franchise Fee:** $26,000, per $100,000 population. **Training:** Initial, onsite, intranet and ongoing support.

LIBRARIES

6921 ■ IEEE Information Center
445 Hoes Ln.
Piscataway, NJ 08855-1331
Fax: (732)981-1209
Co. E-mail: library@ieee.org
URL: http://www.ieee.org
Contact: Sherry Markowitz, Librarian
Scope: Electrical and electronic engineering, computer science. **Services:** Center open to IEEE members and staff. **Founded:** 1980.

6922 ■ Intertek Testing Services - Warnock Hersey Library
1500 Brigantine Dr.
Coquitlam, BC, Canada V3K 7C1
Ph: (604)520-3321
Fax: (604)524-9186
Co. E-mail: lawrence.gibson@intertek.com
URL: http://www.intertek.com/
Scope: Building codes, electrical codes, plumbing codes, standards. **Services:** Library open to potential clients at librarian's discretion. **Holdings:** Standards; codes; handbooks; manuals; directories. **Subscriptions:** 20 journals and other serials.

6923 ■ James Madison University - Carrier Library - Special Collections
MSC 1704, rm. 207
880 Madison Dr.
Harrisonburg, VA 22807
Ph: (540)568-3612
Fax: (540)568-3405
Co. E-mail: library-special@jmu.edu
URL: http://www.lib.jmu.edu/special
Contact: Tracy Harter, Librarian, Special Collections
Scope: Central Shenandoah Valley region. **Services:** Limited copying; scanning; faxing; manuscript finding aids; Library open to the public. **Founded:** 1982. **Holdings:** 4482 books; 100 manuscript collections; 2000 photographs. **Subscriptions:** 89 journals and other serials; 20 newspapers. **Telecommunication Services:** harterts@jmu.edu; merkeljm@jmu.edu.

RESEARCH CENTERS

6924 ■ Tennessee Technological University - Center for Energy Systems Research (CESR)
1020 Stadium Dr., Box 5032
Cookeville, TN 38505
Ph: (931)372-3615
Fax: (931)372-6369
Co. E-mail: deivy@tntech.edu
URL: http://www.tntech.edu/cesr/home
Contact: Prof. Subramaniam Deivanayagam, Director (Acting)
Services: Third party review of technical issues. **Founded:** 1985. **Publications:** *CESR Annual report*. **Awards:** CESR Graduate research assistantships.

ASSOCIATIONS AND OTHER ORGANIZATIONS

6925 ■ American Lighting Association (ALA)
2050 N Stemmons Fwy., Unit 100
Dallas, TX 75207-3206
Ph: (214)698-9898
Free: 800-605-4448
Fax: (214)698-9899
Co. E-mail: skelley@americanlightingassoc.com
URL: http://www.americanlightingassoc.com
Contact: Richard D. Upton, President
E-mail: dupton@americanlightingassoc.com
Description: Manufacturers, manufacturers' representatives, distributors, and retailers of residential lighting fixtures, portable lamps, component parts, accessories, and bulbs. Trains and certifies lighting consultants; conducts showroom sales seminars; disseminates marketing and merchandising information. Compiles statistics. **Founded:** 1945. **Publications:** *American Lighting Association--Membership Directory* (Annual); *Light Up Your Kitchen and Bath*; *Lighting Your Life*; *Lightrays* (Bimonthly). **Educational Activities:** American Lighting Association Workshop (Annual). **Awards:** Hall of Fame Award; Pillars of the Industry (Annual). **Telecommunication Services:** webmaster@americanlightingassoc.com; dupton@americanlightingassoc.com.

6926 ■ International Association of Lighting Designers (IALD)
440 N Wells St., Ste. 210
Chicago, IL 60654
Ph: (312)527-3677
Fax: (312)527-3680
Co. E-mail: iald@iald.org
URL: http://www.iald.org
Contact: Kevin Theobald, President
Description: Represents professionals, educators, students, and others working in the field of lighting design worldwide. Promotes the benefits of quality lighting design and emphasizes the potential impact of lighting on architectural design and environmental quality. Furthers professional standards of lighting designers and seeks to increase their function in the interior design industry. Sponsors national awards program, summer intern program for qualified college students interested in lighting design as a profession, and career development lectures and seminars. **Scope:** lighting. **Founded:** 1969. **Subscriptions:** periodicals. **Publications:** *e-Reflections* (Monthly); *International Association of Lighting Designers--Membership Directory* (Annual); *Why Hire an IALD Lighting Designer.* **Educational Activities:** Lightfair International (Annual). **Awards:** IALD Award (Annual); IALD Scholarship (Annual); Lighting Design Awards; IALD Education Trust Scholarship Program.

6927 ■ National Association of Independent Lighting Distributors (NAILD)
2207 Elmwood Ave.
Buffalo, NY 14216-1009
Ph: (716)875-3670
Fax: (716)875-0734
Co. E-mail: info@naild.org
URL: http://www.naild.org
Contact: Linda Daniel, Administrator
Description: Distributors of specialized lighting products; vendor members are manufacturers and suppliers of lighting goods. Increases effectiveness and profitability through educational programs. Makes available information on the distribution of lighting products develop marketing techniques through an exchange of ideas. Develops methods of exchanging slow-moving inventory among members. Shares solutions to supply and distribution problems. Sponsors educational programs in the areas of accounting, finance, inventory control, general management, personnel training, and product cost analysis. **Scope:** motivational materials. **Founded:** 1977.

6928 ■ National Lighting Bureau (NLB)
8811 Colesville Rd., Ste. G106
Silver Spring, MD 20910
Ph: (301)587-9572
Fax: (301)589-2017
Co. E-mail: info@nlb.org
URL: http://www.nlb.org
Contact: Howard P. Lewis, Chairman
Description: Information source sponsored by trade associations, professional societies, manufacturers, utilities, and agencies of the federal government. Focuses on High-Benefit lighting (tm). Does not promote any specific form of lighting or brand name component. **Founded:** 1976. **Awards:** High-Benefit Lighting Awards (Annual).

REFERENCE WORKS

6929 ■ American Lighting Association--Membership Directory
Pub: American Lighting Association
Contact: Richard D. Upton, President
E-mail: dupton@americanlightingassoc.com
URL(s): www.americanlightingassoc.com. **Released:** Annual; January/February; latest edition 2012. **Covers:** about 110 member manufacturers of lighting fixtures, portable lamps, accessories, components, and bulbs; 720 retail lighting showrooms, 220 manufacturing representative firms, 50 component manufacturing firms. **Entries include:** Company name, address, phone, name and title of chief executive or contact. **Arrangement:** Classified. **Indexes:** Classified by manufacturer; regional manufacturing representatives.

6930 ■ Home Lighting & Accessories--Suppliers Directory Issue
Pub: Doctorow Communications Inc.
Contact: Abbie Liehr, Director
E-mail: abbiel@homelighting.com
URL(s): www.homelighting.com. **Released:** Semiannual **Price:** $15, U.S., Canada, and Mexico 1 year; $20, Elsewhere 1 year; $100, Elsewhere 1 year (air mail); $22.50, U.S., Canada, and Mexico 2 years; $30, Elsewhere 2 years. **Publication includes:** List of almost 1,000 suppliers of lighting fixtures, lamp and lighting parts, and other products primarily for the retail lighting industry. **Entries include:** Company name, address, phone and fax. **Arrangement:** Alphabetical. **Indexes:** Product.

6931 ■ "Homing In On the Future" in Black Enterprise (Vol. 38, October 2007, No. 3, pp. 61)
Pub: Earl G. Graves Publishing Co. Inc.
Ed: Sean Drakes. **Description:** More and more people are wanting new homes wired automated systems that integrate multiple home devices such as computers, audio/visual entertainment, security, communications, utilities, and lighting and environmental controls.

6932 ■ LDA--Lighting Equipment Accessories Directory Issue
Pub: Illuminating Engineering Society of North America
Contact: Rita Harrold, Director
E-mail: rharrold@iesna.org
URL(s): www.iesna.org. **Ed:** Paul Tarricone. **Released:** Annual; June. **Publication includes:** List of over 800 manufacturers and suppliers of custom designed and manufactured lighting products, fixtures, accessories and equipment, parts, housings, and instruments; coverage includes Canada. **Entries include:** Name of firm, address, phone, description of products. **Arrangement:** Alphabetical. **Indexes:** Product, geographical.

STATISTICAL SOURCES

6933 ■ The U.S. Lighting Fixtures Industry
Business Trend Analysts, Inc. Industry Studies
Released: 2001-2002. **Price:** $1450.00. **Description:** This in-depth report analyzes the size, growth, and projected growth of the markets for all types of residential, industrial, commercial, institutional, and vehicular lighting fixtures, on a product-by-product basis.

TRADE PERIODICALS

6934 ■ Architectural Lighting: The Lighting Specifiers Magazine
Pub: Hanley Wood L.L.C.
Contact: Patrick J. Carroll, President
E-mail: pcarroll@hanleywood.com
URL(s): www.archlighting.com/. **Released:** 7/yr. **Price:** $48, Individuals; $60, Canada; $96, Other countries.

6935 ■ Home Lighting & Accessories
Pub: Doctorow Communications Inc.
Contact: Abbie Liehr, Director
E-mail: abbiel@homelighting.com
URL(s): www.homelighting.com. **Released:** Monthly **Price:** $15, U.S., Canada, and Mexico; $20, Other countries; $100, Other countries airmail; $22.50, U.S., Canada, and Mexico two years; $30, Other countries two years.

6936 ■ _LDA_
Pub: Illuminating Engineering Society of North
  America
Contact: Rita Harrold, Director
E-mail: rharrold@iesna.org
URL(s): www.iesna.org/LDA/iesnalda.cfm. **Ed:** Paul
Tarricone. **Released:** Monthly **Price:** $48, Nonmembers; $90, Two years; $72, Other countries; $138,
Two years international.

FRANCHISES AND BUSINESS OPPORTUNITIES

6937 ■ Living Lighting
Franchise Bancorp Inc.
294 Walker Dr., Unit 2
Brampton, ON, Canada L6T 4Z2
Ph: (905)790-9023
Free: 866-463-4124
Fax: (905)790-7059
Co. E-mail: franchises@franchisebancorp.com
URL: http://www.livinglighting.com
Description: Retail and residential lighting. **No. of
Franchise Units:** 27. **Founded:** 1968.. **Franchised:**
1970. **Equity Capital Needed:** $270,000-$470,000.
Franchise Fee: $30,000. **Training:** Yes.

6938 ■ Nite Time Decor Inc.
The Decor Group
PO Box 5183
Lubbock, TX 79408-5183
Free: 866-321-4077
Fax: (806)722-9627
Description: Landscape lighting products and
services. **No. of Franchise Units:** 37. **Founded:**
1986.. **Franchised:** 1999. **Equity Capital Needed:**
$37,500-$74,350. **Franchise Fee:** $16,900. **Royalty
Fee:** 5%. **Training:** Includes 4 days training at
headquarters and ongoing support.

**6939 ■ Outdoor Lighting Perspectives
Franchise, Inc.**
2924 Emerywood Parkway, Ste. 101
Richmond, VA 23294
Ph: (800)722-4668
URL: http://www.olpfranchise.com
Description: Design and installation of landscape
lighting. **No. of Franchise Units:** 70. **No. of**
Company-Owned Units: 1. **Founded:** 1995.. **Franchised:** 1998. **Equity Capital Needed:** $69,000-
$102,000. **Franchise Fee:** $49,000. **Training:** 5 days
of training at corporate location and 3 days within
ninety days of start-up in that city. Product & technical training at manufacturing plant shortly after start-up.

LIBRARIES

6940 ■ TLA Lighting Consultants, Inc. Library
7 Pond St.
Salem, MA 01970
Ph: (978)745-6870
Fax: (978)741-4420
Contact: Thomas M. Lemons, President
Scope: Illumination, optics, lighting systems, architectural lighting design. **Services:** Library not open to
the public. **Founded:** 1970. **Holdings:** 150 books;
5000 bound periodical volumes; 250 reports; 75
manuscripts; 150 patents.

ASSOCIATIONS AND OTHER ORGANIZATIONS

6941 ■ Electronic Literature Organization (ELO)
University of Maryland
Maryland Institute for Technology in the Humanities
B0131 McKeldin Library
College Park, MD 20742
Ph: (301)314-6545
Co. E-mail: hdevinney@gmail.com
URL: http://www.eliterature.org
Contact: Helen DeVinney, Managing Director
Description: Strives to facilitate and promote the writing, publishing, and reading of literature in electronic media. **Founded:** 1999. **Publications:** *Electronic Literature Directory*; *Acid-Free Bits: Recommendations for Long-Lasting Electronic Literature*; *Born-Again Bits: A Framework for Migrating Electronic Literature*; *State of the Arts.*

REFERENCE WORKS

6942 ■ "Boom and Bust in the Book Biz" in Canadian Business (Vol. 83, August 17, 2010, *No. 13-14, pp. 16)*
Pub: Rogers Media Ltd.
Ed: Jordan Timm. **Description:** Electronic book marketplace is booming with Amazon.com's e-book sales for the Kindle e-reader exceeding the hardcover sales. Kobo Inc. has registered early success with its Kobo e-reader and has partnered with Hong Kong telecom giant on an e-book store.

6943 ■ "Media Wars" in Canadian Business (Vol. 83, August 17, 2010, No. 13-14, pp. 32)
Pub: Rogers Media Ltd.
Ed: Thomas Watson. **Description:** Canada's newspaper industry has changed considerably with The Glove, under Philip Crawley, positioned as corporate Canada's newspaper of record. However, the National Post under Paul Godfrey is making a comeback by re-launching it as the flagship of a national chain of so-called digital first news organizations.

TRADE SHOWS AND CONVENTIONS

6944 ■ Bologna Children's Book Fair - Fiera Del Libro Per Ragazzi
Bologna Fiere
Via della Fiera 20
40128 Bologna, Italy
Ph: 39 51 282111
Fax: 39 51 6374004
Co. E-mail: segreteria.generale@bolognafiere.it
URL: http://www.bolognafiere.it
URL(s): www.bookfair.bolognafiere.it. **Frequency:** Annual. **Principal Exhibits:** Children's and juvenile books, text books and electronic books. **Telecommunication Services:** bookfair@bolognafiere.it.

FRANCHISES AND BUSINESS OPPORTUNITIES

6945 ■ Wireless Toyz
Wireless Toyz Franchise LLC
29155 Northwestern Hwy
Southfield,, MI 48034
Ph: (248)426-8200
Free: 866-2FR-ANCH
Fax: (248)671-0346
Co. E-mail: franchise@wirelesstoyz.com
URL: http://www.wirelesstoyz.com
Description: Telecommunication products and services are offered. **No. of Franchise Units:** 160. **No. of Company-Owned Units:** 3. **Founded:** 1995.. **Franchised:** 2001. **Equity Capital Needed:** $75,000 cash minimum. **Franchise Fee:** $30,000. **Training:** 4 weeks in Michigan and 5 days onsite.

TRADE PERIODICALS

6946 ■ Staffing Industry Analysts
Pub: Staffing Industry Analysts Inc.
Contact: Craig Johnson, Analyst
E-mail: basin@staffingindustry.com
Released: Bimonthly, 22/year. **Description:** Focuses on the temporary help and employment services industry. Provides information on economic forecasts, employment indicators, finance, labor and market trends, stocks, and statistics.

VIDEOCASSETTES/ AUDIOCASSETTES

6947 ■ From Law School to Law Practice: What Every Associate Needs to Know—The Set
American Law Institute
American Bar Association Committee on Continuing Education
4025 Chestnut St.
Philadelphia, PA 19104

Ph: (215)243-1600
Free: 800-CLENEWS
Fax: (215)243-1636
Co. E-mail: custserv@ali-aba.org
URL: http://www.ali.org

Released: 1989. **Price:** $190. **Description:** Uses brief dramatizations to outline various skills and strategies for law firm success. Complete with study guide. **Availability:** VHS.

ASSOCIATIONS AND OTHER ORGANIZATIONS

6948 ■ American Staffing Association (ASA)
277 S Washington St., Ste. 200
Alexandria, VA 22314-3675
Ph: (703)253-2020
Fax: (703)253-2053
Co. E-mail: asa@americanstaffing.net
URL: http://www.americanstaffing.net
Contact: Mr. Richard Wahlquist, President
Description: Promotes and represents the staffing industry through legal and legislative advocacy, public relations, education, and the establishment of high standards of ethical conduct. **Founded:** 1966. **Publications:** *Co-Employment Guide*; *ASA Membership and Resource Directory*; *Staffing Success* (Bimonthly); *ASA Managers Guide to Employment Law*. **Educational Activities:** Staffing World (Annual). **Awards:** Staffing VOICE Awards; Chapter Merit Awards; Leadership Hall of Fame Award; Care Award (Annual); Communications Awards (Annual); Employee of the Year (Annual); Leadership Hall of Fame (Annual).

6949 ■ Association of Career Firms North America (ACFI)
8509 Crown Crescent C., Ste. ACF
Charlotte, NC 28227
Ph: (704)849-2500
Fax: (704)845-2420
Co. E-mail: bcrigger@oipartners.net
URL: http://www.acf-northamerica.com
Contact: Bill Crigger, President
Description: Represents firms providing displaced employees, who are sponsored by their organization, with counsel and assistance in job searching and the techniques and practices of choosing a career. Develops, improves and encourages the art and science of outplacement consulting and the professional standards of competence, objectivity, and integrity in the service of clients. Cooperates with other industrial, technical, educational, professional, and governmental bodies in areas of mutual interest and concern. **Scope:** outplacement services. **Founded:** 1982.

6950 ■ Association of Executive Search Consultants (AESC)
12 E 41st St., 17th Fl.
New York, NY 10017
Ph: (212)398-9556
Fax: (212)398-9560
Co. E-mail: info@bluesteps.com
URL: http://www.aesc.org
Contact: Peter M. Felix, President
URL(s): www.bluesteps.com. **Description:** Represents executive search consulting firms worldwide, establishes professional and ethical standards for its members, and serves to broaden public understanding of the executive search process. Specialized form of management consulting, conducted through an exclusive engagement with a client organization. **Founded:** 1959. **Publications:** *eSearch Connection* (Monthly). **Educational Activities:** AESC European

Conference (Annual); AESC North American Conference (Annual). **Awards:** Eleanor Raynolds Award (Annual); Gardner Heidrick Award (Annual).

6951 ■ Career Planning and Adult Development Network (CPADN)
543 Vista Mar Ave.
Pacifica, CA 94044
Ph: (650)773-0982
Fax: (650)359-3089
Co. E-mail: admin@careernetwork.org
URL: http://www.careernetwork.org
Description: Counselors, trainers, consultants, therapists, educators, personnel specialists, and graduate students who work in business, educational, religious, and governmental organizations, and focus on career planning and adult development issues. Seeks to: establish a link between professionals working with adults in a variety of settings; identify and exchange effective adult development methods and techniques; develop a clearer understanding of the directions and objectives of the career planning and the adult development movement. Keeps members informed of developments in career decision-making, career values clarification, preretirement counseling, dual-career families, job search techniques, and mid-life transitions. Cosponsors professional seminars; maintains biographical archives. **Founded:** 1979. **Publications:** *Career Planning & Adult Development Network Newsletter*; *Career Planning & Adult Development Network Newsletter*. **Educational Activities:** International Career Development Conference (Annual); International Career Development Conference (Annual). **Awards:** Professional Resource Award (Annual).

6952 ■ International Association of Workforce Professionals (IAWP)
1801 Louisville Rd.
Frankfort, KY 40601
Ph: (502)223-4459
Free: 888-898-9960
Fax: (502)223-4127
Co. E-mail: iawp@iawponline.org
URL: http://www.iawponline.org
Contact: David Slimp, President
Description: Officials and others engaged in job placement, unemployment compensation, and labor market information administration through municipal, state, provincial, and federal government employment agencies and unemployment compensation agencies. Conducts workshops and research. Offers professional development program of study guides and tests. **Founded:** 1913. **Awards:** Freddy L. Jacobs Scholarships; Administrator of the Year (Annual); Award of Merit (Annual); W. Scott Boyd Group Grants; Logan S. Chambers Individual Scholarships.

6953 ■ National Association of Colleges and Employers (NACE)
62 Highland Ave.
Bethlehem, PA 18017-9481
Ph: (610)868-1421
Free: 800-544-5272

Fax: (610)868-0208
Co. E-mail: mmackes@naceweb.org
URL: http://www.naceweb.org
Contact: Marie Artim, President
Description: Connects more than 5,200 college career services professionals at nearly 2,000 college and universities nationwide, and more than 3,000 HR/staffing professionals focused on college relations and recruiting. Forecasts trends in the job market; tracks legal issues in employment, the job search, and hiring practices; and provides college and employer professionals with benchmarks for their work. Provides research and information to its professional members through website, quarterly surveys of starting salary offers to new college graduates, and surveys of employer and college members. Provides members with primary tools for reaching and educating college students through Job Choices publications. **Founded:** 1956. **Publications:** *NACE Journal* (Quarterly); *NACE--Salary Survey* (Quarterly); *NACE Journal* (Quarterly); *Job Choices*; *Job Choices in Business and Liberal Arts Students* (Annual); *NACE Directory: Who's Who in Career Services and HR/Staffing* (Annual); *NACE Directory: Who's Who in Career Services and HR/Staffing t*; *Directory: Who's Who in Career Services & HR/Staffing* (Annual); *National Association of Colleges and Employers-- Spotlight*; *Job Choices for Business & Liberal Arts Students* (Annual). **Educational Activities:** NACE National Meeting (Annual). **Awards:** Innovation Excellence Awards; Kauffman Award; Academy of Fellows; NACE/Chevron Award; Excellence Awards (Annual); Kauffman Award (Annual); NACE Academy of Fellows (Annual); NACE/Chevron Award (Annual). **Telecommunication Services:** customer_service@naceweb.org; amcewen@naceweb.org.

6954 ■ National Association of Personnel Services (NAPS)
6625 Hwy. 53 E, Ste. 410-201
Dawsonville, GA 30534
Ph: (706)531-0060
Fax: (866)739-4750
Co. E-mail: jsacerdote@recruitinglife.com
URL: http://www.recruitinglife.com
Contact: Conrad Taylor, President
Description: Private employment and temporary service firms. Compiles statistics on professional agency growth and development; conducts certification program and educational programs. Association is distinct from former name of National Association of Personnel Consultants. **Founded:** 1961. **Publications:** *National Directory of Personnel Service Firms* (Annual). **Telecommunication Services:** info@recruitinglife.com.

6955 ■ National Business and Disability Council (NBDC)
201 I.U. Willets Rd.
Albertson, NY 11507
Ph: (516)465-1516
Co. E-mail: jtowles@abilitiesonline.org
URL: http://www.business-disability.com
Contact: John D. Kemp, President
Description: Acts as a resource for employers seeking to integrate people with disabilities into the

workplace and companies seeking to reach them in the consumer market. **Founded:** 1977. **Publications:** *NBDC News* (Quarterly); *Giving Us the Tools: A Human Resources Training Package on Employing Individuals with Disabilities; Interviewing Individuals with Disabilities.* **Awards:** Employee of the Year (Annual); Employer of the Year (Annual); Manager of the Year; Outstanding Advertising Campaign (Annual); Product of the Year (Annual); Valued Customer Award (Annual); Employee of the Year; Employer of the Year; Manager of the Year; Outstanding Advertising Campaign; Product of the Year; Valued Customer Award.

DIRECTORIES OF EDUCATIONAL PROGRAMS

6956 ■ *Adams Jobs Almanac*
Pub: Adams Media Corporation
Contact: Gary Krebs, Director
E-mail: swatrous@adamsmedia.com
URL(s): www.adamsmediastore.com. **Released:** Annual; Latest edition 9th. **Price:** $10, Individuals list price. **Covers:** Job listings nationwide. **Entries include:** Firm or organization name, address, phone, name and title of contact; description of organization, headquarters location, typical titles for entry- and middle-level positions, educational backgrounds desired, fringe benefits offered, stock exchange listing, training programs, internships, parent company, number of employees, revenues, e-mail and web address, projected number of hires. **Database includes:** Information on the basics of job winning and writing resumes and cover letters; electronic job search information. **Indexes:** Alphabetical.

REFERENCE WORKS

6957 ■ *"Albany Molecular on Hiring Spree as Big Pharma Slashes Work Force" in Business Review, Albany New York (December 28, 2007)*
Pub: American City Business Journals, Inc.
Ed: Barbara Pinckney. **Description:** Albany Molecular Research Inc. (AMRI) is an outsourcing company that provides work forces for pharmaceutical companies due to large numbers of downsizings in the year 2007. In 2008, AMRI plans to hire several workers.

6958 ■ *"AT&T To Acquire Black Telecom Firm" in Black Enterprise (Vol. 38, January 2008, No. 6, pp. 24)*
Pub: Earl G. Graves Publishing Co. Inc.
Ed: Alan Hughes. **Description:** Details of AT&T's acquisition of ChaseCom LP, a telecommunications company based in Houston, Texas, are covered.

6959 ■ *"Beyond Auto; Staffing Firm Malace Grabs Revenue Jump" in Crain's Detroit Business (Vol. 26, January 18, 2010, No. 3, pp. 3)*
Pub: Crain Communications Inc.
Ed: Sherri Welch. **Description:** Malace & Associates Inc., the Troy-based human resources management company, expects its diversification into nonautomotive industries to help double its revenues this year. Due to the automotive downturn, between October 2008 and March 2009 the company lost approximately 48 percent of its business.

6960 ■ *"Calling All Recruiters: Agent HR Puts Staffing Agents In Charge" in Black Enterprise (Vol. 38, December 2007, No. 5, pp. 72)*
Pub: Earl G. Graves Publishing Co. Inc.
Ed: Chana Garcia. **Description:** Recruiting and staffing agencies are seeing a drop in services due to slow economic growth. AgentHR partners with full-service recruiters who have three to five year's experience-specialists soliciting their own clients, provide staffing services, and manage their own accounts, thus combining the roles of recruiter and salesperson.

6961 ■ *The Career Guide--Dun's Employment Opportunities Directory*
Pub: Dun and Bradstreet Corp.
Contact: David J. Emery, President
URL(s): dnb.com/uswww.dnblearn.com/index.php?page=the-career-guide. **Released:** Annual **Cov-**

ers: More than 10,000 companies on leading employers throughout the U.S. that provide career opportunities in sales, marketing, management, engineering, life and physical sciences, computer science, mathematics, statistics planning, accounting and finance, liberal arts fields, and other technical and professional areas; based on data supplied on questionnaires and through personal interviews. Also covers personnel consultants; includes some public sector employers (governments, schools, etc.) usually not found in similar lists. **Entries include:** Company name, location of headquarters and other offices or plants; entries may also include name, title, address, and phone of employment contact; disciplines or occupational groups hired; brief overview of company, discussion of types of positions that may be available, training and career development programs, benefits offered, internship and work-study programs. **Arrangement:** Employers are alphabetical; geographically by industry, employer branch offices geographically, disciplines hired geographically, employees offering work-study or internship programs and personnel consultants. **Indexes:** Geographical, SIC code.

6962 ■ *"Growing Strong" in Entrepreneur (Vol. 35, November 2007, No. 11, pp. 36)*
Pub: Entrepreneur Media Inc.
Ed: Nichole L. Torres. **Description:** Amy Langer founded Salo LL with partner John Folkestad. The company is growing fast since its 2002 launch, with over $40 million in projections for 2007. The finance and accounting staffing company tops the list of the fastest-growing women-led companies in North America.

6963 ■ *"Impressive Numbers: Companies Experience Substantial Increases in Dollars, Employment" in Hispanic Business (July-August 2007)*
Pub: Hispanic Business
Ed: Derek Reveron. **Description:** Profiles of five fastest growing Hispanic companies reporting increases in revenue and employment include Brightstar, distributor of wireless products; Greenway Ford Inc., a car dealership; Fred Loya Insurance, auto insurance carrier; and Group O, packaging company; and Diverse Staffing, Inc., an employment and staffing firm.

6964 ■ *"Interbrand's Creative Recruiting" in Business Courier (Vol. 27, November 12, 2010, No. 28, pp. 1)*
Pub: Business Courier
Ed: Dan Monk. **Description:** Global brand consulting firm Interbrand uses a creative recruitment agency to attract new employees into the company. Interbrand uses themed parties to attract prospective employees. The 'Alice In Wonderland' tea party for example, allowed the company to hire five new employees.

6965 ■ *"iSymmetry's Technological Makeover Or, How a Tech Company Finally Grew Up and Discovered the World Wide Web" in Inc. (October 2007)*
Pub: Gruner & Jahr USA Publishing
Description: Profile of iSymmetry, an Atlanta, Georgia-based IT recruiting firm, covering the issues the company faces keeping its technology equipment up-to-date. The firm has devised a program that will replace its old server-based software systems with on-demand software delivered via the Internet, known as software-as-a-service. Statistical information included.

6966 ■ *"The Jobs Man" in Business Courier (Vol. 26, December 25, 2009, No. 35, pp. 1)*
Pub: American City Business Journals, Inc.
Ed: Lucy May. **Description:** Entrepreneur Bob Messer, a volunteer for Jobs Plus Employment Network in Cincinnati's Over-the-Rhine neighborhood, regularly conducts a seminar that aims to help attendees prepare for employment. Jobs Plus founder Burr Robinson asked Messer to create the seminar in order to help unemployed jobseekers. So far, the program has helped 144 individuals with full time jobs in 2009.

6967 ■ *"Matchmakers Anticipating Tech Valley Boom" in Business Review, Albany New York (Vol. 34, November 2, 2007, No. 31, pp. 1)*
Pub: American City Business Journals, Inc.
Ed: Adam Sichko. **Description:** Qualified candidates are coming to permanent placement companies after being downsized elsewhere. The top five projected fastest-growing and top five projected fasted-decreasing jobs in the Capital Region are presented.

6968 ■ *Occupational Outlook Handbook*
Pub: Available from U.S. Government Printing Office
URL(s): www.bls.gov/oco/home.htm. **Released:** Biennial; Latest edition 2012-2013. **Price:** $22, Individuals. **Publication includes:** Various occupational organizations that provide career information on hundreds of occupations. **Entries include:** For organizations--Organization name, address. Principal content of publication is profiles of various occupations, which include description of occupation, educational requirements, job outlook, and expected earnings. **Arrangement:** Organizations are classified by occupation.

6969 ■ *"On the Clock" in Canadian Business (Vol. 82, April 27, 2009, No. 7, pp. 28)*
Pub: Rogers Media
Ed: Sarka Halas. **Description:** Survey of 100 Canadian executives found that senior managers can be out of a job for about nine months before their careers are adversely affected. The nine month mark can be avoided if job seekers build networks even before they lose their jobs. Job seekers should also take volunteer work and training opportunities to increase their changes of landing a job.

6970 ■ *"Overseas Overtures" in Business Journal-Portland (Vol. 24, October 26, 2007, No. 35, pp. 1)*
Pub: American City Business Journals, Inc.
Ed: Robin J. Moody. **Description:** Oregon has a workforce shortage, specifically for the health care industry. Recruiting agencies, such as the International Recruiting Network Inc., answers the high demand for workforce by recruiting foreign employees. The difficulties recruiting companies experience with regards to foreign labor laws are investigated.

6971 ■ *"Priority: Business For Sale" in Inc. (January 2008, pp. 28)*
Pub: Gruner & Jahr USA Publishing
Ed: Elaine Appleton Grant. **Description:** Profile of an employment agency providing registered nurses to hospitals and nursing homes. The company began as an temporary placement agency for IT professionals and is now for sale at the asking price of $4.2 million.

6972 ■ *"Q&A With Devin Ringling: Franchise's Services Go Beyond Elder Care" in Gazette (October 2, 2010)*
Pub: The Gazette
Ed: Bill Radford. **Description:** Profile of franchise, Interim HealthCare, in Colorado Springs, Colorado; the company offers home care services that include wound care and specialized feedings to shopping and light housekeeping. It also runs a medical staffing company that provides nurses, therapists and other health care workers to hospitals, prisons, schools and other facilities.

6973 ■ *"Regional Talent Network Unveils Jobs Web Site" in Crain's Cleveland Business (Vol. 30, June 1, 2009, No. 21, pp. 11)*
Pub: Crain Communications, Inc.
Description: Regional Talent Network launched WhereToFindHelp.org, a Website designed to act as a directory of all Northeast Ohio resources that can help employers recruit and job seekers look for positions. The site also lists organizations offering employment and training services.

6974 ■ *"Sign of the Times: Temp-To-Perm Attorneys" in HRMagazine (Vol. 54, January 2009, No. 1, pp. 24)*
Pub: Society for Human Resource Management
Contact: Henry G. Jackson, President
E-mail: hjackson@shrm.org
Ed: Bill Leonard. **Description:** A growing number of law firms are hiring professional staff on a temp-to-

perm basis according to the president of Professional Placement Services in Florida. Firms can save money while testing potential employees on a temporary basis.

6975 ■ *"Staffing Firms are Picking Up the Pieces, Seeing Signs of Life" in Milwaukee Business Journal (Vol. 27, February 5, 2010, No. 19)*
Pub: American City Business Journals
Ed: Rich Rovito. **Description:** Milwaukee, Wisconsin-based staffing firms are seeing signs of economic rebound as many businesses turned to temporary employees to fill the demands for goods and services. Economic observers believe the growth in temporary staffing is one of the early indicators of economic recovery.

6976 ■ *"Temporary Measures" in Occupational Outlook Quarterly (Vol. 54, Fall 2010, No. 3, pp. 36)*
Pub: U.S. Bureau of Labor Statistics
Description: Data on temporary help services employment from the U.S. Bureau of Labor Statistics suggests good news for all nonfarm workers. The data had been rising steadily for most of 2009.

6977 ■ *"What You Look Like Online" in Black Enterprise (Vol. 37, January 2007, No. 6, pp. 56)*
Pub: Earl G. Graves Publishing Co. Inc.
Ed: Marcia A. Reed-Woodard. **Description:** Of 100 executive recruiters 77 percent stated that they use search engines to check the backgrounds of potential job candidates, according to a survey conducted by ExecuNet. Of those surveyed 35 percent stated that they eliminate potential candidates based on information they find online so it is important to create a positive Web presence which highlights professional image qualities.

6978 ■ *"Winner: Private Company, $100M-$1B" in Crain's Detroit Business (Vol. 25, June 22, 2009, No. 25, pp. E004)*
Pub: Crain Communications Inc. - Detroit
Ed: Sherri Begin Welch. **Description:** Profile of Strategic Staffing Solutions Inc. is presented.

6979 ■ *"Work To Do" in Canadian Business (Vol. 81, July 22, 2008, No. 12-13, pp. 22)*
Pub: Rogers Media Ltd.
Ed: Jane Bao. **Description:** Recruiting firm Manpower revealed that 36 percent of Canadian employers had trouble filling positions in 2007, highlighting the labor shortage and the need to bring in more workers. Underemployment of immigrants costs up to $6 billion to Canada's economy every year. Other views regarding Canada's labor shortage and on its economic impact are presented.

STATISTICAL SOURCES

6980 ■ *RMA Annual Statement Studies*
Pub: Risk Management Association
Contact: Kevin M. Blakey, President
Released: Annual. **Price:** $175.00 2006-07 edition, $105.00. **Description:** Contains composite balance sheets and income statements for more than 360 industries, including the accounting, auditing, and bookkeeping industries. Also contains five years of comparative historical data for discerning trends. Includes 16 commonly used ratios, computed for most of the size groupings for nearly every industry.

TRADE PERIODICALS

6981 ■ *AACE Bonus Briefs*
Pub: American Association for Career Education
Ed: Pat Nellor Wickwire, Editor. **Released:** Quarterly. **Price:** Included in membership. **Description:** Contains brief papers by American Association for Career Education members on current issues in careers, education, and employment.

6982 ■ *AACE Distinguished Member Series*
Pub: American Association for Career Education
Ed: Pat Nellor Wickwire, Editor. **Released:** Periodic. **Price:** Included in membership. **Description:** Publication of the American Association for Career Education. Provides information on careers, education, and employment.

6983 ■ *Journal of Employment Counseling*
Pub: American Counseling Association
Contact: Brian S. Canfield, President
E-mail: bcanfield@counseling.org
URL(s): www.counseling.org/Publications/Journals. aspx. **Ed:** Dr. Roberta A. Neault. **Released:** Quarterly **Price:** $150, Institutions non-member; $173, Institutions.

6984 ■ *National Association of Colleges and Employers--Spotlight*
Pub: National Association of Colleges and Employers
Contact: Marie Artim, President
Ed: Mimi Collins, Editor. **Released:** 21/year. **Description:** Devoted to career planning and employment of college graduates. Recurring features include news of regulations and legislation, technological developments statistics, research, trends, publications, and events related to career development and employment. Remarks: Subscription includes the Journal of Career Planning & Employment.

6985 ■ *Occupational Outlook Quarterly*
Pub: U.S. Government Printing Office
URL(s): www.bls.gov/opub/ooq/ooqhome.htm. **Ed:** Kathleen Green. **Released:** Quarterly **Price:** $30, Two years; $15, Individuals; $42, Other countries 2 years; $6, Single issue; $8.40, Other countries single copy.

6986 ■ *Recruiting Trends*
Pub: Kennedy Information Inc.
Contact: Wayne E. Cooper, President
Ed: Joseph Daniel McCool, Editor, rt-editor@ kennedyinfo.com. **Released:** Bimonthly. **Price:** $249, Included in membership; $249, U.S., Canada, and Mexico; $289. **Description:** Provides strategies and tactics for creating and maintaining a competitive work force.

VIDEOCASSETTES/ AUDIOCASSETTES

6987 ■ *Career Moves: A Winning Strategy*
University of Wisconsin-Madison Center on Education & Work
1025 W. Johnson St., Rm. 964
Madison, WI 53706-1796
Ph: (608)265-6700
Free: 800-862-1071
Co. E-mail: cewmail@education.wisc.edu
URL: http://www.cew.wisc.edu
Released: 19??. **Price:** $48.00. **Description:** Discusses various career issues, including the state of job opportunities, employment and training options, and balancing family and work. **Availability:** VHS.

6988 ■ *Day in the Career Series*
The Bureau for At-Risk Youth
PO Box 1246
Wilkes-Barre, PA 18703-1246
Free: 800-99-YOUTH
Fax: 8002620-1886
Co. E-mail: Email is a form at the site
URL: http://www.at-risk.com
Released: 1994. **Price:** $1575.00. **Description:** Twenty-tape vocational series that allows one to explore the various career opportunities within the top 100 vocations of the '90s. **Availability:** VHS.

6989 ■ *Employability Skills Video Series*
University of Wisconsin-Madison Center on Education & Work
1025 W. Johnson St., Rm. 964
Madison, WI 53706-1796
Ph: (608)265-6700
Free: 800-862-1071
Co. E-mail: cewmail@education.wisc.edu
URL: http://www.cew.wisc.edu
Released: 199?. **Price:** $295.00. **Description:** Eight-part job hunting series focusing on the skills needed for career and job success. Includes "Going to Work" workbook. **Availability:** VHS.

6990 ■ *Empowerment: It's Your Career*
International Training Consultants, Inc.
1838 Park Oaks
Kemah, TX 77565
Free: 800-998-8764
Co. E-mail: itc@trainingitc.com
URL: http://www.trainingitc.com
Released: 19??. **Price:** $495.00. **Description:** Part of the "Empowerment: The Employee Development Series." Examines career development as an organizational system and teaches the employee's role in this system. Provides tools and information which will help employees determine and plan their career goals and interests. Emphasis is placed on individual responsibility for career development. **Availability:** VHS.

6991 ■ *From Law School to Law Practice: What Every Associate Needs to Know—The Set*
American Law Institute
American Bar Association Committee on Continuing Education
4025 Chestnut St.
Philadelphia, PA 19104
Ph: (215)243-1600
Free: 800-CLENEWS
Fax: (215)243-1636
Co. E-mail: custserv@ali-aba.org
URL: http://www.ali.org
Released: 1989. **Price:** $190. **Description:** Uses brief dramatizations to outline various skills and strategies for law firm success. Complete with study guide. **Availability:** VHS.

6992 ■ *Inside Business Today*
GPN Educational Media
1550 Executive Drive
Elgin, IL 60123
Ph: (402)472-2007
Free: 800-228-4630
Fax: (800)306-2330
Co. E-mail: askgpn@smarterville.com
URL: http://www.shopgpn.com
Released: 1989. **Description:** Leaders in business and industry tell their success stories in this extensive series. **Availability:** VHS; 3/4 U.

6993 ■ *Shhh! I'm Finding a Job: The Library and Your Self-Directed Job Search*
Cambridge Educational
c/o Films Media Group
132 West 31st Street, 17th Floor
Ste. 124
New York, NY 10001
Free: 800-257-5126
Fax: (609)671-0266
Co. E-mail: custserve@films.com
URL: http://www.cambridgeol.com
Released: 1993. **Price:** $79.95. **Description:** The library can be a powerful resource in locating and landing the job that's right for you. Learn how to utilize this tool to maximize your strengths and minimize your weaknesses. **Availability:** VHS.

FRANCHISES AND BUSINESS OPPORTUNITIES

6994 ■ *10 Til 2- Part-Time Placement Service*
10 Til 2 Franchising, LLC
3151 S Vaughn Way., Ste. 500
Aurora, CO 80014
Ph: (303)909-3868
Free: 877-999-1022
Fax: (303)617-1371
Description: Part-time employment placement services. **No. of Franchise Units:** 19. **No. of Company-Owned Units:** 2. **Founded:** 2003.. **Franchised:** 2006. **Franchise Fee:** $35,000. **Training:** Yes.

6995 ■ *AAA Employment*
5533 Central Ave.
St. Petersburg, FL 33710
Ph: (727)343-3044
Free: 800-801-5627

Fax: (727)343-2953
Co. E-mail: aaaemployment@ij.net
URL: http://www.aaaemployment.net
Description: Employment agency. **No. of Franchise Units:** 11. **Founded:** 1957.. **Franchised:** 1967. **Equity Capital Needed:** $25,000. **Franchise Fee:** $25,000. **Royalty Fee:** 10%. **Training:** Provides 2 weeks-30 days training.

6996 ■ AHEAD Human Resources, Inc.
AHEAD Human Resources, Inc.
2209 Heather Ln.
Louisville, KY 40218
Free: 877-485-5858
Fax: (502)485-0801
Description: Temporary staffing. **No. of Franchise Units:** 7. **Founded:** 1995.. **Franchised:** 2000. **Equity Capital Needed:** Need working capital. **Franchise Fee:** $17,700-$23,700. **Training:** Yes.

6997 ■ Careers USA
6501 Congress Ave., Ste. 200
Boca Raton, FL 33487
Ph: (561)995-7000
Free: 888-227-3375
Fax: (561)995-7001
Description: Staffing service. **No. of Franchise Units:** 7. **No. of Company-Owned Units:** 18. **Founded:** 1981.. **Franchised:** 1988. **Equity Capital Needed:** $129,700-$170,600. **Franchise Fee:** $14,500. **Royalty Fee:** Varies. **Training:** Provides 2 weeks at headquarters, 1 week at franchisees location and ongoing sales support.

6998 ■ CareersUSA Franchise
Careers Franchising Inc.
6501 Congress Ave., Ste. 200
Boca Raton, FL 33487
Ph: (561)995-7000
Free: 888-CAR-EERS
Fax: (561)995-7001
Co. E-mail: tfeldman@careerusa.com
URL: http://www.careerusa.com
Description: A temporary, temp-to-hire and direct hire placement staffing service specializing in clerical, administrative, accounting and light service personnel in varied industries and organizations. **No. of Franchise Units:** 3. **No. of Company-Owned Units:** 17. **Founded:** 1981.. **Franchised:** 1987. **Equity Capital Needed:** $63,625-$189,075. **Franchise Fee:** $22,500. **Financial Assistance:** Yes. **Training:** Yes.

6999 ■ Express Employment Professionals
8516 NW Expy.
Oklahoma City, OK 73162
Ph: (877)652-6400
Co. E-mail: franchising@expresspersonnel.com
URL: http://www.franchising.expresspersonnel.com
Description: Is an international fullservice staffing corporation with three distinct divisions available in one franchise agreement. The franchised offices provide clients with temporary help, full-time placements, and executive recruitment. **No. of Franchise Units:** 550. **Founded:** 1983.. **Franchised:** 1985. **Equity Capital Needed:** $153,750-$242,500. **Franchise Fee:** $35,000. **Financial Assistance:** Yes. **Training:** 2 week initial training at headquarters, 1 week in certified training office and ongoing field training and support. Followed by additional time in new office with assigned field representative.

7000 ■ Interim HomeStyle Services
1601 Sawgrass Corporate Pkwy.
Sunrise, FL 33323
Ph: (800)338-7786
Free: 800-338-7786
Fax: (954)858-2720
Co. E-mail: johnmarquez@interimhealthcare.com
URL: http://www.interimhealthcare.com
Description: Interim HomeStyle Services is the brand for non-medical services provided by Interim Healthcare, the country's oldest health care franchise organization. **No. of Franchise Units:** 267. **No. of Company-Owned Units:** 22. **Founded:** 1956. **Franchised:** 1966. **Equity Capital Needed:** Medical Staffing $100,000-$125,000; Home Healthcare $250,000-$400,000. **Franchise Fee:** $5,000; $20,000-$30,000. **Training:** Yes.

7001 ■ Labor Finders International, Inc.
11426 N Jog Rd.
Palm Beach Gardens, FL 33418
Ph: (800)864-7749
Fax: (561)273-8163
URL: http://www.laborfinders.com
Description: Personnel services. **No. of Franchise Units:** 256. **No. of Company-Owned Units:** 29. **Founded:** 1975.. **Franchised:** 1980. **Equity Capital Needed:** $96,150-$157,320. **Franchise Fee:** $20,000. **Training:** Sales, operation, and owners training program software, and helpdesk.

7002 ■ Management Recruiters International Inc.
CDI Corp.
75 Erieview Plc., Ste. 100
Cleveland, OH 44114
Ph: (216)416-8467
Co. E-mail: contractstaffing@MRINetwork.com
URL: http://www.mrinetwork.com
Description: Management level and general personnel placement, search and recruiting service on an employer-paid, contingency fee basis. **No. of Franchise Units:** 1,128. **No. of Company-Owned Units:** 32. **Founded:** 1957. **Franchised:** 1965. **Equity Capital Needed:** $112,855-$154,345. **Franchise Fee:** $100,000. **Financial Assistance:** Yes. **Training:** Initial training program of approximately 3 weeks at headquarters, plus an additional on-the-job training program of approximately 3 weeks in licensee's first office. Training thereafter as needed. Also assists in securing suitable office space, lease negotiations, design and layout, office furniture, equipment, telephone systems, etc.

7003 ■ Pridestaff
7535 N Palm Ave., Ste. 101
Fresno, CA 93711-1393
Ph: (559)449-5804
Fax: (559)432-4371
Description: Recruiting Agency. **No. of Franchise Units:** 36. **No. of Company-Owned Units:** 3. **Founded:** 1978.. **Franchised:** 1995. **Equity Capital Needed:** $162,000-$237,000. **Franchise Fee:** $32,000. **Training:** Yes.

7004 ■ Sanford Rose Associates
SRA International, Inc.
1305 Mall of Georgia Blvd., Ste. 160
Buford, GA 30519
Ph: (800)731-7724
Fax: (770)904-0359
Description: Employee search service that uses a database of candidates and custom computer software to allow each office to match employees with client openings. **No. of Franchise Units:** 64. **Founded:** 1959.. **Franchised:** 1970. **Equity Capital Needed:** $91,350-$129,680. **Franchise Fee:** $65,000. **Financial Assistance:** Yes. **Training:** Provides a minimum of 10 days of training at corporate headquarters and an additional 5 days of training in franchisees office.

7005 ■ Snelling Staffing, LLC
Snelling Staffing L.L.C.
4055 Valley View Ln, Ste. 700
Dallas, TX 75244
Ph: (800)411-6401
Fax: (972)239-6879
Co. E-mail: info@snelling.com
URL: http://www.snelling.com
Description: Full-service temporary and permanent personnel service franchise. Computerized national matching network. Services inclusive of sales and marketing, accounting and finance, data processing, engineering, health care and office support. **No. of Franchise Units:** 126. **No. of Company-Owned Units:** 54. **Founded:** 1951. **Franchised:** 1955. **Equity Capital Needed:** $104,700-$183,500. **Franchise Fee:** $25,000. **Royalty Fee:** 4.5/7%. **Training:** Provides 8 days training at headquarters, at franchisee's location as needed, and at field location as needed.

7006 ■ TRC Staffing Services, Inc.
115 Perimeter Center Pl. NE, Ste. 850
Atlanta, GA 30346

Ph: (800)488-8008
Description: Provides office support, clerical, word processing, data processing, marketing and light industrial personnel to businesses. **No. of Franchise Units:** 30. **No. of Company-Owned Units:** 23. **Founded:** 1980.. **Equity Capital Needed:** $15,000. **Franchise Fee:** $75,000 minimum liquid. **Training:** Yes.

7007 ■ White Glove Placement, Inc.
We Know How, Inc.
155 Lorimer St.
Brooklyn, NY 11206
Ph: (718)387-8181
Free: 866-862-8994
Description: Staff hospitals, etc. w/nursing personnel. **No. of Company-Owned Units:** 1. **Founded:** 1995.. **Franchised:** 2004. **Equity Capital Needed:** $89,000-$242,900. **Franchise Fee:** $25,000. **Training:** Yes.

COMPUTERIZED DATABASES

7008 ■ *The Ohio JobBank: The Job Hunter's Guide to Ohio*
57 Littlefield St.
Avon, MA 02322
Ph: (508)427-7100
Free: 800-872-5627
Fax: (508)427-6790
Co. E-mail: orders@adamsmedia.com
URL: http://www.adamsmedia.com
Contact: Gary Krebs, Director
E-mail: swatrous@adamsmedia.com
URL(s): www.adamsmediastore.com. **Released:** Biennial; Latest edition 12th. **Price:** $17.95, Individuals Paperback. **Covers:** 4,800 Employers and employment services in Ohio. **Entries include:** Firm or organization name, address, phone, name and title of contact; description of organization, headquarters location, typical titles for entry- and middle-level positions, educational backgrounds desired, fringe benefits offered, stock exchange listing, training programs, internships, parent company, number of employees, revenues, e-mail and web address, projected number of hires. **Database includes:** Information on the basics of job winning and writing resumes and cover letters; electronic job search information. **Arrangement:** Alphabetical.

7009 ■ *Oregon Career Information System (CIS)*
328 E Broadway
Eugene, OR 97401
Ph: (541)346-3872
Free: 800-495-1266
Fax: (541)346-3823
Co. E-mail: cherylb@orcis.uoregon.edu
URL: http://oregoncis.uoregon.edu
Availability: Online: Oregon Career Information System. **Type:** Directory.

7010 ■ *SkillSearch*
15a Brighton Pl
Brighton BN1 1HJ, United Kingdom
Ph: 1273 287 007
Co. E-mail: brighton@skillsearch.com
URL: http://www.skillsearch.com
Availability: Online: SkillSearch Ltd. **Type:** Directory.

LIBRARIES

7011 ■ Employment Support Center Library
1556 Wisconsin Ave., NW
Washington, DC 20007
Ph: (202)628-2919
Fax: (703)790-1469
Co. E-mail: escjobclubs@yahoo.com
URL: http://jobclubs.angelfire.com/
Contact: Ellie Wegener, Executive Director
Scope: Employment networking, self-esteem, starting your own business, setting up job clubs, training facilitators, maintaining a large job bank, providing job-searching skills. **Services:** Library open to the public. **Founded:** 1984. **Holdings:** 150 articles;

books; periodicals; videos on job search; interviews; reports; manuscripts. **Subscriptions:** 4 journals and other serials; 2 newspapers.

7012 ■ Muskegon Community College - Hendrik Meijer Library - Special Collections
221 S. Quarterline Rd.
Muskegon, MI 49442
Ph: (231)777-0260
Fax: (231)777-0279
Co. E-mail: library@muskegoncc.edu
URL: http://muskegoncc.edu/pages/309.asp
Contact: Carol Briggs-Erickson, Director, Library Services

Scope: Reference. **Services:** Interlibrary loan; copying; wireless Internet access; library open to the public. **Founded:** 1926. **Holdings:** 54,000 books; 600 bound periodical volumes; 2000 archives; 20,000 microfiche; 2000 microfilms. **Subscriptions:** 320 journals and other serials; 10 newspapers. **Telecommunication Services:** carol.briggs-erickson@muskegoncc.edu.

RESEARCH CENTERS

7013 ■ W.E. Upjohn Institute for Employment Research
300 S Westnedge Ave.
Kalamazoo, MI 49007-4686
Ph: (269)343-5541
Fax: (269)343-3308
Co. E-mail: eberts@upjohn.org
URL: http://www.upjohninstitute.org
Contact: Randall W. Eberts, President

Founded: 1945. **Publications:** *Employment Research Newsletter*; *Business Outlook for West Michigan*. **Educational Activities:** W.E. Upjohn Institute for Employment Research Conference (Annual). **Awards:** Upjohn Institute Dissertation Award; W.E. Upjohn Institute for Employment Research Grants, for policy-relevant research on employment issues. **Telecommunication Services:** communications@upjohn.org.

DIRECTORIES OF EDUCATIONAL PROGRAMS

7014 ■ *Directory of Private Accredited Career Schools and Colleges of Technology*
Pub: Accrediting Commission of Career Schools and Colleges of Technology
Contact: Michale S. McComis, Executive Director
Released: On web page. **Price:** Free. **Description:** Covers 3900 accredited post-secondary programs that provide training programs in business, trade, and technical fields, including various small business endeavors. Entries offer school name, address, phone, description of courses, job placement assistance, and requirements for admission. Arrangement is alphabetical.

TRADE PERIODICALS

7015 ■ *Recognition Review*
Pub: Awards and Recognition Association
Contact: Lori Warren, President
Ed: Joseph Agnew, Editor. **Released:** Monthly. **Price:** Included in membership; $42, nonmembers. **Description:** Covers news and general information on the awards and engraving industry. Focuses on the association's trade shows, product developments and additions, Association business, and industry success stories.

VIDEOCASSETTES/ AUDIOCASSETTES

7016 ■ *Machine Embroidery*
Nancy's Notions Ltd.
333 Beichl Ave.
P.O. Box 683
Beaver Dam, WI 53916-0683
Ph: (920)887-7321
Free: 800-725-0361
Fax: (800)255-8119
Co. E-mail: customerservice@nancysnotions.com
URL: http://www.nancysnotions.com
Released: 1987. **Description:** Complete instruction is given in how to use your sewing machine to embroider like a pro. **Availability:** VHS.

7017 ■ *Machine Monogramming*
Nancy's Notions Ltd.
333 Beichl Ave.
P.O. Box 683
Beaver Dam, WI 53916-0683
Ph: (920)887-7321
Free: 800-725-0361
Fax: (800)255-8119
Co. E-mail: customerservice@nancysnotions.com
URL: http://www.nancysnotions.com
Released: 1987. **Description:** How to effectively monogram through the use of a zigzag sewing machine. **Availability:** VHS.

7018 ■ *Machine Monogramming & Embroidery Combo*
Nancy's Notions Ltd.
333 Beichl Ave.
P.O. Box 683
Beaver Dam, WI 53916-0683
Ph: (920)887-7321
Free: 800-725-0361
Fax: (800)255-8119
Co. E-mail: customerservice@nancysnotions.com
URL: http://www.nancysnotions.com
Released: 1987. **Description:** Two instructional programs on monogramming and embroidery using the sewing machine. **Availability:** VHS.

FRANCHISES AND BUSINESS OPPORTUNITIES

7019 ■ Crown Trophy, Inc.
9 Skyline Dr.
Hawthorne, NY 10532
Ph: (800)583-8228
Fax: (914)347-0211
Description: Offers a complete line of trophies and awards. **No. of Franchise Units:** 142. **Founded:** 1978.. **Franchised:** 1987. **Equity Capital Needed:** $50,000-$60,000. **Franchise Fee:** $35,000. **Financial Assistance:** Yes. **Training:** Yes.

7020 ■ Recognition Express
Recognition Express Intl.
6290 Harrison Dr., Ste. 7
Las Vegas, NV 89120
Ph: (702)795-4550
Free: 866-838-5888
Fax: (702)795-4551
Description: Name badges, awards, and specialty products. **No. of Franchise Units:** 10. **Founded:** 1972.. **Franchised:** 1974. **Equity Capital Needed:** $82,100-$118,500 total investment. **Franchise Fee:** $29,500. **Royalty Fee:** 4-6%. **Training:** Provides 5 days training at headquarters, 2 days at franchisee's location and ongoing support.

START-UP INFORMATION

7021 ■ *"EDCO Doling Out Capital Along Border" in Austin Business JournalInc. (Vol. 28, August 1, 2008, No. 20, pp. 1)*
Pub: American City Business Journals

Ed: Sandra Zaragoza. **Description:** Non-profit business incubator Economic Development Catalyst Organization Ventures is searching for promising startup companies. The company is targeting startups in green energy, technology and consumer markets. EDCO has partnered with consumer electronics repair company CherryFusion and technology firm MiniDonations.

7022 ■ *How to Start a Home-Based Consulting Business: Define Your Specialty Build a Client Base Make Yourself Indispensable*
Pub: Globe Pequot Press

Ed: Bert Holtje. **Released:** January 10, 2010. **Price:** $18.95. **Description:** Everything needed for starting and running a successful consulting business from home.

7023 ■ *Starting Green: An Ecopreneur's Guide to Starting a Green Business from Business Plans to Profits*
Pub: Entrepreneur Press
Contact: Perlman Neil, President

Ed: Glenn E. Croston. **Released:** September 9, 2010. **Price:** $21.95. **Description:** Entrepreneur and scientist outlines green business essentials and helps uncover eco-friendly business opportunities, build a sustainable business plan, and gain the competitive advantage.

ASSOCIATIONS AND OTHER ORGANIZATIONS

7024 ■ *Between the Issues*
2705 Fern Ln.
Halifax, NS, Canada B3K 4L7
Ph: (902)429-2202
Fax: (902)405-3716
Co. E-mail: info@ecologyaction.ca
URL: http://www.ecologyaction.ca
Contact: Karen Hollett, Co-Chairperson
Released: Quarterly **Price:** included in membership dues.

7025 ■ *Canada EarthSaver*
349 W. Georgia St.
Vancouver, BC, Canada V6B 3W2
Ph: (604)731-5885
Fax: (604)731-5805
Co. E-mail: office@earthsave.bc.ca
URL: http://www.earthsave.bc.ca
Contact: Dave Steele, President
Released: Bimonthly

7026 ■ **Canadian Environmental Law Association (CELA)**
130 Spadina Ave., Ste. 301
Toronto, ON, Canada M5V 2L4
Ph: (416)960-2284
Fax: (416)960-9392
Co. E-mail: theresa@cela.ca
URL: http://www.cela.ca
Contact: Theresa McClenaghan, Executive Director
Description: Protects and enhances public health and environmental quality throughout Canada. Advocates for comprehensive laws, standards and policies. Seeks to increase public participation in environmental decision-making. **Founded:** 1970. **Publications:** *Intervenor* (Quarterly).

7027 ■ **Canadian Environmental Network (CEN)—Reseau canadien de l'environment (RCEN)**
39 McArthur Ave., Level 1-1
Ottawa, ON, Canada K1L 8L7
Ph: (613)728-9810
Fax: (613)728-2963
Co. E-mail: info@cen-rce.org
URL: http://www.cen-rce.org
Contact: Maggie Paquet, Chairman
Description: Environmental organizations. Seeks to advance the projects and activities of members. Promotes ecologically sustainable development. Serves as a clearinghouse on environmental issues; provides support and assistance to members. **Founded:** 1988. **Publications:** *Canadian Environmental Network News* (Annual). **Awards:** Caucus Achievement Award.

7028 ■ *Canadian Environmental Network News*
39 McArthur Ave., Level 1-1
Ottawa, ON, Canada K1L 8L7
Ph: (613)728-9810
Fax: (613)728-2963
Co. E-mail: info@cen-rce.org
URL: http://www.cen-rce.org
Contact: Maggie Paquet, Chairman
Released: Annual

7029 ■ **Canadian Institute for Environmental Law and Policy (CIELAP)—L'Institut Canadien du Droit et de la Politique de l'Environnement**
729 St. Clair Ave. W, Rm. 13
Toronto, ON, Canada M6C 1B2
Ph: (416)923-3529
Fax: (416)923-5949
Co. E-mail: cielap@cielap.org
URL: http://www.cielap.org
Contact: Thomas Esakin, Executive Director
E-mail: thomas@cielap.org
Description: Works to improve legal and economic policies affecting the environment. Conducts research and disseminates information on current environmental policies. Promotes dialogue among governments, the private sector, and nongovernmental groups. Provides educational programs. **Scope:** A not-for-profit research and education organization that carries out research and development of environmental law and policy to promote the public interest and sustainability. **Founded:** 1970. **Publications:** "CIELAP Brief Ontario's Green Energy and Green Economy Act, 2009," Mar, 2009; "Bringing Local Food Home: Legal, Regulatory and Institutional Barriers to Local Food," Dec, 2008; "Ontario's Waste Management Challenge - Is Incineration an Option," Mar, 2007; "A Survey of National Environmental Education and Education for Sustainable Development Laws and Policies: Lessons for Canada," Oct, 2006; "The Formation, Governance, Financing Mechanisms and Mandate of Public Interest, Community based Environmental Law Centers," Jun, 2006; "Hazardous Waste Fact sheet," Jun, 2006; "Innovative Technologies: Focus on Biotechnology and Nanotechnology," Mar, 2006. **Seminars:** Stakeholder Workshop, Mar, 2007; Working Together for Environmentally Sustainable Innovative Technologies, Nov, 2006. **Telecommunication Services:** thomas@cielap.org; millers@lao.on.ca.

7030 ■ **Canadian Institute of Resources Law (CIRL)—L'institut canadien du droit des ressources - Institut canadien du droit des ressourcesInstitut Canadien du Droit des Ressources;**
University of Calgary
Calgary, AB, Canada T2N 1N4
Ph: (403)220-3200
Fax: (403)282-6182
Co. E-mail: cirl@ucalgary.ca
URL: http://www.cirl.ca
Contact: Allan Ingelson, Executive Director
Description: Promotes research, education, and publication on law relating to Canada's renewable and nonrenewable natural resources. Conducts research and educational programs on topics including the relationship between legal systems, laws, and natural resources, and the development of public policies governing environmental protection and natural resources extraction. Provides advice and assistance to legal and policy-making bodies; gathers and disseminates information on environmental law. **Founded:** 1979. **Publications:** *Resources* (Quarterly); *Canada Energy Law Service* (Biennial); *Resources* (Quarterly). **Educational Activities:** CIRL Courses, on selected topics of resources law for the legal, professional, and academic community. **Telecommunication Services:** josaunde@ucalgary.ca.

7031 ■ **Canadian Network of Toxicology Centres (CNTC)**
University of Guelph
Edmund Bovey Bldg., No. 80, 2nd Fl.
Gordon St.
Guelph, ON, Canada N1G 2W1
Ph: (519)824-4120
Fax: (519)837-3861
Co. E-mail: dwarner@uoguelph.ca
URL: http://www.uoguelph.ca
Contact: Dr. Len Ritter, Executive Director
Description: University based toxicology research centers. Seeks to improve human and environmental health through increased understanding of toxic substances and their impact on the environment.

Coordinates research efforts of research team members; advises government agencies and industrial organizations concerned with the release of toxic substances into the environment. Supports educational programs in toxicology at all levels. Serves as a clearinghouse on toxicology and environmental health issues. **Founded:** 1988. **Publications:** *Toxicology Educators Resource Guide for Secondary School Audiences.*

7032 ■ Canadian Parks and Wilderness Society (CPAWS)—Societe pour la nature et les parcs du Canada
250 City Centre Ave., Ste. 506
Ottawa, ON, Canada K1R 6K7
Ph: (613)569-7226
Free: 800-333-9453
Fax: (613)569-7098
Co. E-mail: info@cpaws.org
URL: http://www.cpaws.org
Contact: Eric Hebert-Daly, Director
E-mail: ehebert-daly@cpaws.org
Description: Individuals and organizations with an interest in the preservation of wilderness areas. Promotes establishment of new protected areas; seeks to improve management of existing parks and wildernesses. Develops proposals for reform of public policies governing wilderness preservation and parks management. Conducts advocacy and educational programs to raise public awareness of wilderness preservation issues. Facilitates formation of partnerships linking environmental groups, aboriginal people's governments and organizations, industries, and government agencies. **Founded:** 1963. **Publications:** *Canadian Wilderness* (Semiannual); *Canadian Wilderness* (Semiannual); *Borealis: The Magazine For Canadian Parks And Wilderness.* **Awards:** J.B. Harkin Conservation Award (Periodic); J. B. Harkin Conservation Award.

7033 ■ Canadian Society of Environmental Biologists (CSEB)—Societe Canadienne des Biologistes l'Environnement
Sta. F
Toronto, ON, Canada M4Y 2N9
Ph: (306)585-1854
Co. E-mail: rjstedwill@live.ca
URL: http://www.cseb-scbe.org
Contact: Robert Stedwill, President
Description: Environmental biologists. Promotes conservation and wise use of Canada's natural resources. Facilitates communication and cooperation among members. Promulgates and enforces professional standards for environmental biology practice, education, and research. Conducts professional training programs; sponsors public education projects to raise awareness of environmental issues. Evaluates conservation and environmental protection programs maintained by government agencies and industries; makes recommendations regarding improvement of conservation practices. **Founded:** 1958. **Publications:** *CSEB Newsletter* (Quarterly). **Educational Activities:** Inland Water Resources (Annual).

7034 ■ Canadian Wilderness
250 City Centre Ave., Ste. 506
Ottawa, ON, Canada K1R 6K7
Ph: (613)569-7226
Free: 800-333-9453
Fax: (613)569-7098
Co. E-mail: info@cpaws.org
URL: http://www.cpaws.org
Contact: Eric Hebert-Daly, Director
E-mail: ehebert-daly@cpaws.org
Released: Semiannual **Price:** included in membership dues.

7035 ■ Connector
PO Box 23
Bluffton, AB, Canada T0C 0M0
Ph: (403)843-6563
Fax: (403)843-4156
Co. E-mail: info@recycle.ab.ca
URL: http://www.recycle.ab.ca
Contact: Jason London, Director
Released: Quarterly **Price:** free.

7036 ■ CSEB Newsletter
Sta. F
Toronto, ON, Canada M4Y 2N9
Ph: (306)585-1854
Co. E-mail: rjstedwill@live.ca
URL: http://www.cseb-scbe.org
Contact: Robert Stedwill, President
Released: Quarterly

7037 ■ Currents
6712 Fisher St. SE, Ste. 160
Calgary, AB, Canada T2H 2A7
Ph: (403)221-8360
Free: 800-909-6040
Fax: (403)221-8368
Co. E-mail: tuc@tucanada.org
URL: http://www.tucanada.org
Contact: Jeff Surtees, Chief Executive Officer
Released: Quarterly

7038 ■ Earth Day Canada (EDC)
111 Peter St., Ste. 503
Toronto, ON, Canada M5V 2H1
Ph: (416)599-1991
Free: 888-283-2784
Fax: (416)599-3100
Co. E-mail: info@earthday.ca
URL: http://www.earthday.ca
Contact: Jed Goldberg, President
Description: Individuals and organizations. Promotes respect for the environment. Seeks to raise public awareness of environmental protection and conservation issues. Conducts educational and charitable programs; makes available children's services. **Founded:** 1970. **Publications:** *Earth Tones* (Quarterly). **Awards:** Hometown Heroes Award (Annual); Toyota Earth Day Scholarship Award (Annual).

7039 ■ Earth Energy Society of Canada (EESC)—Societe de l'Energie solaire du CanadaGeoCanada;
7885 Jock Trail
Ottawa, ON, Canada K0A 2Z0
Ph: (613)222-6920
Fax: (613)822-4987
Co. E-mail: info@earthenergy.ca
URL: http://www.earthenergy.ca
Contact: Mr. Bill Eggertson, Coordinator
Description: Promotes the feasible application of geothermal (earth energy) heat pumps for low-grade thermal energy, both as a standalone technology and as an integral part of the Green Heat Global partnership. **Founded:** 1997.

7040 ■ Earth Tones
111 Peter St., Ste. 503
Toronto, ON, Canada M5V 2H1
Ph: (416)599-1991
Free: 888-283-2784
Fax: (416)599-3100
Co. E-mail: info@earthday.ca
URL: http://www.earthday.ca
Contact: Jed Goldberg, President
Released: Quarterly

7041 ■ EarthSave Canada
349 W. Georgia St.
Vancouver, BC, Canada V6B 3W2
Ph: (604)731-5885
Fax: (604)731-5805
Co. E-mail: office@earthsave.bc.ca
URL: http://www.earthsave.bc.ca
Contact: Dave Steele, President
URL(s): www.earthsave.ca. **Description:** Seeks to increase the awareness of the health, ethical, and environmental impacts of food choices. Promotes transition to a plant-based diet for optimum health, environmental sustainability, and compassion. **Publications:** *Canada EarthSaver* (Bimonthly); *Earthsave Canada--Vegetarian Directory.* **Educational Activities:** Taste of Health (Annual).

7042 ■ Eco News
116 Spadina Ave., Ste. 300
Toronto, ON, Canada M5V 2K6
Ph: (416)323-9521
Free: 877-399-2333

Fax: (416)323-9301
Co. E-mail: info@environmentaldefence.ca
URL: http://environmentaldefence.ca
Contact: Dr. Rick Smith, Executive Director
Price: free.

7043 ■ Ecojustice Canada
131 Water St., Ste. 214
Vancouver, BC, Canada V6B 4M3
Ph: (604)685-5618
Free: 800-926-7744
Fax: (604)685-7813
Co. E-mail: info@ecojustice.ca
URL: http://www.ecojustice.ca
Contact: Devon Page, Executive Director
Description: Represents attorneys and others with an interest in conservation and environmental law. Provides free legal advice and representation to organizations and individuals seeking judgments in cases involving environmental protection. **Founded:** 1990.

7044 ■ Ecology Action Centre (EAC)
2705 Fern Ln.
Halifax, NS, Canada B3K 4L7
Ph: (902)429-2202
Fax: (902)405-3716
Co. E-mail: info@ecologyaction.ca
URL: http://www.ecologyaction.ca
Contact: Karen Hollett, Co-Chairperson
Description: Works to develop solutions to ecological problems. Fosters communication between members. **Founded:** 1971. **Publications:** *Between the Issues* (Quarterly).

7045 ■ L'Enjeu
50, rue Sainte-Catherine Ouest, Ste. 400
Montreal, QC, Canada H2X 3V4
Ph: (514)252-3016
Free: 866-377-3016
Fax: (514)254-5873
Co. E-mail: infoenjeu@enjeu.qc.ca
URL: http://enjeu.qc.ca
Contact: Ginette Caron, Coordinator, Administration
Released: Quarterly

7046 ■ Enviro Business Guide
PO Box 23
Bluffton, AB, Canada T0C 0M0
Ph: (403)843-6563
Fax: (403)843-4156
Co. E-mail: info@recycle.ab.ca
URL: http://www.recycle.ab.ca
Contact: Jason London, Director

7047 ■ Environmental Business Council of New England (EBC-NE)
375 Harvard St., Ste. 2
Brookline, MA 02446
Ph: (617)505-1818
Co. E-mail: ebc@ebcne.org
URL: http://www.ebcne.org
Contact: Daniel K. Moon, President
Description: Firms that manufacture environmental and/or energy products and provide environmental and/or energy services. Fosters the development of an effective and competitive envirotech industry for the purpose of enhancing and maintaining a clean and productive environment. Provides a forum for environmental and energy company executives to network with each other and to meet leading members of the academic, nonprofit, and government communities to discuss issues of concern to the environmental industry. Provides business development and educational services. **Founded:** 1990. **Awards:** EBEE Award (Annual).

7048 ■ Environmental Defence
116 Spadina Ave., Ste. 300
Toronto, ON, Canada M5V 2K6
Ph: (416)323-9521
Free: 877-399-2333
Fax: (416)323-9301
Co. E-mail: info@environmentaldefence.ca
URL: http://environmentaldefence.ca
Contact: Dr. Rick Smith, Executive Director
Description: Provides Canadians with the tools and knowledge needed to protect and improve the environment and health; committed to engaging the

public, finding solutions, and protecting the environmental rights of future generations. **Founded:** 1984. **Publications:** *Eco News.*

7049 ■ Environnement Jeunesse (ENJEU)
50, rue Sainte-Catherine Ouest, Ste. 400
Montreal, QC, Canada H2X 3V4
Ph: (514)252-3016
Free: 866-377-3016
Fax: (514)254-5873
Co. E-mail: infoenjeu@enjeu.qc.ca
URL: http://enjeu.qc.ca
Contact: Ginette Caron, Coordinator, Administration
Description: Youth and adult leaders. Promotes development in youth of a worldview conducive to sustainable use of natural resources. Conducts educational and social programs to raise awareness among youth of environmental consequences of lifestyle choices. **Founded:** 1979. **Publications:** *L'Enjeu* (Quarterly).

7050 ■ *For R Information*
127 Wyndham St. N, Ste. 100
Guelph, ON, Canada N1H 4E9
Ph: (519)823-1990
Fax: (519)823-0084
Co. E-mail: mwa@municipalwaste.ca
URL: http://www.municipalwaste.ca
Contact: Sue McCrae, Chairman
Released: Quarterly

7051 ■ Harmony Foundation—Harmony
1594 Fairfield Rd., Unit 15
Victoria, BC, Canada V8S 1G1
Ph: (250)380-3001
Fax: (250)380-0887
Co. E-mail: harmony@islandnet.com
URL: http://www.harmonyfdn.ca
Contact: Mr. Michael Bloomfield, Executive Director
Description: Environmental educators, community and youth leaders, government officials, and other interested individuals. Seeks to ensure the availability of environmental education resources and skills in schools, workplaces, and the community. Works with educators and community leaders to improve environmental programs; develops and conducts leadership training courses for educators and community leaders. **Founded:** 1985.

7052 ■ *Intervenor*
130 Spadina Ave., Ste. 301
Toronto, ON, Canada M5V 2L4
Ph: (416)960-2284
Fax: (416)960-9392
Co. E-mail: theresa@cela.ca
URL: http://www.cela.ca
Contact: Theresa McClenaghan, Executive Director
Released: Quarterly **Price:** C$20.

7053 ■ *Les Naturalistes*
Jardin botanique de Montreal
4101 Rue Sherbrooke Est, Bureau 262
Montreal, QC, Canada H1X 2B2
Ph: (514)252-3023
Fax: (514)254-8744
Co. E-mail: info@jeunesnaturalistes.org
URL: http://www.jeunesnaturalistes.org
Contact: Andre St-Arnaud, President
Released: Quarterly **Price:** C$25.

7054 ■ Municipal Waste Association (MWA)
127 Wyndham St. N, Ste. 100
Guelph, ON, Canada N1H 4E9
Ph: (519)823-1990
Fax: (519)823-0084
Co. E-mail: mwa@municipalwaste.ca
URL: http://www.municipalwaste.ca
Contact: Sue McCrae, Chairman
Description: Municipal waste management professionals. Promotes more effective and environmentally sustainable removal of solid wastes. Facilitates sharing of municipal waste management, reduction, recycling, and reuse information and facilities. Conducts continuing professional education courses for members; operates job hotline; represents members' interests before government agencies and the

public. Sponsors research; compiles statistics. **Founded:** 1987. **Publications:** *For R Information* (Quarterly). **Awards:** Promotion and Education Awards.

7055 ■ Natural Products Marketing Council (NPMC)
PO Box 550
Truro, NS, Canada B2N 5E3
Ph: (902)893-6511
Co. E-mail: crouseea@gov.ns.ca
URL: http://www.gov.ns.ca/agri/npmc
Contact: Dave Davies, Chairman
Description: Producers and processors of natural food products and wool. Promotes growth and development of the natural products industries. Supervises natural product marketing boards. **Founded:** 1946.

7056 ■ *On Nature*
214 King St. W, Ste. 612
Toronto, ON, Canada M5H 3S6
Ph: (416)444-8419
Free: 800-440-2366
Fax: (416)444-9866
Co. E-mail: info@ontarionature.org
URL: http://www.ontarionature.org
Contact: Caroline Schultz, Executive Director
Released: Quarterly **Price:** C$25, /year for individuals.

7057 ■ Ontario Nature
214 King St. W, Ste. 612
Toronto, ON, Canada M5H 3S6
Ph: (416)444-8419
Free: 800-440-2366
Fax: (416)444-9866
Co. E-mail: info@ontarionature.org
URL: http://www.ontarionature.org
Contact: Caroline Schultz, Executive Director
Description: Works to protect Ontario's nature through research, education and conservation action. Champions woodlands, wetlands and wildlife, and preserves essential habitat through a system of nature reserves. **Founded:** 1931. **Publications:** *On Nature* (Quarterly). **Educational Activities:** Ontario Nature Conference (Annual). **Awards:** J. R. Dymond Public Service Award; W. W. H. Gunn Conservation Award; Carl Nunn Media and Conservation Award; Richards Education Award; W. E. Saunders Natural History Award; Lee Symmes Municipal Award; Achievement Award; Corporate Award.

7058 ■ Pembina Institute for Appropriate Development (PIAD)
219 19 St. NW
Calgary, AB, Canada T2N 2H9
Ph: (403)269-3344
Fax: (403)269-3377
Co. E-mail: info@pembina.org
URL: http://www.pembina.org
Contact: Ed Whittingham, Executive Director
Description: Organizations and individuals with an interest in environmental protection and global development. Promotes increased public awareness of environmental and development issues. Conducts environmental research and educational programs; provides corporate environmental strategic management services, sponsors charitable activities. **Founded:** 1985.

7059 ■ Pitch-In Canada (PIC)
Box 45011, Ocean Park RPO
White Rock, BC, Canada V4A 9L1
Free: 877-474-8244
Fax: (604)535-4653
Co. E-mail: pitch-in@pitch-in.ca
URL: http://www.pitch-in.ca
Contact: Misha Cook, Executive Director
Description: Individuals and organizations with an interest in community beautification and pollution control. Promotes reduction of packaging and other refuse discarded in public and wild places. Conducts educational and public relations programs to discourage littering and stimulate community-based clean-up campaigns, including annual Pitch-In Week. Makes available resources and other support and assistance to local antilittering and clean-up projects. Sponsors

research; compiles statistics. **Founded:** 1967. **Awards:** Clean World Award (Annual); National Civic Pride Recognition Award (Annual).

7060 ■ Pollution Probe Foundation
12 Madison Ave.
Toronto, ON, Canada M5R 2S1
Ph: (416)926-1907
Fax: (416)926-1601
Co. E-mail: pprobe@pollutionprobe.org
URL: http://www.pollutionprobe.org
Contact: Bob Oliver, Chief Executive Officer
Description: Works to define environmental problems through research; seeks to raise public awareness of environmental issues through education; lobbies for environmental protection and remediation before government agencies and industrial associations. Focuses on smog and climate change, reduction and elimination of mercury in water, child health and the environment, indoor air quality, and water quality. **Founded:** 1969. **Publications:** *ProbeAbilities* (Quarterly); *Probe Post: Canada's Environmental Magazine* (Quarterly).

7061 ■ Probe International (PI)
225 Brunswick Ave.
Toronto, ON, Canada M5S 2M6
Co. E-mail: info@probeinternational.org
URL: http://www.probeinternational.org
Contact: Patricia Adams, President
E-mail: patriciaadams@nextcity.com
Description: Seeks to ensure that Canadian foreign aid and trade programs make a positive environmental, social, and economic impact abroad. Monitors projects undertaken or financed by Canadian organizations and corporations; publicizes effects of projects judged to have a negative impact on people in developing regions. **Founded:** 1980. **Publications:** *Probe Alert* (Annual); *Probe Directory of Foreign Direct Investment in the United States* (Triennial). **Telecommunication Services:** patriciaadams@nextcity.com.

7062 ■ *ProbeAbilities*
12 Madison Ave.
Toronto, ON, Canada M5R 2S1
Ph: (416)926-1907
Fax: (416)926-1601
Co. E-mail: pprobe@pollutionprobe.org
URL: http://www.pollutionprobe.org
Contact: Bob Oliver, Chief Executive Officer
Released: Quarterly **Price:** available to members only.

7063 ■ Recycling Council of Alberta (RCA)
PO Box 23
Bluffton, AB, Canada T0C 0M0
Ph: (403)843-6563
Fax: (403)843-4156
Co. E-mail: info@recycle.ab.ca
URL: http://www.recycle.ab.ca
Contact: Jason London, Director
Description: Promotes and facilitates waste reduction, recycling and resource conservation in the province of Alberta. **Founded:** 1987. **Publications:** *Connector* (Quarterly); *Enviro Business Guide.* **Awards:** Rs of Excellence Awards; R's of Excellence (Annual).

7064 ■ *Resources*
University of Calgary
Calgary, AB, Canada T2N 1N4
Ph: (403)220-3200
Fax: (403)282-6182
Co. E-mail: cirl@ucalgary.ca
URL: http://www.cirl.ca
Contact: Allan Ingelson, Executive Director
Released: Quarterly **Price:** free.

7065 ■ Saskatchewan Environmental Society (SES)
Box 1372
Saskatoon, SK, Canada S7K 3N9
Ph: (306)665-1915

Fax: (306)665-2128
Co. E-mail: info@environmentalsociety.ca
URL: http://www.environmentalsociety.ca
Contact: Allyson Brady, Executive Director
Description: Seeks to support and encourage the creation of a global community in which all needs are met in sustainable ways. **Founded:** 1970. **Publications:** *SES Newsletter* (Bimonthly).

7066 ▪ *SES Newsletter*
Box 1372
Saskatoon, SK, Canada S7K 3N9
Ph: (306)665-1915
Fax: (306)665-2128
Co. E-mail: info@environmentalsociety.ca
URL: http://www.environmentalsociety.ca
Contact: Allyson Brady, Executive Director
Released: Bimonthly **Price:** C$40, /subscription.

7067 ▪ Sierra Club of Canada (SCC)
412-1 Nicholas St.
Ottawa, ON, Canada K1N 7B7
Ph: (613)241-4611
Free: 888-810-4204
Fax: (613)241-2292
Co. E-mail: info@sierraclub.ca
URL: http://www.sierraclub.ca
Contact: John Bennett, Executive Director
Description: Individuals and organizations concerned about conservation and environmental protection. Promotes development of public policies mandating environmental responsibility. Seeks to raise public awareness of environmental protection issues. Conducts national campaigns on matters including: increased energy efficiency; clear-cutting of forests; health risks associated with pesticide use; protection of biodiversity. **Founded:** 1963. **Telecommunication Services:** membership@sierraclub.ca.

7068 ▪ Society Promoting Environmental Conservation (SPEC)
2060-B Pine St.
Vancouver, BC, Canada V6J 4P8
Ph: (604)736-7732
Fax: (604)736-7115
Co. E-mail: admin@spec.bc.ca
URL: http://www.spec.bc.ca
Contact: Tara Moreau, President
Description: Promotes environmental research, advocacy, and education. **Founded:** 1969. **Publications:** *SPECTRUM* (Quarterly).

7069 ▪ *SPECTRUM*
2060-B Pine St.
Vancouver, BC, Canada V6J 4P8
Ph: (604)736-7732
Fax: (604)736-7115
Co. E-mail: admin@spec.bc.ca
URL: http://www.spec.bc.ca
Contact: Tara Moreau, President
Released: Quarterly **Price:** free.

7070 ▪ *Toxicology Educators Resource Guide for Secondary School Audiences*
University of Guelph
Edmund Bovey Bldg., No. 80, 2nd Fl.
Gordon St.
Guelph, ON, Canada N1G 2W1
Ph: (519)824-4120
Fax: (519)837-3861
Co. E-mail: dwarner@uoguelph.ca
URL: http://www.uoguelph.ca
Contact: Dr. Len Ritter, Executive Director

7071 ▪ Trout Unlimited Canada (TUC)
6712 Fisher St. SE, Ste. 160
Calgary, AB, Canada T2H 2A7
Ph: (403)221-8360
Free: 800-909-6040
Fax: (403)221-8368
Co. E-mail: tuc@tucanada.org
URL: http://www.tucanada.org
Contact: Jeff Surtees, Chief Executive Officer
URL(s): www. yellowfishroad.org. **Description:** Individuals with interest in trout fishing and conservation of riparian habitats and freshwater ecosystems. Promotes the protection, conservation and restoration of Canada's freshwater ecosystems and their coldwater resources for current and future genera-

tions. Conducts educational programs and restoration projects in areas including responsible disposal of household chemicals and other wastes; sustainable fishing practices such as catch and release; sustainable development; purchase and preservation of unique coldwater habitats. Sponsors research and educational programs; maintains speakers' bureau. **Founded:** 1972. **Publications:** *Currents* (Quarterly). **Awards:** Bill Griffiths Memorial Conservation Award (Annual).

7072 ▪ *Walk Softly*
302 Hawkins St.
Whitehorse, YT, Canada Y1A 1X6
Ph: (867)668-5678
Fax: (867)668-6637
Co. E-mail: ycs@ycs.yk.ca
URL: http://www.yukonconservation.org
Contact: Mary Whitley, President
Released: Quarterly **Price:** included in membership dues.

7073 ▪ Western Canada Wilderness Committee (WCWC)
Station Terminal
Vancouver, BC, Canada V6B 3W2
Ph: (604)683-8220
Free: 800-661-9453
Fax: (604)683-8229
Co. E-mail: info@wildernesscommittee.org
URL: http://www.wildernesscommittee.org
Contact: Diana VanderVeen, Chairperson
Description: Individuals interested in preserving wilderness areas, with emphasis on old-growth forests, and their inhabitants. Promotes social justice as a prerequisite of environmental protection in developing regions. Conducts educational campaigns to raise public awareness of environmental protection issues and the dangers posed to the environment by economic development. Works with local environmental groups and indigenous people associations to insure appropriate and sustainable economic growth in developing regions. Maintains trails in unprotected temperate rainforests on the coast of British Columbia. Acts as hub for a global network of environmental groups. **Founded:** 1980. **Educational Activities:** World Temperate Rainforest Conference. **Awards:** Eugene Rogers Award (Annual).

7074 ▪ *Women and Environments*
215 Spadina Ave., Ste. 400
Toronto, ON, Canada M5T 2C7
Ph: (416)928-0880
Fax: (416)644-0116
Co. E-mail: office@womenshealthyenvironments.ca
URL: http://www.womenshealthyenvironments.ca
Contact: Marie Lorenzo, Chairperson
Released: Quarterly **Price:** C$8, /issue; C$21.97, /year.

7075 ▪ Women's Healthy Environments Network (WHEN)
215 Spadina Ave., Ste. 400
Toronto, ON, Canada M5T 2C7
Ph: (416)928-0880
Fax: (416)644-0116
Co. E-mail: office@womenshealthyenvironments.ca
URL: http://www.womenshealthyenvironments.ca
Contact: Marie Lorenzo, Chairperson
Description: Women experts in environmental studies and issues. Works to implement community development projects to improve the environment. Provides a forum for discussion, information exchange, and the conducting of research related to women in the fields of planning, health, workplace, design, economy, urban and rural sociology, and community development. Initiates and organizes community projects. Advocates environmental protection, anti-discriminatory zoning practices, and the development of affordable housing. **Founded:** 1994. **Publications:** *Women and Environments* (Quarterly); *Whitewash*.

7076 ▪ Young Naturalists' Circle (YNC)—Cercles des Jeunes Naturalistes
Jardin botanique de Montreal
4101 Rue Sherbrooke Est, Bureau 262
Montreal, QC, Canada H1X 2B2
Ph: (514)252-3023

Fax: (514)254-8744
Co. E-mail: info@jeunesnaturalistes.org
URL: http://www.jeunesnaturalistes.org
Contact: Andre St-Arnaud, President
Description: Youth with an interest in nature; nature clubs. Promotes interest in nature and the natural and environmental sciences among youth. Encourages environmental protection. Conducts educational programs; maintains speakers' bureau and museum. **Founded:** 1931. **Publications:** *Les Naturalistes* (Quarterly). **Awards:** Benevole of the Year (Annual); Young Naturalist of the Year (Annual).

7077 ▪ Yukon Conservation Society (YCS)
302 Hawkins St.
Whitehorse, YT, Canada Y1A 1X6
Ph: (867)668-5678
Fax: (867)668-6637
Co. E-mail: ycs@ycs.yk.ca
URL: http://www.yukonconservation.org
Contact: Mary Whitley, President
Description: Seeks to protect Canada's natural environment; particularly that of the Yukon region. Encourages the conservation of Yukon wilderness, wildlife and natural resources. **Founded:** 1968. **Publications:** *Walk Softly* (Quarterly). **Awards:** Ted Parnell Scholarship (Annual).

DIRECTORIES OF EDUCATIONAL PROGRAMS

7078 ▪ *The Guide to Graduate Environmental Programs*
Pub: Island Press-Center For Resource Economics
Contact: Charles Savitt, President
URL(s): www.islandpress.org. **Price:** $29.96, Individuals hardcover; $20, Individuals paperback. **Covers:** Graduate study facilities and 160 programs in the environmental sciences in the U.S. **Entries include:** Facility name, address, phone, program name, profile, Number of students and faculty in the program, requirements for master's and doctoral degrees, faculty/advisee ratio, e-mail contact and Web site address, special program features, auxiliary services.

7079 ▪ *Recycling in America: A Reference Handbook*
Pub: ABC-Clio Inc.
Contact: Ron Boehm, President
E-mail: rboehm@abc-clio.com
URL(s): www.abc-clio.com. **Released:** Latest edition 2nd, November 1997. **Publication includes:** Lists of private, state, and federal agencies and organizations, and online sources. Principal content of publication is a history of recycling; brief biographical section; facts on recycled materials; and laws and regulations.

REFERENCE WORKS

7080 ▪ *"21st Century Filling Station" in Austin Business JournalInc. (Vol. 29, December 11, 2009, No. 40, pp. 1)*
Pub: American City Business Journals
Ed: Jacob Dirr. **Description:** Clean Energy Fuels Corporation announced plans for the construction of a $1 million, 17,000 square foot compressed natural gas fueling station at or near the Austin-Bergstrom International Airport (ABIA). Clean Energy Fuels hopes to encourage cab and shuttle companies in the ABIA to switch from gasoline to natural gas.

7081 ▪ *"$40M Fund Created for Big Energy Project" in Austin Business JournalInc. (Vol. 29, November 27, 2009, No. 38, pp. 1)*
Pub: American City Business Journals
Ed: Christopher Calnan. **Description:** A group of Texas businessmen, called Republic Power Partners LP, is planning to raise $40 million in order to launch an alternative energy project. The 6,000-megawatt initiative would generate solar, biomass and wind power in West Texas and could cost as much as $10 billion.

7082 ■ *"2010: Important Year Ahead for Waterfront"* in *Bellingham Business Journal (Vol. March 2010, pp. 2)*
Pub: Sound Publishing Inc.
Ed: Isaac Bonnell. **Description:** A tentative timeline has been established for the environmental impact statement (EIS) slated for completion in May 2010. The plan for the Waterfront District includes detailed economic and architectural analysis of the feasibility of reusing remaining structures and retaining some industrial icons.

7083 ■ *"2011 FinOvation Awards"* in *Farm Industry News (January 19, 2011)*
Pub: Penton Business Media Inc.
Ed: Jodie Wehrspann. **Description:** The 2011 FinOvation Award winners are announced, covering new products that growers need for corn and soybean crops. Winners range from small turbines and a fuel-efficient pickup to a Class 10 combine and drought-tolerant hybrids.

7084 ■ *"2011 a Record Year for New Wind Energy Installations in Canada"* in *CNW Group (September 26, 2011)*
Pub: CNW Group
Contact: Carolyn McGill-Davidson, President
Description: Canada reports a record for new wind energy projects in 2011 with about 1,338 MW of newly installed wind energy capacity expected to come on line, compared to 690 MW installed in 2010. Statistical data included.

7085 ■ *"2011 U.S. Smart Grid - Saving Energy/Saving Money"* in *Ecology,Environment & Conservation Business (October 8, 2011, pp. 3)*
Pub: HighBeam Research
Description: Highlights of the '2011 U.S. Smart Grid—Saving Energy/Saving Money Customers' Prospective Demand-Response assesses residential energy consumers' willingness to decrease their power consumption in order to mitigate power issues. Statistical details included.

7086 ■ *"The ABCs of a Good Show"* in *Playthings (Vol. 106, October 1, 2008, No. 9, pp. 18)*
Pub: Reed Business Information
Contact: Jeff Greisch, President
Ed: Karyn M. Peterson. **Description:** ABC Kids Expo 2008 made a strong showing with products for babies, kids and new/expecting parents. The new Naturally Kids section promoting eco-friendly products was the highlight of the show.

7087 ■ *"Acing the Test"* in *Contractor (Vol. 57, January 2010, No. 1, pp. 32)*
Pub: Penton Media, Inc.
Ed: Robert P. Mader. **Description:** A ward winning mechanical system retrofitting of a middle school in Ohio is discussed. The school now operates at 37,800 Btu/sq. ft and reduced a significant amount of pollutants from being emitted into the environment.

7088 ■ *"Actiontec and Verizon Team Up for a Smarter Home"* in *Ecology,Environment & Conservation Business (November 5, 2011, pp. 3)*
Pub: HighBeam Research
Description: Verizon is implementing Actiontec Electronics' SG200 Service Gateway as a basic component of its Home Monitoring and Control service. This new smart home service allows customers to remotely check their homes, control locks and appliances, view home-energy use and more using a smartphone, PC, or FiOS TV.

7089 ■ *"Adventures at Hydronicahh"* in *Contractor (Vol. 56, September 2009, No. 9, pp. 52)*
Pub: Penton Media, Inc.
Ed: Mark Eatherton. **Description:** Installation of the heating system of a lakeview room are described. The room's radiant windows are powered by electricity from a solar PV array and a propane-powered hydrogen fuel cell. The system will be programmed to use the most energy available.

7090 ■ *"Adventures at Hydronicahh"* in *Contractor (Vol. 56, November 2009, No. 11, pp. 36)*
Pub: Penton Media, Inc.
Ed: Mark Eatherton. **Description:** Part 6 of the installation of a five stage ground-source heat pump for a hydronic heating system is discussed. The heat exchanger will be bidirectional in the plan described.

7091 ■ *"Adventures at Hydronicahh"* in *Contractor (Vol. 56, October 2009, No. 10, pp. 42)*
Pub: Penton Media, Inc.
Ed: Mark Eatherton. **Description:** Design and installation of a solar thermal system for a hydronic heating project is described. This portion has two 32-square feet of flat plate glazed solar collectors that are tied to a 120-gallon reverse indirect DHW heater.

7092 ■ *"AF Expands in New Green Building in Gothenburg"* in *Ecology,Environment & Conservation Business (September 24, 2011, pp. 2)*
Pub: HighBeam Research
Description: AF signed a ten-year tenancy contract with Skanska for the premises of its new green building in Gothenburg, Sweden. AF offers qualified services and solutions for industrial processes, infrastructure projects and the development of products and IT systems.

7093 ■ *"Agricultural Community Implements Green Technologies, Building Team"* in *Contractor (Vol. 56, September 2009, No. 9, pp. 5)*
Pub: Penton Media, Inc.
Ed: Candace Ruolo. **Description:** John DeWald and Associates has initiated a residential development project which uses green technologies in Illinois. The community features a community center, organic farm and recreational trails. Comments from executives are also provided.

7094 ■ *"Ahead of the Pack"* in *Small Business Opportunities (Fall 2010)*
Pub: Harris Publications Inc.
Description: Profile of an organic fast-food business that is carving out a niche that is gaining favor. Elevation Burger is a unique concept offering healthier burgers in sustainable buildings.

7095 ■ *"Allowing Ethanol Tax Incentive to Expire Would Risk Jobs, RFAas Dinneen Says"* in *Farm Industry News (November 3, 2010)*
Pub: Penton Business Media Inc.
Description: Jobs would be at risk if the ethanol tax incentive expires.

7096 ■ *"Alstom Launches te ECO 122 - 2.7MW Wind Turbine for Low Wind Sites"* in *CNW Group (September 28, 2011)*
Pub: CNW Group
Contact: Carolyn McGill-Davidson, President
Description: Alstom is launching its new ECO 122, a 2.7MW onshore wind turbine that combines high power and high capacity factor (1) to boost energy yield in low wind regions around the world. The ECO 122 will produce about 25 percent increased wind farm yield that current turbines and fewer turbines would be installed in areas.

7097 ■ *"Alternative Energy Calls for Alternative Marketing"* in *Indoor Comfort Marketing (Vol. 70, June 2011, No. 6, pp. 8)*
Pub: Industry Publications Inc.
Ed: Richard Rutigliano. **Description:** Advice for marketing solar energy products and services is given.

7098 ■ *"Alternative Energy is a Major Topic at Agritechnica 2011"* in *Farm Industry News (November 16, 2011)*
Pub: Penton Business Media Inc.
Ed: Mark Moore. **Description:** Sustainable agricultural systems were a hot topic at this year's Agritechnica 2011, held in Germany. Germany is a leader in the development of on-farm biogas systems.

7099 ■ *"American Chemistry Council Launches Flagship Blog"* in *Ecology,Environment & Conservation Business (October 29, 2011, pp. 5)*
Pub: HighBeam Research
Description: American Chemistry Council (ACC) launched its blog, American Chemistry Matters, where interactive space allows bloggers to respond to news coverage and to discuss policy issues and their impact on innovation, competitiveness, job creation and safety.

7100 ■ *"ANATURALCONCEPT"* in *Crain's Cleveland Business (Vol. 30, June 22, 2009, No. 24, pp. 1)*
Pub: Crain Communications, Inc.
Ed: Dan Shingler. **Description:** Cleveland-based Biomimicry Institute, led by Cleveland's Entrepreneurs for Sustainability and the Cuyahoga County Planning Commission, are using biomimicry to incorporate eco-friendliness with industry. Biomimicry studies nature's best ideas then imitates these designs and processes to solve human problems.

7101 ■ *"Answers About Commercial Wind Farms Could Come from Downstate"* in *Erie Times-News (September 27, 2011)*
Pub: Erie Times-News
Ed: Valerie Myers. **Description:** Texas-based Pioneer Green Energy is measuring wind and leasing land in North East Township, Pennsylvania. The firm plans to build a 7,000-acre wind farm along wine-country ridges. About 70 turbines would harness wind in order to generate electricity that would be sold into the eastern power grid.

7102 ■ *"Aquarium's Solar Demonstration Project Exceeds Expectations"* in *Contractor (Vol. 57, February 2010, No. 2, pp. 1)*
Pub: Penton Media, Inc.
Ed: Candace Roulo. **Description:** Seattle Aquarium cafe installed flat-plate solar collectors to preheat water and data has shown that the system has allowed them to off-set almost double their expected consumption of natural gas. It is estimated that rthe solar panels will shrink the aquarium's carbon footprint by 2.5 tons of carbon dioxide each year.

7103 ■ *"Are You Looking for an Environmentally Friendly Dry Cleaner?"* in *Inc. (Vol. 30, December 2008, No. 12, pp. 34)*
Pub: Mansueto Ventures LLC
Ed: Shivani Vora. **Description:** Greenopia rates the greenness of 52 various kinds of businesses, including restaurants, nail salons, dry cleaners, and clothing stores. The guidebooks are sold through various retailers including Barnes & Noble and Amazon.com.

7104 ■ *"Areva Diversifies Further Into Wind"* in *Wall Street Journal Eastern Edition (November 29, 2011, pp. B7)*
Pub: Dow Jones & Company Inc. Enterprise Media Group
Contact: Clare Hart, President
Ed: Max Colchester, Noemie Bisserbe. **Description:** French engineering company Areva SA is diversifying and moving away from nuclear energy projects. One sign of that is its recent discussion to construct 120 wind turbines to be located at two German wind farms. Such a deal, if signed, would be worth about US$1.59 billion.

7105 ■ *"Art Institute of Chicago Goes Green"* in *Contractor (Vol. 56, July 2009, No. 7, pp. 1)*
Pub: Penton Media, Inc.
Ed: Candace Roulo. **Description:** Art Institute of Chicago's Modern Wing museum addition will receive a certification that makes them one of the most environmentally sound museum expansions in the U.S. A modified variable-air-volume system is being used to meet temperature and humidity requirements in the building and it also has a double curtain wall to capture summer heat.

7106 ■ *"Attorney Covers Climate in Copenhagen"* in *Houston Business Journal (Vol. 40, December 25, 2009, No. 33, pp. 1)*
Pub: American City Business Journals
Ed: Ford Gunter. **Description:** Houston environmental attorney Richard Faulk talks to the United Nations Climate Change Conference in Copenhagen, Den-

mark. Faulk believes the conference failed due to political differences between countries like US and China. Faulk believed the discussion of developed and developing countries on verification and limits on carbon emissions is something good that came from the conference.

7107 ■ "Austin to Buy $1.1B of Wind Power from Two" in Austin Business Journal (Vol. 31, August 19, 2011, No. 24, pp. A1).
Pub: American City Business Journals Inc.
Ed: Vicky Garza. Description: Austin City Council is set to approve contracts to purchase wind energy from Duke Energy Corporation and MAP Royalty Inc. The city will get 200MW from Duke and 91MW from MAP and the total contract is estimated to be worth $1.1 million.

7108 ■ "Austin Energy May Build $2.3B Biomass Plant" in Austin Business JournalInc. (Vol. 28, July 25, 2008, No. 19, pp. A1)
Pub: American City Business Journals
Ed: Kate Harrington. Description: An approval from the Austin City Council is being sought by Austin Energy for a 20-year supply contract with Nacogdoches Power LLC to build a $2.3 billion biomass plant in East Texas. The 100-megawatt biomass plant, which is to run on waste wood, will have Austin Energy as its sole buyer.

7109 ■ "Award Win Highlights Slingsby's Green Credentials" in Ecology,Environment & Conservation Business (August 20, 2011, pp. 3)
Pub: HighBeam Research
Description: Slingsby, an industrial and commercial equipment supplier, was joint winner with Hallmark Cards of the Baildon Business in the Community's Yorkshire and Humber Long Term Environmental Improvement Award. The firm cites its commitment to reducing environmental impact.

7110 ■ "Babynut.com to Shut Down" in Bellingham Business Journal (Vol. February 2010, pp. 3)
Pub: Sound Publishing Inc.
Description: Saralee Sky and Jerry Kilgore, owners of Babynut.com will close their online store. The site offered a free online and email newsletter to help mothers through pregnancy and the first three years of their child's life. Products being sold at clearance prices include organic and natural maternity and nursing clothing, baby and toddler clothes, books on pregnancy, and more.

7111 ■ "Be Wary of Dual-Flush Conversion Kits" in Contractor (Vol. 56, September 2009, No. 9, pp. 66)
Pub: Penton Media, Inc.
Ed: John Koeller; Bill Gauley. Description: Recommendation of untested dual-flush conversion devices for tank-type toilets in the United States have been questioned. The products are being advertised as having the ability to convert single-flush to a dual-flush toilet. No evidence of water conservation from using such devices has been recorded.

7112 ■ "BETC Backers Plot Future" in Business Journal Portland (Vol. 27, December 10, 2010, No. 41, pp. 1)
Pub: Portland Business Journal
Ed: Erik Siemers. Description: A coalition of clean energy groups and industrial manufacturers have spearheaded a campaign aimed at persuading Oregon legislators that the state's Business Energy Tax Credit (BETC) is vital in job creation. Oregon's BETC grants tax credits for 50 percent of an eligible renewable or clean energy project's cost. However, some legislators propose BETC's abolition.

7113 ■ "Beware of E15" in Rental Product News (Vol. 33, October 2011)
Pub: Cygnus Business Media
Ed: Curt Bennink. Description: Environmental Protection Agency (EPA) set a new regulation that grants partial waivers to allow gasoline containing up to 15 percent ethanol (E15) to be introduced into commerce for use in model year 2001 and newer light-duty motor vehicles, subject to certain conditions.

7114 ■ "Big Energy Deals Power OptiSolar's Local Growth" in Sacramento Business Journal (Vol. 25, August 22, 2008, No. 25, pp. 1)
Pub: American City Business Journals, Inc.
Ed: Celia Lamb. Description: Solar energy projects are driving Sacramento, California-based OptiSolar's growth. The company is set to begin construction of its first photovoltaic project in Ontario. It also plans to build the world largest photovoltaic project in San Luis Obispo County.

7115 ■ "Big Energy Ideas for Our Times" in Canadian Business (Vol. 83, August 17, 2010, No. 13-14, pp. 49)
Pub: Rogers Media Ltd.
Description: Five ideas Canada must consider in the production of energy are explored. These ideas are run-off-river hydroelectric projects, the tapping of natural gas inside shale formation, the water's role in creating energy, the development of a smart grid, and the reduction of energy consumption.

7116 ■ "Bigger is Definitely Not Better When It Comes to Cooling" in Indoor Comfort Marketing (Vol. 70, May 2011, No. 5, pp. 49)
Pub: Industry Publications Inc.
Ed: Eugene Silberstein. Description: Efficiency is more important when installing air conditioning equipment over size of the unit. Details are provided.

7117 ■ "Biodiesel Poised to Regain Growth" in Farm Industry News (January 21, 2011)
Pub: Penton Business Media Inc.
Description: According to Gary Haer, vice president of sales and marketing for Renewable Energy Group, the biodiesel industry is positioned to regain growth in 2011 with the reinstatement of the biodiesel blendersa tax credt of $1 per gallon.

7118 ■ "Bioheat - Alternative for Fueling Equipment" in Indoor Comfort Marketing (Vol. 70, May 2011, No. 5, pp. 14)
Pub: Industry Publications Inc.
Ed: Gary Hess. Description: Profile of Worley and Obetz, supplier of biofuels used as an alternative for fueling industry equipment.

7119 ■ "Blackwater is LEED Golden for Port of Portland Building" in Contractor (Vol. 56, October 2009, No. 10, pp. 3)
Pub: Penton Media, Inc.
Ed: Robert P. Mader. Description: Worrel Water Technologies' Tidal Wetlands Living Machine recycles blackwater from the toilets and sends it right back to flush the toilets. The Technology is being installed in the new headquarters of the Port of Portland which aims to get awarded a gold certificate from the Leadership in Energy and Environmental Design.

7120 ■ "Brown At Center of Local CleanTech Lobbying Efforts" in Boston Business Journal (Vol. 30, October 15, 2010, No. 36, pp. 1)
Pub: Boston Business Journal
Ed: Kyle Alspach. Description: U.S. Senator Scott Brown has been active in lobbying for energy reform in Massachusetts. Brown has been meeting with business groups seeking the reforms.

7121 ■ "Burner Handles Everything From #2 to B100" in Indoor Comfort Marketing (Vol. 70, May 2011, No. 5, pp. 24)
Pub: Industry Publications Inc.
Description: A new oil burner being offered by AMERIgreen Energy is profiled.

7122 ■ "Burning Issues: Four of Today's Hottest Energy Topics" in Canadian Business (Vol. 83, August 17, 2010, No. 13-14, pp. 45)
Pub: Rogers Media Ltd.
Description: A look at four issues dominating Canada's energy industry is presented. These issues are lack of transmission capacity and difficulty in transferring power across provincial boundaries, the management of intermittency of renewable generation, techniques that would clean up the Alberta's oil sands, and the impending massive use of electric cars in North America.

7123 ■ "The Business of Activism" in Entrepreneur (Vol. 37, September 2009, No. 9, pp. 43)
Pub: Entrepreneur Media, Inc.
Ed: Mary Catherine O'Connor. Description: San Francisco, California-based business incubator Virgance has been promoting sustainable projects by partnering with businesses. The company has launched campaigns which include organizing homeowners in negotiating with solar installers. The company is also planning to expand its workforce.

7124 ■ "Caber Engineering Helps to Reduce Canada's Carbon Footprint" in Ecology,Environment & Conservation Business (July 16, 2011, pp. 7)
Pub: HighBeam Research
Description: Calgary-based Caber Engineering Inc. will assist in the engineering design of the Alberta Carbon Trunk Line (ACTL). The ACTL is Alberta's first sizable commercial carbon capture and storage project focusing on the reduction of environmental impacts while being economically beneficial.

7125 ■ "Campaign Not Stirred by Wind Issue in Roanoke County" in Roanoke Times (September 18, 2011)
Pub: Roanoke Times
Ed: Katelyn Polantz. Description: Wind energy has brought citizens of the Roanoke area into activism this year. Comments from citizen on both sides of the issue are provided.

7126 ■ "Canada's Clean Energy Advantages Offer a Bright Future" in Canadian Business (Vol. 83, August 17, 2010, No. 13-14, pp. 38)
Pub: Rogers Media Ltd.
Ed: Don McKinnon. Description: Canada has clean energy advantages in the greenhouse gas emission-free CANada Deuterium Uranium reactor technology and carbon neutral biomass fuels that were continuously ignored by policy makers. Both are proven to significantly reduce emissions while providing reliable, affordable and secure electricity.

7127 ■ "Canada's Largest Bakery Officially Opened Today" in Ecology,Environment & Conservation Business (October 15, 2011, pp. 7)
Pub: HighBeam Research
Description: Maple Leaf Foods opened Canada's largest commercial bakery in Hamilton, Ontario. The firm's 385,000 square foot Trillium bakery benefits from efficient design flow and best-in-class technologies.

7128 ■ "Canadian Hydronics Businesses Promote 'Beautiful Heat" in Indoor Comfort Marketing (Vol. 70, September 2011, No. 9, pp. 20)
Pub: Industry Publications Inc.
Description: Canadian hydronics companies are promoting their systems as beautiful heat. Hydronics is the use of water as the heat-transfer medium in heating and cooling system.

7129 ■ "Canadian Wind Farm Sued Due to Negative Health Effects" in PC Magazine Online (September 22, 2011)
Pub: PC Magazine
Description: Suncor Energy is being sued by a family in Ontario, Canada. The family claims that Suncor's wind turbines have created health problems for them, ranging from vertigo and sleep disturbance to depression and suicidal thoughts. The family's home is over 1,000 meters from the eight wind turbines, and according to Ontario officials, wind turbines must be a minimum of 550 meters from existing homes.

7130 ■ "Candidates Differ On State's Green Streak" in Business Journal Portland (Vol. 27, October 22, 2010, No. 34, pp. 1)
Pub: Portland Business Journal
Ed: Andy Giegerich. Description: The views of Oregon gubernatorial candidates Chris Dudley and John Kitzhaber on the state's economy and on

environmental policies are presented. Both Dudley, who is a Republican, and his Democratic challenger believe that biomass could help drive the state's economy. Both candidates also pledged changes in Oregon's business energy tax credit (BETC) program.

7131 ■ "CanWEA Unveils WindVision for BC: 5,250 MW of Wind Energy by 2025" in CNW Group (October 4, 2011)
Pub: CNW Group

Contact: Carolyn McGill-Davidson, President

Description: Wind industry leaders are asking British Columbia, Canada policy makers to created conditions to further develop and integrate wind energy in accordance with greenhouse gas emission targets and projected economic growth. Statistical data included.

7132 ■ "The Carbon Equation" in Canadian Business (Vol. 81, October 27, 2008, No. 18, pp. 109)
Pub: Rogers Media Ltd.

Ed: Jack M. Mintz. **Description:** Economic and environmental impacts of the likely rejection of a carbon tax for the cap-and-trade system in Canada are discussed. The Conservative Party is expected tow in the 2008 elections and would likely pursue the cap-and-trade system.

7133 ■ "Carbon Trading: Current Schemes and Future Developments" in Energy Policy (Vol. 39, October 2011, No. 10, pp. 6040-6054)
Pub: Reed Elsevier Reference Publishing

Ed: Slobodan Perdan, Adisa Azapagic. **Description:** Current and future developments regarding carbon trading is highlighted.

7134 ■ "Case IH Announces Strategy to Meet 2014 Clean Air Standards" in Farm Industry News (September 15, 2011)
Pub: Penton Business Media Inc.

Ed: Jodie Wehrspann. **Description:** Case IH will meet EPA's stringent engine emissions limits imposed in 2014, called Tier 4. The limits call for a 90 percent reduction in particulate matter and nitrogen oxides (NOx) over the Tier 3 requirements from a few years ago.

7135 ■ "Cash for Appliances Targets HVAC Products, Water Heaters" in Contractor (Vol. 56, October 2009, No. 10, pp. 1)
Pub: Penton Media, Inc.

Ed: Candace Roulo. **Description:** States and territories would need to submit a full application that specifies their implementation plans if they are interested in joining the Cash for Appliances program funded by the American Recovery and Reinvestment Act. The Department of Energy urges states to focus on heating and cooling equipment, appliances and water heaters since these offer the greatest energy savings potential.

7136 ■ "Catch the Wind Announces Filing of Injunction Against Air Data Systems LLC and Philip Rogers" in CNW Group (September 30, 2011)
Pub: CNW Group

Contact: Carolyn McGill-Davidson, President

Description: Catch the Wind, providers of laser-based wind sensor products and technology, filed an injunction against Optical Air Data Systems (OADS) LLC and its former President and CEO Philip L. Rogers. The complaint seeks to have OADS and Rogers return tangible and intangible property owned by Catch the Wind, which the firm believes to be critical to the operations of their business.

7137 ■ "Catch the Wind to Hold Investor Update Conference Call on October 18, 2011" in CNW Group (October 4, 2011)
Pub: CNW Group

Contact: Carolyn McGill-Davidson, President

Description: Catch the Wind Ltd., providers of laser-based wind sensor products and technology, held a conference call for analysts and institutional investors. The high-growth technology firm is headquartered in Manassas, Virginia.

7138 ■ "CE2 Carbon Capital and Dogwood Carbon Solutions Partner With Missouri Landowners" in Nanotechnolgy Business Journal (Jan. 25, 2010)
Pub: Investment Weekly News

Description: Dogwood Carbon Solutions, a developer of agriculture and forestry based conservation projects, has partnered with CE2 Carbon Capital, one of the largest investors and owners of U.S. carbon commodities and carbon emissions reduction projects, to develop high-quality carbon offsets from over 30,000 acres of privately-owned non-industrial forest in the Ozark mountain region of Arkansas and Missouri.

7139 ■ "CEO Forecast" in Hispanic Business (January-February 2009, pp. 34, 36)
Pub: Hispanic Business

Ed: Jessica Haro, Richard Kaplan. **Description:** As economic uncertainty fogs the future, executives turn to government contracts in order to boost business. Revenue sources, health care challenges, environmental consulting and remediation services, as well as technological strides are discussed.

7140 ■ "Changing Fuel Compositions: What It Means To You and Your Business" in Indoor Comfort Marketing (Vol. 70, June 2011, No. 6, pp. 30)
Pub: Industry Publications Inc.

Ed: Paul Nazzaro. **Description:** Biofuels are outlined and the way it is changing the HVAC/R industry are discussed.

7141 ■ "Charged Up for Sales" in Charlotte Business Journal (Vol. 25, October 15, 2010, No. 30, pp. 1)
Pub: Charlotte Business Journal

Ed: Susan Stabley. **Description:** Li-Ion Motors Corporation is set to expand its production lines of electric cars in Sacramento, California. The plan is seen to create up to 600 jobs. The company's total investment is seen to reach $500 million.

7142 ■ "China Wind Power Generates Stronger First Quarter Results" in Marketwire Canada (September 28, 2011)
Pub: MarketWire Canada

Description: China Wind Power International Corporation, an independent wind power producer in China reported strong growth for the first quarter 2011. Details of the company and its future developments are highlighted.

7143 ■ "China's Transition to Green Energy Systems" in Energy Policy (Vol. 39, October 2011, No. 10, pp. 5909-5919)
Pub: Reed Elsevier Reference Publishing

Ed: Wei Li, Guojun Song, Melanie Beresford, Ben Ma. **Description:** The economics of home solar water heaters and their growing popularity in Dezhous City, China is discussed.

7144 ■ "Chinese Solar Panel Manufacturer Scopes Out Austin" in Austin Business JournalInc. (Vol. 29, October 30, 2009, No. 34, pp. 1)
Pub: American City Business Journals

Ed: Jacob Dirr. **Description:** China's Yingli Green Energy Holding Company Ltd. is looking for a site in order to construct a $20 million photovoltaic panel plant. Both Austin and San Antonio are vying to house the manufacturing hub. The project could create about 300 jobs and give Austin a chance to become a player in the solar energy market. Other solar companies are also considering Central Texas as an option to set up shop.

7145 ■ "City's New Energy Audits to Spawn 'Fantastic' Market" in Austin Business JournalInc. (Vol. 28, November 14, 2008, No. 35, pp. 1)
Pub: American City Business Journals

Ed: Jean Kwon. **Description:** A new law requiring older homes to undergo energy use audits is seen to provide new business for some companies in the Austin, Texas area. The new law is seen to create a new industry of performance testers. Details of the new ordinance are also given.

7146 ■ "Clean-Tech Focus Sparks Growth" in Philadelphia Business Journal (Vol. 28, January 15, 2010, No. 48, pp. 1)
Pub: American City Business Journals

Ed: Peter Key. **Description:** Keystone Redevelopment Group and economic development organization Ben Franklin Technology Partners of Southeastern Pennsylvania have partnered in supporting the growth of new alternative energy and clean technology companies. Keystone has also been developing the Bridge Business Center.

7147 ■ "Clean Wind Energy Tower Transitions from R&D Stage Company" in Professional Services Close-Up (September 30, 2011)
Pub: Close-Up Media

Description: Clean Wind Energy designed and is developing large downdraft towers that use benevolent, non-toxic natural elements to generate electricity and clean water. The firm is closing its internally staffed engineering office in Warrenton, Virginia and transitioning a development team to oversee and coordinate industry consultants and advisors to construct their first dual renewable energy tower.

7148 ■ "Climate Law Could Dig into our Coal-Dusted Pockets" in Business Courier (Vol. 26, November 20, 2009, No. 30, pp. 1)
Pub: American City Business Journals, Inc.

Ed: Lucy May. **Description:** Passage of federal climate legislation into law is set to increase household cost for Greater Cincinnati, according to the calculation by the Brookings Institute. The increase for residents of the area will amount to $244 in 2020 and the city was ranked the sixth-highest rate in the nation, behind Indianapolis.

7149 ■ "Cloudy Skies" in Canadian Business (Vol. 81, October 27, 2008, No. 18, pp. 101)
Pub: Rogers Media Ltd.

Ed: Andrew Wahl. **Description:** Canada's federal government is expected to implement its regulations on greenhouse-gas emissions by January 1, 2010, but companies are worried because the plan took so long and some details are yet to be revealed. Corporate Canada wants a firm, long-range plan similar to the European Union Emissions Trading Scheme in dealing with greenhouse-gas emissions.

7150 ■ "CO2 Emissions Embodied in China-US Trade" in Energy Policy (Vol. 39, October 2011, No. 10, pp. 5980-5987)
Pub: Reed Elsevier Reference Publishing

Ed: Huibin Du, Guozhu Mao, Alexander M. Smith, Xuxu Wang, Yuan Wang, Jianghong Guo. **Description:** Input and output analysis based on the energy per dollar ratio for carbon dioxide emissions involved in China-United States trade is outlined.

7151 ■ "Combo Dorm-Field House Built to Attain LEED Gold" in Contractor (Vol. 56, September 2009, No. 9, pp. 1)
Pub: Penton Media, Inc.

Ed: Candace Roulo; Robert P. Mader. **Description:** North Central College in Illinois has built a new dormitory that is expected to attain Leadership in Energy and Environmental Design Gold certification from the United States Green Building Council. The structure features a geo-exchange heat pump system and radiant floor heat. A description of the facility is also provided.

7152 ■ "Coming Soon: Electric Tractors" in Farm Industry News (November 21, 2011)
Pub: Penton Business Media Inc.

Ed: Jodie Wehrspann. **Description:** The agricultural industry is taking another look at electric farm vehicles. John Deere Product Engineering Center said that farmers can expect to see more diesel-electric systems in farm tractors, sprayers, and implements.

7153 ■ "Community Food Co-op Creates Revolving Loan Program for Local Farmers" in Bellingham Business Journal (Vol.

February 2010, pp. 3)
Pub: Sound Publishing Inc.
Description: Community Food Co-op's Farm Fund received a $12,000 matching grant from the Sustainable Whatcom Fund of the Whatcom Community Foundation. The Farm Fund will create a new revolving loan program for local farmers committed to using sustainable practices.

7154 ■ Consultants and Consulting Organizations Directory
Pub: Cengage Learning Inc.
Contact: Ronald Dunn, President
URL(s): www.gale.cengage.com. **Released:** Annual; New edition expected 37th; February, 2012. **Price:** $1392, Individuals. **Covers:** Over 26,000 firms, individuals, and organizations active in consulting. **Entries include:** Individual or organization name, address, phone, fax, e-mail, URL, specialties, founding date, branch offices, names and titles of key personnel, number of employees, financial data, publications, seminars and workshops. **Arrangement:** By broad subject categories. **Indexes:** Subject, geographical, organization name.

7155 ■ "Consumers Like Green, But Not Mandates" in Business Journal-Milwaukee (Vol. 28, December 10, 2010, No. 10, pp. A1)
Pub: Milwaukee Business Journal
Ed: Sean Ryan. **Description:** Milwaukee, Wisconsin consumers are willing to spend more on green energy, a survey has revealed. Respondents also said they will pay more for efficient cars and appliances. Support for public incentives for homeowners and businesses that reduce energy use has also increased.

7156 ■ "Convert New Customers to Long Term Accounts" in Indoor Comfort Marketing (Vol. 70, February 2011, No. 2, pp. 22)
Pub: Industry Publications Inc.
Description: Marketing to new customers and suggestions for retaining them is covered.

7157 ■ "Corporate Responsibility" in Professional Services Close-Up (July 2, 2010)
Pub: Close-Up Media
Description: List of firms awarded the inaugural Best Corporate Citizens in Government Contracting by the Corporate Responsibility Magazine is presented. The list is based on the methodology of the Magazine's Best Corporate Citizen's List, with 324 data points of publicly-available information in seven categories which include: environment, climate change, human rights, philanthropy, employee relations, financial performance, and governance.

7158 ■ "The Cost of Energy" in Canadian Business (Vol. 83, August 17, 2010, No. 13-14, pp. 39)
Pub: Rogers Media Ltd.
Description: Canada's cheap energy has bred complacency among Canadian companies and most have not strived to conserve or develop other forms of energy. However, even costs of traditional energy such as oil are set to rise, fueled by recent events in Saudi Arabia and the Gulf of Mexico.

7159 ■ "Could This Be Your Next Office Building?" in Austin Business Journal (Vol. 31, May 13, 2011, No. 10, pp. A1)
Pub: American City Business Journals Inc.
Ed: Cody Lyon. **Description:** Falcon Containers moved to a 51-acre site in Far East Austin, Texas and started construction of a 2,500-square-foot headquarters made from eight 40-foot shipping containers. Falcon's CEO Stephen Shang plans to use his headquarters building as a showroom to attract upscale, urban hipsters. Insights on the construction's environmental and social impact are shared.

7160 ■ "Council Power Shift Could Benefit Business" in Business Courier (Vol. 26, November 6, 2009, No. 28, pp. 1)
Pub: American City Business Journals, Inc.
Ed: Lucy May. **Description:** A majority in the Cincinnati City Council, which is comprised of reelected members, might be created by Charlie Winburn's

impending return to the council. It would be empowered to decide on public safety, stock options taxes, and environmental justice. How the presumed majority would affect the city's economic progress is discussed.

7161 ■ "Crude Awakening" in Canadian Business (Vol. 81, October 27, 2008, No. 18, pp. 14)
Pub: Rogers Media Ltd.
Ed: Jeff Sanford. **Description:** Jim Grays believes that a global liquid fuels crisis is coming and hopes the expected transition from oil dependence will be smooth. Charles Maxwell, on the other hand, predicts that a new world economy will arrive in three waves. Views of both experts are examined.

7162 ■ "Customized Before Custom Was Cool" in Green Industry Pro (July 2011)
Pub: Cygnus Business Media
Ed: Gregg Wartgow. **Description:** Profile of Turf Care Enterprises and owner Kevin Vogeler, who discusses his desire to use more natural programs using little or no chemicals in 1986. At that time, that sector represented 20 percent of his business, today it shares 80 percent.

7163 ■ "Cut Energy Waste" in Inc. (Vol. 31, January-February 2009, No. 1, pp. 42)
Pub: Mansueto Ventures LLC
Description: Carbon Control, Edison, and Saver software programs help companies cut carbon emissions by reducing the amount of energy consumed by computers while they are idle.

7164 ■ "David Robinson Column" in Buffalo News (October 2, 2011)
Pub: Buffalo News
Ed: David Robinson. **Description:** New York Power Authority ceased development of an offshore wind farm project. Wind farming in the waters of Lake Erie or Lake Ontario would be too costly. Details of the project are discussed.

7165 ■ "A Day Late and a Dollar Short" in Indoor Comfort Marketing (Vol. 70, March 2011, No. 3, pp. 30)
Pub: Industry Publications Inc.
Ed: Philip J. Baratz. **Description:** A discussion involving futures options and fuel oil prices is presented.

7166 ■ "Despite Economic Upheaval Generation Y is Still Feeling Green: RSA Canada Survey" in CNW Group (October 28, 2010)
Pub: CNW Group
Contact: Carolyn McGill-Davidson, President
Description: Canadian Generation Y individuals believe it is important for their company to be environmentally-friendly and one-third of those surveyed would quit their job if they found their employer was environmentally irresponsible, despite the economy.

7167 ■ "Detroit Hosts Conferences on Green Building, IT, Finance" in Crain's Detroit Business (Vol. 25, June 1, 2009, No. 22, pp. 9)
Pub: Crain Communications Inc. - Detroit
Ed: Tom Henderson. **Description:** Detroit will host three conferences in June 2009, one features green technology, one information technology and the third will gather black bankers and financial experts from across the nation.

7168 ■ "DeWind Delivering Turbines to Texas Wind Farm" in Professional Services Close-Up (September 25, 2011)
Pub: Close-Up Media
Description: DeWind Company has begun shipment of turbines to the 20 MW Frisco Wind Farm located in Hansford County, Texas. DeWind is a subsidiary of Daewoo Shipbuilding and Marine Engineering Company. Details of the project are discussed.

7169 ■ "DOE Proposes New Water Heater Efficiency Standards" in Contractor (Vol. 57, January 2010, No. 1, pp. 3)
Pub: Penton Media, Inc.
Ed: Robert P. Mader. **Description:** U.S. Department of Energy is proposing higher efficiency standards for gas and electric water heaters which will not take ef-

fect until 2015. The proposal calls for gas-fired storage water heaters less than 60 gallons to have an Energy Factor of 0.675 and those larger than 60 gallons to have an Energy Factor of 0.717.

7170 ■ "Dow Champions Innovative Energy Solutions for Auto Industry at NAIAS" in Business of Global Warming (January 25, 2010, pp. 7)
Pub: Investment Weekly News
Description: This year's North American International Auto Show in Detroit will host the 'Electric Avenue' exhibit sponsored by the Dow Chemical Company. The display will showcase the latest in innovative energy solutions from Dow as well as electric vehicles and the technology supporting them. This marks the first time a non-automotive manufacturer is part of the main floor of the show.

7171 ■ "Earth Angels" in Playthings (Vol. 106, September 1, 2008, No. 8, pp. 10)
Pub: Reed Business Information
Contact: Jeff Greisch, President
Ed: Karyn M. Peterson. **Description:** ImagiPlay toy company has partnered with Whole Foods Market to distribute the company's wooden playthings across the country. The company's Earth-friendly business model is outlined.

7172 ■ "East Coast Solar" in Contractor (Vol. 57, February 2010, No. 2, pp. 17)
Pub: Penton Media, Inc.
Ed: Dave Yates. **Description:** U.S. Department of Energy's Solar Decathlon lets 20 college student-led teams from around the world compete to design and build a solar-powered home. A mechanical contractor discusses his work as an advisor during the competition.

7173 ■ Eco Barons: The New Heroes of Environmental Activism
Pub: Ecco/HarperCollins
Ed: Edward Humes. **Released:** January 19, 2010. **Price:** $14.99. **Description:** Profiles of business leaders who have dedicated their lives to saving the planet from ecological devastation.

7174 ■ "Eco-Preneuring" in Small Business Opportunities (July 2008)
Pub: Entrepreneur Media Inc.
Ed: Mary C. Pearl. **Description:** Profile of Wildlife Trust, a rapidly growing global organization dedicated to innovative conservation science linking health and ecology. With partners in nearly twenty countries, Wildlife Trust draws on global strengths in order to respond to well-defined local needs. In the Dominican Republic, they are working with the community and local biologists in order to restore fishing and create jobs in the field of ecotourism.

7175 ■ "Eco Smart Home Will Showcase Green Technology" in Contractor (Vol. 56, September 2009, No. 9, pp. 3)
Pub: Penton Media, Inc.
Ed: Steve Spaulding. **Description:** Eco Smart World Wide is building the Eco Smart Demonstration House to promote the latest in sustainable, renewable and high-efficiency practices and products. The company will use insulated concrete forms in the construction of the building. Features and dimensions of the structure are also presented.

7176 ■ "EMC Greens Its Machines" in Boston Business Journal (Vol. 31, July 15, 2011, No. 25, pp. 3)
Pub: Boston Business Journal
Ed: Kyle Alspach. **Description:** Hopkinton, Massachusetts-based EMC Corporation has been pursuing a sustainability strategy even though it would not directly pay back money to the company or customers who use the products. EMC has been increasingly requiring sustainable practices from its suppliers and evaluating the full lifecycle impacts of its products.

7177 ■ "Energy Consulting Company to Expand" in Austin Business JournalInc. (Vol. 28, November 7, 2008, No. 34, pp. A1)
Pub: American City Business Journals
Ed: Kate Harrington. **Description:** CLEAResult Consulting Inc. is planning to increase its workforce and move its headquarters to a larger office. The

company has posted 1,000 percent increase in revenues. The company's adoption of best practices and setting of benchmark goals are seen as the reason for its growth.

7178 ■ *"Energy Efficiency Ordinance Softened" in Austin Business JournalInc. (Vol. 28, October 3, 2008, No. 29)*
Pub: American City Business Journals
Ed: Jean Kwon. **Description:** City of Austin has eliminated mandatory energy efficiency upgrades to single-family housing as a condition for selling or renting homes or buildings. The new law proposes that an energy performance audit be conducted on single-family homes before being sold and the results of the audit disclosed to perspectives buyers.

7179 ■ *"Energy Is Put to Good Use in Antarctica" in Contractor (Vol. 56, July 2009, No. 7, pp. 32)*
Pub: Penton Media, Inc.
Ed: Carol Fey. **Description:** Recapturing waste heat is an important part of the heating system at the Mc-Murdo Station in Antarctica. The radiators of generators are the heat source and this is supplemented by modular boilers when seasonal demands for heat increase. Waste heat is also used to make 55,000 gallons of fresh water a day.

7180 ■ *Environmental Guide to the Internet*
Pub: Government Institutes
Contact: Judith Rothman, Director
URL(s): www.govinstpress.com. **Ed:** Carol Briggs-Erickson, Toni Murphy. **Released:** Latest edition 4th. **Price:** $83, Individuals Paperback; £51.95, Individuals Paperback. **Covers:** 1,200 resources covering the environment on the Internet, including organizations, products, and resources, including discussion groups, electronic journals, newsgroups, and discussion groups. **Entries include:** Name, online address, description, e-mail address. **Arrangement:** Categories.

7181 ■ *"EPA 'Finalizes' WaterSense for Homes" in Contractor (Vol. 57, January 2010, No. 1, pp. 70)*
Pub: Penton Media, Inc.
Ed: Bob Mader. **Description:** U.S. Environmental Protection Agency released its 'final' version of the WaterSense for Homes standard. The standard's provisions that affect plumbing contractors includes the specification that everything has to be leak tested and final service pressure cannot exceed 60 psi.

7182 ■ *"EPA Grants E15 Waiver for 2001-2006 Vehicles" in Farm Industry News (January 21, 2011)*
Pub: Penton Business Media Inc.
Description: U.S. Environmental Protection Agency waived a limitation on selling gasoline that contains more than 10 percent ethanol for model year 2001-2006 cars and light trucks, allowing fuel to contain up to 15 percent ethanol (E15) for these vehicles.

7183 ■ *"ESolar Partners With Penglai on Landmark Solar Thermal Agreement for China" in Business of Global Warming (January 25, 2010, pp. 8)*
Pub: Investment Weekly News
Description: Penglai Electric, a privately-owned Chinese electrical power equipment manufacturer, and eSolar, a global provider of cost-effective and reliable solar power plants, announced a master licensing agreement in which eSolar will build at least 2 gigawatts of solar thermal power plants in China over the next 10 years.

7184 ■ *"Everett Dowling" in Hawaii Business (Vol. 54, August 2008, No. 2, pp. 32)*
Pub: Hawaii Business Publishing
Ed: Jason Ubay. **Description:** Real estate developer Everett Dowling, president of Dowling Company Inc., talks about the company's sustainable management and services. The company's office has been retrofitted to earn a Leadership in Energy and Environmental Design (LEED) certification. Dowling believes that real estate development can be part of the sustainable solution.

7185 ■ *"Family Takes Wind Turbine Companies to Court Over Gag Clauses on Health Effects of Turbines" in CNW Group (September 12, 2011)*
Pub: CNW Group
Contact: Carolyn McGill-Davidson, President
Description: Shawn and Trisha Drennan are concerned about the negative experiences other have had with wind turbines close to their homes, including adverse health effects. The couple's home will be approximately 650 meters from the Kingsbridge II wind farm project in Ontario, Canada.

7186 ■ *"Federal Buildings to Achieve Zero-Net Energy by 2030" in Contractor (Vol. 56, December 2009, No. 12, pp. 5)*
Pub: Penton Media, Inc.
Ed: Candace Roulo. **Description:** United States president Barack Obama has issued sustainable goals for federal buildings. Federal agencies are also required to increase energy efficiency, conserve water and support sustainable communities. Obama has also announced a $3.4 billion investment in a smart energy creed.

7187 ■ *"Find Private Money for FutureGen Plant" in Crain's Chicago Business (Vol. 34, September 12, 2011, No. 37, pp. 18)*
Pub: Crain Communications Inc.
Description: FutureGen is a clean-coal power plant being developed in Southern Illinois. The need for further funding is discussed.

7188 ■ *"First Suzlon S97 Turbines Arrive in North America for Installation" in PR Newswire (September 28, 2011)*
Pub: United Business Media
Description: Suzlon Energy Ltd., the world's fifth largest manufacturer of wind turbines, will install its first S97 turbine at the Amherst Wind Farm Project. These turbines will be installed on 90-meter hub height towers and at full capacity, will generate enough electricity to power over 10,000 Canadian homes.

7189 ■ *The Flaw of Averages: Why We Underestimate Risk in the Face of Uncertainty*
Pub: John Wiley & Sons, Inc.
Ed: Sam L. Savage. **Released:** June 3, 2009. **Price:** $22.95. **Description:** Personal and business plans are based on uncertainties on a daily basis. The common avoidable mistake individuals make in assessing risk in the face of uncertainty is defined. The explains why plans based on average assumptions are wrong, on average, in areas as diverse as finance, healthcare, accounting, the war on terror, and climate change.

7190 ■ *"Florida's Bright Upside" in Tampa Bay Business Journal (Vol. 29, November 6, 2009, No. 46, pp. 1)*
Pub: American City Business Journals
Ed: Michael Hinman. **Description:** Florida's Public Service Commission (PSC) decision on a power purchase agreement that could add 25 megawatts of solar energy on Tampa Electric Company's offerings is presented. The decision could support the growing market for suppliers and marketers of renewable energy such as Jabil Circuit Inc., which manufactures photovoltaic modules. Details of the agreement are discussed.

7191 ■ *"Floyd County Considers Wind Farms" in Roanoke Times (September 19, 2011)*
Pub: Roanoke Times
Ed: Jeff Sturgeon. **Description:** German firm, Nordex USA Inc. is proposing a $100 million, 30-50 megawatt wind farm atop Wills Ridge, Virginia within the next four years. This project is one of several large wind project considered in the Roanoke and New River valleys of Virginia.

7192 ■ *"Flue Vaccines are Going Green" in Canadian Business (Vol. 83, September 14, 2010, No. 15, pp. 24)*
Pub: Rogers Media Ltd.
Ed: Angelia Chapman. **Description:** Quebec-based Medicago has found a solution to the bottleneck in the production of influenza vaccines by using plant-

based processes instead of egg-based systems. Medicago's US Department of Defense funded research has produced the technology that speeds up the production time for vaccines by almost two-thirds. Insights into Medicago's patented process are also given.

7193 ■ *"For Giving Us a Way To Say Yes To Solar: Lynn Jurich and Edward Fenster" in Inc. (Volume 32, December 2010, No. 10, pp. 110)*
Pub: Inc. Magazine
Description: Profile of entrepreneurs Lynn Jurich and Edward Fenster, cofounders of SunRun. The firm installs solar panels at little or no cost and homeowners sign 20-year contracts to buy power at a fixed price.

7194 ■ *"For Putting Down Roots in Business: Amy Norquist: Greensulate, New York City" in Inc. (Volume 32, December 2010, No. 10, pp. 106)*
Pub: Inc. Magazine
Ed: Christine Lagorio. **Description:** Profile of Amy Norquist who left her position at an environmental nonprofit organization to found Greensulate. Her firm insulates rooftops with lavender, native grasses and succulents called sedum in order to eliminate carbon from the atmosphere.

7195 ■ *"Forum at UNCW to Explore Offshore Wind Farming" in Star-News (October 4, 2011)*
Pub: Star-News
Ed: Kate Elizabeth Queram. **Description:** North Carolina is poised to profit from offshore wind farming, according to regional environmental experts. The Sierra Club, in conjunction with the University of North Carolina Wilmington and Oceana are hosting an offshore wind forum featuring five panelists, focusing on potential impacts on birds and sea life, tourism and cost, as well as other pertinent issues.

7196 ■ *"Fossil Fuel, Renewable Fuel Shares Expected to Flip Flop" in Farm Industry News (April 29, 2011)*
Pub: Penton Business Media Inc.
Description: Total energy use of fossil fuels is predicted to fall 5 percent by the year 2035, with renewable fuel picking it up.

7197 ■ *"FSU's OGZEB Is Test Bed for Sustainable Technology" in Contractor (Vol. 56, October 2009, No. 10, pp. 1)*
Pub: Penton Media, Inc.
Ed: Candace Roulo. **Description:** Florida State University has one of 14 off-grid zero emissions buildings (OGZEB) in the U.S.; it was built to research sustainable and alternative energy systems. The building produces electricity from 30 photovoltaic panels and it also has three AET water heating solar panels on the roof.

7198 ■ *"Fuel King: The Most Fuel-Efficient Tractor of the Decade is the John Deere 8295R" in Farm Industry News (November 10, 2011)*
Pub: Penton Business Media Inc.
Description: Farm Industry News compiled a list of the most fuel-efficient tractors with help from the Nebraska Tractor Test Lab, with the John Deere 8295R PTO winner of the most fuel-efficient tractor of the decade.

7199 ■ *"Fuel for Thought; Canadian Business Leaders on Energy Policy" in Canadian Business (Vol. 81, September 15, 2008, No. 14-15, pp. 12)*
Pub: Rogers Media Ltd.
Ed: Joe Castaldo. **Description:** Most Canadian business leaders worry about the unreliability of the oil supply but feel that Canada is in a better position to benefit from the energy supply crisis than other countries. Many respondents also highlighted the need to invest in renewable energy sources.

7200 ■ *"GE Milestone: 1,000th Wind Turbine Installed in Canada" in CNW Group (October 4, 2011)*
Pub: CNW Group
Contact: Carolyn McGill-Davidson, President
Description: GE installed its 1,000th wind turbine in Canada at Cartier Wind Energy's Gros Morne project

in the Gaspesie Region of Quebec, Canada. As Canada continues to expand its use of wind energy, GE plans to have over 1,100 wind turbines installed in the nation by the end of 2011.

7201 ■ *"Germans Win Solar Decathlon - Again" in Contractor (Vol. 56, November 2009, No. 11, pp. 1)*
Pub: Penton Media, Inc.
Ed: Robert P. Mader. **Description:** Students from Technische Universtat Darmstadt won the U.S. Department of Energy's Solar Decathlon by designing and building the most attractive and efficient solar-powered home. The winner's design produced a surplus of power even during three days of rain and photovoltaic panels covered nearly every exterior surface.

7202 ■ *"Getting the Bioheat Word Out" in Indoor Comfort Marketing (Vol. 70, September 2011, No. 9, pp. 32)*
Pub: Industry Publications Inc.
Description: Ways to market advanced liquid fuels to the public are outlined.

7203 ■ *"Getting Going on Going Green" in HRMagazine (Vol. 53, August 2008, No. 8, pp. 8)*
Pub: Society for Human Resource Management
Contact: Henry G. Jackson, President
E-mail: hjackson@shrm.org
Ed: Rita Zeidner. **Description:** Being eco-friendly can help recruit and retain workers. Resources to help firms create green initiatives are presented.

7204 ■ *"Getting NORA reauthorized is high priority" in Indoor Comfort Marketing (Vol. 70, February 2011, No. 2, pp. 14)*
Pub: Industry Publications Inc.
Description: The importance of reauthorizing the National Oilheat Research Alliance is stressed.

7205 ■ *"The GHG Quandary: Whose Problem Is It Anyway?" in Canadian Business (Vol. 81, September 15, 2008, No. 14-15, pp. 72)*
Pub: Rogers Media Ltd.
Ed: Matthew McClearn. **Description:** Nongovernmental organizations were able to revoke the permit for Imperial Oil Ltd's Kearl oilsands project on the grounds of its expected greenhouse gas emission but the court's ruling was rendered irrelevant by bureaucratic paper-shuffling shortly after. The idea of an environmental impact assessment as a guide to identify the consequences of a project is also discussed.

7206 ■ *"The Global Environment Movement is Bjorn Again" in Canadian Business (Vol. 83, September 14, 2010, No. 15, pp. 11)*
Pub: Rogers Media Ltd.
Ed: Steve Maich. **Description:** Danish academic Bjorn Lomborg is in favor of decisive action to combat climate change in his new book and was given front page treatment by a London newspaper. Environmentalist groups see this as a victory since Lomborg had not previously considered climate change an immediate issue.

7207 ■ *"GM's Volt Woes Cast Shadow on E-Cars" in Wall Street Journal Eastern Edition (November 28, 2011, pp. B1)*
Pub: Dow Jones & Company Inc. Enterprise Media Group
Contact: Clare Hart, President
Ed: Sharon Terlep. **Description:** The future of electric cars is darkened with the government investigation by the National Highway Traffic Safety Administration into General Motor Company's Chevy Volt after two instances of the car's battery packs catching fire during crash tests conducted by the Agency.

7208 ■ *"Go Green Or Go Home" in Black Enterprise (Vol. 41, August 2010, No. 1, pp. 53)*
Pub: Earl G. Graves Publishing Co. Inc.
Ed: Tennille M. Robinson. **Description:** The green economy has become an essential part of every business, however, small business owners need to learn how to participate, including minority owned entrepreneurs.

7209 ■ *"Going Green, Going Slowly" in Playthings (Vol. 106, September 1, 2008, No. 8, pp. 17)*
Pub: Reed Business Information
Contact: Jeff Greisch, President
Ed: Nancy Zwiers. **Description:** Sustainability and greener materials for both product and packaging in the toy industry has become important for protecting our environment. However, in a recent survey nearly 60 percent of responders stated environmental issues did not play a part in purchasing a toy or game for their children.

7210 ■ *"Golden Valley, Fling Hills Plan LNG Plant" in Alaska Business Monthly (Vol. 27, October 2011, No. 10, pp. 9)*
Pub: Alaska Business Publishing Company
Ed: Nancy Pounds. **Description:** Golden Valley Electric Association and Flint Hills Resources have partnered on a natural gas liquefaction facility on the North Slope. The deal will deliver gas at cost to GVEA and Flint Hills and Flint Hills will become more competitive and efficient by burning LNG instead of refined crude oil at the refinery.

7211 ■ *Good Green Guide for Small Businesses: How to Change the Way Your Business Works for the Better*
Pub: A. & C. Black
Ed: Impetus Consulting Ltd. Staff. **Released:** September 1, 2009. **Price:** $19.95. **Description:** Guide for small businesses to take an environmental audit of their company and shows how to minimize the impact of office essentials such as utilities, insulation, recycling and waste, electrical equipment, water systems, lighting options, food and drink, and office cleaning arrangements and products.

7212 ■ *"Gov. Kasich to Put DOD On Short Leash" in Business Courier (Vol. 27, November 26, 2010, No. 30, pp. 1)*
Pub: Business Courier
Ed: Dan Monk. **Description:** Ohio Governor-elect John Kasich proposed the privatization of the Ohio Department of Development in favor of a nonprofit corporation called JobsOhio. Kasich believes that the department has lost its focus by adding to its mission issues such as energy efficiency and tourism.

7213 ■ *"Grainger Show Highlights Building Green, Economy" in Contractor (Vol. 57, February 2010, No. 2, pp. 3)*
Pub: Penton Media, Inc.
Ed: Candace Roulo. **Description:** chief U.S. economist told attendees of the Grainger's 2010 Total MRO Solutions National Customer Show that the economic recovery would be subdued. Mechanical contractors who attended the event also learned about building sustainable, green products, and technologies, and economic and business challenges.

7214 ■ *"Green Acre$ Tope 10 Green Biz To Start Right Now" in Small Business Opportunities (September 2010)*
Pub: Harris Publications Inc.
Description: A list of the top ten green businesses to start in 2010 is provided.

7215 ■ *"Green Acres" in Hawaii Business (Vol. 54, September 2008, No. 3, pp. 48)*
Pub: Hawaii Business Publishing
Ed: Jan Tenbruggencate. **Description:** Bill Cowern's Hawaiian Mahogany is a forestry business that processes low-value trees to be sold as wood chips, which can be burned to create biodiesel. Cowern is planning to obtain certification to market carbon credits and is also working with Green Energy Hawaii for the permit of a biomass-fueled power plant. Other details about Cowern's business are discussed.

7216 ■ *"Green and Clean" in Retail Merchandiser (Vol. 51, July-August 2011, No. 4, pp. 56)*
Pub: Phoenix Media Corporation
Description: Green Valley Grocery partnered with Paragon Solutions consulting firm to make their stores environmentally green.

7217 ■ *"'Green' Cleaner Buys Local Firm" in Puget Sound Business Journal (Vol. 29, December 19, 2008, No. 35, pp. 3)*
Pub: American City Business Journals
Ed: Greg Lamm. **Description:** Washington-based Blue Sky Cleaners has purchased Four Seasons Cleaners. The green company also purchased Queen Anne store and Four Seasons' routes fro Snohomish County through Seattle.

7218 ■ *The Green Collar Economy: How One Solution Can Fix Our Two Biggest Problems*
Pub: HarperCollins Publishers
Ed: Van Jones. **Released:** November 1, 2009. **Price:** $14.99. **Description:** This book offers insight into rebuilding the nation's infrastructure and creating alternative energy sources that could boost the economy through increased employment and higher wages while decreasing our dependence on fossil fuels.

7219 ■ *"Green Counting" in Canadian Business (Vol. 81, October 13, 2008, No. 17, pp. 27)*
Pub: Rogers Media Ltd.
Ed: Joe Castaldo. **Description:** Procter and Gamble research revealed that only 10 percent of North American consumers are willing to accept trade-offs for a greener product. Three out of four North American consumers will not accept a higher price or a decrease in a product's performance for an environmental benefit. Details on green marketing are also discussed.

7220 ■ *"Green Energy Exec Hits State Policy" in Boston Business Journal (Vol. 30, December 3, 2010, No. 45, pp. 1)*
Pub: Boston Business Journal
Ed: Kyle Alspach. **Description:** American Superconductor Corporation President Dan McGahn believes that the state government of Massachusetts is not proactive enough to develop the state into a manufacturing hub for wind power technology. McGahn believes that while Governor Deval Patrick campaigned for wind turbines in the state, his administration does not have the focus required to build the turbines in the state.

7221 ■ *"Green Firm Scouts Sites in Tri-State" in Business Courier (Vol. 27, July 23, 2010, No. 12, pp. 1)*
Pub: Business Courier
Ed: Dan Monk. **Description:** CresaPartners is searching for a manufacturing facility in Cincinnati, Ohio. The company is set to tour about ten sites in the area.

7222 ■ *The Green Guide for Business: The Ultimate Environment for Businesses of All Sizes*
Pub: Profile Books Limited
Ed: Roger East, Hannah Bullock, Chris Goodall. **Released:** May 10, 2010. **Description:** Everyone wants to go green these days, but for small businesses that's easier said than done. How do you measure a company's carbon footprint? Are dryers or hand towels more eco-friendly? Recycled paper or FSC-certified? All these questions and more are explored.

7223 ■ *"Green It Like You Mean It" in Special Events Magazine (Vol. 28, February 1, 2009, No. 2)*
Pub: Special Events Magazine
Ed: Christine Landry. **Description:** Eco-friendly party planners offer advice for planning and hosting green parties or events. Tips include information for using recycled paper products, organic food and drinks. The Eco Nouveau Fashion Show held by Serene Star Productions reused old garments to create new fashions as well as art pieces from discarded doors and window frames for the show; eco-friendly treats and gift bags were highlighted at the event.

7224 ■ *"Green Light" in The Business Journal-Portland (Vol. 25, July 11, 2008, No. 18, pp. 1)*
Pub: American City Business Journals, Inc.
Ed: Erik Siemers. **Description:** Ecos Consulting, a sustainability consulting company based in Portland, Oregon, is seeing a boost in revenue as more busi-

nesses turn to sustainable practices. The company's revenue rose by 50 percent in 2007 and employees increased from 57 to 150. Other details about Ecos' growth are discussed.

7225 ■ *"Green Shift Sees Red"* in Canadian Business (Vol. 81, September 29, 2008, No. 16)
Pub: Rogers Media Ltd.
Ed: Jeff Sanford. **Description:** Green Shift Inc. is suing the Liberal Party of Canada in an $8.5 million lawsuit for using the phrase 'green shift' when they rolled out their carbon tax and climate change policy. The company has come to be recognized as a consultant and provider of green products such as non-toxic, biodegradable cups, plates, and utensils for events.

7226 ■ *"Greenhouse Announces Merger With Custom Q, Inc."* in Investment Weekly (January 30, 2010, pp. 338)
Pub: Investment Weekly News
Description: In accordance with an Agreement and Plan of Share Exchange, GreenHouse Holdings, Inc., an innovative green solutions provider, has gone public via a reverse merger with Custom Q, Inc.

7227 ■ *"Greening the Auto Industry"* in Business Journal-Serving Phoenix & the Valley of the Sun (Vol. 30, July 23, 2010, No. 46, pp. 1)
Pub: Phoenix Business Journal
Ed: Patrick O'Grady. **Description:** Thermo Fluids Inc. has been recycling used oil products since 1993 and could become Arizona's first home for oil filter recycling after retrofitting its Phoenix facility to include a compaction machine. The new service could help establish Thermo Fluids as a recycling hub for nearby states.

7228 ■ *"Greening the Manscape"* in Canadian Business (Vol. 81, October 13, 2008, No. 17, pp. S19)
Pub: Rogers Media Ltd.
Ed: David Lackie. **Description:** Buyer's guide of environmentally friendly grooming products for men is provided. Improved formulations have solved the problems of having synthetic ingredients in grooming products. Details about a face scrub, after shave conditioner, and a nourishing cream made of 91 percent organic ingredients are given, including prices.

7229 ■ *Greening Your Small Business: How to Improve Your Bottom Line, Grow Your Brand, Satisfy Your Customers and Save the Planet*
Pub: Prentice Hall Press
Contact: Dame Marjorie M. Scardino, Chief Executive Officer
Ed: Jennifer Kaplan. **Released:** November 3, 2009. **Price:** $19.95. **Description:** A definitive resource for anyone who wants their small business to be cutting-edge, competitive, profitable, and eco-conscious. Stories from small business owners address every aspect of going green, from basics such as recycling waste, energy efficiency, and reducing information technology footprint, to more in-depth concerns such as green marketing and communications, green business travel, and green employee benefits.

7230 ■ *Guerrilla Marketing Goes Green: Winning Strategies to Improve Your Profits and Your Planet*
Pub: John Wiley & Sons, Inc.
Ed: Jay Conrad Levinson, Shel Horowitz. **Released:** January 10, 2010. **Price:** $21.95. **Description:** The latest tips on green marketing and sustainable business strategies are shared.

7231 ■ *"Guide to Carbon Footprinting"* in American Printer (Vol. 128, June 1, 2011, No. 6)
Pub: Penton Media Inc.
Description: PrintCity Alliance published its new report, 'Carbon Footprint & Energy Reduction for Graphic Industry Value Chain.' The report aims to help improve the environmental performance of printers, converters, publishers, brand owners and their suppliers.

7232 ■ *"Habitat, Home Depot Expand Building Programs"* in Contractor (Vol. 56, September 2009, No. 9, pp. 16)
Pub: Penton Media, Inc.
Description: Habitat for Humanity International and The Home Depot Foundation are planning to expand their Partners in Sustainable Building program. The program will provide funds to help Habitat affiliates build 5,000 homes. Comments from executives are also included.

7233 ■ *Habitats and Ecosystems: An Encyclopedia of Endangered America*
Pub: ABC-Clio Inc.
Contact: Ron Boehm, President
E-mail: rboehm@abc-clio.com
URL(s): www.abc-clio.com. **Released:** Published December 1999. **Price:** $75, Individuals print; £51.95, Individuals. **Covers:** A listing of more than 1,400 of the most hazardous pollution sites since 1980. **Entries include:** Location. **Database includes:** Maps. **Arrangement:** Geographical by state.

7234 ■ *"Hard Rock on Pike"* in Puget Sound Business Journal (Vol. 29, September 5, 2008, No. 20, pp. 1)
Pub: American City Business Journals
Ed: Jeanne Lang Jones. **Description:** A branch of the Hard Rock Cafe is opening in 2009 in the Liberty Building on Pike Street in downtown Seattle, Washington. The location is being renovated as a green building; the restaurant and concert venue will seat 300 patrons and has a rooftop deck and memorabilia shop.

7235 ■ *"Hey, You Can't Do That"* in Green Industry Pro (Vol. 23, September 2011)
Pub: Cygnus Business Media
Ed: Rod Dickens. **Description:** Manufacturers of landscape equipment are making better use of energy resources, such as the use of fuel-injection systems instead of carburetors, lightweight materials, better lubricants, advanced battery technology, and innovative engine designs.

7236 ■ *"Hot Air"* in Canadian Business (Vol. 81, July 22, 2008, No. 12-13, pp. 16)
Pub: Rogers Media Ltd.
Ed: Joe Castaldo. **Description:** Over half of 101 business leaders who were recently surveyed oppose Liberal leader Stephane Dion's carbon-tax proposal, saying that manufacturers in Canada are likely to suffer from the plan. Additional key results of the survey are presented.

7237 ■ *"Hot Air: On Global Warming and Carbon Tax"* in Canadian Business (Vol. 81, October 13, 2008, No. 17, pp. 12)
Pub: Rogers Media Ltd.
Ed: Joe Castaldo. **Description:** Survey of Canadian business leaders revealed that the environment is a key issue in Canada's federal elections. Respondents believe that Prime Minister Stephen Harper's views on global warming and climate change are closer to their own views. Other key information on the survey is presented.

7238 ■ *Hot, Flat and Crowded: Why We Need a Green Revolution - and How It Can Renew America*
Pub: Farrar, Straus and Giroux
Ed: Thomas L. Friedman. **Released:** September 8, 2008. **Price:** $27.95. **Description:** Author explains how global warming, rapidly growing populations, and the expansion of the world's middle class through globalization have impacted the environment.

7239 ■ *Housecleaning Business: Organize Your Business - Get Clients and Referrals - Set Rates and Services*
Pub: Globe Pequot Press
Ed: Laura Jorstad, Melinda Morse. **Released:** June 1, 2009. **Price:** $18.95. **Description:** This book shares insight into starting a housecleaning businesses. It shows how to develop a service manual, screen clients, serve customers, select cleaning products, competition, how to up a home office, using the Internet to grow the business and offering green cleaning options to clients.

7240 ■ *"How Bad Is It?"* in Hawaii Business (Vol. 54, July 2008, No. 1, pp. 35)
Pub: Hawaii Business Publishing
Ed: Jolyn Okimoto Rosa. **Description:** Donald G. Horner, chief executive officer of First Hawaiian Bank, says that the current Hawaiian economic situation is a cyclical slowdown. Maurice Kaya, an energy consultant, says the slowdown is due to overdependence on imported fuels. Other local leaders, such as Constance H. Lau, also discuss their view on the current economic situation in Hawaii.

7241 ■ *"How Green Is The Valley?"* in Barron's (Vol. 88, July 4, 2008, No. 28, pp. 13)
Pub: Dow Jones & Co., Inc.
Description: San Jose, California has made a good start towards becoming a leader in alternative energy technology through the establishment of United Laboratories' own lab in the city. The certification process for photovoltaic cells will be dramatically shortened with this endeavor.

7242 ■ *"IAPMO GTC Debates Supplement"* in Contractor (Vol. 56, September 2009, No. 9, pp. 3)
Pub: Penton Media, Inc.
Ed: Robert P. Mader. **Description:** Green Technical Committee of the International Association of Plumbing and Mechanical Officials is developing a Green Plumbing and Mechanical Supplement. The supplement provides for installation of systems by licensed contractors and installers. Comments from officials are also presented.

7243 ■ *"IAPMO GTC Finalizes Green Supplement"* in Contractor (Vol. 57, January 2010, No. 1, pp. 1)
Pub: Penton Media, Inc.
Description: International Association of Plumbing and Mechanical Officials' Green Technical Committee finalized the Green Plumbing & Mechanical Code Supplement. The supplement was created to provide a set of provisions that encourage sustainable practices and work towards the design and construction of plumbing and mechanical systems.

7244 ■ *"IAPMO GTC Votes to Limit Showers to 2.0-GPM"* in Contractor (Vol. 56, September 2009, No. 9, pp. 1)
Pub: Penton Media, Inc.
Ed: Robert P. Mader. **Description:** Green Technical Committee of the International Association of Plumbing and Mechanical Officials has voted to limit showers to 2.0 GPM. It is also developing a Green Plumbing and Mechanical Supplement. Comments from executives are also supplied.

7245 ■ *"Independence Station Utilizes Sustainable Technologies"* in Contractor (Vol. 56, September 2009, No. 9, pp. 3)
Pub: Penton Media, Inc.
Ed: Candace Ruolo. **Description:** Independence Station building in Oregon is seen to receive the most LEED points ever awarded by the United States Green Building Council. The building will use an ice-based cooling storage system, biofuel cogeneration system and phovoltaic system. Other building features and dimensions are also supplied.

7246 ■ *"Indoor Air Quality - a Tribute to Efficiency"* in Indoor Comfort Marketing (Vol. 70, August 2011, No. 8, pp. 8)
Pub: Industry Publications Inc.
Ed: Matthew Maleske. **Description:** Efficiency of new HVAC/R equipment has helped improve indoor air quality.

7247 ■ *"Industry Escalates Lobbying Efforts For Loan Program"* in Crain's Detroit Business (Vol. 24, September 22, 2008, No. 38, pp. 22)
Pub: Crain Communications Inc.
Ed: Jay Greene; Ryan Beene; Harry Stoffer. **Description:** Auto suppliers such as Lear Corp., which is best known for vehicle seating, also supplies high-voltage wiring for Ford hybrids and is developing other hybrid components. These suppliers are joining

automakers in lobbying for the loan program which would promote the accelerated development of fuel-efficient vehicles.

7248 ■ *"Info Junkie"* in *Crain's Chicago Business (Vol. 34, October 24, 2011, No. 42, pp. 35)*
Pub: Crain Communications Inc.
Ed: Christina Le Beau. **Description:** Greg Colando, president of Flor Inc., an eco-friendly carpet company located I Chicago discusses his marketing program to increase sales.

7249 ■ *"Interested in 12 Billion Dollars?"* in *Indoor Comfort Marketing (Vol. 70, March 2011, No. 3, pp. 18)*
Pub: Industry Publications Inc.
Ed: Matthew Maleske. **Description:** Trends in the indoor quality industry are cited, with insight into expanding an existing indoor heating and cooling business.

7250 ■ *"It's Always 55 Degrees F"* in *Contractor (Vol. 56, September 2009, No. 9, pp. 38)*
Pub: Penton Media, Inc.
Ed: Carol Fey. **Description:** Geothermal-exchange heating and cooling systems can save businesses up to 60 percent on energy costs for heating and cooling. Geothermal systems get heat from the earth during winter. Design, features and installation of geothermal systems are also discussed.

7251 ■ *"It's Not Easy Investing Green"* in *Entrepreneur (Vol. 37, August 2009, No. 8, pp. 64)*
Pub: Entrepreneur Media, Inc.
Ed: Rosalind Resnick. **Description:** Some venture capitalists remain bullish on green investing despite signs of stagnation. One way for an investor to cash in on green investing is to invest in large public companies that are investing big in green initiatives. Being an angel investor to a local clean-tech company is another avenue.

7252 ■ *"Know the Facts About Natural Gas!"* in *Indoor Comfort Marketing (Vol. 70, August 2011, No. 8, pp. 26)*
Pub: Industry Publications Inc.
Description: AEC Activity Update is presented on the American Energy Coalition's Website.

7253 ■ *"Kohler Building Earns LEED Silver Certification"* in *Contractor (Vol. 56, September 2009, No. 9, pp. 12)*
Pub: Penton Media, Inc.
Description: United States Green Building Council has awarded Kohler Co. with the Silver Leadership in Energy and Environmental Design Status. The award has highlighted the company's work to transform its building into a more environmentally efficient structure. A description of the facility is also provided.

7254 ■ *"Large Homes can be Energy Efficient Too"* in *Contractor (Vol. 56, October 2009, No. 10, pp. 5)*
Pub: Penton Media, Inc.
Ed: Candace Roulo. **Description:** Eco Estate at Briggs Chaney subdivision in Silver Spring, Maryland has model houses that use sustainable technologies and products and the homes that will be built on the subdivision will feature some of the technologies featured on the model home. The energy efficient HVAC system of the model homes are discussed.

7255 ■ *"Legislation Introduced"* in *Indoor Comfort Marketing (Vol. 70, July 2011, No. 7, pp. 6)*
Pub: Industry Publications Inc.
Description: New industry legislation is examined by the National Oilheat Research Alliance.

7256 ■ *"Letting the Sunshine In"* in *Barron's (Vol. 89, July 6, 2009, No. 27, pp. 11)*
Pub: Dow Jones & Co., Inc.
Ed: Katherine Cheng. **Description:** Solar energy industry leaders believe the industry needs aid from the US government regarding the funding of its research efforts and lowering solar energy costs. The

climate change bill passed by the US House of Representatives signifies the US government's desire to significantly reduce carbon dioxide emissions.

7257 ■ *"Lincoln Electric Installs Large Wind Tower"* in *Modern Machine Shop (Vol. 84, October 2011, No. 5, pp. 42)*
Pub: Gardner Business Media, Inc.
Contact: Richard G. Kline, President
E-mail: rkline@gardnerweb.com
Description: Lincoln Electric, a welding product manufacturer, constructed a 443-foot-tall wind tower at its plant in Euclid, Ohio. The tower is expected to generate as much as 10 percent of the facility's energy and save as much as $500,000 annually in energy costs.

7258 ■ *"The Lithium Deficit"* in *Canadian Business (Vol. 82, April 27, 2009, No. 7, pp. 17)*
Pub: Rogers Media
Ed: Joe Castaldo. **Description:** Experts are concerned that there may not be enough lithium available to support the expected rise in demand for the natural resource. Lithium is used in lithium ion batteries, the standard power source for electric and hybrid vehicles. Experts believe that the demand for lithium can only be measured once the technology is out in the market.

7259 ■ *"Loan Dollars Sit Idle for Energy Plan"* in *Baltimore Business Journal (Vol. 28, September 10, 2010, No. 18, pp. 1)*
Pub: Baltimore Business Journal
Ed: Scott Dance. **Description:** The Maryland Energy Administration has millions of dollars in Federal stimulus and state energy efficiency cash sitting idle and might be lost once the window for stimulus spending is gone. However, businesses have no interest in betting on renewable energy because some cannot afford to take out more loans. Other challenges faced by these businesses are presented.

7260 ■ *"The Long View: Roberta Bondar on Science and the Need for Education"* in *Canadian Business (Vol. 81, October 27, 2008, No. 18)*
Pub: Rogers Media Ltd.
Ed: Alex Mlynek. **Description:** Roberta Bondar believes that energy and renewable energy is a critical environmental issue faced by Canada today. Bondar is the first Canadian woman and neurologist in space.

7261 ■ *"A Look At Three Gas-Less Cars"* in *Hispanic Business (Vol. 30, September 2008, No. 9, pp. 90)*
Pub: Hispanic Business, Inc.
Ed: Daniel Soussa. **Description:** Three major car manufacturers, Chevrolet, BMW, and Honda, are giving market leader Toyota competition for the next generation of eco-friendly car. The latest and most advanced of the gasoline-less cars designed by the three firms, namely, the Chevrolet Volt, BMW's Hydrogen 7, and the Honda FCX Clarity, are reviewed.

7262 ■ *"Lunch Box Maker Gives Back"* in *Marketing to Women (Vol. 23, November 2010, No. 11, pp. 5)*
Pub: EPM Communications Inc.
Contact: Ira Mayer, President
E-mail: imayer@epmcom.com
Description: Female entrepreneurs launched a new program called, 'Share Your Lunch Project' that encourages mothers to give back and replace their child's lunchbox with their eco-friendly lunch boxes, which are available at select retailers. All proceeds from the project will benefit the World Food Program USA, which feeds children in developing countries.

7263 ■ *"Magpower May Build Solar Panels Here"* in *Austin Business Journal (Vol. 31, May 13, 2011, No. 10, pp. A1)*
Pub: American City Business Journals Inc.
Ed: Christopher Calnan. **Description:** RRE Austin Solar LLC CEO Doven Mehta has revealed plans to partner with Portugal-based Magpower SA, only if Austin energy buys electricity from planned solar

energy farm in Pflugerville. Austin Energy has received 100 bids from 35 companies to supply 200 megawatts of solar- and wind-generated electricity.

7264 ■ *"Making Waves"* in *Business Journal Portland (Vol. 27, November 26, 2010, No. 39, pp. 1)*
Pub: Portland Business Journal
Ed: Erik Siemers. **Description:** Corvallis, Oregon-based Columbia Power Technologies LLC is about to close a $2 million Series A round of investment initiated by $750,000 from Oregon Angel Fund. The wave energy startup company was formed to commercialize the wave buoy technology developed by Oregon State University researchers.

7265 ■ *"Missouri Public Service Commission Chooses APX"* in *Wireless News (January 22, 2010)*
Pub: Investment Weekly News
Description: Missouri Public Service Commission, with the help of APX Inc., an infrastructure provider for environmental and energy markets, has selected the North American Registry as the renewable energy certificate management system for Missouri Renewable Energy Standard compliance. APX will continue to support the state's renewable energy programs and manage their environmental assets.

7266 ■ *"Mixing Business and Pleasure On the Green"* in *Black Enterprise (Vol. 41, October 2010, No. 3, pp. 65)*
Pub: Earl G. Graves Publishing Co. Inc.
Ed: Annya M. Lott. **Description:** Glow Golf, sponsored by Glow Sports, will offer instruction to 150 female corporate executives and entrepreneurs to learn the fundamentals of the game of golf.

7267 ■ *"Molycorp Funds Wind Energy Technology Company"* in *Manufacturing Close-Up (September 19, 2011)*
Pub: Close-Up Media
Description: Molycorp Inc., producer of rare earth oxides (REO) and a REO producer outside of China, announced it will invest in Boulder Wind Power, which has designed a rare earth magnet powered wind turbine generator. This new generator can produce electricity as low as $0.04 per Kilowatt Hour. Boulder Wind Power's patented wind turbine technology allows for use of rare earth permanent magnets that do not require dysprosium, which is relatively scarce.

7268 ■ *"Mr. Clean"* in *Canadian Business (Vol. 81, October 27, 2008, No. 18, pp. 74)*
Pub: Rogers Media Ltd.
Ed: Rachel Pulfer. **Description:** Profile of Nicholas Parker, co-founder of Cleantech Group LLC, a pioneer in clean technology investing. Cleantech, now a global industry, accounts for 10 percent of all venture capital investments made by U.S. companies in 2007.

7269 ■ *The Necessary Revolution: Working Together to Create a Sustainable World*
Pub: Broadway Books
Contact: David Drake, Manager
E-mail: ddrake@randomhouse.com
Ed: Peter M. Senge, Bryan Smith, Nina Kruschwitz, Joe Laur, Sara Schley. **Released:** April 6, 2010. **Price:** $18.00. **Description:** The book outlines various examples for companies to implement sustainable change and go green in the process.

7270 ■ *"N.E.'s Largest Solar Site Set for Scituate Landfill"* in *Boston Business Journal (Vol. 30, December 17, 2010, No. 47, pp. 1)*
Pub: Boston Business Journal
Ed: Kyle Alspach. **Description:** A closed 12-acre landfill in Scituate, Massachusetts is the proposed site for a 2.4-megawatt solar power plant. The town government will buy the power at a discounted rate, saving it $200,000 annually.

7271 ■ *"The New Alchemists"* in *Canadian Business (Vol. 81, October 27, 2008, No. 18, pp. 22)*
Pub: Rogers Media Ltd.
Ed: Joe Castaldo. **Description:** Ethanol industry expects second-generation ethanol or cellulosic biofuels to provide ecologically friendly technologies than

the ethanol made from food crops. Government and industries are investing on producing cellulosic biofuels.

7272 ■ *"A New Alliance For Global Change"* **in Harvard Business Review (Vol. 88, September 2010, No. 9, pp. 56)**

Pub: Harvard Business School Publishing

Ed: Bill Drayton, Valeria Budinich. **Description:** Collaboration between social organizations and for-profit firms through the development of hybrid value chains to target complex global issues is promoted. While social organizations offer links to communities and consumers, firms provide financing and scale expertise.

7273 ■ *"New Book Takes Alternate View on Ontario's Wind Industry"* **in CNW Group (September 19, 2011)**

Pub: CNW Group

Contact: Carolyn McGill-Davidson, President

Description: Dirty Business: The Reality Behind Ontario's Rush to Wind Power, was written by editor and health care writer Jane Wilson of Ottawa, Ontario, Canada along with contributing editor Parker Gallant. The book contains articles and papers on the wind business, including information on illnesses caused from the environmental noise.

7274 ■ *"A New Day is Dawning"* **in Indoor Comfort Marketing (Vol. 70, August 2011, No. 8, pp. 18)**

Pub: Industry Publications Inc.

Ed: Paul Nazzaro. **Description:** New trends in the HVAC/R industry regarding biofuels and bioheat are explored.

7275 ■ *"Next Stage of Green Building will be Water Efficiency"* **in Contractor (Vol. 56, July 2009, No. 7, pp. 41)**

Pub: Penton Media, Inc.

Description: One market report says that water efficiency and conservation will become critical factors in green design, construction, and product selection in the next five years from 2009. The report outlines how critical it will be for the construction industry to address responsible water practices in the future.

7276 ■ *"N.H. Near the LEED in Green Space"* **in New Hampshire Business Review (Vol. 33, March 25, 2011, No. 6, pp. 30)**

Pub: Business Publications Inc.

Description: New Hamphire's architects, contractors and suppliers are among the leaders with LEED-certified space per capita.

7277 ■ *"NStar Feels the Heat"* **in Cape Cod Times (September 30, 2011)**

Pub: Cape Cod Media Group

Ed: Patrick Cassidy. **Description:** Massachusetts energy officials wish to delay a merger between NStar and Northeast Utilities until it is clear how the partnership would meet the state's green energy goals. Governor Deval Patrick supports the proposed Nantucket Sound wind farm.

7278 ■ *"Nuclear Renaissance"* **in Canadian Business (Vol. 83, August 17, 2010, No. 13-14, pp. 46)**

Pub: Rogers Media Ltd.

Description: Nuclear energy has come back into the public's favor in Canada because it has virtually no emissions and is always available anytime of the day. Canada's nuclear industry has also achieved an incomparable record of safe, economic and reliable power generation in three provinces for 48 years.

7279 ■ *"On Growth Path of Rising Star"* **in Boston Business Journal (Vol. 31, June 24, 2011, No. 22, pp. 3)**

Pub: Boston Business Journal

Ed: Kyle Alspach. **Description:** 1366 Technologies Inc. of Lexington, Massachusetts is considered a rising solar power technology company. The firm secured $150 million loan guarantee from the US Department of Energy that could go to the construction of a 1,000 megawatt solar power plant.

7280 ■ *"One on One With SEIA's President, CEO"* **in Contractor (Vol. 57, January 2010, No. 1, pp. 40)**

Pub: Penton Media, Inc.

Ed: Dave Yates. **Description:** Solar Energy Industries Association President and CEO Rhone Resch says that the deployment of solar systems in the U.S. has exploded since 2005 and that there is a need to make inroads for shaping the U.S. energy policy. Resch says one of the hurdles they face is that there are no universal standards.

7281 ■ *"OPEC Exposed"* **in Hawaii Business (Vol. 54, September 2008, No. 3, pp. 2)**

Pub: Hawaii Business Publishing

Ed: Serena Lim. **Description:** Organization of the Petroleum Exporting Countries (OPEC) has said that their effort in developing an alternative energy source has driven prices up. The biofuel sector is criticizing the statement, saying that a research study found that biofuels push petroleum prices down by 15 percent. Details on the effect of rising petroleum prices are discussed.

7282 ■ *"Out of Juice?"* **in Canadian Business (Vol. 81, October 27, 2008, No. 18, pp. 32)**

Pub: Rogers Media Ltd.

Ed: Joe Castaldo. **Description:** Alternative energy experts suggest Canada should be more aggressive and should make major policy changes on energy alternatives despite an Ernst & Young research that rated the country high on renewable energy.

7283 ■ *"Overheating Taking Place? Pay Attention to Details.."* **in Indoor Comfort Marketing (Vol. 70, March 2011, No. 3, pp.)**

Pub: Industry Publications Inc.

Ed: George R. Carey. **Description:** Boiler facts are outlined to help the small HVAC company when servicing customers.

7284 ■ *"An Overview of Energy Consumption of the Globalized World Economy"* **in Energy Policy (Vol. 39, October 2011, No. 10, pp. 5920-2928)**

Pub: Reed Elsevier Reference Publishing

Ed: Z.M. Chen, G.Q. Chen. **Description:** Energy consumption and its impact on the global world economy is examined.

7285 ■ *"Phoenix Conference Reveals Opportunities are Coming"* **in Indoor Comfort Marketing (Vol. 70, March 2011, No. 3, pp. 24)**

Pub: Industry Publications Inc.

Ed: Paul J. Nazzaro. **Description:** Advanced liquid fuels were spotlighted at the Phoenix conference revealing the opportunities for using liquid fuels.

7286 ■ *"Positive Transformational Change"* **in Indoor Comfort Marketing (Vol. 70, April 2011, No. 4, pp. 30)**

Pub: Industry Publications Inc.

Ed: Blaine Fox. **Description:** Management changes taking place at Shark Bites HVAC firm are discussed.

7287 ■ *"PPC's Major Commitment to Biofuel Infrastructure"* **in Indoor Comfort Marketing (Vol. 70, April 2011, No. 4, pp. 6)**

Pub: Industry Publications Inc.

Description: Petroleum Products Corporation's commitment to the biofuel infrastructure is outlined.

7288 ■ *"Pre-Certified LEED Hotel Prototype Reduces Energy Use, Conserves Water"* **in Contractor (Vol. 57, January 2010, No. 1, pp. 3)**

Pub: Penton Media, Inc.

Ed: Candace Roulo. **Description:** Marriott International Inc.'s LEED pre-certified prototype hotel will reduce a hotel's energy and water consumption by 25 percent and save owners approximately $100,000. Their Courtyard Settler's Ridge in Pittsburgh will be the first hotel built based on the prototype.

7289 ■ *"Programs Provide Education and Training"* **in Contractor (Vol. 56, September 2009, No. 9, pp. 56)**

Pub: Penton Media, Inc.

Ed: William Feldman; Patti Feldman. **Description:** Opportunity Interactive's Showroom v2 software provides uses computer graphics to provide educa-

tion and training on HVAC equipment and systems. It can draw heat pump balance points for a specific home. Meanwhile, Simutech's HVAC Training Simulators provide trainees with 'hands-on' HVACR training.

7290 ■ *"PSC Approves $130M TECO Solar Project"* **in Tampa Bay Business Journal (Vol. 30, December 18, 2009, No. 52, pp. 1)**

Pub: American City Business Journals

Ed: Michael Hinman. **Description:** Florida's Public Service Commission has endorsed Tampa Electric Company's plan to add 25 megawatts of solar energy to its portfolio. TECO's plan needed the approval by PSC to defray additional costs for the project through ratepayers.

7291 ■ *"Radiant - the Hottest Topic in .. Cooling"* **in Indoor Comfort Marketing (Vol. 70, February 2011, No. 2, pp. 8)**

Pub: Industry Publications Inc.

Description: Examination of radiant cooling systems, a new trend in cooling homes and buildings.

7292 ■ *"Recycling 202: How to Take Your Recycling Practices to the Next Level"* **in Black Enterprise (Vol. 41, September 2010, No. 2, pp. 38)**

Pub: Earl G. Graves Publishing Co. Inc.

Ed: Tamara E. Holmes. **Description:** Consumer Electronics Association and other organizations, manufacturers and retailers list ways to recycle all household items.

7293 ■ *"Reducing the Book's Carbon Footprint"* **in American Printer (Vol. 128, July 1, 2011, No. 7)**

Pub: Penton Media Inc.

Description: Green Press Initiative's Book Industry Environmental Council is working to achieve a 20 percent reduction in the book industry's carbon footprint by 2020. The Council is made up of publishers, printers, paper suppliers, and non-governmental organizations.

7294 ■ *"Reinventing Marketing to Manage the Environmental Imperative"* **in Journal of Marketing (Vol. 75, July 2011, No. 4, pp. 132)**

Pub: American Marketing Association

Ed: Philip Kotler. **Description:** Marketers must now examine their theory and practices due to the growing recognition of finite resources and high environmental costs. Companies also need to balance more carefully their growth goals with the need to purse sustainability. Insights on the rise of demarketing and social marketing are also given.

7295 ■ *"Renewable Energy Adoption in an Aging Population"* **in Energy Policy (Vol. 39, October 2011, No. 10, pp. 6021-6029)**

Pub: Reed Elsevier Reference Publishing

Ed: Ken Willis, Riccardo Scarpa, Rose Gilroy, Neveen Hamza. **Description:** Attitudes and impacts of renewable energy adoption on an aging population is examined.

7296 ■ *"Renewable Energy Market Opportunities: Wind Testing"* **in PR Newswire (September 22, 2011)**

Pub: United Business Media

Description: Global wind energy test systems markets are discussed. Research conducted covers both non-destructive test equipment and condition monitoring equipment product segments.

7297 ■ *"ReVenture Plan Appears Close to Landing Key Legislative Deal"* **in Charlotte Business Journal (Vol. 25, July 9, 2010, No. 16, pp. 1)**

Pub: Charlotte Business Journal

Ed: John Downey. **Description:** North Carolina lawmakers acted on special legislation that would boost development of Forsite Development 667-acre ReVenture Energy Park. The legislation could also improve chances that Duke Energy Carolinas will contract to purchase the power from the planned 50-megawatt biomass power plant located at the park. How utilities would benefit from the legislation is also discussed.

7298 ■ *"Rivals Blow In"* in Crain's Cleveland Business (Vol. 30, June 1, 2009, No. 21, pp. 1)
Pub: Crain Communications, Inc.

Ed: Chuck Soder. **Description:** U.S. and Canadian competitors are hoping to start construction of offshore wind farm project proposed by Cuyahoga County's Great Lakes Energy Development Task Force. Details of the project are included.

7299 ■ *"Rosewood Site Faces Big Cleanup"* in Baltimore Business Journal (Vol. 27, February 6, 2010, No. 40, pp. 1)
Pub: American City Business Journals

Ed: Daniel J. Sernovitz. **Description:** Environmental assessment report states that Maryland's Rosewood Center for the Developmentally Disabled has significant amounts of toxic chemicals, which could impact Stevenson University's decision to purchase the property. Senator Robert A. Zirkin believes that the state should pay for the cleanup, which is expected to cost millions.

7300 ■ *"Rough Headwinds"* in Boston Business Journal (Vol. 30, November 12, 2010, No. 42, pp. 1)
Pub: Boston Business Journal

Ed: Kyle Alspach. **Description:** Views of residents, as well as key information on First Wind's plan to install wind power turbines in Brimfield, Massachusetts are presented. Residents believe that First Wind's project will devalue properties, compromise quality of life, and ruin the rural quality of Brimfield. First Wind expects to produce 2,000 megawatts of power from wind by 2020.

7301 ■ *"San Diego Museum Receives LEED Certification"* in Contractor (Vol. 57, January 2010, No. 1, pp. 14)
Pub: Penton Media, Inc.

Description: San Diego Natural History Museum received an LEED certification for existing buildings. The certification process began when they committed to displaying the Dead Sea Scrolls in 2007 and they had to upgrade their buildings' air quality and to control for air moisture, temperature, and volume. They reduced their energy consumption by upwards of 20 percent.

7302 ■ *"Sandvik Expands Energy-Saving Program"* in Modern Machine Shop (Vol. 84, September 2011, No. 4, pp. 48)
Pub: Gardner Business Media, Inc.
Contact: Richard G. Kline, President
E-mail: rkline@gardnerweb.com

Description: Sandvik Coromant, based in Fair Lawn, New Jersey, expanded its Sustainable Manufacturing Program that originally was developed to help Japanese-based firms reduce electricity consumption by 15 percent after the recent earthquake that cause loss of electrical power. The program now provides energy reduction through the Sandvick cutting tool technology, application techniques and productivity increases.

7303 ■ *"The Second Most Fuel-Efficient Tractor of the Decade: John Deere 8320R"* in Farm Industry News (November 10, 2011)
Pub: Penton Business Media Inc.

Description: John Deere's 8320R Tractor was ranked second in the Farm Industry News listing of the top 40 most fuel-efficient tractors of the decade, following the winner, John Deere's 8295R PTO tractor.

7304 ■ *"Shaw Joins Green Institute Launch"* in Home Textiles Today (Vol. 31, May 24, 2011, No. 13, pp. 4)
Pub: Reed Business Information
Contact: Jeff Greisch, President

Description: Shaw Industries Group joined the Green Products Innovation Institute, the first nonprofit institute of its kind in America. The institute promotes the concepts of reverse engineering, elimination of waste, safe chemistries, and closed loop technical nutrients.

7305 ■ *"Shifting Gears"* in Business Journal-Serving Phoenix & the Valley of the Sun (Vol. 31, November 12, 2010, No. 10, pp. 1)
Pub: Phoenix Business Journal

Ed: Patrick O'Grady. **Description:** Automotive parts recyclers in Arizona are benefiting from the challenging national economic conditions as well as from the green movement. Recyclers revealed that customers prefer recycled parts more because they are cheaper and are more environmentally friendly. Other information about the automotive parts recycling industry is presented.

7306 ■ *"Slick Science"* in Canadian Business (Vol. 81, September 15, 2008, No. 14-15, pp. 55)
Pub: Rogers Media Ltd.

Ed: Andrew Nikiforuk. **Description:** N-Solv Corp's John Nenniger has discovered a better alternative to steam-assisted gravity drainage methods for extracting bitumen. Nenniger's technique also relies on gravity but replaces steam with propane, which leaves behind impurities like asphaltenes and heavy metals that are too dirty to burn.

7307 ■ *"Small Wind Power Market to Double by 2015 at $634 Million"* in Western Farm Press (September 30, 2011)
Pub: Penton Media, Inc.

Description: Small wind power provides cost-effective electricity on a highly localized level, in both remote settings as well as in conjunction with power from the utility grid. Government incentives are spurring new growth in the industry.

7308 ■ *"Smart Car Sales Take Big Hit in Recession"* in Business Journal-Milwaukee (Vol. 28, December 10, 2010, No. 10, pp. A1)
Pub: Milwaukee Business Journal

Ed: Stacey Vogel Davis. **Description:** Sales of smart cars in Milwaukee declined in 2010. Smart Center Milwaukee sold only 52 new cars through October 2010. Increased competition is seen as a reason for the decline in sales.

7309 ■ *"Snow Melt Systems Offer Practical Solutions"* in Contractor (Vol. 56, October 2009, No. 10, pp. S6)
Pub: Penton Media, Inc.

Ed: Lisa Murton Beets. **Description:** Cases are discussed in which the installation of a snow melt system becomes a necessity. One example describes how limited space means there would be no place to put plowed snow; snow melt systems can also resolve problems that arise due to an excess of melting snow.

7310 ■ *"Solar Choices"* in Contractor (Vol. 56, October 2009, No. 10, pp. 32)
Pub: Penton Media, Inc.

Ed: Tom Scheel. **Description:** Price, performance, and ease of installation of a flat plate versus an evacuated tube collector for a plumbing and heating job are compared. The better choice with regards to weight, aesthetics, efficiency in warm or cool climates, year round load, and space heating is discussed.

7311 ■ *"Solar Credit Lapse Spur Late Demand"* in The Business Journal - Serving Phoenix and the Valley of the Sun (Vol. 28, July 18, 2008)
Pub: American City Business Journals, Inc.

Ed: Patrick O'Grady. **Description:** Businesses looking to engage in the solar energy industry are facing the problems of taxation and limited solar panel supply. Solar panels manufacturers are focusing more on the European market. Political issues surrounding the federal tax credit policy on solar energy users are also discussed.

7312 ■ *"Something Different in the Air? The Collapse of the Schwarzenegger Health Plan in California"* in WorkingUSA (June 2008)
Pub: Blackwell Publishers Ltd.

Ed: Daniel J.B. Mitchell. **Description:** In January 2007, California Governor Arnold Schwarzenegger proposed a state universal health care plan modeled after the Massachusetts individual mandate program.

A year later, the plan was dead. Although some key interest groups eventually backed the plan, it was overwhelmed by a looming state budget crisis and a lack of gubernatorial focus. Although much acclaimed for his stance on greenhouse gases, stem cells, hydrogen highways, and other Big Ideas, diffused gubernatorial priorities and a failure to resolve California's chronic fiscal difficulties let the clock run out on universal health care.

7313 ■ *"Start Connecting Today"* in Indoor Comfort Marketing (Vol. 70, May 2011, No. 5, pp. 34)
Pub: Industry Publications Inc.

Ed: Paul Nazzaro. **Description:** An in-depth discussion regarding the use of biofuels on bioheat use and dealership.

7314 ■ *"Start Moving Toward Advanced Fuels"* in Indoor Comfort Marketing (Vol. 70, March 2011, No. 3, pp. 4)
Pub: Industry Publications Inc.

Ed: Michael L. SanGiovanni. **Description:** Commentary on advanced fuels is presented.

7315 ■ *"Start Thinking About Carbon Assets - Now"* in Harvard Business Review (Vol. 86, September 2008, No. 9, pp. 28)
Pub: Harvard Business School Press

Ed: Alex Rau; Robert Toker. **Description:** Economic and strategic benefits of adopting a corporate carbon assets policy are discussed. Topics include renewable energy and capturing waste energy.

7316 ■ *"State Investment Goes Sour"* in Business Journal Portland (Vol. 26, December 4, 2009, No. 39, pp. 1)
Pub: American City Business Journals Inc.

Ed: Erik Siemers. **Description:** Oregon might recoup only $500,000 of a $20 million loan to Vancouver-based Cascade Grain Products LLC. Cascade Grain's ethanol plant in Clatskanie, OR will be put into auction under the supervision of a bankruptcy court.

7317 ■ *State Wildlife Laws Handbook*
Pub: Government Institutes
Contact: Judith Rothman, Director
URL(s): www.govinstpress.comwildlifelaw.unm.edu/statbook/intro.html. **Price:** $127, Individuals cloth. **Publication includes:** Listing of state fish and wildlife agencies. **Entries include:** Name, address, phone. Principal content of publication is an analysis of wildlife management and protection laws for all fifty states.

7318 ■ *"Stimulus 'Loser' Won't Build Plant in Mass."* in Boston Business Journal (Vol. 30, November 5, 2010, No. 41, pp. 1)
Pub: Boston Business Journal

Ed: Kyle Alspach. **Description:** Boston-Power Inc. no longer plans to build an electric vehicle battery plant in Massachusetts after it failed to obtain stimulus funds from the federal government. The company is instead looking to build a lithium-ion battery plant in China and possibly Europe.

7319 ■ *"The Superpower Dilemma"* in Canadian Business (Vol. 83, August 17, 2010, No. 13-14, pp. 42)
Pub: Rogers Media Ltd.

Description: Canada has been an energy superpower partly because it controls the energy source and the production means, particularly of fossil fuels. However, Canada's status as superpower could diminish if it replaces petroleum exports with renewable technology for using sources of energy available globally.

7320 ■ *"Sustainability Is Top Priority for GreenTown Chicago"* in Contractor (Vol. 56, November 2009, No. 11, pp. 1)
Pub: Penton Media, Inc.

Ed: Candace Roulo. **Description:** GreenTown Chicago 2009 conference tackled energy-efficient practices and technologies, green design and building, and sustainable policies. Water conservation was also a topic at the conference and one mayor who made a presentation said that reducing the water loss in the system is a priority in the city's endeavor.

7321 ■ "Suzlon S88-Powered Wind Farm in Minnesota Secures Long-Term Financing" in PR Newswire (September 21, 2011)
Pub: United Business Media
Description: Suzlon Energy Limited is the world's fifth largest manufacturer of wind turbines. Owners of the Grant County Wind Farm in Minnesota have secured a long-term financing deal for the ten Suzlon S88 2.1 MW wind turbines that generate enough electricity to power 7,000 homes.

7322 ■ "Taxis Are Set to Go Hybrid" in Philadelphia Business Journal (Vol. 30, September 16, 2011, No. 31, pp. 1)
Pub: American City Business Journals Inc.
Ed: Natalie Kostelni. **Description:** Taxis are going hybrid in several major states such as New York, California and Maryland where it is mandated, but it is yet to happen in Philadelphia, Pennsylvania with the exception of one taxi company. Freedom Taxi is awaiting Philadelphia Parking Authority's sign off.

7323 ■ "Think the Oilsands Are an Environmental Disaster?" in Canadian Business (Vol. 83, October 12, 2010, No. 17, pp. 52)
Pub: Rogers Media Ltd.
Ed: Michael McCullough. **Description:** Studies which were commissioned by the Alberta Energy Research Institute in 2008 found that the life-cycle carbon emissions of oil derived from oilsands was 10 percent greater than the average from all sources. Synthetic crude from the oilsands is 38 percent less carbon-intensive than it was 20 years ago due to productivity improvements.

7324 ■ "Thirsty? Now There's a Water Cooler to Suit Every Taste" in Inc. (Vol. 33, October 2011, No. 8, pp. 43)
Pub: Inc. Magazine
Ed: John Brandon. **Description:** Brita's Hydration Station is a wall-mounted unit with a touch-free sensor for dispensing water. This water cooler cuts down on landfill waste and offers special features.

7325 ■ The Three Secrets of Green Business: Unlocking Competitive Advantage in a Low Carbon Economy
Pub: Earthscan
Ed: Gareth Kane. **Released:** February 10, 2010. **Price:** $96.00. **Description:** Small business is coming under increasing pressure from government, customers and campaigning groups to improve environmental performance. Soaring utility and compliance costs are critical financial burdens on small companies.

7326 ■ "Timberland's CEO On Standing Up to 65,000 Angry Activists" in Harvard Business Review (Vol. 88, September 2010, No. 9, pp. 39)
Pub: Harvard Business School Publishing
Ed: Jeff Swartz. **Description:** Timberland Company avoided a potential boycott by taking a two-way approach. It addressed a supplier issue that posed a threat to the environment, and launched an email campaign to keep Greenpeace activists informed of the development of a new supplier agreement.

7327 ■ "Time to Green Your Business" in Gallup Management Journal (April 22, 2011)
Pub: Gallup
Ed: Bryant Ott. **Description:** It's Earth Day, so expect to hear companies touting their commitment to the environment. However, according to Gallup, more companies are finding it more interested to talk about being green than actually taking the steps to become a green business.

7328 ■ "Toolmakers' New Tack" in Crain's Detroit Business (Vol. 25, June 8, 2009,)
Pub: Crain Communications Inc. - Detroit
Ed: Ryan Beene, Amy Lane. **Description:** MAG Industrial Automation Systems LLC and Dowding Machining Inc. have partnered to advance wind-turbine technology. The goal is to cut costs of wind energy to the same level as carbon-based fuel.

7329 ■ "Toward a Better Future" in Canadian Business (Vol. 83, August 17, 2010, No. 13-14, pp. 51)
Pub: Rogers Media Ltd.
Description: A look at certain realities in order to build a better future for Canada's energy industry is presented. Canada must focus on making the oil cleaner, instead of replacing it with another source since dependency on oil will remain in this lifetime. Canada must also develop solutions toward clean technology power sources.

7330 ■ "Traer Turning to Wind Power to Meet Long-Term Energy Needs" in Waterloo Courier (September 20, 2011)
Pub: Lee Enterprises
Ed: Josh Nelson. **Description:** Traer Municipal Utilities is working with Clark Thompson, a Story City wind turbine developer, to erect a wind turbine to supply electrical energy to the city. Details are included.

7331 ■ "Tucson Tech Column" in AZ Daily Star (September 27, 2011)
Pub: Arizona Daily Star
Ed: David Wichner. **Description:** Western Wind Energy, based in Vancouver, British Columbia, Canada is able to harness energy from the sun when the wind is not blowing at the Kingman I Project wind farm. Details of this technology are outlined.

7332 ■ "UA Turns Ann Arbor Green" in Contractor (Vol. 56, September 2009, No. 9, pp. 5)
Pub: Penton Media, Inc.
Ed: Robert P. Mader. **Description:** Instructors at the United Association of Plumbers and Steamfitters have studied the latest in green and sustainable construction and service at the Washtenaw Community College in Michigan. Classes included building information modeling, hydronic heating and cooling and advanced HVACR troubleshooting. The UA is currently focusing on green training.

7333 ■ "Ultra Green Energy Services Opens NJ Biodiesel Transload Facility" in Indoor Comfort Marketing (Vol. 70, June 2011, No. 6, pp. 35)
Pub: Industry Publications Inc.
Description: Profile of Ultra Green Energy Services and the opening of their new biodiesel facility in New Jersey is discussed.

7334 ■ "Ultra Low Sulfur Diesel: The Promise and the Reality" in Indoor Comfort Marketing (Vol. 70, July 2011, No. 7, pp. 22)
Pub: Industry Publications Inc.
Ed: Ed Kitchen. **Description:** Impacts of ultra low sulfur diesel are examined.

7335 ■ "Unilever to Sustainably Source All Paper and Board Packaging" in Ice Cream Reporter (Vol. 23, July 20, 2010, No. 8, pp. 1)
Pub: Ice Cream Reporter
Description: Unilever, a leader in the frozen dessert market, has developed a new sustainable paper and board packaging sourcing policy that will reduce environmental impact by working with suppliers to source 75 percent of paper and board packaging from sustainably managed forests or from recycled material. Unilever is parent company to Breyers, Haagen-Dazs, Klondike, Popsicle and other ice cream brands.

7336 ■ "University Data Center Goes Off-Grid, Is Test Bed" in Contractor (Vol. 57, February 2010, No. 2, pp. 1)
Pub: Penton Media, Inc.
Ed: Candace Roulo. **Description:** Syracuse University's Green Data Center has gone off-grid through the use of natural gas fired turbines. It is expected to use 50 percent less energy than a typical computer center. The center's heating and cooling system setup is also discussed.

7337 ■ "Valener Announces that Gaz Metro has Achieved a Key Step in Acquiring CVPS" in CNW Group (September 30, 2011)
Pub: CNW Group
Contact: Carolyn McGill-Davidson, President
Description: Valener Inc., which owns about 29 percent of Gaz Metro Ltd. Partnership, announced that Gaz Metro welcomes the sale of Central Vermont

Public Service Corporation (CVPS). Valener owns an indirect interest of 24.5 percent in the wind power projects jointly developed by Beaupre Eole General Partnership and Boralex Inc. on private lands in Quebec. Details of the deal are included.

7338 ■ "VeriFone Announces Global Security Solutions Business" in Marketing Weekly News (October 3, 2009)
Pub: Investment Weekly News
Description: Focused on delivering innovative security solutions, VeriFone Holdings, Inc. announced the formation of its Global Security Solutions Business Unit, including VeriShield Protect, an end-to-end encryption to protect cardholder data throughout the merchant and processor systems. The business will focus on consulting, sales and implementation of these new products in order to help retailers and processors protect customer data.

7339 ■ "Volunteers Needed" in Canadian Business (Vol. 81, October 27, 2008, No. 18, pp. 60)
Pub: Rogers Media Ltd.
Ed: Megan Harman. **Description:** Emissions-targeting regulations focus on the biggest polluters, missing out on other companies that leave carbon footprints in things such as shipping and travel. Some companies in Canada have initiated programs to offset their carbon emissions. Critics claim that offsetting does not reduce emissions and the programs merely justify pollution.

7340 ■ "Warm Floors Make Warm Homes" in Contractor (Vol. 56, October 2009, No. 10, pp. S18)
Pub: Penton Media, Inc.
Ed: Lisa Murton Beets. **Description:** Three award winning radiant floor-heating installations are presented. The design and the equipment used for these systems are discussed.

7341 ■ "Was Mandating Solar Power Water Heaters For New Homes Good Policy?" in Hawaii Business (Vol. 54, August 2008, No. 2, pp. 28)
Pub: Hawaii Business Publishing
Description: Senator Gary L. Kooser of District 7 Kauai-Niihau believes that the mandating of energy-efficient water heaters for new single-family homes starting in 2010 will help cut Hawaii's oil consumption. Ron Richmond of the Hawaii Solar Energy Association says that the content of SB 644 has negative consequences as it allows for choice of energy and not just solar, and it also eliminates tax credits for new homebuyers.

7342 ■ "Water Conservation Helps GC's Building Attain LEED Gold Status" in Contractor (Vol. 56, September 2009, No. 9, pp. 5)
Pub: Penton Media, Inc.
Description: Green contractor Marshall Erdman has built a new office building using green design. The facility is seen to become a prime Leadership in Energy and Environmental Design (LEED) building model. Details of the building's design and features are also provided.

7343 ■ "Water Distiller" in Canadian Business (Vol. 81, September 29, 2008, No. 16, pp. 52)
Pub: Rogers Media Ltd.
Ed: Matthew McClearn. **Description:** Les Fairn's invention of a water distiller called a Solarsphere was recognized in the Great Canadian Invention Competition. Fairn's invention resembles a buoy that uses the sun's energy to vaporize dirty water then leaves the impurities behind in a sump. The invention has an application for producing potable water in impoverished countries.

7344 ■ "Western Wind Energy Corporation" in CNW Group (October 4, 2011)
Pub: CNW Group
Contact: Carolyn McGill-Davidson, President
Description: Profile of Western Wind Energy Corporation will complete the installation of 60 wind turbines by the end of 2011. The first 106MW are ready for pre-commissioning with the ability to sell power in November when the site is interconnected.

7345 ■ *"What Are Canada's Industrial Polluters Doing to Reduce Emissions?" in Canadian Business (Vol. , pp.)*
Pub: Rogers Media Ltd.
Ed: Matthew McClearn. **Description:** Efforts by Canada's industrial polluters to reduce emissions are examined. Syncrude Canada plans to reduce sulphur emissions by 60 percent in 2011, while TransAlta invests in emission reduction programs. Environmental groups, however, claim that companies are not doing enough to protect the environment.

7346 ■ *"What Is a Geothermal Heat Pump" in Indoor Comfort Marketing (Vol. 70, August 2011, No. 8, pp. 14)*
Pub: Industry Publications Inc.
Ed: George Carey. **Description:** Examination of geothermal heat pumps is provided, citing new trends in the industry.

7347 ■ *"Where the Future is Made" in Indoor Comfort Marketing (Vol. 70, May 2011, No. 5, pp. 48)*
Pub: Industry Publications Inc.
Description: Research being performed at Brookhaven National Laboratory, located in Upton, New York, is discussed, focusing on new energy sources for our nation.

7348 ■ *"A Whiff of TV Reality" in Houston Business Journal (Vol. 40, January 22, 2010, No. 37, pp. A1)*
Pub: American City Business Journals
Ed: Christine Hall. **Description:** Houston, Texas-based Waste Management Inc.'s president and chief operation officer, Larry O'Donnell shares some of his experience as CBS Television Network reality show 'Undercover Boss' participant. O'Donnell believes the show was a great way to show the customers how tough their jobs are and reveals that the most difficult job was being a sorter at the recycling center.

7349 ■ *"Will Home Buyers Pay for Green Features?" in Contractor (Vol. 56, October 2009, No. 10, pp. 70)*
Pub: Penton Media, Inc.
Ed: Bob Mader. **Description:** National Association of Home Builders commissioned a survey which shows that homeowners are interested in green as long as they do no have to pay much for it. The association did not allow a board member to read the survey which raises questions about how the questions were phrased and how the sample was selected.

7350 ■ *"Wind Gets Knocked Out of Energy Farm Plan" in Buffalo News (September 28, 2011)*
Pub: Buffalo News
Ed: David Robinson. **Description:** New York Power Authority formally killed the proposal for a wind energy farm off the shores of Lake Erie and Lake Ontario. The Authority cited high subsidy costs would be required to make the wind farm economically feasible. Details of the proposal are outlined.

7351 ■ *"Yates Helps Turn Log Home Green" in Contractor (Vol. 56, December 2009, No. 12, pp. 40)*
Pub: Penton Media, Inc.
Description: Upgrading and greening of a log home's HVAC system in Pennsylvania is discussed. F. W. Behler Inc. president Dave Yates was chosen to manage the project. A large coil of R-flex was used to connect the buffer tank to the garage's radiant heat system.

7352 ■ *"Yates Turns Log Home Green - Part Three" in Contractor (Vol. 57, January 2010, No. 1, pp. 5)*
Pub: Penton Media, Inc.
Description: Dave Yates of F.W. Behler Inc. discusses remodeling a log home's HVAC system with geo-to-radiant heat and thermal-solar systems. The solar heater's installation is discussed.

7353 ■ *"You're a What? Wind Turbine Service Technician" in Occupational Outlook Quarterly (Vol. 54, Fall 2010, No. 3, pp. 34)*
Pub: U.S. Bureau of Labor Statistics
Ed: Drew Liming. **Description:** Profile of Brandon Johnson, former member of the Air Force, found a career as a wind turbine service technician.

7354 ■ *"Yudelson Challenges San Antonio Groups" in Contractor (Vol. 56, October 2009, No. 10, pp. 6)*
Pub: Penton Media, Inc.
Description: Green building consultant and author Jerry Yudelson made a presentation for the Central Texas Green Building Council and Leadership San Antonio where he discussed the European approach to sustainability and how it can be used for designing green buildings. Yudelson also discussed how to use sustainable practices for planning 25 years into the future.

SOURCES OF SUPPLY

7355 ■ *Environmental Management Information Systems Report*
Donley Technology
Contact: Elizabeth M. Donley, President
URL(s): www.donleytech.com. **Released:** Latest edition 6th, Published May, 2007. **Price:** $389, Individuals single; $699, Individuals multiple; $999, Individuals company-wide license. **Covers:** 26 software systems that manage environmental data, including inventory and waste tracking, air pollution tracking, report and label generation, mapping, and help with emergency response. **Entries include:** Company name, address, phone, hardware and software requirements, description of system, cost. **Indexes:** Developer/Distributor.

TRADE PERIODICALS

7356 ■ *Composting News*
Pub: McEntee Media Corp.
Ed: Ken McEntee, Editor, ken@recycle.cc. **Released:** Monthly. **Price:** $83, individuals; $93, Canada and Mexico; $105, other countries. **Description:** Covers news and trends in the composting industry. Also reports on compost product prices. Recurring features include letters to the editor, interviews, news of research, a calendar of events, reports of meetings, and notices of publications available.

7357 ■ *E: The Environmental Magazine*
Pub: Earth Action Network
URL(s): www.emagazine.com. **Ed:** Brita Belli. **Released:** Bimonthly **Price:** $24.95, Individuals; $34.95, Two years; $34.95, Canada; $64.95, Other countries.

7358 ■ *Earth Island Journal: An International Environmental News Magazine*
Pub: Earth Island Institute
Contact: John A. Knox, Executive Director
URL(s): www.earthisland.org/journal/. **Ed:** Jason Mark. **Released:** Quarterly **Price:** $9.95, Individuals.

7359 ■ *Environmental Compliance Alert*
Pub: Progressive Business Publications
Ed: Tom Guay, Editor. **Released:** Semimonthly. **Price:** $299. **Description:** Explains the latest air, water and waste regulatory changes affect business in plain English. Recurring features include interviews, news of research, a calendar of events, news of educational opportunities, and a column titled Sharpen Your Judgment.

7360 ■ *Environmental News Network*
Pub: Environmental News Network
URL(s): www.enn.com. **Ed:** Roger Greenway. **Released:** Daily **Price:** $12.95, Individuals world-wide.

7361 ■ *Everyone's Backyard*
Pub: Center For Health, Environment and Justice
Contact: Lois Marie Gibbs, Executive Director
Ed: Stephen U. Lester, Editor. **Released:** Quarterly. **Price:** $35, individuals; $5, single issue. **Description:** Includes information on the grassroots environmental movement. Presents community victories and how the groups organized and succeeded. Supports community activists around the United States.

7362 ■ *The Green Business Letter*
Pub: Tilden Press Inc.
Ed: Joel Makower, Editor. **Released:** Monthly. **Price:** $95 electronic edition; $45 for students and acdemics. **Description:** Helps companies integrate environmental considerations into their operations in a way that creates business value and environmental

improvement. Recurring features include interviews, news of research, reports of meetings, book reviews, and notices of publications available.

7363 ■ *The GreenMoney Journal & Online Guide*
Pub: The Greenmoney Journal
Contact: Cliff Feigenbaum, Editor
E-mail: cliff@greenmoney.com
Released: Bimonthly. **Price:** $50, individuals; $50, Canada plus $10 postage; $50, elsewhere plus $20. **Description:** Encourages and promotes the awareness of socially and environmentally responsible business, investing and consumer resources in publications and online. Our goal is to educate and empower individuals and businesses to make informed financial decisions through aligning their personal, corporate and financial principles. Recurring features include a calendar.

7364 ■ *Inside Cal/EPA*
Pub: Inside Washington Publishers
Contact: Korila Malecha, Manager
Released: Weekly (Fri.). **Price:** $585, U.S. and Canada; $635, elsewhere. **Description:** Reports on environmental legislation, regulation, and litigation.

7365 ■ *Navigator*
Pub: Hudson River Sloop Clearwater Inc.
Ed: Linda Richards, Editor. **Released:** Bimonthly. **Description:** Contains information on environmental issues, globally, nationally, and locally. Recurring features include letters to the editor, interviews, news of research, a calendar of events, and reports of meetings.

7366 ■ *Water Policy Report*
Pub: Inside Washington Publishers
Contact: Korila Malecha, Manager
Released: Biweekly, every other Monday. **Price:** $650, U.S. and Canada; $700, elsewhere. **Description:** Reports on federal water quality programs and policies. Covers topics such as drinking water, toxics, enforcement, monitoring, and state/EPA relations.

7367 ■ *Wind Energy Weekly*
Pub: American Wind Energy Association
Ed: Thomas O. Gray, Editor, tom_gray@igc.org. **Released:** Weekly. **Price:** Included in membership; $595, nonmembers. **Description:** Provides wind energy trade news, plus covers energy and environmental policy. Recurring features include news of research, reports of meetings, job listings, and notices of publications available. Remarks: Available only via E-mail account.

7368 ■ *Windstar Wildlife Garden Weekly*
Pub: WindStar Wildlife Institute
Contact: Thomas D. Patrick, Editor
Released: Weekly. **Price:** Included in membership; $25, nonmembers. **Description:** Communicates how to attract wildlife to one's property and improve wildlife habitat at the same time, including personal experiences. Includes profiles of wildlife and plants, and what to plant and feed. Recurring features include interviews, news of research, reports of meetings, news of educational opportunities, book reviews, and notices of publications available. Also includes a column titled From the President.

7369 ■ *Worm Digest: Worms Deepening Our Connection to Food and Soil*
Pub: Worm Digest
URL(s): www.wormdigest.org. **Ed:** Steven Zorba Frankel, Pete Bogdanov. **Released:** Quarterly **Price:** $69.95, Individuals; $109, Two years.

VIDEOCASSETTES/ AUDIOCASSETTES

7370 ■ *How to Build a Profitable Consulting Practice 1 & 2*
Chesney Communications
2302 Martin St., Ste. 125
Irvine, CA 92612
Ph: (949)263-5500
Free: 800-223-8878

Fax: (949)263-5506
Co. E-mail: videocc@aol.com
URL: http://www.videocc.com
Released: 1987. **Price:** $59.95. **Description:** An entire Howard Shenson seminar about setting up a consulting practice, condensed into two hours. **Availability:** VHS; 3/4 U.

7371 ■ Recycle Rex
Buena Vista Home Entertainment
500 S Buena Vista St.
Burbank, CA 91521-1120
Ph: (800)723-4763
Fax: (818)845-8728
URL: http://www.bvhe.com
Contact: Bob Chapek, President
Released: 1997. **Price:** $199.00. **Description:** Discusses renewable and non-renewable natural resources, recycling, reducing and reusing trash, and how items are made. **Availability:** Video.

TRADE SHOWS AND CONVENTIONS

7372 ■ GLOBE - International Environmental Industry Trade Fair and Conference
GLOBE Foundation of Canada
World Trade Ctr.
999 Canada Pl., Ste. 578
Vancouver, BC, Canada V6C 3E1
Ph: (604)695-5001
Free: 800-274-6097
Fax: (604)695-5019
Co. E-mail: info@globe.ca
URL: http://www.globe.ca
URL(s): www.globe.ca. **Price:** $35, Pre-registered; $1050, Onsite. **Frequency:** Biennial. **Audience:** Trade professionals. **Principal Exhibits:** Environmental equipment, supplies, and services. **Dates and Locations:** , Trade & Convention Centre. **Telecommunication Services:** info@globeseries.com.

CONSULTANTS

7373 ■ ardea consulting
10 1st St.
Woodland, CA 95695
Ph: (530)669-1645
Fax: (530)669-1674
Co. E-mail: birdtox1@ardeacon.com
URL: http://www.ardeacon.com
Contact: Michael Getz, Manager
Scope: Provider of avian and wildlife toxicology and eco toxicology guidance to engineering and environmental firms, government agencies, businesses and non-governmental organizations. Provides ecological risk assessments; assesses contaminant effects on birds and other wildlife; evaluates impacts of pesticides on birds and other wildlife; reviews and compiles scientific field research and data/literature; plans and document pesticide effects studies; collects wildlife specimens or other environmental samples, prepares samples for chemical analysis, and interpret analytical results; drafts project reports and research proposals and reviews ecotoxicology data and reports. **Founded:** 1997. **Publications:** "Estimating the response of ring-necked pheasants to the Conservation Reserve Program," 2008; "Identifying and handling contaminant-related wildlife mortality/morbidity," The Wildlife Society, 2005; "Productivity of American robins exposed to polychlorinated biphenyls," 2003; "Assessing impacts of environmental contaminants on wildlife". **Seminars:** Pheasant breeding bird survey response to the conservation reserve program, 2006; Society of Environmental Toxicology and Chemistry; Niov, 2006; Introduction and Demonstration of the Terrestrial Wildlife Exposure Model (TWEM), Nov, 2004; Society of Environmental Toxicology and Chemistry, Nov, 2004.

7374 ■ Chester Engineers Inc.
155 Coraopolis Heights Rd.
Moon Township, PA 15108-2924
Ph: (412)809-6600
Free: 888-448-6330

Fax: (412)809-6611
Co. E-mail: info_request@atschester.com
URL: http://www.atschester.com
Contact: Robert O. Agbede, President
URL(s): www.chester-engineers.com. **Scope:** Provider of water and wastewater engineering solutions to public and industrial clients across the United States and internationally. Specializes in environmental data management and modeling, water resources engineering, chemical problem solving, environmental investigations, and air quality measurement. **Founded:** 1910.

7375 ■ Monte G. Cole & Associates
4915 Bay St. NE
Purcellville, VA 20132-3214
Ph: (540)338-1122
Fax: (540)338-5041
Contact: Monte Cole, President
E-mail: montecole@friendsofdusty.org
Scope: Firm provides risk management information, software systems, education and insurance consultation, specializing in environmental health and safety issues. **Founded:** 1996.

7376 ■ EnviroBusiness Inc.
21 B St.
Burlington, MA 01803
Ph: (781)273-2500
Free: 800-786-2346
Fax: (781)273-3311
Co. E-mail: info@ebiconsulting.com
URL: http://www.ebiconsulting.com
Contact: Frank E. Previte, Chief Executive Officer
E-mail: fprevite@ebiconsulting.com
Scope: Provides environmental, civil, and structural engineering support to national and international telecommunications companies. Specializes in providing environmental health and safety management consulting and training, occupational health and safety, industrial hygiene, air quality, semiconductor safety, bio-safety, and safety engineering services. Provides environmental health and safety services to renowned institutions in the biotechnology, pharmaceutical, education, energy, education, manufacturing, and marine industries. **Founded:** 1989. **Seminars:** Marina Industry Regulatory Compliance Assistance, Mar, 2007; The Business of Boating in MA, Jan, 2007.

7377 ■ Groupe DGE International Inc.
2586 Ch Hamel
Sherbrooke, QC, Canada J1R 0P8
Ph: (819)820-8881
Fax: (819)820-8808
Co. E-mail: info@dgeinternational.ca
Contact: Sophie Gauvin, President
E-mail: sgauvin@dgeinternational.ca
Scope: Firm specializes in performing environmental management projects like the implementation of ISO 14000 environmental management system, the completion of studies and verifications as well as financial assistance requests for viability studies and implementation of international projects.

7378 ■ Immedia Technologies
107 Sierra Woods Dr.
Ottawa, ON, Canada K0A 1L0
Ph: (613)236-4419
Co. E-mail: info@immtech.com
URL: http://www.immtech.com
Contact: Dan Frederiksen, Technical Director
Scope: Specializing in environmental information solutions.

7379 ■ J.L. Meaher & Associates Inc.
107 St. Francis St., 25th Fl.
Mobile, AL 36602-3334
Ph: (251)433-2676
Fax: (251)433-0708
Co. E-mail: meaherasso@aol.com
Contact: Joseph L. Meaher, President
E-mail: meaheroffice@bellsouth.net
Scope: Offers general forestry consulting, including advice on timber and timberland taxation, estate taxation, planning, timberland sales and purchases. **Founded:** 1974.

7380 ■ Social Venture Partners (SVP)
1601 2nd Ave., Ste. 615
Seattle, WA 98101-1539
Ph: (206)374-8757
Fax: (206)728-0552
Co. E-mail: info@svpseattle.org
URL: http://www.svpseattle.org
Contact: Lisa Merrill, Director
Scope: Organization addresses social and environmental issues in the region. Offers consultation and grants to nonprofits. It seeks to develop philanthropy and volunteerism to achieve positive social change. Using the venture capital approach as a model, committed to giving time, money and expertise to create partnerships with not-for-profit organizations. **Founded:** 1997. **Publications:** "Voices That Matter: Paul Shoemaker, on Becoming a Social Entrepreneur," Oct, 2009; "Immerse Your Donors In You," The Nonprofit Times, Sep, 2009; "New Ideas Shouldn't Necessarily Spawn New Nonprofit Groups," Jan, 2009; "Inside Entrepreneurship: Nonprofit boards will welcome your talents," Dec, 2008; "Charity begins in the office," Nov, 2008.

7381 ■ Stelle & Associates Inc.
4137 S 87th E Ave.
Tulsa, OK 74145
Ph: (918)425-4277
Fax: (918)622-2206
Co. E-mail: scott@stelleassociates.com
URL: http://www.stelleassociates.com
Contact: J. Scott Stelle, President
E-mail: scott@stelleassociates.com
Scope: Consulting consortium which allows highly qualified and experienced specialists an opportunity to function singly or in conjunction with others on projects of any size or duration. Has developed several levels of environmental due diligence to fulfill the need of clients in the most cost effective manner. **Founded:** 1991.

FRANCHISES AND BUSINESS OPPORTUNITIES

7382 ■ Lord & Partners Ltd.
9-741 Muskoka Rd., Ste. 3 N
Huntsville, ON, Canada P1H 2L3
Ph: (705)788-1966
Free: 877-490-6660
Fax: (705)788-1969
Co. E-mail: info@lordandpartners.com
URL: http://www.lordandpartners.com
Description: Unique business to business franchise network serving a growing $30 billion market in representing Canadian manufactured environmentally responsible solutions that replace hazardous traditional chemicals in the workplace and reduce environmental aspects and impacts on the community. **No. of Franchise Units:** 4. **No. of Company-Owned Units:** 2. **Founded:** 1990.. **Franchised:** 2005. **Equity Capital Needed:** $200,000. **Franchise Fee:** $50,000. **Training:** Provides 29 days training on the proven proprietary business, marketing systems, a demo 'showroom on wheels,' with ongoing support for a protected territory.

COMPUTERIZED DATABASES

7383 ■ BioQUEST Library
700 College St.
Beloit, WI 53511
Ph: (608)363-2012
Fax: (608)363-2052
Co. E-mail: bioquest@beloit.edu
URL: http://bioquest.org
Availability: Online: Beloit College - BioQUEST Curriculum Consortium. **Type:** Full-text; Image.

7384 ■ Earthquake Intensity Database, 1638-1985
325 Broadway E/GC3
Boulder, CO 80305-3328
Ph: (303)497-6345

Fax: (303)497-6513
Co. E-mail: susan.mclean@noaa.gov
URL: http://www.ngdc.noaa.gov/mgg
Availability: Online: U.S. National Oceanic and Atmospheric Administration - National Geophysical Data Center - Marine Geology and Geophysics Div. **Type:** Properties; Time Series.

7385 ■ *Energy Detente*
PO Box 6002
Camarillo, CA 93011
Ph: (805)383-2400
Fax: (805)383-2424
Co. E-mail: lsi@lundbergsurvey.com
URL: http://www.lundbergsurvey.com
Availability: Online: Lundberg Survey Inc. **Type:** Full-text.

7386 ■ *Environment & Safety Library™*
1801 S Bell St.
Arlington, VA 22202
Free: 800-372-1033
Co. E-mail: customercare@bna.com
URL: http://www.bna.com
Availability: Online: Bloomberg LP-Bloomberg BNA. CD-ROM: Bloomberg LP-Bloomberg BNA. **Type:** Full-text.

7387 ■ *Environmental Law Reporter® (ELR)*
2000 L St. NW, Ste. 620
Washington, DC 20036
Ph: (202)939-3800
Free: 800-433-5120
Fax: (202)939-3868
Co. E-mail: carothers@eli.org
URL: http://www.eli.org/index.cfm
Contact: John Cruden, President
E-mail: carothers@eli.org
Availability: Online: LexisNexis Group; Environmental Law Institute; Thomson Reuters - Westlaw. **Type:** Full-text.

7388 ■ *Environmental Sciences & Pollution Management*
789 E Eisenhower Pky.
Ann Arbor, MI 48103
Ph: (734)761-4700
Fax: (734)997-4222
Co. E-mail: info@proquest.com
URL: http://www.csa.com
Availability: Online: ProQuest LLC - CSA. **Type:** Bibliographic.

7389 ■ *The Environmentalist*
Van Godewijckstraat 30
NL-3311 GX Dordrecht, Netherlands
Ph: 78 657 6000
Fax: 78 657 6555
URL: http://www.springer.com
Availability: Online: Springer Science + Business Media BV. **Type:** Full-text.

7390 ■ *Geologic Hazards Photos*
325 Broadway E/GC3
Boulder, CO 80305-3328
Ph: (303)497-6345
Fax: (303)497-6513
Co. E-mail: susan.mclean@noaa.gov
URL: http://www.ngdc.noaa.gov/mgg
Availability: Online: U.S. National Oceanic and Atmospheric Administration - National Geophysical Data Center - Marine Geology and Geophysics Div. CD-ROM: U.S. National Oceanic and Atmospheric Administration - National Geophysical Data Center - Marine Geology and Geophysics Div. **Type:** Image.

7391 ■ *Jane's Merchant Ships*
Sentinel House
163 Brighton Rd.
Surrey
Coulsdon CR5 2YH, United Kingdom
Ph: 20 8700 3700
Fax: 20 8763 1006
Co. E-mail: info.uk@janes.com
URL: http://www.janes.com
Availability: Online: IHS Global Ltd.-IHS Jane's: Defense & Security Intelligence & Analysis. **Type:** Full-text; Directory; Image.

7392 ■ *Significant Earthquakes Database*
325 Broadway E/GC3
Boulder, CO 80305-3328
Ph: (303)497-6345
Fax: (303)497-6513
Co. E-mail: susan.mclean@noaa.gov
URL: http://www.ngdc.noaa.gov/mgg
Availability: Online: U.S. National Oceanic and Atmospheric Administration - National Geophysical Data Center - Marine Geology and Geophysics Div. **Type:** Full-text.

LIBRARIES

7393 ■ Andrews & Kurth L.L.P. Library
1350 I St. NW, Ste. 1100
Washington, DC 20005
Ph: (202)662-2700
Fax: (202)662-2739
URL: http://www.andrewskurth.com
Contact: Martha L. Birdseye, Librarian
Scope: Law - civil, environmental, public utilities. **Services:** Interlibrary loan; Library not open to the public. **Founded:** 1900. **Holdings:** 3500 volumes.

7394 ■ Appalachia-Science in the Public Interest Library
50 Lair St.
Mount Vernon, KY 40456-9806
Ph: (606)256-0077
Fax: (606)256-2779
Co. E-mail: aspi@a-spi.org
URL: http://www.a-spi.org
Scope: Appropriate technology, environmental science, solar energy, water and air environments, organic gardening, forest, nature. **Services:** Copying; library open to the public by appointment. **Founded:** 1977. **Holdings:** 7000 books; 8000 periodical volumes; 3000 reports; 3000 microfiche. **Subscriptions:** 100 journals and other serials; 3 newspapers.

7395 ■ Beveridge & Diamond, P.C. Library
1350 I St. NW, Ste. 700
Washington, DC 20005-7202
Ph: (202)789-6000
Fax: (202)789-6190
Co. E-mail: slarson@bdlaw.com
URL: http://www.bdlaw.com
Scope: Law - environmental, pollution, waste disposal, water. **Services:** Interlibrary loan; copying; library open to the public by appointment with restrictions. **Holdings:** 10,000 volumes. **Subscriptions:** 300 journals and other serials.

7396 ■ Bracewell & Patterson Library
2000 K St. NW, Ste. 500
Washington, DC 20006-1872
Ph: (202)828-5876
Fax: (202)223-1225
Contact: Ruth Mendelson, Librarian
Scope: Law - banking, environmental, taxation. **Services:** Interlibrary loan; Library open to the public by appointment with restrictions. **Holdings:** 10,000 volumes; technical reports; videocassettes; audiocassettes.

7397 ■ Cadwalader, Wickersham & Taft Library
700 6th St., N.W.
Washington, DC 20001
Ph: (202)862-2200
Fax: (202)862-2400
Co. E-mail: jane.platt-brown@cwt.com
URL: http://www.cadwalader.com
Contact: Jane Platt-Brown, Director, Library Services
Scope: Law - antitrust, corporate, securities, taxation, business fraud. **Services:** Interlibrary loan; library open to the public by appointment (with restrictions). **Holdings:** 15,000 volumes; microforms; CD-ROM. **Telecommunication Services:** cwtdclibrary@cwt.com.

7398 ■ Bryan Cave LLP Law Library
1155 F St., NW
Washington, DC 20004
Ph: (202)508-6000

Fax: (202)508-6200
Co. E-mail: john.peirce@bryancave.com
URL: http://www.bryancave.com
Contact: John Peirce
Scope: Government and politics; law - commercial, corporate, environmental, intellectual property, taxation. **Services:** Interlibrary loan; copying; faxing; library open to the public with restrictions. **Founded:** 1978. **Holdings:** 11,000 volumes. **Subscriptions:** 200 journals and other serials.

7399 ■ M.H. Chew & Associates Corporate Library
7275 National Dr., Ste. C
Livermore, CA 94550
Ph: (925)443-5071
Fax: (510)373-0624
Co. E-mail: patricia.shannon@mhchew.com
URL: http://www.mhchew.com/
Contact: Patricia Shannon
Scope: Nuclear safety, environmental safety, health physics, radiation protection, risk analysis. **Services:** Interlibrary loan; copying; Library not open to the public. **Founded:** 1993. **Holdings:** 1500 books; 2000 bound periodical volumes; 5000 reports. **Subscriptions:** 100 journals and other serials. **Telecommunication Services:** mel_chew@mhchew.com; corporate@mhchew.com; info@mhchew.com.

7400 ■ Lille D'Easum Library - SPEC Library
2150 Maple St.
Vancouver, BC, Canada V6J 3T3
Ph: (604)736-7732
Fax: (604)736-7115
Scope: Environmental conservation. **Services:** Library open to the public. **Holdings:** 5000 books and reports.

7401 ■ DLA Piper LLP US Library
500 8th St., NW
Washington, DC 20004
Ph: (202)799-4000
Fax: (202)799-5000
URL: http://www.dlapiper.com/us/
Contact: May Guo
Scope: Law - environmental; government contracts, communications, franchising. **Services:** Interlibrary loan; library not open to the public. **Holdings:** 6000 books.

7402 ■ Energy & Environmental Management Library
PO Box 71
Murrysville, PA 15668
Ph: (412)733-0022
Fax: (412)733-0018
Contact: Larry L. Simmons, President
Scope: Environmental compliance in the electric utility, metals production, mining, chemical, petroleum, sanitation, and manufacturing industries. **Services:** Library not open to the public. **Founded:** 1981. **Holdings:** 1000 books. **Subscriptions:** 12 journals and other serials.

7403 ■ ERM - West, Inc. Library
1277 Treat Blvd., Ste. 500
Walnut Creek, CA 94597
Ph: (925)946-0455
Fax: (925)946-9968
URL: http://www.erm.com/
Scope: Environmental issues, groundwater, soils, air, regulations. **Services:** Interlibrary loan; Library not open to the public. **Founded:** 1987. **Holdings:** Government documents. **Subscriptions:** 65 journals and other serials.

7404 ■ Farmington River Watershed Association - Environmental Research Center
749 Hopmeadow St.
Simsbury, CT 06070
Ph: (860)658-4442
Fax: (860)651-7519
Co. E-mail: info@frwa.org
URL: http://www.frwa.org
Contact: Eileen Fielding, Executive Director
Scope: Farmington River watershed, environmental resources. **Services:** Copying; library open to the public with restrictions. **Founded:** 1993. **Holdings:** 500 books; 500 reports. **Telecommunication Services:** efielding@frwa.org.

7405 ■ Forest Alliance of British Columbia Library
1055 Dunsmuir St.
Vancouver, BC, Canada V7X 1L3
Ph: (604)685-7507
Fax: (604)685-5373
URL: http://www.forest.ca
Contact: Elizabeth Steele
Scope: Forestry, environment. **Services:** Library open to the public. **Founded:** 1993.

7406 ■ General Engineering Laboratories, Inc. Library
PO Box 30712
Charleston, SC 29417
Ph: (843)556-8171
Fax: (843)766-1178
Co. E-mail: bob.pullano@gel.com
URL: http://www.gel.net
Contact: James M. Stelling, President
Scope: Environmental analysis, environmental consulting, environmental regulations. **Holdings:** Figures not available.

7407 ■ Georgia Wildlife Federation Conservation Library
11600 Hazelbrand Rd.
Covington, GA 30014
Ph: (770)787-7887
Fax: (770)787-9229
Co. E-mail: dharris@gwf.org
URL: http://www.gwf.org
Contact: DeAnna Harris, Conservator
Scope: Wildlife, conservation. **Services:** Library open to the public by appointment. **Holdings:** 1100 books.

7408 ■ Great Plains RC & D - Environmental Education Library
1505 N. Glenn L. English St.
Cordell, OK 73632-1405
Ph: (580)832-3661
Co. E-mail: greatplainsrcd@yahoo.com
URL: http://www.greatplainsrcd.org
Contact: Alfred Miller, Chairman
Scope: Conservation education, grant researching, agriculture, solid waste and recycling, rural development. **Services:** Library open to the public with restrictions. **Founded:** 1997. **Holdings:** 200 books/binders; 100 videos; 15 CD-ROMs; 50 teacher guides.

7409 ■ Heartland Institute
One S. Wacker Dr., No. 2740
Chicago, IL 60606
Ph: (312)377-4000
Fax: (312)377-5000
Co. E-mail: think@heartland.org
URL: http://www.heartland.org
Contact: Cheryl Parker, Administrative Assistant
Scope: Privatization, deregulation, education reform, healthcare reform, environment, libertarian thought, environmental play, economics. **Services:** Library open to the public by appointment. **Founded:** 1984. **Holdings:** 2500 books; 300 reports; 200 audiocassettes; 100 videotapes. **Subscriptions:** 200 journals and other serials.

7410 ■ Hudson County Improvement Authority Library
Environmental Resource Center
574 Summit Ave., 5th Fl.
Jersey City, NJ 07306
Ph: (201)795-4555
Free: 800-540-0987
Fax: (201)795-0240
Co. E-mail: recycle@hcia.org
URL: http://www.hcia.org
Contact: MaryEllen Gilpin, Director
Scope: Environment. **Services:** Library not open to the public. **Founded:** 1990. **Holdings:** Books; manuals; videocassettes; catalogs; DVDs. **Subscriptions:** 20 journals and other serials; 3 newspapers.

7411 ■ Karpeles Manuscript Library - Duluth Museum
902 E. 1st St.
Duluth, MN 55805
Ph: (218)728-0630
URL: http://www.rain.org/~karpeles/dul.html
Contact: Lee R. Fadden, Director
Scope: Rare manuscripts. **Services:** Library open to the public. **Holdings:** Manuscripts.

7412 ■ Keller and Heckman LLP - Law Firm Library
1001 G St. NW, Ste. 500 W.
Washington, DC 20001
Ph: (202)434-4100
Fax: (202)434-4646
URL: http://www.khlaw.com
Scope: Food and drug, the environment, telecommunications, transportation, intellectual property, International trade. **Services:** Interlibrary loan; Library not open to the public. **Founded:** 1962. **Holdings:** 8000 books. **Subscriptions:** 140 journals and other serials; 8 newspapers.

7413 ■ Maritime College of Forest Technology Library—Ecole des Gardes Forestiers.
1350 Regent St.
Fredericton, NB, Canada E3C 2G6
Ph: (506)458-0653
Free: 866-619-9900
Fax: (506)458-0652
Co. E-mail: info@mcft.ca
URL: http://www.mcft.ca
Contact: Gerald Redmond, Librarian
Scope: Forestry, natural resources, environment, conservation. **Services:** Library not open to the public. **Holdings:** Figures not available. **Subscriptions:** 20 journals and other serials. **Telecommunication Services:** gredmond@mcft.ca.

7414 ■ McKenna Long & Aldridge LLP Law Library
1900 K St. NW, Lower Level
Washington, DC 20006-1108
Ph: (202)496-7500
Fax: (202)496-7756
Co. E-mail: tpapson@mckennalong.com
URL: http://www.mckennalong.com
Scope: Law - government contracts, environmental, litigation, food and drug, International, health care, labor, insurance, energy. **Services:** Interlibrary loan; Library not open to the public. **Founded:** 1940. **Holdings:** 15,000 books; 5000 bound periodical volumes. **Subscriptions:** 400 journals and other serials.

7415 ■ Northcoast Environmental Center Library—NEC.
1385 8th St., Ste. 215
Arcata, CA 95518
Ph: (707)822-6918
Fax: (707)822-6980
Co. E-mail: nec@yournec.org
URL: http://yournec.org
Scope: Logging, mining, fish and wildlife, habitat protection, air and water quality, toxic hazards, recycling, sustainability. **Services:** Interlibrary loan; copying; library open to the public with restrictions. **Founded:** 1971. **Holdings:** 8000 books; 5500 reports; 200 videos; 400 maps. **Subscriptions:** 70 journals and other serials; 10 newspapers.

7416 ■ Petroleum Communication Foundation Library
100-4 Avenue S.W., 409
Calgary, AB, Canada T2P 3N2
Ph: (403)264-6064
Fax: (403)237-6286
Co. E-mail: info@pcf.ca
URL: http://www.pcf.ca
Contact: Tony Laramee, Specialist, Information
Scope: Petroleum, gasoline, oil, environment, natural gas, sour gas, flaring, benzene. **Services:** Copying; Library open to the public. **Founded:** 1975. **Holdings:** 570 books; 10 bound periodical volumes; 400 reports. **Subscriptions:** 26 journals and other serials; 3 newspapers.

7417 ■ S L Ross Environmental Research Ltd. Library
200-717 Belfast Rd., Ste. 200
Ottawa, ON, Canada K1G 0Z4
Ph: (613)232-1564
Fax: (613)232-6660
Co. E-mail: info@slross.com
URL: http://www.slross.com/
Scope: Oil spill research, spill risk assessment, environmental impact. **Services:** Library not open to the public. **Founded:** 1981. **Holdings:** Figures not available.

7418 ■ San Francisco Public Library - Wallace Stegner Environmental Center
100 Larkin St., 5th Fl.
San Francisco, CA 94102
Ph: (415)557-4500
Co. E-mail: citylibrarian@sfpl.org
URL: http://sfpl.org/index.php?pg=0200002201
Contact: Luis Herrera, Librarian
Scope: Environmental literature. **Services:** Center open to the public. **Founded:** 1996. **Holdings:** 1000 books; audiocassettes; videocassettes. **Telecommunication Services:** info@sfpl.org.

7419 ■ Saskatchewan Research Council - Information Services
125-15 Innovation Blvd.
Saskatoon, SK, Canada S7N 2X8
Ph: (306)933-5400
Fax: (306)933-7446
Co. E-mail: info@src.sk.ca
URL: http://www.src.sk.ca
Contact: Colleen Marshall, Coordinator, Information
Scope: Agriculture, biotechnology and food, alternative energy and manufacturing, energy, the environment and forestry, mining and minerals. **Services:** Interlibrary loan. **Founded:** 1947. **Holdings:** 8600 monographs; 3300 SRC-authored publications. **Subscriptions:** 55 periodicals.

7420 ■ SCS Engineers Library
3900 Kilroy Airport Way, Ste. 100
Long Beach, CA 90806-6816
Ph: (562)426-9544
Fax: (562)427-0805
Co. E-mail: lbures@scsengineers.com
Contact: Loran Bures, Librarian
Scope: Environmental and civil engineering, hazardous waste control, landfills, landfill gas, environmental protection. **Services:** Copying; Library not open to the public. **Founded:** 1970. **Holdings:** 50,000 volumes; government reports; trade journals. **Subscriptions:** 115 journals and other serials; 3 newspapers.

7421 ■ Sedgwick County Zoo Library
5555 Zoo Blvd.
Wichita, KS 67212-1698
Ph: (316)660-9453
Fax: (316)942-3781
Co. E-mail: ask@scz.org
URL: http://www.scz.org/
Contact: Mark C. Reed, Executive Director
Scope: Zoology, wildlife conservation. **Services:** Interlibrary loan; copying; library open to the public. **Founded:** 1971. **Holdings:** 1000 books; 100 reports. **Subscriptions:** 10 journals and other serials.

7422 ■ Tetra Tech NUS, Inc. - Technical Information Center
900 Trail Ridge Rd.
Aiken, SC 29803
Ph: (803)649-7963
Fax: (803)642-8454
Co. E-mail: info@tetratech.com
URL: http://www.tetratech.com/about/locations.html
Contact: Debbie Pyron, Manager
Scope: Environment, nuclear energy. **Services:** Library not open to the public. **Holdings:** Reports. **Subscriptions:** 2 newspapers.

7423 ■ United Nations Association of Southern Arizona - Education Resource Center
United Nations Center
6242 E. Speedway Blvd.
Tucson, AZ 85712
Ph: (520)881-7060

Fax: (520)327-0314
Co. E-mail: education@untucson.org
URL: http://untucson.org
Contact: Blake Gentry, Coordinator, Education Resources
Scope: United Nations, War and Peace, international relations, world environment. **Services:** Copying; center open to the public. **Founded:** 1982. **Holdings:** 2000 books; 50 bound periodical volumes. **Subscriptions:** 80 journals and other serials; 2 newspapers.

7424 ■ U.S. Environmental Protection Agency Headquarters Library
Mailcode 3404T
Washington, DC 20460-0001
Ph: (202)566-0556
Fax: (202)260-5153
Co. E-mail: hqchemlibraries@epa.gov
URL: http://www.epa.gov/libraries/hqrepository.html
Scope: Water - pollution, quality, supply; air pollution; noise abatement; radiation; hazardous wastes; solid waste management; resource recovery; pesticides; chemistry and toxicology; social, economic, legislative, legal, administrative, and management aspects of environmental policy. **Services:** Interlibrary loan; SDI; library open to the public with restrictions. **Founded:** 1971. **Holdings:** 16,000 books; 7000 hardcopy documents and technical reports; 400,000 documents and reports from the EPA and its predecessor agencies on microfiche; newspapers, abstracts and indexes, periodicals on microfilm. **Subscriptions:** 20 journals and other serials.

7425 ■ U.S. Environmental Protection Agency Library
Mail Code 3404T
1200 Pennsylvania Ave., NW
Washington, DC 20460
Ph: (202)566-0556
Fax: (202)566-0574
Co. E-mail: hqchemlibraries@epa.gov
URL: http://www.epa.gov/libraries/hqchem.html
Scope: Water pollution, water quality, environmental quality, air pollution, toxic substances, hazardous wastes. **Services:** Interlibrary loan; copying; Library open to the public. **Founded:** 1967. **Holdings:** 3500 books; 10,000 federal and state reports; 200,000 microfiche. **Subscriptions:** 60 journals and other serials.

7426 ■ The Weinberg Group - Washington Information Resources Library
1220 19th St. NW, Ste. 300
Washington, DC 20036
Ph: (202)833-8077
Fax: (202)293-9326
Co. E-mail: library@weinberggrroup.com
URL: http://www.weinberggroup.com
Contact: Ruth Bridges, Manager
Scope: Environment, medicine, chemistry. **Services:** Interlibrary loan; library not open to the public.

Founded: 1987. **Holdings:** 2000 books. **Subscriptions:** 108 journals and other serials; 4 newspapers. **Telecommunication Services:** science@weinberg-group.com.

7427 ■ Williams College Center for Environmental Studies - Matt Cole Memorial Library
Harper House
Williamstown, MA 01267
Ph: (413)597-2346
Fax: (413)597-3489
Co. E-mail: ces@williams.edu
URL: http://ces.williams.edu/?page_id=130
Contact: Norm Parker, Specialist
URL(s): library.williams.edu/. **Scope:** Agriculture, air pollution, biodiversity, climate, regional planning, coastal, ecology, energy, environmental health, environmental law and policy, forestry, hazardous substances, land use and planning, solid waste, water quality, wildlife management habitat. **Services:** Interlibrary loan; library open to the public. **Founded:** 1972. **Holdings:** 7500 books; 2900 bound periodical volumes; 5000 other documents. **Subscriptions:** 250 journals and other serials.

RESEARCH CENTERS

7428 ■ Center for Environmental Research (CER)
2210 S FM 973
Austin, TX 78725
Ph: (512)972-1960
Fax: (512)972-9876
Co. E-mail: kevin.anderson@ci.austin.tx.us
URL: http://www.ci.austin.tx.us/water/cer2.htm
Contact: Kevin M. Anderson, Coordinator
Founded: 1987. **Publications:** *Discovering the Colorado: a vision for the Austin-Bastrop river corridor.* **Educational Activities:** Educational tours and workshops; NGO partnerships. **Awards:** Academic internships.

7429 ■ Harvard University - Belfer Center for Science and International Affairs - Environment and Natural Resources Program (ENRP)
John F. Kennedy School of Government, Box 84
79 JFK St.
Cambridge, MA 02138
Ph: (617)495-1351
Fax: (617)495-1635
Co. E-mail: henry_lee@harvard.edu
URL: http://belfercenter.ksg.harvard.edu/project/43/environment_and_natural_resources.h tml
Contact: Henry Lee, Director
Founded: 1981. **Publications:** *Discussion Papers.* **Awards:** Roy Family Award. **Telecommunication Services:** enrp@ksg.harvard.edu.

7430 ■ Holistic Management International
1010 Tijeras Ave. NW
Albuquerque, NM 87102
Ph: (505)842-5252
Fax: (505)843-7900
Co. E-mail: hmi@holisticmanagement.org
URL: http://www.holisticmanagement.org
Contact: Peter Holter, Chief Executive Officer
Founded: 1984. **Publications:** *Holistic Management Newsletter: In practice.* **Educational Activities:** Holistic Management International Conferences; Holistic Management Courses; Training Program.

7431 ■ SUNY College of Environmental Science and Forestry - Randolph G. Pack Environmental Institute
106 Marshall Hall
1 Forestry Dr.
Syracuse, NY 13210-2787
Ph: (315)470-6636
Fax: (315)470-6915
Co. E-mail: vluzadis@syr.edu
URL: http://www.esf.edu/es/pack
Contact: Prof. Valerie A. Luzadis, Director
Services: Assistance: to local groups on environmental equity projects (Annual). **Founded:** 1986. **Publications:** *Randolph G. Pack Environmental Institute Monographs* (Annual); *Randolph G. Pack Environmental Institute Papers.* **Educational Activities:** Day and half day trips (Annual); Workshops, conferences, forums (3/year). **Awards:** Support awards (Annual); Randolph G. Pack Environmental Institute Internships (Annual). **Telecommunication Services:** envsty@esf.edu.

7432 ■ Texas Center for Policy Studies (TCPS)
707 Rio Grande St., Ste. 200
Austin, TX 78701
Ph: (512)740-4086
Fax: (512)479-8302
Co. E-mail: tcps@texascenter.org
URL: http://www.texascenter.org
Contact: David Hall, Chairperson
Founded: 1983. **Publications:** *TCPS Newsletter* (Biennial); *Project Review.*

7433 ■ University of New Brunswick - New Brunswick Cooperative Fish and Wildlife Research Unit (NBCFWRU)
Faculty of Forestry & Environmental Management
Fredericton, NB, Canada E3B 6C2
Ph: (506)453-4929
Fax: (506)453-3538
Co. E-mail: forbes@unb.ca
URL: http://www.unbf.ca/forestry/centers/cwru.htm
Contact: Graham Forbes, Director
Founded: 1989.

Environmental Store

START-UP INFORMATION

7434 ■ *"EDCO Doling Out Capital Along Border" in Austin Business Journallnc. (Vol. 28, August 1, 2008, No. 20, pp. 1)*
Pub: American City Business Journals
Ed: Sandra Zaragoza. **Description:** Non-profit business incubator Economic Development Catalyst Organization Ventures is searching for promising startup companies. The company is targeting startups in green energy, technology and consumer markets. EDCO has partnered with consumer electronics repair company CherryFusion and technology firm MiniDonations.

7435 ■ *Starting Green: An Ecopreneur's Guide to Starting a Green Business from Business Plans to Profits*
Pub: Entrepreneur Press
Contact: Perlman Neil, President
Ed: Glenn E. Croston. **Released:** September 9, 2010. **Price:** $21.95. **Description:** Entrepreneur and scientist outlines green business essentials and helps uncover eco-friendly business opportunities, build a sustainable business plan, and gain the competitive advantage.

ASSOCIATIONS AND OTHER ORGANIZATIONS

7436 ■ **Center for Environmental Information (CEI)**
249 Highland Ave.
Rochester, NY 14620
Ph: (585)262-2870
Fax: (585)262-4156
Co. E-mail: cei@ceinfo.org
URL: http://www.ceinfo.org
Contact: Stephen Lewandowski, Director
E-mail: stachu14512@yahoo.com
Description: Disseminates information on environmental issues. Conducts annual climate issues conference. **Founded:** 1974. **Publications:** *CEI Sphere* (Quarterly); *Directory of Environmental Organizations in the Rochester Area* (Annual). **Educational Activities:** Center for Environmental Information Conference (Annual). **Awards:** Environmental Stewardship Award (Annual); Hartwell Volunteer Award (Annual); Hugh Cumming Environmental Quality Award (Annual).

7437 ■ **EarthSave International**
20555 Devonshire St., Ste. 105
Chatsworth, CA 91311
Ph: (818)407-0289
Co. E-mail: info@earthsave.org
URL: http://www.earthsave.org
Contact: Jeff Nelson, Chief Executive Officer
Description: Promotes food choices that are healthy for the planet. Seeks to educate, inspire and empower people to take positive action for all life on Earth. **Founded:** 1988. **Publications:** *EarthSave* (Quarterly). **Educational Activities:** EarthSave Summit (Annual).

7438 ■ **Environmental Business Council of New England (EBC-NE)**
375 Harvard St., Ste. 2
Brookline, MA 02446
Ph: (617)505-1818
Co. E-mail: ebc@ebcne.org
URL: http://www.ebcne.org
Contact: Daniel K. Moon, President
Description: Firms that manufacture environmental and/or energy products and provide environmental and/or energy services. Fosters the development of an effective and competitive envirotech industry for the purpose of enhancing and maintaining a clean and productive environment. Provides a forum for environmental and energy company executives to network with each other and to meet leading members of the academic, nonprofit, and government communities to discuss issues of concern to the environmental industry. Provides business development and educational services. **Founded:** 1990. **Awards:** EBEE Award (Annual).

7439 ■ **Natural Products Marketing Council (NPMC)**
PO Box 550
Truro, NS, Canada B2N 5E3
Ph: (902)893-6511
Co. E-mail: crouseea@gov.ns.ca
URL: http://www.gov.ns.ca/agri/npmc
Contact: Dave Davies, Chairman
Description: Producers and processors of natural food products and wool. Promotes growth and development of the natural products industries. Supervises natural product marketing boards. **Founded:** 1946.

7440 ■ **Organic Trade Association (OTA)**
28 Vernon St., Ste. 413
Brattleboro, VT 05301
Ph: (802)275-3800
Fax: (802)275-3801
URL: http://www.ota.com
Contact: Christine Bushway, Executive Director
URL(s): www.theorganicreport.org. **Description:** Producers, processors, distributors, retailers, individuals and others involved in the organic products industry. Promotes the industry; heightens production and marketing standards. Provides certification guidelines. **Founded:** 1985. **Publications:** *The American Organic Standards*; *The Organic Report* (Quarterly); *Guide to the U.S. Organic Foods Production Act of 1990*; *How to Harvest the Profits of Organic Produce*. **Awards:** Organic Leadership Award (Annual).

REFERENCE WORKS

7441 ■ *"21st Century Filling Station" in Austin Business Journallnc. (Vol. 29, December 11, 2009, No. 40, pp. 1)*
Pub: American City Business Journals
Ed: Jacob Dirr. **Description:** Clean Energy Fuels Corporation announced plans for the construction of a $1 million, 17,000 square foot compressed natural gas fueling station at or near the Austin-Bergstrom

International Airport (ABIA). Clean Energy Fuels hopes to encourage cab and shuttle companies in the ABIA to switch from gasoline to natural gas.

7442 ■ *"$40M Fund Created for Big Energy Project" in Austin Business Journallnc. (Vol. 29, November 27, 2009, No. 38, pp. 1)*
Pub: American City Business Journals
Ed: Christopher Calnan. **Description:** A group of Texas businessmen, called Republic Power Partners LP, is planning to raise $40 million in order to launch an alternative energy project. The 6,000-megawatt initiative would generate solar, biomass and wind power in West Texas and could cost as much as $10 billion.

7443 ■ *"2010: Important Year Ahead for Waterfront" in Bellingham Business Journal (Vol. March 2010, pp. 2)*
Pub: Sound Publishing Inc.
Ed: Isaac Bonnell. **Description:** A tentative timeline has been established for the environmental impact statement (EIS) slated for completion in May 2010. The plan for the Waterfront District includes detailed economic and architectural analysis of the feasibility of reusing remaining structures and retaining some industrial icons.

7444 ■ *"2011 FinOvation Awards" in Farm Industry News (January 19, 2011)*
Pub: Penton Business Media Inc.
Ed: Jodie Wehrspann. **Description:** The 2011 FinOvation Award winners are announced, covering new products that growers need for corn and soybean crops. Winners range from small turbines and a fuel-efficient pickup to a Class 10 combine and drought-tolerant hybrids.

7445 ■ *"2011 a Record Year for New Wind Energy Installations in Canada" in CNW Group (September 26, 2011)*
Pub: CNW Group
Contact: Carolyn McGill-Davidson, President
Description: Canada reports a record for new wind energy projects in 2011 with about 1,338 MW of newly installed wind energy capacity expected to come on line, compared to 690 MW installed in 2010. Statistical data included.

7446 ■ *"2011 U.S. Smart Grid - Saving Energy/Saving Money" in Ecology,Environment & Conservation Business (October 8, 2011, pp. 3)*
Pub: HighBeam Research
Description: Highlights of the '2011 U.S. Smart Grid—Saving Energy/Saving Money Customers' Prospective Demand-Response assesses residential energy consumers' willingness to decrease their power consumption in order to mitigate power issues. Statistical details included.

7447 ■ *"The ABCs of a Good Show" in Playthings (Vol. 106, October 1, 2008, No. 9, pp. 18)*
Pub: Reed Business Information
Contact: Jeff Greisch, President
Ed: Karyn M. Peterson. **Description:** ABC Kids Expo 2008 made a strong showing with products for

babies, kids and new/expecting parents. The new Naturally Kids section promoting eco-friendly products was the highlight of the show.

7448 ■ "Acing the Test" in Contractor (Vol. 57, January 2010, No. 1, pp. 32)
Pub: Penton Media, Inc.

Ed: Robert P. Mader. **Description:** A ward winning mechanical system retrofitting of a middle school in Ohio is discussed. The school now operates at 37,800 Btu/sq. ft and reduced a significant amount of pollutants from being emitted into the environment.

7449 ■ "Actiontec and Verizon Team Up for a Smarter Home" in Ecology,Environment & Conservation Business (November 5, 2011, pp. 3)
Pub: HighBeam Research

Description: Verizon is implementing Actiontec Electronics' SG200 Service Gateway as a basic component of its Home Monitoring and Control service. This new smart home service allows customers to remotely check their homes, control locks and appliances, view home-energy use and more using a smartphone, PC, or FiOS TV.

7450 ■ "Adventures at Hydronicahh" in Contractor (Vol. 56, September 2009, No. 9, pp. 52)
Pub: Penton Media, Inc.

Ed: Mark Eatherton. **Description:** Installation of the heating system of a lakeview room are described. The room's radiant windows are powered by electricity from a solar PV array and a propane-powered hydrogen fuel cell. The system will be programmed to use the most energy available.

7451 ■ "Adventures at Hydronicahh" in Contractor (Vol. 56, November 2009, No. 11, pp. 36)
Pub: Penton Media, Inc.

Ed: Mark Eatherton. **Description:** Part 6 of the installation of a five stage ground-source heat pump for a hydronic heating system is discussed. The heat exchanger will be bidirectional in the plan described.

7452 ■ "Adventures at Hydronicahh" in Contractor (Vol. 56, October 2009, No. 10, pp. 42)
Pub: Penton Media, Inc.

Ed: Mark Eatherton. **Description:** Design and installation of a solar thermal system for a hydronic heating project is described. This portion has two 32-square feet of flat plate glazed solar collectors that are tied to a 120-gallon reverse indirect DHW heater.

7453 ■ "AF Expands in New Green Building in Gothenburg" in Ecology,Environment & Conservation Business (September 24, 2011, pp. 2)
Pub: HighBeam Research

Description: AF signed a ten-year tenancy contract with Skanska for the premises of its new green building in Gothenburg, Sweden. AF offers qualified services and solutions for industrial processes, infrastructure projects and the development of products and IT systems.

7454 ■ "Agricultural Community Implements Green Technologies, Building Team" in Contractor (Vol. 56, September 2009, No. 9, pp. 5)
Pub: Penton Media, Inc.

Ed: Candace Ruolo. **Description:** John DeWald and Associates has initiated a residential development project which uses green technologies in Illinois. The community features a community center, organic farm and recreational trails. Comments from executives are also provided.

7455 ■ "Ahead of the Pack" in Small Business Opportunities (Fall 2010)
Pub: Harris Publications Inc.

Description: Profile of an organic fast-food business that is carving out a niche that is gaining favor. Elevation Burger is a unique concept offering healthier burgers in sustainable buildings.

7456 ■ "Allowing Ethanol Tax Incentive to Expire Would Risk Jobs, RFAas Dinneen Says" in Farm Industry News (November 3, 2010)
Pub: Penton Business Media Inc.

Description: Jobs would be at risk if the ethanol tax incentive expires.

7457 ■ "Alstom Launches te ECO 122 - 2.7MW Wind Turbine for Low Wind Sites" in CNW Group (September 28, 2011)
Pub: CNW Group

Contact: Carolyn McGill-Davidson, President

Description: Alstom is launching its new ECO 122, a 2.7MW onshore wind turbine that combines high power and high capacity factor (1) to boost energy yield in low wind regions around the world. The ECO 122 will produce about 25 percent increased wind farm yield that current turbines and fewer turbines would be installed in areas.

7458 ■ "Alternative Energy Calls for Alternative Marketing" in Indoor Comfort Marketing (Vol. 70, June 2011, No. 6, pp. 8)
Pub: Industry Publications Inc.

Ed: Richard Rutigliano. **Description:** Advice for marketing solar energy products and services is given.

7459 ■ "Alternative Energy is a Major Topic at Agritechnica 2011" in Farm Industry News (November 16, 2011)
Pub: Penton Business Media Inc.

Ed: Mark Moore. **Description:** Sustainable agricultural systems were a hot topic at this year's Agritechnia 2011, held in Germany. Germany is a leader in the development of on-farm biogas systems.

7460 ■ "American Chemistry Council Launches Flagship Blog" in Ecology,Environment & Conservation Business (October 29, 2011, pp. 5)
Pub: HighBeam Research

Description: American Chemistry Council (ACC) launched its blog, American Chemistry Matters, where interactive space allows bloggers to respond to news coverage and to discuss policy issues and their impact on innovation, competitiveness, job creation and safety.

7461 ■ "ANATURALCONCEPT" in Crain's Cleveland Business (Vol. 30, June 22, 2009, No. 24, pp. 1)
Pub: Crain Communications, Inc.

Ed: Dan Shingler. **Description:** Cleveland-based Biomimicry Institute, led by Cleveland's Entrepreneurs for Sustainability and the Cuyahoga County Planning Commission, are using biomimicry to incorporate eco-friendliness with industry. Biomimicry studies nature's best ideas then imitates these designs and processes to solve human problems.

7462 ■ "Answers About Commercial Wind Farms Could Come from Downstate" in Erie Times-News (September 27, 2011)
Pub: Erie Times-News

Ed: Valerie Myers. **Description:** Texas-based Pioneer Green Energy is measuring wind and leasing land in North East Township, Pennsylvania. The firm plans to build a 7,000-acre wind farm along wine-country ridges. About 70 turbines would harness wind in order to generate electricity that would be sold into the eastern power grid.

7463 ■ "Aquarium's Solar Demonstration Project Exceeds Expectations" in Contractor (Vol. 57, February 2010, No. 2, pp. 1)
Pub: Penton Media, Inc.

Ed: Candace Roulo. **Description:** Seattle Aquarium cafe installed flat-plate solar collectors to preheat water and data has shown that the system has allowed them to off-set almost double their expected consumption of natural gas. It is estimated that rthe solar panels will shrink the aquarium's carbon footprint by 2.5 tons of carbon dioxide each year.

7464 ■ "Are You Looking for an Environmentally Friendly Dry Cleaner?" in Inc. (Vol. 30, December 2008, No. 12, pp. 34)
Pub: Mansueto Ventures LLC

Ed: Shivani Vora. **Description:** Greenopia rates the greenness of 52 various kinds of businesses, including restaurants, nail salons, dry cleaners, and clothing stores. The guidebooks are sold through various retailers including Barnes & Noble and Amazon.com.

7465 ■ "Areva Diversifies Further Into Wind" in Wall Street Journal Eastern Edition (November 29, 2011, pp. B7)
Pub: Dow Jones & Company Inc. Enterprise Media Group

Contact: Clare Hart, President

Ed: Max Colchester, Noemie Bisserbe. **Description:** French engineering company Areva SA is diversifying and moving away from nuclear energy projects. One sign of that is its recent discussion to construct 120 wind turbines to be located at two German wind farms. Such a deal, if signed, would be worth about US$1.59 billion.

7466 ■ "Art Institute of Chicago Goes Green" in Contractor (Vol. 56, July 2009, No. 7, pp. 1)
Pub: Penton Media, Inc.

Ed: Candace Roulo. **Description:** Art Institute of Chicago's Modern Wing museum addition will receive a certification that makes them one of the most environmentally sound museum expansions in the U.S. A modified variable-air-volume system is being used to meet temperature and humidity requirements in the building and it also has a double curtain wall to capture summer heat.

7467 ■ "Attorney Covers Climate in Copenhagen" in Houston Business Journal (Vol. 40, December 25, 2009, No. 33, pp. 1)
Pub: American City Business Journals

Ed: Ford Gunter. **Description:** Houston environmental attorney Richard Faulk talks to the United Nations Climate Change Conference in Copenhagen, Denmark. Faulk believes the conference failed due to political differences between countries like US and China. Faulk believed the discussion of developed and developing countries on verification and limits on carbon emissions is something good that came from the conference.

7468 ■ "Austin to Buy $1.1B of Wind Power from Two" in Austin Business Journal (Vol. 31, August 19, 2011, No. 24, pp. A1)
Pub: American City Business Journals Inc.

Ed: Vicky Garza. **Description:** Austin City Council is set to approve contracts to purchase wind energy from Duke Energy Corporation and MAP Royalty Inc. The city will get 200MW from Duke and 91MW from MAP and the total contract is estimated to be worth $1.1 million.

7469 ■ "Austin Energy May Build $2.3B Biomass Plant" in Austin Business JournalInc. (Vol. 28, July 25, 2008, No. 19, pp. A1)
Pub: American City Business Journals

Ed: Kate Harrington. **Description:** An approval from the Austin City Council is being sought by Austin Energy for a 20-year supply contract with Nacogdoches Power LLC to build a $2.3 billion biomass plant in East Texas. The 100-megawatt biomass plant, which is to run on waste wood, will have Austin Energy as its sole buyer.

7470 ■ "Award Win Highlights Slingsby's Green Credentials" in Ecology,Environment & Conservation Business (August 20, 2011, pp. 3)
Pub: HighBeam Research

Description: Slingsby, an industrial and commercial equipment supplier, was joint winner with Hallmark Cards of the Baildon Business in the Community's Yorkshire and Humber Long Term Environmental Improvement Award. The firm cites its commitment to reducing environmental impact.

7471 ■ *"Babynut.com to Shut Down" in Bellingham Business Journal (Vol. February 2010, pp. 3)*
Pub: Sound Publishing Inc.
Description: Saralee Sky and Jerry Kilgore, owners of Babynut.com will close their online store. The site offered a free online and email newsletter to help mothers through pregnancy and the first three years of their child's life. Products being sold at clearance prices include organic and natural maternity and nursing clothing, baby and toddler clothes, books on pregnancy, and more.

7472 ■ *"Ben & Jerry's Introduces 'Green' Freezer" in Ice Cream Reporter (Vol. 21, October 20, 2008, No. 11, pp. 1)*
Pub: Ice Cream Reporter
Description: Ben & Jerry's describes its latest concept as a cleaner, greener freezer. The hydrocarbon-based freezer provides great environmental benefits by minimizing the freezer's impact on global warming.

7473 ■ *"BETC Backers Plot Future" in Business Journal Portland (Vol. 27, December 10, 2010, No. 41, pp. 1)*
Pub: Portland Business Journal
Ed: Erik Siemers. **Description:** A coalition of clean energy groups and industrial manufacturers have spearheaded a campaign aimed at persuading Oregon legislators that the state's Business Energy Tax Credit (BETC) is vital in job creation. Oregon's BETC grants tax credits for 50 percent of an eligible renewable or clean energy project's cost. However, some legislators propose BETC's abolition.

7474 ■ *"Beware of E15" in Rental Product News (Vol. 33, October 2011)*
Pub: Cygnus Business Media
Ed: Curt Bennink. **Description:** Environmental Protection Agency (EPA) set a new regulation that grants partial waivers to allow gasoline containing up to 15 percent ethanol (E15) to be introduced into commerce for use in model year 2001 and newer light-duty motor vehicles, subject to certain conditions.

7475 ■ *"Big Energy Ideas for Our Times" in Canadian Business (Vol. 83, August 17, 2010, No. 13-14, pp. 49)*
Pub: Rogers Media Ltd.
Description: Five ideas Canada must consider in the production of energy are explored. These ideas are run-off-river hydroelectric projects, the tapping of natural gas inside shale formation, the water's role in creating energy, the development of a smart grid, and the reduction of energy consumption.

7476 ■ *"Bigger is Definitely Not Better When It Comes to Cooling" in Indoor Comfort Marketing (Vol. 70, May 2011, No. 5, pp. 49)*
Pub: Industry Publications Inc.
Ed: Eugene Silberstein. **Description:** Efficiency is more important when installing air conditioning equipment over size of the unit. Details are provided.

7477 ■ *"Biodiesel Poised to Regain Growth" in Farm Industry News (January 21, 2011)*
Pub: Penton Business Media Inc.
Description: According to Gary Haer, vice president of sales and marketing for Renewable Energy Group, the biodiesel industry is positioned to regain growth in 2011 with the reinstatement of the biodiesel blend-ersa tax credt of $1 per gallon.

7478 ■ *"Bioheat - Alternative for Fueling Equipment" in Indoor Comfort Marketing (Vol. 70, May 2011, No. 5, pp. 14)*
Pub: Industry Publications Inc.
Ed: Gary Hess. **Description:** Profile of Worley and Obetz, supplier of biofuels used as an alternative for fueling industry equipment.

7479 ■ *"Blackwater is LEED Golden for Port of Portland Building" in Contractor (Vol. 56, October 2009, No. 10, pp. 3)*
Pub: Penton Media, Inc.
Ed: Robert P. Mader. **Description:** Worrel Water Technologies' Tidal Wetlands Living Machine recycles blackwater from the toilets and sends it right back to

flush the toilets. The Technology is being installed in the new headquarters of the Port of Portland which aims to get awarded a gold certificate from the Leadership in Energy and Environmental Design.

7480 ■ *"Bold Goals Will Require Time" in Contractor (Vol. 56, October 2009, No. 10, pp. S2)*
Pub: Penton Media, Inc.
Ed: Ted Lower. **Description:** Offering a broad range of courses is the Radiant Panel Association (RPA), an organization that holds education as its top priority. The RPA must lead the industry by raising the educational bar for future installers.

7481 ■ *"Brown At Center of Local CleanTech Lobbying Efforts" in Boston Business Journal (Vol. 30, October 15, 2010, No. 36, pp. 1)*
Pub: Boston Business Journal
Ed: Kyle Alspach. **Description:** U.S. Senator Scott Brown has been active in lobbying for energy reform in Massachusetts. Brown has been meeting with business groups seeking the reforms.

7482 ■ *"Burner Handles Everything From #2 to B100" in Indoor Comfort Marketing (Vol. 70, May 2011, No. 5, pp. 24)*
Pub: Industry Publications Inc.
Description: A new oil burner being offered by AMERIgreen Energy is profiled.

7483 ■ *"Burning Issues: Four of Today's Hottest Energy Topics" in Canadian Business (Vol. 83, August 17, 2010, No. 13-14, pp. 45)*
Pub: Rogers Media Ltd.
Description: A look at four issues dominating Canada's energy industry is presented. These issues are lack of transmission capacity and difficulty in transferring power across provincial boundaries, the management of intermittency of renewable generation, techniques that would clean up the Alberta's oil sands, and the impending massive use of electric cars in North America.

7484 ■ *"The Business of Activism" in Entrepreneur (Vol. 37, September 2009, No. 9, pp. 43)*
Pub: Entrepreneur Media, Inc.
Ed: Mary Catherine O'Connor. **Description:** San Francisco, California-based business incubator Virgance has been promoting sustainable projects by partnering with businesses. The company has launched campaigns which include organizing homeowners in negotiating with solar installers. The company is also planning to expand its workforce.

7485 ■ *"Caber Engineering Helps to Reduce Canada's Carbon Footprint" in Ecology,Environment & Conservation Business (July 16, 2011, pp. 7)*
Pub: HighBeam Research
Description: Calgary-based Caber Engineering Inc. will assist in the engineering design of the Alberta Carbon Trunk Line (ACTL). The ACTL is Alberta's first sizable commercial carbon capture and storage project focusing on the reduction of environmental impacts while being economically beneficial.

7486 ■ *"Campaign Not Stirred by Wind Issue in Roanoke County" in Roanoke Times (September 18, 2011)*
Pub: Roanoke Times
Ed: Katelyn Polantz. **Description:** Wind energy has brought citizens of the Roanoke area into activism this year. Comments from citizen on both sides of the issue are provided.

7487 ■ *"Can HOAs Stop You From Going Green?" in Contractor (Vol. 56, July 2009, No. 7, pp. 39)*
Pub: Penton Media, Inc.
Ed: Susan Linden McGreevy. **Description:** There have been cases concerning homeowners' associations objections to the installation of wind turbines and solar panels. Precedence with the courts show that they will look at several factors when deciding to uphold restrictions on property use including whether

the item encroaches on the rights of others, is likely to adversely affect property values, and also the state of enforcement.

7488 ■ *"Canada's Clean Energy Advantages Offer a Bright Future" in Canadian Business (Vol. 83, August 17, 2010, No. 13-14, pp. 38)*
Pub: Rogers Media Ltd.
Ed: Don McKinnon. **Description:** Canada has clean energy advantages in the greenhouse gas emission-free CANada Deuterium Uranium reactor technology and carbon neutral biomass fuels that were continuously ignored by policy makers. Both are proven to significantly reduce emissions while providing reliable, affordable and secure electricity.

7489 ■ *"Canada's Largest Bakery Officially Opened Today" in Ecology,Environment & Conservation Business (October 15, 2011, pp. 7)*
Pub: HighBeam Research
Description: Maple Leaf Foods opened Canada's largest commercial bakery in Hamilton, Ontario. The firm's 385,000 square foot Trillium bakery benefits from efficient design flow and best-in-class technologies.

7490 ■ *"Canadian Hydronics Businesses Promote 'Beautiful Heat" in Indoor Comfort Marketing (Vol. 70, September 2011, No. 9, pp. 20)*
Pub: Industry Publications Inc.
Description: Canadian hydronics companies are promoting their systems as beautiful heat. Hydronics is the use of water as the heat-transfer medium in heating and cooling system.

7491 ■ *"Canadian Wind Farm Sued Due to Negative Health Effects" in PC Magazine Online (September 22, 2011)*
Pub: PC Magazine
Description: Suncor Energy is being sued by a family in Ontario, Canada. The family claims that Suncor's wind turbines have created health problems for them, ranging from vertigo and sleep disturbance to depression and suicidal thoughts. The family's home is over 1,000 meters from the eight wind turbines, and according to Ontario officials, wind turbines must be a minimum of 550 meters from existing homes.

7492 ■ *"Candidates Differ On State's Green Streak" in Business Journal Portland (Vol. 27, October 22, 2010, No. 34, pp. 1)*
Pub: Portland Business Journal
Ed: Andy Giegerich. **Description:** The views of Oregon gubernatorial candidates Chris Dudley and John Kitzhaber on the state's economy and on environmental policies are presented. Both Dudley, who is a Republican, and his Democratic challenger believe that biomass could help drive the state's economy. Both candidates also pledged changes in Oregon's business energy tax credit (BETC) program.

7493 ■ *"CanWEA Unveils WindVision for BC: 5,250 MW of Wind Energy by 2025" in CNW Group (October 4, 2011)*
Pub: CNW Group
Contact: Carolyn McGill-Davidson, President
Description: Wind industry leaders are asking British Columbia, Canada policy makers to created conditions to further develop and integrate wind energy in accordance with greenhouse gas emission targets and projected economic growth. Statistical data included.

7494 ■ *"The Carbon Equation" in Canadian Business (Vol. 81, October 27, 2008, No. 18, pp. 109)*
Pub: Rogers Media Ltd.
Ed: Jack M. Mintz. **Description:** Economic and environmental impacts of the likely rejection of a carbon tax for the cap-and-trade system in Canada are discussed. The Conservative Party is expected tow in the 2008 elections and would likely pursue the cap-and-trade system.

7495 ■ *"Carbon Trading: Current Schemes and Future Developments"* in *Energy Policy (Vol. 39, October 2011, No. 10, pp. 6040-6054)*

Pub: Reed Elsevier Reference Publishing

Ed: Slobodan Perdan, Adisa Azapagic. **Description:** Current and future developments regarding carbon trading is highlighted.

7496 ■ *"Case IH Announces Strategy to Meet 2014 Clean Air Standards"* in *Farm Industry News (September 15, 2011)*

Pub: Penton Business Media Inc.

Ed: Jodie Wehrspann. **Description:** Case IH will meet EPA's stringent engine emissions limits imposed in 2014, called Tier 4. The limits call for a 90 percent reduction in particulate matter and nitrogen oxides (NOx) over the Tier 3 requirements from a few years ago.

7497 ■ *"Cash for Appliances Targets HVAC Products, Water Heaters"* in *Contractor (Vol. 56, October 2009, No. 10, pp. 1)*

Pub: Penton Media, Inc.

Ed: Candace Roulo. **Description:** States and territories would need to submit a full application that specifies their implementation plans if they are interested in joining the Cash for Appliances program funded by the American Recovery and Reinvestment Act. The Department of Energy urges states to focus on heating and cooling equipment, appliances and water heaters since these offer the greatest energy savings potential.

7498 ■ *"Catch the Wind Announces Filing of Injunction Against Air Data Systems LLC and Philip Rogers"* in *CNW Group (September 30, 2011)*

Pub: CNW Group

Contact: Carolyn McGill-Davidson, President

Description: Catch the Wind, providers of laser-based wind sensor products and technology, filed an injunction against Optical Air Data Systems (OADS) LLC and its former President and CEO Philip L. Rogers. The complaint seeks to have OADS and Rogers return tangible and intangible property owned by Catch the Wind, which the firm believes to be critical to the operations of their business.

7499 ■ *"Catch the Wind to Hold Investor Update Conference Call on October 18, 2011"* in *CNW Group (October 4, 2011)*

Pub: CNW Group

Contact: Carolyn McGill-Davidson, President

Description: Catch the Wind Ltd., providers of laser-based wind sensor products and technology, held a conference call for analysts and institutional investors. The high-growth technology firm is headquartered in Manassas, Virginia.

7500 ■ *"CE2 Carbon Capital and Dogwood Carbon Solutions Partner With Missouri Landowners"* in *Nanotechnolgy Business Journal (Jan. 25, 2010)*

Pub: Investment Weekly News

Description: Dogwood Carbon Solutions, a developer of agriculture and forestry based conservation projects, has partnered with CE2 Carbon Capital, one of the largest investors and owners of U.S. carbon commodities and carbon emissions reduction projects, to develop high-quality carbon offsets from over 30,000 acres of privately-owned non-industrial forest in the Ozark mountain region of Arkansas and Missouri.

7501 ■ *"CEO Forecast"* in *Hispanic Business (January-February 2009, pp. 34, 36)*

Pub: Hispanic Business

Ed: Jessica Haro, Richard Kaplan. **Description:** As economic uncertainty fogs the future, executives turn to government contracts in order to boost business. Revenue sources, health care challenges, environmental consulting and remediation services, as well as technological strides are discussed.

7502 ■ *"Changing Fuel Compositions: What It Means To You and Your Business"* in *Indoor Comfort Marketing (Vol. 70, June 2011,* *No. 6, pp. 30)*

Pub: Industry Publications Inc.

Ed: Paul Nazzaro. **Description:** Biofuels are outlined and the way it is changing the HVAC/R industry are discussed.

7503 ■ *"Charged Up for Sales"* in *Charlotte Business Journal (Vol. 25, October 15, 2010, No. 30, pp. 1)*

Pub: Charlotte Business Journal

Ed: Susan Stabley. **Description:** Li-Ion Motors Corporation is set to expand its production lines of electric cars in Sacramento, California. The plan is seen to create up to 600 jobs. The company's total investment is seen to reach $500 million.

7504 ■ *"Chicago Botanic Garden Builds Green Research Facility"* in *Contractor (Vol. 56, December 2009, No. 12, pp. 5)*

Pub: Penton Media, Inc.

Ed: Candace Roulo. **Description:** Chicago Botanic Garden has built a laboratory and research facility in Illinois. The facility is set to receive a United States Green Building Council LEED Gold certification. The building features a solar photovoltaic array, radiant flooring and water-conserving plumbing products.

7505 ■ *"China Wind Power Generates Stronger First Quarter Results"* in *Marketwire Canada (September 28, 2011)*

Pub: MarketWire Canada

Description: China Wind Power International Corporation, an independent wind power producer in China reported strong growth for the first quarter 2011. Details of the company and its future developments are highlighted.

7506 ■ *"China's Transition to Green Energy Systems"* in *Energy Policy (Vol. 39, October 2011, No. 10, pp. 5909-5919)*

Pub: Reed Elsevier Reference Publishing

Ed: Wei Li, Guojun Song, Melanie Beresford, Ben Ma. **Description:** The economics of home solar water heaters and their growing popularity in Dezhous City, China is discussed.

7507 ■ *"Chinese Solar Panel Manufacturer Scopes Out Austin"* in *Austin Business JournalInc. (Vol. 29, October 30, 2009, No. 34, pp. 1)*

Pub: American City Business Journals

Ed: Jacob Dirr. **Description:** China's Yingli Green Energy Holding Company Ltd. is looking for a site in order to construct a $20 million photovoltaic panel plant. Both Austin and San Antonio are vying to house the manufacturing hub. The project could create about 300 jobs and give Austin a chance to become a player in the solar energy market. Other solar companies are also considering Central Texas as an option to set up shop.

7508 ■ *"City's New Energy Audits to Spawn 'Fantastic' Market"* in *Austin Business JournalInc. (Vol. 28, November 14, 2008, No. 35, pp. 1)*

Pub: American City Business Journals

Ed: Jean Kwon. **Description:** A new law requiring older homes to undergo energy use audits is seen to provide new business for some companies in the Austin, Texas area. The new law is seen to create a new industry of performance testers. Details of the new ordinance are also given.

7509 ■ *"Clean-Tech Focus Sparks Growth"* in *Philadelphia Business Journal (Vol. 28, January 15, 2010, No. 48, pp. 1)*

Pub: American City Business Journals

Ed: Peter Key. **Description:** Keystone Redevelopment Group and economic development organization Ben Franklin Technology Partners of Southeastern Pennsylvania have partnered in supporting the growth of new alternative energy and clean technology companies. Keystone has also been developing the Bridge Business Center.

7510 ■ *"Clean Wind Energy Tower Transitions from R&D Stage Company"* in *Professional Services Close-Up (September 30, 2011)*

Pub: Close-Up Media

Description: Clean Wind Energy designed and is developing large downdraft towers that use benevolent, non-toxic natural elements to generate electricity and clean water. The firm is closing its internally staffed engineering office in Warrenton, Virginia and transitioning a development team to oversee and coordinate industry consultants and advisors to construct their first dual renewable energy tower.

7511 ■ *"Climate Law Could Dig into our Coal-Dusted Pockets"* in *Business Courier (Vol. 26, November 20, 2009, No. 30, pp. 1)*

Pub: American City Business Journals, Inc.

Ed: Lucy May. **Description:** Passage of federal climate legislation into law is set to increase household cost for Greater Cincinnati, according to the calculation by the Brookings Institute. The increase for residents of the area will amount to $244 in 2020 and the city was ranked the sixth-highest rate in the nation, behind Indianapolis.

7512 ■ *"Cloudy Skies"* in *Canadian Business (Vol. 81, October 27, 2008, No. 18, pp. 101)*

Pub: Rogers Media Ltd.

Ed: Andrew Wahl. **Description:** Canada's federal government is expected to implement its regulations on greenhouse-gas emissions by January 1, 2010, but companies are worried because the plan took so long and some details are yet to be revealed. Corporate Canada wants a firm, long-range plan similar to the European Union Emissions Trading Scheme in dealing with greenhouse-gas emissions.

7513 ■ *"CO2 Emissions Embodied in China-US Trade"* in *Energy Policy (Vol. 39, October 2011, No. 10, pp. 5980-5987)*

Pub: Reed Elsevier Reference Publishing

Ed: Huibin Du, Guozhu Mao, Alexander M. Smith, Xuxu Wang, Yuan Wang, Jianghong Guo. **Description:** Input and output analysis based on the energy per dollar ratio for carbon dioxide emissions involved in China-United States trade is outlined.

7514 ■ *"Coming Soon: Electric Tractors"* in *Farm Industry News (November 21, 2011)*

Pub: Penton Business Media Inc.

Ed: Jodie Wehrspann. **Description:** The agricultural industry is taking another look at electric farm vehicles. John Deere Product Engineering Center said that farmers can expect to see more diesel-electric systems in farm tractors, sprayers, and implements.

7515 ■ *"Community Food Co-op Creates Revolving Loan Program for Local Farmers"* in *Bellingham Business Journal (Vol. February 2010, pp. 3)*

Pub: Sound Publishing Inc.

Description: Community Food Co-op's Farm Fund received a $12,000 matching grant from the Sustainable Whatcom Fund of the Whatcom Community Foundation. The Farm Fund will create a new revolving loan program for local farmers committed to using sustainable practices.

7516 ■ *"Consumers Like Green, But Not Mandates"* in *Business Journal-Milwaukee (Vol. 28, December 10, 2010, No. 10, pp. A1)*

Pub: Milwaukee Business Journal

Ed: Sean Ryan. **Description:** Milwaukee, Wisconsin consumers are willing to spend more on green energy, a survey has revealed. Respondents also said they will pay more for efficient cars and appliances. Support for public incentives for homeowners and businesses that reduce energy use has also increased.

7517 ■ *"Convert New Customers to Long Term Accounts"* in *Indoor Comfort Marketing (Vol. 70, February 2011, No. 2, pp. 22)*

Pub: Industry Publications Inc.

Description: Marketing to new customers and suggestions for retaining them is covered.

7518 ■ *"Corporate Responsibility" in Professional Services Close-Up (July 2, 2010)*
Pub: Close-Up Media
Description: List of firms awarded the inaugural Best Corporate Citizens in Government Contracting by the Corporate Responsibility Magazine is presented. The list is based on the methodology of the Magazine's Best Corporate Citizen's List, with 324 data points of publicly-available information in seven categories which include: environment, climate change, human rights, philanthropy, employee relations, financial performance, and governance.

7519 ■ *"The Cost of Energy" in Canadian Business (Vol. 83, August 17, 2010, No. 13-14, pp. 39)*
Pub: Rogers Media Ltd.
Description: Canada's cheap energy has bred complacency among Canadian companies and most have not strived to conserve or develop other forms of energy. However, even costs of traditional energy such as oil are set to rise, fueled by recent events in Saudi Arabia and the Gulf of Mexico.

7520 ■ *"Cost Remains Top Factor In Considering Green Technology" in Canadian Sailings (June 30, 2008)*
Pub: UBM Global Trade
Contact: Leonard J. Corallo, President
Ed: Julie Gedeon. **Description:** Improving its environmental performance remains a priority in the shipping industry; however, testing new technologies can prove difficult due to the harsh conditions that ships endure as well as installation which usually requires a dry dock.

7521 ■ *"Could This Be Your Next Office Building?" in Austin Business Journal (Vol. 31, May 13, 2011, No. 10, pp. A1)*
Pub: American City Business Journals Inc.
Ed: Cody Lyon. **Description:** Falcon Containers moved to a 51-acre site in Far East Austin, Texas and started construction of a 2,500-square-foot headquarters made from eight 40-foot shipping containers. Falcon's CEO Stephen Shang plans to use his headquarters building as a showroom to attract upscale, urban hipsters. Insights on the construction's environmental and social impact are shared.

7522 ■ *"Council Power Shift Could Benefit Business" in Business Courier (Vol. 26, November 6, 2009, No. 28, pp. 1)*
Pub: American City Business Journals, Inc.
Ed: Lucy May. **Description:** A majority in the Cincinnati City Council, which is comprised of reelected members, might be created by Charlie Winburn's impending return to the council. It would be empowered to decide on public safety, stock options taxes, and environmental justice. How the presumed majority would affect the city's economic progress is discussed.

7523 ■ *"Crude Awakening" in Canadian Business (Vol. 81, October 27, 2008, No. 18, pp. 14)*
Pub: Rogers Media Ltd.
Ed: Jeff Sanford. **Description:** Jim Grays believes that a global liquid fuels crisis is coming and hopes the expected transition from oil dependence will be smooth. Charles Maxwell, on the other hand, predicts that a new world economy will arrive in three waves. Views of both experts are examined.

7524 ■ *"Customized Before Custom Was Cool" in Green Industry Pro (July 2011)*
Pub: Cygnus Business Media
Ed: Gregg Wartgow. **Description:** Profile of Turf Care Enterprises and owner Kevin Vogeler, who discusses his desire to use more natural programs using little or no chemicals in 1986. At that time, that sector represented 20 percent of his business, today it shares 80 percent.

7525 ■ *"Cut Energy Waste" in Inc. (Vol. 31, January-February 2009, No. 1, pp. 42)*
Pub: Mansueto Ventures LLC
Description: Carbon Control, Edison, and Saver software programs help companies cut carbon emissions by reducing the amount of energy consumed by computers while they are idle.

7526 ■ *"David Robinson Column" in Buffalo News (October 2, 2011)*
Pub: Buffalo News
Ed: David Robinson. **Description:** New York Power Authority ceased development of an offshore wind farm project. Wind farming in the waters of Lake Erie or Lake Ontario would be too costly. Details of the project are discussed.

7527 ■ *"A Day Late and a Dollar Short" in Indoor Comfort Marketing (Vol. 70, March 2011, No. 3, pp. 30)*
Pub: Industry Publications Inc.
Ed: Philip J. Baratz. **Description:** A discussion involving futures options and fuel oil prices is presented.

7528 ■ *"Despite Economic Upheaval Generation Y is Still Feeling Green: RSA Canada Survey" in CNW Group (October 28, 2010)*
Pub: CNW Group
Contact: Carolyn McGill-Davidson, President
Description: Canadian Generation Y individuals believe it is important for their company to be environmentally-friendly and one-third of those surveyed would quit their job if they found their employer was environmentally irresponsible, despite the economy.

7529 ■ *"Detroit Hosts Conferences on Green Building, IT, Finance" in Crain's Detroit Business (Vol. 25, June 1, 2009, No. 22, pp. 9)*
Pub: Crain Communications Inc. - Detroit
Ed: Tom Henderson. **Description:** Detroit will host three conferences in June 2009, one features green technology, one information technology and the third will gather black bankers and financial experts from across the nation.

7530 ■ *"DeWind Delivering Turbines to Texas Wind Farm" in Professional Services Close-Up (September 25, 2011)*
Pub: Close-Up Media
Description: DeWind Company has begun shipment of turbines to the 20 MW Frisco Wind Farm located in Hansford County, Texas. DeWind is a subsidiary of Daewoo Shipbuilding and Marine Engineering Company. Details of the project are discussed.

7531 ■ *"Doing the Right Thing" in Black Enterprise (Vol. 38, July 2008, No. 12, pp. 50)*
Pub: Earl G. Graves Publishing Co. Inc.
Ed: Tamara E. Holmes. **Description:** More business owners are trying to become more environmentally friendly, either due to their belief in social responsibility or for financial incentives or for both reasons. Tips for making one's business more environmentally responsible are included as well as a listing of resources that may be available to help owners in their efforts.

7532 ■ *"Dow Champions Innovative Energy Solutions for Auto Industry at NAIAS" in Business of Global Warming (January 25, 2010, pp. 7)*
Pub: Investment Weekly News
Description: This year's North American International Auto Show in Detroit will host the 'Electric Avenue' exhibit sponsored by the Dow Chemical Company. The display will showcase the latest in innovative energy solutions from Dow as well as electric vehicles and the technology supporting them. This marks the first time a non-automotive manufacturer is part of the main floor of the show.

7533 ■ *"Earth Angels" in Playthings (Vol. 106, September 1, 2008, No. 8, pp. 10)*
Pub: Reed Business Information
Contact: Jeff Greisch, President
Ed: Karyn M. Peterson. **Description:** ImagiPlay toy company has partnered with Whole Foods Market to distribute the company's wooden playthings across the country. The company's Earth-friendly business model is outlined.

7534 ■ *"East Coast Solar" in Contractor (Vol. 57, February 2010, No. 2, pp. 17)*
Pub: Penton Media, Inc.
Ed: Dave Yates. **Description:** U.S. Department of Energy's Solar Decathlon lets 20 college student-led teams from around the world compete to design and build a solar-powered home. A mechanical contractor discusses his work as an advisor during the competition.

7535 ■ *Eco Barons: The New Heroes of Environmental Activism*
Pub: Ecco/HarperCollins
Ed: Edward Humes. **Released:** January 19, 2010. **Price:** $14.99. **Description:** Profiles of business leaders who have dedicated their lives to saving the planet from ecological devastation.

7536 ■ *"Eco-Preneuring" in Small Business Opportunities (July 2008)*
Pub: Entrepreneur Media Inc.
Ed: Mary C. Pearl. **Description:** Profile of Wildlife Trust, a rapidly growing global organization dedicated to innovative conservation science linking health and ecology. With partners in nearly twenty countries, Wildlife Trust draws on global strengths in order to respond to well-defined local needs. In the Dominican Republic, they are working with the community and local biologists in order to restore fishing and create jobs in the field of ecotourism.

7537 ■ *"Eco Smart Home Will Showcase Green Technology" in Contractor (Vol. 56, September 2009, No. 9, pp. 3)*
Pub: Penton Media, Inc.
Ed: Steve Spaulding. **Description:** Eco Smart World Wide is building the Eco Smart Demonstration House to promote the latest in sustainable, renewable and high-efficiency practices and products. The company will use insulated concrete forms in the construction of the building. Features and dimensions of the structure are also presented.

7538 ■ *"Electronic Design and a Greener Environment" in Canadian Electronics (Vol. 23, June-July 2008, No. 4, pp. 6)*
Pub: Action Communication Inc.
Ed: Nicholas Deeble. **Description:** Companies seeking to minimize their environmental impact are using Design methodologies of Cadence Design Systems Ltd. The company's Low Power Format and Low Power Design Flow help reduce carbon dioxide emissions.

7539 ■ *"EMC Greens Its Machines" in Boston Business Journal (Vol. 31, July 15, 2011, No. 25, pp. 3)*
Pub: Boston Business Journal
Ed: Kyle Alspach. **Description:** Hopkinton, Massachusetts-based EMC Corporation has been pursuing a sustainability strategy even though it would not directly pay back money to the company or customers who use the products. EMC has been increasingly requiring sustainable practices from its suppliers and evaluating the full lifecycle impacts of its products.

7540 ■ *"Energy Consulting Company to Expand" in Austin Business JournalInc. (Vol. 28, November 7, 2008, No. 34, pp. A1)*
Pub: American City Business Journals
Ed: Kate Harrington. **Description:** CLEAResult Consulting Inc. is planning to increase its workforce and move its headquarters to a larger office. The company has posted 1,000 percent increase in revenues. The company's adoption of best practices and setting of benchmark goals are seen as the reason for its growth.

7541 ■ *"Energy Efficiency Ordinance Softened" in Austin Business JournalInc. (Vol. 28, October 3, 2008, No. 29)*
Pub: American City Business Journals
Ed: Jean Kwon. **Description:** City of Austin has eliminated mandatory energy efficiency upgrades to single-family housing as a condition for selling or renting homes or buildings. The new law proposes

that an energy performance audit be conducted on single-family homes before being sold and the results of the audit disclosed to perspectives buyers.

7542 ■ *Environmental Guide to the Internet*
Pub: Government Institutes
Contact: Judith Rothman, Director
URL(s): www.govinstpress.com. Ed: Carol Briggs-Erickson, Toni Murphy. Released: Latest edition 4th. Price: $83, Individuals Paperback; £51.95, Individuals Paperback. Covers: 1,200 resources covering the environment on the Internet, including organizations, products, and resources, including discussion groups, electronic journals, newsgroups, and discussion groups. Entries include: Name, online address, description, e-mail address. Arrangement: Categories.

7543 ■ *"EPA 'Finalizes' WaterSense for Homes" in Contractor (Vol. 57, January 2010, No. 1, pp. 70)*
Pub: Penton Media, Inc.
Ed: Bob Mader. Description: U.S. Environmental Protection Agency released its 'final' version of the WaterSense for Homes standard. The standard's provisions that affect plumbing contractors includes the specification that everything has to be leak tested and final service pressure cannot exceed 60 psi.

7544 ■ *"EPA Grants E15 Waiver for 2001-2006 Vehicles" in Farm Industry News (January 21, 2011)*
Pub: Penton Business Media Inc.
Description: U.S. Environmental Protection Agency waived a limitation on selling gasoline that contains more than 10 percent ethanol for model year 2001-2006 cars and light trucks, allowing fuel to contain up to 15 percent ethanol (E15) for these vehicles.

7545 ■ *"ESolar Partners With Penglai on Landmark Solar Thermal Agreement for China" in Business of Global Warming (January 25, 2010, pp. 8)*
Pub: Investment Weekly News
Description: Penglai Electric, a privately-owned Chinese electrical power equipment manufacturer, and eSolar, a global provider of cost-effective and reliable solar power plants, announced a master licensing agreement in which eSolar will build at least 2 gigawatts of solar thermal power plants in China over the next 10 years.

7546 ■ *"Family Takes Wind Turbine Companies to Court Over Gag Clauses on Health Effects of Turbines" in CNW Group (September 12, 2011)*
Pub: CNW Group
Contact: Carolyn McGill-Davidson, President
Description: Shawn and Trisha Drennan are concerned about the negative experiences other have had with wind turbines close to their homes, including adverse health effects. The couple's home will be approximately 650 meters from the Kingsbridge II wind farm project in Ontario, Canada.

7547 ■ *"Find Private Money for FutureGen Plant" in Crain's Chicago Business (Vol. 34, September 12, 2011, No. 37, pp. 18)*
Pub: Crain Communications Inc.
Description: FutureGen is a clean-coal power plant being developed in Southern Illinois. The need for further funding is discussed.

7548 ■ *"First Suzlon S97 Turbines Arrive in North America for Installation" in PR Newswire (September 28, 2011)*
Pub: United Business Media
Description: Suzlon Energy Ltd., the world's fifth largest manufacturer of wind turbines, will install its first S97 turbine at the Amherst Wind Farm Project. These turbines will be installed on 90-meter hub height towers and at full capacity, will generate enough electricity to power over 10,000 Canadian homes.

7549 ■ *The Flaw of Averages: Why We Underestimate Risk in the Face of Uncertainty*
Pub: John Wiley & Sons, Inc.
Ed: Sam L. Savage. Released: June 3, 2009. Price: $22.95. Description: Personal and business plans are based on uncertainties on a daily basis. The com-

mon avoidable mistake individuals make in assessing risk in the face of uncertainty is defined. The explains why plans based on average assumptions are wrong, on average, in areas as diverse as finance, healthcare, accounting, the war on terror, and climate change.

7550 ■ *"Florida's Bright Upside" in Tampa Bay Business Journal (Vol. 29, November 6, 2009, No. 46, pp. 1)*
Pub: American City Business Journals
Ed: Michael Hinman. Description: Florida's Public Service Commission (PSC) decision on a power purchase agreement that could add 25 megawatts of solar energy on Tampa Electric Company's offerings is presented. The decision could support the growing market for suppliers and marketers of renewable energy such as Jabil Circuit Inc., which manufactures photovoltaic modules. Details of the agreement are discussed.

7551 ■ *"Floyd County Considers Wind Farms" in Roanoke Times (September 19, 2011)*
Pub: Roanoke Times
Ed: Jeff Sturgeon. Description: German firm, Nordex USA Inc. is proposing a $100 million, 30-50 megawatt wind farm atop Wills Ridge, Virginia within the next four years. This project is one of several large wind project considered in the Roanoke and New River valleys of Virginia.

7552 ■ *"Flue Vaccines are Going Green" in Canadian Business (Vol. 83, September 14, 2010, No. 15, pp. 24)*
Pub: Rogers Media Ltd.
Ed: Angelia Chapman. Description: Quebec-based Medicago has found a solution to the bottleneck in the production of influenza vaccines by using plant-based processes instead of egg-based systems. Medicago's US Department of Defense funded research has produced the technology that speeds up the production time for vaccines by almost two-thirds. Insights into Medicago's patented process are also given.

7553 ■ *"For Giving Us a Way To Say Yes To Solar: Lynn Jurich and Edward Fenster" in Inc. (Volume 32, December 2010, No. 10, pp. 110)*
Pub: Inc. Magazine
Description: Profile of entrepreneurs Lynn Jurich and Edward Fenster, cofounders of SunRun. The firm installs solar panels at little or no cost and homeowners sign 20-year contracts to buy power at a fixed price.

7554 ■ *"For Putting Down Roots in Business: Amy Norquist: Greensulate, New York City" in Inc. (Volume 32, December 2010, No. 10, pp. 106)*
Pub: Inc. Magazine
Ed: Christine Lagorio. Description: Profile of Amy Norquist who left her position at an environmental nonprofit organization to found Greensulate. Her firm insulates rooftops with lavender, native grasses and succulents called sedum in order to eliminate carbon from the atmosphere.

7555 ■ *"Forum at UNCW to Explore Offshore Wind Farming" in Star-News (October 4, 2011)*
Pub: Star-News
Ed: Kate Elizabeth Queram. Description: North Carolina is poised to profit from offshore wind farming, according to regional environmental experts. The Sierra Club, in conjunction with the University of North Carolina Wilmington and Oceana are hosting an offshore wind forum featuring five panelists, focusing on potential impacts on birds and sea life, tourism and cost, as well as other pertinent issues.

7556 ■ *"Fossil Fuel, Renewable Fuel Shares Expected to Flip Flop" in Farm Industry News (April 29, 2011)*
Pub: Penton Business Media Inc.
Description: Total energy use of fossil fuels is predicted to fall 5 percent by the year 2035, with renewable fuel picking it up.

7557 ■ *"Franchising's Green Scene" in Entrepreneur (Vol. 37, August 2009, No. 8, pp. 85)*
Pub: Entrepreneur Media, Inc.
Ed: Gwen Moran. Description: Trends in favor of environmentally friendly franchises have been growing for about 25 years but have now become mainstream. The challenges for a prospective green franchisee is that these companies may be tricky to evaluate and they need to ask franchisors a lot of questions to weed out ones that falsely claim to be green.

7558 ■ *"FSU's OGZEB Is Test Bed for Sustainable Technology" in Contractor (Vol. 56, October 2009, No. 10, pp. 1)*
Pub: Penton Media, Inc.
Ed: Candace Roulo. Description: Florida State University has one of 14 off-grid zero emissions buildings (OGZEB) in the U.S.; it was built to research sustainable and alternative energy systems. The building produces electricity from 30 photovoltaic panels and it also has three AET water heating solar panels on the roof.

7559 ■ *"Fuel King: The Most Fuel-Efficient Tractor of the Decade is the John Deere 8295R" in Farm Industry News (November 10, 2011)*
Pub: Penton Business Media Inc.
Description: Farm Industry News compiled a list of the most fuel-efficient tractors with help from the Nebraska Tractor Test Lab, with the John Deere 8295R PTO winner of the most fuel-efficient tractor of the decade.

7560 ■ *"Fuel for Thought; Canadian Business Leaders on Energy Policy" in Canadian Business (Vol. 81, September 15, 2008, No. 14-15, pp. 12)*
Pub: Rogers Media Ltd.
Ed: Joe Castaldo. Description: Most Canadian business leaders worry about the unreliability of the oil supply but feel that Canada is in a better position to benefit from the energy supply crisis than other countries. Many respondents also highlighted the need to invest in renewable energy sources.

7561 ■ *"GE Milestone: 1,000th Wind Turbine Installed in Canada" in CNW Group (October 4, 2011)*
Pub: CNW Group
Contact: Carolyn McGill-Davidson, President
Description: GE installed its 1,000th wind turbine in Canada at Cartier Wind Energy's Gros Morne project in the Gaspesie Region of Quebec, Canada. As Canada continues to expand its use of wind energy, GE plans to have over 1,100 wind turbines installed in the nation by the end of 2011.

7562 ■ *"Germans Win Solar Decathlon - Again" in Contractor (Vol. 56, November 2009, No. 11, pp. 1)*
Pub: Penton Media, Inc.
Ed: Robert P. Mader. Description: Students from Technische Universtat Darmstadt won the U.S. Department of Energy's Solar Decathlon by designing and building the most attractive and efficient solar-powered home. The winner's design produced a surplus of power even during three days of rain and photovoltaic panels covered nearly every exterior surface.

7563 ■ *"Getting the Bioheat Word Out" in Indoor Comfort Marketing (Vol. 70, September 2011, No. 9, pp. 32)*
Pub: Industry Publications Inc.
Description: Ways to market advanced liquid fuels to the public are outlined.

7564 ■ *"Getting Going on Going Green" in HRMagazine (Vol. 53, August 2008, No. 8, pp. 8)*
Pub: Society for Human Resource Management
Contact: Henry G. Jackson, President
E-mail: hjackson@shrm.org
Ed: Rita Zeidner. Description: Being eco-friendly can help recruit and retain workers. Resources to help firms create green initiatives are presented.

7565 ■ *"Getting NORA reauthorized is high priority"* in *Indoor Comfort Marketing* (Vol. 70, February 2011, No. 2, pp. 14)
Pub: Industry Publications Inc.
Description: The importance of reauthorizing the National Oilheat Research Alliance is stressed.

7566 ■ *"The Global Environment Movement is Bjorn Again"* in *Canadian Business* (Vol. 83, September 14, 2010, No. 15, pp. 11)
Pub: Rogers Media Ltd.
Ed: Steve Maich. **Description:** Danish academic Bjorn Lomborg is in favor of decisive action to combat climate change in his new book and was given front page treatment by a London newspaper. Environmentalist groups see this as a victory since Lomborg had not previously considered climate change an immediate issue.

7567 ■ *"GM's Volt Woes Cast Shadow on E-Cars"* in *Wall Street Journal Eastern Edition* (November 28, 2011, pp. B1)
Pub: Dow Jones & Company Inc. Enterprise Media Group
Contact: Clare Hart, President
Ed: Sharon Terlep. **Description:** The future of electric cars is darkened with the government investigation by the National Highway Traffic Safety Administration into General Motor Company's Chevy Volt after two instances of the car's battery packs catching fire during crash tests conducted by the Agency.

7568 ■ *"Go Green Or Go Home"* in *Black Enterprise* (Vol. 41, August 2010, No. 1, pp. 53)
Pub: Earl G. Graves Publishing Co. Inc.
Ed: Tennille M. Robinson. **Description:** The green economy has become an essential part of every business, however, small business owners need to learn how to participate, including minority owned entrepreneurs.

7569 ■ *"Going Green, Going Slowly"* in *Playthings* (Vol. 106, September 1, 2008, No. 8, pp. 17)
Pub: Reed Business Information
Contact: Jeff Greisch, President
Ed: Nancy Zwiers. **Description:** Sustainability and greener materials for both product and packaging in the toy industry has become important for protecting our environment. However, in a recent survey nearly 60 percent of responders stated environmental issues did not play a part in purchasing a toy or game for their children.

7570 ■ *"Golden Valley, Fling Hills Plan LNG Plant"* in *Alaska Business Monthly* (Vol. 27, October 2011, No. 10, pp. 9)
Pub: Alaska Business Publishing Company
Ed: Nancy Pounds. **Description:** Golden Valley Electric Association and Flint Hills Resources have partnered on a natural gas liquefaction facility on the North Slope. The deal will deliver gas at cost to GVEA and Flint Hills and Flint Hills will become more competitive and efficient by burning LNG instead of refined crude oil at the refinery.

7571 ■ *Good Green Guide for Small Businesses: How to Change the Way Your Business Works for the Better*
Pub: A. & C. Black
Ed: Impetus Consulting Ltd. Staff. **Released:** September 1, 2009. **Price:** $19.95. **Description:** Guide for small businesses to take an environmental audit of their company and shows how to minimize the impact of office essentials such as utilities, insulation, recycling and waste, electrical equipment, water systems, lighting options, food and drink, and office cleaning arrangements and products.

7572 ■ *"Got to be Smarter than the Average Bear"* in *Contractor* (Vol. 56, September 2009, No. 9, pp. 82)
Pub: Penton Media, Inc.
Ed: Bob Mader. **Description:** International Association of Plumbing and Mechanical Officials Green Technical Committee has debated the need for contractors to have certifications in installing green

plumbing. Some have argued that qualifications would discourage homeowners from improving their properties. Comments from executives are also included.

7573 ■ *"Gov. Kasich to Put DOD On Short Leash"* in *Business Courier* (Vol. 27, November 26, 2010, No. 30, pp. 1)
Pub: Business Courier
Ed: Dan Monk. **Description:** Ohio Governor-elect John Kasich proposed the privatization of the Ohio Department of Development in favor of a nonprofit corporation called JobsOhio. Kasich believes that the department has lost its focus by adding to its mission issues such as energy efficiency and tourism.

7574 ■ *"Grainger Show Highlights Building Green, Economy"* in *Contractor* (Vol. 57, February 2010, No. 2, pp. 3)
Pub: Penton Media, Inc.
Ed: Candace Roulo. **Description:** chief U.S. economist told attendees of the Grainger's 2010 Total MRO Solutions National Customer Show that the economic recovery would be subdued. Mechanical contractors who attended the event also learned about building sustainable, green products, and technologies, and economic and business challenges.

7575 ■ *"Green Acre$ Tope 10 Green Biz To Start Right Now"* in *Small Business Opportunities* (September 2010)
Pub: Harris Publications Inc.
Description: A list of the top ten green businesses to start in 2010 is provided.

7576 ■ *"Green Acres"* in *Hawaii Business* (Vol. 54, September 2008, No. 3, pp. 48)
Pub: Hawaii Business Publishing
Ed: Jan Tenbruggencate. **Description:** Bill Cowern's Hawaiian Mahogany is a forestry business that processes low-value trees to be sold as wood chips, which can be burned to create biodiesel. Cowern is planning to obtain certification to market carbon credits and is also working with Green Energy Hawaii for the permit of a biomass-fueled power plant. Other details about Cowern's business are discussed.

7577 ■ *"Green and Clean"* in *Retail Merchandiser* (Vol. 51, July-August 2011, No. 4, pp. 56)
Pub: Phoenix Media Corporation
Description: Green Valley Grocery partnered with Paragon Solutions consulting firm to make their stores environmentally green.

7578 ■ *"'Green' Cleaner Buys Local Firm"* in *Puget Sound Business Journal* (Vol. 29, December 19, 2008, No. 35, pp. 3)
Pub: American City Business Journals
Ed: Greg Lamm. **Description:** Washington-based Blue Sky Cleaners has purchased Four Seasons Cleaners. The green company also purchased Queen Anne store and Four Seasons' routes fro Snohomish County through Seattle.

7579 ■ *The Green Collar Economy: How One Solution Can Fix Our Two Biggest Problems*
Pub: HarperCollins Publishers
Ed: Van Jones. **Released:** November 1, 2009. **Price:** $14.99. **Description:** This book offers insight into rebuilding the nation's infrastructure and creating alternative energy sources that could boost the economy through increased employment and higher wages while decreasing our dependence on fossil fuels.

7580 ■ *"The Green Conversation"* in *Harvard Business Review* (Vol. 86, September 2008, No. 9, pp. 58)
Pub: Harvard Business School Press
Description: Six guidelines are presented for addressing and benefiting from environmentally conscious corporate decision making and practices. Topics covered include marketing, supply chain, and leadership.

7581 ■ *"Green Counting"* in *Canadian Business* (Vol. 81, October 13, 2008, No. 17, pp. 27)
Pub: Rogers Media Ltd.
Ed: Joe Castaldo. **Description:** Procter and Gamble research revealed that only 10 percent of North American consumers are willing to accept trade-offs for a greener product. Three out of four North American consumers will not accept a higher price or a decrease in a product's performance for an environmental benefit. Details on green marketing are also discussed.

7582 ■ *"Green Energy Exec Hits State Policy"* in *Boston Business Journal* (Vol. 30, December 3, 2010, No. 45, pp. 1)
Pub: Boston Business Journal
Ed: Kyle Alspach. **Description:** American Superconductor Corporation President Dan McGahn believes that the state government of Massachusetts is not proactive enough to develop the state into a manufacturing hub for wind power technology. McGahn believes that while Governor Deval Patrick campaigned for wind turbines in the state, his administration does not have the focus required to build the turbines in the state.

7583 ■ *"Green Firm Scouts Sites in Tri-State"* in *Business Courier* (Vol. 27, July 23, 2010, No. 12, pp. 1)
Pub: Business Courier
Ed: Dan Monk. **Description:** CresaPartners is searching for a manufacturing facility in Cincinnati, Ohio. The company is set to tour about ten sites in the area.

7584 ■ *The Green Guide for Business: The Ultimate Environment for Businesses of All Sizes*
Pub: Profile Books Limited
Ed: Roger East, Hannah Bullock, Chris Goodall. **Released:** May 10, 2010. **Description:** Everyone wants to go green these days, but for small businesses that's easier said than done. How do you measure a company's carbon footprint? Are dryers or hand towels more eco-friendly? Recycled paper or FSC-certified? All these questions and more are explored.

7585 ■ *"Green It Like You Mean It"* in *Special Events Magazine* (Vol. 28, February 1, 2009, No. 2)
Pub: Special Events Magazine
Ed: Christine Landry. **Description:** Eco-friendly party planners offer advice for planning and hosting green parties or events. Tips include information for using recycled paper products, organic food and drinks. The Eco Nouveau Fashion Show held by Serene Star Productions reused old garments to create new fashions as well as art pieces from discarded doors and window frames for the show; eco-friendly treats and gift bags were highlighted at the event.

7586 ■ *"Green Light"* in *The Business Journal-Portland* (Vol. 25, July 11, 2008, No. 18, pp. 1)
Pub: American City Business Journals, Inc.
Ed: Erik Siemers. **Description:** Ecos Consulting, a sustainability consulting company based in Portland, Oregon, is seeing a boost in revenue as more businesses turn to sustainable practices. The company's revenue rose by 50 percent in 2007 and employees increased from 57 to 150. Other details about Ecos' growth are discussed.

7587 ■ *"Green Shift Sees Red"* in *Canadian Business* (Vol. 81, September 29, 2008, No. 16)
Pub: Rogers Media Ltd.
Ed: Jeff Sanford. **Description:** Green Shift Inc. is suing the Liberal Party of Canada in an $8.5 million lawsuit for using the phrase 'green shift' when they rolled out their carbon tax and climate change policy. The company has come to be recognized as a consultant and provider of green products such as non-toxic, biodegradable cups, plates, and utensils for events.

7588 ■ *"Greenhouse Announces Merger With Custom Q, Inc." in Investment Weekly (January 30, 2010, pp. 338)*

Pub: Investment Weekly News

Description: In accordance with an Agreement and Plan of Share Exchange, GreenHouse Holdings, Inc., an innovative green solutions provider, has gone public via a reverse merger with Custom Q, Inc.

7589 ■ *"Greening the Auto Industry" in Business Journal-Serving Phoenix & the Valley of the Sun (Vol. 30, July 23, 2010, No. 46, pp. 1)*

Pub: Phoenix Business Journal

Ed: Patrick O'Grady. **Description:** Thermo Fluids Inc. has been recycling used oil products since 1993 and could become Arizona's first home for oil filter recycling after retrofitting its Phoenix facility to include a compaction machine. The new service could help establish Thermo Fluids as a recycling hub for nearby states.

7590 ■ *"The Greening of Lunch" in Entrepreneur (Vol. 37, October 2009, No. 10, pp. 44)*

Pub: Entrepreneur Media, Inc.

Ed: Deborah Song. **Description:** Kids Konserve is a self-funded online business selling reusable and recycled lunch kits for kids. The company also aims to increase awareness about waste reduction.

7591 ■ *"Greening the Manscape" in Canadian Business (Vol. 81, October 13, 2008, No. 17, pp. S19)*

Pub: Rogers Media Ltd.

Ed: David Lackie. **Description:** Buyer's guide of environmentally friendly grooming products for men is provided. Improved formulations have solved the problems of having synthetic ingredients in grooming products. Details about a face scrub, after shave conditioner, and a nourishing cream made of 91 percent organic ingredients are given, including prices.

7592 ■ *Greening Your Small Business: How to Improve Your Bottom Line, Grow Your Brand, Satisfy Your Customers and Save the Planet*

Pub: Prentice Hall Press

Contact: Dame Marjorie M. Scardino, Chief Executive Officer

Ed: Jennifer Kaplan. **Released:** November 3, 2009. **Price:** $19.95. **Description:** A definitive resource for anyone who wants their small business to be cutting-edge, competitive, profitable, and eco-conscious. Stories from small business owners address every aspect of going green, from basics such as recycling waste, energy efficiency, and reducing information technology footprint, to more in-depth concerns such as green marketing and communications, green business travel, and green employee benefits.

7593 ■ *Guerrilla Marketing Goes Green: Winning Strategies to Improve Your Profits and Your Planet*

Pub: John Wiley & Sons, Inc.

Ed: Jay Conrad Levinson, Shel Horowitz. **Released:** January 10, 2010. **Price:** $21.95. **Description:** The latest tips on green marketing and sustainable business strategies are shared.

7594 ■ *"Guide to Carbon Footprinting" in American Printer (Vol. 128, June 1, 2011, No. 6)*

Pub: Penton Media Inc.

Description: PrintCity Alliance published its new report, 'Carbon Footprint & Energy Reduction for Graphic Industry Value Chain.' The report aims to help improve the environmental performance of printers, converters, publishers, brand owners and their suppliers.

7595 ■ *"Hey, You Can't Do That" in Green Industry Pro (Vol. 23, September 2011)*

Pub: Cygnus Business Media

Ed: Rod Dickens. **Description:** Manufacturers of landscape equipment are making better use of energy resources, such as the use of fuel-injection

systems instead of carburetors, lightweight materials, better lubricants, advanced battery technology, and innovative engine designs.

7596 ■ *"Hot Air" in Canadian Business (Vol. 81, July 22, 2008, No. 12-13, pp. 16)*

Pub: Rogers Media Ltd.

Ed: Joe Castaldo. **Description:** Over half of 101 business leaders who were recently surveyed oppose Liberal leader Stephane Dion's carbon-tax proposal, saying that manufacturers in Canada are likely to suffer from the plan. Additional key results of the survey are presented.

7597 ■ *"Hot Air: On Global Warming and Carbon Tax" in Canadian Business (Vol. 81, October 13, 2008, No. 17, pp. 12)*

Pub: Rogers Media Ltd.

Ed: Joe Castaldo. **Description:** Survey of Canadian business leaders revealed that the environment is a key issue in Canada's federal elections. Respondents believe that Prime Minister Stephen Harper's views on global warming and climate change are closer to their own views. Other key information on the survey is presented.

7598 ■ *Hot, Flat and Crowded: Why We Need a Green Revolution - and How It Can Renew America*

Pub: Farrar, Straus and Giroux

Ed: Thomas L. Friedman. **Released:** September 8, 2008. **Price:** $27.95. **Description:** Author explains how global warming, rapidly growing populations, and the expansion of the world's middle class through globalization have impacted the environment.

7599 ■ *Housecleaning Business: Organize Your Business - Get Clients and Referrals - Set Rates and Services*

Pub: Globe Pequot Press

Ed: Laura Jorstad, Melinda Morse. **Released:** June 1, 2009. **Price:** $18.95. **Description:** This book shares insight into starting a housecleaning businesses. It shows how to develop a service manual, screen clients, serve customers, select cleaning products, competition, how to up a home office, using the Internet to grow the business and offering green cleaning options to clients.

7600 ■ *"How Green Is The Valley?" in Barron's (Vol. 88, July 4, 2008, No. 28, pp. 13)*

Pub: Dow Jones & Co., Inc.

Description: San Jose, California has made a good start towards becoming a leader in alternative energy technology through the establishment of United Laboratories' own lab in the city. The certification process for photovoltaic cells will be dramatically shortened with this endeavor.

7601 ■ *"How to Keep Your Cool and Your Friends in a Heat Wave" in Canadian Business (Vol. 83, August 17, 2010, No. 13-14, pp. 79)*

Pub: Rogers Media Ltd.

Ed: Angelina Chapin. **Description:** A buyer's guide of menswear clothing for businessmen is presented. The products include an antiperspirant and deodorant, men's dress shorts, shoes and bamboo fabric undershirt.

7602 ■ *"Hydronicahh - Everything in Modulation" in Contractor (Vol. 56, December 2009, No. 12, pp. 24)*

Pub: Penton Media, Inc.

Ed: Mark Eatherton. **Description:** Management and the environmental impact of a home hydronic system are discussed. Radiant windows have the potential to reduce energy consumption. A variable speed delta T pump is required for the construction of a hydronic wood pit.

7603 ■ *"IAPMO GTC Finalizes Green Supplement" in Contractor (Vol. 57, January 2010, No. 1, pp. 1)*

Pub: Penton Media, Inc.

Description: International Association of Plumbing and Mechanical Officials' Green Technical Committee finalized the Green Plumbing & Mechanical Code Supplement. The supplement was created to provide

a set of provisions that encourage sustainable practices and work towards the design and construction of plumbing and mechanical systems.

7604 ■ *"Indoor Air Quality - a Tribute to Efficiency" in Indoor Comfort Marketing (Vol. 70, August 2011, No. 8, pp. 8)*

Pub: Industry Publications Inc.

Ed: Matthew Maleske. **Description:** Efficiency of new HVAC/R equipment has helped improve indoor air quality.

7605 ■ *"Industry Escalates Lobbying Efforts For Loan Program" in Crain's Detroit Business (Vol. 24, September 22, 2008, No. 38, pp. 22)*

Pub: Crain Communications Inc.

Ed: Jay Greene; Ryan Beene; Harry Stoffer. **Description:** Auto suppliers such as Lear Corp., which is best known for vehicle seating, also supplies high-voltage wiring for Ford hybrids and is developing other hybrid components. These suppliers are joining automakers in lobbying for the loan program which would promote the accelerated development of fuel-efficient vehicles.

7606 ■ *"Info Junkie" in Crain's Chicago Business (Vol. 34, October 24, 2011, No. 42, pp. 35)*

Pub: Crain Communications Inc.

Ed: Christina Le Beau. **Description:** Greg Colando, president of Flor Inc., an eco-friendly carpet company located I Chicago discusses his marketing program to increase sales.

7607 ■ *"Interested in 12 Billion Dollars?" in Indoor Comfort Marketing (Vol. 70, March 2011, No. 3, pp. 18)*

Pub: Industry Publications Inc.

Ed: Matthew Maleske. **Description:** Trends in the indoor quality industry are cited, with insight into expanding an existing indoor heating and cooling business.

7608 ■ *"It's Always 55 Degrees F" in Contractor (Vol. 56, September 2009, No. 9, pp. 38)*

Pub: Penton Media, Inc.

Ed: Carol Fey. **Description:** Geothermal-exchange heating and cooling systems can save businesses up to 60 percent on energy costs for heating and cooling. Geothermal systems get heat from the earth during winter. Design, features and installation of geothermal systems are also discussed.

7609 ■ *"It's Not Easy Investing Green" in Entrepreneur (Vol. 37, August 2009, No. 8, pp. 64)*

Pub: Entrepreneur Media, Inc.

Ed: Rosalind Resnick. **Description:** Some venture capitalists remain bullish on green investing despite signs of stagnation. One way for an investor to cash in on green investing is to invest in large public companies that are investing big in green initiatives. Being an angel investor to a local clean-tech company is another avenue.

7610 ■ *"KC Sewer Solutions May Overflow With Green Ideas" in The Business Journal-Serving Metropolitan Kansas City (August 22, 2008)*

Pub: American City Business Journals, Inc.

Ed: Suzanna Stagemeyer. **Description:** Adding green solutions such as small, dispersed basins to catch runoffs and the use of deep rooted natural plants to fix the sewer system of Kansas could probably justify the $2.3 billion worth of funds needed for the project. The city has been ordered by the EPA and the Missouri Department of Natural Resources to fix their sewer systems that are overwhelmed by significant rains.

7611 ■ *"Know the Facts About Natural Gas!" in Indoor Comfort Marketing (Vol. 70, August 2011, No. 8, pp. 26)*

Pub: Industry Publications Inc.

Description: AEC Activity Update is presented on the American Energy Coalition's Website.

7612 ■ *"The Lap of Eco-Luxury"* in *Entrepreneur (Vol. 37, August 2009, No. 8, pp. 38)*
Pub: Entrepreneur Media, Inc.
Ed: Dina Mishev. **Description:** Founder Rob DesLauriers of the Terra Resort Group says that the natural world has taken very good care of him and that he wants to do his part to take care of it. The mattresses that their hotel uses are made from recycled steel springs and their TVs are Energy Star-approved. Their linens are made from organically grown cottons and their walls use by-products from coal burning.

7613 ■ *"Large Homes can be Energy Efficient Too"* in *Contractor (Vol. 56, October 2009, No. 10, pp. 5)*
Pub: Penton Media, Inc.
Ed: Candace Roulo. **Description:** Eco Estate at Briggs Chaney subdivision in Silver Spring, Maryland has model houses that use sustainable technologies and products and the homes that will be built on the subdivision will feature some of the technologies featured on the model home. The energy efficient HVAC system of the model homes are discussed.

7614 ■ *"Legislation Introduced"* in *Indoor Comfort Marketing (Vol. 70, July 2011, No. 7, pp. 6)*
Pub: Industry Publications Inc.
Description: New industry legislation is examined by the National Oilheat Research Alliance.

7615 ■ *"Lincoln Electric Installs Large Wind Tower"* in *Modern Machine Shop (Vol. 84, October 2011, No. 5, pp. 42)*
Pub: Gardner Business Media, Inc.
Contact: Richard G. Kline, President
E-mail: rkline@gardnerweb.com
Description: Lincoln Electric, a welding product manufacturer, constructed a 443-foot-tall wind tower at its plant in Euclid, Ohio. The tower is expected to generate as much as 10 percent of the facility's energy and save as much as $500,000 annually in energy costs.

7616 ■ *"The Lithium Deficit"* in *Canadian Business (Vol. 82, April 27, 2009, No. 7, pp. 17)*
Pub: Rogers Media
Ed: Joe Castaldo. **Description:** Experts are concerned that there may not be enough lithium available to support the expected rise in demand for the natural resource. Lithium is used in lithium ion batteries, the standard power source for electric and hybrid vehicles. Experts believe that the demand for lithium can only be measured once the technology is out in the market.

7617 ■ *"Loan Dollars Sit Idle for Energy Plan"* in *Baltimore Business Journal (Vol. 28, September 10, 2010, No. 18, pp. 1)*
Pub: Baltimore Business Journal
Ed: Scott Dance. **Description:** The Maryland Energy Administration has millions of dollars in Federal stimulus and state energy efficiency cash sitting idle and might be lost once the window for stimulus spending is gone. However, businesses have no interest in betting on renewable energy because some cannot afford to take out more loans. Other challenges faced by these businesses are presented.

7618 ■ *"The Long View: Roberta Bondar on Science and the Need for Education"* in *Canadian Business (Vol. 81, October 27, 2008, No. 18)*
Pub: Rogers Media Ltd.
Ed: Alex Mlynek. **Description:** Roberta Bondar believes that energy and renewable energy is a critical environmental issue faced by Canada today. Bondar is the first Canadian woman and neurologist in space.

7619 ■ *"A Look At Three Gas-Less Cars"* in *Hispanic Business (Vol. 30, September 2008, No. 9, pp. 90)*
Pub: Hispanic Business, Inc.
Ed: Daniel Soussa. **Description:** Three major car manufacturers, Chevrolet, BMW, and Honda, are giving market leader Toyota competition for the next generation of eco-friendly car. The latest and most advanced of the gasoline-less cars designed by the three firms, namely, the Chevrolet Volt, BMW's Hydrogen 7, and the Honda FCX Clarity, are reviewed.

7620 ■ *"Lunch Box Maker Gives Back"* in *Marketing to Women (Vol. 23, November 2010, No. 11, pp. 5)*
Pub: EPM Communications Inc.
Contact: Ira Mayer, President
E-mail: imayer@epmcom.com
Description: Female entrepreneurs launched a new program called, 'Share Your Lunch Project' that encourages mothers to give back and replace their child's lunchbox with their eco-friendly lunch boxes, which are available at select retailers. All proceeds from the project will benefit the World Food Program USA, which feeds children in developing countries.

7621 ■ *"Magpower May Build Solar Panels Here"* in *Austin Business Journal (Vol. 31, May 13, 2011, No. 10, pp. A1)*
Pub: American City Business Journals Inc.
Ed: Christopher Calnan. **Description:** RRE Austin Solar LLC CEO Doven Mehta has revealed plans to partner with Portugal-based Magpower SA, only if Austin energy buys electricity from planned solar energy farm in Pflugerville. Austin Energy has received 100 bids from 35 companies to supply 200 megawatts of solar- and wind-generated electricity.

7622 ■ *"Making Waves"* in *Business Journal Portland (Vol. 27, November 26, 2010, No. 39, pp. 1)*
Pub: Portland Business Journal
Ed: Erik Siemers. **Description:** Corvallis, Oregon-based Columbia Power Technologies LLC is about to close a $2 million Series A round of investment initiated by $750,000 from Oregon Angel Fund. The wave energy startup company was formed to commercialize the wave buoy technology developed by Oregon State University researchers.

7623 ■ *"Mixing Business and Pleasure On the Green"* in *Black Enterprise (Vol. 41, October 2010, No. 3, pp. 65)*
Pub: Earl G. Graves Publishing Co. Inc.
Ed: Annya M. Lott. **Description:** Glow Golf, sponsored by Glow Sports, will offer instruction to 150 female corporate executives and entrepreneurs to learn the fundamentals of the game of golf.

7624 ■ *"Molycorp Funds Wind Energy Technology Company"* in *Manufacturing Close-Up (September 19, 2011)*
Pub: Close-Up Media
Description: Molycorp Inc., producer of rare earth oxides (REO) and a REO producer outside of China, announced it will invest in Boulder Wind Power, which has designed a rare earth magnet powered wind turbine generator. This new generator can produce electricity as low as $0.04 per Kilowatt Hour. Boulder Wind Power's patented wind turbine technology allows for use of rare earth permanent magnets that do not require dysprosium, which is relatively scarce.

7625 ■ *"Mr. Clean"* in *Canadian Business (Vol. 81, October 27, 2008, No. 18, pp. 74)*
Pub: Rogers Media Ltd.
Ed: Rachel Pulfer. **Description:** Profile of Nicholas Parker, co-founder of Cleantech Group LLC, a pioneer in clean technology investing. Cleantech, now a global industry, accounts for 10 percent of all venture capital investments made by U.S. companies in 2007.

7626 ■ *The Necessary Revolution: Working Together to Create a Sustainable World*
Pub: Broadway Books
Contact: David Drake, Manager
E-mail: ddrake@randomhouse.com
Ed: Peter M. Senge, Bryan Smith, Nina Kruschwitz, Joe Laur, Sara Schley. **Released:** April 6, 2010. **Price:** $18.00. **Description:** The book outlines various examples for companies to implement sustainable change and go green in the process.

7627 ■ *"N.E.'s Largest Solar Site Set for Scituate Landfill"* in *Boston Business Journal (Vol. 30, December 17, 2010, No. 47, pp. 1)*
Pub: Boston Business Journal
Ed: Kyle Alspach. **Description:** A closed 12-acre landfill in Scituate, Massachusetts is the proposed site for a 2.4-megawatt solar power plant. The town government will buy the power at a discounted rate, saving it $200,000 annually.

7628 ■ *"The New Alchemists"* in *Canadian Business (Vol. 81, October 27, 2008, No. 18, pp. 22)*
Pub: Rogers Media Ltd.
Ed: Joe Castaldo. **Description:** Ethanol industry expects second-generation ethanol or cellulosic biofuels to provide ecologically friendly technologies than the ethanol made from food crops. Government and industries are investing on producing cellulosic biofuels.

7629 ■ *"A New Alliance For Global Change"* in *Harvard Business Review (Vol. 88, September 2010, No. 9, pp. 56)*
Pub: Harvard Business School Publishing
Ed: Bill Drayton, Valeria Budinich. **Description:** Collaboration between social organizations and for-profit firms through the development of hybrid value chains to target complex global issues is promoted. While social organizations offer links to communities and consumers, firms provide financing and scale expertise.

7630 ■ *"New Book Takes Alternate View on Ontario's Wind Industry"* in *CNW Group (September 19, 2011)*
Pub: CNW Group
Contact: Carolyn McGill-Davidson, President
Description: Dirty Business: The Reality Behind Ontario's Rush to Wind Power, was written by editor and health care writer Jane Wilson of Ottawa, Ontario, Canada along with contributing editor Parker Gallant. The book contains articles and papers on the wind business, including information on illnesses caused from the environmental noise.

7631 ■ *"A New Day is Dawning"* in *Indoor Comfort Marketing (Vol. 70, August 2011, No. 8, pp. 18)*
Pub: Industry Publications Inc.
Ed: Paul Nazzaro. **Description:** New trends in the HVAC/R industry regarding biofuels and bioheat are explored.

7632 ■ *"The Next Great Canadian Idea?"* in *Canadian Business (Vol. 81, July 21, 2008, No. 11, pp. 45)*
Pub: Rogers Media Ltd.
Ed: Sharda Prashad. **Description:** Thane Heins has invented a generator that produces energy in an isolated system which contradicts the law of conservation of energy. Perepiteia generator is referred to as a 'perpetual motion machine.' Other inventions slated for the Canadian invention competition include Rob Matthies' batteries and Frank Naumann's Smart Trap.

7633 ■ *"N.H. Near the LEED in Green Space"* in *New Hampshire Business Review (Vol. 33, March 25, 2011, No. 6, pp. 30)*
Pub: Business Publications Inc.
Description: New Hamphire's architects, contractors and suppliers are among the leaders with LEED-certified space per capita.

7634 ■ *"A Nice Consistency"* in *Inc. (Vol. 31, January-February 2009, No. 1, pp. 94)*
Pub: Mansueto Ventures LLC
Ed: Jason Del Rey. **Description:** PJ Madison spent almost a quarter of its revenue promoting its latest product, organic ice cream. The Texas-based firm saw sales increase dramatically.

7635 ■ *"NStar Feels the Heat"* in *Cape Cod Times (September 30, 2011)*
Pub: Cape Cod Media Group
Ed: Patrick Cassidy. **Description:** Massachusetts energy officials wish to delay a merger between NStar and Northeast Utilities until it is clear how the partner-

ship would meet the state's green energy goals. Governor Deval Patrick supports the proposed Nantucket Sound wind farm.

7636 ■ *"Nuclear Renaissance"* in *Canadian Business (Vol. 83, August 17, 2010, No. 13-14, pp. 46)*
Pub: Rogers Media Ltd.
Description: Nuclear energy has come back into the public's favor in Canada because it has virtually no emissions and is always available anytime of the day. Canada's nuclear industry has also achieved an incomparable record of safe, economic and reliable power generation in three provinces for 48 years.

7637 ■ *"On Growth Path of Rising Star"* in *Boston Business Journal (Vol. 31, June 24, 2011, No. 22, pp. 3)*
Pub: Boston Business Journal
Ed: Kyle Alspach. **Description:** 1366 Technologies Inc. of Lexington, Massachusetts is considered a rising solar power technology company. The firm secured $150 million loan guarantee from the US Department of Energy that could go to the construction of a 1,000 megawatt solar power plant.

7638 ■ *"One on One With SEIA's President, CEO"* in *Contractor (Vol. 57, January 2010, No. 1, pp. 40)*
Pub: Penton Media, Inc.
Ed: Dave Yates. **Description:** Solar Energy Industries Association President and CEO Rhone Resch says that the deployment of solar systems in the U.S. has exploded since 2005 and that there is a need to make inroads for shaping the U.S. energy policy. Resch says one of the hurdles they face is that there are no universal standards.

7639 ■ *"OPEC Exposed"* in *Hawaii Business (Vol. 54, September 2008, No. 3, pp. 2)*
Pub: Hawaii Business Publishing
Ed: Serena Lim. **Description:** Organization of the Petroleum Exporting Countries (OPEC) has said that their effort in developing an alternative energy source has driven prices up. The biofuel sector is criticizing the statement, saying that a research study found that biofuels push petroleum prices down by 15 percent. Details on the effect of rising petroleum prices are discussed.

7640 ■ *"Out of Juice?"* in *Canadian Business (Vol. 81, October 27, 2008, No. 18, pp. 32)*
Pub: Rogers Media Ltd.
Ed: Joe Castaldo. **Description:** Alternative energy experts suggest Canada should be more aggressive and should make major policy changes on energy alternatives despite an Ernst & Young research that rated the country high on renewable energy.

7641 ■ *"Overheating Taking Place? Pay Attention to Details.."* in *Indoor Comfort Marketing (Vol. 70, March 2011, No. 3, pp.)*
Pub: Industry Publications Inc.
Ed: George R. Carey. **Description:** Boiler facts are outlined to help the small HVAC company when servicing customers.

7642 ■ *"An Overview of Energy Consumption of the Globalized World Economy"* in *Energy Policy (Vol. 39, October 2011, No. 10, pp. 5920-2928)*
Pub: Reed Elsevier Reference Publishing
Ed: Z.M. Chen, G.Q. Chen. **Description:** Energy consumption and its impact on the global world economy is examined.

7643 ■ *"Phoenix Conference Reveals Opportunities are Coming"* in *Indoor Comfort Marketing (Vol. 70, March 2011, No. 3, pp. 24)*
Pub: Industry Publications Inc.
Ed: Paul J. Nazzaro. **Description:** Advanced liquid fuels were spotlighted at the Phoenix conference revealing the opportunities for using liquid fuels.

7644 ■ *"Positive Transformational Change"* in *Indoor Comfort Marketing (Vol. 70, April 2011, No. 4, pp. 30)*
Pub: Industry Publications Inc.
Ed: Blaine Fox. **Description:** Management changes taking place at Shark Bites HVAC firm are discussed.

7645 ■ *"PPC's Major Commitment to Biofuel Infrastructure"* in *Indoor Comfort Marketing (Vol. 70, April 2011, No. 4, pp. 6)*
Pub: Industry Publications Inc.
Description: Petroleum Products Corporation's commitment to the biofuel infrastructure is outlined.

7646 ■ *"Provinces Tackle E-Waste Problem"* in *Canadian Electronics (Vol. 23, June-July 2008, No. 4, pp. 1)*
Pub: Action Communication Inc.
Ed: Ken Manchen. **Description:** Canadian provinces are implementing measures concerning the safe and environmentally friendly disposal of electronic waste. Alberta, British Columbia, Nova Scotia, and Saskatchewan impose an e-waste recycling fee on electronic equipment purchases.

7647 ■ *"PSC Approves $130M TECO Solar Project"* in *Tampa Bay Business Journal (Vol. 30, December 18, 2009, No. 52, pp. 1)*
Pub: American City Business Journals
Ed: Michael Hinman. **Description:** Florida's Public Service Commission has endorsed Tampa Electric Company's plan to add 25 megawatts of solar energy to its portfolio. TECO's plan needed the approval by PSC to defray additional costs for the project through ratepayers.

7648 ■ *"A Quick Guide to NATE"* in *Indoor Comfort Marketing (Vol. 70, February 2011, No. 2, pp. 12)*
Pub: Industry Publications Inc.
Description: Guide for training and certification in the North American Technician Excellence award.

7649 ■ *"Radiant - the Hottest Topic in .. Cooling"* in *Indoor Comfort Marketing (Vol. 70, February 2011, No. 2, pp. 8)*
Pub: Industry Publications Inc.
Description: Examination of radiant cooling systems, a new trend in cooling homes and buildings.

7650 ■ *"Recycling 202: How to Take Your Recycling Practices to the Next Level"* in *Black Enterprise (Vol. 41, September 2010, No. 2, pp. 38)*
Pub: Earl G. Graves Publishing Co. Inc.
Ed: Tamara E. Holmes. **Description:** Consumer Electronics Association and other organizations, manufacturers and retailers list ways to recycle all household items.

7651 ■ *"Reducing the Book's Carbon Footprint"* in *American Printer (Vol. 128, July 1, 2011, No. 7)*
Pub: Penton Media Inc.
Description: Green Press Initiative's Book Industry Environmental Council is working to achieve a 20 percent reduction in the book industry's carbon footprint by 2020. The Council is made up of publishers, printers, paper suppliers, and non-governmental organizations.

7652 ■ *"Reinventing Marketing to Manage the Environmental Imperative"* in *Journal of Marketing (Vol. 75, July 2011, No. 4, pp. 132)*
Pub: American Marketing Association
Ed: Philip Kotler. **Description:** Marketers must now examine their theory and practices due to the growing recognition of finite resources and high environmental costs. Companies also need to balance more carefully their growth goals with the need to purse sustainability. Insights on the rise of demarketing and social marketing are also given.

7653 ■ *"Renewable Energy Adoption in an Aging Population"* in *Energy Policy (Vol. 39, October 2011, No. 10, pp. 6021-6029)*
Pub: Reed Elsevier Reference Publishing
Ed: Ken Willis, Riccardo Scarpa, Rose Gilroy, Neveen Hamza. **Description:** Attitudes and impacts of renewable energy adoption on an aging population is examined.

7654 ■ *"Renewable Energy Market Opportunities: Wind Testing"* in *PR Newswire (September 22, 2011)*
Pub: United Business Media
Description: Global wind energy test systems markets are discussed. Research conducted covers both non-destructive test equipment and condition monitoring equipment product segments.

7655 ■ *"ReVenture Plan Appears Close to Landing Key Legislative Deal"* in *Charlotte Business Journal (Vol. 25, July 9, 2010, No. 16, pp. 1)*
Pub: Charlotte Business Journal
Ed: John Downey. **Description:** North Carolina lawmakers acted on special legislation that would boost development of Forsite Development 667-acre ReVenture Energy Park. The legislation could also improve chances that Duke Energy Carolinas will contract to purchase the power from the planned 50-megawatt biomass power plant located at the park. How utilities would benefit from the legislation is also discussed.

7656 ■ *"Rivals Blow In"* in *Crain's Cleveland Business (Vol. 30, June 1, 2009, No. 21, pp. 1)*
Pub: Crain Communications, Inc.
Ed: Chuck Soder. **Description:** U.S. and Canadian competitors are hoping to start construction of offshore wind farm project proposed by Cuyahoga County's Great Lakes Energy Development Task Force. Details of the project are included.

7657 ■ *"Rosewood Site Faces Big Cleanup"* in *Baltimore Business Journal (Vol. 27, February 6, 2010, No. 40, pp. 1)*
Pub: American City Business Journals
Ed: Daniel J. Sernovitz. **Description:** Environmental assessment report states that Maryland's Rosewood Center for the Developmentally Disabled has significant amounts of toxic chemicals, which could impact Stevenson University's decision to purchase the property. Senator Robert A. Zirkin believes that the state should pay for the cleanup, which is expected to cost millions.

7658 ■ *"Rough Headwinds"* in *Boston Business Journal (Vol. 30, November 12, 2010, No. 42, pp. 1)*
Pub: Boston Business Journal
Ed: Kyle Alspach. **Description:** Views of residents, as well as key information on First Wind's plan to install wind power turbines in Brimfield, Massachusetts are presented. Residents believe that First Wind's project will devalue properties, compromise quality of life, and ruin the rural quality of Brimfield. First Wind expects to produce 2,000 megawatts of power from wind by 2020.

7659 ■ *"San Diego Museum Receives LEED Certification"* in *Contractor (Vol. 57, January 2010, No. 1, pp. 14)*
Pub: Penton Media, Inc.
Description: San Diego Natural History Museum received an LEED certification for existing buildings. The certification process began when they committed to displaying the Dead Sea Scrolls in 2007 and they had to upgrade their buildings' air quality and to control for air moisture, temperature, and volume. They reduced their energy consumption by upwards of 20 percent.

7660 ■ *"Sandvik Expands Energy-Saving Program"* in *Modern Machine Shop (Vol. 84, September 2011, No. 4, pp. 48)*
Pub: Gardner Business Media, Inc.
Contact: Richard G. Kline, President
E-mail: rkline@gardnerweb.com
Description: Sandvik Coromant, based in Fair Lawn, New Jersey, expanded its Sustainable Manufacturing Program that originally was developed to help Japanese-based firms reduce electricity consumption by 15 percent after the recent earthquake that cause loss of electrical power. The program now provides energy reduction through the Sandvick cutting tool technology, application techniques and productivity increases.

7661 ■ *"Saudi Overtures"* in *The Business Journal-Portland (Vol. 25, August 15, 2008, No. 23, pp. 1)*
Pub: American City Business Journals, Inc.
Ed: Aliza Earnshaw. **Description:** Saudi Arabia's huge revenue from oil is creating opportunities for Oregon companies as the country develops new cities, industrial zones, and tourism centers. Oregon exported only $46.8 million worth of goods to Saudi Arabia in 2007 but the kingdom is interested in green building materials and methods, renewable energy and water quality control, and nanotechnology all of which Oregon has expertise in.

7662 ■ *"The Second Most Fuel-Efficient Tractor of the Decade: John Deere 8320R"* in *Farm Industry News (November 10, 2011)*
Pub: Penton Business Media Inc.
Description: John Deere's 8320R Tractor was ranked second in the Farm Industry News listing of the top 40 most fuel-efficient tractors of the decade, following the winner, John Deere's 8295R PTO tractor.

7663 ■ *"Seeing Green in Going Green"* in *The Business Journal-Serving Greater Tampa Bay (Vol. 28, July 4, 2008, No. 28, pp. 1)*
Pub: American City Business Journals, Inc.
Ed: Janet Leiser. **Description:** Atlanta, Georgia-based developer IDI Corp. is pushing for Leadership in Energy and Environmental Design certification for the warehouse that is currently under construction at Madison Business Center along Port Sutton and U.S. 41. The industrial building is the first in Tampa Bay to seek certification for LEED as set by the U.S. Green Building Council.

7664 ■ *"Shaw Joins Green Institute Launch"* in *Home Textiles Today (Vol. 31, May 24, 2011, No. 13, pp. 4)*
Pub: Reed Business Information
Contact: Jeff Greisch, President
Description: Shaw Industries Group joined the Green Products Innovation Institute, the first nonprofit institute of its kind in America. The institute promotes the concepts of reverse engineering, elimination of waste, safe chemistries, and closed loop technical nutrients.

7665 ■ *"Shifting Gears"* in *Business Journal-Serving Phoenix & the Valley of the Sun (Vol. 31, November 12, 2010, No. 10, pp. 1)*
Pub: Phoenix Business Journal
Ed: Patrick O'Grady. **Description:** Automotive parts recyclers in Arizona are benefiting from the challenging national economic conditions as well as from the green movement. Recyclers revealed that customers prefer recycled parts more because they are cheaper and are more environmentally friendly. Other information about the automotive parts recycling industry is presented.

7666 ■ *"Should I or Shouldn't I?"* in *Indoor Comfort Marketing (Vol. 70, February 2011, No. 2, pp. 30)*
Pub: Industry Publications Inc.
Ed: Philip J. Baratz. **Description:** Investment tips are shared for investing in futures options.

7667 ■ *"Slick Science"* in *Canadian Business (Vol. 81, September 15, 2008, No. 14-15, pp. 55)*
Pub: Rogers Media Ltd.
Ed: Andrew Nikiforuk. **Description:** N-Solv Corp's John Nenniger has discovered a better alternative to steam-assisted gravity drainage methods for extracting bitumen. Nenniger's technique also relies on gravity but replaces steam with propane, which leaves behind impurities like asphaltenes and heavy metals that are too dirty to burn.

7668 ■ *"Small Wind Power Market to Double by 2015 at $634 Million"* in *Western Farm Press (September 30, 2011)*
Pub: Penton Media, Inc.
Description: Small wind power provides cost-effective electricity on a highly localized level, in both remote settings as well as in conjunction with power from the utility grid. Government incentives are spurring new growth in the industry.

7669 ■ *"Smart Car Sales Take Big Hit in Recession"* in *Business Journal-Milwaukee (Vol. 28, December 10, 2010, No. 10, pp. A1)*
Pub: Milwaukee Business Journal
Ed: Stacey Vogel Davis. **Description:** Sales of smart cars in Milwaukee declined in 2010. Smart Center Milwaukee sold only 52 new cars through October 2010. Increased competition is seen as a reason for the decline in sales.

7670 ■ *"Snow Melt Systems Offer Practical Solutions"* in *Contractor (Vol. 56, October 2009, No. 10, pp. S6)*
Pub: Penton Media, Inc.
Ed: Lisa Murton Beets. **Description:** Cases are discussed in which the installation of a snow melt system becomes a necessity. One example describes how limited space means there would be no place to put plowed snow; snow melt systems can also resolve problems that arise due to an excess of melting snow.

7671 ■ *"Solar Credit Lapse Spur Late Demand"* in *The Business Journal - Serving Phoenix and the Valley of the Sun (Vol. 28, July 18, 2008)*
Pub: American City Business Journals, Inc.
Ed: Patrick O'Grady. **Description:** Businesses looking to engage in the solar energy industry are facing the problems of taxation and limited solar panel supply. Solar panels manufacturers are focusing more on the European market. Political issues surrounding the federal tax credit policy on solar energy users are also discussed.

7672 ■ *"Solar Hot Water Sales Are Hot, Hot, Hot"* in *Contractor (Vol. 56, December 2009, No. 12, pp. 22)*
Pub: Penton Media, Inc.
Ed: Dave Yates. **Description:** Plumbing contractors in the United States can benefit from the increased sales of solar thermal water systems. Licensed plumbers have the base knowledge on the risks associated from heating and storing water. Safety issues associated with solar water heaters are also included.

7673 ■ *"Something Different in the Air? The Collapse of the Schwarzenegger Health Plan in Calfornia"* in *WorkingUSA (June 2008)*
Pub: Blackwell Publishers Ltd.
Ed: Daniel J.B. Mitchell. **Description:** In January 2007, California Governor Arnold Schwarzenegger proposed a state universal health care plan modeled after the Massachusetts individual mandate program. A year later, the plan was dead. Although some key interest groups eventually backed the plan, it was overwhelmed by a looming state budget crisis and a lack of gubernatorial focus. Although much acclaimed for his stance on greenhouse gases, stem cells, hydrogen highways, and other Big Ideas, diffused gubernatorial priorities and a failure to resolve California's chronic fiscal difficulties let the clock run out on universal health care.

7674 ■ *"Start Connecting Today"* in *Indoor Comfort Marketing (Vol. 70, May 2011, No. 5, pp. 34)*
Pub: Industry Publications Inc.
Ed: Paul Nazzaro. **Description:** An in-depth discussion regarding the use of biofuels on bioheat use and dealership.

7675 ■ *"Start Moving Toward Advanced Fuels"* in *Indoor Comfort Marketing (Vol. 70, March 2011, No. 3, pp. 4)*
Pub: Industry Publications Inc.
Ed: Michael L. SanGiovanni. **Description:** Commentary on advanced fuels is presented.

7676 ■ *"Start Thinking About Carbon Assets - Now"* in *Harvard Business Review (Vol. 86, September 2008, No. 9, pp. 28)*
Pub: Harvard Business School Press
Ed: Alex Rau; Robert Toker. **Description:** Economic and strategic benefits of adopting a corporate carbon assets policy are discussed. Topics include renewable energy and capturing waste energy.

7677 ■ *"State Investment Goes Sour"* in *Business Journal Portland (Vol. 26, December 4, 2009, No. 39, pp. 1)*
Pub: American City Business Journals Inc.
Ed: Erik Siemers. **Description:** Oregon might recoup only $500,000 of a $20 million loan to Vancouver-based Cascade Grain Products LLC. Cascade Grain's ethanol plant in Clatskanie, OR will be put into auction under the supervision of a bankruptcy court.

7678 ■ *"Stimulus 'Loser' Won't Build Plant in Mass."* in *Boston Business Journal (Vol. 30, November 5, 2010, No. 41, pp. 1)*
Pub: Boston Business Journal
Ed: Kyle Alspach. **Description:** Boston-Power Inc. no longer plans to build an electric vehicle battery plant in Massachusetts after it failed to obtain stimulus funds from the federal government. The company is instead looking to build a lithium-ion battery plant in China and possibly Europe.

7679 ■ *"The Superpower Dilemma"* in *Canadian Business (Vol. 83, August 17, 2010, No. 13-14, pp. 42)*
Pub: Rogers Media Ltd.
Description: Canada has been an energy superpower partly because it controls the energy source and the production means, particularly of fossil fuels. However, Canada's status as superpower could diminish if it replaces petroleum exports with renewable technology for using sources of energy available globally.

7680 ■ *"Survey Finds State Execs Cool On Climate Change"* in *The Business Journal-Milwaukee (Vol. 25, August 8, 2008, No. 46, pp. A1)*
Pub: American City Business Journals, Inc.
Ed: David Doege. **Description:** According to a survey of business executives in Wisconsin, business leaders do not see climate change as a pressing concern, but businesses are moving toward more energy-efficient operations. The survey also revealed that executives believe that financial incentives can promote energy conservation. Other survey results are provided.

7681 ■ *"Sustainability Is Top Priority for GreenTown Chicago"* in *Contractor (Vol. 56, November 2009, No. 11, pp. 1)*
Pub: Penton Media, Inc.
Ed: Candace Roulo. **Description:** GreenTown Chicago 2009 conference tackled energy-efficient practices and technologies, green design and building, and sustainable policies. Water conservation was also a topic at the conference and one mayor who made a presentation said that reducing the water loss in the system is a priority in the city's endeavor.

7682 ■ *"Suzlon S88-Powered Wind Farm in Minnesota Secures Long-Term Financing"* in *PR Newswire (September 21, 2011)*
Pub: United Business Media
Description: Suzlon Energy Limited is the world's fifth largest manufacturer of wind turbines. Owners of the Grant County Wind Farm in Minnesota have secured a long-term financing deal for the ten Suzlon S88 2.1 MW wind turbines that generate enough electricity to power 7,000 homes.

7683 ■ *"Taxis Are Set to Go Hybrid"* in *Philadelphia Business Journal (Vol. 30, September 16, 2011, No. 31, pp. 1)*
Pub: American City Business Journals, Inc.
Ed: Natalie Kostelni. **Description:** Taxis are going hybrid in several major states such as New York, California and Maryland where it is mandated, but it is yet to happen in Philadelphia, Pennsylvania with the exception of one taxi company. Freedom Taxi is awaiting Philadelphia Parking Authority's sign off.

7684 ■ *"Think the Oilsands Are an Environmental Disaster?"* in *Canadian Business (Vol. 83, October 12, 2010, No. 17, pp. 52)*
Pub: Rogers Media Ltd.
Ed: Michael McCullough. **Description:** Studies which were commissioned by the Alberta Energy Research Institute in 2008 found that the life-cycle carbon emis-

sions of oil derived from oilsands was 10 percent greater than the average from all sources. Synthetic crude from the oilsands is 38 percent less carbon-intensive than it was 20 years ago due to productivity improvements.

7685 ■ *"Thirsty? Now There's a Water Cooler to Suit Every Taste"* in Inc. (Vol. 33, October 2011, No. 8, pp. 43)
Pub: Inc. Magazine
Ed: John Brandon. **Description:** Brita's Hydration Station is a wall-mounted unit with a touch-free sensor for dispensing water. This water cooler cuts down on landfill waste and offers special features.

7686 ■ *The Three Secrets of Green Business: Unlocking Competitive Advantage in a Low Carbon Economy*
Pub: Earthscan
Ed: Gareth Kane. **Released:** February 10, 2010. **Price:** $96.00. **Description:** Small business is coming under increasing pressure from government, customers and campaigning groups to improve environmental performance. Soaring utility and compliance costs are critical financial burdens on small companies.

7687 ■ *"Timberland's CEO On Standing Up to 65,000 Angry Activists"* in Harvard Business Review (Vol. 88, September 2010, No. 9, pp. 39)
Pub: Harvard Business School Publishing
Ed: Jeff Swartz. **Description:** Timberland Company avoided a potential boycott by taking a two-way approach. It addressed a supplier issue that posed a threat to the environment, and launched an email campaign to keep Greenpeace activists informed of the development of a new supplier agreement.

7688 ■ *"Time to Green Your Business"* in Gallup Management Journal (April 22, 2011)
Pub: Gallup
Ed: Bryant Ott. **Description:** It's Earth Day, so expect to hear companies touting their commitment to the environment. However, according to Gallup, more companies are finding it more interested to talk about being green than actually taking the steps to become a green business.

7689 ■ *"Toolmakers' New Tack"* in Crain's Detroit Business (Vol. 25, June 8, 2009,)
Pub: Crain Communications Inc. - Detroit
Ed: Ryan Beene, Amy Lane. **Description:** MAG Industrial Automation Systems LLC and Dowding Machining Inc. have partnered to advance wind-turbine technology. The goal is to cut costs of wind energy to the same level as carbon-based fuel.

7690 ■ *"Top 50 Exporters"* in Hispanic Business (Vol. 30, July-August 2008, No. 7-8, pp. 42)
Pub: Hispanic Business, Inc.
Ed: Hildy Medina. **Description:** Increases in exports revenues reported by food exporters and green companies in a time of economic slowdown in the U.S are described. Food exporters have benefited from the growth of high-volume grocery stores in underdeveloped countries and the German governments' promotion of solar energy has benefited the U.S. solar heating equipment and solar panel manufactures.

7691 ■ *"Toward a Better Future"* in Canadian Business (Vol. 83, August 17, 2010, No. 13-14, pp. 51)
Pub: Rogers Media Ltd.
Description: A look at certain realities in order to build a better future for Canada's energy industry is presented. Canada must focus on making the oil cleaner, instead of replacing it with another source since dependency on oil will remain in this lifetime. Canada must also develop solutions toward clean technology power sources.

7692 ■ *"Traer Turning to Wind Power to Meet Long-Term Energy Needs"* in Waterloo Courier (September 20, 2011)
Pub: Lee Enterprises
Ed: Josh Nelson. **Description:** Traer Municipal Utilities is working with Clark Thompson, a Story City

wind turbine developer, to erect a wind turbine to supply electrical energy to the city. Details are included.

7693 ■ *"Tucson Tech Column"* in AZ Daily Star (September 27, 2011)
Pub: Arizona Daily Star
Ed: David Wichner. **Description:** Western Wind Energy, based in Vancouver, British Columbia, Canada is able to harness energy from the sun when the wind is not blowing at the Kingman I Project wind farm. Details of this technology are outlined.

7694 ■ *"Turning Green Ink to Black"* in The Business Journal-Serving Metropolitan Kansas City (Vol. 26, August 8, 2008, No. 48, pp. 1)
Pub: American City Business Journals, Inc.
Ed: James Dornbrook. **Description:** InkCycle has introduced grenk, a line of environmentally-friendly printer toner and ink cartridges. The cartridges are collected and recycled after use by the company, which separates them into their metal, cardboard, and plastic components.

7695 ■ *"Tweaking On-Board Activities, Equipment Saves Fuel, Reduces CO2"* in Canadian Sailings (June 30, 2008)
Pub: UBM Global Trade
Contact: Leonard J. Corallo, President
Description: Optimizing ship activities and equipment uses less fuel and therefore reduces greenhouse gas emissions. Ways in which companies are implementing research and development techniques in order to monitor ship performance and analyze data in an attempt to become more efficient are examined.

7696 ■ *"UA Turns Ann Arbor Green"* in Contractor (Vol. 56, September 2009, No. 9, pp. 5)
Pub: Penton Media, Inc.
Ed: Robert P. Mader. **Description:** Instructors at the United Association of Plumbers and Steamfitters have studied the latest in green and sustainable construction and service at the Washtenaw Community College in Michigan. Classes included building information modeling, hydronic heating and cooling and advanced HVACR troubleshooting. The UA is currently focusing on green training.

7697 ■ *"Ultra Green Energy Services Opens NJ Biodiesel Transload Facility"* in Indoor Comfort Marketing (Vol. 70, June 2011, No. 6, pp. 35)
Pub: Industry Publications Inc.
Description: Profile of Ultra Green Energy Services and the opening of their new biodiesel facility in New Jersey is discussed.

7698 ■ *"Ultra Low Sulfur Diesel: The Promise and the Reality"* in Indoor Comfort Marketing (Vol. 70, July 2011, No. 7, pp. 22)
Pub: Industry Publications Inc.
Ed: Ed Kitchen. **Description:** Impacts of ultra low sulfur diesel are examined.

7699 ■ *"Unilever to Sustainably Source All Paper and Board Packaging"* in Ice Cream Reporter (Vol. 23, July 20, 2010, No. 8, pp. 1)
Pub: Ice Cream Reporter
Description: Unilever, a leader in the frozen dessert market, has developed a new sustainable paper and board packaging sourcing policy that will reduce environmental impact by working with suppliers to source 75 percent of paper and board packaging from sustainably managed forests or from recycled material. Unilever is parent company to Breyers, Haagen-Dazs, Klondike, Popsicle and other ice cream brands.

7700 ■ *"University Data Center Goes Off-Grid, Is Test Bed"* in Contractor (Vol. 57, February 2010, No. 2, pp. 1)
Pub: Penton Media, Inc.
Ed: Candace Roulo. **Description:** Syracuse University's Green Data Center has gone off-grid through the use of natural gas fired turbines. It is expected to use

50 percent less energy than a typical computer center. The center's heating and cooling system setup is also discussed.

7701 ■ *"Valener Announces that Gaz Metro has Achieved a Key Step in Acquiring CVPS"* in CNW Group (September 30, 2011)
Pub: CNW Group
Contact: Carolyn McGill-Davidson, President
Description: Valener Inc., which owns about 29 percent of Gaz Metro Ltd. Partnership, announced that Gaz Metro welcomes the sale of Central Vermont Public Service Corporation (CVPS). Valener owns an indirect interest of 24.5 percent in the wind power projects jointly developed by Beaupre Eole General Partnership and Boralex Inc. on private lands in Quebec. Details of the deal are included.

7702 ■ *"Volunteers Needed"* in Canadian Business (Vol. 81, October 27, 2008, No. 18, pp. 60)
Pub: Rogers Media Ltd.
Ed: Megan Harman. **Description:** Emissions-targeting regulations focus on the biggest polluters, missing out on other companies that leave carbon footprints in things such as shipping and travel. Some companies in Canada have initiated programs to offset their carbon emissions. Critics claim that offsetting does not reduce emissions and the programs merely justify pollution.

7703 ■ *"Warm Floors Make Warm Homes"* in Contractor (Vol. 56, October 2009, No. 10, pp. S18)
Pub: Penton Media, Inc.
Ed: Lisa Murton Beets. **Description:** Three award winning radiant floor-heating installations are presented. The design and the equipment used for these systems are discussed.

7704 ■ *"Was Mandating Solar Power Water Heaters For New Homes Good Policy?"* in Hawaii Business (Vol. 54, August 2008, No. 2, pp. 28)
Pub: Hawaii Business Publishing
Description: Senator Gary L. Kooser of District 7 Kauai-Niihau believes that the mandating of energy-efficient water heaters for new single-family homes starting in 2010 will help cut Hawaii's oil consumption. Ron Richmond of the Hawaii Solar Energy Association says that the content of SB 644 has negative consequences as it allows for choice of energy and not just solar, and it also eliminates tax credits for new homebuyers.

7705 ■ *"Water Conservation Helps GC's Building Attain LEED Gold Status"* in Contractor (Vol. 56, September 2009, No. 9, pp. 5)
Pub: Penton Media, Inc.
Description: Green contractor Marshall Erdman has built a new office building using green design. The facility is seen to become a prime Leadership in Energy and Environmental Design (LEED) building model. Details of the building's design and features are also provided.

7706 ■ *"Water Distiller"* in Canadian Business (Vol. 81, September 29, 2008, No. 16, pp. 52)
Pub: Rogers Media Ltd.
Ed: Matthew McClearn. **Description:** Les Fairn's invention of a water distiller called a Solarsphere was recognized in the Great Canadian Invention Competition. Fairn's invention resembles a buoy that uses the sun's energy to vaporize dirty water then leaves the impurities behind in a sump. The invention has an application for producing potable water in impoverished countries.

7707 ■ *"Western Wind Energy Corporation"* in CNW Group (October 4, 2011)
Pub: CNW Group
Contact: Carolyn McGill-Davidson, President
Description: Profile of Western Wind Energy Corporation will complete the installation of 60 wind turbines by the end of 2011. The first 106MW are ready for pre-commissioning with the ability to sell power in November when the site is interconnected.

7708 ■ *"What Are Canada's Industrial Polluters Doing to Reduce Emissions?" in Canadian Business (Vol. , pp.)*
Pub: Rogers Media Ltd.
Ed: Matthew McClearn. **Description:** Efforts by Canada's industrial polluters to reduce emissions are examined. Syncrude Canada plans to reduce sulphur emissions by 60 percent in 2011, while TransAlta invests in emission reduction programs. Environmental groups, however, claim that companies are not doing enough to protect the environment.

7709 ■ *"What Is a Geothermal Heat Pump" in Indoor Comfort Marketing (Vol. 70, August 2011, No. 8, pp. 14)*
Pub: Industry Publications Inc.
Ed: George Carey. **Description:** Examination of geothermal heat pumps is provided, citing new trends in the industry.

7710 ■ *"Where the Future is Made" in Indoor Comfort Marketing (Vol. 70, May 2011, No. 5, pp. 48)*
Pub: Industry Publications Inc.
Description: Research being performed at Brookhaven National Laboratory, located in Upton, New York, is discussed, focusing on new energy sources for our nation.

7711 ■ *"A Whiff of TV Reality" in Houston Business Journal (Vol. 40, January 22, 2010, No. 37, pp. A1)*
Pub: American City Business Journals
Ed: Christine Hall. **Description:** Houston, Texas-based Waste Management Inc.'s president and chief operation officer, Larry O'Donnell shares some of his experience as CBS Television Network reality show 'Undercover Boss' participant. O'Donnell believes the show was a great way to show the customers how tough their jobs are and reveals that the most difficult job was being a sorter at the recycling center.

7712 ■ *"Wind Gets Knocked Out of Energy Farm Plan" in Buffalo News (September 28, 2011)*
Pub: Buffalo News
Ed: David Robinson. **Description:** New York Power Authority formally killed the proposal for a wind energy farm off the shores of Lake Erie and Lake Ontario. The Authority cited high subsidy costs would be required to make the wind farm economically feasible. Details of the proposal are outlined.

7713 ■ *"Winning Gold" in The Business Journal-Milwaukee (Vol. 25, August 8, 2008, No. 46, pp. A1)*
Pub: American City Business Journals, Inc.
Ed: Rich Rovito. **Description:** Johnson Controls Inc. of Milwaukee, Wisconsin is taking part in the 2008 Beijing Olympics with the installation of its sustainable control equipment and technology that monitor over 58,000 points in 18 Olympic venues. Details of Johnson Controls' green products and sustainable operations in China are discussed.

7714 ■ *"Yates Helps Turn Log Home Green" in Contractor (Vol. 56, December 2009, No. 12, pp. 40)*
Pub: Penton Media, Inc.
Description: Upgrading and greening of a log home's HVAC system in Pennsylvania is discussed. F. W. Behler Inc. president Dave Yates was chosen to manage the project. A large coil of R-flex was used to connect the buffer tank to the garage's radiant heat system.

7715 ■ *"Yates Turns Log Home Green - Part Three" in Contractor (Vol. 57, January 2010, No. 1, pp. 5)*
Pub: Penton Media, Inc.
Description: Dave Yates of F.W. Behler Inc. discusses remodeling a log home's HVAC system with geo-to-radiant heat and thermal-solar systems. The solar heater's installation is discussed.

7716 ■ *"You're a What? Wind Turbine Service Technician" in Occupational Outlook Quarterly (Vol. 54, Fall 2010, No. 3, pp. 34)*
Pub: U.S. Bureau of Labor Statistics
Ed: Drew Liming. **Description:** Profile of Brandon Johnson, former member of the Air Force, found a career as a wind turbine service technician.

7717 ■ *"Yudelson Challenges San Antonio Groups" in Contractor (Vol. 56, October 2009, No. 10, pp. 6)*
Pub: Penton Media, Inc.
Description: Green building consultant and author Jerry Yudelson made a presentation for the Central Texas Green Building Council and Leadership San Antonio where he discussed the European approach to sustainability and how it can be used for designing green buildings. Yudelson also discussed how to use sustainable practices for planning 25 years into the future.

TRADE PERIODICALS

7718 ■ *Fifth Estate*
Pub: Fifth Estate
URL(s): fifthestate.org/fepages/contact.html. **Released:** Quarterly **Price:** $14, Individuals; $20, Canada and Mexico; Free for prisoners & soldiers; $20, Libraries & institutions.

7719 ■ *Greenpeace Magazine*
Pub: Greenpeace U.S.A.
Contact: Karen Topakian, Chairperson
URL(s): www.greenpeace.org/usa/. **Released:** Quarterly

TRADE SHOWS AND CONVENTIONS

7720 ■ GLOBE - International Environmental Industry Trade Fair and Conference
GLOBE Foundation of Canada
World Trade Ctr.
999 Canada Pl., Ste. 578
Vancouver, BC, Canada V6C 3E1
Ph: (604)695-5001
Free: 800-274-6097
Fax: (604)695-5019
Co. E-mail: info@globe.ca
URL: http://www.globe.ca
URL(s): www.globe.ca. **Price:** $35, Pre-registered; $1050, Onsite. **Frequency:** Biennial. **Audience:** Trade professionals. **Principal Exhibits:** Environmental equipment, supplies, and services. **Dates and Locations:** , Trade & Convention Centre. **Telecommunication Services:** info@globeseries.com.

7721 ■ Natural Products Expo East
Delicious Living
New Hope Natural Media
1401 Pearl St.
Boulder, CO 80302
Ph: (303)939-8440
Fax: (303)998-9020
Co. E-mail: info@newhope.com
URL: http://www.deliciouslivingmag.com
URL(s): www.expoeast.com. **Frequency:** Annual. **Audience:** Retailers, wholesalers, distributors, and brokers from the natural products industry. **Principal Exhibits:** Natural, organic and environmentally sound products, including: alternative health care, vegetarian and allergy-free personal care recycled/recyclable products, biodegradable products, and organic meats. **Dates and Locations:** , Convention Center. **Telecommunication Services:** tradeshows@newhope.com.

7722 ■ Natural Products Expo West
Delicious Living
New Hope Natural Media
1401 Pearl St.
Boulder, CO 80302
Ph: (303)939-8440
Fax: (303)998-9020
Co. E-mail: info@newhope.com
URL: http://www.deliciouslivingmag.com
URL(s): www.expowest.com. **Price:** $325, Non-members guest, on or before early date; $295, Non-members manufacturer, before early date; $295, Non-members supplier, before early date; retail buyer, distributor, practitioner buyer. **Frequency:** Annual. **Audience:** Retailers, wholesalers, distributors, and brokers. **Principal Exhibits:** Natural, organic, and environmentally sound products, including: alternative healthcare, vegetarian and allergy-free items,

cruelty-free personal care, recycled/recyclable products, biodegradable products, and organic meats. **Dates and Locations:** , Convention Center. **Telecommunication Services:** tradeshows@newhope.com.

FRANCHISES AND BUSINESS OPPORTUNITIES

7723 ■ Enviro-Tech Pest Services
Enviro-Tech Pest Franchises, Inc.
PO Box 567
Kearneysville, WV 25430
Ph: (304)728-5090
Free: 800-434-7360
Fax: (304)724-5499
Description: Residential and commercial pest management. **No. of Franchise Units:** 5. **No. of Company-Owned Units:** 2. **Founded:** 1985.. **Franchised:** 2004. **Equity Capital Needed:** $37,500-$56,900. **Franchise Fee:** $24,500. **Royalty Fee:** 5-7%. **Training:** Available 10 days at headquarters with optional training at existing office as needed and ongoing support.

7724 ■ EnviroSpect, Inc.
426 Pine St.
Williamsport, PA 17701
Ph: (570)326-4677
Free: 866-773-2881
URL: http://www.esaenviro.com
Description: Residential and commercial environmental inspections. **No. of Franchise Units:** 4. **Founded:** 2004.. **Franchised:** 2004. **Equity Capital Needed:** $26,600-$39,200. **Franchise Fee:** $25,000. **Royalty Fee:** $400/month. **Training:** Available at headquarters: 52 hours minimum.

LIBRARIES

7725 ■ Center for Environmental Information - CEI Library
55 Saint Paul St.
Rochester, NY 14604-1314
Ph: (585)262-2870
Fax: (585)262-4156
Co. E-mail: cei@ceinfo.org
URL: http://www.ceinfo.org
Contact: George Thomas, Executive Director
Scope: Natural resources, conservation, acid rain, greenhouse effect, environment, energy, environmental education. **Services:** Library open to the public by appointment. **Founded:** 1974. **Telecommunication Services:** gthomas@ceinfo.org.

7726 ■ M.H. Chew & Associates Corporate Library
7275 National Dr., Ste. C
Livermore, CA 94550
Ph: (925)443-5071
Fax: (510)373-0624
Co. E-mail: patricia.shannon@mhchew.com
URL: http://www.mhchew.com/
Contact: Patricia Shannon
Scope: Nuclear safety, environmental safety, health physics, radiation protection, risk analysis. **Services:** Interlibrary loan; copying; Library not open to the public. **Founded:** 1993. **Holdings:** 1500 books; 2000 bound periodical volumes; 5000 reports. **Subscriptions:** 100 journals and other serials. **Telecommunication Services:** mel_chew@mhchew.com; corporate@mhchew.com; info@mhchew.com.

7727 ■ General Engineering Laboratories, Inc. Library
PO Box 30712
Charleston, SC 29417
Ph: (843)556-8171
Fax: (843)766-1178
Co. E-mail: bob.pullano@gel.com
URL: http://www.gel.net
Contact: James M. Stelling, President
Scope: Environmental analysis, environmental consulting, environmental regulations. **Holdings:** Figures not available.

7728 ■ Gradient Corporation - Information Resource Center
20 University Rd.
Cambridge, MA 02138
Ph: (617)395-5000
Fax: (617)395-5001
Co. E-mail: info@gradientcorp.com
URL: http://www.gradientcorp.com
Contact: Ruth Lyddy
Scope: Environmental protection, pollution, environmental chemistry, toxicology, risk assessment. **Services:** Interlibrary loan; Center not open to the public. **Founded:** 1986. **Holdings:** 100,000 books and reports. **Subscriptions:** 60 journals and other serials. **Telecommunication Services:** molson@gradientcorp.com.

7729 ■ National Audubon Society - Aullwood Audubon Center and Farm Library
1000 Aullwood Rd.
Dayton, OH 45414-1129
Ph: (937)890-7360
Fax: (937)890-2382
Co. E-mail: aullwood@gemair.com
URL: http://aullwood.center.audubon.org
Contact: Barbara Trick, Office Manager
Scope: Natural history, environmental education, agriculture, protection of birds. **Services:** Copying; Library open to the public for reference use only. **Founded:** 1957. **Holdings:** 2000 books. **Subscriptions:** 4 journals and other serials.

7730 ■ National Environmental Health Association Library
720 S. Colorado Blvd., Ste. 1000-N
Denver, CO 80246-1926
Ph: (303)756-9090
Free: 866-956-2258
Fax: (303)691-9490
Co. E-mail: staff@neha.org
URL: http://www.neha.org
Contact: Nelson Fabian, Executive Director
Scope: Environmental health concerns, environmental protection. **Services:** Library not open to the public. **Founded:** 1980. **Holdings:** 1000 volumes. **Subscriptions:** 10,055 journals and other serials. **Telecommunication Services:** nfabian@neha.org.

7731 ■ Native Americans for a Clean Environment - Resource Office Native Americans for a Clean Environment
Box 1671
Tahlequah, OK 74465
Ph: (918)458-4322
Contact: Lance Hughes, Executive Director
Scope: Nuclear energy - waste and waste routes, facilities, health effects; national environmental issues; area issues. **Services:** Copying; office will respond to telephone and written inquiries. **Holdings:** Figures not available.

7732 ■ Renew America Library
PO Box 77636
Washington, DC 20013
Ph: (202)721-1545
Fax: (202)232-2617
Co. E-mail: info@renewamerica.us
URL: http://www.renewamerica.us/
Contact: Anna Slafer, Executive Director
Scope: The environment, natural resources. **Services:** Library not open to the public. **Founded:** 1979. **Holdings:** 1400 case studies.

7733 ■ Stantec Consulting Services, Inc. Library
4875 Riverside Dr.
Macon, GA 31210-1117
Ph: (478)474-6100

Fax: (478)474-8933
Co. E-mail: macon@stantec.com
URL: http://www.stantec.com
Contact: Kay Luckie
Scope: Engineers, environmental professionals, architects, surveyors, transportation. **Services:** Library not open to the public. **Founded:** 1970. **Holdings:** 2000 books; 500 bound periodical volumes; 1100 reports; 25,000 archives; 5000 microfilms. **Subscriptions:** 250 journals and other serials; 7 newspapers.

7734 ■ Tetra Tech NUS, Inc. - Technical Information Center
900 Trail Ridge Rd.
Aiken, SC 29803
Ph: (803)649-7963
Fax: (803)642-8454
Co. E-mail: info@tetratech.com
URL: http://www.tetratech.com/about/locations.html
Contact: Debbie Pyron, Manager
Scope: Environment, nuclear energy. **Services:** Library not open to the public. **Holdings:** Reports. **Subscriptions:** 2 newspapers.

7735 ■ U.S. Environmental Protection Agency Headquarters Library
Mailcode 3404T
Washington, DC 20460-0001
Ph: (202)566-0556
Fax: (202)260-5153
Co. E-mail: hqchemlibraries@epa.gov
URL: http://www.epa.gov/libraries/hqrepository.html
Scope: Water - pollution, quality, supply; air pollution; noise abatement; radiation; hazardous wastes; solid waste management; resource recovery; pesticides; chemistry and toxicology; social, economic, legislative, legal, administrative, and management aspects of environmental policy. **Services:** Interlibrary loan; SDI; library open to the public with restrictions. **Founded:** 1971. **Holdings:** 16,000 books; 7000 hardcopy documents and technical reports; 400,000 documents and reports from the EPA and its predecessor agencies on microfiche; newspapers, abstracts and indexes, periodicals on microfilm. **Subscriptions:** 20 journals and other serials.

7736 ■ U.S. Environmental Protection Agency Library
Mail Code 3404T
1200 Pennsylvania Ave., NW
Washington, DC 20460
Ph: (202)566-0556
Fax: (202)566-0574
Co. E-mail: hqchemlibraries@epa.gov
URL: http://www.epa.gov/libraries/hqchem.html
Scope: Water pollution, water quality, environmental quality, air pollution, toxic substances, hazardous wastes. **Services:** Interlibrary loan; copying; Library open to the public. **Founded:** 1967. **Holdings:** 3500 books; 10,000 federal and state reports; 200,000 microfiche. **Subscriptions:** 60 journals and other serials.

7737 ■ URS Library
Crown Corporate Center
2870 Gateway Oaks Dr., Ste. 150
Sacramento, CA 95833-4308
Ph: (916)679-2000
Fax: (916)679-2900
URL: http://www.urscorp.com
Scope: Environment, air quality, hazardous waste. **Services:** Interlibrary loan; Library not open to the public. **Founded:** 1986. **Holdings:** 5000 books; technical and government reports; government agency rules and regulations. **Subscriptions:** 75 journals and other serials.

7738 ■ Williams College Center for Environmental Studies - Matt Cole Memorial Library
Harper House
Williamstown, MA 01267
Ph: (413)597-2346
Fax: (413)597-3489
Co. E-mail: ces@williams.edu
URL: http://ces.williams.edu/?page_id=130
Contact: Norm Parker, Specialist
URL(s): library.williams.edu/. **Scope:** Agriculture, air pollution, biodiversity, climate, regional planning, coastal, ecology, energy, environmental health, environmental law and policy, forestry, hazardous substances, land use and planning, solid waste, water quality, wildlife management habitat. **Services:** Interlibrary loan; library open to the public. **Founded:** 1972. **Holdings:** 7500 books; 2900 bound periodical volumes; 5000 other documents. **Subscriptions:** 250 journals and other serials.

RESEARCH CENTERS

7739 ■ Clark University - George Perkins Marsh Institute - Center for Technology, Environment, and Development (CENTED)
950 Main St.
Worcester, MA 01610-1477
Ph: (508)751-4622
Fax: (508)751-4600
Co. E-mail: rjohnston@clarku.edu
URL: http://www.clarku.edu/departments/marsh/centers/cented.cfm
Contact: Prof. Robert J. Johnston, Director
Founded: 1978. **Publications:** *CENTED Research reports*; *CENTED Working papers*. **Educational Activities:** Distinguished Lecture Series.

7740 ■ Green Seal
1001 Connecticut Ave. NW, Ste. 827
Washington, DC 20036-5525
Ph: (202)872-6400
Fax: (202)872-4324
Co. E-mail: greenseal@greenseal.org
URL: http://www.greenseal.org
Contact: Dr. Arthur B. Weissman, President
Services: Awards seals of approval to products deemed to be environmentally responsible. **Founded:** 1989. **Publications:** *Campus Green Buying Guide*; *Choose Green Report*; *Hotel Green Buying Guide*; *Office Green Buying Guide*. **Awards:** Green Seal Internships. **Telecommunication Services:** aweissman@greenseal.org.

7741 ■ Tellus Institute
11 Arlington St.
Boston, MA 02116-3411
Ph: (617)266-5400
Fax: (617)266-8303
Co. E-mail: info@tellus.org
URL: http://www.tellus.org
Contact: Paul D. Raskin, President
Services: Consulting: on-going, on a fee basis. **Founded:** 1976. **Telecommunication Services:** praskin@tellus.org.

7742 ■ University of Colorado at Boulder - Environmental Program
214 UCB
Boulder, CO 80309
Ph: (303)492-7943
Fax: (303)492-1414
Co. E-mail: bob.sievers@colorado.edu
URL: http://cires.colorado.edu/env_prog/index.html
Contact: Prof. Bob Sievers, Director

REFERENCE WORKS

7743 ■ *"Eliminating All of Your Estate Tax Burden" in Contractor (Vol. 57, January 2010, No. 1, pp. 48)*
Pub: Penton Media, Inc.
Ed: Irv Blackman. **Description:** Suggestions on how family owned businesses can minimize their estate tax burdens are discussed. One of these includes not using life insurance in a business succession plan to move stocks to the children and to never use Section 6166 as part of the overall estate tax plan.

7744 ■ *"Estate Tax Problems may Soon Disappear" in Contractor (Vol. 56, September 2009, No. 9, pp. 60)*
Pub: Penton Media, Inc.
Ed: Irv Blackman. **Description:** Advice on how to effectively plan estate tax in the United States. Pending changes to US estate tax laws are seen to resolve inheritance problems. Captive insurance firms can lower property and casualty insurance costs to transfer businesses to children.

7745 ■ *"Expect Action on Health Care and the Economy" in Contractor (Vol. 57, January 2010, No. 1, pp. 30)*
Pub: Penton Media, Inc.
Ed: Kevin Schwalb. **Description:** The Plumbing-Heating-Cooling Contractors National Association is working to solidify its standing in the public policy arena as the legislative agenda will focus on health care reform, estate tax and immigration reform, all of which will impact the industries.

7746 ■ *"For All It's Worth" in Entrepreneur (Vol. 36, April 2008, No. 4, pp. 46)*
Pub: Entrepreneur Media, Inc.
Ed: Farnoosh Torabi. **Description:** Discusses the federal estate tax system requires that 45 percent of the money beyond $2 million be given to the government. Ways on how to minimize the effects of estate tax on assets include: creating bypass trusts for married couples; setting up an irrevocable life insurance trust to avoid taxation of estate for insurance benefactors; and having annual gift tax exclusion.

7747 ■ *"New Year, New Estate Plan" in Hawaii Business (Vol. 53, February 2008, No. 8, pp. 54)*
Pub: Hawaii Business Publishing
Ed: Antony M. Orme. **Description:** Discusses the start of the new year which can be a time to revise wills and estate plans as failure to do so may create problems of unequal inheritance and increase in estate tax exemption, which could disinherit beneficiaries. Other circumstances that can prompt changes in wills and estate plans are presented.

7748 ■ *"Retailers, Your Will, and More" in Agency Sales Magazine (Vol. 39, July 2009, No. 7, pp. 46)*
Pub: MANA
Ed: Melvin H. Daskal. **Description:** IRS audit guide for small retail businesses is presented. Tips on how to make a will with multiple beneficiaries are discussed together with medical expenses that can not be deducted.

7749 ■ *"Solutions to Family Business Problems" in Contractor (Vol. 56, October 2009, No. 10, pp. 51)*
Pub: Penton Media, Inc.
Ed: Irv Blackman. **Description:** Several common business problems that family owned firms face are presented together with their solutions. These problems include giving the children stock bonus options while another discusses the tax burden when a father wants to transfer the business to his son.

7750 ■ *Stealing MySpace: The Battle to Control the Most Popular Website in America*
Pub: Random House Inc.
Contact: Richard Sarnoff, President
Ed: Julia Angwin. **Released:** 2009. **Price:** $27.00. **Description:** Information regarding Rupert Murdoch's outwitting Viacom's Tom Freston and details of the deal are presented.

TRADE PERIODICALS

7751 ■ *Estate Planners Alert*
Pub: Research Institute of America
Contact: Peter Warwick, President
Released: Monthly. **Price:** $210. **Description:** Spotlights critical developments in estate and financial planning.

7752 ■ *Estate Planning Review*
Pub: CCH Inc.
Contact: Mike Sabbatis, President
Released: Monthly. **Price:** $275. **Description:** Monthly newsletter covering estate and financial planning issues for individuals. Includes coverage of retirement planning, insurance planning and investments.

7753 ■ *Tax Management Estates, Gifts, and Trusts Journal*
Pub: BNA Tax and Accounting
Contact: Glenn B. Davis, Managing Editor
E-mail: gdavis@bna.com
Released: Bimonthly. **Price:** $261. **Description:** Provides practical guidance on and reviews recent developments in estates, gifts, and trusts. Recurring features include sections titled Detailed Analysis, Working Papers, and Bibliography and Reference. **Remarks:** Subscription includes Tax Management Memorandum.

FRANCHISES AND BUSINESS OPPORTUNITIES

7754 ■ **American Prosperity Group (APG)**
3 Sunny Knolls Ct.
Wayne, NJ 07470
Ph: (973)831-4424
Free: 877-885-1274
Co. E-mail: info@1apg.com
URL: http://www.1apg.com
Description: Retirement and estate planning products and services. **No. of Franchise Units:** 15. **No. of Company-Owned Units:** 1. **Founded:** 1991..

Franchised: 2006. **Equity Capital Needed:** $78,300-$121,000. **Franchise Fee:** $50,000. **Royalty Fee:** Varies. **Financial Assistance:** Limited third party financing available. **Training:** Offers 4 weeks at headquarters, 1 week onsite and ongoing support.

COMPUTERIZED DATABASES

7755 ■ *Estate Planning*
2395 Midway Rd.
Carrollton, TX 75006
Free: 800-431-9025
Co. E-mail: ria@thomson.com
URL: http://ria.thomsonreuters.com
Availability: Online: Thomson Reuters - RIA Tax & Accounting Unit. **Type:** Full-text.

7756 ■ *Estates, Gifts, and Trust Journal*
1801 S Bell St.
Arlington, VA 22202
Free: 800-372-1033
Co. E-mail: customercare@bna.com
URL: http://www.bna.com/tax-accounting-t5000
Availability: Online: The Bureau of National Affairs Inc. - Tax and Accounting Division. **Type:** Full-text.

LIBRARIES

7757 ■ **Adler Pollock & Sheehan Law Library**
One Citizens Plaza, 8th Fl.
Providence, RI 02903
Ph: (401)274-7200
Fax: (401)751-4604
Co. E-mail: pdumaine@apslaw.com
URL: http://www.apslaw.com
Contact: Nicholas Rago, Executive Director
Scope: Law - business, corporate, commercial, labor, tax, securities, environmental; estate planning; litigation; public utilities; telecommunications; energy; insurance. **Services:** Interlibrary loan (limited); library not open to the public. **Founded:** 1983. **Holdings:** 5000 books; 500 bound periodical volumes. **Subscriptions:** 40 journals and other serials.

7758 ■ **Connecticut Judicial Branch - Putnam Law Library**
Putnam Courthouse
155 Church St.
Putnam, CT 06260
Ph: (860)928-3716
Fax: (860)963-7531
Co. E-mail: donna.izbicki@jud.ct.gov
URL: http://www.jud.ct.gov/lawlib/
Contact: Donna R. Izbicki, Librarian
Scope: Law. **Services:** Copying; Library open to the public. **Holdings:** 17,000 books. **Subscriptions:** 140 journals and other serials.

7759 ■ **Dewey & LeBoeuf LLP Library**
1301 Ave. of the Americas
New York, NY 10019-6092
Ph: (212)259-8000

Fax: (212)259-6333
URL: http://www.deweyleboeuf.com
Scope: Law - antitrust, securities, taxation, real property, trusts and estates, corporate, bankruptcy, intellectual property. **Services:** Interlibrary loan; library open to members of SLA by appointment. **Founded:** 1915. **Holdings:** 50,000 volumes. **Subscriptions:** 300 journals and other serials.

7760 ■ Fasken Martineau DuMoulin LLP Toronto Library
333 Bay St., Ste. 2400
Bay Adelaide Centre, Box 20
Toronto, ON, Canada M5H 2T6
Ph: (416)366-8381
Fax: (416)364-7813
Co. E-mail: toronto@fasken.com
URL: http://www.fasken.com
Contact: Michele L. Miles, Librarian
Scope: Law - corporate, administrative, real estate, estate; taxation; litigation. **Services:** Interlibrary loan. **Holdings:** 14,000 books; 50 bound periodical volumes; federal and provincial legislation. **Subscriptions:** 500 journals and other serials.

7761 ■ Goodmans Library
333 Bay St., Ste. 3400
Toronto, ON, Canada M5H 2M7
Ph: (416)979-2211
Fax: (416)979-1234
Co. E-mail: msaulig@goodmans.ca
URL: http://www.goodmans.ca
Contact: Mary Saulig
Scope: Law - commercial, corporate, securities, bankruptcy, entertainment, planning, administrative; litigation; real estate; estates and trusts; taxation, e-commerce. **Services:** Interlibrary loan. **Founded:** 1962. **Holdings:** 12,000 volumes. **Subscriptions:** 250 journals and other serials.

7762 ■ Hancock & Estabrook Law Library
1500 AXA Tower 1
100 Madison St.
Syracuse, NY 13202
Ph: (315)565-4500
Fax: (315)565-4600
URL: http://hancocklaw.com
Scope: New York state and federal law; labor relations; taxes; securities; estates and trusts; negligence; products liability; malpractice; municipalities; real property; the environment; healthcare. **Services:** Library not open to the public. **Founded:** 1889. **Holdings:** 20,000 books. **Subscriptions:** 200 journals and other serials.

7763 ■ Hinckley, Allen, & Snyder LLP - Library Services
50 Kennedy Plaza, Ste. 1500
Providence, RI 02903
Ph: (401)274-2000
Fax: (401)277-9600
Co. E-mail: ctrask@haslaw.com
URL: http://www.haslaw.com/
Contact: Carolyn J. Trask, Director, Library Services
Scope: Law: business litigation; construction litigation; tax; commercial/business; labor; health; trusts; estates; financial planning; real estate; intellectual property. **Services:** Interlibrary loan (limited); Library not open to the public. **Holdings:** 8000 books. **Subscriptions:** 125 journals and other serials.

7764 ■ Irell & Manella Library
1800 Ave. of the Stars, Ste. 900
Los Angeles, CA 90067
Ph: (310)277-1010

Fax: (310)203-7199
Co. E-mail: info@irell.com
URL: http://www.irell.com
Scope: Law - intellectual property transactional, intellectual property litigation, federal and state litigation, tax, corporate, corporate securities, entertainment, antitrust, trusts and estates, probate, real estate, insurance, computer law, art law, aviation law. **Services:** Library not open to the public. **Founded:** 1941. **Holdings:** 70,000 volumes; microfiche; audio- and videotapes; CD-ROMs.

7765 ■ Kelley, Drye & Warren LLP Law Library
101 Park Ave.
New York, NY 10178
Ph: (212)808-7800
Fax: (212)808-7897
Co. E-mail: jkirk@kelleydrye.com
URL: http://www.kelleydrye.com
Scope: Law - banking, corporate, securities, trusts and estates, labor, tax; employee benefits. **Services:** Interlibrary loan (limited); library not open to the public. **Holdings:** 40,000 books. **Subscriptions:** 247 journals and other serials; 28 newspapers.

7766 ■ Loeb & Loeb LLP Law Library
10100 Santa Monica Blvd., Ste. 2200
Los Angeles, CA 90067
Ph: (310)282-2000
Fax: (213)282-2200
Co. E-mail: mmayerson@loeb.com
URL: http://www.loeb.com
Contact: Mickey Mayerson, Managing Partner
Scope: Law taxation, litigation, insolvency and workout, entertainment, labor, real estate, corporate, estates and trusts, intellectual property. **Services:** Library not open to the public. **Founded:** 1909. **Holdings:** 34,000 volumes. **Subscriptions:** 200 journals and other serials; 12 newspapers.

7767 ■ Lum, Danzis, Drasco, Positan, & Kleinberg Law Library
103 Eisenhower Pkwy.
Roseland, NJ 07068-1049
Ph: (973)403-9000
Fax: (973)403-9021
URL: http://www.lumlaw.com
Contact: Steven J. Eisenstein
Scope: Law - taxation, labor and employment, corporate, banking, trust and estates, litigation. **Services:** Interlibrary loan; Library not open to the public. **Founded:** 1870. **Holdings:** 20,000 volumes. **Subscriptions:** 25 journals and other serials; 5 newspapers.

7768 ■ Mackenzie Hughes LLP Law Library
101 S. Salina St., Ste. 600
Syracuse, NY 13202
Ph: (315)474-7571
Fax: (315)474-6409
Co. E-mail: info@mackenziehughes.com
URL: http://www.mackenziehughes.com
Scope: Law - general, civil practice, tax, corporation, labor, estate, real estate. **Services:** Interlibrary loan; library open to the public with permission of librarian. **Holdings:** 10,000 books; 50 cassettes; 800 law briefs; 300 memoranda of law. **Subscriptions:** 100 journals and other serials.

7769 ■ National Trust Company Reference Library
1 Adelaide St., E., 3rd Fl.
Toronto, ON, Canada M5C 2W8
Ph: (416)361-3611

Fax: (416)361-5551
Scope: Law; trusts and estates. **Services:** Library not open to the public. **Founded:** 1971. **Holdings:** 3200 books; 3500 annual reports of outside companies. **Subscriptions:** 150 journals and other serials; 8 newspapers.

7770 ■ Nixon Peabody LLP Law Library - Rochester, New York
1300 Clinton Sq.
Rochester, NY 14604
Ph: (585)263-1000
Fax: (585)263-1600
Co. E-mail: glusk@nixonpeabody.com
URL: http://www.nixonpeabody.com
Contact: Glenda Lusk, Office Manager
Scope: Law - corporate, tax, estates, real estate, labor, environmental, litigation. **Services:** Interlibrary loan; library not open to the public. **Holdings:** 35,000 books. **Subscriptions:** 320 journals and other serials.

7771 ■ Ober, Kaler, Grimes & Shriver Library—OberIKaler.
100 Light St.
Baltimore, MD 21202-1036
Ph: (410)685-1120
Fax: (410)547-0699
Co. E-mail: info@ober.com
URL: http://www.ober.com
Contact: Ginger J. Gerton, Librarian
Scope: Law - admiralty, hospital/healthcare, corporate, tax; litigation; estates and trusts. **Services:** Library not open to the public. **Holdings:** 15,000 books.

7772 ■ Putney, Twombly, Hall & Hirson LLP Law Library
521 5th Ave., Fl. 10
New York, NY 10175
Ph: (212)682-0020
Fax: (212)682-9380
Co. E-mail: info@putneylaw.com
URL: http://www.putneylaw.com
Scope: Law - labor, corporate, trust, estate, tax. **Services:** Library not open to the public. **Holdings:** 8000 books. **Subscriptions:** 12 journals and other serials.

7773 ■ Venable LLP Library
750 E. Pratt St., Ste. 900
Baltimore, MD 21201
Ph: (410)244-7400
Fax: (410)244-7742
Co. E-mail: info@venable.com
URL: http://www.venable.com
Contact: Anne Morrison-Low
Scope: Law - tax, labor, corporate, securities, environmental, trusts and estates, government contracts, healthcare, real estate; litigation; International trade; intellectual property; trade regulation; bankruptcy; employee benefits; banking. **Services:** Interlibrary loan; library not open to the public. **Holdings:** 25,000 books; 500 bound periodical volumes. **Subscriptions:** 50 journals and other serials; 5 newspapers.

7774 ■ Willkie Farr & Gallagher Library
787 7th Ave.
New York, NY 10019-6099
Ph: (212)728-8000
Fax: (212)728-8111
URL: http://www.willkie.com
Scope: Law - corporate, tax, real estate, trusts and estates, litigation. **Services:** Interlibrary loan; library not open to the public. **Holdings:** 40,000 books; 400 bound periodical volumes; 7 cabinets of microforms; 45 videotapes. **Subscriptions:** 350 journals and other serials.

ASSOCIATIONS AND OTHER ORGANIZATIONS

7775 ■ **National Auctioneers Association (NAA)**
8880 Ballentine St.
Overland Park, KS 66214
Ph: (913)541-8084
Fax: (913)894-5281
Co. E-mail: support@auctioneers.org
URL: http://www.auctioneers.org
Contact: Christie King, President
E-mail: cking@ckingbenefits.com
Description: Professional auctioneers. Provides continuing education classes for auctioneers, promotes use of the auction method of marketing in both the private and public sectors. Encourages the highest ethical standards for the profession. **Founded:** 1949. **Publications:** *IAL Auction Newsletter* / *Auctionier*, *The Auctioneer*, *Auctioneer--Directory Issue* (Annual). **Educational Activities:** National Auctioneers Association National Convention (Annual). **Awards:** Marketing Competition; International Auctioneers Championship; Hall of Fame Award. **Telecommunication Services:** aucmktinst@aol.com.

FRANCHISES AND BUSINESS OPPORTUNITIES

7776 ■ **Caring Transitions**
10700 Montgomery Rd., Ste. 300
Cincinnati, OH 45242
Ph: (866)708-9420
Fax: (513)563-2691
Description: Sales of estates and household goods. **No. of Franchise Units:** 82. **Founded:** 2006.. **Franchised:** 2006. **Equity Capital Needed:** $38,280-$66,580. **Franchise Fee:** $31,900. **Royalty Fee:** 6%. **Financial Assistance:** Yes. **Training:** Provides 5 days at headquarters, regional/national meetings, sales boot camps and ongoing support.

7777 ■ **Estate Group**
666 High St., Ste. 203
Worthington, OH 43085
Ph: (614)844-4406
Fax: (614)985-0169
Description: Estate settlement & downsizing services. **No. of Franchise Units:** 2. **No. of Company-Owned Units:** 1. **Founded:** 2004.. **Franchised:** 2007. **Equity Capital Needed:** $45,700-$90,600. **Franchise Fee:** $29,000. **Royalty Fee:** Varies. **Financial Assistance:** Limited third party financing available. **Training:** Available at eadquarters 3 days.

ASSOCIATIONS AND OTHER ORGANIZATIONS

7778 ■ Association of Professional Recruiters of Canada (APRC)
c/o IPM Management Training and Development Corporation
1081 Ambleside Dr., Ste. 2210
Ottawa, ON, Canada K2B 8C8
Ph: (613)721-5957
Free: 888-441-0000
Fax: (613)721-5850
Co. E-mail: info@workplace.ca
URL: http://www.workplace.ca/resources/aprc_assoc.html
Contact: Ms. Nathaly Pinchuk, Executive Director
Description: Employment recruiters. Seeks to advance the practice of employment recruiting; promotes ongoing professional development of members. Serves as a forum for the exchange of information among members; sponsors educational programs. **Founded:** 1994.

7779 ■ National Association of Executive Recruiters (NAER)
1 E Wacker Dr., Ste. 2600
Chicago, IL 60601
Ph: (618)398-6027
Co. E-mail: lisom@hhisearch.com
URL: http://www.naer.org
Contact: Jim Schneider, President
Description: Executive recruitment and search specialist firms providing counsel and assistance in identifying and hiring candidates for middle- and senior-level management positions. Promotes and enhances the public image, awareness, and understanding of the executive search profession. Serves as a forum for exchange of ideas among members; conducts educational programs and owners' roundtable. Maintains code of ethics and professional practice guidelines. **Founded:** 1984. **Educational Activities:** National Association of Executive Recruiters Conference (Annual).

REFERENCE WORKS

7780 ■ "Akron Community Foundation Hires Help for CEO Search" in Crain's Cleveland Business (Vol. 28, October 29, 2007, No. 43, pp. 6)
Pub: Crain Communications, Inc.
Ed: Shannon Mortland. **Description:** Waverly Partners LLC, an executive search firm, has been hired by the Akron Community Foundation to search for its next president and CEO as Jody Bacon, the company's current CEO, will retire on July 31, 2008.

7781 ■ "AT&T To Acquire Black Telecom Firm" in Black Enterprise (Vol. 38, January 2008, No. 6, pp. 24)
Pub: Earl G. Graves Publishing Co. Inc.
Ed: Alan Hughes. **Description:** Details of AT&T's acquisition of ChaseCom LP, a telecommunications company based in Houston, Texas, are covered.

7782 ■ "Calling All Recruiters: Agent HR Puts Staffing Agents In Charge" in Black Enterprise (Vol. 38, December 2007, No. 5, pp. 72)
Pub: Earl G. Graves Publishing Co. Inc.
Ed: Chana Garcia. **Description:** Recruiting and staffing agencies are seeing a drop in services due to slow economic growth. AgentHR partners with full-service recruiters who have three to five year's experience-specialists soliciting their own clients, provide staffing services, and manage their own accounts, thus combining the roles of recruiter and salesperson.

7783 ■ "DHR Hires Carr for Sports Group" in Crain's Detroit Business (Vol. 25, June 8, 2009, No. 23, pp. 5)
Pub: Crain Communications Inc. - Detroit
Ed: Sherri Begin Welch. **Description:** Lloyd Carr, former head football coach for University of Michigan, has taken a position with DHR International in order to expand its searches for collegiate and professional sports organizations, recruit athletic directors, head coaches and other executives.

7784 ■ Directory of Executive and Professional Recruiters: 2009-2010
Pub: Kennedy Information Inc.
Contact: Wayne E. Cooper, President
URL(s): www.kennedyinfo.com. **Released:** Annual; latest edition 2009-2010. **Price:** $59.95, Individuals. **Covers:** More than 13,000 key recruiters in 5,700 executive search firms with 7,575 executive search offices in North America; firms operating on a contingent fee basis are listed in separate section. **Entries include:** Firm name, address, phone number and e-mail and web addresses when available, names of contact and other key personnel, brief description of firm's specialties, salary minimum; members of the Association of Executive Search Consultants are identified. For commercial use requests, please contact publisher. **Arrangement:** Alphabetical in separate retainer and contingency sections. **Indexes:** Geography, industry, job function, recruiter specialty, firm.

7785 ■ "Growing Strong" in Entrepreneur (Vol. 35, November 2007, No. 11, pp. 36)
Pub: Entrepreneur Media Inc.
Ed: Nichole L. Torres. **Description:** Amy Langer founded Salo LL with partner John Folkestad. The company is growing fast since its 2002 launch, with over $40 million in projections for 2007. The finance and accounting staffing company tops the list of the fastest-growing women-led companies in North America.

7786 ■ "Impressive Numbers: Companies Experience Substantial Increases in Dollars, Employment" in Hispanic Business (July-August 2007)
Pub: Hispanic Business
Ed: Derek Reveron. **Description:** Profiles of five fastest growing Hispanic companies reporting increases in revenue and employment include Brightstar, distributor of wireless products; Greenway Ford Inc.,

a car dealership; Fred Loya Insurance, auto insurance carrier; and Group O, packaging company; and Diverse Staffing, Inc., an employment and staffing firm.

7787 ■ "iSymmetry's Technological Makeover Or, How a Tech Company Finally Grew Up and Discovered the World Wide Web" in Inc. (October 2007)
Pub: Gruner & Jahr USA Publishing
Description: Profile of iSymmetry, an Atlanta, Georgia-based IT recruiting firm, covering the issues the company faces keeping its technology equipment up-to-date. The firm has devised a program that will replace its old server-based software systems with on-demand software delivered via the Internet, known as software-as-a-service. Statistical information included.

7788 ■ "Job Search Made Easy" in Black Enterprise (Vol. 38, January 2008, No. 6, pp. 54)
Pub: Earl G. Graves Publishing Co. Inc.
Description: Profile of The Marquin Group's job portal called DiversityTalent.com. Marquin considered the challenges faced by corporations when recruiting senior executives; salaries, mortgage and relocation calculators for particular cities are provided.

7789 ■ "The Jobs Man" in Business Courier (Vol. 26, December 25, 2009, No. 35, pp. 1)
Pub: American City Business Journals, Inc.
Ed: Lucy May. **Description:** Entrepreneur Bob Messer, a volunteer for Jobs Plus Employment Network in Cincinnati's Over-the-Rhine neighborhood, regularly conducts a seminar that aims to help attendees prepare for employment. Jobs Plus founder Burr Robinson asked Messer to create the seminar in order to help unemployed jobseekers. So far, the program has helped 144 individuals with full time jobs in 2009.

7790 ■ "Matchmakers Anticipating Tech Valley Boom" in Business Review, Albany New York (Vol. 34, November 2, 2007, No. 31, pp. 1)
Pub: American City Business Journals, Inc.
Ed: Adam Sichko. **Description:** Qualified candidates are coming to permanent placement companies after being downsized elsewhere. The top five projected fastest-growing and top five projected fasted-decreasing jobs in the Capital Region are presented.

7791 ■ "On the Clock" in Canadian Business (Vol. 82, April 27, 2009, No. 7, pp. 28)
Pub: Rogers Media
Ed: Sarka Halas. **Description:** Survey of 100 Canadian executives found that senior managers can be out of a job for about nine months before their careers are adversely affected. The nine month mark can be avoided if job seekers build networks even before they lose their jobs. Job seekers should also take volunteer work and training opportunities to increase their changes of landing a job.

7792 ■ "Overseas Overtures" in Business Journal-Portland (Vol. 24, October 26, 2007, No. 35, pp. 1)
Pub: American City Business Journals, Inc.
Ed: Robin J. Moody. **Description:** Oregon has a workforce shortage, specifically for the health care industry. Recruiting agencies, such as the International Recruiting Network Inc., answers the high demand for workforce by recruiting foreign employees. The difficulties recruiting companies experience with regards to foreign labor laws are investigated.

7793 ■ "Regional Talent Network Unveils Jobs Web Site" in Crain's Cleveland Business (Vol. 30, June 1, 2009, No. 21, pp. 11)
Pub: Crain Communications, Inc.
Description: Regional Talent Network launched WhereToFindHelp.org, a Website designed to act as a directory of all Northeast Ohio resources that can help employers recruit and job seekers look for positions. The site also lists organizations offering employment and training services.

7794 ■ "Sign of the Times: Temp-To-Perm Attorneys" in HRMagazine (Vol. 54, January 2009, No. 1, pp. 24)
Pub: Society for Human Resource Management
Contact: Henry G. Jackson, President
E-mail: hjackson\@shrm.org
Ed: Bill Leonard. **Description:** A growing number of law firms are hiring professional staff on a temp-to-perm basis according to the president of Professional Placement Services in Florida. Firms can save money while testing potential employees on a temporary basis.

7795 ■ "Staffing Firms are Picking Up the Pieces, Seeing Signs of Life" in Milwaukee Business Journal (Vol. 27, February 5, 2010, No. 19)
Pub: American City Business Journals
Ed: Rich Rovito. **Description:** Milwaukee, Wisconsin-based staffing firms are seeing signs of economic rebound as many businesses turned to temporary employees to fill the demands for goods and services. Economic observers believe the growth in temporary staffing is one of the early indicators of economic recovery.

7796 ■ "Talent Scout: How This Exec Finds and Develops Leaders Internally" in Black Enterprise (Vol. 38, November 2007, No. 4, pp. 63)
Pub: Earl G. Graves Publishing Co. Inc.
Ed: Faith Chukwudi. **Description:** Profile of Bernard Bedon, director at Public Group Media. Bedon helps attract, develop, retain, and reward talent in his media group of 10,000 employees worldwide.

7797 ■ "Wanted: African American Professional for Hire" in Black Enterprise (Vol. 37, November 2006, No. 4, pp. 93)
Pub: Earl G. Graves Publishing Co. Inc.
Ed: Joe Watson. **Description:** Excerpt from the book, Without Excuses: Unleash the Power of Diversity to Build Your Business, speaks to the lack of diversity in the corporate arena and why executives, recruiters, and HR professionals claim they are unable to find qualified individuals of different races when hiring.

7798 ■ "What You Look Like Online" in Black Enterprise (Vol. 37, January 2007, No. 6, pp. 56)
Pub: Earl G. Graves Publishing Co. Inc.
Ed: Marcia A. Reed-Woodard. **Description:** Of 100 executive recruiters 77 percent stated that they use search engines to check the backgrounds of potential job candidates, according to a survey conducted by ExecuNet. Of those surveyed 35 percent stated that they eliminate potential candidates based on information they find online so it is important to create a positive Web presence which highlights professional image qualities.

7799 ■ "Winner: Private Company, $100M-$1B" in Crain's Detroit Business (Vol. 25, June 22, 2009, No. 25, pp. E004)
Pub: Crain Communications Inc. - Detroit
Ed: Sherri Begin Welch. **Description:** Profile of Strategic Staffing Solutions Inc. is presented.

TRADE PERIODICALS

7800 ■ Executive Recruiter News
Pub: Kennedy Information Inc.
Contact: Wayne E. Cooper, President
Ed: Joseph Daniel McCool, Editor, ern-editor\@kennedyinfo.com. **Released:** Monthly. **Price:** $229.
Description: The authoritative voice of the recruiting industry, covering news, analysis, practice advice, proprietary data and opinion.

VIDEOCASSETTES/AUDIOCASSETTES

7801 ■ From Law School to Law Practice: What Every Associate Needs to Know—The Set
American Law Institute
American Bar Association Committee on Continuing Education
4025 Chestnut St.
Philadelphia, PA 19104
Ph: (215)243-1600
Free: 800-CLENEWS
Fax: (215)243-1636
Co. E-mail: custserv\@ali-aba.org
URL: http://www.ali.org
Released: 1989. **Price:** $190. **Description:** Uses brief dramatizations to outline various skills and strategies for law firm success. Complete with study guide. **Availability:** VHS.

FRANCHISES AND BUSINESS OPPORTUNITIES

7802 ■ Express Employment Professionals
8516 NW Expy.
Oklahoma City, OK 73162
Ph: (877)652-6400
Co. E-mail: franchising\@expresspersonnel.com
URL: http://www.franchising.expresspersonnel.com
Description: Is an international fullservice staffing corporation with three distinct divisions available in one franchise agreement. The franchised offices provide clients with temporary help, full-time placements, and executive recruitment. **No. of Franchise Units:** 550. **Founded:** 1983.. **Franchised:** 1985. **Equity Capital Needed:** $153,750-$242,500. **Franchise Fee:** $35,000. **Financial Assistance:** Yes. **Training:** 2 week initial training at headquarters, 1 week in certified training office and ongoing field training and support. Followed by additional time in new office with assigned field representative.

7803 ■ FORTUNE Personnel Consultants (FPC)
1140 Avenue of the Americas, 5th Fl.
New York, NY 10036-2711
Ph: (212)302-1141
Free: 800-886-7839
Fax: (212)302-2422
Co. E-mail: rherzoq\@fpcnational.com
URL: http://www.fpcnational.com
Description: Executive recruiting firm. **No. of Franchise Units:** 63. **No. of Company-Owned Units:** 1. **Founded:** 1959.. **Franchised:** 1973. **Equity Capital Needed:** $93,075-$138,550. **Franchise Fee:** $50,000. **Royalty Fee:** 7\
. **Financial Assistance:** In-house financial assistance available with franchise fee. **Training:** Offers 2 weeks training at headquarters, 5 days at franchisee's location with ongoing training, mentoring and coaching.

7804 ■ FPC/F-O-R-T-U-N-E Personnel Consultants
145 West 45th St., 8th Fl.
New York, NY 10036
Ph: (800)886-7839
URL: http://www.fpcnational.com
Description: Executive recruiting firm. Franchise owners enjoy all of today's technologies, including a national computerized exchange program. **No. of Franchise Units:** 71. **Founded:** 1959. **Franchised:** 1973. **Equity Capital Needed:** $93,070-$138,550. **Franchise Fee:** $50,000. **Training:** Yes.

7805 ■ Management Recruiters International Inc.
CDI Corp.
75 Erieview Plc., Ste. 100
Cleveland, OH 44114
Ph: (216)416-8467
Co. E-mail: contractstaffing\@MRINetwork.com
URL: http://www.mrinetwork.com
Description: Management level and general personnel placement, search and recruiting service on an employer-paid, contingency fee basis. **No. of Franchise Units:** 1,128. **No. of Company-Owned Units:** 32. **Founded:** 1957. **Franchised:** 1965. **Equity Capital Needed:** $112,855-$154,345. **Franchise Fee:** $100,000. **Financial Assistance:** Yes. **Training:** Initial training program of approximately 3 weeks at headquarters, plus an additional on-the-job training program of approximately 3 weeks in licensee's first office. Training thereafter as needed. Also assists in securing suitable office space, lease negotiations, design and layout, office furniture, equipment, telephone systems, etc.

7806 ■ Pridestaff
7535 N Palm Ave., Ste. 101
Fresno, CA 93711-1393
Ph: (559)449-5804
Fax: (559)432-4371
Description: Recruiting Agency. **No. of Franchise Units:** 36. **No. of Company-Owned Units:** 3. **Founded:** 1978.. **Franchised:** 1995. **Equity Capital Needed:** $162,000-$237,000. **Franchise Fee:** $32,000. **Training:** Yes.

7807 ■ Sanford Rose Associates
SRA International, Inc.
1305 Mall of Georgia Blvd., Ste. 160
Buford, GA 30519
Ph: (800)731-7724
Fax: (770)904-0359
Description: Employee search service that uses a database of candidates and custom computer software to allow each office to match employees with client openings. **No. of Franchise Units:** 64. **Founded:** 1959.. **Franchised:** 1970. **Equity Capital Needed:** $91,350-$129,680. **Franchise Fee:** $65,000. **Financial Assistance:** Yes. **Training:** Provides a minimum of 10 days of training at corporate headquarters and an additional 5 days of training in franchisees office.

COMPUTERIZED DATABASES

7808 ■ SkillSearch
15a Brighton Pl
Brighton BN1 1HJ, United Kingdom
Ph: 1273 287 007
Co. E-mail: brighton\@skillsearch.com
URL: http://www.skillsearch.com
Availability: Online: SkillSearch Ltd. **Type:** Directory.

COMPUTER SYSTEMS/SOFTWARE

7809 ■ PcHunter
200 East Del Mar Blvd., Ste. 91105
Pasadena, CA 91105
Ph: (310)458-1997
Free: 800-995-4868
Fax: (310)458-2177
Co. E-mail: sales\@microj.com
URL: http://www.microj.com
Price: Contact MicroJ Systems. **Description:** Available for PC Computers. System provides a recruitment-management program for employment agencies.

START-UP INFORMATION

7810 ■ *Design and Launch Your Online Boutique in a Week*
Pub: Entrepreneur Press

Ed: Melissa Campanelli. **Released:** June 26, 2008. **Price:** $17.95. **Description:** Tips for starting an on-line boutique in a short amount of time are given. The books shows how to build the online boutique with designer goods or your own product, ways to create eye-catching content, online tools to handle payments and accept orders, marketing and advertising techniques, and customer service.

7811 ■ *In Fashion: From Runway to Retail, Everything You Need to Know to Break Into the Fashion Industry*
Pub: Crown Business Books

Ed: Annemarie Iverson. **Released:** August 10, 2010. **Price:** $16.99. **Description:** Whether your dream is to photograph models, outfit celebrities, design fashions, this book provides details into every aspect for working in the fashion industry.

7812 ■ *"Money Matters: Using Sound Resources, You Can Find Capital For Your Business" in Black Enterprise (Vol. 38, November 2007, No. 4)*
Pub: Earl G. Graves Publishing Co. Inc.

Ed: Carolyn M. Brown. **Description:** Profile of fashion designer Kara Saun who inspired an angel investor from Connecticut to help launch her Fall 2006 clothing line.

7813 ■ *Start Your Own Fashion Accessories Business*
Pub: Entrepreneur Press
Contact: Perlman Neil, President

Released: March 1, 2009. **Price:** $17.95. **Description:** Entrepreneurs wishing to start a fashion accessories business will find important information for setting up a home workshop and office, exploring the market, managing finances, publicizing and advertising the business and more.

REFERENCE WORKS

7814 ■ *"Apparel" in Retail Merchandiser (Vol. 51, July-August 2011, No. 4, pp. 14)*
Pub: Phoenix Media Corporation

Description: NPD Group Inc. released current sales statistics for the women's apparel market along with men's apparel. It also reported annual shoes sales for 2010. Statistical data included.

7815 ■ *"As Seen On TV" in Canadian Business (Vol. 80, November 5, 2007, No. 22, pp. 93)*
Pub: Rogers Media

Ed: Zena Olijnyk. **Description:** StarBrand Media Inc. is one of the companies providing fans with information on how and where to purchase the items that television characters are using. StarBrand created

the style section found on different television shows' Websites, such as that of the Gossip Girl and Small-ville. The benefits of using sites like StarBrand are evaluated.

7816 ■ *"Better Than New" in Bellingham Business Journal (Vol. February 2010, pp. 16)*
Pub: Sound Publishing Inc.

Ed: Ashley Mitchell. **Description:** Profile of family owned Better Than New clothing store that sells overstock items from department stores and clothing manufacturers. The stores location makes it easy to miss and its only advertising is a large sign posted outside. This is the sixth store owned by the couple, Keijeo and Sirba Halmekanqas.

7817 ■ *"The Bottom Line" in Retail Merchandiser (Vol. 51, July-August 2011, No. 4, pp. 60)*
Pub: Phoenix Media Corporation

Description: Hanky Panky believes that comfort and style don't have to be mutually exclusive when designing their line of intimate apparel for women. The lingerie retailer was launched in 1977.

7818 ■ *"Buying Chanel (All Of It)" in Conde Nast Portfolio (Vol. 2, June 2008, No. 6, pp. 34)*
Pub: Conde Nast Publications
Contact: David Carey, President

Ed: Willow Duttge. **Description:** Overview of the luxury company Chanel and an estimated guess as to what the company is worth.

7819 ■ *"A Change Would Do You Good" in Canadian Business (Vol. 80, November 19, 2007, No. 23, pp. 15)*
Pub: Rogers Media

Ed: Geoff Kirbyson. **Description:** Western Glove Works will be manufacturing clothing offshore, including Sheryl Crow's jeans collection, in countries such as China and the Philippines. The company decided to operate offshore after 86 years of existence due to the high price of manufacturing jeans in Canada. Western Glove's focus on producing celebrity-endorsed goods is discussed.

7820 ■ *"Common Thread" in Entrepreneur (Vol. 36, March 2008, No. 3, pp. 144)*
Pub: Entrepreneur Media Inc.

Ed: Sara Wilson. **Description:** Profile of Stacey Benet and her business, Alice and Olivia, and how she jumpstarted her career in the clothing industry after she wore a self-designed pair of pants that caught the attention of a Barney's New York representative is presented.

7821 ■ *"Consignment Shop Closes Without Warning to Customers, Landlord" in Sun Journal (June 30, 2010)*
Pub: Freedom Communications Inc.

Ed: Laura Oleniacz. **Description:** Off The Racks consignment shop located on Glenburnie Road in New Bern, North Carolina closed without warning to customers or its landlord. The consignors who donated clothing to the store were left unpaid.

7822 ■ *"Consignment Shop Offers Children's Clothes, Products" in Frederick News-Post (August 19, 2010)*
Pub: Federick News-Post

Ed: Ed Waters Jr. **Description:** Sweet Pea Consignments for Children offers used items for newborns to pre-teens. The shop carries name brand clothing as well as toys, books and baby products.

7823 ■ *"Crowdsourcing their Way into One Big Mess" in Brandweek (Vol. 51, October 25, 2010, No. 38, pp. 26)*
Pub: Nielsen Business Media, Inc.

Ed: Gregg S. Lipman. **Description:** The Gap, was counting on crowdsourcing to provide feedback for its new logo, but it did not prove positive for the retailer. However, a massive outcry of negative opinion, via crowdsourcing, may not always equal valid, constructive criticism.

7824 ■ *"Designers' Hats Foretell a Big Comeback Next Fall" in Charlotte Observer (February 8, 2007)*
Pub: Knight-Ridder/Tribune Business News

Ed: Crystal Dempsey. **Description:** According to designer experts, hats are making a comeback and will make a big fashion statement, fall 2007.

7825 ■ *"Doing Good: Fair Fashion" in Entrepreneur (Vol. 35, October 2007, No. 10, pp. 36)*
Pub: Entrepreneur Media Inc.

Ed: J.J. Ramberg. **Description:** Indigenous Designs was launched in 1993, when organic clothing was not yet popular. However, the company has become successful in the industry, with $4 million dollars in revenue, owing to the growing environment awareness of consumers. A history of how the company was formed and an overview of their production process are provided.

7826 ■ *"Fall Fever" in Canadian Business (Vol. 81, October 13, 2008, No. 17, pp. S12)*
Pub: Rogers Media Ltd.

Description: Buyer's guide of men's suits and jackets for fall are presented, including a suit by Boss Hugo Boss recommended for fun in the city after finishing work. Designers Ermenegildo, Michael Kors, and Arnold Brant are also highlighted.

7827 ■ *"Finishing Touches: the Fashion Statement is in the Detail" in Black Enterprise (Vol. 37, January 2007, No. 6, pp. 106)*
Pub: Earl G. Graves Publishing Co. Inc.

Ed: Sonia Alleyne. **Description:** Men are discovering the importance of dressing for success. Paying attention to the details such as shoes, socks, cuffs, and collars are just as important as finding the right suit.

7828 ■ *"Former Apprentice Candidate Launches Jewelry Line" in Black Enterprise (Vol. 37, October 2006, No. 3, pp. 36)*
Pub: Earl G. Graves Publishing Co. Inc.

Ed: Philana Patterson. **Description:** Star of the second season of NBC's The Apprentice, Stacie J, has launched a line of jewelry and accessories which will be sold at Claire's stores nationwide.

7829 ■ *Fugitive Denim: A Moving Story of People and Pants in the Borderless World of Global Trade*
Pub: W.W. Norton & Company
Ed: Rachel Snyder. **Released:** April 2009. **Price:** $16.95. **Description:** In-depth study of the global production and processes of how jeans are designed, sewn, and transported as well as how the cotton for denim is grown, regulated, purchased and processed.

7830 ■ *"Going Western with a Touch of Style" in Women In Business (Vol. 63, Summer 2011, No. 2, pp. 8)*
Pub: American Business Women's Association
Ed: Maureen Sullivan. **Description:** Tips on ways women should dress up in Western style are presented. The wearing of Western-style denims is recommended. Use of accessories such as belt buckles, boots and hats is also encouraged.

7831 ■ *"H&M Offers a Dress for Less" in Canadian Business (Vol. 83, September 14, 2010, No. 15, pp. 20)*
Pub: Rogers Media Ltd.
Ed: Laura Cameron. **Description:** Swedish clothing company H&M has implemented loss leader strategy by pricing some dresses at extremely low prices. The economy has forced retailers to keep prices down despite the increasing cost of manufacturing, partly due to Chinese labor becoming more expensive. How the trend will affect apparel companies is discussed.

7832 ■ *"Haute Flyers" in Canadian Business (Vol. 80, November 19, 2007, No. 23, pp. 68)*
Pub: Rogers Media
Ed: Rachel Pulfer. **Description:** Duckie Brown has been nominated by the Council of Fashion Designers of America as best menswear designer in the U.S. for 2007, along with leaders Calvin Klein and Ralph Lauren. The New York-based company was formed the day after September 11, 2001, but the timing did not hamper its growth. The works and plans of owners Steven Cox and Daniel Silver are described.

7833 ■ *"Hot Kicks, Cool Price" in Black Enterprise (Vol. 37, December 2006, No. 5, pp. 34)*
Pub: Earl G. Graves Publishing Co. Inc.
Ed: Topher Sanders. **Description:** Stephon Marbury of the New York Nicks introduced a new basketball shoe, the Starbury One, costing $14.98. The shoes are an addition to the Starbury clothing line and although the privately owned company would not disclose figures; stores sold out of a month's worth of inventory in merely three days.

7834 ■ *"How to Keep Your Cool and Your Friends in a Heat Wave" in Canadian Business (Vol. 83, August 17, 2010, No. 13-14, pp. 79)*
Pub: Rogers Media Ltd.
Ed: Angelina Chapin. **Description:** A buyer's guide of menswear clothing for businessmen is presented. The products include an antiperspirant and deodorant, men's dress shorts, shoes and bamboo fabric undershirt.

7835 ■ *Hug Your Customers*
Pub: Hyperion Books
Ed: Jack Mitchell. **Price:** $19.95. **Description:** The CEO of Mitchells/Roberts, two very successful clothing stores, professes his belief in showering customers with attention. His secrets for long-term business success include advice about attracting a good staff, lowering marketing costs, and maintaining higher gross margins and revenues.

7836 ■ *"Insider" in Canadian Business (Vol. 80, Winter 2007, No. 24, pp.)*
Pub: Rogers Media
Ed: Zena Olijnyk. **Description:** Luluemon Athletica started in 1998 after Dennis Wilson takes a yoga class and notices a demand from women for breathable clothes. The company opened their first outlet in Vancouver in November 2000 then opened their first U.S. store in 2003 until finally going public July 27, 2007 where its stocks doubled in value within days of trading.

7837 ■ *"Island Co.: Isle Style" in Entrepreneur (Vol. 35, October 2007, No. 10, pp. 172)*
Pub: Entrepreneur Media Inc.
Ed: Sara Wilson. **Description:** Island Co., producer of travel clothing and swimsuits was formed by Spencer Antle in 2002. Its office projects the Caribbean atmosphere, a strategy Antle used to promote the company's theme to its clients. Future plans for the company are also indicated.

7838 ■ *"It's In the Bag" in Entrepreneur (Vol. 36, April 2008, No. 4, pp. 122)*
Pub: Entrepreneur Media, Inc.
Ed: Celeste Hoang. **Description:** Sandy Stein launched Alexx Inc in 2004, which markets keychains, called Finders Key Purse, with unique designs to help find keys easier inside the purse. Some of the key ring designs are hearts, sandals, and crowns. The company has approximately $6 million worth of sales in 2007.

7839 ■ *"It's So You! Consignment Chop Owner Thrilled to See Vision Come to Fruition" in News-Herald (August 27, 2010)*
Pub: News-Herald
Ed: Brandon C. Baker. **Description:** Profile of Laurel Howes and her It's So You! Boutique. The consignment shop is located in Willoughby's Pine Ride Plaza in Ohio. The shop targets all women, but particularly those who are not that comfortable with shopping consignment.

7840 ■ *"Izod, Loft Outlets Coming To Tanger" in New Hampshire Business Review (Vol. 33, March 25, 2011, No. 6, pp. 30)*
Pub: Business Publications Inc.
Description: Izod and Lots stores will open at the Tanger Outlet Center in Tilton, New Hampshire. Both stores will feature fashions and accessories.

7841 ■ *"Let It Shine: Organization Helps Disadvantaged Girls See Their Worth" in Black Enterprise (Vol. 38, February 2008, No. 7, pp. 142)*
Pub: Earl G. Graves Publishing Co. Inc.
Ed: George Alexander. **Description:** Wilson Mourning, founder of the clothing label Honey Child, attributes her success to her mother and other positive women who helped her through her adolescence. Mourning created a mentoring organization that helps young girls in the Miami, Florida area to develop life skills.

7842 ■ *"Life's Work: Manolo Blahnik" in Harvard Business Review (Vol. 88, December 2010, No. 12, pp. 144)*
Pub: Harvard Business School Publishing
Ed: Alison Beard. **Description:** Shoe designer Manolo Blahnik recounts his beginnings in the shoe industry and the influence art has had on his work, as well as balancing art and commerce. He also discusses the importance of quality materials and craftsmanship and the benefits of managing an independent, family-owned business.

7843 ■ *"Making It Work" in Retail Merchandiser (Vol. 51, July-August 2011, No. 4, pp. 43)*
Pub: Phoenix Media Corporation
Ed: Anthony DiPaolo. **Description:** Profile of Anthony DiPaolo and his purchase of the Work 'N Gear retail store in 2002. The brick and mortar shop sells work wear and healthcare apparel and DiPaolo believes customer respect is essential to his success.

7844 ■ *Mass Merchandisers & Off-Price Apparel Buyers*
Pub: Briefings Media Group
Contact: Alan M. Douglas, President
E-mail: adouglas@douglaspublications.com
URL(s): www.douglaspublications.comwww.thesalesmansguide.com **Released:** Annual; latest edition 2011-2012. **Price:** $329, Individuals directory price; $659, Individuals directory/CD combo price. **Covers:** 7,900 buyers and 3,400 companies in mass merchandise and off-price apparel industry. **Entries include:** Company name, address, phone, fax, e-mail, URL, names and titles of key personnel, geographical area served, branch office or subsidiary names and addresses, products and/or services provided, sales volume, parent company name. **Arrangement:** Geographical. **Indexes:** Store/company name, new listings, jobbers, online retailers.

7845 ■ *"Midas Touch" in Entrepreneur (Vol. 36, April 2008, No. 4, pp. 160)*
Pub: Entrepreneur Media, Inc.
Ed: Sara Wilson. **Description:** Lana Fertelmeister is a model-turned-jewelry designer. Her company, Lana Jewelry, designs fine jewelry for women. Her jewelry line is available in more than 100 stores worldwide and has been worn by celebrities like Cameron Diaz and Sandra Bullock.

7846 ■ *"Research and Markets Adds: 2011 U.S. Women's & Children's Clothing Wholesale Report" in Health & Beauty Close-Up (October 16, 2010)*
Pub: Close-Up Media Inc.
Description: The Women's & Children's Clothing Wholesale Report is an annual report containing timely and accurate industry statistics, forecasts and demographics.

7847 ■ *"Retail News: Children's Boutique Relocates to Conway" in Sun News (June 4, 2010)*
Pub: The Sun News
Description: Little Angel's Children's Boutique and Big Oak Frame Shop have moved to downtown locations in Conway, South Carolina. Little Angel's will sell children's clothing and accessories, shoes and gifts, while the frame shop will offer custom framing along with the sale of stationary, invitations and local prints.

7848 ■ *"Rule of the Masses: Reinventing Fashion Via Crowdsourcing" in WWD (Vol. 200, July 26, 2010, No. 17, pp. 1)*
Pub: Conde Nast Publications
Contact: David Carey, President
Ed: Cate T. Corcoran. **Description:** Large apparel brands and retailers are crowdsourcing as a way to increase customer loyalty and to build their businesses.

7849 ■ *"Spell It Out" in Entrepreneur (Vol. 36, April 2008, No. 4, pp. 123)*
Pub: Entrepreneur Media, Inc.
Ed: Emily Weisberg. **Description:** IM:It is an apparel and accessories company that markets products with instant messaging (IM) acronyms and emoticons. Examples of these are 'LOL' and 'GTG'. Other details on IM:It products are discussed.

7850 ■ *They Made America*
Pub: Little Brown Company/Time Warner Book Group
Ed: Harold Evans, Gail Buckland, David Lefer. **Released:** 2006. **Price:** $18.95. **Description:** Coffee table book highlighting entrepreneurship; this book is filled with interesting illustrated portraits of entrepreneurs and innovators like Thomas Edison, George Doriot (a venture capital pioneer), and Ida Rosenthal (inventor of the Maidenform bra).

7851 ■ *"The Ultimate Home Shopping Network" in Austin Business JournalInc. (Vol. 28, October 17, 2008, No. 31, pp. A1)*
Pub: American City Business Journals
Ed: Sandra Zaragoza. **Description:** New York-based Etcetera sells their clothing through more than 850 fashion consultants in the U.S. Central Texas is one of the company's top markets and the company is looking to increase its fashion consultants in the area from five to about 20 since they believe there is plenty of room to expand their customer base in the area.

7852 ■ *"Web Sight: Do You See What I See?" in Entrepreneur (Vol. 35, October 2007, No. 10, pp. 58)*
Pub: Entrepreneur Media Inc.
Ed: Heather Clancy. **Description:** Owners of Trunkt, a boutique in New York that showcases independent designs, have created a new style of Website called Trunkt.org. The Website allows buyers to select the products they want to see and designers can choose

anytime which of their items will be displayed on the site. An explanation of the strategy that helped bring Trunkt closer to its clients is presented.

7853 ■ "Well-Heeled Startup" in Business Journal Portland (Vol. 27, November 12, 2010, No. 37, pp. 1)
Pub: Portland Business Journal
Ed: Erik Siemers. Description: Oh! Shoes LLC expects to receive about $1.5 million in funding from angel investors, while marketing a new line of high heel shoes that are comfortable, healthy, and attractive. The new line of shoes will use the technology of athletic footwear while having the look of an Italian designer. Oh! Shoes hopes to generate $35 million in sales by 2014.

7854 ■ "Women Prioritize Luxury Spending" in Marketing to Women (Vol. 22, July 2009, No. 7, pp. 8)
Pub: EPM Communications Inc.
Contact: Ira Mayer, President
E-mail: imayer@epmcom.com
Description: In 2008, women spent 7 percent less on luxury items than in the previous year, according to Unity Marketing. Some luxury items, such as facial care products, are faring better than others. Statistical data included.

VIDEOCASSETTES/ AUDIOCASSETTES

7855 ■ Accessories
Meridian Education Corp.
132 West 31st Street, 17th Floor
New York, NY 10001
Ph: (609)671-0266
Free: 800-257-5126
Co. E-mail: custmserv@films.com
URL: http://meridian.films.com
Released: 1990. Price: $45.00. Description: Describes all sorts of accessories and how they can be used to stretch any wardrobe. Also details the differences between fad pieces and the timeless classics which can be used over and over again. Availability: VHS.

7856 ■ Accessory Allure
Cambridge Educational
c/o Films Media Group
132 West 31st Street, 17th Floor
Ste. 124
New York, NY 10001
Free: 800-257-5126
Fax: (609)671-0266
Co. E-mail: custserve@films.com
URL: http://www.cambridgeol.com
Released: 1987. Price: $29.95. Description: This video shows viewers how to make the most of their wardrobe by using scarves, earrings, hats, and other accessories. Availability: VHS.

TRADE SHOWS AND CONVENTIONS

7857 ■ Baltimore Women's Show
S & L Productions, Inc.
1916 Crain Hwy., Ste. 16
Glen Burnie, MD 21061
Ph: (410)863-1180
Fax: (410)863-1187
URL: http://www.mdhomeandgarden.com
URL(s): www.spoilyourself.com. Frequency: Annual. Audience: Women 25-65 yrs. Principal Exhibits: Products and services for women.

7858 ■ Beauty Fair
The Finnish Fair Corp.
PO Box 21
FIN-00521 Helsinki, Finland
Ph: 358 40 4503250

Fax: 358 9 142358
Co. E-mail: info@finnexpo.fi
URL: http://web.finnexpo.fi/en/Yritys/finnishfair/Pages/default.aspx
URL(s): www.finnexpo.fi. Frequency: Annual. Audience: General public. Principal Exhibits: Beauty and fashion, cosmetics and services; hair products and services; clothing, showes, bags, accessories, jewelry, education, and publications.

7859 ■ Florida Fashion Focus Show
Southern Apparel Exhibitors, Inc.
1856 Sheridan St.
Evanston, IL 60201
Ph: (847)475-1856
Free: 888-249-1377
Co. E-mail: info@saemiami.com
URL: http://www.saemiami.com
Contact: John Harper, President
E-mail: harper@saemiami.com
URL(s): www.floridafashionfocus.com/. Frequency: 5/year. Audience: Trade buyers. Principal Exhibits: Ladies ready-to-wear clothing; handbags, jewelry, and accessories. Order-writing for future delivery. Dates and Locations: Merchandise Mart. Telecommunication Services: Info@FocusTradeshow.com.

7860 ■ Mitteldeutsche Handwerksmesse: Central German Handicrafts Fair
Leipziger Messe GmbH
Messe-Allee 1
04356 Leipzig, Germany
Ph: 0341 6 78-0
Fax: 0341 6 78-8762
Co. E-mail: info@leipziger-messe.de
URL: http://www.leipziger-messe.de
Contact: Dr. Arend Oetker, Director
URL(s): www.handwerksmesse-leipzig.de. Frequency: Annual. Audience: General public. Principal Exhibits: Building and conversion, home, arts and crafts, health, lifestyle, food crafts, vehicles, rare handicrafts.

7861 ■ Mode Accessories International Exposition
Two Plus One Group Inc.
220 Duncan Mill Rd., Ste. 618
Toronto, ON, Canada M3B 3J5
Ph: (416)510-0114
Fax: (416)510-0165
Co. E-mail: twoplusone@mode-accessories.com
URL: http://www.mode-accessories.com
Contact: Alice Chee, President
E-mail: achee@mode-accessories.com
URL(s): www.mode-accessories.com. Frequency: Semiannual. Audience: Fashion accessory retailers, women's wear boutiques, gift shops. Principal Exhibits: Fashion accessories, fashion apparel. Dates and Locations: International Plaza Hotel.

7862 ■ Pittsburgh Women's Show
Trigger Agency
3539 Clipper Mill Rd.
Baltimore, MD 21211
Free: 800-830-3976
Fax: (410)878-9911
Co. E-mail: info@triggeragency.com
URL: http://www.triggeragency.com/
Contact: Greg Nivens, President
E-mail: gnivens@triggeragency.com
URL(s): www.pittsburghwomensshow.com. Price: $7, free for children 15 and under. Frequency: Annual. Audience: Trade and public. Principal Exhibits: Products and services for women relating to health, fitness, business, careers, and finance.

7863 ■ Women's and Children's Apparel and Accessories Mart
Dallas Market Center Co.
2100 Stemmons Fwy.
Dallas, TX 75207
Ph: (214)655-6100

Free: 800-DAL-MKTS
Co. E-mail: lvillarreal@dmcmail.com
URL: http://www.dallasmarketcenter.com/
Audience: Apparel and accessories and home furnishings retailers. Principal Exhibits: Regional Merchandising Mart servicing department and specialty store buyers nationwide.

FRANCHISES AND BUSINESS OPPORTUNITIES

7864 ■ Apricot Lane
Country Visions, Inc.
3333 Vaca Valley Pky., Ste. 900
Vacaville, CA 95688
Free: 800-825-8883
Co. E-mail: franchiseinfo@apricotlanefranchise.com
URL: http://www.apricotlanefranchise.com
Description: Specialty retail franchise that combines opportunities from the gift and fashion accessory industries to other affordable fashion jewelry, handbags, accessories and gifts in the styles and trends customers are looking for. No. of Franchise Units: 71. Founded: 1991.. Franchised: 1992. Equity Capital Needed: $100,000. Franchise Fee: $29,500. Training: Site selection and lease negotiation assistance; turnkey store design and construction; sales point system; home training program and onsite training; initial inventory orders; grand opening marketing kit; and onsite merchandising.

7865 ■ Clothes Mentor
CMF Holdings LLC
Description: New/used women's clothing and accessories. No. of Franchise Units: 40. No. of Company-Owned Units: 1. Founded: 2001. Franchised: 2007. Equity Capital Needed: $175,000. Franchise Fee: $20,000. Training: Includes 2 weeks training at headquarters and ongoing support.

LIBRARIES

7866 ■ George Brown College of Applied Arts & Technology - Archives
500 Macpherson Ave., Rm. F-103
Toronto, ON, Canada M5T 2T9
Ph: (416)415-5000, x4771
Fax: (416)415-4772
Co. E-mail: rmacaula@georgebrown.ca
URL: http://www.georgebrown.ca
Contact: Robert Macaulay, Archivist
Scope: College history, labor relations, fashion industry, post-secondary education, nursing schools, collegiate sports. Services: Copying; archives open to the public with restrictions and by appointment only. Founded: 1975. Holdings: 190 cubic meters of records and manuscripts; 2700 linear meters publications, clippings, photographs, filsm, audio and video recordings.

7867 ■ Conde Nast Publications Library and Information Services
4 Times Sq.
New York, NY 10036
Ph: (212)286-2860
Co. E-mail: communications@condenast.com
URL: http://www.condenastdigital.com
Contact: Sarah Chubb, President
Scope: Fashion, houses, gardens, home furnishings, interior design, health, personalities, photographs. Services: Library not open to public. Founded: 1935. Holdings: 7000 volumes. Subscriptions: 200 journals and other serials; 4 newspapers.

7868 ■ Fashion Institute of Technology - Gladys Marcus Library
7th Ave. at 27th St.
E-Bldg. E502
New York, NY 10001-5992
Ph: (212)217-4340
Fax: (212)217-4371
Co. E-mail: greta_earnest@fitnyc.edu
URL: http://www.fitnyc.edu/library.asp
Contact: Prof. N.J. Wolfe, Director, Library Services
Scope: Costume, fashion, interior design, management engineering technology, fashion buying and merchandising, textiles, toy design, packaging

design, advertising. **Services:** Interlibrary loan; copying; library open to the public for reference use only by appointment. **Founded:** 1944. **Holdings:** 130,260 books; 113,265 nonprint units; 20,637 bound periodical volumes; 125,000 fashion slides; 4712 reels of microfilm; 438 CD-ROM serials and digital monographs. **Subscriptions:** 4000 journals and other serials. **Telecommunication Services:** nj_wolfe@fitnyc.edu.

•

REFERENCE WORKS

7869 ■ *National E-mail and Fax Directory*
Pub: Cengage Learning Inc.
Contact: Ronald Dunn, President
URL(s): www.gale.cengage.com. **Released:** Annual;
Latest edition 26th; April, 2011. **Price:** $265, Individuals. **Covers:** Approximately 130,000 fax numbers and
nearly 85,000 e-mail addresses for businesses,
government agencies, and other institutions and
organizations. **Entries include:** Company or organization name, address, phone, fax, and e-mail addresses. **Arrangement:** Same information provided
alphabetically and classified by subject. **Indexes:**
Subject.

FRANCHISES AND BUSINESS OPPORTUNITIES

7870 ■ **Pak Mail**
7173 S Havan St., Ste. 600
Centennial, CO 80112
Ph: (800)833-2821
Fax: (800)336-7363
Co. E-mail: sales@pakmail.org
URL: http://www.pakmail.com
Description: One-stop shop offers the customer a
convenient location to send packages, make copies,
send or receive a fax or rent a private mailbox. **No.
of Franchise Units:** 500. **Founded:** 1983.. **Franchised:** 1984. **Equity Capital Needed:** $130,000-
$164,300 total investment. **Franchise Fee:** $29,950.
Financial Assistance: Yes. **Training:** Provides training, education & ongoing support to build your business.

START-UP INFORMATION

7871 ■ *"Fast-Forward Fortune" in Small Business Opportunities (July 2010)*
Pub: Harris Publications Inc.
Description: Profile of Steve Dalbec and his home-based Home Video Studio where he earns income by offering a wide variety of video services to clients from duplicating CDs, video to DVD transfer, sports videos and more. Dalbec believes this is the perfect home-based business.

7872 ■ *"Fun And Easy Gold Mines" in Small Business Opportunities (Fall 2008)*
Pub: Entrepreneur Media Inc.
Description: Twenty-five businesses that cater to the booming children's market are profiled; day care services, party planning, special events video-making, tutoring, personalized children's toys and products and other services geared toward the kids market are included.

ASSOCIATIONS AND OTHER ORGANIZATIONS

7873 ■ *Action Newsletter*
151 Slater St., Ste. 902
Ottawa, ON, Canada K1P 5H3
Free: 800-656-7440
Fax: (613)233-0073
Co. E-mail: angela.tupper@cmpa.ca
URL: http://www.cftpa.ca
Contact: Norm Bolen, President
Released: Quarterly

7874 ■ *Annual Review*
4067, Boul. Saint-Laurent, Ste. 200-A
Montreal, QC, Canada H2W 1Y7
Ph: (514)522-8240
Co. E-mail: info@imaa.ca
URL: http://www.imaa.ca
Contact: Kevin Allen, President
Released: Annual

7875 ■ Association for Information Media and Equipment (AIME)
PO Box 9844
Cedar Rapids, IA 52409-9844
Ph: (319)654-0608
Fax: (319)654-0609
URL: http://www.aime.org
Contact: Betty Gorsegner Ehlinger, Executive Director
Description: Producers and distributors of nontheatrical film/video and video related-technologies; organizations that use film and video-related technologies; manufacturer/vendors of related equipment and services; interested others. Promotes the use of motion media in the instructional and informational fields; works to educate schools and libraries regarding copyright laws as applied to film and video; offers networking opportunities among members and the sharing of information; lobbies for increased funds for school media materials; compiles statistics; sponsors

market research. **Founded:** 1986. **Publications:** *AIME News* (Quarterly); *Copyright Law: What Every School, College and Public Library Should Know and Copyright: New Issues.*

7876 ■ Association of Moving Image Archivists (AMIA)
1313 N Vine St.
Hollywood, CA 90028
Ph: (323)463-1500
Fax: (323)463-1506
Co. E-mail: amia@amianet.org
URL: http://www.amianet.org
Description: Works to advance the field of moving image archiving by fostering cooperation among individuals and institutions concerned with the collection, description, preservation, exhibition, and use of moving image materials (film and video). Seeks to improve public awareness of preservation needs through educational programs. **Scope:** moving image conservation. **Founded:** 1991. **Subscriptions:** books business records clippings monographs periodicals. **Publications:** *The Moving Image* (Semiannual). **Awards:** Rick Chace Foundation Scholarships; Mary Pickford Scholarships; CFI Sid Solow Scholarships; Sony Pictures Scholarships; Universal Studios Preservation Scholarships; Silver Light Award (Annual); Kodak Fellowships in Film Preservation; Dan and Kathy Leab Award (Annual).

7877 ■ *Canadian Journal of Film Studies*
c/o Paul S. Moore, Pres.
Ryerson University
350 Victoria St.
Toronto, ON, Canada M5B 2K3
Co. E-mail: psmoore@ryerson.ca
URL: http://www.filmstudies.ca
Contact: Paul S. Moore, President
Released: Semiannual **Price:** C$35, /year; C$45, /year for institutions.

7878 ■ Canadian Media Production Association (CMPA)
151 Slater St., Ste. 902
Ottawa, ON, Canada K1P 5H3
Free: 800-656-7440
Fax: (613)233-0073
Co. E-mail: angela.tupper@cmpa.ca
URL: http://www.cftpa.ca
Contact: Norm Bolen, President
Description: Represents film, television and interactive media companies across the country. Promotes and stimulates the Canadian production industry. Seeks to negotiate and manage labour agreements, and actively lobby the federal and provincial governments on various policy areas including taxation, trade, copyright, broadcasting and film. **Publications:** *Action Newsletter* (Quarterly); *Guide* (Annual). **Awards:** Chetwynd Award for Entrepreneurial Excellence; Jack Chisholm Award for Lifetime Achievement.

7879 ■ Content Delivery and Storage Association (CDSA)
39 N Bayles Ave.
Port Washington, NY 11050

Ph: (516)767-6720
Fax: (516)883-5793
Co. E-mail: mporter@cdsaonline.org.org
URL: http://www.cdsaonline.org
Contact: Martin Porter, Executive Director
Description: Serves as the advocate for the growth and development of all recording media and as a forum for the exchange of information regarding global trends and innovations. Provides members an opportunity to join forces and be a strong industry voice allowing them to grow and expand their business. Encompasses all facets of the recording media. **Founded:** 1970. **Publications:** *Mediaware* (9/year).

7880 ■ *Continuity*
c/o Paul S. Moore, Pres.
Ryerson University
350 Victoria St.
Toronto, ON, Canada M5B 2K3
Co. E-mail: psmoore@ryerson.ca
URL: http://www.filmstudies.ca
Contact: Paul S. Moore, President
Released: Quarterly

7881 ■ Directors Guild of Canada (DGC)—La Guilde Canadienne des Realisateurs
111 Peter St., Ste. 402
Toronto, ON, Canada M5V 2H1
Ph: (416)482-6640
Free: 888-972-0098
Fax: (416)482-6639
Co. E-mail: mail@dgc.ca
URL: http://www.dgc.ca
Contact: Sturla Gunnarsson, President
Description: Creative and logistical personnel in the film and television industries. Facilitates professional and economic advancement of members. Promotes and seeks to advance the quality and vitality of Canadian feature film and television production. Develops and maintains standards of training and practice; negotiates and enforces contracts and other collective agreements with employers on behalf of members; maintains dispute settlement and arbitration mechanisms. Facilitates communication among members; makes available member benefit and insurance programs; conducts lobbying activities. **Founded:** 1962. **Publications:** *Montage* (Quarterly).

7882 ■ Documentary Organisation of Canada (DOC)—Documentaristes du Canada
215 Spadina Ave., Ste. 126
Toronto, ON, Canada M5T 2C7
Ph: (416)599-3844
Free: 877-467-4485
Fax: (416)979-3936
Co. E-mail: info@docorg.ca
URL: http://www.docorg.ca
Contact: Katie McKenna, Chairperson
Description: Independent filmmakers. Promotes excellence in filmmaking; seeks to advance the economic interests of independent filmmakers. Provides professional development opportunities. Represents members' interests before government, industry organizations and the public; sponsors promotional programs. **Founded:** 1983. **Publications:** *POV* (Quarterly).

7883 ■ Film Studies Association of Canada (FSAC)—Association Canadienne D'etudes Cinematographiques
c/o Paul S. Moore, Pres.
Ryerson University
350 Victoria St.
Toronto, ON, Canada M5B 2K3
Co. E-mail: psmoore@ryerson.ca
URL: http://www.filmstudies.ca
Contact: Paul S. Moore, President
Description: Film studies institutes, educators, and students. Promotes the study and appreciation of the history and art of film and related media. Conducts research and educational programs. **Founded:** 1976. **Publications:** *Canadian Journal of Film Studies* (Semiannual); *Continuity* (Quarterly). **Awards:** Gerald Pratley Scholarship (Annual); Gerald Pratley Awards.

7884 ■ Guide
151 Slater St., Ste. 902
Ottawa, ON, Canada K1P 5H3
Free: 800-656-7440
Fax: (613)233-0073
Co. E-mail: angela.tupper@cmpa.ca
URL: http://www.cftpa.ca
Contact: Norm Bolen, President
Released: Annual **Price:** C$65, each.

7885 ■ Independent Media Arts Alliance (IMAA)—Alliance Des Arts Mediatiques Independants
4067, Boul. Saint-Laurent, Ste. 200-A
Montreal, QC, Canada H2W 1Y7
Ph: (514)522-8240
Co. E-mail: info@imaa.ca
URL: http://www.imaa.ca
Contact: Kevin Allen, President
Description: Regroups over 85 artist-run centres across Canada including production, distribution and exhibition. Represents and advocates for independent media artists. **Scope:** visual arts, media arts. **Founded:** 1980. **Subscriptions:** artwork. **Publications:** *Annual Review* (Annual). **Educational Activities:** National Conference on Media Arts (Annual).

7886 ■ InfoComm International
11242 Waples Mill Rd., Ste. 200
Fairfax, VA 22030
Ph: (703)273-7200
Free: 800-659-7469
Co. E-mail: customerservice@infocomm.org
URL: http://www.infocomm.org
Contact: Greg Jeffreys, President
Description: Represents for-profit individuals and organizations that derive revenue from the commercialization or utilization of communications technology. Ensures the credibility and desirability of its members' products and services by representing the communications industry to the public, business, education, and governments. **Founded:** 1939. **Publications:** *ICIA Membership Directory* (Annual); *Info-Community News* (Quarterly). **Awards:** Distinguished Achievement Award; ICIA Achievement Awards (Annual).

7887 ■ International Animated Film Association - Canada (ASIFA-Canada)—Association Internationale du Film d'Animation
CP 5226
St. Laurent, QC, Canada H4L 4Z8
Co. E-mail: asifacanada@mail.com
URL: http://www.awn.com/asifa-canada
Description: Producers of animated films. Promotes excellence in film animation. Promotes and publicizes members' productions; serves as a clearinghouse on film animation; represents members' interests. **Founded:** 1960. **Awards:** Priz Heritage-Norman-Mclaren (Biennial).

7888 ■ International Association of Audio Visual Communicators (IAAVC)
c/o The CINDY Competitions
PO Box 270779
Flower Mound, TX 75027
Ph: (469)464-4180

Fax: (469)464-4170
Co. E-mail: sheemonw@cindys.com
URL: http://www.cindys.com
URL(s): www.iaavc.org. **Description:** Media producers, managers, and creative and technical people in industry, government, education, and technical, promotional, and enrichment fields. **Scope:** competition categories and award winners. **Founded:** 1957. **Educational Activities:** International Association of Audio Visual Communicators Competition; International Association of Audio Visual Communicators Composium (Periodic). **Awards:** CINDY Awards; International Competition Cinema in Industry (Semiannual); Visual Communicators Department of the Year (Annual).

7889 ■ International Documentary Association (IDA)—International Documentary Foundation
1201 W 5th St., Ste. M270
Los Angeles, CA 90017
Ph: (213)534-3600
Fax: (213)534-3610
Co. E-mail: michael@documentary.org
URL: http://www.documentary.org
Contact: Michael Lumpkin, Executive Director
Description: Individuals and organizations involved in nonfiction film and video. Objectives are: to promote nonfiction film and video; to encourage the progress of the documentary arts and sciences; to support the efforts of nonfiction film and videomakers throughout the world. Provides a forum for documentaries and allied members of the film and video industries to meet and discuss areas of mutual interest related to all aspects of nonfiction film and video arts, sciences, production, financing, and distribution. Holds screenings of all Oscar-nominated documentaries. **Founded:** 1982. **Publications:** *Documentary* (Quarterly). **Awards:** Career Achievement Award; Preservation and Scholarship Award; AVID Excellence in Editing Award; Jacqueline Donnet Emerging Filmmaker Award; ABCNews VideoSource Award; Pare Lorentz Award; Career Achievement Award (Annual); IDA Awards (Annual); Preservation and Scholarship (Annual).

7890 ■ Media Communications Association-International (MCA-I)
c/o MCA-I Madison Chapter
Madison, WI 53705-0135
Ph: (608)443-2464
Free: 888-899-6224
Fax: (608)443-2474
Co. E-mail: steve.king@screentime.co.nz
URL: http://www.mca-i.org
Contact: Mike Brown, President
Description: Individuals engaged in multimedia communications needs analysis, scriptwriting, producing, directing, consulting,. and operations management in the video, multimedia, and film fields. Seeks to advance the benefits and image of media communications professionals. **Scope:** A nonprofit, international organization established for the advancement of professional video communications. It supplies a primary channel of communication among video users, industry manufacturers, distributors and service companies. Through publications, seminars, monthly chapter meetings, international conferences and teleconferences, the ITVA shares and disseminates information on the use of video for communication in business, industry, health care, government, education and other fields. The association is currently involved in exploring such issues as interactive video, telecommunications, video management and production, program development, engineering, advanced electronics field production and cable's role in corporate communications. **Founded:** 1968. **Subscriptions:** video recordings. **Publications:** "Don't Forget Traditional Media"; "MCA-I 2006 Demographic Survey". **Awards:** Board of Directors Award (Annual); The Chuck Webb Award (Annual); G. Warren Scholarship Award (Annual); Shining Star Award (Annual). **Seminars:** Getting Started with Final Cut Pro, Colorado, Sep, 2009; The Business of Television Writing, Georgia, Aug, 2009; Final Cut Studio 3 Upgrade Workshop, New York, Aug, 2009; Jeffrey Alan Schechter's 'My Story Can Beat Up Your Story', California, Aug, 2009; Getting Started with

Dream weaver, Colorado, Aug, 2009. **Telecommunication Services:** loiswei@aol.com. **Special Services:** Final Draft AV; Impatica; MCA-I Pro-Track™.

7891 ■ Montage
111 Peter St., Ste. 402
Toronto, ON, Canada M5V 2H1
Ph: (416)482-6640
Free: 888-972-0098
Fax: (416)482-6639
Co. E-mail: mail@dgc.ca
URL: http://www.dgc.ca
Contact: Sturla Gunnarsson, President
Released: Quarterly

7892 ■ Motion Picture Association - Canada
55 St. Clair Ave. W, Ste. 210
Toronto, ON, Canada M4V 2Y7
Ph: (416)961-1888
Fax: (416)968-1016
Co. E-mail: info@mpa-canada.org
URL: http://www.mpa-canada.org
Contact: Wendy Noss, Executive Director
Description: Film studios and distributors; marketers and distributors of television programming. Promotes increased distribution of American films in Canada. Conducts marketing and promotional activities. **Founded:** 1920.

7893 ■ POV
215 Spadina Ave., Ste. 126
Toronto, ON, Canada M5T 2C7
Ph: (416)599-3844
Free: 877-467-4485
Fax: (416)979-3936
Co. E-mail: info@docorg.ca
URL: http://www.docorg.ca
Contact: Katie McKenna, Chairperson
Released: Quarterly **Price:** free for members; C$18, for nonmembers; C$23, for institutions.

7894 ■ University Film and Video Association (UFVA)
3800 Barham Blvd., Ste. 103
Los Angeles, CA 90068
Free: 866-647-8382
Co. E-mail: ufvahome@aol.com
URL: http://www.ufva.org
Contact: Norman Hollyn, President
Description: Professors and video/filmmakers concerned with the production and study of film and video in colleges and universities. Conducts research programs; operates placement service; presents annual grants. **Founded:** 1947. **Awards:** Carole Fielding Student Grant (Annual).

7895 ■ Wedding and Event Videographers Association International (WEVA)
8499 S Tamiami Trail
PMB 208
Sarasota, FL 34238
Ph: (941)923-5334
Fax: (941)921-3836
Co. E-mail: info@weva.com
URL: http://www.weva.com
Contact: Roy Chapman, Chairman Founder
URL(s): www.wevaexpo.com. **Description:** Professional wedding and event videographers. Serves as a trade organization representing members' commercial interests. Provides educational programs and resources to wedding and event videographers. **Founded:** 1995. **Publications:** *Wedding and Event Videography Resource Guide*; *The Business of Wedding and Special Event Videography*. **Awards:** Creative Excellence Award (Annual).

DIRECTORIES OF EDUCATIONAL PROGRAMS

7896 ■ Directory of Private Accredited Career Schools and Colleges of Technology
Pub: Accrediting Commission of Career Schools and Colleges of Technology
Contact: Michale S. McComis, Executive Director
Released: On web page. **Price:** Free. **Description:** Covers 3900 accredited post-secondary programs that provide training programs in business, trade, and

technical fields, including various small business endeavors. Entries offer school name, address, phone, description of courses, job placement assistance, and requirements for admission. Arrangement is alphabetical.

7897 ■ Film & Television Directory: The Production Maker Source
Pub: Peter Glenn Publications
Contact: Gregory James Blount, President
E-mail: gjames@pgdirect.com
URL(s): www.pgdirect.com/ftintro.asp. **Released:** Biennial **Price:** $30, Individuals. **Covers:** More than 11,000 producers/production companies, crews, support services, and film commissions in the film, music, and video industries in the United States and parts of Canada. **Entries include:** Company name, address, phone, fax, E-mail and URL addresses, name and title of contact. **Arrangement:** Classified by line of business. **Indexes:** Product/service; advertisers by name.

7898 ■ The Ultimate Directory of Film Technicians: A Necrology of Dates and Places of Births and Deaths of More than 9,000 Producers, Directors, Screenwriters, Composers, Cinematographers. . .
Pub: Scarecrow Press Inc.
Contact: Patricia Zline, Manager
E-mail: pzline@rowman.com
URL(s): https://rowman.com/ISBN/978-0-8108-3546-7. **Price:** $70, Individuals Hardback; £44.95, Individuals Hardback. **Covers:** Film technicians from the beginning of the film industry to the present, including executives, producers, directors, screenwriters, cinematographers, set and costume designers, composers, art directors, choreographers, publicists, and editors. **Entries include:** Birth and death dates and career information.

REFERENCE WORKS

7899 ■ "A&E Networks" in Brandweek (Vol. 49, April 21, 2008, No. 16, pp. SR9)
Pub: VNU Business Media, Inc.
Ed: Anthony Crupi. **Description:** Provides contact information for sales and marketing personnel for the A&E Networks as well as a listing of the station's top programming and an analysis of the current season and the target audience for those programs running in the current season. A&E has reinvented itself as a premium entertainment brand over the last five years and with its $2.5 million per episode acquisition of The Sopranos, the station signaled that it was serious about getting back into the scripted programming business. The acquisition also helped the network compete against other cable networks and led to a 20 percent increase in prime-time viewers.

7900 ■ "ABC" in Brandweek (Vol. 49, April 21, 2008, No. 16, pp. SR6)
Pub: VNU Business Media, Inc.
Ed: John Consoli. **Description:** Provides contact information for sales and marketing personnel for the ABC network as well as a listing of the station's top programming and an analysis of the current season and the target audience for those programs running in the current season.

7901 ■ "ACTRA Phones It In" in Canadian Business (Vol. 80, January 15, 2007, No. 2, pp. 8)
Pub: Rogers Media
Ed: Denis Seguin. **Description:** The strike held by the members of the ACTRA or Canadian Cinema, Television and Radio Artists from January 8 2007, due to the contract dispute with the trade association representing Canadian producers, is discussed.

7902 ■ "Alliance Unit Signs Movie Distribution Deal" in Globe & Mail (January 24, 2006, pp. B6)
Pub: CTVglobemedia Publishing Inc.
Ed: Grant Robertson. **Description:** The details on the distribution agreement between Movie Distribution Income Fund and Weinstein Co. are presented. Movie Distribution Income Fund is a unit of Alliance Atlantis Communication Inc.

7903 ■ "Autoline Goes West" in Michigan Vue (Vol. 13, July-August 2008, No. 4, pp. 6)
Pub: Entrepreneur Media Inc.
Ed: Dave Gibbons. **Description:** Profile of Blue Sky Productions, a Detroit-based production company that produces the nationally syndicated television series 'Autoline', which traditionally probes inside the Detroit auto industry; the company recently decided to shoot in Southern California, an area that now has an immense auto industry but has been virtually ignored by the media. Blue Sky originally slated four shows but ended up producing eleven due to the immense amount of material they discovered concerning the state of California's auto market.

7904 ■ "Beyond YouTube: New Uses for Video, Online and Off" in Inc. (October 2007, pp. 53-54)
Pub: Gruner & Jahr USA Publishing
Ed: Leah Hoffmann. **Description:** Small companies are using video technology for embedding messages into email, broadcasting live interactive sales and training seminars, as well as marketing campaigns. Experts offer insight into producing and broadcasting business videos.

7905 ■ "Boxing, Tech Giants Team to Help Teens" in Hispanic Business (January-February 2009, pp. 44)
Pub: Hispanic Business
Ed: Daniel Soussa. **Description:** Microsoft and Oscar de la Hoya are providing teens a head start for careers in the sciences by offering a competition in the categories of photography, short films or Web-based games.

7906 ■ "Business Through Hollywood's Lens" in Harvard Business Review (Vol. 88, October 2010, No. 10, pp. 146)
Pub: Harvard Business School Publishing
Ed: Batia Wiesnefeld, Gino Cattani. **Description:** The authors contend that businesses are likely to be portrayed as villains in movies because corruption has higher entertainment draw. However, movies also depict popular opinion, which encourages businesses to be accountable and to help build communities.

7907 ■ "Buzz Marketing for Movies" in Business Horizons (September-October 2007, pp. 395)
Pub: Elsevier Technology Publications
Ed: Iris Mohr. **Description:** Application of buzz marketing through the context of movie differentiation strategies such as cosmetic movie features, differentiation to reach market segments, growing a movie segment, positioning to support the movie image, positioning to extend the movie image, and differentiation via non-traditional channels are all discussed.

7908 ■ Canadian Society of Cinematographers--Directory
Pub: Canadian Society of Cinematographers
Contact: Joan Hutton, President
URL(s): www.csc.ca. **Released:** Biennial **Covers:** Over 400 directors of photography, videographers, operators, assistants, and focus pullers in Canada. **Entries include:** Name, address, phone, fax, biographical data, description of activities. **Arrangement:** Alphabetical. **Indexes:** Geographical.

7909 ■ "CBS" in Brandweek (Vol. 49, April 21, 2008, No. 16, pp. SR6)
Pub: VNU Business Media, Inc.
Ed: John Consoli. **Description:** Provides contact information for sales and marketing personnel for the CBS network as well as a listing of the station's top programming and an analysis of the current season and the target audience for those programs running in the current season.

7910 ■ "CBS Television Distribution" in Brandweek (Vol. 49, April 21, 2008, No. 16, pp. SR13)
Pub: VNU Business Media, Inc.
Ed: Marc Berman. **Description:** Provides contact information for sales and marketing personnel for CBS Television Distribution as well as a listing of the station's top programming and an analysis of the cur-

rent season and the target audience for those programs running in the current season. Due to the unprecedented, decade-plus advantage of first-run leaders such as Wheel of Fortune, Oprah, Judge Judy and Entertainment Tonight, CBS is poised to remain a leader among the syndicates.

7911 ■ "Cineplex Sees Past the Big Picture" in Globe & Mail (February 8, 2007, pp. B9)
Pub: CTVglobemedia Publishing Inc.
Ed: Shirley Won. **Description:** Cineplex Entertainment LP reported $4.6 million profit in the final quarter of 2006. The movie chain is introducing video-game tournaments and live rock concerts to improve sales.

7912 ■ "Comcast Networks" in Brandweek (Vol. 49, April 21, 2008, No. 16, pp. SR9)
Pub: VNU Business Media, Inc.
Ed: Anthony Crupi. **Description:** Provides contact information for sales and marketing personnel for the Comcast networks as well as a listing of the station's top programming and an analysis of the current season and the target audience for those programs running in the current season. Experts believe Comcast will continue to acquire more stations into their portfolio.

7913 ■ "Commotion Pictures; Bill C-10: Is It Censorship or Merely Inept?" in Canadian Business (Vol. 81, March 31, 2008, No. 5, pp. 10)
Pub: Rogers Media
Ed: Denis Seguin. **Description:** Filmmakers are claiming that Bill C-10 amounts to censorship as it could retract a production's eligibility for a tax credit if it is deemed offensive. However, the bill's backers say that the bill protects against tax dollars being directed at productions that run contrary to public policy.

7914 ■ "The CW" in Brandweek (Vol. 49, April 21, 2008, No. 16, pp. SR8)
Pub: VNU Business Media, Inc.
Ed: John Consoli. **Description:** Provides contact information for sales and marketing personnel for the CW network as well as a listing of the station's top programming and an analysis of the current season and the target audience for those programs running in the current season. Purchases of advertising feel that Warner Bros. and CBS made a mistake merging The WB and UPN into the new CW rather than folding UPN into the more-established WB; compared to last season ratings are down more than 20 percent across the board.

7915 ■ "Deal Made for Pontiac Home of Film Studio" in Crain's Detroit Business (Vol. 25, June 1, 2009, No. 22, pp. 3)
Pub: Crain Communications Inc. - Detroit
Ed: Daniel Duggan. **Description:** Details of the $75 million movie production and training facility in Pontiac, Michigan are revealed.

7916 ■ Directors Guild of America--Directory of Members
Pub: Directors Guild of America Inc.
Contact: Taylor Hackford, President
URL(s): www.dga.org. **Ed:** Darrell L. Hope. **Released:** Annual; February; Latest edition 2009. **Price:** $25, plus $6 shipping. **Covers:** Over 11,000 motion picture and television directors and their assistants providing films and tapes for entertainment, commercial, industrial, and other non-entertainment fields; international coverage. **Entries include:** DGA member name; contact or representative address, phone; specialty; brief description of experience and credits. **Arrangement:** Alphabetical. **Indexes:** Geographical, women and minority members, agents.

7917 ■ "Discovery Networks" in Brandweek (Vol. 49, April 21, 2008, No. 16, pp. SR9)
Pub: VNU Business Media, Inc.
Ed: Anthony Crupi. **Description:** Provides contact information for sales and marketing personnel for the Discovery networks as well as a listing of the station's top programming and an analysis of the current season and the target audience for those programs running in the current season. The networks flagship station returned to the top 10 in 2007, averaging 1.28 million viewers.

7918 ■ *"Disney-ABC Domestic Television Distribution"* in *Brandweek (Vol. 49, April 21, 2008, No. 16, pp. SR13)*
Pub: VNU Business Media, Inc.
Ed: Marc Berman. **Description:** Provides contact information for sales and marketing personnel for Disney-ABC Domestic Television Distribution as well as a listing of the station's top programming and an analysis of the current season and the target audience for those programs running in the current season.

7919 ■ *"The Display Group Is Super-Sized"* in *Michigan Vue (Vol. 13, July-August 2008, No. 4, pp. 34)*
Pub: Entrepreneur Media Inc.
Description: Profile of the Display Group, located in downtown Detroit, this company provides custom designed mobile marketing displays as well as special event production services for trade show displays. The rental house and design service is also beginning to see more business due to the film initiative, which provides incentives for films that are shooting in Michigan.

7920 ■ *"Elemental Nabs $5.5 Million"* in *The Business Journal-Portland (Vol. 25, July 18, 2008, No. 19, pp. 1)*
Pub: American City Business Journals, Inc.
Ed: Aliza Earnshaw. **Description:** Elemental Technologies Inc., a Portland, Oregon-based software company got $5.5 million in new funding, bringing its total invested capital to $7.1 million in nine months since October 2008. The company plans to launch Badaboom, software for converting video into various formats, later in 2008.

7921 ■ *"Ex-MP? Ex-con? Exactly!"* in *Canadian Business (Vol. 83, October 12, 2010, No. 17, pp. 16)*
Pub: Rogers Media Ltd.
Ed: James Cowan. **Description:** British author Jeffrey Archer's novels could be made into movies. Archer sold 250 million books in 63 countries, which include political thrillers, spy novels, and crime capers.

7922 ■ *"Exiting Stage Left"* in *Baltimore Business Journal (Vol. 28, June 18, 2010, No. 6, pp. 1)*
Pub: Baltimore Business Journal
Ed: Scott Dance. **Description:** Film professionals including crew members and actors have been leaving Maryland to find work in other states such as Michigan, Louisiana, and Georgia where bigger budgets and film production incentives are given. Other consequences of this trend in local TV and film production are discussed.

7923 ■ *"Film Giants Disney, Pixar Talk Marriage"* in *Globe & Mail (January 19, 2006, pp. B1)*
Pub: CTVglobemedia Publishing Inc.
Ed: Merissa Marr; Nick Wingfield. **Description:** The plans of Walt Disney Co. to acquire Pixar Animation Studios are presented.

7924 ■ *"Film Incentives: A Hit or a Flop?"* in *Michigan Vue (Vol. 13, July-August 2008, No. 4, pp. 10)*
Pub: Entrepreneur Media Inc.
Description: Michigan's new film incentive legislation is fulfilling its core purpose, according to Lisa Dancsok of the Michigan Economic Development Corp. (MEDC), by kickstarting the state's entry into the multi-billion dollar industry; the initiative is considered to be very competitive with other states and countries and is thought to be a way in which to help revitalize Michigan's struggling economy.

7925 ■ *"For DVD Company, No Extra Innings: Capturing a Season Takes Fast Work"* in *Boston Business Journal (Vol. 27, December 7, 2007)*
Pub: American City Business Journals Inc.
Ed: Terry Lefton. **Description:** Details of the development of MLB's annual World Series film by MLB Productions are discussed. The company is compelled to produce the film in a short period of time

due to a promised November 27, 2007 delivery date. According to Elizabeth Scott, MLB vice president of programming and business affairs, she was concerned about the things that could directly affect sales.

7926 ■ *"Fox"* in *Brandweek (Vol. 49, April 21, 2008, No. 16, pp. SR3)*
Pub: VNU Business Media, Inc.
Ed: John Consoli. **Description:** Provides contact information for sales and marketing personnel for the Fox network as well as a listing of the station's top programming and an analysis of the current season and the target audience for those programs running in the current season. In terms of upfront advertising dollars, it looks as if Fox will be competing against NBC for third place due to its success at courting the 18-49-year-old male demographic.

7927 ■ *"Fox Cable Entertainment Networks"* in *Brandweek (Vol. 49, April 21, 2008, No. 16, pp. SR10)*
Pub: VNU Business Media, Inc.
Ed: Anthony Crupi. **Description:** Provides contact information for sales and marketing personnel for the Fox Cable Entertainment networks as well as a listing of the station's top programming and an analysis of the current season and the target audience for those programs running in the current season.

7928 ■ *"Free Fall"* in *Canadian Business (Vol. 79, September 11, 2006, No. 18, pp. 28)*
Pub: Rogers Media
Ed: Zena Olijnyk. **Description:** Second quarter results of Imax Corp are reviewed. The company's performance and its future prospects are also presented.

7929 ■ *"Frost and Sullivan"* in *Investment Weekly News (December 19, 2009, pp. 150)*
Pub: Investment Weekly News
Description: Demand for video analytics solutions concerning security and business intelligence is growing, especially in such regions as the Middle East, Europe and Africa. Significant advancements in the field of intelligent analysis of video hold promising opportunities in security applications.

7930 ■ *"How Pixar Fosters Collective Creativity"* in *Harvard Business Review (Vol. 86, September 2008, No. 9, pp. 64)*
Pub: Harvard Business School Press
Ed: Ed Catmull. **Description:** Pixar Animation Studios illustrates peer-culture methods for fostering product development. These include allowing any employee to communicate with any other employee, providing a safe environment for new ideas, and watching the academic community closely for innovations.

7931 ■ *"Imax Becomes Toast of Movie Industry"* in *Globe & Mail (January 10, 2006, pp. B2)*
Pub: CTVglobemedia Publishing Inc.
Ed: Grant Robertson. **Description:** The United States-based mainstream theatres company Imax Corp., has reported a 35 percent rise in its ticket sales, showing the growing interest of the American audience in the Imax formatted films. A complete focus on this trend is presented.

7932 ■ *"Imax in Play as It Explores Options"* in *Globe & Mail (March 10, 2006, pp. B3)*
Pub: CTVglobemedia Publishing Inc.
Ed: Shirley Won. **Description:** Imax Corp. has put up itself for sale, and has also confirmed that it has received unsolicited offers for purchase.

7933 ■ *"It's a New Game: Killerspin Pushes Table Tennis to Extreme Heights"* in *Black Enterprise (Vol. 37, October 2006, No. 3, pp. 73)*
Pub: Earl G. Graves Publishing Co. Inc.
Ed: Bridget McCrea. **Description:** Profile of Robert Blackwell and his company Killerspin L.L.C., which is popularizing the sport of table tennis. Killerspin has hit $1 million in revenues due to product sales primarily generated through the company's website, magazines, DVDs, and event ticket sales.

7934 ■ *"Johnny Royal of Luthier Society Unveils Archimedes 1.0 Trailer"* in *Internet Wire (October 22, 2009)*
Pub: Comtex News Network, Inc.
Description: Luthier Society, a social media and viral branding agency, has released the first viral video for the company's ROI weighted-value software platform named Archimedes 1.0; users of the software will be able to determine the depth of their outreach efforts, saturation rate, value of their Internet presence and the geo-spatial location of their audience; this will give a true, monetized value for ROI (Return on Investment) in social media marketing.

7935 ■ *"Johnson's Taps Online Animation"* in *Marketing to Women (Vol. 21, April 2008, No. 4, pp. 3)*
Pub: EPM Communications Inc.
Contact: Ira Mayer, President
E-mail: imayer@epmcom.com
Description: Johnson's has launched a new integrated campaign for its baby lotion in an effort to appeal to the growing number of moms online.

7936 ■ *"Kawasaki's New Top Gun"* in *Brandweek (Vol. 49, April 21, 2008, No. 16, pp. 18)*
Pub: VNU Business Media, Inc.
Description: Discusses Kawasaki's marketing plan which included designing an online brochure in which visitors could create a video by building their own test track on a grid and then selecting visual special effects and musical overlay. This engaging and innovative marketing technique generated more than 166,000 unique users within the first three months of being launched.

7937 ■ *"The Last Ingredient?"* in *Canadian Business (Vol. 81, October 13, 2008, No. 17, pp. 88)*
Pub: Rogers Media Ltd.
Ed: Rachel Pulfer. **Description:** Views and information on Cookie Jar Group's plan to acquire rights for Strawberry Shortcake and the Care Bears are discussed. The move would make Cookie Jar a major player in the global children's entertainment market. Cookie Jar chief executive, Michael Hirsh is believed to be securing funds for the planned $195 million acquisition.

7938 ■ *"The Life Changers"* in *Canadian Business (Vol. 81, October 27, 2008, No. 18, pp. 86)*
Pub: Rogers Media Ltd.
Description: The first season of 'The Life Changers' was produced in September 2007 to feature stories about research and development (R&D) efforts by universities in Atlantic Canada. The program addresses the need to inform the public about university R&D and its outcomes.

7939 ■ *"Lifetime Networks"* in *Brandweek (Vol. 49, April 21, 2008, No. 16, pp. SR10)*
Pub: VNU Business Media, Inc.
Ed: Anthony Crupi. **Description:** Provides contact information for sales and marketing personnel for the ABC network as well as a listing of the station's top programming and an analysis of the current season and the target audience for those programs running in the current season. Lifetime will still produce its original signature movies but will now focus its emphasis more clearly on series development in order to appeal to a younger, hipper female demographic.

7940 ■ *"Lights, Camera, Action: Tools for Creating Video Blogs"* in *Inc. (Volume 32, December 2010, No. 10, pp. 57)*
Pub: Inc. Magazine
Ed: John Brandon. **Description:** A video blog is a good way to spread company news, talk about products, and stand out among traditional company blogs. New editing software can create two- to four-minute blogs using a webcam and either Windows Live Essentials, Apple iLife 2011, Powerdirector 9 Ultra, or Adobe Visual Communicator 3.

7941 ■ "Lights, Camera..Incentive" in Austin Business JournalInc. (Vol. 28, October 10, 2008, No. 30, pp. 1)
Pub: American City Business Journals
Ed: Sandra Zaragoza. Description: Film industry insiders are saying that state level tax breaks are needed to boost the sector, together with the help of the $700 billion bailout bill, which is expected to provide $470 million in tax incentives to the movie industry. Other details on filmmakers' call for more tax incentives for Texas' film industry are discussed.

7942 ■ "Like Being There" in Canadian Business (Vol. 79, August 14, 2006, No. 16-17, pp. 77)
Pub: Rogers Media
Ed: Gerry Blackwell. Description: Latest video conferencing facilities at the Halo Collaboration Studio, are discussed.

7943 ■ "Looking Like a Million Bucks" in Entrepreneur (Vol. 37, August 2009, No. 8, pp. 102)
Pub: Entrepreneur Media, Inc.
Ed: Jason Daley. Description: Sunset Tan's Jeff Bozz says he and Devin Haman are executive producers of the show and that that they want to stretch the truth a bit and make fun of it. Haman says the business is all about VIP service for everyone and that they want all their clients to feel like celebrities.

7944 ■ "Making Sense of Ambiguous Evidence" in Harvard Business Review (Vol. 86, September 2008, No. 9, pp. 53)
Pub: Harvard Business School Press
Ed: Lisa Burrell. Description: Documentary filmmaker Errol Morris emphasizes the role of perception in portraying objective reality, and how investigation and analysis enhance the accuracy of that portrayal.

7945 ■ Media Review Digest: The Only Complete Guide to Reviews of Non-Print Media
Pub: Pierian Press
Contact: Carroll Edward Wall, President
E-mail: cewall@pierianpress.org
URL(s): pierianpress.com. Ed: C. Edward Wall. Released: Annual Price: $295, Individuals. Publication includes: List of producers and suppliers of entertainment and educational media, including film, video, audio, and miscellaneous resources. Entries include: Name, address. Principal content of publication is a list of citations and cross-references to reviews found in non-print entertainment and educational media. Arrangement: Classified by type of media, then by company name.

7946 ■ "Moosylvania Releases Latest XL Marketing Trends Report" in Wireless News (October 6, 2009)
Pub: Close-Up Media
Description: Moosylvania, a digital promotion and branding agency that also has an on-site research facility, has released its 2nd XL Marketing Trends Report which focuses on digital video; the study defines the top digital video trends marketers must focus on now and well into the future and notes that in 2010, Mobile Web Devices, such as smart phones will outnumber computers in this country. Statistical data included.

7947 ■ "Moving Pitchers" in Entrepreneur (Vol. 37, December 2009, No. 12, pp. 46)
Pub: Entrepreneur Media, Inc.
Ed: Gwen Moran. Description: Online videos have become accessible for business development and marketing due to the decline in production costs and the growth in viewership. Research company comScore reveals that 153 million Internet users in the U.S. watched an online video in August 2009. The benefits of using online videos to further market one's company are explained.

7948 ■ "MTV Networks" in Brandweek (Vol. 49, April 21, 2008, No. 16, pp. SR10)
Pub: VNU Business Media, Inc.
Ed: Anthony Crupi. Description: Provides contact information for sales and marketing personnel for the MTV networks as well as a listing of the station's top programming and an analysis of the current season and the target audience for those programs running in the current season. MTV networks include MTV, VH1, Nickelodeon and Comedy Central.

7949 ■ My Life From Scratch: A Sweet Journey of Starting Over, One Cake at a Time
Pub: Broadway Books
Contact: David Drake, Manager
E-mail: ddrake@randomhouse.com
Released: June 8, 2010. Price: $14.00. Description: Lively account of Old World recipes, Bullock-Prado, a former Hollywood film developer and sister to actress Sandra Bullock, recounts the joys and heartbreak of running her own patisserie in Montpelier, Vermont. Having fled Los Angeles with her husband, Ray for the simpler pleasures of a small town near the Green Mountains, she opened her own bake shop, Gesine Confectionary in 2004, mostly on the fame of the macaroons she refashioned from her German mother's favorite almond treat, mandelhoernchen (and the casual mention of her sister in an interview). Her memoir follows one day in a busy baker's life, from waking at 3 a.m. to prepare the batter and bake her croissants, scones, and sticky buns, before opening her shop at 7 a.m., through the hectic lunch, and 3 p.m. tea time.

7950 ■ "NBC" in Brandweek (Vol. 49, April 21, 2008, No. 16, pp. SR6)
Pub: VNU Business Media, Inc.
Ed: John Consoli. Description: Provides contact information for sales and marketing personnel for the NBC network as well as a listing of the station's top programming and an analysis of the current season and the target audience for those programs running in the current season. NBC also devised a new strategy of announcing its prime-time schedule 52 weeks in advance which was a hit for advertisers who felt this gave them a better opportunity to plan for product placement. Even with the station's creative sales programs, they could face a challenge from Fox in terms of upfront advertisement purchases.

7951 ■ "NBC Universal Cable" in Brandweek (Vol. 49, April 21, 2008, No. 16, pp. SR11)
Pub: VNU Business Media, Inc.
Ed: Anthony Crupi. Description: Provides contact information for sales and marketing personnel for the NBC Universal Cable networks as well as a listing of the station's top programming and an analysis of the current season and the target audience for those programs running in the current season. The network's stations include USA, Sci Fi and Bravo. Ad revenue for the network grew 30 percent in the first quarter.

7952 ■ "NBC Universal Domestic Television Distribution" in Brandweek (Vol. 49, April 21, 2008, No. 16, pp. SR13)
Pub: VNU Business Media, Inc.
Ed: Marc Berman. Description: Provides contact information for sales and marketing personnel for NBC Universal Domestic Television Distribution as well as a listing of the station's top programming and an analysis of the current season and the target audience for those programs running in the current season.

7953 ■ "A Network of One: Local Writer Adds Web Interviews to Creative Output" in La Crosse Tribune (September 14, 2009)
Pub: La Crosse Tribune
Ed: Geri Parlin. Description: Profile of Andrew Revels, a freelance and aspiring writer, who has created a website in order to help gain attention for his own writing as well as for other local artists, musicians and comedians. His latest endeavor includes interviewing local talent and broadcasting the interviews on his site each week.

7954 ■ "New Recession-Proof Internet Marketing Package Allows Businesses to Ramp Up Web Traffic and Profits" in PR Newswire (Jan. 25, 2010)
Pub: PR Newswire Association, LLC
Description: Profile of Reel Web Design, a leading marketing firm in New York City that caters to small to medium sized businesses with smaller budgets that need substantial return on investment; Reel Web Design offers video production and submission, web design and maintenance and press release writing among additional services.

7955 ■ "New Recession-Proof Internet Marketing Package Allows Businesses to Ramp Up Web Traffic and Profits" in PR Newswire (Jan. 25, 2010)
Pub: PR Newswire Association, LLC
Description: Profile of Reel Web Design, a leading marketing firm in New York City that caters to small to medium sized businesses with smaller budgets that need substantial return on investment; Reel Web Design offers video production and submission, web design and maintenance and press release writing among additional services.

7956 ■ "New TurnHere Survey Reveals Online Video Trends" in Internet Wire (October 22, 2009)
Pub: Comtex News Network, Inc.
Description: TurnHere, Inc., the leading online video marketing services company, released the findings of its recent survey regarding current and future trends in online video among marketing agencies and brand recognition; the report found that online video has and will continue to play a prominent role in the realm of marketing edging out both search and email marketing campaigns. Additional highlights and statistical data included.

7957 ■ "No Risk? No Reward" in Canadian Business (Vol. 79, September 11, 2006, No. 18, pp. 93)
Pub: Rogers Media
Ed: Dennis Seguin. Description: Box office performances of the Canadian films are presented. Strategies to revitalize the film businesses in Canada are suggested.

7958 ■ "No Straight Lines: How Video Visionary Julien 'Little X' Lutz Creates His Images" in Black Enterprise (Vol. 38, January 2008)
Pub: Earl G. Graves Publishing Co. Inc.
Ed: Sonia Alleyne. Description: Profile of Julien Lutz, who turned his passion for drawing into a successful career.

7959 ■ "Northern Overexposure" in Canadian Business (Vol. 79, August 14, 2006, No. 16-17, pp. 36)
Pub: Rogers Media
Description: Fall in revenue from foreign film productions in Canada due to its overexposure, and incentives offered by other nations to foreign film productions, are discussed.

7960 ■ "Note to Marketers: A Viral Video Has a Life of Its Own" in Advertising Age (Vol. 80, October 5, 2009, No. 33, pp. 29)
Pub: Crain's Communications
Ed: Ken Wheaton. Description: Internet marketers do not decide whether or not an online video goes viral. It is the audience that decides what online videos to spread and such fare is usually passed around due to its content being downright witty or creative or so laughably bad that the audience wants to share it.

7961 ■ "Online Marketing and Promotion of Canadian Films via Social Media Tools" in CNW Group (January 27, 2010)
Pub: Comtex News Network, Inc.
Description: Telefilm Canada announced the launch of a pilot initiative aimed at encouraging the integration of online marketing and the use of social media tools into means of distribution ahead of a films' theatrical release. During this pilot phase Web-Cine 360 will target French-language feature films.

7962 ■ "Out to Draw Work, Talent" in Crain's Detroit Business (Vol. 24, April 14, 2008, No. 15, pp. 3)
Pub: Crain Communications, Inc.
Ed: Bill Shea. Description: Profile of Southfield-based Kinetic Post Inc., a growing post-production house that offers video, audio, animation, print, online and related services to corporations and advertising agencies.

7963 ■ "People; E-Commerce, Online Games, Mobile Apps" in Advertising Age (Vol. 80, October 19, 2009, No. 35, pp. 14)
Pub: Crain's Communications
Ed: Nat Ives. Description: Profile of People Magazine and the ways in which the publisher is moving its magazine forward by exploring new concepts in a time of declining newsstand sales and advertising pages; among the strategies are e-commerce such as the brand People Style Watch in which consumers are able highlight clothing and jewelry and then connect to retailers' sites and a channel on Taxi TV, the network of video-touch screens in New Your City taxis.

7964 ■ "People; E-Commerce, Online Games, Mobile Apps: This Isn't Your Mom's People" in Advertising Age (Vol. 80, October 19, 2009, No. 35)
Pub: Crain's Communications
Ed: Nat Ives. Description: Profile of People Magazine and the ways in which the publisher is moving its magazine forward by exploring new concepts in a time of declining newsstand sales and advertising pages; among the strategies are e-commerce such as the brand People Style Watch in which consumers are able highlight clothing and jewelry and then connect to retailers' sites and a channel on Taxi TV, the network of video-touch screens in New Your City taxis.

7965 ■ "Picture of Success" in Black Enterprise (Vol. 38, December 2007, No. 5, pp. 71)
Pub: Earl G. Graves Publishing Co. Inc.
Ed: Sheiresa McRae. Description: Profile of Kenya Cagle, president and CEO of Caglevision Inc., an independent motion picture production company. Cagle, former off-Broadway child actor, kept his company afloat with financial backing and support from friends, employees, and business colleagues.

7966 ■ The Pixar Touch: The Making of a Company
Pub: Pantheon Books
Ed: David A. Price. Released: 2009. Price: $27.95. Description: Profile of how Pixar's founders turned their computer-animated films into a successful movie studio.

7967 ■ "Port in the Storm" in Canadian Business (Vol. 81, October 13, 2008, No. 17, pp. 101)
Pub: Rogers Media Ltd.
Ed: Calvin Leung. Description: Interport Inc.'s state-of-the-art studio complex in Toronto is discussed. The strong Canadian dollar, along with disputes within the movie industry, are creating challenges for the studio to secure Hollywood projects. Interport plans to compete for Hollywood projects based on quality.

7968 ■ "Pretentious and Loving It" in Entrepreneur (Vol. 37, August 2009, No. 8, pp. 34)
Pub: Entrepreneur Media, Inc.
Ed: Eric Mahoney. Description: Pitchfork.com features reviews of albums from independent artists. Their most innovative section is Pitchfork.tv, featuring videos of bands, and Forkcast along with their Features section that contains articles about bands and their histories.

7969 ■ "Promoting Academic Programs Using Online Videos" in Business Communication Quarterly (December 2007, pp. 478)
Pub: SAGE Publications USA
Contact: Blaise R. Simqu, President
Ed: Thomas Clark, Julie Stewart. Description: Xavier Entrepreneurial Center successfully used online videos to promote the effectiveness of its academic programs. Online videos are a cost-effective way of publicizing academic programs.

7970 ■ "Push Is On To Build Region's Prospects In Film Industry" in Crain's Cleveland Business (Vol. 28, November 19, 2007, No. 46, pp. 1)
Pub: Crain Communications, Inc.
Ed: Jay Miller. Description: Overview of a bill that has been introduced by state Representative Thomas Patton that would grant a 25 percent state income tax credit on investments of $300,000 or more in motion picture or television productions filmed in Ohio.

7971 ■ "The Rage Offstage at Marvel" in Barron's (Vol. 88, June 30, 2008, No. 26, pp. 19)
Pub: Dow Jones & Co., Inc.
Ed: Bill Alpert. Description: Lawsuits against Marvel Entertainment and Stan Lee are pushing the claims from Peter F. Paul that Stan Lee Media was undone by the actions of the accused. Paul's associates argue that Stan Lee Media owns rights to Marvel characters and that they want half the profits that Marvel is making.

7972 ■ "Ready, Aim, (Cool) Fire" in Saint Louis Business Journal (Vol. 32, September 2, 2011, No. 1, pp. 1)
Pub: Saint Louis Business Journal
Ed: E.B. Solomont. Description: Coolfire Originals' CEO Jeff Keane is co-producing 'Welcome Sweetie Pie's' with Los Angeles, California-based Pilgrims Films and Television Films for the Oprah Winfrey Network. The reality show focuses on restaurant owner Robbie Montgomery of Sweetie Pie's in St. Louis, Missouri.

7973 ■ "Recovery on Tap for 2010?" in Orlando Business Journal (Vol. 26, January 1, 2010, No. 31, pp. 1)
Pub: American City Business Journals
Ed: Melanie Stawicki Azam, Richard Bilbao, Christopher Boyd, Anjali Fluker. Description: Economic forecasts for Central Florida's leading business sectors in 2010 are presented. These sectors include housing, film and TV, sports business, law, restaurants, aviation, tourism and hospitality, banking and finance, commercial real estate, retail, health care, insurance, higher education, and manufacturing. According to some local executives, Central Florida's economy will slowly recover in 2010.

7974 ■ "Red One and The Rain Chronicles" in Michigan Vue (Vol. 13, July-August 2008, No. 4, pp. 30)
Pub: Entrepreneur Media Inc.
Ed: Evan Cornish. Description: Troy-based film school the Motion Picture Institute (MPI) implemented the latest technology by shooting the second of their trilogy, 'The Rain Chronicles', on the Red One camera. This is the first feature film in Michigan to utilize this exciting new camera, which includes proprietary software for rendering and color correction. Brian K. Johnson heads up the visual effects team as visual effects supervisor and lead CG artist. His company, Dream Conduit Studios, had to tackle the task of employing the new work flow through a post-production pipeline that would allow him to attack complex visual effects shots, many of which were shot with a moving camera, a technique rarely seen in films at this budgetary level where the camera is traditionally locked off.

7975 ■ "Regal Venture Puts Imax Back in the Spotlight" in Globe & Mail (March 13, 2007, pp. B5)
Pub: CTVglobemedia Publishing Inc.
Ed: Shirley Won. Description: Imax Corp. has signed new contract with cinema hall operating giant Regal Entertainment Corp. for constructing two more giant screen theaters. Share prices of Imax Corp. have increased sharply after this announcement.

7976 ■ "ROIonline Announces Streaming Video Products" in Marketing Weekly News (December 5, 2009, pp. 155)
Pub: Investment Weekly News
Description: ROIonline LLC, an Internet marketing firm serving business-to-business and the industrial marketplace, has added streaming video options to the Internet solutions it offers its clients; due to the huge increase of broadband connections, videos are now commonplace on the Internet and can often convey a company's message in a must more efficient, concise and effective way that will engage a website's visitor thus delivering a high return on a company's investment.

7977 ■ "S3 Entertainment Group Partners with WFW International for Film Services in Michigan" in Michigan Vue (July-August 2008)
Pub: Entrepreneur Media Inc.
Description: William F. White (WFW), one of North America's largest production equipment providers has partnered with S3 Entertainment Group (S3EG), a Michigan-based full-service film production services company due to the new incentives package which currently offers the highest incentives in the United States, up to 42 percent. S3EG will actively store, lease, manage, distribute and sell WFW's equipment to the growing number of production teams that are filming in the state.

7978 ■ "Screen Time" in Canadian Business (Vol. 81, October 13, 2008, No. 17, pp. 93)
Pub: Rogers Media Ltd.
Ed: Calvin Leung. Description: Young Canadian entertainment business up-and-comers like Ari Lantos and Brian Mossof plan to produce movies that cold earn and entertain audiences rather than focusing on winning awards. English movies continue to struggle in Canada, while French-language films continue to thrive. Details on Canada's movie industry are furnished.

7979 ■ "Scripps Networks" in Brandweek (Vol. 49, April 21, 2008, No. 16, pp. SR12)
Pub: VNU Business Media, Inc.
Ed: Anthony Crupi. Description: Provides contact information for sales and marketing personnel for the Scripps networks as well as a listing of the station's top programming and an analysis of the current season and the target audience for those programs running in the current season. Scripps networks include HGTV and the Food Network. HGTV boasts on of the industry's best commercial-retention averages, keeping nearly 97 percent of its viewers during advertising breaks.

7980 ■ "Several Studio Projects in Production" in Crain's Detroit Business (Vol. 26, January 18, 2010, No. 3, pp. 21)
Pub: Crain Communications, Inc.
Ed: Bill Shea. Description: Overview of several projects in development in the metro Detroit area due to Michigan's film industry incentives which include a 25 percent tax credit for infrastructure projects.

7981 ■ The SHOOT Directory for Commercial Production and Postproduction
Pub: Nielsen Business Media Inc.
Contact: Toni Nevitt, President
URL(s): www.shootonline.com. Ed: Robert Goldrich. Released: Annual; latest edition June 2004. Price: $99, plus shipping and handling charges. Covers: Companies that provide television commercial production and postproduction services, including film video and audio production, duplication, editing, animation, film-to-tape transfer, and standards conversion in the U.S. and Canada. Entries include: Company name, address, phone, fax, names and titles of key personnel. Arrangement: Classified by type of company. Indexes: Geographical.

7982 ■ "Show and Tell" in Entrepreneur (Vol. 36, May 2008, No. 5, pp. 54)
Pub: Entrepreneur Media, Inc.
Ed: Heather Clancy. Description: FreshStart Telephone uses recorded video testimonials of customers, by using Pure Digital Flip Video that downloads content directly to the computer, and uploads it in the company's website to promote their wireless phone service.

7983 ■ "Small Businesses Benefiting from Movie-Struck Hub" in Boston Business Journal (Vol. 27, October 12, 2007, No. 37, pp. 1)
Pub: American City Business Journals Inc.
Ed: Naomi R. Kooker. Description: Revision of the Massachusetts' film tax credits has attracted filming of major motion pictures in the state and local businesses have benefited. A list of businesses that saw boosts from the movie-making industry's presence is presented.

7984 ■ *"Sony Pictures Television"* in *Brandweek (Vol. 49, April 21, 2008, No. 16, pp. SR13)*
Pub: VNU Business Media, Inc.
Ed: Marc Berman. **Description:** Provides contact information for sales and marketing personnel for Sony Pictures Television Distribution as well as a listing of the station's top programming and an analysis of the current season and the target audience for those programs running in the current season.

7985 ■ *"State Expects Increase of $50 Million from Film Bills; Come Back, Al Roker"* in *Crain's Detroit Business (March 24, 2008)*
Pub: Crain Communications, Inc.
Ed: Bill Shea. **Description:** Overview of the new film initiative and its incentives designed to entice more film work to Michigan; the measures could bring $50 million to $100 million in movie production work for the rest of this year compared to the $4 million total the state saw last year. Also discusses the show 'DEA' which was filmed in Detroit and stars Al Roker.

7986 ■ *"State Film Business Tops $1.3 Billion"* in *The Business Journal-Portland (Vol. 25, August 22, 2008, No. 24, pp. 1)*
Pub: American City Business Journals, Inc.
Ed: Andy Giegerich. **Description:** Oregon's film industry has generated $1.39 billion in direct and indirect economic impact in 2007, a 55 percent rise from 2005 levels. The growth of the industry is attributed to tax incentives issued in 2007, which attracted film production companies from other states.

7987 ■ *"Sticking to Stories; Havey Ovshinksy Changes Method, Keeps the Mission"* in *Crain's Detroit Business (Vol. 24, March 31, 2008)*
Pub: Crain Communications, Inc.
Ed: Daniel Duggan. **Description:** Profile of Harvey Ovshinsky, an award-winning documentary filmmaker who has reinvented his work with corporations who want to market themselves with the transition to digital media. His company, HKO Media, takes Ovshinsky's art of storytelling and enhances it through multimedia operations on the Internet through a joint venture with a man he once mentored, Bob Kernen.

7988 ■ *"Summit, Lions Gate are in Talks to Merge Studios"* in *Wall Street Journal Eastern Edition (November 29, 2011, pp. B2)*
Pub: Dow Jones & Company Inc. Enterprise Media Group
Contact: Clare Hart, President
Ed: Erica Orden, Michelle Kung. **Description:** Movie studio Summit Entertainment LLC is in talks with television producer Lions Gate Entertainment Corporation about a possible merger. Previous talks have taken place, but no deal was ever reached. Such a deal would create a large, independent studio able to compete in the market with the big Hollywood giants.

7989 ■ *"Suspense Hangs Over Fledgling Film Industry"* in *Crain's Detroit Business (Vol. 26, January 18, 2010, No. 3, pp. 3)*
Pub: Crain Communications Inc.
Ed: Bill Shea. **Description:** Overview of the film incentive package which has fostered a growth in the industry with 52 productions completed in 2009, bringing in $223.6 million in gross in-state production expenditures of which the state will refund $87.2 million. Opposition to the incentives has been growing among legislatures who believe that the initiatives cost more than they ultimately bring into the state. Experts believe that the initiatives will remain since they have already fostered economic growth and are good for the state's image.

7990 ■ *"Telemundo"* in *Brandweek (Vol. 49, April 21, 2008, No. 16, pp. SR8)*
Pub: VNU Business Media, Inc.
Ed: John Consoli. **Description:** Provides contact information for sales and marketing personnel for the Telemundo network as well as a listing of the station's top programming and an analysis of the current season and the target audience for those programs running in the current season.

7991 ■ *"This Just In. State House Introduces Film-Industry Stimulus Bills"* in *Crain's Detroit Business (Vol. 24, March 3, 2008, No. 9)*
Pub: Crain Communications Inc. - Detroit
Description: House Bills 5841-5856 would give Michigan the most competitive incentives in the U.S. to encourage projects by film industry. Provisions of the bill are outlined.

7992 ■ *"Ticket Tiff Erupts Over Fund Ads"* in *Globe & Mail (January 31, 2007, pp. B1)*
Pub: CTVglobemedia Publishing Inc.
Description: The opposition of Cineplex Entertainment LP to Mackenzie Financial Corp.'s advertisement about high cost of movie ticket is discussed.

7993 ■ *"Turner Broadcasting System"* in *Brandweek (Vol. 49, April 21, 2008, No. 16, pp. SR13)*
Pub: VNU Business Media, Inc.
Ed: Anthony Crupi. **Description:** Provides contact information for sales and marketing personnel for the Turner Broadcasting System networks as well as a listing of the station's top programming and an analysis of the current season and the target audience for those programs running in the current season. Recent acquisitions are also discussed.

7994 ■ *"Twentieth Television"* in *Brandweek (Vol. 49, April 21, 2008, No. 16, pp. SR16)*
Pub: VNU Business Media, Inc.
Ed: Marc Berman. **Description:** Provides contact information for sales and marketing personnel for Twentieth Television as well as a listing of the station's top programming and an analysis of the current season and the target audience for those programs running in the current season.

7995 ■ *University Film and Video Association--Membership Directory*
Pub: University Film and Video Association
Contact: Melinda Levin, President
E-mail: melinda@unt.edu
URL(s): www.ufva.org. **Released:** Annual **Covers:** about 800 persons concerned with the production and study of motion pictures and video in colleges and universities. **Entries include:** Name, affiliation, address, phone. **Arrangement:** Alphabetical. **Indexes:** Affiliation, geographical.

7996 ■ *"Univision"* in *Brandweek (Vol. 49, April 21, 2008, No. 16, pp. SR8)*
Pub: VNU Business Media, Inc.
Ed: John Consoli. **Description:** Provides contact information for sales and marketing personnel for the Univision network as well as a listing of the station's top programming and an analysis of the current season and the target audience for those programs running in the current season. Univision is the No. 1 network on Friday nights in the 18-34 demographic, beating all English-language networks.

7997 ■ *"Video Surveillance Enters Digital Era, Makes Giant Strides"* in *Arkansas Business (Vol. 26, September 28, 2009, No. 39, pp. 1)*
Pub: Journal Publishing Inc.
Ed: Jamie Walden. **Description:** Arkansas business owners are finding that the newest technology in video surveillance is leading to swift apprehension of thieves due to the high-quality digital imagery now being captured on surveillance equipment. Motion detection software for these systems is enhancing the capabilities of these systems and providing opportunities for businesses that would normally have problems integrating these systems.

7998 ■ *"A View to a Killer Business Model"* in *Black Enterprise (Vol. 40, December 2009, No. 5, pp. 50)*
Pub: Earl G. Graves Publishing Co., Inc.
Ed: Sonya A. Donaldson. **Description:** Profile of Gen2Media Corp., a production, technology and Internet marketing firm based in Florida with offices in New York; Gen2Media is utilizing the advances in technology to now include video in its online marketing offerings.

7999 ■ *"Warner Bros. Domestic Television Distribution"* in *Brandweek (Vol. 49, April 21, 2008, No. 16, pp. SR16)*
Pub: VNU Business Media, Inc.
Ed: Marc Berman. **Description:** Provides contact information for sales and marketing personnel for Warner Bros. Domestic Television Distribution as well as a listing of the station's top programming and an analysis of the current season and the target audience for those programs running in the current season.

8000 ■ *"We May Finally Find the Silver Lining"* in *Crain's Detroit Business (Vol. 24, April 7, 2008, No. 14, pp. 8)*
Pub: Crain Communications, Inc.
Description: Discusses a possible economic turnaround for Michigan which could be brought forth with such things as the new film initiative incentives which may make filming in the state more appealing than filming in Canada due to the weakened state of the dollar and more exportation from Michigan companies.

8001 ■ *"Why Some Get Shaften By Google Pricing"* in *Advertising Age (Vol. 79, July 14, 2008, No. 7, pp. 3)*
Pub: Crain Communications, Inc.
Ed: Abbey Klaassen. **Description:** Google's search advertising is discussed as well as the company's pricing structure for these ads.

SOURCES OF SUPPLY

8002 ■ *DVD Replication Directory*
Corbell Publishing Co.
URL(s): www.corbell.com/. **Released:** Annual; Latest edition 5th, 2007. **Price:** $457, plus 40 shipping. **Covers:** Over 100 video duplicators in the U.S. and Canada. **Entries include:** Name, address, phone, fax, url, e-mail address, names and titles of key personnel, financial data, types of accounts, geographical area served, number of employees, formats duplicated, other services offered. **Database includes:** Statistics. **Arrangement:** Alphabetical. **Indexes:** Company name.

STATISTICAL SOURCES

8003 ■ *RMA Annual Statement Studies*
Pub: Risk Management Association
Contact: Kevin M. Blakey, President
Released: Annual. **Price:** $175.00 2006-07 edition, $105.00. **Description:** Contains composite balance sheets and income statements for more than 360 industries, including the accounting, auditing, and bookkeeping industries. Also contains five years of comparative historical data for discerning trends. Includes 16 commonly used ratios, computed for most of the size groupings for nearly every industry.

TRADE PERIODICALS

8004 ■ *AV Video & Multimedia Producer*
Pub: Phillips Business Information Inc. Access Intelligence L.L.C.
Contact: Heather Farley, President
E-mail: hfarley@accessintel.com
URL(s): www.accessintel.com/. **Released:** Monthly

8005 ■ *Digital Content Producer*
Pub: NewBay Media, LLC
URL(s): digitalcontentproducer.com. **Released:** Monthly

8006 ■ *ICG Magazine*
Pub: International Cinematographers Guild
URL(s): icgmagazine.com. **Released:** Monthly

8007 ■ *Journal of Film and Video*
Contact: Stephen Tropiano, Editor
URL(s): www.press.uillinois.edu/journals/jfv.html. **Ed:** Stephen Tropiano. **Released:** Quarterly **Price:** $75, Individuals print; $95, Individuals print & online; $75, Institutions print; $95, Institutions print & online; $30, Students print with UFVA membership.

8008 ■ *Videography: The Magazine of Professional Video Production, Technology, and Applications*
Pub: NewBay Media, LLC
URL(s): www.videography.com/. **Ed:** Cristina Clapp.
Released: Monthly **Price:** Free.

8009 ■ *Videomaker Magazine*
Pub: York Publishing Inc.
Contact: Matt York, President
URL(s): www.videomaker.com. **Released:** Monthly
Price: $19.97, Individuals.

VIDEOCASSETTES/ AUDIOCASSETTES

8010 ■ *Hollywood Directors and Their Craft*
First Light Video Publishing
2321 Abbot Kinney Blvd.
Venice, CA 90291
Ph: (310)577-8581
Free: 800-262-8862
Fax: (310)574-0886
Co. E-mail: sale@firstlightvideo.com
URL: http://www.firstlightvideo.com
Released: 1994. **Description:** Seven directors (Clint Eastwood, John Badham, Robert Wise, Delbert Mann, Abraham Polonsky, Michael Schultz, and John Flynn) analyze their working methods. Covers career preparation, choosing a project, the writer, casting, pre-production, the cinematographer, on the set, working with actors, the editor, previews and premieres, the development of personal style, and social responsibility. **Availability:** VHS.

8011 ■ *Making a Video Program*
Stagestep
4701 Bath St., #46B
Philadelphia, PA 19137
Ph: (215)636-9000
Free: 800-523-0960
Fax: (267)672-2912
Co. E-mail: stagestep@stagestep.com
URL: http://stagestep.com
Released: 19??. **Price:** $148.95. **Description:** An overview of the video production process, from scriptwriting and preproduction planning to editing, titling, and preview screening. **Availability:** VHS.

8012 ■ *Sound Success*
York Publishing Inc.
1350 E 9th St.
Chico, CA 95927
Ph: (530)891-8410
Free: 800-284-3226
Fax: (530)891-8443
Co. E-mail: customerservice@videomaker.com
URL: http://www.videomaker.com
Contact: Matt York, President
Released: 1997. **Price:** $12.95. **Description:** Discusses types of mics, overcoming audio problems indoors and out, and how music can enhance your videos. **Availability:** VHS.

TRADE SHOWS AND CONVENTIONS

8013 ■ *Home Media Expo*
Home Entertainment Events
201 Sandpointe Ave., Ste. 500
Santa Ana, CA 92707
Free: 800-854-3112
Fax: (714)513-8848
URL: http://www.homemediaexpo.com
URL(s): www.homemediaexpo.com. **Frequency:** Annual. **Audience:** Video/DVD store owners, employees, and distributors (trade only). **Principal Exhibits:**

Mainstream and adult products; interactive media; Internet; studios; novelty products; adult toys; service providers; Internet service providers; video and DVD equipment, supplies, and services; Blu-ray discs.

CONSULTANTS

8014 ■ *Creative Resource Publishing*
W2974 Butternut Ln.
Green Lake, WI 54941-9614
Ph: (920)295-3824
Fax: (920)424-3133
Contact: Al Folker, Owner
Scope: Provider of video production consulting including studio planning, video publishing, scripting, cable television franchising and sales, corporate television and insurance sales training. Serves all industries and public agencies. **Founded:** 1982. **Publications:** "Targeting Workplace Trauma". **Seminars:** How to Deal With Aggressive News Reporters; Opportunities in Video Publishing. **Special Services:** Web Design and Site Management.

8015 ■ *Full Voice*
3217 Broadway Ave., Ste. 300
Kansas City, MO 64111
Ph: (816)941-0011
Free: 800-684-8764
Fax: (816)931-8887
Co. E-mail: info@infullvoice.com
URL: http://www.fullvoice.us
Contact: Michienne Dixon, Principal
Scope: Vocal performance training firm offering consulting services and personal training sessions in the implementation of effective vocal communication techniques for the development of business relationships and career enhancement. Formalizes a program of proven techniques into a practical method of helping individuals improve their ability to better present themselves when speaking in a professional situation. Industries served: All. **Founded:** 1992. **Publications:** "You Can Sound Like You Know What You're Saying". **Seminars:** You Can Sound Like You Know What You're Saying; The Psychology of Vocal Performance; Security. . .the Ability to Accept Change; Knowing. . .the Key to Relaxed Public Communication; The Effective Voice for Customer Service Enhancement; You Can Speak With Conviction; How To Make Yours a Championship Team; Functional English For Foreign Trade. **Special Services:** FULL VOICE™.

FRANCHISES AND BUSINESS OPPORTUNITIES

8016 ■ *Home Video Studio*
8148 Raven Rock Dr.
Indianapolis, IN 46256
Ph: (317)964-8048
Free: 800-464-8220
Fax: (317)577-1522
Description: Home based video studio. **No. of Franchise Units:** 70. **No. of Company-Owned Units:** 2. **No. of Operating Units:** 75. **Founded:** 1991.. **Franchised:** 2006. **Equity Capital Needed:** $69,050-$97,300. **Franchise Fee:** $25,000. **Royalty Fee:** 7%. **Financial Assistance:** Limited third party financing available. **Training:** Yes.

8017 ■ *Videomasters Inc.*
2200 Dunbarton Dr., Ste. D
Chesapeake, VA 23325
Free: 800-836-9461
Fax: (757)424-8693
Description: Video and audio products are available. **No. of Franchise Units:** 80. **Founded:** 1980.. **Franchised:** 1982. **Equity Capital Needed:** $36,950. **Franchise Fee:** $950 annually. **Training:** Yes.

COMPUTERIZED DATABASES

8018 ■ *BaselineFT's In Production Database*
3415 S Sepulveda Blvd., Ste. 200
Los Angeles, CA 90034
Ph: (310)482-3400
Free: 800-858-3669
Fax: (310)393-7799
URL: http://www.baselineresearch.com
Availability: Online: Baseline LLC. **Type:** Full-text.

COMPUTER SYSTEMS/ SOFTWARE

8019 ■ *Authorware 7 | Macro Media*
345 Park Ave.
San Jose, CA 95110
Ph: (408)536-6000
Free: 800-288-4797
Fax: (408)537-6000
URL: http://www.adobe.com
Price: Contact Adobe. **Description:** Available for Apple Macintosh Plus, SE, or II computers. System provides post production, storyboarding, and special effects functions.

LIBRARIES

8020 ■ *California Film Commission - Location Resource Center Library*
7080 Hollywood Blvd., Ste. 900
Los Angeles, CA 90028-6906
Ph: (323)860-2960
Free: 800-858-4749
Fax: (323)860-2972
Co. E-mail: lmosher@film.ca.gov
URL: http://www.film.ca.gov
Contact: Lisa Mosher, Librarian Specialist, Research Services
URL(s): ca.reel-scout.com/loc_search.aspx?. **Scope:** Motion picture film locations. **Services:** Library open to the public. **Founded:** 1985. **Holdings:** 500 books; 300,000 photographs. **Subscriptions:** 6 journals and other serials.

8021 ■ *University of North Carolina School of the Arts - Semans Library*
UNC School of the Arts
1533 S. Main St.
Winston-Salem, NC 27127
Ph: (336)770-3270
Fax: (336)770-3271
Co. E-mail: rebeccab@uncsa.edu
URL: http://www.uncsa.edu/library
Contact: Christia Thomason
Scope: Music, art and design, theater, film, dance, humanities. **Services:** Interlibrary loan; Library open to the public. **Founded:** 1965. **Holdings:** 111,000 books; 9000 bound periodical volumes; 50,000 music scores; 45,000 sound recordings; 5200 DVDs and videos. **Subscriptions:** 470 journals and other serials; 25 newspapers.

8022 ■ *Watkins College of Art, Design, & Film Library*
2298 Rosa L. Parks Blvd.
Nashville, TN 37228
Ph: (615)277-7427
Fax: (615)383-4849
Co. E-mail: library@watkins.edu
URL: http://www.watkins.edu/library
Contact: Lisa Williams, Director, Library Services
Scope: Film, fine arts, interior design, graphic design, photography. **Services:** Interlibrary loan; Library open to the public for reference use only. **Holdings:** 11,600 books; 1200 videotapes and films. **Subscriptions:** 50 journals and other serials; 11 newspapers. **Telecommunication Services:** lwilliams@watkins.edu.

START-UP INFORMATION

8023 ■ *"On Their Own: Bronx High School Students Open a Bank Branch"* in *Black Enterprise* (Vol. 38, February 2008, No. 7, pp. 42)
Pub: Earl G. Graves Publishing Co. Inc.
Ed: Jessica Jones. **Description:** Students at Fordham Leadership Academy for Business and Technology in New York City opened a student-run bank branch at their high school. The business paid high school seniors $11 per hour to work as tellers. Students were also taught interviewing basics.

ASSOCIATIONS AND OTHER ORGANIZATIONS

8024 ■ **Accounting and Finance Benchmarking Consortium**
4606 FM 1960 W, Ste. 250
Houston, TX 77069-9949
Ph: (281)440-5044
URL: http://www.afbc.org
Description: Accounting and finance managers of corporations with an interest in benchmarking. Promotes the use of benchmarking, wherein businesses compare their processes with those of their competitors, as a means of improving corporate efficiency and profitability. Facilitates exchange of information among members; conducts target operations, procurement, development, and maintenance studies; identifies model business practices. **Founded:** 1998.

8025 ■ **Advisor Voice**
390 Queens Quay W, Ste. 209
Toronto, ON, Canada M5V 3A2
Ph: (416)444-5251
Free: 800-563-5822
Fax: (416)444-8031
Co. E-mail: info@advocis.ca
URL: http://www.advocis.ca
Contact: Steve Howard, President
E-mail: showard@advocis.ca
Released: Monthly

8026 ■ **ADVOCIS (TFAAC)—Association des assureurs-vie du Canada**
390 Queens Quay W, Ste. 209
Toronto, ON, Canada M5V 3A2
Ph: (416)444-5251
Free: 800-563-5822
Fax: (416)444-8031
Co. E-mail: info@advocis.ca
URL: http://www.advocis.ca
Contact: Steve Howard, President
E-mail: showard@advocis.ca
Description: Professional association for Canadian insurance and financial advisors with members representing most cities and towns across the country. Founding member of the Financial Planners Standards Council (FPSC), the body that grants the CFP designation. Members provide financial advice, and market and sell financial products to over 9 million Canadians. **Founded:** 2003. **Publications:** *Advisor Voice* (Monthly); *Advocis* (Monthly).

8027 ■ **Canadian Association of Insolvency and Restructuring Professionals (CAIRP)—Canadian Insolvency Foundation (CIF)Association Canadienne des Professionnels de l'Insolvabilite et de la reorganisation;**
277 Wellington St. W
Toronto, ON, Canada M5V 3H2
Ph: (416)204-3242
Fax: (416)204-3410
Co. E-mail: info@cairp.ca
URL: http://www.cairp.ca
Contact: Guylaine Houle, Chairperson
Description: Promotes excellence in the field of insolvency and business recovery services. Lobbies for reform of bankruptcy laws; sponsors continuing professional development courses; delivers qualification program for bankruptcy transfers in conjunction with the federal government. **Founded:** 1979. **Publications:** *Rebuilding Success* (Semiannual). **Awards:** Lloyd Houlden Research Fellowships. **Telecommunication Services:** norm.kondo@cairp.ca.

8028 ■ **Canadian Credit Institute Educational Foundation (CCIEF)—Fondation Scolaire de l'Institut Canadien du Credit**
c/o Credit Institute of Canada
219 Dufferin St., Ste. 216C
Toronto, ON, Canada M6L 3J1
Ph: (416)572-2615
Fax: (416)572-2619
Co. E-mail: geninfo@creditedu.org
URL: http://www.creditedu.org
Contact: Reggie Delovtich, General Manager
Description: Financial institutions and providers of financial planning services. Promotes adherence to high standards of ethics and practice by members. Provides financial support to credit initiatives. **Founded:** 1967.

8029 ■ **Canadian Institute of Financial Planning (CIFP)—Institut Canadien de Planification Finaniere**
3660 Hurontario St., Ste. 600
Mississauga, ON, Canada L5B 3C4
Free: 866-635-5526
Co. E-mail: cifp@cifps.ca
URL: http://www.cifp.ca/Desktop/English/Index.asp
Contact: Keith Costello, President
Description: Works to promote excellence in the field of financial planning. Facilitates communication and cooperation among members, which includes financial planning professionals. Sponsors continuing professional education courses.

8030 ■ **Canadian Investor Relations Institute (CIRI)—Institut Canadien de Relations avec les Investisseurs**
601, 67 Yonge St.
Toronto, ON, Canada M5E 1J8
Ph: (416)364-8200
Fax: (416)364-2805
Co. E-mail: enquiries@ciri.org
URL: http://www.ciri.org
Contact: Tom Enright, President
Description: Executives responsible for communication between public corporations, investors and the financial community; dedicated to advancing the stature and credibility of the investor relations profession and the competency of members. **Founded:** 1992. **Publications:** *Newsline* (Bimonthly).

8031 ■ **Financial Managers Society (FMS)**
100 W Monroe St., Ste. 1700
Chicago, IL 60603-1907
Ph: (312)578-1300
Free: 800-275-4367
Fax: (312)578-1308
Co. E-mail: info@fmsinc.org
URL: http://www.fmsinc.org
Contact: Dick Yingst, President
E-mail: dyingst@fmsinc.org
Description: Works for the needs of finance and accounting professionals from banks, thrifts and credit unions. Offers career-enhancing education, specialized publications, national leadership opportunities and worldwide connections with other industry professionals. **Founded:** 1948. **Publications:** *Financial Managers Society--Membership and Peer Consulting Directory* (Annual); *Record Retention Manual; Financial Managers Society--Membership and Peer Consulting Directory* (Annual); *Membership and Peer Consulting Directory of the Financial Managers Society, Inc.*. **Educational Activities:** Financial Managers Society Annual Conference (Annual); The Finance & Accounting Forum for Financial Institutions (Annual).

8032 ■ **Financial Planning Association (FPA)**
7535 E Hampden Ave., Ste. 600
Denver, CO 80231
Ph: (303)759-4900
Free: 800-322-4237
Fax: (303)759-0749
Co. E-mail: webfeedback@fpanet.org
URL: http://www.fpanet.org
Contact: Martin Kurtz, Chairman
Description: Works to support the financial planning process in order to help people achieve their goals and dreams. Believes that everyone needs objective advice to make smart financial decisions and that when seeking the advice of a financial planner, the planner should be a CFP professional. **Founded:** 2000. **Publications:** *FPA This Week* (Weekly); *FPA Journal of Financial Planning* (Monthly). **Educational Activities:** Broker/Dealer Conference (Annual). **Awards:** Chapter Recognition Awards (Annual); P. Kemp Fain Jr. Award.

8033 ■ **Financial Women International (FWI)**
200 N Glebe Rd., Ste. 820
Arlington, VA 22203
Free: 866-236-2007

Fax: (866)807-6081
Co. E-mail: info@fwi.org
URL: http://www.fwifoundation.org
Contact: Nancy Kinder, President
Description: Individuals working in or with the financial services industry. Maintains FWI Educational Foundation. **Founded:** 1921. **Publications:** *Today's Financial Women*. **Awards:** Member of the Year (Annual); Partner in Success Award (Annual).

8034 ■ Financial Women's Association of New York (FWA)
215 Park Ave. S, Ste. 1712
New York, NY 10003-1619
Ph: (212)533-2141
Fax: (212)928-3008
Co. E-mail: fwaoffice@fwa.org
URL: http://www.nywici.org/links/link_fwa.html
Contact: Anne Izzillo, President
Description: Persons of professional status in the field of finance in the New York metropolitan area. Works to promote and maintain high professional standards in the financial and business communities; provide an opportunity for members to enhance one another's professional contacts; achieve recognition of the contribution of women to the financial and business communities; encourage other women to seek professional positions within the financial and business communities. Activities include educational trips to foreign countries; college internship program including foreign student exchange; high school mentorship program; Washington and international briefings; placement service for members. Maintains speakers' bureau. **Founded:** 1956. **Publications:** *FWA Connections* (11/year); *Financial Women's Association of New York--Directory* (Annual); *Financial Women's Association of New York--Directory* (Annual). **Awards:** Career Achievement Award (Annual); Woman of the Year Award (Annual).

8035 ■ FORUM
Released: Monthly

8036 ■ LIMRA International
300 Day Hill Rd.
Windsor, CT 06095
Ph: (860)688-3358
Free: 800-235-4672
Fax: (860)298-9555
Co. E-mail: webmaster@limra.com
URL: http://www.limra.com
Contact: Robert A. Kerzner, President
Description: Life insurance and financial services companies. Conducts market, consumer, economic, financial, and human resources research; monitors industry distribution systems and product and service developments. Provides executive and field management development schools and seminars. Offers human resource development consulting services, including needs analysis and program design, evaluation, and implementation. **Scope:** A research and management consulting organization specializing in insurance marketing. Company research services apply scientific techniques to the areas of performance appraisal, manpower utilization, employee and consumer opinion sampling, and market analysis. Management consultation services include strategic planning, field cost controls and a computer modeling service. Also offers financial services consulting including defining distribution strategy, developing a distribution channel, organizational development and operations consulting. **Founded:** 1916. **Subscriptions:** 6000 archival material books periodicals. **Publications:** "28 Ways to Improve Your Sales Performance"; "Advanced Selection Interview Guide"; "LIMRA's Market Facts"; "Looking Ahead"; "Cross Selling". **Educational Activities:** LIMRA International Conference (Annual). **Seminars:** Compensation and Motivation Plans that Deliver Results, Bangkok, Aug, 2009; Sales Compensation Seminar, Simsbury, May, 2009; Growth by Design; Strategic Marketing Review. **Telecommunication Services:** customer.service@limra.com. **Special Services:** Career Profile.

8037 ■ National Association of Personal Financial Advisors (NAPFA)
3250 N Arlington Heights Rd., Ste. 109
Arlington Heights, IL 60004
Ph: (847)483-5400

Free: 800-366-2732
Fax: (847)483-5415
Co. E-mail: info@napfa.org
URL: http://www.napfa.org
Contact: Susan M. John, Chairwoman
Description: Full-time, fee-only financial planners. Serves as a network for fee-only planners to discuss issues relating to practice management, client services, and investments selection. Works to encourage and advance the practice of fee-only financial planning by developing the skills of members and increasing the awareness of fee-only financial planning of consumers. **Founded:** 1983. **Publications:** *NAPFA Advisor* (Monthly); *NAPFA Membership Directory* (Annual); *NAPFA NewsLink* (Bimonthly). **Educational Activities:** National Association of Personal Financial Advisors National Conference. **Awards:** Special Membership Award; Special Achievement Award; Distinguished Service Award (Annual); Special Membership Award (Annual); Robert J. Underwood Distinguished Service Award.

8038 ■ Newsline
601, 67 Yonge St.
Toronto, ON, Canada M5E 1J8
Ph: (416)364-8200
Fax: (416)364-2805
Co. E-mail: enquiries@ciri.org
URL: http://www.ciri.org
Contact: Tom Enright, President
Released: Bimonthly

8039 ■ Rebuilding Success
277 Wellington St. W
Toronto, ON, Canada M5V 3H2
Ph: (416)204-3242
Fax: (416)204-3410
Co. E-mail: info@cairp.ca
URL: http://www.cairp.ca
Contact: Guylaine Houle, Chairperson
Released: Semiannual

DIRECTORIES OF EDUCATIONAL PROGRAMS

8040 ■ The Canadian Book of Charities: The Guide to Intelligent Giving
Pub: Mavora Publications Inc.
Contact: Yvonne Trapman, Director
URL(s): www.canadian-charities.com. **Ed:** Yvette Vali. **Released:** Annual; Latest edition 2008. **Price:** $24.95, Single issue including taxes and shipping. **Covers:** Charitable organizations throughout Canada; information on giving charitable gifts; tax treatment of charitable donations; and more. **Entries include:** Contact information. **Arrangement:** Alphabetical, regional.

REFERENCE WORKS

8041 ■ "3Par: Storing Up Value" in Barron's (Vol. 90, August 30, 2010, No. 35, pp. 30)
Pub: Barron's Editorial & Corporate Headquarters
Ed: Mark Veverka. **Description:** Dell and Hewlett Packard are both bidding for data storage company 3Par. The acquisition would help both Dell and Hewlett Packard provide customers with a one-stop shop as customers move to a private cloud in the Internet.

8042 ■ "13D Filings" in Barron's (Vol. 88, March 24, 2008, No. 12, pp. M13)
Pub: Dow Jones & Company, Inc.
Description: HealthCor Management called as problematic the plan of Magellan Health Services to use its high cash balances for acquisitions. Carlson Capital discussed with Energy Partners possible changes in the latter's board. Investor Carl Icahn suggested that Enzon Pharmaceuticals consider selling itself or divest some of its assets.

8043 ■ "13D Filings" in Barron's (Vol. 88, March 10, 2008, No. 10, pp. M11)
Pub: Dow Jones & Company, Inc.
Description: Barington Capital and Clinton Group sent a letter to Dillard's demanding a list of the company's stockholders. Elliott Associates an-

nounced that it is prepared to take over Packeteer for $5.50 a share. Strongbow capital suggested a change in leadership in Duckwall-ALCO Stores.

8044 ■ "13D Filings: Investors Report to the SEC" in Barron's (Vol. 88, March 31, 2008, No. 13, pp. M10)
Pub: Dow Jones & Company, Inc.
Description: Obrem Capital Management wants Micrel to rescind Micrel's shareholder-rights plan and to boost its board to six members from five. Patricia L. Childress plans to nominate herself to the board of Sierra Bancorp, and Luther King Capital Management may consider a competing acquisition proposal for Industrial Distribution Group.

8045 ■ "13D Filings: Investors Report to the SEC" in Barron's (Vol. 88, March 17, 2008, No. 11, pp. M11)
Pub: Dow Jones & Company, Inc.
Description: Nanes Delorme wants Vaalco Energy to keep an investment bank to start an open-bid process to sell the company. West Creek Capital plans to nominate two directors at the 2008 annual meeting of the Capital Senior Living just as ValueVest Management wants to nominate the same number of people at Ampex's annual meeting.

8046 ■ "13D Filings: Investors Report to the SEC" in Barron's (Vol. 89, July 13, 2009, No. 28, pp. M9)
Pub: Dow Jones & Co., Inc.
Description: Bulldog Investors wants Hicks Acquisition Co. to liquidate and return money to shareholders and they believe that the acquisition of Graham Packaging by Hicks will not be completed in a timely manner. Discovery Group raised their holdings to 5.2 percent of Nobel Learning Communities.

8047 ■ "13D Filings: Investors Report to the SEC" in Barron's (Vol. 89, July 27, 2009, No. 30, pp. M14)
Pub: Dow Jones & Co., Inc.
Description: Duquesne Capital Management is opposed to Alpha Natural Resources' proposed merger with Foundation Coal Holdings since it is against the long-term interest of shareholders. Lime Rock Partners increased their holdings of Tesco to 5,234,516 shares while Nova A/S increased their holdings of BioMimetic Therapeutics to 3,729,065 shares.

8048 ■ "A 16-Year Housing Slump? It Could Happen" in Barron's (Vol. 88, March 17, 2008, No. 11, pp. 27)
Pub: Dow Jones & Company, Inc.
Ed: Gene Epstein. **Description:** Housing remains a good protection against inflation but over very long periods. Inflation-adjusted stock prices did even better but have greater volatility. Commodities, on the other hand, underperformed both housing and stocks as inflation hedges. House prices tend to rise faster than the consumer price index is because land is inherently limited.

8049 ■ "75 Most Powerful Blacks on Wall Street" in Black Enterprise (Vol. 37, October 2006, No. 3, pp. 136)
Pub: Earl G. Graves Publishing Co. Inc.
Ed: Carolyn M. Brown. **Description:** Profiles of seventy-five African American top executives. The listing is a compilation of the brightest and best venture capitalists, asset managers, CEOs, traders, and investment bankers.

8050 ■ "The 100 Most Bullish Stocks" in Canadian Business (Vol. 81, Summer 2008, No. 9, pp. 81)
Pub: Rogers Media Ltd.
Ed: Megan Harman; Lauren McKeon. **Description:** 100 of the most bullish stocks are taken from the list of the 500 best-performing stocks. The idea is to narrow the list help investors in their investment decisions since it is difficult to choose from a large list. Analysts rate the companies with 5 being the most bullish and 1 the least. Other details of the roster are presented.

8051 ■ *"401(k) Keys to Stable Value"* in *Barron's (Vol. 88, March 10, 2008, No. 10, pp. 40)*

Pub: Dow Jones & Company, Inc.

Ed: Tom Sullivan. **Description:** Stable-value funds offer investors stability in a period of volatility in financial markets, attracting $888 million in funds. The Securities and Exchange Commission approved the launch of actively managed exchange-traded funds.

8052 ■ *"2008: Year of the Rat Race"* in *Mergers & Acquisitions: The Dealmaker's Journal (March 1, 2008)*

Pub: SourceMedia, Inc.

Ed: Danelle Fugazy. **Description:** Although China still presents opportunities to Western investors, many are discovering that much more research needs to be done concerning doing business in that country before investing there becomes truly mainstream. According to one source, there are at least 300,000 small state-owned enterprises in China and millions of middle-market privately owned companies; the Chinese stock market can only handle about 50 to 70 IPOs a year and lists about 1,500 companies at a time.

8053 ■ *Access to Finance*

Pub: Brookings Institution Press

Ed: Barr. **Released:** December 2006. **Price:** $39.95. **Description:** Challenges to help make financial systems more inclusive to promote successful venture in new markets while utilizing new technologies and government policies to expand financial access to smaller companies.

8054 ■ *"ACE Agrees to Pay Out $266 Million to Investors"* in *Globe & Mail (February 17, 2006, pp. B1)*

Pub: CTVglobemedia Publishing Inc.

Ed: Brent Jang. **Description:** Canada-based commercial aviation firm ACE Aviation Holdings has agreed to pay 266 million dollars to its investors after filing a bankruptcy one year ago. Complete details of this pay off are discussed.

8055 ■ *"ACE Back in Unfriendly Skies"* in *Globe & Mail (February 14, 2006, pp. B17)*

Pub: CTVglobemedia Publishing Inc.

Ed: Brent Jang. **Description:** ACE Aviation Holdings Inc. reported $258 million profit for 2005. The opinions of analysts on the share price of the company for 2006 are presented.

8056 ■ *"Advance America Closing All Pa. Stores"* in *American Banker (Vol. 172, December 20, 2007, No. 244, pp. 11)*

Pub: SourceMedia Inc.

Ed: William Launder. **Description:** Advance America Cash Advance Centers Inc. is closing its 66 locations in Pennsylvania while it awaits a state Supreme Court ruling about the excessively high fees it carries for loan products.

8057 ■ *"Advertising May Take a Big Hit in Southwest/AirTran Merger"* in *Baltimore Business Journal (Vol. 28, October 1, 2010, No. 21, pp. 1)*

Pub: Baltimore Business Journal

Ed: Gary Haber. **Description:** Advertising on television stations and the publishing industry in Baltimore could drop as a result of the merger between rival discount airlines Southwest Airlines and AirTran Airways. Southwest is among the top advertisers in the U.S., spending $126 million in 2009. No local jobs are expected to be affected because neither airline uses a local advertising firm.

8058 ■ *"After Price Cuts, Competition GPS Makers Lose Direction"* in *Brandweek (Vol. 49, April 21, 2008, No. 16, pp. 16)*

Pub: VNU Business Media, Inc.

Ed: Steve Miller. **Description:** Garmin and TomTom, two of the leaders in portable navigation devices, have seen lowering revenues due to dramatic price cuts and unexpected competition from the broadening availability of personal navigation on mobile phones. TomTom has trimmed its sales outlook for its first quarter while Garmin's stock dropped 40 percent since February.

8059 ■ *"Ag Firms Harvest Revenue Growth"* in *The Business Journal-Serving Metropolitan Kansas City (Vol. 26, July 18, 2008, No. 45, pp. 1)*

Pub: American City Business Journals, Inc.

Ed: Steve Vockrodt. **Description:** Five of the biggest agricultural companies in the Kansas City area, except one, reported multibillion-dollar revenue increases in 2007. The companies, which include Lansing Trade Group, posted a combined $9.5 billion revenue growth. The factors that affected the revenue increase in the area's agricultural companies, such as prices and high demand, are also examined.

8060 ■ *"AIG Fixed; Is Michigan Next?"* in *Crain's Detroit Business (Vol. 24, September 22, 2008, No. 38, pp. 1)*

Pub: Crain Communications Inc.

Ed: Jay Greene. **Description:** Michigan's economic future is examined as is the mortgage buyout plan and American International Group Inc.'s takeover by the U.S. government.

8061 ■ *"Air Canada Boss Gains $3.5 Million in Options"* in *Globe & Mail (January 19, 2007, pp. B5)*

Pub: CTVglobemedia Publishing Inc.

Ed: Brent Jang. **Description:** Air Canada chairman Robert Milton's sale of 200,000 shares in stock options is discussed.

8062 ■ *"Algoma Resolves Hedge Fund Fight"* in *Globe & Mail (March 8, 2006, pp. B1)*

Pub: CTVglobemedia Publishing Inc.

Ed: Greg Keenan. **Description:** Algoma Steel Inc. has ended a dispute with Paulson and Co., a New York hedge fund, by offering to pay $200 million special dividend, appointing new directors, and continue to go for a sale.

8063 ■ *"Algoma Shares Soar on Growing Sale Rumors"* in *Globe & Mail (February 13, 2007, pp. B1)*

Pub: CTVglobemedia Publishing Inc.

Ed: Andrew Willis; Greg Keenan. **Description:** The stock prices of Algoma Steel Inc. have touched record high of $40 on the Toronto Stock Exchange. The growing rumors about the possible takeover bid is the major reason for the stock price growth.

8064 ■ *"All Eyes On Iris"* in *Canadian Business (Vol. 81, July 22, 2008, No. 12-13, pp. 20)*

Pub: Rogers Media Ltd.

Ed: Jack Mintz. **Description:** Provincial governments in Canada are believed to be awaiting Alberta Finance Minister Iris Evans' financial and investment policies as well as Evans' development of a new saving strategy. Alberta is the only Canadian province that is in position to invest in sovereign wealth funds after it eliminated its debt in 2005.

8065 ■ *"All Revved Up"* in *Barron's (Vol. 90, September 13, 2010, No. 37, pp. 18)*

Pub: Barron's Editorial & Corporate Headquarters

Ed: Christopher C. Williams. **Description:** Shares of Advance Auto Parts has returned 55 percent in a span of three years and the stock could still reach the mid-60s by 2011 from its price of 46.07 in the second week of September 2010. The shares are trading at just 13 times the 2011 earnings.

8066 ■ *"All-Star Advice 2010"* in *Black Enterprise (Vol. 41, October 2010, No. 3, pp. 97)*

Pub: Earl G. Graves Publishing Co. Inc.

Ed: Renita Burns, Sheiresa Ngo, Marcia Wade Talbert. **Description:** Financial experts share tips on real estate, investing, taxes, insurance and debt management.

8067 ■ *"Amit Wadhwaney"* in *Canadian Business (Vol. 80, March 12, 2007, No. 6, pp. 22)*

Pub: Rogers Media

Ed: Rachel Pulfer. **Description:** Manager of Third Avenue International Value Fund, Amit Wadhwaney, shares his views on buying Canadian agricultural and forestry stocks.

8068 ■ *"Analysts Not Fazed By Constellation's Halt to New Nuclear Plants"* in *Baltimore Business Journal (Vol. 28, October 22, 2010, No. 24)*

Pub: Baltimore Business Journal

Ed: Scott Dance. **Description:** Wall Street analysts believe that Constellation Energy Group Inc.'s decision to pull out of the nuclear construction business would not change their outlook on the company. New nuclear power had been one of Constellation's long-term goals, but the company pulled the plug on the project. It is believed that most investors were not expecting any payoff from the venture.

8069 ■ *"And In This Briefcase"* in *Mergers & Acquisitions: The Dealmaker's Journal (March 1, 2008)*

Pub: SourceMedia, Inc.

Description: ACG San Diego decided to address the impact the changes in the economy will have on potential private equity transactions as well as what criteria private equity firms are looking for when assessing a company. At the opening of the chapter's 2008 breakfast meeting, real-world case studies were utilized with the audiences' participation in order to assess pre-deal risk scenarios.

8070 ■ *"The Annual Entitlement Lecture: Trustees of Medicare and Social Security Issue Another Dismal Report"* in *Barron's (March 31, 2008)*

Pub: Dow Jones & Company, Inc.

Ed: Thomas G. Donlan. **Description:** Expenditures on Medicare hospital insurance and the revenues available to pay for it have led to a gap of capital valued at $38.6 trillion. Slashing the benefits or raising taxes will not solve the gap which exists unless the government saves the money and invests it in private markets.

8071 ■ *"Apartment Tower in River North Fetches More Than $90 Million"* in *Crain's Chicago Business (Vol. 34, October 24, 2011, No. 42, pp. 17)*

Pub: Crain Communications Inc.

Ed: Alby Gallun. **Description:** Apartment tower in River North was sold for over $90 million to a Texas pension fund adviser. Details are included.

8072 ■ *"Are You Ready for Dow 20,000?"* in *Barron's (Vol. 88, March 24, 2008, No. 12, pp. 26)*

Pub: Dow Jones & Company, Inc.

Ed: Jonathan R. Laing. **Description:** Stock strategist James Finucane forecasts that the Dow Jones Industrial Average will rise from its 12,361 level to as high as 20,000 from 2008 to 2009. He believes that stock liquidation and a buildup of cash provide the perfect conditions for a huge rally.

8073 ■ *"As Capital Gains Tax Hike Looms, Merger Activity Percolates"* in *Baltimore Business Journal (Vol. 28, August 27, 2010, No. 16, pp. 1)*

Pub: Baltimore Business Journal

Ed: Scott Dance. **Description:** Concerns for higher capital gains taxes in 2011 have been provoking buyers and sellers to engage in mergers and acquisitions activity, which is expected to gain momentum before the end of 2010. Companies that had saved cash during the recession have been taking advantage of the buyer's market. Other trends in local and national mergers and acquisitions activity are presented.

8074 ■ *"Asia Breathes a Sigh of Relief"* in *Business Week (September 22, 2008, No. 4100, pp. 32)*

Pub: McGraw-Hill Companies, Inc.

Ed: Bruce Einhorn; Theo Francis; Chi-Chu Tschang; Moon Ihlwan; Hiroko Tashiro. **Description:** Foreign bankers, such as those in Asia, that had been investing heavily in the United States began to worry as the housing crisis deepened and the impact on Freddie Mac and Fannie Mae became increasingly clear. Due to the government bailout, however, central banks will most likely continue to buy American debt.

8075 ■ *"ATS Secures Investment From Goldman Sachs"* in *The Business Journal - Serving Phoenix and the Valley of the Sun (Vol. 29, September 26, 2008, No. 4, pp. 1)*
Pub: American City Business Journals, Inc.
Ed: Patrick O'Grady. **Description:** Goldman Sachs made an investment to American Traffic Solutions Inc. (ATS) which will allow it to gain two seats on the board of the red-light and speed cameras maker. The investment will help ATS maintain its rapid growth which is at 83 percent over the past 18 months leading up to September 2008.

8076 ■ *"Attend To Your Corporate Housekeeping"* in *Women Entrepreneur (December 4, 2008)*
Pub: Entrepreneur Media Inc.
Ed: Nina Kaufman. **Description:** Business owners can lose all the benefits and privileges of the corporate form if they do not follow proper corporate formalities such as holding an annual meeting, electing officers and directors and adopting or passing corporate resolutions. Creditors are able to take from one's personal assets if such formalities have not been followed.

8077 ■ *"Au Revoir Or Goodbye?"* in *Barron's (Vol. 88, July 14, 2008, No. 28, pp. 5)*
Pub: Dow Jones & Co., Inc.
Ed: Alan Abelson. **Description:** Former Senator Phil Gramm's opinion that the U.S. is a 'nation of whiners' as they moan about recession is another example of the disconnection between Washington and Wall Street on one hand and the real world on the other. It would be a catastrophe for most of the world if Fannie Mae and Freddie Mac were to go under and take their trillions of mortgage debt with them.

8078 ■ *"Auction-Rate Cash Frees Up"* in *The Business Journal-Portland (Vol. 25, August 15, 2008, No. 23, pp. 1)*
Pub: American City Business Journals, Inc.
Ed: Aliza Earnshaw. **Description:** FEI Co. and RadiSys Corp. have received notices that UBS AG will buy back the auction-rate securities that were sold to them in around two years from 2008. FEI had $110.1 million invested in auction-rate securities while RadiSys holds $62.8 million of these securities.

8079 ■ *"Auto Supplier Stock Battered In Wake Of Wall Street Woes"* in *Crain's Detroit Business (Vol. 24, September 29, 2008, No. 39, pp. 4)*
Pub: Crain Communications Inc.
Ed: Ryan Beene. **Description:** Due to the volatility of the stock market and public perception of the $700 billion banking bailout, auto suppliers are now facing a dramatic drop in their shares. Statistical data included.

8080 ■ *"BABs in Bond Land"* in *Barron's (Vol. 89, July 6, 2009, No. 27, pp. 14)*
Pub: Dow Jones & Co., Inc.
Ed: Jim McTague. **Description:** American Recovery and Reinvestment Act has created taxable Build America Bonds (BAB) to finance new construction projects. The issuance of the two varieties of taxable BABs is expected to benefit the municipal bond market.

8081 ■ *"Back in the Race"* in *Barron's (Vol. 88, March 17, 2008, No. 11, pp. 43)*
Pub: Dow Jones & Company, Inc.
Ed: Leslie P. Norton. **Description:** Katherine Schapiro was able to get Sentinel International Equity's Morningstar classification to blended fund from a value fund rating after joining Sentinel from her former jobs at Strong Overseas Fund. Schapiro aims to benefit from the global rebalancing as the U.S.'s share of the world economy shrinks.

8082 ■ *"Back on Track-Or Off the Rails?"* in *Business Week (September 22, 2008, No. 4100, pp. 22)*
Pub: McGraw-Hill Companies, Inc.
Ed: Peter Coy; Tara Kalwarski. **Description:** Discusses the possible scenarios the American economy may undergo due to the takeover of Fannie Mae and Freddie Mac. Statistical data included.

8083 ■ *"Bad-Loan Bug Bites Mid-Tier Banks; More Pain, Tighter Lending Standards Ahead, CEOs Say"* in *Crain's Chicago Business (May 5, 2008)*
Pub: Crain Communications, Inc.
Ed: Steve Daniels. **Description:** Mid-sized commercial banks form the bedrock of Chicago's financial-services industry and they are now feeling the results of the credit crisis that has engulfed the nation's largest banks and brokerages. Commercial borrowers are seeing tighter terms on loans and higher interest rates while bank investors are unable to forecast lenders' earnings performance from quarter to quarter. Statistical data included.

8084 ■ *"Bad Loans Start Piling Up"* in *Crain's New York Business (Vol. 24, January 7, 2008, No. 1, pp. 2)*
Pub: Crain Communications, Inc.
Ed: Tom Fredrickson. **Description:** Problems in the subprime mortgage industry have extended to other lending activities as evidenced by bank charge-offs on bad commercial and industrial loans which have more than doubled in the third quarter.

8085 ■ *Bad Money*
Pub: Viking Press/Penguin Group
Ed: Kevin Phillips. **Released:** April 15, 2008. **Description:** How the financial sector has hijacked the American economy, aided by Washington's ruinous faith in the efficiency of markets.

8086 ■ *"Bad Paper"* in *Canadian Business (Vol. 80, November 19, 2007, No. 23, pp. 34)*
Pub: Rogers Media
Ed: Al Rosen. **Description:** The Canadian government froze the market for non-bank asset-backed commercial paper (ABCP) August 2007, which means holders will be unable to withdraw investments. The crisis and value of ABCP are discussed.

8087 ■ *"Bailout Forgets the 'Little Guys"* in *The Business Journal-Milwaukee (Vol. 25, September 26, 2008, No. 53, pp. A1)*
Pub: American City Business Journals, Inc.
Ed: Rich Kirchen. **Description:** Community Bankers of Wisconsin and the Wisconsin Bankers Association are urging members to approach congressional representatives and remind them to include local banks in building the $700 billion bailout plan. WBA president and CEO Kurt Bauer thinks that it is only fair to include smaller institutions in the bailout. The initial bailout plan and its benefit for the smaller banks are examined.

8088 ■ *"Bailout May Force Cutbacks, Job Losses"* in *The Business Journal - Serving Phoenix and the Valley of the Sun (Vol. 29, September 26, 2008, No. 4, pp. 1)*
Pub: American City Business Journals, Inc.
Ed: Mike Sunnucks. **Description:** Economists say the proposed $700 billion bank bailout could affect Arizona businesses as banks could be forced to reduce the amount and number of loans it has thereby forcing businesses to shrink capital expenditures and then jobs. However, the plan could also stimulate the economy by taking bad loans off banks balance sheets according to another economist.

8089 ■ *"BancVue to Expand"* in *Austin Business JournalInc. (Vol. 29, November 27, 2009, No. 38, pp. 1)*
Pub: American City Business Journals
Ed: Kate Harrington. **Description:** Significant growth of BancVue in the past six years has prompted the company to look for a site that could increase its office space from 25,000 square feet to 65,000 square feet. BancVue offers bank and credit union software solutions and is planning to lease or buy a property in Austin, Texas.

8090 ■ *"Bank Bullish on Austin"* in *Austin Business JournalInc. (Vol. 29, November 13, 2009, No. 36, pp. A1)*
Pub: American City Business Journals
Ed: Kate Harrington. **Description:** American Bank's presence in Austin, Texas has been boosted by new management and a new 20,000 square foot building. This community bank intends to focus on building

relationship with commercial banking customers. American Bank also plans to extend investment banking, treasury management, and commercial lending services.

8091 ■ *"Bank Forces Brooke Founder To Sell His Holdings"* in *The Business Journal-Serving Metropolitan Kansas City (October 10, 2008)*
Pub: American City Business Journals, Inc.
Ed: James Dornbrook. **Description:** Robert Orr who is the founder of Brooke Corp., a franchise of insurance agencies, says that he was forced to sell virtually all of his stocks in the company by creditors. First United Bank held the founder's stock as collateral for two loans worth $5 million and $7.9 million, which were declared in default in September 2008. Details of the selling of the company's stocks are provided.

8092 ■ *"Bank on It"* in *Hawaii Business (Vol. 53, November 2007, No. 5, pp. 60)*
Pub: Hawaii Business Publishing
Ed: Kathleen Bryan. **Description:** Many Baby Boomers that are preparing to retire would like to give back and make a difference. One way is to make gifts of Individual Retirement Assets (IRA). During 2007 people over 70 years can make withdrawals from an IRA and donate it without realizing the income as taxable.

8093 ■ *"Bank Sticks to Rate Rise Script but 'Modest' is the Salient Word"* in *Globe & Mail (January 25, 2006, pp. B5)*
Pub: CTVglobemedia Publishing Inc.
Ed: Heather Scoffield. **Description:** The reasons behind the decision of Bank of Canada to increase interest rate, which is posted at 3.5 percent, are presented.

8094 ■ *"Banking Bailout: Boost or Bust?"* in *Crain's Detroit Business (Vol. 24, September 29, 2008, No. 39, pp. 1)*
Pub: Crain Communications Inc.
Ed: Amy Lane. **Description:** Economic insiders discuss the banking bailout and how it might impact the state of Michigan.

8095 ■ *"Banking Crisis Rattles Local Businesses"* in *Puget Sound Business Journal (Vol. 29, October 10, 2008, No. 25, pp. 1)*
Pub: American City Business Journals
Ed: Kirsten Grind. **Description:** Customers of Washington Mutual in the Puget Sound region started withdrawing large sums of cash due to fears of the banks unstable condition.

8096 ■ *"A Banking Play Without Banking Plagues"* in *Barron's (Vol. 88, March 31, 2008, No. 13, pp. 26)*
Pub: Dow Jones & Company, Inc.
Ed: Jack Willoughby. **Description:** Fiserv's shares have been dragged down by about 20 percent which presents an appealing entry point since the shares could rise by 30 percent or more by 2009. The company enables banks to post and open new checks and keeps track of loans which are not discretionary processes of banks.

8097 ■ *"Banking on Twitter"* in *Baltimore Business Journal (Vol. 27, February 6, 2010, No. 40, pp. 1)*
Pub: American City Business Journals
Ed: Gary Haber. **Description:** Ways that banks are using Twitter, Facebook and other social networking sites to provide customer services is discussed. First Mariner Bank is one of those banks that are finding the social media platform as a great way to reach customers. Privacy issues regarding this marketing trend are examined.

8098 ■ *"The Bankrate Double Pay"* in *Barron's (Vol. 88, March 24, 2008, No. 12, pp. 27)*
Pub: Dow Jones & Company, Inc.
Ed: Neil A. Martin. **Description:** Shares of Bankrate may rise as much as 25 percent from their level of $45.08 a share due to a strong cash flow and bal-

ance sheet. The company's Internet business remains strong despite weakness in the online advertising industry and is a potential takeover target.

8099 ■ *"Bankruptcies Shoot Up 68 Percent"* in Sacramento Business Journal (Vol. 25, July 18, 2008, No. 20, pp. 1)
Pub: American City Business Journals, Inc.
Ed: Kathy Robertson. **Description:** Personal bankruptcy in the Sacramento area rose by 88 percent for the first half of 2008 while business bankruptcies rose by 50 percent for the same period. The numbers of consumer bankruptcy reflects the effect of high debt, rising mortgage costs, and declining home values on U.S. households.

8100 ■ *"Bankruptcy Blowback"* in Business Week (September 22, 2008, No. 4100, pp. 36)
Pub: McGraw-Hill Companies, Inc.
Ed: Jessica Silver-Greenberg. **Description:** Changes to bankruptcy laws which were enacted in 2005 after banks and other financial institutions lobbied hard for them are now suffering the consequences of the laws which force more troubled borrowers to let their homes go into foreclosure; lenders suffer financially every time they have to take on a foreclosure and the laws in which they lobbied so hard to see enacted are now becoming a problem for these lending institutions. Details of the changes in the laws are outlined as are the affects on the consumer, the economy and the lenders.

8101 ■ *"Banks Fall Short in Online Services for Savvy Traders"* in Barron's (Vol. 88, March 17, 2008, No. 11, pp. 35)
Pub: Dow Jones & Company, Inc.
Ed: Theresa W. Carey. **Description:** Banc of America Investment Services, WellsTrade, and ShareBuilder are at the bottom of the list of online brokerages because they offer less trading technologies and product range. Financial shoppers miss out on a lot of customized tools and analytics when using these services.

8102 ■ *"Banks Fret About Gist Of Bailout"* in The Business Journal-Serving Metropolitan Kansas City (Vol. 27, September 26, 2008, No. 2)
Pub: American City Business Journals, Inc.
Ed: James Dornbrook. **Description:** Banks from the Kansas City area hope that the proposed $700 billion bailout will not send the wrong message. UMB Financial Corp. chairman says that he hopes that the bailout would benefit companies that were more risk restrained and punish those that took outsized risk. Other bank executives' perceptions on the planned bailout are given.

8103 ■ *"Banks Seeing Demand for Home Equity Loans Slowing"* in Crain's Cleveland Business (Vol. 28, December 3, 2007, No. 48, pp. 1)
Pub: Crain Communications, Inc.
Ed: Shawn A. Turner. **Description:** Discusses the reasons for the decline in demand for home equity loans and lines of credit. Statistical data included.

8104 ■ *"Barbarians Set Bar Low With Lowly Canadian Telco"* in Globe & Mail (March 31, 2007, pp. B1)
Pub: CTVglobemedia Publishing Inc.
Ed: Derek DeCloet. **Description:** The efforts of the private equity fund Kohlberg, Kravis, Roberts and Co. to acquire the Canadian telecommunications firm BCE are described.

8105 ■ *"Bargain Hunting In Vietnam"* in Barron's (Vol. 88, July 14, 2008, No. 28, pp. M6)
Pub: Dow Jones & Co., Inc.
Ed: Elliot Wilson. **Description:** Vietnam's economy grew by just 6.5 percent for the first half of 2008 and its balance of payments ballooned to $14.4 billion. The falling stock prices in the country is a boon for bargain hunters and investing in the numerous domestic funds is one way of investing in the country. Some shares that investors are taking an interest in are also discussed.

8106 ■ *"Barron's Lipper Fund Listings"* in Barron's (Vol. 89, July 13, 2009, No. 28, pp. 19)
Pub: Dow Jones & Co., Inc.
Description: Statistical tables are presented which show the assets and return of mutual funds up to a ten year period. The listing covers funds with at least $200 million in assets.

8107 ■ *"BASF Launches $4.9 Billion Bid for Rival Engelhard"* in Globe & Mail (January 4, 2006, pp. B7)
Pub: CTVglobemedia Publishing Inc.
Ed: Mike Esterl; Steve Levine. **Description:** The plans of BASF AG, to acquire Engelhard Corp. for $4.9 billion, are presented.

8108 ■ *"Battered U.S. Auto Makers in Grip of Deeper Sales Slump"* in Globe & Mail (April 4, 2007, pp. B1)
Pub: CTVglobemedia Publishing Inc.
Ed: Greg Keenan. **Description:** The fall in Canadian sales and market share of Ford Motor Co., General Motors Corp. and Chrysler Group is discussed.

8109 ■ *"Battle of the Titans"* in Canadian Business (Vol. 81, March 17, 2008, No. 4, pp. 15)
Pub: Rogers Media
Ed: Rachel Pulfer. **Description:** Regulatory authorities in Canada gave Thomson Corp and Reuters Group PLC the permission to go ahead with their merger. The merged companies could eclipse Bloomberg LP's market share of 33 percent. Authorities also required Thomson and Reuters to sell some of their databases to competitors.

8110 ■ *"BCE's Aliant Trust Spinoff Valued at About $8.5 Billion"* in Globe & Mail (March 8, 2006, pp. B1)
Pub: CTVglobemedia Publishing Inc.
Ed: Catherine McLean. **Description:** The details pertaining to the spinoff of Aliant Inc.'s landline business into an income trust by BCE Inc. are presented. The trust is valued at $8.5 billion.

8111 ■ *"BDC Launches New Online Business Advice Centre"* in Internet Wire (July 13, 2010)
Pub: Comtex
Description: The Business Development Bank of Canada (BDC) offers entrepreneurs the chance to use their new online BDC Advice Centre to seek advice regarding the challenges of entrepreneurship. Free online business tools and information to help both startups and established firms are also provided.

8112 ■ *"The Bear Arrives - With Bargain Hunters"* in Barron's (Vol. 88, July 7, 2008, No. 27, pp. M3)
Pub: Dow Jones & Co., Inc.
Ed: Kopin Tan. **Description:** US stock markets have dropped 20 percent below their highs, entering the bear market at the end of June 2008. It was also the worst performance of the stock markets during June. Wine maker Constellation Brands, however, reported a 50 percent rise in net income for the first quarter of 2008.

8113 ■ *"Bear Market Tough On Investors"* in The Business Journal-Milwaukee (Vol. 25, July 4, 2008, No. 41, pp. A1)
Pub: American City Business Journals, Inc.
Ed: Rich Kirchen. **Description:** Public companies and their investors in the Milwaukee area suffered as the bear market took hold of the Wisconsin stock market. There were 18 stocks out of the 36 publicly traded stocks that have fallen into the bear market, meaning a 20 percent decline from the market peak in the fall of 2007. The impacts of the bear market on investors are evaluated.

8114 ■ *"The Bear's Back"* in Barron's (Vol. 88, July 7, 2008, No. 27, pp. 17)
Pub: Dow Jones & Co., Inc.
Ed: Randall W. Forsyth; Vito Racanelli. **Description:** US stock markets have formally entered the bear market after the Dow Jones Industrial Average

dropped 20 percent from its high as of June 2008. Investors remain uncertain as to how long the bear market will persist, especially with the US economy on the edge of recession.

8115 ■ *"The Beauty of Banking's Big Ugly"* in Barron's (Vol. 89, July 27, 2009, No. 30, pp. 31)
Pub: Dow Jones & Co., Inc.
Ed: Andrew Bary. **Description:** Appeal of the shares of Citigroup comes from its sharp discount to its tangible book value and the company's positive attributes include a strong capital position, high loan-loss reserves, and their appealing global-consumer. The shares have the potential to generate nice profits and decent stock gains as the economy turns.

8116 ■ *"Behind the Numbers: When It Comes to Earnings, Look for Quality, Not Just Quantity"* in Black Enterprise (July 2008, pp. 35)
Pub: Earl G. Graves Publishing Co. Inc.
Ed: Chris Keenan. **Description:** It is important for investors to examine the quality of a company's earnings rather than fixate on the quantity of those earnings. Advice is given regarding issues investors can look at when trying to determine the potential growth of a firm.

8117 ■ *"Bertha's Birth Stirs Juice"* in Barron's (Vol. 88, July 14, 2008, No. 28, pp. M11)
Pub: Dow Jones & Co., Inc.
Ed: Tom Sellen. **Description:** Price of frozen concentrated orange juice, which has risen to four-month highs of $1.3620 in July 2008 is due, in part, to the hurricane season that has come earlier than normal in the far eastern Atlantic thereby possibly harming the 2008-2009 Florida orange crop. Future tropical-storm development will affect the prices of this commodity.

8118 ■ *"Best Cash Flow Generators"* in Canadian Business (Vol. 81, Summer 2008, No. 9, pp. 73)
Pub: Rogers Media Ltd.
Ed: Calvin Leung. **Description:** Table showing the five-year annualized growth rate and one-year stock performance of companies that have grown their cash flow per share at an annualized rate of 15 percent or more over the past five years. Analysts project that the cash flow trend will continue. Other details of the stock performance index are presented.

8119 ■ *"Best Defensive Stocks"* in Canadian Business (Vol. 81, Summer 2008, No. 9, pp. 67)
Pub: Rogers Media Ltd.
Ed: Calvin Leung. **Description:** Stocks of the companies presented have market capitalization of greater than $1 billion and dividend gains of at least 2 percent. A table showing the average one-year total return of the stocks is provided.

8120 ■ *"The Best Five-Month Run Since 1938"* in Barron's (Vol. 89, August 3, 2009, No. 31, pp. M3)
Pub: Dow Jones & Co., Inc.
Ed: Kopin Tan. **Description:** US stock markets ended July 2009 registering the highest five-month rise since 1938. The shares of Cablevision could rise as the company simplifies its structure and spins off its Madison Square Garden unit. The shares of Potash Corp. could fall as the company faces lower earnings due to falling potash purchases.

8121 ■ *"Best Growth Stocks"* in Canadian Business (Vol. 81, Summer 2008, No. 9, pp. 61)
Pub: Rogers Media Ltd.
Ed: Calvin Leung. **Description:** Table showing the one-year performance of growth stocks is presented. Edmonton-based Stantec Inc. expects to advance its sales and profits by 15 percent to 20 percent per year through tapping international markets and acquisitions. Analysts forecast a 17.1 percent growth rate annually over the next 3 to 5 years.

8122 ■ "Best Growth Stocks" in Canadian Business (Vol. 82, Summer 2009, No. 8, pp. 28)
Pub: Rogers Media
Ed: Calvin Leung. **Description:** Canadian stocks that are considered as the best growth stocks, and whose price-earnings ratio is less than their earnings growth rate, are suggested. Suggestions include pharmaceutical firm Paladin Labs, which was found to have 13 consecutive years of revenue growth. Paladin Labs acquires or licenses niche drugs and markets them in Canada.

8123 ■ "Best Income Trust" in Canadian Business (Vol. 81, Summer 2008, No. 9, pp. 69)
Pub: Rogers Media Ltd.
Ed: Calvin Leung. **Description:** Table showing five-year annualized growth rate and one-year stock performance of real estate investment trusts firms in Canada is presented. Calgary-based Boardwalk REIT is projected to grow the fastest among North American REITs over the next two years. Other details on the stock performance analysis are presented.

8124 ■ "Best Managed Companies" in Canadian Business (Vol. 81, Summer 2008, No. 9, pp. 71)
Pub: Rogers Media Ltd.
Ed: Calvin Leung. **Description:** Table showing the five-year annualized growth rate and one-year stock performance of companies that have grown their cash flow per share at an annualized rate of 15 percent or more over the past five years. Analysts project that the cash flow trend will continue. Other details of the stock performance index are presented.

8125 ■ "Best Turnaround Stocks" in Canadian Business (Vol. 81, Summer 2008, No. 9, pp. 65)
Pub: Rogers Media Ltd.
Ed: Calvin Leung. **Description:** Share prices of Sierra Wireless Inc. and EXFO Electro Optical Engineering Inc. have fallen over the past year but have good chance at a rebound considering that the companies have free cash flow and no long-term debt. One-year stock performance analysis of the two companies is presented.

8126 ■ "Best Turnaround Stocks" in Canadian Business (Vol. 82, Summer 2009, No. 8, pp. 32)
Pub: Rogers Media
Ed: Calvin Leung. **Description:** Canadian companies that are believed to have the potential for the best turnaround stocks are presented. Suggested stocks include those of Migao Corporation, which is rated by most research firms as a Buy. Migao produces potash-based fertilizers for the Chinese market.

8127 ■ "Best Value Stocks" in Canadian Business (Vol. 81, Summer 2008, No. 9, pp. 63)
Pub: Rogers Media Ltd.
Ed: Calvin Leung. **Description:** Table showing the one-year performance of bargain or best-value stocks is presented. These stocks are undervalued compared to their North American peers, but it is projected that their five-year average return on equity is greater.

8128 ■ "Best Value Stocks" in Canadian Business (Vol. 82, Summer 2009, No. 8, pp. 30)
Pub: Rogers Media
Ed: Calvin Leung. **Description:** Canadian companies that are believed to have the best value stocks are suggested. Suggestions include publishing firm Glacier Media, which has reported a four-fold growth in sales in the last three years. While publishers like Glacier Media face challenges such as declining circulation, the firm's industry diversification is expected to help it weather the economic downturn.

8129 ■ "Bet on the Subcontinent" in Canadian Business (Vol. 81, April 14, 2008, No. 6, pp. 27)
Pub: Rogers Media
Ed: Calvin Leung. **Description:** Morgan Stanley Capital International India Index is down 28 percent for the first half of 2008 but this index rebounded 6 percent in 2002 then skyrocketed 65 percent in 2003. The economic reforms in the 1990's have created a growing middle class and households that can afford discretionary items will grow from eight million to 94 million by 2025. India's equity market could outperform developed markets if its economy grows at its current rate.

8130 ■ "Betting Big, Winning Big" in Barron's (Vol. 88, March 17, 2008, No. 11, pp. 49)
Pub: Dow Jones & Company, Inc.
Ed: Lawrence C. Strauss. **Description:** Bruce Berkowitz explains that the reason that his portfolio is concentrated is because getting more positions makes the portfolio more average compared to putting the money into your 10th or 20th-best idea. Berkowitz's picks include Berkshire Hathaway, Well-Care Health Plus, Sears Holdings, and Mohawk Industries.

8131 ■ "Betting on a Happy Ending" in Barron's (Vol. 88, July 7, 2008, No. 27, pp. 14)
Pub: Dow Jones & Co., Inc.
Ed: Dimitra DeFotis. **Description:** Shares of Time Warner, priced at $14.69 each, appear under-priced as financial analysts discount the value of the company. The company should be worth more than $20 a share as the company is spinning off Time Warner Cable.

8132 ■ "Betting On Volatile Materials" in Barron's (Vol. 88, July 14, 2008, No. 28, pp. M11)
Pub: Dow Jones & Co., Inc.
Ed: John Marshall. **Description:** Economic slowdowns in the U.S., Europe and China could cause sharp short-term declines in the materials sector. The S&P Materials sector is vulnerable to shifts in the flow of funds. Statistical data included.

8133 ■ "Beware this Chinese Export" in Barron's (Vol. 90, August 30, 2010, No. 35, pp. 21)
Pub: Barron's Editorial & Corporate Headquarters
Ed: Bill Alpert, Leslie P. Norton. **Description:** A look at 158 China reverse-merger stocks in the U.S. reveal that the median underperformed the index of U.S. listed Chinese companies by 75 percent in their first three years. These reverse merger stocks also lagged the Russell 2000 index of small cap stocks by 66 percent.

8134 ■ "Beware the Ides of March" in Canadian Business (Vol. 81, April 14, 2008, No. 6, pp. 13)
Pub: Rogers Media
Ed: Jeff Sanford. **Description:** Financial troubles of Bear Stearns in March, 2008 was part of the credit crunch that started in the summer of 2007 in the U.S. when subprime mortgages that were written for people who could barely afford the payments started defaulting. The bankruptcy protection given to 20 asset backed commercial paper trusts is being fought by the investors in these securities who could stand to lose 40 percent of their money under the agreement.

8135 ■ "Beware of Rotting Money" in Barron's (Vol. 89, July 13, 2009, No. 28, pp. 31)
Pub: Dow Jones & Co., Inc.
Ed: Thomas G. Donlan. **Description:** Inflation can take hold of a country and do it great harm; it is caused by people, most particularly central bankers in charge of the world's reserve currency. Arrogant economists pushed the belief that the government can engineer the economy and it is argued that there is trouble ahead when the government tries to control the economy.

8136 ■ "Beyond Microsoft and Yahoo!: Some M&A Prospects" in Barron's (Vol. 88, March 17, 2008, No. 11, pp. 39)
Pub: Dow Jones & Company, Inc.
Ed: Eric J. Savitz. **Description:** Weak quarterly earnings report for Yahoo! could pressure the company's board to cut a deal with Microsoft. Electronic Arts is expected to win its hostile $26-a-share bid for Take-Two Interactive Software. Potential targets and buyers for mergers and acquisitions are mentioned.

8137 ■ "The Big 50" in Canadian Business (Vol. 81, Summer 2008, No. 9, pp. 125)
Pub: Rogers Media Ltd.
Description: Large publicly held corporations are ranked based on market capitalization and stock performance. Potash Corp. of Saskatchewan topped the roster with 169.3 percent of return and even surpassing its 2007 result of 107 percent. A table showing the 2008 rankings of the companies is presented.

8138 ■ "Big Gains Brewing at Anheuser-Busch InBev" in Barron's (Vol. 90, August 30, 2010, No. 35, pp. 34)
Pub: Barron's Editorial & Corporate Headquarters
Ed: Christopher C. Williams. **Description:** Anheuser-Busch InBev is realizing cost synergies and it posted better than expected returns two years after the merger that formed the company. One analyst believes its American depositary receipt could be worth as much as 72 in a year.

8139 ■ "Big Trouble at Sony Ericsson" in Barron's (Vol. 88, March 24, 2008, No. 12, pp. M9)
Pub: Dow Jones & Company, Inc.
Ed: Angelo Franchini. **Description:** Sony Ericsson is facing trouble as it warned that its sales and net income before taxes will fall by nearly half for the first quarter of 2008. The joint venture of Sony and Ericsson has a global mobile phone market share of nine percent as of 2007, fourth largest in the world.

8140 ■ "Blackstone Set to Sell Stake" in Globe & Mail (March 17, 2007, pp. B6)
Pub: CTVglobemedia Publishing Inc.
Ed: Tennille Tracy. **Description:** The plan of Blackstone Group to sell 10 percent of its stake to raise $4 billion and its proposal to go for initial public offering is discussed.

8141 ■ "Blackstone's Outlook Still Tough" in Barron's (Vol. 88, March 17, 2008, No. 11, pp. 19)
Pub: Dow Jones & Company, Inc.
Ed: Andrew Bary. **Description:** Earnings for the Blackstone Group may not recover soon since the company's specialty in big leveraged buyouts is floundering and may not recover until 2009. The company earns lucrative incentive fees on its funds but those fees went negative in the fourth quarter of 2007 and there could be more fee reversals in the future.

8142 ■ "A Bleak Earnings View" in Barron's (Vol. 88, March 10, 2008, No. 10, pp. 15)
Pub: Dow Jones & Company, Inc.
Description: Analysts expect consumer discretionary profits in the S&P 500 to drop 8.4 percent in the first quarter of 2008. A less confident consumer is expected to pull profits down, putting forecasts of earnings growth in the S&P 500 at risk. Statistical data included.

8143 ■ "Bloody Monday for Bear?" in Barron's (Vol. 88, March 17, 2008, No. 11, pp. M14)
Pub: Dow Jones & Company, Inc.
Ed: Steven M. Sears. **Description:** Shares of Bear Stearns could slip further at the start of the trading week unless the company is bought out or bolstered by some other development over the weekend. Prices of the company's shares in the options market suggests about a 30 percent chance that the stock falls below $20 before March expirations expire.

8144 ■ "Blue-Collar Broker" in Boston Business Journal (Vol. 31, July 15, 2011, No. 25, pp. 1)
Pub: Boston Business Journal
Ed: Tim McLaughlin. **Description:** Richard F. Connolly Jr. was ranked 91st in Barron's latest annual ranking of top financial advisers and his team at Morgan Stanley Smith Barney oversee an estimated $3.7 billion in assets. However, anyone who knew him knows that he's just a blue-collar broker from Woburn who loves golf.

8145 ■ "BMW Revs Up for a Rebound" in Barron's (Vol. 89, July 13, 2009, No. 28, pp. M7)
Pub: Dow Jones & Co., Inc.
Ed: Jonathan Buck. **Description:** Investors may like BMW's stocks because the company has maintained its balance sheet strength and has an impressive production line of new models that should boost sales in the next few years. The company's sales are also gaining traction, although their vehicle delivery was down 1.7 percent year on year on June 2009, this was still the best monthly sales figure for 2009.

8146 ■ "Boar Market: Penny-Wise Consumers Favoring Pork" in Crain's Chicago Business (Vol. 31, April 14, 2008, No. 15, pp. 4)
Pub: Crain Communications, Inc.
Ed: Bruce Blythe. **Description:** Interview with Alan Cole who is the president of Cedar Hill Associates Inc. and who discusses ways in which his company is taking advantage of the record highs of oil and natural gas as well as his overall outlook on the market.

8147 ■ "Board This Powertrain" in Barron's (Vol. 89, July 27, 2009, No. 30, pp. 30)
Pub: Dow Jones & Co., Inc.
Ed: Naureen S. Malik. **Description:** Siemens' American Depositary Receipts have risen 60 percent from their March 2009 low and they should continue heading higher. The company has solid earnings and revenue growth since they lead in growing markets such as alternative energy and health-care infrastructure. Their shares also look cheap at 1.9 times book value.

8148 ■ "Boeing Earns Its Wings With Strong Quarter" in Crain's Chicago Business (Vol. 31, April 28, 2008, No. 17, pp. 4)
Pub: Crain Communications, Inc.
Ed: Daniel Rome Levine. **Description:** Interview with Michael A. Crowe, the senior managing director at Mesirow Financial Investment Management, who discusses highlights from the earnings season so far, his outlook for the economy and the stock market as well as what his company is purchasing. Mr. Crowe also recommends shares of five companies.

8149 ■ "BofA Cutting 70 Charlotte Tech Jobs" in Charlotte Observer (January 31, 2007)
Pub: Knight-Ridder/Tribune Business News
Ed: Rick Rothacker. **Description:** Bank of America announced the elimination of 70 technology positions at their Charlotte, North Carolina facility. The move is part of the company's effort to increase efficiency.

8150 ■ "BofA May Part With U.S. Trust" in Boston Business Journal (Vol. 31, May 20, 2011, No. 17, pp. 1)
Pub: Boston Business Journal
Ed: Tim McLaughlin. **Description:** Bank of America Corporation is willing to sell its U.S. Trust private banking division to improve its capital ratio. The unit remains to be the corporation's core asset and posted $696 million revenue in the first quarter 2010 in contract with Merrill Lynch Global Wealth Management's $3.5 billion. Analysts say that U.S. Trust would fetch more than $3 billion.

8151 ■ "BofA Will Reach the Top with Countrywide Deal" in Business North Carolina (Vol. 28, March 2008, No. 3, pp. 36)
Pub: Business North Carolina
Description: Bank of America, headquartered in Charlotte, North Carolina, will add Countrywide to its let of credits. Countrywide is the largest U.S. mortgage lender. Statistical data included.

8152 ■ "Bonds v. Stocks: Who's Right About Recession?" in Barron's (Vol. 90, August 23, 2010, No. 34, pp. M3)
Pub: Barron's Editorial & Corporate Headquarters
Ed: Kopin Tan. **Description:** The future of treasury securities and stocks should the U.S. enter or avoid a recession are discussed. The back to school business climate and BHP Billiton's bid for Potash Corporation of Saskatchewan are also discussed.

8153 ■ "The Book On Indigo" in Canadian Business (Vol. 81, July 22, 2008, No. 12-13, pp. 29)
Pub: Rogers Media Ltd.
Ed: Thomas Watson. **Description:** Indigo Books & Music Inc. reported record sales of $922 million resulting in a record net profit of $52.8 million for the 2008 fiscal year ended March 29, 2008. Earnings per share were $2.13, greater than Standard & Poor's expected $1.70 per share. Additional information concerning Indigo Books is presented.

8154 ■ "Boring Bonds Gain Pizzazz as Investors Flock to Debt Issues" in Baltimore Business Journal (Vol. 28, June 11, 2010, No. 5, pp. 1)
Pub: Baltimore Business Journal
Ed: Gary Haber. **Description:** Companies and nonprofit organizations have increased the pace of bond offerings in order to take advantage of the bonds' appeal among willing investors. Companies mostly issued corporate bonds to replace existing debt at lower interest rates and save them money from interest payments.

8155 ■ "Boston Hedge Fund Pours Money Into Real Estate Projects" in Charlotte Business Journal (Vol. 25, December 3, 2010, No. 37, pp. 1)
Pub: Charlotte Business Journal
Ed: Will Boye. **Description:** Boston-based hedge fund Baupost Group has been financing real estate project in Charlotte, North Carolina including more than 80 acres just north of uptown. Aside from purchasing the $23.8 million note for the Rosewood Condominiums from Regions Financial Corporation, the Baupost Group is also negotiating with Regions to buy the $93.9 million debt of the EipCentre real estate project.

8156 ■ "Bottler Will Regain Its Pop" in Barron's (Vol. 88, March 17, 2008, No. 11, pp. 56)
Pub: Dow Jones & Company, Inc.
Ed: Alexander Eule. **Description:** Discusses he 30 percent drop in the share price of PepsiAmericas Inc. from their 2007 high which presents an opportunity to buy into the company's dependable U.S. market and fast growing Eastern European business. The bottler's Eastern European operating profits in 2007 grew to $101 million from $21 million in 2006.

8157 ■ "Bottom-Fishing and Speed-Dating in India" in Barron's (Vol. 88, March 24, 2008, No. 12, pp. M12)
Pub: Dow Jones & Company, Inc.
Ed: Elliot Wilson. **Description:** Indian stocks have fallen hard in 2008, with Mumbai's Sensex 30 down 30 percent from its January 2008 peak of 21,000 to 14,995 in March. The India Private Equity Fair 2008 attracted 140 of the world's largest private equity firms and about 24 of India's fastest-growing corporations. Statistical data included.

8158 ■ "Bountiful Barrels: Where to Find $140 Trillion" in Barron's (Vol. 88, July 14, 2008, No. 28, pp. 40)
Pub: Dow Jones & Co., Inc.
Ed: Andrew Bary. **Description:** Surge in oil prices has caused a large transfer of wealth to oil-producing countries thereby reshaping the global economy. Oil reserves of oil exporting countries are now valued at $140 trillion. Economist Stephen Jen believes that this wealth will be transformed into paper assets as these countries invest in global stocks and bonds.

8159 ■ "Bracing for a Bear of a Week" in Barron's (Vol. 88, March 17, 2008, No. 11, pp. 24)
Pub: Dow Jones & Company, Inc.
Ed: Jacqueline Doherty. **Description:** JPMorgan Chase and the Federal Reserve Bank of New York's opening of a line of credit to Bear Stearns cut the stock price of Bear Stearns by 47 percent to 30 followed by speculation of an imminent sale. JP Morgan may be the only potential buyer for the firm and some investors say Bears could be sold at $20 to $30. Bears prime assets include its enormous asset base worth $395 billion.

8160 ■ "Briefly" in Crain's Detroit Business (Vol. 25, June 15, 2009, No. 24, pp. 18)
Pub: Crain Communications Inc. - Detroit
Ed: Tom Henderson, Jay Greene. **Description:** Details of the merger between Pl= anning Alternatives Ltd. and Oakland Wealth Management are highlighted. The two investment advisory firms will have a combined staff of 12 and will maintain two offices.

8161 ■ "Bristol-Myers Close to Settling Lawsuit" in Globe & Mail (January 23, 2006, pp. B6)
Pub: CTVglobemedia Publishing Inc.
Ed: Barbara Martinez. **Description:** The details of shareholder case against Bristol-Myers Squibb Co. are presented. The dispute is over the company's claim on the efficiency of Vanlev drug.

8162 ■ "Brooke Agents Claim Mistreatment" in The Business Journal-Serving Metropolitan Kansas City (Vol. 27, October 24, 2008, No. 7, pp. 1)
Pub: American City Business Journals, Inc.
Ed: James Dornbrook. **Description:** Franchisees of Brooke Corp., an insurance franchise, face uncertainty as their bills remain unpaid and banks threaten to destroy their credit. The company bundled and sold franchisee loans to different banks, but the credit crunch left the company with massive debts and legal disputes.

8163 ■ "Building Portfolios for a World of 2.5 Percent Gains" in Barron's (Vol. 88, July 7, 2008, No. 27, pp. L9)
Pub: Dow Jones & Co., Inc.
Ed: Karen Hube. **Description:** Interview with Harold Evenski whom is a financial planner running a fee-only planning practice; he continues to caution investors against pursuing short-term gains and focusing on long-term trends. He advises investors against investing in commodity and real estate stocks and is concerned about the possible effects of high inflation.

8164 ■ Business Black Belt: Develop the Strength, Flexibility and Agility to Run Your Company
Pub: Career Press, Inc.
Ed: Burke Franklin. **Released:** November 1, 2010. **Price:** $15.99. **Description:** Manual offering insights that will enable anyone to become successful in small business. Seventy short chapters included topics such as attitude, management, marketing, selling, employees, money, MBAs, lawyers, consultants, and investors.

8165 ■ "The Business End of Staying in Business" in Contractor (Vol. 56, September 2009, No. 9, pp. 51)
Pub: Penton Media, Inc.
Ed: Al Schwartz. **Description:** Advice on how to manage a new plumbing business in the United States are offered. The transition from being a workman to an employer is seen as one that accompanies a steep learning curve. The importance of managing cash flow is also highlighted.

8166 ■ "Business Still Expected to Take Hit in 2008" in Business Journal-Serving Phoenix and the Valley of the Sun (December 28, 2007)
Pub: American City Business Journals, Inc.
Ed: Chris Casacchia. **Description:** Community banks in 2008 are still projected to suffer from the repercussions of the subprime mortgage and credit crises. Meanwhile, the asset devaluation of big banks and global investment companies are higher than that of smaller banks. The third quarter and fourth quarter losses of banks such as Bear Stearns are discussed as well.

8167 ■ "Business Through Hollywood's Lens" in Harvard Business Review (Vol. 88, October 2010, No. 10, pp. 146)
Pub: Harvard Business School Publishing
Ed: Batia Wiesnefeld, Gino Cattani. **Description:** The authors contend that businesses are likely to be portrayed as villains in movies because corruption

has higher entertainment draw. However, movies also depict popular opinion, which encourages businesses to be accountable and to help build communities.

8168 ■ *"C.A. Bancorp Inc. (TSX:BKP) Announces First Quarter 2007 Financial Results" in Canadian Corporate News (May 16, 2007)*

Pub: Comtex News Network Inc.

Description: Financial report for the first quarter of 2007 for C.A. Bancorp Inc., a publicly traded Canadian merchant bank and asset manager providing investors access to a range of private equity and alternative asset class investment opportunities. Statistical data and highlights included.

8169 ■ *"Calming Customers" in The Business Journal-Portland (Vol. 25, August 29, 2008, No. 25, pp. 1)*

Pub: American City Business Journals, Inc.

Ed: Kirsten Grind; Rob Smith. **Description:** Credit unions and banks in the Portland area are reaching out to clients in an effort to reassure them on the security of their money and the firms' financial stability. Roy Whitehead of Washington Federal Savings, for instance, wrote 41,000 customers of the bank to reassure them. The strategies of different banks and credit unions to answer their client's worries are discussed.

8170 ■ *"Cambodia Calls" in Barron's (Vol. 89, July 27, 2009, No. 30, pp. M7)*

Pub: Dow Jones & Co., Inc.

Ed: Leslie P. Norton. **Description:** Interest in frontier markets could jump if enthusiasm about growth in the developed world gathers steam. Cambodia is the latest market to get attention where a handful of investors are trying to set up funds. One investor believes that Cambodia is back open for business but others are still cautious about investing in the country.

8171 ■ *"Canadian Banks Too Timid in China, Beijing Tells Flaherty" in Globe & Mail (January 22, 2007, pp. B1)*

Pub: CTVglobemedia Publishing Inc.

Ed: Steven Chase. **Description:** The article discusses Canadian banks' investments on China according to the views of federal Finance Minister Jim Flaherty.

8172 ■ *"The Canadians Are Coming!" in Canadian Business (Vol. 80, October 22, 2007, No. 21, pp. 15)*

Pub: Rogers Media

Ed: Rachel Pulfer. **Description:** Toronto-Dominion Bank declared its acquisition of the New Jersey-based Commerce Bancorp for C$8.5 billion. Royal Bank of Canada has scooped up Trinidad-based Financial Group for C$2.2 billion. Details of the foreign acquisitions, as well as the impact of high Canadian dollars on the mergers are discussed.

8173 ■ *"Candidates Won't Bash Fed; Rate Cuts Bash Savers" in Barron's (Vol. 88, March 24, 2008, No. 12, pp. 31)*

Pub: Dow Jones & Company, Inc.

Ed: Jim McTague. **Description:** Candidates in the 2008 US presidential election, like the current administration, do not and will not bash the Federal Reserve. The Federal Reserve's aggressive interest rate cuts hurt the incomes of people depending on their savings accounts.

8174 ■ *"Capturing Generation Y: Ready, Set, Transform" in Credit Union Times (Vol. 21, July 14, 2010, No. 27, pp. 20)*

Pub: Summit Business Media

Ed: Senthil Kumar. **Description:** The financial services sector recognizes that Generation Y will have a definite impact on the way business is conducted in the future. The mindset of Generation Y is social and companies need to use networking tools such as Facebook in order to reach this demographic.

8175 ■ *"The Case of the Deflated IPO" in Boston Business Journal (Vol. 29, June 24, 2011, No. 7, pp. 1)*

Pub: American City Business Journals Inc.

Ed: Scott Dance. **Description:** IPO market is on the rebound from the recession but for some companies in Maryland, the time is not yet ripe to go public. One

of the companies that chooses to wait for better timing is SafeNet Inc. and it is eyeing some possible acquisitions while doing so.

8176 ■ *"Cash Flow Myths" in Canadian Business (Vol. 80, March 12, 2007, No. 6, pp. 25)*

Pub: Rogers Media

Ed: Al Rosen. **Description:** Expert advice to Canadian investors about understanding the cash flow statements of companies before investing money is presented.

8177 ■ *"Cemex Paves a Global Road to Solid Growth" in Barron's (Vol. 88, March 10, 2008, No. 10, pp. 24)*

Pub: Dow Jones & Company, Inc.

Ed: Sandra Ward. **Description:** Shares of Cemex are expected to perform well with the company's expected strong performance despite fears of a US recession. The company has a diverse geographical reach and benefits from a strong worldwide demand for cement.

8178 ■ *"Centrue Sets Down New Roots in St. Louis; Bank Looks to Expand in Exurbs of Chicago" in Crain's Chicago Business (May 5, 2008)*

Pub: Crain Communications, Inc.

Ed: H. Lee Murphy. **Description:** Centrue Financial Corp. has moved its headquarters from Ottawa to suburban St. Louis in search of higher-growth markets. The banks acquisitions and expansion plans are also discussed.

8179 ■ *"Certified Financial Planner Board of Standards Reacts to Jobs Program" in Professional Services Close-Up (September 14, 2011)*

Pub: Close-Up Media Inc.

Description: Certified Financial Planner Board of Standards Consumer Advocate, Eleanor Blayney, believe that people should be looking inward at their own ability to change their employment future. She shares tips for the job market to help out.

8180 ■ *The Changing Geography of Banking and Finance*

Pub: Springer Publishing Company

Ed: Pietro Alessandrini, Michele Fratianni, Alberto Zazzaro. **Released:** May 1, 2009. **Price:** $139.00. **Description:** The two contrasting trends that have emerged from the integration and consolidation processes of the banking industry in both Europe and the United States in the 1990s is examined.

8181 ■ *"Check Provider Says It Plans to Close Call Center in Charlotte" in Charlotte Observer (February 6, 2007)*

Pub: Knight-Ridder/Tribune Business News

Ed: Rick Rothacker. **Description:** Clarke American Checks Inc. is closing its call center located in Charlotte, North Carolina. Clarke provides checks and other services to financial institutions and customers.

8182 ■ *"Chuck's Big Chance" in Barron's (Vol. 89, July 13, 2009, No. 28, pp. L3)*

Pub: Dow Jones & Co., Inc.

Ed: Leslie P. Norton. **Description:** Charles Schwab is cutting prices and rolling out new products to lure customers and the company is well positioned to benefit from Wall Street's misery. Their shares are trading at just 17 times earnings, which should be at least a multiple of 20.

8183 ■ *"CIBC Spends $1.1 Billion on Caribbean Expansion" in Globe & Mail (March 14, 2006, pp. B1)*

Pub: CTVglobemedia Publishing Inc.

Ed: Sinclair Stewart. **Description:** Canadian Imperial Bank of Commerce (CIBC), the fifth-largest bank of Canada, is planning to spend $1.1billion to buy major share of Barbados-based First Caribbean International Bank. The details of the acquisition plan are presented.

8184 ■ *"Citadel Hires Three Lehman Execs" in Chicago Tribune (October 2, 2008)*

Pub: McClatchy-Tribune Information Services

Ed: James P. Miller. **Description:** Citadel Investment Group LLC, Chicago hedge-fund operator, has hired three former senior executives of bankrupt investment banker Lehman Brothers Holding Inc. Citadel believes that the company's hiring spree will help them to further expand the firm's capabilities in the global fixed income business.

8185 ■ *"Citi Ruling Could Chill SEC, Street Legal Pacts" in Wall Street Journal Eastern Edition (November 29, 2011, pp. C1)*

Pub: Dow Jones & Company Inc. Enterprise Media Group

Contact: Clare Hart, President

Ed: Jean Eaglesham, Chad Bray. **Description:** A $285 million settlement was reached between the Securities and Exchange Commission and Citigroup Inc. over allegations the bank misled investors over a mortgage-bond deal. Now, Judge Jed S. Rakoff has ruled against the settlement, a decision that will affect the future of such attempts to prosecute Wall Street fraud. Rakoff said that the settlement was 'neither fair, nor reasonable, nor adequate, nor in the public interest.'.

8186 ■ *"Citigroup Moves to Buy Japan's Nikko" in Globe & Mail (March 7, 2007, pp. B12)*

Pub: CTVglobemedia Publishing Inc.

Ed: Jonathan Soble; Dan Wilchins. **Description:** Citigroup Inc. offered $10.8 billion to acquire troubled Nikko Cordial Corp., Japan's largest securities firm.

8187 ■ *"Citizens Unveils Mobile App for Business Customers" in New Hampshire Business Review (Vol. 33, March 25, 2011, No. 6, pp. 27)*

Pub: Business Publications Inc.

Description: Citizens Financial Group offers a new mobile banking application that allows business customers to manage cash and payments from a mobile device.

8188 ■ *"Clash of the Titans" in Canadian Business (Vol. 80, March 12, 2007, No. 6, pp. 27)*

Pub: Rogers Media

Ed: Andrew Wahl. **Description:** The frequent allegations of Google Inc. and Microsoft Corp. against each other over copyright and other legal issues, with a view to taking away other's market share, is discussed.

8189 ■ *"Climbing the Wall of Worry, Two Steps at a Time" in Barron's (Vol. 89, July 13, 2009, No. 28, pp. L16)*

Pub: Dow Jones & Co., Inc.

Ed: Brian Blackstone. **Description:** Statistical table that shows the performance of different mutual funds for the second quarter of 2009 is presented. The data shows that on average, the 8,272 diversified equity funds gained 17 percent for this quarter.

8190 ■ *"CNinsure Offers Safety in Numbers" in Barron's (Vol. 90, September 13, 2010, No. 37, pp. 29)*

Pub: Barron's Editorial & Corporate Headquarters

Ed: Teresa Rivas. **Description:** China's insurance holding company CNinsure has a long growth future due to the nascent insurance market in the country. It has also been diversifying its offerings and it has a broad network in the nation. The shares of the company are trading cheaply at nearly 14 times its 2011 earnings, and is considered a good point for investors.

8191 ■ *"Coca-Cola Looks Ready to Pause" in Barron's (Vol. 88, March 10, 2008, No. 10, pp. 18)*

Pub: Dow Jones & Company, Inc.

Ed: Michael Santoli. **Description:** Shares of Coca-Cola are expected to turn sideways or experience a slight drop from $59.50 each to the mid-50 level. The company has seen its shares jump 40 percent since 2006, when it was in a series of measures to improve profitability.

8192 ■ "Cogeco Profit Jumps 47 Percent in First Quarter" in Globe & Mail (January 13, 2006, pp. B3)
Pub: CTVglobemedia Publishing Inc.
Ed: Catherine McLean. **Description:** The reasons behind 47 percent increase in first quarter 2006 profits for Cogeco Inc. are presented.

8193 ■ A Colossal Failure of Common Sense: The Inside Story of the Collapse of Lehman Brothers
Pub: Crown Business
Ed: Lawrence G. McDonald, Patrick Robinson. **Released:** 2009. **Price:** $27.00. **Description:** Former employee of Lehman Brothers details the failure of leadership that led to the demise of the company.

8194 ■ "Coming: Cheaper Oil and a Stronger Buck" in Barron's (Vol. 88, March 24, 2008, No. 12, pp. 53)
Pub: Dow Jones & Company, Inc.
Ed: Lawrence C. Strauss. **Description:** Carl C. Weinberg, the chief economist of High Frequency Economics, forecasts that Chinese economic growth will slow down and that oil prices will drop to $80 a barrel in 2008. He also believes that the US dollar will start rising the moment the Federal Reserve stops cutting interest rates.

8195 ■ "Coming Soon: Bailouts of Fannie and Freddie" in Barron's (Vol. 88, July 14, 2008, No. 28, pp. 14)
Pub: Dow Jones & Co., Inc.
Ed: Jonathan R. Laing. **Description:** Assurances from the government that Fannie Mae and Freddie Mac are adequately capitalized and able to carry on their duties as guarantors or owners of over $5 trillion of U.S. home mortgages are designed to keep both entities afloat until they attempt to raise $10 billion in new equity. The government would assume any losses in a bailout and owners of the banks' papers would profit as yields drop.

8196 ■ "Commentary. On Federal Reserve's Cut of Interest Rates" in Small Business Economic Trends (January 2008, pp. 3)
Pub: National Federation of Independent Business
Description: Federal Reserve cut interest rates and announced its economic outlook on September 18, 2007 to stimulate spending. The cut in interest rates, however, may not help in supporting consumer spending because savers may lose interest income. The expected economic impact of the interest rate cuts and the U.S. economic outlook are also discussed.

8197 ■ "Commentary. Small Business Economic Trends" in Small Business Economic Trends (March 2008, pp. 3)
Pub: National Federation of Independent Business
Ed: William C. Dunkelberg, Holly Wade. **Description:** Commentary on the economic trends for small businesses in the U.S. is presented. Analysis of the labor market and low interest rates is given. The effect of the Federal Reserve's policy announcement on small business owner optimism is also discussed.

8198 ■ "Commentary. Small Business Economic Trends" in Small Business Economic Trends (February 2008, pp. 3)
Pub: National Federation of Independent Business
Ed: William C. Dunkelberg, Holly Wade. **Description:** Commentary on the economic trends for small businesses in the U.S. is presented. Analysis of the U.S. Federal Reserve Board's efforts to prevent a recession is given. Reduction in business inventories is also discussed.

8199 ■ "Commodities: Who's Behind the Boom?" in Barron's (Vol. 88, March 31, 2008, No. 13, pp. 3)
Pub: Dow Jones & Company, Inc.
Ed: Gene Epstein. **Description:** Proliferation of mutual funds and exchange traded funds tied to commodities indexes has helped speculative buying reach unusual levels. Index funds are estimated to account for 40 percent of all bullish bets on commodities. Commodities could drop by 30 percent as speculators retreat. Statistical data included.

8200 ■ "Commodity Speculation: Over the Top?" in Barron's (Vol. 89, July 13, 2009, No. 28, pp. 22)
Pub: Dow Jones & Co., Inc.
Ed: Gene Epstein. **Description:** Commodity Futures Trading Commission is planning to impose position limits on speculators of oil and other commodities as energy costs rebound from their lows. These regulations make much sense and these position limits would greatly diminish the cash commitment of the commodity index traders if these were imposed on speculators and swaps dealers properly.

8201 ■ "Compelling Opportunities" in Barron's (Vol. 88, March 10, 2008, No. 10, pp. 39)
Pub: Dow Jones & Company, Inc.
Ed: Neil A. Martin. **Description:** Michael L. Reynal, portfolio manager of Principal International Emerging Markets Fund, is bullish on the growth prospects of stocks in emerging markets. He is investing big on energy, steel, and transportation companies.

8202 ■ "Competitors Line Up to Save Failing Banks" in The Business Journal - Serving Phoenix and the Valley of the Sun (Vol. 28, July 25, 2008, No. 47, pp. 1)
Pub: American City Business Journals, Inc.
Ed: Chris Casacchia. **Description:** Financial institutions in Arizona are positioning themselves as possible buyers in the event of failure of one of their competitors. These banks have already approached the Federal Deposit Insurance Corp. about their ability to take over their more troubled competitors.

8203 ■ "Compounding Opportunity" in Hispanic Business (October 2007, pp. 72, 74-75)
Pub: Hispanic Business
Ed: Hildy Medina. **Description:** New banks are targeting Hispanic entrepreneurs.

8204 ■ "Comtech's Winning Streak" in Crain's New York Business (Vol. 24, January 7, 2008, No. 1, pp. 3)
Pub: Crain Communications, Inc.
Description: Comtech Telecommunications Corp., a designer and manufacturer of equipment that helps military track troops and vehicles on the field, has been one of the stock market's biggest winners over the past decade. Statistical data included.

8205 ■ "Connect the Thoughts" in Canadian Business (Vol. 81, October 27, 2008, No. 18, pp. 8)
Pub: Rogers Media Ltd.
Ed: Jeff Sanford. **Description:** Thomas Homer-Dixon believes the financial crisis that hit Wall Street is a systemic crisis and may result in the reconfiguration of financial markets in ways that people may never understand. He also thinks the U.S. may borrow against its assets, making it a weaker nation.

8206 ■ "Conquering Your Fear of Fees" in Entrepreneur (Vol. 37, October 2009, No. 10, pp. 86)
Pub: Entrepreneur Media, Inc.
Ed: Rosalind Resnick. **Description:** Entrepreneurs should study money management charges carefully before investing. They should understand how different forms of investments work and how much money managers and mutual funds charge for their services.

8207 ■ "Consumers Finding It Harder to Get and Keep Credit" in Chicago Tribune (January 10, 2009)
Pub: McClatchy-Tribune Information Services
Ed: Susan Chandler. **Description:** Five tips to maintain a good credit rating in these economic times are outlined and discussed.

8208 ■ "Conversation Starters for the Holiday" in Barron's (Vol. 89, July 6, 2009, No. 27, pp. 7)
Pub: Dow Jones & Co., Inc.
Ed: Michael Santoli. **Description:** Investors are concerned that the US will experience high inflation due to low interest rates and improved money supply.

US consumer spending has increased to 70 percent of gross domestic product, brought by health-care spending increases, while savings rates have risen to 6.9 percent.

8209 ■ "A Conversation With Money Manager William Vellon" in Crain's Chicago Business (Vol. 31, November 17, 2008, No. 46, pp. 4)
Pub: Crain Communications, Inc.
Ed: Mike Colias. **Description:** Interview with William Vellon, the executive vice-president of Kingsbury Capital Investment Advisors; Vellon discusses ways in which the government can help the financial sector, his client base and bargains that investors should consider.

8210 ■ "A Conversation With; Ron Gatner, Jones Lang LaSalle" in Crain's Detroit Business (Vol. 24, October 6, 2008, No. 40, pp. 9)
Pub: Crain Communications, Inc.
Description: Interview with Ron Gatner who is a corporate real estate adviser with the real estate company Jones Lang LaSalle as well as the company's executive vice president and part of the tenant advisory team; Gatner speaks about the impact that the Wall Street crisis is having on the commercial real estate market in Detroit.

8211 ■ "Cool on Chicago Office Properties" in Crain's Chicago Business (Vol. 31, March 31, 2008, No. 13, pp. 16)
Pub: Crain Communications, Inc.
Ed: Eddie Baeb. **Description:** Investors predict values on Chicago office buildings to drop 1.3 percent over the next year.

8212 ■ "Copper Giant to Spin Off Silver Assets" in Globe & Mail (February 27, 2006, pp. B1)
Pub: CTVglobemedia Publishing Inc.
Ed: Sinclair Stewart; Andrew Willis. **Description:** The reasons behind the sale of silver mining assets by Codelco are presented.

8213 ■ "Copper, Zinc Prices Hammered" in Globe & Mail (February 3, 2007, pp. B7)
Pub: CTVglobemedia Publishing Inc.
Ed: John Partridge. **Description:** The decline in the global prices of copper and zinc metals in January 2007 is discussed. Copper prices fell by 12 percent while zinc prices dropped by 6.3 percent.

8214 ■ "Copy Karachi?" in Barron's (Vol. 88, June 30, 2008, No. 26, pp. 5)
Pub: Dow Jones & Co., Inc.
Ed: Randall W. Forsyth. **Description:** Karachi bourse had a historic 8.6 percent one-day gain because the bourse banned short-selling for a month and announced a 30 billion rupee fund to stabilize the market. The shares of General Motors are trading within the same values that it had in 1974. The reasons for this decline are discussed.

8215 ■ "Corn May Get Shucked By Soy" in Barron's (Vol. 88, March 31, 2008, No. 13, pp. M12)
Pub: Dow Jones & Company, Inc.
Ed: Angie Pointer. **Description:** Acreage allotted to soybeans could jump by 12 percent from 2007's 63.6 million as the price for soybeans reaches record highs. Corn acreage could drop by 6.7 percent as other crops expand and higher fertilizer prices shift farmers away from corn.

8216 ■ "Corporate Elite Show Resilience" in The Business Journal-Serving Greater Tampa Bay (Vol. 28, August 1, 2008, No. 32, pp. 1)
Pub: American City Business Journals, Inc.
Ed: Margie Manning; Alexis Muellner. **Description:** Stocks of the largest public companies in Tampa Bay, Florida, outperformed the S&P 500 index by 28 percent in the first half of 2008. The escalation is attributed to the growth orientation of the companies in the area and the lack of exposure to the real estate and financial services sectors.

8217 ■ "Corus Eases Off Ailing Condo Market; Office Developers Get Majority of 1Q Loans" in Crain's Chicago Business (April 28, 2008)

Pub: Crain Communications, Inc.

Ed: H. Lee Murphy. **Description:** Corus Bankshares Inc., a specialist in lending for the condominium high-rise construction market, is diversifying its portfolio by making loans to office developers and expects to be investing in hotels through the rest of the year. Corus' $7.57 billion loan portfolio is also discussed in detail as well as the company's earnings and share price. Statistical data included.

8218 ■ "Cost Cuts Lead Dealers to Record Profits" in Globe & Mail (March 24, 2006, pp. B3)

Pub: CTVglobemedia Publishing Inc.

Ed: Omar El Akkad. **Description:** The reasons behind posting of $4.3 billion profit by Canadian securities sector, for 2005, are presented.

8219 ■ "Countdown" in Canadian Business (Vol. 81, March 3, 2008, No. 3, pp. 27)

Pub: Rogers Media

Ed: Al Rosen. **Description:** According to a recent poll only 42 percent of portfolio managers in Canada are aware that the country is planning to adopt the International Financial Reporting Standards beginning 2011. The shift to the new standards will have significant impacts on investment values and will be the biggest revolution in Canadian financial reporting. The effects of the transition on portfolio managers and investors are analyzed.

8220 ■ "CPI, Coal Lead Local Stock Decline" in Saint Louis Business Journal (Vol. 32, October 14, 2011, No. 7, pp. 1)

Pub: Saint Louis Business Journal

Ed: Greg Edwards. **Description:** Coal companies and CPI Corporation were among those whose stocks have declined in St. Louis, Missouri. The stocks of local firms have plunged by 28 percent during the first nine months of 2011.

8221 ■ "Crain's Picks Top '08 Stocks" in Crain's New York Business (Vol. 24, January 7, 2008, No. 1, pp. 3)

Pub: Crain Communications, Inc.

Ed: Aaron Elstein. **Description:** Listing of five stocks that Crain's believes can deliver solid gains for shareholders.

8222 ■ Crash Proof 2.0: How to Profit From the Economic Collapse

Pub: John Wiley & Sons, Inc.

Ed: Peter D. Schiff. **Released:** September 22, 2009. **Price:** $27.95. **Description:** Factors that will affect financial stability in the coming years are explained. A three step plan to battle the current economic downturn is also included.

8223 ■ "The Credit Crisis Continues" in Barron's (Vol. 88, March 10, 2008, No. 10, pp. M12)

Pub: Dow Jones & Company, Inc.

Ed: Randall W. Forsyth. **Description:** Short-term Treasury yields dropped to new cyclical lows in early March 2008, with the yield for the two-year Treasury note falling to 1.532 percent. Spreads of the mortgage-backed securities of Fannie Mae and Freddie Mac rose on suspicion of collapses in financing.

8224 ■ "Credit Crisis Puts Market in Unprecedented Territory" in Crain's New York Business (Vol. 24, January 7, 2008, No. 1, pp. 14)

Pub: Crain Communications, Inc.

Ed: Aaron Elstein. **Description:** Banks are being forced to take enormous losses due to investors who are refusing to buy anything linked to subprime mortgages and associated securities.

8225 ■ "Credit Unions Cast Wary Eye at Paulson Plan, But Not Panicking Yet" in The Business Review Albany (Vol. 35, April 11, 2008, No. 1)

Pub: The Business Review

Ed: Barbara Pinckney. **Description:** Credit unions are suspicious of US Treasury Secretary Henry Paulson's plan to establish a single federally insured depository institution charter for all institutions covered by federal deposit insurance. The charter would replace national banks, federal savings associations, and federal credit union charters.

8226 ■ "Credit Unions Gain: New Members Sign Up, Fleeing Banks" in Puget Sound Business Journal (Vol. 29, October 10, 2008, No. 25, pp. 1)

Pub: American City Business Journals

Ed: Kirsten Grind. **Description:** Credit unions are gaining new members due to customers' lack of confidence in federal banks.

8227 ■ "Critics: Efforts to Fix Loans Won't Stop Foreclosure Wave" in Business First Columbus (Vol. 25, November 14, 2008, No. 12, pp. A1)

Pub: American City Business Journals

Ed: Adrian Burns. **Description:** Efforts by U.S. banks to help homeowners pay mortgages are seen to have little if any impact on foreclosures. Banks have announced plans to identify and aid troubled borrowers. Statistical data included.

8228 ■ Currency Internationalization: Global Experiences and Implications for the Renminbi

Pub: Palgrave Macmillan

Ed: Wensheng Peng, Chang Shu. **Released:** January 5, 2010. **Price:** $100.00. **Description:** A collection of academic studies relating to the potential internationalization of China's remninbi. It also discusses the increasing use of China's remninbi currency in international trade and finance.

8229 ■ "Customers Turned Off? Not at Best Buy" in Barron's (Vol. 88, March 24, 2008, No. 12, pp. 29)

Pub: Dow Jones & Company, Inc.

Ed: Sandra Ward. **Description:** Shares of Best Buy, trading at $42.41 each, are expected to rise to an average of $52 a share due to the company's solid fundamentals. The company's shares have fallen 20 percent from their 52-week high and are attractive given the company's bright prospects in the video game sector and high-definition video.

8230 ■ "CVRD Inco Strike Shuts Sudbury Mines" in Globe & Mail (April 2, 2007, pp. B1)

Pub: CTVglobemedia Publishing Inc.

Ed: Andy Hoffman. **Description:** The closure of nickel mining operations at the Sudbury mines due to the strike by employees of CVRD Inco Ltd. is described. The prospects of a rise in the prices of nickel are discussed, besides the production of metals in Canada.

8231 ■ "Cyclicals, Your Day Is Coming" in Barron's (Vol. 89, July 27, 2009, No. 30, pp. 24)

Pub: Dow Jones & Co., Inc.

Ed: Dimitra DeFotis. **Description:** Cyclical stocks are likely to be big winners when the economy improves and 13 stocks that have improving earnings, decent balance sheets, and dividends are presented. These candidates include U.S. Steel, Alcoa, Allegheny Tech, Dow Chemical, and Nucor.

8232 ■ "Darkness Falling.." in Barron's (Vol. 89, July 20, 2009, No. 29, pp. 13)

Pub: Dow Jones & Co., Inc.

Description: Newsletter writer Arch Crawford believes that market indicators signal a possible downturn in US stock markets. High risk areas also include China and Japan .

8233 ■ "Data Dispel Some Notions About Value of Stock Buybacks" in Crain's Cleveland Business (Vol. 28, November 19, 2007, No. 46, pp. 9)

Pub: Crain Communications, Inc.

Ed: Megan Johnston. **Description:** According to new research on buybacks and their benefits, companies engaged in stock buybacks frequently do not enjoy a nice boost in their share prices despite the conventional wisdom that states that investors like stock buybacks.

8234 ■ "Dating Games" in Canadian Business (Vol. 79, September 25, 2006, No. 19, pp. 23)

Pub: Rogers Media

Ed: John Gray. **Description:** Increasing stock option scandals in Canada and American companies is discussed.

8235 ■ "Deal Braces Cramer for Growth Run" in The Business Journal-Serving Metropolitan Kansas City (Vol. 26, July 4, 2008, No. 43, pp. 1)

Pub: American City Business Journals, Inc.

Ed: James Dornbook. **Description:** Gardner, Kansas-based Cramer Products Inc. bought 100 percent of the stocks of Louisville, Kentucky-based Active Ankle Inc. from 26 private investors increasing its revenue by 20 percent. The latter is the second largest vendor of Cramer. Other details of the merger are presented.

8236 ■ "Deal or No Deal?" in Canadian Business (Vol. 80, January 15, 2007, No. 2, pp. 38)

Pub: Rogers Media

Ed: Andrew Wahl; Zena Olijnyk; Jeff Sanford; Erin Pooley. **Description:** The trends in the stock prices of companies like Loblaw Companies Ltd., Domtar Inc. and Biovail Corp., from January 2006 to January 2007, are analyzed.

8237 ■ "The Deal - Rhymes With Steal - Of A Lifetime" in Barron's (Vol. 88, March 24, 2008, No. 12, pp. 24)

Pub: Dow Jones & Company, Inc.

Ed: Andrew Bary. **Description:** JPMorgan Chase's impending acquisition of Bear Stearns for $2.50 a share is a huge steal for the former. JPMorgan is set to acquire a company with a potential annual earnings of $1 billion while the Federal Reserve funds Bear's illiquid assets by providing $30 billion in nonrecourse loans.

8238 ■ "Dean Foods" in Ice Cream Reporter (Vol. 23, November 20, 2010, No. 12, pp. 8)

Pub: Ice Cream Reporter

Description: The impact of higher commodity prices can be seen in the recent news from Dean Foods, the largest U.S. dairy company, which reported that rising butterfat and other dairy commodity costs have led to lower-than-expected quarterly profits after it cut prices to compete with private-label brands.

8239 ■ "Debutante NYSE Soars 20 Percent" in Globe & Mail (March 9, 2006, pp. B1)

Pub: CTVglobemedia Publishing Inc.

Ed: John Partridge. **Description:** The debutant share trading of NYSE Group Inc. is discussed. The prices rose by 20 percent before closing.

8240 ■ "Decision CEO Cool to Acquisitions" in Globe & Mail (April 19, 2007, pp. B6)

Pub: CTVglobemedia Publishing Inc.

Ed: Andy Hoffman. **Description:** The increase in the shares of Denison Mines Corp. due to hike in Uranium prices is discussed.

8241 ■ "Decline in Assets Is Costly for Advisers" in The Business Journal-Serving Metropolitan Kansas City (Vol. 27, October 24, 2008)

Pub: American City Business Journals, Inc.

Ed: James Dornbrook. **Description:** Financial advisers in the Kansas City, Missouri area are forced to cut costs as their assets have decreased sharply due to the huge drop in stock prices. American Century Investments was forced to diversify into foreign assets and cut 90 jobs as its assets dropped to $84 billion. Diversification has softened the impact of the steep decline in stock prices for Waddell & Reed Financial Inc.

8242 ■ *A Demon of Our Own Design: Markets, Hedge Funds, and the Perils of Financial Innovation*
Pub: John Wiley and Sons, Inc.
Ed: Richard Bookstaber. **Released:** December 2008. **Price:** $16.95 paperback. **Description:** Longtime hedge-fund manager offers his take on a market and investment system that he believes is needlessly complex owing to investment banks, hedge funds, innovation, regulation, and safeguards and further compounded by investor and market instabilities. These complexities could create a large-scale disaster.

8243 ■ *"Detecting Crookery" in Canadian Business (Vol. 80, February 12, 2007, No. 4, pp. 23)*
Pub: Rogers Media
Ed: Al Rosen. **Description:** Expert advice to Canadian investors on proper financial reporting is presented and ways to protect their investments are discussed.

8244 ■ *"Detroit Hosts Conferences on Green Building, IT, Finance" in Crain's Detroit Business (Vol. 25, June 1, 2009, No. 22, pp. 9)*
Pub: Crain Communications Inc. - Detroit
Ed: Tom Henderson. **Description:** Detroit will host three conferences in June 2009, one features green technology, one information technology and the third will gather black bankers and financial experts from across the nation.

8245 ■ *"Deutsche Bank Joins the Club" in Barron's (Vol. 88, March 31, 2008, No. 13, pp. M6)*
Pub: Dow Jones & Company, Inc.
Ed: Arindam Nag. **Description:** Deutsche Bank's tangible leverage has worsened sharply in the past year from 2.1 percent to 2.3 percent during 2002-2006 to only 1.6 percent. The bank has also been accumulating a lot of illiquid assets and its Level-3 assets are three times its tangible equity.

8246 ■ *"Diana Sands; Vice-President of Investor Relations, Boeing Co." in Crain's Chicago Business (Vol. 31, May 5, 2008, No. 18, pp. 32)*
Pub: Crain Communications, Inc.
Ed: John Rosenthal. **Description:** Profile of Diana Sands who is the vice-president of investor relations at Boeing Co. which entails explaining the company's performance to securities analysts and institutional investors.

8247 ■ *"Diary of a Short-Seller" in Conde Nast Portfolio (Vol. 2, June 2008, No. 6, pp. 44)*
Pub: Conde Nast Publications
Contact: David Carey, President
Ed: Jesse Eisinger. **Description:** Profile of David Einhorn who is a fund manager that spoke out against finance company Allied Capital whose stock fell nearly 20 percent the day after Einhorn's critique; Einhorn subsequently had to contend with attacks against his credibility as well as investigations by the S.E.C.; Einhorn's experience illuminates our current economic crisis.

8248 ■ *"Diaz Announces Financial and Operating Results for the First Three Months of 2007" in Canadian Corporate News (May 16, 2007)*
Pub: Comtex News Network Inc.
Description: Diaz Resources Ltd., an oil and gas exploration and production company, announced its financial results during the first quarter of 2007 which were hampered by lower gas prices and declining production volumes but anticipates the financial results should steadily improve in the second quarter of 2007.

8249 ■ *"Dick Haskayne" in Canadian Business (Vol. 81, March 31, 2008, No. 5, pp. 72)*
Pub: Rogers Media
Ed: Andy Holloway. **Description:** Dick Haskayne says that he learned a lot about business from his dad who ran a butcher shop where they had to make

a decision on buying cattle and getting credit. Haskayne says that family, friends, finances, career, health, and infrastructure are benchmarks that have to be balanced.

8250 ■ *Dictionary of Finance, Investment and Banking*
Pub: Palgrave Macmillan
Ed: Erik Banks. **Released:** 2010. **Price:** $42.95. **Description:** Comprehensive dictionary covering terms used in finance, investment and banking sectors.

8251 ■ *Dictionary of Real Estate Terms*
Pub: Barron's Educational Series Inc.
Contact: Alex Holtz, President
E-mail: aholtz@berronseduc.com
Ed: Jack P. Friedman, Jack C. Harris, J. Bruce Lindeman. **Released:** October 2008. **Price:** $13.99. **Description:** More than 2,500 real estate terms relating to mortgages and financing, brokerage law, architecture, rentals and leases, property insurance, and more.

8252 ■ *"Different This Time?" in Canadian Business (Vol. 81, April 14, 2008, No. 6, pp. 38)*
Pub: Rogers Media
Ed: Matthew McClearn. **Description:** Irving Fisher believed that the low interest rates of the 1920's spurred investors to borrow and use the money to speculate with the proceeds thereby increasing the debt to unmanageable levels prior to the stock market crash in Oct. 29, 1929. The U.S. economic conditions in 1929 and U.S. economic conditions in 2008 are discussed.

8253 ■ *"Digging Deep for Gold" in Barron's (Vol. 88, March 24, 2008, No. 12, pp. 49)*
Pub: Dow Jones & Company, Inc.
Ed: Suzanne McGee. **Description:** David Iben, manager of the Nuveen Tradewinds Value Opportunities Fund, looks for value in companies and industries where the consensus of analysts is negative. He started investing in gold stocks well before gold prices started to rise.

8254 ■ *The Directory of Venture Capital and Private Equity Firms: 2009*
Pub: Grey House Publishing
Contact: Richard Gottlieb, President
E-mail: rhg2@greyhouse.com
Ed: Laura Mars-Proietti. **Released:** April 1, 2009. **Price:** $450.00. **Description:** Updated and expanded edition that includes new entries offering access to more than 3,500 domestic and international venture capital and private equity firms; detailed contact information and extensive data on investments and funds is included.

8255 ■ *"Disappearing Act" in Globe & Mail (April 21, 2007, pp. B1)*
Pub: CTVglobemedia Publishing Inc.
Ed: David Parkinson. **Description:** The effects of the buyout of BCE Inc. on the trends of stock prices at the Toronto Stock Exchange are described.

8256 ■ *"Discount Beers Take Fizz Out Of Molson" in Globe & Mail (February 10, 2006, pp. B3)*
Pub: CTVglobemedia Publishing Inc.
Ed: Omar El Akkad. **Description:** The reasons behind the decline in profits by 60 percent for Molson Coors Brewing Co., during fourth quarter 2005, are presented.

8257 ■ *"Dividing to Conquer" in Barron's (Vol. 88, March 31, 2008, No. 13, pp. 22)*
Pub: Dow Jones & Company, Inc.
Ed: Andrew Bary. **Description:** Altria's spin off of Philip Morris International could unlock substantial value for both domestic and international cigarette concerns. The strong brands and ample payouts from both companies will most likely impress investors.

8258 ■ *"Do-It-Yourself Portfolio Management" in Barron's (Vol. 89, July 13, 2009, No. 28, pp. 25)*
Pub: Dow Jones & Co., Inc.
Ed: Mike Hogan. **Description:** Services of several portfolio management web sites are presented. These web sites include MarketRiders E.Adviser, TD Ameritrade and E.

8259 ■ *"Do the Math" in Canadian Business (Vol. 79, October 9, 2006, No. 20, pp. 17)*
Pub: Rogers Media
Ed: Al Rosen. **Description:** Faulty practices followed by regulators in Canadian stock market are discussed. The need for authorities to protect investors against these frauds are emphasized.

8260 ■ *"Dr. Mark Holder" in Crain's Cleveland Business (Vol. 30, June 29, 2009, No. 25, pp. 14)*
Pub: Crain Communications, Inc.
Ed: Kathy Ames Carr. **Description:** Dr. Mark Holder is the director of the financial engineering program at Kent State University. Dr. Holder discusses his role to help teach his students how to market themselves for finance jobs in a down economy.

8261 ■ *"Doctor's Orders" in Canadian Business (Vol. 79, November 20, 2006, No. 23, pp. 73)*
Pub: Rogers Media
Ed: Jeff Sanford. **Description:** George Cohon, the founder of McDonald's in Canada and Russia, speaks about the Canadian market and the experience of starting McDonald's in Canada.

8262 ■ *"DoEs and DonEts" in Canadian Business (Vol. 79, July 17, 2006, No. 14-15, pp. 29)*
Pub: Rogers Media
Ed: Andy Holloway; Erin Pooley; Thomas Watson. **Description:** Strategic tips for planning systematic investments, in order to make life more enjoyable after retirement, are elucidated.

8263 ■ *"Dofasco Quarterly Profit Plunges on Lower Steel Prices, Rising Costs" in Globe & Mail (February 4, 2006, pp. B3)*
Pub: CTVglobemedia Publishing Inc.
Ed: Shirley Won. **Description:** Dofasco Inc. posted 71% decline in profits for fourth quarter 2005. The revenue drop is attributed to fall in steel prices.

8264 ■ *"Dofasco Warms to New Thyssen Bid" in Globe & Mail (January 4, 2006, pp. B1)*
Pub: CTVglobemedia Publishing Inc.
Ed: Greg Keenan. **Description:** The details on ThyssenKrupp AG's bid for Dofasco Inc., at $63 a share, are presented.

8265 ■ *"The Dogs of TSX" in Canadian Business (Vol. 81, Summer 2008, No. 9, pp. 77)*
Pub: Rogers Media Ltd.
Ed: Calvin Leung. **Description:** Table showing the one-year stock performance of the ten highest dividend-yielding stocks on the S&P/TSX 60 Composite Index is presented. This technique is similar to the 'Dogs of the Dow' approach. The idea in this investment strategy is to buy equal amounts of stocks from these companies and selling them a year later, and then repeat the process.

8266 ■ *"The Dogs of the TSX" in Canadian Business (Vol. 82, Summer 2009, No. 8, pp. 42)*
Pub: Rogers Media
Ed: Calvin Leung. **Description:** David Stanley revealed in an analysis of the ten companies on the S&P/TSX 60 index with the highest dividend yields, known as the Dogs of TSX, the dogs delivered an annual return of 13 percent between 1987 to 2005. The Dogs is a stock-picking method that involves buying the ten companies on the S&P/TSX 60 index with the highest dividend yields, and then selling them a year later.

8267 ■ *"The Dominance of Doubt" in Barron's (Vol. 89, July 13, 2009, No. 28, pp. M3)*
Pub: Dow Jones & Co., Inc.
Description: Five straight down days leading up to July 10, 2009 in the U.S. stock market reminds one strategist of 1982 when there was a feeling that things could never be the same again. One analyst is bullish on the stocks of Apple Inc. and sees the stocks rising to at least 180 in 12 months. The prospects of the shares of GM and Ford are also discussed.

8268 ■ *"Don't Bet Against The House"* in *Barron's (Vol. 88, July 14, 2008, No. 28, pp. 20)*
Pub: Dow Jones & Co., Inc.
Ed: Sandra Ward. **Description:** Shares of Nasdaq OMX have lost more than 50 percent of their value from November 2007 to July 2008 but the value of these shares could climb 50 percent on the strength of world security exchanges. Only 15 percent of the company's revenues come from the U.S. and the shares are trading at 12.5 times the amount expected for 2008.

8269 ■ *"Don't Expect Quick Fix"* in The *Business Journal-Serving Metropolitan Kansas City (Vol. 27, October 3, 2008, No. 3, pp. 1)*
Pub: American City Business Journals, Inc.
Ed: James Dornbrook. **Description:** United States governmental entities cannot provide a quick fix solution to the current financial crisis. The economy requires a systemic change in the way people think about credit. The financial services industry should also focus on core lending principles.

8270 ■ *"Don't Get Lulled by the Calm"* in *Barron's (Vol. 89, July 27, 2009, No. 30, pp. M13)*
Pub: Dow Jones & Co., Inc.
Ed: Steven M. Sears. **Description:** Options traders expect volatility to return in the fall of 2009 and to bring correlation with it. September and October are typically the most volatile months and the trick is to survive earnings season.

8271 ■ *"Don't' Hang Up On FairPoint"* in *Barron's (Vol. 88, July 7, 2008, No. 27, pp. M5)*
Pub: Dow Jones & Co., Inc.
Ed: Fleming Meeks. **Description:** Shares of Fair-Point Communications, priced at $6.63 each, are undervalued and should be worth over $12 each. The company increased its size by more than five times by acquiring Verizon's local telephone operations in Vermont, New Hampshire, and Maine, but must switch customers in those areas into their system by the end of September 2007.

8272 ■ *"Dow Jones Gives Apple-Loving Sales Professionals a Boost"* in *Information Today (Vol. 26, February 2009, No. 2, pp. 30)*
Pub: Information Today, Inc.
Description: Dow Jones Sales Triggers for iPhone and iPod program helps sales professionals stay current to prospects and customers in their fields by providing real-time news on business changes, including management moves, mergers, and new investments. The application presents events that trigger best opportunities and allows users to look up companies and executives to retrieve information.

8273 ■ *"Downtown Bank Got High Marks for Irwin Purchase, Is Looking For More"* in *Business Courier (Vol. 27, September 3, 2010, No. 18, pp. 1)*
Pub: Business Courier
Ed: Steve Watkins. **Description:** First Financial Bancorp is looking to acquire more troubled banks following its purchase of Irwin Union Bank. The bank has reported a $383 million bargain purchase gain during the third quarter of 2009.

8274 ■ *"Drilling Deep and Flying High"* in *Barron's (Vol. 88, June 30, 2008, No. 26, pp. 34)*
Pub: Dow Jones & Co., Inc.
Ed: Kenneth Rapoza. **Description:** Shares of Petrobras could rise another 25 percent if the three deepwater wells that the company has found proves as lucrative as some expect. Petrobras will become an oil giant if the reserves are proven.

8275 ■ *"Drug-Maker Plans IPO"* in *Business Courier (Vol. 24, November 23, 2008, No. 32, pp. 1)*
Pub: American City Business Journals, Inc.
Ed: James Ritchie; Steve Watkins. **Description:** Xanodyne Pharmaceuticals Inc. filed plans with the Securities and Exchange Commission on November

9, 2007 for an initial public offering. The company, with annual sales of $75 million, had lost $222 million since it was founded in 2001.

8276 ■ *"Drug, Seed Firms Offer Antidote For Inflation"* in *Crain's Chicago Business (Vol. 31, April 21, 2008, No. 16, pp. 4)*
Pub: Crain Communications, Inc.
Ed: Daniel Rome Levine. **Description:** Interview with Jerrold Senser, the CEO of Institutional Capital LLC in Chicago, in which he discusses the ways that the company is adjusting to the economic slowdown and rising inflation, his favorite firms for investment and his prediction of an economic turnaround; he also recommends five companies he feels are worth investing in.

8277 ■ *"Drug Trial Halt at YM Sets Stage for Selloff"* in *Globe & Mail (January 31, 2007, pp. B3)*
Pub: CTVglobemedia Publishing Inc.
Ed: Leonard Zehr. **Description:** The decision of YM Biosciences Inc. to stop its trial of cancer drug tesmilifene and stocks following government concern over the safety of the drug is discussed.

8278 ■ *"Dueling Visions"* in *Barron's (Vol. 89, July 27, 2009, No. 30, pp. 13)*
Pub: Dow Jones & Co., Inc.
Ed: Michael Santoli. **Description:** Goldman Sachs' market strategists believe the stock market has entered a 'sustained-rally' mode while Morgan Stanley's strategist believes this is a 'rally to sell into'. What is not known in the stock market is how much of a 'V'-shaped recovery in earning the market rebound has already priced in.

8279 ■ *"Dynamic Duo"* in *Barron's (Vol. 88, March 10, 2008, No. 10, pp. 45)*
Pub: Dow Jones & Company, Inc.
Ed: Shirley A. Lazo. **Description:** General Dynamics, the world's sixth-largest military contractor, raised its dividend payout by 20.7 percent from 29 cents to 35 cents a share. Steel Dynamics, producer of structural steel and steel bar products, declared a 2-for-1 stock split and raised its quarterly dividend by 33 percent to a split-adjusted 10 cents a share.

8280 ■ *"easyhome Ltd. Discovers Employee Fraud at an Easyfinancial Kiosk Company"* in *Internet Wire (October 14, 2010)*
Pub: Comtex
Description: Canada's leading merchandise leasing company and provider of financial services, easyhome Ltd., reported employee fraud totaling $3.4 million that was perpetrated against the firm's easyfinancial services business.

8281 ■ *"Economic Prognosis"* in *Barron's (Vol. 89, July 13, 2009, No. 28, pp. 11)*
Pub: Dow Jones & Co., Inc.
Ed: Karen Hube. **Description:** Loomis Sayles Bond Fund manager Dan Fuss believes that the economy is bottoming and that recovery will be long and drawn out. Fuss guesses that the next peak in 10-year Treasury yields will be about 6.25% in around 4 and a half or five years ahead of 2009.

8282 ■ *"An Educated Play on China"* in *Barron's (Vol. 88, June 30, 2008, No. 26, pp. M6)*
Pub: Dow Jones & Co., Inc.
Ed: Mohammed Hadi. **Description:** New Oriental Education & Technology Group sells English-language courses to an increasingly competitive Chinese workforce that values education. The shares in this company have been weighed down by worries on the impact of the Beijing Olympics on enrollment and the Sichuan earthquake. These shares could be a great way to get exposure to the long-term growth in China.

8283 ■ *"Effect of Oil Prices on the Economy"* in *Canadian Business (Vol. 81, September 15, 2008, No. 14-15, pp. 5)*
Pub: Rogers Media Ltd.
Ed: Joe Chidley. **Description:** Rise of oil prices above $100 in February 2008 and $140 in July signals the birth of a 'new economy' according to commentators; this shift is causing uneasiness from

oil industry professionals who are unsure of how this trend could be sustained. Oil dropped below $120 in August, which could slow down global economic growth followed by oil demand, then oil prices.

8284 ■ *"Egg Fight: The Yolk's on the Short"* in *Barron's (Vol. 88, July 7, 2008, No. 27, pp. 20)*
Pub: Dow Jones & Co., Inc.
Ed: Christopher C. Williams. **Description:** Shares of Cal-Maine Foods, the largest egg producer and distributor in the US, are due for a huge rise because of the increase in egg prices. Short sellers, however, continue betting that the stock, priced at $31.84 each, will eventually go down.

8285 ■ *"The Emerging Capital Market for Nonprofits"* in *Harvard Business Review (Vol. 88, October 2010, No. 10, pp. 110)*
Pub: Harvard Business School Publishing
Ed: Robert S. Kaplan, Allen S. Grossman. **Description:** Demonstration of how nonprofits can use intermediaries to grow their organizational structures, giving them improved scale and impact is offered. Some intermediaries play a mutual-fund role and conduct due diligence, while others act as venture capital funds and implement strategy.

8286 ■ *"The Emperor Strikes Back"* in *Canadian Business (Vol. 80, March 26, 2007, No. 7, pp. 48)*
Pub: Rogers Media
Ed: Rachel Pulfer. **Description:** The financial performance of Fairfax Financial Holdings Ltd. in 2006 is presented. The efforts of chief executive Prem Watsa to lead the company towards growth track are also presented.

8287 ■ *"EnCana Axes Spending on Gas Wells"* in *Globe & Mail (February 16, 2006, pp. B1)*
Pub: CTVglobemedia Publishing Inc.
Ed: Dave Ebner. **Description:** The reasons behind EnCana Corp.'s cost spending measures by $300 million on natural gas wells are presented. The company projects 2 percent cut in gas and oil sales for 2006.

8288 ■ *"End of the Beginning"* in *Canadian Business (Vol. 81, November 10, 2008, No. 19, pp. 17)*
Pub: Rogers Media Ltd.
Ed: David Wolf. **Description:** The freeze in the money markets and historic decline in equity markets around the world finally forced governments into aggressive coordinated action. The asset price inflation brought on by cheap credit will now work in reverse and the tightening of credit will be difficult economically. Canada is exposed to the fallout everywhere, given that the U.S, the U.K. and Japan buy 30 percent of Canada's output.

8289 ■ *"End of an Era"* in *Barron's (Vol. 88, July 7, 2008, No. 27, pp. 3)*
Pub: Dow Jones & Co., Inc.
Ed: Alan Abelson. **Description:** June 2008 was a very bad month for US stocks, with investors losing as much as 41.9 percent in the first half of 2008 signaling an end to the financial environment that prevailed around the world since the 1980's. The US job market lost 62,000 jobs in June 2008.

8290 ■ *"The End of the Line for Line Extensions?"* in *Advertising Age (Vol. 79, July 7, 2008, No. 26, pp. 3)*
Pub: Crain Communications, Inc.
Description: After years of double-digit growth, some of the most heavily extended personal-care products have slowed substantially or even declined in the U.S. Unilever's Dove and P&G's Pantene and Olay are two such brands that have been affected. Statistical data included.

8291 ■ *"Energy Firms Face Stricter Definitions"* in *Globe & Mail (March 26, 2007, pp. B3)*
Pub: CTVglobemedia Publishing Inc.
Ed: David Ebner. **Description:** The Alberta Securities Commission has imposed strict securities regulations on oil and gas industries. Energy industries will have to submit revenue details to stake holders.

8292 ■ *"Energy, MLPs: Pipeline to Profits"* in *Barron's* (Vol. 89, July 27, 2009, No. 30, pp. 9)
Pub: Dow Jones & Co., Inc.
Ed: Dimitra DeFotis. **Description:** Energy master limited partnership stocks are range-bound in the next few months from July 2009 but there are there are some opportunities that remain. These include Energy Transfer Equity, Enterprise GP holdings, NuStar GP Holdings, and Plains All American Pipeline.

8293 ■ *"Engine of Growth: U.S. Industry Funk hasn't Hurt Cummins or Its Investors"* in *Barron's* (Vol. 88, July 14, 2008, No. 28, pp. 43)
Pub: Dow Jones & Co., Inc.
Ed: Shirley A. Lazo. **Description:** Engine maker Cummins increased its quarterly common dividend by 40 percent to 17.5 cents per share from 12.5 cents. CVS Caremark's dividend saw a hike of 18.4 percent from 9.5 cents to 11.25 cents per share while its competitor Walgreen is continuing its 75th straight year of dividend distribution and its 33rd straight year of dividend hikes.

8294 ■ *"Essential Releases Record First Quarter Results"* in *Canadian Corporate News* (May 14, 2007)
Pub: Comtex News Network Inc.
Description: The first quarter of 2007 saw record financial performance despite numerous challenges for Essential Energy Services Trust. Statistical data included.

8295 ■ *"ETF Score Card"* in *Barron's* (Vol. 89, July 13, 2009, No. 28, pp. 51)
Pub: Dow Jones & Co., Inc.
Description: Statistical table is presented which shows the net assets of various exchange-traded funds is presented. The table also shows the total return of these funds up to a three-year time period.

8296 ■ *"European Stocks on Deck"* in *Barron's* (Vol. 89, July 27, 2009, No. 30, pp. M7)
Pub: Dow Jones & Co., Inc.
Ed: Vito J. Racanelli. **Description:** European stocks are cheap and these trade at a discount to U.S. equities rarely seen in the past 40 years. This represents an opportunity for Americans and trends show that Europe's stocks outperform when there is a discrepancy between the price to earnings ratio in European stocks versus U.S. stocks and when sentiment on European equities are downbeat.

8297 ■ *"Europe's Meltdown"* in *Canadian Business* (Vol. 83, June 15, 2010, No. 10, pp. 76)
Pub: Rogers Media Ltd.
Ed: Bryan Borzykowski. **Description:** As European countries such as Greece, Spain, and Portugal struggle with debt problems, it is worth noting that its equities trade at a 30 percent discount to the U.S. and that a 10 percent drop in the Euro translates to a 10 percent rise in profitability for exporters. Investors may also want to focus on business-to-business operations rather than consumer-focused ones.

8298 ■ *"Everyone Out of the Pool"* in *Barron's* (Vol. 89, July 20, 2009, No. 29, pp. 18)
Pub: Dow Jones & Co., Inc.
Ed: Sandra Ward. **Description:** Shares of Pool Corp. could drop as continued weakness in the housing market weakens the market for swimming pool equipment. The company's shares are trading at $18.29, about 20 times projected 2009 earnings of $0.91 a share.

8299 ■ *"Expect a Rally as Waders Dive In"* in *Barron's* (Vol. 89, July 20, 2009, No. 29, pp. 11)
Pub: Dow Jones & Co., Inc.
Ed: Vito J. Racanelli. **Description:** US stock markets may experience a rally in the autumn of 2009 as skeptical investors start to return to the market. The Standard & Poor's Index may jump to the 1025-1050 point levels during this rally.

8300 ■ *"Experts: Market Shaky But Resilient"* in *The Business Journal-Serving Metropolitan Kansas City* (Vol. 27, September 19, 2008, No. 1)
Pub: American City Business Journals, Inc.
Ed: Steve Vockrodt. **Description:** Investment advisers believe that the local investors in Kansas City who have a long-term approach towards their portfolios may come out even or even experience gains despite the Wall Street financial crisis. The impacts of the crisis are expected to take time to reach the area of Kansas City. The potential impacts of the Wall Street meltdown are examined further.

8301 ■ *"Falling Markets' Nastiest Habits"* in *Barron's* (Vol. 88, July 7, 2008, No. 27, pp. 7)
Pub: Dow Jones & Co., Inc.
Ed: Michael Santoli. **Description:** US market conditions reflect a bear market, with the S&P 500 index falling 20 percent below its recent high as of June 2008. The bear market is expected to persist in the immediate future, although bear market rallies are likely to occur.

8302 ■ *"Falling Share Prices Will Convince Big Oil Producers to Pay Up to Drill"* in *Globe & Mail* (April 21, 2007, pp. B1)
Pub: CTVglobemedia Publishing Inc.
Ed: Boyd Erman. **Description:** The effect of the increase in operational costs and the decline in share prices, on the exploration of petroleum deposits in Canada, is described.

8303 ■ *"Fannie and Freddie: How They'll Change"* in *Business Week* (September 22, 2008, No. 4100, pp. 30)
Pub: McGraw-Hill Companies, Inc.
Ed: Jane Sasseen. **Description:** Three possible outcomes of the fate of struggling mortgage giants Freddie Mac and Fannie Mae after the government bailout are outlined.

8304 ■ *"Fast Revival Unlikely For Indian 'Net Stocks"* in *Barron's* (Vol. 88, July 7, 2008, No. 27, pp. 12)
Pub: Dow Jones & Co., Inc.
Ed: Leslie P. Norton. **Description:** Shares of Indian Internet companies Rediff.com and Sify are not likely to stage a rebound due to weak financial results. Rediff.com shares have declined 39.2 percent in 2008, while Sify shares are down 35.8 percent.

8305 ■ *"February Hot for Mutual Fund Sales"* in *Globe & Mail* (March 3, 2006, pp. B10)
Pub: CTVglobemedia Publishing Inc.
Ed: Keith Damsell. **Description:** The details on Canadian mutual fund sector, which posted $4.7 billion for February 2005, are presented.

8306 ■ *"The Fed Still Has Ammunition"* in *Barron's* (Vol. 90, August 30, 2010, No. 35, pp. M9)
Pub: Barron's Editorial & Corporate Headquarters
Ed: Randall W. Forsyth. **Description:** Federal Reserve chairman Ben Bernanke said the agency still has tools to combat deflation and a second downturn but these strategies are not needed at this time. The prospects of the Federal Open Market Committee's purchasing of treasuries are also discussed.

8307 ■ *"Fed Tackles Bear of a Crisis"* in *Barron's* (Vol. 88, March 17, 2008, No. 11, pp. M10)
Pub: Dow Jones & Company, Inc.
Ed: Randall W. Forsyth. **Description:** Emergency funding package for Bear Stearns from the Federal Reserve Bank of New York through JPMorgan Chase is one of the steps taken by the central bank shore up bank liquidity. Prior to the emergency funding, the central bank announced the Term Securities Lending Facility to allow dealers to borrow easily saleable Treasuries in exchange for less-liquid issues.

8308 ■ *"Federal Bailout, Three Years Later"* in *Business Owner* (Vol. 35, September-October 2011, No. 5, pp. 6)
Pub: DL Perkins Company
Description: State of the economy and small business sector three years after the government stimulus and bailout programs were instituted.

8309 ■ *"Feeling the Heat: Effects of Stress, Commitment, and Job Experience On Job Performance"* in *Academy of Management Journal* (Aug. 2007)
Pub: Academy of Management
Contact: Ming-Jer Chen, President
Ed: Larry W. Hunter, Sherry M.B. Thatcher. **Description:** Links between bank branch employees' felt job stress, organizational commitment, job experience, and performance is analyzed. Results found are uniform with the attention view of stress.

8310 ■ *"Fees Come Down; Markets Come Down More"* in *Barron's* (Vol. 89, July 13, 2009, No. 28, pp. L8)
Pub: Dow Jones & Co., Inc.
Ed: J.R. Brandstrader. **Description:** Investors spent less on mutual fund fees in 2009 than they did in the last 25 years. These fees include administration, accounting, and legal expense. Despite the popularity of money market funds which has contributed to this decline, the short-term yields of these funds fell in the last year.

8311 ■ *"A Few Points of Contention"* in *Barron's* (Vol. 88, July 14, 2008, No. 28, pp. 3)
Pub: Dow Jones & Co., Inc.
Ed: Michael Santoli. **Description:** Headline inflation tends to revert to the lower core inflation, which excludes food and energy in its calculation over long periods. Prominent private equity figures believe that regulators should allow more than the de facto 10 percent to 25 percent limit of commercial banks to hasten the refunding of the financial sector.

8312 ■ *"Fewer Banks Offer Big Gifts to Lure Clients"* in *Globe & Mail* (March 14, 2006, pp. D1)
Pub: CTVglobemedia Publishing Inc.
Ed: Chris Reidy. **Description:** Fewer banks are offering gifts to lure the customers in this year in the wake of less favorable interest rates in the spring season. The market climate is analyzed.

8313 ■ *"Fifth Third CEO Kabat: A World of Difference"* in *Business Courier* (Vol. 26, January 1, 2010, No. 37, pp. 1)
Pub: American City Business Journals, Inc.
Ed: Steve Watkins. **Description:** CEO Kevin Kabat of Cincinnati-based Fifth Third Bancorp believes that the bank's assets of $111 billion and stock value of more than $10 indicate the recovery from the low stock prices posted in February 2009. He attributes the recovery from the federal government's stress test finding in May 2009 that Fifth Third needs to generate $1.1 billion.

8314 ■ *"The File On..Skoda Minotti"* in *Crain's Cleveland Business* (Vol. 28, October 8, 2007, No. 40, pp. 26)
Pub: Crain Communications, Inc.
Ed: Kimberly Bonvissuto. **Description:** Overview of Skoda Minotti, the accounting and financial services firm located in Mayfield Village; the company has 140 employees and an expanded slate of services.

8315 ■ *"Finalist: BlackEagle Partners L.L.C."* in *Crain's Detroit Business* (Vol. 24, March 24, 2008, No. 12, pp. 12)
Pub: Crain Communications, Inc.
Ed: Brent Snavely. **Description:** Overview of private-equity firm, BlackEagle Partners L.L.C., an upstart that acquired Rockford Products Corp. in order to improve the performance of the company who does business with several major tier-one automotive suppliers; Rockford manufactures highly engineered chassis and suspension components for automakers and the automotive aftermarket.

8316 ■ *"The Finance Function In A Global Corporation"* in *Harvard Business Review* (Vol. 86, July-August 2008, No. 8, pp. 108)
Pub: Harvard Business School Press
Ed: Mihir A. Desai. **Description:** Designing and implementing a successful finance function in a global setting is discussed. Additional topics include the internal capital market, managing risk and budgeting capital internationally.

8317 ■ *"Financial Education: Boomer's Spending Hurts Retirement"* in *Employee Benefit News (Vol. 25, November 1, 2011, No. 14, pp. 18)*
Pub: SourceMedia Inc.

Ed: Ann Marsh. **Description:** Financial planners and employers need to educate clients and employees about retirement planning. Boomers are spending money that should be saved for their retirement.

8318 ■ *Financing Your Small Business*
Pub: Barron's Educational Series Inc.
Contact: Alex Holtz, President
E-mail: aholtz@berronseduc.com

Ed: Robert Walter. **Released:** December 2003. **Description:** Tips for raising venture capital, dealing with bank officials, and initiating public offerings of stock shares for small business.

8319 ■ *"Finding Good Bets Down on the Farm"* in *Crain's Chicago Business (Vol. 31, March 24, 2008, No. 12, pp. 4)*
Pub: Crain Communications, Inc.

Ed: Daniel Rome Levine. **Description:** Interview with money manager Jeff James, the portfolio manager for Driehaus Capital Management LLC, who discusses the Federal Reserve and recommends several companies in which to make investments.

8320 ■ *"Finger-Pointing Time"* in *Barron's (Vol. 88, March 10, 2008, No. 10, pp. 9)*
Pub: Dow Jones & Company, Inc.

Ed: Michael Santoli. **Description:** Discusses who is to blame for the financial crisis brought about by the credit crunch in the United States; the country's financial markets will eventually digest this crisis but will bottom out first before the situation improves.

8321 ■ *"First Financial Aiming for Banking Big Leagues"* in *Business Courier (Vol. 26, December 4, 2009, No. 32, pp. 1)*
Pub: American City Business Journals, Inc.

Ed: Steve Watkins. **Description:** First Financial Bancorp could dominate the community banking market of Greater Cincinnati after buying failed banks with the supervision of the FDIC. Details of the transactions are presented.

8322 ■ *"FirstMerit's Top Executive Turns Around Credit Quality"* in *Crain's Cleveland Business (Vol. 28, October 15, 2007, No. 41, pp. 3)*
Pub: Crain Communications, Inc.

Ed: Shawn A. Turner. **Description:** Discusses the ways in which chairman and CEO Paul Greig has been able to improve FirstMerit Corp.'s credit quality and profit margin. Strategies included selling more than $70 million in bad loans, hiring a new chief credit officer and redirecting its focus on cross-selling its wealth and investment services to its commercial customers. Statistical data included.

8323 ■ *"FIS-Metavante Deal Paying Off for Many"* in *Business Journal-Milwaukee (Vol. 28, December 17, 2010, No. 11, pp. A1)*
Pub: Milwaukee Business Journal

Ed: Rich Kirchen. **Description:** Jacksonville, Florida-based Fidelity National Information Services Inc., also known as FIS, has remained committed to Milwaukee, Wisconsin more than a year after purchasing Metavante Technologies Inc. FIS has transferred several operations into Metropolitan Milwaukee and has continued its contribution to charitable organizations in the area.

8324 ■ *"A Flawed Yardstick for Banks"* in *Barron's (Vol. 88, July 14, 2008, No. 28, pp. M6)*
Pub: Dow Jones & Co., Inc.

Ed: Arindam Nag. **Description:** Return on equity is no longer the best measure for investors to judge banks by in a post-subprime-crises world. Investors should consider the proportion of a bank's total assets that are considered risky and look out for any write-downs of goodwill when judging a bank's financial health.

8325 ■ *"Florida's Housing Gloom May Add To Woes of National City"* in *Crain's Cleveland Business (Vol. 28, October 29, 2007, No. 43, pp. 1)*
Pub: Crain Communications, Inc.

Ed: Shawn A. Turner. **Description:** Already suffering by bad loans in the troubled mortgage market, National City Corp. is attempting to diversify its geographic presence beyond the slow-growth industrial Midwest by acquiring two Florida firms. Analysts worry that the acquisitions may end up making National City vulnerable to a takeover if the housing slump continues and credit quality becomes more of an issue for the bank.

8326 ■ *"Flying High?"* in *Canadian Business (Vol. 80, April 9, 2007, No. 8, pp. 42)*
Pub: Rogers Media

Ed: Thomas Watson. **Description:** The increase in Bombardier Inc.'s income by 30 percent to $112 million and increase in its share prices are discussed. The caution of analysts about its accounting methods that may adversely hit the company in future, too is discussed.

8327 ■ *Fooling Some of the People All of the Time*
Pub: John Wiley & Sons, Inc.

Ed: David Einhorn. **Released:** March 10, 2010. **Price:** $29.95. **Description:** A chronicle of the ongoing saga between author, David Einhorn's hedge fund, Greenlight Capital, and Allied Capital, a leader in the private finance industry.

8328 ■ *Fool's Gold: How the Bold Dream of a Small Tribe at J.P. Morgan Was Corrupted by Wall Street Greed*
Pub: Free Press

Ed: Gillian Tett. **Released:** 2009. **Price:** $26.00. **Description:** An explanation of how swaps and CDOs, which were invented by J.P. Morgan, ended up creating more risk not controlling it.

8329 ■ *"For Baxter, A Lingering PR Problem; Ongoing Focus On Heparin Deaths Ups Heat On CEO"* in *Crain's Chicago Business (April 21, 2008)*
Pub: Crain Communications, Inc.

Ed: Mike Colias. **Description:** Baxter International Inc.'s recall of the blood-thinning medication heparin has exposed the company to costly litigation and put the perils of overseas drug manufacturing in the spotlight. Wall Street investors predict that an indefinite halt in production of the drug should not hurt the company's bottom line since heparin represents a tiny sliver of the business. Since Baxter began recalling the drug in January its shares have continued to outpace most other medical stocks.

8330 ■ *"For Buffet Fans, the Price Is Right"* in *Barron's (Vol. 89, July 13, 2009, No. 28, pp. 17)*
Pub: Dow Jones & Co., Inc.

Ed: Andrew Bary. **Description:** Shares of Warren Buffett's Berkshire Hathaway have fallen to $85,000 and these are cheap since they are trading at just 1.2 times estimated book value and are well below its peak of $149,000. One fan of the stock expects it to top $110,000 in the next year from June 2009.

8331 ■ *"For Gilead, Growth Beyond AIDS"* in *Barron's (Vol. 88, June 30, 2008, No. 26, pp. 18)*
Pub: Dow Jones & Co., Inc.

Ed: Jay Palmer. **Description:** First-quarter 2008 revenue for Gilead Sciences grew by 22 percent and an earnings gain of 19 percent thanks to their HIV-treatment drugs that comprised over two-thirds of the company's sales in 2007. An analyst has a 12-month target from June, 2008 of 65 per share. The factors behind the company's prospects are also discussed.

8332 ■ *"Ford Canada's Edsel of a Year: Revenue Plummets 24 Percent in '05"* in *Globe & Mail (February 2, 2006, pp. B1)*
Pub: CTVglobemedia Publishing Inc.

Ed: Greg Keenan. **Description:** Ford Motor Company of Canada Ltd. posted 24% decline in revenues for 2005. The drop in earnings is attributed to plant shutdown in Oaksville, Canada.

8333 ■ *"Former Mayor Driving $500 Million Real Estate Equity Fund"* in *The Business Journal - Serving Phoenix and the Valley of the Sun (Vol. 28, August 15, 2008, No. 50, pp. 1)*
Pub: American City Business Journals, Inc.

Ed: Jan Buchholz. **Description:** Paul John, the former mayor of Phoenix, is establishing a $500 million real estate asset management fund. The fund is dubbed Southwest Next Capital Management and has attracted three local partners, namely Joseph Meyer, Jay Michalowski, and James Mullany, who all have background in finance and construction.

8334 ■ *"The Four Cheapest Plays in Emerging Markets"* in *Barron's (Vol. 89, July 27, 2009, No. 30, pp. 34)*
Pub: Dow Jones & Co., Inc.

Ed: Lawrence C. Strauss. **Description:** Portfolio manager Arjun Divecha of the GMO Emerging Markets III Fund says that the main thing in investing in emerging markets is getting the country right since getting it wrong makes it harder to add value. Divecha says that the four countries that they are positive on are Turkey, Russia, South Korea, and Thailand.

8335 ■ *"Fraud Alleged at Norshield; Investors Out $215 Million"* in *Globe & Mail (March 8, 2007, pp. B1)*
Pub: CTVglobemedia Publishing Inc.

Ed: Paul Waldie. **Description:** The investigation of the diversion of $215 million in investors' money by the management of Norshield Asset Management (Canada) Ltd. is described.

8336 ■ *"Freak Weather Dampens Intrawest Forecast"* in *Globe & Mail (February 8, 2006, pp. B3)*
Pub: CTVglobemedia Publishing Inc.

Ed: Peter Kennedy. **Description:** Intrawest Corp. dropped its earnings forecast by 7 percent. The impact of weather on earnings is discussed.

8337 ■ *"Friends With Money"* in *Canadian Business (Vol. 81, Summer 2008, No. 9, pp. 22)*
Pub: Rogers Media Ltd.

Description: Two of the most well connected managers in Canadian capital markets Rob Farquharson and Brian Gibson will launch Panoply Capital Asset Management in June. The investment management company aims to raise a billion dollars from institutions and high-net worth individuals.

8338 ■ *"From Buyout to Busted"* in *Business Week (September 22, 2008, No. 4100, pp. 18)*
Pub: McGraw-Hill Companies, Inc.

Ed: Emily Thornton; Deborah Stead. **Description:** Bankruptcy filings by private equity-backed companies are at a record high with 134 American firms taken private (or invested in) by buyout firms that have filed for protection this year under Chapter 11; this is 91 percent higher than the previous year, which had set a record when 70 of such companies filed for protection under Chapter 11.

8339 ■ *"From Fastenal, a Boost"* in *Barron's (Vol. 89, July 20, 2009, No. 29, pp. M13)*
Pub: Dow Jones & Co., Inc.

Ed: Shirley A. Lazo. **Description:** Fastenal increased its semi-annual common payout from $0.35 to $0.37 a share. Core Laboratories declared a special dividend of $0.75 a share along with its quarterly payout of $0.10. Ryder System and Landstar System raised their payouts to $0.23 and $0.045 a share respectively.

8340 ■ *"The Frugal Billionaire"* in *Canadian Business (Vol. 79, Winter 2006, No. 24, pp. 63)*
Pub: Rogers Media

Ed: Joe Castaldo. **Description:** The achievements of David Cheriton are described, along with his investments in various firms, including Google Inc.

8341 ■ *"Full-Court Press for Apple"* in *Barron's* (Vol. 88, March 24, 2008, No. 12, pp. 47)

Pub: Dow Jones & Company, Inc.

Ed: Mark Veverka. **Description:** Apple Inc. is facing more intellectual property lawsuits in 2008, with 30 patent lawsuits filed compared to 15 in 2007 and nine in 2006. The lawsuits, which involve products such as the iPod and the iPhone, present some concern for Apple's shareholders.

8342 ■ *"Function Over Forms?"* in *Barron's* (Vol. 88, June 30, 2008, No. 26, pp. 17)

Pub: Dow Jones & Co., Inc.

Ed: Eric Savitz. **Description:** Securities and Exchange Commission (SEC) chairman Christopher Cox wants the SEC to consider an overhaul of the forms used to meet the agency's disclosure requirements. Cox also said that the U.S. Generally Accepted Accounting Standards has too many rules with exceptions and alternative interpretations.

8343 ■ *"Funds 'Friend' Facebook"* in *Barron's* (Vol. 89, July 27, 2009, No. 30, pp. 30)

Pub: Dow Jones & Co., Inc.

Ed: Leslie P. Norton. **Description:** Mutual-fund companies are the latest entrants to the 'social media' space and several companies have already set up Facebook and Twitter pages. The use of this technology pose special challenges for compliance and regulators especially since the Financial Industry Regulatory Authority reminds companies that advertising, sales and literature are governed by regulations.

8344 ■ *"The Future of Private Equity"* in *Canadian Business* (Vol. 80, March 26, 2007, No. 7, pp. 19)

Pub: Rogers Media

Ed: Jack Mintz. **Description:** The impact growing Canadian economy and competition in global business on the performance of private equity funds is analyzed.

8345 ■ *"Future's Brighter for Financial Stocks"* in *Barron's* (Vol. 89, July 20, 2009, No. 29, pp. 14)

Pub: Dow Jones & Co., Inc.

Ed: Jacqueline Doherty. **Description:** Shares of US financial companies are projected to rise as their earnings start to normalize. Earnings of these companies have been hurt by credit losses but have been bolstered by one-time gains.

8346 ■ *"Futures Shock for the CME"* in *Crain's Chicago Business* (Vol. 31, November 10, 2008, No. 45, pp. 8)

Pub: Crain Communications, Inc.

Ed: Ann Saphir. **Description:** Chicago-based CME Group Inc., the largest futures exchange operator in the U.S., is facing a potentially radically altered regulatory landscape as Congress weighs sweeping reform of financial oversight. The possible merger of the CFTC and the Securities and Exchange Commission are among CME's concerns. Other details of possible regulatory measures are provided.

8347 ■ *"Futures of the Street"* in *Barron's* (Vol. 88, June 30, 2008, No. 26, pp. 27)

Pub: Dow Jones & Co., Inc.

Ed: Michael Santoli. **Description:** Prospects of the securities industry in terms of jobs and profit sources are discussed. Suggestions on what the industry needs with regards to its use of capital are also discussed.

8348 ■ *"Gas Glut Pummels Prices"* in *Barron's* (Vol. 89, July 27, 2009, No. 30, pp. M8)

Pub: Dow Jones & Co., Inc.

Ed: Christine Buurma. **Description:** Natural gas-futures prices have fallen 73 percent and the glut of output from onshore gas fields and the weak demand signals that a rebound is not near. An analyst expects U.S. production to show increasingly steep declines but the oversupply situation is not good for prices.

8349 ■ *"Gateway Delays Start"* in *The Business Journal-Serving Metropolitan Kansas City* (Vol. 27, October 31, 2008, No. 8, pp. 1)

Pub: American City Business Journals, Inc.

Ed: Rob Roberts. **Description:** Economic problems caused, in part, by the Wall Street crisis has resulted in the setback of a proposed mixed-use redevelopment project, The Gateway. The $307 million project, which includes the Kansas Aquarium, will be delayed due to financing problems. Details of the project are given.

8350 ■ *"GE Looking to Extend Hot Streak"* in *Business Courier* (Vol. 24, January 25, 2008, No. 42, pp. 1)

Pub: American City Business Journals, Inc.

Ed: John Newberry. **Description:** GE Aviation has enjoyed strong revenues and sales due to increase aircraft engine orders. It has an engine backlog order of $19 million as of the end of 2007. Data on the aviation company's revenues, operating profit and total engine orders for the year 2004 to 2007 are presented.

8351 ■ *"General Motors Can't Kick Incentives-But They Work"* in *Advertising Age* (Vol. 79, July 7, 2008, No. 26, pp. 3)

Pub: Crain Communications, Inc.

Ed: Jean Halliday. **Description:** General Motors Corp. was able to maintain their market share just as Toyota Motor Corp. was beginning to pass the manufacturer; GM lured in customers with a sales incentive that they heavily advertised and subsequently helped build demand; investors, however, were not impressed and GM shares were hammered to their lowest point in 50 years after analysts speculated the company might go bankrupt.

8352 ■ *"Generation Y - An Opportunity for a Fresh Financial Start"* in (September 11, 2010, pp. 241)

Pub: VerticalNews

Description: Eleanor Blayney, the consumer advocate for the Certified Financial Planner Board of Standards, offers a financial strategy for Generation Y individuals starting their financial planning. The first segment of the non-profit's Lifelong Financial Strategies initiative is called 'Starting Out', and focuses on ways Generation Y people can avoid pitfalls of earlier generations by making smart financial decisions.

8353 ■ *"Genzyme: Underrated Oversold"* in *Barron's* (Vol. 88, March 24, 2008, No. 12, pp. 58)

Pub: Dow Jones & Company, Inc.

Ed: Johanna Bennett. **Description:** Shares of bio-technology company Genzyme appear oversold and underrated at their $71.86 level. The company's finances are on a solid foundation, with revenues over $3.8 billion in 2007 and forecasts of $4.5-4.7 billion in revenue for 2008.

8354 ■ *"Get It While Its Hot"* in *Canadian Business* (Vol. 80, January 15, 2007, No. 2, pp. 49)

Pub: Rogers Media

Ed: John Gray. **Description:** The rise in the demand for processed uranium and increase in the number of investors interested to invest in metal industries is discussed.

8355 ■ *"Get Off The Rollercoaster"* in *Michigan Vue* (Vol. 13, July-August 2008, No. 4, pp. 19)

Pub: Entrepreneur Media Inc.

Ed: Donald N. Hobley Jr. **Description:** Benefits of creating and implementing a solid financial plan during these rocky economic times are examined. Things to keep in mind before meeting with a financial planner include risk assessment, investment goals, the length of time required to meet those goals and the amount of money one has available to invest.

8356 ■ *"Getting In on the Ground Floor"* in *Barron's* (Vol. 89, July 27, 2009, No. 30, pp. 32)

Pub: Dow Jones & Co., Inc.

Ed: Jacqueline Doherty. **Description:** Shares of AvalonBay Communities have fallen 61 percent in the past two and a half years to July 2009 but at $56, the stock is trading near the asset value. The shares could rise as the economy improves and if the recovery takes longer, investors will be rewarded with a yield of 3.5 percent.

8357 ■ *"Getting More Out of Retirement"* in *Agency Sales Magazine* (Vol. 39, November 2009, No. 10, pp. 48)

Pub: MANA

Ed: Joshua D. Mosshart. **Description:** Overview of the Tax Increase Prevention and Reconciliation Act, which lets employees convert to a Roth IRA in 2010. The benefits of conversion depend on age and wealth and it is best to consult a tax advisor to determine the best strategy for retirement planners.

8358 ■ *"Getting Out of an IRS Mess"* in *Black Enterprise* (Vol. 37, December 2006, No. 5, pp. 53)

Pub: Earl G. Graves Publishing Co. Inc.

Ed: Carolyn M. Brown. **Description:** Owing back taxes to the IRS can lead to huge penalties and interest. Here are some tips on how to handle paying the IRS what you owe them.

8359 ■ *"Giants Now Admit They Roam Planet Earth; Time To Buy?"* in *Barron's* (Vol. 88, March 31, 2008, No. 13, pp. 39)

Pub: Dow Jones & Company, Inc.

Ed: Eric J. Savitz. **Description:** Oracle's third-quarter results showed that top-line growth fell short of expectations but the company is expected to fare better than most applications companies in the downturn. Google had a flat growth in the number of people who click their online ads. The time for investors in the tech sector with a long-term horizon has arrived.

8360 ■ *"Give a Little Back"* in *Canadian Business* (Vol. 79, November 20, 2006, No. 23, pp. 17)

Pub: Rogers Media

Ed: Jack Mintz. **Description:** The plans of Jim Flaherty, Canada's minister of finance, to remove the corporate tax bias on income paid to pension plans are discussed.

8361 ■ *"Give Me Liberty With DirecTV"* in *Barron's* (Vol. 89, July 13, 2009, No. 28, pp. M5)

Pub: Dow Jones & Co., Inc.

Ed: Fleming Meeks. **Description:** Shares of Liberty Entertainment look cheap at $25.14 and the same goes for DirecTV at $23.19. A merger between the two companies was announced and the deal will likely close by September 2009. Barclays Capital has a target of $30 for Liberty Media and $32 for DirecTV.

8362 ■ *"Global Good Time"* in *Canadian Business* (Vol. 80, January 15, 2007, No. 2, pp. 53)

Pub: Rogers Media

Ed: Thomas Watson. **Description:** Speculations on the stock prices of global emerging markets for 2007 are presented.

8363 ■ *"Global Steel Makers Circle Stelco"* in *Globe & Mail* (April 19, 2007, pp. B3)

Pub: CTVglobemedia Publishing Inc.

Ed: Greg Keenan. **Description:** The details of the take over bids offered to Stelco Inc. are presented. Due to these bids the shares of Stelco Inc rose up to 70 percent.

8364 ■ *"Gold Handshake"* in *Canadian Business* (Vol. 79, September 11, 2006, No. 18, pp. 25)

Pub: Rogers Media

Ed: John Gray. **Description:** Goldcorp Inc.'s company's planned takeover of Glamis Gold Ltd. is discussed. Implications of the merger on its investors are presented.

8365 ■ *"Gold Still Has That Glitter"* in *Barron's* (Vol. 89, July 20, 2009, No. 29, pp. M8)

Pub: Dow Jones & Co., Inc.

Ed: Allen Sykora. **Description:** Gold prices appear to be ready for an increase starting in the fall of 2009 due to an increase in demand. The price of the August 2009 gold contract fell to as low as $904.08 an ounce before recovering to $937.50.

8366 ■ *"A Good Book Is Worth a Thousand Blogs"* in *Barron's (Vol. 88, July 14, 2008, No. 28, pp. 42)*

Pub: Dow Jones & Co., Inc.

Ed: Gene Epstein. **Description:** Nine summer book suggestions on economics are presented. The list includes 'The Revolution' by Ron Paul, 'The Forgotten Man' by Amity Shales, 'The Commitments of Traders Bible' by Stephen Briese, and 'Economic Facts and Fallacies' by Thomas Sowell.

8367 ■ *"Good Going, Partners: Energy-Asset Firms Do Their Parents Proud"* in *Barron's (Vol. 89, July 27, 2009, No. 30, pp. M8)*

Pub: Dow Jones & Co., Inc.

Ed: Shirley A. Lazo. **Description:** Four master limited partnerships boosted their dividends. Sunoco Logistics raised theirs by 11.2 percent, El Paso Pipeline by 12 percent, Holly Energy upped their dividends by a penny, and Western Gas hiked their dividend to 31 cents per unit.

8368 ■ *"A Good Step, But There's a Long Way to Go"* in *Business Week (September 22, 2008, No. 4100, pp. 10)*

Pub: McGraw-Hill Companies, Inc.

Ed: James C. Cooper. **Description:** Despite the historic action by the U.S. government to nationalize the mortgage giants Freddie Mac and Fannie Mae, rising unemployment rates may prove to be an even bigger roadblock to bringing back the economy from its downward spiral. The takeover is meant to restore confidence in the credit markets and help with the mortgage crisis but the rising rate in unemployment may make many households unable to take advantage of any benefits which arise from the bailout. Statistical data included.

8369 ■ *"Good Things Happen When We Buy Local"* in *Crain's Detroit Business (Vol. 24, October 6, 2008, No. 40, pp. 7)*

Pub: Crain Communications, Inc.

Description: Michigan is facing incredibly difficult economic times. One way in which each one of us can help the state and the businesses located here is by purchasing our goods and services from local vendors. The state Agriculture Department projected that if Michigan households earmarked $10 per week in their grocery purchases to made-in-Michigan products, this would generate $30 million a week in economic impact.

8370 ■ *"Google's Next Stop: Below 350?"* in *Barron's (Vol. 88, March 10, 2008, No. 10, pp. 17)*

Pub: Dow Jones & Company, Inc.

Ed: Jacqueline Doherty. **Description:** Share prices of Google Inc. are expected to drop from their level of $433 each to below $350 per share. The company is expected to miss its earnings forecast for the first quarter of 2008, and its continued aggressive spending on non-core areas will eventually bring down earnings.

8371 ■ *"Gordon Nixon"* in *Canadian Business (Vol. 80, November 5, 2007, No. 22, pp. 9)*

Pub: Rogers Media

Ed: Rachel Pulfer. **Description:** Royal Bank of Canada (RBC) CEO, Gordon Nixon, believes the Canadian financial services segment is heavily regulated. Nixon also feels that it has become difficult for local banks to enter the market since foreign banks can easily come in and compete with them. His views on RBC's success are provided.

8372 ■ *"Gordon Nixon Q&A"* in *Canadian Business (Vol. 80, November 5, 2007, No. 22, pp. 9)*

Pub: Rogers Media

Ed: Rachel Pulfer. **Description:** Royal Bank of Canada (RBC) chief executive officer Gordon Nixon believes that the Canadian financial services segment is heavily regulated. Nixon also feels that it has become difficult for local banks to enter the market since foreign banks can easily come in and compete with Canadian banks. His views on RBC's success are provided.

8373 ■ *"Graduates to the TSX in 2008"* in *Canadian Business (Vol. 81, Summer 2008, No. 9, pp. 79)*

Pub: Rogers Media Ltd.

Ed: Calvin Leung. **Description:** Table showing the market capitalization and stock performance of the companies that jumped to the TSX Venture Exchange is presented. The 17 companies that made the leap to the list will have an easier time raising capital, although leeway must be made in investing since they are still new businesses.

8374 ■ *"The Great Deleveraging"* in *Canadian Business (Vol. 81, October 13, 2008, No. 17, pp. 45)*

Pub: Rogers Media Ltd.

Ed: Jeff Sanford. **Description:** 'Hell Week' of financial crisis on Wall Street is believed to have started with the downgrade of AIG Inc.'s credit rating. AIG is a major player in the credit derivatives market, and its bankruptcy would have affected firms on Wall Street.

8375 ■ *"The Great Fall"* in *Barron's (Vol. 88, March 10, 2008, No. 10, pp. 5)*

Pub: Dow Jones & Company, Inc.

Ed: Alan Abelson. **Description:** Discusses the US economy is considered to be in a recession, with the effects of the credit crisis expected to intensify as a result. Inflation is estimated at 4.3 percent in January 2008, while 63,000 jobs were lost in February 2008.

8376 ■ *"The Great Moderation"* in *Canadian Business (Vol. 80, February 12, 2007, No. 4, pp. 25)*

Pub: Rogers Media

Ed: David Wolf. **Description:** Caution over the changes to stock inventory levels and their adverse impact on the Canadian economy is discussed.

8377 ■ *"Great Stocks Cheap"* in *Canadian Business (Vol. 80, January 15, 2007, No. 2, pp. 31)*

Pub: Rogers Media

Ed: Calvin Leung. **Description:** The stock performance of top 10 international companies like Furgo, Moody's Investor Service, Adidas Group and Nestle is analyzed.

8378 ■ *"Green Assets Powering Boralex Shares"* in *Globe & Mail (March 30, 2007, pp. B10)*

Pub: CTVglobemedia Publishing Inc.

Ed: Richard Blackwell. **Description:** The impact of econ-friendly power plant portfolio on the stock performance of Kingsey Falls-based Boralex Inc. is analyzed.

8379 ■ *"The Green Trap"* in *Canadian Business (Vol. 80, April 9, 2007, No. 8, pp. 19)*

Pub: Rogers Media

Ed: Al Rosen. **Description:** Expert advice to companies on investing in environmental-friendly measures is presented.

8380 ■ *"Greenberg Sues U.S. Over AIG Rescue"* in *Wall Street Journal Eastern Edition (November 22, 2011, pp. C3)*

Pub: Dow Jones & Company Inc.

Ed: Liam Pleven, Serena Ng. **Description:** Former Chief Executive Officer of American International Group Inc., Maurice R. 'Hank' Greenberg, has filed a lawsuit against the United States and the Federal Reserve Bank of New York on behalf of shareholders and his company, Starr International Company Inc., claiming that the government was wrong in taking control of the insurance giant and used it to move tens of millions of dollars to the trading partners of AIG.

8381 ■ *"A Greenish Light for Financial-Sector Funds"* in *Barron's (Vol. 88, March 24, 2008, No. 12, pp. 52)*

Pub: Dow Jones & Company, Inc.

Ed: Tom Sullivan. **Description:** Financial sector funds have lost value in 2008 through 17 March, and investors are advised to reduce investments in the financial sector. Exchange-traded funds present a good way to own financial stocks.

8382 ■ *"Greg Stringham"* in *Canadian Business (Vol. 81, March 3, 2008, No. 3, pp. 8)*

Pub: Rogers Media

Ed: Michelle Magnan. **Description:** Canadian Association of Petroleum Producers' Greg Stringham thinks that the new royalty plan will result in companies pulling out their investments for Alberta's conventional oil and gas sector. Stringham adds that Alberta is losing its competitive advantage and companies must study their cost profiles to retrieve that advantage. The effects of the royalty system on Alberta's economy are examined further.

8383 ■ *"A Gripping Read: Bargains & Noble"* in *Barron's (Vol. 88, March 17, 2008, No. 11, pp. 20)*

Pub: Dow Jones & Company, Inc.

Ed: Jonathan R. Laing. **Description:** Barnes & Noble's earnings forecast for the fiscal year ending in January, 2008 to be $1.70 to $1.90 per share which is way lower than the $2.12 analyst consensus. The company also said that sales at stores one-year old or older dropped 0.5 percent in the fourth quarter. However, the shares are now cheap at 4.9 times enterprise value with some analysts putting a price target of 41 per share.

8384 ■ *Grow Your Money: 101 Easy Tips to Plan, Save and Invest*

Pub: HarperBusiness

Ed: Jonathan D. Pond. **Released:** December 2007. **Price:** $26.95. **Description:** In what should be required reading for anyone entering the work world, the author offers helpful investment and financial definitions, debt-management strategies, retirement and home ownerships considerations and more.

8385 ■ *"Growth Back on CIBC's Agenda"* in *Globe & Mail (March 3, 2006, pp. B1)*

Pub: CTVglobemedia Publishing Inc.

Ed: Sinclair Stewart. **Description:** The details on business growth of Canadian Imperial Bank of Commerce, which posted $547 million profit for first quarter 2006, are presented.

8386 ■ *"Handleman Liquidation Leaves Questions For Shareholders"* in *Crain's Detroit Business (Vol. 24, October 6, 2008, No. 40, pp. 4)*

Pub: Crain Communications, Inc.

Ed: Nancy Kaffer. **Description:** Discusses Handleman Co., a Troy-based music distribution company, and their plan of liquidation and dissolution as well as how shareholders will be affected by the company's plan. Handleman filed its plan to liquidate and dissolve assets with the Securities and Exchange Commission in mid-August, following several quarters of dismal earnings.

8387 ■ *"Hank and Ben: Hedgies' BFFs"* in *Barron's (Vol. 88, March 31, 2008, No. 13, pp. 50)*

Pub: Dow Jones & Company, Inc.

Ed: Tom Sullivan. **Description:** David Ballin of Alternative Investment Solutions says that everything in the financial markets is tainted and beaten-up which presents an extraordinary opportunity for hedge funds as long as they back up their decisions with sharp and intensive research. He adds that money managers should short suspect stocks and go long on undeservedly battered stocks in the same sector.

8388 ■ *"Hank Paulson On the Housing Bailout and What's Ahead"* in *Business Week (September 22, 2008, No. 4100, pp. 19)*

Pub: McGraw-Hill Companies, Inc.

Ed: Maria Bartiromo. **Description:** Interview with Treasury Secretary Henry Paulson in which he discusses the bailout of Fannie Mae and Freddie Mac as well as the potential impact on the American economy and foreign interests and investments in the country. Paulson has faith that the government's actions will help to stabilize the housing market.

8389 ■ *"A Harbinger?"* in *The Business Journal-Milwaukee (Vol. 25, August 29, 2008, No. 49, pp. A1)*

Pub: American City Business Journals, Inc.

Ed: Rich Kirchen. **Description:** Stock prices of Marshall & Ilsley Corp. (M&I) and MGIC Investment Corp. are expected to rebound after insiders were reported to have bought stocks of the companies. M&I director David Lubar bought $4.3 million, while MGIC CEO and chairman Curt Culver bought 20,000 stocks of MGIC. Other views and information on the insiders' purchase of stocks are presented.

8390 ■ *"Hartco Income Fund Announces the Completion of the CompuSmart Strategic Review"* in *Canadian Corporate News (May 14, 2007)*
Pub: Comtex News Network Inc.
Description: Hartco Income Fund announced that it has completed the process of exploring strategic options for CompuSmart and found that it should implement a plan to sell select stores and assets while consolidating remaining CompuSmart locations over the next sixty days.

8391 ■ *"Has Microsoft Found a Way to Get at Yahoo?"* in *Advertising Age (Vol. 79, July 7, 2008, No. 26, pp. 4)*
Pub: Crain Communications, Inc.
Ed: Abbey Klaassen. **Description:** Microsoft's attempt to acquire Yahoo's search business is discussed as is Yahoo's plans for the future at a time when the company's shares have fallen dangerously low.

8392 ■ *"Hastily Enacted Regulation Will Not Cure Economic Crisis"* in *Crain's Chicago Business (Vol. 31, May 5, 2008, No. 18, pp. 18)*
Pub: Crain Communications, Inc.
Ed: Stephen P. D'Arcy. **Description:** Policymakers are looking for ways to respond to what is possibly the greatest financial crisis of a generation due to the collapse of the housing market, the credit crisis and the volatility of Wall Street.

8393 ■ *"Hawaii's Identity Crisis"* in *Hawaii Business (Vol. 53, November 2007, No. 5, pp. 10)*
Pub: Hawaii Business Publishing
Ed: Kelli Abe Trifonovitch. **Description:** Some Hawaiians have shown that the Superferry controversy makes it seem to the rest of the world as if they do not know what they are doing, and intensifies several issues regarding the stability of investing in Hawaii. With or without the Superferry, there is still no evidence that investors are afraid to put their money in Hawaii.

8394 ■ *"Hawaii's Top Twenty Financial Advisors"* in *Hawaii Business (Vol. 53, February 2008, No. 8, pp. 32)*
Pub: Hawaii Business Publishing
Description: Listing of Hawaii's top 20 financial advisors is presented. Details on the methodology used to create the rankings are discussed.

8395 ■ *"HBDiversityStockIndex"* in *Hispanic Business (October 2009, pp. 1)*
Pub: Hispanic Business
Description: Data covering the Hispanic Business Diversity Stock Index is highlighted. The HBDSI was up 0.12 percent through September 3, 2009. Statistical data included.

8396 ■ *"Headwinds From the New Sod Slow Aer Lingus"* in *Barron's (Vol. 88, March 10, 2008, No. 10, pp. M6)*
Pub: Dow Jones & Company, Inc.
Ed: Sean Walters; Arindam Nag. **Description:** Aer Lingus faces a drop in its share prices with a falling US market, higher jet fuel prices, and lower long-haul passenger load factors. British media companies Johnston Press and Yell Group are suffering from weaker ad revenue and heavier debt payments due to the credit crunch.

8397 ■ *"The Heat Is On"* in *Crain's Chicago Business (Vol. 31, April 28, 2008, No. 17, pp. 4)*
Pub: Crain Communications, Inc.
Ed: Steve Daniels. **Description:** Discusses Nicor Inc., a natural-gas utility serving 2 million customers in Chicago's suburbs, and its potential acquirers; shares of the company have dropped 17 percent this

year making Nicor the second-worst among 31 utilities in an index tracked by Standrd & Poor's. Statistical data included.

8398 ■ *"Heat's On, but Glacier Not Retreating"* in *Globe & Mail (January 26, 2006, pp. B3)*
Pub: CTVglobemedia Publishing Inc.
Ed: Grant Robertson. **Description:** The details on Glacier Ventures International Corp., which acquired Hollinger International Inc.'s assets, are presented.

8399 ■ *"Hello, 9000! The Dow's Run Is Far From Over"* in *Barron's (Vol. 89, July 27, 2009, No. 30, pp. 20)*
Pub: Dow Jones & Co., Inc.
Ed: Andrew Bary. **Description:** Another 10 percent gain is possible for the rest of 2009 as the Dow Jones Industrial Average moved above 9000 level for the week ending July 24, 2009. Blue chip stocks could do well in the next 10 years.

8400 ■ *"Here are the Stocks of the Decade"* in *Business Courier (Vol. 26, December 18, 2009, No. 34, pp. 1)*
Pub: American City Business Journals, Inc.
Ed: Steve Watkins. **Description:** Listing of companies with stocks that made big gains since December 1999 to November 30, 2009 is presented.

8401 ■ *"Here's How Buffett Spent 2007"* in *Barron's (Vol. 88, March 10, 2008, No. 10, pp. 48)*
Pub: Dow Jones & Company, Inc.
Ed: Andrew Bary. **Description:** Earnings of Berkshire Hathaway may decline in 2008 due to a tighter insurance market, but its portfolio is expected to continue growing. Warren Buffett purchased $19.1 billion worth of stocks in 2007.

8402 ■ *"The Hidden Tax"* in *Canadian Business (Vol. 81, April 14, 2008, No. 6, pp. 28)*
Pub: Rogers Media
Ed: Al Rosen. **Description:** Accounting fraud could take out a sizable sum from one's retirement fund when computed over a long period of time. The much bigger tax on savings is the collective impact of the smaller losses that do not attract the attention they deserve. Ensuring that investors are not unnecessarily taxed 2 percent of their total investments every year outweighs the benefit of a 2 percent reduction in personal tax rates.

8403 ■ *"H.I.G. Capital Announces Acquisition of Next Generation Vending"* in *Benzinga.com (October 29, 2011)*
Pub: Benzinga.com
Ed: Benzinga Staff. **Description:** H.I.G. Capital LLC, a leader in global private investments, acquired Next Generation Vending and Food Service Inc. Next Generation is a provider of vending services for corporate and institutional clients in Northeastern United States.

8404 ■ *"High-Yield Turns Into Road Kill"* in *Barron's (Vol. 88, July 7, 2008, No. 27, pp. M7)*
Pub: Dow Jones & Co., Inc.
Ed: Emily Barrett. **Description:** High-yield bonds have returned to the brink of collapse after profits have recovered from the shock brought about by the collapse of Bear Stearns. The high-yield bond market could decline again due to weakness in the automotive sector, particularly in Ford and General Motors.

8405 ■ *"Higher Freight Rates Keep CPR Rolling in Profit"* in *Globe & Mail (February 1, 2006, pp. B3)*
Pub: CTVglobemedia Publishing Inc.
Ed: Brent Jang. **Description:** Canadian Pacific Railway Ltd. posted $135.4 million in revenues for fourth quarter 2005. The company's earnings projections for 2006 and workforce reduction plans are presented.

8406 ■ *"His Banking Industry Software Never Caught On, so Bill Randle is Now Targeting the Health Care Market"* in *Inc. (March 2008)*
Pub: Gruner & Jahr USA Publishing
Ed: Alex Salkever. **Description:** Profile of Bill Randle, bank executive turned entrepreneur; Randle tells how he changed his focus for his company from banking software to healthcare software. The firm employs ten people who secure online billing and recordkeeping systems for hospitals and insurers. Randle discusses critical decisions that will impact his firm in the coming year. Three experts offer advice.

8407 ■ *"Hispantelligence Report"* in *Hispanic Business (July-August 2009, pp. 8)*
Pub: Hispanic Business
Description: After forty years, Hispanic-owned businesses have grown to more than three million, according to a U.S. Census report. The Hispanic business stock index is also presented. Statistical data included.

8408 ■ *"Hit the Books"* in *Black Enterprise (Vol. 38, July 2008, No. 12, pp. 42)*
Pub: Earl G. Graves Publishing Co. Inc.
Ed: Mellody Hobson. **Description:** Four books that deal with investing are discussed as is the idea that reading even 15 minutes a day from one of these books will give you tools that far exceed what you can learn from magazines and the business section of your daily newspaper.

8409 ■ *"Hits and Misses"* in *Canadian Business (Vol. 80, December 25, 2006, No. 1, pp. 69)*
Pub: Rogers Media
Ed: Calvin Leung. **Description:** The performance of stocks of several Canadian companies is discussed.

8410 ■ *"Hitting Bottom?"* in *Barron's (Vol. 88, March 24, 2008, No. 12, pp. 21)*
Pub: Dow Jones & Company, Inc.
Ed: Jacqueline Doherty. **Description:** Brokerage houses and banks may stabilize in 2008 as a result of regulatory responses brought about by the near-collapse of Bear Stearns. Some of their shares may rise by as much as 20 percent from 2008 to 2009.

8411 ■ *"Hold Your Nose, Say 'Da'"* in *Canadian Business (Vol. 79, September 11, 2006, No. 18, pp. 151)*
Pub: Rogers Media
Ed: Thomas Watson. **Description:** The changing business environment and investment opportunities in Russia despite its instable democracy are discussed. Russia's potential and its ability to attract productive investment are presented.

8412 ■ *"Hollinger Shares Plummet on Reports"* in *Globe & Mail (March 10, 2007, pp. B5)*
Pub: CTVglobemedia Publishing Inc.
Ed: Richard Blackwell. **Description:** The fall in the share prices of Hollinger Inc. to 49 percent soon after the company filed its annual statements is discussed.

8413 ■ *"The Home Game"* in *Canadian Business (Vol. 80, October 8, 2007, No. 20, pp. 68)*
Pub: Rogers Media
Ed: Rachel Pulfer. **Description:** Analysis of Canada's banking industry is presented. Trends show that Canadian banks avoid risks in their investments, and usually choose to take safer paths. Experts believe these trends affect the country's economy and that Canadian banks do not play a significant role in economic development.

8414 ■ *"A Home of Her Own"* in *Hawaii Business (Vol. 53, October 2007, No. 4, pp. 51)*
Pub: Hawaii Business Publishing
Ed: Maria Torres-Kitamura. **Description:** It was observed that the number of single women in Hawaii purchasing their own home has increased, as that in the whole United States where the percentage has increased from 14 percent in 1995 to 22 percent in 2006. However, First Hawaiian Bank's Wendy Lum

thinks that the trend will not continue in Hawaii due to lending restrictions. The factors that women consider in buying a home of their own are presented.

8415 ■ *"Home Sweet Home?" in Canadian Business (Vol. 79, September 11, 2006, No. 18, pp. 17)*
Pub: Rogers Media

Ed: David Wolf. **Description:** Fading attractiveness of the Canadian stock market for its domestic investors is discussed. Changing investor's trends toward cross-border investments are presented.

8416 ■ *"Homebuilders Continue to be Our Nemesis" in Contractor (Vol. 56, July 2009, No. 7, pp. 50)*
Pub: Penton Media, Inc.

Ed: Bob Mader. **Description:** Homebuilders rank high on the greed scale along with Wall Street brokers. There is this one instance when a builder gave copies of another contractor's quotes that have just been blackened out and another instance when one builder let other bidders visit a site while the current mechanical contractor is working.

8417 ■ *"Honesty Doesn't Pay" in Canadian Business (Vol. 79, Winter 2006, No. 24, pp. 28)*
Pub: Rogers Media

Ed: Al Rosen. **Description:** The effects of the outlook of financial analysts and investment bankers, on their career prospects, are described.

8418 ■ *"Hong Kong's Boom in IPO" in Barron's (Vol. 89, July 13, 2009, No. 28, pp. M7)*
Pub: Dow Jones & Co., Inc.

Ed: Nick Lord. **Description:** Hong Kong's IPO (initial public offering) market is booming with 13 Chinese IPOs already on the market for the year as July 2009. One of them is Bawang International which raised $214 million after generating $9 billion in order which makes it 42 times oversubscribed.

8419 ■ *House of Cards*
Pub: Doubleday, a Division of Random House

Ed: William D. Cohan. **Released:** March 10, 2009. **Price:** $27.95. **Description:** The fall of Bear Stearns and the beginning of the Wall Street Collapse.

8420 ■ *House of Cards: A Tale of Hubris and Wretched Excess on Wall Street*
Pub: Anchor Press

Ed: William D. Cohan. **Released:** February 9, 2010. **Price:** $16.95. **Description:** A historical account of the events leading up to the Bear Stearns implosion.

8421 ■ *"Housing Hedge" in Canadian Business (Vol. 79, July 17, 2006, No. 14-15, pp. 66)*
Pub: Rogers Media

Ed: Jeff Sanford. **Description:** The idea of starting a hedge scheme for housing is presented using the advent of pension schemes as an example to follow.

8422 ■ *"How to Avoid the Three Big Mistakes" in Barron's (Vol. 88, March 10, 2008, No. 10, pp. 30)*
Pub: Dow Jones & Company, Inc.

Ed: Karen Hube. **Description:** Investors, particularly those having retirement investments, are advised to diversify their investments, refrain from market timing, and minimize payments to maximize investment gains. An investor committing these mistakes could lose as much as $375,000 dollars over ten years.

8423 ■ *"How to Beat the Pros" in Canadian Business (Vol. 81, Summer 2008, No. 9, pp. 59)*
Pub: Rogers Media Ltd.

Ed: Calvin Leung. **Description:** Table showing the results of the Investor 500 beat the S&P/TSX composite index is presented. The average total return, best performing stocks and total return of the 2007 stock screen are provided.

8424 ■ *"How CoolBrand's Thrills Turned to Chills" in Globe & Mail (January 25, 2007, pp. B1)*
Pub: CTVglobemedia Publishing Inc.

Ed: Keith McArthur. **Description:** The key reasons behind the sudden share price fall of ice cream giant CoolBrands International Inc. are discussed.

8425 ■ *"How to Deal" in Canadian Business (Vol. 81, November 10, 2008, No. 19, pp. 36)*
Pub: Rogers Media Ltd.

Ed: Calvin Leung. **Description:** The Great Depression, Japan's Lost Decade, and the Swedish Banking Crisis is compared to the 2008 financial crisis in the U.S. The chances for recession in the U.S. are discussed along with investment strategies to survive.

8426 ■ *"How Foreigners Could Disrupt U.S. Markets" in Barron's (Vol. 90, September 13, 2010, No. 37, pp. 30)*
Pub: Barron's Editorial & Corporate Headquarters

Ed: Jim McTague. **Description:** An informal meeting by the House Homeland Security Panel concluded that U.S. stock exchanges and related trading routes can be the subject of attacks from rogue overseas traders. A drop in funding for the U.S. Department of Defense is discussed.

8427 ■ *"How to Handle a Bank Error: Act Quickly When You See a Mistake on Your Statement" in Black Enterprise (Vol. 41, December 2010, No. 5)*
Pub: Earl G. Graves Publishing Co. Inc.

Ed: Sheiresa Ngo. **Description:** Contact your bank or financial institution immediately after discovering an error in your account.

8428 ■ *"How High Can Soybeans Fly?" in Barron's (Vol. 88, March 10, 2008, No. 10, pp. M14)*
Pub: Dow Jones & Company, Inc.

Ed: Kenneth Rapoza. **Description:** Prices of soybeans have risen to $14.0875 a bushel, up 8.3 percent for the week. Increased demand, such as in China and in other developing economies, and the investment-driven commodities boom are boosting prices.

8429 ■ *"How Interest Rate Changes Affect You" in Agency Sales Magazine (Vol. 39, September-October 2009, No. 9, pp. 50)*
Pub: MANA

Ed: Lee Eisinberg. **Description:** Falling interest rates make the prices of previously issued bonds rise and new issues are offered at lower rates. For stock investors, rising interest rates can have a positive or negative effect. Terminologies related to investing are explained.

8430 ■ *How to Make Money in Stocks: A Winning System in Good Times and Bad*
Pub: The McGraw-Hill Companies

Ed: William J. O'Neil. **Released:** June 12. 2009. **Price:** $16.95. **Description:** The bestselling guide to buying stocks, from the founder of Investor's Business Daily. The technique is based on a study of the greatest stock market winners dating back to 1953 and includes a seven-step process for minimizing risk, maximizing return, and finding stocks that are ready to perform.

8431 ■ *"How Not to Raise Bank Capital" in Barron's (Vol. 88, June 30, 2008, No. 26, pp. M6)*
Pub: Dow Jones & Co., Inc.

Ed: Sean Walters. **Description:** French bank Natixis wants to raise 1 billion euros from cash provided by their two major owners. Natixis will reimburse Banque Populaire and Caisses d'Epargne with hybrid securities so this move will not benefit Natixis' core Tier 1 ratio. This has also given the impression that the company is afraid of a full rights issue which could shake investors' faith in the bank.

8432 ■ *"How Our Picks Beat The Bear" in Barron's (Vol. 88, July 14, 2008, No. 28, pp. 18)*
Pub: Dow Jones & Co., Inc.

Ed: Andrew Bary. **Description:** Performance of the stocks that Barron's covered in the first half of 2008 is discussed; some of the worst picks and most

rewarding pans have been in the financial sector while the best plays were in the energy, materials, and the transportation sectors.

8433 ■ *"How Sweet It Will Be" in Barron's (Vol. 89, July 13, 2009, No. 28, pp. M13)*
Pub: Dow Jones & Co., Inc.

Ed: Debbie Carlson. **Description:** Raw sugar experienced a rally in the first half of 2009 and the long term outlook for sugar prices is still good. However, there is a likely near-term correction due to the onset of Brazilian harvest that could be 20.7 percent higher for 2009 as compared to the previous year and October contracts could fall to 15.61 cents per pound.

8434 ■ *"HSBC Canada Posts 8.8 Percent Profit Gain in 2006" in Globe & Mail (February 20, 2007, pp. B14)*
Pub: CTVglobemedia Publishing Inc.

Ed: Andrew Willis. **Description:** HSBC Bank Canada reported profits of $497 million in 2006. The financial results of the company for 2006 are presented.

8435 ■ *"Ian Gordon" in Canadian Business (Vol. 81, Summer 2008, No. 9, pp. 10)*
Pub: Rogers Media Ltd.

Ed: Matthew McClearn. **Description:** Bolder Investment Partners' Ian Gordon discussed the economic theory promulgated by Russian economist Nikolai Kondratieff. The cycle begins with a rising economy then followed by deflationary depression. Details of his views on the Kondratieff cycle and its application to the current economy are presented.

8436 ■ *"Identity Crisis: The Battle For Your Data" in Canadian Business (Vol. 81, March 17, 2008, No. 4, pp. 12)*
Pub: Rogers Media

Description: Nigel Brown explains that businesses must protect their data through encryption and tightening up access to data. Brown also points out that banks and merchants bear most of the costs for identity fraud and leaves individuals with a lot of pain and heartache in clearing their name.

8437 ■ *"If You Go Into the Market Today.." in Canadian Business (Vol. 82, Summer 2009, No. 8, pp. 18)*
Pub: Rogers Media

Ed: Jeff Sanford. **Description:** Opinions of experts and personalities who are known to have bear attitudes towards the economy were presented in the event 'A Night with the Bears' in Toronto in April 2009. Known bears that served as resource persons in the event were Nouriel Roubini, Eric Sprott, Ian Gordon, and Meredith Whitney. The bears were observed to have differences regarding consumer debt.

8438 ■ *"An Ill Wind: Icelandic Bank Failures Chill Atlantic Canada" in Canadian Business (Vol. 81, November 10, 2008, No. 19, pp. 10)*
Pub: Rogers Media Ltd.

Ed: Charles Mandel. **Description:** Bank failures in Iceland have put a stop to flights ferrying Icelanders to Newfoundland to purchase Christmas gifts, thereby threatening Newfoundland's tourism industry. The credit of Newfoundland's fisheries is also being squeezed since most of Atlantic Canadian seafood processors hold lines of credit from Icelandic banks.

8439 ■ *"Immigration Issues Frustrate Owners From Overseas" in The Business Journal-Serving Greater Tampa Bay (Vol. 28, August 15, 2008)*
Pub: American City Business Journals, Inc.

Ed: Margie Manning. **Description:** Investors who availed the E-2 visa program believe that the tightened restrictions on the visa program has trapped them in the United States. The E-2 investor visa program was designed to attract investors into the U.S., but restrictions were tightened after the September 11, 2001 attacks. Other views and information on E-2 and its impact on investors are presented.

8440 ■ *"The Impact of Brand Quality on Shareholder Wealth" in Journal of Marketing (Vol. 75, September 2011, No. 5, pp. 88)*
Pub: American Marketing Association

Ed: Sundar G. Bharardwaj, Kapil R. Tuli, Andre Bonfrer. **Description:** The effects of brand quality on idiosyncratic risk, systematic risk, and stock returns are investigated. Findings reveal that unexpected changes in brand quality negatively associated with idiosyncratic risk changes and positively related to stock returns. However, unexpected changes in brand quality will reduce shareholder wealth due to positive relationship with changes n systematic risk.

8441 ■ *"Imports Frothing Up Beer Market" in Globe & Mail (February 16, 2006, pp. B4)*
Pub: CTVglobemedia Publishing Inc.
Ed: Andy Hoffman. **Description:** The reasons behind the rise in market share of beer imports, in Canada, are presented.

8442 ■ *"In the Bag?" in Canadian Business (Vol. 81, March 3, 2008, No. 3, pp. 57)*
Pub: Rogers Media
Ed: Calvin Leung. **Description:** American stocks are beginning to appear cheap amidst the threat of a worldwide economic slowdown, United States economic crisis and declining stock portfolios. Investors looking for bargain stocks should study the shares of Apple and Oshkosh Corp. Evaluation of other cheap-looking stocks such as the shares of Coach and 3M is also given.

8443 ■ *"In China, Railways to Riches" in Barron's (Vol. 88, July 7, 2008, No. 27, pp. M9)*
Pub: Dow Jones & Co., Inc.
Ed: Assif Shameen. **Description:** Shares of Chinese railway companies look to benefit from multimillion-dollar investments aimed at upgrading the Chinese railway network. Investment in the sector is expected to reach $210 billion for the 2006-2010 period.

8444 ■ *"In India, A Gold-Price Threat?" in Barron's (Vol. 88, June 30, 2008, No. 26, pp. M12)*
Pub: Dow Jones & Co., Inc.
Ed: Melanie Burton. **Description:** Gold purchases in India are falling as record prices take its toll on demand. Gold imports to India fell by 52 percent in May 2008 from the previous year and local prices are higher by one-third from the previous year to 12,540 rupees for 10 grams.

8445 ■ *"In Praise of How Not to Invest" in Barron's (Vol. 89, July 13, 2009, No. 28, pp. 11)*
Pub: Dow Jones & Co., Inc.
Ed: Vito J. Racanelli. **Description:** One research study found that the shares of companies that have growing market shares and expanding asset bases underperform. This is contrary to the widely held premise that stock prices for these companies rise. It is argued that this result is caused by these companies' tendency to sacrifice profitability to grab market share and this is reflected in their stock prices.

8446 ■ *"In Sickness and In Wealth Management" in Hispanic Business (Vol. 30, March 2008, No. 3, pp. 28)*
Pub: Hispanic Business
Ed: Rick Munarriz. **Description:** Discusses the investment and wealth management firms owned and operated by Hispanics. There are only a handful of these firms owned by Hispanics, as most of them prefer capital preservation by investing in hard assets like cash and real estate than in capital appreciation.

8447 ■ *"In Surging Oil Industry, Good Fortune Comes In Stages" in Barron's (Vol. 88, July 7, 2008, No. 27, pp. 12)*
Pub: Dow Jones & Co., Inc.
Ed: Sandra Ward. **Description:** Shares of US land oil and gas driller Helmerich and Payne, priced at $69 each, are estimated to be at peak levels. The shares are trading at 17 times 2008 earnings and could be in for some profit taking.

8448 ■ *"In the Wake of Pet-Food Crisis, Iams Sales Plummet Nearly 17 Percent" in Advertising Age (Vol. 78, May 14, 2007, No. 18, pp. 3)*
Pub: Crain Communications, Inc.
Ed: Jack Neff. **Description:** Although the massive U.S. pet-food recall impacted more than 100 brands, Procter & Gamble Co.'s Iams lost more sales and market share than any other industry player. According-

ing to Information Resources Inc. data, the brand's sales dropped 16.5 percent in the eight-week period ended April 22. Many analysts feel that the company could have handled the crisis in a better manner.

8449 ■ *"Inflation Woes: Secure Your Portfolio Against Rising Prices" in Black Enterprise (Vol. 37, January 2007, No. 6, pp. 40)*
Pub: Earl G. Graves Publishing Co. Inc.
Ed: Donald Jay Korn. **Description:** Inflation has a huge impact on investing and it is important to take the steady increase on cost into account when looking at your financial goals and investing in your future. Statistical data included.

8450 ■ *"Inland Snaps Up Rival REITs" in Crain's Chicago Business (Vol. 31, November 17, 2008, No. 46, pp. 3)*
Pub: Crain Communications, Inc.
Ed: Alby Gallun. **Description:** Discusses Inland American Real Estate Trust Inc., a real estate investment trust that is napping up depressed shares of publicly traded competitors, a possible first step toward taking over these companies; however, with hotel and retail properties accounting for approximately 70 percent of its portfolio, the company could soon face its own difficulties.

8451 ■ *"Inmet Selling Nunavut Mining Properties" in Globe & Mail (February 15, 2006, pp. B6)*
Pub: CTVglobemedia Publishing Inc.
Ed: Allan Robinson. **Description:** The details on Wolfden Resources Inc.'s acquisition of mining assets of Inmet Mining Corp. are presented.

8452 ■ *"Insider" in Canadian Business (Vol. 81, March 31, 2008, No. 5, pp. 76)*
Pub: Rogers Media
Ed: John Gray. **Description:** Discusses a comparison of an average Canadian family's finances in 1990 with the data from 2007. The average family in 2007 has over $80,000 in debt compared to just under $52,000 in 1990. However, Canadians have also been accumulating solid assets such as homes and stocks. This means that Canadian debt load has fallen from 22 percent in 1990 to 20 percent in 2007 when taken as a percentage of total net worth.

8453 ■ *"Insider" in Canadian Business (Vol. 81, March 3, 2008, No. 3, pp. 96)*
Pub: Rogers Media
Description: History of gold usage and gold trading is presented in a timeline. Gold was a symbol of power and wealth in 2500 B.C., and in 1500 B.C., it became the first currency to be recognized internationally. Other remarkable events in the gold industry and laws that covered gold are discussed.

8454 ■ *"An Insurance Roll-Up In Danger of Unraveling" in Barron's (Vol. 88, March 17, 2008, No. 11, pp. 51)*
Pub: Dow Jones & Company, Inc.
Ed: Bill Alpert. **Description:** Shares of National Financial Partners have fallen below their initial offering price as sputtering sales and management turnover leave many investors wondering. One of the company's star brokers is being sued for their 'life settlement' contracts while another broker is being pursued by the IRS for unpaid taxes.

8455 ■ *"Intangible Assets" in Canadian Business (Vol. 79, July 17, 2006, No. 14-15, pp. 17)*
Pub: Rogers Media
Ed: Al Rosen. **Description:** Need for investors to check the actual worth of a company and not to get carried away by the inflated claims made by the company is emphasized.

8456 ■ *"International ETFs: Your Passport to the World" in Barron's (Vol. 89, July 13, 2009, No. 28, pp. L10)*
Pub: Dow Jones & Co., Inc.
Ed: John Hintze. **Description:** International exchange traded funds give investors more choices in terms of investment plays and there are 174 U.S. ETF listings worth $141 billion as of July 2009. Sug-

gestions on how to invest in these funds based on one's conviction on how the global economy will unfold are presented.

8457 ■ *"International Nickel Ventures Corporation Reports Results for the First Quarter 2007" in Canadian Corporate News (May 16, 2007)*
Pub: Comtex News Network Inc.
Description: Profile of International Nickel Ventures Corporation (INV) including its financial report for the first quarter of fiscal 2007, its partnership and possible acquisition of Teck Cominco Limited, and its plans for the future. Statistical data included.

8458 ■ *The Internationalization of Asset Ownership in Europe*
Pub: Cambridge University Press
Contact: Richard Ziemacki, President
E-mail: rziemacki@cambridge.org
Ed: Harry Huizinga, Lars Jonung. **Released:** November 2005. **Price:** $112.00. **Description:** Ten financial experts provide analysis of the growth and the implications of foreign ownership in Europe's financial markets.

8459 ■ *"Investment Manager Disciplined" in Sacramento Business Journal (Vol. 25, July 4, 2008, No. 18, pp. 1)*
Pub: American City Business Journals, Inc.
Ed: Mark Anderson. **Description:** Community Capital Management's David A. Zwick is permanently barred by the Securities and Exchange Commission (SEC) from associating with any broker or dealer, after investigations revealed that he took part in paying kickbacks to a bond trader. Other views and information on Community Capital, and on the SEC investigation on Zwick, are presented.

8460 ■ *"Investors Lost Patience A Long Time Ago" in Globe & Mail (January 21, 2006, pp. B5)*
Pub: CTVglobemedia Publishing Inc.
Ed: Konrad Yakabuski. **Description:** The financial impasse at Quebecor World Inc., under chief executive officer Pierre Karl Peladeau, is discussed.

8461 ■ *"Investors Shrug Off the Turmoil" in Globe & Mail (March 1, 2007, pp. B1)*
Pub: CTVglobemedia Publishing Inc.
Ed: Geoffrey York. **Description:** The decision of Chinese investors to continue to buy stocks despite the decade's biggest market crash is discussed. The rise in the stock price indexes of China is described.

8462 ■ *"Is the VIX in Denial?" in Barron's (Vol. 88, July 7, 2008, No. 27, pp. M12)*
Pub: Dow Jones & Co., Inc.
Ed: Lawrence McMillan. **Description:** Volatility Index (VIX) of the Chicago Board Options Exchange did not rise significantly despite the drop in the US stock markets, rising to near 25. This market decline, however, will eventually result in investor panic and the rise of the VIX.

8463 ■ *"Islamic Banks Get a 'Libor' of Their Own" in Wall Street Journal Eastern Edition (November 25 , 2011, pp. C4)*
Pub: Dow Jones & Company Inc. Enterprise Media Group
Contact: Clare Hart, President
Ed: Katy Burne. **Description:** The London interbank offered rate, or Libor, has been used by banks internationally for years. It is the rate at which banks lend money to each other. The rate has not been used by Islamic banks, but now sixteen banks have come up with the Islamic Interbank Benchmark Rate.

8464 ■ *"It Could Be Worse" in Barron's (Vol. 89, July 27, 2009, No. 30, pp. 5)*
Pub: Dow Jones & Co., Inc.
Ed: Alan Abelson. **Description:** Media sources are being fooled by corporate America who is peddling an economic recovery rather than reality as shown by the report of a rise in existing home sales which boosted the stock market even if it was a seasonal phenomenon. The phrase 'things could be worse' sums up the reigning investment philosophy in the U.S. and this has been stirring up the market.

8465 ■ *"It Takes More Than One" in Black Enterprise (Vol. 38, July 2008, No. 12, pp. 38)*
Pub: Earl G. Graves Publishing Co. Inc.

Ed: James A. Anderson. **Description:** Interview with Eric Small, the CEO of SBK-Brooks Investment Corp., whom discusses the importance of versatility when trying to find the best investment choices; the primary factors investors should be mindful of; his current stock picks; and recommendations for investing in an uncertain and volatile market.

8466 ■ *"Itochu Joins KKR in Samson Buyout" in Wall Street Journal Eastern Edition (November 25 , 2011, pp. B7)*
Pub: Dow Jones & Company Inc. Enterprise Media Group

Contact: Clare Hart, President

Description: Samson Investment Company is the target of a $7.2 billion leveraged buyout by a consortium led by US investment firm Kohlberg Kravis Roberts & Company and Tokyo-based Itochu Corporation, part of the consortium is coming in on the deal for a 25 percent holding, for which it will pay $1.04 billion.

8467 ■ *"It's Good to be Goldman" in Barron's (Vol. 89, July 20, 2009, No. 29, pp. 5)*
Pub: Dow Jones & Co., Inc.

Ed: Randall W. Forsyth. **Description:** Profits of Goldman Sachs rose to $3.44 billion in the second quarter of 2009, aided by federal financial stimulus programs. CIT Group is facing bankruptcy and may need up to $6 billion to survive. The federal economic stimulus programs are benefiting Wall Street more than the US economy itself.

8468 ■ *"It's Time to Wise Up: Income Trusts" in Canadian Business (Vol. 79, November 6, 2006, No. 22, pp. 24)*
Pub: Rogers Media

Ed: Mark Rosen. **Description:** The effects bogus financial reporting of income trusts on investors are analyzed.

8469 ■ *"Ivernia Mine Closing Could Boost Lead" in Globe & Mail (April 4, 2007, pp. B5)*
Pub: CTVglobemedia Publishing Inc.

Ed: Andy Hoffman. **Description:** The closing of Ivernia Inc.'s mine in view of government investigation into alleged lead contamination at the port of Esperance is discussed. The likely increase in the price of lead is also discussed.

8470 ■ *"Jamieson Eyes $175 Million Trust IPO" in Globe & Mail (March 7, 2006, pp. B1)*
Pub: CTVglobemedia Publishing Inc.

Ed: Sinclair Stewart; Leonard Zehr. **Description:** The reasons behind $175 million initial public offering plans of Jamieson Laboratories Ltd. are presented.

8471 ■ *"Jean Coutu Resuscitates Bottom Line" in Globe & Mail (January 11, 2006, pp. B5)*
Pub: CTVglobemedia Publishing Inc.

Ed: Bertrand Marotte. **Description:** The details on Jean Coutu Group (PJC) Inc., which posted $30.8 million profits for second quarter 2005, are presented.

8472 ■ *"Judge Gives RIM One Last Chance" in Globe & Mail (February 25, 2006, pp. B5)*
Pub: CTVglobemedia Publishing Inc.

Ed: Barrie McKenna; Paul Waldie. **Description:** United States District Court Judge James Spencer offers more time for Research In Motion Ltd. (RIM) to settle the patent infringement dispute with NTP Inc. RIM's shares increase by 6.2 percent following the decision.

8473 ■ *"The Judgment Deficit" in Harvard Business Review (Vol. 88, September 2010, No. 9, pp. 44)*
Pub: Harvard Business School Publishing

Ed: Amar Bhide. **Description:** The importance of individual, decentralized initiative and judgment in the capitalist system is outlined. While financial models have their use, they cannot always account appropriately for the inherent uncertainty in economic decision making.

8474 ■ *"Juiced on Energy" in Barron's (Vol. 88, July 14, 2008, No. 28, pp. 33)*
Pub: Dow Jones & Co., Inc.

Ed: Leslie P. Norton. **Description:** Brad Evans and his team at Heartland Value Plus were able to outperform their peers by significantly undercommitting to financials and overexposing themselves with energy stocks. Brad Evans believes that there is a lot of value left in energy stocks such as natural gas.

8475 ■ *"Julie Holzrichter; Managing Director of Operations, CME Group Inc." in Crain's Chicago Business (Vol. 31, May 5, 2008, No. 18)*
Pub: Crain Communications, Inc.

Ed: Ann Saphir. **Description:** Profile of Julie Holzrichter who works as the managing director of operations for CME Group Inc. and is known as a decisive leader able to intercept and solve problems.

8476 ■ *"Just Hang Up" in Barron's (Vol. 88, March 10, 2008, No. 10, pp. 45)*
Pub: Dow Jones & Company, Inc.

Ed: Tiernan Ray. **Description:** Sprint's shares are expected to continue falling while the company attempts to attract subscribers by cutting prices, cutting earnings in the process. The company faces tougher competition from better-financed AT&T and Verizon Communications.

8477 ■ *"Keeping the Faith in Fuel-Tech" in Barron's (Vol. 88, March 24, 2008, No. 12, pp. 20)*
Pub: Dow Jones & Company, Inc.

Ed: Christopher C. Williams. **Description:** Shares of air pollution control company Fuel-Tech remain on track to reach $40 each from their $19 level due to a continued influx of contracts. The stock has suffered from lower-than-expected quarterly earnings and tougher competition but stand to benefit from increased orders.

8478 ■ *"Kid Rock" in Canadian Business (Vol. 81, Summer 2008, No. 9, pp. 54)*
Pub: Rogers Media Ltd.

Ed: John Gray. **Description:** Damien Reynolds is the founder, chairman and chief executive officer of Vancouver-based Longview Capital Partners. The investment bank, founded in 2005, is one of the fastest-growing companies in British Columbia. The recent economic downturn has battered the stocks of the company and its portfolio of junior miners.

8479 ■ *King of Capital*
Pub: John Wiley and Sons, Inc.

Ed: Amey Stone; Mike Brewster. **Released:** 2004. **Price:** $16.95. **Description:** Biography of Sandy Weill describes how he became a billionaire business giant by creating successful companies from smaller, sometimes failing firms; creating successful new products where none previously existed; and making deals no one thought possible. He is also responsible for changing the landscape of the banking industry and insurance business when he created Citigroup in 1998, the world's largest financial services firm.

8480 ■ *"The Latin Beat Goes On" in Barron's (Vol. 88, July 7, 2008, No. 27, pp. L5)*
Pub: Dow Jones & Co., Inc.

Ed: Tom Sullivan. **Description:** Latin American stocks have outperformed other regional markets due to rising commodities prices and favorable economic climate. Countries such as Brazil, Mexico, Chile, and Peru provide investment opportunities, while Argentina and Venezuela are tougher places to invest.

8481 ■ *"Laugh or Cry?" in Barron's (Vol. 88, March 24, 2008, No. 12, pp. 7)*
Pub: Dow Jones & Company, Inc.

Ed: Alan Abelson. **Description:** Discusses the American economy which is just starting to feel the effect of the credit and housing crises. JPMorgan Chase purchased Bear Stearns for $2 a share, much lower than its share price of $60, while quasi-government entities Fannie Mae and Freddie Mac are starting to run into trouble.

8482 ■ *"Leaders and Lagards" in Barron's (Vol. 89, July 13, 2009, No. 28, pp. 14)*
Pub: Dow Jones & Co., Inc.

Ed: J.R. Brandstrader. **Description:** Statistical table that shows the returns of different mutual funds in different categories that include U.S. stock funds, sector funds, world equity funds, and mixed equity funds is presented. The data presented is for the second quarter of 2009.

8483 ■ *"Leaders and Lagards" in Barron's (Vol. 89, July 13, 2009, No. 28, pp. 14)*
Pub: Dow Jones & Co., Inc.

Ed: J.R. Brandstrader. **Description:** Statistical table that shows the returns of different mutual funds in different categories that include U.S. stock funds, sector funds, world equity funds, and mixed equity funds is presented. The data presented is for the second quarter of 2009.

8484 ■ *"Leaders Weigh In On Fannie Mae, Freddie Mac Failure, Fed Bailout" in The Business Journal - Serving Phoenix and the Valley of the Sun (Vol. 28, September 12, 2008, No. 53, pp. 1)*
Pub: American City Business Journals, Inc.

Ed: Chris Casacchia; Mike Sunnucks; Jan Buchholz. **Description:** Fannie Mae and Freddie Mac's federal takeover was a move to help stabilize the financial market and it helped bring down interest rates in the past week. Local executives from Arizona's Phoenix area share their thoughts on the immediate effect of the takeover and its upside and downside.

8485 ■ *"Legg's Compensation Committee Chair Defends CEO Fetting's Pay" in Boston Business Journal (Vol. 29, July 22, 2011, No. 11, pp. 1)*
Pub: American City Business Journals Inc.

Ed: Gary Haber. **Description:** Legg Mason Inc. CEO Mark R. Fetting has been awarded $5.9 million pay package and he expects to receive questions regarding it in the coming shareholders meeting. However, Baltimore, Maryland-based RKTL Associates chairman emeritus Harold R. Adams believes Fetting has done a tremendous job in bringing Legg's through a tough market.

8486 ■ *"Lehman's Hail Mary Pass" in Business Week (September 22, 2008, No. 4100, pp. 28)*
Pub: McGraw-Hill Companies, Inc.

Ed: Matthew Goldstein; David Henry; Ben Levison. **Description:** Overview of Lehman Brothers' CEO Richard Fuld's plan to keep the firm afloat and end the stock's plunge downward; Fuld's strategy calls for selling off a piece of the firm's investment management business.

8487 ■ *"Lenders" in The Business Journal - Serving Phoenix and the Valley of the Sun (Vol. 28, July 25, 2008, No. 47, pp. 1)*
Pub: American City Business Journals, Inc.

Ed: Jan Buchholz. **Description:** Private equity lender Investor Mortgage Holdings Inc. has continued growing despite the crisis surrounding the real estate and financial industries and has accumulated a $700 million loan portfolio. Private lending has become increasingly important in financing real estate deals as commercial credit has dried up.

8488 ■ *"Lenders Capitalize on a Thinning Bulge Bracket" in Mergers & Acquisitions: The Dealmaker's Journal (March 1, 2008)*
Pub: SourceMedia, Inc.

Description: Regardless of what the economic markets look like, private equity firms will continue to invest capital and mid-market finance firms are becoming very attractive acquisition opportunities since not as much capital is needed to buy them.

8489 ■ *"Lending Door Slams" in Puget Sound Business Journal (Vol. 29, October 24, 2008, No. 27, pp. 1)*
Pub: American City Business Journals

Ed: Jeanne Lang Jones, Kirsten Grind. **Description:** KeyBank's closure of its Puget Sound unit that services single-family homebuilders is part of a nationwide shutdown that includes similar closures in other cities. Bank of America is adopting more conservative terms for homebuilding loans while Union Bank of California is still offering credit for market rate housing.

8490 ■ *"Lending Idea Gets Mixed Review"* in *Tampa Bay Business Journal (Vol. 29, October 30, 2009, No. 45, pp. 1)*
Pub: American City Business Journals
Ed: Kent Hoover, Margie Manning. **Description:** Tampa Bay area, Florida's community banks have expressed disapproval to the proposal of President Obama to increase lending to small business, wherein the government will provide cheap capital through US Treasury Troubled Asset Relief Program (TARP). The banks were hesitant on the plan because of the strings attached to TARP.

8491 ■ *"Less Malaise in Malaysia"* in *Barron's (Vol. 88, March 17, 2008, No. 11, pp. M12)*
Pub: Dow Jones & Company, Inc.
Ed: Assif Shameen. **Description:** Shares of Malaysia's Bursa have been in freefall while the Malaysia government prolongs its pitch to sell a 10 percent stake of the exchange to NYSE Euronext. Asian bourses had produced very good returns for five years and charge some of the highest fees for exchanges. A key growth driver for Asian bourses could be the derivatives markets and exchange-traded funds.

8492 ■ *"Let Us Count the Ways"* in *Barron's (Vol. 88, July 7, 2008, No. 27, pp. M10)*
Pub: Dow Jones & Co., Inc.
Ed: Bennet Sedacca. **Description:** Investors are advised to remain cautious after the drop in stock prices in June 2008. The stock markets remain in the downtrend after reaching a peak in October 2007 and are on the verge of a collapse.

8493 ■ *"A Lifetime of Making Deals"* in *Crain's Detroit Business (Vol. 24, March 24, 2008, No. 12, pp. 11)*
Pub: Crain Communications, Inc.
Ed: Tom Henderson. **Description:** Profile of Walter 'Bud' Aspature who received Crain's Lifetime Achievement Award for mergers and acquisitions; Aspature is chairman and co-founder of Amherst Partners L.L.C., an investment banking firm that does evaluations and financings, specializes in turnarounds and advises private and public companies on mergers and acquisitions.

8494 ■ *"Lifetime Planning with a Twist"* in *Contractor (Vol. 56, July 2009, No. 7, pp. 40)*
Pub: Penton Media, Inc.
Ed: Irv Blackman. **Description:** Private Placement Life Insurance lets wealthy investors make their investment gains tax-free and can be set up so investors can make tax-free loans from the policy. This can be used on a younger member of the family as a wealth-building strategy if the investor is uninsurable.

8495 ■ *"A Limited Sphere of Influence"* in *Mergers & Acquisitions: The Dealmaker's Journal (March 1, 2008)*
Pub: SourceMedia, Inc.
Ed: Ken MacFadyen. **Description:** Changes to the interest rate has had little impact on the mergers and acquisitions market since the federal funds rate does not link directly to the liquidity available to the M&A market; lenders are looking at cash flows and are likely to remain cautious due to other factors impacting the market.

8496 ■ *"Listen to Bond Market on Tembec"* in *Globe & Mail (January 25, 2006, pp. B1)*
Pub: CTVglobemedia Publishing Inc.
Ed: Derek DeCloet. **Description:** The feasibility of Tembec Inc.'s restructuring efforts is discussed.

8497 ■ *"Listen Up: There's a Revolution in the Cubicle"* in *Barron's (Vol. 89, July 27, 2009, No. 30, pp. 18)*
Pub: Dow Jones & Co., Inc.
Ed: Jay Palmer. **Description:** Plantronics will be among the first beneficiaries when the unified communications revolution arrives in the office. Plantron-

ics' shares could rise to around 30 in 2009 from the 20s as of July 2009. Unified communications could create a huge new multimillion-dollar market for Plantronics.

8498 ■ *"The Little Biotech that Could"* in *Barron's (Vol. 89, July 27, 2009, No. 30, pp. 19)*
Pub: Dow Jones & Co., Inc.
Ed: Christopher C. Williams. **Description:** OSI Pharmaceuticals' shares is a compelling investment bet among small biotech firms due to its Tarceva anticancer drug which has a 23 percent market share as well as their strong balance sheet. OSI is planning to expand the use of Tarceva which could re-ignite sales and one analyst expects the shares to trade in the 40s one year from July 2009.

8499 ■ *"Loblaw Posts 40 Percent Profit Drop as it Scrambles to Lower Costs"* in *Globe & Mail (February 9, 2006, pp. B1)*
Pub: CTVglobemedia Publishing Inc.
Ed: Marina Strauss. **Description:** The reasons behind 40 percent decline in profits for Lobalaw Companies Ltd., for fourth quarter 2005, are presented.

8500 ■ *"Local Firms Will Feel Impact Of Wall St. Woes"* in *The Business Journal-Milwaukee (Vol. 25, September 19, 2008, No. 52, pp. A1)*
Pub: American City Business Journals, Inc.
Ed: Rich Kirchen. **Description:** Wall Street's crisis is expected to affect businesses in Wisconsin, in terms of decreased demand for services and products and increased financing costs. Businesses in Milwaukee area may face higher interest rates and tougher loan standards. The potential impacts of the Wall Street crisis on local businesses are examined further.

8501 ■ *"Locally Based Stocks Escape Worst of Market's Turmoil"* in *Crain's Detroit Business (Vol. 24, September 22, 2008, No. 38, pp. 4)*
Pub: Crain Communications Inc.
Ed: Daniel Duggan. **Description:** Locally-based companies did not take as big a hit as might be expected with the shock to the financial markets last week; this is due mainly to the fact that the region does not have heavy exposure to energy or capital markets.

8502 ■ *"Long - And Leery"* in *Barron's (Vol. 88, March 31, 2008, No. 13, pp. 47)*
Pub: Dow Jones & Company, Inc.
Ed: Jack Willoughby. **Description:** Tom Claugus' Bay Resource Partners hedge fund has returned 20 percent annually since it started in 1993. Claugus says that he is as aggressively long as he has ever been despite the dangers of the U.S. market. Claugus' stock picks include Canadian Natural Resources, NII Holdings, and Discover Financial.

8503 ■ *"Loop 360 Offices Planned"* in *Austin Business JournalInc. (Vol. 28, December 5, 2008, No. 38, pp. A1)*
Pub: American City Business Journals
Ed: Kate Harrington. **Description:** Nearly 356,000 square feet of office space is planned in the South Capital of Texas Highway Corridor, also known as Loop 360 in Austin. Riverside Developers plans to wait until the economy improves before starting construction.

8504 ■ *"Lotus Starts Slowly, Dodges Subprime Woes"* in *Crain's Detroit Business (Vol. 24, April 14, 2008, No. 15, pp. 3)*
Pub: Crain Communications, Inc.
Ed: Tom Henderson. **Description:** Discusses Lotus Bancorp Inc. and their business plan, which although is not right on target due to the subprime mortgage meltdown, is in a much better position than its competitors due to the quality of their loans.

8505 ■ *"Lower Prices No Shoo-In as Telcos Near Deregulation"* in *Globe & Mail (March 28, 2007, pp. B1)*
Pub: CTVglobemedia Publishing Inc.
Ed: Catherine McLean. **Description:** The fall in market share and low quality of service among other issues that may disallow telecommunication industries in Canada from setting their phone rates is discussed.

8506 ■ *"Lundin Deal Leaves Nickel Market Thin"* in *Globe & Mail (April 5, 2007, pp. B4)*
Pub: CTVglobemedia Publishing Inc.
Ed: Andy Hoffman. **Description:** The likely acquisition of Rio Narcea Gold Mines Ltd. by Lundin Mining Corp. and the decreasing number of nickel mining companies on the list of Toronto Stock Exchange are discussed.

8507 ■ *"Luster Lost"* in *Saint Louis Business Journal (Vol. 32, September 16, 2011, No. 3, pp. 1)*
Pub: Saint Louis Business Journal
Ed: E.B. Solomont. **Description:** Express Cripts shares have plunged 22.71 percent since late July amid regulatory concerns, as the luster of the second-largest deal announced for 2011 wore off. Express Scripts has become the largest pharmacy benefit manager in the country after the $29 billion deal to take rival Medco Health Solutions.

8508 ■ *"Magna Banks on Big Cash Hoard"* in *Globe & Mail (March 1, 2006, pp. B3)*
Pub: CTVglobemedia Publishing Inc.
Ed: Greg Keenan. **Description:** The details on Magna International Inc., which posted decline in profits at $639 million for 2005, are presented.

8509 ■ *"Magna Shares Sink on Tepid Outlook"* in *Globe & Mail (January 13, 2006, pp. B1)*
Pub: CTVglobemedia Publishing Inc.
Ed: Greg Keenan. **Description:** The impact of Magna International Inc.'s sales projection for 2006, on its shares, is discussed.

8510 ■ *Major Financial Institutions of the World*
Pub: Graham & Whiteside
URL(s): www.gale.cengage.com. **Ed:** Alison Gallico, Susan Hoernig, Kate Wilson, Carolina Dunsford. **Released:** Latest edition 16th; Published May, 2012. **Price:** $1460, Individuals. **Covers:** More than 10,000 worldwide financial corporations, including banks, insurance companies, investment companies, and leasing companies. Also includes contact information for senior executives. **Entries include:** Most listings include name, address, phone, telex, names of executives, principal activities, names of principal shareholders; subsidiary companies and financial summary where available. **Availability:** Online: Cengage Learning Inc. **Type:** Directory.

8511 ■ *"Making It Click"* in *Barron's (Vol. 88, March 17, 2008, No. 11, pp. 31)*
Pub: Dow Jones & Company, Inc.
Ed: Theresa W. Carey. **Description:** Listing of 23 online brokers that are evaluated based on their trade experience, usability, range of offerings, research amenities, customer service and access, and costs. TradeStation Securities takes the top spot followed by thinkorswim by just a fraction.

8512 ■ *"M&I Execs May Get Golden Parachutes"* in *Business Journal-Milwaukee (Vol. 28, December 31, 2010, No. 14, pp. A3)*
Pub: Milwaukee Business Journal
Ed: Rich Kirchen. **Description:** Marshall and Isley Corporation's top executives have a chance to receive golden-parachute payments it its buyer, BMO Financial Group, repays the Troubled Asset Relief Program (TARP) loan on behalf of the company. One TARP rule prevents golden-parachute payments to them and the next five most highly paid employees of TARP recipients.

8513 ■ *"M&T On the March?"* in *Baltimore Business Journal (Vol. 28, November 12, 2010, No. 27, pp. 1)*
Pub: Baltimore Business Journal
Ed: Gary Haber. **Description:** Information on the growth of M&T Bank, as well as its expansion plans are presented. M&T recently acquired Wilmington Trust and took over $500 million in deposits from the failed K Bank. Analysts believe that M&T would continue its expansion through Washington DC and Richmond, Virginia, especially after a bank executive acknowledged that the markets in those areas are attractive.

8514 ■ "Many Roads Lead to Value" in Barron's (Vol. 88, March 10, 2008, No. 10, pp. 46)
Pub: Dow Jones & Company, Inc.
Ed: Lawrence C. Strauss. Description: David J. Williams, lead manager of Excelsior Value & Restructuring Fund, invests in struggling companies and those companies whose turnarounds show promise. Morgan Stanley, Lehman Brothers, and Petroleo Brasileiro are some of the companies he holds shares in, while he has unloaded shares of Citigroup, Freddie Mac, and Sallie Mae.

8515 ■ "Market Recoups Its Losses - And Its Optimism" in Barron's (Vol. 89, July 20, 2009, No. 29, pp. M3)
Pub: Dow Jones & Co., Inc.
Ed: Kopin Tan. Description: US stock markets gained heavily in the third week of July 2009, rising by about 7 percent during the week. The shares of human resource management companies could be overpriced as they are trading at very high price-earnings multiples. Baxter International faces a class-action suit due to its alleged conspiracy with CSL to fix blood-plasma product prices.

8516 ■ "Market Swings Intensify Yearning for Bonds" in Globe & Mail (March 9, 2007, pp. B9)
Pub: CTVglobemedia Publishing Inc.
Ed: Keith Damsell. Description: The rise in demand for proper fixed-income bonds in Canada as a result of uncertainties in the equity market is discussed. Some big Canadian fixed-income funds are presented.

8517 ■ "Market Volatility and Your Retirement" in Agency Sales Magazine (Vol. 39, August 2009, No. 8, pp. 48)
Pub: MANA
Ed: Joshua D. Mosshart. Description: Strategies for retirees in managing investments amid market volatility are presented. Retirees should keep their withdrawal assumptions conservative, maintain sensible asset allocation, review and rebalance their portfolio and allow a financial professional to guide them. Insights on market volatility are also given.

8518 ■ "Market Watch" in Barron's (Vol. 88, March 24, 2008, No. 12, pp. M18)
Pub: Dow Jones & Company, Inc.
Ed: Ashraf Laidi; Marc Pado; David Kotok. Description: Latest measures implemented by the Federal Reserve to address the credit crisis did not benefit the US dollar, with the Japanese yen and the euro recouping earlier losses against the dollar. Goldman Sachs reported earnings of $3.23 per share, claiming a stronger liquidity position. The US markets bottomed early on 22 January 2007, according to evidence.

8519 ■ "Market Watch" in Barron's (Vol. 89, July 20, 2009, No. 29, pp. M10)
Pub: Dow Jones & Co., Inc.
Ed: Peter Greene; Michael Darda; Ian Wyatt; Stephanie Pomboy. Description: Concerns about a possible increase in US inflation rates are overblown as the country remains in a deflationary environment. Goldman Sachs's second quarter 2009 earnings have already been priced in as its shares rose. Germany's plans of a possible dollar bond sale are in anticipation of a rise in the euro's value.

8520 ■ "Market Watch: A Sampling of Advisory Opinion" in Barron's (Vol. 88, March 17, 2008, No. 11, pp. M10)
Pub: Dow Jones & Company, Inc.
Ed: Paul Schatz; William Gibson; Michael Darda. Description: S&P 500 bank stocks were down 46 percent from their 2007 peak while the peak to through fall in 1989-1990 was just over 50 percent. This suggests that the bottom on the bank stocks could be near. The Federal Reserve Board announced they will lend up to $200 billion to primary lenders in exchange other securities.

8521 ■ "Markets Defy the Doomsayers" in Barron's (Vol. 88, March 24, 2008, No. 12, pp. M5)
Pub: Dow Jones & Company, Inc.
Ed: Leslie P. Norton. Description: US stock markets registered strong gains, with the Dow Jones Industrial

Average rising 3.43 percent on the week to close at 12,361.32, in a rally that may be seen as short-covering. Shares of Hansen Natural are poised for further drops with a slowdown in the energy drink market.

8522 ■ "The Market's (Very) Tender Spring Shoots" in Barron's (Vol. 88, March 31, 2008, No. 13, pp. M3)
Pub: Dow Jones & Company, Inc.
Ed: Kopin Tan. Description: Expansion in price-earnings multiples and a lower credit-default risk index has encouraged fans of the spring-awakening theory. Shares of industrial truckers have gone up 32 percent in 2008 and some shares are pushing five-year highs brought on by higher efficiency and earnings from more load carried. The prospects of the shares of Foot Locker are also discussed.

8523 ■ The Match King: Ivar Kreuger, the Financial Genius Behind a Century of Wall Street Scandals
Pub: Basic Books
Ed: Frank Portnoy. Released: 2009. Price: $26.95.
Description: Ivar Kreuger, the so-called Match King, used a pyramid scheme to become the financier to European leaders.

8524 ■ "The Medium 150" in Canadian Business (Vol. 81, Summer 2008, No. 9, pp. 129)
Pub: Rogers Media Ltd.
Description: Medium-sized companies are ranked based on market capitalization and stock performance. Timminico Ltd. topped the roster with 1,294.2 percent returns, while Petrominerales Ltd. ranked second with 325.4 percent. A table showing the 2008 rankings of the companies is presented.

8525 ■ "Merchant Cash-Advance Company Enters Canada" in Cardline (Vol. 8, February 29, 2008, No. 9, pp. 1)
Pub: SourceMedia Inc.
Description: Merchant cash-advance company is expanding operations into Canada.

8526 ■ "Merrill Lynch in Talks to Buy BlackRock Stake" in Globe & Mail (February 13, 2006, pp. B4)
Pub: CTVglobemedia Publishing Inc.
Ed: Dennis K. Breman; Randall Smith. Description: Financial services firm Merrill Lynch and Co. is planning to acquire money managing company BlackRock Inc. for 8 million dollars. Sources report that this deal would create 1-trillion dollar huge fund management venture.

8527 ■ "Mettle Detector" in Canadian Business (Vol. 79, July 17, 2006, No. 14-15, pp. 63)
Pub: Rogers Media
Ed: Calvin Leung. Description: The difficulties faced in completing the Certified Financial Analyst course, and the rewards one can expect after its completion, are discussed.

8528 ■ "MF Global Moved Clients' Funds to BNY Mellon" in Wall Street Journal Eastern Edition (November 19 , 2011, pp. B2)
Pub: Dow Jones & Company Inc.
Ed: Aaron Lucchetti. Description: Since the collapse of securities brokerage MF Global Holdings Ltd., one question has remained: where did the hundreds of millions of dollars in customers' accounts go? It has been revealed that MF Global moved those millions from its own brokerage unit to Bank of New York Mellon Corporation in August of this year, just two months before filing for bankruptcy protection.

8529 ■ "MFS Survey: Generation X/Y Perplexed and Conservative about Future Investing" in Wireless News (November 16, 2010)
Pub: Close-Up Media Inc.
Description: Generation X and Y tend to have a conservative approach to investing according to a survey conducted by MFS Investment Management. Statistical data included.

8530 ■ "Micro-Cap Companies" in Canadian Business (Vol. 81, Summer 2008, No. 9, pp. 157)
Pub: Rogers Media Ltd.
Description: Micro-cap companies have lower than $221 million in terms of market capitalization. Burnaby, British Columbia-based Fancamp Exploration Ltd. topped the roster with 1,116.7 percent in return. A table showing the 2008 rankings of the companies is presented.

8531 ■ "Microsoft's Big Gamble" in Canadian Business (Vol. 81, March 3, 2008, No. 3, pp. 13)
Pub: Rogers Media
Ed: Andrew Wahl. Description: Microsoft Corp. is taking a big risk in buying Yahoo, as it is expected to pay more than $31 a share to finalize the acquisition. The deal would be seven and a half times bigger than any other that Microsoft has entered before, an execution of such deal is also anticipated to become a challenge for Microsoft. Recommendations on how Microsoft should handle the integration of the two businesses are given.

8532 ■ "Mine Woes Could Rouse Zinc" in Barron's (Vol. 88, July 7, 2008, No. 27, pp. M12)
Pub: Dow Jones & Co., Inc.
Ed: Andrea Hotter. Description: Prices of zinc could increase due to supply problems in producing countries such as Australia and China. London Metal Exchange prices for the metal have dropped about 36 percent in 2008.

8533 ■ "Mining Executive Telfer Pocketed Millions" in Globe & Mail (April 5, 2007, pp. B4)
Pub: CTVglobemedia Publishing Inc.
Ed: Andy Hoffman. Description: The issue of huge compensation for former executive of both Goldcorp Inc. and UrAsia Energy Ltd., Ian Telfer, for his efficient management of stock options is discussed.

8534 ■ "Mining Goldman for Insight" in Barron's (Vol. 89, July 20, 2009, No. 29, pp. M8)
Pub: Dow Jones & Co., Inc.
Ed: Steven M. Sears. Description: Methods of investing in options for companies with earnings estimates from Goldman Sachs are discussed. These methods take advantage of increased volatility generated by earnings revisions.

8535 ■ "Misguided" in Canadian Business (Vol. 81, July 22, 2008, No. 12-13, pp. 30)
Pub: Rogers Media Ltd.
Ed: Al Rosen. Description: Canada's securities regulations are discussed; differing views on using principles-based and rules-based securities regulations are also presented.

8536 ■ "Misplaced Trust" in Canadian Business (Vol. 79, October 23, 2006, No. 21, pp. 65)
Pub: Rogers Media
Ed: John Gray. Description: The reasons for the drop in the share prices of the income trusts of Retrocom Investment Management Inc. are analyzed.

8537 ■ "Missing MF Global Funds Could Top $1.2 Billion" in Wall Street Journal Eastern Edition (November 22 , 2011, pp. A1)
Pub: Dow Jones & Company Inc.
Ed: Aaron Lucchetti, Dan Strumpf. Description: As the investigation into the collapse of securities brokerage MF Global Holdings Ltd. continues, the question of what happened to customers' funds has to be answered. Now, it is believed that the actual amount of missing funds is much more than the $600 million originally thought, and could be well over $1.2 billion.

8538 ■ "A Mixed-Bag Quarter" in Barron's (Vol. 88, July 7, 2008, No. 27, pp. 19)
Pub: Dow Jones & Co., Inc.
Ed: Shirley A. Lazo. Description: Seven component companies of the Dow Jones Industrial Average increased their dividend payouts in the second quarter of 2008 despite the weak performance of the

index. Five companies in the Dow Jones Transportation index and three in the Dow Jones Utilities also increased their dividends.

8539 ■ "Modern-Day Midas Hasn't Lost Touch" in Globe & Mail (January 19, 2006, pp. B4)
Pub: CTVglobemedia Publishing Inc.
Ed: Shirley Won. **Description:** The investment plans of chief executive officer Rob McEwen of U.S. Gold Corp. are presented.

8540 ■ "Molson Coors Ends Ill-Fated Foray Into Brazil" in Globe & Mail (January 17, 2006, pp. B1)
Pub: CTVglobemedia Publishing Inc.
Ed: Andy Hoffman. **Description:** The details of loss incurred by Molson Coors Brewing Co., from the sale of Cervejarias Kaiser SA to Fomento Economico Mexicano S.A. de C.V., are presented.

8541 ■ "Moms Mull Money" in Marketing to Women (Vol. 21, February 2008, No. 2, pp. 6)
Pub: EPM Communications Inc.
Contact: Ira Mayer, President
E-mail: imayer@epmcom.com
Description: According to a survey by Countrywide Bank, women, especially mothers, are more concerned about their financial fitness than men.

8542 ■ "MoneyGram In Pact With Payday Lender" in American Banker (Vol. 173, March 7, 2008, No. 46, pp. 6)
Pub: SourceMedia Inc.
Ed: William Launder. **Description:** Details of pact between MoneyGram International Inc. and Advance America Cash Advance Centers are examined.

8543 ■ "Montreal Exchange Buoyed by U.S. Takeover Moves" in Globe & Mail (March 16, 2007, pp. B1)
Pub: CTVglobemedia Publishing Inc.
Ed: Sinclair Stewart. **Description:** The rise in the share prices of Montreal Exchange due to the derivatives exchange's bid to acquire the Chicago Board of Trade is discussed. The trends pertaining to the consolidation of global stock markets are described.

8544 ■ "Moody and Paranoid" in Barron's (Vol. 88, March 10, 2008, No. 10, pp. M14)
Pub: Dow Jones & Company, Inc.
Ed: Steven M. Sears. **Description:** Discusses the options market which remains liquid but is cautious of possible failures, especially for financial companies. Investors are in absolute fear when trading with options involving the financial sector.

8545 ■ "More Gains in the Pipeline" in Barron's (Vol. 89, August 3, 2009, No. 31, pp. M5)
Pub: Dow Jones & Co., Inc.
Ed: Fleming Meeks. **Description:** Shares of El Paso Corp. could recover as the company concludes a deal with a private-equity group to fund pipeline construction. The company's shares are trading at $10.06 and could move up to $12 as bad news has already been priced into the stock.

8546 ■ "More Jobs Moving Out of City" in Business Courier (Vol. 24, March 14, 2008, No. 49, pp. 1)
Pub: American City Business Journals, Inc.
Ed: Steve Watkins; Laura Baverman. **Description:** UBS Financial Services Inc. is moving Gradison to Kenwood Town Place in Sycamore Township a year after UBS acquired Gradison. The township does not have a tax on earnings so the move will save Gradison's employees the 2.1 percent Cincinnati tax.

8547 ■ "Mortgage Securities Drop Hits Home" in The Business Journal-Serving Metropolitan Kansas City (Vol. 27, October 17, 2008, No. 5)
Pub: American City Business Journals, Inc.
Ed: Rob Roberts. **Description:** Sale of commercial mortgage-backed securities (CMBS) in Kansas City, Missouri have declined. The area may avoid layoffs if the United States government succeeds in stabilizing the economy. Major CMBS players in the area include Midland Loan Services Inc. and KeyBank Real Estate Capital.

8548 ■ "Mortgages Going Under" in Black Enterprise (Vol. 41, December 2010, No. 5, pp. 20)
Pub: Earl G. Graves Publishing Co. Inc.
Description: Nearly one-fifth of the country's homeowners are underwater in their mortgages, which means they owe more on their home than the home's worth. Statistical data included.

8549 ■ "Move Over - Or Out" in Puget Sound Business Journal (Vol. 29, November 28, 2008, No. 32, pp. 1)
Pub: American City Business Journals
Ed: Kirsten Grind. **Description:** Real estate agents in the state of Washington are either moving to smaller real estate firms or quitting the industry due to the weak housing market. Lesser-known firms are experiencing an influx of experienced real estate agents, while 2,800 agents in the state have left the industry.

8550 ■ "Mover and Sheika" in Conde Nast Portfolio (Vol. 2, June 2008, No. 6, pp. 104)
Pub: Conde Nast Publications
Contact: David Carey, President
Ed: John Arlidge. **Description:** Profile of Princess Sheika Lubna who is the first female foreign trade minister in the Middle East, the United Arab Emirates biggest business envoy, paving the way for billions in new investment, and also a manufacturer of her own perfume line.

8551 ■ "'Mr. CEO, Please Do Elaborate On Your Firm's Metrics" in Business Courier (Vol. 24, February 29, 2008, No. 47, pp. 1)
Pub: American City Business Journals, Inc.
Ed: Jon Newberry. **Description:** Discusses a rogue caller who goes by the name of Joe Herrick, Steven Nissan and Joe Harris has joined in over a dozen conference calls, asking chief executive officers on their plans and commenting on the companies' operations. The mystery caller attempts to pass himself off as a financial analyst. Transcripts of some conference calls, in which the rogue caller is involved, are provided.

8552 ■ "Mr. Deeds" in Canadian Business (Vol. 81, March 31, 2008, No. 5, pp. 24)
Pub: Rogers Media
Ed: Thomas Watson. **Description:** Ron Sandler has the right experience to save Northern Rock PLC get through its liquidity problems. Sandler is known for saving Lloyd's of London in the mid-90's and he is not afraid to make enemies. Ron Sandler's assignment to help Northern Rock comes at a time when the health of the U.K. housing is not great.

8553 ■ "MTI Faces Touch Choices" in The Business Review Albany (Vol. 35, April 4, 2008, No. 53, pp. 1)
Pub: The Business Review
Ed: Richard A. D'Errico. **Description:** Mechanical Technology Inc.'s auditor, PricewaterhouseCoopers LLP is concerned about the company's limited current cash and its $105 million accumulated deficit. MTI has already sold 1.45 million of its PlugPower Inc. shares, but still considers to sell more of the Plug stock. The problems at MTI and the difficult decisions it has to face to solve them are examined.

8554 ■ "Muddy Portfolio Raises a Question: Just What Is National City Worth?" in Crain's Detroit Business (Vol. 24, April 7, 2008, No. 14)
Pub: Crain Communications, Inc.
Ed: Jay Miller. **Description:** National City Bank is looking at strategies to help it deal with its credit and loan problems which are reflected in its falling stock price. One possible solution is a merger with another bank, however most national banks are facing their own home-loan portfolio issues and may be unable to tackle another company's unresolved problems. Statistical data included.

8555 ■ "Mutual Fund Sales of $23.4 Billion Best Since 2001" in Globe & Mail (January 5, 2006, pp. B3)
Pub: CTVglobemedia Publishing Inc.
Ed: Omar El Akkad. **Description:** The details on $23.4 billion net sales of mutual fund sector, in Canada, are presented.

8556 ■ "Naked Investing" in Canadian Business (Vol. 80, January 15, 2007, No. 2, pp. 27)
Pub: Rogers Media
Ed: Al Rosen. **Description:** The need for Canadian investors to learn important facts about income trusts before investing in them is discussed.

8557 ■ "Nancy Hughes Anthony" in Canadian Business (Vol. 81, October 13, 2008, No. 17, pp. 104)
Pub: Rogers Media Ltd.
Ed: Andy Holloway. **Description:** Profile of Nancy Hughes Anthony, who believes her experience operating large enterprises as a public servant helped her earn positions that ultimately brought her to her current position as chief executive and president of the Canadian Bankers Association. She also thinks there should be more public-private sector coordination within industries.

8558 ■ "Nanoready?" in Entrepreneur (Vol. 36, May 2008, No. 5, pp. 20)
Pub: Entrepreneur Media, Inc.
Ed: Andrea Cooper. **Description:** Experts predict that the medicine and energy sectors are among those that will see nanotechnology innovations in the coming years, and that nanotechnology will produce significant commercial value in new products. Some entrepreneurs are investing in nanotech and are partnering with universities. Details on nanotech funding concerns are discussed.

8559 ■ "Nationwide Bank Ready for December Conversion" in Business First-Columbus (October 12, 2007, pp. A1)
Pub: American City Business Journals, Inc.
Ed: Adrian Burns. **Description:** Nationwide Bank will increase marketing to its customers, including the 45,000 that came from the acquisition of Nationwide Federal Credit Union in December 2006. Upgrading its online banking system and Website will bring the company and its services closer to clients. The influence of the insurance industry on the bank's marketing strategy is also examined.

8560 ■ "Need Grub? Start Texting at Kroger" in Business Courier (Vol. 24, December 21, 2008, No. 36, pp. 1)
Pub: American City Business Journals, Inc.
Ed: Laura Baverman. **Description:** Discusses the University of Cincinnati which is teaming up to release a technology platform called Macopay that would link a cell phone to a bank account and allow a person to make payments at participating retailers by sending a text message. Details with regard to the new service and its growth potential are discussed.

8561 ■ "Needed: A Strategy; Banking In China" in The Economist (Vol. 390, January 3, 2009, No. 8612, pp. 54)
Pub: The Economist Newspaper Inc.
Description: International banks are competing for a role in China but are finding obstacles in their paths such as a reduction in the credit their operations may receive from Chinese banks and the role they can play in the public capital markets which remain limited.

8562 ■ "Nerds on Wall Street: Math, Machines and Wired Markets
Pub: John Wiley & Sons, Inc.
Ed: David J. Leinweber. **Released:** May 27, 2009. **Price:** $39.95. **Description:** The history of technology and how it will transform investing and trading on Wall Street is outlined.

8563 ■ "Netflix Gets No Respect" in Barron's (Vol. 89, July 27, 2009, No. 30, pp. 26)
Pub: Dow Jones & Co., Inc.
Ed: Tiernan Ray. **Description:** Netflix met expectations when they announced their second quarter sales but their shares still fell by almost 10 percent. Analysts say their entry into the 'streaming video' business is a mixed bag since customers are increasingly buying the cheaper monthly plan and this is dragging the economics of the business.

8564 ■ *"NetSpend, Payday Firm in Pact"* in *American Banker (Vol. 173, February 22, 2008, No. 7, pp. 7)*
Pub: SourceMedia Inc.
Ed: Daniel Wolfe. **Description:** NetSpend Corporation of Austin, Texas is providing its prepaid cards to Advance America Cash Advance Centers Inc., a Spartanburg, South Carolina payday lender.

8565 ■ *"The New Arsenal of Risk Management"* in *Harvard Business Review (Vol. 86, September 2008, No. 9, pp. 92)*
Pub: Harvard Business School Press
Ed: Kevin Bueler; Andrew Freeman; Ron Hulme. **Description:** Goldman Sachs Group Inc. is used to illustrate methods for successful risk management. The investment bank's business principles, partnerships, and oversight practices are discussed.

8566 ■ *"New Century's Fall Has a New Culprit"* in *Barron's (Vol. 88, March 31, 2008, No. 13, pp. 20)*
Pub: Dow Jones & Company, Inc.
Ed: Jonathan R. Laing. **Description:** Court examiner Michael Missal reports that New Century Financial's auditor contributed to New Century's demise by its negligence in permitting improper and imprudent practices related to New Century's accounting processes. New Century's bankruptcy filing is considered the start of the subprime-mortgage crisis.

8567 ■ *"New Drug Could Revitalize Amgen"* in *Barron's (Vol. 88, July 7, 2008, No. 27, pp. 23)*
Pub: Dow Jones & Co., Inc.
Ed: Johanna Bennett. **Description:** Shares of the biotechnology company Amgen could receive a boost from the release of the anti-osteoporosis drug denosumab. The shares, priced at $48.84 each, are trading at 11 times expected earnings for 2008 and could also be boosted by cost cutting measures.

8568 ■ *"A New Kid on the Block"* in *Barron's (Vol. 88, March 17, 2008, No. 11, pp. 58)*
Pub: Dow Jones & Company, Inc.
Ed: Thomas G. Donlan. **Description:** Discusses the Federal Reserve which has offered to lend $100 billion in cash to banks and $200 billion in Treasuries to Wall Street investment banks that have problems with liquidity. The reluctance of the banks to lend money to meet a margin call on securities that could still depreciate is the reason why the agency is going into the direct loan business.

8569 ■ *"New Law Lets Shareholders Play Hardball With Firms"* in *Globe & Mail (January 2, 2006, pp. B1)*
Pub: CTVglobemedia Publishing Inc.
Ed: Janet McFarland. **Description:** Business lawyer Wes Voorheis discusses about the launching of Bill 198 by plaintiffs' lawyers on behalf of ordinary retail investors.

8570 ■ *"New Money"* in *Entrepreneur (Vol. 36, February 2008, No. 2, pp. 62)*
Pub: Entrepreneur Media Inc.
Ed: C.J. Prince. **Description:** Tips on how to handle business finance, with regard to the tightened credit standards imposed by leading institutions, are provided. These include: selling receivables, margining blue chips, and selling purchase orders.

8571 ■ *"The New Nimble"* in *Barron's (Vol. 90, August 30, 2010, No. 35, pp. S12)*
Pub: Barron's Editorial & Corporate Headquarters
Ed: Suzanne McGee. **Description:** Financial advisors are making investments based on short-lived market trends due to the uncertainty in the long-term market. This strategy can be demanding and advisors should only try it if they are confident about their skill in spotting short-term trends.

8572 ■ *"The New Risk Tolerance"* in *Entrepreneur (Vol. 37, September 2009, No. 9, pp. 66)*
Pub: Entrepreneur Media, Inc.
Ed: Rosalind Resnick. **Description:** Offers advice on where to invest personal money in the United States. One could lose money from investing in gold and treasuries. High-quality corporate bonds and Treasury Inflation-Protected Securities are seen as ideal investments.

8573 ■ *"New Thinking for a New Financial Order"* in *Harvard Business Review (Vol. 86, September 2008, No. 9, pp. 26)*
Pub: Harvard Business School Press
Ed: Diana Farell. **Description:** Factors driving the current global economy are analyzed with a focus on the influence of new public and private sectors and the impact of unregulated markets.

8574 ■ *"A New Way to Tell When to Fold"* in *Barron's (Vol. 88, July 7, 2008, No. 27, pp. 27)*
Pub: Dow Jones & Co., Inc.
Ed: Theresa W. Carey. **Description:** Overview of the Online trading company SmartStops, a firm that aims to tell investors when to sell the shares of a particular company. The company's Web site categorizes stocks as moving up, down, or sideways, and calculates exit points for individual stocks based on an overall market trend.

8575 ■ *"New Ways to Catch a Thief"* in *Barron's (Vol. 88, March 10, 2008, No. 10, pp. 37)*
Pub: Dow Jones & Company, Inc.
Ed: Theresa W. Carey. **Description:** Online brokerage firms employ different methods to protect the accounts of their customers from theft. These methods include secure Internet connections, momentary passwords, and proprietary algorithms.

8576 ■ *"New Year, New Estate Plan"* in *Hawaii Business (Vol. 53, February 2008, No. 8, pp. 54)*
Pub: Hawaii Business Publishing
Ed: Antony M. Orme. **Description:** Discusses the start of the new year which can be a time to revise wills and estate plans as failure to do so may create problems of unequal inheritance and increase in estate tax exemption, which could disinherit beneficiaries. Other circumstances that can prompt changes in wills and estate plans are presented.

8577 ■ *"The Next Government Bailout?"* in *Barron's (Vol. 88, March 10, 2008, No. 10, pp. 21)*
Pub: Dow Jones & Company, Inc.
Ed: Jonathan Laing. **Description:** Fannie Mae may need a government bailout as it faces huge hits brought about by the effects of the housing crisis. The shares of the government-sponsored enterprise have dropped 65 percent since the housing crisis began.

8578 ■ *"Nightmare on Wall Street"* in *Canadian Business (Vol. 81, October 13, 2008, No. 17, pp. 9)*
Pub: Rogers Media Ltd.
Ed: Rachel Pulfer. **Description:** Information on events that happened on Wall Street on the week that started September 15, 2008, as well on its effect on financial markets around the world, are presented. Lehman Brothers filed for bankruptcy on September 15, 2008 after negotiations with Barclays Group and Bank of America failed. Details on AIG and Morgan Stanley are also presented.

8579 ■ *"No Fast Cash Class"* in *Black Enterprise (Vol. 37, December 2006, No. 5, pp. 72)*
Pub: Earl G. Graves Publishing Co. Inc.
Description: There are no shortcuts to a obtaining a career as a financial planner. Certified Financial Planner Board of Standards has specific requirements for certification which include having a bachelor's degree from an accredited U.S. school before candidates are even eligible for taking the certification exam. Other criteria and requirements are discussed.

8580 ■ *"No Surprises"* in *Canadian Business (Vol. 79, September 25, 2006, No. 19, pp. 49)*
Pub: Rogers Media
Ed: Jeff Sanford. **Description:** The increasing income trust sector in Canada is discussed.

8581 ■ *"Nortel Plays Big to Settle Lawsuits"* in *Globe & Mail (February 9, 2006, pp. B1)*
Pub: CTVglobemedia Publishing Inc.
Ed: Catherine McLean. **Description:** The details on Nortel Networks Corp.'s settlement of cases with shareholders are presented.

8582 ■ *"Not In My Backyard"* in *Entrepreneur (Vol. 36, May 2008, No. 5, pp. 42)*
Pub: Entrepreneur Media, Inc.
Ed: Farnoosh Torabi. **Description:** More investors are turning to overseas real estate investments as the U.S. market sees a slowdown. Analysts say that risk-averse investors opt for funds with record of strong returns and U.S. real estate investment trusts that partner with foreign businesses for transparency purposes. Other details about foreign real estate investments are discussed.

8583 ■ *"A Novel Fix for the Credit Mess"* in *Barron's (Vol. 88, March 31, 2008, No. 13, pp. 10)*
Pub: Dow Jones & Company, Inc.
Ed: Michael Santoli. **Description:** Due to the common bank-leverage factor of 10, the $250 billion of lost bank capital would have supported $2.5 trillion in lending capacity. Jeffrey Lewis suggests onerous regulations on bank-holding companies that own 10 to 25 percent, as they are partly to blame. Statistical data included.

8584 ■ *"Now in Play, Score Keeps Head Up and Stick on Ice"* in *Globe & Mail (January 20, 2007, pp. B5)*
Pub: CTVglobemedia Publishing Inc.
Ed: Grant Robertson. **Description:** The hike in the shares of Score Media Inc. due to its new services is presented.

8585 ■ *"Now That's Rich"* in *Canadian Business (Vol. 80, February 12, 2007, No. 4, pp. 92)*
Pub: Rogers Media
Ed: Thomas Watson. **Description:** The effort of chief executive officer of Stelco Inc. Rodney Mott in resolving the issue of financial loss of the company by taking up backdating options for share price is discussed.

8586 ■ *"Now You See It.."* in *Canadian Business (Vol. 81, November 10, 2008, No. 19, pp. 20)*
Pub: Rogers Media Ltd.
Ed: Sharda Prashad. **Description:** Total return swaps were offered by Deutsche Bank AG and UBS AG to foreign investors for them to avoid paying taxes on the proceeds of their shares of Fording Canadian Coal Trust when Teck Cominco offered to buy the company. This means that the Canadian government is losing tax revenue from foreigners and it is argued that a simpler tax system would avoid this practice.

8587 ■ *"Number of Mechanic's Liens Triple Since 2005"* in *The Business Journal - Serving Phoenix and the Valley of the Sun (Vol. 28, August 22, 2008, No. 51, pp. 1)*
Pub: American City Business Journals, Inc.
Ed: Jan Buchholtz. **Description:** Experts are blaming the mortgage and banking industries for the tripling of mechanic's liens that were filed in Arizona from 2005 through August 6, 2008. The rise in mechanic's liens is believed to indicate stress in the real estate community. Other views and information on the rise of mechanic's liens filed in Arizona are presented.

8588 ■ *"The Numbers Speak For Themselves"* in *Barron's (Vol. 88, July 14, 2008, No. 28, pp. 16)*
Pub: Dow Jones & Co., Inc.
Ed: Bill Alpert. **Description:** Discusses quant fund managers versus traditional long-short equity funds after quants outperformed traditional funds in the year 2000. Causes for the underperformance are outlined and statistical data is included.

8589 ■ *"Nvidia Shares Clobbered After Gloomy Warning"* in *Barron's (Vol. 88, July 7, 2008, No. 27, pp. 25)*
Pub: Dow Jones & Co., Inc.
Ed: Eric J. Savitz. **Description:** Shares of graphics chip manufacturer Nvidia suffered a 30 percent drop in its share price after the company warned that revenue and gross margin forecasts for the quarter ending July 27, 2008 will be below expectations. Stan

Glasgow, chief operating officer of Sony Electronics, believes the US economic slowdown will not affect demand for the company's products. Statistical data included.

8590 ■ *"Nvidia's Picture Brighter Than Stock Price Indicates" in Barron's (Vol. 88, March 24, 2008, No. 12, pp. 46)*
Pub: Dow Jones & Company, Inc.
Ed: Eric J. Savitz. **Description:** Shares of graphics chip maker Nvidia, priced at $18.52 each, do not indicate the company's strong position in the graphics chip market. The company's shares have dropped due to fears of slower demand for PCs, but the company is not as exposed to broader economic forces.

8591 ■ *"N.Y. Investors Reject AnorMed Board Proposal" in Globe & Mail (February 21, 2006, pp. B11)*
Pub: CTVglobemedia Publishing Inc.
Ed: Leonard Zehr. **Description:** The reasons behind the denial of investors over the restructuring plans of AnorMed are presented.

8592 ■ *"Nymex Dissidents Rattle Sabers" in Crain's Chicago Business (Vol. 31, April 21, 2008, No. 16, pp. 2)*
Pub: Crain Communications, Inc.
Ed: Ann Saphir. **Description:** Two groups of New York Mercantile Exchange members say they have more than enough votes to stop CME Group Inc.'s $10 billion deal to acquire the oil and metals exchange and they are threatening a proxy fight if the Chicago exchange doesn't raise its offer.

8593 ■ *"OccuLogix Shares Plummet 65 Percent" in Globe & Mail (February 4, 2006, pp. B5)*
Pub: CTVglobemedia Publishing Inc.
Ed: Leonard Zehr. **Description:** The shares of Occu-Logix drop by 65% in Canada. The decline in share price is attributed to failure of blood filtering system.

8594 ■ *"October 2009: Recovery Plods Along" in Hispanic Business (October 2009, pp. 10-11)*
Pub: Hispanic Business
Ed: Dr. Juan Solana. **Description:** Economist reports on a possible economic recovery which will not be allowed to rely on a strong domestic demand in order to sustain it. Consumers, looking to counterbalance years of leverage financing based on unrealistic, ever-increasing home and portfolio valuations, are saving rather than spending money.

8595 ■ *"Office Market May Turn Down" in Crain's New York Business (Vol. 24, January 14, 2008, No. 2, pp. 26)*
Pub: Crain Communications, Inc.
Description: Although still dominated by Wall Street, the downturn in the economy is raising fears that the continuing fallout from the subprime mortgage crisis could result in layoffs that will derail the office market.

8596 ■ *"Ohio Commerce Draws Closer to Profitability" in Crain's Cleveland Business (Vol. 28, October 29, 2007, No. 43, pp. 14)*
Pub: Crain Communications, Inc.
Ed: Shawn A. Turner. **Description:** Overview of the business plan of Ohio Commerce Bank, a de novo, or startup bank that is close to turning the corner to profitability. The bank opened in November 2006 and focuses on dealing with small businesses totaling $5 million or less in annual revenues.

8597 ■ *"Oil Patch Expects Richer Shell Offer" in Globe & Mail (January 3, 2006, pp. B1)*
Pub: CTVglobemedia Publishing Inc.
Ed: Andrew Willis; Patrick Brethour. **Description:** The concerns investors over the feasibility of Royal Dutch Shell PLC's acquisition of Shell Canada Ltd., for $7.6 billion, are presented. Shell Canada Ltd. reports rise in shares by ten percent.

8598 ■ *"Oil Picks and Pans" in Canadian Business (Vol. 79, August 14, 2006, No. 16-17, pp. 67)*
Pub: Rogers Media
Ed: Graham Scott. **Description:** A survey on investments in Canadian energy companies and the inflation caused by oil price hike, are discussed.

8599 ■ *"Oil's Going Down, Down, Down" in Canadian Business (Vol. 79, October 9, 2006, No. 20, pp. 148)*
Pub: Rogers Media
Ed: Ian McGugan. **Description:** Strategies for investors to benefit from the fall in global crude oil prices are discussed.

8600 ■ *"Ok, So Now What?" in Canadian Business (Vol. 79, November 6, 2006, No. 22, pp. 113)*
Pub: Rogers Media
Ed: Calvin Leung. **Description:** Details of healthy income-generating corporations, such as Cedar Fair L.P., are presented.

8601 ■ *"The Old Railway is on a Roll" in Globe & Mail (January 26, 2006, pp. B1)*
Pub: CTVglobemedia Publishing Inc.
Description: The reasons behind 5 percent rise in shares for Canadian National Railway Co. are presented.

8602 ■ *"On the Trail of the Bear" in Canadian Business (Vol. 81, March 17, 2008, No. 4, pp. 28)*
Pub: Rogers Media
Ed: Thomas Watson. **Description:** Discusses the conservative rule of thumb which is to invest in equity markets when a five to ten percent market rally is sustained for more than a few months. Bear markets on the S&P 500 bear markets in the 20th century only lasts over a year based on average. It is also good to remember that bear markets are followed by bulls that exceed the previous market highs.

8603 ■ *"One-Time Area Trust Executive Finds Trouble in N.H." in The Business Journal-Serving Metropolitan Kansas City (September 12, 2008)*
Pub: American City Business Journals, Inc.
Ed: Steve Vockrodt. **Description:** About 200 investors, some from Missouri's Kansas City area, claim that they had conducted business with Noble Trust Co. The trust company was placed under New Hampshire Banking Department's conservatorship after $15 million was discovered to be missing from its account. It is alleged that the money was lost in a Colorado Ponzi scheme.

8604 ■ *"Opportunity Now Lies at Short End of the Market" in Barron's (Vol. 88, June 30, 2008, No. 26, pp. M9)*
Pub: Dow Jones & Co., Inc.
Ed: Michael S. Derby. **Description:** Renewed credit concerns and the lesser chance of a Federal Reserve interest rate hike boosted the bond market. Some portfolio managers are more bullish on short-dated securities as they expect the market to adjust to a more appropriate outlook.

8605 ■ *"An Opportunity for Patience" in Barron's (Vol. 88, June 30, 2008, No. 26, pp. M5)*
Pub: Dow Jones & Co., Inc.
Ed: Fleming Meeks. **Description:** Shares of Louisiana-Pacific are near their 52-week low at $8.95 per share making them look like a better buy than they were at $11.51 in May, 2008. The company is a to player in a cyclical business and its balance sheet is sound compared to its peers with net debt at just $84 million or 20 percent of total capital.

8606 ■ *"Optimize.ca Supplies Free Online Financial Advice" in Entertainment Close-Up (October 9, 2010)*
Pub: Close-Up Media Inc.
Description: Optimize.ca provides free online financial advice, focusing on instant savings for their mutual funds and other banking products while improving rates of return and overall financial health.

8607 ■ *"Oracle: No Profit of Doom" in Barron's (Vol. 88, March 31, 2008, No. 13, pp. 40)*
Pub: Dow Jones & Company, Inc.
Ed: Mark Veverka. **Description:** Oracle's revenues grew by 21 percent but fell short of expectation and their profits came in at the low-end of expectations.

The company's shares dropped 8 percent but investors are advised to pay more attention to the company's earnings expansion rather than revenue growth in a slow economy. Nokia's Rick Simonson points out that their markets in Asia and particularly India is growing so they are not as affected by the U.S. economic conditions.

8608 ■ *"The Oracle's Endgame; Wrigley Investment Isn't What Many Call a Classic Buffett Play" in Crain's Chicago Business (May 5, 2008)*
Pub: Crain Communications, Inc.
Ed: Ann Saphir. **Description:** Discusses Warren Buffett's deal with Mars Inc. to buy Wm. Wrigley Jr. Co., a move which would make Mr. Buffett a minority shareholder in a privately held company, a departure from his typical investment strategy. Mr. Buffett's Berkshire Hathaway Inc. agreed to provide $4.4 billion to help finance the $23 billion deal to pay another $2.1 billion for an equity stake in the company once it became a subsidiary of Mars.

8609 ■ *"Out of Fashion" in Barron's (Vol. 88, March 17, 2008, No. 11, pp. 48)*
Pub: Dow Jones & Company, Inc.
Ed: Robin Goldwyn Blumenthal. **Description:** Shares of Perry Ellis International and G-III Apparel Group have taken some beating in the market despite good growth earnings prospects. Perry Ellis sees earnings growth of 8 to 11 percent for fiscal 2009, while G-III Apparel expects earnings growth of 25 percent.

8610 ■ *"Over A Barrel" in Canadian Business (Vol. 81, July 21, 2008, No. 11, pp. 13)*
Pub: Rogers Media Ltd.
Ed: Thomas Watson. **Description:** Analysts predict that the skyrocketing price of fuel will cause a crackdown in the market as purported in the peak oil theory. It is forecasted that the price of oil will reach $200 per barrel. Details of the effect of the increasing oil prices on the market are presented.

8611 ■ *"Over a Barrel" in Canadian Business (Vol. 80, February 12, 2007, No. 4, pp. 52)*
Pub: Rogers Media
Ed: Andrew Nikiforuk. **Description:** The potential of tar sands of Alberta in becoming the largest source of oil in the world and huge investments of Canadian companies to mine for the oil there are discussed.

8612 ■ *"Packaging Firm Wraps Up Remake; Overseas Plants Help Firm Fatten Margins" in Crain's New York Business (January 7, 2008)*
Pub: Crain Communications, Inc.
Description: Sealed Air Corp., a packaging manufacturer, has seen its share price fall nearly 20 percent over the past two years, making it one of the worst performers in the packaging sector.

8613 ■ *"Pain Ahead as Profit Pressure Increases" in Crain's Chicago Business (Vol. 31, May 5, 2008, No. 18, pp. 4)*
Pub: Crain Communications, Inc.
Ed: Daniel Rome Levine. **Description:** Interview with David Klaskin, the chairman and chief investment officer at Oak Ridge Investments LLC, who discusses the outlook for the economy and corporate earnings, particularly in the housing and auto industries, the impact of economic stimulus checks, the weakness of the dollar and recommendations of stocks that individual investors may find helpful.

8614 ■ *Paper Fortunes: Modern Wall Street: Where It's Been and Where It's Going*
Pub: St. Martin's Press LLC
Ed: Roy C. Smith. **Released:** 2010. **Price:** $35.00. **Description:** Comprehensive history of Wall Street and lessons learned with insight into ways Wall Street will reinvent itself in this new economy.

8615 ■ *"Patchy Oil Profits" in Canadian Business (Vol. 80, February 12, 2007, No. 4, pp. 89)*
Pub: Rogers Media
Ed: Michelle Magnan. **Description:** The fall in fourth-quarter earnings of several oil and gas companies in Canada, in view of rise in their expenditure, is discussed.

8616 ■ *"Paterson Plots Comeback With Internet IPO"* in Globe & Mail (February 20, 2006, pp. B1)
Pub: CTVglobemedia Publishing Inc.
Ed: Grant Robertson. **Description:** The initial public offering plans of chief executive officer Scott Paterson of JumpTV.com are presented.

8617 ■ *"Peak Performer"* in Canadian Business (Vol. 81, October 13, 2008, No. 17, pp. 30)
Pub: Rogers Media Ltd.
Ed: Andrea Jezovit. **Description:** Jerry Del Missier's promotion as president of Barclays Capital (BarCap) has made him the likely successor to BarCap chief executive Bob Diamond. Diamond believes the technology Jerry Del Missier built on BarCap is producing record performance for the company. Public opinion on Jerry Del Missier, as well as his views, is discussed.

8618 ■ *"Penny Chief Shops For Shares"* in Barron's (Vol. 88, July 7, 2008, No. 27, pp. 29)
Pub: Dow Jones & Co., Inc.
Ed: Teresa Rivas. **Description:** Myron Ullman III, chairman and chief executive officer of J.C. Penney, purchased $1 million worth of shares of the company. He now owns 393,140 shares of the company and an additional 1,282 on his 401(k) plan.

8619 ■ *"Peter Bynoe Trades Up"* in Black Enterprise (Vol. 38, July 2008, No. 12, pp. 30)
Pub: Earl G. Graves Publishing Co. Inc.
Ed: Alexis McCombs. **Description:** Chicago-based Loop Capital Markets L.L.C. has named Peter Bynoe managing director of corporate finance. Bynoe was previously a senior partner at the law firm DLA Piper U.S. L.L.P., where he worked on stadium deals.

8620 ■ *"Pioneer Bank Ready to Expand"* in Austin Business JournalInc. (Vol. 28, December 19, 2008, No. 40, pp. 1)
Pub: American City Business Journals
Ed: Christopher Calnan. **Description:** Pioneer Bank, an 18-month old community bank based in Dripping Springs, Texas is planning to raise $6 million to open branches in the Austin area, including Hays County locations such as San Marcos, Buda, and Kyle. Pioneer's deposits have growing from $2.2 million to $54 million in 18 months.

8621 ■ *"Place Restrictions on Your Stock Shares"* in Business Owner (Vol. 35, July-August 2011, No. 4, pp. 14)
Pub: DL Perkins Company
Description: It is critical for any small business owner to be certain that the buyer or recipient of any part of the company represents that the stock is being acquired or given for investment purposes only.

8622 ■ *"A Place in the Sun"* in Canadian Business (Vol. 81, July 22, 2008, No. 12-13, pp. 56)
Pub: Rogers Media Ltd.
Description: Experts believe that it is the best time for Canadians to own a retirement home in the U.S., where real estate prices are up to 50 percent below their peak. Other views concerning the economic conditions occurring in the United States, as well as on the implications for Canadians planning to invest in the country are presented.

8623 ■ *"Planning Ahead: Steven Taylor Mulls a Second Career After Retirement"* in Black Enterprise (Vol. 37, November 2006, No. 4, pp. 82)
Pub: Earl G. Graves Publishing Co. Inc.
Ed: Sheryl Nance Nash. **Description:** Many workers are unprepared for retirement. Profile of Steven Taylor, a soon to retire dietary correctional officer who looked to Walt Clark, president of Clark Capital Financial in Maryland, to assess his retirement goals. Detailed advice and statistical data included.

8624 ■ *"Playing Citigroup's Woes"* in Barron's (Vol. 88, March 31, 2008, No. 13, pp. M7)
Pub: Dow Jones & Company, Inc.
Ed: Steven M. Sears. **Description:** Citigroup's first-quarter earnings estimate was slashed to a $1.15-per-share-loss from 28 cents. A strategist recom-

mends buying the company's shares at Sept. 20, 2008 put and selling a Sept. 17.50 put with a maximum profit of $166 if the shares is at or below $17.50 at expiration.

8625 ■ *"Playing Defense"* in Crain's Chicago Business (Vol. 31, November 10, 2008, No. 45, pp. 4)
Pub: Crain Communications, Inc.
Ed: Monee Fields-White. **Description:** Chicago's money managers are increasingly investing in local companies such as Caterpillar Inc., a maker of construction and mining equipment, Kraft Foods Inc. and Baxter International Inc., a manufacturer of medical products, in an attempt to bolster their portfolios. These companies have a history of surviving tough economic times.

8626 ■ *"PNC Begins Search for New Local HQ"* in Baltimore Business Journal (Vol. 28, June 4, 2010, No. 4, pp. 1)
Pub: Baltimore Business Journal
Ed: Daniel J. Sernovitz. **Description:** PNC Financial Services Group Inc. is searching for a new headquarters building in Greater Baltimore, Maryland. The company is seeking about 150,000 square feet for its regional operations. However, PNC could also end up moving out of Baltimore for space in the surrounding suburbs.

8627 ■ *"Polite Conversation"* in Mergers & Acquisitions: The Dealmaker's Journal (March 1, 2008)
Pub: SourceMedia, Inc.
Description: In January, industry leaders and dealmakers met at Davos to discuss topics ranging from the possibility of a recession to what lies ahead in the deal market.

8628 ■ *"The Power of Alumni Networks"* in Harvard Business Review (Vol. 88, October 2010, No. 10, pp. 34)
Pub: Harvard Business School Publishing
Ed: Lauren H. Cohen, Christopher J. Malloy. **Description:** Research indicates that members of alumni associations tend to invest in similar ways; implications for the mutual funds sector are discussed.

8629 ■ *"Private Equity Firms Focus on Failing Banks"* in Baltimore Business Journal (Vol. 28, July 16, 2010, No. 10, pp. 1)
Pub: Baltimore Business Journal
Ed: Gary Haber. **Description:** Four deals in which assets of failed banks were acquired by private equity firms have been approved by the Federal Deposit Insurance Corporation in the past couple of years. Bay Bank FSK, for example, purchased Bay National Bank's assets in July 2010. Forecasts on more private equity acquisitions in the community banking industry are given.

8630 ■ *"Private Equity Firms Shopping Valley For Deals"* in The Business Journal - Serving Phoenix and the Valley of the Sun (Vol. 29, September 19, 2008, No. 3, pp. 1)
Pub: American City Business Journals, Inc.
Ed: Mike Sunnucks. **Description:** Private equity firms from California, Boston, New York, and overseas are expected to invest in growth-oriented real estate markets that include Phoenix. Real estate experts revealed that privately held investment and acquisition firms are looking to invest in real estate markets hit by the housing crisis. Views and information on private equity firms' real estate investments are presented.

8631 ■ *"Private TV Industry's Profit Climbs Four Percent"* in Globe & Mail (March 29, 2006, pp. B6)
Pub: CTVglobemedia Publishing Inc.
Ed: Simon Tuck. **Description:** The private television industry in Canada is experiencing 4 percent increase in its profits, i.e. $242.2 millions. The revenues of CTV contributed more to this increase in profits.

8632 ■ *"Profico Takes Itself Off the Market"* in Globe & Mail (March 14, 2006, pp. B1)
Pub: CTVglobemedia Publishing Inc.
Ed: Deborah Yedlin; Dave Ebner. **Description:** Profico Energy Management Ltd., Canada's largest junior energy explorer, has backed off its potential acquisi-

tion plans. The decreased prices of the natural gas are the main reasons that caused Profico to back off from the acquisition plan.

8633 ■ *"Profit Predictions Look Too Plump"* in Barron's (Vol. 88, March 31, 2008, No. 13, pp. 37)
Pub: Dow Jones & Company, Inc.
Ed: Johanna Bennett. **Description:** Full-year forecast points to a 14 percent gain for 2008 but the second-half profit increases would have to grow at a fast rate and peak at 61 percent in the fourth quarter to achieve this. Trends in the U.S. economic conditions are also discussed.

8634 ■ *"Public Opinion"* in Entrepreneur (Vol. 36, April 2008, No. 4, pp. 28)
Pub: Entrepreneur Media, Inc.
Ed: Aliza Sherman. **Description:** According to a 2007 report from Group and Organization Management, women in top positions can lead publicly traded companies to stock price and earnings growth. Some women business owners say that going public has provided them with the capital to grow. Details on the potential of women-managed publicly traded companies are discussed.

8635 ■ *"Put It on MasterCard"* in Barron's (Vol. 89, July 27, 2009, No. 30, pp. 16)
Pub: Dow Jones & Co., Inc.
Ed: Bill Alpert. **Description:** Shares of MasterCard trade at a discount at just 15 times its anticipated earnings and some believe that these shares may be a better play in an economic recovery. The prospects of these shares are compared with those of Visa.

8636 ■ *"Putting SogoTrade Through Its Paces"* in Barron's (Vol. 89, July 27, 2009, No. 30, pp. 27)
Pub: Dow Jones & Co., Inc.
Ed: Theresa W. Carey. **Description:** SogoTrade options platform streams options quotes in real time and lets users place a trade in several ways. The site also features notable security tactics and is a reasonable choice for bargain-seekers. OptionsXpress' Xtend platform lets users place trades and get real time quotes.

8637 ■ *"Putting the World at Your Fingertips"* in Barron's (Vol. 88, July 7, 2008, No. 27, pp. L13)
Pub: Dow Jones & Co., Inc.
Ed: Neil A. Martin. **Description:** Currency-traded exchange funds allow investors to diversify their assets and take advantage of investment opportunities such as speculation and hedging. Investors can use these funds to build positions in favor of or against the US dollar.

8638 ■ *"Q&A: David Labistour"* in Canadian Business (Vol. 81, March 17, 2008, No. 4, pp. 10)
Pub: Rogers Media
Ed: Lauren McKeon. **Description:** David Labistour says that the difference between being a co-op retailer and a corporate-owned retailer in the case of Mountain Equipment Co-op (MEC) is that the company is owned by their customers and not by shareholders. Labistour also says that MEC works with their factories to ensure that these maintain ethical standards in the manufacturing process.

8639 ■ *"Qualcomm Could Win Big as the IPhone 3G Calls"* in Barron's (Vol. 88, July 4, 2008, No. 28, pp. 30)
Pub: Dow Jones & Co., Inc.
Ed: Eric J. Savitz. **Description:** Apple iPhone 3G's introduction could widen the smartphone market thereby benefiting handset chipmaker Qualcomm in the process. Qualcomm Senior V.P., Bill Davidson sees huge potential for his company's future beyond phones with their Snapdragon processor. The prospects of Sun Microsystems' shares are also discussed.

8640 ■ *"Quality at Bargain Prices"* in Black Enterprise (Vol. 41, December 2010, No. 5, pp. 30)
Pub: Earl G. Graves Publishing Co. Inc.
Ed: James A. Anderson. **Description:** Monica L. Walker, CEO of Holland Capital Management, sug-

gests investors to watch prevailing trends in the financial market and to focus on using bottom-up analysis to identify companies meeting their investment criteria.

8641 ■ *The Quants*
Pub: Crown Business Books
Ed: Scott Patterson. **Released:** January 25, 2011. **Price:** $16.00. **Description:** The story of four rich and powerful men, along with Jim Simons, the founder of the most successful hedge fund in history and how they felt and what they thought in the days and weeks during the crash of Wall Street.

8642 ■ *"Quarreling Parties Keep Schenectady Redevelopment Plan In Limbo" in The Business Review Albany (Vol. 35, April 4, 2008, No. 53)*
Pub: The Business Review
Ed: Michael DeMasi. **Description:** First National Bank of Scotia chairman Louis H. Buhrmaster opposes the Erie Boulevard design project. as it could negatively affect access to the bank. Buhrmaster, aslo a vice president for Schenectady Industrial Corp, prohibits environmental assessment at the former American Locomotive property. The issues affecting the progress of the planned redevelopment at Schenectady are analyzed.

8643 ■ *"Quebecor World Cuts Dividend" in Globe & Mail (January 20, 2006, pp. B1)*
Pub: CTVglobemedia Publishing Inc.
Description: The reasons behind the decrease in dividend by Quebecor World Inc., and its impact on investors, are discussed.

8644 ■ *"A Questionable Chemical Romance" in Barron's (Vol. 88, July 14, 2008, No. 28, pp. 28)*
Pub: Dow Jones & Co., Inc.
Ed: Andrew Bary. **Description:** Dow Chemical paid $78-a-share for the surprise takeover of Rohm & Haas. The acquisition is reducing Dow Chemical's financial flexibility at a time when chemical companies are being affected by high costs and a weak U.S. economy.

8645 ■ *"Quick Earnings Revival Unlikely" in Barron's (Vol. 88, June 30, 2008, No. 26, pp. 31)*
Pub: Dow Jones & Co., Inc.
Ed: Johanna Bennett. **Description:** Analysts are pushing back their prediction of a U.S. economy turnaround to 2009. A recession in the first half of 2008 may not have happened but unemployment is rising and house prices continue to fall.

8646 ■ *Raising Capital*
Pub: Greenwood Publishing Group, Inc.
Ed: David Nour. **Released:** March 1, 2009. **Price:** $39.95. **Description:** An overview to help entrepreneurs find capital for starting and maintaining a small business is presented. The author shows how to develop long-term relationships with financial partners and ways to attract financing to fund the startup and growth phases of any business. Entrepreneurs tell how they raised money from friends, family, angel investors, banks and venture capitalists and private equity firms.

8647 ■ *"Raptor Opens Consultancy" in Austin Business Journal (Vol. 31, July 8, 2011, No. 18, pp. 1)*
Pub: American City Business Journals Inc.
Ed: Christopher Calnan. **Description:** Boston hedge fund operator Raptor Group launched Raptor Accelerator, a consulting business providing sales and advisory services to early-stage companies in Central Texas. Aside from getting involved with the startups in which the Raptor Group invests, Raptor Accelerator will target firms operating in the sports, media, entertainment, and content technology sectors.

8648 ■ *"Ratio-Cination" in Canadian Business (Vol. 79, October 23, 2006, No. 21, pp. 164)*
Pub: Rogers Media
Ed: Ian McGugan. **Description:** Tips for investors, on how to make market observations before selecting companies for purchasing stocks, are presented.

8649 ■ *"The RBC Dynasty Continues" in Globe & Mail (January 30, 2006, pp. B1)*
Pub: CTVglobemedia Publishing Inc.
Ed: Gordon Pitts. **Description:** The details on business growth of Royal Bank of Canada, under chief executive officer Gordon Nixon, are presented.

8650 ■ *"Ready for the Back Burner" in Barron's (Vol. 88, March 17, 2008, No. 11, pp. 47)*
Pub: Dow Jones & Company, Inc.
Ed: Vito J. Racanelli. **Description:** McDonald's has promised to return $15 billion to $17 billion to shareholders in 2007-2009 but headwinds are rising for the company. December, 2007 same-store sales were flat and the company's traffic growth in the U.S. is slowing. Its shares are likely to trade in tandem with the market until recession fears recede.

8651 ■ *"Ready for a Rally?" in The Economist (Vol. 390, January 3, 2009, No. 8612, pp. 54)*
Pub: The Economist Newspaper Inc.
Description: Analysts predict that the recession could end by 2010. The current economic crisis is presented in detail.

8652 ■ *"Real Estate Woes Mount for State's Smaller Banks" in Boston Business Journal (Vol. 27, November 30, 2007, No. 44, pp. 1)*
Pub: American City Business Journals Inc.
Ed: Craig M. Douglas. **Description:** Massachusetts banking industry is facing a steep increase on loan defaults such as in home mortgages and condominium projects, contrary to public belief that the local industry is safe from the real estate meltdown. The dollar value of local banks' nonperforming loans doubled in 2007, and is rising statewide. Other banking issues in the state are discussed.

8653 ■ *"Recession Fears Power Gold" in Barron's (Vol. 88, March 17, 2008, No. 11, pp. M14)*
Pub: Dow Jones & Company, Inc.
Ed: Melanie Burton. **Description:** Gold prices have been more attractive as the U.S. dollar weakens and the Dow Jones Industrial Average has slipped almost 10 percent in 2008. The rate cuts from the Federal Reserve Board has also spurred inflation fears adding upward pressure to the price of the metal.

8654 ■ *"Recession Management" in Canadian Business (Vol. 81, March 3, 2008, No. 3, pp. 62)*
Pub: Rogers Media
Ed: Joe Castaldo. **Description:** Some companies such as Capital One Financial Corp. are managing their finances as if a recession has already taken place to prepare themselves for the looming economic downturn. Intel Corp., meanwhile shows how increasing its investments during a recession could be advantageous. Tips on how companies can survive a recession are provided.

8655 ■ *"Reduce the Risk of Failed Financial Judgments" in Harvard Business Review (Vol. 86, July-August 2008, No. 8, pp. 24)*
Pub: Harvard Business School Press
Ed: Robert G. Eccles; Edward J. Fiedl. **Description:** Utilization of business consultants, evaluators, appraisers, and actuaries to decrease financial management risks is discussed.

8656 ■ *"The REIT Stuff" in Canadian Business (Vol. 80, March 26, 2007, No. 7, pp. 72)*
Pub: Rogers Media
Description: The stock performance of various real estate investment trusts in Canada is analyzed.

8657 ■ *"REIT's Decry Foreign Limits on Investment" in Globe & Mail (March 29, 2007, pp. B4)*
Pub: CTVglobemedia Publishing Inc.
Ed: Elizabeth Church. **Description:** The planned legislation by Canadian government for regulation foreign investments by real estate investment trusts is discussed.

8658 ■ *"Reports of Banks' Revival were Greatly Exaggerated" in Barron's (Vol. 88, July 7, 2008, No. 27, pp. L14)*
Pub: Dow Jones & Co., Inc.
Ed: Jack Willoughby. **Description:** Performance of mutual funds improved for the second quarter of 2008 compared to the previous quarter, registering an average gain of 0.13 percent; funds focusing on natural resources rose the highest, their value rising by an average of 24.50 percent.

8659 ■ *"Research Reports" in Barron's (Vol. 88, March 24, 2008, No. 12, pp. M10)*
Pub: Dow Jones & Company, Inc.
Description: Investors are recommending purchasing shares of Ampco Pittsburgh due to an expected surge in earnings. Deteriorating credit quality presents problems for the shares of BankAtlantic Bancorp, whose price targets have been lowered from $7 to $5 each. Shares of Helicos Biosciences are expected to move sideways from their $6 level. Statistical data included.

8660 ■ *"Research Reports" in Barron's (Vol. 88, March 10, 2008, No. 10, pp. M13)*
Pub: Dow Jones & Company, Inc.
Description: Research reports on different company stocks by investment analysts are given. Shares of Cal Dive are rated Outperform by analysts, citing the shares' continued attractiveness and the company's acquisition of Horizon. Analysts recommend buying the shares of California Water Service Group.

8661 ■ *"Research Reports" in Barron's (Vol. 89, July 20, 2009, No. 29, pp. M12)*
Pub: Dow Jones & Co., Inc.
Description: Shares of Bank of the Ozarks, Broadpoint Gleacher Securities Group, Halozyme Therapeutics, and Take Two Interactive are rated as Buy. The shares of Fluor and PetMed Express are rated as Outperform, while those of Humana and Janus Capital Group are rated as Hold and Underweight respectively.

8662 ■ *"Research Reports: How Analysts Size Up Companies" in Barron's (Vol. 88, March 31, 2008, No. 13, pp. M13)*
Pub: Dow Jones & Company, Inc.
Ed: Anita Peltonen. **Description:** Sirius Satellite's shares are ranked Outperform as it awaits approval from the Federal Communications Commission in its merger with XM. TiVo's shares are ranked Avoid as the company is in a sector that's being commoditized. Verizon Communications' rising dividend yield earns it a Focus List ranking. The shares of Bear Stearns, Churchill Downs, Corning, and Deerfield Triarc Capital are also reviewed. Statistical data included.

8663 ■ *"Research Reports: How Analysts Size Up Companies" in Barron's (Vol. 88, March 17, 2008, No. 11, pp. M13)*
Pub: Dow Jones & Company, Inc.
Ed: Anita Peltonen. **Description:** Shares of Applied Industrial Technologies are ranked Market Perform while the shares of Google get a buy rating. Salix Pharmaceuticals gets a Sell/Above-Average risk rating. The shares of Dune Energy, Franklin Resources, Internet Brands, Piper Jaffray, and Texas Instruments are also rated.

8664 ■ *"Research Reports: How Analysts Size Up Companies" in Barron's (Vol. 88, June 30, 2008, No. 26, pp. M11)*
Pub: Dow Jones & Co., Inc.
Ed: Anita Peltonen. **Description:** Shares of Developers Diversified Realty Corp. get a 'Long-Term Buy' rating while the shares of HealthSouth Corp. and Onyx Pharmaceutical get a rating of 'Underperform' and a 'Buy' rating respectively. The shares of American Capital Agency, American Public Education, Bankrate, and Werner Enterprises are also ranked.

8665 ■ *"Research Reports: How Analysts Size Up Companies" in Barron's (Vol. 88, July 14, 2008, No. 28, pp. M13)*
Pub: Dow Jones & Co., Inc.
Ed: Anita Peltonen. **Description:** Shares of Bankrate and AutoZone both get a 'Buy' rating from analysts while Zions Bancorporation's shares are downgraded

8666 ■ *"Research Reports: How Analysts Size Up Companies" in Barron's (Vol. 89, July 13, 2009, No. 28, pp. M11)*

Pub: Dow Jones & Co., Inc.

Description: Shares of Alaska Air Group get a 'Hold' rating while the shares of Art Technology Group and Cathay General Bancorp both get a 'Buy' rating. The shares of HCC Insurance Holdings, HMS Holdings, H&R Block, Intel, McDonald's, People's United Financial, Pride International, Sino Forest, and Virgin Media are also given ratings.

8667 ■ *"Research Reports: How Analysts Size Up Companies" in Barron's (Vol. 89, July 27, 2009, No. 30, pp. M12)*

Pub: Dow Jones & Co., Inc.

Ed: Anita Peltonen. **Description:** Shares of Allscripts-Misys gets an 'Outperform' rating while the shares of M&T Bank and Precision Castparts get a 'Sell' and 'Hold' rating respectively. The shares of Supervalu, Syniverse Holdings, Valley National Bancorp, Volterra, and Wesco are also rated.

8668 ■ *"Research Reports: How Analysts Size Up Companies" in Barron's (Vol. 90, September 13, 2010, No. 37, pp. M12)*

Pub: Barron's Editorial & Corporate Headquarters

Description: Shares of Adtran and Redwood City-based Informatica both get an 'Outperform' rating while the shares of Phillips-Van Heusen get a 'Neutral' rating. The shares of Melco Crown Entertainment, Sonic Solutions, Jamba, Warnaco Group are also rated.

8669 ■ *"Research Reports: How Analysts Size Up Companies" in Barron's (Vol. 90, August 23, 2010, No. 34, pp. M13)*

Pub: Barron's Editorial & Corporate Headquarters

Description: Shares of Sirius XM Radio, Target and Deere and Company received an eBuyE rating, while shares of Research in Motion got an eNeutralE rating.

8670 ■ *"Retail Woes: The Shoe Doesn't Fit for Gerald Loftin's Stock Picks" in Black Enterprise (Vol. 38, July 2008, No. 12, pp. 40)*

Pub: Earl G. Graves Publishing Co. Inc.

Ed: Steve Garmhausen. **Description:** Each of the three stocks that Gerald Loftin picked in May 2007 have lost money; DSW, the designer shoe retailer, fell by 63.7 percent; paint and coatings retailer Sherwin-Williams Co. fell by 7.2 percent; and Verizon Communications Inc. fell by 1.4 percent. Statistical data included.

8671 ■ *"Return to Wealth; Bank Strategy" in The Economist (Vol. 390, January 3, 2009, No. 8612, pp. 56)*

Pub: The Economist Newspaper Inc.

Description: UBS' strategy to survive these trying economic times is presented. Statistical data included. UBS has a stronger balance-sheet than most of its investment-banking peers and has reduced its portfolio.

8672 ■ *"The Right Time for REITs" in Barron's (Vol. 88, July 14, 2008, No. 28, pp. 32)*

Pub: Dow Jones & Co., Inc.

Ed: Mike Hogan. **Description:** Discusses the downturn in U.S. real estate investment trusts so these are worth considering for investment. Several Websites that are useful for learning about real estate investment trusts for investment purposes are presented.

8673 ■ *"Risk Management Starts at the Top" in Business Strategy Review (Vol. 21, Spring 2010, No. 1, pp. 18)*

Pub: Wiley-Blackwell

Ed: Paul Strebel, Hongze Lu. **Description:** Authors question why, at the end of 2008, Citigroup, Merrill Lynch and UBS had well over $40 billion in sub-prime write-downs and credit losses, while some of their

competitors were much less exposed. Their research into the situation revealed correlations of great import to today's firms.

8674 ■ *"Risk and Reward" in Canadian Business (Vol. 81, October 13, 2008, No. 17, pp. 21)*

Pub: Rogers Media Ltd.

Ed: Calvin Leung. **Description:** Macro-economist and currency analyst Mark Venezia believes that stable financial institutions, free-market reforms, and the role of central banks in keeping inflation and exchange rates stable could make emerging-market bonds strong performers for better future returns. Venezia's other views on emerging-market bonds are discussed.

8675 ■ *"Rock Festival: High Spirited Conventioneers Celebrate Their Good Fortune" in Canadian Business (Vol. 81, March 31, 2008, No. 5)*

Pub: Rogers Media

Ed: Jeff Sanford. **Description:** Soaring prices of commodities in the mining industry have been very good for the attendees of the 76th annual conference of the Prospectors & Developers Association of Canada. A speaker at the conference expects commodity prices to come off a bit but not fall dramatically as it did in the 1980's.

8676 ■ *"Rogue's Gallery" in Canadian Business (Vol. 81, November 10, 2008, No. 19, pp. 44)*

Pub: Rogers Media Ltd.

Ed: Rachel Pulfer. **Description:** Laissez-faire capitalism or poor oversight of Fannie Mae and Freddie Mac are causes for the financial crisis in the U.S., depending or Democrat or Republican viewpoint. Events leading up to the 2008 financial crisis are covered.

8677 ■ *"Roundtable - The Auto Sector Shifts Gears" in Mergers & Acquisitions: The Dealmaker's Journal (March 1, 2008)*

Pub: SourceMedia, Inc.

Description: Industry professionals discuss the current state of the automotive sector as well as what they predict for the future of the industry; also provides information for investors about opportunities in the sector.

8678 ■ *"Rules Will Tighten, Bankers are Told: House Panel Chairman Expects More Regulation" in Charlotte Observer (February 6, 2007)*

Pub: Knight-Ridder/Tribune Business News

Ed: Binyamin Appelbaum. **Description:** House Financial Services Committee will impose more federal regulation on banks offering mortgages.

8679 ■ *"Ryder's Shock Absorbers Are In Place" in Barron's (Vol. 88, March 24, 2008, No. 12, pp. 19)*

Pub: Dow Jones & Company, Inc.

Ed: Christopher C. Williams. **Description:** Shares of Ryder System Inc. are expected to continue rising on the back of rising earnings, forecast at $5.20 a share for 2009. The shares of the truck freight company hit a 52-week high of $62.27 each and may reach $70 a share.

8680 ■ *Safety Net*

Pub: Crown Business Books

Ed: James Glassman. **Released:** February 22, 2011. **Price:** $23.00. **Description:** Ways to build a financial investment strategy that protects you, while ensuring growth in a strong financial future are presented.

8681 ■ *"St. Elizabeth Fights for Share at St. Lukes" in Business Courier (Vol. 27, November 12, 2010, No. 28, pp. 1)*

Pub: Business Courier

Ed: James Ritchie. **Description:** Key information on how St. Elizabeth Healthcare helps partner St. Luke's Hospitals increase market share in the healthcare industry are presented. Some of St. Luke's hospitals, such as the St. Elizabeth Fort Thomas in Kentucky, are struggling with low occupancy rates, prompting St. Elizabeth to invest about $24 million to help St. Luke's increase its market share.

8682 ■ *"Sales Gave W&S Record '07" in Business Courier (Vol. 24, March 14, 2008, No. 49, pp. 1)*

Pub: American City Business Journals, Inc.

Ed: Jon Newberry. **Description:** Western & Southern Financial Group was able to achieve a record $365 million in net income thanks in large part to the double-digit increases in profits by its W&S Agency Group field offices and non-insurance businesses. The sale of their Integrated Investment Services Subsidiary and shares in several Marriot hotels also added to the record profit.

8683 ■ *"Samll Fortunes" in Business Courier (Vol. 27, July 23, 2010, No. 12, pp. 1)*

Pub: Business Courier

Ed: Steve Watkins. **Description:** Small banks in Cincinnati, Ohio have been faring well despite the economic crisis, a survey has revealed. Sixty percent of local small banks have capital levels above 15.8 percent median. But regulators are seen to close more banks in 2010 than since the financial crises began.

8684 ■ *"Satellite Down, Stock Up: Raytheon Is On Target With Ten Percent Dividend Increase" in Barron's (Vol. 88, March 31, 2008, No. 13)*

Pub: Dow Jones & Company, Inc.

Ed: Shirley A. Lazo. **Description:** Raytheon hiked their quarterly dividend to 28 cents per share from 25.5 cents. Aircastle slashed their quarterly common dividend by 64 percent for them to retain additional capital that can be used to increase their liquidity position.

8685 ■ *"Schwab: Lower Returns Ahead" in Barron's (Vol. 89, July 13, 2009, No. 28, pp. L4)*

Pub: Dow Jones & Co., Inc.

Ed: Leslie P. Norton. **Description:** Charles Schwab says that 8 percent to 10 percent equity-market returns are not realistic these days and that 4 percent to 5 percent are more realistic in the next four to five years from 2009. Schwab expects inflation to be close to 10 percent per annum in a couple of years.

8686 ■ *"Score One for 'Barron's" in Barron's (Vol. 89, July 13, 2009, No. 28, pp. 14)*

Pub: Dow Jones & Co., Inc.

Ed: Andrew Bary. **Description:** 57 companies that were bullishly covered on 'Barron's' for the first half of 2009 were up an average of 20.4 percent compared to the 10.2 percent gain in the relevant market indexes. The bearish stock picks by 'Barron's' were down 3.4 percent compared to a 6.4 percent for the benchmarks.

8687 ■ *"Scotiabank Targets More Baby Boomers" in Globe & Mail (March 4, 2006, pp. B5)*

Pub: CTVglobemedia Publishing Inc.

Ed: Elizabeth Church. **Description:** Bank of Nova Scotia posted $844 million profit for first quarter 2006. The plans of the bank to achieve baby boomer client base are presented.

8688 ■ *"Scottsdale Bank Plans 4Q Opening" in The Business Journal - Serving Phoenix and the Valley of the Sun (Vol. 28, August 15, 2008, No. 50)*

Pub: American City Business Journals, Inc.

Ed: Chris Casacchia. **Description:** Arizona's Department of Financial Institutions has approved Scottsdale Business Bank, a community bank which plans to open in the fourth quarter of 2008. The bank, which is to be located near McCormick Ranch in Scottsdale, Arizona, will cater to small business owners in the professional sector, such as accountants and doctors.

8689 ■ *"Screening for the Best Stock Screens" in Barron's (Vol. 90, September 13, 2010, No. 37, pp. 36)*

Pub: Barron's Editorial & Corporate Headquarters

Ed: Mike Hogan. **Description:** Pros and cons of the new and revised stock screening tools from Zack, Finviz.com, and GuruFocus are discussed. FinVix. com is more capable for screening through stocks and the service is free.

8690 ■ *"Sears' Lampert Solid in Game of Valuation Chicken"* in *Globe & Mail (February 25, 2006, pp. B2)*
Pub: CTVglobemedia Publishing Inc.
Ed: Eric Reguly. **Description:** The feasibility of share value of Sears Canada Inc., following Sears Holdings Corp.'s acquisition, is discussed.

8691 ■ *"SEC Doesn't Buy Biovail's Claims"* in *Barron's (Vol. 88, March 31, 2008, No. 13, pp. 20)*
Pub: Dow Jones & Company, Inc.
Ed: Bill Alpert. **Description:** Overstatement of earnings and chronic fraudulent conduct has led the SEC to file a stock fraud suit against Biovail, Eugene Melnyk and three others present or former employees of Biovail. Melnyk had the firm file suit in 2006 that blames short-sellers and stock researchers for the company's drop in share price.

8692 ■ *"SEC Report On Rating Agencies Falls Short"* in *Barron's (Vol. 88, July 14, 2008, No. 28, pp. 35)*
Pub: Dow Jones & Co., Inc.
Ed: Jack Willoughby. **Description:** The Securities and Exchange Commissions report on credit-rating firms should have drawn attention to the slipshod practices in the offerings of collateralized debt obligations. The report fell short of prescribing correctives for the flawed system of these agencies' relationship with their clients.

8693 ■ *"Selling Pressures Rise in China"* in *Barron's (Vol. 88, March 10, 2008, No. 10, pp. M9)*
Pub: Dow Jones & Company, Inc.
Ed: Mohammed Hadi. **Description:** There are about 1.6 trillion yuan worth of shares up for sale in Chinese stock markets in 2008, adding to the selling pressures in these markets. The Chinese government has imposed restrictions to prevent a rapid rise in selling stocks.

8694 ■ *"Sense of Discovery"* in *Business Journal Portland (Vol. 27, November 19, 2010, No. 38, pp. 1)*
Pub: Portland Business Journal
Ed: Erik Siemers. **Description:** Tigard, Oregon-based Exterro Inc. CEO Bobby Balachandran announced plans to go public without the help of an institutional investor. Balachandran believes Exterro could grow to a $100 million legal compliance software company in the span of three years. Insights on Exterro's growth as market leader in the $1 billion legal governance software market are also given.

8695 ■ *"Sentiment Split on Financials"* in *Barron's (Vol. 88, March 24, 2008, No. 12, pp. M14)*
Pub: Dow Jones & Company, Inc.
Ed: Steven M. Sears. **Description:** Experts in the financial sector are split as to whether or not the worst of the financial crisis brought on by the credit crunch is over. Some options traders are trading on are defensive puts, expecting the worst, while investors buying calls are considered as bullish.

8696 ■ *"Serious Signal Flashing?"* in *Barron's (Vol. 88, July 7, 2008, No. 27, pp. 11)*
Pub: Dow Jones & Co., Inc.
Description: Discusses the Hindenburg Omen, named after the airship disaster of May 1937, which is considered a predictor of market crashes and has appeared twice in June 2008. There is a 25 percent probability that the US stock market will suffer a crash in the July-October 2008 period.

8697 ■ *"A Shallow Pool"* in *Canadian Business (Vol. 81, Summer 2008, No. 9, pp. 44)*
Pub: Rogers Media Ltd.
Ed: Joe Castaldo. **Description:** Bank of Canada projected in its 'Monetary Policy Report' a growth rate of 1.4 percent in 2008 and does not expect the economy to fully recover until mid-2010. The Canadian stock market has been recovering although slowly with just a 1.6 percent gain by April 30. Other details on the Canadian equity market are presented.

8698 ■ *"Shanghai Butterfly"* in *Canadian Business (Vol. 80, March 12, 2007, No. 6, pp. 69)*
Pub: Rogers Media
Ed: Thomas Watson. **Description:** The volatile nature of Shanghai stock markets and its impact on investors and the economy is discussed.

8699 ■ *"Shipwreck Floats Nickel's Boat"* in *Globe & Mail (January 24, 2007, pp. B1)*
Pub: CTVglobemedia Publishing Inc.
Ed: John Partridge. **Description:** The rise in the price of nickel to $38,300 a tonne following a shipwreck in which 1,000 tonnes of the metal was lost is discussed.

8700 ■ *"Shorts Story"* in *Barron's (Vol. 89, July 6, 2009, No. 27, pp. 16)*
Pub: Dow Jones & Co., Inc.
Ed: Gene Epstein. **Description:** Shares of Compass Minerals, J2 Global Communications, K12, Middleby, and Pactiv should be shorted by investors. These companies suffer from weaknesses in their business models, making them vulnerable to a share price decline.

8701 ■ *"Shorts Story"* in *Barron's (Vol. 89, July 6, 2009, No. 27, pp. 16)*
Pub: Dow Jones & Co., Inc.
Ed: Gene Epstein. **Description:** Shares of Compass Minerals, J2 Global Communications, K12, Middleby, and Pactiv should be shorted by investors. These companies suffer from weaknesses in their business models, making them vulnerable to a share price decline.

8702 ■ *"Should the Fed Regulate Wall Street?"* in *Barron's (Vol. 88, March 24, 2008, No. 12, pp. M15)*
Pub: Dow Jones & Company, Inc.
Ed: Randall W. Forsyth. **Description:** Greater regulation of the financial sector by the Federal Reserve is essential for it to survive the crisis it is experiencing. The resulting regulation could be in complete contrast with the deregulation the sector previously experienced.

8703 ■ *"Silver Standard Reports First Quarter 2007 Results"* in *Canadian Corporate News (May 14, 2007)*
Pub: Comtex News Network Inc.
Description: Silver Standard Resources Inc. reports a first quarter loss of $1.6 million compared with the first quarter of 2006 in which the loss was $1.1 million. Statistical data included.

8704 ■ *"Six Great Stock Funds for the Long Haul"* in *Barron's (Vol. 89, July 13, 2009, No. 28, pp. L5)*
Pub: Dow Jones & Co., Inc.
Ed: Lawrence C. Strauss; Tom Sullivan. **Description:** Six mutual funds that have solid long-term performance, transparency, savvy stock picking, and discipline are presented. The managers of these funds are also evaluated. These funds include the T. Rowe Price Emerging Market Stock Fund, Fairholme, and Dodge & Cox Stock.

8705 ■ *"Six Things You Can Do To Ride Out A Turbulent Market"* in *Hispanic Business (Vol. 30, March 2008, No. 3, pp. 20)*
Pub: Hispanic Business
Ed: Hildy Medina; Michael Bowker. **Description:** Top financial experts' views on managing investment portfolios during turbulent periods in the stock market are reported. Experts prefer investing in health care, short term investments, international bonds and preferred stocks or just maintain cash until such times as the market settles.

8706 ■ *"A Slice of Danish; Fixing Finance"* in *The Economist (Vol. 390, January 3, 2009, No. 8612, pp. 55)*
Pub: The Economist Newspaper Inc.
Description: Denmark's mortgage-holders and the county's lending system is presented.

8707 ■ *"The Small 300"* in *Canadian Business (Vol. 81, Summer 2008, No. 9, pp. 137)*
Pub: Rogers Media Ltd.
Description: Small cap-companies are ranked based on market capitalization and stock performance. Calgary-based Grande Cache Coal Corp. topped the roster with 1,000 percent of return resulting from strong sales. A table showing the 2008 rankings of the companies is presented.

8708 ■ *The Small Business Owner's Manual: Everything You Need to Know to Start Up and Run Your Business*
Pub: Career Press, Incorporated
Ed: Joe Kennedy. **Released:** June 2005. **Price:** $19.99 (US), $26.95 (Canadian). **Description:** Comprehensive guide for starting a small business, focusing on twelve ways to obtain financing, business plans, selling and advertising products and services, hiring and firing employees, setting up a Web site, business law, accounting issues, insurance, equipment, computers, banks, financing, customer credit and collection, leasing, and more.

8709 ■ *"Smaller Banks Could Face Tough 2008"* in *Austin Business JournalInc. (Vol. 28, January 2, 2009, No. 1, pp. 3)*
Pub: American City Business Journals
Ed: Christopher Calnan. **Description:** The turbulence in the banking industry is expected to reach Texas in 2009 and industry insiders believe there will be a shift in deposits from small, regional banks to larger banks due to low consumer confidence. One economist says that a large number of banks are going to go out of business in 2009.

8710 ■ *"Smart Investor's Shopping List: Coke, Walgreen, Drill Bits; A Conversation with Money Manager Paula Dorion-Gray"* in *Crain's Chicago Business*
Pub: Crain Communications, Inc.
Ed: Bruce Blythe. **Description:** Interview with Paula Dorion-Gray, president of Dorion-Gray Retirement Planning Inc., discusses the state of the investing environment, favored industries, industries to avoid, and her approach towards investing.

8711 ■ *"Smart Medicine"* in *Canadian Business (Vol. 80, February 26, 2007, No. 5, pp. 73)*
Pub: Rogers Media
Ed: Zena Olijnyk. **Description:** The stock price stability and future earnings prospects of Canadian bio-technology firm YM Biosciences are analyzed.

8712 ■ *"The Smell of Fear: Is a Bottom Near?"* in *Barron's (Vol. 88, March 17, 2008, No. 11, pp. M3)*
Pub: Dow Jones & Company, Inc.
Ed: Kopin Tan. **Description:** Liquidity problems at Bear Stearns frightened investors in markets around the world due to the fear of the prospects of a big bank's failure. Shares of health maintenance organizations got battered led by WellPoint, and Humana but longer-term investors who could weather short-term volatility may find value here. The value of J. Crew shares is also discussed.

8713 ■ *"A Socko Payout Menu: Rural Phone Carrier Plots to Supercharge Its Shares"* in *Barron's (Vol. 88, June 30, 2008, No. 26, pp. M5)*
Pub: Dow Jones & Co., Inc.
Ed: Shirley A. Lazo. **Description:** CenturyTel boosted its quarterly common payout to 70 cents from 6.75 cents per share die to its strong cash flows and solid balance sheet. Eastman Kodak's plan for a buyback will be partially funded by its $581 million tax refund. CME Group will buyback stocks through 2009 worth $1.1 billion.

8714 ■ *"Solace for the Freshly Flaherty'd"* in *Canadian Business (Vol. 79, November 6, 2006, No. 22, pp. 114)*
Pub: Rogers Media
Ed: Ian McGugan. **Description:** Tips to manage investments with relation to cash distribution tax on income trusts are presented.

8715 ■ *"Some Big Biotechs Buying Own Stock"* in *Boston Business Journal (Vol. 30, November 5, 2010, No. 41, pp. 1)*
Pub: Boston Business Journal

Ed: Julie M. Donnelly. **Description:** Biotechnology companies such as Biogen Idec and Genzyme Corporation are conducting stock buybacks as they look to invest their cash holdings. Other analysts see the buybacks as reluctance in committing to longer-term investments.

8716 ■ *"Some Relief Possible Following Painful Week"* in *Barron's (Vol. 88, July 14, 2008, No. 28, pp. M3)*
Pub: Dow Jones & Co., Inc.

Ed: Kopin Tan. **Description:** Dow Chemical is offering a 74 percent premium to acquire Rohm & Haas' coatings and electronics materials operations. Frontline amassed a 5.6 percent stake in rival Overseas Shipholding Group and a merger between the two would create a giant global fleet with pricing power. Highlights of the U.S. stock market during the week that ended in July 11, 2008 are discussed. Statistical data included.

8717 ■ *"Something to Like"* in *Canadian Business (Vol. 81, April 14, 2008, No. 6, pp. 22)*
Pub: Rogers Media

Ed: Jack Mintz. **Description:** Jim Flaherty's policy on tax-free savings account (TFSA) will allow Canadians to accumulate wealth at a much faster rate and these accounts could be especially good for people who are subject to high effective taxes on savings. Investors should put their money into a Registered Retirement Savings Plan (RRSP) when it comes to risky investments but the TFSA is better than an RRSP if investors expect very high taxes on withdrawals from their RRSP.

8718 ■ *"The Spark's Back in Sanyo"* in *Barron's (Vol. 88, March 31, 2008, No. 13, pp. M9)*
Pub: Dow Jones & Company, Inc.

Ed: Jay Alabaster. **Description:** Things are looking up for Sanyo Electric after its string of calamities that range from major losses brought on by earthquake damage to its semiconductor operations and its near collapse and bailout. The company looks poised for a rebound as they are on track for their first net profit since 2003 and could beat its earnings forecast for 2008.

8719 ■ *"Spectre of Iran War Spooks Oil Markets"* in *Globe & Mail (March 28, 2007, pp. B1)*
Pub: CTVglobemedia Publishing Inc.

Ed: Shawn McCarthy. **Description:** The increase in the price of crude oil by $5 a barrel to reach $68 in the United States following speculation over war against Iran, is discussed.

8720 ■ *"Spread Your Wings"* in *Canadian Business (Vol. 81, March 17, 2008, No. 4, pp. 31)*
Pub: Rogers Media

Ed: Megan Harman. **Description:** Financing from angel investors is one avenue that should be explored by startups. Angel investors are typically affluent individuals who invest their own money. Angel investors usually want at least 10 times their initial investment within eight years but they benefit the businesses through their help in decision-making and the industry expertise they provide.

8721 ■ *"Sprint Tries to Wring Out Positives"* in *The Business Journal-Serving Metropolitan Kansas City (Vol. 26, August 8, 2008, No. 48)*
Pub: American City Business Journals, Inc.

Ed: Suzanna Stagemeyer. **Description:** Sprint Nextel Corp. reported that 901,000 subscribers left the company in the quarter ending June 30, 2008; fewer than the nearly 1.1 million it lost in the previous quarter. Customer turnover also dropped to just less than 2 percent, compared to 2.45 percent in the first quarter of 2008.

8722 ■ *"Staffing Firm Grows by Following Own Advice-Hire a Headhunter"* in *Crain's Detroit Business (Vol. 24, October 6, 2008, No. 40, pp. 1)*
Pub: Crain Communications, Inc.

Ed: Sherri Begin. **Description:** Profile of Venator Holdings L.L.C., a staffing firm that provides searches for companies in need of financial-accounting and technical employees; the firm's revenue has increased from $1.1 million in 2003 to a projected $11.5 million this year due to a climate in which more people are exiting the workforce than are coming in with those particular specialized skills and the need for a temporary, flexible workforce for contract placements at companies that do not want to take on the legacy costs associated with permanent employees. The hiring of an external headhunter to find the right out-of-state manager for Venator is also discussed.

8723 ■ *"Stand-Up Guy"* in *Barron's (Vol. 88, July 7, 2008, No. 27, pp. L11)*
Pub: Dow Jones & Co., Inc.

Ed: Suzanne McGee. **Description:** James O'Shaughnessy, a mutual fund manager with O'Shaughnessy Asset Management, is bullish on both financial and energy stocks. He was formerly involved with Bear Stearns until he left the firm in March 2008.

8724 ■ *Start Your Own Blogging Business, Second Edition*
Pub: Entrepreneur Press
Contact: Perlman Neil, President

Released: July 1, 2010. **Price:** $17.95. **Description:** Interviews with professional bloggers from some of the most popular blogs on the Internet will help anyone interested in starting their own blogging business.

8725 ■ *"State of Play"* in *Canadian Business (Vol. 79, June 19, 2006, No. 13, pp. 25)*
Pub: Rogers Media

Ed: Andrew Wahl; Zena Olijnyk; Jeff Sanford. **Description:** Top 100 information technology companies in Canada are ranked by their market capitalization as of June 1. The statistics that show the revenues of these companies are also presented.

8726 ■ *"State Shock Prices Take Large Tumble"* in *The Business Journal-Milwaukee (Vol. 25, September 12, 2008, No. 51, pp. A1)*
Pub: American City Business Journals, Inc.

Ed: Rich Rovito. **Description:** Weak economic times have caused the stocks of most publicly traded companies in Wisconsin to dip in 2008. Companies that appeared on the worst performing stocks list also experienced drops in share price to as much as 70 percent. Information about the companies that experienced increases in stock prices is also presented. Statistical data included.

8727 ■ *"Stay Calm, Bernanke Urges Markets"* in *Globe & Mail (March 1, 2007, pp. B1)*
Pub: CTVglobemedia Publishing Inc.

Ed: Brian McKenna. **Description:** The views of Ben Bernanke, the chief of the United States Federal Reserve Board, on the future trends of the United States' economy are presented. The effect of the global stock market trends on the American stock markets is discussed.

8728 ■ *"Stelco Investors Told Their Stock Now Worthless"* in *Globe & Mail (January 23, 2006, pp. B4)*
Pub: CTVglobemedia Publishing Inc.

Ed: Greg Keenan. **Description:** The reasons behind Ontario Superior Court's approval of Stelco Inc.'s restructuring proposal are presented.

8729 ■ *"Stock Analysts' Pans"* in *Canadian Business (Vol. 81, Summer 2008, No. 9, pp. 75)*
Pub: Rogers Media Ltd.

Ed: Calvin Leung. **Description:** Table showing the one-year stock performance of companies that are least loved by analysts and are rated either to be a Hold or Sell. These companies should not be included in the investment portfolio, at least in the short term.

8730 ■ *"Stock Car Racing"* in *Canadian Business (Vol. 81, September 15, 2008, No. 14-15, pp. 29)*
Pub: Rogers Media Ltd.

Ed: Thomas Watson. **Description:** Some analysts predict a Chapter 11-style tune-up making GM and Ford a speculative turnaround stock. However, the price of oil could make or break the shares of the Big Three U.S. automobile manufacturers and if oil goes up too high then a speculative stock to watch is an electric car company called Zenn Motor Co.

8731 ■ *"Stock Delisting Could Hamper First Mariner"* in *Boston Business Journal (Vol. 29, July 29, 2011, No. 12, pp. 1)*
Pub: American City Business Journals Inc.

Ed: Gary Haber. **Description:** Possible delisting of First Mariner Bancorp from the Nasdaq stock exchange could adversely impact the bank's ability to attract institutional investors. Some institutions limit their investments to companies trading on the Nasdaq.

8732 ■ *"Stockgroup Completes US $4.5 Million Financing"* in *Canadian Corporate News (May 16, 2007)*
Pub: Comtex News Network Inc.

Description: Stockgroup, a financial media company focused on collaborative technologies and user-generated content, will use the proceeds of the private placement for acquisitions and general working capital.

8733 ■ *Street Fighters: The Last 72 Hours of Bears Stearns, the Toughest Firm on Wall Street*
Pub: Portfolio

Ed: Kate Kelly. **Released:** 2009. **Price:** $25.95. **Description:** An account of the investment bank, Bears Stearns fight for survival is documented.

8734 ■ *"Stressed Out: 7 Banks Rated 'At Riks"* in *Saint Louis Business Journal (Vol. 32, September 16, 2011, No. 3, pp. 1)*
Pub: Saint Louis Business Journal

Ed: Greg Edwards. **Description:** St. Louis, Missouri has seven banks that are well above the 100 percent level that is considered 'at risk' based on a risk measurement called the Texas ratio. The banks are the Sun Security bank, 1st Advantage Bank, Superior Bank, Truman Bank, Reliance Bank, St. Louis Bank and Meramec Valley Bank.

8735 ■ *"Struggling Community Banks Find Little Help In Wall Street Bailout"* in *Crain's Detroit Business (Vol. 24, September 29, 2008)*
Pub: Crain Communications Inc.

Ed: Tom Henderson. **Description:** Both public and private Michigan bands have been hit hard by poorly performing loan portfolios and although their problems were not caused by high-risk securities but by a longtime statewide recession and a housing slump, these community banks have little hope of seeing any of the bailout money that has been allotted for the larger institutions.

8736 ■ *"Stymiest's RBC Compensation Triggers Shareholder Outrage"* in *Gl obe & Mail (January 28, 2006, pp. B3)*
Pub: CTVglobemedia Publishing Inc.

Ed: Sinclair Stewart. **Description:** The concerns of shareholders over the issue of Royal Bank of Canada's $6.6 million pay package for chief executive officer Barbara Stymiest, in 2004, are presented.

8737 ■ *"Subprime Hits Huntington"* in *Business First-Columbus (November 23, 2007, pp. A1)*
Pub: American City Business Journals, Inc.

Ed: Adrian Burns. **Description:** Huntington Bancshares Inc. picked up a $1.5 billion exposure to the country's subprime mortgage mess. It caused the bank to set aside $450 million to cover increases in loan losses. When Huntington acquired Sky Financial, it absorbed a 17-year relationship Sky had with Franklin Credit Corporation, which is a subprime lender and servicer.

8738 ■ "The Suits Look Better Than the Shares" in Barron's (Vol. 88, March 31, 2008, No. 13, pp. 25)

Pub: Dow Jones & Company, Inc.

Ed: Bill Alpert. **Description:** Jos. A. Bank's inventory has increased sharply raising questions about the company's growth prospects. The company's shares have already dropped significantly from 46 to 23 and could still continue its slide. The company is also battling a class action suit where plaintiffs allege that the Bank inventories were bloated.

8739 ■ "SunBank Plans Expansion Via Wall-Mart" in Business Journal-Serving Phoenix and the Valley of the Sun (Vol. 10, November 9, 2007)

Pub: American City Business Journals, Inc.

Ed: Chris Casacchia. **Description:** SunBank plans to install 12 to 14 branches in Wal-Mart stores in Arizona and hire 100 bankers by the end of 2008. Wal-Mart also offers financial products at other stores through partnerships with other banks.

8740 ■ "Surprise Package" in Business Courier (Vol. 27, June 25, 2010, No. 8, pp. 1)

Pub: Business Courier

Ed: Dan Monk, Jon Newberry, Steve Watkins. **Description:** More than 60 percent of the chief executive officers (CEOs) in Greater Cincinnati's 35 public companies took a salary cut in 2009, but stock grants resulted in large paper gains for the CEOs. The salary cuts show efforts of boards of directors to observe austerity. Statistics on increased values of stock awards for CEOs, median pay for CEOs, and median shareholder return are also presented.

8741 ■ "A Survival Guide for Crazy Times" in Canadian Business (Vol. 81, March 3, 2008, No. 3, pp. 61)

Pub: Rogers Media

Ed: David Wolf. **Description:** Investors should ensure that their portfolios are positioned defensively more than the average as the U.S. and Canadian markets face turbulent times. They should not assume that U.S. residential property is a good place to invest only because prices have dropped and the Canadian dollar is showing strength. Other tips that investors can use during unstable periods are supplied.

8742 ■ "Surviving the Storm" in Canadian Business (Vol. 81, July 22, 2008, No. 12-13, pp. 50)

Pub: Rogers Media Ltd.

Ed: Jeff Sanford. **Description:** Investment adviser Harry Dent and finance professor Paul Marsh discuss their views and forecasts on the United States' economic condition. Dent believes advisors should concentrate on wealth preservation rather than on returns. Other views regarding U.S. economic conditions are also presented.

8743 ■ "A Swifter, Better Marketplace" in Barron's (Vol. 89, July 13, 2009, No. 28, pp. M13)

Pub: Dow Jones & Co., Inc.

Ed: Eric W. Noll. **Description:** Listed-derivatives market is moving towards greater trading through computerized systems with an emphasis on speed and innovation. The market for listed options is also being changed by new techniques from other markets such as algorithmic trading, dark pools, and new-order priority systems.

8744 ■ "Sykes Group Targets GunnAllen" in The Business Journal-Serving Greater Tampa Bay (Vol. 28, September 5, 2008, No. 37, pp. 1)

Pub: American City Business Journals, Inc.

Ed: Margie Manning. **Description:** GAH Holdings LLC. a newly formed investment company by John H. Sykes of Sykes Enterprises Inc., will add capital to Tampa Bay Area investment banking firm GunnAllen Holdings Inc. The capital infusion is to aid GunnAllen Holdings in expanding and diversifying as GAH becomes its largest shareholder.

8745 ■ "Take a Flyer on Choice" in Canadian Business (Vol. 79, October 23, 2006, No. 21, pp. 163)

Pub: Rogers Media

Description: The variations in the stock market prices of companies like Nike Inc. and Black & Decker Corp. from October 2005-06 are discussed.

8746 ■ "Take It to the Bank" in Barron's (Vol. 89, July 13, 2009, No. 28, pp. 20)

Pub: Dow Jones & Co., Inc.

Ed: Jim McTague. **Description:** Banks are one of the safest place to put one's principal due to the temporary increase in the Federal Deposit Insurance Corp.'s insurance of bank accounts up to $250,000 and also because of the Cdars (Certificates of Deposit Registry Service) program which spreads the deposit to several banks thereby making the account covered as if it the money was deposited at multiple banks.

8747 ■ "Takeover Frenzy Stokes Steel Stocks" in Globe & Mail (February 7, 2006, pp. B1)

Pub: CTVglobemedia Publishing Inc.

Description: The impact of merger speculations, on shares of steel companies such as Ipsco Inc., is discussed.

8748 ■ "Taking Collections" in Investment Dealers' Digest (Vol. 75, October 9, 2009, No. 38, pp. 19)

Pub: SourceMedia, Inc.

Ed: Aleksandrs Rozens. **Description:** Although the nation's debt-collection industry has grown with increased reliance by consumers on credit, valuations of these firms have lessened due to the economy which has hurt some of the success of these firms in obtaining the debt back from consumers who are experiencing trying economic times.

8749 ■ "Taking the Over-the-Counter Route to US" in Barron's (Vol. 88, July 7, 2008, No. 27, pp. 24)

Pub: Dow Jones & Co., Inc.

Ed: Eric Uhlfelder. **Description:** Many multinational companies have left the New York Stock Exchange and allowed their shares to trade over-the-counter. The companies have taken advantage of a 2007 SEC rule allowing publicly listed foreign companies to change trading venues if less than 5 percent of global trading volume in the past 12 months occurred in the US.

8750 ■ "Tamara Vrooman" in Canadian Business (Vol. 80, November 19, 2007, No. 23, pp. 9)

Pub: Rogers Media

Ed: Regan Ray. **Description:** Profile of Tamara Vrooman, newly appointed CEO of Canada's largest credit union, Vancity. Vrooman believes that Vancity has an advantage over big bank when it comes to the flexibility of products the company offers. The role of Vancity and credit unions in the banking sector of Canada is discussed.

8751 ■ "Tanganyika Announces First Quarter 2007 Results" in Canadian Corporate News (May 14, 2007)

Pub: Comtex News Network Inc.

Description: Tanganyika Oil Company Ltd., announced the interim operating and financial results for the first quarter ending March 31, 2007. Statistical data included.

8752 ■ "Tao of Downfall" in International Journal of Entrepreneurship and Small Business (Vol. 11, August 31, 2010, No. 2, pp. 121)

Pub: Publishers Communication Group

Ed: Wenxian Zhang, Ilan Alon. **Description:** Through historical reviews and case studies, this research seeks to understand why some initially successful entrepreneurs failed in the economic boom of past decades. Among various factors contributing to their downfall are a unique political and business environment, fragile financial systems, traditional cultural influences and personal characteristics.

8753 ■ "Tech's Payout Problem" in Barron's (Vol. 90, September 13, 2010, No. 37, pp. 19)

Pub: Barron's Editorial & Corporate Headquarters

Ed: Andrew Bary. **Description:** Big tech companies have the potential to be good dividend payers, but instead just hoard their cash for acquisitions and share buybacks. If these companies offered more dividends, they could boost their shares and attract more income-oriented investors.

8754 ■ The Ten Laws of Enduring Success

Pub: Crown Business Books

Ed: Maria Bartiromo, Catherine Whitney. **Released:** March 1, 2011. **Price:** $15.00. **Description:** A new meaning for success is described by financial expert, Maria Bartiromo, with advice on how to adapt with the changing times.

8755 ■ "TerraVest Income Fund Releases 2007 First Quarter Financial Results" in Canadian Corporate News (May 14, 2007)

Pub: Comtex News Network Inc.

Description: Overview of TerraVest Income Fund's financial results for the quarter ended March 31, 2007 in which the net earnings increased 36.7 percent to $3.7 million from the 2006 first quarter. Statistical data included.

8756 ■ "That's About It for Quantitative Easing" in Barron's (Vol. 89, July 20, 2009, No. 29, pp. M11)

Pub: Dow Jones & Co., Inc.

Ed: Brian Blackstone. **Description:** US Federal Reserve appears to have decided to halt quantitative easing, causing bond prices to drop and yields to rise. The yield for the 1-year Treasury bond rose more than 0.3 percentage point to about 3.65 percent.

8757 ■ "There's More Upside in Germany" in Barron's (Vol. 90, September 6, 2010, No. 36, pp. M7)

Pub: Barron's Editorial & Corporate Headquarters

Ed: Jonathan Buck. **Description:** Germany's stocks have gone up since the beginning of 2010, and investors can still benefit. These stocks will benefit from Germany's stellar economic performance and the relative weakness of the Euro. The prospects of the shares of Daimler and Hochtief are discussed.

8758 ■ "They Have Issues: New Black-Owned Investment Bank Nets $90 Million In Managed Issues" in Black Enterprise (Vol. 38, March 2008)

Pub: Earl G. Graves Publishing Co. Inc.

Ed: Marcia A. Wade. **Description:** Castle Oak Securities LP has co-managed multiple deals for more than 35 blue-chip clients. Their first deal earned $300 million for General Electric Capital Corporation and Castle Oak has since co-managed nine more deals with GE Capital, seven for Citigroup, six for American Express, and three for Goldman Sachs.

8759 ■ "They've Fallen, But They Can Get Up" in Barron's (Vol. 88, March 10, 2008, No. 10, pp. 43)

Pub: Dow Jones & Company, Inc.

Ed: Kopin Tan. **Description:** Shares of senior housing companies present buying opportunities to investors because of their low prices. Companies such as Brookdale Senior Living are not as dependent on housing prices but have suffered declines in share prices.

8760 ■ "Time to Change Direction" in Canadian Business (Vol. 79, October 23, 2006, No. 21, pp. 21)

Pub: Rogers Media

Ed: Jack Mintz. **Description:** The decision of BCE Inc. to get converted into an income trust is discussed. The economic factors responsible for the conversion of firms to income trusts are analyzed.

8761 ■ "Time to Leave the Party?" in Barron's (Vol. 88, March 24, 2008, No. 12, pp. M16)

Pub: Dow Jones & Company, Inc.

Ed: Andrea Hotter. **Description:** Prices of commodities such as gold, copper, crude oil, sugar, cocoa, and wheat have fallen from their all-time highs set in the middle of March 2008. Analysts, however, caution that this decline in prices may be temporary, and that a banking crisis may trigger new price rises in commodities.

8762 ■ *"Time for a Little Pruning"* in *Barron's (Vol. 89, July 6, 2009, No. 27, pp. 13)*
Pub: Dow Jones & Co., Inc.
Ed: Dimitra DeFotis. **Description:** Investors are advised to avoid the shares of Whole Foods, American Tower, T. Rowe Price, Iron Mountain, Intuitive Surgical, Salesforce.com, and Juniper Networks due to their high price to earnings ratios. The shares of Amazon.com, Broadcom, and Expeditors International of Washington remain attractive to investors despite their high price to earnings ratios due to their strong growth.

8763 ■ *"A Timely Boon for Small Investors"* in *Barron's (Vol. 88, March 24, 2008, No. 12, pp. 48)*
Pub: Dow Jones & Company, Inc.
Ed: Theresa W. Carey. **Description:** Nasdaq Data Store's new program called Market Replay allows investors to accurately track stock price movements. The replay can be as long as a day of market time and allows investors to determine whether they executed stock trades at the best possible price.

8764 ■ *"Tiptoeing Beyond Treasuries"* in *Barron's (Vol. 88, March 31, 2008, No. 13, pp. M6)*
Pub: Dow Jones & Company, Inc.
Ed: Michael S. Derby. **Description:** Risk-free assets like treasuries are still a good place for cash even if market conditions have calmed down and Treasury yields are low. Investors looking for yield and safety might want to consider Treasury inflation-indexed securities that are attractive given new inflation pressures.

8765 ■ *"Tofutti Brands"* in *Ice Cream Reporter (Vol. 23, September 20, 2010, No. 10, pp. 6)*
Pub: Ice Cream Reporter
Description: Tofutti Brands announced net sales at $4.5 million for second quarter 2010.

8766 ■ *"A Tonic for Irrationality"* in *Barron's (Vol. 89, July 13, 2009, No. 28, pp. 12)*
Pub: Dow Jones & Co., Inc.
Description: Financial-personality assessment being introduced by Barclays Wealth, measures six personality aspects related to financial behavior through a profile that measures such traits including risk tolerance, composure and perceived financial expertise. The profile helps the company create a portfolio that are structured to meet their client's personality needs.

8767 ■ *"Too Much Information?"* in *Black Enterprise (Vol. 37, December 2006, No. 5, pp. 59)*
Pub: Earl G. Graves Publishing Co. Inc.
Ed: James C. Johnson. **Description:** African American business owners often face the dilemma of whether or not to divulge their minority status when soliciting new customers and financial institutions. The quality of the products or services is always the key factor and race should never define one's business; however, it is appropriate to market oneself as a minority or women-owned business, especially if the company is in an industry where those clients are offered top-tier contracts.

8768 ■ *"Too Much Precaution About Biotech Corn"* in *Barron's (Vol. 88, March 17, 2008, No. 11, pp. 54)*
Pub: Dow Jones & Company, Inc.
Ed: Mark I. Schwartz. **Description:** In the U.S., 90 percent of cultivated soybeans are biotech varietals as well as 60 percent of the corn. Farmers have significantly reduced their reliance on pesticides in the growing of biotech corn. Biotech cotton cultivation has brought hundreds of millions of dollars in net financial gains to farmers. The European Union has precluded the cultivation or sale of biotech crops within its border.

8769 ■ *"Too Much too Soon"* in *Barron's (Vol. 89, July 27, 2009, No. 30, pp. 33)*
Pub: Dow Jones & Co., Inc.
Ed: Leslie P. Norton. **Description:** Shares of hhgregg have risen 85 percent in the year leading up to July 2009 and analysts believe the stock could hit 25. However, their 113 outlets are concentrated in states where unemployment is above 10 percent and expanding into areas already overstored. Competition is also rife and credit availability is still tight.

8770 ■ *"Tool-o-Rama"* in *Barron's (Vol. 90, September 6, 2010, No. 36)*
Pub: Barron's Editorial & Corporate Headquarters
Description: New trading tool features from several online brokers are discussed. The new features from Fidelity, ChoiceTrade, JunoTrade and TradeKing are examined. Investors can now screen exchanged traded funds in the same way as stocks with Fidelity, while ChoiceTrade can run in any browser without the need to install additional plug-ins.

8771 ■ *"Top 10 Retirement Mistakes and How to Avoid Them"* in *Canadian Business (Vol. 83, July 20, 2010, No. 11-12, pp. 39)*
Pub: Rogers Media Ltd.
Ed: Jacqueline Nelson, Angelina Chapin. **Description:** Some of the top retirement mistakes is relying on selling one's house to find a retirement. Other mistakes are paying too much for investments and planning to work in retirement since no one can be sure that they will be healthy enough to accomplish this. Suggestions to avoid these pitfalls are discussed.

8772 ■ *"Top 50 By 1-Year Return"* in *Canadian Business (Vol. 81, Summer 2008, No. 9, pp. 121)*
Pub: Rogers Media Ltd.
Description: Table showing the top 50 Canadian companies ranked in terms of one-year return is presented. Toronto, Canada-based Timminco Ltd. topped the roster with a 1,294.2 percent in one-year return. However, the share prices of the company were affected by the recent controversy in its silicon purification process.

8773 ■ *"Top 50 By 5-Year Return"* in *Canadian Business (Vol. 81, Summer 2008, No. 9, pp. 123)*
Pub: Rogers Media Ltd.
Description: Table showing the rankings of the top 50 Canadian companies in terms of five-year return is presented. Silver Wheaton Corp. topped the roster with a 178.5 percent in five-year return. The company's share prices have skyrocketed despite increasing silver prices.

8774 ■ *"Top 50 in the Capital Market"* in *Canadian Business (Vol. 81, Summer 2008, No. 9, pp. 117)*
Pub: Rogers Media Ltd.
Description: Research in Motion Ltd. topped the list of companies in Canada in terms of market capitalization. The company's share prices surge to 119.8 percent in the year ended April 4. A table showing the top 50 Canadian companies in terms of market capitalization is presented.

8775 ■ *"Top 50 In Profits"* in *Canadian Business (Vol. 81, Summer 2008, No. 9, pp. 116)*
Pub: Rogers Media Ltd.
Description: Royal Bank of Canada topped the Investor 500 by profits list despite the slower economic growth in Canada and the U.S. The bank was in the runner-up position in the 2007. RBC's growth strategy is through hefty acquisitions in the U.S. A table ranking the top 50 companies in Canada in terms of profits is presented.

8776 ■ *"Top 50 In Total Revenue"* in *Canadian Business (Vol. 81, Summer 2008, No. 9, pp. 119)*
Pub: Rogers Media Ltd.
Description: Table showing the top 50 Canadian companies in terms of total revenue is presented. Manulife Financial Corp. topped the list with revenue

of 34.5 billion. The financial services firm is the 6th largest provider of life insurance in the world and the second largest in North America.

8777 ■ *"Top Law Firms Join Forces"* in *Business Journal Portland (Vol. 27, December 3, 2010, No. 40, pp. 1)*
Pub: Portland Business Journal
Ed: Andy Giegerich. **Description:** Law Firms Powell PC and Roberts Kaplan LLP will forge a collaboration, whereby 17 Roberts Kaplan attorneys will join the Portland, Oregon-based office of Lane Powell. The partnership is expected to strengthen the law firms' grip on Portland's banking clients.

8778 ■ *"Tory or Liberal, Blue or Red, the Impact of the Election is All in Your Head"* in *Globe & Mail (January 14, 2006, pp. B19)*
Pub: CTVglobemedia Publishing Inc.
Ed: Derek DeCloet. **Description:** The effect of the outcome of 2006 Canadian federal elections on stock markets is discussed.

8779 ■ *"The Trader's Edge"* in *Barron's (Vol. 88, March 31, 2008, No. 13, pp. 56)*
Pub: Dow Jones & Company, Inc.
Ed: Dan McGuire. **Description:** There is a $3,000 a year annual limit to deducting investor's losses and normal investment expenses are purportedly deductible as miscellaneous expenses on Schedule A only to the extent that they exceed two percent of adjusted gross income. Professional gamblers who can use Schedule C are unable deduct a net gaming loss against income from any other sources.

8780 ■ *"Traditional VS. Roth IRA"* in *Black Enterprise (Vol. 37, October 2006, No. 3, pp. 58)*
Pub: Earl G. Graves Publishing Co. Inc.
Ed: K. Parker; Carolyn M. Brown. **Description:** Government taxes the traditional IRAs different than it taxes Roth IRAs.

8781 ■ *"Treasuries Buffeted by Stocks"* in *Barron's (Vol. 89, July 27, 2009, No. 30, pp. M9)*
Pub: Dow Jones & Co., Inc.
Ed: Randall W. Forsyth. **Description:** Warren Buffett favors equities over long-term government bonds or stocks even with the Dow index at an eight-month high. The 10-year Treasury was up two basis points to 3.67 percent as of July 24, 2009. Corporate bond issuance hit a record $1.79 trillion for the first half of 2009.

8782 ■ *"Treasuries Rally Despite Huge Supply"* in *Barron's (Vol. 89, July 13, 2009, No. 28, pp. M10)*
Pub: Dow Jones & Co., Inc.
Ed: Randall W. Forsyth. **Description:** Prices of U.S. Treasuries were sent higher and their yields lower despite four auctions of coupon securities because of the strong appetite for government securities around the world. The reopening of the 10-year note in the week ending July 10, 2009 drew the strongest bidding since 1995.

8783 ■ *"A Trend Is His Friend"* in *Barron's (Vol. 89, July 27, 2009, No. 30, pp. 28)*
Pub: Dow Jones & Co., Inc.
Ed: Eric Uhlfelder. **Description:** Global Diversified Program fund under Quality Capital Management is managed through a trading system called the Advanced Resource Allocator which rebalances short-term tactical moves to gather quick profits. CEO Aref Karim's allocations are based on risk and he says their sentiments toward the market conditions are agnostic.

8784 ■ *"The Trials of Brian Hunter"* in *Canadian Business (Vol. 81, March 3, 2008, No. 3, pp. 64)*
Pub: Rogers Media
Ed: Thomas Watson. **Description:** Brian Hunter was a considered a brilliant trader in Wall Street before he was blamed for the fall of the Amaranth hedge fund. Some people blame Hunter for placing bets based on unpredictable weather when he was a trader for

Amaranth Advisors LLC. The accusation against Hunter that he conspired to manipulate natural gas prices is also discussed.

8785 ■ "Trilogy Metals Inc.: Private Placement" in Canadian Corporate News (May 16, 2007)
Pub: Comtex News Network Inc.
Description: Trilogy Metals Inc. announces a private placement of 10,000,000 units at $0.08 per unit in an effort to raise total gross proceeds of $800,000 which will be allocated to working capital, new acquisitions, and to service existing debt.

8786 ■ "Trust Buyouts Not My Fault, Flaherty Says" in Globe & Mail (April 3, 2007, pp. B1)
Pub: CTVglobemedia Publishing Inc.
Ed: Tara Perkins; Doug Saunders; Steven Chase. **Description:** The causes of the acquisition of Canadian firms by foreign investors are discussed by the Canadian Finance Minister Jim Flaherty.

8787 ■ "Trust Distrust" in Canadian Business (Vol. 79, July 17, 2006, No. 14-15, pp. 61)
Pub: Rogers Media
Ed: John Gray. **Description:** The need to frame better trust deeds in order to protect the investor's money as well as their returns is examined.

8788 ■ "TUSK Announces 2007 First Quarter Results" in Canadian Corporate News (May 14, 2007)
Pub: Comtex News Network Inc.
Description: TUSK Energy Corp. announced its financial and operating results for the first quarter ending March 31, 2007.

8789 ■ "TV Revenue Slide Hits CanWest Profit" in Globe & Mail (January 13, 2006, pp. B3)
Pub: CTVglobemedia Publishing Inc.
Ed: Grant Robertson. **Description:** CanWest Global Communications Corp. posted drop in profits by 14 percent for first quarter 2006. The downward trend in profits is attributed to low television revenues.

8790 ■ "UBS Buys Out Canadian Partner" in Globe & Mail (January 20, 2006, pp. B1)
Pub: CTVglobemedia Publishing Inc.
Ed: Andrew Willis. **Description:** The details on UBS AG's acquisition of UBS Securities Canada Inc. are presented.

8791 ■ "An Unfair Knock on Nokia" in Barron's (Vol. 88, March 10, 2008, No. 10, pp. 36)
Pub: Dow Jones & Company, Inc.
Ed: Mark Veverka. **Description:** Discusses the decision by the brokerage house Exane to recommend a Sell on Nokia shares, presumably due to higher inventories, which is unfounded. The news that the company's inventories are rising is not an indicator of falling demand for its products. The company is also benefiting from solid management and rising market share.

8792 ■ "Unify Corp. Back in the Black, Poised to Grow" in Sacramento Business Journal (Vol. 25, August 29, 2008, No. 26, pp. 1)
Pub: American City Business Journals, Inc.
Ed: Melanie Turner. **Description:** It was reported that Unify Corp. returned to profitability in the fiscal year ended April 30, 2008 with a net income of $1.6 million, under the guidance of Todd Wille. Wille, who took over as the company's chief executive officer in October 2000, was named as Turnaround CEO of the Year in June 2008 for his efforts.

8793 ■ "Universal Energy Group Releases March 31, 2007 Financial Statements" in Canadian Corporate News (May 14, 2007)
Pub: Comtex News Network Inc.
Description: Universal Energy Group Ltd., a company that sells electricity and natural gas to small to mid-size commercial and small industrial customers as well as residential customers, announced the release of its March 31, 2007 financial statements.

Management's analysis and discussion of the company's financial condition and results of operations are listed. Statistical data included.

8794 ■ "Unpleasant Surprise" in Barron's (Vol. 88, March 24, 2008, No. 12, pp. 60)
Pub: Dow Jones & Company, Inc.
Ed: Shirley A. Lazo. **Description:** Discusses the $175 million that footwear company Genesco received in a settlement with Finish Line and UBS is considered as a stock distribution and is taxable as dividend income. Railroad company CSX raised its quarterly common payout from 15 cents to 18 cents.

8795 ■ "The Upside of Fear and Loathing" in Barron's (Vol. 88, March 24, 2008, No. 12, pp. 11)
Pub: Dow Jones & Company, Inc.
Ed: Michael Santoli. **Description:** Fear and risk aversion prevalent among investors may actually serve to cushion the decline and spark a rally in US stock prices. Surveys of investors indicate rising levels of anxiety and bearishness, indicating a possible positive turnaround.

8796 ■ "USAmeriBank Deals for Growth" in The Business Journal-Serving Greater Tampa Bay (Vol. 28, September 26, 2008, No. 40, pp. 1)
Pub: American City Business Journals, Inc.
Ed: Margie Manning. **Description:** It is believed that the pending $14.9 million purchase of Liberty Bank by USAmeriBank could be at the forefront of a trend. Executives of both companies expect the deal to close by the end of 2008. USAmeriBank will have $430 million in assets and five offices in Pinellas, Florida once the deal is completed.

8797 ■ "Valener Announces that Gaz Metro has Achieved a Key Step in Acquiring CVPS" in CNW Group (September 30, 2011)
Pub: CNW Group
Contact: Carolyn McGill-Davidson, President
Description: Valener Inc., which owns about 29 percent of Gaz Metro Ltd. Partnership, announced that Gaz Metro welcomes the sale of Central Vermont Public Service Corporation (CVPS). Valener owns an indirect interest of 24.5 percent in the wind power projects jointly developed by Beaupre Eole General Partnership and Boralex Inc. on private lands in Quebec. Details of the deal are included.

8798 ■ "Valenti: Roots of Financial Crisis Go Back to 1998" in Crain's Detroit Business (Vol. 24, October 6, 2008, No. 40, pp. 25)
Pub: Crain Communications, Inc.
Ed: Tom Henderson; Nathan Skid. **Description:** Interview with Sam Valenti III who is the chairman and CEO of Valenti Capital L.L.C., a wealth-management firm; Valenti discusses in detail the history that led up to the current economic crisis as well as his prediction for the future of the country.

8799 ■ "Virtus.com Wins 'Best of Industry' WebAward for Excellence in Financial Services" in Investment Weekly News (October 24, 2009)
Pub: Investment Weekly News
Description: Web Marketing Association honored Virtus.com, the Website of Virtus Investment Partners, Inc., for Outstanding Achievement in Web Development and Acsys Interactive was awarded the Financial Services Standard of Excellence Award for developing the site. The site was part of a rebranding effort and is a one-stop portal for both financial advisors and their investors.

8800 ■ "Virtus.com Wins 'Best of Industry' WebAward for Excellence in Financial Services" in Investment Weekly News (Oct. 24, 2009, pp. 227)
Pub: Investment Weekly News
Description: Web Marketing Association honored Virtus.com, the Website of Virtus Investment Partners, Inc., for Outstanding Achievement in Web Development and Acsys Interactive was awarded the Financial Services Standard of Excellence Award for

developing the site. The site was part of a rebranding effort and is a one-stop portal for both financial advisors and their investors.

8801 ■ "Vital Signs: The Big Picture" in Canadian Business (Vol. 81, Summer 2008, No. 9, pp. 153)
Pub: Rogers Media Ltd.
Description: Results of the Investor 500 showing percentage of companies with positive returns, most actively traded companies over the past six months and market capitalization by industry are presented. Stock performance and revenues of publicly held corporations in Canada are also provided.

8802 ■ "Vive La Resistance: Competing Logics and the Consolidation of U.S. Community Banking" in Academy of Management Journal (August 2007)
Pub: Academy of Management
Contact: Ming-Jer Chen, President
Ed: Christopher Marquis, Michael Lounsbury. **Description:** Ways in which competing logics facilitate resistance to institutional change is presented, highlighting on banking professionals' resistance to large, national banks acquisitions of smaller, local banks.

8803 ■ "Voice: Rebuilding Trust" in Business Strategy Review (Vol. 21, Summer 2010, No. 2, pp. 79)
Pub: Blackwell Publishers Ltd.
Ed: David De Cremer. **Description:** An examination of the financial sector's attempt to rebuild trust is given. Three steps to jump start the process are explored.

8804 ■ "Voice: Rebuilding Trust" in Business Strategy Review (Vol. 21, Summer 2010, No. 2, pp. 79)
Pub: Wiley-Blackwell
Ed: David De Cremer. **Description:** The financial world's attempts to rebuild trust are charted. Three steps to jump-start that process are outlined.

8805 ■ "Wachovia Gears Up for Major Arizona Expansion" in Business Journal-Serving Phoenix and the Valley of the Sun (Vol. 5, Oct. 5, 2007)
Pub: American City Business Journals, Inc.
Ed: Chris Casacchia. **Description:** Wachovia, America's fourth-largest bank is finalizing a deal to build its Arizona headquarters in downtown Phoenix. The bank plans to add an additional 100 employees by June 2008 and double its financial network to 30 offices in four years. Wachovia will also convert fifteen World Savings Bank branches it acquired in 2006 through Golden West Financial Corporation.

8806 ■ "Wait for the Call" in Canadian Business (Vol. 80, April 9, 2007, No. 8, pp. 74)
Pub: Rogers Media
Ed: Andrew Wahl. **Description:** The effort of chief executive of BCE Inc. Michael Sabia to deal with rumors about the company's private equity deal with Kohlberg Kravis Roberts & Co. is discussed.

8807 ■ "Wall Street Is No Friend to Radical Innovation" in Harvard Business Review (Vol. 88, July-August 2010, No. 7-8, pp. 28)
Pub: Harvard Business School Publishing
Ed: Julia Kirby. **Description:** Research indicates that investors are skittish about backing a business that proposes significant changes to its product or service status quo.

8808 ■ "W&S to Trim Rich Retirement Plan" in Business Courier (Vol. 27, October 15, 2010, No. 24, pp. 1)
Pub: Business Courier
Ed: Dan Monk. **Description:** Insurance firm Western & Southern Financial Group announced that it will reduce the pension benefits of its 4,000 associates by more than 30 percent starting January 1, 2011. The move is expected to reduce annual retirement payments by several thousand dollars per associate. Western is a Fortune 500 company and has $34 billion in total assets.

8809 ■ *"Want People to Save? Force Them"* in *Harvard Business Review (Vol. 88, September 2010, No. 9, pp. 36)*
Pub: Harvard Business School Publishing
Ed: Dan Ariely. **Description:** Contrasts in U.S. attitudes towards savings and government regulation with those of Chile, where all employees are required to save 11 percent of their salary in a retirement account, are highlighted.

8810 ■ *"Want Some of This?"* in *Canadian Business (Vol. 80, April 9, 2007, No. 8, pp. 71)*
Pub: Rogers Media
Ed: Jeff Sanford. **Description:** The economic impact of growing private equity in Canada is discussed.

8811 ■ *"The Way to the Market's Heart?"* in *Canadian Business (Vol. 80, March 26, 2007, No. 7, pp. 74)*
Pub: Rogers Media
Ed: Erin Pooley. **Description:** The financial and stock performance of Canadian biotechnology companies Medicure Inc. and Angiotech Pharmaceuticals Inc. are analyzed.

8812 ■ *"The Wealth Portfolio"* in *Canadian Business (Vol. 79, Winter 2006, No. 24, pp. 146)*
Pub: Rogers Media
Ed: Jeff Sanford. **Description:** The trends pertaining to the pricing of shares of public enterprises, at the Montreal stock exchange, are described.

8813 ■ *"Website for Women 50 Launches"* in *Marketing to Women (Vol. 21, April 2008, No. 4, pp. 5)*
Pub: EPM Communications Inc.
Contact: Ira Mayer, President
E-mail: imayer@epmcom.com
Description: Vibrantnation.com is an online community targeting women over age 50; members can share recommendations on a variety of topics such as vacation spots, retailers and financial issues.

8814 ■ *"A Week of the Worst Kind of Selling"* in *Barron's (Vol. 88, June 30, 2008, No. 26, pp. M3)*
Pub: Dow Jones & Co., Inc.
Ed: Kopin Tan. **Description:** In the week that ended in June 27, 2008 the selloff in the U.S. stock market was brought on by mounting bank losses and the spread of economic slowdown on top of high oil prices. The 31 percent decrease in the share price of Ingersoll-Rand since October 2007 may have factored in most of its risks. The company has completed its acquisition of Trane to morph into a refrigeration-equipment company.

8815 ■ *"Welcome to the Neighborhood"* in *Hawaii Business (Vol. 53, October 2007, No. 4, pp. 48)*
Pub: Hawaii Business Publishing
Ed: Jolyn Okimoto Rosa. **Description:** Finance Factors is planning to build branches in Manoa, and Liliha, as part of its strategy to position itself in high-yield areas. The company chose Manoa and Liliha due to thee sites' rich deposits. Its strategy with regards to the branches' location and to the building design is discussed.

8816 ■ *"Wells Fargo Will Soon Lead Local Banks in Deposits"* in *Austin Business JournalInc. (Vol. 28, December 5, 2008, No. 38, pp. A1)*
Pub: American City Business Journals
Ed: Christopher Calnan. **Description:** Acquisition of Wachovia Corporation by Wells Fargo and Company will leave the latter as the top bank for deposits in Austin, Texas. The merged bank will have deposits of more than $ billion, more than the $3.9 billion deposits Bank of America maintains in the area.

8817 ■ *"Wenzel Downhole Tools Ltd. Announces First Quarter Results for 2007"* in *Canadian Corporate News (May 14, 2007)*
Pub: Comtex News Network Inc.
Description: Wenzel Downhole Tools Ltd., a manufacturer, renter, and seller of drilling tools used in gas and oil exploration, announced its financial results for the first quarter ended March 31, 2007 which includes achieved revenues of $14.5 million. Statistical data included.

8818 ■ *"Weyerhaeuser's REIT Decision Shouldn't Scare Investors Away"* in *Barron's (Vol. 88, June 30, 2008, No. 26, pp. 18)*
Pub: Dow Jones & Co., Inc.
Ed: Christopher Williams. **Description:** Weyerhaeuser Co.'s management said that a conversion to a real estate investment trust was not likely in 2009 since the move is not tax-efficient as of the moment and would overload its non-timber assets with debt. The company's shares have fallen by 19.5 percent. However, the company remains an asset-rich outfit and its activist shareholder is pushing for change.

8819 ■ *"What Ever Happened to TGIF?"* in *Barron's (Vol. 88, March 10, 2008, No. 10, pp. M3)*
Pub: Dow Jones & Company, Inc.
Ed: Kopin Tan. **Description:** US stock markets fell in early March 2008 to their lowest level in 18 months, venturing close to entering a bear market phase. The S&P 500 has dropped an average of 0.78 percent on Fridays for 2008.

8820 ■ *What Has EX-IM Bank Done for Small Business Lately?: Congressional Hearing*
Pub: DIANE Publishing Company
Ed: Donald A. Manzullo. **Description:** Covers Congressional hearing: Witnesses: Philip Merrill, President and CEO, Export Import Bank of the U.S.; Victoria Hadfield, President, Semiconductor Equipment and Materials International (SEMI), North America; and Michael Vaden, President and CEO, Rutland Plastic Technologies, Inc. Attachments: April 1, 2005, letter to Chairman Philip Merrill from Semiconductor Manufacturing International Corporation (SMIC); Attachment A - Chronology of SMIC Transaction; Attachment B-Appendices; Appendix A: March 21, 2005, letter from EX-IM Chairman Philip Merrill to Congressman Donald A. Manzullo from the State of Illinois; and Appendix B: Congressional letter written on SMIC and equipment suppliers behest. Includes charts and tables.

8821 ■ *"What Has Sergey Wrought?"* in *Barron's (Vol. 89, July 13, 2009, No. 28, pp. 8)*
Pub: Dow Jones & Co., Inc.
Ed: Alan Abelson. **Description:** Sergey Aleynikov is a computer expert that once worked for Goldman Sachs but he was arrested after he left the company and charged with theft for bringing with him the code for the company's proprietary software for high-frequency trading. The stock market has been down for four straight weeks as of July 13, 2009 which reflects the reality of how the economy is still struggling.

8822 ■ *"What You Should Know If Your Bank Fails"* in *Black Enterprise (Vol. 41, December 2010, No. 5, pp. 29)*
Pub: Earl G. Graves Publishing Co. Inc.
Ed: John Simons. **Description:** The Federal Deposit Insurance Corporation announced that the number of banks in trouble has reached the highest level since March 1993. Advice from the FDIC is cited. Statistical data included.

8823 ■ *"What'll You Have Tonight?"* in *Barron's (Vol. 88, July 4, 2008, No. 28, pp. 22)*
Pub: Dow Jones & Co., Inc.
Ed: Neil A. Martin. **Description:** Shares of Diageo could rise by 30 percent a year from June 2008 after it slipped due to U.S. sales worries. The company also benefits from the trend toward more premium alcoholic beverage brands worldwide especially in emerging markets.

8824 ■ *"What's In a Name?"* in *Barron's (Vol. 88, March 17, 2008, No. 11, pp. 7)*
Pub: Dow Jones & Company, Inc.
Ed: Alan Abelson. **Description:** Eliot Spitzer's resignation incidentally caused the stock market to go up by 400 points. The Federal Reserve Board's new Term Securities Lending Facility provides liquidity to the big lenders by funneling $200 billion in the form of 28-day loans of Treasuries. The analysis of Paul Brodsky and Lee Quaintance of QB Partners on the demand for commodities is also discussed.

8825 ■ *"What's In a Relationship? The Case of Commercial Lending"* in *Business Horizons (Vol. 51, March-April 2008, No. 2, pp. 93)*
Pub: Elsevier Advanced Technology Publications
Description: Academic literature on relationship lending and banking to small and medium enterprises is analyzed. This practice is best suited to some SME types but creates special challenges for bank managers. Relationship lending may also be better delivered by community banks.

8826 ■ *"What's More Important: Stag or Inflation?"* in *Barron's (Vol. 88, July 14, 2008, No. 28, pp. M8)*
Pub: Dow Jones & Co., Inc.
Ed: Randall W. Forsyth. **Description:** Economists are divided on which part of stagflation, an economic situation in which inflation and economic stagnation occur simultaneously and remain unchecked for a period of time, is more important. Some economists say that the Federal government is focusing on controlling inflation while others see the central bank as extending its liquidity facilities to the financial sector.

8827 ■ *"When to Roll Over"* in *Black Enterprise (Vol. 37, November 2006, No. 4, pp. 50)*
Pub: Earl G. Graves Publishing Co. Inc.
Ed: Carolyn M. Brown. **Description:** Being proactive and rolling over your funds if you own stock of your former employee will give you more control over your money, especially if the company merges or is sold.

8828 ■ *"Where Are the Vultures?"* in *Mergers & Acquisitions: The Dealmaker's Journal (March 1, 2008)*
Pub: SourceMedia, Inc.
Ed: Ken MacFadyen. **Description:** Although the real estate market is distressed, not many acquisitions are being made by distress private equity investors; this is due, in part, to the difficulty in assessing real estate industry firms since it is a sector which is so localized.

8829 ■ *"Where the Money Is"* in *Conde Nast Portfolio (Vol. 2, June 2008, No. 6, pp. 113)*
Pub: Conde Nast Publications
Contact: David Carey, President
Description: Revenue generated from treatments for common brain disorders that are currently on the market are listed.

8830 ■ *"Where Oil-Rich Nations Are Placing Their Bets"* in *Harvard Business Review (Vol. 86, September 2008, No. 9, pp. 119)*
Pub: Harvard Business School Press
Ed: Rawi Abdelal; Ayesha Khan; Tarun Khanna. **Description:** Investment strategies of the Gulf Cooperation Council nations are examined in addition to how these have impacted the global economy and capitalism.

8831 ■ *"Where to Stash Your Cash"* in *Barron's (Vol. 88, March 17, 2008, No. 11, pp. 41)*
Pub: Dow Jones & Company, Inc.
Ed: Mike Hogan. **Description:** Investors are putting their money in money-market mutual funds seeking fractionally better yields and a safe haven from the uncertainties that was brought about by subprime lending. These funds, however, are hovering near 3.20 percent which is less than the 4 percent inflation rate.

8832 ■ *"Where To Look for Income"* in *Women In Business (Vol. 63, Summer 2011, No. 2, pp. 50)*
Pub: American Business Women's Association
Ed: William J. Lynott. **Description:** Advice on ways to invest in the US market are presented, with information on Certificates of Deposit and Money Markets included.

8833 ■ *"Whiplashed? That's a Bullish Sign"* in *Barron's (Vol. 88, March 31, 2008, No. 13, pp. 34)*
Pub: Dow Jones & Company, Inc.
Ed: Richard W. Arms. **Description:** Huge volatility often occurs just ahead of a substantial rally, according to an analysis of the volatility in the Dow Jones

Index since 2000. The Average Percentage Change based on a 10-day moving average of volatility is a way to measure the level of fear in the market and reveals when buying or selling have been overdone.

8834 ■ "Whistling Past the Graveyard?" in Barron's (Vol. 88, March 17, 2008, No. 11, pp. 15)
Pub: Dow Jones & Company, Inc.
Ed: Michael Santoli. **Description:** Discusses the Federal Reserve's move to provide $200 billion to the system which can be seen as an effort to avoid the liquidity problems that Bear Stearns suffered. The Federal Reserve's move seems to frighten investors rather than reassure them.

8835 ■ "Who Gets the Last Laugh?" in Barron's (Vol. 88, March 31, 2008, No. 13, pp. 17)
Pub: Dow Jones & Company, Inc.
Ed: Leslie P. Norton. **Description:** Nord/LB will take a charge of 82.5 million euros to cover potential losses apparently related to Vatas' refusal to take the shares of Remote MDx Inc. after buying the shares. Remote MDx's main product is an ankle bracelet to monitor criminals; the firm has lost over half of its market cap due to the Nord/LB troubles and questions about its revenues.

8836 ■ "Why Intel Should Dump Its Flash-Memory Business" in Barron's (Vol. 88, March 10, 2008, No. 10, pp. 35)
Pub: Dow Jones & Company, Inc.
Ed: Eric J. Savitz. **Description:** Intel Corp. must sell its NAND flash-memory business as soon as it possibly can to the highest bidder to focus on its PC processor business and take advantage of other business opportunities. Apple should consider a buyback of 10 percent of the company's shares to lift its stock.

8837 ■ "Why It Pays to be in the Boardroom" in Globe & Mail (January 16, 2006, pp. B1)
Pub: CTVglobemedia Publishing Inc.
Ed: Janet McFarland. **Description:** The reasons behind higher stock compensation for board directors, in Canada, are presented. The survey is conducted by Patrick O'Callaghan & Associates and Korn/Ferry International.

8838 ■ "Why the Rally Should Keep Rolling..for Now" in Barron's (Vol. 89, July 27, 2009, No. 30, pp. M3)
Pub: Dow Jones & Co., Inc.
Ed: Kopin Tan. **Description:** Stocks rallied for the second straight week as of July 24, 2009 and more companies reported better than expected earnings but the caveat is that companies are beating estimates chiefly by slashing expenses and firing workers. The regulatory risks faced by CME Group and the IntercontinentalExchange are discussed as well as the shares of KKR Private Equity Investors LP.

8839 ■ "Why the Rout in Financials Isn't Over" in Barron's (Vol. 88, June 30, 2008, No. 26, pp. 23)
Pub: Dow Jones & Co., Inc.
Ed: Robin Goldwyn Blumenthal. **Description:** Top market technician Louise Yamada warns that the retreat in the shares of financial services is not yet over based on her analysis of stock charts. Yamada's analysis of the charts of Citigroup, Fifth Third Bancorp and Merrill Lynch are discussed together with the graphs for these shares. Statistical data included.

8840 ■ "Why WestJet's Culture Guru Chooses to Fly Under the Radar" in Globe & Mail (January 22, 2007, pp. B1)
Pub: CTVglobemedia Publishing Inc.
Ed: Brent Jang. **Description:** The views of co-founder Donald Bell of WestJet Airlines Ltd. on company's shares and services are presented.

8841 ■ "Wielding a Big Ax" in Barron's (Vol. 89, July 13, 2009, No. 28, pp. 26)
Pub: Dow Jones & Co., Inc.
Ed: Shirley A. Lazo. **Description:** Weyerhaeuser cut their quarterly common payout by 80 percent from 25 cents to a nickel a share which they say will help them preserve their long-term value and improve their performance. Paccar also cut their quarterly dividend

by half to nine cents a share. Walgreen however, boosted their quarterly dividend by 22.2 percent to 13.75 cents a share.

8842 ■ "Will the Force Be With Salesforce?" in Barron's (Vol. 88, March 24, 2008, No. 12, pp. 20)
Pub: Dow Jones & Company, Inc.
Ed: Mark Veverka. **Description:** Shares of Salesforce.com are likely to drop from the $44.83-a-share level in the face of a deteriorating economy and financial sector and thus lower demand for business software. The company is unlikely to deliver on its ambitious earnings forecasts for 2008 especially with strengthening competition from Oracle.

8843 ■ "Wind Point Partners Closes Southfield HQ" in Crain's Detroit Business (Vol. 26, January 18, 2010, No. 3, pp. 18)
Pub: Crain Communications Inc.
Ed: Tom Henderson. **Description:** Wind Point Partners, a private-equity firm that expanded its headquarters to Southfield in 1997, has closed down its Michigan operations opting to move its headquarters back to Illinois.

8844 ■ "With Mine Approval, Crystallex's Value as Target Seen on Rise" in Globe & Mail (March 28, 2006, pp. B3)
Pub: CTVglobemedia Publishing Inc.
Ed: Wendy Stueck. **Description:** Crystallex International Corp. obtains Venezuelan Ministry of Basic Industry and Mining's authorization on Las Cristinas mining project. The impact of the approval, which posted rise in shares by 21 percent for the company, is discussed.

8845 ■ "Wobbling Economy" in The Business Journal-Serving Metropolitan Kansas City (Vol. 27, September 26, 2008, No. 2, pp. 1)
Pub: American City Business Journals, Inc.
Ed: Rob Roberts. **Description:** Real estate developers in Kansas City Metropolitan Area are worried of the possible impacts of the crisis at Wall Street. They expect tightening of the credit market, which will result in difficulty of financing their projects. The potential effects of the Wall Street crisis are examined further.

8846 ■ "Woes Portend Consumer Shift" in The Business Journal-Serving Metropolitan Kansas City (Vol. 27, September 26, 2008, No. 2, pp. 1)
Pub: American City Business Journals, Inc.
Ed: Suzanna Stagemeyer. **Description:** Black Bamboo owner Tim Butt believes that prolonged tightening of the credit market will result in consumer spending becoming more cash-driven that credit card driven. The financial crisis has already constricted spending among consumers. Forecasts for the US economy are provided.

8847 ■ "A World of Opportunity: Foreign Markets Offer Diversity to Keen Investors" in Canadian Business (Vol. 81, Summer 2008, No. 9)
Pub: Rogers Media Ltd.
Ed: Andrew Wahl. **Description:** International Monetary Fund projected in its 'World Economy Outlook' that there is a 25 percent chance that a global recession will occur in 2008 and 2009. Global growth rate is forecasted at 3.7 percent in 2008. Inflation in Asia emerging markets and forecasts on stock price indexes are presented.

8848 ■ "World's Best CEOs" in Barron's (Vol. 88, March 24, 2008, No. 12, pp. 33)
Pub: Dow Jones & Company, Inc.
Ed: Andrew Bary. **Description:** Listing of the 30 best chief executive officers worldwide which was compiled through interviews with investors and analysts, analysis of financial and stock market performance, and leadership and industry stature.

8849 ■ "The Worst Lies Ahead for Wall Street; More Losses Certain" in Crain's New York Business (Vol. 24, January 21, 2008, No. 3, pp. 1)
Pub: Crain Communications, Inc.
Ed: Aaron Elstein. **Description:** Due to the weakening economy, many financial institutions will face further massive losses forcing them to borrow more

at higher interest rates and dragging down their earnings for years to come. The effects on commercial real estate and credit card loans are also discussed as well as the trend to investing in Asia and the Middle East.

8850 ■ "Xstrata's Takeover Bid Comes Up Short in Shareholder's Eyes" in Globe & Mail (March 27, 2007, pp. B16)
Pub: CTVglobemedia Publishing Inc.
Ed: Andy Hoffman. **Description:** The share holders of LionOre Mining International have expressed dissatisfaction over $4.6 billion take over by Xstrata PLC. Share holders are demanding more prices for share value.

8851 ■ "Yahoo! - Microsoft Pact: Alive Again?" in Barron's (Vol. 89, July 27, 2009, No. 30, pp. 8)
Pub: Dow Jones & Co., Inc.
Ed: Mark Veverka. **Description:** Yahoo! reported higher than expected earnings in the second quarter of 2009 under CEO Carol Bartz who has yet to articulate her long-term vision and strategy for turning around the company. The media reported that Yahoo! and Microsoft are discussing an advertising-search partnership which should benefit both companies.

8852 ■ "YoCream" in Ice Cream Reporter (Vol. 23, September 20, 2010, No. 10, pp. 6)
Pub: Ice Cream Reporter
Description: YoCream reported a sales increase for third quarter 2010 at 15.6 percent and net income increasing 25 percent to $2,141,000 for that quarter.

8853 ■ "You Won't Go Broke Filling Up On These Stocks" in Barron's (Vol. 88, July 14, 2008, No. 28, pp. 38)
Pub: Dow Jones & Co., Inc.
Ed: Assif Shameen. **Description:** Due to high economic growth, pro-business policies and a consumption boom, the Middle East is a good place to look for equities. The best ways in which to gain exposure to this market include investing in the real estate industry and telecommunications markets as well as large banks that serve corporations and consumers.

8854 ■ "Young People Speak Out On Credit Union Board Involvement" in Credit Union Times (Vol. 21, July 14, 2010, No. 27, pp. 20)
Pub: Summit Business Media
Ed: Myriam Di Giovanni. **Description:** Results of a Credit Union Times survey of Generation Y individuals about serving on Credit Union boards across the country are examined.

8855 ■ "Your 2010 Windfall" in Small Business Opportunities (July 2010)
Pub: Harris Publications Inc.
Description: Make this a year of fiscal health and wealth. A survey says most will strive to save this year.

8856 ■ "Your Exposure to Bear Stearns" in Barron's (Vol. 88, March 17, 2008, No. 11, pp. 45)
Pub: Dow Jones & Company, Inc.
Ed: Tom Sullivan; Jack Willoughby. **Description:** Bear Stearns makes up 5.5 percent of Pioneer Independence's portfolio, 1.4 percent of Vanguard Windsor II's portfolio, 1.2 percent of Legg Mason Value Trust, about 1 percent of Van Kampen Equity & Income, and 0.79 percent of Putnam Fund for Growth & Income. Ginnie Mae securities are now trading at 1.78 percentage points over treasuries due to the mortgage crises.

8857 ■ Your Guide to Arranging Bank and Debt Financing for Your Own Business in Canada
Pub: Productive Publications
Ed: Iain Williamson. **Released:** December 31, 2000. **Description:** Bank financing for small businesses in Canada is discussed.

8858 ■ *"Zell Takes a Gamble on Tribune" in Globe & Mail (April 3, 2007, pp. B1)*
Pub: CTVglobemedia Publishing Inc.
Ed: Sinclair Stewart. **Description:** The purchase of the majority share in Tribune Co. by Samuel Zell is described. Samuel Zell's plans to keep the company's assets intact are discussed.

8859 ■ *"Zucker Closes Deal on HBC With Sweeter Takeover Offer" in Globe & Mail (January 27, 2006, pp. B1)*
Pub: CTVglobemedia Publishing Inc.
Ed: Marina Strauss; Sinclair Stewart; Jacquie McNish. **Description:** Jerry Zucker, vice-president of InterTech Group Inc., has finalized a deal to buy retail store Hudson Bay Co. for 1.1 billion dollars. The shares will be purchased at a rate of 15.25 dollars per share in an all cash transaction. Complete details of the buyout are discussed.

TRADE PERIODICALS

8860 ■ *Bacard's Global Investor*
Pub: Ferney Scribes Inc.
Ed: Andre Bacard, Editor. **Released:** Monthly. **Price:** $129, U.S.. **Description:** Provides monthly updates of select no-load global and international funds, model portfolios, foreign market graphs, monthly analysis and current recommendations. Recurring features include news of research and a column titled Mutual Fund in the Spotlight.

8861 ■ *Banking & Financial Services Policy Report: A Journal on Trends in Regulation and Supervision*
Pub: Aspen Publishers Inc.
Contact: Mark Dorman, President
URL(s): www.aspenpublishers.com/Product. asp?catalog_name=Aspen&category_name =&product_id=SS0730689X. **Released:** 12/yr. **Price:** $790, Individuals with free standard shipping on U.S prepaid orders.

8862 ■ *Deposit Growth Strategies*
Pub: Siefer Consultants Inc.
Ed: Joe Sheller, Editor. **Released:** Monthly. **Price:** $329, U.S.; $259 charter rate. **Description:** Cover methods to increase deposits at financial institutions, as well as marketing strategies for deposit growth. Both personal accounts and commercial accounts are covered.

8863 ■ *Fidelity Investor*
Pub: FundWorks, Inc.
Contact: Karen Frost
Ed: James H. Lowell, III, Editor. **Released:** Monthly. **Price:** $199. **Description:** Contains investment advice covering Fidelity mutual funds. Recurring features include interviews, model portfolios, performance reviews, and best buys.

8864 ■ *Financial and Estate Planning*
Pub: CCH Inc.
Contact: Mike Sabbatis, President
URL(s): tax.cchgroup.com/FEP/default. **Ed:** Sidney Kess. **Released:** Monthly **Price:** $1479, Individuals CD-ROM; $1465, Individuals print.

8865 ■ *Financial Services Review: The Journal of Individual Financial Management*
Pub: Cadmus Journal Services
URL(s): www.drsm.org/FSR_journal/Financial_Services_Review_home.htm. **Ed:** Stuart Michelson. **Released:** Quarterly

8866 ■ *Global Custodian*
Pub: Asset International Inc.
URL(s): home.globalcustodian.com. **Ed:** Giles Turner. **Released:** 5/yr. **Price:** €405, Individuals online only; €515, Individuals print and online; €360, Individuals print only.

8867 ■ *International Tax and Public Finance*
Pub: Springer Netherlands
Contact: Zachary Rolnik, Managing Director
E-mail: zrolnik@wkap.com
URL(s): www.springerlink.com/content/102915/. **Ed:** Ruud A. De Mooij. **Released:** Bimonthly **Price:** €1111, Institutions print or online; €1333, Institutions print & enchanced access.

8868 ■ *Journal of Financial Planning*
Pub: Financial Planning Association
Ed: Marv Tuttle, Editor, marv.tuttle@fpanet.org. **Released:** 12/year. **Price:** Included in membership; $119, nonmembers; $144, Canada; $154, elsewhere. **Description:** Provides coverage of industry events and developments as well as happenings within the association. Carries articles on regulatory, ethical, and public relations aspects of the industry. Recurring features include letters to the editor, news of members, a calendar of events, feature articles, and original contributions.

8869 ■ *Journal of IT Financial Management*
Pub: I.T. Financial Management Association
Contact: Terence Quinlan, Director
URL(s): www.isfma.com/index.cfm. **Released:** Triennial

8870 ■ *NACOMEX Insider*
Pub: NACOMEX USA Inc.
Ed: Robert Zises, Editor, zises@nacomex.com. **Released:** Quarterly. **Price:** $199, U.S.. **Description:** Provides information on historical values, current tactics, and residual value forecasting for ad valorem tax, bankruptcy, loss compensation, and related purposes. Recurring features include news of research and a column titled Industry Round-up.

8871 ■ *National Financing Law Digest*
Pub: Strafford Publications Inc.
Contact: Richard M. Ossoff, President
E-mail: richardossoff@straffordpub.com
Ed: Jennifer Vaughan, Editor. **Released:** Monthly. **Price:** $687. **Description:** Digest offers complete coverage of workouts, bankruptcy, lender's liability, and the growing number of court decisions releated to the changing economic climate. Reports on state and federal cases of national significance.

8872 ■ *The Neatest Little FundLetter*
Pub: Jason Kelly
Ed: Jason Kelly, Editor. **Released:** Monthly. **Price:** $75, U.S.; $100, elsewhere. **Description:** Aims to help readers use the various tools to create and manage their own mutual fund portfolio better than professional managers. Also includes how-to articles and model portfolios. Columns titled Kelly's Quicklist, FundFolio, and FundFilter.

8873 ■ *Plan Sponsor: Insight on Plan Design & Investment Strategy*
Pub: Asset International Inc.
URL(s): www.plansponsor.com. **Released:** Monthly **Price:** $229, Individuals; $259, Canada; $390, Other countries; Free to members.

8874 ■ *Quarterly Journal of Finance and Accounting*
Pub: University of Nebraska
URL(s): www.qjbe.unl.edu. **Ed:** Gordon V. Karels. **Released:** Quarterly **Price:** $35, Individuals; $55, Institutions; $47, Other countries; $65, Institutions, other countries.

VIDEOCASSETTES/ AUDIOCASSETTES

8875 ■ *Ask for the Order. . .and Get It!*
Dartnell Corp.
2222 Sedwick Dr.
Durham, NC 34112
Ph: (239)417-2079
Free: 800-223-8720
Fax: (800)508-2592
Co. E-mail: customerservice@dartnellcorp.com
URL: http://www.dartnellcorp.com
Contact: Kenneth F. Kahn, Publisher
Released: 1972. **Description:** Hammers home a key principle of salesmanship—to get an order you must ask for it; from the "Tough-Minded Salesmanship" series. **Availability:** VHS; 3/4 U; Special order formats.

8876 ■ *Basics of Successful Investing*
Tapeworm Video Distributors
25876 The Old Road #141
Stevenson Ranch, CA 91381
Ph: (661)257-4904

Fax: (661)257-4820
Co. E-mail: sales@tapeworm.com
URL: http://www.tapeworm.com
Released: 19??. **Price:** $29.95. **Description:** Guides viewers through the basics of money management and financial planning. **Availability:** VHS.

8877 ■ *The Charles J. Givens Financial Library*
Nightingale-Conant Corp.
6245 W. Howard St.
Niles, IL 60714
Ph: (847)647-0300
Free: 800-560-6081
URL: http://www.nightingale.com
Released: 1990. **Price:** $399.00. **Description:** Givens shares advice on practical ways to manage money and build wealth. Comes with six 90-minute audio cassettes and a reference manual. **Availability:** VHS.

8878 ■ *The Cold Call*
Video Arts, Inc.
c/o Aim Learning Group
8238-40 Lehigh
Morton Grove, IL 60053-2615
Free: 877-444-2230
Fax: (416)252-2155
Co. E-mail: service@aimlearninggroup.com
URL: http://www.aimlearninggroup.com
Released: 1976. **Price:** $695.00. **Description:** This program demonstrates the specific skills and disciplines of telephone selling, and the dangers of ignoring them. **Availability:** VHS; 8 mm; 3/4 U; Special order formats.

8879 ■ *The Competitive Edge*
Film Library/National Safety Council California Chapter
4553 Glencoe Ave., Ste. 150
Marina Del Rey, CA 90292
Ph: (310)827-9781
Free: 800-421-9585
Fax: (310)827-9861
Co. E-mail: California@nsc.org
URL: http://www.nsc.org/nsc_near_you/FindYourLocalChapter/Pages/California.aspx
Released: 1989. **Description:** This program emphasizes finding out your customer's most immediate concern, and selling to that concern. **Availability:** VHS; 3/4 U.

8880 ■ *Corporate Financial Management: Emerging Trends and Recent Developments*
Bisk Education
9417 Princess Palm Ave.
Tampa, FL 33619
Free: 800-874-7877
Co. E-mail: info@bisk.com
URL: http://www.bisk.com
Released: 19??. **Price:** $179.00. **Description:** Discusses financial management techniques and recent developments in corporate finance. Furnishes information on Activity-Based Cost Management (ABC), Total Quality Management (TQM), and Internal Controls and Management Accounting. Includes workbook and quizzer. **Availability:** VHS.

8881 ■ *Financial Management Workshops*
Bullfrog Films, Inc.
PO Box 149
Oley, PA 19547
Ph: (610)779-8226
Free: 800-543-3764
Fax: (610)370-1978
Co. E-mail: video@bullfrogfilms.com
URL: http://bullfrogfilms.com
Released: 1985. **Description:** This complete personal financial instructional program is available on separate tapes or as a package. **Availability:** VHS; 3/4 U.

8882 ■ *Financial Planning and Management*
RMI Media
1365 N. Winchester St.
Olathe, KS 66061-5880
Ph: (913)768-1696
Free: 800-745-5480

Fax: (800)755-6910
Co. E-mail: actmedia@act.org
URL: http://www.actmedia.com
Released: 1978. **Description:** A series of programs which offer ideas on cost cutting and controlling the family budget. Programs are available individually. **Availability:** VHS; 3/4 U.

8883 ■ Good Money Management
Cambridge Educational
c/o Films Media Group
132 West 31st Street, 17th Floor
Ste. 124
New York, NY 10001
Free: 800-257-5126
Fax: (609)671-0266
Co. E-mail: custserve@films.com
URL: http://www.cambridgeol.com
Released: 1986. **Description:** This tape demonstrates how to personally manage and properly distribute your income. **Availability:** VHS.

8884 ■ A Happy Beginning
Resources for Education & Management, Inc.
1804 Montreal Ct., Ste. A
Tucker, GA 30084
Released: 1971. **Description:** An examination of closing the sale, asking for the order, and answering the customer's objections. How to become a confident sale closer. **Availability:** VHS; 3/4 U.

8885 ■ How to Close the Sale
Dartnell Corp.
2222 Sedwick Dr.
Durham, NC 34112
Ph: (239)417-2079
Free: 800-223-8720
Fax: (800)508-2592
Co. E-mail: customerservice@dartnellcorp.com
URL: http://www.dartnellcorp.com
Contact: Kenneth F. Kahn, Publisher
Released: 1981. **Description:** This program shows salespeople how to ask for the order, and how to get it. **Availability:** VHS; 3/4 U; Special order formats.

8886 ■ How to Take the Butt Out of a Sales Rebuttal
Dartnell Corp.
2222 Sedwick Dr.
Durham, NC 34112
Ph: (239)417-2079
Free: 800-223-8720
Fax: (800)508-2592
Co. E-mail: customerservice@dartnellcorp.com
URL: http://www.dartnellcorp.com
Contact: Kenneth F. Kahn, Publisher
Released: 1967. **Description:** A look at how to cope with the difficult problem of rebutting a customer's objection-without being objectionable. **Availability:** VHS; 3/4 U; Special order formats.

8887 ■ Investing for Women by Women
Tapeworm Video Distributors
25876 The Old Road #141
Stevenson Ranch, CA 91381
Ph: (661)257-4904
Fax: (661)257-4820
Co. E-mail: sales@tapeworm.com
URL: http://www.tapeworm.com
Released: 1996. **Price:** $34.95. **Description:** Discusses stock market investing and retirement planning options for women. **Availability:** VHS.

8888 ■ Knowing the Prospect
Resources for Education & Management, Inc.
1804 Montreal Ct., Ste. A
Tucker, GA 30084
Released: 1971. **Description:** Shows the relationship of product or service benefits to the sales prospect's personal goals, and illustrates the value of knowing a prospect's needs. Ignores the fast-talking sales pitch. **Availability:** VHS; 3/4 U.

8889 ■ Making It Live
Resources for Education & Management, Inc.
1804 Montreal Ct., Ste. A
Tucker, GA 30084
Released: 1971. **Description:** This tape demonstrates a key to sales success-knowing your product or service and telling your story with enthusiasm and conviction. **Availability:** VHS; 3/4 U.

8890 ■ Managing Your Personal Finances
RMI Media
1365 N. Winchester St.
Olathe, KS 66061-5880
Ph: (913)768-1696
Free: 800-745-5480
Fax: (800)755-6910
Co. E-mail: actmedia@act.org
URL: http://www.actmedia.com
Released: 1989. **Price:** $89.00. **Description:** The ability to handle personal expenses and finance accounts is a must for any adult in today's society. **Availability:** VHS; 3/4 U.

8891 ■ More Awkward Customers
Video Arts, Inc.
c/o Aim Learning Group
8238-40 Lehigh
Morton Grove, IL 60053-2615
Free: 877-444-2230
Fax: (416)252-2155
Co. E-mail: service@aimlearninggroup.com
URL: http://www.aimlearninggroup.com
Released: 1973. **Description:** This program shows the importance of knowing your stock and services so that you can deal professionally with awkward customers. **Availability:** 3/4 U.

8892 ■ Networking for Your Personal & Financial Growth
Chesney Communications
2302 Martin St., Ste. 125
Irvine, CA 92612
Ph: (949)263-5500
Free: 800-223-8878
Fax: (949)263-5506
Co. E-mail: videocc@aol.com
URL: http://www.videocc.com
Released: 1989. **Price:** $49.95. **Description:** Anne Boe talks about the importance of networking to financial success, and points out that 80 percent of all millionaires are networkers. **Availability:** VHS; 3/4 U.

8893 ■ Overcoming Objections
Film Library/National Safety Council California Chapter
4553 Glencoe Ave., Ste. 150
Marina Del Rey, CA 90292
Ph: (310)827-9781
Free: 800-421-9585
Fax: (310)827-9861
Co. E-mail: California@nsc.org
URL: http://www.nsc.org/nsc_near_you/FindYourLocalChapter/Pages/California.aspx
Released: 1987. **Description:** This film emphasizes the importance of understanding the customer's point of view. **Availability:** VHS; 3/4 U.

8894 ■ Prescription for Complaints
Video Arts, Inc.
c/o Aim Learning Group
8238-40 Lehigh
Morton Grove, IL 60053-2615
Free: 877-444-2230
Fax: (416)252-2155
Co. E-mail: service@aimlearninggroup.com
URL: http://www.aimlearninggroup.com
Released: 1975. **Price:** $695.00. **Description:** This program shows a six-step, objective method for dealing with customer complaints. **Availability:** VHS; 8 mm; 3/4 U; Special order formats.

8895 ■ Presenting the Story
Resources for Education & Management, Inc.
1804 Montreal Ct., Ste. A
Tucker, GA 30084
Released: 1971. **Description:** How a salesman can best communicate benefits to a customer. Emphasis is on preparation of the story and practice. **Availability:** VHS; 3/4 U.

8896 ■ The Road to Wise Money Management: Planning, Credit, and Your First Paycheck
Cambridge Educational
c/o Films Media Group
132 West 31st Street, 17th Floor
Ste. 124
New York, NY 10001
Free: 800-257-5126
Fax: (609)671-0266
Co. E-mail: custserve@films.com
URL: http://www.cambridgeol.com
Released: 1989. **Price:** $79.00. **Description:** A comprehensive guide to managing personal finances, including checkbook maintenance, credit, savings, short- and long-term goals, and details of a paycheck. Includes a study guide. **Availability:** VHS.

8897 ■ Self-Motivation in Selling
Learning Communications L.L.C.
5520 Trabuco Rd.
Irvine, CA 92620-5705
Free: 800-622-3610
Fax: (949)727-4323
Co. E-mail: sales@learncom.com
URL: http://www.learncom.com
Contact: Lloyd W. Singer, President
Released: 1979. **Description:** A look at how to avoid sales slumps and maintain peak performances. Four untitled programs cover frustrations and turndowns, seeking feedback, how to keep personal problems from affecting performance, and how sales managers can keep their people motivated. **Availability:** VHS; 3/4 U.

8898 ■ So You Want to Be a Success at Selling?
Video Arts, Inc.
c/o Aim Learning Group
8238-40 Lehigh
Morton Grove, IL 60053-2615
Free: 877-444-2230
Fax: (416)252-2155
Co. E-mail: service@aimlearninggroup.com
URL: http://www.aimlearninggroup.com
Released: 1982. **Price:** $790.00. **Description:** Four videos that describe the fundamental skills of selling, from the initial research to the close. Part 1 focuses on the preparation, including client research and product knowledge. Part 2 looks at the skills and techniques of sales presentation. Part 3 shows how to deal with problem clients. Part 4 demonstrates the tactics for successfully closing a sale. Also available as a complete seminar kit. **Availability:** VHS; 8 mm; 3/4 U; Special order formats.

8899 ■ U.S. News & World Report: Building Your Fortune
Anchor Bay Entertainment
1699 Stutz Dr.
Troy, MI 48084
Ph: (248)816-0909
Free: 800-786-8777
Fax: (248)816-3335
Released: 1990. **Price:** $14.95. **Description:** Guidance and information on securing your future via financial planning and tax strategies. **Availability:** VHS.

8900 ■ When You're Turned Down—Turn On!
Dartnell Corp.
2222 Sedwick Dr.
Durham, NC 34112
Ph: (239)417-2079
Free: 800-223-8720

Fax: (800)508-2592
Co. E-mail: customerservice@dartnellcorp.com
URL: http://www.dartnellcorp.com
Contact: Kenneth F. Kahn, Publisher
Released: 1977. **Description:** Examines the question: When is a turndown a true rejection and when is it just a disguised objection?; from the "Tough—Minded Salesmanship" series. **Availability:** VHS; 3/4 U; Special order formats.

TRADE SHOWS AND CONVENTIONS

8901 ■ ABA/BMA National Conference for Community Bankers
American Bankers Association (ABA)
1120 Connecticut Ave. NW
Washington, DC 20036
Ph: (202)663-5564
Free: 800-226-5377
Fax: (202)663-7543
Co. E-mail: custserv@aba.com
URL: http://www.aba.com
Contact: Edward L. Yingling, President

Frequency: Annual. **Audience:** Chairmen and presidents, mainly of banks with less than $500 million in assets, community bank CEOs, bank directors, and other community bank executives. **Principal Exhibits:** Products and services related to investment management, customer service improvements, advertising, asset/liability management, bank management, electronic data interchange, employee recruitment/training, insurance, strategic planning models, including preparation for the 21st century, new revenue sources, cost control techniques, mainframe computers, market research, MCIF technology, minicomputers in community banking applications, software: platform, optical disk, and loan pricing, sweep accounts, and relationship banking for community bankers.

8902 ■ BMA Annual Marketing Forum
American Bankers Association (ABA)
1120 Connecticut Ave. NW
Washington, DC 20036
Ph: (202)663-5564
Free: 800-226-5377
Fax: (202)663-7543
Co. E-mail: custserv@aba.com
URL: http://www.aba.com
Contact: Edward L. Yingling, President

Frequency: Annual. **Audience:** Bankers including community bank CEOs, marketing directors, sales managers, advertising directors, public relations managers. **Principal Exhibits:** Financial services marketing offering banking solutions in advertising services, bank equipment/systems, computer software, database marketing, direct marketing/sales, incentive/premium programs, insurance services, investment services, marketing consulting, merchandising, publishing, research, retail delivery, sales training, service quality, signage, and telemarketing.

8903 ■ BMA Private Wealth Sales Management Workshop, an ABA Program
American Bankers Association (ABA)
1120 Connecticut Ave. NW
Washington, DC 20036
Ph: (202)663-5564
Free: 800-226-5377
Fax: (202)663-7543
Co. E-mail: custserv@aba.com
URL: http://www.aba.com
Contact: Edward L. Yingling, President

Frequency: Annual. **Audience:** Trust, private banking and asset management officers, bank brokerage managers, sales managers, business development managers, and regional department managers. **Principal Exhibits:** Provides marketing education and information, professional growth and networking resources to marketing professionals in the financial services industry.

8904 ■ The Bond Market Association - Fixed Income Summit Expo on E-Commerce & Technology
Flagg Management, Inc.
353 Lexington Ave.
New York, NY 10016
Ph: (212)286-0333
Fax: (212)286-0086
Co. E-mail: flaggmgmt@msn.com
URL: http://www.flaggmgmt.com
URL(s): www.sifma.org. **Frequency:** Annual. **Audience:** Bond Market Association members, government bond officers, fixed income brokers and dealers. **Principal Exhibits:** Online services, Internet systems, fixed-income trading and executions systems, real-time systems, Internet and other new products and solutions; online trading and execution systems; bond market services; online research and global markets information. **Telecommunication Services:** sweiss@bondmarkets.com.

8905 ■ Financial Managers Society Annual Conference
Financial Managers Society (FMS)
100 W Monroe St., Ste. 1700
Chicago, IL 60603-1907
Ph: (312)578-1300
Free: 800-275-4367
Fax: (312)578-1308
Co. E-mail: info@fmsinc.org
URL: http://www.fmsinc.org
Contact: Dick Yingst, President
E-mail: dyingst@fmsinc.org

URL(s): www.fmsinc.org. **Price:** $849, Pre-registered, members; $1049, Pre-registered, non-members. **Frequency:** Annual. **Audience:** CEOs, CFOs, treasurers, controllers, investment officers, internal auditors of banks, thrift and credit unions. **Principal Exhibits:** Companies offering products/services to CEOs, CFOs, treasurers, controllers, investment officers, and internal auditors of banks, thrifts, and credit unions. **Telecommunication Services:** info@fmsinc.org.

8906 ■ Futures and Options Expo
Futures Industry Association (FIA)
2001 Pennsylvania Ave. NW, Ste. 600
Washington, DC 20006
Ph: (202)466-5460
Fax: (202)296-3184
Co. E-mail: info@futuresindustry.org
URL: http://www.futuresindustry.org
Contact: Michael C. Dawley, Chairman

URL(s): www.futuresindustry.org. **Price:** $800, Members full, early bird; $950, Non-members full, early bird. **Frequency:** Annual. **Audience:** Futures commission merchants, futures exchanges, clearing houses, brokers, commodity trading advisors, banks, and money managers. **Principal Exhibits:** Equipment, supplies, and services for the futures, options and derivatives industries. **Dates and Locations:** , Hyatt Regency. **Telecommunication Services:** tvitale-chan@futuresindustry.org.

8907 ■ National Agricultural Bankers Conference
American Bankers Association (ABA)
1120 Connecticut Ave. NW
Washington, DC 20036
Ph: (202)663-5564
Free: 800-226-5377
Fax: (202)663-7543
Co. E-mail: custserv@aba.com
URL: http://www.aba.com
Contact: Edward L. Yingling, President

URL(s): www.aba.com. **Price:** $830, Pre-registered, members; $900, Pre-registered, members; $830, Pre-registered, members; $900, Pre-registered, members. **Frequency:** Annual. **Audience:** Bank CEOs, mainly from community banks in rural areas, executive vice presidents, senior vice presidents, economists, analysts. **Principal Exhibits:** The latest developments in the agricultural lending business, as well as strategies for better market share, profitability and customer service. **Telecommunication Services:** jblanchf@aba.com.

CONSULTANTS

8908 ■ Bedford Associates Inc.
211 Greenwood Ave., 2-2
Bethel, CT 06801
Ph: (203)846-0230
Fax: (203)846-1487
Co. E-mail: nick.kroot@bedford.com
URL: http://www.bedford.com
Contact: Jose Badia, Principal
E-mail: jose.badia@bedford.com
Scope: Offers expertise in the areas of computer information systems design and management. Services include airline systems consulting; transaction processing facility (TPF) and airline control system (ALCS) services; system development and maintenance; step by step (SST) and C-view sales, support and maintenance; supplemental staffing (either on site or remotely); web development services. **Founded:** 1980. **Publications:** *Advanced Telecommunications Abuse Control System (ATACS)*.

8909 ■ Alan Biller and Associates—Alan D. Biller & Associates Inc.
535 Middlefield Rd., Ste. 230
Menlo Park, CA 94025
Ph: (650)328-7283
Fax: (650)323-4417
Co. E-mail: support@adbiller.com
URL: http://www.adbiller.com
Contact: Dr. Alan D. Biller, President
E-mail: adbiller@adbiller.com
URL(s): www.alanbiller.com. **Scope:** Offers services from investment advising to pension planning, especially Taft Hartley Planning. Serves as expert witness in cases related to Investments and Fiduciary Standards. **Founded:** 1982. **Publications:** "Fourteen Things to Expect From Your Investment Consultant"; "First Principles of Performance Evaluation"; "Organization and Structure of a Fund"; "Hedge Fund Hoopla: As Taft-Hartley Funds Get Interested, What Should Trustees Ask?"; "Does Private Equity Have a Role in Your Portfolio?"; "Soft-Dollars Harm to Pension Funds, Markets"; "Baubles, Bangles and Bright Shiny Things"; "Equity Style Benchmarks for Fund Analysis"; "A Plan Sponsor's Guide to Commissions".

8910 ■ Samuel E. Bodily Associates
Office:172, 100 Darden Blvd.
Charlottesville, VA 22903
Ph: (434)924-4813
Fax: (434)243-7677
Contact: Samuel E. Bodily, Principal
E-mail: bodilys@virginia.edu
Scope: Consultant specializes in financial analysis, capital investment, business/product/market planners, financial risk analysis and decision sciences. **Founded:** 1977. **Publications:** "I Can't Get No Satisfaction: How Bundling and Multi-Part Pricing Can Satisfy Consumers and Suppliers," Feb, 2006; "Organizational Use of Decision Analysis," Oct, 2004; "Real Options," Oct, 2004.

8911 ■ Everett & Co.
3126 S Franklin St.
Englewood, CO 80113
Ph: (303)761-7999
Fax: (303)781-8296
Contact: Robert W. Everett, Manager
Scope: Provides strategic real estate solutions and project management. **Founded:** 1993.

8912 ■ Financial Computer Support Inc.
14 Commerce Dr.
Oakland, MD 21550-3940
Ph: (301)334-1800
Fax: (301)334-1896
Co. E-mail: sales@fcsi.com
URL: http://www.fcsi.com
Contact: David Huxford, Jr., President
Scope: Independent user group which provides computer and administrative support for financial planners, money managers, and insurance agents. Serves finance and insurance industries. **Founded:** 1981. **Publications:** "Check Out Carmen Petote," Jul, 2006; "Control the Information Flow with Rep Level Access," Feb, 2005.

8913 ■ M. S. Franks & Company Inc.
11 La Cuesta Rd.
Orinda, CA 94563
Ph: (925)254-1469
Co. E-mail: msf@msfranksco.com
URL: http://www.msfranksco.com
Contact: Richard F. Kijewski, Manager
Scope: Offers services in cash management, check processing, general ledger, financial reporting, loan processing, international, branch operations and merger integrations. Specializes in operations design to financial service companies with a focus on impact analysis, user requirements, work flow analysis and design, project communications, development of training programs and material, project management. **Founded:** 1990. **Seminars:** Facilitating Great Meetings; Creating Great Project Documentation; Producing Great Meeting Notes.

8914 ■ Arnold S. Goldin & Associates Inc.
5030 Champion Blvd., Ste. G-6231
Boca Raton, FL 33496
Ph: (561)994-5810
Fax: (561)994-5860
Co. E-mail: arnold@goldin.com
URL: http://www.goldin.com
Contact: Arnold S. Goldin, Principal
E-mail: arnold@goldin.com
Scope: An accounting and management consulting firm. Serves clients worldwide. Provides management services. Handles monthly write-ups and tax returns. **Founded:** 1978.

8915 ■ InfoSource Management Services Inc.
PO Box 590
Sicamous, BC, Canada V0E 2V0
Ph: (250)804-6113
Fax: (250)836-3667
Contact: Sherry Leggett, President
Scope: Firm provides customized financial reports that highlight the areas where change will improve the bottom line. **Founded:** 1995.

8916 ■ Integrated Business Information Systems Ltd.
22 Colonial Pl.
New Haven, CT 06515
Ph: (203)397-1523
Fax: (203)397-1523
Contact: Dr. Michael L. Schneider, President
E-mail: mischni@idt.net
Scope: Provider of financial and marketing software applications, design and development for PC LAN, Wang VS and IBM AS or 400 computers. Offers sales and support for several software products from other vendors, including Tele-magic, Real world, Lotus Notes and Power Builder. Industries served: Finance, marketing, investment, airlines, insurance and reinsurance worldwide. **Founded:** 1994. **Publications:** "Future Scope".

8917 ■ Nikmal Financial Services
23 Victoria Heights Rd.
Hyde Park, MA 02136
Ph: (617)361-2101
Fax: (617)249-2093
Contact: Selma H. Lamkin, President
E-mail: selma@nikmal.com
Scope: Services provided include seminars and workshops on personal finance, small business management, economic awareness courses; preparation of personal and business tax returns; training of financial personnel; and financial management services including accounting and auditing, tax reports, record-keeping, and all payroll taxes. Serves private industries as well as government agencies. **Founded:** 1984. **Publications:** "What is Wrong with Our Legal System and How to Fix It," American Training Institute, 2002. **Seminars:** Preparing Your Business Plan; Financial Planning for the Not-So-Wealthy.

8918 ■ Olson Research Associates Inc. (ORA)
10290 Old Columbia Rd.
Columbia, MD 21046-2379
Free: 888-657-6680
Fax: (410)290-6726
Co. E-mail: info@olsonresearch.com
URL: http://www.olsonresearch.com
Contact: Brad Olson, President
URL(s): blogs.olsonresearch.com. **Scope:** A firm of consultants, educators and publishers providing consulting services, simulation models, financial risk management reporting, educational programs and books for financial institutions. **Founded:** 1970. **Publications:** "Risk Management Digest"; "Strategic Financial Management," Ivy Press Inc; "The Double Whammy," Oct, 2000. **Seminars:** Policy Development Workshops; Seminars for Bank Directors; Financial Risk Management and Interest Rate Risk; Getting the Maximum Benefit From A/L Benchmarks; Revising Your ALCO Policies.

8919 ■ Rose & Crangle Ltd.
117 N 4th St.
Lincoln, KS 67455
Ph: (785)524-5050
Fax: (785)524-3130
Co. E-mail: rcltd@nckcn.com
URL: http://www.roseandcrangle.com
Contact: Robert D. Crangle, President
E-mail: rcltd@nckcn.com
Scope: Provider of evaluation, planning and policy analyzes for universities, associations, foundations, governmental agencies and private companies engaged in scientific, technological or educational activities. Special expertise in the development of new institutions. Special skills in providing planning and related group facilitation workshops. **Founded:** 1984. **Publications:** "Preface to Bulgarian Integration Into Europe and NATO: Issues of Science Policy And research Evaluation Practice," Ios Press, 2006; "Allocating Limited National Resources for Fundamental Research," 2005.

8920 ■ SS & C Technologies
33 W Monroe, Ste. 420
Chicago, IL 60603-2401
Ph: (312)443-7501
Free: 800-234-0556
Fax: (312)443-7509
Co. E-mail: solution@sscinc.com
URL: http://www.ssctech.com
Contact: Normand A. Boulanger, President
Scope: Software development, consulting service, and turnkey systems provides servicing the investment/private wealth management, the financial/accounting services, and other markets requiring technical systems integration solutions. **Founded:** 1986. **Special Services:** Sun Solaris/MS NT Server Platforms. Software partners with Lotus Notes; Microsoft; Sybase; Ardent (Universe); and others.

8921 ■ Thornton Financial FNIC
1024 Centre Ave., Bldg. E
Fort Collins, CO 80526-1849
Ph: (970)221-2089
Fax: (970)484-5206
Contact: Jo-Ellen M. Thornton, Owner
Scope: Offers personal financial planning and small business planning which focuses on written plans, capitalization, strategic planning, and marketing. Also offers career and life planning. **Founded:** 1981. **Seminars:** Capitalizing the Small Business; Financial Independence at Any Income Level; Small Business Management.

8922 ■ Weich & Bilotti Inc.
600 Worcester Rd., 4th Fl.
Framingham, MA 01702
Ph: (508)663-1600
Fax: (508)663-1682
Co. E-mail: info@weich-bilotti.com
Contact: Mervyn D. Weich, Director
E-mail: mweich@weich-bilotti.com
Scope: Specializes in business plans, venture capital, computer information systems, turnaround/interim management, retail consulting, start-up process, college recruiting and IS and IT personnel. **Founded:** 1995.

FRANCHISES AND BUSINESS OPPORTUNITIES

8923 ■ The Comprehensive Financial Planning System
T&M Financial, Inc.
3706 SW Topeka Blvd., Ste. 400
Topeka, KS 66609
Ph: (785)266-8333
Fax: (785)266-7819
Description: Client-based financial planning. **No. of Franchise Units:** 5. **No. of Company-Owned Units:** 1. **Founded:** 1962.. **Franchised:** 2004. **Equity Capital Needed:** $11,400. **Financial Assistance:** Yes. **Training:** Yes.

8924 ■ 4Pillars Consulting Group Inc.
Franchise Development
2300-2850 Shaughnessy St.
Port Coquitlam, BC, Canada V3C 6K5
Ph: (250)384-7112
Free: 866-600-2364
Fax: (866)591-2941
Co. E-mail: franchise@4pillars.ca
URL: http://www.4pillars.ca
Description: Independent debt restructuring firm providing Financial Restructuring Solutions to individuals and families who suffer from debt and cash flow difficulties. The 4 Pillars system allows our consultants to successfully help thousands of Canadians avoid bankruptcy and eliminate debt. **No. of Franchise Units:** 42. **No. of Company-Owned Units:** 1. **Founded:** 2002.. **Franchised:** 2002. **Equity Capital Needed:** $74,000. **Franchise Fee:** $39,500. **Financial Assistance:** Financing up to $15,000 available for franchise fee. **Training:** Provides 2 weeks training and ongoing support.

8925 ■ The Interface Financial Group
2182 DuPont Dr., Ste. 221
Irvine, CA 92612-1320
Ph: (905)475-5701
Free: 800-387-0860
Fax: (866)475-8688
Co. E-mail: dtbanf@interfacefinancial.biz
URL: http://www.interfacefinancial.com
Description: Franchise buys quality accounts receivables from client companies at a discount to provide short-term working capital to expanding businesses. **No. of Franchise Units:** 192. **Founded:** 1971.. **Franchised:** 1991. **Equity Capital Needed:** $100,000. cash investment; $88,300-$139,300 total investment. **Franchise Fee:** $39,000. **Royalty Fee:** 8%. **Training:** Yes.

8926 ■ Weigh House Investors Services
4141 Yonge St., Ste. 304
Toronto, ON, Canada M2P 2A8
Ph: (416)640-0550
Free: 866-918-0550
Fax: (416)640-0552
Co. E-mail: info@weighhouse.com
URL: http://www.secondopinions.ca
Description: Second Opinion offices offer financial consulting services to retail and corporate clients. We remain completely independent and unbiased and do not sell products of any kind. Our only fee is an hourly fee paid directly by our clients which gives us a major competitive advantage. Our main services include: PerformanceCHECKa, PortfolioCHECKa, and Manager SEARCH. **No. of Franchise Units:** 2. **No. of Company-Owned Units:** 1. **Founded:** 2004.. **Franchised:** 2007. **Equity Capital Needed:** $50.00. **Franchise Fee:** $30,000. **Training:** Yes.

COMPUTERIZED DATABASES

8927 ■ ABA Banking Journal
345 Hudson St., 12th Fl.
New York, NY 10014
Ph: (212)620-7200
Free: 800-895-4389
URL: http://www.simmonsboardman.com
Contact: Arthur J. McGinnis, Jr., President
E-mail: amcginnis@sbpub.com
Availability: Online: LexisNexis Group; Simmons-Boardman Publishing Corp.; Intuit Inc. - Intuit Financial Services. **Type:** Full-text.

8928 ■ ABI/INFORM®
789 E Eisenhower Pkwy.
Ann Arbor, MI 48106-1346
Ph: (734)761-4700
Free: 800-521-0600
Co. E-mail: info@il.proquest.com
URL: http://www.il.proquest.com
Contact: Matt Dunie, President
Availability: Online: ProQuest Co.; ProQuest LLC-Dialog; ProQuest LLC - Dialog; LexisNexis Group; STN International; Wolters Kluwer Health - Ovid.
Type: Full-text; Bibliographic; Image.

8929 ■ American Banker Financial Publications
1 State St. Plz., 27th Fl.
New York, NY 10004
Ph: (212)803-8200
Free: 800-221-1809
Fax: (212)843-9600
Co. E-mail: custserv@AmericanBanker.com
URL: http://www.americanbanker.com
Availability: Online: ProQuest LLC - Dialog. **Type:** Full-text.

8930 ■ Banking Information Source™
789 E Eisenhower Pkwy.
Ann Arbor, MI 48106-1346
Ph: (734)761-4700
Free: 800-521-0600
Co. E-mail: info@il.proquest.com
URL: http://www.il.proquest.com
Contact: Matt Dunie, President
Availability: Online: ProQuest Co.; ProQuest LLC - Dialog; ProQuest LLC - Dialog; LexisNexis Group.
Type: Bibliographic; Full-text.

8931 ■ BANKSCOPE
Rivierstaete
Amsteldijk 166
NL-1079 LH Amsterdam, Netherlands
Ph: 20 5400 100
Fax: 20 5400 111
Co. E-mail: info@bvdinfo.com
URL: http://www.bvdinfo.com
Availability: Online: Bureau van Dijk Electronic Publishing. **Type:** Directory; Numeric; Statistical; Image.

8932 ■ Barron's Online
1 World Financial Ctr.
200 Liberty St.
New York, NY 10281
Ph: (212)416-2000
Fax: (212)416-4348
Co. E-mail: info@dowjones.com
URL: http://www.dowjones.com
Availability: Online: Dow Jones & Company Inc.
Type: Full-text; Numeric; Statistical.

8933 ■ BlockDATA®
3 Times Sq.
New York, NY 10036
Ph: (646)223-4000
Co. E-mail: salesinquires@thomsonreuters.com
URL: http://thomsonreuters.com/products_services/financial
Availability: Online: Thomson Reuters - Financial Unit. **Type:** Full-text; Numeric.

8934 ■ The Bond Buyer Online
1 State St. Plz., 27th Fl.
New York, NY 10004
Ph: (212)803-8200
Free: 800-221-1809
Co. E-mail: custserv@sourcemedia.com
URL: http://www.sourcemedia.com
Availability: Online: ProQuest LLC - Dialog; ProQuest LLC - Dialog; Investcorp International Inc. - SourceMedia Inc. **Type:** Directory; Full-text.

8935 ■ Business Wire
44 Montgomery St., 39th Fl.
San Francisco, CA 94104
Ph: (415)986-4422
Free: 800-227-0845

Fax: (415)788-5335
Co. E-mail: SF_sales_group@bizwire.com
URL: http://www.businesswire.com
Availability: Online: ProQuest LLC - Dialog; Dow Jones & Company Inc.; Mzinga Inc.; LexisNexis Group; Bloomberg L.P. **Type:** Full-text.

8936 ■ CANNEX
1200 Bay St., Ste. 1001
Toronto, ON, Canada M5R 2A5
Ph: (416)926-0882
Free: 800-387-1269
Fax: (416)926-0706
Co. E-mail: cannex@cannex.com
URL: http://www.cannex.com
Availability: Online: CANNEX Financial Exchanges Ltd. **Type:** Numeric.

8937 ■ Capital Stock
60 E 42nd St.
New York, NY 10165
Ph: (212)986-9300
Fax: (212)986-5857
Co. E-mail: data@haver.com
URL: http://www.haver.com
Availability: Online: Haver Analytics - HaverSelect.
Type: Time Series.

8938 ■ CNQ Market Data Feed
Exchange Twr., 3rd Fl.
130 King St. W
Toronto, ON, Canada M5X 1J2
Ph: (416)947-4670
Free: 888-873-8392
Fax: (416)947-4662
Co. E-mail: info@tsx.com
URL: http://www.tmx.com
Availability: Online: TMX Group Inc. **Type:** Numeric.

8939 ■ Dial-Data™
95 Rockwell Pl.
Brooklyn, NY 11217
Ph: (718)522-7373
Free: 800-367-5968
Co. E-mail: info@trackdata.com
URL: http://www.trackdata.com
Availability: Online: Track Data Corp. **Type:** Numeric.

8940 ■ Dividend Record
55 Water St.
New York, NY 10041
Ph: (212)438-2000
Free: 800-523-4534
Fax: (212)438-7375
Co. E-mail: questions@standardandpoors.com
URL: http://www.standardandpoors.com
Availability: Online: The McGraw-Hill Cos., Inc.- Standard & Poor's Financial Services LLC. **Type:** Numeric.

8941 ■ e-JEP
2014 Broadway, Ste. 305
Nashville, TN 37203
Ph: (615)322-2595
Fax: (615)343-7590
Co. E-mail: aeainfo@vanderbilt.edu
URL: http://www.vanderbilt.edu/AEA
Contact: Angus Deaton, President
Availability: Online: American Economic Association; Thomson Reuters - Westlaw. CD-ROM: American Economic Association. **Type:** Full-text.

8942 ■ EDR Sanborn® Maps
440 Wheelers Farms Rd.
Milford, CT 06461
Ph: (203)783-0300
Free: 800-352-0050
Fax: (203)231-6802
Co. E-mail: jhan@edrnet.com
URL: http://www.edrnet.com
Availability: Online: Environmental Data Resources Inc. **Type:** Image.

8943 ■ Ford Equity Research Databases
11722 Sorrento Valley Rd., Ste. I
San Diego, CA 92121
Ph: (858)755-1327
Free: 800-842-0207

Fax: (858)455-6316
Co. E-mail: info@fordequity.com
URL: http://www.fordequity.com
Type: Numeric.

8944 ■ IGM CorporateWatch
Graybar Bldg., Ste. 616
420 Lexington Ave.
New York, NY 10170
Ph: (212)509-5802
Fax: (212)949-4189
Co. E-mail: sales@informagm.com
URL: http://www.informagm.com/gml
Availability: Online: informa global markets. **Type:** Full-text; Numeric.

8945 ■ InvestmentNews
711 3rd Ave.
New York, NY 10017
Ph: (212)210-0111
Free: 888-909-9111
Fax: (212)210-0200
Co. E-mail: rcrain@adage.com
URL: http://www.crain.com
URL(s): www.investmentnews.com/. **Availability:** Online: Crain Communications Inc. **Type:** Full-text; Numeric.

8946 ■ MarketScope®
55 Water St.
New York, NY 10041
Ph: (212)438-2000
Free: 800-523-4534
Fax: (212)438-7375
Co. E-mail: questions@standardandpoors.com
URL: http://www.standardandpoors.com
Availability: Online: The McGraw-Hill Cos., Inc.- Standard & Poor's Financial Services LLC. **Type:** Numeric; Full-text.

8947 ■ Municipal Futures Data-Line®
22 Thomson Pl.
Boston, MA 02210
Ph: (617)856-2900
Free: 800-367-8215
Fax: (617)856-5610
Co. E-mail: clientservice@tm3.com
URL: http://www.tm3.com
Availability: Online: Thomson Reuters - Municipal Market Monitor. **Type:** Full-text; Numeric.

8948 ■ Municipal Market Data-Line®
22 Thomson Pl.
Boston, MA 02210
Ph: (617)856-2900
Free: 800-367-8215
Fax: (617)856-5610
Co. E-mail: clientservice@tm3.com
URL: http://www.tm3.com
Availability: Online: Thomson Reuters - Municipal Market Monitor. **Type:** Full-text; Numeric.

8949 ■ opTrack™ Service
95 Rockwell Pl.
Brooklyn, NY 11217
Ph: (718)522-7373
Free: 800-367-5968
Co. E-mail: info@trackdata.com
URL: http://www.trackdata.com
Availability: Online: Track Data Corp. **Type:** Full-text.

8950 ■ Pink Sheets
304 Hudson St., 2nd Fl.
New York, NY 10013
Ph: (212)896-4400
Fax: (212)868-3848
Co. E-mail: info@otcmarkets.com
URL: http://www.otcmarkets.com
Availability: Online: Solera Holdings Inc. - Audatex North America Inc.; Bloomberg L.P.; OTC Markets Group Inc. **Type:** Full-text; Numeric.

8951 ■ Securities Law Daily™
1801 S Bell St.
Arlington, VA 22202

Free: 800-372-1033
Co. E-mail: customercare@bna.com
URL: http://www.bna.com
Availability: Online: Bloomberg LP-Bloomberg BNA; Thomson Reuters - Westlaw. **Type:** Full-text.

8952 ■ *Securities Regulation & Law Report™*
1801 S Bell St.
Arlington, VA 22202
Free: 800-372-1033
Co. E-mail: customercare@bna.com
URL: http://www.bna.com
Availability: Online: LexisNexis Group; Bloomberg LP-Bloomberg BNA; Thomson Reuters - Westlaw. **Type:** Full-text.

8953 ■ *Trendvest Ratings*
923 First Colonial Rd., No. 1805
Virginia Beach, VA 23454
Ph: (757)412-4301
Fax: (757)412-4302
Co. E-mail: editor@trendvest.com
URL: http://www.trendvest.com
Availability: Online: Trendvest Management Inc. **Type:** Full-text; Numeric.

8954 ■ *U.S. Weekly Statistics*
60 E 42nd St.
New York, NY 10165
Ph: (212)986-9300
Fax: (212)986-5857
Co. E-mail: data@haver.com
URL: http://www.haver.com
Availability: Online: Haver Analytics - HaverSelect. **Type:** Statistical; Numeric.

8955 ■ *Value Line DataFile*
220 E 42nd St.
New York, NY 10017-5806
Ph: (212)907-1500
Free: 800-654-0508
Fax: (212)818-9747
Co. E-mail: vlcr@valueline.com
URL: http://www.valueline.com
Contact: Howard A. Brecher, President
Availability: Online: FactSet Research Systems Inc.; Citigroup Inc. - Institutional Clients Group - Global Markets. **Type:** Time Series; Numeric.

8956 ■ *Value Line Electronic Convertibles*
220 E 42nd St.
New York, NY 10017-5806
Ph: (212)907-1500
Free: 800-654-0508
Fax: (212)818-9747
Co. E-mail: vlcr@valueline.com
URL: http://www.valueline.com
Contact: Howard A. Brecher, President
Availability: Online: Value Line Inc. **Type:** Numeric.

8957 ■ *Value Line Estimates and Projections File*
220 E 42nd St.
New York, NY 10017-5806
Ph: (212)907-1500
Free: 800-654-0508
Fax: (212)818-9747
Co. E-mail: vlcr@valueline.com
URL: http://www.valueline.com
Contact: Howard A. Brecher, President
Availability: Online: FactSet Research Systems Inc.; GIT Satellite LLC. **Type:** Numeric.

LIBRARIES

8958 ■ Bank of Nova Scotia Archives
44 King St. W., 19th Fl.
Toronto, ON, Canada M5H 1H1
Co. E-mail: archives@scotiabank.com
URL: http://www.scotiabank.com
Contact: Jane Nokes, Director
Scope: Banking, finance, economics, business. **Services:** Archives open to the public. **Founded:** 1900. **Holdings:** Records; art; antiques; photographs.

8959 ■ Compass Lexecon Library
332 S. Michigan Ave., Ste. 1300
Chicago, IL 60604

Ph: (312)322-0845
Fax: (312)322-0881
Co. E-mail: cgriffin@lexecon.com
Contact: Christine Griffin, Office Manager
Scope: Economics, securities, finance, government, business, reference. **Services:** Library not open to the public. **Subscriptions:** 54 journals and other serials; 5 newspapers.

8960 ■ Fiscal Agents - Financial Information Service - Research Department - Library
PO Box 5000
Oakville, ON, Canada L6J 5C7
Ph: (905)842-2790
Fax: (905)844-8552
Co. E-mail: library@fiscalagents.com
URL: http://www.fiscalagents.com/
Contact: David J. Newman
Scope: Industry, trust services, investment products, insurance. **Services:** Copying; Library open to the public at librarian's discretion. **Founded:** 1977. **Holdings:** 12 reports. **Subscriptions:** 3 newspapers. **Telecommunication Services:** mailroom@fiscalagents.com.

8961 ■ Huddleston, Bolen LLP Law Library
611 3rd Ave.
Huntington, WV 25701
Ph: (304)529-6181
Fax: (304)522-4312
URL: http://www.huddlestonbolen.com/
Scope: Taxation/estate, corporate/securities/banking, federal litigation, labor. **Services:** Library not open to the public. **Holdings:** 35,000 books.

8962 ■ Independent Community Bankers of America Information Center
1615 L St. NW, 9th Fl.
Washington, DC 20036
Ph: (202)659-8111
Free: 800-422-8439
Fax: (202)659-3604
Co. E-mail: library@icba.org
URL: http://www.icba.org
Contact: Susan R. Fournier, Director
Scope: Banking and finance, legislative and regulatory documents, small bank operations, bank structure. **Services:** Interlibrary loan; library not open to the public. **Holdings:** 3500 books, periodicals, and clippings; 300 audio/visual items. **Subscriptions:** 240 journals and other serials. **Telecommunication Services:** susan.fournier@icba.org.

8963 ■ Ontario Teachers' Pension Plan Board - Knowledge Centre
5650 Yonge St.
North York, ON, Canada M2M 4H5
Ph: (416)228-5900
Fax: (416)730-5374
Co. E-mail: inquiry@otpp.com
URL: http://www.otpp.com/wps/wcm/connect/otpp_en/home
Scope: Pension management, investment, economics, finance. **Services:** Library not open to the public. **Founded:** 1995. **Holdings:** 900 books. **Subscriptions:** 30 journals and other serials.

8964 ■ Principal Financial Group - Online Library
711 High St.
Des Moines, IA 50392-0510
Free: 800-986-3343
URL: http://www.principal.com
Contact: Kay Kelly, Consultant
Scope: Human Resources research. **Services:** Library not open to the public. **Founded:** 1994. **Holdings:** Figures not available.

8965 ■ Russell Reynolds Associates, Inc. Library
155 N. Wacker Dr., Ste. 4100
Chicago, IL 60606-1732
Ph: (312)993-9696

Fax: (312)993-9658
Co. E-mail: alison.ranney@russellreynolds.com
URL: http://www.russellreynolds.com/
Scope: Business, financial services, banking. **Services:** Interlibrary loan; copying; reference; library open to the public by appointment. **Holdings:** 1000 books; company Annual reports; subject files. **Subscriptions:** 50 journals and other serials.

8966 ■ Willamette Management Associates Library
8600 W. Bryn Mawr Ave., Ste. 950
Chicago, IL 60631
Ph: (773)399-4300
Fax: (773)399-4310
Co. E-mail: vaplatt@willamette.com
URL: http://www.willamette.com
Contact: Victoria A. Platt, Specialist
Scope: Business valuation, tax, gift and estate, finance. **Services:** Interlibrary loan; copying. Library not open to the public. **Founded:** 1969. **Telecommunication Services:** cmblalock@willamette.com.

RESEARCH CENTERS

8967 ■ Boston University - Morin Center for Banking and Financial Law
School of Law, Rm. 1524
765 Commonwealth Ave.
Boston, MA 02215
Ph: (617)353-3023
Free: 888-285-7003
Fax: (617)353-2444
Co. E-mail: ckhurley@bu.edu
URL: http://www.bu.edu/law/morincenter
Contact: Prof. Cornelius K. Hurley, Director
Founded: 1978. **Publications:** *Annual Review of Banking Law; Review of banking and financial law* (Semiannual); *Review of Financial Law* (Semiannual). **Educational Activities:** Edward Lane-Retiker Speaker Series, on current issues in banking and financial institutions law and policy, once per semester, open to the public; Morin Center for Banking and Financial Law Lectures, on current issues in banking and financial institutions law for financial institution executives and legal counsel or other interested parties. **Telecommunication Services:** banklaw@bu.edu.

8968 ■ Filene Research Institute
PO Box 2998
Madison, WI 53701-2998
Ph: (608)231-8550
Fax: (608)238-4709
Co. E-mail: markm@filene.org
URL: http://filene.org
Contact: Mark Meyer, Chief Executive Officer
Founded: 1989. **Publications:** *Investigative reports; Filene Research Institute Research reports; Special reports.* **Educational Activities:** Research colloquia workshops. **Awards:** Research grants to academic researchers and consultants.

8969 ■ McGill University - Desmarais Global Finance Centre (DGFC)
Desautels Faculty of Management
1001 Sherbrooke St. W
Montreal, QC, Canada H3A 1G5
Ph: (514)398-8144
Fax: (514)398-3876
Co. E-mail: vihang.errunza@mcgill.ca
URL: http://www.mcgill.ca/desautels/dgfc
Contact: Prof. Vihang R. Errunza, Director
Founded: 1998. **Educational Activities:** DGFC Seminars, conferences.

8970 ■ Princeton University - Bendheim Center for Finance (BCF)
Department of Economics
26 Prospect Ave.
Princeton, NJ 08540-5296
Ph: (609)258-0770

Fax: (609)258-0771
Co. E-mail: jessicab@princeton.edu
URL: http://www.princeton.edu/bcf
Contact: Jessica O'Leary, Manager
Founded: 1997. **Educational Activities:** BCF Conferences (Annual); BCF Seminars (Weekly), for university students and staff, as well as invited guests, held every Wednesday.

8971 ■ Research Foundation of CFA Institute
PO Box 3668
Charlottesville, VA 22903-0668
Ph: (434)951-5499
Free: 800-247-8132
Fax: (434)951-5370
Co. E-mail: rf@cfainstitute.org
URL: http://www.cfainstitute.org/about/foundation/
    Pages/index.aspx
Contact: John D. Rogers, President
Founded: 1965. **Publications:** *Research Foundation of CFA Institute Monographs.* **Telecommunication Services:** john.rogers@cfainstitute.org.

8972 ■ Stetson University - Roland and Sara George Investments Institute
421 N Woodland Blvd., Unit 8398
DeLand, FL 32723
Ph: (386)822-7100
Free: 800-688-0101
Fax: (386)822-7491
Co. E-mail: lbelcher@stetson.edu
URL: http://business.stetson.edu/george/
Contact: Prof. Lawrence J. Belcher, Director
Founded: 1989. **Educational Activities:** Public forums, on investing; Investment Seminars for academics and practitioners (Annual). **Telecommunication Services:** admissions@stetson.edu.

8973 ■ University of Chicago - Center for Research in Security Prices (CRSP)
105 W Adams St., Ste. 1700
Chicago, IL 60603
Ph: (312)263-6400

Fax: (312)263-6430
Co. E-mail: subscriptions@crsp.chicagobooth.edu
URL: http://www.crsp.chicagogsb.edu
Contact: David Barclay, Chief Operating Officer
Founded: 1960. **Telecommunication Services:** david.barclay@crsp.chicagobooth.edu.

8974 ■ University of Pennsylvania - Rodney L. White Center for Financial Research
3254 Steinberg Hall-Dietrich Hall
Philadelphia, PA 19104-6367
Ph: (215)898-7616
Fax: (215)573-8084
Co. E-mail: rlwctr@finance.wharton.upenn.edu
URL: http://finance.wharton.upenn.edu/~rlwctr
Contact: Dr. Donald B. Keim, Director
Founded: 1969. **Educational Activities:** Rodney L. White Center for Financial Research Seminars (Annual). **Telecommunication Services:** keim@wharton.upenn.edu.

ASSOCIATIONS AND OTHER ORGANIZATIONS

8975 ■ International Institute of Fisheries Economics and Trade (IIFET)
Oregon State University
Corvallis, OR 97331-3601
Ph: (503)737-2228
Fax: (503)737-3447
Co. E-mail: iifet@oregonstate.edu
URL: http://oregonstate.edu/dept/iifet
Contact: Dr. Rebecca Metzner, President
Description: Individuals from the fisheries industry, government, and universities. Objectives are to: promote discussion on factors affecting seafood trade and fisheries management; facilitate cooperative research projects and data exchange. **Founded:** 1982. **Publications:** *Conference Proceedings* (Biennial); *IIFET Newsletter* (Semiannual); *International Institute of Fisheries Economics and Trade--Membership Directory* (Annual). **Educational Activities:** International Institute of Fisheries Economics and Trade Conference (Biennial); International Institute of Fisheries Economics and Trade Conference (Biennial). **Awards:** Best Student Paper Award (Biennial); Distinguished Service Award (Biennial); Best Student Paper Award; Distinguished Service Award.

8976 ■ Maine Lobstermen's Association (MLA)
21 Western Ave., Ste. 1
Kennebunk, ME 04043
Ph: (207)967-4555
Fax: (866)407-3770
Co. E-mail: info@mainelobstermen.org
URL: http://www.mainelobstermen.org
Contact: David Cousens, President
Description: Licensed lobstermen and supporting business. Gives Maine's lobstermen a voice and influence at the highest levels of government. **Founded:** 1954.

8977 ■ Northwest Fisheries Association (NWFA)
2208 NW Market St., Ste. 318
Seattle, WA 98107
Ph: (206)789-6197
Fax: (206)789-8147
Co. E-mail: info@northwestfisheries.org
URL: http://www.northwestfisheries.org
Contact: Susan Chesney, President
Description: Primary and secondary seafood processors, seafood brokers, distributors, and direct support industries. Provides a positive business climate for members and enhances the flow of information throughout the Pacific fishing and seafood industry. **Founded:** 1951.

8978 ■ Southeastern Association of Fish and Wildlife Agencies (SEAFWA)
PO Box 2040
Maggie Valley, NC 28751
Ph: (850)545-6001
URL: http://www.seafwa.org
Contact: Carter Smith, President
Description: Directors of state game and fish commissions in 16 southern states, and the Commonwealth of Puerto Rico, and the Virgin Islands. Aims to: protect the right of jurisdiction of southeastern states over their wildlife resources on public and private lands; study state and federal wildlife legislation and regulations as they affect the area; consult with and make recommendations to federal wildlife and public land agencies on federal management programs and programs involving federal aid to southeastern states; serve as a clearinghouse for exchange of ideas on wildlife management and research techniques. Sponsors: Cooperative Fish Disease Study at Auburn University in Alabama; Cooperative Wildlife Disease Study at the University of Georgia in Athens. **Founded:** 1947. **Publications:** *Southeastern Association of Fish and Wildlife Agencies Proceedings* (Annual). **Educational Activities:** Southeastern Association of Fish and Wildlife Agencies Conference (Annual).

REFERENCE WORKS

8979 ■ "Convictions Under the Fisheries Act" in Canadian Corporate News (May 16, 2007)
Pub: Comtex News Network Inc.
Description: Fisheries and Oceans Canada is mandated to protect and conserve marine resources and thus released a list of fishers fined for various offences under the Fisheries Act in March and April.

8980 ■ "Counting Crabs: Supply Dips, Putting Crimp on Memorial Day Feast" in Boston Business Journal (Vol. 29, June 3, 2011, No. 4, pp. 1)
Pub: American City Business Journals Inc.
Ed: Scott Dance. **Description:** Restaurateurs in Baltimore City experienced low supply of crabs this Memorial Day 2011 owing to the early season and the fact that many small crabbers took time off during the weekend. Sales were cut in half compared with previous Memorial Day weekends and prices rose to as much as $185 to $200 per box of crabs. Normal supply is expected, though, as summer pushes on.

8981 ■ "An Ill Wind: Icelandic Bank Failures Chill Atlantic Canada" in Canadian Business (Vol. 81, November 10, 2008, No. 19, pp. 10)
Pub: Rogers Media Ltd.
Ed: Charles Mandel. **Description:** Bank failures in Iceland have put a stop to flights ferrying Icelanders to Newfoundland to purchase Christmas gifts, thereby threatening Newfoundland's tourism industry. The credit of Newfoundland's fisheries is also being squeezed since most of Atlantic Canadian seafood processors hold lines of credit from Icelandic banks.

8982 ■ "Life After Cod" in Globe & Mail (March 18, 2006, pp. B1)
Pub: CTVglobemedia Publishing Inc.
Ed: Gordon Pitts. **Description:** Canadian fishing industry is under threat because of Chinese processing competition, high energy costs, rise of powerful retailers and the rise of Canadian dollar value. Fishing industry of Canada is analyzed.

8983 ■ "The Mood of a Nation" in Canadian Business (Vol. 81, April 14, 2008, No. 6, pp. 56)
Pub: Rogers Media
Ed: Joe Castaldo. **Description:** Independent Fish Harvesters Inc. processes more kilograms a year and has had to hire more workers but its managers worry about how a slowdown in the U.S. economy will affect his business. A planned shopping complex in Mirabel Quebec, the manufacturing industry in Kitchener, Ontario, and a cattle farming business in Sarnia, Ontario are discussed to provide a snapshot of the challenges that business in Canada are facing as recession looms.

8984 ■ "Oil Rich" in Canadian Business (Vol. 79, Winter 2006, No. 24, pp. 57)
Pub: Rogers Media
Ed: Calvin Leung. **Description:** The efforts of John Risley, the Chairman of the Candaian firm Clearwater Fine Foods Inc., to educate consumers about the health aspects of seafood, are described.

8985 ■ "Paying the Price" in Baltimore Business Journal (Vol. 28, July 9, 2010, No. 9, pp. 1)
Pub: Baltimore Business Journal
Ed: Emily Mullin. **Description:** Crab prices have never been higher in Baltimore, Maryland and businesses have been led to count on strengthening demand for seafood. For instance, the average price for a dozen large crabs has increased by 5 percent to $58.90. How restaurants have responded to the increase in prices is discussed, along with factors that might have caused the harvest of smaller crabs.

8986 ■ "Something's Fishy" in Canadian Business (Vol. 83, September 14, 2010, No. 15, pp. 71)
Pub: Rogers Media Ltd.
Ed: Matthew McClearn. **Description:** The Marine Stewardship Council (MSC) is offering a widely recognized blue check mark to certify that the seafood being sold has not been overfished, nor harvested in a way that harms the ecosystems. However, the MSC certification of Fraser sockeye salmon has put into question its credibility.

TRADE PERIODICALS

8987 ■ Seafood Price-Current
Pub: Urner Barry Publications Inc.
Contact: Paul B. Brown, Jr., President
Ed: Paul B. Brown, Jr., Editor. **Released:** Semiweekly. **Price:** $383. **Description:** Provides seafood market price quotations for fresh and frozen fin and shell fish throughout the United States.

8988 ■ Shrimp Notes
Pub: Shrimp World Inc.
Ed: William D. Chauvin, Editor, chauvin@shrimpcom.com. **Released:** Monthly. **Description:** Analyzes fac

tors determining the shrimp market status, including U.S. shrimp imports, domestic production, and economic factors.

LIBRARIES

8989 ■ Oregon State University - Seafoods Research Laboratory Library
2001 Marine Dr., Rm. 253
Astoria, OR 97103
Ph: (503)325-4531
Fax: (503)325-2753
Co. E-mail: sue.hansell@oregonstate.edu
URL: http://osuseafoodlab.oregonstate.edu/
Contact: Dr. Gil Sylvia, Director (Acting)

Scope: Fisheries, marine food science and technology, fish processing, seafood safety. **Founded:** 1945. **Holdings:** 380 volumes.

RESEARCH CENTERS

8990 ■ North Central Regional Aquaculture Center (NCRAC)
13 Natural Resources Bldg.
Michigan State University
East Lansing, MI 48824-1222
Ph: (517)353-1962
Fax: (517)353-7181
Co. E-mail: batters2@msu.edu
URL: http://www.ncrac.org
Contact: Dr. Ted R. Batterson, Director

Services: Information exchange between industry and researchers. **Founded:** 1988. **Educational Activities:** Cooperative research projects; Extension educational programs. **Telecommunication Services:** ncrac@iastate.edu.

8991 ■ Northeastern Regional Aquaculture Center (NRAC)
2113 Animal Sciences Bldg.
University of Maryland
College Park, MD 20742-2317

Ph: (301)405-6085
Fax: (301)314-9412
Co. E-mail: rharrell@umd.edu
URL: http://www.nrac.umd.edu
Contact: Dr. Reginal Harrell, Director

Services: Offers information exchange between industry and researchers. **Founded:** 1985. **Publications:** *Northeastern Aquaculture.* **Educational Activities:** Cooperative research projects; Extension educational programs. **Telecommunication Services:** nrac@umd.edu.

8992 ■ Southern Regional Aquaculture Center (SRAC)
127 Experiment Station Rd.
Stoneville, MS 38776-0197
Ph: (662)686-3285
Fax: (662)686-3320
Co. E-mail: ctucker@drec.msstate.edu
URL: http://www.msstate.edu/dept/srac
Contact: Dr. Craig S. Tucker, Director

Services: Information exchange between industry and researchers. **Founded:** 1987. **Educational Activities:** Cooperative research projects; Extension educational programs. **Telecommunication Services:** srac@drec.msstate.edu.

ASSOCIATIONS AND OTHER ORGANIZATIONS

8993 ■ **American Fisheries Society (AFS)**
5410 Grosvenor Ln., Ste. 110
Bethesda, MD 20814-2199
Ph: (301)897-8616
Fax: (301)897-8096
Co. E-mail: main@fisheries.org
URL: http://www.fisheries.org
Contact: Ghassan N. Rassam, Executive Director
Description: International scientific organization of fisheries and aquatic science professionals, including fish culturists, fish biologists, water quality scientists, fish health professionals, fish technologists, educators, limnologists, and oceanographers. Promotes the development of all branches of fishery science and practice, and the conservation, development, and wise utilization of fisheries, both recreational and commercial. Strengthens professional standards by certifying fisheries scientists, stressing professional ethics, and providing forums for the exchange of scientific and management information. Represents members through written and verbal testimony before legislative and administrative bodies concerning aquatic environmental issues. Maintains over 30 committees. **Founded:** 1870. **Publications:** *AFS Membership Directory and Handbook* (Annual); *Fisheries* (Monthly); *Journal of Aquatic Animal Health* (Quarterly); *North American Journal of Aquaculture* (Quarterly); *North American Journal of Fisheries Management* (Bimonthly); *Transactions of the American Fisheries Society* (Bimonthly); *Fisheries*; *AFS Membership Directory and Handbook* (Annual); *American Fisheries Society--Membership Directory and Handbook*; *North American Journal of Aquaculture*; *North American Journal of Fisheries Management*; *Fisheries* (Monthly); *North American Journal of Fisheries Management* (Bimonthly); *North American Journal of Aquaculture* (Quarterly); *Transactions of the American Fisheries Society* (Bimonthly); *Journal of Aquatic Animal Health* (Quarterly); *Directory of North American Fisheries & Aquatic Scientists*. **Educational Activities:** American Fisheries Society Annual Meeting (Annual); American Fisheries Society Meeting (Annual). **Awards:** Excellence in Fisheries Education Award; Award of Excellence; Distinguished Service Award; Meritorious Service Award; Dr. J. Frances Allen Scholarship; John E. Skinner Memorial Fund Award; Carl R. Sullivan Fishery Conservation Award; Student Writing Contest; Carl R. Sullivan International Membership Award; President's Fishery Conservation Award; Honorary Membership; Clarence W. Watson Award; William E. Ricker Resource Conservation Award. **Telecommunication Services:** info@fisheries.org; grassam@fisheries.org.

8994 ■ **American Institute of Fishery Research Biologists (AIFRB)**
c/o Allen Shimada, Treas.
7909 Sleaford Pl.
Bethesda, MD 20814
Co. E-mail: allen.shimada@noaa.gov
URL: http://www.aifrb.org
Contact: Steve Cadrin, President
Description: Professional scientific and educational organization formed to: advance the theory and practice of fishery science in pursuit of greater scientific understanding of living marine and freshwater natural resources, their habitat, their biological and physical environment, and their fisheries; support the education of students and the general public, and the professional development and recognition of researchers, practitioners, and institutions in fishery science and related areas of natural resource management public policy, and public affairs; and foster the application of scientific knowledge to the sustainable use, conservation and sound management of living aquatic resources and their allied human applications (having commercial, recreational, subsistence, and aesthetic or intrinsic value to society). **Founded:** 1956. **Publications:** *BRIEFS* (Bimonthly). **Educational Activities:** Board of Control (Annual). **Awards:** AIFRB Distinguished Service Award (Annual); AIFRB Outstanding Achievement Award (Annual); AIFRB Research Assistance Award (Annual); W. F. Thompson Award; W.F. Thompson Best Paper (Annual); Outstanding Achievement Award - Individual; Outstanding Achievement Award - Group.

8995 ■ *Atlantic Salmon*
15 Rankine Mill Rd.
Chamcook, NB, Canada E5B 3A9
Ph: (506)529-4581
Free: 800-565-5666
Fax: (506)529-1070
Co. E-mail: savesalmon@asf.ca
URL: http://www.asf.ca
Contact: Bill Taylor, President
E-mail: btaylor@asf.ca
Released: Quarterly

8996 ■ **Atlantic Salmon Federation (ASF)**
15 Rankine Mill Rd.
Chamcook, NB, Canada E5B 3A9
Ph: (506)529-4581
Free: 800-565-5666
Fax: (506)529-1070
Co. E-mail: savesalmon@asf.ca
URL: http://www.asf.ca
Contact: Bill Taylor, President
E-mail: btaylor@asf.ca
Description: Represents the interest of conservationists, scientists, government personnel, and salmon anglers. Promotes the preservation and better management of Atlantic salmon stocks. Encourages international cooperation; coordinates education and research in the field. Maintains aquarium exhibits. **Founded:** 1982. **Publications:** *Atlantic Salmon Journal: Conservation-minded salmon angler* (Quarterly); *Atlantic Salmon* (Quarterly). **Educational Activities:** Atlantic Salmon Federation Conference (Semiannual). **Awards:** Affiliate of the Year (Annual); ASF Olin Fellowships (Annual); ASF Roll of Honor (Annual); Lee Wulff Conservation Award (Annual); T.B. Fraser Award (Annual); Atlantic Salmon Federation Olin Fellowships. **Telecommunication Services:** btaylor@asf.ca.

8997 ■ **Florida Tropical Fish Farms Association (FTFFA)**
PO Box 1519
Winter Haven, FL 33882
Ph: (863)293-5710
Fax: (863)299-5154
Co. E-mail: flassn@aol.com
URL: http://www.ftffa.com
Contact: Art Rawlins, President
Description: Growers of tropical fish and aquatic plants; associate members are manufacturers and suppliers of allied products in Florida and elsewhere in the U.S. Seeks to elevate trade standards and promote the industry. Sponsors quarterly meeting to hear speakers on the care of tropical fish, applicable laws, and other aspects of the trade. Resources include an organization-owned co-op. **Founded:** 1964. **Publications:** *Florida Tropical Fish Farms Association--Membership Directory* (Annual). **Awards:** FTFFA Hall of Fame (Annual).

8998 ■ *Fraser River Panel Annual Report*
600-1155 Robson St.
Vancouver, BC, Canada V6E 1B5
Ph: (604)684-8081
Fax: (604)666-8707
Co. E-mail: info@psc.org
URL: http://www.psc.org
Contact: Don Kowal, Executive Secretary

8999 ■ **International Association of Astacology (IAA)**
c/o Antonio Garza de Yta, Sec.
Auburn University
Dept. of Fisheries and Allied Aquaculture
203 Swingle Hall
Auburn University, AL 36849-5419
Ph: (334)844-4786
Fax: (334)844-9208
Co. E-mail: agarza@crm-agc.com
URL: http://iz.carnegiemnh.org/crayfish/iaa/index.htm
Contact: James Fetzner, President
URL(s): iz.carnegiemnh.org/crayfish/IAA/. **Description:** Individuals from industry, academia, and state and federal government wildlife agencies. Promotes the scientific study and cultivation of freshwater crayfish. Sponsors 8 working groups in areas such as biology, ecology, and zoogeography. **Founded:** 1972. **Publications:** *Directory of Astacologists* (Biennial). **Awards:** Honorary Life Membership (Periodic). **Telecommunication Services:** garzaan@auburn.edu.

9000 ■ **International Institute of Fisheries Economics and Trade (IIFET)**
Oregon State University
Corvallis, OR 97331-3601
Ph: (503)737-2228
Fax: (503)737-3447
Co. E-mail: iifet@oregonstate.edu
URL: http://oregonstate.edu/dept/iifet
Contact: Dr. Rebecca Metzner, President
Description: Individuals from the fisheries industry, government, and universities. Objectives are to: promote discussion on factors affecting seafood trade and fisheries management; facilitate cooperative research projects and data exchange. **Founded:** 1982. **Publications:** *Conference Proceedings* (Biennial); *IIFET Newsletter* (Semiannual); *International Institute of Fisheries Economics and Trade--*

Membership Directory (Annual). **Educational Activities:** International Institute of Fisheries Economics and Trade Conference (Biennial); International Institute of Fisheries Economics and Trade Conference (Biennial). **Awards:** Best Student Paper Award (Biennial); Distinguished Service Award (Biennial); Best Student Paper Award; Distinguished Service Award.

9001 ■ *Journal of Northwest Atlantic Fishery Science*
PO Box 638
Dartmouth, NS, Canada B2Y 3Y9
Ph: (902)468-5590
Fax: (902)468-5538
Co. E-mail: info@nafo.int
URL: http://www.nafo.int
Contact: Ricardo Federizon, Manager

9002 ■ *Meeting Proceedings*
PO Box 638
Dartmouth, NS, Canada B2Y 3Y9
Ph: (902)468-5590
Fax: (902)468-5538
Co. E-mail: info@nafo.int
URL: http://www.nafo.int
Contact: Ricardo Federizon, Manager
Released: Annual

9003 ■ National Shellfisheries Association (NSA)
c/o Dr. Sandra Shumway, Ed.
University of Connecticut
Dept. of Marine Sciences
1080 Shennecossett Rd.
Groton, CT 06340-6097
Ph: (631)653-6327
Fax: (631)653-6327
Co. E-mail: secretariat@shellfish.org
URL: http://shellfish.org
Contact: Mr. R. Leroy Creswell, President
URL(s): www.shellfish.org. **Description:** Biologists, hydrographers, public health workers, shellfish producers, and fishery administrators. Encourages research on mollusks and crustaceans, with emphasis on those forms of economic importance known as shellfish. **Founded:** 1908. **Educational Activities:** National Shellfisheries Association Meeting (Annual). **Awards:** David Wallace Award.

9004 ■ North Pacific Anadromous Fish Commission (NPAFC)
889 W Pender St., Ste. 502
Vancouver, BC, Canada V6C 3B2
Ph: (604)775-5550
Fax: (604)775-5577
Co. E-mail: secretariat@npafc.org
URL: http://www.npafc.org
Contact: Mr. Vladimir Fedorenko, Executive Director
Description: Represents administrators and scientists devoted to the conservation of salmon in the North Pacific Ocean. Seeks to prohibits commercial salmon fishing on the high seas of the Pacific, between the United States, Canada, Japan, Republic of Korea and Russian Federation. Coordinates fisheries enforcement and scientific researches on the high seas of the North Pacific. **Founded:** 1993. **Subscriptions:** archival material books periodicals. **Publications:** *NPAFC Annual Report* (Annual); *NPAFC Bulletin*; *NPAFC Technical Report*; *Statistical Yearbook* (Annual).

9005 ■ Northwest Atlantic Fisheries Organization (NAFO)—Organisation des Peches de l'Atlantique Nord-Ouest
PO Box 638
Dartmouth, NS, Canada B2Y 3Y9
Ph: (902)468-5590
Fax: (902)468-5538
Co. E-mail: info@nafo.int
URL: http://www.nafo.int
Contact: Ricardo Federizon, Manager
Description: Contracting parties working to investigate, protect, and conserve the fishery resources of the Northwest Atlantic Ocean. Provides resource management. Compiles statistics; maintains research programs. **Founded:** 1979. **Publications:** *Journal of*

Northwest Atlantic Fishery Science; *Meeting Proceedings* (Annual); *Scientific Council Reports* (Annual); *NAFO List of Fishing Vessels* (Irregular).

9006 ■ *NPAFC Annual Report*
889 W Pender St., Ste. 502
Vancouver, BC, Canada V6C 3B2
Ph: (604)775-5550
Fax: (604)775-5577
Co. E-mail: secretariat@npafc.org
URL: http://www.npafc.org
Contact: Mr. Vladimir Fedorenko, Executive Director
Released: Annual

9007 ■ *NPAFC Bulletin*
889 W Pender St., Ste. 502
Vancouver, BC, Canada V6C 3B2
Ph: (604)775-5550
Fax: (604)775-5577
Co. E-mail: secretariat@npafc.org
URL: http://www.npafc.org
Contact: Mr. Vladimir Fedorenko, Executive Director
Released: published as necessary.

9008 ■ *NPAFC Technical Report*
889 W Pender St., Ste. 502
Vancouver, BC, Canada V6C 3B2
Ph: (604)775-5550
Fax: (604)775-5577
Co. E-mail: secretariat@npafc.org
URL: http://www.npafc.org
Contact: Mr. Vladimir Fedorenko, Executive Director
Released: published as necessary.

9009 ■ Pacific Coast Shellfish Growers Association (PCSGA)
120 State Ave. NE
PMB No. 142
Olympia, WA 98501
Ph: (360)754-2744
Fax: (360)754-2743
Co. E-mail: pcsga@pcsga.org
URL: http://www.pcsga.org
Contact: David Steele, President
Description: Oyster, clam, mussel, scallop, geoduck growers, openers, packers and shippers in Alaska, California, Oregon, Washington, Hawaii and Mexico. **Founded:** 1930. **Awards:** Applied Research Student Scholarship Award (Annual).

9010 ■ Pacific Salmon Commission (PSC)
600-1155 Robson St.
Vancouver, BC, Canada V6E 1B5
Ph: (604)684-8081
Fax: (604)666-8707
Co. E-mail: info@psc.org
URL: http://www.psc.org
Contact: Don Kowal, Executive Secretary
Description: Formed by treaty between Canada and the United States for the conservation, management and optimum production of Pacific Salmon. **Founded:** 1985. **Publications:** *Fraser River Panel Annual Report*; *Pacific Salmon Commission Annual Report*.

9011 ■ *Pacific Salmon Commission Annual Report*
600-1155 Robson St.
Vancouver, BC, Canada V6E 1B5
Ph: (604)684-8081
Fax: (604)666-8707
Co. E-mail: info@psc.org
URL: http://www.psc.org
Contact: Don Kowal, Executive Secretary

9012 ■ *Scientific Council Reports*
PO Box 638
Dartmouth, NS, Canada B2Y 3Y9
Ph: (902)468-5590
Fax: (902)468-5538
Co. E-mail: info@nafo.int
URL: http://www.nafo.int
Contact: Ricardo Federizon, Manager
Released: Annual

9013 ■ Southeastern Fisheries Association (SFA)
1118-B Thomasville Rd.
Tallahassee, FL 32303
Ph: (850)224-0612

Fax: (850)222-3663
Co. E-mail: bobfish@aol.com
URL: http://seafoodsustainability.us/Home_Page.html
Contact: Bob Jones, Executive Director
Description: Producers, distributors and suppliers of seafood in the South Atlantic and Gulf of Mexico areas. Disseminates information on legislation, both proposed and implemented, that affects fishermen in that area. Promotes and represents commercial fishermen's interests in legislative, industrial and environmental matters. Provides HAACP training on-site. **Founded:** 1952. **Publications:** *International Conference on Shrimp Bycatch*; *Importing Seafood - A Buyer's Guide.*

9014 ■ *Statistical Yearbook*
889 W Pender St., Ste. 502
Vancouver, BC, Canada V6C 3B2
Ph: (604)775-5550
Fax: (604)775-5577
Co. E-mail: secretariat@npafc.org
URL: http://www.npafc.org
Contact: Mr. Vladimir Fedorenko, Executive Director
Released: Annual

9015 ■ U.S. Trout Farmers Association (USTFA)
PO Box 1647
Pine Bluff, AR 71613
Ph: (870)850-7900
Fax: (870)850-7902
Co. E-mail: ustfa@thenaa.net
URL: http://www.ustfa.org
Contact: Jerry Zinn, Chairman
Description: Trout farmers, suppliers, academics, students, and individuals interested in the trout farming industry. Promotes the trout farming industry and recreational trout fishing. Establishes Trout Farmers Quality Assurance Program; monitors legislation related to the aquaculture industry. **Founded:** 1954. **Publications:** *Trout Talk* (Quarterly). **Educational Activities:** U.S. Trout Farmers Association Meeting (Annual). **Awards:** Clark and Mimi White Distinguished Service Award (Annual).

REFERENCE WORKS

9016 ■ *"Counting Crabs: Supply Dips, Putting Crimp on Memorial Day Feast" in Boston Business Journal (Vol. 29, June 3, 2011, No. 4, pp. 1)*
Pub: American City Business Journals Inc.

Ed: Scott Dance. **Description:** Restaurateurs in Baltimore City experienced low supply of crabs this Memorial Day 2011 owing to the early season and the fact that many small crabbers took time off during the weekend. Sales were cut in half compared with previous Memorial Day weekends and prices rose to as much as $185 to $200 per box of crabs. Normal supply is expected, though, as summer pushes on.

9017 ■ *Fisheries of the United States*
Pub: National Marine Fisheries Service Fisheries Statistics & Economics Division, F/ST1

URL(s): www.st.nmfs.gov/st1/www.st.nmfs.noaa.gov/st1/publications.html. **Ed:** Barbara K. O'Bannon. **Released:** Annual; Latest edition 2009. **Price:** $20, Individuals s/n 003-020-00178-5. **Covers:** fisheries throughout the country as compiled in government statistical reports. **Database includes:** Annual fishery statistics, such as worldwide consumption, supply, employment.

9018 ■ *"An Ill Wind: Icelandic Bank Failures Chill Atlantic Canada" in Canadian Business (Vol. 81, November 10, 2008, No. 19, pp. 10)*
Pub: Rogers Media Ltd.

Ed: Charles Mandel. **Description:** Bank failures in Iceland have put a stop to flights ferrying Icelanders to Newfoundland to purchase Christmas gifts, thereby threatening Newfoundland's tourism industry. The credit of Newfoundland's fisheries is also being squeezed since most of Atlantic Canadian seafood processors hold lines of credit from Icelandic banks.

9019 ■ *"Life After Cod" in Globe & Mail (March 18, 2006, pp. B1)*
Pub: CTVglobemedia Publishing Inc.
Ed: Gordon Pitts. **Description:** Canadian fishing industry is under threat because of Chinese processing competition, high energy costs, rise of powerful retailers and the rise of Canadian dollar value. Fishing industry of Canada is analyzed.

9020 ■ *"The Mood of a Nation" in Canadian Business (Vol. 81, April 14, 2008, No. 6, pp. 56)*
Pub: Rogers Media
Ed: Joe Castaldo. **Description:** Independent Fish Harvesters Inc. processes more kilograms a year and has had to hire more workers but its managers worry about how a slowdown in the U.S. economy will affect his business. A planned shopping complex in Mirabel Quebec, the manufacturing industry in Kitchener, Ontario, and a cattle farming business in Sarnia, Ontario are discussed to provide a snapshot of the challenges that business in Canada are facing as recession looms.

9021 ■ *"Oil Rich" in Canadian Business (Vol. 79, Winter 2006, No. 24, pp. 57)*
Pub: Rogers Media
Ed: Calvin Leung. **Description:** The efforts of John Risley, the Chairman of the Candaian firm Clearwater Fine Foods Inc., to educate consumers about the health aspects of seafood, are described.

9022 ■ *"Paying the Price" in Baltimore Business Journal (Vol. 28, July 9, 2010, No. 9, pp. 1)*
Pub: Baltimore Business Journal
Ed: Emily Mullin. **Description:** Crab prices have never been higher in Baltimore, Maryland and businesses have been led to count on strengthening demand for seafood. For instance, the average price for a dozen large crabs has increased by 5 percent to $58.90. How restaurants have responded to the increase in prices is discussed, along with factors that might have caused the harvest of smaller crabs.

9023 ■ *"Small Fish, Big Box Stores" in Hawaii Business (Vol. 53, November 2007, No. 5, pp. 55)*
Pub: Hawaii Business Publishing
Ed: Jolyn Okimoto Rosa. **Description:** Ohana Seafoods can be found at big-box stores such as Costco, Marukai and Don Quijote. Owner Jeffrey Yee spends his weekend at a farmers market to have direct contact with his customers and get feedback right away. Ohana offers ready-to-cook fish products, sauces and fish.

9024 ■ *"Something's Fishy" in Canadian Business (Vol. 83, September 14, 2010, No. 15, pp. 71)*
Pub: Rogers Media Ltd.
Ed: Matthew McClearn. **Description:** The Marine Stewardship Council (MSC) is offering a widely recognized blue check mark to certify that the seafood being sold has not been overfished, nor harvested in a way that harms the ecosystems. However, the MSC certification of Fraser sockeye salmon has put into question its credibility.

TRADE PERIODICALS

9025 ■ *Alternative Aquaculture Network*
Pub: Alternative Aquaculture Association
Ed: Steven Van Gorder, Editor. **Released:** Quarterly. **Description:** Provides research and practical information on the application of low-energy/high-productivity methods for small and medium scale aquaculture. Covers developments in integrated and recirculating methods of aquaculture, emphasizing energy efficiency and resource conservation. Recurring features include editorials, letters to the editor, book reviews, and a calendar of events.

9026 ■ *Aquaculture Magazine*
Pub: Achill River Corp.
URL(s): www.aquaculturemag.com/. **Ed:** Greg Gallagher. **Released:** Bimonthly **Price:** $24, Individuals; $30, Canada and Mexico; $44, Two years; $50, Canada and Mexico 2 years; $60, Other countries.

9027 ■ *Fishery Bulletin*
Pub: U.S. Government Printing Office
URL(s): fishbull.noaa.gov. **Released:** Quarterly **Price:** $32, Individuals; $44.80, Other countries.

9028 ■ *National Fisherman*
Pub: National Fisherman
URL(s): www.nationalfisherman.com. **Released:** Monthly **Price:** $14.95, Individuals; $24.95, Canada; $39.95, Other countries; $26.95, Two years; $46.95, Two years Canada; $76.95, Two years other countries.

9029 ■ *North American Journal of Aquaculture*
Pub: American Fisheries Society
Contact: Ghassan N. Rassam, Executive Director
URL(s): afsjournals.orgwww.tandfonline.com/toc/unaj20/current. **Ed:** Christopher C. Kohler, Bruce A. Barton. **Released:** Quarterly **Price:** $350, Individuals online; $399, Individuals print & online.

TRADE SHOWS AND CONVENTIONS

9030 ■ **American Fisheries Society Annual Meeting**
American Fisheries Society (AFS)
5410 Grosvenor Ln., Ste. 110
Bethesda, MD 20814-2199
Ph: (301)897-8616
Fax: (301)897-8096
Co. E-mail: main@fisheries.org
URL: http://www.fisheries.org
Contact: Ghassan N. Rassam, Executive Director
URL(s): www.fisheries.org. **Price:** $295, Pre-registered, members; $395, Onsite registered, members; $395, Pre-registered, non-members; $495, Onsite registered, non-members. **Frequency:** Annual. **Audience:** Fisheries biologists, administrators, and related professionals. **Principal Exhibits:** Equipment, supplies, and services related to fishery and marine biology.

CONSULTANTS

9031 ■ **Aquatic Control Inc.**
418 W State Rd., Ste. 258
Seymour, IN 47274
Ph: (812)497-2410
Free: 800-753-5253
Fax: (812)497-2460
Co. E-mail: sales@aquaticcontrol.com
URL: http://www.aquaticcontrol.com
Contact: Michael Whitacre, Manager
E-mail: mikew@aquaticcontrol.com
Scope: Provider of consulting services in aquatic and terrestrial ecology, including fish and wildlife population management, industrial fish and wild life enhancement programs, aquatic weed control, fish stocking, management of cooling reservoirs, and lake aeration equipment, consultation installation and maintenance. **Founded:** 1966.

9032 ■ **Canadian Fishery Consultants Ltd. (CFCL)**
1489 Hollis St.
Halifax, NS, Canada B3J 2R7
Ph: (902)422-4698
Fax: (902)422-8147
Co. E-mail: cfcl@canfish.com
URL: http://www.canfish.com
Contact: Alan Perry, President
E-mail: alanp@cbcl.ca
Scope: Natural resources management consultants specialize in supplying professional expertise to sectors within the fishing/aquaculture industry. Offers a range of expertise dealing with the culturing, harvesting, processing, and marketing of fish species. Projects executed have involved financial and technical feasibility studies; design, evaluation, and retrofitting of fish processing facilities; resource analysis; site selection; design of fish culturing facilities; and increasing commercial use of fish processing wastes and by-catch. Industries served: fisheries, resource sector, processing/fish handling industry, government departments, environmental sectors, port authorities,

international financing institutions. **Founded:** 1980. **Seminars:** Care of Live Shellfish During Shipping; Use of Fish Offal in Aquaculture Feed; Hold Live Fish and Shellfish; Exporting Goods and Services to the Caribbean.

9033 ■ **Southern Fish Culturists Inc.**
7608 US Highway 441 S
Leesburg, FL 34749
Ph: (352)787-1360
Contact: W. Chet Ross, Director
Scope: Provider of counseling services in problems of aquatic ecology: Effects of pollution on aquatic organisms, fish kill evaluations, environmental assessments, fish and bait culture, fisheries management and aquatic weed control. Serves private industries as well as government agencies. **Founded:** 1953.

LIBRARIES

9034 ■ **Auburn University - International Center for Aquaculture and Aquatic Environments Library—ICAAE.**
Dept. of Fisheries and Allied Aquacultures
203 Swingle Hall
Auburn University, AL 36849
Ph: (334)844-4786
Fax: (334)844-9208
Co. E-mail: fish@auburn.edu
URL: http://www.ag.auburn.edu/fish/international/academic-exchanges/
Contact: Bryan L. Duncan, Director
Scope: Aquaculture in fresh, brackish, and marine water; aquatic plants management; nutrition and feeds; parasites and disease; limnology; water quality and management for aquaculture; International development for fisheries and aquaculture. **Founded:** 1970. **Holdings:** 2500 books; Annual reports of the Fisheries Resources Unit, 1936 to present; 10,000 slides and pictures; 250 dissertations; 550 theses. **Telecommunication Services:** duncabl@auburn.edu.

9035 ■ **Columbia River Inter-Tribal Fish Commission - StreamNet Library**
729 NE Oregon St., Ste. 190
Portland, OR 97232-2107
Ph: (503)238-0667
Fax: (503)235-4228
Co. E-mail: oftl@critfc.org
URL: http://www.streamnetlibrary.org/
Contact: Lenora A. Oftedahl, Librarian
Scope: Fisheries science, habitat and watersheds, fisheries management, Columbia River Basin. **Services:** Interlibrary loan; copying; scanning; document delivery; library open to the public. **Founded:** 1992. **Holdings:** 60,000 volumes. **Subscriptions:** 20 journals and other serials.

9036 ■ **Desmond-Fish Library**
472 Rte. 403
Garrison, NY 10524
Ph: (845)424-3020
Fax: (845)424-4061
Co. E-mail: donick@highlands.com
URL: http://dfl.highlands.com
Contact: Polly Townsend
Scope: Hudson River art and history, Hamilton Fish. **Services:** Interlibrary loan; Wi-Fi; copying; library open to the public. **Founded:** 1980. **Holdings:** 29,000 books. **Subscriptions:** 80 journals and other serials. **Telecommunication Services:** dflstaff@highlands.com.

9037 ■ **Fisheries Museum of the Atlantic Library**
68 Bluenose Dr.
Lunenburg, NS, Canada B0J 2C0
Ph: (902)634-4794
Free: 866-579-4909
Fax: (902)634-8990
Co. E-mail: fma@gov.ns.ca
URL: http://museum.gov.ns.ca/fma/en/home/default.aspx
Contact: Heather-Anne Getson, Historian
Scope: Fisheries history, history, naval architecture, natural history of fish. **Services:** Library open to the public for reference use only. **Founded:** 1967. **Hold-**

ings: 2000 books; reports; archival material; 134 reels of microfilm; audio/visual materials. **Subscriptions:** 24 journals and other serials; 2 newspapers.

9038 ■ Oklahoma Fisheries Research Laboratory Library
500 E. Constellation St.
Norman, OK 73072-7900
Ph: (405)325-7288
Fax: (405)325-7631
Co. E-mail: gregsumm@aol.com
URL: http://www.biosurvey.ou.edu/fishlab.html
Contact: Greg L. Summers, Director
Scope: Freshwater fisheries, aquatic ecology, fish, limnology, fishery management, animal genetics. **Services:** Copying; library open to the public for reference use only. **Founded:** 1948. **Holdings:** 68,000 volumes.

9039 ■ U.S. National Oceanic & Atmospheric Administration - Library and Information Services Division - Central Library—NOAA.
1315 East-West Hwy.
SSMC 3, 2nd Fl.
Silver Spring, MD 20910
Ph: (301)713-2600, x124
Fax: (301)713-4598
Co. E-mail: library.reference@noaa.gov
URL: http://www.lib.noaa.gov
Contact: Neal Kaske, Director
Scope: Geodesy, surveying, oceanography, geophysics, geodetic and hydrographic surveying, photogrammetry, nautical and aeronautical cartography, fisheries, geodetic astronomy, meteorology, climatology, hydrology, atmospheric physics, ocean engineering, mathematics, computer science. **Services:** Interlibrary loan; copying; SDI; Library open to the public for reference use only. **Founded:** 1846. **Holdings:** 800,000 volumes; 100,100 bound periodical volumes; 100,400 bound documents; 19,500 microfiche; 34,000 reports, maps, charts, data publications. **Subscriptions:** 9040 journals and other serials.

RESEARCH CENTERS

9040 ■ Aquatic Research Institute
2242 Davis Ct.
Hayward, CA 94545
Ph: (510)782-4058
Fax: (510)784-0945
Co. E-mail: rofen@novalek.com
Contact: Dr. Robert R. Rofen, Director
Services: Consulting: in aquatic sciences and technology. **Founded:** 1962.

9041 ■ Auburn University - Alabama Agricultural Experiment Station - Department of Fisheries and Allied Aquacultures
203 Swingle Hall
Auburn, AL 36849
Ph: (334)844-4786
Fax: (334)844-9208
Co. E-mail: goodmrk@auburn.edu
URL: http://www.ag.auburn.edu/fish
Contact: Randall K. Goodman, Director
Founded: 1970. **Publications:** *Newsletter Quarterly* (Quarterly). **Educational Activities:** Aquaculture Training Program, from mid-March to mid-July; Master of Aquaculture Program; Philosophy Degree Programs, in aquaculture and fisheries; Department of Fisheries and Allied Aquacultures Short courses, for fisheries biologists and aquaculturists. **Telecommunication Services:** fish@auburn.edu.

9042 ■ Canadian Centre for Fisheries Innovation (CCFI)—Le Centre Canadien pour l'Innovation dans les Pecheries
PO Box 4920
Saint John's, NL, Canada A1C 5R3
Ph: (709)778-0517

Fax: (709)778-0516
Co. E-mail: robert.verge@mi.mun.ca
URL: http://www.ccfi.ca
Contact: Robert Verge, Managing Director
Services: Research and development, technology transfer, workshops, and information dissemination: to the Canadian fishery and aquaculture industry. **Founded:** 1989. **Publications:** *CCFI Annual report*; *Project Reports.* **Telecommunication Services:** ccfi@mi.mun.ca.

9043 ■ Maine Aquaculture Innovation Center (MAIC)
5717 Corbett Hall, Rm. 436
Orono, ME 04469-5717
Ph: (207)581-2263
Fax: (207)581-1479
Co. E-mail: maic@maineaquaculture.org
URL: http://www.maineaquaculture.org
Contact: Christopher V. Davis, Executive Director
Founded: 1989.

9044 ■ Memorial University of Newfoundland - Centre for Aquaculture and Seafood Development (CASD)
Fisheries & Marine Institute
Saint John's, NL, Canada A1C 5R3
Ph: (709)778-0532
Free: 800-563-5799
Fax: (709)778-0670
Co. E-mail: heather.manuel@mi.mun.ca
URL: http://www.mi.mun.ca/casd
Contact: Heather Manuel, Director
Services: Offers analytical services: such as nutritional, microbial, and quality assessments; Provides assistance: to companies in selecting equipment, processing, and quality control and productivity concerns. **Founded:** 1989. **Educational Activities:** Educational services and technical workshops, in harvesting, aquaculture, processing and industrial engineering. **Telecommunication Services:** casd@mi.mun.ca.

9045 ■ Oceanic Institute (OI)
41-202 Kalanianaole Hwy.
Waimanalo, HI 96795
Ph: (808)259-7951
Fax: (808)259-5971
Co. E-mail: hr@oceanicinstitute.org
URL: http://www.oceanicinstitute.org
Contact: Anthony C. Ostrowski, President
Services: Technical services. **Founded:** 1960. **Publications:** *OI Annual report* (Annual); *OI Research papers* (Periodic). **Educational Activities:** OI Training courses, in marine aquaculture practices; OI Workshops, in marine aquaculture practices.

9046 ■ State University of New York at Stony Brook - Living Marine Resources Institute (LIMRI)
School of Marine & Atmospheric Sciences
Stony Brook, NY 11794-5000
Ph: (631)632-8700
Fax: (631)632-8820
Co. E-mail: wwise@notes.cc.sunysb.edu
URL: http://www.somas.stonybrook.edu/institutes/lmri.html
Services: Public lectures. **Founded:** 1985. **Educational Activities:** Conferences and symposia (Periodic), on issues related to fisheries and their effects on the environment.

9047 ■ University of British Columbia - Fisheries Centre
Aquatic Ecosystems Research Laboratory
2202 Main Mall
Vancouver, BC, Canada V6T 1Z4
Ph: (604)822-2731
Fax: (604)822-8934
Co. E-mail: r.sumaila@fisheries.ubc.ca
URL: http://www.fisheries.ubc.ca
Contact: Prof. Ussif Rashid Sumaila, Director
Founded: 1992. **Publications:** *Fisheries Centre Research reports* (Bimonthly). **Educational Activities:** Fisheries Centre Seminars (Weekly), during

spring and fall, open to all; Fisheries Centre Workshops (Biennial). **Awards:** Research Scholarships. **Telecommunication Services:** office@fisheries.ubc.ca.

9048 ■ University of Idaho - Aquaculture Research Institute (ARI)
Bldg. 2260, Poultry Hill
Moscow, ID 83844-2260
Ph: (208)837-9096
Fax: (208)837-6047
Co. E-mail: rhardy@uidaho.edu
URL: http://www.webs.uidaho.edu/aquaculture
Contact: Prof. Ronald W. Hardy, Director
Services: Aquaculture industry assistance. **Founded:** 1988. **Publications:** *Idaho Aquaculture News* (Quarterly). **Educational Activities:** K-12 outreach activities; Workshops, short courses. **Awards:** ARI Graduate research assistantships. **Telecommunication Services:** aqua@uidaho.edu.

9049 ■ University of Maryland - Crane Aquaculture Facility
2145 Animal Sciences Ctr.
Department of Animal & Avian Sciences
College Park, MD 20742-2311
Ph: (301)405-1366
Fax: (301)405-7980
Co. E-mail: curry@umd.edu
URL: http://ansc.umd.edu/facilities/index.cfm?directory=MERC_aqua_unit.cfm
Contact: Dr. Curry Woods, Supervisor
Services: Provides juvenile to mature striped bass for outside research, demonstrations, and donations; Technology transfer for aquaculture industry. **Founded:** 1983.

9050 ■ University of Memphis - Ecological Research Center (ERC)
Park Ave. Campus
Memphis, TN 38152
Ph: (901)678-2594
Fax: (901)327-8001
Co. E-mail: bsimco@memphis.edu
URL: http://www.memphis.edu/erc
Contact: Dr. Bill A. Simco, Director
Founded: 1973.

9051 ■ University of New Hampshire - New Hampshire Sea Grant College Program
Chase Ocean Engineering Lab
24 Colovos Rd.
Durham, NH 03824-3505
Ph: (603)862-7007
Fax: (603)862-0241
Co. E-mail: jonathan.pennock@unh.edu
URL: http://www.seagrant.unh.edu
Contact: Jonathan R. Pennock, Director
Founded: 1976. **Educational Activities:** Coastal Floating Lab Program; Great Bay Coast Watch Program; Great Bay Living Lab Program; Sea Grant Extension Program; Sea Trek Program; UNH Marine Docent Program.

9052 ■ Western Regional Aquaculture Center (WRAC)
School of Aquatic & Fishery Sciences, Box 355020
University of Washington
Seattle, WA 98195-5020
Ph: (206)543-4291
Fax: (206)685-4674
Co. E-mail: grahamy@u.washington.edu
URL: http://www.fish.washington.edu/wrac
Contact: Dr. Graham Young, Executive Director
Services: Information exchange between industry and researchers. **Founded:** 1985. **Publications:** *Waterlines* (Semiannual). **Educational Activities:** Cooperative research projects; Extension educational programs. **Telecommunication Services:** wrac@u.washington.edu.

ASSOCIATIONS AND OTHER ORGANIZATIONS

9053 ■ **American Floorcovering Alliance (AFA)**
210 W Cuyler St.
Dalton, GA 30720
Ph: (706)278-4101
Free: 800-288-4101
Fax: (706)278-5323
Co. E-mail: afa@americanfloor.org
URL: http://www.americanfloor.org
Contact: Wanda J. Ellis, Executive Director
URL(s): www.floor-tek.com. **Description:** Floorcovering manufacturers and companies providing services or supplies to the floor covering industry. Promotes the floor covering industry. Provides insurance programs for members. **Founded:** 1979. **Publications:** *Floor Covering Weekly* (Weekly); *Floor Focus* (Monthly); *Floor Tek Source Guide* (Biennial); *Industry Profile* (Quarterly); *Floor Tek Source Guide* (Biennial). **Educational Activities:** Floor-Tek (Biennial).

9054 ■ **Carpet and Rug Institute (CRI)**
PO Box 2048
Dalton, GA 30722-2048
Ph: (706)278-3176
Free: 800-882-8846
Fax: (706)278-8835
Co. E-mail: snewberry@carpet-rug.org
URL: http://www.carpet-rug.org
Contact: Werner Braun, President
Description: Represents the carpet and rug industry; sources of extensive carpet information for consumers, writers, interior designers, specifiers, facility managers, architects, builders and building owners and managers. **Scope:** functional and financial benefits of carpet, selection, installation, construction, fiber characteristics, maintenance, technical, environment and carpet. **Founded:** 1968. **Publications:** *Carpet and Rug Manufacturing Plants and Corporate Locations in the U.S. and Canada* (Annual).

9055 ■ **Floor Covering Installation Contractors Association (FCICA)**
7439 Millwood Dr.
West Bloomfield, MI 48322
Ph: (248)661-5015
Fax: (248)661-5018
Co. E-mail: keo@fcica.com
URL: http://www.fcica.com
Contact: Gerry Swift, Chairman
Description: Installation contractors, carpet manufacturers, and suppliers to the installation trade. Aims to establish acceptable levels of performance for the carpet installation industry; to promote standards of business ethics; to encourage quality installations. Acts as liaison with retailers, manufacturers, and suppliers; represents the industry before government agencies regarding proposed or enacted regulation and legislation. Fosters the sale and use of the industry's products and services. Serves as clearinghouse for resolving problems of mutual interest inside and outside the industry. Assists local installation workrooms/ contractors' groups. Sponsors training programs. **Founded:** 1982. **Publications:** *The Flooring Contractor* (Quarterly). **Educational Activities:** Mid-Year Meeting (Annual).

9056 ■ **North American Association of Floor Covering Distributors (NAFCD)**
401 N Michigan Ave., Ste. 2200
Chicago, IL 60611
Ph: (312)321-6836
Fax: (312)673-6962
Co. E-mail: info@nafcd.org
URL: http://www.nafcd.org
Contact: Michelle Parrilli Miller, Executive Director
Description: Floor covering distributors and firms selling to them. Aims to promote, protect, and advance the best interests of wholesale floor covering distribution; to foster sound business principles in all phases of floor covering wholesaling; to increase the use of wholesale floor covering products by the retailer; to improve understanding between manufacturers and wholesalers of floor covering products, and increase distribution of floor covering and related products through wholesale distribution channels; to improve the conditions under which the industry must operate; to collect and disseminate pertinent industry data; to assist its members through education, research, and training. **Founded:** 1971. **Publications:** *National Association of Floor Covering Distributors--Membership* (Annual). **Awards:** Young Executive of the Year (Annual).

9057 ■ **Resilient Floor Covering Institute (RFCI)**
115 Broad St., Ste. 201
LaGrange, GA 30240-2757
Ph: (706)882-3833
Fax: (706)882-3880
Co. E-mail: info@rfci.com
URL: http://www.rfci.com
Contact: Dean Thompson, President
Description: Supports the manufacturers of vinyl composition tile, solid vinyl tile, or sheet vinyl and rubber tile and people who use its products. Provides technical information and data regarding the resilient flooring industry. **Founded:** 1929.

9058 ■ **Terrazzo Tile and Marble Association of Canada (TTMAC)**
163 Buttermill Ave., Unit 8
Concord, ON, Canada L4K 3X8
Ph: (905)660-9640
Free: 800-201-8599
Fax: (905)660-0513
Co. E-mail: association@ttmac.com
URL: http://www.ttmac.com
Contact: Estelle Davis, President
Description: Aims to develop a method of standardizing terrazzo, tile and marble installation techniques. Works as a technical resource and liaison for architects, designers and engineers. **Founded:** 1944.

9059 ■ **World Floor Covering Association (WFCA)**
2211 E Howell Ave.
Anaheim, CA 92806
Ph: (714)978-6440
Free: 800-624-6880
Fax: (714)978-6066
Co. E-mail: wfca@wfca.org
URL: http://www.wfca.org
Contact: D. Christopher Davis, President
URL(s): wfca-pro.org. **Description:** Retail floorcovering store owners and managers; floorcovering distributors and manufacturers. Provides liaison, through a Washington, DC lobbyist, between the membership and government organizations that affect the business. Conducts seminars promoting professional development and increased profits; compiles business activity statistics; sponsors research. **Founded:** 1995. **Publications:** *World Floor Covering Association--Annual Management Report.* **Educational Activities:** Surfaces (Annual); Surfaces (Annual). **Awards:** Hall of Fame (Annual).

REFERENCE WORKS

9060 ■ **"Behind the Scenes: Companies At the Heart of Everyday Life" in Inc. (February 2008, pp. 26-27)**
Pub: Gruner & Jahr USA Publishing
Ed: Athena Schindelheim. **Description:** Profiles of companies providing services to airports, making the environment safer and more efficient, as well as more comfortable for passengers and workers. Centerpoint Manufacturing provides garbage bins that can safely contain explosions producing thousands of pounds of pressure; Infax, whose software displays arrival and departure information on 19-foot-wide screens; Lavi Industries, whose products include security barricades, hostess stands, and salad-bar sneeze guards; and SATech maker of rubber flooring that helps ease discomfort for workers having to stand for long periods of time.

9061 ■ **Floor Covering Weekly--Annual Product Source Guide**
Pub: FCW
Contact: Thomas Young, Manager, Production
E-mail: tdyoung@hearst.com
URL(s): floorcoveringweekly.com. **Ed:** Santiago Montero. **Released:** Annual; Latest edition 2011. **Price:** $66, Canada; $61, Individuals; $101, Two years; $184, Out of country. **Publication includes:** Lists of manufacturers and importers of carpet, rugs, carpet cushion, fiber, resilient wood, and ceramic floor coverings; separate listing of distributors by state, retail groups and associations. **Entries include:** For manufacturers--Company name, address, phone, regional sales offices, names and titles of key personnel, local distributors, products. For distributors--Company name, address, phone, manufacturers represented. **Arrangement:** Alphabetical. **Indexes:** Geographical by distributor.

9062 ■ **"Ground Floor Opportunity" in Small Business Opportunities (July 2008)**
Pub: Entrepreneur Press
Contact: Perlman Neil, President
Description: Profile of Doug Disney, the founder of the booming franchise Tile Outlet Always in Stock, which sells ceramic and porcelain tile and stone

products at wholesale prices; Disney found inspiration in a book he read in two days and that motivated him to expand his venture into a huge franchise opportunity.

9063 ■ "Info Junkie" in Crain's Chicago Business (Vol. 34, October 24, 2011, No. 42, pp. 35)

Pub: Crain Communications Inc.

Ed: Christina Le Beau. **Description:** Greg Colando, president of Flor Inc., an eco-friendly carpet company located I Chicago discusses his marketing program to increase sales.

9064 ■ North American Association of Floor Covering Distributors--Membership Directory

Pub: North American Association of Floor Covering Distributors

URL(s): www.nafcd.org. **Released:** Annual **Covers:** Association happenings and approximately 300 member distributors and suppliers of floor coverings. **Entries include:** Company name, location (code indicates if a branch location), products, contacts.

9065 ■ "Take the Right Approach to Concrete Polishing Rentals" in Rental Product News (Vol. 33, June 2011)

Pub: Cygnus Business Media

Ed: Jenny Lescohier. **Description:** A recent trend in flooring is concrete polishing for a practical, beautiful and sustainable way to decorate homes and businesses. Things to keep in mind when assessing the value of adding concrete polishing equipment to an existing rental store are evaluated.

STATISTICAL SOURCES

9066 ■ Carpets and Rugs Market U.S.A.

Pub: Rector Press, Ltd.

Contact: Lewis Sckolnick, President

Released: 2009. **Price:** Contact Rector Press.

9067 ■ RMA Annual Statement Studies

Pub: Risk Management Association

Contact: Kevin M. Blakey, President

Released: Annual. **Price:** $175.00 2006-07 edition, $105.00. **Description:** Contains composite balance sheets and income statements for more than 360 industries, including the accounting, auditing, and bookkeeping industries. Also contains five years of comparative historical data for discerning trends. Includes 16 commonly used ratios, computed for most of the size groupings for nearly every industry.

9068 ■ Standard & Poor's Industry Surveys

Pub: Standard & Poor's Corp.

Released: Annual. **Price:** $3633.00. **Description:** Two-volume book that examines the prospects for specific industries, including trucking. Also provides analyses of trends and problems, statistical tables and charts, and comparative company analyses.

TRADE PERIODICALS

9069 ■ FCICA Update

Pub: Floor Covering Installation Contractors Association

Released: Bi-Weekly. **Description:** Features articles on members and conferences in the floor covering installation industry. Recurring features include interviews, news of research, and a calendar of events.

9070 ■ Floor Covering News

Pub: RO-EL Productions Inc.

URL(s): www.floorcoveringnews.net/. **Ed:** Albert Wahnon. **Released:** Biweekly

9071 ■ Floor Covering Weekly

Pub: FCW

Contact: Thomas Young, Manager, Production

E-mail: tdyoung@hearst.com

URL(s): floorcoveringweekly.com. **Released:** Weekly **Price:** $60, U.S. and Canada; $110, U.S. and Canada two years.

9072 ■ Floor Focus

Pub: Floor Focus Inc.

URL(s): www.floordaily.net/FloorFocus/. **Ed:** Brian Hamilton. **Released:** Monthly **Price:** $49.95, Individuals; $59.95, Out of country; $99.95, Other countries.

9073 ■ ICS Cleaning Specialist: Information for Today's Floor Care Professional

Pub: Specialist Publications Inc.

URL(s): www.icsmag.com. **Ed:** Jeffrey Stouffer. **Released:** Monthly **Price:** Free.

9074 ■ National Floor Trends Magazine

Pub: Specialist Publications Inc.

URL(s): www.ntlfloortrends.com/. **Ed:** Arpi Nalbandian, Jeff Golden. **Released:** Monthly **Price:** Free.

9075 ■ Rug News

Pub: Rug News Magazine

URL(s): www.museumbooks.com/rugnews/index. php. **Ed:** Dasha Morgan. **Released:** Monthly **Price:** $78, Individuals; $100, Canada; $162, Other countries; $442, Other countries to India by air; $120, Individuals delivered via first class mail.

9076 ■ Strategy

Pub: North American Association of Floor Covering Distributors

Ed: Dennis Coyle, Editor. **Released:** BIM. **Price:** Included in membership. **Description:** Provides news of the Association and the floor covering industry. Recurring features include news of members, notices of publications available, news of educational opportunities, reports of meetings, and a calendar of events.

TRADE SHOWS AND CONVENTIONS

9077 ■ Chicago Design Show

Merchandise Mart Properties Inc.

222 Merchandise Mart, Ste. 470

Chicago, IL 60654

Ph: (312)527-4141

Free: 800-677-6278

URL: http://www.merchandisemart.com

URL(s): www.merchandisemart.com. **Frequency:** Annual. **Audience:** Interior design trade professionals and consumers. **Principal Exhibits:** Contemporary design in furniture, fashion, food.

CONSULTANTS

9078 ■ Surface Technologies Inc. (STI)

18 Willotta Dr.

Suisun City, CA 94534-1446

Ph: (707)864-6313

Free: 800-241-2982

Contact: Richard E. Larson, President

Scope: Specializes in carpet, tile, wood, stone, and vinyl floor covering inspection and testing. Evaluates floor covering samples for durability, clean ability, and longevity of appearance. Trains hotel and other institutional personnel to maintain, clean, and repair floor coverings. Industries served include floor and wall covering and upholstery fabric manufacturers, as well as producers of all types of architectural surfaces. **Founded:** 1998. **Seminars:** Complaint Reduction Program; Selling Floor Covering Defensively; Turn Complaints into More Business; Presented to department stores and floor covering specialty stores.

FRANCHISES AND BUSINESS OPPORTUNITIES

9079 ■ Carpet Network

109 Gaither Dr., Ste. 302

Mt. Laurel, NJ 08054

Ph: (800)821-1635

Free: 800-428-1067

URL: http://www.carpetnetwork.com

URL(s): www.aboutgreenfloors.com. **Description:** Mobile carpet and window treatment business. **No. of Franchise Units:** 27. **Founded:** 1992.. **Franchised:** 1992. **Equity Capital Needed:** $68,485-

$92,705. **Franchise Fee:** $39,500. **Royalty Fee:** 7-2%. **Financial Assistance:** Limited third party financing available. **Training:** 2 week training program consisting of 1 week home study course including video aids; 1 week at Carpet Network College, located in Mt. Laurel, NJ. Ongoing personalized support by the home office, 24-hr. toll-free help-Line, newsletters, workshops, marketing and operational support, global website and intranet system.

9080 ■ Floor Coverings International

Floor Coverings International, Ltd.

5250 Triangle Pky., Ste. 100

Norcross, GA 30082-5201

Ph: (800)955-4324

Free: 800-342-5324

Fax: (404)366-4606

Description: Mobile floor covering retailer. **No. of Franchise Units:** 110. **Founded:** 1988.. **Franchised:** 1988. **Equity Capital Needed:** $90,000-$100,000. **Franchise Fee:** $30,000. **Financial Assistance:** Yes. **Training:** Yes.

9081 ■ The Mad Matter

The Mad Matter Franchise Corp.

PO Box 128

Cumming, GA 30028

Ph: (800)685-1144

Fax: (770)887-9240

Description: Sale and installation of specialty flooring. **No. of Company-Owned Units:** 2. **Founded:** 1992.. **Franchised:** 2003. **Equity Capital Needed:** Estimated $69,000-$121,000, includes franchise fee. **Franchise Fee:** $30,000-$50,000. **Training:** Yes.

9082 ■ MarbleLife

MarbleLife, Inc.

300 Northstar Ct.

Sandord, FL 32771

Ph: (407)302-4171

Fax: (407)302-9311

Description: Stone restoration and preservation. **No. of Franchise Units:** 55. **Founded:** 1989.. **Franchised:** 1990. **Equity Capital Needed:** $25,000 liquid; net worth $150,000. **Franchise Fee:** $15,000-$75,000. **Financial Assistance:** Yes. **Training:** Yes.

9083 ■ Mr. Sandless Inc.

2970 Concord Rd.

Aston, PA 19014

Ph: (610)364-2080

Free: 877-966-3360

Fax: (610)364-2081

URL: http://www.mrsandless.com

Description: Sandless wood floor refinishing. **No. of Franchise Units:** 212. **No. of Company-Owned Units:** 12. **No. of Operating Units:** 268. **Founded:** 2004.. **Franchised:** 2005. **Equity Capital Needed:** $12,350-$62,605. **Franchise Fee:** $2,500-$16,000. **Royalty Fee:** 5%. **Financial Assistance:** Third party financing available and assistance with franchise fee. **Training:** Provides 1 week at headquarters and ongoing support.

9084 ■ N-Hance

1530 N 1000 West

Logan, UT 84321

Ph: (435)755-0099

Free: 866-642-6231

Fax: (435)604-8452

URL: http://www.nhance.com

URL(s): www.nhancefranchise.com. **Description:** Wood floor and cabinet renewal systems. **No. of Franchise Units:** 201. **No. of Company-Owned Units:** 218. **Founded:** 2001.. **Franchised:** 2003. **Equity Capital Needed:** $30,500-$125,900. **Franchise Fee:** $21,200-$47,000. **Royalty Fee:** $220-$660/month. **Financial Assistance:** Limited in-house financing available. **Training:** Offers 1 week on training at headquarters and ongoing support.

9085 ■ Prosource Wholesale Floorcoverings

CCA Global Partners

4301 Earth City Expy.

Earth City, MO 63045

Free: 800-466-6984 Fax: (314)506-0953
Co. E-mail: mjameson@pswwholesale.com
URL: http://www.prosourcefloors.com
Description: Members-only wholesale flooring showroom. **No. of Franchise Units:** 138. **No. of Company-Owned Units:** 3. **Founded:** 1990.. **Franchised:** 1991. **Equity Capital Needed:** $750,000 net worth; $375,000 minimum investment. **Franchise Fee:** $46,450. **Financial Assistance:** Yes. **Training:** Initial training provided at headquarters in St. Louis and ongoing support.

9086 ■ Re-Bath, LLC
421 W Alameda Dr.
Tempe, AZ 85282
Ph: (480)844-1575
Fax: (480)833-7199
Description: Custom-manufactured, high-impact acrylic bathtub liners, wall systems and shower liners designed to go over existing bathtubs, ceramic tile walls and shower bases. **No. of Franchise Units:** 225. **Founded:** 1979.. **Franchised:** 1991. **Equity Capital Needed:** $3,500-$89,000. **Franchise Fee:** $6,000-$40,000. **Financial Assistance:** Yes. **Training:** Phases of installation, operations, sales and marketing. Both classroom and hands-on training.

LIBRARIES

9087 ■ Congoleum Corporation Technical Research Library
PO Box 3127
Mercerville, NJ 08619-0127
Ph: (609)584-3601
Fax: (609)584-3305
URL: http://www.congoleum.com
Contact: Joanne L. Stout
Scope: Plastics, chemistry, paper, floor coverings, coatings. **Services:** Library not open to the public. **Founded:** 1920. **Holdings:** 1500 books; official patent gazettes (current year). **Subscriptions:** 35 journals and other serials.

ASSOCIATIONS AND OTHER ORGANIZATIONS

9088 ■ American Institute of Floral Designers (AIFD)
720 Light St.
Baltimore, MD 21230
Ph: (410)752-3318
Fax: (410)752-8295
Co. E-mail: aifd@assnhqtrs.com
URL: http://www.aifd.com
Contact: Tom Bowling, President
Description: Active floral designers, associates, retired floral designers and other individuals. Works to promote the profession and art of floral design. Maintains student chapter. **Founded:** 1965. **Awards:** AIFD Award of Design Influence (Periodic); AIFD Award of Merit - Industry (Annual); AIFD Award of Merit - Non Industry (Annual); Award of Distinguished Service to AIFD (Annual); Special Award of Recognition (Periodic); Award of Design Influence; Award of Merit - Industry; Special Award of Recognition; Award of Distinguished Service to AIFD.

9089 ■ Canadian Ornamental Plant Foundation (COPF)
PO Box 26029
Guelph, ON, Canada N1E 6W1
Ph: (519)341-6761
Free: 800-265-1629
Fax: (519)341-6748
Co. E-mail: info@copf.org
URL: http://www.copf.org
Contact: Peggy Walsh Craig, Director, Communications
Description: Growers and breeders of ornamental plants. Encourages development of new plant strains. Strengthens relations between growers and breeders; provides support to research projects. **Founded:** 1964. **Publications:** COPF News (Quarterly). **Awards:** Keith Laver Award.

9090 ■ Canadian Rosarian
116 Belsize Dr.
Toronto, ON, Canada M4S 1L7
Co. E-mail: canrosesociety@aol.com
URL: http://www.canadianrosesociety.org
Contact: Shari-Lyn Safir, President
Released: Annual **Price:** included in membership dues.

9091 ■ Canadian Rose Society (CRS)
116 Belsize Dr.
Toronto, ON, Canada M4S 1L7
Co. E-mail: canrosesociety@aol.com
URL: http://www.canadianrosesociety.org
Contact: Shari-Lyn Safir, President
Description: Noncommercial rose growers and rose enthusiasts. Promotes the hobby of rose breeding and growing. Conducts educational programs; sponsors competitions; maintains speakers' bureau. **Founded:** 1914. **Publications:** Canadian Rosarian (Annual); The CRS CommPoster (5/year); The Annual (Annual).

9092 ■ COPF News
PO Box 26029
Guelph, ON, Canada N1E 6W1
Ph: (519)341-6761
Free: 800-265-1629
Fax: (519)341-6748
Co. E-mail: info@copf.org
URL: http://www.copf.org
Contact: Peggy Walsh Craig, Director, Communications
Released: Quarterly

9093 ■ The CRS CommPoster
116 Belsize Dr.
Toronto, ON, Canada M4S 1L7
Co. E-mail: canrosesociety@aol.com
URL: http://www.canadianrosesociety.org
Contact: Shari-Lyn Safir, President
Released: 5/year **Price:** included in membership dues.

9094 ■ Flowers Canada (FC)
99 5th Ave., Ste. 305
Ottawa, ON, Canada K1S 5P5
Free: 800-447-5147
Fax: (866)671-8091
Co. E-mail: flowers@flowerscanada.org
URL: http://flowerscanada.ca
Contact: James Fuller, Chairman
Description: Retail florists, distributors, and greenhouse operators. Promotes growth and development in the domestic floriculture industry. Provides technical and promotional services to floral retailers, producers, and distributors; sponsors continuing professional development and educational programs for members. Represents members' interests before government agencies; serves as a liaison between members and related trade organizations. Makes available discount credit card, insurance, automotive fleet, lodging, and other business services to members. **Founded:** 1897. **Subscriptions:** reports photographs. **Publications:** News Vine (Bimonthly). **Awards:** Flowers Canada Friend of Floriculture (Periodic); Walter Good Award (Annual).

9095 ■ Heritage Rose Foundation (HRF)
PO Box 831414
Richardson, TX 75083
Co. E-mail: steprose@mac.com
URL: http://www.heritagerosefoundation.org
Contact: Stephen Scanniello, President
Description: Individuals interested in old-fashioned roses. Collects, preserves, studies, and promotes old-fashioned roses. Locates commercial sources of specific old-fashioned roses and identifies "mystery" roses; provides information on growing roses from cuttings and photographing them to facilitate identification. Conducts educational programs. **Founded:** 1986. **Publications:** Heritage Rose Foundation News (Quarterly); Rosa Mundi (Semiannual).

9096 ■ News Vine
99 5th Ave., Ste. 305
Ottawa, ON, Canada K1S 5P5
Free: 800-447-5147
Fax: (866)671-8091
Co. E-mail: flowers@flowerscanada.org
URL: http://flowerscanada.ca
Contact: James Fuller, Chairman
Released: Bimonthly

9097 ■ Society of American Florists
1601 Duke St.
Alexandria, VA 22314-3406
Ph: (703)836-8700
Free: 800-336-4743
Fax: (703)836-8705
Co. E-mail: info@safnow.org
URL: http://www.safnow.org
Contact: Leo M. Roozen, Chairman of the Board
Description: Growers, wholesalers, retailers, and allied tradesmen in the floral industry. Lobbies Congress on behalf of the industry; sponsors educational programs; promotes the floral industry; prepares materials for consumers and for high school and college students; provides business resources. Sponsors Floricultural Hall of Fame, American Academy of Floriculture, and Professional Floral Commentators International. Compiles statistics; sponsors competitions. **Publications:** Dateline: Washington; SAF Floral Management (Monthly); Floral Management (Monthly); Floral Management--Buyers Guide Issue (Irregular); Who's Who in Floriculture (Biennial). **Educational Activities:** Congressional Action Days (Annual). **Awards:** Floriculture Hall of Fame; Sylvia Cup Design Competition.

9098 ■ Wholesale Florist and Florist Supplier Association (WF&FSA)
Horn Point Harbor Marina
105 Eastern Ave., Ste. 104
Annapolis, MD 21403
Ph: (410)940-6580
Free: 888-289-3372
Fax: (410)263-1659
Co. E-mail: info@wffsa.org
URL: http://www.wffsa.org
Contact: Patricia A. Lilly, Executive Vice President
Description: Proprietorships, partnerships or corporations conducting wholesale businesses in fresh flowers, greens, or plants, or engaged in the manufacture and/or wholesaling of florist supplies; others actively engaged in the floral industry are associate members. Preserves and strengthens the wholesale florists' position in the floral industry. Provides a unified voice to promote the wholesalers' contributions to the industry. **Founded:** 1926. **Awards:** Leland T. Kintzele Award (Annual).

DIRECTORIES OF EDUCATIONAL PROGRAMS

9099 ■ Directory of Private Accredited Career Schools and Colleges of Technology
Pub: Accrediting Commission of Career Schools and Colleges of Technology
Contact: Michale S. McComis, Executive Director
Released: On web page. **Price:** Free. **Description:** Covers 3900 accredited post-secondary programs that provide training programs in business, trade, and

technical fields, including various small business endeavors. Entries offer school name, address, phone, description of courses, job placement assistance, and requirements for admission. Arrangement is alphabetical.

REFERENCE WORKS

9100 ■ *"Cold-Storage Cargo Facility a Late Bloomer" in Houston Business Journal (Vol. 40, August 28, 2009, No. 16, pp. 1A)*
Pub: American City Business Journals
Ed: Jennifer Dawson. **Description:** Trammell Crow Company leased half of the 61,000 square foot IAH International Air Cargo Centre II to Tradewinds Cargo Handling. The facility, located at George Bush Intercontinental Airport, is intended to be a destination of fresh flowers and food from Latin America.

9101 ■ *"Floral-Design Kiosk Business in Colorado Springs Blossoming" in Colorado Springs Business Journal (September 24, 2010)*
Pub: Dolan Media Newswires
Ed: Monica Mendoza. **Description:** Profile of Shellie Greto and her mother Jackie Martin who started a wholesale flower business in their garage. The do-it-yourself floral arrangement firm started a kiosk business in supermarkets called Complete Design.

9102 ■ *"Flower Confidential' in Business Horizons (Vol. 51, January-February 2008, No. 1, pp. 73)*
Pub: Elsevier Advanced Technology Publications
Ed: Mimi Dollinger. **Description:** Review of the book, 'Flower Confidential: The Good, the Bad, and the Beautiful Business of Flowers', which offers insight for anyone starting or running a successful flower shop.

9103 ■ *Flower Confidential: The Good, the Bad, and the Beautiful in the Business of Flowers*
Pub: Algonquin Publishing
Ed: Amy Stewart. **Released:** January 4, 2007. **Price:** $23.95. **Description:** Author mixes botany, history and commerce for small business owners running a florist shop.

9104 ■ *"Holiday Bloom: Event Designer Collin Abraham Heightens Glamour With Florals" in Black Enterprise (Vol. 41, November 2010, No. 4)*
Pub: Earl G. Graves Publishing Co. Inc.
Ed: Sean Drakes. **Description:** Profile of Collin Abraham, who works out of his Harlem boutique to arrange unique floral pieces to complement the social gatherings and main events he plans for his clients.

9105 ■ *"Verizon Small Business Awards Give Companies a Technology Edge" in Hispanic Business (July-August 2009, pp. 32)*
Pub: Hispanic Business
Ed: Patricia Marroquin. **Description:** Verizon Wireless awards grants to twenty-four companies in California. The winning businesses ranged from barbershop to coffee shop, tattoo parlor to florist.

9106 ■ *"VISA: Canadians Spend $97 Million on Mom This Mother's Day" in Canadian Corporate News (May 16, 2007)*
Pub: Comtex News Network Inc.
Description: Visa Canada finds that Canadians are spending more on Mother's Day in recent years. Since 2002, sales of jewelry, flowers, and cards have climbed steadily in the week before Mother's Day weekend.

9107 ■ *Wholesale Florist & Florist Supplier Association--Membership Directory*
Pub: Wholesale Florists & Florist Supplier Association
URL(s): www.wffsa.org. **Released:** Biennial; summer/winter. **No. of Listings:** 1,275. **Entries include:** Company name, address, phone, names of executives, list of products or services. **Arrangement:** Geographical. **Indexes:** Alphabetical.

STATISTICAL SOURCES

9108 ■ *RMA Annual Statement Studies*
Pub: Risk Management Association
Contact: Kevin M. Blakey, President
Released: Annual. **Price:** $175.00 2006-07 edition, $105.00. **Description:** Contains composite balance sheets and income statements for more than 360 industries, including the accounting, auditing, and bookkeeping industries. Also contains five years of comparative historical data for discerning trends. Includes 16 commonly used ratios, computed for most of the size groupings for nearly every industry.

TRADE PERIODICALS

9109 ■ *California Garden*
Pub: San Diego Floral Association
Contact: Barbara Clark, President
URL(s): www.sdfloral.org/magazine.htm. **Released:** Bimonthly

9110 ■ *Flora Magazine*
Pub: Cenflo Inc.
URL(s): www.cenflo.com/flora.html. **Released:** Bimonthly **Price:** $32.95, Individuals; $54, Two years; $16.95, Students; $52.95, Canada; $92, Canada 2 years.

9111 ■ *Florists' Review Magazine*
Pub: Florist's Review Enterprises Inc.
Contact: David Coake, Director
URL(s): www.floristsreview.com/main/. **Ed:** Kelsey E. Smith. **Released:** Monthly **Price:** $42, Individuals; $72, Two years; $82, Individuals three years; $55, Canada; $85, Canada 2 years; $60, Other countries; $90, Other countries 2 years.

9112 ■ *Flowers&*
Pub: Teleflora
Contact: Phil Kleweno, President
URL(s): www.myteleflora.com/flowers-and-magazine. aspx. **Released:** Monthly **Price:** $66, Individuals; $90, Canada; $54, Students one time; $102, Out of area.

9113 ■ *Fresh Facts*
Pub: Fresh Produce and Floral Council
Contact: Carissa Mace, President
Ed: Linda Stine, Editor. **Released:** Weekly. **Price:** Free. **Description:** Discusses trends and issues in fresh fruit, vegetable, and floral supply.

9114 ■ *Green Profit Magazine*
Pub: Ball Publishing
Contact: Anissa Lobrillo, Director
URL(s): www.ballpublishing.com/GreenProfit/CoverStory.aspx?articleid=18051. **Ed:** Chris Beytes. **Released:** 9/yr.

9115 ■ *Greenhouse Management and Production*
Pub: G.I.E. Media Inc.
Contact: Chris Foster, President
URL(s): www.greenhousemanagementonline.com/. **Ed:** David Kuack. **Released:** Monthly

9116 ■ *Michigan Florist: A publication of the Michigan Floral Association*
Pub: Michigan Floral Association
URL(s): www.michiganfloral.org/. **Ed:** Heidi Anderson. **Released:** Bimonthly **Price:** $50, Members; $5, Single issue.

VIDEOCASSETTES/ AUDIOCASSETTES

9117 ■ *Floral Design*
Silver Mine Video Inc.
31316 Via Colinas, Ste. 104
Westlake Village, CA 91362-6715
Ph: (818)707-0300

Fax: (818)707-1606
Co. E-mail: quksil@aol.com
URL: http://www.quicksilverrecords.zoomshare.com
Contact: Howard L. Silver, President
Released: 19??. **Price:** $29.95. **Description:** Presents easy to make flower arrangements. **Availability:** VHS.

9118 ■ *Floral Fundamentals*
Nancy's Notions Ltd.
333 Beichl Ave.
P.O. Box 683
Beaver Dam, WI 53916-0683
Ph: (920)887-7321
Free: 800-725-0361
Fax: (800)255-8119
Co. E-mail: customerservice@nancysnotions.com
URL: http://www.nancysnotions.com
Released: 1989. **Description:** Kathy demonstrates how to arrange flowers in three different styles: the mound, the triangle, and the centerpiece. **Availability:** VHS.

9119 ■ *Flower Arrangements Made Easy*
Tapeworm Video Distributors
25876 The Old Road #141
Stevenson Ranch, CA 91381
Ph: (661)257-4904
Fax: (661)257-4820
Co. E-mail: sales@tapeworm.com
URL: http://www.tapeworm.com
Released: 19??. **Price:** $14.95. **Description:** Expert floral designer Kim Alexander demonstrates how to create three fresh flower arrangements. **Availability:** VHS.

9120 ■ *The Flower Shop Series*
RMI Media
1365 N. Winchester St.
Olathe, KS 66061-5880
Ph: (913)768-1696
Free: 800-745-5480
Fax: (800)755-6910
Co. E-mail: actmedia@act.org
URL: http://www.actmedia.com
Released: 1987. **Description:** Flower expert Phil Easter demonstrates the art of floral design using various themes. **Availability:** VHS; 3/4 U.

TRADE SHOWS AND CONVENTIONS

9121 ■ *Great Lakes Floral Expo*
Michigan Floral Association
1152 Haslett Rd.
Haslett, MI 48840
Ph: (517)575-0110
Fax: (517)575-0115
Co. E-mail: rcrittenden@michiganfloral.org
URL: http://www.michiganfloral.org
URL(s): www.michiganfloral.org. **Frequency:** Annual. **Principal Exhibits:** Floral equipment, supplies, and services.

9122 ■ *Northeast Floral Expo*
Connecticut Florists Association
590 Main St., Bart Ctr.
Monroe, CT 06468
Free: 800-352-6946
Fax: (203)261-5429
Co. E-mail: ctflorists@aol.com
URL: http://www.flowersplantsinct.com/cfaindex.htm
URL(s): www.northeastfloralexpo.com/. **Frequency:** Annual. **Audience:** Florists and related trade professionals. **Principal Exhibits:** Florist supplies, cut flowers, potted plants, wire services, and dried and artificial flowers and plants. **Dates and Locations:** , Radisson Center Hotel. **Telecommunication Services:** ctflorists@aol.com.

9123 ■ *Nursery/Landscape Expo*
Texas Nursery & Landscape Association
7730 S. IH-35
Austin, TX 78745-6698
Ph: (512)280-5182
Free: 800-880-0343

Fax: (512)280-3012
Co. E-mail: info@tnlaonline.org
URL: http://www.txnla.org
URL(s): www.txnla.org. **Frequency:** Annual. **Audience:** Nursery, landscape and related trades professionals. **Principal Exhibits:** Plant materials including foliage, bedding plants, trees, palms; allied products including machinery, equipment and supplies for horticulture and landscape industry. **Dates and Locations:** , Convention Center.

9124 ■ OFA Short Course
Ohio Florists Association
2130 Stella Ct., Ste. 200
Columbus, OH 43215-1033
Ph: (614)487-1117
Fax: (614)487-1216
Co. E-mail: ofa@ofa.org
URL: http://www.ofa.org
Contact: Mike McCabe, Executive Director
E-mail: mike@mccabesflowers.com
URL(s): www.ofa.org. **Frequency:** Annual. **Audience:** Growers, retailers, garden centers, and other trade professionals. **Principal Exhibits:** Exhibits for the greenhouse grower and related industries. **Dates and Locations:** , Convention Center.

9125 ■ Tropical Plant Industry Exhibition
Florida Nursery Growers and Landscape
1533 Park Ctr. Dr.
Orlando, FL 32835-5705
Ph: (407)295-7994
Free: 800-375-3642
Fax: (407)295-1619
Co. E-mail: info@fngla.org
URL: http://www.fngla.org
URL(s): www.fngla.org. **Price:** $15, Pre-registered by early-bird date; $30, after early-bird date. **Frequency:** Annual. **Audience:** Trade. **Principal Exhibits:** Large foliage plants; horticultural, interiorscape, florist, and interior foliage industry products. **Dates and Locations:** Broward County Convention Center. **Telecommunication Services:** shaines@fngla.org.

CONSULTANTS

9126 ■ The Landplan Collaborative Ltd.
319 Woolwich St.
Guelph, ON, Canada N1H 3W4
Ph: (519)824-8664
Fax: (519)824-6776
Co. E-mail: landplan@thelandplan.com
URL: http://www.thelandplan.com
Contact: Owen R. Scott, President
E-mail: oscott@thelandplan.com
Scope: Offers consulting services in landscape architecture, environmental planning, heritage research and planning and resource planning. Also plan and design rural, urban, regional and heritage landscapes; manage projects and procure government approvals; provide expert testimony to boards and tribunals and teaching skills to universities and colleges. **Founded:** 1976.

FRANCHISES AND BUSINESS OPPORTUNITIES

9127 ■ Flowerama of America
3165 W Airline Hwy.
Waterloo, IA 50703

Ph: (800)728-6004
Fax: (319)291-8676
Co. E-mail: info@flowerama.com
URL: http://www.flowerama.com
Description: Franchise program operates under the concepts of mass-merchandising and cash-and-carry floral sales. **No. of Franchise Units:** 71. **No. of Company-Owned Units:** 8. **Founded:** 1971.. **Franchised:** 1972. **Equity Capital Needed:** $50,000-$100,000 (cash). **Franchise Fee:** $35,000. **Financial Assistance:** Yes. **Training:** 4-6 week training program (held at the corporate offices in Waterloo, Iowa). Store layouts and design, assistance during construction, store set-up and product merchandising are provided.

9128 ■ Grower Direct Fresh Cut Flowers Inc.
9613-41 Ave., Ste. 201
Edmonton, AB, Canada T6E 5X7
Ph: (780)436-7774
Fax: (780)436-3336
Co. E-mail: franchises@grower.com
URL: http://www.growerdirect.com
Description: Supplies top quality, fresh cut flowers and marketing expertise to its retail outlets. **No. of Franchise Units:** 41. **No. of Company-Owned Units:** 1. **Founded:** 1991. **Franchised:** 1993. **Equity Capital Needed:** $55,000-$75,000. **Franchise Fee:** $15,000. **Training:** Provides 10 days training.

9129 ■ KaBloom Ltd
305 Harvard St.
Brookline, MA 02446
Free: 800-KaB-loom
Co. E-mail: info@kabloom.com
URL: http://www.kabloom.com
Description: Flower shops. **No. of Franchise Units:** 116. **No. of Company-Owned Units:** 7. **Founded:** 1998.. **Franchised:** 2001. **Equity Capital Needed:** $176,000-$302,000. **Franchise Fee:** $30,000. **Royalty Fee:** 4.5-5.5%. **Training:** 3 weeks at corporate headquarters and ongoing support provided.

9130 ■ Suspended In Time, Inc.
122 S Mountainway Dr.
Orem, UT 84058
Ph: (801)227-0075
Free: 866-756-0059
Fax: (801)221-1003
Co. E-mail: info@suspendedintime.com
URL: http://www.suspendedintime.com
Description: With the remarkable discovery of Suspended in Time's technology in floral preservation over the last 10 years, we are expanding our business opportunities. This is not a Freeze Dry Method. We offer an excellent dealership package with low start-up fees. This preservation process only takes an average of 3-5 days to complete. **No. of Franchise Units:** 47. **Founded:** 1997.. **Equity Capital Needed:** $4,886. **Training:** Training provided at the corporate location 3, 10 hour days, which includes lunch - large discount on room accommodations and ongoing support as long as needed.

LIBRARIES

9131 ■ American Floral Art School - Floral Library
2519 W. Altgeld Ave., Ste. 100
Chicago, IL 60647-1910

Ph: (312)922-9328
Co. E-mail: americanfl@americanfloralartschool.com
URL: http://www.americanfloralartschool.com
Contact: James Moretz, Director
Scope: Flower arrangement and symbolism, floral design, language of flowers. **Services:** Library is accessible on a restricted basis. **Founded:** 1965. **Holdings:** 6000 books; 500 uncataloged items; periodicals; photographs; videotapes. **Subscriptions:** 60 journals and other serials; 2 newspapers. **Telecommunication Services:** jamesflowerman@aol.com.

9132 ■ American Horticultural Society Library
7931 E. Boulevard Dr.
Alexandria, VA 22308
Ph: (703)768-5700
Free: 800-777-7931
Fax: (703)768-8700
Co. E-mail: tunderwood@ahs.org
URL: http://www.ahs.org/
Contact: Tom Underwood, Executive Officer
Scope: Horticulture. **Services:** Copying; Library open to the public by appointment. **Holdings:** 5000 books.

9133 ■ Chicago Park District - Garfield Park Conservatory
300 N. Central Park Ave.
Chicago, IL 60624-1945
Ph: (312)746-5100
Fax: (773)638-1777
URL: http://www.garfield-conservatory.org/
Contact: Mary Eysenbach, Director
Scope: Horticulture. **Services:** Library not open to the public. **Founded:** 1907. **Holdings:** 600 books. **Subscriptions:** 2 journals and other serials.

9134 ■ State Botanical Garden of Georgia Library
Callaway Bldg.
University of Georgia
2450 S. Milledge Ave.
Athens, GA 30605
Ph: (706)542-1244
Co. E-mail: garden@uga.edu
URL: http://www.botgarden.uga.edu
Scope: Plants, gardening, horticulture, botany, conservation, ethnobotany, landscape design, floral crafts. **Services:** Library open to the public for reference use only. **Founded:** 1975. **Holdings:** 2000 books; 85 videotapes; CD-ROMs; archives; manuscripts. **Subscriptions:** 14 journals and other serials.

9135 ■ U.S. National Arboretum Library
3501 New York Ave., NE
Washington, DC 20002-1958
Ph: (202)245-2726
Fax: (202)245-4575
Co. E-mail: everlyr@ars.usda.gov
URL: http://www.usna.usda.gov/
Contact: Robin Everly, Librarian
Scope: Botany, taxonomy, floristics, horticulture, gardening, plant genetics and breeding. **Services:** Interlibrary loan (through National Agricultural Library only); Library open to the public by appointment for onsite research only. **Founded:** 1966. **Holdings:** 10,000 books; 500 periodical titles. **Subscriptions:** 165 journals and other serials.

START-UP INFORMATION

9136 ■ *The 100 Best Businesses to Start When You Don't Want To Work Hard Anymore*
Pub: Career Press Inc.

Ed: Lisa Rogak. **Price:** $16.99. **Description:** Author helps burned-out workers envision a new future as a small business owner. Systems analysis, adventure travel outfitting, bookkeeping, food delivery, furniture making, and software development are among the industries examined.

ASSOCIATIONS AND OTHER ORGANIZATIONS

9137 ■ *Canadian Foodservice Industry Operations Report*
316 Bloor St. W
Toronto, ON, Canada M5S 1W5
Ph: (416)923-8416
Free: 800-387-5649
Fax: (416)923-1450
Co. E-mail: info@crfa.ca
URL: http://www.crfa.ca
Contact: Garth Whyte, President
Released: Biennial

9138 ■ **Canadian Restaurant and Foodservices Association (CRFA)—Association Canadienne des Restaurateurs et des Services Alimentaires**
316 Bloor St. W
Toronto, ON, Canada M5S 1W5
Ph: (416)923-8416
Free: 800-387-5649
Fax: (416)923-1450
Co. E-mail: info@crfa.ca
URL: http://www.crfa.ca
Contact: Garth Whyte, President

Description: Restaurant and food service corporations, hotels, caterers, and food service suppliers and educators. Seeks to create a favorable business environment for members. Represents members' interests before government; conducts trade research. Makes available group buying programs and other services to members; owns and operates three industry trade shows. **Scope:** hospitality industries. **Founded:** 1944. **Subscriptions:** books periodicals. **Publications:** *Foodservice Facts* (Annual); *Legislation Guide* (Quarterly); *Canadian Foodservice Industry Operations Report* (Biennial); *CRFA National Hospitality News*. **Educational Activities:** Canadian Food and Beverage Show (Annual); ApEx; Canadian International Food and Beverage Show (Annual).

9139 ■ *Foodservice Facts*
316 Bloor St. W
Toronto, ON, Canada M5S 1W5
Ph: (416)923-8416
Free: 800-387-5649

Fax: (416)923-1450
Co. E-mail: info@crfa.ca
URL: http://www.crfa.ca
Contact: Garth Whyte, President
Released: Annual

9140 ■ **Foodservice & Packaging Institute Inc. (FPI)**
201 Park Washington Ct.
Falls Church, VA 22046
Ph: (703)538-3550
Fax: (703)538-2817
Co. E-mail: fpi@fpi.org
URL: http://www.fpi.org
Contact: John Burke, President
E-mail: jburke@fpi.org
Description: Manufacturers of raw material and machinery; suppliers and distributors of: single-use cups, plates and related items for service of food and/or beverages; nestable containers for food packaging and containers for oven usage, placemats and doilies, egg cartons and trays for prepackaging meat and produce. Promotes sanitation and the environmentally-responsible use of food and beverage packaging. Compiles market data. **Founded:** 1933. **Publications:** *Executive Briefs* (Biweekly); *Single Service News* (Semiannual). **Awards:** FPI Foodservice Packaging Innovation Awards (Annual); Samuel J. Crumbine Consumer Protection Award (Annual); Samuel J. Crumbine Consumer Protection Award.

9141 ■ **International Flight Services Association (IFSA)**
1100 Johnson Ferry Rd., Ste. 300
Atlanta, GA 30342
Ph: (404)252-3663
Fax: (404)252-0774
Co. E-mail: ifsa@kellencompany.com
URL: http://www.ifsanet.com
Contact: David Loft, President
Description: Works to serve the needs and interests of the airline and railway personnel, in-flight and railway caterers and suppliers responsible for providing passenger foodservice on regularly scheduled travel routes. **Scope:** catering the in-flight food service industry. **Founded:** 1966. **Subscriptions:** 1. **Awards:** President's Award; President's Award (Annual); Lois Campbell Scholarship Awards; Tommy Depaola Scholarship Awards; Harvey and Laura Alpert Scholarship Awards.

9142 ■ **International Foodservice Manufacturers Association (IFMA)**
2 Prudential Plz.
180 N Stetson Ave., Ste. 4400
Chicago, IL 60601
Ph: (312)540-4400
Fax: (312)540-4401
Co. E-mail: ifma@ifmaworld.com
URL: http://www.ifmaworld.com
Contact: Michael J. Licata, President
Description: Represents food, equipment and supply manufacturers in the foodservice industry, as well as related marketing service organizations, foodservice trade publications, distributors and brokers. Aims

to shape the future of foodservice by creating an environment for positive change and actionable solutions benefiting manufacturers and their foodservice channel partners. **Founded:** 1952. **Publications:** *IFMA World* (9/year); *International Foodservice Manufacturers Association: Membership Directory*; *International Foodservice Manufacturers Association--Membership Directory* (Annual); *Encyclopedia of the Foodservice Industry* (Irregular). **Educational Activities:** Chain Operators Exchange (Annual). **Awards:** Gold Plate Award (Annual); Silver Plate Award (Annual).

9143 ■ *Legislation Guide*
316 Bloor St. W
Toronto, ON, Canada M5S 1W5
Ph: (416)923-8416
Free: 800-387-5649
Fax: (416)923-1450
Co. E-mail: info@crfa.ca
URL: http://www.crfa.ca
Contact: Garth Whyte, President
Released: Quarterly

9144 ■ **National Council of Chain Restaurants (NCCR)**
325 7th St. NW, Ste. 1100
Washington, DC 20004
Ph: (202)783-7971
Free: 800-673-4692
Fax: (202)737-2849
Co. E-mail: info@nrf.com
URL: http://www.nccr.net
Contact: Rob Green, Executive Director
Description: Represents chain restaurant companies. Works to advance sound public policy that best serves the interests of restaurant businesses and the millions of people they employ. **Founded:** 1965. **Educational Activities:** Membership, Tax Forum and Food Safety (Quarterly).

9145 ■ **National Restaurant Association Educational Foundation (NRAEF)**
175 W Jackson Blvd., Ste. 1500
Chicago, IL 60604-2814
Ph: (312)715-1010
Free: 800-765-2122
Fax: (312)583-9841
Co. E-mail: info@restaurant.org
URL: http://www.nraef.org
Contact: Mary M. Adolf, President
E-mail: madolf@nraef.org
Description: Serves as an educational foundation supported by the National Restaurant Association and all segments of the foodservice industry including restaurateurs, foodservice companies, food and equipment manufacturers, distributors and trade associations. Advances the professional standards of the industry through education and research. Offers video training programs, management courses and careers information. Conducts research and maintains hall of fame. **Founded:** 1987. **Publications:** *Foodservice/Hospitality College Directory* (Irregular); *Directory of Computer Hardware and Software for the Food Service Industry*. **Awards:** College of Diplomates Award; Al Schuman Ecolab Undergradu-

ate Entrepreneurial Scholarships; Thad and Alice Eure Ambassador of Hospitality Award. **Telecommunication Services:** lmckee@nraef.org; scholars@ nraef.org.

REFERENCE WORKS

9146 ■ *"Alliance to End Hunger to Hold Press Conference on Fasting, Prayer and Budget Cuts"* in Food & Beverage Close-Up (March 28, 2011)
Pub: Close-Up Media
Description: A coalition of religious and other leaders are launching a new campaign to protect programs for vulnerable people. Partners include: Alliance to End Hunger, American Jewish World Service, Bread for the World, Congressional Hunger Center, Feeding America, Food for the Hungry, Islamic Relief USA, Meals on Wheels Association of America, New Manna Inc., ONE, Society of Saint Andrews, Sojourners, and World Food Program USA.

9147 ■ *"Aramark Rolls Out Ballpark Food Truck"* in Nation's Restaurant News (Vol. 45, August 8, 2011, No. 16, pp. 4)
Pub: Penton Media Inc.
Contact: John French, President
Ed: Ron Ruggless. **Description:** Aramark installed its first ballpark food truck serving Asian-inspired noodle bowls at the outfield concourse at Coors Field in Colorado.

9148 ■ *"Cluster Truck Events Updates on Curbside Dining Sweeps in Las Vegas"* in Food & Beverage Close-Up (November 4, 2011)
Pub: Close-Up Media
Description: Gourmet food trucks will provide mobile dining for attendees of the South Point Gourmet Food Truck Fest held in Las Vegas, Nevada November 5, 2011.

9149 ■ *"Coastal Luxury Management Reports Los Angeles Food and Wine Tickets On Sale"* in Food & Beverage Close-Up (August 24, 2011)
Pub: Close-Up Media
Description: Wolfgang Puck's Sunday Brunch and Charity Auction will raise money for Saint Vincent Meals on Wheels program.

9150 ■ *"Consumers Who Saw a Food Truck This Summer"* in Nation's Restaurant News (Vol. 45, September 26, 2011, No. 20, pp. 8)
Pub: Penton Media Inc.
Contact: John French, President
Description: A guide to the number of customers encountering food trucks during summer 2011 is presented by region.

9151 ■ *"Counter Service"* in Nation's Restaurant News (Vol. 45, September 26, 2011, No. 20, pp. 8)
Pub: Penton Media Inc.
Contact: John French, President
Description: As food trucks continue their momentum, a study was conducted showing how many consumer would visit a food truck. Nearly two thirds of 18-44 year olds would likely visit a food truck, while individuals over the age of 65 only 38 percent would eat from a food truck.

9152 ■ *"Counter Service: We Gear Up Some Food Truck Stats"* in Nation's Restaurant News (Vol. 45, August 8, 2011, No. 16, pp. 6)
Pub: Penton Media Inc.
Contact: John French, President
Description: According to a recent survey, people do not see food truck service as a trend and 84 percent of social media users said they would visit food trucks at least once a week.

9153 ■ *"Food-Truck Learnings Travel Indoors"* in Nation's Restaurant News (Vol. 45, June 27, 2011, No. 13, pp. 3)
Pub: Penton Media Inc.
Contact: John French, President
Ed: Lisa Jennings. **Description:** Challenges faced by owners of food truck businesses are discussed. Ways a food truck can be used to promote a restaurant's menu are covered.

9154 ■ *"Gallo Family Vineyards to Raise Funds for Meals On Wheels"* in Food & Beverage Close-Up (November 4, 2011)
Pub: Close-Up Media
Description: Gallo family is committed to raising funds for Meals On Wheels Association of America and hosts a fundraiser annually.

9155 ■ *"Having Words with Matt Maroni: Chef-Owner, Gaztro-Wagon, Chicago"* in Nation's Restaurant News (Vol. 45, April 4, 2011, No. 7, pp. 62)
Pub: Penton Media, Inc.
Ed: Mike Dempsey. **Description:** Profile of Matt Maroni, chef and owner of Gaztro-Wagon in Chicago, Illinois is presented. Maroni tells how he found his niche in the food truck industry.

9156 ■ *"Howl-o-ween"* in Decatur Daily (October 25, 2011)
Pub: Decatur Daily
Ed: Catherine Godbey. **Description:** Animal Friends Humane Society provides free pet food and cat litter to Meals on Wheels clients.

9157 ■ *"Keep On Truckin"* in Boston Business Journal (Vol. 31, August 5, 2011, No. 28, pp. 3)
Pub: Boston Business Journal
Ed: Lisa van der Pool. **Description:** Food truck business is booming in Boston with more than 25 trucks dotting the area including 15 new truck locations approved by the city in July 2011. The business is rather costly to start because it requires more than $100,000 capital and the food truck can run between $50,000 to $100,000.

9158 ■ *"Learn New Ideas from Experienced Menu Makers"* in Nation's Restaurant News (Vol. 45, June 27, 2011, No. 13, pp. 82)
Pub: Penton Media Inc.
Contact: John French, President
Ed: Nancy Kruse. **Description:** National Restaurant Association Restaurant, Hotel-Motel Show featured the Food Truck Spot, a firm committed to all aspects of mobile catering, foodtruck manufacturers, leasers of fully equipped truck and a food-truck franchising group.

9159 ■ *"Meals on Wheels Filling 'Blizzard Bags"* in Tulsa World (November 5, 2011)
Pub: Tulsa World
Ed: Sara Plummer. **Description:** Cathy Perlingiere, director of volunteer services for Meals on Wheels of Metro Tulsa, Oklahoma reports that they do not deliver meals when the Tulsa Public Schools close because of weather so they try to prepare 'blizzard bags' with nonperishable food items to cover about three meals for when drivers cannot deliver.

9160 ■ *"More Volunteers Needed to Make a Difference"* in Times-News (October 18, 2011)
Pub: Times-News
Ed: Roselee Papandrea. **Description:** Meals on Wheels program in the Burlington, North Carolina area is seeking volunteers to deliver meals to senior citizens.

9161 ■ *"New Technology, Growing Fan Base Fuel Truck Trend"* in Nation's Restaurant News (Vol. 45, June 13, 2001, No. 12, pp. 16)
Pub: Penton Media Inc.
Contact: John French, President
Ed: Ron Ruggless. **Description:** Food trucks drove more interest at this year's National Restaurant Association Restaurant Hotel-Motel Show in Chicago. The trend continues to show long-term growth.

9162 ■ *"Oberweis Tests Home Ice Cream Delivery"* in Ice Cream Reporter (Vol. 21, November 20, 2008, No. 12, pp. 1)
Pub: Ice Cream Reporter
Description: Oberwies Dairy launched its Treat Delivery Program in the Saint Louis area. The program allows customers to order milkshakes, ice cream cones, sundaes and scoops of ice cream and they are delivered to their home or office. Oberweis is a fourth generation family run business.

9163 ■ *"Silver Key Seeks Volunteer Drivers in Colorado Springs"* in Colorado Springs Business Journal (October 21, 2011)
Pub: Dolan Media
Ed: Amy Gillentine. **Description:** Silver Keyis look for drivers to use their own vehicles to deliver Meals on Wheels to area seniors. For many of these senior citizens, it is the only outside contact they have an entire day.

9164 ■ *"Speakers Address Authenticity, R&D Evolution"* in Nation's Restaurant News (Vol. 45, October 24, 2011, No. 32, pp. 32)
Pub: Penton Media Inc.
Contact: John French, President
Ed: Bret Thorn. **Description:** Culinary trends are discussed, along with an examination of the food truck trend and how this small sector is creating a great influence on food and communication with customers and delivery expectations.

9165 ■ *"Substantial Deal Expected to Create Jobs, Help Industrial Market"* in Tampa Bay Business Journal (Vol. 30, January 8, 2010, No. 3)
Pub: American City Business Journals
Ed: Janet Leiser. **Description:** Food distribution firm Gordon Food Service (GFS) is on the brink of purchasing Albertson's million-square-foot warehouse along with 158 acres of space. The deal between GFS and Albertson's could expand GFS' presence in west Central Florida. A history of GFS' growth is included.

9166 ■ *"Tap Into Food Truck Trend to Rev Up Sales, Build Buzz"* in Nation's Restaurant News (Vol. 45, February 7, 2011, No. 3, pp. 18)
Pub: Penton Media, Inc.
Ed: Brian Sacks. **Description:** Food truck trend is growing, particularly in New York City, Philadelphia, Washington DC, and Los Angeles, California. Man entrepreneurs are using a mobile food component to market their food before opening a restaurant.

9167 ■ *"Tualatin Senior Center Under Construction"* in Daily Journal of Commerce (October 21, 2011)
Pub: Dolan Media
Ed: Angela Webber. **Description:** Juanita Pohl Center in Tualatin Community Park is the home to TualatinAEs Meals on Wheels program that delivers meals to seniors in the area.

9168 ■ *"Working the Streets"* in Baltimore Business Journal (Vol. 28, July 30, 2010, No. 12, pp. 1)
Pub: Baltimore Business Journal
Ed: Amanda Pino. **Description:** Reports show that street vendors are popping up on new corners in Baltimore, Maryland, with city-inspected stainless steel food carts in tow. Applications for street vending licenses shot up at the end of 2009 and into this summer. It is believed that pinning down the exact number of vendors operating at any one point is difficult.

TRADE PERIODICALS

9169 ■ *Canadian Pizza Magazine*
Pub: Annex Publishing & Printing Inc.
URL(s): www.canadianpizzamag.comwww.annexweb.com/. **Ed:** Laura Aiken. **Released:** 8/yr. **Price:** $18, Canada.

9170 ■ *IDDBA Legis-Letter*
Pub: International Dairy-Deli-Bakery Association
Contact: Steve Beekhuizen, President
Ed: Carol L. Christison, Editor, cchristison@iddba. org. **Price:** Included in membership. **Description:** Reports on legislative activity concerning the supermarket dairy-deli-bakery industry.

9171 ■ *WrapUp*
Pub: International Dairy-Deli-Bakery Association
Contact: Steve Beekhuizen, President
Ed: Carol L Christison, Editor, cchristison@iddba.org. **Released:** Quarterly. **Price:** Included in membership. **Description:** Reports on news, activities, and topics of interest to the Association.

VIDEOCASSETTES/ AUDIOCASSETTES

9172 ■ *Food Service Industry Video Series: Career Opportunities*
Meridian Education Corp.
132 West 31st Street, 17th Floor
New York, NY 10001
Ph: (609)671-0266
Free: 800-257-5126
Co. E-mail: custmserv@films.com
URL: http://meridian.films.com
Released: 1991. **Price:** $45.00. **Description:** Presents information on education and training for a variety of careers in the food service industry: cook, chef, waiter/waitress, counter attendant, short-order cook, dishwasher, hostess, bookkeeper, maintenance, purchasing, management, cashier, dietitian, busperson, baker and more. **Availability:** VHS.

9173 ■ *Food Service Industry Video Series: Employee Skills*
Meridian Education Corp.
132 West 31st Street, 17th Floor
New York, NY 10001
Ph: (609)671-0266
Free: 800-257-5126
Co. E-mail: custmserv@films.com
URL: http://meridian.films.com
Released: 1991. **Price:** $45.00. **Description:** Presents information on preparing for a job interview in the food service industry and the skills necessary to be successful in that field. **Availability:** VHS.

9174 ■ *Food Service Industry Video Series: Food Preparation*
Meridian Education Corp.
132 West 31st Street, 17th Floor
New York, NY 10001
Ph: (609)671-0266
Free: 800-257-5126
Co. E-mail: custmserv@films.com
URL: http://meridian.films.com
Released: 1991. **Price:** $45.00. **Description:** Overviews food preparation techniques in all areas of food service including entrees, salads, and bakery. Also includes information on food service presentation. **Availability:** VHS.

9175 ■ *Food Service Industry Video Series: Management Skills*
Meridian Education Corp.
132 West 31st Street, 17th Floor
New York, NY 10001
Ph: (609)671-0266
Free: 800-257-5126
Co. E-mail: custmserv@films.com
URL: http://meridian.films.com
Released: 1991. **Price:** $45.00. **Description:** Overviews the skills necessary for success as a manager in the food service industry, including math skills, adaptability, costs, record keeping and more. **Availability:** VHS.

9176 ■ *Food Service Industry Video Series: Safety and Sanitation*
Meridian Education Corp.
132 West 31st Street, 17th Floor
New York, NY 10001
Ph: (609)671-0266
Free: 800-257-5126
Co. E-mail: custmserv@films.com
URL: http://meridian.films.com
Released: 1991. **Price:** $45.00. **Description:** Presents viewers with information on sanitation in a food service environment. **Availability:** VHS.

9177 ■ *Food Services*
RMI Media
1365 N. Winchester St.
Olathe, KS 66061-5880
Ph: (913)768-1696
Free: 800-745-5480
Fax: (800)755-6910
Co. E-mail: actmedia@act.org
URL: http://www.actmedia.com
Released: 1987. **Description:** Methods of food preparation and equipment maintenance used in the food industry are discussed. **Availability:** VHS; 3/4 U.

TRADE SHOWS AND CONVENTIONS

9178 ■ ApEx
Canadian Restaurant and Foodservices Association (CRFA)
316 Bloor St. W
Toronto, ON, Canada M5S 1W5
Ph: (416)923-8416
Free: 800-387-5649
Fax: (416)923-1450
Co. E-mail: info@crfa.ca
URL: http://www.crfa.ca
Contact: Garth Whyte, President
URL(s): www.crfa.ca/tradeshows/apex. **Audience:** Trade. **Principal Exhibits:** Products and services for the restaurant and hospitality industry, as well as institutions, convenience stores, delis and bakeries. **Telecommunication Services:** escanlan@crfa.ca.

FRANCHISES AND BUSINESS OPPORTUNITIES

9179 ■ Cena
12501 N Hwy. 395, Ste. 3
Spokane, WA 99218
Ph: (509)448-1725
Free: 888-667-2362
Fax: (509)448-9380
Description: Meal preparation/assembly center and wine shop. **No. of Franchise Units:** 10. **No. of Company-Owned Units:** 1. **Founded:** 2004.. **Franchised:** 2005. **Equity Capital Needed:** $148,400-$205,500; express/kiosk option available. **Franchise Fee:** $30,000. **Royalty Fee:** 5%. **Training:** Provides 4 days training at headquarters, 3 days onsite and ongoing support.

9180 ■ Coffee Perks
Coffee Perks Franchise Inc.
Description: Office coffee and food-service distribution. **No. of Franchise Units:** 4. **No. of Company-Owned Units:** 1. **Founded:** 1993.. **Franchised:** 2004. **Equity Capital Needed:** $50,000-$250,000, depending on market size. **Franchise Fee:** $18,000 plus. **Training:** Yes.

9181 ■ Farmer Boys
Farmer Boys Food, Inc.
3452 University Ave.
Riverside, CA 92501
Ph: (909)275-9900
Fax: (909)275-9930
Description: Restaurants and food delivery services. **No. of Franchise Units:** 48. **No. of Company-Owned Units:** 17. **Founded:** 1981.. **Founded:** 1997. **Equity Capital Needed:** $515,375-$795,505. **Franchise Fee:** $40,000. **Royalty Fee:** 5%. **Financial Assistance:** Limited third party financing available. **Training:** Yes. **Telecommunication Services:** franchising@farmerboys.com.

9182 ■ The Firkin Group of Pubs
Firkin Pub International, Inc.
20 Steelcase Rd. W, No. 1C
Markham, ON, Canada L3R 1B2
Ph: (905)305-9792
Fax: (905)305-9719
Co. E-mail: larry@firkinpubs.com
URL: http://www.firkinpubs.com
Description: Restaurants and food delivery services. **No. of Franchise Units:** 21. **No. of Company-Owned Units:** 11. **Founded:** 1987.. **Franchised:** 1999. **Equity Capital Needed:** $350,000. **Franchise Fee:** $30,000. **Training:** Training provided at headquarters and ongoing support.

9183 ■ Hooters of America, Inc.
1815 The Exchange
Atlanta, GA 30339
Ph: (770)951-2040
Fax: (770)933-9464
Description: Business of restaurant and food delivery services. **No. of Franchise Units:** 210. **No. of Company-Owned Units:** 90. **Founded:** 1985.. **Franchised:** 1988. **Equity Capital Needed:** $800,000. **Franchise Fee:** $75,000. **Training:** Yes.

9184 ■ Insomnia Cookies Franchising LLC
650 5th Ave., 31st Fl.
New York, NY 10019
Ph: (212)286-2403
Fax: (866)422-8402
Description: Cookies & baked goods stores/late-night delivery. **No. of Company-Owned Units:** 14. **Founded:** 2002.. **Franchised:** 2006. **Equity Capital Needed:** $65,600-$111,400. **Franchise Fee:** $25,000. **Royalty Fee:** 6%. **Training:** Offer 2-3 weeks training at headquarters, 2-3 weeks at franchisee's location, at other franchisee/corporate locations as needed and ongoing support.

9185 ■ Let's Eat
2202 North Westshore Blvd., Suite 200
Tampa, FL 33607
Ph: (813)258-0555
Fax: (813)258-9100
Description: Meal preparation service. **No. of Franchise Units:** 5. **No. of Company-Owned Units:** 3. **Founded:** 2004.. **Franchised:** 2005. **Equity Capital Needed:** $99,000-$193,500. **Franchise Fee:** $25,500-$26,500. **Royalty Fee:** 6%.

9186 ■ The Lunch Lady Group Inc.
151 Spinnaker Way, Unit 11
Concord, ON, Canada L4K 4C3
Ph: (905)660-5994
Free: 800-603-6656
Fax: (905)660-0972
Co. E-mail: franchise@thelunchlady.ca
URL: http://www.thelunchlady.ca
Description: Offering HOT lunches delivered to Public School children. **No. of Franchise Units:** 40. **No. of Company-Owned Units:** 2. **Founded:** 1995.. **Franchised:** 2001. **Equity Capital Needed:** $10,000-$20,000 start-up capital required; $80,000-$100,000 investment required. **Franchise Fee:** $25,000. **Training:** Offers 2 week training program and ongoing support.

9187 ■ Mancino's, Samuel Italian Eatery
Nu-Ventures Inc.
1324 W Milham
Portage, MI 49024
Ph: (269)226-4400
Free: 888-432-8379
Fax: (269)226-4466
Description: Franchise of restaurants and food delivery services of food. **No. of Franchise Units:** 38. **Founded:** 1959.. **Franchised:** 1994. **Equity Capital Needed:** $200,000-$250,000. **Franchise Fee:** $30,000. **Training:** Yes.

9188 ■ Off the Grill Franchising, LLC
1728 General George Patton Dr., Ste. 200
Brentwood, TN 37027
Ph: (615)370-0700
Fax: (615)371-1405
Description: Carry out and delivery; steaks, burgers, and chicken. **No. of Franchise Units:** 13. **No. of Company-Owned Units:** 2. **Founded:** 1999.. **Franchised:** 1999. **Equity Capital Needed:** $250,000. **Franchise Fee:** $25,000. **Training:** Yes.

9189 ■ Padows's Hams & Deli
Padow's Deli Inc.
9864 W Broad St.
Glen Allen, VA 23060
Ph: (804)965-6262
Description: Retail and mail order food. **No. of Franchise Units:** 10. **No. of Company-Owned Units:** 2. **Founded:** 1936.. **Franchised:** 1995. **Equity Capital Needed:** $250,000-$400,000. **Franchise Fee:** $25,000-$35,000. **Training:** Yes.

9190 ■ **Sarpino's Pizzeria Canada Ltd.**
Sarpino's World LTD
1133 Regent St., Ste. 203
Fredericton, NB, Canada E3B 3Z2
Ph: (506)462-9270
Fax: (506)451-8692
Co. E-mail: rbuckingham@nb.aibn.com
URL: http://www.sarpinos.com
Description: Pizzeria. **No. of Franchise Units:** 9.
No. of Company-Owned Units: 1. **Founded:** 2001..
Franchised: 2002. **Equity Capital Needed:**
$195,000-$235,000. **Franchise Fee:** $25,000. **Training:** Provides 2 weeks training.

LIBRARIES

9191 ■ **American Institute of Food
Distribution, Inc. - Information and Research
Center—The Food Institute.**
1 Broadway Plaza, 2nd Fl.
Elmwood Park, NJ 07407
Ph: (201)791-5570
Fax: (201)791-5222
Co. E-mail: jkastrinsky@foodinstitute.com
URL: http://www.foodinstitute.com/
Contact: Brian Todd, President
Scope: Food industry. **Services:** Center open to the
public on fee basis. **Founded:** 1928. **Subscriptions:**
400 journals and other serials. **Publications:** *Food
Business Mergers and Acquisitions.* **Telecommunication Services:** food1@foodinstitute.com.

9192 ■ **Coca-Cola Company - The
INFOSOURCE**
PO Box 1734
Atlanta, GA 30301
Ph: (404)515-4636
Fax: (404)253-4575
Co. E-mail: koinfo@na.ko.com
URL: http://www.coca-cola.com
Contact: Barbara Kahn-Aitken
Scope: Business, Legal, Marketing, Technical -
including beverages, soft drinks, fruit juices, food
technology, nutrition, chemistry, engineering.
Founded: 1967. **Telecommunication Services:**
coca-cola@na.ko.com.

9193 ■ **ConAgra Grocery Products - R&D
Technical Library**
3353 Michelson Dr.
Irvine, CA 92612-0650
Ph: (949)437-2859
Fax: (949)437-3372
Co. E-mail: gilbertson@yahoo.com
URL: http://www.conagrafoods.com
Contact: Christopher L. Gilbertson
Scope: Food science, technology, and packaging.
Services: Library not open to the public. **Founded:**
2002. **Holdings:** 4500 books; 1000 bound periodical
volumes; 98 VF drawers of patents; 1300 government documents; 4 VF drawers of Annual reports.

9194 ■ **Food Marketing Institute Information
Service**
2345 Crystal Dr., Ste. 800
Arlington, VA 22202
Ph: (202)452-8444
Fax: (202)429-4519
Co. E-mail: fmi@fmi.org
URL: http://www.fmi.org
Contact: Ms. Leslie G. Sarasin, President
URL(s): www.fmi.org/facts_figs. **Scope:** Food distribution. **Services:** Interlibrary loan; copying; service
open to the public by appointment. **Founded:** 1952.
Holdings: 7000 volumes. **Subscriptions:** 100
journals and other serials.

9195 ■ **Noble and Associates Library**
2155 W. Chesterfield Blvd.
Springfield, MO 65807
Ph: (417)875-5000
Co. E-mail: julie.tumy@noble.net
URL: http://www.noble.net
Contact: Julie Tumy, President
Scope: Food, food service, advertising, construction,
agriculture. **Services:** Interlibrary loan; copying; SDI;
Library not open to the public. **Holdings:** 500 books;
1000 reports. **Subscriptions:** 300 journals and other
serials; 5 newspapers.

9196 ■ **Technomic, Inc. - Knowledge Center**
300 S. Riverside Plz., Ste. 1200
Chicago, IL 60606-6637
Ph: (312)506-3929
Fax: (312)876-1158
Co. E-mail: curban@technomic.com
URL: http://www.technomic.com
Contact: Chris Urban, Director
Scope: Management, food/food service, restaurants.
Founded: 1976. **Holdings:** 250 books. **Subscriptions:** 70 journals and other serials.

RESEARCH CENTERS

9197 ■ **National Restaurant Association -
Quality Assurance Executive Study Group**
1200 17th St. NW
Washington, DC 20036
Ph: (202)331-5900
Free: 800-424-5156
Fax: (202)331-2429
Co. E-mail: nmadison@restaurant.org
URL: http://www.restaurant.org/education/study-
    groups/qa
Contact: Dawn Sweeney, President
Educational Activities: Educational meetings; Study
group meetings (Semiannual).

Freight Forwarding Service

ASSOCIATIONS AND OTHER ORGANIZATIONS

9198 ■ Express Delivery and Logistics Association (XLA)
400 Admiral Blvd.
Kansas City, MO 64106-1508
Ph: (816)221-0254
Free: 888-838-0761
Fax: (816)472-7765
Co. E-mail: jim@expressassociation.org
URL: http://www.expressassociation.org
Contact: Jim Conway, Executive Director
Description: Represents air couriers, small package express delivery companies, airlines and associated industry members (75); supports companies and facilities such as airlines and airports. Seeks to: provide industry forum for ideas, educate members about new technologies within the industry; represent air couriers before governmental bodies; inform members of legislation affecting the industry; develop and maintain relationships among members. Conducts seminars and workshops. **Founded:** 1976. **Publications:** *XLA Alert* (Periodic); *XLA Express* (Quarterly); *XLA Extra* (Biweekly). **Educational Activities:** AirCargo (Annual).

9199 ■ National Customs Brokers and Forwarders Association of America (NCBFAA)
1200 18th St. NW, No. 901
Washington, DC 20036
Ph: (202)466-0222
Fax: (202)466-0226
Co. E-mail: staff@ncbfaa.org
URL: http://www.ncbfaa.org
Contact: Darrell Sekin, Jr., President
Description: Treasury-licensed customs brokers, FMC-licensed independent ocean freight forwarders, and CNS-registered air cargo agents; associate members in 25 foreign countries. Seeks to maintain high standards of business practice throughout the industry. Monitors legislative and regulatory issues affecting customs brokers and forwarders; conducts seminars on new developments and techniques in the industry; provides forum for exchange among brokers and forwarders. Conducts educational programs. **Founded:** 1897. **Publications:** *National Customs Brokers & Forwarders Association of America--Membership Directory* (Annual); *The National Customs Brokers & Forwarders Association of America Membership Directory*; *National Customs Brokers and Forwarders Association of America Membership Directory*; *NCBFAA Membership Directory: The Who's Who of American Customs Brokers and International Freight Forwarders* (Annual). **Educational Activities:** Government Affairs Conference (Annual).

9200 ■ National Industrial Transportation League (NITL)
1700 N Moore St., Ste. 1900
Arlington, VA 22209
Ph: (703)524-5011
Fax: (703)524-5017
Co. E-mail: info@nitl.org
URL: http://www.nitl.org
Contact: Terry L. Bunch, Chairperson
Description: Seeks to promote adequate national and international transportation; encourages the exchange of ideas and information concerning traffic and transportation; and cooperates with regulatory agencies and other transportation companies in developing an understanding of legislation. **Founded:** 1907. **Publications:** *The Notice, NITL* (Weekly). **Educational Activities:** TransComp (Annual).

9201 ■ Overseas Automotive Council (OAC)
PO Box 13966
Research Triangle Park, NC 27709-3966
Ph: (919)406-8846
Fax: (919)549-4824
Co. E-mail: jdenton@mema.org
URL: http://www.aftermarketsuppliers.org/Councils/OAC
Contact: John Brunke, Chairman
Description: Multi-faceted resource for individuals involved in the international marketing and sales of automotive products manufactured in the United States. Provides a forum, which enhances the prestige of the American automotive industry, promoting friendly trade relationships with understanding of the various cultures involved. **Founded:** 1923. **Publications:** *Overseas Automotive Council--Membership Roster* (Annual).

REFERENCE WORKS

9202 ■ American Motor Carrier Directory
Pub: UBM Global Trade
Contact: Leonard J. Corallo, President
URL(s): www.cbizmedia.com. **Released:** Annual; December. **Publication includes:** Lists of all licensed Less Than Truckload (LTL) general commodity carriers in the United States; includes specialized motor carriers and related services; includes refrigerated carriers, heavy haulers, bulk haulers, riggers, and specified commodity carriers; state and federal regulatory bodies governing the trucking industry; tariff publishing bureaus; freight claim councils; industry associations, etc. **Entries include:** For carriers and services--Company name, address of headquarters and terminals, phones, tariffs followed, names of executives, insurance, and equipment information, services or commodities handled. Principal content of publication is listing of direct point-to-point services of LTL general commodity carriers throughout the United States and to Canada and Mexico. **Arrangement:** Alphabetical.

9203 ■ "Cold-Storage Cargo Facility a Late Bloomer" in Houston Business Journal (Vol. 40, August 28, 2009, No. 16, pp. 1A)
Pub: American City Business Journals
Ed: Jennifer Dawson. **Description:** Trammell Crow Company leased half of the 61,000 square foot IAH International Air Cargo Centre II to Tradewinds Cargo Handling. The facility, located at George Bush Intercontinental Airport, is intended to be a destination of fresh flowers and food from Latin America.

9204 ■ "Con-Way Project Back in High Gear" in Business Journal Portland (Vol. 27, November 5, 2010, No. 36, pp. 1)
Pub: Portland Business Journal
Ed: Wendy Culverwell. **Description:** Trucking firm Con-Way Inc. intends to sell parcels of land from a property comprising 16 blocks and 20 prime acres west of the Pearl District in Portland, Oregon. In 2009, Con-Way abandoned plans to sell the property. As Con-Way reclaims control over design and usage of the property, it also expressed willingness to cooperate with a master developer on a related real estate project.

9205 ■ "Could This Be Your Next Office Building?" in Austin Business Journal (Vol. 31, May 13, 2011, No. 10, pp. A1)
Pub: American City Business Journals Inc.
Ed: Cody Lyon. **Description:** Falcon Containers moved to a 51-acre site in Far East Austin, Texas and started construction of a 2,500-square-foot headquarters made from eight 40-foot shipping containers. Falcon's CEO Stephen Shang plans to use his headquarters building as a showroom to attract upscale, urban hipsters. Insights on the construction's environmental and social impact are shared.

9206 ■ Directory of Freight Forwarders and Custom House Brokers
Pub: International Wealth Success, Inc.—IWS
URL(s): www.iwsmoney.com/exportimport.htm. **Released:** Annual; January. **Price:** $20, Individuals. **Covers:** Several hundred freight forwarders and custom house brokers involved in international trade. **Entries include:** Company or firm name, address, phone. **Arrangement:** Geographical.

9207 ■ "Freeing the Wheels of Commerce" in Hispanic Business (July-August 2007, pp. 50, 52, 54)
Pub: Hispanic Business
Ed: Keith Rosenblum. **Description:** SecureOrigins, a border-based partnership with high-tech innovators is working to move goods faster, more efficiently, and securely.

9208 ■ "Is 'Tsunami' of Freight in our Future?" in Business Courier (Vol. 26, November 27, 2009, No. 31, pp. 1)
Pub: American City Business Journals, Inc.
Ed: Dan Monk. **Description:** Freight companies are planning for cargo-container shipping facilities on the riverfront of Cincinnati in light of the completion of the $5 billion Panama Canal expansion in 2015. The city's capability to utilize the growth in freight has been under investigation by authorities.

9209 ■ "Martin Marietta Expands Rock Solid Port Manatee Presence" in Tampa Bay Business Journal (Vol. 30, January 8, 2010,

No. 3, pp. 1)
Pub: American City Business Journals
Ed: Jane Meinhardt. **Description:** Raleigh, North Carolina-based Martin Marietta Materials Inc. has been granted by Florida's Manatee County Port Authority with a 30-year, $42 million contract. Through the contract, an aggregate terminal will be built by Martin Marietta at the port. Construction work is anticipated to start in earl 2010 with terminal operations commencing by late summer 2010.

9210 ■ Messenger Courier Association of America--Network Guide and Membership Directory
Pub: Messenger Courier Association of America
Contact: Bob DeCaprio, Executive Director
URL(s): www.mcaa.com. **Released:** Annual; January. **Price:** $235. **Covers:** Approximately 500 member air courier companies. **Entries include:** Company name, office personnel, warehouse facilities area served. **Arrangement:** Geographical by airport city.

9211 ■ National Customs Brokers & Forwarders Association of America--Membership Directory
Pub: National Customs Brokers and Forwarders Association of America
Contact: Darrell Sekin, Jr., President
URL(s): www.ncbfaa.org. **Released:** Annual; Latest edition 2011 New edition expected 2012. **Price:** $30, Individuals per copy. **Covers:** About 600 customs brokers, international air cargo agents, and freight forwarders in the United States. **Entries include:** Company name, address, phone, telex, fax, cable address, year established, FMC license number, contact, branch or affiliate cities, and line of business. **Arrangement:** Classified by membership class, then alphabetical. **Indexes:** Geographical.

9212 ■ Official Export Guide
Pub: UBM Global Trade
Contact: Leonard J. Corallo, President
URL(s): www.cbizmedia.comwww.officialexportguide.com. **Released:** Annual; January; inter-edition supplements. **Price:** $449.50, sale price; $899, regular price. **Covers:** Customs officials, port authorities, embassies and consulates, chambers of commerce, foreign trade zones, and other organizations and agencies involved in international trade; prospective foreign buyers; related trade services. **Entries include:** Generally, organization or company name, address, phone, phone, telex, fax, names and titles of key personnel. **Database includes:** For each country, description of seaport, airport, and trade zone facilities, documentary requirements, trade, and discussion of export prospects; Export Administration Regulations. **Arrangement:** Geographical, then classified by service.

9213 ■ Quick Caller Area Air Cargo Directory QC
Pub: Fourth Seacoast Publishing Company Inc.
Contact: Tom Buysse, Office Manager, Finance
URL(s): www.quickcalleronline.com/shipping_directories/air_cargo.htm. **Released:** Annual; Latest edition 2010. **Price:** $21.95, Individuals each, plus shipping charges; payment must accompany order; $19.95, Individuals 2-12 copies. **Covers:** firms in the east (New York/New Jersey metro area edition); midwest (Detroit and Chicago editions); New England (Boston edition); the south (Miami/Orlando/Florida and Atlanta editions); and the west (San Francisco/Oakland Bay area and Los Angeles editions) and Pacific Northwest (Seattle/Portland/Vancouver edition); includes airlines, charter services, air freight forwarders, and related air freight services, including trucking, warehousing, and packaging. **Entries include:** Firm name, location, description of services. **Arrangement:** By line of business/service.

9214 ■ Smart Mail
Pub: Pitney Bowes Inc.
Contact: Marc Lautenbach, President
URL(s): www.pitneybowes.com. **Released:** Quarterly **Covers:** Courier companies that provide same day, overnight and second-day delivery service of small packages throughout the United States. **Entries in-**

clude: Courier name, rates, phone, destinations, delivery times, types of service, hours of operation, company profile. **Arrangement:** Geographical.

9215 ■ "StorageByMail Lets Customers Ship Away Their Clutter" in Inc. (Vol. 33, April 2011, No. 3, pp. 92)
Pub: Inc. Magazine
Ed: Issie Lapowsky. **Description:** StorageByMail allows people to put items into storage by mailing them to the company. The firm charges a monthly fee, customers describe contents of each box, and ship to the Jersey City facility using a preprinted label. StorageByMail pays the $25 shipment charge.

9216 ■ "Truckers Walk Strike Line" in Puget Sound Business Journal (Vol. 29, October 24, 2008, No. 27, pp. 1)
Pub: American City Business Journals
Ed: Steve Wilhelm. **Description:** Teamsters Local 174 went on strike against Oak Harbor Freight Lines Inc. over alleged company violations of federal labor laws. The union also accuses the company of engaging directly with employees and holding mandatory meetings about contract negotiations.

9217 ■ "Virginia Albanese: President and CEO" in Inside Business (Vol. 13, September-October 2011, No. 5, pp. NC4)
Pub: Great Lakes Publishing Co.
Ed: Jeannie Roberts. **Description:** Profile of Virginia Albanese, CEO of FedEx's Custom Critical Division in Akron, Ohio. Albanese discusses her philosophy on business leadership.

STATISTICAL SOURCES

9218 ■ RMA Annual Statement Studies
Pub: Risk Management Association
Contact: Kevin M. Blakey, President
Released: Annual. **Price:** $175.00 2006-07 edition, $105.00. **Description:** Contains composite balance sheets and income statements for more than 360 industries, including the accounting, auditing, and bookkeeping industries. Also contains five years of comparative historical data for discerning trends. Includes 16 commonly used ratios, computed for most of the size groupings for nearly every industry.

TRADE PERIODICALS

9219 ■ Fastline--Bluegrass Truck Edition
Pub: Fastline
URL(s): www.fastline.com/v100/index.aspx. **Released:** 13/yr. **Price:** $20, Individuals; $35, Two years; $45, Canada and Mexico; $95, Other countries.

9220 ■ Fastline--Florida Truck Edition
Pub: Fastline
URL(s): www.fastline.com/v100/index.aspx. **Released:** 13/yr. **Price:** $20, Individuals; $35, Two years; $45, Canada and Mexico; $95, Other countries.

9221 ■ Fastline--Georgia Truck Edition
Pub: Fastline
URL(s): www.fastline.com/v100/index.aspx. **Released:** 13/yr. **Price:** $20, Individuals; $35, Two years; $45, Canada and Mexico; $95, Other countries.

9222 ■ Fastline--Tennessee Truck Edition
Pub: Fastline
URL(s): www.fastline.com/v100/index.aspx. **Released:** Monthly **Price:** $20, Individuals; $35, Two years; $45, Canada and Mexico; $95, Other countries; $40, Individuals 3 years.

9223 ■ Fastline--Tri-State Truck Edition
Pub: Fastline
URL(s): www.fastline.com/v100/index.aspx. **Released:** 13/yr. **Price:** $20, Individuals; $35, Two years; $45, Canada and Mexico; $95, Other countries.

9224 ■ Mailing Systems Technology (MAST)
Pub: RB Publishing Co.
Contact: Shelby Murphy, Editor
URL(s): mailingsystemstechnology.com/me2/default.asp. **Ed:** Dan O'Rourke.

9225 ■ Trans Digest
Pub: Transportation Consumer Protection Council Inc.
Ed: Stephen W. Beyer, Editor. **Released:** Monthly. **Price:** Included in membership. **Description:** Provides the shipping community with news relating to the transportation of goods, including agency actions and decisions, legislative developments, and court decisions. Recurring features include recent court decisions; questions & answers; tariff watch; notices of seminars and educational materials.

TRADE SHOWS AND CONVENTIONS

9226 ■ TransComp
National Industrial Transportation League
1700 N. Moore St., Ste. 1900
Arlington, VA 22209
Ph: (703)524-5011
Fax: (703)524-5017
Co. E-mail: info@nitl.org
URL: http://www.nitl.org
Contact: Bruce Carlton, President
E-mail: carlton@nitl.org
URL(s): www.nitl.org/trans.htm. **Frequency:** Annual. **Audience:** Transportation professionals. **Principal Exhibits:** Computer services, software, and innovations for transportation operations. Motor, rail, air, water and International modal carriers, freight payment services, EDI, custom brokers, bar coding, tariff watch services and other products and services for enhancing domestic and international freight transportation management. **Telecommunication Services:** gilanshah@nitl.org.

FRANCHISES AND BUSINESS OPPORTUNITIES

9227 ■ eShipping
173 English Landing Dr., Ste. 210
Parkville, MD 64152
Ph: (816)505-0198
Fax: (816)880-0047
Description: Freight and shipping services. **No. of Franchise Units:** 13. **No. of Company-Owned Units:** 4. **Founded:** 2001.. **Franchised:** 2006. **Equity Capital Needed:** $30,755-$64,150. **Franchise Fee:** $22,500-$23,700. **Royalty Fee:** 35%. **Training:** Provides 3-4 days training and ongoing support.

9228 ■ United Shipping Solutions
6985 Union Park Ctr., Ste. 565
Midvale, UT 84047
Ph: (801)352-0012
Free: 866-744-7486
Fax: (801)352-0339
Description: Transportation services. **No. of Franchise Units:** 126. **Founded:** 2002.. **Franchised:** 2002. **Equity Capital Needed:** $53,700-$103,500. **Franchise Fee:** $50,000-$53,000. **Royalty Fee:** 6%. **Training:** Offers 7 days at headquarters, 7 days at franchisees location and ongoing training as needed (recurrent and/or advanced).

COMPUTERIZED DATABASES

9229 ■ MileMaker®
8255 Central Park Ave.
Skokie, IL 60076
Ph: (847)329-8100
Free: 800-234-4069
Fax: (847)329-6361
Co. E-mail: info@randmcnally.com
URL: http://www.randmcnally.com
Contact: Robert S. Apatoff, President
Availability: Online: Rand McNally & Co. **Type:** Directory; Numeric.

LIBRARIES

9230 ■ Airlines for America (A4A)
1301 Pennsylvania Ave. NW, Ste. 1100
Washington, DC 20004-7017
Ph: (202)626-4000
Free: 800-497-3326
Fax: (202)626-4264

Co. E-mail: a4a@airlines.org
URL: http://www.airlines.org
Contact: Nicholas E. Calio, President
URL(s): www.air-transport.org. **Description:** Airlines engaged in transporting persons, goods and mail by aircraft between fixed terminals on regular schedules. **Scope:** Transportation, civil aviation history. **Services:** Interlibrary loan; copying; Library open to the public by appointment. **Founded:** 1936. **Holdings:** 12,000 volumes; 12 VF drawers of pamphlets and

Annual reports; 350 reels of microfilm; 3 drawers of microfiche; 500 report files. **Subscriptions:** 120 journals and other serials; 10 newspapers. **Publications:** *Air Transport*; *Air Transport* (Annual); *Economic* (Annual). **Educational Activities:** Air Transport Association Engineering, Maintenance and Material Forum. **Telecommunication Services:** ata@airlines. org; pubs@airlines.org; ata@air-lines.org.

CPSIA information can be obtained
at www.ICGtesting.com
Printed in the USA
FFOW051102250313
1030FF

9 781414 479583